P R E N T I C E   H A L L

Advanced Mathematics A Precalculus Approach

◆ *Builds a solid foundation of advanced mathematics skills and concepts*
◆ *Provides the tools to implement the NCTM Curriculum and Professional Standards*

Comprehensive Coverage

Student Text

◆ Cohesive course, clearly written, ensures student success
◆ Allows students to become involved in the development of their own mathematical understanding
◆ Balances solid mathematics with contemporary approaches

Communication

◆ Provides the opportunity to communicate mathematics in a variety of ways; Writing in Mathematics

Reasoning

◆ Encourages involvement in developing and applying mathematical concepts; Thinking Critically, Challenge

Connections

◆ Connects mathematics to the real world
◆ Integrates related topics and other disciplines
◆ Develops students' mathematical power
◆ Gives students the ability to use mathematics in today's world

Technology

◆ Develops and explores concepts using multiple forms of technology, including the graphing calculator and computer software

Modeling

◆ Represents real world problems as mathematical models

Review and Assessment

◆ Ongoing review and self-evaluation ensure success; Review, Chapter Summary and Review, Cumulative Review, Test Yourself, Chapter Test

Addresses Current Curriculum Issues

◆ Implementation of NCTM Curriculum Standards
◆ Alternative Assessment
◆ Alternative Learning
◆ Cooperative Learning
◆ Technology
◆ Multicultural Opportunities

PLUS . . . Superior and Flexible Support

Teacher's Edition

◆ Chapter Overview and Lesson Plan for every lesson, including background information, suggestions, examples, quizzes, enrichment; Course Recommendations, Resources, and more

Teacher's Resource Book

◆ Organized by chapter
◆ Practice, Enrichment for every lesson
◆ Testing Program
◆ Transparencies
◆ TI-81 Emulation Software

Solutions Manual

◆ Complete solutions to all Student Edition exercises

Advanced Mathematics
A Precalculus Approach

Contemporary...
Unique...
Relevant...

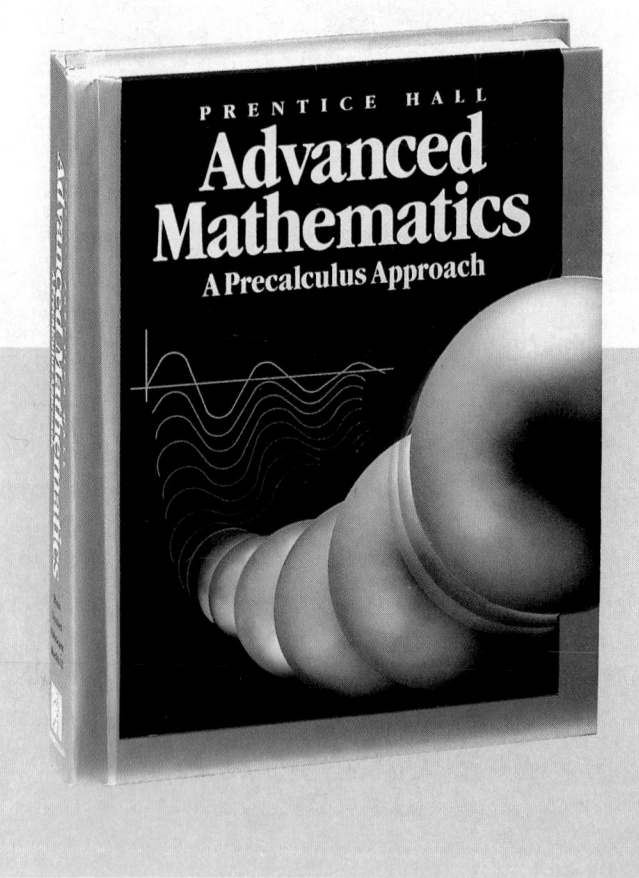

STUDENT TEXT

Builds a solid foundation of advanced mathematical skills and concepts

- Represents real world problems as mathematical models
- Develops strategies for problem solving
- Connects mathematics to daily life
- Integrates related topics and other disciplines
- Develops concepts through the use of technology
- Provides opportunities to communicate mathematically
- Provides on-going review and self-evaluation
- Implements the NCTM Curriculum Standards

TEACHER'S EDITION

Support to help meet the challenges of teaching

- Chapter Overviews, suggestions, examples, quizzes, and enrichment
- Addresses current curriculum issues...
    Authentic Assessment — Alternative Learning Styles
    Cooperative Learning Techniques — Multicultural Connections
- Technology use and instruction
- Tools to implement the NCTM Curriculum and Professional Standards

TEACHER'S RESOURCE BOOK
Wealth of ideas and support materials

- Organized by Chapter for convenient access
- Practice and Enrichment
- Current Testing program...including
  Authentic and Performance Assessment
  Up-to-date College Board Entrance Exam Reviews
- Transparencies
- Graphing Utility included for use with program

SOLUTIONS MANUAL
Covers every exercise

- Complete solutions to all Student Text exercises

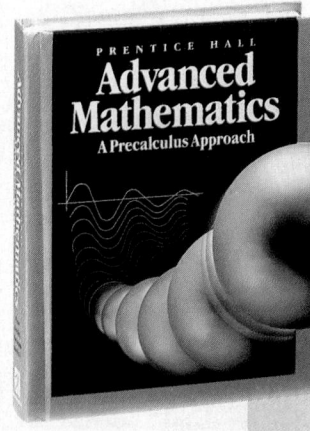

PRENTICE HALL

Advanced
Mathematics
A Precalculus Approach

P R E N T I C E   H A L L

Advanced Mathematics
A Precalculus Approach

STUDENTS DEVELOP THEIR MATHEMATICAL POWER

- Developing techniques to represent real world problems as mathematical models
- Gaining the ability to use mathematics in today's world
- Learning to communicate mathematically
- Improving their thinking critically skills
- Connecting and integrating mathematics in real-life situations
- Using technology to develop concepts therefore enhancing their understanding of mathematics
- Benefiting from on-going review and self-evaluation

TEACHERS DEVELOP THEIR MATHEMATICAL POWER

- Tools to implement the NCTM Curriculum and Professional Standards
- A curriculum that addresses current issues
- Authentic Assessment Projects
- Cooperative Learning Techniques
- Strategies to address Alternative Learning Styles
- Suggestions for using technology to develop concepts
- Multicultural Connections

PRENTICE HALL

Advanced Mathematics
A Precalculus Approach

Merilyn Ryan, S.S.J.
Marvin E. Doubet
Mona Fabricant
Theron D. Rockhill

Prentice Hall dedicates this
mathematics program to
all mathematics educators
and their students.

Prentice Hall
Englewood Cliffs, New Jersey
Needham, Massachusetts

Contents

ISBN 0-13-715798-3

2 3 4 5 6 7 8 9 10   96 95 94 93 92

Prentice Hall
A Division of Simon & Schuster
Englewood Cliffs, New Jersey 07632

THE STUDENT TEXT

Teaching mathematics continues to undergo change since the National Council of Teachers of Mathematics published its Curriculum and Evaluation Standards in 1989 and its Professional Standards in 1991.

The Curriculum and Evaluation Standards have provided a vision of what the mathematics curriculum should include, and the Professional Standards are providing a vision of what teaching can be. Prentice Hall is committed to providing teachers with the support they need to help realize that vision.

Prentice Hall is also committed to helping you create a learning environment in which students have access to experiences and challenges that lead to their development of mathematical power. Solid lesson development, critical thinking and discussion activities, application-based lessons, and writing in mathematics activities make it easier for teachers to foster students' understanding of concepts and procedures.

Throughout its mathematics program, Prentice Hall provides you with the tools for discourse— integration of technology, critical thinking activities, manipulatives, and the opportunities for students to communicate mathematics in a variety of ways.

In this Teacher's Edition, current issues are addressed (pages T10 to T19) to help you to implement the Standards.

The National Council of Teachers of Mathematics
CURRICULUM STANDARDS

1 Mathematics as Problem Solving
2 Mathematics as Communication
3 Mathematics as Reasoning
4 Mathematics as Connections
5 Algebra
6 Functions
7 Geometry from a Synthetic Perspective
8 Geometry from an Algebraic Pespective
9 Trigonometry
10 Statistics
11 Probability
12 Discrete Mathematics
13 Conceptual Underpinning of Calculus
14 Mathematical Structure

In addition, side column commentary addresses Alternative Assessment. Alternative Learning Styles, Cooperative Learning, Critical Thinking, Multicultural Opportunities, and Using Technology.

ABOUT THE PROGRAM

The initial planning and subsequent development of *Prentice Hall Advanced Mathematics* was achieved with input from over 5000 teachers and supervisors, along with recommendations from subject matter scholars and consultants. The result is that our secondary mathematics program is designed by teachers for teachers.

During each development phase, field testing and pilots were implemented for on-going review and evaluation of the program. Teachers and subject matter scholars assessed content, factual accuracy, conceptual integrity, and value.

Each of the components received the same careful research and development as did the Student Edition. Prentice Hall is creating and publishing materials that work in the classroom. The cooperation and involvement between publisher and teacher is a continual process. Students, along with teachers, provide us with insight into new and creative ideas that will ensure that every student succeeds. Planning, writing, editing, and evaluation personally involve all school personnel.

THE NCTM STANDARDS

This comprehensive program allows students to develop a solid foundation of advanced mathematics skills and concepts better than current programs because it was specifically written for high school students. The flexibility of the program provides teachers with a variety of approaches to make mathematics work. *Prentice Hall Advanced Mathematics* actively involves students in their learning. They develop their mathematical power through Modeling, Technology, Cooperative Learning, Projects, Critical Thinking, Writing, and connecting mathematics to the real world.

In this program, students develop and remember the skills and strategies necessary to select a successful approach to any problem. The flexibility of the program develops their ability to use mathematical models and technology to investigate, reason, predict, and interpret, so that they may solve problems with confidence.

Prentice Hall Advanced Mathematics provides the power for students to operate the latest technological tools, interpret statistical data, use spreadsheets, and represent real world problems and mathematical models.

A student's mathematical power depends directly on his or her ability to take advantage of today's tools and *Prentice Hall Advanced Mathematics* has been developed to help you develop your students' mathematical power.

♦ Each chapter begins with a two-page mini-lesson that explores *mathematical modeling. Thinking Critically* questions and a *Project* provide students with opportunities to investigate topics further, independently or with classmates.

♦ *Mathematical modeling* is the process of devising a mathematical representation of nonmathematical phenomenon. Often a mathematical model provides an efficient means of solving real world problems. An introduction and explanation of mathematical modeling is given in Chapter 1. *Modeling* sections in lessons present worked-out examples of mathematical modeling. In addition, a modeling lesson is presented at the beginning of each chapter.

♦ Each lesson begins with *Lesson Objectives* that tell students what is expected of them and a *Focus* that connects mathematics to an interesting topic or related discipline.

♦ *Completely worked-out Examples* provide instruction to help your students successfully complete their assignments. Solutions are given step by step with reasons given in blue type.

♦ *Important concepts* are highlighted to emphasize their importance and for easy reference. Review concepts are labeled *Recall*.

Technology is an integral part of this book. The technology logo identifies discussion of techniques for using technology, and suggests when using technology is beneficial and appropriate. A graphing utility (a graphing calculator or computer software) is a valuable tool to use in this course. A graphing calculator has all the capabilities of a scientific calculator, and can also plot and graph functions on the display screen, view formulas and solutions in their entirety, zoom in and trace graphs, and more.

♦ *Class and Practice Exercises* build a solid foundation of mathematics skills. Answers to selected exercises are given in the back of the student text.

- *Thinking Critically* exercises help improve students' reasoning skills.
- *Application* exercises connect mathematics to daily life and to other disciplines.
- *Writing in Mathematics* exercises help students acquire communication skills.
- *Review* exercises integrated within the Practice Exercises review previously learned skills and concepts. These exercises are denoted by ® in the Teacher's Edition only. Additional review exercises are given at the end of lessons.

♦ *Challenge* exercises at the end of a lesson expand students' critical thinking and reasoning abilities.

♦ The complete review and assessment program provides opportunities for student self-evaluation, along with alternative assessment opportunities.

- *Review* exercises at the end of lessons help students remember skills and concepts already learned. In addition, review exercises, denoted by ® in the Teacher's Edition only, are integrated within the Practice Exercises to provide on-going review.
- *Test Yourself* is a tool for self-evaluation which is given midway and at the end of each chapter.
- *Summary and Review* is a two-page review of the chapter; it includes important vocabulary.
- *Chapter Test* is a one-page test that provides effective preparation for tests.
- *Cumulative Review* provides one to three pages of review exercises from all previous chapters. Multiple-choice and quantitative analysis questions, as well as free-response questions, prepare students for placement tests.

The Teacher's Edition is designed to provide both the experienced and the novice advanced mathematics teacher with more features than ever before to help meet the challenges of teaching, plan effectively, and implement the NCTM Curriculum Standards.

♦ *Recommended Course Sequences* are provided on page T20 for courses in Precalculus, Topics in Advanced Mathematics, Analytic Geometry, Discrete Mathematics, and Finite Mathematics.
♦ Each chapter begins with a *Chapter Overview* which includes the following:

  • *Summary* A brief description of the chapter's content
  • *Mathematical Power* Further information about the two-page mini-modeling lesson
  • *Features* A complete listing of the chapter features, including a listing of the *Modeling* in the chapter, and the *Prentice Hall Advanced Mathematics Program* resources for the chapter
  • *Review and Assessment* A complete listing of the available reviews and tests in the Student Edition and Teacher's Resource Book

Throughout the book, nearly full-size student text pages have answers in place. Answers that do not fit on the student page are placed in the side column or in the back of the Teacher's Edition. Answers to *Thinking Critically* questions asked in the lesson development are given at the bottom of the Teacher's Edition page. Answers to *Writing in Mathematics* questions are also given at the bottom of the Teacher's Edition page.

♦ Teaching suggestions that address current curriculum issues are given in the side column. Each *Lesson Plan* contains the following:

  • *Vocabulary* A listing of important terms introduced in the lesson
  • *Materials/Manipulatives* Concrete materials and programs that may be used to develop lesson concepts. Suggestions for using Materials and Manipulatives are marked by Ⓜ.
  • *Technology* Technological tools and program resources that may be used to develop lesson concepts

  • *Focus* Further information about the *Focus* that begins the lesson, which includes discussion of cultural diversity in mathematics
  • *Instruction* Includes specific teaching suggestions for the lesson that include *Alternative Learning Styles*, Modeling, Critical Thinking, Cooperative Learning, and Multicultural opportunities
  • *Guided Practice* Includes examples that parallel the examples in the student text. Suggestions for correcting *Common Errors* and for utilizing *Technology* are given.
  • *Closure* Contains suggestions to help students summarize the lesson
  • *Independent Practice* Includes an Assignment Guide; comments on the Review exercises in the Practice Exercises, labeled Ⓡ; comments on appropriate use of technology in the exercises. Labels (A, B, C) indicating degree of difficulty are provided in the exercises only in the Teacher's Edition.
  • *Lesson Follow-Up* Includes a *Lesson Quiz* and *Alternative Assessment* suggestions
  • *Project* Discusses ways in which projects at the ends of some lessons can be used effectively for Cooperative Learning
  • *Enrichment* A particularly challenging application or conceptual extension of the subject matter presented in the lesson

SUPERIOR, FLEXIBLE SUPPORT

TEACHER'S RESOURCE BOOK

♦ Organized by chapter
♦ Practice and Enrichment for every lesson
♦ Applications, Technology, Teacher and Student Aids
♦ Current Testing program, including Authentic and Performance Assessment and Up-to-date College Entrance Exam Reviews
♦ Graphing Utility included

SOLUTIONS MANUAL

♦ Complete solutions to all Student Edition exercises

DEVELOPING · MATHEMATICAL · POWER

One of the primary goals of the Prentice Hall mathematics program is to help students gain mathematical power. What is mathematical power? According to the National Council of Teachers of Mathematics *Curriculum and Evaluation Standards for School Mathematics,* mathematical power means

> . . . an individual's abilities to explore, conjecture, and reason logically, as well as the ability to use a variety of mathematical methods effectively to solve nonroutine problems. This notion is based on the recognition of mathematics as more than a collection of concepts and skills to be mastered; it includes methods of investigating and reasoning, means of communication, and notions of context. In addition, for each individual, mathematical power involves the development of personal self-confidence.

Mathematical power is not acquired quickly or easily. It is built over time, through hard work and determination on the student's part, through patience and encouragement on the teacher's part. There are many aspects to be considered in developing mathematical power. The following pages are designed to help you explore some of the critical issues that affect mathematical teaching today. *Prentice Hall Advanced Mathematics: A Precalculus Approach* is designed to help you incorporate these ideas into your own teaching style. References are made to specific features of the text and to their use in building mathematical power.

MATHEMATICAL MODELING

Mathematical modeling may be defined as the process of devising a mathematical representation of some nonmathematical phenomenon. Like physical models (model planes, model cars, and so on), mathematical models (functions, graphs, equations, and so on) may be used to gain important information about the situation being modeled. A mathematical model often provides an efficient means of solving real world problems and, in some cases, the only practical means of solving a problem.

As recommended in the NCTM *Curriculum and Evaluation Standards,* students need to see the connections between the mathematics that they are studying and real world problems. Throughout this book mathematical modeling is used to emphasize the link between mathematics and applied problems. For example, the *Focus* at the beginning of a lesson often provides a general introduction to a real world situation, which is later modeled using mathematics taught in the lesson. In the lesson exercises the students are asked to solve one or more application problems related to this model.

Students using this textbook will learn that mathematical problem solving is more than just solving a list of equations. Problem solving is usually done in the context of a real world situation. In nearly every lesson in this book students will encounter real world applications. They will learn firsthand that a wide variety of real problems can be modeled and solved using precalculus mathematics.

Classes using this textbook will have frequent opportunities to explore and discuss mathematical models that use advanced mathematics. Beginning in Chapter 1 with linear and quadratic models and ending with calculus-based modeling applications in Chapter 16, every chapter includes at least two lessons in which real world phenomena are modeled mathematically. For example, in Chapter 8 (Inequalities and Linear Programming) the problem of deploying airplanes and crews for a massive airlift is modeled and solved by using linear inequalities. In Chapter 9 (Exponential and Logarithmic Functions) the spread of a measles outbreak is modeled by an exponential function. This frequent presentation of modeling applications throughout the text serves to reinforce student understanding of mathematical modeling as a connecting link between mathematics and real world problems.

Industry now expects new employees to enter the workplace prepared to use many mathematical modeling tools. Some of the models and applications presented in Chapter 12 (Matrices and Vectors), Chapter 14 (Probability), and Chapter 15 (Statistics) illustrate real world problems that your students may encounter when they enter the workplace. In these chapters they have the opportunity to investigate some typical applications of advanced mathematics found in industrial occupations.

Serious mathematical modeling of real world

phenomena very often includes the use of computer programs for computation and simulation. Numerous exercise sets and lesson projects include opportunities for students to write computer programs. For students who have learned how to program a computer or a programmable calculator, these programming assignments provide reinforcement of their programming skills and a chance to experience the application of computer programming to mathematical problem solving.

Students who continue their academic study after completing this course will certainly encounter the use of mathematical modeling in a wide range of disciplines. Researchers in nearly every academic discipline now make use of mathematical modeling. The vocabulary of mathematical modeling is present in textbooks used across the college curriculum. The report "Everybody Counts: A Report to the Nation on the Future of Mathematics Education," published in 1989 by the National Research Council, stressed the urgent need to increase the emphasis on model building in teaching mathematics. It is important that students obtain an orientation to mathematical modeling in their mathematics courses, especially in an advanced mathematics course. Students who use this textbook will gain an appreciation and understanding of the emerging role of mathematical modeling in our society.

COMMUNICATION

Communication is essential to life, yet it is an ongoing process and a challenge for each of us. The process of mathematical communication, both in and out of the classroom, is no different. Working out a problem and explaining the method helps teach students the language of mathematics, and as students become more comfortable with that language, their explanations and methods become clearer and smoother. A strong vocabulary can be made stronger yet with regular practice, and the Prentice Hall approach weaves the mathematical vocabulary through each page of each lesson. A *Vocabulary* section is also included in each chapter's two-page *Summary and Review*.

Learning mathematics is a matter of building on what is already understood, and the stronger the structure, the longer it will stand. Communication is an important part of that structure. Frequently, students understand the idea behind a concept, yet it is not until they put it into words that it crystallizes

in their minds. It is at this point that the concept becomes a part of their own mathematical reference. To aid in the development of this "concept crystallization," exercises and features requiring class discussion, *Writing in Mathematics,* and *Thinking Critically* are interwined throughout the student text. These are ideal points of departure for students keeping a math journal. The *Closure* in the Teacher's Edition side column contains further suggestions in this direction.

A student's ability to communicate builds on itself. When students are more comfortable speaking mathematically, they are more likely to ask probing questions. A vocabulary that expands inquiry also allows for more sophisticated responses. When homework assignments challenge students to speculate and imagine, the results often surprise the students themselves. In the words of the NCTM *Curriculum and Evaluation Standards,* "facility with the language of mathematics is an integral part of thinking mathematically, solving problems, and reflecting on one's own mathematical experiences."

REASONING

Every teacher has had students show up in class with a whole section of homework missing. Maybe the problems were worded differently from the ones the day before, or they do not ask for exactly the same thing; one way or another, some students will say, "We never went over these in class!" *You* know you went over that material; the problem is, *they* don't. In the classroom, teachers have the chance to express a problem in a variety of ways, to change parameters, and to help students find their way through to the result. At home, students may need the same sort of directed questioning that you are able to provide in the classroom. The lessons in this text are interspersed with critical thinking questions designed to help students stop and think about what they have just read. *Thinking Critically* questions incorporated into the exercise sets will do a great deal to focus attention on the mathematics rather than on the "right answer." Questions like these establish a habit of analyzing problems; and when students start thinking about old problems, picking them apart and examining their logic, they are less afraid to tackle new ones.

In mathematics courses, the logic that leads to an answer is usually more important than the answer itself. The right answer is no guarantee that students know what a problem is all about. What math teacher has not heard the question, "What's wrong with the way I did it? I got the right answer, didn't I?" The challenge is to involve students constantly in logical thinking, deciding when an alternate method is valid, and when it is not. When students are given an assignment in which a number of open-ended questions are included, there is opportunity to shift the emphasis from rote learning to method and reasoning. Every exercise set in this text includes a number of questions that ask students to discuss, to present possibilities, or to speculate about why something happens. Students who learn to think may forget a particular technique over time; but they will not forget how to reason out a new one.

CONNECTIONS

Every teacher has a private list of perfect examples, foolproof analogies, favorite stories, and jokes for drawing a parallel and illustrating a concept to students. These are mathematical connections. By focusing on these connections, the student recalls something familiar—a shape, a process, an experience—and uses it as a springboard to understanding a new mathematical idea. Teachers are constantly looking for these springboards, and the Prentice Hall teaching program provides them with many opportunities to "make new connections."

Each chapter opens with a two-page mini-modeling lesson on *Mathematical Modeling* that provides connections between real world applications and technology. These lessons capture the student's—and the teacher's—interest immediately with topics like earthquake prediction, game show probabilities, and computer-generated imagery. The *Project* at the end provides an ideal opportunity for using the real world to illuminate the world of mathematics. Students use the content of the chapter to accomplish the project; and in the process, new mathematical ideas take on real shape and meaning.

At the beginning of each lesson is a *Focus* that provides an immediate connection to the mathematics in the lesson, through other disciplines, through real world applications, or through historical information. Many of the lessons contain a special *Modeling* section that provides similar connections specifically related to the content of the lesson. In addition, the *Practice Exercises* at the end of each lesson include a variety of applications to fields outside mathematics.

Students so often want to know how they will use their mathematics in "real life"; teachers so often want to find "real life" models to explain the mathematics they are teaching. Mathematical connections work both ways, opening up unlimited possibilities for students and teachers alike, and providing motivation and elucidation and a sense of purpose that can benefit everyone involved.

TECHNOLOGY

The use of technology pervades our society and is increasing throughout the workplace, in the professions, and across all academic disciplines. Technology is becoming increasingly dependent on mathematics, and users of mathematics are making greater use of technology. Computer programs and calculators are now used routinely for most mathematical problem solving taking place in the real world, outside of the classroom. The changing role of computers and calculators in the practice of mathematics must have an impact on the teaching and learning of mathematics in the classroom. Within the next few years, the new symbolic manipulation software (Mathematica, Derive, Theorist, and Maple, to name a few) will begin to transform the course of study in mathematics.

One goal of this textbook is to provide a vehicle for teaching advanced mathematics with a focus on current real world applications, using the latest technology. The graphing calculator (perhaps more appropriately called the hand-held computer) has become the tool of choice for many people using mathematics to solve applied problems. These calculators are designed not only for graphing but also for performing a wide range of tasks, including operations with matrices and calculations for probability and statistics. As noted in "Restructuring School Mathematics: A Philosophy and Framework for Curriculum" published by the Mathematical Sciences Education Board, calculators and computers should be used throughout the mathematics curriculum as "fast pencils" for computation and for function sketching. This text reflects that point of view by incorporating calculators and graphing utilities throughout the text.

The use of graphing utilities in this book is in keeping with the recommendations of the NCTM *Curriculum and Evaluation Standards*. The availability of a *graphing utility* (computer software or graphing calculator) for classroom use in an advanced mathematics course will increase student understanding of many mathematical concepts. Students who have access to such a utility can examine the graphs of many complicated equations in the time it would take them to graph one by hand. Furthermore, if students have access to a graphing utility, they can use this tool as an instrument for verifying conjectures and for unparalleled experimentation. In every chapter of this book there are opportunities for teachers and students to utilize this technology for enhancing learning.

This symbol is found throughout the student text to highlight material that discusses using technology such as graphing calculations or computer software. The symbol is also given above *Practice Exercise* sets that utilize technology. Frequently, the symbol highlights methods for using a graphing utility to advantage. The zoom feature of a graphing utility, for example, can be used to approximate roots of an equation, locate maximum and minimum points of a function, or to find where the graphs of two functions intersect.

Teachers who can obtain access to a graphing utility for use in the classroom will certainly enhance their teaching of advanced mathematics. A computer or a graphing calculator with overhead display capabilities will reinforce student understanding of advanced mathematics concepts as well as expose students to this important use of technology. Some schools have found that they can purchase a classroom set of graphing calculators for about the cost of one or two computers. Also, many students elect to buy their own graphing calculators.

ASSESSMENT

How do teachers know when their students understand the material? How do the students know? Both usually rely on the results of tests and quizzes, performance on homework, and on class participation. These are all forms of assessment—but they are not the only forms. Traditional tests alone fail to give a complete picture of students' mathematical reasoning ability. The NCTM *Curriculum and Evaluation Standards* recommends "using multiple assessment techniques, including written, oral, and demonstration formats." Alternative forms of assessment are *not* just for the student who "doesn't test well"—they are for everyone.

One of the options available to teachers who want to test "the whole student" is the systematic use of observations. Your own instincts as a teacher are an invaluable assessment tool, especially when they are reinforced with specific areas of observation. These are a few of the questions you may want to ask yourself as you evaluate a student's progress. Does the student

Work better alone or in a group?
Help others?
Listen to the ideas of others?
Organize information?
Verbalize and define concepts?
Finish tasks?
Accept guidance and/or corrections from others?
Use a variety of strategies to solve problems?

Another way to evaluate a student's thinking process is to interview the student individually. This gives the student the opportunity to show areas of real achievement that you may not have focused on. At the same time it may alert you to a false sense of security on the student's part. Here are some types of questions you may find helpful in an interview with a student:

What did you learn?
Where do you think you had difficulty?
What parts do you think you handled well?
What skills do you need to practice more?
Is there a project you would especially like to work on?
What steps did you take to solve the problem?
What other approach could you have used?
How did you check your answer?

More and more, students are finding that one path to success is keeping a portfolio. This is a collection of work the student has produced over a period of time, material that exhibits creativity, organization, accuracy, thoroughness, synthesis, or any of a hundred other characteristics that make good math. Students who keep a portfolio of mathwork have something solid to point to with pride, to say, "I did this, and it makes sense." Assessing a student's portfolio is a valuable way to evaluate the student's

Ability to think and work independently
Ability to use mathematics creatively
Willingness to apply mathematics to real life situations
Pride in accomplishment

Performance assessment allows you to evaluate students as they work to complete a multi-step project or task. The performance itself could take a variety of forms, whether initiated by student or teacher. It may be an exhibit, a play, a project, an investigation. It could be a report, a set of interviews, artwork. The actual form is not important; what is important is what the performance tells about the student's progress.

Regardless of the form assessment takes, it is important for the teacher to decide in advance what criteria to use for judging students. At the same time, it helps students and teachers if assessment matches instruction. If classwork involves proofs, so must assessment. If days are spent on problem solving, assessment must also center on problem solving. And if students are using calculators in class, they should be using calculators during assessment as well.

An authentic assessment uses a wide range of methods to measure a wide range of learning experience. Each chapter in this textbook provides a choice of three forms of assessment. The *Chapter Test* found at the end of the chapter is one form of assessment. In the same page of the Teacher's Edition is an *Alternative Assessment* in the side column, providing a different perspective on the student's progress through the chapter. Finally, *Projects* found at the beginning of the chapter and at the end of many exercise sets present an ideal opportunity for performance assessment.

Assessment is one of the most important aspects of learning. It tells teachers whether or not they can introduce a new topic. It gives students confidence and lets them know they are on the right track; or it can help them refocus their energy if they are not. Best of all, when done well, it becomes a learning experience in its own right.

MULTICULTURAL OPPORTUNITIES

One of the greatest challenges of the 1990s is to improve student awareness of the contributions to mathematics of cultures other than their own. In order to meet the challenge of the NCTM's *Curriculum and Evaluation Standards,* students need to appreciate mathematics in its historical context. Mathematics has had its roots in different parts of the world, and contributions made by many scholars have lasted through centuries. The great mathematicians, past and present, have been men and women from all around the globe, oppressed and privileged, educated and self-educated. Recognizing these facts can bring the vitality of ethnic and cultural diversity to the curriculum. More important, students may seek their own opportunities in mathematics when they discover that mathematics has always been a field open to all.

The Prentice Hall mathematics program offers a wide spectrum of opportunity for cross-cultural discussion. Many features and applications use Western and non-Western cultures as points of reference; several focus on subgroups within our own American cuture. When a mathematical challenge presents material through a discussion of origami, or the Berlin Airlift, or sign-language interpretation, all students are enriched by a greater knowledge and appreciation of experiences beyond their own lives.

COOPERATIVE LEARNING

In addition to traditional teacher demonstrations and teacher-led discussions, greater opportunities should be provided for small-group work, individual explorations, peer instruction, and whole-class discussions in which the teacher serves as a moderator.

NCTM *Curriculum and Evaluation Standards*

One of the greatest challenges in teaching today is the challenge of making cooperative learning work in the classroom. Most teachers acknowledge the potential benefits of cooperative learning situations, but are often wary about the practical aspects: How does one keep students accountable, or evenly grouped, or on the topic? These are legitimate concerns that must be addressed individually; they are problems that will not solve themselves. But once the logistics are in place, the cooperative, collaborative classroom becomes an invigorating workplace for students and teachers.

Cooperative learning situations demand that students put their thoughts into words, a learning process in itself. Most teachers find that they know their subjects better through teaching; cooperative learning gives every student that opportunity. And when students hear each other's ideas, they gain the advantage of multiple perspectives offered by the others in the group.

The *Projects* found throughout the text work well either as individual or team assignments. Many of the projects are transdisciplinary in focus (one, for example, involves the influence of the Sherman Anti-Trust Act on athletics). Such projects are accomplished best when a diverse group shares abilities and interests, working toward a common goal.

Several projects involve writing computer programs. These projects are ideal cooperative situations for a class with mixed programming experience, because they allow the programmers to share their skills and the nonprogrammers to gain a valuable lesson in the importance of sequencing. When students collaborate on such a project, they learn more than just the mathematics.

COOPERATIVE LEARNING TIPS

◆ Create heterogeneous teams of students. Identify the six highest achievers and six lowest achievers in the class; assign one of each to a group. Assign others to create a cross-section of gender, past performance levels, and ethnicity. Keep groups long enough for students to feel like a team—6 to 8 weeks.

◆ Take time to explain what you are doing and why. Emphasize that the primary goal is to learn a concept. Use groups for both one-day and multi-day discussions and problem solving.

◆ Give teams a get-acquainted activity, such as planning an imaginary party with limited resources. Allow time for students to organize and pick team names.

◆ Explain when you will assist. Monitor by walking around and listening, but try not to intervene too quickly if students encounter difficulties. The goal is for groups to work through ideas themselves. Ask how they chose strategies, what difficulties they encountered, how they decided if answers were reasonable.

◆ Individual accountability can take many forms, such as quizzes or written explanations. Base group scores on individual improvement over previous performance. Group scores accumulate toward reward levels.

◆ Establish a signal for quiet, but expect a more lively atmosphere. Your goal is to generate the kind of peer support, excitement, and camaraderie often found among sports teams. These are some of the most powerful motivating qualities known in social psychology.

LEARNING STYLES

Learning styles are cognitive, conceptual, affective and behavioral patterns that are typical, consistent and stable processes which people use in their learning.

Pat Guild, Ed.D.
Coordinator of Learning Style Programs,
Seattle Pacific University

This is one definition of learning styles. What does it mean for you as a mathematics teacher? It means, first and foremost, *approach.*

Experienced teachers know that no single approach to a given topic will work with all of their students all of the time. Some students understand ideas best when they are shown one clear definition, while some need multiple examples. For some students, the most meaningful examples are those put into words; for others, a series of images brings a point across more clearly. In order to teach to the whole group, teachers usually find it necessary to vary their approach—that is, to teach material with an eye toward the different learning styles of their students. This is what *alternative learning styles* are all about.

Researchers have identified many different learning styles. One school of thought divides learners into those who are "field-dependent" and "field-independent," sometimes categorized as "whole-to-part" and "part-to-whole," respectively. The field-dependent learner is most comfortable when shown "the big picture" first, leaving the details for later. The field-independent learner, on the other hand, learns best in an analytic, sequential fashion, mastering one step before progressing to the next. The field-dependent learner is more likely to ask, "What are we going to use this for?" while the field-independent learner is more likely to ask, "Could you go over the third step again?"

The traditional approach to teaching mathematics has been the field-independent approach, taking the subject a unit at a time and building on the foundation thus established. *Prentice Hall Advanced Mathematics: A Precalculus Approach* follows this approach and structure. However, to accommodate the needs of the field-dependent learner as well, *Advanced Mathematics* contains the following whole-to-part, field-dependent features:

A list of *Objectives* at the beginning of each lesson, showing the student the lesson goals

A *Focus* at the beginning of each lesson, providing a real context for the material of the lesson

A variety of *Applications* within each exercise set, to show the student a "purpose" before focusing on the mathematics of the problem.

Examples that teach: Several chapters, particularly Chapter 14 (Probability), include problem solving methods that are taught by example, rather than by instruction, and then generalized.

A *Summary and Review* at the end of each chapter to allow students to get an idea of the chapter as a whole

A modeling *Project* explained at the opening of each chapter, designed to bring much of the chapter material together toward a common real world goal

Beyond these specific features, the Prentice Hall approach itself offers opportunities for both types of learners. Most material is originally presented in a step-by-step fashion, with a field-independent emphasis on sequence and cause and effect. The *Examples* found in every lesson of the text, on the other hand, provide a total picture of how a problem is solved, for the field-dependent learner: The student can see the entire problem completely worked out and can then focus on the specific steps. This combined approach is used throughout most of the text, providing a detailed, stepwise explanation of the logic behind an idea, and showing an example of how that idea is put into play.

In addition to the dual categories of field dependence and independence, researchers have further categorized learning styles based on the medium or modality of learning—that is, the physical method used in learning, as opposed to the direction of the approach. Some of the modalities frequently listed are the auditory, the visual, the tactile, the kineshetic, and the linguistic.

The auditory learner may be more successful with a lecture than a demonstration or may find that music can help bring meaning to a topic. This student, like the linguistic learner, is likely to be creative in using mnemonic devices and may have a good memory for vocabulary, dates, formulas, names, and lists in general.

The visual learner, as expected, is likely to succeed in constructions, graphs, and diagrams. Often an idea that is unclear when expressed in words makes sense to the visual learner when drawn as a diagram on the blackboard. Projects that allow such students to create a visual display help not only the students who create the project but also those who examine it later on display.

The tactile and kinesthetic learners are more comfortable with hands-on approaches to instruction, such as modeling or using manipulatives like algebra tiles, geoboards, and geometric solids. The Teacher's Edition contains side column references to *Materials/ Manipulatives* for each lesson. Often a graphing calculator in hand can help bridge the gap to understanding for these students who learn best by doing and experimenting.

RESOURCES

General

Booklets and Periodicals

National Council of Teachers of Mathematics. *An Agenda for Action: Recommendations for School Mathematics of the 1980's*. Reston, VA: NCTM, 1980.

National Council of Teachers of Mathematics. *Curriculum and Evaluation Standards for School Mathematics*. Reston, VA: NCTM, 1989.

National Council of Teachers of Mathematics. *Journal for Research in Mathematics Education*, January, March, May, July, and November. Reston, VA: NCTM.

National Council of Teachers of Mathematics. *The Mathematics Teacher*. Monthly September through May. Reston, VA: NCTM. Annually since 1926.

National Council of Teachers of Mathematics. *Professional Standards for Teaching Mathematics*. Reston, VA: NCTM, 1991.

Books

Abbot, Edwin A. *Flatland*. New York: Barnes and Noble, 1963.

Barnsley, Michael. *Fractals Everywhere*. San Diego, CA: Academic Press, Inc., 1988.

Bell, Eric Temple. *Mathematics: Queen & Servant of Science*. Washington, DC: Mathematical Association of America, 1979.

Boles, Martha, and Rochelle Newman. *The Golden Relationship: Art, Math, Nature*. Bradford, MA: Pythagorean Press, 1983.

Cooney, Thomas J., Edward J. Davis, and K. B. Henderson. "Teaching and Understanding of

Proof." *Dynamics of Teaching Secondary School Mathematics*. Prospect Heights, IL: Waveland Press, Inc., 1975.

Davison, David M., Marsha Landau, Leah McCracken, and Linda Thompson. *Pre-Algebra*. Needham, MA: Prentice Hall, 1992.

Eves, Howard. *An Introduction to the History of Mathematics*. New York: Holt Rinehart and Winston, 1976.

Gardner, Martin. *The Second Scientific American Book of Mathematical Puzzles and Diversions*. Chicago: University of Chicago Press, 1987.

"Geometry in the Mathematics Curriculum." *Thirty-Sixth Yearbook of the National Council of Teachers of Mathematics*. Reston, VA: NCTM, 1973.

Graham, Neill. *Computers and Computing*. St. Paul, MN: West Publishing Company, 1983.

Grinstein, Louise S., and Paul J. Campbell. *Women of Mathematics: A Bibliographic Sourcebook*. Westport, CT: Greenwood Press, 1987.

"Historical Topics for the Mathematics Classroom." *Thirty-first Yearbook of the National Council of Teachers of Mathematics*. Reston, VA: NCTM, 1969.

"The Ideas of Algebra, K–12." *The 1988 Yearbook of the National Council of Teachers of Mathematics*. Reston, VA: NCTM, 1988.

Jacobs, Harold R. *Mathematics: A Human Endeavor*. 2nd ed. San Francisco: W. H. Freeman, 1982.

Krulik, Stephen (ed.). "Problem Solving in School Mathematics." *1980 Yearbook of the National Council of Teachers of Mathematics*. Reston, VA: NCTM, 1980.

"Learning and Teaching Geometry, K–12." *1987 Yearbook of the National Council of Teachers of Mathematics*. Reston, VA: NCTM, 1987.

Mathematical Sciences Education Board. *Reshaping School Mathematics: A Philosophy and Framework for Curriculum*. Washington, DC: National Academy Press, 1990.

Papert, Seymour. *Mindstorms: Children, Computers, and Powerful Ideas*. New York: Basic Books, 1980.

Perl, T. *Math Equals: Biographies of Women Mathematicians and Related Activities*. Menlo Park, CA: Addison-Wesley Publishing Co., 1978.

Peterson, Ivars. *The Mathematical Tourist*. New York: W. H. Freeman, 1988.

Polya, George. *How to Solve It: A New Aspect of Mathematical Method*. 2nd ed. Princeton, NJ: Princeton University Press, 1973.

Sobel, Max, and Evan M. Maletsky. *Teaching Mathematics: A Sourcebook of Aids, Activities, and Strategies*. 2nd ed. Englewood Cliffs, NJ: Prentice Hall, 1988.

Tobias, Sheila. *Overcoming Math Anxiety*. New York: W. W. Norton Company, 1978.

Usiskin, Zalman. *Van Hiele Levels and Achievement in Secondary School Geometry*, Department of Education, University of Chicago, ERIC Document No. SE 038 813.

West, Beverly H., et al. *The Prentice-Hall Encyclopedia of Mathematics*. Englewood Cliffs, NJ: Prentice-Hall Inc., 1982.

Assessment

Designing District Evaluation Instruments for Math and Science Process Skills, an educators' network established in 1987 by the Association for Supervision and Curriculum Development. Contact Shelley Lipowich, 6321 N. Canon Del Pajaro, Tucson, AZ 85715.

"Educational Assessment—Policy and Use." No. 8, March 1990. American Education Research Association, 1310 South 6th Street, Champaign, IL 61820.

Kulm, Gerald (ed.). *Assessing Higher Order Thinking in Mathematics*. Washington, DC: American Association for the Advancement of Science, 1990.

Mathematics Portfolio Project, Vermont Department of Education, 120 State St., Montpelier, VT 05602.

Mitchell, Ruth. "A Caveat for Test Publishers," *Basic Education*, Vol. 31, No. 8. Washington, DC: Council for Basic Education, 1990.

"New Math Assessment," *Instructor*, April 1991.

Resnick, Lauren, and Daniel Resnick, "Tests as Standards of Achievement in Schools," *The Uses of Standardized Tests in American Education*. Princeton, NJ: Educational Testing Service, 1989.

Stenmark, Jean (ed.). Mathematics Assessment: *Myths, Models, Good Questions, and Practical Suggestions*. Reston, VA: NCTM, 1991.

"Testing: Where We Stand." Arlington, VA: American Association of School Administrators, 1989.

Multicultural Concerns

Browne, J. and J. P. Perez. *Multicultural Education Course of Study for Grades Kindergarten*

Through Twelve 1979–1981. Los Angeles, CA: Los Angeles County School District.

Careccio, John. "Mathematical Heritage of Zambia," *The Arithmetic Teacher,* May 1970, pp. 391–395.

Cocking, Rodney, and Jose Mestre (eds.). *Linguistic and Cultural Influences on Learning Mathematics.* Hillsdale, NJ: Lawrence Erlbaum Associates, 1988.

Gilligan, Carol. *In a Different Voice.* Cambridge, MA: Harvard University Press, 1982.

Guild, Pat B., and Stephen Garger. *Marching to Different Drummers.* ASCD, 1985. Write to: Pat Guild Associates, PO BOX 99131, Seattle, WA 98119.

Kenschaft, Patricia C. "Black Men and Women in Mathematical Research," *Journal of Black Studies,* December, 1987, pp. 170–190.

Making Mathematics Work for Minorities. Washington DC: Mathematical Sciences Education Board, 1990.

Mallory, Garrick. *Picture Writing of the American Indians.* New York: Dover, 1972.

A Nation at Risk: The Imperative for Educational Reform. Washington, DC: U.S. Government Printing Office, 1983.

Neugebauer, O. *The Exact Science in Antiquity.* New York: Dover, 1972.

Newel, Virginia K., and Gipson, Rich, Stubblefield. *Black Mathematicians and Their Work.* Ardmore, PA: Dorrance and Company, 1980.

Newman, James. *The World of Mathematics.* New York: Simon & Schuster, 1956.

"The Rhind Papyrus," *Scientific American,* August 1952.

Takaki, Ronald. *Strangers from a Different Shore.* Boston: Little, Brown, 1989.

Zaslavsky, Claudia. *Africa Counts.* Boston: Prindle, Weber & Schmidt, 1973.

Learning Styles

Allen, W. H., and R. L. Van Sickle. "Learning Teams and Low Achievers." *Social Education,* 1984.

Faggella, Kathy, and Janet Horowitz. "Different Child, Different Style: Seven Ways to Reach and Teach All Children," *Instructor,* September 1990.

Feldman, Edmund Burke. *Varieties of Visual Experience.* New York: Harry N. Abrams, 1981.

Guild, Pat B., and Steven Garger. *Marching to Different Drummers.* ASCD, 1985.

Guild, Pat B., and Louise McKinney. *Using Learning Styles to Help Students Be Successful.* Write to: Pat Guild Associates, PO Box 99131, Seattle, WA 98119.

Kim, Scott. *Inversions.* New York: W. H. Freeman, 1989.

Moore, David W., Sharon A. Moore, Patricia M. Cunningham, James W. Cunningham. *Developing Readers and Writers in the Content Areas.* New York: Longman, 1986.

Skemp, Richard R. *The Psychology of Learning Mathematics.* Middlesex, England: Penguin Books, 1971.

Slawsky, Norman. "The Artist as Mathematician," *Mathematics Teacher,* April, 1977.

Tufte, Edward R. *Envisioning Information.* Cheshire, CT: Graphics Press, 1990.

Technology

Borenson, Henry. "The Graphics Calculator: A Helpful Tool," *Mathematics Teacher,* November 1990.

Coburn, Terrence G., Shirely Hoogenboom, and Judy Goodnow. *The Problem Solver with Calculators.* Sunnyvale, CA: Creative Publications, Inc., 1989.

Devaney, Robert L. *Chaos, Fractals, and Dynamics: Computer Experiments in Mathematics.* Menlo Park, CA: Addison-Wesley, 1990.

Devlin, Keith. *Microchip Mathematics—Number Theory for Computer Users.* Cheshire, England: Shiva Publishing, 1984.

The Elementary Mathematician, COMAP, Inc., 60 Lowell Street, Arlington, MA 02174.

Graham, Neill. *Computers and Computing.* St. Paul, MN: West Publishing Company, 1983.

Graham, Ronald Lewis, Donald Ervin Knuth, Oren Patashnik. *Concrete Mathematics: A Foundation for Computer Science.* Menlo Park, CA: Addison-Wesley, 1989.

Papert, Seymour. *Mindstorms: Children, Computers, and Powerful Ideas.* New York: Basic Books, 1980.

Swadener, Mar, and William Blubaugh. "Teaching Mathematics with a Vision: Integrating Computers into Instruction," *Teaching and Learning Mathematics in the 1990s.* Reston, VA: NCTM, 1990.

Warger, Cynthia (ed.). *Technology in Today's Schools.* Alexandria, VA: Association for Supervision and Curriculum Development, 1990.

Available software packages

Apple 128K	Macintosh	IBM PC

For Algebra and Trigonometry:

Apple 128K	Macintosh	IBM PC
Algeblaster	Algeblaster	Algeblaster
Algebra Drill	Bradford Graph Wiz	Graphing Equations
Algebra Drill & Practice 1		Algebra Drill & Practice 1
Algebra Drill & Practice 2		Algebra Drill & Practice 2
ARBPLOT		ARBPLOT
Interpreting Graphs		Interpreting Graphs
NCTM Short Programs Disks		NCTM Short Programs Disks
Chalkboard Graphics		MathCad
Disk Learning in Trigonometry		TI-81 Emulation

For Geometry:

Apple 128K	Macintosh	IBM PC
Geometric Presupposer		Geometric Presupposer
Geometric Supposer:	Geometric Supposer:	Geometric Supposer:
Triangles	Triangles	Triangles
Quadrilaterals	Quadrilaterals	Quadrilaterals
Circles		Circles
Logic and Euclidean Geometry	Bradford 3D Images	
LogoWriter	LogoWriter	LogoWriter
	Geometer's Sketchpad	

Symbolic manipulation:

Apple 128K	Macintosh	IBM PC
	Maple	Derive
	Mathematica	Mathematica
	Theorist	

Spreadsheets:

Apple 128K	Macintosh	IBM PC
Appleworks	Excel	Quattro
	Microsoft Works	Lotus 1-2-3

Videotapes

What is Statistics?	Annenberg
Picturing Distributions	Annenberg
Time Series	Annenberg
Models for Growth	Annenberg
Describing Relationships	Annenberg
What Is Probability?	Annenberg
Vectors	Annenberg
Gravity, Electricity, Magnetism	Annenberg
Harmonic Motion	Annenberg
Waves	Annenberg
Angular Momentum	Annenberg
Probability and Its Uses	Coronet
FUTURES with Jaime Escalante	PBS Videotapes

RECOMMENDED · COURSE · SEQUENCES

Prentice Hall's *Advanced Mathematics: A Precalculus Approach* offers a wide spectrum of topics to match a variety of approaches to senior-level advanced mathematics courses. The following lists of topics are suggestions that meet the objectives of five senior-level courses.

Precalculus

For students who plan to take calculus and other college-level mathematics courses

Chapter 1	Functions
Chapter 2	Graphing Functions
Chapter 3	Trigonometric Functions
Chapter 4	Graphs and Inverses of Trigonometric Functions
Chapter 5	Applications of Trigonometry
Chapter 6	Trigonometric Identities and Equations
Chapter 7	Polynomial Functions
Chapter 8	Inequalities and Linear Programming
Chapter 9	Exponential and Logarithmic Functions
Chapter 10	Polar Coordinates and Complex Numbers
Chapter 11	Conic Sections
Chapter 13	Sequences and Series
Chapter 16	Limits and an Introduction to Calculus

Topics in Advanced Mathematics

For students who may not choose to continue their study of mathematics after high school

Chapter 1	Functions
Chapter 2	Graphing Functions
Chapter 3	Trigonometric Functions
Chapter 4	Graphs and Inverses of Trigonometric Functions
Chapter 5	Applications of Trigonometry
Chapter 7	Polynomial Functions
Chapter 8	Inequalities and Linear Programming
Chapter 9	Exponential and Logarithmic Functions
Chapter 11	Conic Sections (Lessons 11.1 to 11.4)
Chapter 13	Sequences and Series
Chapter 14	Probability
Chapter 15	Statistics and Data Analysis

Analytic Geometry

Chapter 1	Functions
Chapter 2	Graphing Functions
Chapter 3	Trigonometric Functions
Chapter 4	Graphs and Inverses of Trigonometric Functions
Chapter 7	Polynomial Functions
Chapter 8	Inequalities and Linear Programming
Chapter 9	Exponential and Logarithmic Functions
Chapter 10	Polar Coordinates and Complex Numbers
Chapter 11	Conic Sections
Chapter 12	Vectors (Lessons 12.5 to 12.10)
Chapter 16	Limits and an Introduction to Calculus

Discrete Mathematics

Chapter 8	Inequalities and Linear Programming
Chapter 12	Matrices and Vectors
Chapter 13	Sequences and Series
Chapter 14	Probability
Chapter 15	Statistics and Data Analysis

Many of the applications and modeling features throughout the text also reflect a discrete mathematics approach.

Finite Mathematics

Chapter 1	Functions
Chapter 2	Graphing Functions
Chapter 3	Trigonometric Functions
Chapter 4	Graphs and Inverses of Trigonometric Functions
Chapter 7	Polynomial Functions
Chapter 8	Inequalities and Linear Programming
Chapter 9	Exponential and Logarithmic Functions
Chapter 11	Conic Sections (Lessons 11.1 to 11.4)
Chapter 12	Matrices (Lessons 12.1 to 12.4)
Chapter 13	Sequences and Series
Chapter 14	Probability
Chapter 15	Statistics and Data Analysis

PRENTICE HALL

Advanced Mathematics
A Precalculus Approach

Merilyn Ryan, S.S.J.
Marvin E. Doubet
Mona Fabricant
Theron D. Rockhill

*Prentice Hall dedicates this
mathematics program to
all mathematics educators
and their students.*

Prentice Hall
Englewood Cliffs, New Jersey
Needham, Massachusetts

PRENTICE HALL

Advanced Mathematics A Precalculus Approach

AUTHORS

Merilyn Ryan, S.S.J.
Associate Professor of Mathematics
Chestnut Hill College
Philadelphia, Pennsylvania

Mona Fabricant
Professor of Mathematics
Queensborough Community College
Bayside, New York

Marvin E. Doubet
Mathematics Department Chair
Deerfield High School
Deerfield, Illinois

Theron D. Rockhill
Professor of Mathematics
SUNY College at Brockport
Brockport, New York

CONSULTANTS

Barbara Adams
St. Rose High School
Belmar, New Jersey

Judy B. Basara
Mathematics Curriculum Chairman
St. Hubert High School
Philadelphia, Pennsylvania

Gail M. Baumann
Mathematics Teacher
H. B. Plant High School
Tampa, Florida

Donna Beers
Mathematics Department
Simmons College
Boston, Massachusetts

Mary K. Butler, S.S.J.
St. Rose High School
Belmar, New Jersey

Sylva Cohn
Formerly Associate Professor of Mathematics
State University of New York at Stony Brook
Stony Brook, New York

Wade Ellis, JR.
Mathematics Instructor
West Valley College
Saratoga, California

Calvin T. Long
Professor of Mathematics
Washington State University
Pullman, Washington

Composition, film, and computer-generated art: Monotype Composition Company, Inc.
Cover Design: Martucci Studio
Chapter Opener Design: Function Thru Form

ISBN 0-13-715780-0

3 4 5 6 7 8 9 10   96 95 94 93 92

Prentice Hall
A Division of Simon & Schuster
Englewood Cliffs, New Jersey 07632

Photo Research: omni–communications, Inc.
Photo credits appear on pages 909 and 937.

Staff Credits
Editorial: Rosemary Calicchio, Enid Nagel, Debra Berger, Mary Ellen Cheasty, Michael Ferejohn, Tony Maksoud, John Nelson, Alan MacDonell, Ann Fattizzi
Design: Laura Jane Bird, Art Soares
Production: Lynn Contrucci, Suse Cioffi, Lorraine Moffa
Photo Research: Libby Forsyth, Emily Rose, Martha Conway
Publishing Technology: Andrew Grey Bommarito, Gwendollyn Waldron, Deborah Jones, Monduane Harris, Michael Colucci, Gregory Myers, Cleasta Wilburn
Marketing: Julie Scarpa, Everett Draper, Michelle Sergi
Prepress Production: Laura Sanderson, Kathryn Dix, Denise Herckenrath, Natalia Bilash
Manufacturing: Rhett Conklin, Gertrude Szyferblatt
National Consultants: Susan Berk, Charlotte Mason

Formulas

Fundamental Identities (p. 168)

$$\csc \theta = \frac{1}{\sin \theta} \quad \sec \theta = \frac{1}{\cos \theta} \quad \cot \theta = \frac{1}{\tan \theta}$$

$$\tan \theta = \frac{\sin \theta}{\cos \theta} \quad \cot \theta = \frac{\cos \theta}{\sin \theta}$$

$$\sin^2 \theta + \cos^2 \theta = 1 \qquad 1 + \cot^2 \theta = \csc^2 \theta$$
$$1 + \tan^2 \theta = \sec^2 \theta$$

$$\sin(-\theta) = -\sin \theta \qquad \cos(-\theta) = \cos \theta$$
$$\tan(-\theta) = -\tan \theta \qquad \cot(-\theta) = -\cot \theta$$
$$\sec(-\theta) = \sec \theta \qquad \csc(-\theta) = -\csc \theta$$

Sum and Difference Identities (pp. 287, 288)

$$\sin(\alpha \pm \beta) = \sin \alpha \cos \beta \pm \cos \alpha \sin \beta$$
$$\cos(\alpha \pm \beta) = \cos \alpha \cos \beta \mp \sin \alpha \sin \beta$$
$$\tan(\alpha \pm \beta) = \frac{\tan \alpha \pm \tan \beta}{1 \mp \tan \alpha \tan \beta}$$

Double/Half-Angle Formulas (pp. 298, 299)

$$\sin 2\alpha = 2 \sin \alpha \cos \alpha \qquad \cos 2\alpha = \cos^2 \alpha - \sin^2 \alpha$$

$$\tan 2\alpha = \frac{2 \tan \alpha}{1 - \tan^2 \alpha}, \quad \tan \alpha \neq \pm 1$$

$$\sin \frac{\alpha}{2} = \pm \sqrt{\frac{1 - \cos \alpha}{2}} \qquad \cos \frac{\alpha}{2} = \pm \sqrt{\frac{1 + \cos \alpha}{2}}$$

$$\tan \frac{\alpha}{2} = \pm \sqrt{\frac{1 - \cos \alpha}{1 + \cos \alpha}}, \quad \cos \alpha \neq -1$$

Product/Sum Identities (p. 306)

$$2 \cos \alpha \cos \beta = \cos(\alpha - \beta) + \cos(\alpha + \beta)$$
$$2 \sin \alpha \sin \beta = \cos(\alpha - \beta) - \cos(\alpha + \beta)$$
$$2 \sin \alpha \cos \beta = \sin(\alpha + \beta) + \sin(\alpha - \beta)$$
$$2 \cos \alpha \sin \beta = \sin(\alpha + \beta) - \sin(\alpha - \beta)$$

Law of Sines/Law of Cosines (pp. 251, 265)

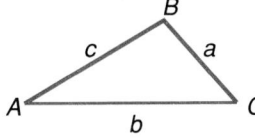

Law of sines: $\dfrac{\sin A}{a} = \dfrac{\sin B}{b} = \dfrac{\sin C}{c}$

Law of cosines: $a^2 = b^2 + c^2 - 2bc \cos A$
$b^2 = a^2 + c^2 - 2ac \cos B$
$c^2 = a^2 + b^2 - 2ab \cos C$

Distance from a Point to a Line (p. 107)

$$d = \frac{|Ax_1 + By_1 + C|}{\sqrt{A^2 + B^2}}$$

Logarithms (pp. 456, 461)

$$\log_b MN = \log_b M + \log_b N \qquad \log_b(N^r) = r \log_b N$$
$$\log_b \frac{M}{N} = \log_b M - \log_b N \qquad \log_b x = \frac{\log_a x}{\log_a b}$$

Financial Formulas (pp. 470, 471)

Compound interest: $A = P\left(1 + \dfrac{r}{n}\right)^{nt}$

Continuous compound interest: $A = Pe^{rt}$

General Form of a Conic (p. 566)

$$Ax^2 + Bxy + Cy^2 + Dx + Ey + F = 0$$

Vectors (pp. 645, 654)

Norm of a vector: $\quad \|\mathbf{v}\| = \sqrt{x^2 + y^2}$
Dot product: $\quad \mathbf{v} \cdot \mathbf{w} = v_1 w_1 + v_2 w_2$

Polar Coordinates (p. 490)

To convert from rectangular coordinates to polar:

$$r = \sqrt{x^2 + y^2}$$

$$\theta = \text{Tan}^{-1} \frac{y}{x}, \text{ if } x > 0 \quad \theta = \text{Tan}^{-1}\left(\frac{y}{x}\right) + \pi, \text{ if } x < 0$$

To convert from polar coordinates to rectangular:

$$x = r \cos \theta \qquad \qquad y = r \sin \theta$$

Complex Numbers (pp. 504, 510, 512, 517)

Polar form: $z = r(\cos \theta + i \sin \theta)$
Product: $z_1 z_2 = r_1 r_2 [\cos(\theta_1 + \theta_2) + i \sin(\theta_1 + \theta_2)]$
Quotient: $\dfrac{z_1}{z_2} = \dfrac{r_1}{r_2}[\cos(\theta_1 - \theta_2) + i \sin(\theta_1 - \theta_2)]$
DeMoivre's theorem: $z^n = r^n(\cos n\theta + i \sin n\theta)$

Combinations and Permutations (pp. 750, 751)

$$_nC_r = \frac{_nP_r}{r!} = \frac{n!}{r!(n-r)!} \qquad _nP_r = \frac{n!}{(n-r)!}$$

Binomial Theorem (p. 709)

$$(a + b)^n = \binom{n}{0}a^n + \binom{n}{1}a^{n-1}b + \binom{n}{2}a^{n-2}b^2 +$$

$$\cdots + \binom{n}{n-1}ab^{n-1} + \binom{n}{n}b^n$$

Sequences and Series (pp. 692, 693, 722)

Partial sum of an arithmetic series:

$$S_n = \frac{n[2a_1 + (n-1)d]}{2}$$

Partial sum of a geometric series:

$$S_n = \frac{a_1(1 - r^n)}{1 - r}, \quad r \neq 1$$

Sum of an infinite geometric series:

$$S = \frac{a}{1 - r}, \text{ if } |r| < 1$$

iii

Contents

1 Functions

CONNECTIONS: *Transportation • Electronics • Driving Safety • Ecology • Consumerism • Engineering • Construction • Drafting • Robotics • Manufacturing • Electricity • Physics • Optics • Business • Economics • Sports • Chemistry • Cryptography • Finance*

2 Graphing Functions

CONNECTIONS: *Gardening • Finance • Sports • Robotics • Cryptography • Depreciation • Medicine • Space Science • Anthropology • Physical Fitness • Electricity • Conservation • Fund Raising • Physics • Construction • Marketing • Labor • Manufacturing • Civil Engineering • Architecture • Urban Planning • Communication*

Trigonometric Functions

CONNECTIONS: *Astronomy • Mechanics • Entertainment • Horology • Physics • Geography • Navigation • Mechanics • Sports • Construction • Architecture • Automotive Technology • Recreation • Engineering • Forestry • Surveying • Space Science*

Graphs and Inverses of Trigonometric Functions

CONNECTIONS: *Construction • Architecture • Astronomy • Helioseismology • Acoustics • Electricity • Physics • Recreation • Oceanography • Consumerism • Optics • Space Science • Sports • Physiology • Finance • Mechanics • Entertainment • Engineering • Marine Studies*

5 Applications of Trigonometry

CONNECTIONS: *Security • Geography • Construction • Entertainment • Photography • Aviation • Mechanics • Engineering • Surveying • Navigation • Aeronautics • Landscaping • Construction • Advertising • Programming • Manufacturing*

6 Trigonometric Identities and Equations

CONNECTIONS: *Security • Landscaping • Surveying • Forestry • Aviation • Cryptography • Engineering • Consumerism • Sports • Physics • Music • Medicine • Geography • Electricity • Robotics • Biology • Pharmacology*

7 Polynomial Functions

CONNECTIONS: *Landscaping • Computer Technology • Engineering • Manufacturing • Demographics • Space Science • Business • Physics • Ecology • Construction • Surveying • Programming • Architecture • Chemistry • Sociology*

8 Inequalities and Linear Programming

CONNECTIONS: *Construction • Finance • Aviation • Pharmaceuticals • Traffic Control • Manufacturing • Budgeting • Business • Consumerism • Physics • Sports • Conservation • Economics • Space Science • Forestry • Shipping • Recreation • Transportation • Design • Time Management • Nutrition • Communication*

Exponential and Logarithmic Functions

CONNECTIONS: Bacteria Growth • Carbon-14 Dating • Light Intensity • Engineering • Mechanics • Physics • Banking • Geology • Demographics • Space Science • Consumer Awareness • Acoustics • Seismology • Chemistry • Electricity • Radioactive Decay • Banking • Finance • Depreciation • Investment • Health Care

Polar Coordinates and Complex Numbers

CONNECTIONS: Business • Geology • Pharmacology • Physics • Packaging • Astronomy • Chemistry • Radioactive Decay • Electricity • Biology • Programming • Landscaping • Acoustics • Economics

11 Conic Sections

CONNECTIONS: *Landscaping • Design • Archaeology • Construction • Programming • Astronomy • Space Science • Entertainment • Engineering • Navigation • Sports • Physics • Ballistics • Business • Surveying • Gardening • Technology • Communications*

12 Matrices and Vectors

CONNECTIONS: *Manufacturing • Health/Fitness • Shipping • Consumerism • Business • Education • Networking • Communication • Recreation • Traffic Engineering • Sports • Economics • Construction • Cryptography • Investment • Civil Engineering • Aviation • Physics • Navigation • Space Exploration*

13 Sequences and Series

CONNECTIONS: *Travel • Number Theory • Finance • Philately • Programming • Etymology • Aquaculture • Biology • Botany • Technology • Medicine • Real Estate • Economics • Physics • Sports • Genealogy • Business • Computer Science • Ecology • Nature • Design • Civil Engineering • Construction*

14 Probability

CONNECTIONS: *Search and Rescue • Medicine • Sales • Meteorology • Zoology • Travel • Restaurant Management • Biology • Politics • Manufacturing • Management • Sports • Consumerism • Gardening • Programming • Entertainment • International Relations • Marketing • Education • Business • Recreation • Health • Survey Research*

15 Statistics and Data Analysis

CONNECTIONS: *Employment • Health • Marketing • Conservation • Education • Meteorology • Programming • Sports • Fund Raising • Economics • Publishing • Political Science • Business • Sociology • Astronomy • Geography • Medicine • Automotive Engineering • Botany • Linguistics • Zoology • Demographics*

16 Limits and an Introduction to Calculus

CONNECTIONS: *Chemistry • Physics • Biology • Business • Manufacturing • Sports • Construction • Automotive Technology • Mechanics • Ecology • Agriculture • Navigation • Economics • Meteorology • Demographics*

NCTM Correlation

NCTM Standards are listed on page T7.

Lesson	NCTM Standards
1.1	1, 2, 3, 4, 5, 6, 8, 10, 12, 14
1.2	2, 3, 4, 5, 8, 12, 14
1.3	1, 2, 3, 4, 5, 6, 8, 12
1.4	2, 3, 4, 5, 6, 8
1.5	1, 2, 3, 4, 5, 6, 12
1.6	2, 3, 4, 5, 6, 14
1.7	1, 2, 3, 4, 5, 6, 14
2.1	2, 3, 4, 5, 6, 14
2.2	2, 3, 4, 5, 6, 8, 14
2.3	1, 2, 3, 4, 5, 6, 8, 12
2.4	1, 2, 3, 5, 12, 14
2.5	1, 2, 3, 4, 5, 6, 12, 13
2.6	1, 2, 3, 4, 5, 6, 8, 12, 13
2.7	1, 2, 3, 4, 5, 6, 7, 8
2.8	1, 2, 3, 4, 5, 6, 8
3.1	1, 2, 3, 4, 5, 8, 9
3.2	2, 3, 4, 5, 8, 12, 14
3.3	1, 2, 3, 4, 5, 8
3.4	2, 3, 4, 5, 6, 9
3.5	2, 3, 4, 5, 6, 9
3.6	2, 3, 4, 5, 6, 8, 9
3.7	1, 2, 3, 4, 5, 6, 9, 12, 13
3.8	2, 3, 5, 6, 9
3.9	2, 3, 5, 6, 9
4.1	2, 3, 4, 5, 6, 12
4.2	1, 2, 3, 4, 5, 6, 9, 12
4.3	2, 3, 4, 5, 6, 9, 12
4.4	2, 3, 4, 5, 6, 9, 12
4.5	1, 2, 3, 4, 5, 6, 9, 13
4.6	1, 2, 3, 4, 5, 6, 9, 13
4.7	1, 2, 3, 4, 5, 9, 13
5.1	1, 2, 3, 4, 5, 6, 8, 9
5.2	1, 2, 3, 4, 5, 6, 8, 9
5.3	1, 2, 3, 4, 5, 6, 8, 9
5.4	1, 2, 3, 4, 5, 6, 8, 9
5.5	1, 2, 3, 4, 5, 6, 8, 9
6.1	1, 2, 3, 4, 5, 6, 8, 9
6.2	2, 3, 4, 8, 9
6.3	1, 3, 4, 5, 8, 9
6.4	1, 2, 3, 4, 5, 13
6.5	1, 2, 3, 4, 5, 6, 9
6.6	1, 2, 3, 4, 5, 6, 9

Lesson	NCTM Standards
7.1	2, 3, 4, 5, 8
7.2	1, 2, 3, 4, 5, 6, 13
7.3	1, 3, 5, 6, 8
7.4	1, 3, 5, 6, 8
7.5	1, 3, 4, 6, 8, 13
7.6	1, 4, 5, 6, 8, 13, 14
7.7	1, 3, 4, 5, 6
7.8	3, 4, 5, 13, 14

Lesson	NCTM Standards
8.1	1, 2, 3, 4, 5, 8, 12, 14
8.2	1, 2, 3, 4, 5, 6, 8
8.3	1, 2, 3, 4, 5, 6, 8
8.4	1, 2, 3, 4, 5, 6, 8
8.5	1, 2, 3, 4, 5, 6, 8
8.6	1, 2, 3, 4, 5, 6, 8, 12
8.7	1, 2, 3, 4, 5, 6, 8, 12

Developing Mathematical Power

Modeling   1, 2–10, 12, 54–55, 76, 90, 96, 109, 118–119, 128–129, 136, 162, 180–181, 195, 217–218, 229–230, 242–243, 246, 265–266, 284–285, 298–299, 319–320, 328–329, 346, 367, 384–385, 414–415, 420–421, 438–439, 449–450, 471, 486–487, 511, 517–518, 532–533, 552–553, 576–577, 586–587, 594–595, 622–623, 628–629, 649–650, 672–673, 685–686, 724, 731, 740–741, 765, 778–779, 787–788, 796–797, 828, 834, 840, 850–851, 868, 890–891

Communication

Writing in Mathematics   9, 17, 22, 29, 31, 37, 42, 49, 62, 71, 78, 84, 86, 91, 92, 93, 98, 99, 105, 111, 113, 124, 131, 132, 139, 146, 151, 157, 164, 174, 189, 196, 198, 206, 212, 228, 234, 248, 254, 262, 263, 268, 277, 278, 291, 295, 309, 315, 322, 334, 335, 336, 342, 347, 355, 361, 369, 378, 391, 398, 400, 410, 424, 429, 430, 444, 450, 459, 464, 479, 481, 492, 501, 507, 514, 520, 526, 537, 538, 539, 546, 547, 548, 554, 555, 562, 563, 569, 574, 580, 581, 588, 601, 602, 609, 615, 618, 643, 652, 653, 665, 678, 687, 696, 704, 713, 726, 727, 733, 747, 759, 774, 781, 782, 789, 804, 808, 815, 821, 830, 835, 843, 844, 858, 863, 875, 880, 892

Reasoning

Thinking Critically   1, 4, 5, 7, 8, 9, 16, 17, 21–23, 28, 29–31, 34, 35, 36, 37, 41–43, 45, 46, 47, 48, 55, 58, 60, 61, 62, 65, 66, 70, 71, 76, 77, 78, 81, 83–85, 87, 91–93, 96, 97, 98, 99, 103, 104, 105, 106, 108, 109, 111–113, 119, 123, 124, 131, 135, 139, 144–146, 148, 149, 150, 154, 156, 157, 158, 160, 161, 163, 164, 170, 174, 175, 181, 187, 188, 192, 193, 198, 201, 203, 204, 206, 210, 211, 212, 213, 220, 227, 231, 233, 243, 247, 248, 249, 253–255, 260, 261, 267, 269, 276, 277, 285, 291, 295, 299, 301, 302–304, 309, 315, 318, 322, 323, 328, 333, 334–336, 338, 340, 341, 347, 348, 353–355, 357, 359, 360, 362, 367, 368, 369, 374, 378, 379, 385, 387, 390, 391, 392, 397, 398, 399, 403, 404, 405, 410, 411, 414, 415, 417, 419, 420, 423, 424, 428, 429, 431, 439, 443–445, 450, 451, 458, 459, 464, 465, 472–474, 479, 480, 487, 489, 492, 493, 501, 502, 505, 507, 514, 521, 523, 525, 527, 533, 536, 539, 546, 551, 555, 562, 573, 574, 580, 581, 595, 600, 601, 605, 607–609, 615, 617, 618, 620, 624, 631, 637, 638, 643, 644, 651, 653, 657, 658, 662, 664, 665, 673, 677, 678, 680, 682, 684, 687, 688, 694, 696, 703, 711, 712, 713, 716, 717, 718, 719, 722, 725, 726, 727, 734, 741, 745, 747, 752, 754, 758, 760, 767, 769, 774, 779, 780, 781, 788, 789, 797, 802, 803, 806, 808, 809, 810, 812, 813–816, 820, 821, 822, 824, 828, 829, 831, 835, 836, 843, 844, 845, 851, 858, 863, 869, 874, 875, 881, 892, 893

Challenge   17, 37, 72, 93, 106, 132, 146, 165, 199, 221, 256, 271, 296, 316, 342, 363, 375, 400, 417, 452, 474, 502, 521, 548, 569, 582, 610, 625, 644, 658, 689, 713, 727, 754, 776, 810, 831, 864, 881

Developing Mathematical Power

Summary

The technique of using linear and quadratic functions to model real world problems is introduced. The properties of the real number system and the Cartesian coordinate system are discussed as necessary background for the study of relations and functions. The algebra of functions and inverse relations and functions are discussed. Then certain special functions are introduced.

Chapter Objectives

- To use a linear or a quadratic equation as a mathematical model
- To define a mathematical system called a field
- To identify the properties of the set of real numbers and its subsets
- To graph ordered pairs on a coordinate plane
- To graph equations
- To determine the domain and range of relation or function
- To determine whether a given relation is a function
- To determine whether two functions are equal
- To define the sum, difference, product, and quotient of functions
- To form and evaluate composite functions
- To find the inverse of a relation or function
- To determine if the inverse of a function is a function
- To define and graph special functions

1 Functions

Mathematical Power

Modeling   Most of you are familiar with physical models of objects such as cars, airplanes, or buildings. These models may be simpler than the actual objects, or a different size, but the purpose of each of them is to *represent* something in the real world. By examining this representation, you can gain new perspective on the objects being modeled.

Mathematical models, such as graphs, equations, or geometric figures, are also used to represent real world structures and relationships. By using a mathematical model, you can often simplify and, thus, gain understanding about a complex real world problem. After working with the mathematical model, you can translate the results back to the real world situation. If your model was an accurate representation of the problem, then your conclusions may provide a workable solution.

Mathematical models, like physical models, usually describe only limited aspects of the real world and, even then, may yield only approximate answers. If the limitations and approximations are not acceptable for your purposes, then you need to construct a better model by incorporating refinements.

Features

Modeling

Creating a mathematical model requires time, imagination, and usually a great deal of data. Experiments with physical models are often used to generate data for a mathematical model. While mathematical modeling cannot be done mechanically, the following steps can help you in using modeling to solve a real world problem.

Problem Solving Skills

1. *State the question.* A question may be too vague or too big. If the question is vague, make it precise. If it is too big, break it into manageable parts on which you can focus individually.

2. *Identify relevant factors.* Decide which quantities and relationships are important and which can be omitted.

3. *Translate into mathematics.* Represent each quantity with an appropriate mathematical entity, for example, a variable, function, or geometric figure. Express each relationship by an equation, inequality, graph, or other mathematical representation.

4. *Perform the necessary mathematical procedures.* Developing the model rarely gives the answer directly. Usually you will have to do some computation, solve equations, or prove other relationships.

5. *Draw conclusions.* If your model captured the critical features of the problem, you should be able to state or predict something about the real world situation being modeled. Summarize your results.

6. *Evaluate the model.* Decide if your model was a good one. Did the model lead you to make a correct prediction about the real world problem? If not, you may need to modify your model.

Thinking Critically Suppose a student is trying to develop a tire that will provide the best traction, and is working with the mathematical model $C = 2\pi r$, where C is the circumference of the tire and r is the radius. Discuss possible shortcomings of this model.

Project Choose one product that interests you, such as a car or a bicycle or even an article of clothing. Then choose one aspect of that product that you think you could improve. Create a physical model and defend the changes in the model that you are suggesting.

1

Mathematical Power

Motivate the discussion by pointing out that modeling goes to the root of how mathematics is used to analyze the real world. The goal of modeling is to capture some essential aspects of a situation in a way that can be dealt with mathematically, thus making it possible for a problem to be studied conveniently on paper (or computer screen). Elicit from students examples of situations modeled by graphs, equations, and geometric figures. Emphasize that many situations can give rise to the same mathematical model. As an exercise, have students suggest different real world situations that could be modeled by the equation $x + y = 100$.

When you discuss the steps for modeling, remind students that half of the battle of trying to solve a difficult problem is knowing the right questions to ask. Also mention that, for complex situations, it is often helpful to look at an easier, special case first.

Thinking Critically Some reasons for using mathematical models are: to save time and money; to avoid experiments that may endanger life or property; to study the behavior of products or processes before they exist; to examine several possibilities simultaneously.

Vocabulary
mathematical model

Ⓜ **Materials/Manipulatives**
driver's manual
graph paper
transparencies
VCR

Technology
calculator
graphing utility

FOCUS

Students should be quite familiar
with the workings of a video cassette
recorder. You might find it effective
to have them collect data from their
own VCRs and compare and contrast the results to the data presented in the Focus. Also, once the
students recognize the quadratic
relationship in the table and the
graph, they will be prompted to ask
"Why?" Encourage them to speculate on what type of mechanism
powers the counter on a VCR.

1.1 Introduction to Modeling

Objectives: To use a linear equation as a mathematical model
To use a quadratic equation as a mathematical model

Focus

Suppose you are watching a video
movie. After 15 minutes, you leave to
answer the phone without turning off
the video tape. After another 15 minutes,
you return and want to rewind the tape
to see the part you missed. The counter
on the VCR registers 686, so you decide that you should rewind the tape until it
registers half of 686, or 343. When you do this, you find that you have rewound
to a point in the movie that came well *before* you received the phone call. *Why?*

The data in the table at
the right relates counter
readings on the VCR to
elapsed time. The
graph shows that this
relationship is not
linear; that is, the
counter readings do not
increase at a constant
rate.

Counter reading x	Elapsed time y (min)
0	0
32	1
64	2
93	3
123	4
151	5
281	10
397	15
500	20
600	25
686	30
850	40
1000	50

Organizing and graphing data are two important tools used in *data analysis*.
They allow you to visualize the particular relationships that are suggested in a
real world problem. Data analysis is used extensively in the process of *modeling,*
a method by which real world phenomena are described mathematically.

To understand a complicated system in the real world, it is often helpful to
create a simplified representation of that system. Suppose you are giving
directions to your house. You might draw a simplified map of the route, leaving
out the streets that are not necessary. This simplified map is an example
of a model. A **mathematical model,** then, is a mathematical representation of
some aspect of a real world system. One kind of mathematical model is an
equation.

In Example 1, a linear equation is found to fit the given data. The slope m of a
line is the ratio of the change in vertical distance to the change in horizontal
distance.

2   Chapter 1 Functions

Recall

If $P(x_1, y_1)$ and $Q(x_2, y_2)$ are two points on a line and m is the slope and b is the y-intercept, then

$$m = \frac{y_2 - y_1}{x_2 - x_1} \qquad x_1 \neq x_2 \qquad \textit{Slope of a line}$$

Two equations of a line are

$$y = mx + b \qquad \textit{Slope-intercept form}$$
$$y - y_1 = m(x - x_1) \qquad \textit{Point-slope form}$$

When you find an equation that seems to fit the data, substitute other points to see if a true statement results. Once you verify that the equation is a valid model, use the equation to answer questions or make predictions.

Example 1 *Transportation* A tourist has a pamphlet which contains the following list of taxi fares for various distances. How much should the tourist expect to pay for a taxi ride that covers 9.5 mi?

Miles driven	1	2	3	5	10	15
Cost ($)	1.65	2.90	4.15	6.65	12.90	19.15

From the graph it appears that the equation that models this set of data is linear. To find the equation, choose two points from the data set, $(1, 1.65)$ and $(2, 2.90)$. Use the two points to find the slope of the line that contains them.

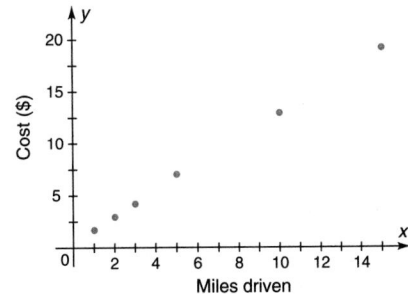

$$m = \frac{y_2 - y_1}{x_2 - x_1} \qquad \textit{Slope of a line}$$

$$m = \frac{2.90 - 1.65}{2 - 1} \qquad \textit{Substitute.}$$

$$m = 1.25$$

Now use the point-slope form to find the equation of the line.

$$y - y_1 = m(x - x_1) \qquad \textit{Point-slope form}$$
$$y - 1.65 = 1.25(x - 1) \qquad \textit{Substitute.}$$
$$y = 1.25x + 0.40$$

The equation can be interpreted as follows: The cost of a trip is an initial $0.40 plus $1.25 for each additional mile.

Substitute other points to see if the equation is a valid model. Then use the equation to find the cost of the 9.5-mi ride.

$$y = 1.25(9.5) + 0.40 = 12.275$$

The tourist can expect to pay about $12.28 for a 9.5-mi taxi ride.

1.1 Introduction to Modeling **3**

For Example 1

1. For many drugs, the dosage administered is a function of body weight. A nurse has a dosage card from the manufacturer of Antrocol Elixir for children which contains the following list of recommended dosages for various body weights. Find the proper dosage, to the nearest tenth of a milliliter, for a child weighing 39 lb.

Body weight x (lb)	Dosage y (mL)
15	0.5
27	0.9
33	1.1
46	1.5
52	1.7
65	2.2

1.3 mL

2. Below is a chart relating the distance w between parallel sides of a bolthead and the diameter d of a bolt that fits that bolthead. What is the diameter of a bolt that would fit into a bolthead if the distance between parallel sides is 0.6875 in.?

Distance between sides w (in.)	Diameter of the bolt d (in.)
1.0625	0.625 $\left(\frac{5}{8}\right)$
1.2500	0.750 $\left(\frac{3}{4}\right)$
1.4375	0.875 $\left(\frac{7}{8}\right)$
1.6250	1.000 (1)
1.8125	1.125 $\left(1\frac{1}{8}\right)$

0.375 in. or $\frac{3}{8}$ in.

In any modeling situation, certain *assumptions* are made. In Example 1, it was assumed that the relationship was linear and that the fare increased continuously as the mileage increased. Actually, most taxi fares increase in *increments* such as one-tenth of a mile. Such a case would be better modeled by a step function, which will be discussed in Lesson 1.7. However, the continuous linear model is sufficient for finding an approximate price for the tourist to pay.

In many problem situations the data does not suggest a linear relationship. The data and the graph in the Focus, for example, suggest that the relationship between the counter reading and the elapsed time on a VCR is quadratic. *How would you find an equation that fits the data in the table?*

> **Recall**
>
> The graph of a *quadratic function* defined by an equation of the form $y = ax^2 + bx + c$ is a parabola.

To find the coefficients a, b, and c of the equation, you may need to solve a system of equations as shown in Example 2. When solving equations using real world data, values are usually not exact. Throughout the text the equals symbol will be used in equations with approximate values, but the context should make it clear when approximate values are being used, as in Example 2. When using a calculator, values should not be rounded until the end of a calculation.

Example 2 *Electronics* Use the data taken from the VCR described in the Focus to find an equation that relates the counter reading to the elapsed time of the tape. Round the values of the coefficients to five decimal places.

Since the graph of the data appears to form a parabola, the relationship may be quadratic. The point $(0, 0)$ is in the data set, so you can substitute for x and y in the quadratic equation to find c.

$$y = ax^2 + bx + c$$
$$0 = a(0)^2 + b(0) + c$$
$$0 = c$$

Then the equation that models the data is

$$y = ax^2 + bx$$

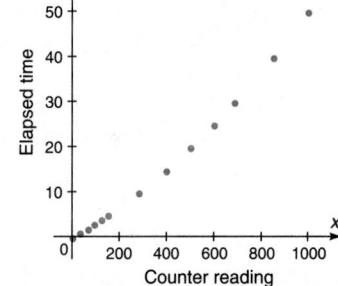

To find the coefficients a and b that fit the set of data, choose two points from the data and substitute them for x and y. This will give a system of two linear equations which can be solved for a and b. The values of a and b will depend on which points you choose to substitute. In this case, the points $(64, 2)$ and $(500, 20)$ are used.

$$2 = a(64)^2 + b(64)$$
$$20 = a(500)^2 + b(500)$$

$$\begin{cases} 2 = 4096a + 64b \\ 20 = 250{,}000a + 500b \end{cases}$$ *Solve the system for a and b.*

$$\begin{array}{ll} -250 = -512{,}000a - 8000b & \text{\textit{Multiply the first equation by} } -125. \\ \underline{320 = 4{,}000{,}000a + 8000b} & \text{\textit{Multiply the second equation by} } 16. \\ 70 = 3{,}488{,}000a \\ a = 0.00002007 & \text{\textit{Approximate value}} \end{array}$$

Substitute for a in one of the original equations and solve for b. When using a calculator, store the value of a in the memory and use that value in further calculations. This will help to cut down on errors due to rounding. Save your rounding for the last step.

$$2 = 4096(0.00002007) + 64b \qquad \text{\textit{Substitute for a.}}$$

$$b = \frac{2 - 4096(0.00002007)}{64} = 0.0299655963$$

Rounding to five decimal places yields $a = 0.00002$ and $b = 0.02997$. The equation that relates the counter reading x to the elapsed time y on the tape is

$$y = 0.00002x^2 + 0.02997x$$

The coefficients in the above model are dependent on the points chosen from the data set. A different choice of points would yield different coefficients. Therefore, check other data points to see if the equation models the data accurately. If 123 is substituted for x, the value of y is 3.98889. If 850 is substituted for x, the value of y is 39.9245. *Do these values suggest that the equation is a fairly accurate model of the data? Explain.*

You can use a model to make predictions about the variable. If the value of y is known, you may need to use the quadratic formula.

> **Recall**
>
> The solutions of a quadratic equation $ax^2 + bx + c = 0$, $a \neq 0$, are given by the *quadratic formula*
> $$x = \frac{-b \pm \sqrt{b^2 - 4ac}}{2a}$$

Example 3 *Electronics* Use the equation in Example 2 to predict the counter reading on a VCR after one hour of playing time.

$$\begin{array}{ll} y = 0.00002x^2 + 0.02997x \\ 60 = 0.00002x^2 + 0.02997x & \text{\textit{Substitute.}} \\ 0 = 0.00002x^2 + 0.02997x - 60 \\ x = \dfrac{-0.02997 \pm \sqrt{(0.02997)^2 - 4(0.00002)(-60)}}{2(0.00002)} & \text{\textit{Quadratic formula}} \\ x = 1137.9107 \quad \text{or} \quad x = -2636.4107 \end{array}$$

The counter will read 1138 to the nearest unit.

For Example 2
The dosages of some medications are calculated proportionally to a person's body surface area measured in square meters. The chart below relates the surface area A for children of normal height to their body weight x. Find a model that relates the surface area to the weight of a child of normal height. Round the values of the coefficients to five decimal places.

Weight x (lb)	Surface area A (m²)
0	0
3	0.13
8	0.24
15	0.36
20	0.44
24	0.50

Using the points (8, 0.24) and (24, 0.50), the model is $A = -0.00057x^2 + 0.03458x$.

Common Error Students may round before completing the calculations and thereby have an error in the model. Remind these students to save the rounding for the last step.

For Example 3
Use the equation in Example 2 to predict the body surface area of a child of normal height for each of the following weights.
1. 11 lb 0.31 m²
2. 4 lb 7 oz 0.14 m²

Common Error If mixed measurements are stated in a problem, some students may forget to change the expression to a single equivalent unit of measurement. It is important that students understand that all measurements should correspond to the units of measurement used in the statement of the relationship.

Thinking Critically
Yes, the values (123, 3.98939) and (850, 39.9705) suggest that the equation $y = 0.00002x^2 + 0.2997x$ is a fairly accurate model of the data because these values are approximately the same as the values given in the table, (123, 4) and (850, 40).

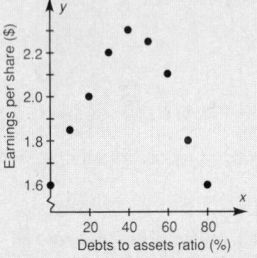
The equation in Example 3 yields two values for *x*, one positive and one negative. Since the counter reading cannot be negative, only the positive value is correct. Negative values are not in the *replacement set* for the variable representing counter reading. Remember that the *solution set* of an equation must be a subset of the replacement set. A real world problem may impose more restrictions on the replacement set than the equation that is used to model it. It is especially important in a modeling situation to refer back to the original problem when checking your answers.

An equation will not always fit the data as well as those in Examples 1 and 2. Often you must analyze the graph and use your judgment to find the equation that best models a set of data.

The stopping distance of an automobile is a function of the speed of the automobile at the time the driver recognizes the need to stop. The data in the table shows average stopping distances on dry pavement for various speeds. This data can be used to determine a mathematical model for the stopping distance of an automobile driven on dry pavement.

Speed (mi/h)	Stopping distance (ft)
0	0
20	47
30	88
40	149
50	243
60	366

First determine what kind of equation would best fit the data. Plotting the data points on a graph can often help you make this determination.

The data for stopping distances is plotted at the right. The points do not all seem to lie on a line. Therefore, the mathematical relationship between stopping distance and speed is probably not linear. However, the graph appears to resemble the shape of a parabola, so a quadratic function may be a more appropriate model for this data.

Example 4 *Driving Safety* Using the three data points (0, 0), (20, 47), and (30, 88), determine an equation for stopping distance in terms of speed. Round the coefficients to the nearest thousandth.

$y = ax^2 + bx + c$	*Find a, b, and c.*
$0 = 0a + 0b + c$	*Substitute (0, 0) for x and y.*
$0 = c$	
$47 = (20)^2a + 20b + c$	*Substitute (20, 47) for x and y.*
$47 = 400a + 20b$	*Substitute 0 for c.*
$88 = (30)^2a + 30b + c$	*Substitute (30, 88) for x and y.*
$88 = 900a + 30b$	*Substitute 0 for c.*

Solve the system of equations by the addition method.

6 Chapter 1 Functions

$$\begin{cases} 47 = 400a + 20b \\ 88 = 900a + 30b \end{cases}$$

$$\begin{aligned} -141 &= -1200a - 60b &&\text{\textit{Multiply both sides of the first equation by} } -3. \\ \underline{176} &= \underline{1800a + 60b} &&\text{\textit{Multiply both sides of the second equation by} } 2. \\ 35 &= 600a &&\text{\textit{Add the equations.}} \\ a &= 0.058333333 \end{aligned}$$

Solve for b by substituting for a in the first equation.

$$47 = 400(0.058333333) + 20b$$

$$b = \frac{47 - 400(0.058333333)}{20} \qquad \text{\textit{Calculation-ready form}}$$

$$b = 1.183333333$$

To the nearest thousandth, $a = 0.058$ and $b = 1.183$. Substituting for a, b, and c yields the equation

$$y = 0.058x^2 + 1.183x$$

Remember that once a model is found, it is necessary to test the model for different values of the data to see how accurate it is.

Example 5 *Driving Safety* Using the equation to predict stopping distance developed in Example 4, test the model for speeds of 40 and 50 mi/h.

$$y = 0.058x^2 + 1.183x$$

For $x = 40$ mi/h: $\begin{aligned}[t] y &= 0.058(40)^2 + 1.183(40) \\ y &= 140.12 \approx 140 \end{aligned}$

The model predicts that at 40 mi/h it will take 140 ft for the car to stop. According to the data in the table, it will actually take the car 149 ft to stop.

For $x = 50$ mi/h: $\begin{aligned}[t] y &= 0.058(50)^2 + 1.183(50) \\ y &= 204.15 \approx 204 \end{aligned}$

The model predicts that at 50 mi/h it will take 204 ft for the car to stop. According to the data in the table, it will actually take the car 243 ft to stop. *What conclusions can you draw about the reliability of this model? Is it sufficiently accurate for a driver to safely predict stopping distance?*

The equation derived in Example 4 does not fit the data exactly. However, there are many ways to improve a model's accuracy. One method is to start with a different set of data points and see if the resulting equation provides a more accurate model. Try to choose points that represent different parts of the curve. Another method is to use a graphing calculator or computer to plot the data points and to graph the equation of the model. Make slight adjustments to the coefficients in the equation until the graph fits the data well. Later in this course you will learn statistical methods for finding an equation of "best fit."

1.1 Introduction to Modeling   **7**

Thinking Critically
Students' conclusions may vary, but they should reflect the notion that the model is fairly accurate for low speeds but not for high speeds. Students should also note that a difference of 39 ft, when referring to stopping distance of a car, is very significant.

CLOSURE
Have students write a paragraph or two in their math journals summarizing the procedure for finding a mathematical model (equation) that best fits a set of data.

INDEPENDENT PRACTICE
Assignment Guide
Basic: 1–16, 20–21, 23, Project
Average: 8–26, Project
Enriched: 13–30, Project

Teacher's Resource Book
  Practice, page 1

Note: Any answers that do not appear on the student pages of this text can be found in the side columns, or in the Additional Answers Section that begins on page 947.

Ⓡ Review
Exercises 3, 12, 16, and 20 review concepts and methods of solving various types of linear equations, including equations with parentheses, literal equations, systems of three equations in three variables, and fractional equations.

Technology
Students should be encouraged to use technology when trying to find the equations and graphs in the exercises. This will improve accuracy and also invite more serious analysis of their findings.

Project
The project introduces the concept of depreciation. Encourage students to attempt to explain why an item like a car depreciates in value over time. The students' findings in this project may prove useful later in the course when they study exponential functions.

LESSON FOLLOW-UP

Lesson Quiz

1. The weight W of a steel beam with uniform cross-sectional area is a function of its length L. A manufacturer of steel beams collected the following data. Find a linear model for determining the weight of a beam if its length is known.

Length L (ft)	Weight W (lb)
0	0
6	270
8	360
10	450
12	540

$W = 45L$

2. Use the model in Exercise 1 to find the weight of a 7.3-ft beam.
328.5 lb

3. For a given resistance the power P developed in a circuit is a function of the current I. The following data was collected for a given circuit. Find a quadratic model for determining the power in the circuit when the current is known. Round the coefficients to the nearest hundredth.

Current I (amps)	Power P (W)
0	0
1.2	11.8
1.7	23.7
2.3	43.4
2.5	51.3

Using the points (1.2, 11.8) and (2.5, 51.3) yields $P = 8.22I^2 - 0.03I$

4. Use the model you found in Exercise 3 to determine the power developed in the circuit if the current is 1.9 amps. 29.6 W

Additional Answers
Class Exercises

1.

Class Exercises

Ecology   A community offered students a chance to earn money while helping clean up litter. The table below lists their earnings based on the number of bags of litter they collected.

Number of bags	1	3	5	8	11	12
Earnings ($)	0.80	3.60	6.40	10.60	14.80	16.20

1. Graph the data and determine if a linear or quadratic relationship is appropriate. linear

2. Use the first two data points to find a model for the method of payment. $y = 1.4x - 0.6$

3. Test the model found in Exercise 1 for 11 bags and 12 bags. Draw a conclusion about the accuracy of the model. $14.80; $16.20; The model appears to be accurate.

4. Use the model to predict the earnings of a student who collects 20 bags. $27.40

5. **Thinking Critically**   If the community were posting an advertisement for this opportunity, how might the method of payment be phrased?
Earn $0.80 for the first bag and $1.40 for each additional bag.

6. Using the data points (0, 0), (30, 88), and (60, 366) and Example 4, find an equation for stopping distance. $y = 0.106x^2 - 0.233x$

7. Compare the results of applying the models in Example 4 and Exercise 6 for the speed of 50 mi/h. 204 ft; 253 ft; The model in Exercise 6 is a better predictor.

Practice Exercises   Use appropriate technology.

Consumerism   Carlos made six long distance calls to his mother's house last month on weekday afternoons. The length and cost of each call is listed below.

Length of call (min)	1	3	6	14	15	32
Cost ($)	0.37	0.59	0.92	1.80	1.91	3.78

A 1. Use the data points (6, 0.92) and (14, 1.80) to find a linear model for the company's billing system. $y = 0.11x + 0.26$

2. Use the model developed in Exercise 1 to predict the cost of a 23-min call. $2.79

Ⓡ 3. Solve for x: $7(3x + 6) - 11 = -(x + 2)$ $x = -\frac{3}{2}$

The following data was collected by measuring the distance d which an object falls for various lengths of time t. A negative distance means that the object is d feet *below* the point from which it was dropped.

Time (s)	0	1	2	3	4
Distance (ft)	0	−16	−64	−143	−250

4. Plot the points in the table on a graph. Analyze the graph to determine if a linear or quadratic model best fits the data. quadratic

5. Using the first three data points in the table, find an equation that relates the distance an object falls to time. $d = -16t^2$

6. **Thinking Critically**   Test the equation found in Exercise 5 for times of 3 and 4 s. What conclusions can you draw about the accuracy of the model?

8   Chapter 1 Functions

Additional Answers, Practice Exercises
6. −144 ft; −256 ft; Answers may vary. In general, the model is a good predictor for times of less than 4 s but is less accurate beyond 4 s.

7. Use the model determined in Exercise 5 to predict the distance that an object will fall in 7.25 s. 841 ft

Engineering A new radial tire has a tread depth of 0.28 in. Testing of this tire showed the following relationship between number of miles driven and the tread depth of the tire.

Number of miles driven	0	5000	12,000	23,000
Tread depth (in.)	0.28	0.26	0.21	0.15

8. Graph the data given and determine if a linear model best fits the data. yes
9. Using the data points (5000, 0.26) and (12,000, 0.21), find an equation which expresses tread depth as a function of the number of miles driven.
10. Test the model developed in Exercise 9 using the point (23,000, 0.15). 0.13 in.; Model is off by 0.02 in.
11. Using the model developed in Exercise 9, predict after how many miles new tires would need to be purchased if tires must be replaced when the tread is 0.06 in. 33,199 mi

Ⓡ 12. Solve for x in terms of a and b: $3ax - 2a^2 = 6bx$

13. **Thinking Critically** Suppose you are solving a real world problem and you are not given instructions on how to round your answer. How might you go about deciding on a rounding procedure?

B 14. *Recreation* The all-weather ice-skating rink has determined that when the temperature is 32°F at 8 a.m., they can expect 100 skaters in the morning session. For each 5°F rise in temperature, 7 fewer skaters will attend this session. Find the linear equation that relates the number of skaters to the temperature. $y = -1.4x + 144.8$

15. Use the equation derived in Exercise 14 to find the number of skaters for the morning session if the temperature is 43°F at 8 a.m. 85

Ⓡ 16. Solve the system of equations using the addition method: $\begin{cases} x + y + z = 0 \\ 2x + 3y = 2 \\ y - 3z = 2.5 \end{cases}$ $(-0.5, 1, -0.5)$

17. *Construction* A zookeeper has 500 ft of fencing and wants to build a rectangular pen. Find a quadratic equation that relates the area of the pen to its length. $A = 250\ell - \ell^2$

18. Graph the equation derived in Exercise 17 representing the length on the horizontal axis and the area on the vertical axis.

19. Use the graph to determine the value of the length that will yield the maximum area. Use the equation to verify the maximum. 125 ft

Ⓡ 20. Solve: $\dfrac{m}{m-7} = \dfrac{m}{m-7} + 11$ and indicate any restrictions on the solution. No solution. $m \neq 7$

21. **Writing in Mathematics** A real world problem may have more restrictions on its replacement set than the mathematical equation that models it. Write a paragraph explaining why this is so.

22. **Thinking Critically** Examine the graph in Exercise 18 to determine which part of the graph does not pertain to the problem situation. Explain.

Writing in Mathematics
21. Although a function or equation may be defined for all values of the independent variable, when the independent variable represents a measurable quantity such as time, the replacement set may need to be restricted to nonnegative numbers. If the independent variable represents the number of items to be manufactured, the replacement set may need to be restricted to whole numbers.

Alternative Assessment
Have students choose a situation or problem that they encounter in everyday life such as estimating the cost of a taxi ride or a phone call, measuring the area of a ball field, or keeping track of their grades. Have them collect a set of data for this problem and determine a mathematical model. Each student should justify his or her choice of model and prepare a presentation of the material to be given to the class.

Enrichment
An employee of a company agrees to take a pay cut this year but is guaranteed that his salary will be restored to its original level next year. If his pay is cut by $x\%$ this year, by what percent will it have to be increased next year? $\dfrac{x}{1-x}$

Additional Answers

4.

8.

9. $y = -0.0000071x + 0.2957143$

12. $x = \dfrac{2a^2}{3a - 6b}$

13. Examine the test data to determine the accuracy needed and only round answers at the last step.

18.

22. When the curve falls on or below the x-axis, the result is a negative area or an area of 0, both of which are inappropriate.

23. **Thinking Critically**   Suppose you have a three-digit counter on your VCR and the number 999 is followed by 000. Use the model in Example 2 to find what the counter reading would be after a movie that ran 2 h 55 min. 302

Mechanical Engineering   A ballistics expert, studying trajectory, uses a device that fires projectiles at a constant velocity but varies the angles at which they are launched. Below is a table showing the horizontal distances that the projectiles travel for various launch angles.

Angle (degrees)	0	15	30	45	60	75	90
Distance (m)	0	104	181	209	180	105	0

C 24. Plot the points in the table and determine what type of equation would best model the data. quadratic

25. Use the data points (0, 0), (15, 104), and (30, 181) to find an appropriate equation relating the launch angle to the horizontal distance traveled. $y = -0.06x^2 + 7.83x$

26. Repeat Exercise 25 using points (15, 104), (45, 209), and (75, 105).

27. **Thinking Critically**   Make tables of values for the equations derived in Exercises 25 and 26, and graph each equation. Compare the tables and graphs to the original data. What conclusions can you draw about the accuracy of the two models?

28. **Writing in Mathematics**   Write a paragraph explaining what the data reveals about the relationship between the launch angle and the horizontal distance traveled. Why is the distance 0 for 90°?

29. **Thinking Critically**   Using the equation derived in Exercise 25, what prediction can you make about the horizontal distance traveled by a projectile launched at an angle of 150°? 176 m in the opposite direction

30. Suppose you have a three-digit counter on your VCR and after rewinding a 20-min segment of tape, the counter reading is 545. Use the model in Example 2 to determine the reading before the tape was rewound. 886

Project

Find newspapers or magazines giving new and used car prices. Find a car you would like to own and make a graph comparing the value of the car every year from the time of purchase until it is 8 years old. Using the data in the graph, make a model that predicts the value of the car after a given number of years.

Review

Factor.

1. $x^2 - 10xy + 25y^2$ $(x - 5y)^2$ 2. $25x^2 - y^2$ $(5x - y)(5x + y)$

3. Solve the inequality $|2x - 7| < 15$ and graph the solution set. $-4 < x < 11$

4. Determine the coordinates of all points that are 5 units from the y-axis and 3 units from the x-axis. (5, 3), (5, -3), (-5, 3), (-5, -3)

5. Simplify $-3x^2y^{-4}$ if $x = -3$ and $y = 2$. $\frac{-27}{16}$

10   Chapter 1 Functions

1.2 The Real Number System

Objectives: To define a mathematical system called a field
To identify the properties of the set of real numbers and its subsets

Focus

The Greeks contributed greatly to the development of mathematics in general and of geometry in particular. In an attempt to use logic to describe phenomena in the natural world, Greek thinkers provided the foundation on which much of contemporary mathematics was built. But even the Greeks could not foresee the extent of their contributions. Their studies of the relationships that exist in geometric planes and solids would be extended to include abstractions that they could not comprehend.

One important aspect of the Greeks' study of geometry is the technique of *geometric construction.* This is the practice of creating or duplicating a figure using only a compass and a straightedge. Geometric constructions can be directly applied in areas such as drafting. But they can also be used to illustrate abstract concepts about the *real number system.*

It is important to have an understanding of the properties of the real number system. The set of **real numbers** $\Re$ is the union of the set of rational numbers Q and the set of irrational numbers. The set of rational numbers has several subsets which can be used to describe different real world phenomena.

Recall	
Natural numbers	$N = \{1, 2, 3, 4, \ldots\}$
Whole numbers	$W = \{0, 1, 2, 3, 4, \ldots\}$
Integers	$Z = \{\ldots, -3, -2, -1, 0, 1, 2, 3, \ldots\}$

Rational numbers are defined as numbers that can be written in the form $\frac{a}{b}$, where a and b are integers and $b \neq 0$. Each rational number can be written as a terminating or repeating decimal. Numbers such as $\frac{3}{4}$, $\frac{11}{2}$, -0.05, 2.3, and $0.272727 \ldots$ are all rational.

1.2 The Real Number System   **11**

Vocabulary
associative property
binary operation
closure property
commutative property
distributive property
field
identity property
integers
inverse property
irrational numbers
natural numbers
rational numbers
real numbers
reflexive property
substitution property
symmetric property
transitive property
whole numbers

Ⓜ **Materials/Manipulatives**
compass
straightedge

Technology
calculator
computer

FOCUS

The use of geometric constructions to better understand the real number system is a first step in introducing analytic geometry. The correspondence between the set of real numbers and the number line can later be extended to introduce the correspondence between the set of ordered pairs and the coordinate plane.

Ⓜ • Use a compass and straightedge to review the following constructions before discussing Example 1:

Construct an angle congruent to a given angle.

Construct a segment or ray perpendicular to a given line at a point on the line.

• Demonstrate how to find the inverse of any element in a table. Point out that if the corresponding row for any element does not contain the identity element, the given element has no inverse. Ask students what it would mean if the identity element appeared twice in one row.

Alternative Learning Styles

Some students need to explore concrete examples and find patterns before discussing abstract mathematical ideas. Have students use a calculator to find values of numbers such as $\sqrt{5}$, $\sqrt{3}$, $\frac{1}{2}$, $\frac{1}{3}$, and $\frac{2}{7}$ and determine a pattern in the decimal part of these numbers which will classify a number as rational or irrational.

GUIDED PRACTICE

For Example 1

1. Locate $-\frac{2}{3}$ on the number line.

Draw a ray through zero on the number line. Mark off three equal lengths on the ray. Draw a segment from P to the point -1 on the number line. Copy $\angle P$ at Q. The coordinate of R is $-\frac{2}{3}$.

Irrational numbers are real numbers that are not rational numbers. The set of irrational numbers contains numbers such as $\sqrt{2}$, $\sqrt[3]{5}$, π, and e. The sets of rational and irrational numbers have no elements in common and are therefore mutually exclusive.

A calculator performs operations with rational numbers. The calculator manipulates irrational numbers by converting them to very accurate decimal approximations. To reduce rounding errors in your calculations, remember to confine your rounding to the last step and to store decimal approximations in the calculator's memory when necessary. Also, for greater accuracy, use the calculator keys designated for irrational numbers, such as π or e.

Modeling

How can you use geometric constructions to represent real numbers on a number line?

Just as modeling can be used to make a real world problem more understandable, it can also be used to make an abstract concept more concrete. For example, the techniques of geometric construction can be used to illustrate the idea that every element in the set of real numbers can be represented on a number line. Draw a line with a straightedge and choose a point on it to represent 0. You can then choose some unit length and use a compass to locate points for the integers. Geometric constructions can also be used to find points on the number line that represent rational numbers and points that represent irrational numbers.

Example 1 Locate each point on the number line.

    a. $\frac{3}{5}$ **b.** $\sqrt{2}$

a. Draw a ray through zero on the number line. Mark off five equal lengths on the ray and label the end of the third length Q and the fifth length P. Draw $\overline{PA}$. Copy $\angle P$ at Q. Since $\overline{QR}$ is parallel to $\overline{PA}$, the coordinate of R is $\frac{3}{5}$.

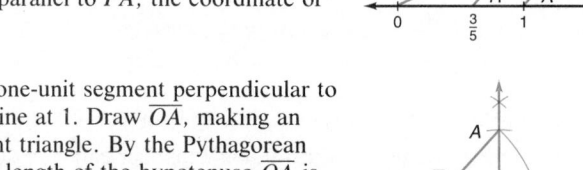

b. Construct a one-unit segment perpendicular to the number line at 1. Draw $\overline{OA}$, making an isosceles right triangle. By the Pythagorean theorem, the length of the hypotenuse $\overline{OA}$ is $\sqrt{2}$. Use a compass to locate this value on the number line.

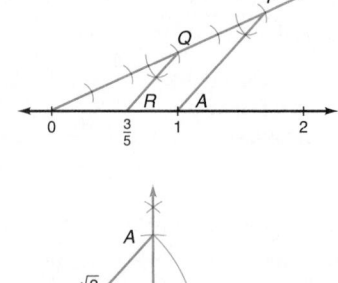

12   Chapter 1 Functions

The Real Number System

Theoretically, any real number can be located on the number line. Geometric constructions provide an excellent model of the *one-to-one correspondence* between the set of real numbers and the set of points on the number line.

A **binary operation** sets up a correspondence between any two elements in a set and another element in the set. Addition, subtraction, multiplication, and division are familiar binary operations on the set of real numbers. The set of real numbers and the two binary operations of addition and multiplication form an important mathematical structure called a **field** that has the properties listed below. The operations of addition and multiplication are related by the distributive property.

Field Properties of the Set of Real Numbers

Let a, b, and c be real numbers.

	Addition Properties	Multiplication Properties
Closure	$a + b$ is a unique real number.	ab is a unique real number.
Commutative	$a + b = b + a$	$ab = ba$
Associative	$(a + b) + c = a + (b + c)$	$(ab)c = a(bc)$
Identity	There exists a unique real number zero, 0, such that $a + 0 = 0 + a = a$.	There exists a unique real number one, 1, such that $a \cdot 1 = 1 \cdot a = a$.
Inverse	For each real number a, there is a unique real number $-a$ such that $a + (-a) = (-a) + a = 0$.	For each *nonzero* real number a, there is a unique real number $\frac{1}{a}$ such that $a\left(\frac{1}{a}\right) = \left(\frac{1}{a}\right)a = 1$.
Distributive	$a(b + c) = ab + ac$	

Example 2 Name the field property of the real number system illustrated in each statement.

a. $2\pi r = 2r\pi$
b. $0.625(1.6) = 1$
c. $1 + 0$ is a real number
d. $2[3.27 + (-3.27)] = 2(0)$

a. commutative, multiplication
b. multiplicative inverse
c. closure, addition
d. additive inverse

The set of real numbers with the operations of addition and multiplication is only one example of a field. A field is any set, finite or infinite, with two binary operations having all the properties listed above. For a finite set, the field properties can be verified by checking all possible combinations of all elements. Of course, if a property does not hold for any combination of elements, then a field is not formed.

1.2 The Real Number System **13**

2. Locate $\sqrt{5}$ on the number line.

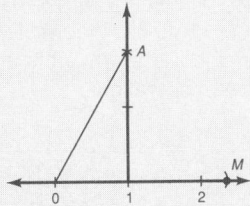

Construct a perpendicular segment 2 units long to the number line at 1. Draw $\overline{OA}$, forming a right triangle. Then $\overline{OA}$ is $\sqrt{5}$ units long. Using a compass and $\overline{OA}$ as the radius, with O as the center, draw $\overline{AM}$. Then the coordinate of M is $\sqrt{5}$.

For Example 2
Name the field property of the real number system illustrated in each statement.

1. $\sqrt{7} \cdot 1 = 1 \cdot \sqrt{7} = \sqrt{7}$
   multiplicative identity

2. $\left(2 + \frac{2}{3}\right) + \frac{1}{3} = 2 + 1$
   associative, addition

3. $(5 \cdot 0)(2) = (5 \cdot 0)$
   associative, multiplication

Example 3 The operations ⊕ and ⊗ are defined on the set $S = \{0, 1, 2, 3\}$ in the tables below. Determine if this set forms a field under these operations.

⊕	0	1	2	3
0	0	1	2	3
1	1	2	3	0
2	2	3	0	1
3	3	0	1	2

⊗	0	1	2	3
0	0	0	0	0
1	0	1	2	3
2	0	2	0	2
3	0	3	2	1

Test to determine if the operation of ⊕ is commutative.

$2 \oplus 3 = 1$ *Find the intersection of the row for 2 and the column for 3.*

$3 \oplus 2 = 1$ *Find the intersection of the row for 3 and the column for 2.*

A test of all the elements shows that for all elements a and b in S,

$$a \oplus b = b \oplus a$$

Therefore, the operation ⊕ is commutative. Similarly, it can be shown that all the field properties are satisfied for the operation ⊕. The identity element for ⊕ is 0.

The identity element for ⊗ is 1. Since there is no 1 in the row for 2, the element 2 has no inverse under the operation ⊗. Therefore, the set S with the operations ⊕ and ⊗ does not form a field.

The field properties, along with the properties of equality listed below, can be used to prove theorems about real numbers.

Properties of Equality	
$a = a$	**Reflexive property**
If $a = b$, then $b = a$.	**Symmetric property**
If $a = b$ and $b = c$, then $a = c$.	**Transitive property**
If $a = b$, then b may be substituted for a.	**Substitution property**

Example 4 Using the field properties of real numbers and the properties of equality, prove the theorem:

If a, b, and c are real numbers and $a = b$, then $ca = cb$.

Proof

a, b, c are real numbers	*Given*
ca and cb are real numbers	*Closure*
$ca = ca$	*Reflexive property*
$a = b$	*Given*
$ca = cb$	*Substitute b for a.*

14   Chapter 1 Functions

Class Exercises

Using a compass and a straightedge, locate each point on the number line.

1. $-\frac{1}{3}$

2. $\frac{7}{5}$

3. $\sqrt{5}$

Given that r and m are real numbers and $r \neq 0$, complete each sentence and name the field property illustrated.

4. $r + \underline{?} = \underline{?} + r = r$ 0; 0; add. ident.

5. $r \cdot \underline{?} = \underline{?} \cdot r = 1$ $\frac{1}{r}; \frac{1}{r}$; mult. inv.

6. $(\underline{?} + 2) + 5 = 3 + (2 + 5)$ 3; assoc. add.

7. $m \cdot \underline{?} = \underline{?} \cdot m = m$ 1; 1; mult. ident.

8. $r(2 + \underline{?}) = 2r + rm$ m; dist.

9. $\underline{?} + \underline{?}$ is a unique real number. r; m; closure add.

Determine which of the following subsets of the real numbers have the given property: *natural numbers, whole numbers, integers, rational numbers, irrational numbers.*

10. closed under addition N, W, Z, Q

11. closed under subtraction Z, Q

12. additive inverse Z, Q, irrational

13. multiplicative inverse Q, irrational

Analyze each statement. If the statement is true, explain why. If the statement is false, state a counterexample.

14. Every integer is a rational number. true; Integers can be written as rationals in $\frac{a}{b}$ form.

15. The rational numbers are closed under multiplication. true; The product of rationals is rational.

16. The irrational numbers are closed under addition. false; $\pi + (-\pi) = 0$, 0 is not irrational.

17. e is a real number. true; e is irrational and all irrationals are real.

Practice Exercises

Using a compass and a straightedge, locate each point on the number line.

A **1.** $-\frac{3}{5}$

2. $\frac{7}{4}$

3. $\sqrt{10}$

4. $2\sqrt{5}$

5. 2.5

Given that m and n are real numbers, name the property of the real number system illustrated by each statement.

6. $(7 + 3) + 4 = 7 + (3 + 4)$ assoc. add.

7. $8 + (-8) = (-8) + 8 = 0$ add. inv.

8. $(3m)n = 3(mn)$ assoc. mult.

9. $m + n = n + m$ comm. add.

10. $9 \cdot 1 = 1 \cdot 9 = 9$ mult. ident.

11. mn is a unique real number. closure, mult.

12. $2(3 + 5) = 2 \cdot 3 + 2 \cdot 5$ dist.

13. $mn = nm$ comm. mult.

14. *Drafting* A draftsman wants to make a diagram of a room with all lengths measured in inches. How could he construct a sketch of a crossbeam of length $\frac{1}{2}\sqrt{2}$ in. using a compass and a straightedge?

Ⓡ **15.** Solve the equation for z: $2z^3 = 10z$ z = 0, $\sqrt{5}$, $-\sqrt{5}$

State whether each of the given sets is closed under the operations of addition, subtraction, multiplication, and division.

16. whole numbers add., mult.

17. rational numbers add., subt., mult., div.

18. positive odd integers mult.

1.2 The Real Number System   **15**

CLOSURE
Group students in pairs and have them explain to each other how to locate a rational and an irrational number on the number line. Then have them summarize the field properties in their math journals.

INDEPENDENT PRACTICE
Assignment Guide
Basic: 1–21, 23–26, 34, 36–37, Project
Average: 3–4, 14–39, Project
Enriched: 21–45, Project

Teacher's Resource Book
Practice, page 2

Ⓡ **Review**
Exercises 15, 23, and 34 review concepts of factoring and solving equations. Exercise 19 reviews the concept of finding average speed for a round trip, and Exercise 36 reviews the concept of finding the equation of a line parallel to a given line.

Project
The painting that accompanies the project is George Seurat's "La Parade" and is a vivid example of the use of the golden rectangle in art. Students with an interest in fine art might want to research other famous works in which the golden rectangle is used, including those in architecture.

LESSON FOLLOW-UP
Lesson Quiz
1. Using a compass and straightedge, locate $\frac{5}{6}$ on the number line.

2. List three field properties for the operation of addition and give an example of each. The field properties for addition are closure, commutative, associative, identity, and inverse. Examples will vary.

3. The operations ∗ and # are defined on the set $S = \{a, b, c\}$ in the tables below. Determine if this set forms a field under these operations.

∗	a	b	c
a	a	a	a
b	b	b	b
c	c	c	c

#	a	b	c
a	b	a	d
b	a	b	b
c	d	d	a

The set S with the operations ∗ and # is not a field.

Reasons:
The identity element under ∗ is not unique.
The operation ∗ is not commutative.
The set is not closed under #.
There is no identity element under #.
The operation # is not commutative.

4. Using the field properties of real numbers and the properties of equality, prove the theorem:

If $ab = ac$ and $a \neq 0$, then $b = c$.

Statements	Reasons
1. a, b, and c are real numbers	1. Given
2. $ab = ac$	2. Given
3. $a \neq 0$	3. Given
4. $\frac{1}{a}$ is a real number	4. Closure
5. $\frac{1}{a} = \frac{1}{a}$	5. Reflexive
6. $\frac{1}{a}(ab) = \frac{1}{a}(ac)$	6. Def. of mult.
7. $\left(\frac{1}{a} \cdot a\right)b = \left(\frac{1}{a} \cdot a\right)c$	7. Assoc.
8. $1 \cdot b = 1 \cdot c$	8. Mult. inverse
9. $b = c$	9. Mult. identity

Ⓡ 19. Robert drove to the shore at an average speed of 55 mi/h and returned home over the same route at the average speed of 45 mi/h. It took him 2 hours longer on the return trip. What was his average speed for the entire trip? 49.5 mi/h

20. **Thinking Critically** A *unary* operation sets up a correspondence between one element of a set and another element of the set. Name two unary operations on the set of real numbers. Give an example of each.

Given that a, b, c, and x are real numbers, prove each theorem.

B 21. If $a = b$, then $a + c = b + c$.

22. If $x + a = b$, then $x = b - a$.

Ⓡ 23. Factor completely: $3x^3 - 6x^2 - 189x$ $3x(x + 7)(x - 9)$

Under the operations of addition and multiplication, determine which field properties *do not* hold for each set. Give an example.

24. positive even integers

25. $\{0, 3, 6, 9, \ldots\}$

26. integers divisible by 5

27. negative odd integers

28. $\left\{0, \frac{1}{2}, \frac{1}{4}, \frac{1}{8}, \frac{1}{16}, \ldots\right\}$

29. $\{-1, 0, 1\}$ closure add.: $1 + 1 = 2 \notin \{-1, 0, 1\}$

30. $\{\ldots, -1.5, -1, -0.5, 0, 0.5, 1, 1.5, \ldots\}$ closure mult.: $(0.5)(0.5) = (0.25) \notin$ of the set, mult. inv.: $1.5a = a1.5 = 1$, $a \notin$ of the set.

Determine whether each set forms a field under the operations of addition and multiplication.

31. the set of rational numbers yes

32. the set of natural numbers no

33. The operations of ⊕ and ⊗ are defined on the set $\{0, 1, 2\}$ in the tables below. Determine if this set forms a field under these operations. If your answer is no, name a field property that does not hold. yes

⊕	0	1	2
0	0	1	2
1	1	2	0
2	2	0	1

⊗	0	1	2
0	0	0	0
1	0	1	2
2	0	2	1

Ⓡ 34. Solve for y: $2 - \frac{4}{y} = \frac{16}{y^2}$ $y = 4, -2$

35. **Thinking Critically** The drawing at the right illustrates that for a right triangle with hypotenuse of length $m + n$, the length of the altitude from the right angle to the hypotenuse is $\sqrt{mn}$. How can this information be used to locate $\sqrt{8}$ on a number line?

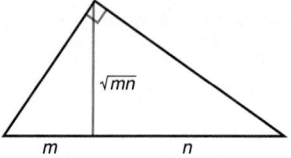

Ⓡ 36. Find the equation, in standard form, of the line that goes through the point $(-3, -3.5)$ and is parallel to the line $6x - 5y = 12$. $y = 1.2x + 0.1$

37. **Writing in Mathematics** In Lewis Carroll's *School of Mathematics* there is a "padded and soundproof room for irrational numbers." Contrast and compare the uses of the word "irrational" in everyday language and in mathematics.

16 Chapter 1 Functions

Additional Answers

20. Answers may vary. Examples: squaring a number, $6^2 = 36$; absolute value of a number, $|-2| = 2$

21.
Statements	Reasons
1. a, b, and c are real numbers	1. Given
2. $a + c$ is a real number	2. Closure
3. $a + c = a + c$	3. Reflexive
4. $a = b$	4. Given
5. $a + c = b + c$	5. Subst.

22.
Statements	Reasons
1. $x + a = b$	1. Given
2. $x + a + (-a)$ $= b + (-a)$	2. Add. prop.
3. $x + 0$ $= b + (-a)$	3. Add. inv.
4. $x = b + (-a)$	4. Add. iden.
5. $x = b - a$	5. Def. of subt.

38. *Drafting*   A draftsman is making a diagram of a guest house with all lengths measured in centimeters. How could he construct a rafter of length $2\sqrt{3}$ cm using a compass and a straightedge? Use Exer. 35. $m = 6, n = 2$ since $2\sqrt{3} = \sqrt{12}$

39. Writing in Mathematics   The set Z and the set W are both infinite sets, yet Z contains all the elements of W as well as elements not in W. Explain how this can be so.

Given a set $S = \{a, b, c, d\}$ and the operations of $*$ and $\#$ defined by the following tables.

$*$	a	b	c	d
a	a	b	c	d
b	b	a	d	c
c	c	d	a	b
d	d	c	b	a

$\#$	a	b	c	d
a	b	b	c	d
b	b	c	d	a
c	c	d	a	b
d	d	a	b	d

C **40.** Name the identity element for $*$, if it exists. a

41. Name the inverse for each element under $*$, if it exists. a; b; c; d, respectively

42. Name the field properties that hold under $*$. closure, ident., comm., assoc., inv.

43. Name the identity element for $\#$, if it exists. no identity element

44. Name the inverse for each element under $\#$, if it exists. no inverses

45. Thinking Critically   State the distributive property for $\#$ over $*$. Does the distributive property hold? $a \# (b * c) = a \# b * a \# c$; no

---

Project

Research what is meant by a *golden rectangle* and use your findings to determine a method for locating the point $\dfrac{1 + \sqrt{5}}{2}$ on a number line.

Challenge

1. If a and b are two nonnegative integers, the result of the operation a MOD b is the integer remainder after a and b are divided. For example,

11 MOD 2 = 1
because $11 \div 2 = 5$ with a remainder of 1

Find 8 MOD 3, 8 MOD 1, and 8 MOD 10. Is the set of nonnegative integers closed under the operation MOD? Why or why not? 2; 0; 8; Yes, the remainders are nonnegative.

2. Determine an equation to represent the number of diagonals in a regular polygon in terms of the number of sides. $y = \dfrac{x^2}{2} - \dfrac{3x}{2}, x \geq 3$

Alternative Assessment
Have students research the history of irrational numbers and write a report. They should include biographical information on at least one mathematician who played a role in the development of irrational numbers.

Enrichment
Define an operation on the set $S = \{0, 1, 2, 3, 4, 5\}$ which is closed, associative, has an identity element, and in which each element has an inverse but which is not commutative. One example is given below. Answers may vary.

$*$	0	1	2	3	4	5
0	0	1	2	3	4	5
1	1	0	3	2	5	4
2	2	5	0	4	3	1
3	3	4	1	5	2	0
4	4	3	5	1	0	2
5	5	2	4	0	1	3

Additional Answers
24. add. ident.: $0 \notin$ positive even integers
add. inv.: $2 + a = a + 2 = 0, a \notin$ positive even integers
mult. ident.: $1 \notin$ positive even integers
mult. inv.: $2 \cdot a = a \cdot 2 = 1, a \notin$ positive even integers

25. add. inv.: $3 + a = a + 3 = 0, a \notin \{0, 3, 6, 9, \ldots\}$
mult. ident.: $1 \notin \{0, 3, 6, 9, \ldots\}$
mult. inv.: $3 \cdot a = a \cdot 3 = 1, a \notin \{0, 3, 6, 9, \ldots\}$

26. mult. ident.: $1 \notin$ integers divisible by 5
mult. inv.: $5 \cdot a = a \cdot 5 = 1, a \notin$ integers divisible by 5

27. clos. add.: $-3 + (-5) = -8, -8 \notin$ negative odd integers
clos. mult.: $(-3)(-5) = 15, 15 \notin$ negative odd integers
add. ident.: $0 \notin$ negative odd integers
add. inv.: $-1 + a = a + (-1) = 0, a \notin$ negative odd integers
mult. ident.: $1 \notin$ negative odd integers
mult. inv.: $-3 \cdot a = a \cdot (-3) = 1, a \notin$ negative odd integers

---

Writing in Mathematics
37. The word *irrational* in everyday use means behavior in a manner not based on reasoning. This is the sense in which Lewis Carroll is using the word. Mathematically, an irrational number is a number that cannot be expressed as a ratio of integers.
39. If you juxtapose the two sets, theoretically you can pair each whole number with each integer, which shows a one-to-one correspondence between Z and W.

Vocabulary
abscissa
Cartesian coordinate system
coordinate axes
coordinate plane
graph
ordinate
origin
quadrants
rectangular coordinate system
x-axis
x-intercept
y-axis
y-intercept

Ⓜ Materials/Manipulatives
graph paper

Technology
graphing utility

FOCUS

Heinrich Schwabe (1789–1875) discovered the cyclical nature of sunspot activity. An amateur astronomer, he began observing the sun in 1826 and noticing that the number of sunspots ranged from a low of 0 to a high of over 200 spots in a given cycle. Have students research sunspot activity in the last 20 years.

INSTRUCTION

- Point out that when graphing information, it is important to choose scales that allow all the data to be displayed on the graph.
- Demonstrate for students how a graph is affected by changing the scales on the axes. You can use the graphs in Examples 1 and 2 to do this.
- The equations in Practice Exercises 27 to 32 are all used in real world applications. You may want to have students research the contexts in which they are used.

1.3 The Cartesian Coordinate System

Objectives: To graph ordered pairs on a coordinate plane
To graph equations

Focus

Sunspots, which can be seen using special telescopic lenses, are dark patches on the surface of the sun. They are believed to be caused by immense concentrations of magnetic fields in particular regions of the sun's surface. These magnetic fields, along with cooler temperatures, cause the gases in the sunspot region to be duller in appearance. Sunspot activity is taken into account when planning space missions.

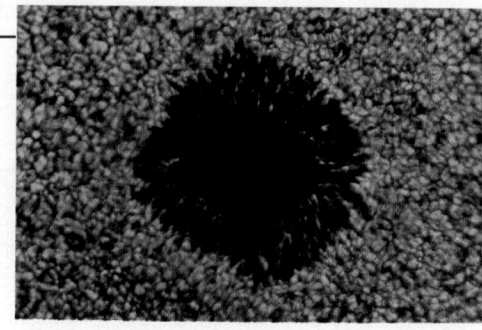

At the right is a graph of sunspot activity from 1850 to 1970 as reported by NASA. A graph often discloses interesting facets of the data. This graph shows that the phenomenon seems to occur in 11-year cycles.

The mathematical development that allows you to visualize the data for sunspot activity is the *Cartesian coordinate system.* As you have seen, there is a one-to-one correspondence between the set of real numbers and the set of points on the real number line. Extending this concept, there is a one-to-one correspondence between the set of the points on the plane and the set of *ordered pairs* of real numbers. One reference system used to represent this correspondence is called a **rectangular,** or **Cartesian, coordinate system.**

Draw one horizontal number line, called the **x-axis,** and one vertical number line perpendicular to it, called the **y-axis.** Their point of intersection is at the zero value on each line and is called the **origin.** The *x*- and *y*-axes together are called the **coordinate axes,** and the plane in which they lie is called the **coordinate plane.** On the *x*-axis the positive direction is to the right, and on the *y*-axis the positive direction is upward. The coordinate axes divide the coordinate plane into four parts called **quadrants.**

Coordinate Plane

18 Chapter 1 Functions

Each point P in the xy-plane can be assigned a unique ordered pair (x, y). The x-coordinate, or **abscissa,** gives the distance and direction of P from the y-axis, and the y-coordinate, or **ordinate,** gives the distance and direction of P from the x-axis.

Given a set S of ordered pairs of numbers, each element of the set can be represented by a point in the plane. The **graph** of S is the set of all such points.

Consider a set of ordered pairs generated from a real world situation. Working on a coal seam 1000 ft below the surface, a robot can mine enough coal in 30 seconds to meet the electric needs of a typical suburban household for 1 year.

Example 1 *Robotics* Let x represent the number of seconds a robot works, and y the number of years of electricity provided for one household. Determine the missing numbers in the chart below and draw a graph of the set of points.

x	0	30	45	60	70	80
y	0	1		2		

Since the rate at which the robot produces coal is a linear relationship, use proportions.

$$\frac{30}{1} = \frac{45}{x} \qquad \frac{30}{1} = \frac{70}{x} \qquad \frac{30}{1} = \frac{80}{x}$$
$$x = 1.5 \qquad x \approx 2.3 \qquad x \approx 2.7$$

x	0	30	45	60	70	80
y	0	1	1.5	2	2.3	2.7

Since the values of x and y are very different, the scales on the axes are different.

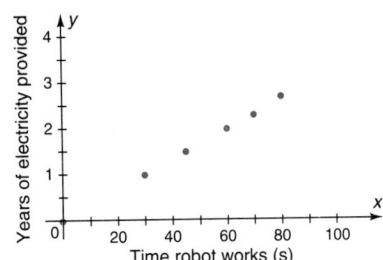

The graph of an equation in two variables is the set of all points whose coordinates satisfy the equation. One method of graphing equations is to use a table of values. Choose several values for x and find the corresponding values for y. Plot a sufficient number of points to get a clear picture of the behavior of the graph, and then connect the points with a smooth line or curve.

Example 2 *Manufacturing* A company is manufacturing a new calculator. From a market survey, a linear model for the relationship between the demand y for the product and the price x of the product is developed. Graph the linear model $4x + y = 330$.

Solve the equation for y.
$$y = -4x + 330$$

Make a table of values.

x	0	10	50
y	330	290	130

1.3 The Cartesian Coordinate System **19**

GUIDED PRACTICE
For Example 1
A plant that manufactures toaster ovens has completely automated its production line. Let x represent the number of hours per day the assembly line functions at maximum capacity, and y the number of ovens produced. Fill in the missing numbers in the chart below and draw a graph of the set of points.

x	15	17	19	21	24
y			1045		1320

$(15, 825)$; $(17, 935)$; $(21, 1155)$

For Example 2
There is a linear relationship between the number of returns for defects r of an automatic tennis ball machine and the number of hours each batch of machines is tested per week, h. Graph the linear model $16h + r = 2150$ using h as the independent variable and approximate the intercepts from the graph.

x-intercept: $(134, 0)$;
y-intercept: $(0, 2150)$

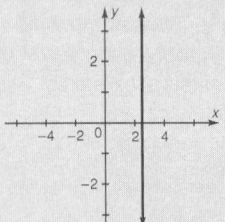
The points where the graph of an equation intersects the axes are called *intercepts* and often provide valuable information. In Example 2, when the price x is 0, the graph intersects the y-axis at $y = 330$. Therefore, the maximum demand for this product is 330 units. When the demand y is 0, the graph intersects the x-axis at $x = 82.5$. Therefore, if the price of the calculator is $82.50 or more, there is virtually no market for it. The point $(0, 330)$ is the **y-intercept** and the point $(82.5, 0)$ is the **x-intercept.**

Equations can be graphed much more quickly and efficiently using *graphing utilities*. A **graphing utility** is a program used in a graphing calculator or a computer to graph an equation. Use the following procedure.

To use a graphing utility:

- Solve the equation for y.
- Enter the minimum and maximum values for x and y that are pertinent to the problem. On a graphing calculator, use the *range* key to do this. Note that the *range* key on the calculator refers to the minimum and maximum values on both the horizontal and vertical axes as well as the scale (scl) on each axis.
- Use the *graph* key or command to graph the equation.
- Adjust the range values until a reasonable portion of the graph is determined. The visible portion is called a **viewing rectangle** and its dimensions are given as [x-min, x-max] by [y-min, y-max].

Example 3 Graph: $y = x^2 + 4x + 5$

The graph of $y = x^2 + 4x + 5$ is a parabola that opens upward with vertex $(-2, 1)$. The viewing rectangle is chosen so the vertex and the y-intercept are visible.

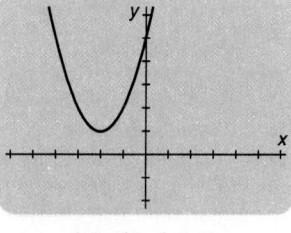

[-6, 6] by [-2, 6]

Range settings		Viewing rectangle
x-min: -6	y-min: -2	$[-6, 6]$ by $[-2, 6]$
x-max: 6	y-max: 6	
x-scl: 1	y-scl: 1	

When graphing an equation with the variables x and y, x is assumed to be the **independent variable.** When graphing equations with variables other than x and y, the independent variable must be specified. The independent variable is represented on a graph by the horizontal axis.

Class Exercises

The ordered pair (x, y) represents a point in a coordinate plane. Name the quadrant, point, or axis that satisfies the given conditions.

1. $x > 0$ and $y < 0$ IV
2. $x < 0$ and $y < 0$ III
3. $x = 0$ and $y = 0$ origin
4. $x = 0$ y-axis
5. $y = 0$ x-axis
6. $x > 0$ I, IV

20 Chapter 1 Functions

Approximate each ordered pair from the graph of sunspot activity in the Focus and reproduced at the right.

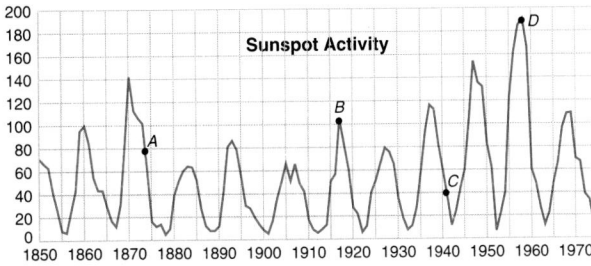

Sunspot Activity

7. A (1873, 80)

8. B (1917, 100)

9. C (1942, 40)

10. D (1957, 190)

Graph each equation.

11. $2y = -4x + 6$

12. $x = 3$

13. $y = x^2 - 3x + 4$

14. $m = -n + 2$, where n is the independent variable

Practice Exercises

 Use appropriate technology.

Plot each set of points on a rectangular coordinate system. Choose an appropriate scale.

A **1.** (30, 0.5), (45, 0.7), (60, 0.9), (90, 1)

2. (4, 10), (−5, 1), (−9, −9), (3, −15)

3. $\left(-1, \frac{1}{2}\right), \left(-2, \frac{1}{4}\right), \left(-3, \frac{1}{8}\right), \left(-4, \frac{1}{16}\right)$

4. (1.6, −270), (3.1, −180), (−4.7, −90), (1.6, 90)

Ⓡ **5.** Locate $\frac{2}{3}$ on the number line.

Complete the table of values for each graph.

6.

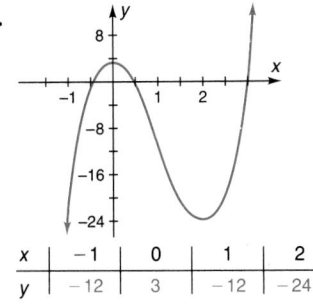

x	−1	0	1	2
y	−12	3	−12	−24

7.

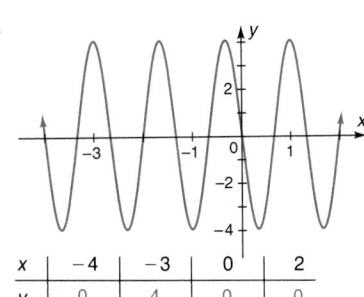

x	−4	−3	0	2
y	0	4	0	0

Graph each equation.

8. $3y - 5x = 4$

9. $1.5x = 7.5y$

10. $y = -2x^2$

11. $y = x^2 - 2$

12. $0.2x = 5y + 1$

13. $y = x^2 + 2$

14. $y = -x^3$

15. $y = 2x^3$

Ⓡ **16.** Name the field properties that are satisfied for the set of whole numbers under the operation of multiplication. closure, comm., assoc., mult. ident.

17. Thinking Critically Given an equation $ax + by = c$, where a, b, and c are nonzero integers, describe a method for choosing an integral value for x so that the corresponding y will also be an integer. x so that $c - ax$ is a multiple of b

1.3 The Cartesian Coordinate System **21**

Additional Answers, Class Exercises

11.

12.

13.

14.

Test Yourself

Teacher's Resource Book
  Tests—Quiz, form A, page 1
  Tests—Quiz, form B, page 1

Lesson Quiz

1. Approximate each ordered pair from the graph.

A(28, 1.25); B(−20, 2.5);
C(−45, −1.25); D(45, 0)

2. Graph $y = x^2 + 2$.

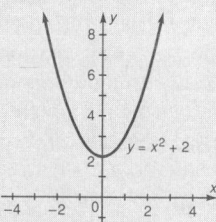

3. Graph $3x − 20 = 0$.

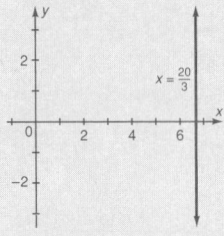

4. The resale value y of a Tiffany lamp is a function of its age x, in years, and can be approximated by the equation $y = 17,500(1 + 0.04x)$. Graph the equation and approximate the value of a 37-year-old lamp.

The value of a 37-year-old lamp is $43,400.

18. *Depreciation* The resale value y of a certain model of an American car can be calculated using the formula $y = 22,000(1 − 0.07x)$, where x is the age of the car in years. Graph the equation and approximate the value of the car after 7.5 years. $11,000

19. *Electricity* The voltage V of a circuit can be determined by the formula $V = 6R$, where R is the resistance in ohms. Graph the equation using R as the independent variable and approximate the voltage for a circuit with a resistance of 3.2 ohms. 19 V

20. **Writing in Mathematics** Write a word problem for which the solution is a linear equation.

Graph each equation.

B 21. $y = −25x^2 + 1000$ 22. $y = 0.05x^3 − x$ 23. $x = \dfrac{4}{y}$ 24. $\sqrt{y − 1} = x + 4$

Ⓡ 25. Factor completely: $15x^4 − x^3 − 2x^2$ $x^2(5x − 2)(3x + 1)$

26. **Writing in Mathematics** Explain why a real world problem may restrict the graph of the equation that models it, and give examples of restrictions.

Graph each equation using the indicated variable for the independent variable.

27. $5F = 9C + 160$; C 28. $\frac{4}{5}q + \frac{1}{5}h = 70$; q 29. $h = −16t^2 + 64t$; t

30. $S = 0.5n(n + 1)$; n 31. $A = \frac{1}{\pi}c^2$; c 32. $V = \frac{4}{3}\pi r^3$; r

Ⓡ 33. Solve for x: $x^2 + 2 = 0$ $\pm i\sqrt{2}$. No solution in $\mathfrak{R}$.

34. *Construction* A carpenter wants to make sure that all the staircases in a certain building rise at a 35° angle. She uses the equation $h = 0.7r$ to relate the height h of the staircase with the horizontal distance covered, or "run," r. Graph this equation for $0 \le r \le 30$, using r for the independent variable.

35. **Thinking Critically** The equation in Exercise 29 relates the height of an object fired directly upward to the time that elapses after firing. If the object travels in a path that is straight up and straight down, why then does the graph behave the way it does?

36. *Physics* The distance d, in meters, that an object falls after t seconds is given by the formula $d = 4.9t^2$. Graph this equation for $0 \le t \le 6$, where t is the independent variable.

37. **Writing in Mathematics** Although making a table of values can be helpful when graphing a function that you are not familiar with, other graphing techniques are often more efficient. Explain some of the difficulties that can occur when you depend on a table of values for a graph.

Point (x, y) is a *lattice point* if both x and y are integers. For the given values of x, graph the lattice points that satisfy each equation.

C 38. $4y − 5x = 6$, where $x \in \{0, 2, 4, 16, 18\}$ 39. $y = \frac{1}{3}x + \frac{1}{3}$, where $x \in \{0, 2, 4, 5, 6, 8\}$

22   Chapter 1 Functions

Writing in Mathematics
20. Answers may vary.
26. Answers may vary. One possible example is that a graph of the amount earned for a given number of hours worked would be restricted to nonnegative numbers.

40. **Thinking Critically** Given the formula $y = \dfrac{x}{c} + \dfrac{1}{c}$, where c is a nonzero integer, determine a formula for choosing integral values of x that will result in integral values of y. $x = nc - 1, n \in Z$

41. Graph: $y = x^3 - 3$ 42. Graph: $y = \sqrt{x - 4}$

43. *Education* A teacher gives a final exam in two parts, oral and written. Each part is based on a score of 100 points. The oral part is worth 25% of the exam grade and the written part is worth 75%. A student uses the equation $0.25x + 0.75y = 70$ to find all the possible combinations of scores that will result in an exam grade of 70. Graph this equation for $0 \leq x \leq 100$ and $0 \leq y \leq 100$.

44. **Thinking Critically** How can the graph in Exercise 43 be used to show all the possible combinations of scores that will result in an exam grade of 70 or above? Shade the portion of the plane above and including the line segment.

45. *Driving Safety* A formula that gives the safe turning radius (in feet) of a certain car in relation to its velocity (in miles per hour) is $r = 3v^2$. Graph this equation in the first quadrant of the coordinate plane, where v is the independent variable.

46. **Writing in Mathematics** Explain how your choice of the scales for the axes can affect the way that a graph models a real world problem.

Test Yourself

1. At Debbie's Bagels, one dozen bagels cost $6.00. Each additional bagel costs 40 cents. Find the linear equation that models the cost in terms of the number of bagels purchased. $y = 1.20 + 0.40x, x \geq 12$ **1.1**

2. Use the equation determined in Exercise 1 to find the number of bagels that can be purchased for $9.20. 20

3. A farmer has 300 ft of fencing and wants to enclose a rectangular field. Find a quadratic equation that relates the area of the field to its width. $A = -w^2 + 150w$

Given that a, b, and c are real numbers, name the property of the real number system illustrated by each statement.

4. $a(b + c) = ab + ac$ distributive 5. $a + 0 = 0 + a = a$ Add. identity **1.2**

Under the operations of addition and multiplication, which field properties do not hold for each set? Provide an example for each property that does not hold.

6. Integers divisible by 4 7. $\left\{ \ldots, -1, -\dfrac{2}{3}, -\dfrac{1}{3}, 0, \dfrac{1}{3}, \dfrac{2}{3}, 1, \ldots \right\}$

Plot each set of points on a rectangular coordinate system. Choose an appropriate scale.

8. $(20, -2), (30, -3), (40, -4), (50, -5)$ 9. $(5, 0.3), (6, 0.6), (7, 0.9), (8, 1.0)$ **1.3**

Graph each equation.

10. $2x + y = 4$ 11. $y = -x^2 + 1$

5. Graph $y = x^3 - 5$ using a graphing utility and find the intercepts.

x-intercept: (1.7, 0); y-intercept: (0, −5)

Alternative Assessment
Ask students to find a graph in a newspaper or magazine. Then have them write a report that explains what the scales on the graph represent and why they think these particular scales were chosen. They should include in their reports at least five pieces of data that can be read from the graph.

Enrichment
Using a table of values, graph $y = \dfrac{4}{x - 2} + 1$. Check your answer using a graphing utility and approximate the intercepts.

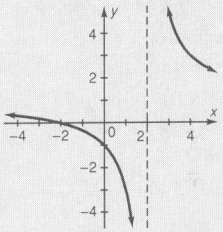

x-intercept: (−1.8, 0); y-intercept: (0, −1)

Additional Answers
41.

42.

Vocabulary
domain
equal functions
function
horizontal line test
mapping
one-to-one function
range
relation
vertical line test

Ⓜ **Materials/Manipulatives**
transparencies

Technology
graphing utility

FOCUS

Students may be interested in the fact that computers are used to solve most complicated ciphers. An interesting twist, though, is that the one-to-one nature of many ciphers enables them to be used to check a computer's logic. A sentence is entered and the computer is asked to translate it into a code. Then the coded message is entered and the computer is asked to translate it back into English. If the computer does not output the original sentence, the system may need some adjustments.

1.4   Relations and Functions

Objectives: To determine the domain and range of a relation or function
To determine whether a given relation is a function
To determine whether two functions are equal

Focus

For centuries people have used *ciphers*, or codes, to keep confidential information secure. Effective ciphers are essential to the military, to financial institutions, and to computer programmers. The study of the techniques used in creating and decoding these ciphers is called *cryptography*.

One of the earliest methods of coding a message was a simple substitution function. For example, each letter in a message might be replaced by the letter that is three places later in the alphabet. Thus, A is replaced by D, B is replaced by E, and so on. A follows Z in this method. Using this coding scheme,

I GET IT   becomes   L JHW LW

This scheme was used by Julius Caesar and is called the Caesar Cipher. To decode such a message, replace each letter by the letter three places before it. Every coding scheme will have a corresponding "inverse" scheme to decode it. Can you break the code and decipher the message below?

XLWVH ZIV NZWV GL YV YILPVM

A cipher such as the Caesar Cipher is a correspondence, or *mapping*, between two sets. Each element in one set is "mapped" onto an element in another. In mathematics, a mapping of this kind is called a *relation*.

A simple cipher might assign to each letter in the alphabet a natural number so that 1 represents *a*, 2 represents *b*, and so on. This correspondence can be written as the set of ordered pairs $\{(a, 1), (b, 2), \ldots, (z, 26)\}$. A set of ordered pairs is called a **relation**. The **domain** *D* of the relation is the set of all the first coordinates of the ordered pairs, and the **range** *R* is the set of all the second coordinates. The correspondence between the elements of the domain and the range of a relation is called a **mapping**. In the diagram, letters of the alphabet are mapped onto the natural numbers.

A special type of relation which plays an important role in mathematics is called a *function*.

> A **function** *f* is a relation in which each element in the domain is mapped to *exactly one* element in the range.

Since a function is a relation, it is a set of ordered pairs. In set notation a function f can be written $f = \{(x, y): y = f(x)\}$. The expression $f(x)$ denotes the *value* of f at x and is read "f of x." Also, $f(x)$ as well as f is used to refer to the function itself. The *range* of the function, denoted R_f, is the set of all values $f(x)$ where x is in the *domain*, denoted D_f. Subscripts are used to distinguish different functions.

Relations and functions can be expressed in different ways. A mapping of sets like the one shown above is one example of a function. A function may also be expressed as a rule, such as $f(x) = x^2$. This function is the set of ordered pairs such that the second element is the square of the first. The domain of this function is the set of real numbers. *What is the range?*

Example 1 Given $f(x) = x^2 + 3$, evaluate each of the following:

$\quad$ **a.** $f(-4)$ $\quad$ **b.** $f(m)$ $\quad$ **c.** $f(x + h)$ $\quad$ **d.** $\dfrac{f(x + h) - f(x)}{h}$, $h \neq 0$

a. $f(x) = x^2 + 3$
$\quad f(-4) = (-4)^2 + 3 = 19$

b. $f(x) = x^2 + 3$
$\quad f(m) = m^2 + 3$

c. $f(x) = x^2 + 3$
$\quad f(x + h) = (x + h)^2 + 3 = x^2 + 2xh + h^2 + 3$

d. $f(x) = x^2 + 3$
$\quad \dfrac{f(x + h) - f(x)}{h} = \dfrac{(x^2 + 2xh + h^2 + 3) - (x^2 + 3)}{h} = \dfrac{2xh + h^2}{h} = 2x + h$

The expression $\dfrac{f(x + h) - f(x)}{h}$ in Example 1d is called a difference quotient and is used in the study of limits, which will be presented later in this course.

If a function is given by a rule and no domain is specified, then the domain of the function is the set of all real numbers for which $f(x)$ is also a real number. Any values of x that result in division by zero or require taking an even root of a negative number will not be in the domain. When the variable occurs in the denominator, determine the values of x that make the denominator zero and eliminate these values from the domain. When the variable occurs in a radical of even index, determine the values of x that make the radicand nonnegative.

When the range of a function $y = f(x)$ is not easily determined from the equation, graph the function and determine the range from the graph as shown.

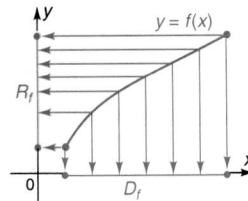

- Encourage students to draw mappings and study the pattern of the arrows. Point out that a relation is a function if one and only one arrow emanates from each element in set X.
- Remind students that the equation of a vertical line is $x = a$.
Ⓜ • Use transparencies to illustrate the use of the vertical line test to determine whether a graph represents a function.

Alternative Learning Styles
Many students need a more visual representation of a function to understand its definition. Drawing mappings to illustrate the domain and range can be helpful.

GUIDED PRACTICE
For Example 1
1. Given $g(x) = -5x + 7$, evaluate $g(x + 2)$ and $\dfrac{g(x + 2) - g(x)}{2}$.

$\quad g(x + 2) = -5x - 3$
$\quad \dfrac{g(x + 2) - g(x)}{2} = -5$

2. Given $m(x) = 2x^2 - 3x$, evaluate $m(x - a)$ and $\dfrac{m(x - a) - m(x)}{-a}$, $a \neq 0$.

$\quad m(x - a) = 2x^2 - 4ax + 2a^2 - 3x + 3a$
$\quad \dfrac{m(x - a) - m(x)}{-a} = 4x - 2a - 3$

Common Error In the expression $f(x + h) - f(x)$, many students do not write parentheses around $f(x)$ and then forget to distribute the negative sign. Stress the importance of writing the parentheses. Remind students that after the expression is simplified, all the terms should have factors of h or a power of h.

26

For Example 2

Find the domain and range of each function. Then graph the function using a graphing utility and determine the range from the graph.

1. $g(x) = \dfrac{1}{x^2}$

$D = \{x: x \neq 0\}$
$R = \{y: y > 0\}$

2. $h(x) = \dfrac{2x}{\sqrt{5 - x}}$

$D = \{x: x < 5\}$
$R = \{y: y \in \mathcal{R}\}$

Common Error When a radical occurs in the denominator of the fraction, students sometimes forget to exclude the values that make other variables zero. Remind students that in the numerator the radicand must be nonnegative for y to be a real number but in the denominator the radicand must be positive.

For Example 3

Determine whether each pair of functions is equal.

1. $f(x) = 3(x - 2)^2$ and
$g(x) = 3x^2 - 12x + 12$
Functions are equal.

2. $h(x) = 3x^{-2}$ and $m(x) = \dfrac{1}{3x^2}$

Functions are not equal.
$D_h = D_m$ but $h(x) \neq m(x)$

For Example 4

Determine whether each equation represents a function.

1. $x^2 + y = 5$
$a^2 + b = 5 \qquad a^2 + c = 5$
$a^2 = 5 - b \qquad a^2 = 5 - c$
$5 - b = 5 - c$
$b = c$
Therefore, $x^2 + y = 5$ is a function.

2. $x^2 + y^2 = 25$
$a^2 + b^2 = 25 \qquad a^2 + c^2 = 25$
$b = \pm\sqrt{25 - a^2} \quad c = \pm\sqrt{25 - a^2}$

If $b = +\sqrt{25 - a^2}$ and
$c = -\sqrt{25 - a^2}$, then $b \neq c$. Therefore, the relation $x^2 + y^2 = 25$ is not a function.

Example 2 Find the domain of each function. Then graph the function using a graphing utility and determine the range from its graph.

a. $g(x) = \sqrt{x - 3}$ **b.** $f(x) = \dfrac{x}{x^2 - 4}$

a. $g(x) = \sqrt{x - 3}$ *Radical has an even index, 2.*
$x - 3 \geq 0$ *Radicand must be nonnegative.*
$x \geq 3$

$D_g = \{x: x \geq 3\}$

Graph $g(x)$.

Since $x - 3 \geq 0$, then $\sqrt{x - 3} \geq 0$.

$R_g = \{y: y \geq 0\}$

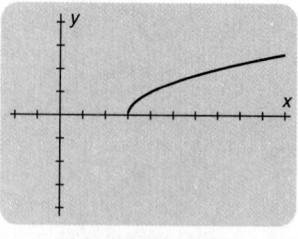

[−2, 10] by [−4, 4]

b. $f(x) = \dfrac{x}{x^2 - 4}$ *Variable occurs in denominator.*

$f(x) = \dfrac{x}{(x - 2)(x + 2)}$ *Factor denominator.*

$(x - 2)(x + 2) = 0$ *Set denominator equal to 0.*

$x = 2$ or $x = -2$

$D_f = \{x: x \neq 2 \text{ and } x \neq -2\}$

Graph $f(x)$. From the graph the range appears to be the set of real numbers.

$R_f = \{y: y \in \mathcal{R}\}$

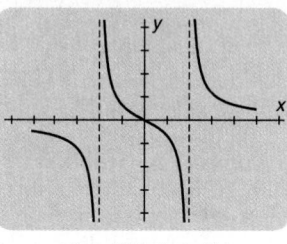

[−6, 6] by [−4, 4]

Notice that in Example 2 the functions $f(x)$ and $g(x)$ are graphed on the x- and y-axes. This is because the definition of a function is given as a set of ordered pairs (x, y) such that $y = f(x)$. Thus, the rule for a function can sometimes be given as an equation in two variables such as x and y. Since many graphing utilities require a function to be in the form $y = f(x)$ before it can be input, and since the Cartesian coordinate system was defined in terms of x- and y-axes, it is important to recognize the different forms in which a function rule may appear.

Two functions f and g are **equal functions** if the following two conditions are satisfied:

> The domain of f is equal to the domain of g.
> For all x in the domain, $f(x) = g(x)$.

Example 3 Determine whether each pair of functions is equal.

a. $f(x) = \sqrt{x^2}$ and $g(x) = |x|$

b. $h(x) = x - 2$ and $k(x) = \dfrac{x^2 - 2x}{x}$

a. $f(x) = \sqrt{x^2}$ and $g(x) = |x|$

The domain of both $f(x)$ and $g(x)$ is the set of all real numbers.

For any positive real number a,

$$f(a) = \sqrt{(a)^2} = a \qquad\qquad g(a) = |a| = a$$
$$f(-a) = \sqrt{(-a)^2} = a \qquad\qquad g(-a) = |-a| = a$$
$$f(0) = \sqrt{(0)^2} = 0 \qquad\qquad g(0) = |0| = 0$$

Therefore, for all real numbers, $f(x) = g(x)$.

Since the domain of f is equal to the domain of g and $f(x) = g(x)$ for all x, f and g are equal functions.

b. $h(x) = x - 2$ and $k(x) = \dfrac{x^2 - 2x}{x}$

The domain of $h(x)$ is the set of all real numbers. The domain of $k(x)$ is the set of all real numbers except 0. Since the domains of h and k are not equal, h and k are not equal functions.

In Example 4b the graph of $h(x)$ is "unbroken," or *continuous*. The graph of $k(x)$ has a gap at the point $(0, -2)$ and is said to be *discontinuous* at that point. The concept of continuity will be discussed formally in Chapter 16.

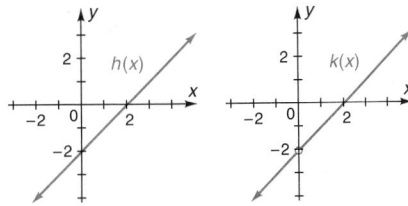

An alternative definition of a function states:

> If a relation contains the ordered pairs (a, b) and (a, c), then that relation is a function if and only if $b = c$.

Example 4 Show that the relation $xy = -4$ is a function.

$$xy = -4 \qquad\qquad \textit{Use the alternative definition of a function.}$$
$$ab = -4 \quad ac = -4 \qquad \textit{Substitute the ordered pairs } (a, b) \textit{ and } (a, c).$$
$$a = \frac{-4}{b} \quad a = \frac{-4}{c}$$
$$\frac{-4}{b} = \frac{-4}{c} \qquad\qquad \textit{Since } a = a$$
$$-4c = -4b$$
$$c = b \qquad\qquad \text{Therefore, } xy = -4 \text{ is a function.}$$

A relation can be represented as a set of ordered pairs, a mapping, or a rule. A graph is another representation of a relation. The **vertical line test** is a useful tool when trying to determine if the graph of a relation represents a function. Let each value of x in the domain of a relation be represented by a vertical line drawn in the plane. If every vertical line intersects the graph no more than once, the graph represents a function.

1.4 Relations and Functions   **27**

For Example 5
Use the vertical line test to determine which of the given graphs represents a function.

1.

function

2.

function

3.

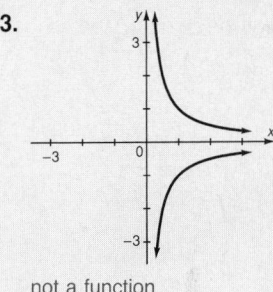

not a function

CLOSURE

Have students summarize the concepts of relations and functions in their math journals. Make sure they list examples of each from their own experiences, not necessarily mathematical.

INDEPENDENT PRACTICE

Assignment Guide
Basic: 1–29, 38, 43, 49, Project
Average: 5, 15, 27–56, Project
Enriched: 30–59, Project

Teacher's Resource Book
  Practice, page 4

Example 5 Use the vertical line test to determine which of the given graphs represents a function.

a.

b.

c.
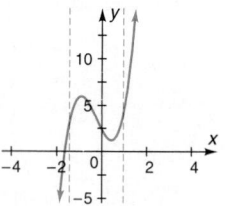

Function
Every vertical line
intersects the graph
no more than once.

Not a function
At least one vertical
line intersects the
graph more than once.

Function
Every vertical line
intersects the graph
no more than once.

A function f is called a **one-to-one** function if for any two elements of the domain of f, $f(x_1) = f(x_2)$ if and only if $x_1 = x_2$. To determine whether the graph of a function represents a one-to-one function, use the **horizontal line test**. Draw horizontal lines in the plane. If every horizontal line intersects the graph of the function no more than once, the graph represents a one-to-one function. *Which graph in Example 5 represents a one-to-one function?*

Class Exercises

Give the domain and range of each relation. Determine if each mapping represents a function.

1.

2.

3.
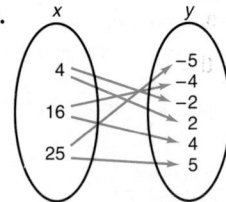

Given $f(x) = 3x^2$ and $g(x) = -2x$, evaluate each of the following.

4. $f(-3)$ 27

5. $g(-3)$ 6

6. $f(x + h)$
   $3x^2 + 6xh + 3h^2$

7. $g(x - h)$ $-2x + 2h$

Determine whether each graph represents a function. For each function, determine whether it is one-to-one.

8.
One-to-one
function

9.
Function

10.
Not a
function

11.
One-to-one
function
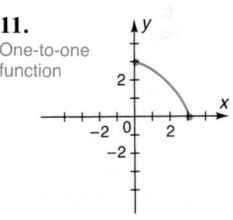

28   Chapter 1 Functions

State the domain of each function and determine if each pair of functions is equal.

12. $f(x) = 2x^2 + 4x$; $g(x) = 2(x^2 + x) + 2x$ $\quad D_f = \{x : x \in \mathcal{R}\}$; $D_g = \{x : x \in \mathcal{R}\}$; equal

13. $h(x) = \dfrac{5x^3 + 5x}{5x}$; $m(x) = x^2 + 1$ $\quad D_h = \{x : x \neq 0\}$; $D_m = \{x : x \in \mathcal{R}\}$; not equal

14. Determine the domain of the function $f(x) = \dfrac{1}{x^2}$. Graph the function using a graphing utility, and determine the range from the graph.

Practice Exercises Use appropriate technology.

State the domain and range of each relation. Determine if each mapping represents a function.

A **1.**

2.

3.

4.
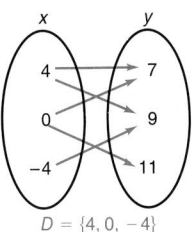

$D = \{4, 0, -4\}$
$R = \{7, 9, 11\}$
not a function

Ⓡ **5.** Express using positive exponents: $3x^{-3}y^2 \cdot \dfrac{3y^2}{x^3}$

Determine whether each equation represents a function.

6. $3y = x + 12$ function

7. $2y = \dfrac{3}{x}$ function

8. Thinking Critically Find a relation that is not a function for which the horizontal line test applies. Answers may vary; $x = y^2$ or $x = a$, $a \in \mathcal{R}$.

State the domain and range of each relation.

9. $g(x) = \dfrac{x - 5}{18 - 3x - x^2}$ $\quad D_g = \{x : x \neq -6, x \neq 3\}$; $R_g = \{y : y \in \mathcal{R}\}$

10. $h(x) = 3\sqrt{-3 - x}$ $\quad D_h = \{x : x \leq -3\}$; $R_h = \{y : y \geq 0\}$

11. Writing in Mathematics A function $f(x)$ has a domain that includes all real numbers except -2 and 2 and a range that includes all real numbers greater than 3. Describe how these restrictions affect the graph.

Determine whether each graph represents a function. For each function, determine whether it is one-to-one.

12.
One-to-one function

13.
Not a function

14.
Function
Not one-to-one
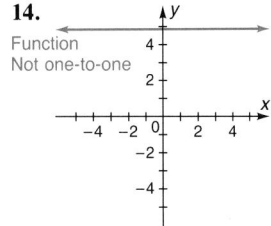

Writing in Mathematics
11. The continuity of the graph will be broken where $x = 2$ and $x = -2$. Also, the graph will not dip *below* the line $y = 3$.

---

5. Determine if each graph represents a function. State if the function is one-to-one.

a.

function; not one-to-one

b.
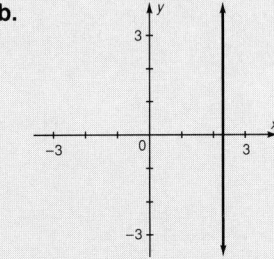

not a function

Alternative Assessment
Instruct students to find a relationship for two sets of data in their everyday experience that can be represented as a set of ordered pairs. Then have them write the set of ordered pairs and determine if the relation is a function. For example, there is a relationship between the top row of keys (numbers) and the special symbols !, @, #, and so forth on a keyboard or typewriter.

Additional Answers
Class Exercises
1. $D = \{2, 5, 11\}$; $R = \{1, 8, 14\}$; function
2. $D = \{-3, -1, 0, 1, 3\}$; $R = \{0, 1, 9\}$; function
3. $D = \{4, 16, 25\}$;
$R = \{-5, -4, -2, 2, 4, 5\}$;
not a function

Practice Exercises
1. $D = \{a, b, c, d\}$; $R = \{0, 2, 4, 6\}$; function
2. $D = \{1, 2, 3, 4\}$; $R = \{a, b, c\}$; function
3. $D = \{-1, -2, 1, 2\}$; $R = \{1, 16\}$; function

30

Ⓡ 15. Simplify: $\sqrt[5]{64x^6y^3}$ $2x\sqrt[5]{2xy^3}$

Given $f(x) = 3x + 4$ and $g(x) = x^2$, evaluate each of the following:

16. $f(2a)$ 6a + 4

17. $g(4a)$ 16a²

18. $g(b^2)$ b⁴

19. $f(\sqrt{b})$ 3√b + 4

20. $f(x - 2)$ 3x − 2

21. $g(x - 4)$ x² − 8x + 16

Find the domain of each function. Graph the function using a graphing utility and determine the range from the graph.

22. $f(x) = \dfrac{1}{x - 2}$ $D_f = \{x: x \neq 2\}$; $R_f = \{y: y \neq 0\}$

23. $g(x) = \dfrac{x}{x + 1}$ $D_g = \{x: x \neq -1\}$; $R_g = \{y: y \neq 1\}$

Find the domain of each function and determine if each pair of functions is equal.

24. $T(x) = 3x^2 + 9x$; $H(x) = 3(x^2 + 3x)$

25. $H(x) = \sqrt{4x - 16}$; $T(x) = 2\sqrt{x - 4}$

26. $f(x) = 4x + 2$; $g(x) = \dfrac{8x^2 + 4x}{2x}$

27. $m(x) = \dfrac{x^2 - 25}{x - 5}$; $n(x) = x + 5$

28. *Business*   The profit from a new computer program is a function of the number x sold and can be expressed by the rule $P(x) = 7.2x - 90$. Evaluate $P(50)$, $P(100)$, and $P(150)$. 270; 630; 990

29. *Optics*   The proper distance, in meters, of a camera with a 50-mm lens from an object being photographed is a function of the magnification x of the lens and can be expressed by the rule $D(x) = 0.05(1 + x)$. Evaluate $D(15)$, $D(40)$, $D(60)$. 0.8; 2.05; 3.05

Given $f(x) = -3x + 2$ and $g(x) = x^2 - 1$, evaluate each of the following:

Ⓑ 30. $f(\sqrt{5})$ −3√5 + 2

31. $g(\pi)$ π² − 1

32. $g(x + 2)$ x² + 4x + 3

33. $f(x - 4)$ −3x + 14

34. $f(x^3)$ −3x³ + 2

35. $g(x^2)$ x⁴ − 1

36. $\dfrac{f(t + h) - f(t)}{h}$, $h \neq 0$ −3

37. $\dfrac{g(m + h) - g(m)}{h}$, $h \neq 0$ 2m + h

Ⓡ 38. Factor completely: $a^2b^5c - a^2b^3c^3$ a²b³c(b − c)(b + c)

Find the domain of each function and determine if each pair of functions is equal.

39. $f(x) = \dfrac{2x^2 + 3x - 2}{x + 2}$; $g(x) = 2x - 1$

40. $h(x) = \dfrac{2x^2 + x - 3}{x - 1}$; $m(x) = 2x + 3$

41. $f(x) = |2x + 3|$; $g(x) = \sqrt{(2x + 3)^2}$

42. $T(x) = 5x - 2$; $P(x) = \sqrt{(5x - 2)^2}$

Ⓡ 43. Solve for M, indicating any restrictions on the variables: $K = \dfrac{MR - 2\pi M}{3}$

44. Thinking Critically   Accept or reject the following statement and justify your reply: "If two functions can be written in the same form, they are equal."

Graph each equation and determine if the graph represents a function. For each function, determine if it is one-to-one.

45. $y = 3x^2 - 2$

46. $y = -\dfrac{1}{2}x + 8$

47. $y = -2$

48. $x = 5$

45.

one-to-one function

46.

one-to-one function

47.

function; not one-to-one

48.

not a function

Ⓡ 49. If you have three coins in your pocket totaling 35 cents and one of those coins falls out of your pocket, what is the probability that you will still have 30 cents in your pocket? 2/3

50. Writing in Mathematics Reword the definition of a one-to-one function. Write your definition in sentence form.

51. *Biology* The weight of the muscles of a man is a function of his body weight x and can be expressed as $W(x) = 0.4x$. Determine the domain of this function. $D_W = \{x: x > 0\}$

52. *Physics* The distance an object falls is a function of time t and can be expressed as $s(t) = -16t^2$. Graph the function and determine if it is one-to-one.

Determine the domain of each function. Graph the function using a graphing utility, and determine the range from the graph. $D_T = \{x: x > 2 \text{ or } x < -2\};$ $R_T = \{y: y > 0\}$

C 53. $g(x) = \dfrac{1}{x}$ $\qquad$ **54.** $f(x) = \dfrac{1}{x^2}$ $\qquad$ **55.** $T(x) = \dfrac{1}{\sqrt{x^2 - 4}}$ $\qquad$ **56.** $R(x) = \dfrac{1}{\sqrt[3]{x}}$

$D_g = \{x: x \neq 0\}; R_g = \{y: y \neq 0\}$ $\quad$ $D_f = \{x: x \neq 0\}; R_f = \{y: y > 0\}$ $\qquad\qquad$ $D_R = \{x: x \neq 0\};$ $R_R = \{y: y \neq 0\}$

Determine if each of the following pairs of functions is equal.

57. $f(x) = |x + 1|$; $g(x) = |x| + 1$ not equal

58. $f(x) = |x - n|$; $g(x) = n - x$, given that n is a real number and $x < n$ equal

59. Thinking Critically Given that a is a real number and $f(a) = 3a - 4 = g(a)$, but $f(x) \neq g(x)$, construct two functions f and g which make these statements true. Answers may vary. $f(x) = 3x - 4$; $g(x) = \dfrac{(3x - 4)(x)}{x}$

Project

Construct your own cipher. Then see if you can determine a mathematical formula with which to solve it.

Review

Solve each equation.

1. $2d^2 - 4d + 1 = 0$ $d = 1 \pm \dfrac{\sqrt{2}}{2}$ $\qquad$ **2.** $3x^2 - 7x + 8 = 0$ $\dfrac{7 \pm i\sqrt{47}}{6}$

3. The sum of three integers is 48. The second number is 12 more than the first and the third number is twice the first. Find the numbers. 9, 21, 18

Given set $A = \{-5, -3, -1, 0, 1, 2\}$ and set $B = \{-3, -2, 0, 1, 2\}$, determine.

4. $A \cap B$ $\{-3, 0, 1, 2\}$ $\qquad\qquad$ **5.** $A \cup B$ $\{-5, -3, -2, -1, 0, 1, 2\}$

6. $\angle A$ is complementary to $\angle B$. If $\angle A$ is $37°$, determine $\angle B$. 53°

7. Graph $y = 3x + 4$.

8. Divide $(8a^4 + 52a^3 - 4a^2 + 10a + 12) \div (4a + 2)$ $2a^3 + 12a^2 - 7a + 6$

9. Simplify: $\dfrac{5 + 3(-2 + 5)^2}{2^3(3 - (7 - (4 + 2)))}$ 2

10. Find the volume of a prism with a 4 cm by 4 cm base and height of 6 cm. 96 cm³

1.4 Relations and Functions **31**

Additional Answers

52.

not one-to-one

53.

54.

55.

56.

Review

7.

Writing in Mathematics
50. Answers may vary. Example: A function is one-to-one if and only if for any two distinct values of x their images are also distinct values.

Vocabulary
composite function
composition of functions

Ⓜ **Materials/Manipulatives**
local newspaper's business section
foreign coins
ads for airline fares

Technology
symbolic manipulator

FOCUS

The number of units of one currency needed to buy a unit of another currency is called the foreign exchange rate. These rates are usually published daily in the business section of the newspaper. Have students choose two countries they would like to visit and find the foreign exchange rate of the American dollar for each of these countries.

INSTRUCTION

Ⓜ • When discussing Example 2, have students analyze the airline fare ads to determine if airfare is truly based on mileage alone. They may be surprised to find that it is sometimes less expensive to fly to a destination 2000 mi away than to one that is 500 mi away. Have students suggest reasons for this.

• After discussing Example 5, divide students into small groups and have each group select two countries. Using the newspaper to find current foreign exchange rates for the countries, have them find functions f and g such that the function f represents the exchange rate of dollars into the first country's currency, and the function g the exchange rate of the first country's currency into the second country's currency. Then have them find a function $h = f \circ g$ such that $f \circ g$ represents the exchange rate of dollars into the second country's currency.

1.5 Algebra of Functions

Objectives: To define the sum, difference, product, and quotient of functions
To form and evaluate composite functions

Focus

Eric participated in a one-year student exchange program. He studied in Kenya for 6 months and then in Japan. When Eric arrived in Kenya, he exchanged his American dollars for Kenya shillings. On that particular day, one dollar was worth 19.27 Kenya shillings. When Eric arrived in Japan, he exchanged his Kenya shillings for Japanese yen. One shilling was worth 7.16 Japanese yen. On any given day, the exchange rates for dollars in terms of shillings and for shillings in terms of yen can each be expressed as a formula. Applying these formulas in a specified order yields a new formula for the exchange rate of dollars in terms of yen, an example of *composition* of functions.

In the situation described in the Focus, the exchange rates can be expressed as functions. For instance, dollars d can be expressed as a function of shillings s by the rule $d = f(s) = 19.27s$. Once a function is found to model a situation, it can be combined with other functions mathematically.

Given two functions f and g, new functions $f + g$, $f - g$, $f \cdot g$, and f/g can be formed by adding, subtracting, multiplying, and dividing.

Sum	$(f + g)(x) = f(x) + g(x)$
Difference	$(f - g)(x) = f(x) - g(x)$
Product	$(f \cdot g)(x) = f(x) \cdot g(x)$
Quotient	$(f/g)(x) = \left(\dfrac{f}{g}\right)(x) = \dfrac{f(x)}{g(x)},\ g(x) \neq 0$

The domain of each resulting function consists of those values of x common to the domains of f and g. The domain of the quotient function is further restricted by excluding all values that make $g(x) = 0$.

32   Chapter 1 Functions

Example 1 Given $f(x) = \dfrac{1}{x-3}$ and $g(x) = 2x$, find each function and state its domain.

     a. $f + g$ **b.** $f - g$ **c.** $f \cdot g$ **d.** f/g

a. $(f + g)(x) = f(x) + g(x) = \dfrac{1}{x-3} + 2x = \dfrac{1 + 2x(x-3)}{x-3} = \dfrac{2x^2 - 6x + 1}{x-3}$

a. $D_f = \{x: x \neq 3\}$ and $D_g = \{x: x \in \mathcal{R}\}$

     $D_{f+g} = \{x: x \neq 3\}$, since the domain of $(f + g)(x)$ is comprised of all the elements that the domains of f and g have in common.

b. $(f - g)(x) = f(x) - g(x) = \dfrac{1}{x-3} - 2x = \dfrac{1 - 2x(x-3)}{x-3} = \dfrac{-2x^2 + 6x + 1}{x-3}$

b. $D_{f-g} = \{x: x \neq 3\}$

c. $(f \cdot g)(x) = f(x) \cdot g(x) = \dfrac{1}{x-3} \cdot 2x = \dfrac{2x}{x-3}$

c. $D_{f \cdot g} = \{x: x \neq 3\}$

d. $(f/g)(x) = \dfrac{f(x)}{g(x)} = \dfrac{1}{x-3} \div 2x = \dfrac{1}{x-3} \cdot \dfrac{1}{2x} = \dfrac{1}{2x^2 - 6x}$

d. $D_{f/g} = \{x: x \neq 0, \ x \neq 3\}$ *Why is $x = 0$ omitted from the domain?*

Functions are often combined when modeling real world situations.

Example 2   *Transportation*   The total cost of airfare on a given route, excluding taxes and promotions, is comprised of the base cost C and the fuel surcharge S. Both C and S are functions of the mileage m; $C(m) = 0.30m + 40$ and $S(m) = 0.02m$. Determine a function for the total cost of a ticket in terms of the mileage, and find the airfare for flying 1573 mi.

$(C + S)(m)$ represents the total cost of a ticket in terms of mileage.

     $(C + S)(m) = C(m) + S(m)$ *Definition of the sum function.*

               $= (0.30m + 40) + 0.02m$

               $= 0.32m + 40$

     $(C + S)(1573) = 0.32(1573) + 40$ *Calculation-ready form*

                   $= 543.36$ The ticket will cost $543.36.

Another method of combining two functions is by successive applications of the functions in a specific order. This binary operation is called **composition of functions.**

> Given two functions f and g, the **composite function** $f \circ g$ is defined by $(f \circ g)(x) = f(g(x))$ and is read "f of g of x." The domain of $(f \circ g)(x)$ is the set of elements x in the domain of g such that $g(x)$ is in the domain of f.

1.5 Algebra of Functions   **33**

Thinking Critically

The domain does not include $x = 0$ because the expression $\dfrac{1}{2x^2 - 6x}$ is undefined for that value. The denominator cannot equal zero.

GUIDED PRACTICE

For Example 1

For each pair of functions find each function $f + g$, $f - g$, $f \cdot g$, f/g and state its domain.

1. $f(x) = \sqrt{x + 1}$; $g(x) = \sqrt{x - 1}$

   $(f + g)(x) = \sqrt{x + 1} + \sqrt{x - 1}$

   $D_{f+g} = \{x: x \geq 1\}$

   $(f - g)(x) = \sqrt{x + 1} - \sqrt{x - 1}$

   $D_{f-g} = \{x: x \geq 1\}$

   $(f \cdot g)(x) = \sqrt{x^2 - 1}$

   $D_{f \cdot g} = \{x: x \geq 1\}$

   $(f/g)(x) = \dfrac{\sqrt{x + 1}}{\sqrt{x - 1}}$

   $D_{f/g} = \{x: x > 1\}$

Common Error   Some students may add the radicands together. Remind students that only like radicals may be added.

Some students may forget to eliminate $x = 1$ from the domain of f/g. Remind these students that when a radical is in the denominator, the radicand must be a positive number.

2. $f(x) = x + 5$; $g(x) = x^2 - 5x + 4$

   $(f + g)(x) = x^2 - 4x + 9$

   $D_{f+g} = \{x: x \in \mathcal{R}\}$

   $(f - g)(x) = -x^2 + 6x + 1$

   $D_{f-g} = \{x: x \in \mathcal{R}\}$

   $(f \cdot g)(x) = x^3 - 21x + 20$

   $D_{f \cdot g} = \{x: x \in \mathcal{R}\}$

   $(f/g)(x) = \dfrac{x + 5}{x^2 - 5x + 4}$

   $D_{f/g} = \{x: x \neq 1 \text{ and } x \neq 4\}$

For Example 2

The efficiency of an engine with a given heat output, in calories, can be calculated by finding the ratio of two functions of heat input, D and N, where $D(I) = I - 5700$ and $N(I) = I$. Write a function for the efficiency of the engine in terms of heat input. Find the efficiency when the heat input is 17,200 calories.

$E(I) = \dfrac{I - 5700}{I}$; $E(17,200) \approx 0.67$

For Example 3

For each pair of functions evaluate $(f \circ g)(x)$ and $(g \circ f)(x)$.

1. $f(x) = x - 3$; $g(x) = 2x^2 - 1$
   $(f \circ g)(x) = 2x^2 - 4$
   $(g \circ f)(x) = 2x^2 - 12x + 17$

2. $f(x) = 2x + 3$; $g(x) = \dfrac{x - 3}{2}$
   $(f \circ g)(x) = x = (g \circ f)(x)$

For Example 4

For each pair of functions find the domain of $(f \circ g)(x)$ and $(g \circ f)(x)$.

1. $f(x) = x^2$; $g(x) = \sqrt{x}$
   $(f \circ g)(x) = x \quad D_{f \circ g} = \{x : x \in \mathcal{R}\}$
   $(g \circ f)(x) = |x| \quad D_{g \circ f} = \{x : x \in \mathcal{R}\}$

Common Error Some students may write the domain of $(f \circ g)(x)$ as the set of real numbers. Remind them that the definition of the domain of $(f \circ g)(x)$ is the set of elements in the domain of g such that $g(x)$ is in the domain of f and $D_g = \{x : x \geq 0\}$.

2. $f(x) = x^3 + 5$; $g(x) = \dfrac{1}{x}$

   $(f \circ g)(x) = \dfrac{1 + 5x^3}{x^3}$
   $D_{f \circ g} = \{x : x \neq 0\}$
   $(g \circ f)(x) = \dfrac{1}{x^3 + 5}$
   $D_{g \circ f} = \{x : x \neq -\sqrt[3]{5}\}$

A composite function $f \circ g$ can be illustrated as shown:

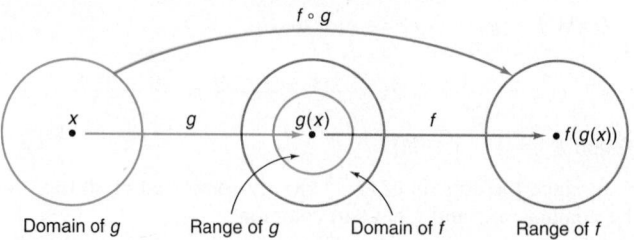

Domain of g Range of g Domain of f Range of f

In the composition $f \circ g$, the domain of f must contain the range of g. Sometimes the domain of g must be restricted so that $g(x)$ is in the domain of f. The composition of two functions $f \circ g$ is the operation of applying g and then f. The composition $g \circ f$ is the operation of applying f and then g.

Example 3 Given $f(x) = x^2$ and $g(x) = 2x + 5$, evaluate each function.
      a. $(f \circ g)(x)$ **b.** $(g \circ f)(x)$

a. $(f \circ g)(x) = f(g(x))$ *Definition of $f \circ g$*
             $= f(2x + 5)$ *Substitute $2x + 5$ for $g(x)$.*
             $= (2x + 5)^2$ *$f(x) = x^2$*
             $= 4x^2 + 20x + 25$

b. $(g \circ f)(x) = g(f(x))$ *Definition of $g \circ f$*
             $= g(x^2)$ *Substitute x^2 for $f(x)$.*
             $= 2(x^2) + 5$ *$g(x) = 2x + 5$*
             $= 2x^2 + 5$

Notice that composition of functions is not commutative. *Will the domains of $f \circ g$ and $g \circ f$ necessarily be the same?*

Example 4 Given $f(x) = \sqrt{x - 2}$ and $g(x) = 3x$, find the domain of
      a. $(g \circ f)(x)$ **b.** $(f \circ g)(x)$

a. $(g \circ f)(x) = g(f(x))$
             $= g(\sqrt{x - 2})$
             $= 3(\sqrt{x - 2})$
             $= 3\sqrt{x - 2}$

    $D_{g \circ f} = \{x : x \geq 2\}$, since $x - 2$ must be nonnegative.

b. $(f \circ g)(x) = f(g(x))$
             $= f(3x)$
             $= \sqrt{3x - 2}$

    $D_{f \circ g} = \left\{x : x \geq \dfrac{2}{3}\right\}$, since $3x - 2$ must be nonnegative.

34   Chapter 1 Functions

Thinking Critically
The domains of $(f \circ g)$ and $(g \circ f)$ will not necessarily be the same. See Example 4.

Composite functions may be useful in real world situations.

Example 5 *Economics*   The wholesale price P for a box of computer disks is a function of the manufacturing cost per disk x in dollars. If there are 25 disks per box and the manufacturer includes a $15 markup, then $P = W(x) = 25x + 15$. The retail price Q includes a 20% markup, $Q = R(P) = P + 0.20P$.
a. Determine a function which gives the retail price Q in terms of x.
b. Determine the retail price of a box of disks that costs $0.37 per disk to manufacture.

a. $Q = R(P) = R(W(x))$ $\qquad\qquad$ $P = W(x)$
$\quad = R(25x + 15)$
$\quad = (25x + 15) + 0.20(25x + 15)$
$\quad = 30x + 18$

b. The retail price of a box of disks that costs $0.37 per disk to manufacture is

$Q = 30(0.37) + 18 = \$29.10$

Given a composite function $f \circ g$, it is sometimes possible to decompose it into two functions, f and g. Since $(f \circ g)(x) = f(g(x))$, it is helpful to think of $g(x)$ as the "inner" function and $f(x)$ as the "outer" function.

Example 6   Determine two functions f and g such that $(f \circ g)(x) = \sqrt{2x}$.

Let $g(x) = 2x$ $\qquad$ *Inner function*
Let $f(x) = \sqrt{x}$ $\qquad$ *Outer function*
$(f \circ g)(x) = f(g(x))$ $\qquad$ *Check.*
$\qquad\quad = f(2x)$ $\qquad\quad$ *Apply g.*
$\qquad\quad = \sqrt{2x}$ $\qquad\quad$ *Apply f.*

Are there other functions f and g such that $(f \circ g)(x) = \sqrt{2x}$?

Class Exercises

For each pair of functions, find $f + g, f - g, f \cdot g,$ and f/g. State the domain of each new function.

1. $f(x) = 3x^2 + 2; \ g(x) = 2x + 4$ $\qquad$ **2.** $f(x) = x^3 - 3; \ g(x) = 2x^3 + 4$

3. $f(x) = \sqrt{x - 1}; \ g(x) = 3x$ $\qquad$ **4.** $f(x) = \dfrac{1}{x - 2}; \ g(x) = \dfrac{1}{x}$

For each pair of functions, evaluate $(f \circ g)(-5)$ and $(g \circ f)(2)$.

5. $f(x) = x^3; \ g(x) = -x$ $\ $ 125; -8 $\qquad$ **6.** $f(x) = \dfrac{1}{x}; \ g(x) = 3x$ $\ \dfrac{-1}{15}; \dfrac{3}{2}$

For each pair of functions, find $(f \circ g)(x)$ and $(g \circ f)(x)$.

7. $f(x) = x + 3; \ g(x) = 5x$ $\ $ 5x + 3; 5x + 15 $\qquad$ **8.** $f(x) = \sqrt{x}; \ g(x) = x^2$ $\ $ |x|; x

Determine two functions f and g such that $h(x) = (f \circ g)(x)$.

9. $h(x) = 3(4x + 1)^2$ $\ $ f(x) = 3x²; g(x) = 4x + 1 $\qquad$ **10.** $h(x) = \dfrac{1}{x + 1}$ $\ $ f(x) = $\frac{1}{x}$; g(x) = x + 1

1.5 Algebra of Functions $\quad$ **35**

Thinking Critically
Yes. For example, $f(x) = \sqrt{6x}$ and $g(x) = \frac{x}{3}$.

Assignment Guide
Basic: 1–25, 33–35
Average: 7, 9, 16–40
Enriched: 22–48

Teacher's Resource Book
  Practice, page 5

Ⓡ **Review**
Exercises 7, 9, 17, 33, and 35 review concepts of factoring, applying formulas, solving equations, and finding the domain and range of a function.

LESSON FOLLOW-UP

Lesson Quiz

1. The cost of having one-page flyers printed is comprised of the per page cost of the paper P and the per page cost of printing C. Both P and C are functions of the number of flyers printed. $P(n) = 0.03n$ and $C(n) = 0.07n + 75$. Write a function for the total cost T of printing a set of flyers in terms of the number of flyers printed and find the cost for printing 2500 flyers.
$T(n) = 0.1n + 75$; $T(2500) = \$325$

2. Given $f(x) = 4x - 1$ and $g(x) = \dfrac{x + 1}{4}$, find $(f \circ g)(x)$ and $(g \circ f)(x)$.
$(f \circ g)(x) = x = (g \circ f)(x)$

3. Given $f(x) = \sqrt{3x - 1}$ and $g(x) = 2x$, find the domains of $(f \circ g)(x)$ and $(g \circ f)(x)$.
$(f \circ g)(x) = \sqrt{6x - 1}$;
$D_{f \circ g} = \left\{x : x \geq \dfrac{1}{6}\right\}$
$(g \circ f)(x) = 2\sqrt{3x - 1}$;
$D_{g \circ f} = \left\{x : x \geq \dfrac{1}{3}\right\}$

---

11. *Physics*   A spherical balloon is being inflated at a constant rate. The radius r, in inches, of the sphere as it is being inflated is a function of time t, in minutes, given by $r = f(t) = 1.85t$. The volume V of a sphere is related to the radius by the formula $V = g(r) = \dfrac{4\pi r^3}{3}$. Find $g(f(t))$ and interpret its meaning. $8.44\pi t^3$; Volume of the sphere is a function of time.

Practice Exercises

For each pair of functions, find $f + g$, $f - g$, $f \cdot g$, and f/g. State the domain of each new function.

A **1.** $f(x) = 3x$; $g(x) = 4x$

2. $f(x) = 2x$; $g(x) = -3x$

3. $f(x) = \dfrac{3x}{x - 2}$; $g(x) = 2x$

4. $f(x) = \dfrac{-x}{x + 3}$; $g(x) = 4$

5. $f(x) = \sqrt{x}$; $g(x) = 4x^2$

6. $f(x) = \sqrt{2x}$; $g(x) = -x$

Ⓡ **7.** Factor $x^3 - 125$ over the set of real numbers. $(x - 5)(x^2 + 5x + 25)$

8. Thinking Critically   If $p(x) = (f/g)(x)$, $g(x) \neq 0$, under what conditions will $p(x) = 0$? When $f(x) = 0$

Ⓡ **9.** If the diameter of a circle is 5, what is the circumference? 5π

10. *Business*   Talaiya is a salesperson whose annual earnings can be represented by the function $T(x) = 25{,}000 + 0.05x$, where x is the dollar value of the merchandise she sells. Her husband Pierre is also in sales, and his earnings are represented by the function $P(x) = 20{,}000 + 0.06x$. Find $(T + P)(x)$ and determine the total family income if they each sell $250,000 worth of merchandise. $45{,}000 + 0.11x$; $\$72{,}500$

For each pair of functions evaluate $(f \circ g)(-2)$ and $(g \circ f)(-2)$.

11. $f(x) = -x$; $g(x) = 2x + 7$ -3; 11

12. $f(x) = x^2 + 1$; $g(x) = 1 - x$ 10; -4

For each pair of functions, find $(f \circ g)(-x)$ and $(g \circ f)(x)$.

13. $f(x) = 3x - 4$; $g(x) = 3x + 1$ $-9x - 1$; $9x - 11$

14. $f(x) = x^2$; $g(x) = x + 3$ $x^2 - 6x + 9$; $x^2 + 3$

15. $f(x) = \sqrt{x + 3}$; $g(x) = 2x$ $\sqrt{-2x + 3}$; $2\sqrt{x + 3}$

16. $f(x) = x + 1$; $g(x) = \sqrt{5x}$ $\sqrt{-5x} + 1$; $\sqrt{5x + 5}$

Ⓡ **17.** Use the quadratic formula to solve $4x^2 + 6x - 10 = 0$. $x = 1, -2.5$

Determine two functions f and g such that $h(x) = (f \circ g)(x)$.

18. $h(x) = \sqrt{x + 1}$
$f(x) = \sqrt{x}$; $g(x) = x + 1$

19. $h(x) = (x - 3)^3$
$f(x) = x^3$, $g(x) = x - 3$

20. $h(x) = \dfrac{4}{x}$ $f(x) = 4x$; $g(x) = \dfrac{1}{x}$

21. $h(x) = -\dfrac{x}{3}$
$f(x) = \dfrac{x}{3}$; $g(x) = -x$

Given the functions $f(x) = \sqrt{x}$, $g(x) = x^2$, $h(x) = x + 1$, and $m(x) = x - 1$, find each of the following and state the domain.

B **22.** $(g \circ f)(a)$ a; $a \geq 0$

23. $(f \circ h)(a)$

24. $(f \circ g)(x)$

25. $(m - f)(x)$

26. $(m \circ h)(x)$

27. $(h \circ m)(x)$

28. $(f/g)(a + b)$

29. $(g + h)(c + d)$

Determine two functions f and g such that $h(x) = (f \circ g)(x)$.

30. $h(x) = \sqrt[3]{x + 3}$ $f(x) = \sqrt[3]{x}$; $g(x) = x + 3$

31. $h(x) = \sqrt[4]{x + 4}$ $f(x) = \sqrt[4]{x}$; $g(x) = x + 4$

32. $h(x) = \dfrac{1}{\sqrt{x}}$ $f(x) = \dfrac{1}{x}$; $g(x) = \sqrt{x}$

36   Chapter 1 Functions

® 33. Determine the domain of $f(x) = \dfrac{2x}{x^2 - 5x - 24}$. $D_f = \{x: x \neq 8, x \neq -3\}$

34. **Writing in Mathematics** Write a paragraph explaining how to find the composite function $f \circ g$ given f and g.

® 35. Determine a rule for the relation $\{(-2, 4), (0, 0), (2, -4), (4, -8)\}$. State the domain and range. $y = -2x$; $D = \{-2, 0, 2, 4\}$; $R = \{4, 0, -4, -8\}$

36. **Thinking Critically** If $f(x)$ and $g(x)$ are one-to-one functions, determine if $(f + g)(x)$ is necessarily a one-to-one function. Explain.

37. *Consumerism* An auto mechanic charges $35 per hour for labor plus $45 for parts for a tuneup on a six-cylinder car. The cost of a tuneup is a function of time determined by the formula $C(t) = 35t + 45$. The amount of time for the tuneup is determined by a formula given in the manual, $A(x) = 0.5x$, where x is a numerical code for the particular make of car. Write a formula for the cost of a tuneup in terms of the numerical code. If the numerical code for a certain car is 3, determine the final cost of the tuneup. $17.5x + 45$; $97.50

38. *Currency Exchange* The function for exchanging dollars for Kenya shillings on a given day is $f(x) = 19.27x$, where x represents the number of dollars. On the same day the function for exchanging Kenya shillings for Japanese yen is $g(y) = 7.16y$, where y represents the number of shillings. Write a function which will give the exchange rate of dollars in terms of yen. $137.97x$

Given $f(x) = x^2 + x$ and $g(x) = 2x$, solve each equation.

C 39. $(f \circ g)(x) = (f - g)(x)$ $x = 0, -1$ 40. $(g \circ f)(x) = (f \circ g)(x) - 18$ $x = 3, -3$
41. $(f + g)(x) = (f \cdot g)(x)$ $x = 0, \dfrac{-3}{2}, 1$ 42. $(f \circ g)(x) = (g \circ g)(x)$ $x = 0, \dfrac{1}{2}$

Find two different pairs of functions f and g such that $h(x) = (f \circ g)(x)$.

43. $h(x) = \dfrac{1}{x^3}$ $f(x) = \dfrac{1}{x}, g(x) = x^3$; $f(x) = x^3, g(x) = \dfrac{1}{x}$ 44. $h(x) = (\sqrt{x} - 2)^3$ $f(x) = (\sqrt{x})^3, g(x) = x - 2$; $f(x) = x^3, g(x) = \sqrt{x} - 2$
45. $h(x) = x$ $f(x) = x^2, g(x) = \sqrt{x}$; $f(x) = x + 5$; $g(x) = x - 5$ 46. $h(x) = c$, where c is a constant $f(x) = x, g(x) = c$; $f(x) = 2x - c, g(x) = c$
47. **Thinking Critically** Graph the functions $f(x) = x^3$ and $g(x) = \sqrt[3]{x}$ on the same coordinate plane. Find $f \circ g$ and graph it on the plane as well. Explain your results.

48. *Business* The owner of a small restaurant can prepare a particular gourmet meal at a cost of $10. He estimates that if the menu price of the meal is x dollars, then the number of customers who will order that meal at that price in an evening is given by the function $N(x) = 40 - x$. Express his nightly revenue, cost, and profit on this meal as functions of x.

Challenge

1. The volume of a sphere with radius r is tripled. Determine the new radius R in terms of the original radius. $R = \sqrt[3]{3}\,r$

2. Graph $f(x) = \sqrt{25 - x^2}$ and find the area of the region bounded by $f(x)$ and the x-axis. $\dfrac{25\pi}{2}$

4. The number of hair dryers that a factory produces in one day is a function of the number of hours the assembly line is in operation and is given by $n = P(t) = 300t - 6t^2$. The cost, in dollars, for producing n hair dryers is given by the function $C(n) = 6n + 50$.
   a. Write a function for the cost of producing the hair dryers in terms of the number of hours the assembly line is in production.
   b. Determine the cost of producing hair dryers on a day when the assembly line is in production for 15 h.
   a. $(C \circ P)(t) = -36t^2 + 1800t + 50$
   b. $(C \circ P)(15) = $18,950

5. Determine two functions f and g such that $h(x) = (f \circ g)(x)$ given $h(x) = \sqrt{2x - 7} + 5$.
   $g(x) = 2x - 7$; $f(x) = \sqrt{x} + 5$
   Answers may vary.

Alternative Assessment

Have the students write a paragraph explaining how to find the composition of two functions. Ask them to discuss any difficulties they are still having in finding the composition of functions.

Enrichment

Given $Q(x) = \sqrt{\sqrt{x} - 1} - 5$, find functions f, g, and h, such that $Q(x) = (f \circ g \circ h)(x)$ and determine the domain of $Q(x)$.
Answers may vary. $f(x) = \sqrt{x} - 5$; $g(x) = \sqrt{x} - 1$; $h(x) = x$; $D_Q = \{x: x \geq 1\}$

Additional Answers
Challenge

2.

Writing in Mathematics
34. Write the rule for the function g. Then write the rule for the function f and substitute the rule for g for each occurrence of the variable in this rule. Simplify the expression.

Vocabulary
inverse
inverse function

Ⓜ **Materials/Manipulatives**
telephone
tracing paper
transparencies

Technology
graphing utility

FOCUS

Divide the class into small groups and have each group research a method of coding. Have each group prepare an index card with the rule for decoding written on the front and the rule for coding written on the back. On a second index card have the group write a coded message with the correct decoded message on the back. Then have each group exchange cards and try to decode the message using the rule on the index card. If they are successful, they can write a new coded message using the rule on the back of the index card and pass it on to the next group.

INSTRUCTION

Ⓜ • Use the dial or buttons on a telephone to illustrate a function whose inverse is not a function. Let X be the set of letters on the telephone (have students list the domain which excludes Q and Z) and Y be the set of numbers. Ask students to determine if the relation that maps each letter to a number is a function. Then have them find the inverse relation and determine *if* it is a function.
• When discussing the notation for inverse function, stress the fact that f^{-1} is not the reciprocal of f.
• Use transparencies with graphs of $h(x)$ and $h^{-1}(x)$, as well as the graph of $y = x$ to reinforce Example 4.

1.6 Inverse Functions

Objectives: *To find the inverse of a relation or a function*
To determine if the inverse of a function is a function

Focus

Public key encryption schemes are important tools used by banks and other organizations to code secret data for transmission. These codes use numbers of approximately 200 digits that are difficult to factor into prime numbers. This method for coding was invented in 1977 by a group of mathematicians. In order to decode the data transmission, the order of the steps used to do the coding must be reversed. A formula which reverses the steps of a function is called the *inverse* of the function. Using approximately 1000 computers, researchers recently factored a 155-digit number into three smaller numbers. Although the security of present public key encryption systems is still not threatened, this feat illustrates that any security system must be constantly modified to keep up with the growth in technology.

Factoring a 155-Digit Number
13,407,807,929,942,597,099,574,024,998,205,846,127, 479,365,820,592,393,377,723,561,443,721,764,030,073, 546,976,801,874,298,166,903,427,690,031,858,186,486, 050,853,753,882,811,946,569,946,433,649,006,084,097
equals
2,424,823
times
7,455,602,825,647,884,208,337,395,736,200,454,918, 783,366,342,657
times
741,640,062,627,530,801,524,787,141,901,937,474,059, 940,781,097,519,023,905,821,316,144,415,759,504,705, 008,092,818,711,693,940,737

Given a relation represented by a set of ordered pairs, the **inverse** of the relation can be found by interchanging the first and second coordinates of each pair in the original relation. The inverse of a relation is a relation; but the inverse of a function may not be a function.

Example 1   Given the relation $\{(2, 4), (-2, 4), (3, 9), (-3, 9)\}$, determine if it is a function. Then, find its inverse and determine if the inverse is a function.

Using the mapping at the right, it can be determined that for each x there is one and only one corresponding y. Therefore, the relation is a function.

The inverse of the relation is

$\{(4, 2), (4, -2), (9, 3), (9, -3)\}$ *Interchange the first and second coordinates.*

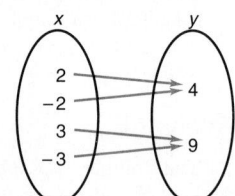

The inverse is not a function since 4 is paired with 2 and -2 and 9 is paired with 3 and -3.

38   Chapter 1 Functions

Let $f(x) = 2x - 4$ and $g(x) = \frac{1}{2}x + 2$. Consider the composite functions $f \circ g$ and $g \circ f$.

$$(f \circ g)(x) = f(g(x)) = f\left(\frac{1}{2}x + 2\right) = 2\left(\frac{1}{2}x + 2\right) - 4 = x + 4 - 4 = x$$

$$(g \circ f)(x) = g(f(x)) = g(2x - 4) = \frac{1}{2}(2x - 4) + 2 = x - 2 + 2 = x$$

Since both $f \circ g$ and $g \circ f$ equal x, the original element in the domain, the functions f and g are *inverse functions*.

A function f has an **inverse function** g if and only if $f(g(x)) = x$ for all x in the domain of $g(x)$ and $g(f(x)) = x$ for all x in the domain of $f(x)$.

The inverse function of a function f is denoted f^{-1} or $f^{-1}(x)$. Thus $(f \circ f^{-1})(x) = (f^{-1} \circ f)(x) = x$. Note that f^{-1} is not the reciprocal of the function f. The reciprocal of f, $\frac{1}{f(x)}$, is denoted $[f(x)]^{-1}$.

The range of f is the domain of f^{-1} and the domain of f is the range of f^{-1}. For example, when

$$f = \{(q, t), (r, u), (s, v)\}$$

then $$f^{-1} = \{(t, q), (u, r), (v, s)\}$$

To find the inverse of a function expressed as an equation, interchange x and y and solve for y.

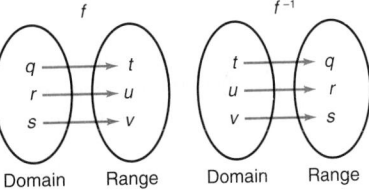

Domain   Range   Domain   Range

Example 2   Find the inverse function of $f(x) = \frac{2x}{3} - 6$. Graph the function, its inverse, and the line $y = x$ on the same set of axes.

$y = \frac{2x}{3} - 6$ $y = f(x)$

$x = \frac{2y}{3} - 6$ *Interchange x and y.*

$y = \frac{3x}{2} + 9$ *Solve for y to obtain f^{-1}.*

The viewing rectangle is set so that the intercepts and point of intersection are visible.

[−30, 30] by [−20, 20]
x scl: 5   y scl: 5

The graphs of a function and its inverse are symmetric with respect to the line $y = x$. In Example 2, notice that if the coordinate plane were folded along the line $y = x$, the graphs of f and f^{-1} would coincide.

When you interpret a model, the inverse function can provide you with valuable information.

1.6 Inverse Functions   **39**

GUIDED PRACTICE

For Example 1
Determine if each relation is a function. Then find the inverse of the relation and determine if the inverse is a function.

1. $\{(2, a), (2, b), (3, d), (3, e)\}$
   The relation is not a function since 2 maps onto a and b and 3 maps onto d and e. The inverse is $\{(a, 2), (b, 2), (d, 3), (e, 3)\}$ and is a function.

Common Error   Some students view a relation as a function only if it is one-to-one. Stress the fact that a many-to-one relation is a function but a one-to-many relation is not a function. Mappings can help to illustrate this point.

2. $\{(a, 2a), (b, 2b), (c, 2c), (d, 2d)\}$
   The relation is a function. The inverse is $\{(2a, a), (2b, b), (2c, c), (2d, d)\}$ and is a function.

For Example 2
Find the inverse of each function. Graph the function, its inverse, and the line $y = x$ on the same set of axes.

1. $f(x) = x^3 + 1$
   Inverse: $y = \sqrt[3]{x - 1}$

39

2. $y = \dfrac{1}{x}$

Inverse: $y = \dfrac{1}{x}$

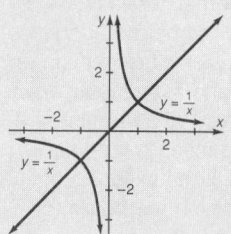

Technology Graphing utilities often display graphs that are not "square" and therefore the visual relationship between the graphs of a function and its inverse may be distorted. Make sure that students are aware of this and instruct them to use the *square zoom* feature if their calculators are equipped with one.

For Example 3

The linear model $h(\ell) = 2.8\ell + 71.5$ can be used to approximate the height, in centimeters, of a female from the length ℓ of her humerus bone (bone from the shoulder to the elbow). Using volunteers, test the model to determine its accuracy. Then find the inverse of $h(\ell)$ and interpret the meaning of h and ℓ in the inverse.

$h^{-1}(\ell) = 0.36\ell - 25.54$, where ℓ is the height and $h^{-1}(\ell)$ is the length of the bone.

Common Error Some students may not change the meaning of ℓ from length to height. Remind these students that when finding the inverse of a relation or function, the variables are interchanged.

Example 3 *Sports* A linear model that can be used to predict the year y in which the world record will be set for running the mile in a given time x is

$$f(x) = 2538.3243 - 146.5827x$$

In 1985, Steve Cram of England ran the mile in 3:46.31 (3 min, 46.31 s).
a. Test the linear model to see how accurate it was for Steve Cram's record.
b. Find the inverse of $f(x)$ and interpret its meaning.

a. Evaluate $f(3{:}46.31)$. Change 3:46.31 into decimal form.

$$3{:}46.31 = 3 + \frac{46.31}{60} \qquad \text{\textit{Calculation-ready form}}$$

$$= 3.771833333 \text{ min}$$

$$f(3.771833333) = 2538.3243 - 146.5827(3.771833333) \approx 1985$$

b. $y = 2538.3243 - 146.5827x$

$x = 2538.3243 - 146.5827y$ *Interchange x and y.*

$y = \dfrac{2538.3243}{146.5827} - \dfrac{x}{146.5827}$

$y = 17.3167 - 0.0068x$ *Round to four decimal places to be consistent with the original function.*

Since the variables were interchanged, x now represents the year and y now represents the running time. This model can be used to predict the running time record that will be set in a given year.

Do all functions have inverses that are also functions? Notice that the mapping at the right is not one-to-one. The function f has an inverse, but that inverse is not a function. The inverse is a relation. For a function f to have an inverse function, the function must be *one-to-one*. That is, for any two elements in the domain of f, $f(x_1) = f(x_2)$ if and only if $x_1 = x_2$.

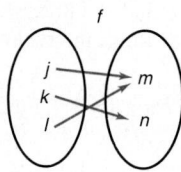

The horizontal line test is a useful tool in determining whether or not a function has an inverse function. If any horizontal line that is drawn on the graph of a function passes through no more than one point on the graph, then the function will have an inverse function.

Example 4 Graph the function $h(x) = x^2 + 2$. Use the horizontal line test to determine whether $h^{-1}(x)$ is a function.

The viewing rectangle is set at

$$[-6, 6] \text{ by } [-1, 7].$$

Using the horizontal line test, $h(x)$ does not have an inverse function.

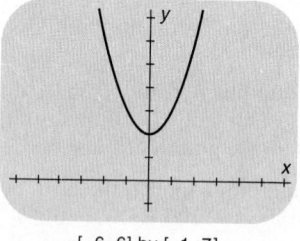

[−6, 6] by [−1, 7]

It is often possible to restrict the domain of a function to make it one-to-one and ensure that it has an inverse function.

Example 5 Restrict the domain of $h(x) = x^2 + 2$ to make it one-to-one and find the inverse function of $h(x)$ with the restricted domain. For this domain, what is the range of $h(x)$?

Looking at the graph in Example 4, if the domain is restricted to the nonnegative numbers, $h(x)$ will be one-to-one.

$$y = x^2 + 2$$
$$x = y^2 + 2 \qquad \textit{Interchange x and y.}$$
$$y = \sqrt{x - 2} \qquad h^{-1}(x)$$

The inverse function of $h(x) = x^2 + 2$, $x \geq 0$ is $h^{-1}(x) = \sqrt{x - 2}$.
The range of h is $\{x : x \geq 2\}$, which is the domain of $h^{-1}(x)$.
The range of h^{-1} is $\{x : x \geq 0\}$, which is the domain of $h(x)$.

Class Exercises

Find the inverse of each relation. Determine if the inverse is a function.

1. $\{(1, -5), (3, -3), (4, -2)\}$

2. $\{(a, c), (a, d), (b, e), (b, g)\}$

3. $y = 3x - 1$ $\ y = \frac{x}{3} + \frac{1}{3}$; function

4. $y = x^2$ $\ y = \pm\sqrt{x}$; not a function

Find the inverse function for each function. Restrict the domain of the original function, if necessary.

5. $f(x) = 4x - 6$ $\ f^{-1}(x) = \frac{x}{4} + \frac{3}{2}$

6. $g(x) = \sqrt{x} - 3$
$\ g^{-1}(x) = (x + 3)^2$

7. $h(x) = x^3$ $\ h^{-1}(x) = \sqrt[3]{x}$

8. $f(x) = \sqrt{x + 1}$
$\ f^{-1}(x) = x^2 - 1$

9. $f(x) = -x^2$
$\ f^{-1}(x) = -\sqrt{-x}$; $D_f = \{x : x \leq 0\}$

10. $g(x) = \frac{1}{x}$ $\ g^{-1}(x) = \frac{1}{x}$

Graph each function, its inverse, and the line $y = x$ on the same set of axes.

11. $f(x) = x - 1$

12. $g(x) = 2x + 1$

13. $h(x) = x^2 - 3$, $x \geq 0$

Graph each function and use the horizontal line test to determine if the function has an inverse function.

14. $f(x) = x^2$

15. $g(x) = x^2 + 4x + 3$

16. $h(x) = -x^3$

17. $f(x) = -2x$

18. Thinking Critically Think of a function f whose inverse is not a function. Then graph a portion of f that does pass the horizontal line test. What does this tell you about the importance of examining the complete graph?

Practice Exercises Use appropriate technology.

Find the inverse function for each function. Restrict the domain of the original function if necessary.

A **1.** $\{(5, 2), (7, 4), (9, 6)\}$ $\ \{(2, 5), (4, 7), (6, 9)\}$

2. $\{(a, b), (a, c), (b, d), (b, f)\}$
$\ \{(b, a), (c, a), (d, b), (f, b)\}$

3. $f(x) = 3x$ $\ f^{-1}(x) = \frac{x}{3}$

4. $f(x) = 4x$ $\ f^{-1}(x) = \frac{x}{4}$

5. $g(x) = -3x + 1$ $\ g^{-1}(x) = \frac{-x}{3} + \frac{1}{3}$

6. $g(x) = -2x - 3$ $\ g^{-1}(x) = \frac{-x}{2} - \frac{3}{2}$

7. $h(x) = \frac{1}{2x}$ $\ h^{-1}(x) = \frac{1}{2x}$

8. $h(x) = \frac{1}{x - 3}$ $\ h^{-1}(x) = \frac{1}{x} + 3$

1.6 Inverse Functions **41**

For Example 4
Graph each function and determine whether its inverse is a function.
1. $f(x) = x^3 - 5$

$f(x)$ is one-to-one and therefore its inverse is a function.

2. $g(x) = 2$

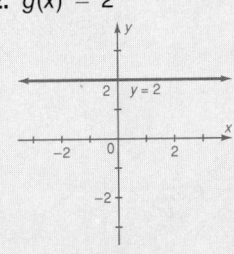

$g(x)$ is not one-to-one and therefore its inverse is not a function.

For Example 5
Restrict the domain of the function $g(x) = (x - 1)^2$ to make it one-to-one and then find the inverse function. State the domain and range of the inverse function.
$D_g = \{x : x \geq 1\}$ or $\{x : x \leq 1\}$
$R_g = \{y : y \geq 0\}$ or $\{y : y \geq 0\}$
Inverse:
$g^{-1}(x) = \sqrt{x} + 1$ or $g^{-1}(x) = -\sqrt{x} + 1$
$D_{g^{-1}} = \{x : x \geq 0\}$ or $\{x : x \geq 0\}$
$R_{g^{-1}} = \{y : y \geq 1\}$ or $\{y : y \leq 1\}$

CLOSURE

Have students summarize the procedures for finding the inverse of a relation or a function and for determining if the inverse of a function is a function.

INDEPENDENT PRACTICE

Assignment Guide
Basic: 1–23, 26–28, 36
Average: 9, 13–38
Enriched: 21–47

Teacher's Resource Book
  Practice, page 6

41

LESSON FOLLOW-UP

Lesson Quiz

1. Find the inverse of the relation $\{(4, 2), (-4, 2), (6, 3), (7, 1)\}$. Determine if the inverse is a function. inverse: $\{(2, 4), (2, -4), (3, 6), (1, 7)\}$; The inverse is not a function since the element 2 maps onto 4 and -4.

2. Graph $f(x) = (x - 2)^4$ and determine if f has an inverse function.

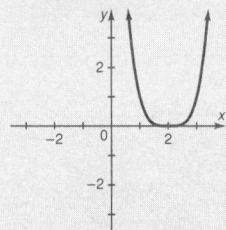

Since f is not a one-to-one function, it does not have an inverse function.

3. Find the inverse function of $g(x) = 5x - 1$.
$g^{-1}(x) = \dfrac{x + 1}{5}$

4. Restrict the domain of $h(x) = x^2 - 3$ so that it will have an inverse function. Find $h^{-1}(x)$ and determine the domain and range of h^{-1}.
$D_h = \{x: x \ge 0\}$ or $\{x: x \le 0\}$
$h^{-1}(x) = \sqrt{x + 3}$ or $h^{-1}(x) = -\sqrt{x + 3}$
$D_{h-1} = \{x: x \ge -3\}$ or $\{x: x \ge -3\}$
$R_{h-1} = \{y: y \ge 0\}$ or $\{y: y \le 0\}$

5. Restrict the domain of each function so that it is one-to-one.

   a. $g(x) = (x - 5)^2$ **b.** $h(x) = \dfrac{1}{x^2}$

   a. $D_g = \{x: x \ge 5\}$ or $\{x: x \le 5\}$
   b. $D_h = \{x: x > 0\}$ or $\{x: x < 0\}$

® 9. Given $f(x) = x^2$ and $g(x) = x - 2$, evaluate $(g \circ f)(-3)$ and $(f \circ g)(-3)$. 7; 25

Graph each function, its inverse, and the line $y = x$ on the same set of axes.

10. $g(x) = 2x - 1$ 11. $g(x) = -x + 2$ 12. $h(x) = \frac{2}{3}x + 1$

13. $h(x) = \frac{1}{2}x - 2$ 14. $f(x) = 2x^2 + 2$ 15. $f(x) = x^3$

16. **Thinking Critically** Construct a linear function that is its own inverse. Draw a graph to show that the graph of the function and its inverse are symmetric to the line $y = x$. Answers may vary. Refer students to Exercise 7.

Determine whether $f(x)$ and $g(x)$ are inverse functions.

17. $f(x) = 3x + 6$; $g(x) = \frac{x}{3} - 2$ Inverse functions

18. $f(x) = -x + 7$; $g(x) = -x + 7$ Inverse functions

19. $f(x) = x^2 - 3$, $x \ge 0$; $g(x) = \sqrt{x + 3}$ Inverse functions

20. *Chemistry* The formula for converting from Fahrenheit to Celsius temperatures is $y = \dfrac{5x}{9} - \dfrac{160}{9}$. Find the inverse of this function and determine whether the inverse is also a function. $y = \frac{9}{5}x + 32$; Inverse is a function.

21. *Cryptography* A simple cipher takes a number and codes it using the function $f(x) = 4x + 3$. Find the inverse of this function, and determine whether the inverse is also a function. $f^{-1}(x) = \frac{1}{4}x - \frac{3}{4}$; Inverse is a function.

Restrict the domain of each function so that it will have an inverse function. Then graph the inverse function.

B 22.

23.

24.
25.
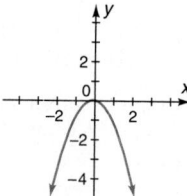

® 26. Find the slope and y-intercept of the line $2x + 3y = -7$. $\frac{-2}{3}$; $\frac{-7}{3}$

® 27. Given $f(x) = x^2$ and $g(x) = |x|$, find $g \circ f$ and $f \circ g$. x^2; x^2

28. **Writing in Mathematics** What limitations do you see in using the model discussed in Example 3 of this lesson?

Determine whether $f(x)$ and $g(x)$ are inverse functions, restricting the domains as necessary. State the domain and range of each function.

29. $f(x) = \sqrt{x + 2}$; $g(x) = x^2 - 2$ 30. $f(x) = 4x$; $g(x) = 0.25x$

31. $f(x) = \sqrt[3]{x} - 3$; $g(x) = (x - 3)^3$ 32. $f(x) = -2x + 5$; $g(x) = 2x - 5$

33. $f(x) = \dfrac{x - 1}{x}$; $g(x) = \dfrac{1}{1 - x}$ 34. $f(x) = \dfrac{x + 1}{x}$; $g(x) = \dfrac{1}{x + 1}$

42   Chapter 1 Functions

Writing in Mathematics

28. Answers may vary. One obvious flaw is that the model, if interpreted too literally, suggests that by the year 2539 the mile will be run in negative time.

35. Thinking Critically Construct a nonlinear function f such that $f = f^{-1}$.

Ⓡ **36.** Solve the system of equations: $\begin{cases} 7x - y = 6 \\ 2x - y + z = 3 \\ y + z = 3 \end{cases}$ (1, 1, 2)

Find the inverse function of each function. Restrict the domain of the original function, if necessary.

C **37.** $f(x) = \sqrt{2 - x}$ $f^{-1}(x) = -x^2 + 2$ **38.** $f(x) = x^2 + 4$ $f^{-1}(x) = \sqrt{x - 4}; D_f = \{x: x \geq 0\}$

39. $f(x) = x^2 - 6x + 4$ **40.** $f(x) = -\sqrt{x} - 1$

41. $f(x) = -x^2 + 4$ $f^{-1}(x) = \sqrt{4 - x}; D_f = \{x: x \leq 0\}$ **42.** $f(x) = x^2 - 3x + 4$

43. Prove: $(f^{-1})^{-1} = f$

44. Prove that the function $f(x) = ax + b$ is a one-to-one function if $a \neq 0$, but it is not a one-to-one function if $a = 0$.

45. Prove that a one-to-one function can have at most one inverse function.

46. Use a graphing utility to graph $f(x) = \dfrac{x - 1}{x}$ and $g(x) = \dfrac{1}{1 - x}$. Do these functions appear to be inverses? Compare your conclusion with your answer to Exercise 33.

47. Use a graphing utility to graph $f(x) = \dfrac{x + 1}{x}$ and $g(x) = \dfrac{1}{1 + x}$. Do these functions appear to be inverses? Compare your conclusion with your answer to Exercise 34.

Review

1. 15 is what percent of 50? 30%

Make a mapping diagram for each relation and determine whether each is a function.

2. $\{(1, 4), (2, 4), (3, 4)\}$ yes   **3.** $\{(z, 10), (z, 20), (z, 30)\}$ no

Evaluate $g(f(x))$ and $f(g(x))$ for $x = -2, 0, a + b$.

4. $f(x) = -x$, $g(x) = |x|$ **5.** $f(x) = x - 5$, $g(x) = 2x^2$

6. In the coordinate plane give the inequality for the set of all points below the x-axis. $y < 0$

Solve for x.

7. $5 - \sqrt{x - 4} = 3$ $x = 8$ **8.** $4\sqrt[4]{x} - 3 = 1$ $x = 1$

Express each as a rational number in the form $\dfrac{a}{b}$.

9. $3.\overline{14}$ $3\frac{14}{99} = \frac{311}{99}$ **10.** $0.\overline{9}$ $\frac{9}{9} = 1$

11. The sum of four numbers is 129. The second is eight more than the first. The third is three times the second. The fourth is two times the sum of the first and second. Find the numbers. 9, 17, 51, 52

1.6 Inverse Functions   **43**

43

Review
2. 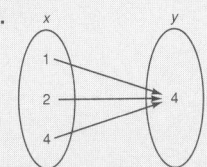 **3.**

4. $2, 0, |a + b|; -2, 0, -|a + b|$
5. $98, 50, 2a^2 + 4ab + 2b^2 - 20a - 20b + 50$; $3, -5, 2a^2 + 4ab + 2b^2 - 5$

Vocabulary
absolute value function
closed interval
constant function
decreasing function
greatest integer function
half-open interval
increasing function
interval notation
open interval
piecewise function
step function

Ⓜ **Materials/Manipulatives**
long distance phone rate schedule
postal scale
postal mailing rate schedule
transparencies

Technology
graphing utility

FOCUS

Sign language interpreting is a unique and rewarding field. Students may be interested in learning more about this career opportunity and about the culture of the deaf community.

INSTRUCTION

Ⓜ • With the use of an inexpensive postal scale, develop a group learning experience to illustrate Example 1. Working in small groups, have students make up envelopes of various weights. Then have them weigh and mark each envelope with the weight and the cost of mailing by the U.S. Postal Service.
• Have students use the postal rate schedule to graph the cost of mailing a letter (or package) as a function of weight or distance.
• When discussing piecewise functions, use transparencies to compare the process of graphing the piecewise function to graphing several different functions each with a restricted domain.

1.7 Absolute Value, Greatest Integer, and Piecewise Functions

Objective: *To define and graph special functions*

Focus

Sign language interpreting is a rewarding profession. An interpreter for the deaf facilitates communication between a hearing person and a deaf person by translating spoken language to sign language and the reverse. A sign language interpreter requires manual dexterity as well as excellent command of the languages being used.

Freelance interpreters often use a unique billing system. For assignments, the charge is a fixed rate, such as $20 per hour, with a 2-hour minimum and with the full hourly rate charged for any part of an hour worked. If the interpreter works more than 8 hours in a single day, the fixed rate may increase to $30 per hour or part of an hour. This billing system cannot be modeled with a linear function. However, a *piecewise step function* can accurately represent the billing system.

The function which models the sign language interpreter's billing system does not increase continuously. Instead, it increases in "jumps" or "steps," and its graph is horizontal between steps. This kind of function is called a **step function.**

For working any portion of the first 2 hours, the interpreter receives $40. For working between 2 and 3 hours, the interpreter receives $60. A graph of the function which models the interpreter's charges for the first 8 hours is shown at the right. The open circles on the graph indicate that those points are not included. The solid dots, however, are points on the graph. The function is *discontinuous* at 2, 3, 4, 5, 6, and 7.

Many other real world situations, such as charges for postage and taxi rides, can be modeled by step functions.

Example 1   *Civil Service*   At the right are the 1991 United States rates for mailing a first class letter weighing up to 6 oz. Graph the cost of mailing a letter as a function of the weight of the letter.

FIRST CLASS LETTER RATES	
For package not exceeding (oz)	Rate:
1	$0.29
2	$0.52
3	$0.75
4	$0.98
5	$1.21
6	$1.44

44   Chapter 1 Functions

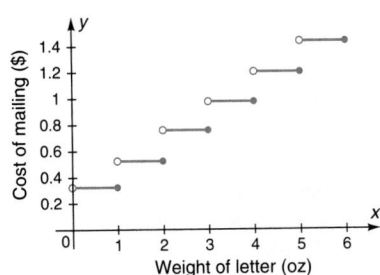

Why is there an open circle for a weight of zero ounce?

Where is the function discontinuous?

A special step function is the **greatest integer function** which assigns to each real number the greatest integer that is less than or equal to that number and is denoted by $f(x) = [\![x]\!]$. On most computers and calculators, the greatest integer function is denoted INT. These examples demonstrate how the function is applied.

$$[\![-4]\!] = -4 \qquad [\![-3.6]\!] = -4 \qquad [\![2.3]\!] = 2 \qquad [\![2.9]\!] = 2$$

Why is the greatest integer in -3.6 equal to -4?

Example 2 Graph $f(x) = [\![x]\!]$ for $-4 \le x < 4$. State the domain and range of this function.

$a \le x < b$	$f(x) = [\![x]\!]$
$-4 \le x < -3$	-4
$-3 \le x < -2$	-3
$-2 \le x < -1$	-2
$-1 \le x < 0$	-1
$0 \le x < 1$	0
$1 \le x < 2$	1
$2 \le x < 3$	2
$3 \le x < 4$	3

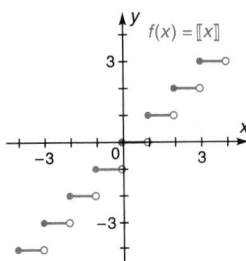

The domain is the set of real numbers.

The range is the set of integers.

Where is the greatest integer function discontinuous?

Another special function is the **absolute value function** which is denoted by $f(x) = |x|$. For any real number a, if $f(x) = |x|$ then

$$f(a) = a \text{ for } a \ge 0 \qquad \text{and} \qquad f(a) = -a \text{ for } a < 0$$

On most computers and calculators, the absolute value function is denoted ABS.

Example 3 Graph $f(x) = |x|$. State the domain and range.

x	$f(x) = |x|$
-4	4
-3	3
-2	2
-1	1
0	0
1	1
2	2
3	3
4	4

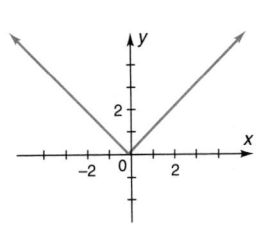

The domain is the set of real numbers.

The range is $\{y: y \ge 0\}$.

1.7 Absolute Value, Greatest Integer, and Piecewise Functions   **45**

GUIDED PRACTICE

For Example 1
A long distance call between two cities costs $0.90 for the first 3 minutes and $0.25 for each additional minute or part thereof. Graph the cost of a call as a function of the length of the call.

For Example 2
1. Graph $g(x) = [\![2x]\!]$ for $-2 \le x \le 2$

2. Graph $h(x) = [\![x]\!] - 1$ for $-3 \le x \le 3$

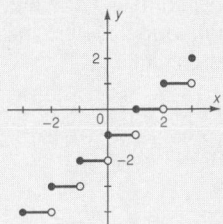

Technology Having students graph these functions on a graphing utility will illustrate clearly why they are called step functions.

Thinking Critically
There is an open circle on the graph for a weight of 0 oz because a letter weighing 0 oz does not exist, and therefore there is no cost.

The greatest integer function is discontinuous where x is an integer.

The greatest integer for -3.6 is equal to -4 because -4 is less than -3.6. By definition $[\![x]\!]$ is the greatest integer that is less than or equal to x.

46

On a number line or axis, an interval with endpoints a and b can be expressed using **interval notation** such as $(a, b]$. If an endpoint is included in the interval a bracket is used, and if an endpoint is not included a parenthesis is used. An interval with both endpoints included is called a **closed interval** $[a, b]$, and an interval with neither endpoint included is called an **open interval** (a, b). Intervals with one endpoint included are called **half-open intervals,** $(a, b]$ and $[a, b)$. To indicate that an interval extends indefinitely, the symbols ∞ and $-\infty$ are used. The entire real number line is expressed as the interval $(-\infty, \infty)$.

A function which is defined differently over various parts of its domain is called a **piecewise function.** Interval notation is useful for expressing each part of the domain for which the function has a specific definition. When graphing a piecewise function, be careful to assign the correct range value for each interval.

Example 4 Graph the function and state its domain and range: $f(x) = \begin{cases} 2x - 1, & x < 0 \\ \sqrt{x}, & x \geq 0 \end{cases}$

The graph is linear over $(-\infty, 0)$.

The graph is curved over $[0, \infty)$.

D_f: $\{x: x \in R\}$

R_f: $\{y: y < -1 \text{ or } y \geq 0\}$

Where is the function discontinuous?

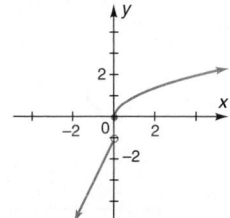

When graphing a function, it is useful to know the intervals in which it is increasing, decreasing, or constant. A function f is *increasing* on an interval if, for any two real numbers x_1 and x_2 in the interval, $f(x_2) > f(x_1)$ when $x_2 > x_1$. If a function is increasing for all real numbers in its domain, it is called an **increasing function.** A function f is *decreasing* on an interval if, for any two real numbers x_1 and x_2 in the interval, $f(x_2) < f(x_1)$ when $x_2 > x_1$. If the function f is decreasing for all real numbers in its domain, then the function is a **decreasing function.** A function f is *constant* on an interval if, for any two real numbers x_1 and x_2 in the interval, $f(x_1) = f(x_2)$. If the function f is constant for all real numbers in its domain, then the function is a **constant function.**

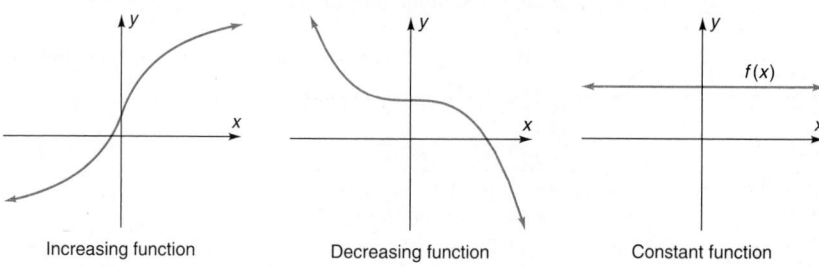

Increasing function   Decreasing function   Constant function

46 Chapter 1 Functions

Example 5 From the graph, determine the open intervals for which $f(x)$ is increasing, decreasing, or constant.

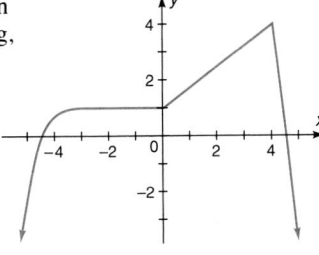

Increasing: $\begin{cases} (-\infty, -3) \\ (0, 4) \end{cases}$

Decreasing: $(4, \infty)$

Constant: $(-3, 0)$

Class Exercises

Graph each function and determine the domain and range.

1. $f(x) = 2[\![x]\!]$

2. $f(x) = |x| + 1$

3. $g(x) = \begin{cases} 2x, & x < 0 \\ x + 3, & 0 \le x \le 5 \end{cases}$

4. $f(x) = \begin{cases} x^2, & x \le 0 \\ -x^2, & x > 0 \end{cases}$

5. $h(x) = |x + 1|$

6. $T(x) = [\![x - 2]\!]$

Determine the open intervals in which each function is increasing, decreasing, or constant.

7.

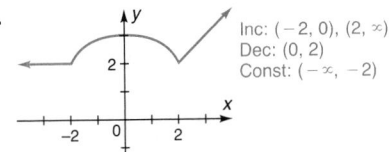

Inc: $(-2, 0), (2, \infty)$
Dec: $(0, 2)$
Const: $(-\infty, -2)$

8.

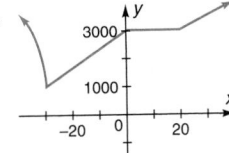

Inc: $(-30, 0), (20, \infty)$
Dec: $(-\infty, -30)$
Const: $(0, 20)$

9. Graph the cost of parking as a function of hours parked.

Hours parked	Fee ($)
Less than 1 h	5
At least 1 h but less than 2 h	7
At least 2 h but less than 3 h	9
At least 3 h but less than 4 h	10
At least 4 h but less than 24 h	12

Practice Exercises Use appropriate technology.

Graph each function and determine the domain and range.

A **1.** $f(x) = |2x|$

2. $g(x) = |-2x|$

3. $f(x) = -[\![x]\!]$

4. $f(x) = [\![-x]\!]$

5. $f(x) = \begin{cases} -x, & x < 0 \\ x, & x \ge 0 \end{cases}$

6. $g(x) = \begin{cases} x^2, & x \le 5 \\ x, & x > 5 \end{cases}$

7. $h(x) = \begin{cases} 2x + 1, & x < 0 \\ \sqrt{x}, & x \ge 0 \end{cases}$

8. $g(x) = \begin{cases} x^3, & x < 1 \\ \sqrt[3]{x}, & x \ge 1 \end{cases}$

9. $M(x) = \begin{cases} 2x + 1, & x < 1 \\ 3, & x \ge 1 \end{cases}$

10. $T(x) = \begin{cases} 3x - 1, & x < 2 \\ 6, & x \ge 2 \end{cases}$

Ⓡ **11.** Solve for x: $5x^3 - 35x^2 + 60x = 0$ $x = 0, 3, 4$

12. Thinking Critically Express the absolute value function as a piecewise function. Compare this function to the definition of absolute value.

Ⓡ **13.** Name 5 subsets of the real numbers to which the number 8 belongs. $N, W, Z, \mathcal{R}$, Rational

1.7 Absolute Value, Greatest Integer, and Piecewise Functions **47**

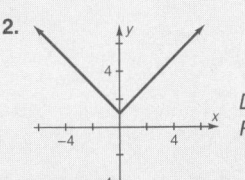
47

LESSON FOLLOW-UP

Test Yourself

Teacher's Resource Book
Tests—Quiz, form A, page 2
Tests—Quiz, form B, page 2

Lesson Quiz

1. Graph $f(x) = [\![x]\!]$ for $-2 \le x < 5$.

2. Graph $g(x) = -|2x|$ and state the domain and range.

$D_g = \{x: x \in \mathcal{R}\}$; $R_g = \{y: y \le 0\}$

3. Graph the function:

$$h(x) = \begin{cases} x^2, & x < 0 \\ |x|, & x \ge 0 \end{cases}$$

State the domain and range and determine if the function is continuous.

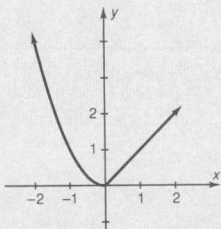

$D_h = \{x: x \in \mathcal{R}\}$; $R_g = \{y: y \ge 0\}$
The function is continuous.

Determine the open intervals in which each graph is increasing, decreasing, or constant.

14.

Inc: $(0, \infty)$
Dec: $(-\infty, 0)$

15.

Const: $(-\infty, \infty)$

16.

Inc: $(0, 2)$
Dec: $(-\infty, 0)$
Const: $(2, \infty)$

17.

Inc: $(0, 4)$
Dec: $(-\infty, 0)$
Const: $(4, \infty)$

18. *Transportation* Graph the cost of a taxi ride as a function of the mileage traveled.

> **TAXI FARE**
>
> **$1.50** Initial Charge
> **25¢** Per ⅕ Mile

ℝ **19.** Find the inverse function of $f(x) = 2x^3 - 1$, if it exists. $f^{-1}(x) = \sqrt[3]{\dfrac{x+1}{2}}$

Graph each function and determine the domain and range.

B **20.** $f(x) = |2x| - 3$　　　　**21.** $g(x) = 4|x| - 2$　　　　**22.** $h(x) = -|x + 2|$

23. $g(x) = |2 - x|$　　　　**24.** $f(x) = [\![x]\!] - 1$　　　　**25.** $g(x) = [\![x - 1]\!]$

26. $f(x) = \begin{cases} \dfrac{1}{x}, & x < 0 \\ 3x, & x \ge 0 \end{cases}$ 　　　　**27.** $g(x) = \begin{cases} \dfrac{1}{x-2}, & x < 2 \\ -2x, & x \ge 2 \end{cases}$

28. $h(x) = \begin{cases} -3, & x < 0 \\ 2x, & 0 \le x \le 4 \\ 2x - 10, & x > 4 \end{cases}$ 　　　　**29.** $g(x) = \begin{cases} 5, & x < 0 \\ 4x, & 0 \le x \le 3 \\ 2x - 3, & x > 3 \end{cases}$

ℝ **30.** Determine if $y = \sqrt{x + 2}$, $x \ge -2$, and $y = x^2 - 2$, $x \ge 0$, are inverse functions. yes

31. Thinking Critically Graph a number of increasing functions and determine a relationship between increasing functions and one-to-one functions.

ℝ **32.** Solve graphically: $\begin{cases} y = 2x + 4 \\ y = x^2 \end{cases}$ and estimate the answer to the nearest tenth.

Graph each function and determine in which open intervals it is increasing, decreasing, or constant.

33. $f(x) = |-2x + 5|$ 　　　　　　　　**34.** $g(x) = [\![2x + 4]\!]$

35. *Transportation* Graph the cost of renting a car as a function of the number of days the car is rented. See the chart at the right.

Number of days car is rented	Charge ($)
1 day or part of a day	18
2 days or 1 day and part of a day	36
3 days or 2 days and part of a day	54
4 days or 3 days and part of a day	72

Graph each function and determine the domain and range.

C **36.** $f(x) = |[\![x]\!]|$ 　　　　　　　　**37.** $g(x) = \sqrt{|x - 2|}$

38. $h(x) = [\![|1 - x|]\!]$ 　　　　　　　　**39.** $f(x) = |x| - [\![x]\!]$

48　Chapter 1 Functions

Additional Answers

33.

Increasing: $(2.5, +\infty)$
Decreasing: $(-\infty, 2.5)$

34.

Constant: . . . $[-3, -2.5)$, $[-2.5, -2)$, $[-2, -1.5)$, . .

35.

Determine a piecewise function for each graph. Use the equations $y = x$, $y = -x$, $y = x^2$, $y = -x^2$, $y = x^3$, or $y = -x^3$. Assume any overlapping points are defined by the left most graph.

40.

41.

42.

43.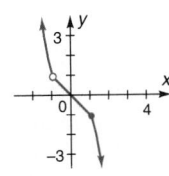

44. *Finance*   The income tax rules for a certain state are defined in the table below. Graph this piecewise function.

If your adjusted income is:	You pay:
Less than $20,000	2% × your adjusted income
Between $20,000 and $50,000	$400 + 2.5% × (your adjusted income − $20,000)
More than $50,000	$1150 + 3% × (your adjusted income − $50,000)

45. Writing in Mathematics   Analyze the graph at the right and create a real world situation for which the graph might serve as a model.

46. Determine a piecewise function that models the interpreter's charges described in the Focus.

Test Yourself

Given $f(x) = 2x^2$ and $g(x) = -x - 3$, evaluate each of the following.

1. $f(-4)$ 32   **2.** $g(-4)$ 1   **3.** $f(a + b)$ $2a^2 + 4ab + 2b^2$ **4.** $g(a + b)$ $-a - b - 3$ **1.4**

Given $f(x) = \dfrac{2}{x + 3}$ and $g(x) = x + 1$, find each function and state its domain.

5. $f + g$ **6.** $f - g$ **7.** $f \cdot g$ **8.** f/g **1.5**

For each set of functions, evaluate $(f \circ g)(2)$ and $(g \circ f)(2)$.

9. $f(x) = -x + 3$; $g(x) = \dfrac{x^2}{2}$ $1; \frac{1}{2}$ **10.** $f(x) = x^2 + 1$; $g(x) = 3x + 4$ 101; 19

Find the inverse function for each function. Restrict the domain of the original function, if necessary.

11. $f(x) = -2x + 3$ $f^{-1}(x) = -\frac{1}{2}x + \frac{3}{2}$ **12.** $g(x) = \dfrac{1}{\sqrt{x + 2}}$ $g^{-1}(x) = \frac{1}{x^2} - 2$ **1.6**

Determine whether $f(x)$ and $g(x)$ are inverse functions.

13. $f(x) = \dfrac{3x}{2} - 6$; $g(x) = \dfrac{2x}{3} + 4$ yes   **14.** $f(x) = x^3 - 1$; $g(x) = \sqrt[3]{x + 1}$ yes

Graph each function and determine the domain and range.

15. $f(x) = \begin{cases} \dfrac{x}{2} + 1, & x < -2 \\ \sqrt[3]{x + 1}, & x \geq -2 \end{cases}$ **16.** $g(x) = -2\llbracket x \rrbracket$ **1.7**

1.7 Absolute Value, Greatest Integer, and Piecewise Functions   **49**

Writing in Mathematics
45. Students should describe a situation in which values fluctuate, increasing over an interval linearly, nonlinearly, leveling off, and then decreasing.

4. From the graph, determine the open intervals for which $f(x)$ is increasing, decreasing, or constant.

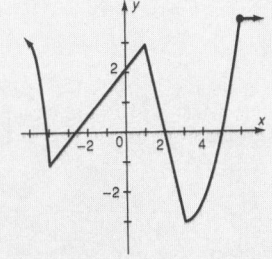

Increasing: $(-4, 1)$; $(3, 5.5)$
Decreasing: $(-\infty, -4)$; $(1, 3)$
Constant: $(5.5, \infty)$

Chapter 1   Summary and Review

Vocabulary

abscissa (19)
absolute value function (45)
binary operation (13)
Cartesian coordinate system (18)
closed interval (46)
composite function (33)
composition of functions (33)
constant function (46)
coordinate axes (18)
coordinate plane (18)
decreasing function (46)
domain (24)
equal functions (26)
field properties (13)
function (24)
graph (19)
graphing utility (20)
greatest integer function (45)
half-open interval (46)
horizontal line test (28)
increasing function (46)
independent variable (20)
integers (11)
interval notation (46)
inverse (38)

inverse function (39)
irrational numbers (12)
natural numbers (11)
mapping (24)
mathematical model (2)
one-to-one (28)
open interval (46)
ordinate (19)
origin (18)
piecewise function (46)
quadrants (18)
range (24)
rational numbers (11)
real numbers (11)
rectangular coordinate system (18)
relation (24)
step function (44)
vertical line test (27)
viewing rectangle (20)
whole numbers (11)
x-axis (18)
x-intercept (20)
y-axis (18)
y-intercept (20)

Introduction to Modeling   Mathematical equations can be used to model many real   1.1
world situations.

1. A large cheese pizza from Maria's Pizzeria costs $8.00. Each additional topping costs $1.25. Find an equation that models the cost of the pizza in terms of the number of toppings. $y = 1.25x + 8$

2. Use the equation in Exercise 1 to find the number of additional toppings on a pizza that costs $11.75. 3

3. Use the three data points $(0, 0)$, $(50, 243)$, and $(60, 366)$ to find an equation that models stopping distance in terms of speed. $y = 0.124x^2 - 1.34x$

The Real Number System   The set of real numbers $\mathcal{R}$ is the set of all rational   1.2
and irrational numbers. The real numbers under the operations of addition and multiplication form a field.

Under the operations of addition and multiplication, which field properties do not hold for each set? Provide an example.

4. positive odd integers

5. $\{0, 4, 8, 12, \ldots\}$

50   Chapter 1 Functions

The Cartesian Coordinate System Each point on the coordinate plane can be represented by a unique ordered pair of real numbers (x, y).

1.3

Graph each equation.

6. $x + 2y = 8$

7. $y = x^2 - 1$

8. $y = \frac{1}{2}x^3$

Relations and Functions A function f is a mapping between two sets, X and Y, such that for each element x in X there is associated exactly one element y in Y.

1.4

Given $g(x) = x^2 + 2$, evaluate each of the following.

9. $g(3b)$ $9b^2 + 2$

10. $g(-a)$ $a^2 + 2$

11. $g(a - b)$ $a^2 - 2ab + b^2 + 2$

Find the domain and range of each function.

12. $h(x) = \dfrac{1}{x + 2}$

13. $f(x) = \dfrac{x}{x^2 - x - 2}$

14. $g(x) = \sqrt{x + 5}$

Algebra of Functions Given two functions f and g, new functions can be formed by adding, subtracting, multiplying, and dividing the functions. The composition $(f \circ g)(x) = f(g(x))$ is the operation of applying g and then f to values of x.

1.5

Given $f(x) = \dfrac{1}{x - 1}$ and $g(x) = 3x$, find each function and state its domain.

15. $f + g$

16. $f - g$

17. $f \cdot g$

18. f/g

For each pair of functions, evaluate $(f \circ g)(-1)$ and $(g \circ f)(-1)$.

19. $f(x) = 2x + 5$; $g(x) = 3x - 1$ $-3; 8$

20. $f(x) = x^2$; $g(x) = x - 3$ $16; -2$

Inverse Functions Two functions f and g are inverse functions if and only if $f(g(x)) = x$ for all x in the domain of $g(x)$ and $g(f(x)) = x$ for all x in the domain of $f(x)$.

1.6

Find the inverse function for each function. Restrict the domain of the original function if necessary.

21. $f(x) = -x + 4$ $f^{-1}(x) = -x + 4$

22. $g(x) = \dfrac{1}{x + 2}$ $g^{-1}(x) = \dfrac{1}{x} - 2$

Determine whether $f(x)$ and $g(x)$ are inverse functions.

23. $f(x) = 2x - 8$; $g(x) = \frac{1}{2}x + 4$ yes

24. $f(x) = x^3 + 2$; $g(x) = \sqrt[3]{x + 2}$ no

Absolute Value, Greatest Integer, and Piecewise Functions Real world situations cannot always be modeled by continuous equations. Special functions include step, greatest integer, absolute value, and piecewise functions.

1.7

Graph each function and determine its domain and range.

25. $f(x) = \begin{cases} |x|, & x \le 0 \\ \sqrt{x}, & x > 0 \end{cases}$

26. $g(x) = [\![x]\!] + 2$

Additional Answers

6.

7.

8.
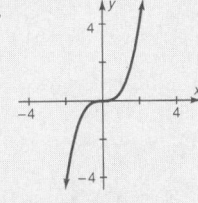

12. $D_h = \{x: x \ne -2\}$; $R_h = \{y: y \ne 0\}$

13. $D_f = \{x: x \ne -1, 2\}$; $R_f = \{y: y \in \Re\}$

14. $D_g = \{x: x \ge -5\}$; $R_g = \{y: y \ge 0\}$

15. $\dfrac{3x^2 - 3x + 1}{x - 1}$; $D_{f+g} = \{x: x \ne 1\}$

16. $\dfrac{-3x^2 + 3x + 1}{x - 1}$; $D_{f-g} = \{x: x \ne 1\}$

17. $\dfrac{3x}{x - 1}$; $D_{f \cdot g} = \{x: x \ne 1\}$

18. $\dfrac{1}{3x^2 - 3x}$; $D_{f/g} = \{x: x \ne 0, 1\}$

25.

$D_f = \{x: x \in \Re\}$
$R_f = \{y: y \ge 0\}$

26.

$D_g = \{x: x \in \Re\}$
$R_g = \{y: y \in Z\}$

Additional Answers

3. closed under addition; not closed under subtraction, $-3 - (-4) = 1$; not closed under multiplication, $(-3)(-4) = 12$; not closed under division, $-2 \div -3 = \frac{2}{3}$

4.

12. $-x + \frac{1}{x}; D_{f+g} = \{x: x \neq 0\}$

13. $-x - \frac{1}{x}; D_{f-g} = \{x: x \neq 0\}$

14. $-1; D_{f \cdot g} = \{x: x \in \mathcal{R}\}$

15. $-x^2; D_{f/g} = \{x: x \in \mathcal{R}\}$

16. $-\frac{1}{x}; D_{f \circ g} = \{x: x \neq 0\}$

17. $-\frac{1}{x}; D_{g \circ f} = \{x: x \neq 0\}$

20.

$D_f = \{x: x \in \mathcal{R}\}$
$R_f = \{y: y \in \mathcal{R}\}$

21.

$D_g = \{x: x \in \mathcal{R}\}$
$R_g = \{y: y \in Z\}$

Chapter 1 Test

1. The cost of having a carpet installed is $25.00 for delivery and $1.50 per square yard for the actual installation. Find a linear equation that models the cost of having a carpet delivered and installed. $y = 25 + 1.50x$

2. Use the equation found in Problem 1 to find the number of square yards of carpet installed if the bill for delivery and installation is $60.25 without the tax. 23.5

3. State whether the set of negative whole numbers is closed under the operations of addition, subtraction, multiplication, and division. Provide a counterexample for each operation under which it is not closed.

4. Graph $y = x^2 - 2$.

Given $f(x) = x^2 - 1$, evaluate each of the following.

5. $f(-2)$ 3

6. $f(a + b)$ $a^2 + 2ab + b^2 - 1$

7. $f\left(\frac{2}{x}\right)$ $\frac{4 - x^2}{x^2}$

Find the domain and range of each function.

8. $f(x) = \dfrac{1}{x + 4}$ $D_f = \{x: x \neq -4\}$
$R_f = \{y: y \neq 0\}$

9. $g(x) = \sqrt{x - 1.5}$ $D_g = \{x: x \geq 1.5\}$
$R_g = \{y: y \geq 0\}$

10. $h(x) = \dfrac{3}{x^2 - x - 20}$ $D_h = \{x: x \neq -4, 5\}$
$R_h = \{y: y \neq 0\}$

11. $f(x) = \dfrac{4}{x^2 - 3x}$ $D_f = \{x: x \neq 0, 3\}$
$R_f = \left\{y: y > 0, y \leq \dfrac{-16}{9}\right\}$

Given $f(x) = -x$ and $g(x) = \dfrac{1}{x}$, find each function and state its domain.

12. $f + g$

13. $f - g$

14. $f \cdot g$

15. f/g

16. $f \circ g$

17. $g \circ f$

Find the inverse function for each function. Restrict the domain of the original function if necessary.

18. $f(x) = \dfrac{\sqrt{x}}{2}$ $f^{-1}(x) = 4x^2$

19. $g(x) = \dfrac{1}{2x - 3}$ $g^{-1}(x) = \dfrac{1 + 3x}{2x}$

Graph each function and determine its domain and range.

20. $f(x) = \begin{cases} x + 1, & x < 0 \\ x - 1, & x \geq 0 \end{cases}$

21. $g(x) = [\![x - 3]\!]$

Challenge

Find a counterexample to show that the product of two increasing functions is not always an increasing function. $f(x) = x, g(x) = x, (f \cdot g)(x) = x^2$

52   Chapter 1 Functions

Cumulative Review

Select the best choice for each question.

1. Name the field property of the real number system illustrated by $2.5(0.4) = 1$. **1.2**
   A
   A. multiplicative inverse
   B. additive inverse   C. commutative
   D. transitive   E. reflexive

2. Given $f(x) = 4x^2 - 3$, evaluate $f(-4)$. **1.4**
   D
   A. -67 B. -61 C. 69
   D. 61   E. 67

3. Which type of function does the graph represent? **1.7**
   B

   A. increasing
   B. decreasing
   C. constant
   D. reciprocal   E. inverse

4. A rent-a-car for the Senior Week trip costs $95 a week. Each extra day costs an additional $10. The linear equation that models the cost of the car in terms of the number of days is: **1.1**
   C
   A. $y = 85x + 10$ B. $y = 85x + 95$
   C. $y = 10x + 95$ D. $y = 95x + 10$
   E. $y = 95x - 10$

5. The domain of the function $g(x) = \sqrt{x - 4}$ is **1.4**
   E
   A. $D = \{x: x \le 4\}$ B. $D = \{x: x \ge 2\}$
   C. $D = \{x: x \le -2\}$
   D. $D = \{x: x \ge -4\}$
   E. $D = \{x: x \ge 4\}$

6. Given that a and b are real numbers, name the property of multiplication of real numbers illustrated by the statement $(7a)b = 7(ab)$. **1.2**
   C
   A. commutative   B. symmetric
   C. associative   D. transitive
   E. reflexive

7. The inverse of the relation $\{(2, -3), (5, -4), (8, -2)\}$ is **1.6**
   D
   A. $\{(-2, 3), (-5, 4), (-8, 2)\}$
   B. $\{(2, 3), (5, 4) (8, 2)\}$
   C. $\{(-2, -3), (-5, -4), (-8, 2)\}$
   D. $\{(-3, 2), (-4, 5), (-2, 8)\}$
   E. $\{(-3, -2), (-4, -5), (-2, -8)\}$

8. Given $f(x) = x^2$ and $g(x) = 3x - 4$, evaluate $(f \circ g)(x)$. **1.5**
   A
   A. $9x^2 - 24x + 16$ B. $9x^2 - 12x + 8$
   C. $9x^2 + 24x + 16$ D. $9x^2 - 12x + 16$
   E. $9x^2 + 12x + 8$

Determine if each statement is always true, sometimes true, or never true.

9. The independent variable is represented on a graph by the horizontal axis. always   **1.3**

10. The graph of a quadratic function defined by an equation $y = ax^2 + bx + c$, $a \ne 0$, is a parabola. always   **1.1**

11. f^{-1} is the notation that represents the reciprocal function. never   **1.6**

12. $\sqrt{2}$ can be located on the number line by using a geometric construction. always   **1.2**

13. A function is a relation in which each element in the domain is mapped to exactly one element in the range. always   **1.4**

14. A function is discontinuous sometimes   **1.7**

15. Numbers such as $\frac{1}{4}$, $\frac{13}{2}$, -0.08, 3.2, and $0.434343 \ldots$ are irrational. never   **1.2**

16. If a graph passes the vertical line test, then the vertical line intersects the graph more than once. never   **1.4**

Summary

Symmetry with respect to a point and symmetry with respect to a line are discussed from a geometric and algebraic viewpoint. Symmetry, reflections, translations, and dilations are used to graph transformations of functions. Familiarity with graphing basic functions and their transformations is stressed. Linear and quadratic functions with applications are presented. Then, general polynomial functions are introduced with emphasis on the use of technology to graph the functions. Coordinate proofs and the distance from a point to a line are also presented.

Chapter Objectives

- To determine the symmetry of a graph and to use symmetry to sketch a graph
- To graph functions using reflections in the x-axis, y-axis, and the line $y = x$
- To graph functions using translations and dilations
- To determine the equations of linear functions and graph them
- To find real and imaginary solutions to quadratic equations
- To graph a quadratic function using the axis of symmetry, vertex, and intercepts
- To approximate the real zeros of quadratic and polynomial functions from their graphs
- To determine the minimum or maximum of the graph of a quadratic function
- To solve polynomial equations by factoring techniques
- To prove geometric theorems using coordinate geometry
- To solve maximum and minimum problems using coordinate geometry
- To determine the distance from a point to a line and between parallel lines

2 Graphing Functions

Mathematical Power

Modeling   Do you sometimes wonder if it is really true that the more time you spend studying, the more you will learn? Behavioral scientists and psychologists are interested in the answers to this and other questions about learning. They conduct extensive learning experiments to collect data, and graphically represent their results with a *learning curve*. Below are two situations that yield very different learning curves.

In one learning experiment, subjects were given lists of items to study, and a specific amount of time to study each list. They were then tested on the number of items that they could recall. A graphic representation of the resulting data was made by plotting the effective study time t on the horizontal axis, and the proportion of items remembered for each time $P(t)$ on the vertical axis. The graph that best fit the data points is a straight line, as shown below; that is, study time and the proportion of items remembered are linearly related.

The equation of the line determined by the data points is

$$P(t) = 0.059t + 0.025$$

The slope of the line is 0.059. This means that for each 1-second increase in study time, the proportion of items recalled increases by 0.059.

54

Features

Modeling

2.3 Temperature scales	Projects 63, 72, 79, 93, 99, 113
2.5 Transition curves	Challenge 72, 93, 106
2.6 Polynomial functions as models	Review 63, 79, 99
2.8 Indirect measurement	

In another experiment, subjects were given some kind of puzzle to solve, such as a maze, and the time that each subject took to solve the puzzle was recorded. The subjects were then given the same puzzle to solve again and again, and for each solution the time was recorded. When the solution time was plotted against the number of trials, the graph showed a steep curve that is asymptotic to the *x*-axis. You will study this learning curve in greater depth in a later chapter.

Both of the graphs generated by the data in these experiments illustrate very definite and unique patterns. In the process of modeling, graphing is a powerful step that allows you to discover patterns and decide on a logical course of action.

Thinking Critically   For a linear learning curve such as the one described above, what restrictions might be needed on the domain of the defining function? When would a learning curve be finite? Could a learning curve ever be infinite? Explain your answers and give examples of learning situations to illustrate each case.

Project   Conduct your own experiments similar to the ones described here. Give subjects lists of 20 words and allow them to study the lists for various time limits. Test their retention and record your findings graphically. Then give subjects some puzzle to complete, such as a complex maze, and record the time it takes to complete it. Represent these findings graphically as well. Remember to conduct each experiment several times. Comment on the patterns that emerge in your graphs.

Mathematical Power

Since functions are used to describe relationships among variables, they are a basic tool for creating real world models. Moreover, the graphical display of functional relationships helps the model-maker to draw conclusions and make predictions.

The linear example here can be used to review the difference between the *dependent* and *independent* variable. Explain that by convention the independent variable is plotted on the horizontal axis and the dependent variable is shown on the vertical axis. In this case, time is the independent variable because time affects learning.

Emphasize how the key steps in modeling (see Chapter 1) were applied here. Guide students to summarize the process by having them explain what question the researchers sought to answer, what mathematical representation was used, and what conclusions could be drawn.

Thinking Critically   Because $P(t)$ represents a percentage, students should understand that the domain of the function should be restricted to values of t that cause $P(t)$ to be greater than or equal to 0 and less than or equal to 1. Students should also understand that a finite curve denotes a case of complete learning; memorizing the alphabet or a set of multiplication facts are simple examples. Some students may offer philosophical objections to the notion of an infinite learning curve, but for the purposes of this lesson it is meant to apply to a situation where learning continues indefinitely.

55

Review and Assessment

Student Text
- Test Yourself   86, 113
- Summary and Review   114–115
- Chapter Test   116

Teacher's Resource Book
- Tests   5–8
- Practice   8–15

Vocabulary
even function
odd function
symmetry with respect to a line
symmetry with respect to a point

ⓜ **Materials/Manipulatives**
compass
graph paper
scissors
tracing paper

Technology
graphing utility

FOCUS

First practiced almost a thousand years ago, the Japanese art of paper-folding is still very popular in Japan today. Have students research the topic of origami. Have each student make one shape using the techniques of origami and demonstrate his or her project to the class.

INSTRUCTION

ⓜ To help students see the symmetry of a circle about every line through its center, have students draw a circle on paper using a compass. Then have them draw four extended diameters of the circle and fold the circle on each extended diameter to check the symmetry.

2.1 Symmetry

Objectives: *To determine the symmetry of a graph*
To use symmetry to sketch a graph

Focus

Origami is the ancient art of folding paper into models of animals, trees, musical instruments, people, or other forms. *Symmetrical* folds are made in sheets of paper; glue and scissors are rarely needed. A Scottish sculptor named George Wyllie folded an 80-by-120 ft sheet of paperlike material into a boat, the world's largest piece of shipshape origami. It sailed from London to New York, arriving on July 13, 1990.

Symmetry is evident in many forms. Birds and airplanes would find it difficult to fly if their two wings were not the same size and shape. Ships cannot move safely through the water if weight is not distributed symmetrically. Patterns on floor and wall coverings are symmetric because people find symmetry aesthetically pleasing.

It is important to understand the mathematical meaning of symmetry.

Two points P and Q are **symmetric with respect to a line** ℓ if ℓ is the perpendicular bisector of $\overline{PQ}$.

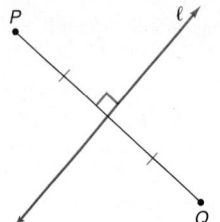

Two points P and Q are **symmetric with respect to a point** M if M is the midpoint of $\overline{PQ}$.

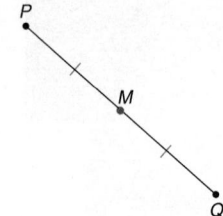

Knowing that a graph has point or line symmetry will help you draw it. For example, a parabola exhibits line symmetry, and a circle exhibits both point and line symmetries. In fact, a circle is symmetric with respect to every line through its center. When a figure that has line symmetry is folded on its line of symmetry, the two halves coincide exactly.

56 Chapter 2 Graphing Functions

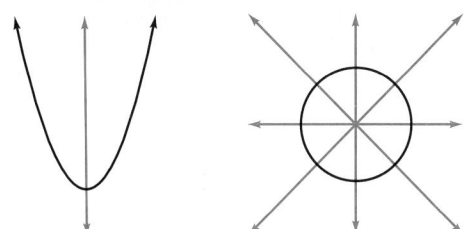

Symmetries important in graphing are line symmetry about the x and y-axes and point symmetry about the origin. The relationships between coordinates of points symmetric with respect to the y-axis, the x-axis, and the origin are shown below.

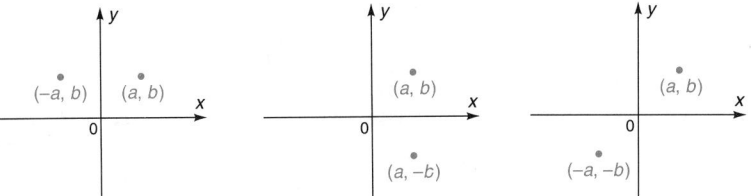

Symmetry with respect to the y-axis   **Symmetry with respect to the x-axis**   **Symmetry with respect to the origin**

Determining Symmetries of a Graph		
Symmetric with respect to	*Definition*	*Test*
y-axis	If (a, b) is on the graph, then $(-a, b)$ is also on the graph.	Substituting $-x$ for x results in an equivalent equation.
x-axis	If (a, b) is on the graph, then $(a, -b)$ is also on the graph.	Substituting $-y$ for y results in an equivalent equation.
Origin	If (a, b) is on the graph, then $(-a, -b)$ is also on the graph.	Substituting $-x$ for x *and* $-y$ for y results in an equivalent equation.

Example 1 Given the point $(3, -2)$, determine a point that satisfies the specified symmetry.
a. origin   **b.** y-axis   **c.** x-axis

a. $(-3, 2)$ **b.** $(-3, -2)$ **c.** $(3, 2)$

If you know that a graph has a certain symmetry or symmetries, then you can draw a portion of the graph and use your knowledge of symmetry to complete it.

2.1 Symmetry   **57**

GUIDED PRACTICE

For Example 1
Given the point $\left(-5, -\frac{1}{2}\right)$, determine the coordinates of a point that satisfies the specified symmetry.

1. y-axis $\left(5, -\frac{1}{2}\right)$

2. origin $\left(5, \frac{1}{2}\right)$

3. x-axis $\left(-5, \frac{1}{2}\right)$

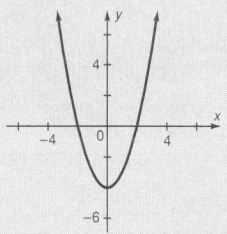
Example 2 Determine the symmetries of each equation. Then graph, using the properties of symmetry.

a. $y = x^4 - 2x^2$ **b.** $x = y^2$

a. $y = x^4 - 2x^2$

y-axis	x-axis	Origin
$y = (-x)^4 - 2(-x)^2$	$-y = x^4 - 2x^2$	$-y = (-x)^4 - 2(-x)^2$
$y = x^4 - 2x^2$	$y = -x^4 + 2x^2$	$y = -x^4 + 2x^2$
equivalent	not equivalent	not equivalent

Since an equivalent equation results when x is substituted for $-x$ in the original equation, the graph is symmetric with respect to the y-axis.

Construct a table by substituting values for x such that $x \geq 0$ and then finding the corresponding y-values to the nearest tenth. Graph these points and connect them with a smooth curve. Use symmetry about the y-axis to complete the graph.

$y = x^4 - 2x^2$

x	0	0.5	1	$\sqrt{2}$	2
y	0	−0.4	−1	0	8

b. $x = y^2$

y-axis	x-axis	Origin
$-x = y^2$	$x = (-y)^2$	$-x = (-y)^2$
$x = -y^2$	$x = y^2$	$x = -y^2$
not equivalent	equivalent	not equivalent

Since an equivalent equation results when $-y$ is substituted for y in the original equation, the graph is symmetric with respect to the x-axis.

Construct a table by substituting values for y such that $y \geq 0$ and then finding the corresponding x-values. Graph these points and connect them with a smooth curve. Use symmetry about the x-axis to complete the graph.

$x = y^2$

y	0	1	2	3
x	0	1	4	9

To see symmetry with respect to the y-axis geometrically, visualize folding the graph along the y-axis. One side of the graph will coincide with the other. To see symmetry with respect to the x-axis geometrically, visualize folding the graph along the x-axis. One side of the graph will coincide with the other. *How can you fold a graph to see origin symmetry geometrically?*

You can also use a graphing utility to help you determine the symmetry of the graph of an equation. The zoom-square feature will give you a viewing rectangle where the scales on the x- and y-axes produce a nearly square grid.

58   Chapter 2 Graphing Functions

Example 3 Use a graphing utility to graph each equation. Then determine whether the graph appears to be symmetric with respect to the x-axis, y-axis, origin, or none of these.

   a. $y = \frac{1}{4}x^3$ **b.** $y = -\sqrt{16 - x^2}$ **c.** $y = 2x + 4$

a.

[−7.5, 7.5] by [−5, 5]
Origin

b.

[−7.5, 7.5] by [−5, 5]
y-axis

c.

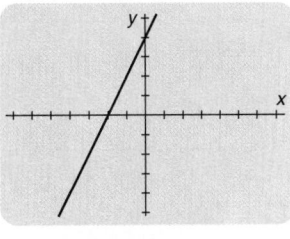

[−7.5, 7.5] by [−5, 5]
None of these

The two points (5, 2) and (2, 5) are symmetric with respect to the line $y = x$. This is true because the line $y = x$ bisects the segment connecting the two points. In general, any two points with coordinates (a, b) and (b, a) are symmetric with respect to the line $y = x$. The graph of an equation may also be symmetric with respect to the line $y = x$. To test for this symmetry, interchange x and y in the equation and solve for y. If the new equation is equivalent to the original equation, then the graph will be symmetric with respect to the line $y = x$.

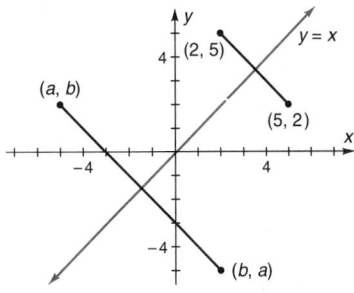

Symmetry with respect to the line $y = x$

Example 4 Determine the symmetries of the equation $y = \frac{1}{x}$.

y-axis	x-axis	*Origin*	$y = x$
$y = \dfrac{1}{-x}$	$-y = \dfrac{1}{x}$	$-y = \dfrac{1}{-x}$	$x = \dfrac{1}{y}$
	$y = -\dfrac{1}{x}$	$y = \dfrac{1}{x}$	$y = \dfrac{1}{x}$
not equivalent	not equivalent	equivalent	equivalent

Since $y = \frac{1}{x}$ is symmetric to the origin and the line $y = x$, only values such that $x \geq 0$ and $x \leq y$ need to be determined. Complete the graph using symmetry.

x	0.1	0.2	0.25	0.33	0.5	1
y	10	5	4	3	2	1

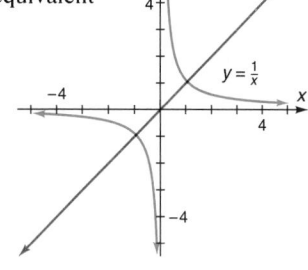

For Example 3
Use a graphing utility to graph the equation $y = (x - 2)^2$. Then determine the symmetries of the graph.

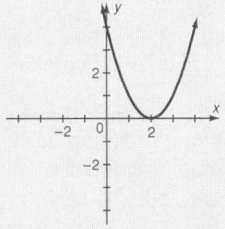

From the graph, it can be seen that the curve is symmetric with respect to the line $x = 2$.

Technology Students should be made aware that verifying symmetry of a function using a graphing utility involves more than just looking at the graph. The zoom and trace functions should be used to check points on the graph.

Common Error Some students may claim that when $-x$ is substituted for x, the equation $y = (-x - 2)^2$ is equivalent to $y = (x - 2)^2$ because the expression $(-x - 2)$ is squared. Have these students square the expression to see that the equations are not equivalent.

For Example 4
Determine the symmetries of the equation $y = \frac{1}{x^2}$. Then graph. y-axis

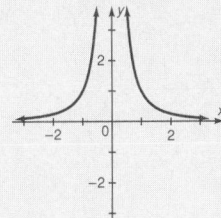

59

Determine whether each function is even, odd, or neither.

1. $f(x) = \dfrac{x^3}{x^2 + 1}$ odd

2. $g(x) = \dfrac{1}{x^2} + 2$ even

Technology Have students graph each function using a graphing utility and then use a trace to verify that the function is even, odd, or neither.

For Example 6
Complete each graph using only the given information.

1. $f(x) = -f(-x)$

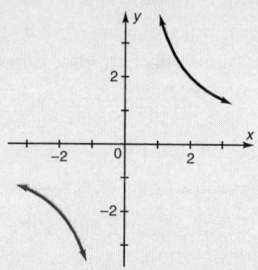

2. The graph is symmetric with respect to both the x- and y-axes.

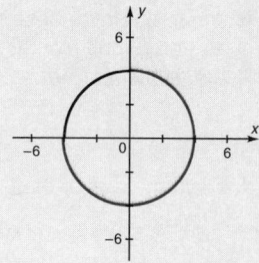

A function whose graph is symmetric with respect to the y-axis is called *even*, and a function whose graph is symmetric to the origin is called *odd*.

> For any function f, if $f(-x) = f(x)$, then f is an **even function**.
> For any function f, if $f(-x) = -f(x)$, then f is an **odd function**.

Even function   Odd function

If $f(x) \neq 0$, can a function f be both even and odd? Explain.

Example 5   Determine whether each function is even, odd, or neither.
       a. $f(x) = 2x^5 + 4x^3$ **b.** $g(x) = 2x^4 - x^3 + x^2 - 2$

a. $f(-x) = 2(-x)^5 + 4(-x)^3$ **b.** $g(-x) = 2(-x)^4 - (-x)^3 + (-x)^2 - 2$
          $= -2x^5 - 4x^3$ $= 2x^4 + x^3 + x^2 - 2$
          $= -(2x^5 + 4x^3)$

Since $f(-x) = -f(x)$, the function is odd.   Since $g(-x) \neq g(x)$ and $g(-x) \neq -g(x)$, $g(x)$ is neither even nor odd.

You can use the fact that a function is even or odd to complete a graph.

Example 6   Complete each graph using only the given information.
       a. $f(x)$ is an even function.   **b.** The relation is symmetric with respect to the line $y = x$.

a.   **b.**

Class Exercises

For each point, determine another point that satisfies the specified symmetry.

1. $(-2, 6)$; y-axis (2, 6)

2. $(-1, 3)$; origin (1, -3)

3. $(-16, -12)$; x-axis (-16, 12)

4. $(3.9, -2.2)$; $y = x$ (-2.2, 3.9)

5. Thinking Critically If a graph is symmetric with respect to the x-axis and the y-axis, is it also symmetric with respect to the origin? yes

Determine the symmetries of each equation. Then graph, using the properties of symmetry.

6. $x^2 + y^2 = 25$
x-axis, y-axis, origin, $y = x$

7. $y = |x| + 1$ y-axis

8. $x^2y = 1$ y-axis

9. $y = -\dfrac{2}{x}$ origin, $y = x$

Determine whether each function is even, odd, or neither.

10. $f(x) = x^3 - 3x^2 + 2x - 1$ neither

11. $g(x) = 2x^4 - x^2 + 2$ even

Practice Exercises

 Use appropriate technology.

For each point, determine another point that satisfies the specified symmetry.

A 1. $(-5, 3)$; origin (5, -3)

2. $(-3, 9)$; y-axis (3, 9)

3. $(-3.5, -6.5)$; $y = x$ (-6.5, -3.5)

4. $(4.1, -1.3)$; x-axis (4.1, 1.3)

Ⓡ 5. *Gardening* The area of a rectangular flower garden is $a^2 + 15ab - 3250b^2$. Find algebraic expressions for the length and the width. $(a - 50b)$, $(a + 65b)$

Determine whether the graph of each equation is symmetric with respect to the x-axis, y-axis, origin, or none of these. Then graph each equation, using the properties of symmetry when possible.

6. $y = 9 - x^2$ y-axis

7. $y^2 = x$ x-axis

8. $y = |x - 1|$ none

9. $y = 2 + x^2$ y-axis

10. $y = x^3 - 3$ none

11. $y^3 = x$ origin

12. $y = x^2 - 5$ y-axis

13. $y = |x + 2|$ none

14. Thinking Critically Find a relationship between the exponents that appear in a function and whether the function is even or odd.

Ⓡ 15. *Finance* The closing prices of RWB stock for the first week in April can be represented by the relation $\left\{(10, \text{Monday}), \left(10\frac{1}{4}, \text{Tuesday}\right), \left(10\frac{1}{2}, \text{Wednesday}\right), \left(10\frac{1}{4}, \text{Thursday}\right), \text{ and } (11, \text{Friday})\right\}$. Does this relation represent a function? no

Complete each graph using the given information.

16. Symmetric with respect to the x-axis

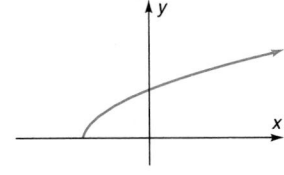

17. Symmetric with respect to the origin

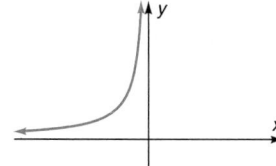

2.1 Symmetry **61**

Additional Answers, Class Exercises

6.

7.

8.

9.

LESSON FOLLOW-UP

Lesson Quiz

Determine whether each equation or function is symmetric with respect to the *x*-axis, *y*-axis, the origin, or the line *y* = *x*. Then sketch each graph using the properties of symmetry.

1. $y^2 - 3 = x$ x-axis

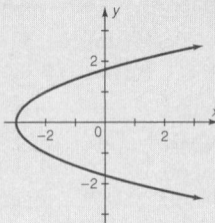

2. $f(x) = x^4 + 2$ y-axis

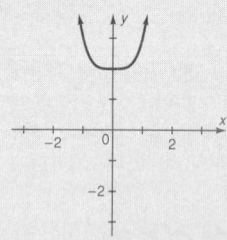

3. Use a graphing utility to graph and determine the symmetries of the equation $y = \sqrt{x^2 + 4}$.

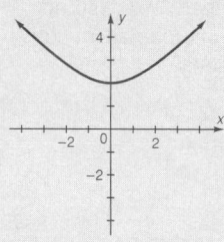

4. Explain how a function can be both even and odd. If a function is both even and odd then $f(-x) = f(x) = -f(x)$. This is true when $f(x) = 0$.

---

18. $f(x)$ is an even function.

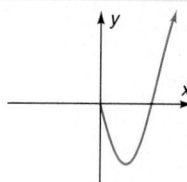

19. Symmetric with respect to $y = x$

Draw each graph on a sheet of tracing paper. Fold the graph along the *x*-axis, the *y*-axis, or along the *x*-axis and the *y*-axis to determine its symmetry.

20.

x-axis

21.

x-axis, y-axis, origin

22.

23.

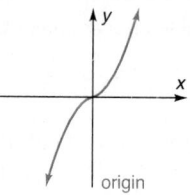

origin

Determine whether each function is even, odd, or neither.

B **24.** $f(x) = 4x^4 + 2x^2 + x$ neither

25. $g(x) = 5x^5 + 3x^3 + x$ odd

26. $h(x) = 2|x|$ even

27. $f(x) = \dfrac{x^3 - x}{x^5 + x}$ even

Determine the symmetries of each equation and then graph.

28. $x^2 = -y + 4$ **29.** $y = (x + 1)^2$ **30.** $xy^2 = 3$ **31.** $x - 1 = |y|$
y-axis   none   x-axis   x-axis

32. Thinking Critically   Analyze the following statement: "f is a function whose graph is symmetric to the *y*-axis and the origin."

ⓡ **33.** *Sports*   Golfer Betsy Prince must obtain an average qualifying score of at most 75. If her average score on her first three rounds is 79, what is the most she can score on her fourth round and still qualify? 63

34. Writing in Mathematics   Explain why an even function is symmetric with respect to the *y*-axis.

ⓡ **35.** *Sports*   Latiefa runs at a rate of 8.5 mi/h and walks at a rate of 4.5 mi/h. How long will it take her to cover 20 mi if she walks half the distance and runs the other half? 3.4 h

36. Thinking Critically   The graph of $y = (x - 2)^2$ is not symmetric with respect to the *x*-axis, *y*-axis, or the origin. Use a graphing utility to graph the equation. Does there appear to be any other line symmetry?

ⓡ **37.** Three of the exterior angles of a pentagon have measures of 62°, 74°, and 56°. If the other two exterior angles are congruent, what is the measure of each? 84°

62   Chapter 2 Graphing Functions

Writing in Mathematics

34. If a function is even then $f(-x) = f(x)$, which means that for every point (x, y) on the graph, there is also a point $(-x, y)$ on the graph. This is also the definition of a graph symmetric to the *y*-axis.

Complete each graph using the given information.

38. $f(x)$ is symmetric with respect to $x = 3$.

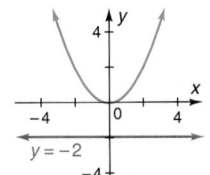

39. A relation is symmetric with respect to $y = -2$.

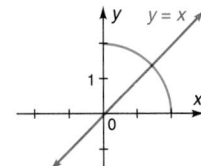

40. $g(x)$ is symmetric with respect to $y = x$ and is neither odd nor even.

Determine whether each is true or false. If false, provide a counterexample.

C **41.** $f + g$ is an odd function if f and g are both odd functions. true

42. $f - g$ is an even function if f and g are both even functions. true

43. $\dfrac{f}{g}$ is an odd function if f and g are both odd functions. false

44. $\dfrac{f}{g}$ is an odd function if f and g are both even functions. false

45. $f \cdot g$ is an even function if f and g are both odd functions. true

46. $f \cdot g$ is an even function if f is an odd function and g is an even function. false

47. Graph a function that contains the point (2, 5) and is symmetric with respect to the y-axis.

48. Graph a relation that contains the points (0, 2) and $(-3, -2)$ and is symmetric with respect to both the x- and y-axes.

Graph each function from the given information. Use the graph to complete the definition of each piecewise-defined function.

49. $f(x) = \begin{cases} x - 2, & 0 \le x \le 2 \\ x^2 - 2x, & x > 2 \end{cases}$

f is symmetric with respect to the y-axis.

50. $g(x) = \begin{cases} x^3, & 0 < x < 1 \\ x, & x \ge 1 \end{cases}$

g is symmetric with respect to the origin.

Project

Create a model using origami valley, mountain, and reverse folds. Share the model with classmates and discuss various techniques that can be used to design it.

Review

Solve.

1. $\dfrac{s}{s-9} = 13 + \dfrac{s}{s-9}$ $\varnothing$

2. $-\dfrac{42}{y} = \dfrac{y-25}{3}$ 18, 7

Given $f(x) = -x^2 - 2x$ and $g(x) = 2x + 4$, determine each of the following.

3. $(f \circ g)(x)$ $-4x^2 - 20x - 24$

4. $(g \circ f)(x)$ $-2x^2 - 4x + 4$

5. Factor $x^3 - 125y^3$ completely. $(x - 5y)(x^2 + 5xy + 25y^2)$

2.1 Symmetry **63**

Complete each graph using only the given information.

5. $f(x)$ is symmetric to the line $y = x$.

6. $g(x)$ is even.

47.

48.

49.

50.

63

Vocabulary
congruent graphs
dilation
horizontal shift
reflection
transformations
translations
vertical shift

Ⓜ **Materials/Manipulatives**
pipe cleaners
transparencies

Technology
graphing utility

FOCUS

The word *robot* was coined in 1921 by playwright Karl Capek to describe the mechanical people in his play *RUR.* Robots are not only being used in industry but are proving invaluable in medicine. Robots can be programmed to do a biopsy of a brain tumor and can accurately locate the tumor to within 0.002 of an inch.

INSTRUCTION

- Encourage students to be familiar with the basic set of functions or curves so that they can graph them without plotting many points.
- When presented with a function, students should be able to graph it by first identifying the basic curve and then using transformations such as reflections about the *y*-axis, *x*-axis, or line *y* = *x*, vertical and horizontal translations, and dilations.

2.2 Reflections and Transformations

Objectives: *To graph functions using reflections in the x-axis, y-axis, and the line y = x*
To graph functions using translations and dilations

Focus

The science of robotics uses computer technology to help automate the workplace. Robots are used to perform routine, strenuous, dangerous, or repetitive tasks. They may appear to think. However, every move they make has been programmed in advance by a human being. A simple robot can be programmed to place a gear in a certain position. To accomplish this task, the robot's arm can move left, right, up or down. To ensure that the arm of the robot places the gear precisely where it belongs, the correct *vertical* and *horizontal shifts* must be determined.

Knowing how to graph quickly without plotting numerous points is an invaluable skill. Familiarity with the shapes of some basic functions will help you graph other functions. Understanding and using symmetry and transformations will then enable you to strengthen your graphing abilities.

Identity function
$f(x) = x$

Squaring function
$f(x) = x^2$

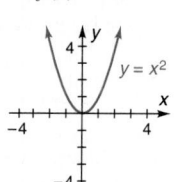

Cubing function
$f(x) = x^3$

Square root function
$f(x) = \sqrt{x}$

Absolute value function
$f(x) = |x|$

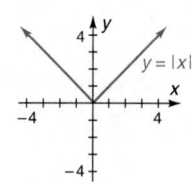

Reciprocal function
$f(x) = \dfrac{1}{x}$

64   Chapter 2 Graphing Functions

In this lesson, you will study the following types of **transformations:** *reflections,* *translations,* and *dilations.* Reflections and translations produce graphs *congruent* to the original graph; that is, the size and shape of the graph does not change. Dilations produce graphs with shapes related to those of the original graph.

Given graph G, the **reflection** G' in line m is the graph symmetric to G with respect to m. A reflection is the mirror image of the graph where line m is the *mirror* of the reflection. The resulting graph is congruent to the original graph. Every point in G has a corresponding *image* in G', except when the point lies on m. In this case, the point is its own image. Reflections in the x-axis, the y-axis, and the line $y = x$ are very useful when graphing.

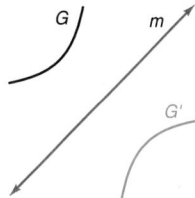

Reflections of $y = f(x)$

The graph of $y = -f(x)$ is the reflection of the graph of f in the x-axis.
The graph of $y = f(-x)$ is the reflection of the graph of f in the y-axis.
The graph of $y = f^{-1}(x)$ is the reflection of the graph of f in $y = x$.

Example 1 Find the line in which g is a reflection of f. Then graph f and g.

a. $f(x) = |x|$; $g(x) = -|x|$ **b.** $f(x) = \sqrt{x}$; $g(x) = \sqrt{-x}$

c. $f(x) = -\dfrac{x}{3} + 2$; $g(x) = -3x + 6$

a. $f(x) = |x|$ is the absolute value function. Since $g(x) = -f(x)$, g is the reflection of f in the x-axis. Therefore, for every point (a, b) on the graph of f, $(a, -b)$ is on the graph of its reflection g. The graph of g is symmetric to the graph of f with respect to the x-axis.

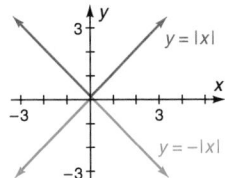

b. $f(x) = \sqrt{x}$ is the square root function. Since $g(x) = f(-x)$, g is the reflection of f in the y-axis. Therefore, for every point (a, b) on the graph of f, $(-a, b)$ is on the graph of g. The graph of g is symmetric to the graph of f with respect to the y-axis. *What is the domain of f? Of g?*

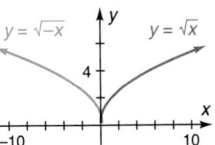

c. Since $f(x) = -\dfrac{x}{3} + 2$ is a linear function, determine whether $g(x) = -3x + 6$ is its inverse.

$$(f \circ g)(x) = -\frac{(-3x + 6)}{3} + 2 = x - 2 + 2 = x$$

$$(g \circ f)(x) = -3\left(-\frac{x}{3} + 2\right) + 6 = x - 6 + 6 = x$$

Since f and g are inverses, $g(x) = f^{-1}(x)$. For each point (a, b) on the graph of f, (b, a) is on the graph of g. The graph of g is the reflection of the graph of f in the line $y = x$.

2.2 Reflections and Transformations   **65**

Thinking Critically
The domain of f is $\{x: x \geq 0\}$, and the domain of g is $\{x: x \leq 0\}$.

Alternative Learning Styles

Ⓜ A tactile approach to transformations may be helpful to many students. To help students see rigid transformations of curves, have them draw a basic curve and then bend a pipe cleaner to model its shape. Students can translate and/or reflect this shape to the correct location on the grid and trace it.

GUIDED PRACTICE

For Example 1
Use reflections of a basic curve to graph each transformation.
1. $f(x) = x^2$, graph $f(x)$, $-f(x)$, and $f(-x)$.

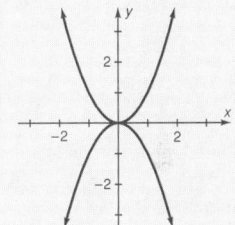

2. $g(x) = \dfrac{1}{x}$, graph $g(x)$, $-g(x)$, and $g^{-1}(x)$.

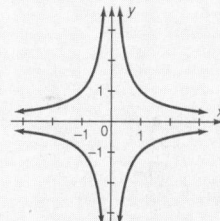

Technology Have students check their results using a graphing utility. Have them use the basic curve to help determine the range of the reflected curve. For a curve reflected about the y-axis, the X max setting of the range for the reflected curve should be the opposite of the X min setting for the basic curve.

For Example 2

Let the arm of a robot be represented as the line segment from (0, 2) to (10, 2) with the "hand" at (10, 2). If a gear must be placed at (12, 5), determine the horizontal and vertical shift through which the arm must be programmed to move. The arm is shifted right 2 units and up 3 units.

For Example 3

Use vertical shifts of the graph of $f(x) = x^3$ to graph the transformations $f(x) + 4$ and $f(x) - 1$.

A model of the arm of a simple robot can be made using a line segment graphed on coordinate axes. Then, horizontal and vertical shifts can be used to describe the movements of the arm.

Example 2 *Robotics* Let the arm of the robot be represented as the line segment from (0, 0) to (6, 0) with the "hand" at (6, 0). If a gear must be placed at (2, −3), determine the horizontal and vertical shifts through which the arm must be programmed to move. The arm may only be moved horizontally or vertically.

If the arm is shifted left 4 units, it will be directly above the point on which the gear must be placed. Then a downward shift of 3 units will place the "hand" precisely on the point (2, −3).

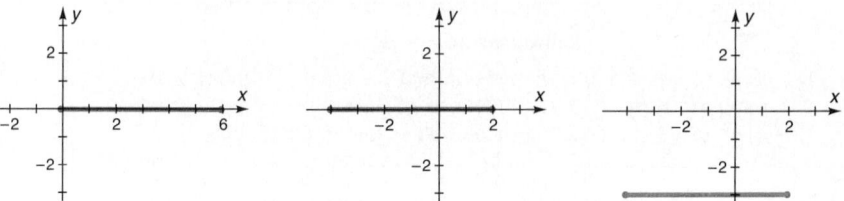

Does the order in which the translations are done affect the final placement of the arm of the robot? Explain.

Graphing can be simplified by using *translations* of basic functions. A **translation** of a graph is a vertical or horizontal shift of the graph that produces a congruent graph.

Example 3 Graph $f(x) = |x|$, $g(x) = |x| + 2$, and $h(x) = |x| - 3$ on the same set of axes. Find a relationship among the graphs.

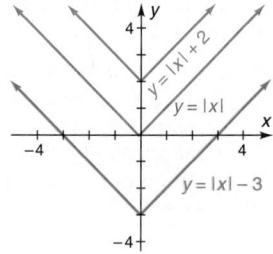

For every (a, b) on the graph of f, $(a, b + 2)$ is on the graph of g. The graph of g is a translation of the graph of f by an upward vertical shift of 2 units.

For every (a, b) on the graph of f, $(a, b - 3)$ is on the graph of h. The graph of h is a translation of the graph of f by a downward vertical shift of 3 units.

Adding a constant to a function produces a *vertical shift*. If a vertical translation is written $f(x) + d$, then a positive value for d produces an upward shift and a negative value for d produces a downward shift.

In order to produce a *horizontal shift*, a constant must be added to the x value of a function; that is, the graph of $f(x + k)$ is a horizontal transformation of k units of the graph of $f(x)$. If a horizontal translation is written $f(x - c)$, then a positive value for c produces a shift to the right and a negative value for c produces a shift to the left.

66 Chapter 2 Graphing Functions

Thinking Critically
No. A movement of 4 left and 2 down is equivalent to a movement of 2 down and 4 left.

Example 4   Graph $f(x) = |x|$, $g(x) = |x - 1|$, and $h(x) = |x + 2|$ on the same set of axes. Find a relationship among the graphs.

For every (a, b) on the graph of f, $(a + 1, b)$ is on the graph of g. The graph of g is a translation of the graph of f by a horizontal shift to the right of 1 unit.

For every (a, b) on the graph of f, $(a - 2, b)$ is on the graph of h. The graph of h is a translation of the graph of f by a horizontal shift to the left of 2 units.

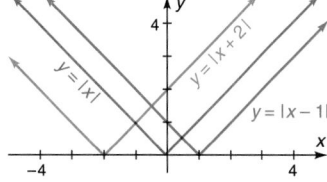

Both vertical and horizontal shifts can be used to translate a graph.

Translations of $y = f(x)$

The graph of $y = f(x - c) + d$ is a horizontal and vertical translation of the graph of $y = f(x)$.

Horizontal translation of $|c|$ units
If $c < 0$, the shift is to the left.
If $c > 0$, the shift is to the right.

Vertical translation of $|d|$ units
If $d < 0$, the shift is downward.
If $d > 0$, the shift is upward.

Dilation is a third type of transformation. Multiplying a function by a positive constant vertically *stretches* or *compresses* its graph; that is, the graph moves away from the x-axis or toward the x-axis.

Example 5   Graph $f(x) = x^2$, $g(x) = 2x^2$, and $h(x) = \frac{1}{3}x^2$ on the same set of axes. Locate $f(2)$, $g(2)$, and $h(2)$. Then state a relationship among the graphs.

Since $f(2) = 4$, $g(2) = 8$, and $h(2) = \frac{4}{3}$, the points $(2, 4)$, $(2, 8)$, and $\left(2, \frac{4}{3}\right)$ are on the graphs of f, g, and h, respectively.

For every (a, b) on the graph of f, $(a, 2b)$ is on the graph of g. The graph of g is a stretching of the graph of f. For every (a, b) on the graph of f, $\left(a, \frac{b}{3}\right)$ is on the graph of h. The graph of h is a compression of the graph of f.

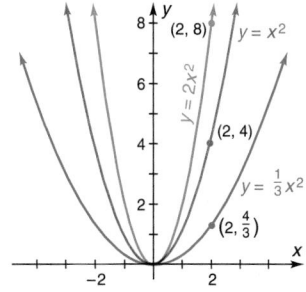

Dilations of $y = f(x)$

The graph of $y = af(x)$ is a vertical dilation of the graph of $f(x)$ of $|a|$ units.

If $a > 1$, the graph moves away from the x-axis.
If $0 < a < 1$, the graph moves toward the x-axis.

For Example 4
Use horizontal shifts of the graph of $f(x) = x^2$ to graph the transformations $f(x + 1)$ and $f(x - 2)$.

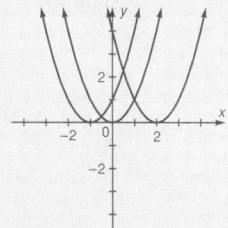

Common Error   When translating the graph of $f(x + 1)$ some students may translate the curve to the right instead of to the left. Have these students write the translation in standard form as $f[x - (-1)]$ or check at least one point on the translated graph in the equation.

For Example 5
Use dilations of the graph of $f(x) = |x|$ to graph the transformations $\frac{1}{2}f(x)$ and $2f(x)$.

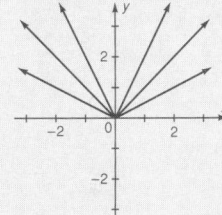

For Example 6

Graph the function $g(x) = \frac{1}{2}|x + 1| - 1$ by determining the basic function and then using transformations.

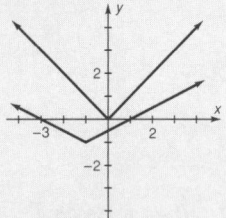

For Example 7

The graph of $f(x)$ is shown below. Graph the transformation.

$m(x) = -f(x + 1)$

Thus, transformations of graphs of functions include reflections, translations, and dilations. To graph a transformation of a given function, determine the basic function, reflect it, dilate it, and then translate it.

Example 6 Graph $y = -\frac{1}{2}x^3 + 2$ by determining the basic function and then using transformations.

$$y = -\frac{1}{2}x^3 + 2$$
$$b(x) = x^3 \qquad \textit{Determine the basic function.}$$
$$t(x) = -\frac{1}{2}x^3 + 2 \qquad \textit{Identify the transformations.}$$

Basic function Reflection in x-axis Dilation of $\frac{1}{2}$ unit Upward vertical shift of 2 units

The graph of a transformation of a function can be determined by analyzing its equation.

Example 7 The graph of $f(x)$ is shown at the left below. Graph $y = f(-x) - 4$.

Analyze the equation $y = f(-x) - 4$.

Reflection in the y-axis. Vertical shift downward of 4 units.

 A graphing utility can be used to determine the relationship between two graphs.

68 Chapter 2 Graphing Functions

Example 8 Use a graphing utility to graph the equations $y_1 = x^3 - 2x + 1$ and $y_2 = (x - 4)^3 - 2(x - 4) + 1$ on the same set of axes. How are the two graphs related?

[-7.5, 7.5] by [-5, 5]

The graph of y_2 is the graph of y_1 translated 4 units to the right.

Class Exercises

Graph each reflection in the given line.

1. x-axis

2. y-axis

3. line $y = x$

4. x-axis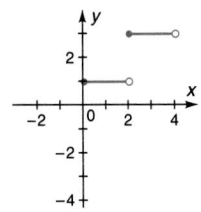

For each pair of functions, find the line in which g is a reflection of f. Then graph f and g.

5. $f(x) = 2x - 20$; $g(x) = \frac{1}{2}x + 10$ $y = x$

6. $f(x) = x^2 + 5$; $g(x) = -x^2 - 5$ x-axis

Determine the basic function for each equation. Identify all transformations.

7. $y = \sqrt{x - 3}$

8. $y = (x + 3)^2$

9. $y - 2 = x^2$

10. $y = -[\![x + 2]\!]$

The graphs of f and g are shown below. Graph each transformation.

11. $y = -f(x + 3)$

12. $y = -g(x) + 2$

13. $y = g(x - 1) - 5$

14. $y = f(-x) + 1$

15. $y = 2f(x)$

16. $y = \frac{1}{2}g(x)$

Practice Exercises

 Use appropriate technology.

Graph each reflection in the given line.

A **1.** x-axis

2. y-axis

3. y-axis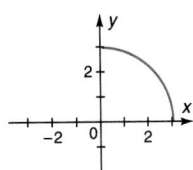

2.2 Reflections and Transformations **69**

Additional Answers, Practice Exercises

1. **2.** **3.**

For Example 8
Use a graphing utility to graph the equations $y_1 = x^2 - 1$ and $y_2 = 4(x - 2)^2$ on the same set of axes. How are the two graphs related?

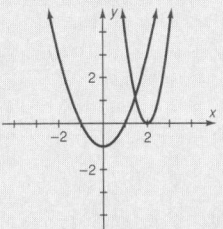

y_2 is dilated by a factor of 4, shifted 2 units to the right, and 1 unit up from y_1.

CLOSURE

Let $f(x)$ be the basic function. Have students record in their math journals the function notation used to describe the following transformations.
• Reflection of $f(x)$ in the x-axis
• Reflection of $f(x)$ in the y-axis
• Reflection of $f(x)$ in the line $y = x$
• Translation of $f(x)$ 4 units to the left
• Translation of $f(x)$ 2 units up

INDEPENDENT PRACTICE

Assignment Guide
Basic: 1–25, 33–36
Average: 1–25, 27–43 odd, Project
Enriched: 1–29 odd, 30–56 even, Project

Teacher's Resource Book
Practice, page 9

Ⓡ **Review**
Exercises 7, 11, 21, 33, and 35 review concepts such as finding inverse functions, using formulas, graphing linear equations, finding width of a rectangle, and naming properties of number sets.

Project
When researching robots, students may want to look for references in science fiction literature. The project thus provides an opportunity for cross-curricular learning.

69

4.

5.

6.

8.

9.

12.

13.

4. x-axis   **5.** line $y = x$ **6.** x-axis

Ⓡ **7.** *Cryptography*   A simple cipher takes a number and codes it using the function $f(x) = 5x - 2$. Find the inverse of this function. $f^{-1}(x) = \frac{x}{5} + \frac{2}{5}$

For each pair of functions, find the line in which g is a reflection of f. Then graph f and g.

8. $f(x) = x^2 - 2$; $g(x) = 2 - x^2$ x-axis   **9.** $f(x) = x^3$; $g(x) = \sqrt[3]{x}$ $y = x$

10. Thinking Critically   A function $f(x)$ is symmetric to the y-axis. Analyze $y = f(x - a)$ to determine its line of symmetry. $x = a$

Ⓡ **11.** *Depreciation*   The resale value y of a certain pickup truck can be calculated using the formula $y = 18,000(1 - 0.10x)$, where x is the age of the truck in years. Find the approximate value of the truck after $3\frac{1}{2}$ years. $11,700

The graphs of f and g are shown below. Graph each transformation.

12. $y = f(x - 4)$
13. $y = g(x) - 4$
14. $y = g(x + 2) - 3$
15. $y = 2f(x)$
16. $y = -g(x)$
17. $y = f(x + 5) + 1$

Use a graphing utility to graph each pair of equations on the same set of axes. Determine how the two equations are related.

18. $y_1 = 2\sqrt{x - 1}$ and $y_2 = -2\sqrt{x - 1}$ reflections about x-axis
19. $y_1 = x^2 + 4x$ and $y_2 = (x + 2)^2 + 4(x + 2) - 3$
20. $y_1 = x^3 - 3x^2$ and $y_2 = x^3 + 3x^2 - 4$

Ⓡ **21.** In Rye Brook, a taxi ride costs $1.25 for the first $\frac{1}{4}$ mile and 10 cents for each additional $\frac{1}{8}$ mile. In Middlebury, a taxi ride costs $1.00 for the first $\frac{1}{4}$ mile and 10 cents for each additional $\frac{1}{8}$ mile. Graph the linear equations that model the fares in each city, and state how the two equations are related.

Graph each equation by determining the basic function and then using transformations.

22. $y = x - 2$ $y = x$ **23.** $y = x + 4$ $y = x$ **24.** $y = \sqrt{x - 2}$ $y = \sqrt{x}$ **25.** $y = \sqrt{x + 5}$ $y = \sqrt{x}$
B **26.** $y = 2[\![x]\!] + 1$ $y = [\![x]\!]$ **27.** $y = 3[\![x]\!] - 1$ $y = [\![x]\!]$ **28.** $y = \frac{1}{x - 3}$ $y = \frac{1}{x}$ **29.** $y = 2|x - 4|$ $y = |x|$

70   Chapter 2 Graphing Functions

14.

15.

16.

17.

30. Writing in Mathematics Compare and contrast the meaning of the word *dilation* as used in everyday speech and as a transformation of a graph.

For each pair of functions, find the line in which g is a reflection of f. Then graph f and g.

31. $f(x) = x^3 + 4$; $g(x) = \sqrt[3]{x - 4}$

32. $f(x) = (x - 2)^3$; $g(x) = (-2 - x)^3$

Ⓡ **33.** *Gardening* The width of a rectangular garden whose perimeter is 80 yd is 2 yd less than its length. Find its width. 19 yd

34. Writing in Mathematics Study the reflection of a ruler in a mirror. Write a paragraph describing how to draw the reflection of the ruler.

Ⓡ **35.** Name the field properties satisfied by the set of whole numbers under the operation of addition.

36. Thinking Critically Construct a function whose reflection in the line $y = x$ is itself. State the symmetries of the function.

Use the basic functions and transformations to determine the equation of each function from its graph.

37.
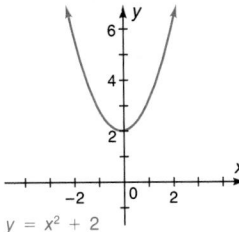
$y = x^2 + 2$

38.
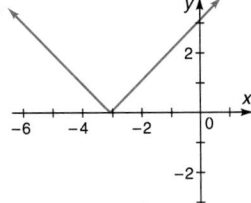
$y = |x + 3|$

39.
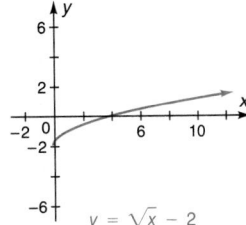
$y = \sqrt{x} - 2$

40.
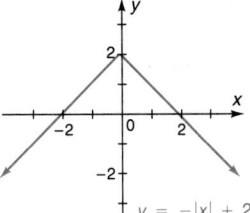
$y = -|x| + 2$

41.
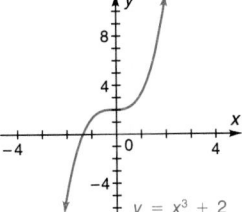
$y = x^3 + 2$

42.
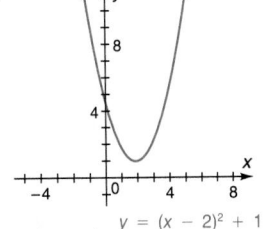
$y = (x - 2)^2 + 1$

43.
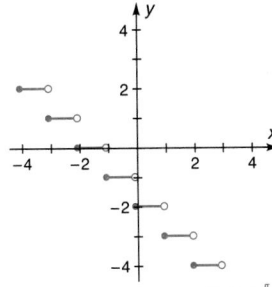
$y = -[\![x + 2]\!]$

44.
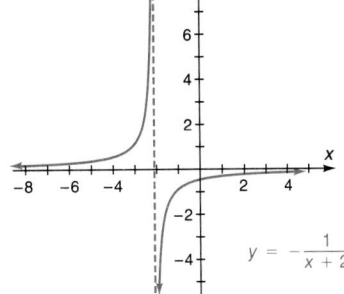
$y = -\dfrac{1}{x + 2}$

2.2 Reflections and Transformations **71**

Lesson Quiz

1. Graph the reflection of $f(x)$ in the line $y = x$.

2. Determine the basic function for the equation $y = -\frac{1}{4}(x + 2)^3$ and identify all transformations. The basic function is $y = x^3$. It is reflected in the x-axis, vertically compressed by a factor of $\frac{1}{4}$, and translated left 2 units.

3. $f(x) = \sqrt{x}$; graph $f(x)$ and $f(-x)$.
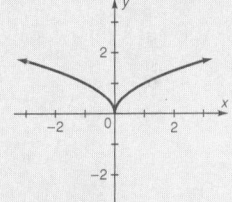

4. Graph $g(x) = (x + 3)^2 - 1$ using transformations.
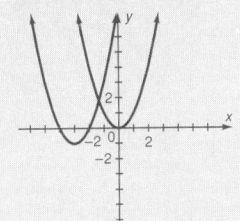

5. $h(x)$ is a cubic function. Write the equation from the graph.

$y = (x + 4)^3$

Alternative Assessment

Have students choose any example from Exercises 19 to 26 that was not assigned for homework, and explain in detail a strategy for graphing the function. They should then illustrate their explanations by using the strategy to draw the graph.

Enrichment

For $f(x) = \dfrac{1}{x^2}$, sketch $f(x)$ and $f(-x - 2)$.

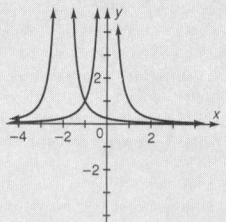

Graph each function and its reflection in the given line. Then determine an equation for the graph of the reflection.

C **45.** $f(x) = |x| + 1$; x-axis
46. $f(x) = |x| - 2$; y-axis
47. $f(x) = [\![x]\!] + 1$; y-axis
48. $f(x) = [\![x]\!] - 2$; x-axis

49. Describe the effect on the range of the greatest integer function $f(x) = [\![x]\!]$ of a vertical dilation of $\dfrac{1}{a}$, $a > 1$. Vertical distance between the steps decreases as a increases.

Use transformations to graph each function.

50. $f(x) = \sqrt{-x + 1}$
51. $h(x) = -[\![x + 3]\!]$

52. $f(x) = \begin{cases} 3x, & x < 0 \\ -x^2 + 2, & x \geq 0 \end{cases}$
53. $g(x) = \begin{cases} \sqrt{-x} - 2, & x < 0 \\ (-x - 1)^2, & x \geq 0 \end{cases}$

Graph each function.

54. $f(x) = [\![x]\!]^2$
55. $f(x) = [\![x - 2]\!]^2$
56. $f(x) = [\![x]\!]^2 + 1$

Project

Research the use of robots in an area of interest to you. Prepare a talk about the tasks they perform, why they are used, problems encountered, and the plans for future use of robots in that field.

Challenge

1. The height of a conical drinking cup is 10 cm and the radius is 2 cm at the top. Find the volume capacity of the cup. The cup is then filled with water to a height of 5 cm. Can you reason that since the height of the water is one-half the height of the cup, the volume of water must therefore be one-half the volume of the cup? Explain.

2. Find the smallest positive integral value for x that makes the following true:

$$\sqrt{\sqrt{\sqrt{\sqrt{\sqrt{x}}}}} > 1.4 \quad \text{47,435}$$

3. The difference of the squares of two consecutive even integers is 356. Find the numbers. 90, 88

4. If the numerator and denominator of a fraction are each decreased by 1, the result is $\dfrac{5}{8}$; but if the numerator and denominator are each increased by 1, the result is $\dfrac{2}{3}$. Find the fraction. $\dfrac{11}{17}$

5. Factor $a^6 - b^6$ completely. $(a - b)(a^2 + ab + b^2)(a + b)(a^2 - ab + b^2)$

6. A method for approximating the square root of a number x was discovered using the formula $\sqrt{x} = p + \dfrac{x - p^2}{2p + 1}$, where p is the square root of the nearest perfect square less than x. Use this formula to approximate the square root of 175. 13.22

72   Chapter 2 Graphing Functions

Additional Answers

54. **55.** **56.**

2.3 Linear Functions

Objectives: To graph linear functions
To determine the equation of a linear function

Focus

Japan has developed a high-speed train where magnetic fields produced by superconducting magnets "levitate" vehicles over the tracks so there is essentially no friction. The levitation occurs from the repulsive force between the magnet on the train and the eddy currents produced in the train track. Superconducting materials have negligible resistance at temperatures near absolute zero. Absolute zero, the point where all molecular motion stops, forms the basis of a temperature scale known as the absolute, or Kelvin, scale which is used extensively in scientific work.

Temperature is measured on several different scales. The Fahrenheit scale, used in daily weather reports, was developed by the German physicist Gabriel Fahrenheit, who also designed the first mercury thermometer. The Celsius scale, part of the metric system, sets the freezing point of water at 0°C and the boiling point at 100°C.

The relationship between the Fahrenheit and Celsius scales can be represented by a linear function. A **linear function** is a function of the form

$$f(x) = mx + b$$

where m and b are constants. The graph of f is a line. A linear function can be represented by a linear equation, $y = mx + b$.

The standard form of a linear equation in two variables is $Ax + By + C = 0$, where A and B are not both zero. The steepness or **slope** of a line is defined as the ratio of the change in the vertical distance to the change in the horizontal distance between any two points on the line.

Consider the line ℓ that contains the points (x_1, y_1) and (x_2, y_2). The slope of this line is defined by the following equation:

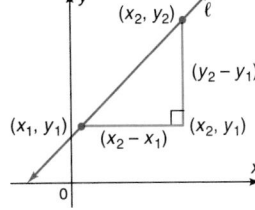

$$m = \frac{\Delta y}{\Delta x} = \frac{y_2 - y_1}{x_2 - x_1} = \frac{f(x_2) - f(x_1)}{x_2 - x_1}$$

The Greek letter delta Δ is interpreted as "the change in," but is read as "delta."

2.3 Linear Functions   **73**

LESSON PLAN

Vocabulary
linear function
slope

Ⓜ **Materials/Manipulatives**
Celsius thermometer
Fahrenheit thermometer

Technology
graphing utility

FOCUS

A discussion of the Kelvin temperature scale provides an opportunity to relate mathematics to material that students may be learning in their science classes.

INSTRUCTION

- Emphasize the difference between a linear function and a linear equation. In particular point out that the linear equation $x = a$ is not a function.
- Note the four forms of equations of lines: *point-slope, two-point, slope-intercept,* and *standard* forms. Give students two points and have them write the equation of the line containing the two points in four different forms. Then discuss the information that can be read directly from each equation such as slope, points on the line, and y-intercepts.

Alternative Learning Styles

Ⓜ Many students find performing physical experiments helpful in understanding mathematical concepts. In the physics lab have students measure the temperatures of liquids using both a Celsius thermometer and a Fahrenheit thermometer. Students may wish to test their data in the function obtained in Example 2 and discuss their results.

For Example 1

A teacher wants to test the hypothesis that the number of arithmetical errors made by a student on a simple arithmetic computation test is a linear function of the room temperature. A student makes 8 mistakes per 50 computations at 68°F and 14 mistakes per 50 computations at 76°F. Assuming the teacher's hypothesis is correct, determine the linear function that relates the number of mistakes a student makes per 50 computations to the room temperature. Then find the number of mistakes a student would be expected to make if the room temperature is 92°F.

$M = \frac{3}{4}T - 43$; $f(92) = 26$ mistakes

Common Error Some students may try to use the number 50 (50 computations) to determine the linear function. Explain that this is just a standard measure against which the number of errors is computed.

The definition of slope leads to many forms of the equation of a line that are useful for determining the rule of a linear function. The *point-slope form* of the equation of a line is

$$y - y_1 = m(x - x_1) \qquad \text{Since } m = \frac{y_2 - y_1}{x_2 - x_1}$$

The form is used to determine the equation of a line when the slope m and the coordinates of one point (x_1, y_1) are known.

Example 1 *Medicine* A new fever-reducing drug was tried on patients who had the flu, and the following was determined. On the average, a patient's temperature would be lowered by 0.08 degree in the first 15 min for each 1 mg of the drug administered. A patient's fever was reduced to 98.6°F 15 min after receiving 50 mg of the drug. Determine the linear function that relates the patient's temperature after 15 min to the number of milligrams of the drug administered, and determine the patient's initial temperature.

Let y be the patient's temperature after 15 min.
Let x be the number of milligrams of the drug administered.

$$m = \frac{\text{change in temperature}}{\text{change in dosage}}$$

$$= \frac{-0.08}{1} \qquad \textit{The temperature is decreasing.}$$

The patient's temperature is 98.6°F for 50 mg of the drug.

$$
\begin{aligned}
y - y_1 &= m(x - x_1) &\textit{Point-slope form}\\
y - 98.6 &= -0.08(x - 50) &(x_1, y_1) = (50, 98.6)\\
y &= 102.6 - 0.08x
\end{aligned}
$$

To determine the initial temperature, find the y-intercept by substituting zero for x.

$$
\begin{aligned}
y &= 102.6 - 0.08(0)\\
y &= 102.6
\end{aligned}
$$

The initial temperature was 102.6°F.

Recall from geometry that two points determine a line. When the coordinates of two points (x_1, y_1) and (x_2, y_2) are known, the *two-point form* of the equation of a line

$$y - y_1 = \left(\frac{y_2 - y_1}{x_2 - x_1}\right)(x - x_1)$$

can be used to determine the equation of the line.

Notice that the two-point form is simply a modification of the point-slope form in which the formula for the slope is substituted for m. If you are using a computer to find the equations of lines given two points, this formula allows you to input the coordinates of the points directly without first solving for the slope.

74 Chapter 2 Graphing Functions

Example 2 *Physics* The temperature at which water freezes is 0°C, or 32°F. The temperature at which water boils is 100°C, or 212°F. Use this data to find a linear function that relates Celsius temperature to Fahrenheit temperature. Using a graphing utility, graph the function, letting x stand for the independent variable F and y stand for the dependent variable C.

Using F for Fahrenheit and C for Celsius, the data points are $(32, 0)$ and $(212, 100)$. Use the two-point form of the equation of the line to find the function rule.

$$C - 0 = \frac{100 - 0}{212 - 32}(F - 32) \quad \textit{Two-point form}$$

$$C = \frac{5}{9}(F - 32)$$

[0, 225] by [0, 100]
x scl: 25 y scl: 20

Use the original data points to help you determine an appropriate viewing window.

All nonvertical lines are functions. A linear equation in *slope-intercept form*, $y = mx + b$, is easily graphed by plotting the value of b, the y-intercept, on the y-axis and using the slope to determine a second point.

Example 3 Given a linear equation in standard form $40x - 30y + 6000 = 0$, express the equation in slope-intercept form. Then graph the function.

$$40x - 30y + 6000 = 0$$

$$40x - 30y = -6000$$

$$y = \frac{4}{3}x + 200$$

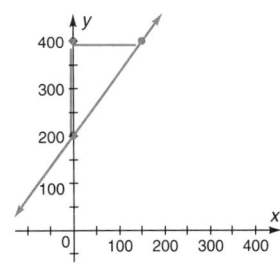

The slope is $\frac{4}{3}$ and the y-intercept is 200.

Plot the y-intercept. Since the slope is *positive*, plot a point 4 units *up* and 3 units to the right. Connect the two points with a line.

The equation of a vertical line a units from the y-axis is $x = a$. The equation of a horizontal line b units from the x-axis is $y = b$.

Note that a vertical line is not a function. *Why?* All vertical lines are parallel and all horizontal lines are parallel. Also, a vertical line is perpendicular to a horizontal line.

Given two linear equations, you can determine if their graphs are parallel lines, perpendicular lines, or neither. Two nonvertical lines are parallel if and only if they have the same slope. Two nonvertical lines are perpendicular if and only if their slopes are negative reciprocals.

2.3 Linear Functions   **75**

For Example 2
One inch corresponds to 2.54 cm. One foot corresponds to 30.48 cm. Use this data to find a linear equation that expresses standard measurement as a function of metric measurement. Graph the function.
$y = 0.3937x$, where x is number of centimeters, and y is number of inches.

Common Error Some students may forget to write 1 ft as 12 in.

Technology When minimum and maximum values of a quantity are given, students may use these values to determine the appropriate viewing window. Values slightly smaller and larger than the actual minimum and maximum, respectively, may be chosen.

For Example 3
Given a linear equation in standard form $0.55x + 0.85y = 675$, express the equation in slope-intercept form. Then graph the function.
$y = -0.647x + 794$

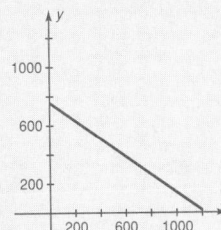

75

Modeling

Discuss what is meant by the Kelvin scale and the Celsius scale using "the same size units." Explain that, for any temperature, the measure in degrees Celsius differs from that in degrees Kelvin by 273.15°, so that $C = K - 273.15$. Substituting $K - 273.15$ for y in the equation $y = \frac{5}{9}(x - 32)$ gives the formula for converting degrees Fahrenheit x to degrees Kelvin K.

For Example 4

Determine if the given lines are parallel, perpendicular, or neither.
1. $2y + 3x = 3$; $y = -1.5x - 0.7$
   parallel
2. $5y - 15x = -4$; $3y + x = 5$
   perpendicular

Technology Some students may find it helpful to verify the parallelism or perpendicularity of lines by graphing them on a graphing utility.

CLOSURE

Pair students and have them describe each of the four forms of linear equations. For each form, have students discuss the conditions where it is more appropriate to use that form over the others.

INDEPENDENT PRACTICE

Assignment Guide
Basic: 1–20, 22–27, 32
Average: 1–16, 18–34, Project
Enriched: 6–8, 15–40, Project

Teacher's Resource Book
Practice, page 10

ℝ Review
Exercises 5, 9, 11, 17, 21, 23, 27, and 29 review concepts such as graphing functions, finding symmetry of functions, evaluating composite functions, naming subsets, identifying field properties, and determining if the graph represents a one-to-one function.

Modeling

What is the relationship between the Kelvin and Fahrenheit scales?

The Celsius temperature scale is the one often preferred by scientists because it is part of the metric system. However, studies in physics involving the relationship between the temperature and the volume of a gas revealed an interesting feature of the Celsius scale. It was found that when the pressure of a gas is kept constant, the volume of the gas increases or decreases with the temperature at a constant rate. The temperature that causes the volume of any gas to drop to zero is $-273.15°C$. Any temperature less than this would cause the volume to be less than zero which is, of course, impossible. Thus, $-273.15°C$ is the lowest temperature possible and is called *absolute zero*. The Kelvin scale uses the same size units as the Celsius scale but assigns the value 0°K to absolute zero temperature.

Example 4   In Example 2, Fahrenheit temperature F and Celsius temperature C were related by the equation $C = \frac{5}{9}(F - 32)$. A formula for converting degrees Kelvin C to degrees Fahrenheit F is $F = 1.8C - 459.67$. Determine if the graphs of these two lines are parallel, perpendicular, or neither.

Find the slope of each line.

$$5F - 9C = 160 \qquad\qquad F = 1.8C - 459.67$$

$$C = \frac{5}{9}F - \frac{160}{9} \qquad C = \frac{1}{1.8}F + \frac{459.67}{1.8}$$

$$\frac{5}{9} = \frac{1}{1.8} \qquad \text{Since the slopes are equal, the lines are parallel.}$$

What interpretation can you give to the fact that the lines are parallel?

Class Exercises

Using the given information, find the equation of the line.

1. The line has slope $-\frac{1}{2}$ and passes through the point $(3, 4)$. $x + 2y = 11$
2. The line passes through the points $(6, 1)$ and $(-3, 2)$. $x + 9y = 15$
3. The line is parallel to the x-axis and is 3 units below it. $y = -3$
4. The x-intercept is $(-7, 0)$ and the y-intercept is $(0, 0.4)$. $2x - 35y = -14$
5. *Physics*   The change in pressure of a gas per one degree drop in temperature is -0.05. The initial pressure at 70°F is 15.2 lb/in². Write a linear model for the pressure of the gas with a constant volume as a function of temperature. $0.05x + y = 18.7$

Thinking Critically
The only change from one formula to another is adding a constant.

Graph each linear function.

6. $y = -\frac{1}{14}x + 9$ **7.** $4y - 3x = 16$

Determine if the given lines are parallel, perpendicular, or neither.

8. $0.3x + 0.4y = -0.7$; $2y - 4x = 6$ neither

9. $5x - 2y = 5$; $100x + 250y = 500$ perpendicular

10. *Physics* The weight of a person on the earth and on the moon is given in the table. Graph the data and find a linear equation representing the weight y of a person on the moon as a function of his weight x on the earth. $y = \frac{x}{6}$

Weight on earth (lb)	Weight on moon (lb)
120	20
132	22
156	26
162	27

Practice Exercises   Use appropriate technology.

Business To rent a car from the RENT-ME Car Rental Company costs $25 per day plus $0.07 per mile. For the number of days indicated, find a linear function for the cost C of renting the car as a function of the number of miles driven d.

A **1.** The car is rented for two days. $C = 0.07d + 50$

   2. The car is rented for five days. $C = 0.07d + 125$

   3. Graph the function in Exercise 1 and estimate the bill from the graph for a person who drove 356 mi.

   4. Graph the function in Exercise 2 and estimate the bill from the graph for a person who drove 685 mi.

Ⓡ **5.** Graph $f(x) = (x - 2)^3 + 1$ using transformations.

   6. Graph the linear equation $35x - 25y = -75$.

Find an equation of each line in standard form.

   7. The slope of the line is $\frac{5}{9}$ and the line passes through the point $(-18, 0)$. $5x - 9y = -90$

   8. The line passes through the points $(5, 4)$ and $(0, 7)$. $3x + 5y = 35$

Ⓡ **9.** Determine the symmetry of $f(x) = x^3 - x$. origin

   10. Thinking Critically Consider the standard form and the slope-intercept form of a line. How could you determine the slope of a line directly from the standard form $Ax + By + C = 0$? $m = -\frac{A}{B}$

Ⓡ **11.** Given $f(x) = 2x^2 + 1$ and $g(x) = -3x$, evaluate $(g \circ f)(-4)$. -99

Electricity The electrical resistance R of a certain resistor has been measured for different temperatures t in Celsius.

Temperature (°C)	Resistance (ohms)
10	5.70
13	5.79
15	5.85
16	5.88
19	5.97

   12. Graph the data with temperature on the horizontal axis and resistance on the vertical axis.

   13. Determine the slope of the line that contains the points. 0.03

   14. Determine an equation giving the resistance as a function of the temperature. $R = 0.03t + 5.4$

2.3 Linear Functions   **77**

Lesson Quiz

1. There is a linear relationship between the number of hamburgers sold by a large food chain each week and the number of discount coupons handed out the previous week. When 500 coupons were distributed, 1200 hamburgers were sold. When 650 coupons were distributed, 1450 hamburgers were sold. Determine the linear function that relates the two quantities and determine how many coupons need to be distributed to sell 1600 hamburgers. $y = 1.67x + 366.67$; 740 coupons

2. The temperature at which water freezes is 0°C or 32°F. The temperature at which water boils is 100°C or 212°F. Use this data to find a linear function for converting from Celsius to Fahrenheit. Graph the function. $F = \frac{9}{5}C + 32$, or $F = 1.8C + 32$

3. Write an equation of a line in standard form whose slope is $\frac{2}{3}$ and which passes through the point $(0, -5)$. $2x - 3y = 15$

4. Using a graphing utility, graph the linear equation $0.34x + 0.45y = 0.06$. Explain how you determined an appropriate viewing window and scale. Answers may vary. Example: Find the x- and y-intercepts.

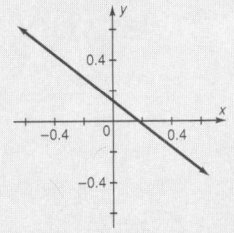

Additional Answers, Practice Exercises

3.

4.

5.

6.

Determine if the given lines are parallel, perpendicular, or neither.

15. $7x - 4y = 3$; $8y - 14x = 2$ parallel

16. $0.1x = 0.2y + 3$; $-2y - 4x = 7$ perpendicular

Ⓡ **17.** Name three subsets of the set of real numbers.

Space Science A ball thrown in space where there is virtually zero gravity would travel in a straight line at a constant speed. The data at the right was collected.

Time (s)	Distance (ft)
0.2	8.5
0.5	16.6
0.7	22.0
1.5	43.6

Ⓑ **18.** Graph the data and estimate the number of seconds needed for the ball to travel 37.2 ft. 1.3 s

19. Determine the slope of the line that contains the points. 27

20. Find an equation giving the distance traveled as a function of time. $d = 27t + 3.1$

Ⓡ **21.** Identify the field properties of the real number system that are satisfied for the set of positive even integers under the operation of multiplication.

22. *Anthropology* The height h of a female can be approximated from the length ℓ of her humerus using the linear function $h(\ell) = 2.8\ell + 71.5$. Graph the linear function and estimate the length of the humerus bone of a female that is 157 cm tall. 31 cm

Ⓡ **23.** Graph $f(x) = -x^2 + 4$ using transformations.

24. Thinking Critically Express the linear equation $Ax + By = C$ so that the x- and y-intercepts can be determined directly from the equation.

Physical Fitness A comfortable walking speed for power walking for a person in moderate shape is 2 m every 3 s.

25. Determine a linear function for the distance the person walks at this rate in a given time. $d = \dfrac{2}{3}t$

26. Graph the function in Exercise 25 and estimate the time it would take the person to walk 36.5 m. 54.75 s

Ⓡ **27.** Determine if the graph at the right represents a one-to-one function. no

28. Find an equation of a line parallel to the line $3x - 5y = 17$ and passing through the origin. $y = \dfrac{3}{5}x$

Ⓡ **29.** Graph $y = -x^3 - 2$ using transformations.

30. Find an equation of a line perpendicular to the line $0.3y = 0.4x + 0.32$ and passing through the point $(0, 0.09)$. $3x + 4y = 0.36$

Energy Conservation The relationship between the thickness of a new insulation material and its R-factor is given in the chart to the right.

Thickness (in.)	R-factor
1.5	1.095
2.1	1.533
4.3	3.139
5.7	4.162
6.1	4.453

31. Graph the data.

32. Find an equation in slope-intercept form for the R-factor as a function of the thickness of the material. $R = 0.73t$

33. Interpret the meaning of the y-intercept.

34. Writing in Mathematics Explain in a few sentences the meaning of the words "if and only if" in the statement, "Two nonvertical lines are parallel if and only if their slopes are equal."

78 Chapter 2 Graphing Functions

Writing in Mathematics

34. *If and only if* is a biconditional. The statement can be divided into two statements: If two nonvertical lines are parallel, then their slopes are equal; If the slopes of two nonvertical lines are equal, then the lines are parallel.

Business   A refrigerator salesperson is paid a fixed amount per week plus a commission on the number of units sold. The fixed amount is $100 and the commission for that week is $22 per unit sold.

C   **35.** Find a linear function representing the salesperson's pay for that week. $p = 22w + 100$

36. Determine the domain of the linear function in Exercise 35. Justify your answer.

37. Graph the function and determine if it is continuous.

The identity function $I(x) = x$ is compressed by a factor of $\frac{1}{2}$ and translated 3 units to the right and 4 units up.

38. Find an equation of the transformed function. $y = \frac{1}{2}(x - 3) + 4$

39. Find an equation of the line perpendicular to the equation in Exercise 38 and passing through a point on the y-axis, 0.7 unit below the x-axis. $2x + y = -0.7$

40. Find the equation of the line which is a downward shift of 6 units of the line in Exercise 38, and show that this new line is perpendicular to the line in Exercise 39.

Project

New materials are being developed that superconduct at more reasonable temperatures so that the energy expended to maintain extremely low temperatures of original superconducting materials can be reduced. Investigate uses of superconducting materials in generating plants and high-speed ground transportation.

Review

1. Find the inverse of the relation $\{(1, 4), (2, 4), (3, 4), (4, 0), (5, 0), (6, 0)\}$. State the domain and range and determine if the new relation is a function.

2. Factor completely: $25x^2 + 50xy + 25y^2$ $25(x + y)^2$

3. If $ab = 0$, what do you conclude about the numbers a and b? $a = 0$ or $b = 0$

4. Solve: $\dfrac{1}{x + 3} < 0$ $x < -3$

5. The width of a photo is 6 cm less than the length. The frame that surrounds the photo is 2 cm wide and has an area of 120 cm². Determine the dimensions of the photo. $\ell = 16$ cm; $w = 10$ cm

6. Everett travels 21.5 mi by car to go to work. He travels part of the trip along a country road at an average speed of 30 mi/h. The other part of the trip, he travels on a highway at the rate of 50 mi/h. The time he travels on the highway is twice the time he travels on the country road. Determine the total time for the trip. ≈ 30 min

7. If $f(x) = x - 1$, evaluate and simplify: $\dfrac{f(x) - f(2)}{x - 2}$ 1

Solve for x.

8. $\dfrac{5}{x} - \dfrac{2}{3} = \dfrac{14}{3x}$ $\frac{1}{2}$

9. $\dfrac{x + 2}{x^2 + x} - \dfrac{3}{x + 1} = 0$ 1

2.3 Linear Functions   **79**

Vocabulary
complex number
zero-product property

ⓜ **Materials/Manipulatives**
paper
scissors
tape

Technology
programmable calculator
symbolic manipulator

FOCUS

If air resistance is ignored, all objects would fall with the same velocity. The formula for finding velocity is $v = at + v_0$, where a is acceleration, t is time, and v_0 is the initial velocity. Near the surface of the earth the acceleration due to gravity is considered to be uniform at -32 ft/s^2 or -9.8 m/s^2. The negative sign is used to indicate that the pull of gravity is toward the center of the earth. Thus, near the surface of the earth, since all objects fall with the same acceleration, objects with equal initial velocities fall with the same velocity.

INSTRUCTION

Many real world situations can be modeled by quadratic equations. For Examples 1 and 3, be sure students understand how the first equation in each solution is derived. Encourage students having difficulty interpreting these equations to substitute one or more values for the variable x and find the respective revenue or volume.

2.4   Solving Quadratic Equations

Objective: To find real and imaginary solutions to quadratic equations

Focus

When an object is projected into the air, it is pulled back to the earth by the force of gravity. This same force holds the moon in orbit around the earth and the planets in orbit around the sun. All objects in the universe are attracted toward each other according to Isaac Newton's *law of universal gravitation.*

What prevents all the objects in a room from falling toward one another? The strength of the gravitational attraction between objects is dependent on their masses and the distances between them. They are not pulled toward one another because their masses are so small relative to the mass of the earth. What prevents the moon from falling to the earth? The force of gravity attracting two masses decreases as the square of the distance between their centers increases. Thus, the gravitational attraction between the earth and the moon is only strong enough to keep the moon in orbit. Quadratic equations can be used to model problems involving this inverse square law.

A quadratic equation in one variable is an equation of the form $ax^2 + bx + c = 0$, where $a \neq 0$ and a, b, and c are real numbers. The *solutions* of a quadratic equation are those values which, when substituted for the variable, make the equation true. If the equation is factorable over the integers, one method for finding the solutions is to *factor* and use the *zero-product property.*

> **Recall**
>
> **Zero-Product Property**
> For all real numbers a and b, $ab = 0$ if and only if $a = 0$ or $b = 0$.

Example 1   *Fund Raising*   The All City High School is running a fund-raiser to buy a new printer for the computer lab. It is selling hats with the school logo. The hats are donated by a local company. A survey of the students is taken and it is determined that 50 students will pay $5 for the hat. For each decrease of 25 cents, 10 more students will purchase a hat. The school must raise $390, but it would also like to allow as many students as possible to purchase hats. Determine the price at which the school should sell the hats.

80   Chapter 2 Graphing Functions

Let x represent the number of 25 cent decreases. Then the price and the number sold can be represented by $5 - 0.25x$ and $50 + 10x$, respectively.

$(5 - 0.25x)(50 + 10x) = R(x)$	*Price times number sold equals revenue.*
$(5 - 0.25x)(50 + 10x) = 390$	*Total revenue is $390.*
$-2.5x^2 + 37.5x + 250 = 390$	
$-2.5x^2 + 37.5x - 140 = 0$	*Express in standard form.*
$x^2 - 15x + 56 = 0$	*Divide by -2.5.*
$(x - 7)(x - 8) = 0$	*Factor.*
$x - 7 = 0$ or $x - 8 = 0$	*Zero-product property*
$x = 7$ or $x = 8$	

For $x = 7$, the price is $5 - 7(0.25) = \$3.25$, and the number of students who will purchase the hats is $[50 + 10(7)] = 120$.

For $x = 8$, the price is $5 - 8(0.25) = \$3.00$, and the number of students who will purchase the hats is $50 + 10(8) = 130$.

Therefore, the school should sell the hats for $3.00.

Quadratic equations can also be solved by *completing the square*. One side of an equation can be made into a perfect square trinomial,

$$x^2 + 2hx + h^2 = (x + h)^2$$

by using the relationship that the constant term h^2 is the square of one-half the coefficient of x.

Example 2 *Physics* A ball is thrown upward and outward from the roof of a building. The height of the ball is modeled by the equation $s = -16t^2 + 64t + 128$, where s is the height of the ball in feet and t is the elapsed time in seconds. There is an awning on the building 20 ft from the ground. Find the time at which the ball will hit the awning to the nearest second.

20 ft

To find the time at which the ball will hit the awning, substitute the height of the awning for s in the equation and solve for t by completing the square.

$s = -16t^2 + 64t + 128$	
$20 = -16t^2 + 64t + 128$	*The awning is 20 ft from the ground.*
$16t^2 - 64t = 108$	*Place the constant term on one side.*
$t^2 - 4t = 6.75$	*The coefficient of t^2 must be 1.*
$t^2 - 4t + 4 = 6.75 + 4$	*Add $\left[\frac{1}{2}(4)\right]^2$, or 4, to both sides.*
$(t - 2)^2 = 10.75$	*Factor the trinomial.*
$t - 2 = \pm\sqrt{10.75}$	*If $a^2 = k$, $a = \pm\sqrt{k}$.*
$t = 5$ or $t = -1$	To the nearest second

The ball will hit the awning in approximately 5 s. *Why is the answer -1 s rejected?*

2.4 Solving Quadratic Equations **81**

Thinking Critically
It does not make sense to have negative time.

Alternative Learning Styles

Ⓜ Some students may benefit from the use of manipulatives to model the factors used to obtain a quadratic equation. For Example 3, have students construct an open-top box from a sheet of paper by cutting out a square from each corner, folding up the sides and taping them. Have students measure and compare the dimensions of the flat sheet and the bottom of the box.

GUIDED PRACTICE
For Example 1
A company makes novelty items for holidays. In the month of February the projected revenue on Valentine's Day items is modeled by the function $R(x) = 21x^2 + 75x + 235$, where x is the number of items produced in hundreds. The cost of producing x items is modeled by the function $C(x) = 4x^2 + 7x + 1200$. Assume every item produced is sold. Due to production problems, at the end of February the company determines it has a loss of $200. Find the number of items it sold during the month. 500 items

Common Error Some students may use 200 instead of -200 in the equation. Point out that if there is a loss, the cost is more than the revenue and therefore revenue minus cost is a negative number.

For Example 2
A small rocket is fired into the air from an initial height of 50 ft above ground level. The height, s in feet, of the rocket at any time, t in seconds, in modeled by the equation $s = -16t^2 + 320t + 50$. Find the time at which the rocket will be 25 ft from the ground to the nearest second. 20 s

Two packaging machines working together can shrink-wrap 300 boxes in $2\frac{1}{4}$ h. If the older machine takes 3 h longer than the newer machine to do the same job, determine, to the nearest tenth, how long it would take the older machine working alone to wrap 600 boxes. 13 h

Common Error Some students may try to use the 300 and 600 boxes in the initial equation. Point out that shrink-wrapping 300 boxes represents 1 complete job and shrink-wrapping 600 boxes represents 2 complete jobs.

Technology Interested students may wish to program the quadratic formula on either a programmable calculator or a computer so that by inputting the values of *a*, *b*, and *c* in a quadratic equation, they may obtain solutions for *x*.

Recall that any quadratic equation, $ax^2 + bx + c = 0$, can be solved by using the *quadratic formula*

$$x = \frac{-b \pm \sqrt{b^2 - 4ac}}{2a}$$

This formula can be derived by completing the square for the equation $ax^2 + bx + c = 0$.

Example 3 A rectangular rug is in the middle of a room. There is a uniform width of floor that shows around the rug. The dimensions of the rug are 16 ft by 21 ft. The area of the room is 780 ft². Determine the dimensions of the room to the nearest tenth of a foot.

Let *x* represent the uniform width of the floor. Then $21 + 2x$ represents the length of the room and $16 + 2x$ represents the width.

$$(21 + 2x)(16 + 2x) = 780 \qquad A = \ell w$$
$$336 + 74x + 4x^2 = 780$$
$$2x^2 + 37x - 222 = 0 \qquad a = 2, \ b = 37, \ c = -222$$
$$x = \frac{-37 \pm \sqrt{37^2 - 4(2)(-222)}}{2(2)} \qquad \textit{Quadratic formula}$$
$$x = 4.8 \quad \text{or} \quad x = -23.3 \qquad \text{To the nearest tenth}$$

The length of the room is $21 + 2(4.8) = 30.6$ ft, and the width is $16 + 2(4.8) = 25.6$ ft.

A quadratic equation can have zero, one, or two real solutions. In the quadratic formula, $x = \frac{-b \pm \sqrt{b^2 - 4ac}}{2a}$, the value of the radicand $b^2 - 4ac$ determines the number of real solutions of the quadratic equation $ax^2 + bx + c = 0$. The radicand $b^2 - 4ac$ is called the *discriminant* of the equation.

If $b^2 - 4ac > 0$, the equation has two real solutions.
If $b^2 - 4ac = 0$, the equation has one real solution.
If $b^2 - 4ac < 0$, the equation has zero real solutions.

When the value of the discriminant is negative, the solutions of the quadratic equation are *imaginary numbers* because the square root of a negative number is an imaginary number.

> **Recall**
>
> The imaginary unit *i* is equal to $\sqrt{-1}$. A **complex number** is a number that can be written in the form $a + bi$, where *a* and *b* are real numbers. A number of the form $a + bi$, where $b \neq 0$, is called an imaginary number. A number of the form bi, where $b \neq 0$, is called a *pure imaginary number*. The complex numbers $a + bi$ and $a - bi$ are called *complex conjugates*.

Example 4 Determine the nature of the solutions of the quadratic equation $3x^2 + 7x + 5 = 0$. Then solve it.

$b^2 - 4ac = (7)^2 - 4(3)(5) = -11$ *Find the discriminant: $a = 3$, $b = 7$, $c = 5$*

Since $b^2 - 4ac < 0$, there are no real solutions. The solutions will be imaginary numbers.

$x = \dfrac{-(7) \pm \sqrt{(7)^2 - 4(3)(5)}}{2(3)} = \dfrac{-7 \pm \sqrt{-11}}{6}$ *Use the quadratic formula.*

$x = -\dfrac{7}{6} + \dfrac{i\sqrt{11}}{6}$ or $x = -\dfrac{7}{6} - \dfrac{i\sqrt{11}}{6}$ *The solutions are complex conjugates.*

The *complex conjugates* theorem which is discussed in Lesson 7.5 states that if a complex number $a + bi$ is a solution of a polynomial equation with real coefficients, then its conjugate $a - bi$ is also a solution of the equation. *What is the product of $(a + bi)(a - bi)$?*

Example 5 One solution of a quadratic equation with real coefficients is $2 + 3i$. Express the quadratic equation in standard form.

If $2 + 3i$ is a solution, then $2 - 3i$ must also be a solution. If $x = s$ is a solution of a quadratic equation, then $x - s$ must be a factor.

$[x - (2 + 3i)][x - (2 - 3i)] = 0$ $(x - s_1)(x - s_2) = 0$
$x^2 - (2 - 3i)x - (2 + 3i)x + (2 + 3i)(2 - 3i) = 0$
$x^2 - 2x + 3ix - 2x - 3ix + (4 + 9) = 0$ $(a + bi)(a - bi) = a^2 + b^2$
$x^2 - 4x + 13 = 0$

Class Exercises

1. **Thinking Critically** How would you determine whether to solve a quadratic equation by factoring, by completing the square, or by using the quadratic formula?

Solve each quadratic equation by an appropriate method.

2. $x^2 - 10x + 70 = 0$ $5 \pm 3i\sqrt{5}$

3. $x^2 - 6x - 27 = 0$ $9; -3$

4. $3x^2 - 5x + 7 = 0$ $\dfrac{5}{6} \pm \dfrac{i\sqrt{59}}{6}$

5. $6x^2 - 5x - 4 = 0$ $\dfrac{4}{3}, -\dfrac{1}{2}$

Determine a quadratic equation in standard form with real coefficients that has the given solution.

6. $2i$ $x^2 + 4 = 0$

7. $1 - 3i$ $x^2 - 2x + 10 = 0$

8. $-2 + i$ $x^2 + 4x + 5 = 0$

9. *Space Science* A rocket is shot vertically upward. Its distance from the ground at time t, in seconds, is determined by the equation $s = -16t^2 + 128t$. Determine its height after 4 s. At what time will it hit the ground? 256 ft; 8 s

10. *Construction* A border is to be placed around a rectangular garden whose perimeter is 50 ft. The front border costs $5 per foot, and the side and back borders cost $3 per foot. If the total cost of the border is $191, find the dimensions of the garden. $w = 4.5$ ft; $\ell = 20.5$ ft

2.4 Solving Quadratic Equations   **83**

Thinking Critically
$a^2 + b^2$

For Example 4
Determine the nature of the solutions of each quadratic equation.
1. $9x^2 - 12x + 4 = 0$
   $b^2 - 4ac = 0$
   There is one distinct solution.
2. $10x^2 + x = 21$
   $b^2 - 4ac = 841 > 0$
   There are two real distinct solutions.

For Example 5
Find a quadratic equation in standard form with real coefficients that has the given solution.
1. $-5i$ $x^2 + 25 = 0$
2. $4 + 2i$ $x^2 - 8x + 20 = 0$

Common Error Some students may inadvertently drop signs of values when multiplying.

CLOSURE

Pair students to discuss the three methods for solving quadratic equations and to compare the advantages and disadvantages of each method.

INDEPENDENT PRACTICE

Assignment Guide
Basic: 1–24, 26–27, 33
Average: 1–21 odd, 22–40
Enriched: 1–31 odd, 32–47

Teacher's Resource Book
   Practice, page 11

Ⓡ **Review**
Exercises 7, 15, 25, 27, 33, and 35 review concepts such as graphing functions, finding inverse functions, finding quotients of complex numbers, modeling work problems, and naming field properties of numbers.

Additional Answers
Class Exercises
1. If the discriminant equals zero or the equation is a recognizable perfect square, then factor. Otherwise, complete the square or use the quadratic formula.

LESSON FOLLOW-UP

Test Yourself

Teacher's Resource Book
  Tests—Quiz, form A, page 5
  Tests—Quiz, form B, page 5

Lesson Quiz

1. Solve $6x^2 - 5x - 6$ by factoring.
   $x = -\frac{2}{3}$ or $x = \frac{3}{2}$

2. A rectangular open-top box is to be made by cutting 3 in. squares from each corner of a sheet of metal and folding up the edges. The length of the finished box must be 4 in. longer than twice the width. If the volume of the box must be 150 in.³, determine the dimensions of the flat sheet of metal needed to construct the box. 10.1 in. by 18.2 in.

3. An object is thrown into the air from a height of 6 ft above ground level. The height of the object, *s* in feet, at any time, *t* in seconds, can be modeled by the equation $s = -16t^2 + 18t + 6$. Find the time at which the object will hit the ground to the nearest tenth of a second. 1.4 s

4. Determine the nature of the solutions of the quadratic equation $6x^2 = 2x - 3$.
   $b^2 - 4ac = -68 < 0$; There are no real solutions.

5. One solution of a quadratic equation with real coefficients is $1 - i$. Express the quadratic equation in standard form. $x^2 - 2x + 2 = 0$

Additional Answers

7.

Practice Exercises   Use appropriate technology.

Solve each quadratic equation by factoring.

A **1.** $x^2 + 12x + 32 = 0$ $-8, -4$ **2.** $x^2 - 16x + 55 = 0$ $5, 11$ **3.** $2t^2 + t - 1 = 0$ $\frac{1}{2}, -1$

Solve each quadratic equation by completing the square. Round answers to the nearest tenth.

4. $x^2 + 4x = 16$ $2.5, -6.5$ **5.** $2x^2 - 2x = 3$ $1.8, -0.8$ **6.** $3y^2 - 6y = 15$ $3.4, -1.4$

Ⓡ **7.** Graph $f(x) = 2x^2 - 4x + 5$.

8. Writing in Mathematics Describe the method of completing the square for a quadratic equation of the form $ax^2 + bx + c = 0$.

Determine the number of real solutions of each quadratic equation. Find all solutions using the quadratic formula. Round answers to the nearest tenth.

9. $3x^2 - 4x - 2 = 0$ 2 **10.** $5x^2 - x + 3 = 0$ 0 **11.** $2x^2 - 4x + 2 = 0$ 1
12. $3y^2 - 2y = 0$ 2 **13.** $-5m^2 = 2m - 7$ 2 **14.** $-2z = 3z^2 + 6$ 0

Ⓡ**15.** Graph $f(x) = -|x| - 3$.

16. Thinking Critically Given that the discriminant of a quadratic equation of the form $ax^2 + bx + c = 0$ is negative, analyze the structure of the quadratic formula and determine the values of *b* that will result in the solutions being pure imaginary numbers. $b = 0$

Find a quadratic equation in standard form with real coefficients that has the given solution.

17. $3i$ $x^2 + 9 = 0$ **18.** $4 - i$ $x^2 - 8x + 17 = 0$ **19.** $-1 + 2i$ $x^2 + 2x + 5 = 0$

20. *Marketing* A company determines that it can sell 100 calculators per month if the selling price is \$25. For each \$2 decrease in the price, the number of calculators sold per month increases by 20. Find the revenue function and determine the price the company should sell the calculators for if they want a revenue of \$3000 for the month. $R(x) = 2500 + 300x - 40x^2$; \$5 or \$2.50

21. *Space Science* A rocket is shot vertically into the air. Its height at any time *t*, in seconds, can be determined by the equation $s = -16t^2 + 184t$. When will it reach its maximum height of 529 ft? Round to the nearest second. 6 s

Solve each quadratic equation by factoring.

B**22.** $2x^2 + x - 28 = 0$ $-4, \frac{7}{2}$ **23.** $12x^2 = 11x + 56$ $-\frac{7}{4}, \frac{8}{3}$ **24.** $28x^2 + 13x = 6$ $-\frac{3}{4}, \frac{2}{7}$

Ⓡ**25.** Find the inverse function of $f(x) = 9x^3 - 1$. $f^{-1}(x) = \sqrt[3]{\frac{x + 1}{9}}$

26. Writing in Mathematics Explain why the value of the discriminant, $b^2 - 4ac$, determines the number of real solutions of a quadratic equation.

Ⓡ**27.** Determine the quotient of $3 + 4i$ and $2 - i$. $\frac{2 + 11i}{5}$

Solve each quadratic equation by completing the square. Round all answers to the nearest tenth. *Hint:* Let $u = \frac{1}{x}$.

28. $-\frac{1}{2} - \frac{4}{x} + \frac{2}{x^2} = 0$ $0.5, -8.5$ **29.** $\frac{1}{4} - \frac{8}{x} = \frac{4}{x^2}$ $32.5, -0.5$

84   Chapter 2 Graphing Functions

Writing in Mathematics

8. Isolate the constant term. Divide each term by the coefficient of x^2. Then take $\frac{1}{2}$ the value of the coefficient of *x*, square it, and add this number to both sides of the equation. Take the square root of both sides and solve for *x*.

26. The discriminant is the value of the radicand in the quadratic formula. If the radicand is negative, the radical is an imaginary number. If the radicand is positive, the radical is real.

Find a quadratic equation in standard form with real coefficients that has the given solution.

30. $\dfrac{3 + i\sqrt{2}}{4}$ $16x^2 - 24x + 11 = 0$ **31.** $\dfrac{4 - i\sqrt{5}}{2}$ $4x^2 - 16x + 21 = 0$ **32.** $\dfrac{-2 - i\sqrt{3}}{3}$ $9x^2 + 12x + 7 = 0$

Ⓡ **33.** *Labor* Ron and Mary Beth are hired to stock shelves in a supermarket. It takes them 4 hours working together to complete the job. It would take Ron 6 more hours than Mary Beth to do the job alone. If one of them were absent, how long would the other one need to complete the job alone? Mary Beth: 6 h; Ron: 12 h

34. *Physics* A ball is thrown vertically upward from the roof of a building 120 ft high so that its distance from the roof at any time t, in seconds, is given by the equation $s = -16t^2 + 43t$. Determine after how many seconds the ball will hit the roof. If on the way down the ball were to fall over the side of the building, determine after how many seconds it would hit the ground. *Hint*: The distance below the roof is considered to be negative. 2.7 s, 4.4 s

Ⓡ **35.** Name the field properties that hold for the set of irrational numbers under the operation of addition. add. inv., comm., assoc.

36. *Business* A record store sells CDs at $9.50 each. For a CD on the top of the chart, the store expects to sell 150 CDs per week. For each 50 cent decrease in the price, the store will sell approximately 20 more CDs per week. The store wants to make a profit of $1050. If each CD costs the store $3.00, determine the price at which they should sell the CDs. $8.25 or $8

Solve each equation by writing it in quadratic form.

37. $x - 4\sqrt{x} = 21$ 49

38. $6x^4 + 2 = 7x^2$ ±0.7, ±0.8

Ⓒ *Manufacturing* A sheet of metal is to be cut in the shape of a square with two notches. One notch is 3 in. wide with length 0.8 times the length of the square. The other notch is 1 in. wide with length 0.2 times the length of the side of the square.

39. Write a quadratic equation to represent the area of the metal sheet with the notches removed in terms of the length of the side of the square. $A = s^2 - 2.6s$

40. Determine the dimensions of the notches if the area of the metal sheet with the notches removed is 4.7 ft². 3 in. × 21.9 in. and 1 in. × 5.5 in.

41. Solve the equation $ax^2 + bx + c = 0$ to derive the quadratic formula.

42. Derive a formula for the sum of the solutions of the quadratic equation $ax^2 + bx + c = 0$ in terms of the coefficients a and b.

43. Derive a formula for the product of the solutions of the quadratic equation $ax^2 + bx + c = 0$ in terms of the coefficients.

44. One solution of a quadratic equation with real coefficients is $m - i\sqrt{n}$. Find the equation. $x^2 - 2mx + m^2 + n = 0$

45. **Thinking Critically** The path of a projectile is parabolic unless it is acted upon by some outside force. Explain what is meant by this and give some examples of such forces. Discuss how this affects the process of modeling projectile motion. ex: wind, gravity

1.

2.

5.

6.

7.

8.

9.

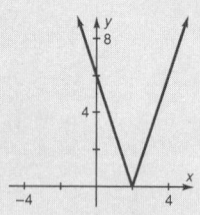

46. *Construction* A slab of concrete is poured in 60°F weather. The total area of the slab upon drying is 16.2 ft². The width of the slab increases 0.25 ft for every 10° rise in temperature. The length of the slab increases by 0.5 ft for every 10° rise in temperature. When the temperature reaches 95°F, the perimeter of the slab is 21.45 ft. Find the original dimensions of the slab of concrete. 3.6 ft × 4.5 ft

47. **Writing in Mathematics** The quadratic equation $s = -16t^2 + 22t + 6$ models the height of a projectile thrown into the air. Write a paragraph explaining the significance of the values of a, b, and c in this equation.

Test Yourself

Determine the symmetries of each equation. Then use the properties of symmetry to graph each equation.

1. $y = x^3 - 2$ none

2. $xy^2 = 1$ x-axis

2.1

Determine whether each function is even, odd, or neither.

3. $f(x) = x^4 + 2x^2 + 3$ even

4. $g(x) = 3x^4 - 2x^3 + x + 5$
   neither

Graph each reflection in the given line.

5. *x*-axis

6. *y*-axis

7. $y = x$

2.2

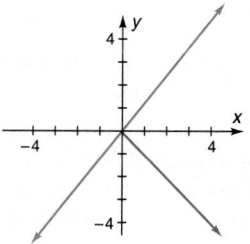

Graph each equation by determining the basic function and then using transformations.

8. $y = \sqrt{x + 3}$

9. $y = 3|x - 2|$

10. Find an equation of a line perpendicular to the line $2x - 3y + 8 = 0$ and passing through the point $(4, -5)$. 3x + 2y = 2

2.3

11. During an energy crisis, the price of unleaded gasoline had increased at a constant rate of 5 cents per gallon per week for 8 weeks. At the end of the eighth week the price had reached $1.65 per gallon. Find an equation in standard form giving the price of gasoline as a linear function of time and draw the graph. 5x − y + 125 = 0

Solve each equation.

12. $3x^2 - 13x = -4$ $\frac{1}{3}$, 4

13. $6x^4 + 4 = 11x^2$ $\pm\frac{2\sqrt{3}}{3}, \pm\frac{\sqrt{2}}{2}$

2.4

14. Determine the nature of the solutions of $2x^2 - 4x + 5 = 0$. Find all solutions. complex conjugates; $1 \pm \frac{i\sqrt{6}}{2}$

86 Chapter 2 Graphing Functions

Writing in Mathematics
47. The equation $s = -16t^2 + 22t + 6$ represents the height of an object at time t. The coefficient of t^2, −16, is $\frac{1}{2}$ the acceleration of gravity as it pulls the object toward the center of the earth. The coefficient of t, 22, is the initial velocity with which the object is thrown. The constant term, 6, is the initial height above ground level from which the object was thrown.

Graphing Quadratic Functions

Objectives: *To graph a quadratic function using the axis of symmetry, vertex, and intercepts*
To approximate the real zeros of a quadratic function from its graph
To determine the minimum or maximum of the graph of a quadratic function

Focus

When constructing a new highway, civil engineers have to contour and level the road, taking into account the *gradient*, or slope, of the land. One important factor to be considered is the distance at which a driver will be able to see upcoming road conditions. To connect two stretches of road where the slopes of the land are different, the engineers must design a transition curve. The curve that will provide the smoothest transition is the parabola.

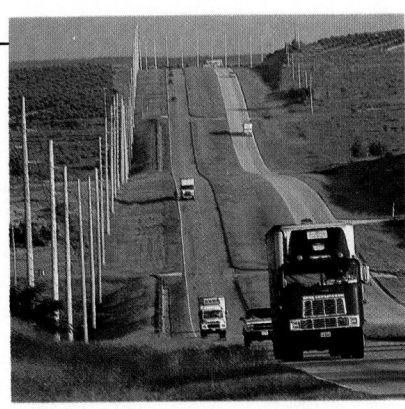

In the previous lesson, you studied quadratic *equations* of the form $ax^2 + bx + c = 0$, $a \neq 0$. A quadratic *function* is a function of the form $f(x) = ax^2 + bx + c$, where a, b, and c are real numbers and $a \neq 0$. The graph of a quadratic function is a *parabola* symmetric about the vertical line $x = \frac{-b}{2a}$.

This line is called the **axis of symmetry.**

To determine the equation of the axis of symmetry, examine the solutions of the corresponding quadratic equation, $ax^2 + bx + c = 0$. Its real solutions are $\frac{-b + \sqrt{b^2 - 4ac}}{2a}$ and $\frac{-b - \sqrt{b^2 - 4ac}}{2a}$, and the graph of the function intersects the x-axis at these points. The axis of symmetry intersects the x-axis at the midpoint of the segment connecting the x-intercepts. The x-coordinate of the midpoint is the average of the two solutions, $\frac{-b}{2a}$. Thus, the equation of the axis of symmetry is $x = \frac{-b}{2a}$. If the solutions are imaginary, the equation of the axis of symmetry is also $x = \frac{-b}{2a}$. *Why?*

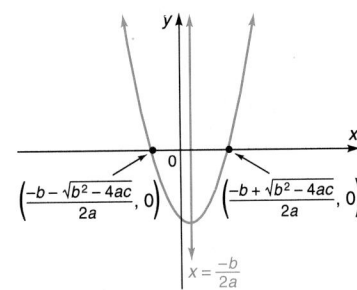

2.5 Graphing Quadratic Functions **87**

Thinking Critically

Whether its solutions are real or complex, a quadratic function is symmetric about the vertical line that passes through its vertex. The equation of that line is $x = -\frac{b}{2a}$.

LESSON PLAN

Vocabulary
axis of symmetry
gradient
maximum value of a parabola
minimum value of a parabola
transition curve
vertex
x-intercept
y-intercept

Ⓜ **Materials/Manipulatives**
MAA video: "Highway Slope Design"
pipe cleaners
transparencies

Technology
graphing utility
relief map

FOCUS

The longest interstate highway runs from Seattle, Washington to Boston, Massachusetts, a distance of 3087.65 mi. The steepest street in the world is Baldwin Street in Dunedin, New Zealand with a gradient of approximately 78%.

INSTRUCTION

• Students are introduced to another method of graphing parabolas: finding and graphing the axis of symmetry, the vertex, the *x*-intercepts, and the *y*-intercept. Encourage students to record on index cards the derivations and formulas for finding each of these features.

Ⓜ • For Example 3, have students draw the basic curve and stretch it. Then have them bend a pipe cleaner to fit the shape of the curve. Rigid transformations of the curve can be demonstrated by translating and reflecting the pipe cleaner curve.

GUIDED PRACTICE

For Example 1

Determine the x- and y-intercepts, axis of symmetry, and vertex of the quadratic function $f(x) = -3x^2 + 4x - 1$, and then graph it. Check, using a graphing utility.

x-intercepts: $\frac{1}{3}$, 1; y-intercept: -1

axis of symmetry: $x = \frac{2}{3}$;

vertex: $\left(\frac{2}{3}, \frac{1}{3}\right)$

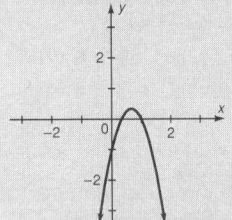

A quadratic function $f(x) = ax^2 + bx + c$ can be graphed by finding the axis of symmetry, the vertex, and the intercepts. The *y-intercept* has coordinates $(0, f(0))$. The *x-intercepts* have coordinates $(s_1, 0)$ and $(s_2, 0)$ where s_1 and s_2 are the real solutions of the quadratic equation $ax^2 + bx + c = 0$. The point where the parabola intersects the axis of symmetry is called the **vertex** and has coordinates $\left(\frac{-b}{2a}, f\left(\frac{-b}{2a}\right)\right)$.

Example 1 Determine the x- and y-intercepts, axis of symmetry, and vertex of the function $f(x) = x^2 + 2x - 8$, and then graph it.

To find the x-intercepts, factor the associated quadratic equation.

$$0 = x^2 + 2x - 8$$
$$0 = (x + 4)(x - 2)$$
$$x = -4 \quad \text{or} \quad x = 2$$

The x-intercepts are $(-4, 0)$ and $(2, 0)$.

The y-intercept has coordinates $(0, f(0))$.

$$f(0) = 0^2 + 2(0) - 8$$
$$f(0) = -8$$

The y-intercept is $(0, -8)$.

The equation of the axis of symmetry is $x = -1$, since

$$x = \frac{-b}{2a} = \frac{-2}{2(1)} = -1.$$

Since $f(-1) = (-1)^2 + 2(-1) - 8 = -9$, the vertex is located at $(-1, -9)$.

Since a quadratic equation can have zero, one, or two real solutions, the graph of a quadratic function can have zero, one, or two x-intercepts. These x-intercepts are called the real **zeros** of the function. The number of zeros of a quadratic function can be determined from its graph.

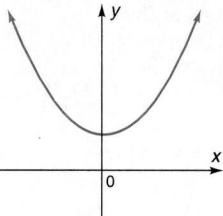

Does not intersect the x-axis; no real zeros

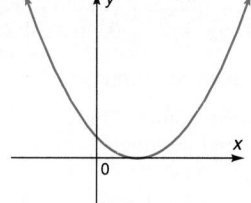

Tangent to the x-axis; one real zero

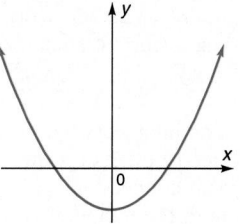

Intersects the x-axis twice; two real zeros

To use a graphing utility to solve a quadratic function, determine the vertex to decide how to set the viewing rectangle. Then use the zoom and trace features to approximate the real zeros to the desired accuracy.

88 Chapter 2 Graphing Functions

Example 2 Use a graphing utility to estimate the real zeros of the quadratic function $f(x) = 3x^2 - 9x + 2$ to the nearest tenth.

Determine the vertex: $\dfrac{-b}{2a} = \dfrac{-(-9)}{2(3)} = 1.5$. Use the zoom and trace features to locate the x-intercepts at approximately 0.2 and 2.8. Thus, the real zeros are approximately 0.2 and 2.8.

[−2, 5] by [−5, 5]

The graph of a quadratic function can be interpreted as a series of transformations of the squaring function $f(x) = x^2$. Express the function in the form $f(x) = a(x - h)^2 + k$. The value of $|a|$ determines the dilation of the parabola. If $a < 0$, the parabola is reflected in the x-axis. The value of k determines the vertical shift, and the value of h determines the horizontal shift.

The function $f(x) = ax^2 + bx + c$, $a \neq 0$, can be written in the form $f(x) = a(x - h)^2 + k$ by completing the square.

$$f(x) = ax^2 + bx + c$$
$$f(x) = a\left(x^2 + \frac{b}{a}x\right) + c \qquad \text{Factor out } a, \text{ the coefficient of } x^2.$$
$$f(x) = a\left(x^2 + \frac{b}{a}x + \frac{b^2}{4a^2}\right) + c - \frac{b^2}{4a} \qquad \text{Add } \left[\frac{1}{2}\left(\frac{b}{a}\right)\right]^2 = \frac{b^2}{4a^2} \text{ to } x^2 + \frac{b}{a}x \text{ to complete}$$
$$f(x) = a\left(x + \frac{b}{2a}\right)^2 + c - \frac{b^2}{4a}. \qquad \text{the square and subtract } a\left(\frac{b^2}{4a^2}\right) = \frac{b^2}{4a}.$$

Example 3 Express the function $f(x) = -2x^2 + 4x + 3$ in the form $f(x) = a(x - h)^2 + k$, and then use transformations of the graph of $f(x) = x^2$ to graph it.

$$f(x) = -2(x^2 - 2x) + 3 \qquad \text{Factor out } -2.$$
$$f(x) = -2(x^2 - 2x + 1) + 3 + 2 \qquad \text{Complete the square.}$$
$$f(x) = -2(x - 1)^2 + 5$$

The graph of $f(x) = x^2$ is reflected in the x-axis, vertically dilated by a factor of 2, and shifted 1 unit to the right and 5 units upward.

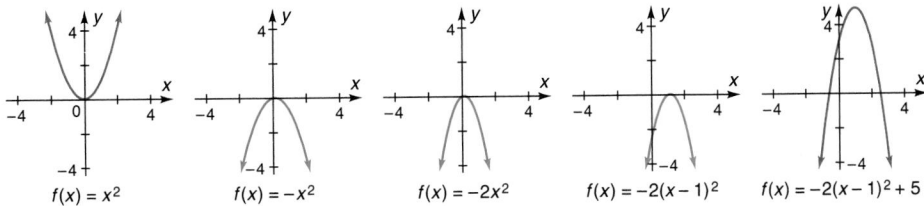

$f(x) = x^2$ $f(x) = -x^2$ $f(x) = -2x^2$ $f(x) = -2(x-1)^2$ $f(x) = -2(x-1)^2 + 5$

The parabola in Example 3 has its vertex at (1, 5). In general, for a quadratic function of the form $f(x) = a(x - h)^2 + k$, the axis of symmetry is $x = h$ and the vertex is at (h, k).

2.5 Graphing Quadratic Functions **89**

For Example 2
Using a graphing utility, graph the function $g(x) = -15x^2 + 3x - 5$ and estimate its real zeros, if any, to the nearest tenth.

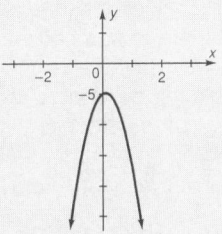

no real zeros

Technology Have students use the zoom and trace features to estimate the real zeros.

For Example 3
Graph the quadratic function $g(x) = \frac{1}{2}x^2 + x - \frac{1}{2}$ using transformations.
$g(x) = \frac{1}{2}(x + 1)^2 - 1$

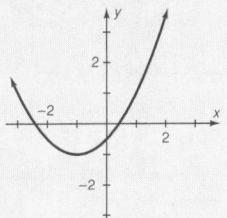

The vertex of a parabola is at the greatest or least value of the function $f(x) = ax^2 + bx + c$. The value is called a **maximum** if $a < 0$, and a **minimum** if $a > 0$. Finding this maximum or minimum value is necessary in many problem-solving situations.

Modeling

An engineer is building a road on mountainous terrain. How can he design a transition curve to connect points P_1 and P_2 so that the highway will provide maximum safety for the driver?

The graph at the right models the transition curve to be designed. The engineers designing the highway must find the curve that will provide the smoothest transition from point P_1 to point P_2. This *transition curve* will be in the shape of a parabola. To determine the coefficients of this curve, engineers use the formula $m = 2ax + b$, which relates the slope of any line tangent to the parabola at a point $P(x, y)$ and the coefficients a and b of the transition curve. This formula can be derived using differential calculus.

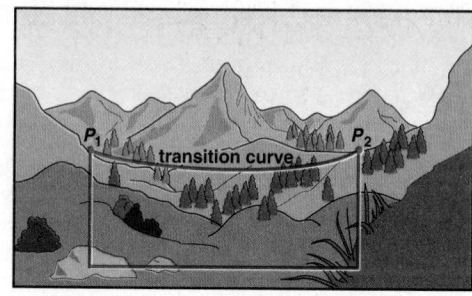

Example 4 *Civil Engineering* Engineers want to install a storm drain at the lowest point on the transition curve sketched above. The gradient or slope of the terrain at point P_1 is −4%, and the gradient at point P_2 is 2.5%. Point P_1 is at an elevation of 950 ft, and the distance between the points is 1200 ft. Determine the equation of this curve and find the coordinates of the storm drain, to the nearest whole number.

Since the transition curve is a parabola, its equation is of the form $y = ax^2 + bx + c$. Use the formula $m = 2ax + b$ to find a and b.

Line through point P_1	Line through point P_2
$-0.04 = 2a(0) + b$	$0.025 = 2a(1200) - 0.04$
$b = -0.04$	$a = 0.000027083$

Since the y-intercept of the curve is 950, $c = 950$. Thus, the equation is $y = 0.000027083x^2 - 0.04x + 950$.

The lowest or minimum point on the curve will be the vertex of the parabola. The coordinates of the vertex are $\left(\dfrac{-b}{2a}, f\left(\dfrac{-b}{2a}\right)\right)$.

$$x = \frac{-(-0.04)}{2(0.00002783)} = 738$$
$$f(738) = 0.000027083(738)^2 - 0.04(738) + 950 = 935$$

The drain is located at the point (738, 935).

Class Exercises

Express each quadratic function in the form $f(x) = a(x - h)^2 + k$. Then use transformations of the graph of $f(x) = x^2$ to graph each function.

1. $f(x) = \frac{1}{3}x^2 - 2$ $f(x) = \frac{1}{3}(x - 0)^2 - 2$

2. $f(x) = -2x^2 - 5$ $f(x) = -2(x - 0)^2 - 5$

3. $f(x) = 2x^2 - 4x + 4$ $f(x) = 2(x - 1)^2 + 2$

4. $f(x) = x^2 + 4x - 9$ $f(x) = (x + 2)^2 - 13$

Use a graphing utility to estimate the real zeros of each quadratic function.

5. $f(x) = \frac{1}{2}x^2 + 4x + 10$ none

6. $f(x) = -3x^2 + 12x - 12$ 2 (mult. 2)

Determine the axis of symmetry, the vertex, and the x- and y-intercepts of each quadratic function. Graph each function.

7. $f(x) = 3x^2 - 6x + 4$

8. $f(x) = -4x^2 + x + 3$

9. $f(x) = -16x^2 + 96x$

10. $f(x) = -16x^2 + 22x + 20$

11. *Urban Planning* A city charges $1.15 to ride the bus. The present ridership is estimated at 20,000 people per day. It is determined that for every 5 cent decrease in the fare the ridership would increase by 1000 people per day. Determine the revenue function, $R(x) = $ (fare) · (number of riders), and graph it. Find the fare that will yield the maximum revenue.

Practice Exercises Use appropriate technology.

Determine the axis of symmetry, the vertex, and the x- and y-intercepts of each quadratic function. Graph each function.

A 1. $f(x) = 4x^2 - 4$

2. $f(x) = -3x^2 + 3$

3. $f(x) = x^2 - 2x - 3$

4. $f(x) = x^2 + 4x - 5$

5. $f(x) = \frac{2}{3}x^2 - \frac{1}{3}x - 1$

6. $f(x) = \frac{4}{5}x^2 + \frac{1}{5}x - 1$

Use a graphing utility to estimate the real zeros of each quadratic function.

7. $f(x) = x^2 + 4x + 4$ -2 (mult. 2)

8. $f(x) = 2x^2 - x - 3$ $-1, 1.5$

9. $f(x) = -3x^2 - 5x + 2$ $-2, 0.3$

10. Writing in Mathematics Explain how to use the axis of symmetry to obtain the right half of a graph if the left side is known.

Ⓡ **11.** Determine the symmetry of $f(x) = -x^3 + 3x$. origin

12. Thinking Critically Analyze the quadratic function $f(x) = ax^2 + c, a \neq 0$, and draw a conclusion about the vertex of its graph. $(0, c)$

Ⓡ **13.** Graph $f(x) = |x| + 2$.

Express each quadratic function in the form $f(x) = a(x - h)^2 + k$. Then use transformations of the graph of $f(x) = x^2$ to graph each function.

14. $f(x) = -x^2 + 4x + 6$

15. $f(x) = -2x^2 + 2x - 1$

16. $f(x) = 3x^2 + 30x - 4$

17. $f(x) = 6x^2 - 36x + 7$

18. $f(x) = x^2 + 4x + 7$

19. $f(x) = -2x^2 + 12x - 18$

20. *Civil Engineering* Engineers are designing a stretch of highway in a valley. They want to install a storm drain at its lowest point. The equation for the transition curve is $y = 0.00004x^2 - 0.05x + 1100$. Determine the coordinates of the storm drain, to the nearest unit. $(625, 1084)$

2.5 Graphing Quadratic Functions **91**

Writing in Mathematics
10. Answers may vary. Example: Reflect the left side of the graph about the axis of symmetry to obtain the right side.

INDEPENDENT PRACTICE

Assignment Guide
Basic: 1–24, 27–35 odd
Average: 1–29 odd, 30–40, Project
Enriched: 1–39 odd, 40–49, Project

Teacher's Resource Book
  Practice, page 12

Ⓡ **Review**
Exercises 11, 13, 21, 25, 27, and 29 review concepts such as finding symmetry of functions, graphing functions, determining whether a function is one-to-one, finding inverse functions and composite functions.

Additional Answers
Class Exercises

7.
x-int: none;
y-int: (0, 4);
axis: $x = 1$;
vertex: (1, 1)

8.
x-int: $\left(-\frac{3}{4}, 0\right)$,
(1, 0);
y-int: (0, 3);
axis: $x = \frac{1}{8}$;
vertex: $\left(\frac{1}{8}, \frac{49}{16}\right)$

9.
x-int: (0, 0), (6, 0); y-int: (0, 0);
axis: $x = 3$;
vertex: (3, 144)

10.
x-int: $\left(-\frac{5}{8}, 0\right)$,
(2, 0);
y-int: (0, 20);
axis: $x = \frac{11}{16}$;
vertex:
$\left(\frac{11}{16}, \frac{441}{16}\right)$

LESSON FOLLOW-UP

Lesson Quiz

1. Graph $f(x) = 2x^2 + 12x + 17$ using transformations.
$f(x) = 2(x + 3)^2 - 1$

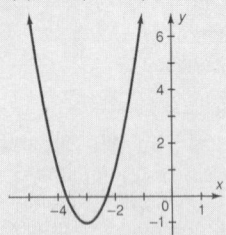

2. Using a graphing utility, estimate the real zeros, if any, of the quadratic function $f(x) = 4x^2 - 13x + 5$ to the nearest tenth.

0.5, 2.8

3. Civil engineers are designing a stretch of highway in a valley and want to put a storm drain at its lowest point. The equation that models the transition curve for this stretch of highway is $y = 0.00002x^2 - 0.01x + 780$. Determine the coordinates of the drain to the nearest unit.
(250, 779)

4. Find the x- and y-intercepts, axis of symmetry, and vertex of the quadratic function $f(x) = 3x^2 - 9x - 12$.
x-int: $(-1, 0)$, $(4, 0)$; y-int: $(0, -12)$;
axis of symmetry: $x = \frac{3}{2}$;
vertex: $\left(\frac{3}{2}, -\frac{75}{4}\right)$

Ⓡ 21. Determine whether the function $f(x) = -\dfrac{3}{x}$ is one-to-one.   yes

22. *Business*   A baker sells 1-lb loaves of whole wheat bread for $1.89 each. He usually sells 30 loaves per day. By taking a survey of his customers, he determines that for each 10 cent per loaf decrease in the price, he will increase the number of loaves he sells each day by 4. Determine the function that represents his revenue and graph it.

Express each quadratic function in the form $f(x) = a(x - h)^2 + k$. Then use transformations of the graph of $f(x) = x^2$ to graph each function.

B 23. $f(x) = \frac{1}{2}x^2 - x + 2$ 24. $f(x) = -\frac{1}{3}x^2 + 2x + 4$

Ⓡ 25. Find the inverse function of $f(x) = x^2 + 4x + 4$. Restrict the domain, if necessary. $f^{-1}(x) = \sqrt{x} - 2$; $D = \{x: x \geq 0\}$

26. **Writing in Mathematics**   Explain why a quadratic function that has no real zeros will never cross the x-axis.

Ⓡ 27. For $f(x) = x^2$ and $g(x) = -2x$, determine $(g \circ f)(x)$. $-2x^2$

28. **Thinking Critically**   Determine the values of k for which $y = a(x - h)^2 + k$ has exactly two zeros when $a < 0$ and when $a > 0$.

Ⓡ 29. Graph: $f(x) = \begin{cases} 2x^2, & x < 0 \\ -x^2 + 3, & x > 0 \end{cases}$

Find the quadratic equation that is represented by the graph of each parabola.

30.
$y = (x + 3)^2 + 1$

31.
$y = 4(x - 3)^2 - 4$

32.
$y = -\frac{1}{2}(x - 1)^2$

33.
$y = -\frac{1}{4}(x + 2)^2$

34.
$y = 2(x + 4)^2 - 2$

35.
$y = 10x^2$

36. *Architecture*   The arch of a rounded window is approximately the shape of a parabola whose equation is $y = -\frac{1}{2}x^2 + 4$. Graph the parabola and estimate the coordinates of the points where the edges of the frame of the arch touch the window sill.

37. *Civil Engineering*   Engineers are designing a stretch of highway on a mountain. They plan to put a lookout station at the highest point, called the summit. The equation of the transition parabola is $y = -0.0000333x^2 + 0.03x + 120$. Determine the coordinates of the summit.   (450, 127)

92   Chapter 2 Graphing Functions

Writing in Mathematics

26. The real zeros of a function are its x-intercepts. The x-intercepts are the points where the curve crosses the x-axis. If a quadratic function does not have real zeros, it will not have any x-intercepts and therefore cannot cross the x-axis.

38. *Physics* A person throws a ball directly upward. The height of the ball, in feet, after t seconds is given by the equation $s(t) = -16t^2 + 32t + 3$. Graph the equation and determine the maximum height reached by the ball.

39. Graph the function $f(x) = 0.5x^2 + 2.5x - 1.5$ by representing it as a series of transformations.

C **40. Writing in Mathematics** Write a real world application exercise in which the solution requires solving a quadratic equation.

41. Thinking Critically Analyze $f(x) = ax^2 + c$, $a \neq 0$. Determine a method for finding the number of zeros, given values for a and c.

Find the quadratic equation that is represented by the graph of each parabola.

42.

43.

44.

45.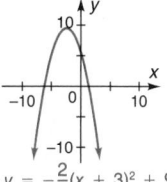

$y = \frac{1}{5}(x - 15)^2 + 10$ $y = -\frac{3}{2}x^2 + 6$ $y = \frac{1}{25}(x + 50)^2 - 300$ $y = -\frac{2}{3}(x + 3)^2 + 9$

46. *Metalwork* The sides of a rectangular sheet of metal 40 cm wide are folded up to form a rain gutter. The sides of the gutter will be of equal length and perpendicular to the base. Find the length of the sides for the rain gutter that will have the maximum cross-sectional area. 10 in.

$40 - 2x$

47. Thinking Critically Let $f(x) = x^2 + bx$. Choose some values for b, including both negative and positive values. Graph these functions on the same coordinate axes. Describe the pattern of the graphs.

48. A parabolic arch whose shape can be modeled by the function $f(x) = -2x^2 + 2x + 71.5$ has a vertical support every 2 ft. Find the coordinates of the points where the vertical supports are placed, to the nearest tenth of a foot.

49. Determine the sum of the heights of the vertical supports described in Exercise 48, to the nearest tenth of a foot. 280 ft

2 ft 2 ft 2 ft 2 ft

Project

Describe some safety features with which engineers should be concerned when designing a road. What were some of the potential hazards that were avoided by the designers of a road in your area?

Challenge

Solve for x: $\dfrac{x}{x - 1} = \dfrac{y^2 - 3y - 3}{y^2 - 3y - 4}$ $y^2 - 3y - 3$

2.5 Graphing Quadratic Functions   **93**

5. The discriminant of the quadratic function $f(x) = ax^2 + bx + c$ is 0. Describe how to determine when $f(x) < 0$, $f(x) = 0$, and $f(x) > 0$. Since the discriminant is 0, $f(x)$ has one distinct real zero which occurs at the maximum or minimum of the parabola.

Therefore $f(x) = 0$ at $x = \dfrac{-b}{2a}$.

If $a > 0$, $f(x) > 0$ for all values of x except $x = \dfrac{-b}{2a}$.

If $a < 0$, $f(x) < 0$ for all values of x except $x = \dfrac{-b}{2a}$.

Alternative Assessment

Ask students to describe how and when a graphing calculator can be used to find the zeros of a quadratic function. Ask them also to explain when it would not be helpful. Have them defend and illustrate their answers.

Enrichment

Using a graphing utility, find the solution set of the system of quadratic equations to the nearest tenth.

$\begin{cases} f(x) = 3x^2 - 4x - 3 \\ g(x) = -2x^2 + 3x + 2 \end{cases}$

$\{(-0.5, -0.1), (1.9, 0.4)\}$

Additional Answers

38.

19 ft

39.

Vocabulary
leading coefficient
multiple zero
polynomial equation
polynomial function

Ⓜ **Materials/Manipulatives**
transparencies

Technology
graphing utility
symbolic manipulator

FOCUS

The symbolism for polynomials has changed considerably over the years. In the early 1600s Fermat described the simplest case of a linear equation in Latin as: *D in A aequetur B in E,* where *in* means "multiplied by" and *aequetur* means "equal to." Today Fermat's equation is written as *Dx = By,* or *y = ax.* Viete, in the late 1500s, wrote the third power of *A* as *A cubus* and the second power of *A* as *A quadratus.* In 1631 Harriot, in a mathematical paper called *Clavis mathematicae,* wrote an expression as *AAAAAAA.* Around this same time another mathematician, Oughtred, wrote this expression as *Aqqc,* shorthand for *A quadratus quadratus cubus,* or *A* squared squared cubed. Today the expression is simply written as A^7.

INSTRUCTION

The following outline for solving polynomial equations by factoring may prove helpful for some students.
1. Factor out the GCF.
2. If the remaining polynomial has three terms, determine if it can be written in quadratic form.
3. If the remaining polynomial has four terms, try factoring by grouping the terms.
4. If the remaining polynomial is the sum or difference of two cubes, recall the applicable factoring formula.

2.6 Solving Polynomial Equations

Objectives: To solve polynomial equations by factoring techniques
To approximate the real zeros of a polynomial function from its graph

Focus

Unlike mammals, many species of fish continue to grow during their entire lifespan. For this reason, the largest recorded weight of certain fish may be significantly larger than the average weight for that species. The largest striped bass, for example, weighed 78 lb 8 oz—more than twice the average weight of the species. It is interesting to note, however, that the rate of growth of a fish is much greater when measured by weight rather than by length. The model that best relates the weight of a fish to its length is a polynomial function of degree 3, $w(\ell) = a\ell^3$.

A **polynomial function** of degree n in one variable is a function of the form

$$f(x) = a_n x^n + a_{n-1} x^{n-1} + \cdots + a_1 x + a_0 \qquad a_n \neq 0$$

where n is a nonnegative integer and $a_n, a_{n-1}, \cdots, a_0$ are real numbers. The **leading coefficient** of the polynomial is a_n. The *zeros* are the values of x for which $f(x) = 0$.

You are already familiar with the following polynomial functions:

The *constant function*, $f(x) = a$, $a \neq 0$, of degree zero
The *linear function*, $f(x) = ax + b$, $a \neq 0$, of degree 1
The *quadratic function*, $f(x) = ax^2 + bx + c$, $a \neq 0$, of degree 2

A polynomial function of degree n, $n \geq 1$, has exactly n zeros in the complex number system.

A **polynomial equation** of degree n in one variable x is an equation of the form $a_n x^n + a_{n-1} x^{n-1} + \cdots + a_1 x + a_0 = 0$, $a_n \neq 0$, where n is a nonnegative integer and $a_n, a_{n-1}, \cdots, a_0$ are real numbers. To find the zeros of a polynomial function, solve the corresponding polynomial equation. The *solutions* of the equation are the *zeros* of the function. Sometimes a zero is repeated, in which case it is called a *multiple zero.* When a zero occurs k times, it is said to have **multiplicity** k. One method that can be used to solve certain polynomial equations is to factor and then use the zero-product property. Remember to factor out the greatest common factor (GCF) first.

94 Chapter 2 Graphing Functions

Example 1 Find the zeros of the polynomial function $f(x) = 2x^5 + 8x^4 - 154x^3$.

$$2x^5 + 8x^4 - 154x^3 = 0 \qquad \text{\textit{Solve the equation} } f(x) = 0.$$
$$2x^3(x^2 + 4x - 77) = 0 \qquad \text{\textit{The GCF is} } 2x^3.$$
$$2x^3(x + 11)(x - 7) = 0 \qquad \text{\textit{Factor.}}$$
$$2x^3 = 0 \quad \text{or} \quad x + 11 = 0 \quad \text{or} \quad x - 7 = 0 \qquad \text{\textit{Zero-product property}}$$
$$x = 0 \quad \text{or} \quad x = -11 \quad \text{or} \quad x = 7 \qquad \text{\textit{Solve for x.}}$$

The solutions, -11, 0 (multiplicity 3), and 7, of the equation $2x^5 + 8x^4 - 154x^3 = 0$ are the zeros of the function $f(x) = 2x^5 + 8x^4 - 154x^3$. Check by substituting the values of x into the original equation.

A polynomial equation can sometimes be solved by arranging the terms in groups so that a factor common to all the groups may be found.

Example 2 Solve the polynomial equation $2x^3 + 6x^2 - 5x - 15 = 0$.

$$2x^3 + 6x^2 - 5x - 15 = 0$$
$$(2x^3 + 6x^2) - (5x + 15) = 0 \qquad \text{\textit{Group terms.}}$$
$$2x^2(x + 3) - 5(x + 3) = 0 \qquad \text{\textit{Factor each group.}}$$
$$(2x^2 - 5)(x + 3) = 0 \qquad \text{\textit{The GCF is} } x + 3.$$
$$x + 3 = 0 \quad \text{or} \quad 2x^2 - 5 = 0$$
$$x = -3 \quad \text{or} \quad x = \frac{\sqrt{10}}{2} \quad \text{or} \quad x = -\frac{\sqrt{10}}{2}$$

Some higher-degree equations can be expressed in *quadratic form* and then solved using factoring, completing the square, or the quadratic equation. Introducing a *dummy variable* may be helpful.

Example 3 Solve the polynomial equation $12t^4 - 5t^2 - 2 = 0$. Round answers to the nearest hundredth.

$$12t^4 - 5t^2 - 2 = 0$$
$$12(t^2)^2 - 5(t^2)^1 - 2 = 0 \qquad \text{\textit{Express in quadratic form.}}$$
$$12u^2 - 5u - 2 = 0 \qquad \text{\textit{Use a dummy variable. Let} } u = t^2.$$
$$(3u - 2)(4u + 1) = 0 \qquad \text{\textit{Factor.}}$$
$$3u - 2 = 0 \quad \text{or} \quad 4u + 1 = 0 \qquad \text{\textit{Zero-product property}}$$
$$u = \frac{2}{3} \quad \text{or} \quad u = -\frac{1}{4} \qquad \text{\textit{Solve for u.}}$$
$$t^2 = \frac{2}{3} \quad \text{or} \quad t^2 = -\frac{1}{4} \qquad u = t^2$$
$$t = \pm 0.82 \quad \text{or} \quad t = \pm 0.5i \qquad \text{To the nearest hundredth}$$

As with a quadratic function, you can estimate the real zeros of a polynomial function using a graphing utility. Use the zoom and trace features to determine the real zeros to the desired accuracy.

Students may find the use of visual aids such as transparencies helpful in expressing high degree equations in quadratic form. For Example 3, u is the dummy variable equal to t^2. Superimpose u^2 over t^4, and u over t^2. Have students solve for u and then for t.

GUIDED PRACTICE

For Example 1
Find the zeros of each polynomial function.
1. $f(x) = -3x^4 + 18x^3 - 27x^2$
   0 (multiplicity 2),
   3 (multiplicity 2)
2. $g(x) = 4x^7 - 49x^5$
   0 (multiplicity 5), $\pm\frac{7}{2}$

For Example 2
Solve each polynomial equation.
1. $4x^4 + 16x^3 - 7x^2 - 28x = 0$
   $0, -4, \pm\frac{\sqrt{7}}{2}$
2. $27x^3 - 9x^2 - 3x + 1 = 0$
   $\frac{1}{3}$ (multiplicity 2), $-\frac{1}{3}$

For Example 3
Solve each polynomial equation. Remember:

$$a^3 + b^3 = (a + b)(a^2 - ab + b^2)$$
$$a^3 - b^3 = (a - b)(a^2 + ab + b^2)$$

1. $f(x) = x^6 + 7x^3 - 8$
   $1, \frac{-1 \pm i\sqrt{3}}{2}, -2, 1 \pm i\sqrt{3}$

Common Error When solving a cubic of the form $x^3 + a = 0$, some students may just solve the equation for x^3 and then take the cube root of both sides. Remind students that a cubic equation has three roots, and in order to find the complex roots, they must factor this type of cubic using one of the formulas given above.

2. $g(x) = 3x^4 - 147$
   $\pm\sqrt{7}, \pm i\sqrt{7}$

Use a graphing utility to approximate the real zeros of each function to the nearest tenth.

1. $P(x) = 4x^4 + 3x^3 - 2x - 1$

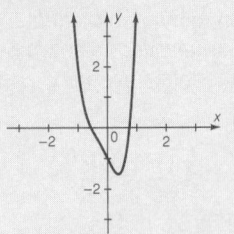

−0.6, 0.7

2. $P(x) = x^6 + x^4 + x^2 + 3$

No real zeros

Technology To use a trace to locate a zero, watch the value of *y*. When *y* changes from positive to negative or vice versa, the graph crosses the *x*-axis. A zero will occur between the two corresponding values of *x*.

Modeling
Discuss the usefulness of this model to predict the weight of a bass fish. Students may wish to research other situations where a polynomial function is used to make a prediction.

Example 4 Use a graphing utility to estimate the real zeros of the function $f(x) = 2x^3 + 6x^2 - x - 4$ to the nearest hundredth.

Graph *f* and use the zoom and trace features to locate the *x*-intercepts at −2.94, −0.86, and 0.79. Thus, the real zeros are −2.94, −0.86, and 0.79.

[−6, 3] by [−8, 8]
x scl: 1   y scl: 2

Modeling

How can a fisherman estimate the weight of a fish if he knows the length of the fish?

A bass fisherman fishing in a New York State lake wishes to model the weight of a fish using only one piece of information. He finds that the length of the fish is the best single estimator. This information can be modeled using the polynomial function

$$w(\ell) = a\ell^3 \qquad \text{where } a \text{ is a constant}$$

This model is developed for one type of fish (bass) taken from a single lake. It uses only one measurement. A more reliable model might use the length of the fish *and* the circumference of the fish to estimate the weight. *What other factors might make the model more reliable?*

Example 5 *Sports* The average measurements for bass caught in a certain lake are given in the table below.
  a. Use three points to find an equation of the form $w(\ell) = a\ell^3$ to model the data. Round *a* to four decimal places.
  b. Use the data to predict the length of a 40-oz bass.

Length of fish (in.)	10.5	12	13.5	14.5	16
Weight of fish (oz)	14	21	30	36	49

a. Use $21 = a(12)^3$ to obtain $a \approx 0.0122$.
Use $36 = a(14.5)^3$ to obtain $a \approx 0.0118$.
Use $49 = a(16)^3$ to obtain $a \approx 0.0120$.

Since the average of these three estimates for *a* is 0.0120, a reasonable model for the weight of a bass in terms of its length is $w(\ell) = 0.0120\ell^3$.

b. $40 = 0.0120\ell^3$
  $14.9 = \ell$

The length of a 40-oz bass should be approximately 14.9 in.

Will you obtain the exact value for a if you select three alternate length and weight values? Does the model obtained above provide a good fit for the data?

96 Chapter 2 Graphing Functions

Thinking Critically
No. The model provides a relatively accurate fit for the data.

$$a^3 + b^3 = (a + b)(a^2 - ab + b^2)$$
$$a^3 - b^3 = (a - b)(a^2 + ab + b^2)$$

Example 6 *Storage* The Leuzzis bought a modular storage unit in the shape of a cube with 3-ft sides. They wish to buy a second cube to increase their total storage space to 35 ft³. Determine a polynomial equation to represent the problem. Find all the solutions of this equation and interpret the results.

Let x represent the length of the new unit. The volume of the new cube is x^3 and the volume of the unit they have is 3^3, or 27 ft³.

$$x^3 + 27 = 35 \qquad \textit{The sum of the volumes is 35 ft}^3.$$
$$x^3 - 8 = 0$$
$$(x - 2)(x^2 + 2x + 4) = 0 \qquad a^3 - b^3 = (a - b)(a^2 + ab + b^2)$$
$$x - 2 = 0 \quad \text{or} \quad x^2 + 2x + 4 = 0$$
$$x = 2 \quad \text{or} \qquad x = \frac{-2 \pm \sqrt{2^2 - 4(1)(4)}}{2(1)} = -1 \pm i\sqrt{3}$$

Since 2 is the only real solution, the new cube should have sides of length 2 ft.

Class Exercises

Solve each polynomial equation. If a solution occurs more than once, state its multiplicity.

1. $x^4 + 6x^3 + 9x^2 = 0$ 0 (mult. 2), -3 (mult. 2) **2.** $x^3 + x^2 - 9x - 9 = 0$ -1, ± 3

3. $x^4 - 5x^2 - 36 = 0$ ± 3, $\pm 2i$ **4.** $t^6 + 7t^3 - 8 = 0$ $-2, 1, \dfrac{-1 \pm i\sqrt{3}}{2}, 1 \pm i\sqrt{3}$

Use a graphing utility to estimate the real zeros of each polynomial function to the nearest tenth.

5. $f(x) = x^3 + 2x^2 - 16x - 32$ ± 4, -2 **6.** $f(x) = 28x^6 + 13x^5 - 6x^4$ 0 (mult. 4), -0.8, 0.3

7. $f(x) = x^3 - 27$ $\dfrac{-3 \pm 3i\sqrt{3}}{2}$, 3 **8.** $f(a) = 3a^6 - 24a^3$ 0 (mult. 3), 2, $-1 \pm i\sqrt{3}$

9. Thinking Critically Determine a formula for factoring the sum of two squares. $a^2 + b^2 = (a + bi)(a - bi)$

Practice Exercises

⊓⊔ Use appropriate technology.

Solve each polynomial equation. If a solution occurs more than once, state its multiplicity.

A **1.** $2x^3 - 13x^2 - 15x = 0$ 0, $\dfrac{15}{2}$, -1 **2.** $-2x^5 + 24x^4 - 70x^3 = 0$ 0 (mult. 3), 5, 7

3. $3x^4 - 3x^3 - 36x^2 = 0$ 0 (mult. 2), -3, 4 **4.** $10x^3 - 23x^2 + 12x = 0$ 0, $\dfrac{4}{5}$, $\dfrac{3}{2}$

5. $8x^3 + 4x^2 - 2x - 1 = 0$ $-\dfrac{1}{2}$ (mult. 2), $\dfrac{1}{2}$ **6.** $9x^3 - 108x^2 + x - 12 = 0$ 12, $\pm\dfrac{1}{3}i$

Use a graphing utility to estimate the real zeros of each polynomial function to the nearest tenth.

7. $f(x) = 4x^3 - 108$ 3 **8.** $f(x) = x^3 - 64$ 4

9. $f(x) = x^4 - 6x^2 - 16$ ± 2.8 **10.** $f(x) = x^6 - 19x^3 + 84$ 1.9, 2.3

2.6 Solving Polynomial Equations **97**

For Example 5
The power needed to propel a speedboat varies directly as the cube of the speed of the boat where the constant of proportionality is 0.014. The maximum speed of one boat is twice the maximum speed of another. If the difference in horse-power between the boats is 29, find a function to determine the speed of each boat. Give the speed of each boat to the nearest tenth of a knot.
Let s = speed of slower boat
Let $2s$ = speed of faster boat
$P(s) = 0.014[(2s)^3 - s^3]$
$29 = 0.014[(2s)^3 - s^3]$
$29 = 0.014(7s^3)$
$29 = 0.098s^3$
$s^3 = 295.92$
s = 6.7 knots; $2s$ = 13.4 knots

For Example 6
A rectangular fish tank with a square bottom whose height is half the length of its side contains 4000 in.³ of water. What are the dimensions of the tank? 20 in. by 20 in. by 10 in.

CLOSURE

Have students write a few sentences in their math journals describing when factoring by grouping would be an appropriate method of solving a polynomial function and when writing an equation in quadratic form would be an appropriate method.

INDEPENDENT PRACTICE

Assignment Guide
Basic: 1–21, 23, 25, 35
Average: 1–25 odd, 27–37, Project
Enriched: 1–37 odd, 38–46, Project

Teacher's Resource Book
    Practice, page 13

Exercises 11, 13, 15, 21, and 33 review concepts such as graphing using transformations, finding symmetries of functions, determining equations of lines, determining whether a relation is a function, and rewriting functions.

Project

Students can gather data for the project by looking in record books or almanacs, or by contacting local officials in charge of fishing regulations.

LESSON FOLLOW-UP

Lesson Quiz

Find the zeros for each polynomial function by factoring.

1. $f(x) = 5x^4 - 20x^2$
0 (multiplicity 2), ± 2

2. $h(x) = 4x^3 + 28x^2 + 2x + 14$
$-7, \pm\frac{i\sqrt{2}}{2}$

3. $g(x) = 10x^4 - 13x^2 - 3$
$\pm\frac{\sqrt{6}}{2}, \pm\frac{i\sqrt{5}}{5}$

4. Using a graphing utility, approximate the zeros of the polynomial function $f(x) = x^5 - 2x^2 + x - 1$.

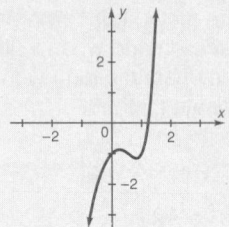

One zero: $x \approx 1.2$

5. A rectangular shipping container with a capacity of 216 ft³ is to be sectioned off so that one part will be a cube. If the capacity of the remaining section must be no less than 152 ft³, determine the size of the largest cube that can be sectioned off. 4 ft³

R **11.** Graph $y = x^2 + 4x - 2$ using transformations.

12. **Thinking Critically**   Use a graphing utility to graph the set of functions $g(x) = ax^3 + b, a \neq 0$. Draw conclusions about the shapes of the graphs when $a < 0$ and when $a > 0$. What is the effect of b? Express your answers in terms of translations of the basic function $f(x) = x^3$.

R **13.** Determine the symmetries of $f(x) = 2x^4 - 2x^2 + 4$. y-axis

14. **Thinking Critically**   Analyze the cubic equation $ax^3 + b = 0, a \neq 0$. Determine the number of real solutions if a and b are real numbers.

R **15.** Determine the equation in standard form of the line with slope $\frac{2}{3}$ that passes through (0, 6). $2x - 3y = -18$

16. **Writing in Mathematics**   Explain why all polynomial equations cannot be solved using only the techniques presented in this lesson.

17. **Thinking Critically**   Solve the polynomial equation in Example 2 by rearranging the terms and factoring by grouping. How does this affect the solution? $-3, \pm\frac{\sqrt{10}}{2}$; no change

18. Use grouping to solve the equation $x^4 + 8x^3 - 8x - 64 = 0$. $2, -8, -1 \pm i\sqrt{3}$

19. *Manufacturing*   A swimming pool manufacturer makes rectangular pools so that the sides are in the ratio $1:2:3$. If the pool holds 2058 ft³ of water when filled to the top, find the dimensions of the pool. 7 ft × 14 ft × 21 ft

20. **Thinking Critically**   How would you determine the cubic polynomial that has the solutions $-3, -2$, and 7? multiply $(x + 3)(x + 2)(x - 7)$

R **21.** Determine whether the relation $\{(2, 3), (2, -3), (4, 2), (5, 7)\}$ is a function. no

Use a graphing utility to estimate the real zeros of each polynomial function to the nearest tenth.

B **22.** $f(x) = 49x^4 + 7x^2 - 72$ ± 1.1 **23.** $f(m) = 30m^4 + 58m^2 - 4$ ± 0.3

24. $f(t) = 10t^6 - 7290t^3$ 0 (mult. 3), 9   **25.** $f(a) = 5a^7 - 2560a^4$ 0 (mult. 4), 8

26. $f(x) = 5x^3 - 10x^2 + 2x - 4$ 2   **27.** $f(x) = 3x^3 - 6x^2 - 8x + 16$ 2, ± 1.6

28. $f(x) = 0.02x^7 - 0.13x^5 - 0.15x^3$ **29.** $f(x) = 5x^5 + 70x^3 + 225x$ 0
0 (mult. 3), ± 2.7

Find all the zeros of each polynomial function.

30. $f(x) = x^4 - 3x^3 - 8x + 24$ 3, 2, $-1 \pm i\sqrt{3}$ **31.** $f(x) = 8x^4 - 40x^3 + x - 5$ 5, $-\frac{1}{2}, \frac{1 \pm i\sqrt{3}}{4}$

32. **Writing in Mathematics**   Describe in sentence form characteristics of a polynomial of degree n, $n > 2$, that can be expressed in quadratic form.

R **33.** Express $f(x) = 5x^2 + 10x - 79$ in the form $f(x) = a(x - h)^2 + k$.

34. Solve $x^5 + 4x^4 - 10x^3 - 27x^2 - 108x + 270 = 0$ to the nearest tenth. *Hint*: Factor into two groups of three terms each.

35. **Thinking Critically**   Suppose $6x^3 + 30x^2 - x - 5 = 0$ is expressed in the form $6x^3 + 30x^2 = x + 5$. Can the equation then be solved by dividing both sides by $x + 5$? Explain.

36. *Construction*   An executive has 1620 ft³ of storage space. She wants to increase her space 45% by adding a room in the shape of a cube. Find the dimensions of the room. 9 ft × 9 ft × 9 ft

98   Chapter 2 Graphing Functions

Writing in Mathematics

16. To solve a polynomial equation means to find all its roots, real and complex. If the polynomial function is not factorable, the only other possibility presented in this lesson is to graph it. However, only the real zeros can be approximated from the graph.

32. After factoring out the GCF, the polynomial should have three terms so that the exponents of variable, written in decreasing order, are of the form u, $\frac{1}{2}u$, and 0.

37. Writing in Mathematics   Write a word problem in which the solution requires solving a cubic equation of the form $ax^3 = b$.

Solve each polynomial equation for x in terms of a.

C 38. $11x^4 - 122a^2x^2 = -11a^4$ $\pm\dfrac{a\sqrt{11}}{11}, \pm a\sqrt{11}$ **39.** $12x^6 + 5a^3x^3 - 3a^6 = 0$ $\dfrac{a\sqrt[3]{9}}{3}, -\dfrac{a\sqrt[3]{6}}{2}$

40. $6x^6 + 39a^6x^3 = -18a^{12}$ $-a^2\sqrt[3]{6}, -\dfrac{a^2\sqrt[3]{4}}{2}$ **41.** $6x^4 = 11x^2a^4 - 4a^8$ $\pm\dfrac{2a^2\sqrt{3}}{3}, \pm\dfrac{a^2\sqrt{2}}{2}$

Solve each polynomial equation. Round answers to the nearest tenth.

42. $7x^6 - 7 = 0$ **43.** $10x^4 - 31x^2 + 15 = 0$ **44.** $6x^4 - 11x^2 + 3 = 0$
$\pm 1, -0.5 \pm 0.9i, 0.5 \pm 0.9i$ $\pm 0.8, \pm 1.6$ $\pm 1.2, \pm 0.6$

45. *Irrigation*   A drainage ditch is 4 m longer than it is wide and 1 m wider than it is deep. Find the dimensions of the ditch if it can hold 12 m³ of water.   1 m × 2 m × 6 m

46. Thinking Critically   Consider the equation $\dfrac{x+4}{x^2+4x} = \dfrac{x}{x^2+6x}$. Cross-multiplying yields the polynomial equation $x^3 + 10x^2 + 24x = x^3 + 4x^2$. Solve this equation for x and comment on the results.

Project

Determine the average length and weight measurements for a species of fish that are caught in your area. Write an equation of the form $w(\ell) = a\ell^3$ to model the data.

Review

Determine the equation of the line satisfying the given conditions:

1. Passes through the point $(5, 3)$ and is parallel to the y-axis $x = 5$
2. Passes through the point $(-2, -4)$ and has slope of -2 $y = -2x - 8$
3. Passes through the point $(5, 7)$ and is parallel to the line $y = x$ $y = x + 2$
4. Find the dimensions of a rectangle whose perimeter is 76 in. if the length is two more than three times the width. $w = 9$ in.; $\ell = 29$ in.
5. Suppose it is known that if 60 pear trees are planted in a certain orchard, the average yield per tree will be 1400 pears per year. For each additional tree planted in the same orchard, the annual yield per tree will drop by 20 pears. How many trees should be planted in order to produce the maximum crop of pears per year? 65

Find the inverse of each of the following functions and determine if the inverse is also a function.

6. $f(x) = (x - 2)^2 + 4$ no   7. $f(x) = |x| - 3$ no

Determine the domain of each of the following:

8. $f(x) = \dfrac{3x - 4}{x^2 + 2x - 35}$ $\{x: x \in \mathcal{R}, x \neq 5, -7\}$ 9. $f(x) = \sqrt{x^2 + 6x + 8}$ $\{x: x \geq -2 \text{ or } x \leq -4\}$

Simplify each of the following:

10. $\dfrac{4 + 3i}{3 - 2i}$ $\dfrac{6 + 17i}{13}$ 11. $\dfrac{2 - i}{1 + i}$ $\dfrac{1 - 3i}{2}$

Alternative Assessment
Instruct students to write several values for x, and then write the equation for which the values are solutions. Have them discuss the conditions on the values for x to obtain:
1. a fourth degree equation
2. an equation that can be expressed in quadratic form solvable only by using the quadratic formula
3. a fifth degree function having only one term

Enrichment
Using a graphing utility, graph each function and draw a conclusion about the effect of horizontal and vertical shifts on the real zeros of a polynomial function.

$$f(x) = 2x^4 - 3x^2 - 2;$$
$$f(x - 2) \qquad f(x) + 4$$

$$g(x) = x^3 + 3x^2 + 4;$$
$$g(x + 1) \qquad g(x) - 5$$

A horizontal shift does not alter the number of zeros of a function. For $f(x - a)$, the zeros shift a units. A vertical shift may either increase or decrease the number of zeros.

Additional Answers
33. $f(x) = 5(x + 1)^2 - 84$
34. $-5.7, 1.7, 3, -1.5 + 2.6i,$
$-1.5 - 2.6i$
35. No. If you divide by $x + 5$ you will lose the solution $x = -5$.
46. Solving the polynomial equation yields $x = 0$ and $x = -4$. However, both of these solutions must be rejected because they cause the original equation to be undefined.

Writing in Mathematics
37. Answers may vary. Students' answers may include applications similar to Examples 5 and 6.

LESSON PLAN

Vocabulary

distance formula
midpoint formula

Technology

graphing utility

FOCUS

Satellites are an essential part of modern day communication networks. Following the earthquake in Mexico in September 1985, the only method of communication between the U.S. and Mexico was through a satellite belonging to NASA. It is a satellite that supports the hotline between the White House and the Kremlin. Private homes, using small dish antennae, will soon be able to receive direct satellite broadcasts.

INSTRUCTION

- For Example 1, students may find it helpful to model the equation of a parabola and the perimeter function on a graphing utility at the same time. For each *x*-value, check that the corresponding rectangle inscribed in the parabola has a perimeter equal to the *y*-coordinate on the graph of the perimeter function.
- Point out that when using the distance formula to determine and compare lengths of sides of a figure, students should leave the answers in radical form to avoid rounding errors.
- Remind students that all vertical lines are parallel and all horizontal lines are parallel.

Alternative Learning Styles

Many students benefit from a review of mathematical theorems that are needed to solve the problems in this lesson. Listing the theorems given on page 101 is recommended.

2.7 Coordinate Proofs

Objectives: To prove geometric theorems using coordinate geometry
To solve maximum and minimum problems using coordinate geometry

Focus

A satellite is said to be in *geosynchronous* orbit if it is orbiting above the equator and revolving at the same rate as the earth is rotating. A transmission from a geosynchronous satellite 22,000 mi above the earth can reach approximately 40% of the earth's surface. Communications satellites are often the link between transmission of data such as television programs and the reception of the data in individual homes.

Cable companies send scrambled messages through a satellite which are then decoded by special devices in subscribers' homes. One variable that must be considered when designing these systems is the *distance* between the transmitting dish and the satellite at any given time. *Analytic or coordinate geometry* may be used to plan the design.

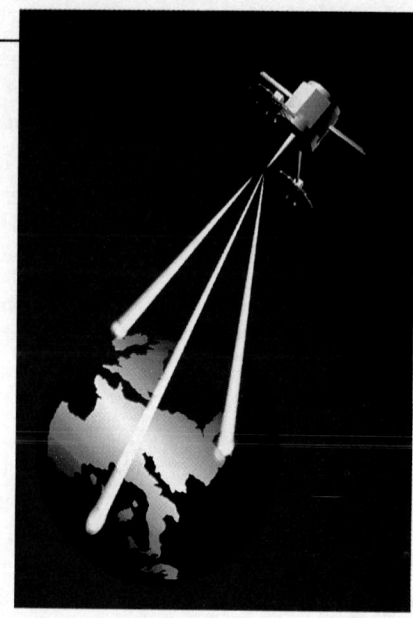

In analytic or coordinate geometry, figures are drawn on the coordinate plane and appropriate coordinates are assigned to the vertices. These drawings can be used as a tool to solve problems and prove geometric theorems.

In Lesson 2.5 you learned that the vertex of a parabola, $y = ax^2 + bx + c$, is a maximum point if $a < 0$ and a minimum point if $a > 0$. Coordinate geometry can be used to solve maximum and minimum problems that involve a parabola. A general strategy for solving maximum and minimum problems follows:

- Draw a diagram and label the vertices of the geometric figure.
- Determine an equation for the quantity to be maximized or minimized.
- Use the information in the problem to express the equation in terms of one variable.
- Analyze the equation to determine a maximum or minimum value.

At Raging Waters Park in Salt Lake City, Utah, water slide designers used a parabolic curve to construct an exciting water ride which allows riders to actually fly above the ride for a few seconds and then make a smooth landing.

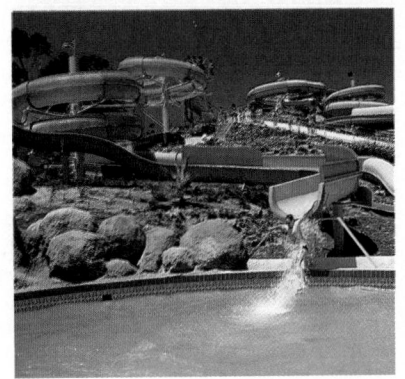

Example 1 *Engineering* A second parabolic slide is to be built with a rectangular storage shed under one arch of the slide. The equation of the parabola is $y = 20 - 0.32x^2$. Using a two-dimensional model of the curve and the storage shed, determine the maximum perimeter, in feet, of the front side of this shed.

Draw a diagram and label the vertices of the rectangle. Place one side of the rectangle along the x-axis and choose the coordinates as shown to make it easier to determine the equation of the perimeter, which is the quantity to be maximized. The perimeter is $P = 4x + 2y$.

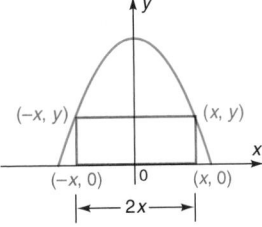

Then express the equation in terms of one variable. Since the storage shed is to be built under the parabolic arch, (x, y) is on the parabola $y = 20 - 0.32x^2$.

$$P = 4x + 2(20 - 0.32x^2) \quad \text{Substitute } 20 - 0.32x^2 \text{ for } y.$$
$$P(x) = -0.64x^2 + 4x + 40 \quad \text{The perimeter of the rectangle is a function of } x.$$

The graph of this function P is a parabola. Since $a < 0$, the parabola has a maximum point at its vertex, $\left(\dfrac{-b}{2a}, P\left(\dfrac{-b}{2a}\right)\right)$.

$$x = \frac{-b}{2a} = \frac{-4}{2(-0.64)} = 3.125$$
$$P(3.125) = -0.64(3.125)^2 + 4(3.125) + 40 = 46.25$$

The maximum perimeter of the storage shed is 46.25 ft.

To determine the *distance between any two points* $P(x_1, y_1)$ and $Q(x_2, y_2)$ in the coordinate plane, form a right triangle, and then apply the Pythagorean theorem.

Given $P(x_1, y_1)$ and $Q(x_2, y_2)$, draw a line through P parallel to the x-axis and a line through Q parallel to the y-axis. The lines intersect at $R(x_2, y_1)$. Triangle PRQ is a right triangle.

$$PR = |x_2 - x_1| \qquad RQ = |y_2 - y_1|$$
$$(PQ)^2 = (PR)^2 + (RQ)^2 \qquad \text{Pythagorean theorem}$$
$$(PQ)^2 = |x_2 - x_1|^2 + |y_2 - y_1|^2$$
$$(PQ)^2 = (x_2 - x_1)^2 + (y_2 - y_1)^2 \qquad \text{For any real number } r, |r|^2 = r^2.$$
$$PQ = \sqrt{(x_2 - x_1)^2 + (y_2 - y_1)^2}$$

2.7 Coordinate Proofs **101**

Theorems For an *acute triangle*, the sum of the squares of the lengths of the two shortest sides is greater than the square of the length of the longest side.

For an *obtuse triangle*, the sum of the squares of the lengths of the two shorter sides is less than the square of the length of the longest side.

A quadrilateral is a *parallelogram* if and only if both pairs of opposite sides are parallel.

A quadrilateral is a *parallelogram* if and only if both pairs of opposite sides are of equal length.

A quadrilateral is a *rectangle* if and only if both pairs of opposite sides are of equal length, and it has one right angle.

A quadrilateral is a *rhombus* if and only if all sides are of equal length.

A quadrilateral is a *square* if and only if all sides are of equal length, and it has one right angle.

Three points P, Q, and R are *collinear* with Q between P and R if and only if $PQ + QR = PR$.

GUIDED PRACTICE

For Example 1
Determine the maximum perimeter of a rectangle inscribed in a parabolic arch modeled by the equation $y = 7 - 3x^2$ so that the base of the rectangle is along the x-axis.

$$P(x) = -6x^2 + 4x + 14$$
$$x = \frac{-b}{2a} = \frac{-4}{-12} = 0.33$$
$$P(0.33) = 14.7$$

Common Error When finding the perimeter, some students forget to double the value of x to determine the length of the base.

Distance Formula

The distance d between any two points $P(x_1, y_1)$ and $Q(x_2, y_2)$ in the coordinate plane is

$$d = \sqrt{(x_2 - x_1)^2 + (y_2 - y_1)^2}$$

Example 2 *Communications* A geosynchronous satellite is at a point 22,000 mi above a point on the earth. A television transmission from California is sent to the satellite which then transmits the signals to New York. Using the two-dimensional model at the right, determine whether triangle TRS is obtuse.

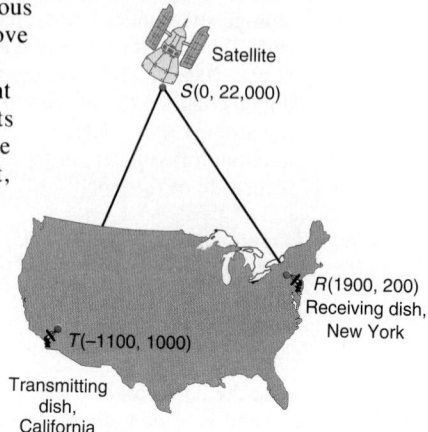

If $\triangle TRS$ is obtuse, then the sum of the squares of the lengths of the two shortest sides is less than the square of the length of the longest side. Use the distance formula to find TR, RS, and ST.

$$TR = \sqrt{[1900 - (-1100)]^2 + [200 - 1000]^2} = \sqrt{9,640,000}$$
$$RS = \sqrt{(0 - 1900)^2 + (22,000 - 200)^2} = \sqrt{478,850,000}$$
$$ST = \sqrt{(-1100 - 0)^2 + (1000 - 22,000)^2} = \sqrt{442,210,000}$$

Determine whether $TR^2 + ST^2 < RS^2$.

$$(\sqrt{9,640,000})^2 + (\sqrt{442,210,000})^2 \overset{?}{<} (\sqrt{478,850,000})^2$$
$$451,850,000 < 478,850,000$$

Therefore, $\triangle TRS$ is obtuse.

The midpoint of a line segment divides it into two segments of equal length.

Midpoint Formula

The coordinates of the midpoint M of the line segment with endpoints $P(x_1, y_1)$ and $Q(x_2, y_2)$ are

$$M\left(\frac{x_1 + x_2}{2}, \frac{y_1 + y_2}{2}\right)$$

$Q(x_2, y_2)$

$M\left(\frac{x_1 + x_2}{2}, \frac{y_1 + y_2}{2}\right)$

$P(x_1, y_1)$

When you use the midpoint formula to solve a problem, label the vertices of a geometric figure using coordinates $2a$, $2b$, and so on. *Why?*

102 Chapter 2 Graphing Functions

Thinking Critically
It will be easier to do the calculations if the coordinates are given as multiples of 2.

Example 3 Prove that the line segments joining the midpoints of the successive sides of any quadrilateral form a parallelogram.

Draw a diagram and label the vertices. Use the midpoint formula to find the coordinates of A, B, C, and D.

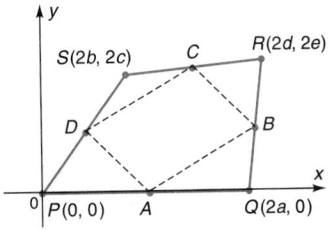

$$A\left(\frac{0+2a}{2}, \frac{0+0}{2}\right) = A(a, 0)$$

$$B\left(\frac{2a+2d}{2}, \frac{0+2e}{2}\right) = B(a+d, e)$$

$$C\left(\frac{2b+2d}{2}, \frac{2c+2e}{2}\right) = C(b+d, c+e)$$

$$D\left(\frac{0+2b}{2}, \frac{0+2c}{2}\right) = D(b, c)$$

If both pairs of opposite sides of a quadrilateral are parallel, then it is a parallelogram. Two lines are parallel if their slopes are equal. Show that $\overline{AB}$ is parallel to $\overline{CD}$ and $\overline{AD}$ is parallel to $\overline{BC}$.

$$m = \frac{y_2 - y_1}{x_2 - x_1} \quad \text{\textit{Definition of slope}}$$

$$m_{\overline{AB}} = \frac{e-0}{(a+d)-a} = \frac{e}{d} \qquad m_{\overline{CD}} = \frac{c-(c+e)}{b-(b+d)} = \frac{e}{d}$$

$$m_{\overline{AD}} = \frac{c-0}{b-a} = \frac{c}{b-a} \qquad m_{\overline{BC}} = \frac{(c+e)-e}{(b+d)-(a+d)} = \frac{c}{b-a}$$

$$m_{\overline{AB}} = m_{\overline{CD}} \quad \text{and} \quad m_{\overline{AD}} = m_{\overline{BC}}$$

Since both pairs of opposite sides of $ABCD$ are parallel, it is a parallelogram. *What is another method for proving $ABCD$ is a parallelogram?*

Class Exercises

1. Determine whether $P(-4, 1)$, $Q(6, -1)$, and $R(-3, 6)$ are the vertices of a right triangle. yes

2. Show that $P(1, 1)$, $Q(5, 4)$, $R(9, 1)$, and $S(5, -2)$ are the vertices of a rhombus. $PQ = QR = RS = SP = 5$

3. Given that x_1 and x_2 are real zeros of a quadratic function $f(x) = ax^2 + bx + c$, show that the x-coordinate of the vertex of the graph of this function is equal to the x-coordinate of the midpoint of the line segment connecting the zeros.

4. Prove that $P(0, 0)$, $Q(a, 0)$, $R(a, a)$, and $S(0, a)$ are the vertices of a square.

5. Prove that $P(0, 0)$, $Q(a, 0)$, $R(a+b, c)$, and $S(b, c)$ are the vertices of a parallelogram.

6. Prove that the diagonals of a square are perpendicular.

7. Prove that in a right triangle, the midpoint of the hypotenuse is equidistant from the three vertices.

8. Three vertices of a rectangle are $(5, -1)$, $(5, 3)$, and $(-2, 3)$. Find the fourth vertex. $(-2, -1)$

2.7 Coordinate Proofs **103**

For Example 3
Prove that the length of the line joining the midpoints of any two sides of a triangle is one-half the length of the third side.

$M_{\overline{PR}}(-c, b)$ and $M_{\overline{RQ}}(a, b)$

Length $M_{\overline{PR}}M_{\overline{RQ}} = \sqrt{(a+c)^2}$
$\qquad = |a+c|$

Length of $\overline{PQ} = \sqrt{(2a+2c)^2}$
$\qquad = 2\sqrt{(a+c)^2}$
$\qquad = 2|a+c|$

CLOSURE
Have students work in groups to compose a list of example problems that can be solved by using the distance formula, the midpoint formula, and/or the definition of slope. For example: How can you show that a quadrilateral with a given set of vertices is a parallelogram? Use the distance formula to show that opposite sides are congruent; use the distance formula to show that diagonals are congruent; use the midpoint formula to show that the midpoints of the diagonals are the same; and so on.

INDEPENDENT PRACTICE
Assignment Guide
Basic: 1–20, 23
Average: 1–17 odd, 18–30, 33
Enriched: 1–25 odd, 26–38

Teacher's Resource Book
  Practice, page 14

Thinking Critically
You can show that both pairs of opposite sides are of equal length.

Exercises 3, 7, 11, 21, 25, and 29 review the concepts of solving polynomial equations, finding equations of lines, graphing functions, determining whether a function is one-to-one, and naming field properties.

LESSON FOLLOW-UP

Lesson Quiz

1. Derive the distance formula for the distance between any two points $P(x_1, y_1)$ and $P(x_2, y_2)$.

The segment that connects $P(x_1, y_1)$ and $P(x_2, y_2)$ is the hypotenuse of a right triangle with legs of lengths $|x_2 - x_1|$ and $|y_2 - y_1|$. By the Pythagorean theorem the length of the segment is $\sqrt{(x_2 - x_1)^2 + (y_2 - y_1)^2}$.

2. Show that quadrilateral $ABCD$ with vertices $A(4, -1)$, $B(7, -5)$, $C(11, -2)$ and $D(8, 2)$ is a rhombus.
$AB = BC = CD = AD = 5$

3. The front of a storage building is parabolic in shape and can be modeled by the equation $y = 25 - 0.21x^2$. Determine the maximum perimeter of a rectangular set of doors that could be installed in the front wall of this building to the nearest tenth of a foot. $P(x) = 4x + 50 - 0.42x^2$; Maximum value occurs at $x = 4.76$; $P(4.76) = 59.5$ ft

4. Explain how to find the midpoint of a line segment. The x-coordinate of the midpoint of a line segment with endpoints $P(x_1, y_1)$ and $P(x_2, y_2)$ is the average of the x-coordinates and the y-coordinate of the midpoint is the average of the y-coordinates.

Practice Exercises

 Use appropriate technology.

A 1. Find the maximum perimeter of a rectangle whose top vertices are on the curve $y = 12 - 0.2x^2$ and whose bottom vertices are on the x-axis. 34

2. Show that $P(-3, 2)$, $Q(-2, -1)$, $R(0, 3)$, and $S(-1, 6)$ are vertices of a parallelogram. $m_{\overline{PQ}} = m_{\overline{RS}} = -3$; $m_{\overline{QR}} = m_{\overline{SP}} = 2$

R 3. Find the zeros of the polynomial $f(x) = 6x^3 - 7x^2 + 2x$. $0, \frac{1}{2}, \frac{2}{3}$

4. Show that $P(2, 2)$, $Q(6, 10)$, and $R(8, 4)$ are vertices of an isosceles triangle. $QR = PR = \sqrt{40}$

5. Prove that the line joining the midpoints of two sides of a triangle is parallel to the third side.

6. Prove that the length of the line joining the midpoints of two sides of a triangle is equal to one-half the length of the third side.

R 7. Determine an equation of a line in standard form that is perpendicular to the line $2y = -x + 3$ and passes through the point $(4, 5)$. $2x - y - 3 = 0$

8. The median of a trapezoid is the line segment joining the midpoints of the nonparallel sides. Prove that the median of a trapezoid is parallel to the bases.

9. **Thinking Critically** A rectangle is drawn on the coordinate plane so that one side is on the x-axis and the midpoint of that side is the origin. Determine the coordinates of this rectangle. How would you find the coordinates of the vertices of this rectangle if it were translated k units to the right and p units up?

10. An isosceles trapezoid is a trapezoid with legs of equal length. Prove that the diagonals of an isosceles trapezoid are equal in length.

R 11. Graph $y = -x^3 + 3$.

12. Prove that the length of the median of any trapezoid is one-half the sum of the lengths of the bases.

13. Prove that the diagonals of a rectangle are equal in length.

14. *Design* A table top in the shape of a parallelogram is decorated with two strips of leather joining the midpoints of the opposite sides. Prove that these two strips of leather bisect each other.

15. *Communications* A satellite dish placed 1800 ft above ground level is located halfway between a transmission station and a receiving station, both of which are at ground level. If the distance between the stations is exactly $1200\sqrt{3}$ ft, determine whether the triangle formed by the transmission station, the satellite dish, and the receiving station is equilateral. yes

16. *Construction* A road is to be constructed to pass through a small mountain. A two-dimensional model for the shape of the mountain is the curve with equation $y = 24 - x^2$. A rectangular passageway is to be made through the center of the mountain. Let the x-axis represent the road. Then use a two-dimensional model in which the top vertices of the rectangle touch the curve and the bottom vertices are on the x-axis to find the maximum perimeter of the rectangle. 50 ft

104 Chapter 2 Graphing Functions

Additional Answers

5. Let the vertices of the triangle be $P(0, 2c)$, $Q(-2a, 0)$, and $R(2b, 0)$. Let E and F be the midpoints of $\overline{PQ}$ and $\overline{PR}$, respectively. So $E(-a, c)$ and $F(b, c)$. Then $m_{\overline{EF}} = 0$ and $m_{\overline{QR}} = 0$, and are therefore parallel.

6. Use the information from #5. $QR = 2a + 2b = 2(a + b)$; $EF = a + b$; $EF = \frac{1}{2}QR$

17. **Writing in Mathematics** Given $f(x) = ax^2 + bx + c$, $a \neq 0$, what does the point $P\left\{\dfrac{-b}{2a}, f\left(\dfrac{-b}{2a}\right)\right\}$ represent? Explain.

B 18. Determine whether the points $P(2, 2)$, $Q(5, 6)$ and $R(7, 2)$ are the vertices of an equilateral, isosceles, or scalene triangle. isosceles

19. Determine whether the points $P(-4, 8)$, $Q(0, -5)$, and $R(-1, -1)$ are collinear. no

20. How could rounding affect your answer to Exercise 19? no change

® 21. Determine whether the graph of $f(x) = -x^2 + 3x + 1$ represents a one-to-one function. no

22. Prove that if two medians of a triangle are equal in length, the triangle is isosceles.

23. Prove that the sum of the squares of the lengths of the four sides of any parallelogram is equal to the sum of the squares of the lengths of the two diagonals.

24. Prove that the sum of the squares of the lengths of the three medians of any triangle is equal to three-fourths the sum of the squares of the lengths of the three sides.

® 25. Name the field properties that hold for the set of real numbers under the operation of division. none

26. **Thinking Critically** A triangle has vertices $P(0, 0)$, $Q(a, 0)$ and $R(b, c)$. Find a relationship among a, b, and c so that triangle PQR is a right triangle.

27. Referring to Example 3, use another method to prove that $ABCD$ is a parallelogram. Show $AB = CD$ and $AD = CB$.

28. A triangle has vertices $R(800, 300)$, $S(0, 18,000)$, and $T(-400, 400)$. Determine whether the triangle is acute. *Hint*: A triangle is acute if the sum of the squares of the lengths of the two shortest sides is greater than the square of the length of the longest side. no

® 29. Prove that the lines represented by $ax - by = c$ and $bx + ay = c$ are perpendicular. $m_1 = \dfrac{a}{b}$; $m_2 = -\dfrac{b}{a}$; perpendicular

30. *Engineering* An engineer designing a straight stretch of road using the coordinate plane, marks off the points $P(-2, -9)$, $Q(2, -3)$, and $R(6, 3)$. Determine if these points are collinear. yes

C 31. *Recreation* An amusement park has designated a rectangular picnic area for its visitors along the ocean. The area is 25,000 ft². A fence is to be erected around only three sides since one side is adjacent to the water. Express the required feet of fence as a function of the length of the unfenced side. $f(\ell) = \ell + \dfrac{50,000}{\ell}$

32. Show that the points $P(x_1, y_1)$, $M\left(\dfrac{x_1 + x_2}{2}, \dfrac{y_1 + y_2}{2}\right)$, and $Q(x_2, y_2)$ are collinear.

33. **Writing in Mathematics** In the 1939 version of the picture *The Wizard of Oz*, the scarecrow says, "The sum of the square roots of any two sides of an isosceles triangle is equal to the square root of the remaining side." Explain why this statement is incorrect. Which theorem was he probably trying to quote?

2.7 Coordinate Proofs **105**

Alternative Assessment

Have students research the roles of Maria Gaetana Agnesi and Charlotte Angas Scott in the development of analytic or coordinate geometry, then prepare an oral report. Students should provide examples of the relevant mathematics.

Enrichment

Find the maximum perimeter of the rectangle that can be drawn under the curve $y = -0.5x^2 + 3x + 5.5$ so that its base is along the x-axis. Express the equation in the form $y = -0.5(x - 3)^2 + 10$. Then find the maximum perimeter for the rectangle under the curve $y = -0.5x^2 + 10$. The areas of the rectangles will be the same since the curves are congruent. $P(x) = -x^2 + 4x + 20$; the maximum occurs at $x = 2$; $P(2) = 24$.

Additional Answers

23. Let the four vertices be $A(0, 0)$, $B(a, 0)$, $C(a + b, c)$, and $D(b, c)$, where $AB = CD = a$ and $BC = AD = \sqrt{b^2 + c^2}$. $AB^2 + BC^2 + CD^2 + AD^2 = a^2 + b^2 + c^2 + a^2 + b^2 + c^2 = 2a^2 + 2b^2 + 2c^2$; $AC = \sqrt{a^2 + 2ab + b^2 + c^2}$; $BD = \sqrt{a^2 - 2ab + b^2 + c^2}$; $AC^2 + BD^2 = 2a^2 + 2b^2 + 2c^2$

26. $c \neq 0$ and $b = 0$ or a

Writing in Mathematics
17. The point represents the x and y values of the maximum or minimum point on the graph of the parabola.
33. Assume the theorem is true. Then $\sqrt{a} + \sqrt{a} = \sqrt{b}$, $2\sqrt{a} = \sqrt{b}$, $4a = b$. In any triangle the sum of the lengths of any two sides must be greater than the third side. Then $a + a > b$ but $b = 4a$. This contradiction shows that scarecrow's statement is false. He was probably trying to quote the Pythagorean theorem.

34. $\left(\dfrac{x_1 + 2x_2}{3}, \dfrac{y_1 + 2y_2}{3}\right)$

35.

From Exercise 34, the point on the median that is $\frac{2}{3}$ the distance from P to N is $\left(\dfrac{2a + 2b}{3}, \dfrac{2c}{3}\right)$. The point that is $\frac{2}{3}$ the distance from Q to L is $\left(\dfrac{2a + 2b}{3}, \dfrac{2c}{3}\right)$ and the point that is $\frac{2}{3}$ the distance from R to M is $\left(\dfrac{2a + 2b}{3}, \dfrac{2c}{3}\right)$. Since that point is common to all 3 medians, that is where they all meet.

36. $(x - h)^2 + (y - k)^2 = r^2$, where (h, k) is the midpoint of the hypotenuse.

34. Find the coordinates of a point located two-thirds of the distance between $P(x_1, y_1)$ and $Q(x_2, y_2)$.

35. Prove that the medians of a triangle must meet at a point that is located two-thirds of the distance from each vertex to the midpoint of the opposite side. *Hint*: See Exercise 34.

36. The center of a circle that circumscribes a right triangle is at the midpoint of the hypotenuse of the right triangle. Determine an equation of the circle.

37. Thinking Critically If $A(4x_1, y_1)$ are the coordinates of one endpoint of AB and $M\left(2x_1 + 3x_2, \dfrac{y_1}{2}\right)$ are the coordinates of the midpoint, find the coordinates of the other endpoint B. $(6x_2, 0)$

38. Find the maximum perimeter of a rectangle whose top vertices are on the curve $y = c - ax^2$, $a > 0$ and $c > 0$, and whose bottom vertices are on the line $y = b$, $0 < b < c$.

Challenge

1. List all the subsets of $\{\{\varnothing\}, \varnothing\}$. $\{\{\varnothing\}\}, \{\varnothing\}, \{\{\varnothing\}, \varnothing\}, \varnothing$

2. Determine the remainder on dividing $x^8 + x^6 + x^4 + x^2 + x + 1$ by $x - 1$. 6

3. Simplify: $\left(-\dfrac{1}{64}\right)^{-\frac{2}{3}}$ 16

4. In which quadrants are the set of points satisfying the pair of inequalities $y > x$ and $y > 3 - x$ contained? I and II

5. The medians $\overline{AD}$ and $\overline{CE}$ of triangle ABC intersect at M. The midpoint of $\overline{AE}$ is P. If the area of triangle EMP is k times the area of triangle ABC, determine k. $\frac{1}{12}$

6. Determine the difference between the larger solution and the smaller solution of $x^2 - kx + \dfrac{k^2 - 1}{4} = 0$. 1

7. A side of square $ABCD$ is 10 in. long. A circle is drawn through the vertices A and D and is tangent to side BC. Determine the radius of the circle. 6.25

8. Find x if the reciprocal of $x + 2$ is $x - 2$. $\pm\sqrt{5}$

9. Determine the value of $x + y$ if $2^x = 8^{y-1}$ and $9^y = 3^{x-8}$. 41

10. For what real values of m are the equations $y = (m - 1)x + 2$ and $y = (2m + 1)x + 3$ satisfied by at least one pair of real numbers (x, y)? $\{m: m \neq -2\}$

11. Determine what pairs of integers (a, b) satisfy the equation $a + b = ab$. $(0, 0), (2, 2)$

12. Determine the area of the circle if eight times the reciprocal of the circumference of the circle equals the diameter of the circle. 2

13. Determine the length of each side of a regular hexagon if opposite sides are 18 in. apart. $6\sqrt{3}$

14. Simplify: $\left(\dfrac{x^2 + 1}{x}\right)\left(\dfrac{y^2 + 1}{y}\right) + \left(\dfrac{x^2 - 1}{y}\right)\left(\dfrac{y^2 - 1}{x}\right)$ $2xy + \dfrac{2}{xy}$

38.

$p = 4x + 2(c - ax^2 - b)$
$p = 4x + 2c - 2ax^2 - 2b$
$p = -2ax^2 + 4x + 2(c - b)$

Maximum occurs at $x = \dfrac{1}{a}$.

The maximum perimeter is $\dfrac{2(1 + ac - ab)}{a}$.

2.8 Distance from a Point to a Line

Objectives: To determine the distance from a point to a line
To determine the distance between two parallel lines

Focus

Distances may often be computed without measurement. The acceleration due to gravity and the speed of sound can be used to measure vertical distances. To estimate the depth of a deep well, all you need is a rock and a stopwatch. By measuring the total time it takes for the rock to fall to the bottom and the time it takes for the sound of the splash to travel back up to the top, assuming the point at which the rock hits is the bottom, you can determine the depth of the well.

In Lesson 2.7, the distance formula was used to determine the distance between two points. The distance from a point $P(x_1, y_1)$ to a *horizontal line* $y = a$ is $|y_1 - a|$, and the distance to a *vertical line* $x = b$ is $|x_1 - b|$. The **distance d from the point $P(x_1, y_1)$ to a nonvertical line** $Ax + By + C = 0$ is

$$d = \frac{|Ax_1 + By_1 + C|}{\sqrt{A^2 + B^2}}$$

To derive the formula, let $Q(x_2, y_2)$ be the intersection of a perpendicular from P to the line ℓ. Let R be the intersection with ℓ of a vertical line through P. Since $Ax + By + C = 0$, $y = -\frac{A}{B}x - \frac{C}{B}$. Then R has coordinates $R\left(x_1, -\frac{A}{B}x_1 - \frac{C}{B}\right)$. *Why?*

Note that $PR = \left| -\frac{A}{B}x_1 - \frac{C}{B} - y_1 \right|$.

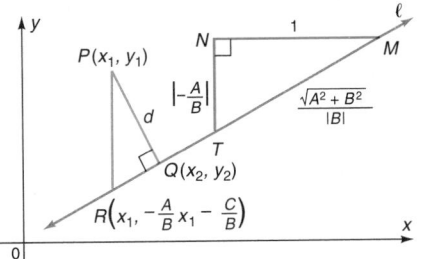

Since the slope of line ℓ is $-\frac{A}{B}$, draw $\triangle MNT$ with its hypotenuse on the line so that leg $\overline{NT}$ has length $\left| -\frac{A}{B} \right|$ and leg $\overline{MN}$ has length 1. Then, using the Pythagorean theorem, the length of the hypotenuse $\overline{MT}$ is

$$MT = \sqrt{\left| -\frac{A}{B} \right|^2 + 1^2} = \frac{\sqrt{A^2 + B^2}}{|B|} \qquad \sqrt{B^2} = |B|$$

Since both triangles are right triangles and $\angle QRP$ and $\angle MTN$ are congruent, $\triangle PQR$ is similar to $\triangle MNT$. Therefore,

$$\frac{d}{1} = \frac{\left| -\frac{A}{B}x_1 - \frac{C}{B} - y_1 \right|}{\frac{\sqrt{A^2 + B^2}}{|B|}} \qquad \textit{Multiply numerator and denominator by } |B|.$$

$$d = \frac{|-Ax_1 - By_1 - C|}{\sqrt{A^2 + B^2}} = \frac{|Ax_1 + By_1 + C|}{\sqrt{A^2 + B^2}} \qquad \textit{For any real number } r, |-r| = |r|.$$

LESSON PLAN

Vocabulary
distance between two parallel lines
distance from a point to a line

Technology
graphing utility
symbolic manipulator

FOCUS

Encourage students to think about ways that they use indirect measurement. To encourage creative thinking, pose problems such as the following:
- Lightening strikes. How can you tell how far away it is from you?
- Your watch has stopped. How can you use it to tell what time it is?

INSTRUCTION

- Be sure students carefully read each line of the derivation for the distance of a point to a line. Students should be able to recognize the application of geometric concepts such as the distance formula, slope formula, Pythagorean theorem, congruent angles and similar triangles.
- Encourage students to describe in their own words how the formula for the distance from a point to a line is derived. Have them provide reasons for how and why the two similar triangles are formed.
- For Example 3, discuss how the equation $y_3 = y_2 - y_1$ represents the distance between the power line and the ground. Note that y_3 is the difference in y-values of the two given equations at each value of x. Since y_3 represents only vertical distance and there are other distances that may be shorter, it is an approximation. However, it is a good one for lines with slopes close to 0.

GUIDED PRACTICE

For Example 1

An aluminum awning has a wrought iron support bar attached to the building and the awning so that it is perpendicular to the awning. From the graphical representation determine the length of the support bar to the nearest tenth of a foot.

Equation of awning: $0.25x + y - 9 = 0$
Length of support bar: 1.6 ft

Example 1 A wooden board is placed so that it leans against a loading dock to provide a ramp. The board is supported by a metal beam perpendicular to the ramp and placed on a 1-ft-tall support. On a two-dimensional model of the ramp, the ramp is drawn so that it has slope $\frac{2}{5}$ and passes through the origin. The coordinates of the bottom of the metal beam are (7, 1). Find the length of the beam to the nearest hundredth of a foot.

Since the slope is $\frac{2}{5}$ and the point where the ramp touches the ground is the y-intercept (0, 0), an equation of the line representing the ramp is $y = \frac{2}{5}x$, or $2x - 5y = 0$.

To find the distance from the bottom of the beam to the ramp, use the formula for the distance from a point to a nonvertical line.

$$d = \frac{|Ax_1 + By_1 + C|}{\sqrt{A^2 + B^2}} \qquad A = 2,\ B = -5,\ C = 0;\ P(x_1, y_1) = P(7, 1)$$

$$= \frac{|2(7) - 5(1) + 0|}{\sqrt{2^2 + (-5)^2}} = 1.67 \qquad \text{To the nearest hundredth}$$

The length of the beam is approximately 1.67 ft.

The distance between two parallel lines is the length of the line segment between the two lines that is perpendicular to both. To find the *distance between two parallel lines*, choose a point on one line and find the distance from that point to the other line.

Example 2 The third rail of a straight stretch of train tracks is to be constructed so that it is equidistant from both side rails. Using a computer-assisted design program, the tracks can be modeled on a coordinate plane. Find the distance, in feet, from the third rail to either side rail. Round the answer to the nearest hundredth.

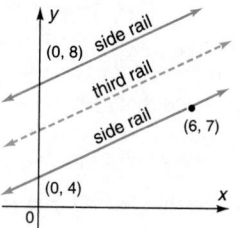

Find an equation representing one side rail.

$$y - y_1 = \left(\frac{y_2 - y_1}{x_2 - x_1}\right)(x - x_1) \qquad \textit{Use the two-point formula for an equation of a line.}$$

$$y - 4 = \left(\frac{7 - 4}{6 - 0}\right)(x - 0) \qquad (x_1, y_1) = (0, 4)\ \textit{and}\ (x_2, y_2) = (6, 7)$$

$$y - 4 = 0.5x, \text{ or } 0.5x - y + 4 = 0 \qquad Ax + By + C = 0$$

The point $R(0, 6)$ is on the third rail. *Why?*

$$d = \frac{|Ax_1 + By_1 + C|}{\sqrt{A^2 + B^2}} = \frac{|(0.5)(0) + (-1)(6) + 4|}{\sqrt{(0.5)^2 + (-1)^2}} = 1.79 \quad \text{To the nearest hundredth}$$

The distance from the third rail to either side rail is 1.79 ft.

Can you solve this problem without finding a point on the third rail?

108   Chapter 2 Graphing Functions

Thinking Critically
The point (0, 6) is the midpoint betrween the points (0, 4) and (0, 8).

Yes. You could simply find the distance between the side rails and halve it.

It is sometimes necessary to compute the distance from a point on a curve to a line. If you know the coordinates of the point, then you can use the above distance formula. However, if you need the minimum distance from a curve to a line, this formula may not be sufficient to solve the problem.

 In some cases, you can use a graphing utility to approximate the distance.

Example 3 *Electrical Engineering* A high-voltage power line is suspended between two towers on a mountain. The line $y_1 = 0.5x - 1$ represents ground level along the mountain slope. The power line hangs in a parabolic arc represented by $y_2 = 0.15x^2 - x + 7$. Use a graphing utility to determine the minimum distance between the power line and the ground.

It is possible to graph both curves on a graphing utility and then approximate the minimum distance between the line and the parabola. However, you can obtain a more accurate approximation of the minimum distance by graphing the equation $y_3 = y_2 - y_1$, which represents the distance between the power line and the ground.

$$y_3 = y_2 - y_1$$
$$= (0.15x^2 - x + 7) - (0.5x - 1)$$
$$= 0.15x^2 - 1.5x + 8$$

Graph y_3, and use the zoom and trace features to locate the minimum point at approximately $x = 5.00$ and $y = 4.25$. Thus, the minimum distance from the power line to the ground is 4.25 m.

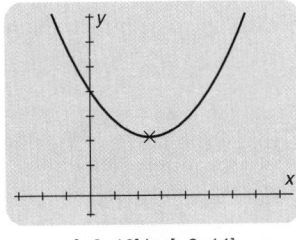

[−6, 16] by [−2, 14]
x scl: 2   y scl: 2

Modeling

How can a property owner determine the depth of a well on his land if he cannot measure it directly?

The distance in feet which a rock falls in t_1 seconds to the bottom of a well is $d = 0.5gt_1^2$ where g is 32 ft/s, the acceleration due to gravity. Thus, $d = 0.5(32)t_1^2 = 16t_1^2$. In t_2 seconds, the sound of the splash travels back to the top of the well at 1100 ft/s, the speed of sound in air. Thus, $d = 1100t_2$. Setting the two expressions for d equal gives

$$16t_1^2 = 1100t_2$$

If the total time $T = t_1 + t_2$ has been measured with a stopwatch, then substituting $t_2 = T - t_1$ into the above equation yields

$$16t_1^2 = 1100(T - t_1) \quad \text{or} \quad 16t_1^2 + 1100t_1 - 1100T = 0$$

Thus, if you know the elapsed time between dropping a rock into a well and hearing the splash, you can determine the depth of the well. *What factors might contribute to errors when using the above model?*

2.8 Distance from a Point to a Line   **109**

For Example 2
Three decorative beams are placed on a wall so that the center beam is equidistant from the two end beams. From the graphical model determine the distance of the center beam from either end beam to the nearest tenth of a foot.

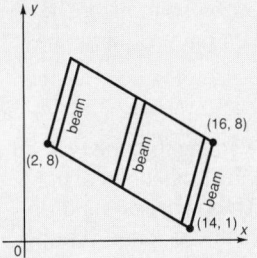

Equation of the beam with endpoints (14, 1) and (16, 8): $3.5x - y - 48 = 0$
Distance: 6.7 ft

For Example 3
A circular ferris wheel is erected over a sloped piece of ground represented in the equation $0.2x - y = 9.6$. The ferris wheel frame can be modeled by the equation $x^2 + y^2 = 20$. Using a graphing utility, approximate the minimum distance from the frame of the ferris wheel to the ground to the nearest hundredth of a foot. about 5.04 ft

Common Error Some students may use $-\sqrt{20 - x^2}$ instead of $\sqrt{20 - x^2}$ to graph the function. Explain that the minimum distance will occur from the bottom half of the ferris wheel which is represented by $\sqrt{20 - x^2}$.

Thinking Critically
The method presented only gives the distance from the top of the well to the surface of the water. It does not account for the depth of the well below the water line.

109

Modeling

Interested students may wish to simulate the experiment in Example 4 under a teacher's supervision. If students do not have access to a well, they can drop a rock from a height such as a third story window into a barrel of water on the ground. They can use a stop watch to measure the time it takes the rock to hit the water.

For Example 4

An old survey states that the well on a particular parcel of land is about 100 ft deep. The owner of the property drops a rock into the well and finds that the total time it takes to reach the bottom of the well and for the sound to travel back to the top of the well is 2.8 s. Determine if the old survey correctly stated the depth of the well.
Equation: $16t_1^2 + 1100t_1 - 3080 = 0$
$t_1 = 2.69$ s; According to the owner's calculations the well should be about 116 ft deep.

CLOSURE

Have students write in their own words the methods that can be used to find the minimum distance between:
1. a point and a line
2. two parallel lines
3. any function and a line (provided they do not intersect)

INDEPENDENT PRACTICE

Assignment Guide

Basic: 1–21, 23–27 odd
Average: 1–9 odd, 12–35, Project
Enriched: 1–25 odd, 26–43, Project

Teacher's Resource Book
Practice, page 15

Example 4 *Indirect Measurement* A rock was dropped into a well. The total time T for the rock to reach the bottom of the well and for the sound to travel back to the top of the well was 4.5 s. Find the depth of the well to the nearest foot.

$$16t_1^2 + 1100t_1 - 1100T = 0$$
$$16t_1^2 + 1100t_1 - 4950 = 0 \qquad \textit{Substitute 4.5 for T.}$$
$$t_1 = \frac{-1100 \pm \sqrt{(1100)^2 - 4(16)(-4950)}}{2(16)} \qquad \textit{Use the quadratic formula.}$$
$$t_1 = 4.24 \text{ or } t_1 = -72.99$$
$$d = 16(4.24)^2 = 288 \text{ ft} \qquad \textit{Use } t_1 = 4.24 \text{ and } d = 16t_1^2.$$

The depth of the well is approximately 288 ft. *Why was $t_1 = -72.99$ eliminated?*

Class Exercises

Express the equation of the given line in the form $Ax + By + C = 0$. Then find the distance from the given point $P(x_1, y_1)$ to that line. Round answers to the nearest hundredth.

1. $y = 3x + 2$; $P(3, 4)$
$3x - y + 2 = 0$; 2.21

2. $x = 3$; $P(5, 7)$
$x - 3 = 0$; 2

3. $0.02x - 0.12y = 0.07$; $P(-1, 2)$
$0.02x - 0.12y - 0.07 = 0$; 2.71

4. The line has slope $\frac{1}{3}$ and y-intercept 4; $P(1, -1)$. $x - 3y + 12 = 0$; 5.06

5. The line passes through the points $(4, 2)$ and $(-4, 5)$; $P(4, 0)$. $3x + 8y - 28 = 0$; 1.87

6. Find the distance between the lines $y = \frac{1}{2}x + 4$ and $y = \frac{1}{2}x - 3$. 6.26

7. *Communications* A communications system is modeled on the coordinate plane. The top of the transmitting tower is located at $(-6, -25)$, and the receiving dish is located at $(4, 11)$. If the signal travels on a straight path from the tower to the dish, find the distance from an antenna located at $(9, 5)$ to the path of transmission.
$36x - 10y - 34 = 0$; 6.42

8. *Construction* The shoulders of the eastbound and westbound lanes of a straight stretch of highway shown below are parallel. Assuming the median is constructed parallel to the shoulders, determine the distance from the median to either shoulder.
$7x - 8y + 18 = 0$; 3.48

Practice Exercises Use appropriate technology.

Express the equation of the given line in the form $Ax + By + C = 0$. Then find the distance from the given point $P(x_1, y_1)$ to that line. Round answers to the nearest hundredth.

A 1. x-axis; $P(4, 3)$ $y = 0$; 3

2. y-axis; $P(-5, -7)$ $x = 0$; 5

3. $3x + 4y = 2$; $P(5, -1)$ $3x + 4y - 2 = 0$; 1.8

4. $2x - 3y = -3$; $P(-6, 0)$
   $2x - 3y + 3 = 0$; 2.50

5. The line has slope -2 and y-intercept 5; $P(4, -2)$.
   $2x + y - 5 = 0$; 0.45

6. The line has slope $-\frac{1}{2}$ and passes through the point $(2, -6)$; $P(-7, -3)$.
   $x + 2y + 10 = 0$; 1.34

7. The line is parallel to the x-axis and passes through the point $(4, -2)$; $P(0, 0)$. $y + 2 = 0$; 2

Find the distance between each pair of parallel lines to the nearest hundredth.

8. $2x - 3y - 4 = 0$; $4x - 6y - 2 = 0$ 0.83

9. $-x + 3y = -7$; $2x - 6y = 1$ 2.06

10. **Thinking Critically**   Determine a formula for the distance of a point $P(x_1, y_1)$ from the line $x = h$. Explain your answer.

R 11. Use factoring to solve the equation $12x^2 + 14x - 10 = 0$. $\frac{1}{2}, -\frac{5}{3}$

12. *Communications*   A telephone line is strung from a pole to the top of a house. If a perpendicular wire is to be connected from a point on the window to the telephone line, determine the length of the wire. 5.01

R 13. Graph: $f(x) = 3(x - 1)^3$

14. *Architecture*   A triangular sculpture is to be placed in a garden. If the equation of the base of the sculpture when drawn on a coordinate plane is $3x - 4y = 7$ and the vertex of the triangle is at $(6, 4)$, determine the height of the triangle. 1

15. Use a graphing utility to approximate the minimum vertical distance between $y_1 = x^2 - x + 8$ and $y_2 = 0.5x - 2$. 9.4375

16. *Design*   A pair of jeans is to have a buttonhole midway between two parallel rows of stitches on a slant pocket. The designer draws a sketch of the pocket pictured at the right. Determine the distance from the buttonhole to either line of stitching.

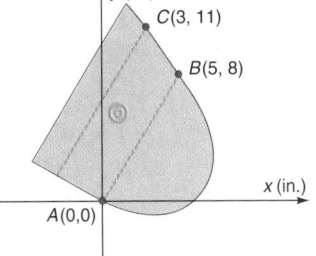

R 17. Use coordinate geometry to prove that the lengths of the diagonals of a square are equal.

18. *Indirect Measurement*   A rock was dropped into a dry well. The total time T for the rock to reach the bottom of the well and for the sound to travel back to the top of the well was 6.7 s. Determine the depth of the well to the nearest foot. 605 ft

19. **Writing in Mathematics**   In the derivation of the formula for the distance from a point to a line, the slope of the line ℓ is given as $-\frac{A}{B}$. Explain why this is true.

2.8 Distance from a Point to a Line   **111**

Writing in Mathematics
19. A linear equation in standard form, $Ax + By + C = 0$, can be rewritten in slope-intercept form, $y = -\frac{A}{B}x - \frac{C}{B}$, where the slope is the coefficient of x, $-\frac{A}{B}$.

® Review
Exercises 11, 13, 17, 23, 27, and 29 review the concepts and skills of factoring polynomials, graphing functions, writing proofs using coordinate geometry, finding the maximum or minimum point of the graph of a function, and defining a field.

LESSON FOLLOW-UP

Test Yourself

Teacher's Resource Book
   Tests—Quiz, form A, page 6
   Tests—Quiz, form B, page 6

Lesson Quiz
1. Find the distance from the point $(9, -3)$ to the line $y = -2x + 5$ to the nearest hundredth.
   4.47 units

2. Find the distance between the lines $x - 3y + 2 = 0$ and $9y = 3x - 6$ to the nearest hundredth.
   The lines are parallel. Therefore, the distance from any point on one line to the other line is 1.26 units.

3. A metal stake is placed perpendicular to the ground which can be represented by the equation $0.2x + y = -1.5$. The top of the stake has coordinates $(7, 8.5)$. Determine the distance from the top of the stake to the ground to the nearest tenth of a foot. 11.2 ft

4. Using a graphing utility, find the minimum distance between f and g to the nearest hundredth.
   $f(x) = x^2 + 3x - 1$
   $g(x) = -0.2x - 6$ 2.44 units

5. A rock was dropped into a well and the total time T for the rock to reach the bottom of the well and for the sound to travel back to the top of the well was 1.3 s. Find the depth of the well to the nearest foot.
   $16t_1^2 + 1100t_1 - 1430 = 0$
   $t_1 = 1.28$ s
   The depth of the well is 26 ft.

111

Express the equation of the given line in standard form. Then find the distance from the given point $P(x_1, y_1)$ to that line. Round answers to the nearest hundredth.

B **20.** The line is perpendicular to the line $2y = 3x - 4$ and passes through the origin; $P(2, -5)$. $2x + 3y = 0$; 3.05

21. The line is perpendicular to the line $x = 3$ and passes through the point $(0, 4)$; $P(-1, 5)$. $y - 4 = 0$; 1

22. Thinking Critically   Analyze the formula for the distance from a point to a line given below. Explain why this formula is not defined for a vertical line.

$$\frac{d}{1} = \frac{\left| \dfrac{-Ax_1}{B} - \dfrac{C}{B} - y_1 \right|}{\dfrac{\sqrt{A^2 + B^2}}{|B|}}$$

® **23.** Determine the maximum or minimum point of the graph of the function $f(x) = 4x^2 - 8x + 2$. (1, -2)

24. Find the equations of all lines parallel to the line $2x - 3y = 0$ located 3 units from this line. $2x - 3y \pm 3\sqrt{13} = 0$

25. Find the equations of all lines parallel to the line $-5x + 2y = 0$ located 4 units from this line. $5x - 2y \pm 4\sqrt{29} = 0$

26. If $P(x_1, y_1)$ is a point such that the ratio of its distance from the x-axis to its distance from the y-axis is 1:2, express its coordinates in terms of x_1. $(2x_1, x_1)$

® **27.** Use coordinate geometry to prove that the points $P(2, 1)$, $Q(2, -3)$, and $R(5, -3)$ are vertices of a right triangle.

28. *Architecture*   An A-frame house is built so that the front is a triangle. A two-dimensional sketch of the front of the house shows that the equation of the base of the triangle is $y = 0.07x + 1$. The length of the base is 15 ft. The vertex opposite the base is located at (7, 10). Find the area of the triangle. 63.67 ft²

® **29.** State the definition of a field.

30. One method for finding the minimum distance between two curves f and g is to graph $f - g$ and determine the minimum value of this new function. Explain what the graph of $f - g$ represents. the difference of the functions

31. Use a graphing utility to approximate, to the nearest hundredth, the minimum vertical distance between the two functions $y_1 = 0.01x^4 - x + 4$ and $y_2 = -x^2 + 4x - 5$. 3.07

32. *Safety*   A high-wire artist sets up his wire so that it is at an angle to the horizontal. If the safety net must be 3 ft from the wire at all times, determine the equation of the line representing the safety net pictured at the right. $0.125x - y + 3.98 = 0$

33. *Indirect Measurement*   A survey indicates that the well on a piece of property has a depth of 450 ft. A rock is dropped into the well. The total time T for the rock to reach the bottom of the well and for the sound to travel back to the top of the well is 5.6 s. Determine whether the survey is correct. no

112   Chapter 2 Graphing Functions

34. **Thinking Critically** State some reasons why the depth of the well given in the survey might differ from the depth you calculated in Exercise 33.

35. *Construction* The model for a walkway has a ramp with equation $y = 0.4x + 3$. If a supporting beam is at $(4, 0)$, determine the length of the beam to the nearest foot. 4 ft

C 36. Find a formula for the distance from a point $P(x_1, y_1)$ to a line using slope m and y-intercept b.

37. Find the slope of each line that passes through the point $(6, 7)$ and is tangent to the circle $x^2 + y^2 = 25$. 7.34, 0.30

38. Find the slope of each line that passes through the point $(5, 2)$ and is tangent to the circle $(x - 1)^2 + (y + 2)^2 = 12$. 7.87, 0.13

39. Find an equation for the set of all points P such that the distance between P and the x-axis is four times the distance between P and the y-axis. $|y| = 4|x|$

40. Given two parallel lines $y = 2x - 3$ and $y = 2x + 5$, determine an equation of a line parallel to these lines such that the ratio of its distance from the first line to its distance from the second line is $1 : 3$. $2x - y - 7 = 0$

41. Find the distance from $P(2, 5)$ to the line that passes through the origin and is tangent to $y = -2x^2 + 2x + 2.5$ at its maximum. 1.15

42. **Writing in Mathematics** Write a riddle, story, problem, or poem in which the main theme explains how to find the depth of a well.

43. **Thinking Critically** Determine an expression for the distance from the origin to the line $Ax + By + C = 0$.

Project

How can you measure the depth of an ocean?

Test Yourself

1. Determine the axis of symmetry, vertex, and the x- and y-intercepts of $f(x) = -3x^2 + 4x - 3$. Then graph. 2.5

Express each quadratic function in the form $f(x) = a(x - h)^2 + k$. Then use transformations of the graph of $f(x) = x^2$ to graph each function.

2. $f(x) = \frac{1}{4}x^2 - 2x + 3$ $f(x) = \frac{1}{4}(x - 4)^2 - 1$ 3. $f(x) = -\frac{1}{2}x^2 + 4x - 2$ $f(x) = -\frac{1}{2}(x - 4)^2 + 6$

Solve each polynomial equation. Round answers to the nearest hundredth.

4. $2x^4 - 6x^3 - 56x^2 = 0$ 5. $6y^6 - 11y^3 + 4 = 0$ 6. $x^3 - 2x^2 + 4x = 0$ 2.6
   7, -4, 0 (mult. 2)   1.10, 0.79   0, $1 \pm 1.73i$

7. Determine whether $P(0, 2)$, $Q(3, 0)$, and $R(-2, -1)$ are the vertices of a right triangle. yes 2.7

8. Find the distance from the point $P(3, -2)$ to the line $4x + 2y - 3 = 0$ to the nearest hundredth. 1.12 2.8

2.8 Distance from a Point to a Line   **113**

1.

2.

5.

6.

7.

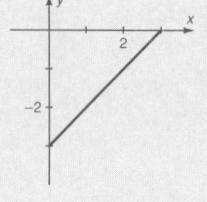

Chapter 2   Summary and Review

Vocabulary

axis of symmetry (87)
dilation (67)
distance formula (102)
distance from a point to a
  line (107)
even function (60)
leading coefficient (94)
linear function (73)
maximum (90)

midpoint formula (102)
minimum (90)
multiplicity (94)
odd function (60)
origin symmetry (57)
polynomial equation (94)
polynomial function (94)
reflection (65)
slope (73)

symmetric with respect to
  a line and a point (56)
transformations (65)
translation (66)
vertex of a parabula (88)
x-axis symmetry (57)
y-axis symmetry (57)
$y = x$ symmetry (59)
zeros of a function (88)

Symmetry   There are tests for symmetry with respect to the y-axis, the x-axis, the
origin, and the line $y = x$.   2.1

Determine the symmetries of each equation. Then use the properties of
symmetry to graph each equation.
                                   not symmetric to x-, y-axes, origin, or the line $y = x$
  1. $y = x^2 - 3$ y-axis
  2. $y = |x - 2|$

Determine whether each function is even, odd, or neither.
  3. $f(x) = 2x^3 + 3x - 4$ neither
  4. $g(x) = 5x^4 - 3x^2 + 6$ even

Transformations   Reflections, translations, and dilations are three types of   2.2
transformations that are essential to graphing.

Graph the reflection of each function in the given line.

  5. x-axis
  6. y-axis
  7. line $y = x$

Graph each equation by determining the basic function and then using transformations.
  8. $y = \sqrt{x - 4}$
  9. $y = \frac{1}{4}x^3 - 2$

Linear Functions   A linear function can be expressed in the form $f(x) = mx + b$,   2.3
where m and b are constants.

10. Find an equation of a line parallel to the line $2x + 5y = 11$ and passing
through the point $(-3, 4)$. $2x + 5y = 14$

11. The cost C for renting a car for one day is given by the linear function
$C = 0.10n + 25$, where n is the number of miles driven. Graph the
function and estimate the cost for driving 275 mi.

Solving Quadratic Equations   A quadratic equation in one variable is an equation of   2.4
the form $ax^2 + bx + c = 0$, where a, b, and c are real numbers and $a \neq 0$.

114   Chapter 2 Graphing Functions

8.

9.

11.

Solve each quadratic equation.

12. $2x^2 - 7x = 4$ $\quad 4, -\frac{1}{2}$

13. $4x^4 + 3 = 7x^2$ $\quad \pm 1, \pm\frac{\sqrt{3}}{2}$

14. A ball is thrown vertically into the air. The height of the ball is modeled by $s(t) = 48t - 16t^2$, where s is the height of the ball in feet and t is the elapsed time in seconds. Find the time at which the ball will reach a height of 32 ft. $\quad$ 1 s and 2 s

Graphing Quadratic Functions A quadratic function is a function of the form $f(x) = ax^2 + bx + c$, where a, b, and c are real numbers and $a \neq 0$. Its graph is a parabola symmetric about the vertical line $x = -\frac{b}{2a}$, called the axis of symmetry.

2.

Determine the axis of symmetry, the vertex, and the x- and y-intercepts of each quadratic function. Graph each function.

15. $f(x) = -2x^2 + 4x - 3$

16. $f(x) = 3x^2 + 5x - 2$

Express each quadratic function in the form $f(x) = a(x - h)^2 + k$. Then use transformations of the graph of $f(x) = x^2$ to graph each function.

17. $f(x) = 3x^2 + 6x - 2$ $\quad f(x) = 3(x + 1)^2 - 5$

18. $f(x) = \frac{1}{2}x^2 - 2x + 3$ $\quad f(x) = \frac{1}{2}(x - 2)^2 + 1$

Solving Polynomial Equations A polynomial equation of degree n in one variable x is an equation of the form $a_nx^n + a_{n-1}x^{n-1} + \cdots + a_1x + a_0 = 0$, $a_n \neq 0$, where n is a nonnegative integer and $a_n, a_{n-1}, \ldots, a_0$ are real numbers. The zeros of a polynomial function are the values of x for which $f(x) = 0$.

2.6

Solve each polynomial equation.

19. $8x^3 - 27 = 0$ $\quad \frac{3}{2}, \frac{-3 \pm 3i\sqrt{3}}{4}$

20. $x^3 - 2x^2 - 48x = 0$ $\quad 0, 8, -6$

Use a graphing utility to estimate the real zeros of each polynomial function to the nearest tenth.

21. $f(x) = x^4 - 13x^2 + 40$ $\quad \pm 2.8, \pm 2.2$

22. $f(x) = 3x^3 + 2x^2 - 9x - 6$ $\quad -0.7, \pm 1.7$

Coordinate Proofs Given any two points $P(x_1, y_1)$ and $Q(x_2, y_2)$:

2.7

Distance PQ: $d = \sqrt{(x_2 - x_1)^2 + (y_2 - y_1)^2}$ $\quad$ Midpoint of PQ: $M\left(\frac{x_1 + x_2}{2}, \frac{y_1 + y_2}{2}\right)$

23. Determine whether the points $P(2, 5)$, $Q(2, -2)$, and $R(6, -1)$ are vertices of an isosceles triangle. $\quad$ no

24. Prove that the median of any trapezoid is parallel to the bases.

Distance from a Point to a Line Given a nonvertical line in the form $Ax + By + C = 0$ and a point $P(x_1, y_1)$ not on the line, the distance from $P(x_1, y_1)$ to the line is

2.8

$$d = \frac{|Ax_1 + By_1 + C|}{\sqrt{A^2 + B^2}}$$

25. Find the distance from the point $P(-1, 3)$ to the line $3x - 4y + 2 = 0$ to the nearest hundredth. $\quad$ 2.60

26. Find the distance between the lines $3x - 2y = -5$ and $6x - 4y + 8 = 0$ to the nearest hundredth. $\quad$ 0.28

15.
x-int: none;
y-int: $(0, -3)$;
axis: $x = 1$;
vertex: $(1, -1)$

16.
x-int: $\left(\frac{1}{3}, 0\right)$, $(-2, 0)$;
y-int: $(0, -2)$;
axis $x = -\frac{5}{6}$;
vertex: $\left(-\frac{5}{6}, -\frac{49}{12}\right)$

17.

18.

24.

slope of $\overline{SR} = \frac{2c - 2c}{2b - 2d} = 0$;

slope of $\overline{PQ} = \frac{0 - 0}{2a - 0} = 0$;

slope of $\overline{MN} = \frac{c - c}{b - d} = 0$;

Since the slopes are the same, $\overline{SR} \| \overline{PQ} \| \overline{MN}$.

Additional Answers

1.

2.

5.

6.

7.

8.

9.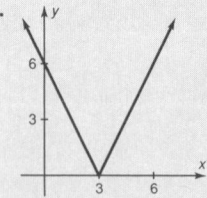

116

Chapter 2   Test

Determine the symmetries of each equation and then graph.

1. $y = x^4 - 4$ y-axis

2. $x^2y = 2$ y-axis

Determine whether each function is even, odd, or neither.

3. $f(x) = 2x^4 + 3x^2 + 4$ even

4. $g(x) = 3x^5 + 2x^3 + x^2 + 1$ neither

Graph the reflection of each function in the given line.

5. x-axis

6. y-axis

7. line $y = x$

Graph each equation by determining the basic function and using transformations.

8. $y = \dfrac{1}{x - 2}$

9. $y = 2|x - 3|$

10. Find an equation of a line parallel to the line $3x - 2y + 6 = 0$ and passing through the point $\left(\frac{1}{2}, -3\right)$. $6x - 4y - 15 = 0$

11. Water is being pumped into a tank at the rate of 8 gal/min. At this moment, the tank contains 40 gal. Determine the linear equation that expresses gallons g as a function of time t in minutes. Graph the equation. $g(t) = 8t + 40$

Solve each quadratic equation.

12. $3x^2 - 7x - 6 = 0$ $-\frac{2}{3}$, 3

13. $x^4 - x^2 - 4 = 0$ ± 1.6, $\pm 1.2i$

14. The height s, in feet, of a ball thrown into the air is given by $s = -16t^2 + 96t + 112$, where t is the time in seconds. Find the maximum height.   256 ft

Determine the axis of symmetry, the vertex, and the x- and y-intercepts of each quadratic function. Graph each function.

15. $f(x) = 3x^2 - 4x + 2$

16. $f(x) = -2x^2 + 6x - 5$

Express each quadratic function in the form $f(x) = a(x - h)^2 + k$. Then use transformations of the graph of $f(x) = x^2$ to graph each function.

17. $f(x) = 3x^2 - 6x + 2$ $f(x) = 3(x - 1)^2 - 1$

18. $f(x) = \frac{1}{4}x^2 + 3x - 3$ $f(x) = \frac{1}{4}(x + 6)^2 - 12$

Solve each polynomial equation.

19. $3x^3 + 17x^2 - 28x = 0$ 0, $\frac{4}{3}$, -7

20. $x^3 - 4x^2 + 4x - 16 = 0$ 4, $\pm 2i$

21. Prove that the diagonals of a parallelogram bisect each other.

22. Find the distance from the point $P(-2, 5)$ to the line $3x - 4y = 6$.   6.4

Challenge

Is it possible for a quadratic equation to have solutions of -2 and $3 + i$? Explain.

116   Chapter 2 Graphing Functions

15.
x-int: none;
y-int: (0, 2);
axis: $x = \frac{2}{3}$;
vertex: $\left(\frac{2}{3}, \frac{2}{3}\right)$

16.
x-int: none;
y-int: (0, −5);
axis: $x = \frac{3}{2}$;
vertex: $\left(\frac{3}{2}, -\frac{1}{2}\right)$

Cumulative Review

$5y - 2x = 15$

1. Solve the quadratic equation $8x^2 + 22x - 21 = 0$ by factoring. $-\frac{7}{2}, \frac{3}{4}$ 2.4

2. Find the slope of the line that passes through the points $(-2, 5)$ and $(-6, -4)$. $\frac{9}{4}$ 2.3

3. In the relation $xy = -6$ is y a function of x? yes   1.4

4. Given the point $(4, -5)$, determine a point that satisfies symmetry with respect to the origin. $(-4, 5)$ 2.1

5. Express the quadratic function $f(x) = x^2 - 6x + 3$ in the form $f(x) = a(x - h)^2 + k$. $f(x) = (x - 3)^2 - 6$ 2.5

6. Find the distance from the point $P(6, -2)$ to the line $4x - 2y = 1$ to the nearest hundredth. 6.04   2.8

7. Determine the basic function for $y = (x - 5)^2$. $f(x) = x^2$ 2.2

8. If graphing an equation with the variables x and y, the variable x is assumed to be the independent variable. Is the independent variable represented on a graph by the horizontal or the vertical axis? horizontal   1.3

9. Find the midpoint of the line that joins the points $(6, -2)$ and $(-5, 2)$. $\left(\frac{1}{2}, 0\right)$ 2.7

10. Find the equation of the line that has slope $-\frac{2}{3}$ and passes through the point $(-6, 1)$. $2x + 3y = -9$ 2.3

11. Find the distance between the points $(-3, 7)$ and $(-8, 4)$ to the nearest hundredth. 5.83   2.7

12. Given $f(x) = \sqrt{x - 5}$ and $g(x) = 2x$, find the domain of $(g \circ f)(x)$. $D = \{x : x \geq 5\}$ 1.5

13. Determine the axis of symmetry and the vertex of the quadratic function $f(x) = -14x^2 + 56x$. axis of symmetry: $x = 2$; vertex: $(2, 56)$ 2.5

14. Find the zeros of the polynomial function $f(x) = 4x^5 + 8x^4 - 60x^3$. -5; 3; 0 (mult. 3)   2.6

15. Determine whether the function $f(x) = 4x^5 - x^3$ is odd, even, or neither. odd   2.1

16. Graph the linear function $5y - 2x = 15$.   2.3

17. Find a quadratic equation in standard form with real coefficients that has $1 - 2i$ as a solution. $x^2 - 2x + 5 = 0$ 2.4

Determine if each statement is always true, sometimes true, or never true.

18. Transformations of graphs of functions include reflections, translations, and dilations. always   2.2

19. Quadratic equations can be solved by completing the square. always   2.4

20. The x-intercepts of a quadratic function have coordinates $(0, s_1)$ and $(1, s_2)$, where s_1 and s_2 are the real solutions of the quadratic equation $ax^2 + bx + c = 0$. never   2.5

21. If two medians of a triangle are equal in length, the triangle is isosceles. always   2.7

22. The inverse of a relation is a relation but the inverse of a function may be not a function. always   1.6

Summary

Angle measures in both degrees and radians are presented, with applications to angular and linear velocity. The six trigonometric functions are defined using the unit circle, and methods for determining exact values of these functions for certain angles are examined. Use of technology to obtain trigonometric values is also discussed. Trigonometric identities are studied both as a source of insight into relationships among the six functions, and as a way of handling some tasks involving these functions more efficiently.

Chapter Objectives

- To measure angles in rotations, degrees, and radians
- To find measures of coterminal angles
- To convert between degree measure and radian measure
- To measure arcs and sectors of circles
- To solve problems involving angular and linear velocity
- To define the sine and cosine functions
- To evaluate the sine and cosine functions of an angle given a point on its terminal side
- To define the trigonometric functions
- To evaluate the trigonometric functions of angles
- To find the six trigonometric functions of special and quadrantal angles
- To find decimal approximations for values of the trigonometric functions
- To find the measure of an angle for which the value of a trigonometric function is known
- To introduce and prove the reciprocal, ratio, Pythagorean, and odd-even identities
- To use the fundamental identities to prove other trigonometric identities

3 Trigonometric Functions

Mathematical Power

Modeling   You are, no doubt, familiar with many real world phenomena that are described using angles. Ballistics, navigation, and surveying are just a few of the many fields that make extensive use of angle measurement. But did you know angle measure is also important in the study of seismology? Below is a description of how angles are used to classify and analyze earthquakes.

The earth's rocky crust contains many faults or fractures. If the walls of rock on opposite sides of a fault begin to slide past each other, but then become locked together, energy builds up in the walls. When movement begins again, this energy is released—and an earthquake occurs.

In an effort to find a reliable method of earthquake prediction, scientists construct a model, or geological map, of major fault locations. They use a method called *strike-and-dip* notation to describe the orientation of faults and other structural deformations of the earth's crust. The strike is the direction of the fault in the horizontal plane. By convention, the strike is given as an acute angle measured from true north. The dip is the angle between the horizontal and the direction of the steepest slope of the fault. *Low-angle* faults have a dip of less than 45° and *high-angle* faults have a dip greater than 45°. The diagram below shows a fault striking N 30° E and dipping 40° toward the southeast.

118

Analyzing fault patterns and watching for signs of activity help scientists to predict the likelihood of an earthquake in a region. Geologists identify different types of movement along faults. The term used to denote the displacement of once-adjacent points is called *slip*.

The figure below shows three kinds of slip. A *dip slip*, designated by *A*, indicates movement on a fault parallel to the fault dip. A *strike slip*, *B*, indicates movement parallel to the fault strike. An *oblique slip*, *C*, indicates movement at an angle to both the strike and dip of the fault.

Fault plane

Fault dip

Fault strike

Most of the world's faults that show the greatest amount of movement—sometimes as much as hundreds of kilometers—are of the strike-slip type. The San Andreas fault in California is a famous example of a strike-slip fault. Once a fault has been designated with strike-and-dip angles, it can be further analyzed using *trigonometry*, a branch of mathematics that has some "earth-shattering" applications.

Thinking Critically   A horizontal deformity is denoted on a geological map by the symbol ⊕. What do you think the dip angle is for a horizontal deformity?

Project   Obtain a large outline map of the United States. Do research to find the location of major faults in this country and, if possible, the strike-and-dip measures and the type of fault. Create your own geological model by indicating the information on the map. Can you draw any conclusions about regions of potential danger? What safety precautions might be recommended in these regions?

119

Mathematical Power

Using basic angle measurements, geologists construct a model, called a *geological map,* to describe the geometry of the earth's surface. In this case, working with the model is easier, safer, and much less expensive than sending teams out on repeated field trips. By studying the model for deformations and abrupt changes, geologists can discover patterns of faulting and identifying regions of potential earthquake danger. Moreover, using computer simulations in combination with the available data, researchers can explore the possibilities of future events.

The danger of an earthquake is greater along high-angle faults. Emphasize that the different types of fault movement describe the *relative* changes of the rock walls on either side. Students may already know that the *Richter scale* is used to measure the amount of energy released by an earthquake.

Because mineral ores are often trapped in fault zones, mining tunnels may be constructed along the fault. Miners actually stand on the block on one side of the fault (called the *footwall*) with the face of the other block (called the *hanging wall*) above their heads.

Thinking Critically   A horizontal form has no dip. Also, strike is not defined for a horizontal form. Referring to the original definition and drawing pictures may help students to visualize this information.

Vocabulary
angle
coterminal angles
degrees
initial side
standard position
terminal side

Ⓜ **Materials/Manipulatives**
globe
protractor

Technology
scientific calculator

FOCUS

A discussion of the tilt of the earth can incite critical thinking. You may want to use a globe or some other three-dimensional model to help students to visualize the earth's orbit. Emphasize that the tilt angle of the earth is the important factor in determining the seasons and the length of daylight. It may interest students that the earth is actually further from the sun during summer (in the Northern Hemisphere) than during winter.

INSTRUCTION

Ⓜ • Remind students that a protractor may be used to measure an angle in degrees. Point out that in some applications only the size of an angle is of interest, while in others the direction of rotation is also important, and so the notion of negative measure is introduced.

• Connect students' experiences with angle measurement in geometry by recalling definitions of terms such as *acute angle, obtuse angle, right angle,* and *straight angle.*

• The computer language LOGO uses degree measure extensively to construct designs and geometric figures. Students familiar with this language might explain this application to the class.

120

3.1 Angles in the Coordinate Plane

Objectives: To measure angles in rotations and degrees
To find the measures of coterminal angles

Focus

The earth is tilted on its axis at an angle of 23.5°. As the illustration shows, the north-south line is at an angle with the orientation of the earth as it revolves around the sun. The measure of latitude for the farthest point above or below the equator from which the sun can shine directly overhead is also 23.5°. This happens on the first day of summer. The seasons of the year are caused by the tilt. When the northern part of the earth is tilted toward the sun, summer occurs in the northern hemisphere. When it is tilted away from the sun, winter occurs.

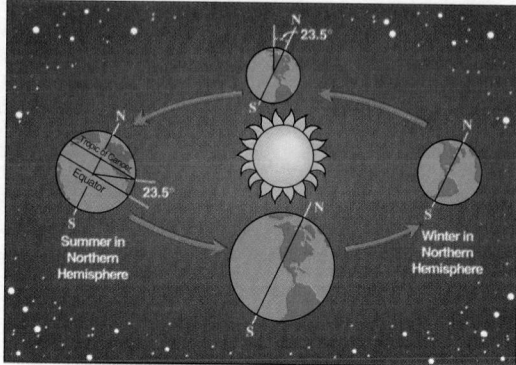

The term *trigonometry* comes from the Greek words *trigonon* and *metron,* meaning *triangle* and *measure.* This practical branch of mathematics was originally created to answer questions in geography and astronomy. Today its applications range from piano tuning to studying the orbits of atomic particles. Two fundamental concepts needed for the study of trigonometry are *angle* and *angle measure.*

In trigonometry, an **angle** is formed by rotating a ray about its endpoint. The starting position of the ray is the **initial side** of the angle; the ending position is its **terminal side.** The endpoint of the ray is called the **vertex** of the angle. An angle in **standard position** has its initial side on the positive *x*-axis and its vertex at the origin.

The measure of an angle describes the amount and direction of rotation required to get from the initial side to the terminal side. If the rotation is counterclockwise, the angle has *positive* measure. If the rotation is clockwise, the angle has *negative* measure. An angle in standard position is said to lie in the quadrant in which its terminal side falls.

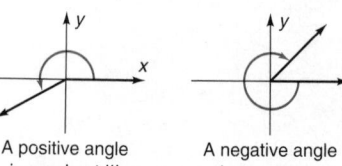

A positive angle in quadrant III

A negative angle in quadrant I

120 Chapter 3 Trigonometric Functions

One way to measure angles is in **degrees**. An angle generated by one complete counterclockwise rotation measures 360°; one generated by a complete clockwise rotation measures −360°. Degree measures of other angles are found by considering fractional parts or multiples of a rotation.

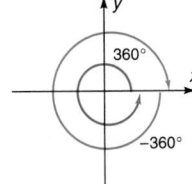

Example 1 Find the degree measure of the angle for each given rotation, and draw the angle in standard position.

a. $\frac{3}{4}$ rotation, counterclockwise   b. $\frac{1}{2}$ rotation, clockwise

c. $2\frac{1}{3}$ rotation, counterclockwise   d. $\frac{7}{6}$ rotation, clockwise

a. $\frac{3}{4}(360°) = 270°$ b. $\frac{1}{2}(-360°) = -180°$

     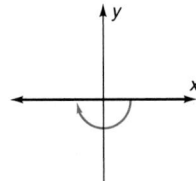

c. $\frac{7}{3}(360°) = 840°$ d. $\frac{7}{6}(-360°) = -420°$

     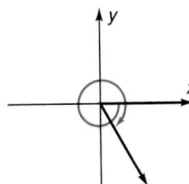

The movements of the hands of a clock, the indicator on a speedometer, and the markings on a dial may all be measured in degrees. In real world applications in which an object rotates in only one direction, angles are commonly referred to as positive, regardless of the direction of the rotation. For example, the minute hand of a clock is said to rotate through 90° in 15 min.

Example 2 *Astronomy* The earth completes one rotation on its axis every 24 hours. Through how many degrees does a point on the earth rotate in
a. 8 hours   b. 7 days

a. $8\ h = \frac{8}{24}d = \frac{1}{3}d$ b. $7(360°) = 2520°$

$\frac{1}{3}(360°) = 120°$

3.1 Angles in the Coordinate Plane **121**

GUIDED PRACTICE

For Example 1
Find the degree measure of the angle for each given rotation, and draw the angle in standard position.

1. $\frac{2}{3}$ rotation clockwise −240°

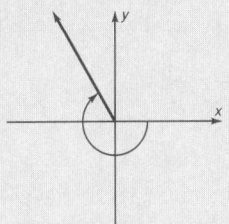

2. $\frac{11}{6}$ rotation counterclockwise 660°

For Example 2
The hour hand of the clock makes one rotation in 12 h. Through how many degrees does the hour hand rotate in each of the following times?
1. 9 h 270°   2. 18 h 540°

For Example 3

1. Express 40°40′5″ in decimal degrees. 48.668°
2. Express 15.345° in degrees-minutes-seconds. 15°20′42″

Technology Some scientific calculators have built-in functions to convert from degrees-minutes-seconds to decimal degrees and conversely with commands such as DEG and DMS. These are not standard commands, however, and it is important to consult the instruction manual for specifics.

For Example 4

Identify all angles coterminal with the given angle. Then find the coterminal angle whose measure is between 0° and 360°.

1. −200°
   (−200 + 360k)°, k ∈ Z; 160°
2. −450°
   (−450 + 360k)°, k ∈ Z; 270°

CLOSURE

Group students in pairs and have them explain to each other the procedures for measuring angles in degrees and rotations, and how to find the measures of all angles coterminal with a given angle.

INDEPENDENT PRACTICE

Assignment Guide
Basic: 1–25, 27, 31–33, 35, Project
Average: 11–40, Project
Enriched: 22–47, Project

Teacher's Resource Book
  Practice, page 16

Ⓡ **Review**
Exercises 11, 13, 27, 31, 33, and 35 review concepts of symmetry, determining equations of lines, solving quadratic equations, and finding the distance between two points.

Project
The suggested project provides an excellent opportunity for cross-curricular learning, as it has strong connections to themes common in science fiction literature.

Degrees may be divided into smaller parts in two ways, by using decimals and by using *minutes* and *seconds*. As with time measurement, each degree is divided into 60 minutes, and each minute into 60 seconds. Minutes are represented symbolically by ′ and seconds by ″. For example, 36°50′10″ denotes an angle of 36 degrees, 50 minutes, and 10 seconds. Three-place decimal form is approximately accurate to the nearest second.

Example 3 Express:
  a. 36°50′10″ in decimal degrees
  b. 50.525° in degrees-minutes-seconds

a. $36°50′10″ = 36° + 50′\left(\frac{1°}{60′}\right) + 10″\left(\frac{1°}{3600″}\right)$

$\approx 36.836°$

b. $50.525° = 50° + 0.525°\left(\frac{60′}{1°}\right)$

$= 50° + 31.5′$

$= 50° + 31′ + 0.5′\left(\frac{60″}{1′}\right)$

$= 50°31′30″$

Many calculators can convert between degrees-minutes-seconds and decimal degrees using built-in functions. It is important to consult the calculator's instruction manual to learn how to use these functions and to interpret the results. Since calculators have come into widespread use, decimal notation is used more frequently than minutes-seconds notation.

Angles of different measures in standard position can have the same terminal side. Such angles are called **coterminal** angles. All the angles shown below are coterminal. Observe that their measures differ by integral multiples of 360°.

| 60° | 420° = 60° + 360° | 1140° = 60° + 3(360)° | −300° = 60° + (−1)360° |

In fact, any angle coterminal with an angle of 60° will have measure 60° plus an integral multiple of 360°, or (60 + 360k)°, where k is an integer. This observation may be generalized to all pairs of coterminal angles as follows:

> If θ is the degree measure of an angle, then all angles coterminal with this angle have degree measure θ + 360k, where k is an integer.

122 Chapter 3 Trigonometric Functions

Example 4   Identify all angles coterminal with an angle of $-45°$. Then find the coterminal angle whose measure is between $0°$ and $360°$.

All angles coterminal with $-45°$ are $(-45 + 360k)°$, $k \in Z$.

For $k = 1$, $(-45 + 360)° = 315°$ and $0° < 315° < 360°$.

Class Exercises

Find the degree measure of the angle for each rotation. Draw the angle in standard position.

1. $\frac{3}{4}$ rotation, clockwise $-270°$

2. $\frac{5}{3}$ rotation, counterclockwise $600°$

3. 0.375 rotation, counterclockwise $135°$

4. 2.25 rotation, clockwise $-810°$

In which quadrant does each of these angles lie?

5. $30°$ I

6. $120°$ II

7. $-150°$ III

8. $-312°$ I

Express each angle measure in decimal degrees.

9. $40°17'45''$ $40.30°$

10. $129°10'37''$ $129.18°$

Express each angle measure in degrees-minutes-seconds.

11. $13.49°$ $13°29'24''$

12. $52.66°$ $52°39'36''$

Identify all angles coterminal with the given angle. Then find the coterminal angle whose measure is between $0°$ and $360°$.

13. $-75°$ $[-75 + 360k]°$, $k \in Z$; $285°$

14. $700°$ $[700 + 360k]°$, $k \in Z$; $340°$

15. $-275°$ $[-275 + 360k]°$, $k \in Z$; $85°$

16. *Entertainment*   A compact disc rotates at a speed of 500 revolutions per minute (rpm). Through how many degrees does it rotate to play a song that lasts 2.05 min? $369,000°$

17. Thinking Critically   Explain why any angle is coterminal with exactly one angle of measure θ, where $0° \le \theta < 360°$. The angles with measure between $0°$ and $360°$ represent every possible position for the terminal side of an angle in standard position.

Practice Exercises

 Use appropriate technology.

Find the degree measure of the angle for each rotation. Draw the angle in standard position.

A **1.** $\frac{5}{8}$ rotation, clockwise $-225°$

2. $\frac{3}{5}$ rotation, counterclockwise $216°$

3. $\frac{7}{9}$ rotation, counterclockwise $280°$

4. $\frac{17}{4}$ rotation, clockwise $-1530°$

5. $\frac{3}{10}$ rotation, clockwise $-108°$

6. $\frac{5}{6}$ rotation, counterclockwise $300°$

Find the quadrant or axis on which the terminal side of each angle lies.

7. $-125°$ III

8. $540°$ negative x-axis

9. $215°$ III

10. $101°5'16''$ II

Ⓡ **11.** Determine the symmetry of $f(x) = x^3 - x$. origin

3.1 Angles in the Coordinate Plane   **123**

Class Exercises

1. $-270°$

2. $600°$

3. $135°$

4. $-810°$

LESSON FOLLOW-UP

Lesson Quiz

1. Find the degree measure of the angle for a 1.2 rotation clockwise, and sketch the angle in standard position. −432°

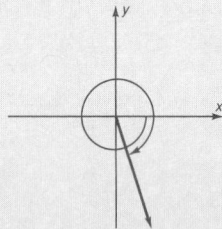

2. The hour hand of a clock makes one rotation in 12 h. Through how many degrees does the hour hand rotate in 2 h? 60°

3. Express 38°10′25″ in decimal degrees. 38.174°

4. Express 27.11° in degrees-minutes-seconds. 27°6′36″

5. Identify all angles coterminal with an angle of −75°. Then find the coterminal angle whose measure is between 0° and 360°. (−75 + 360k)°; 285°

6. A gear rotates at a rate of 750 rotations per minute. Through how many degrees does it rotate in 1 s? 4500°

12. Find the quadrant or axis in which the terminal side of an angle of 2.5 clockwise rotations lies. negative x-axis

Ⓡ 13. Determine the equation of the line determined by the points (0.5, 6) and (−1, 3.5). $y = \frac{5}{3}x + \frac{31}{6}$

Express each angle measure in decimal degrees.

14. 67°30′56″ 67.52°   15. −5°10′24″ −5.17°   16. 16°5′44″ 16.10°   17. −48°15″ −48.00°

Express each angle measure in degrees-minutes-seconds.

18. 33.47° 33°28′12″   19. 20.11° 20°6′36″   20. −56.2° −56°12′   21. −10.33° −10°19′48″

Ⓑ 22. *Mechanics* A large gear rotates at a rate of 3 rotations per minute. Through how many degrees does it rotate in 5 min? In 40 s? 5400°; 720°

23. *Entertainment* Some single songs are recorded on one side of records that rotate at a rate of 45 rpm. Through how many degrees does one of these records rotate in 20 s? 5400°

24. Draw the angle in quadrant I whose terminal side is on $y = 4x$.

25. Draw the angle in quadrant IV whose terminal side is on $y = -2x$.

26. Draw the angle in quadrant II whose terminal side is on $\frac{1}{2}x + y = 0$.

Ⓡ 27. If $\theta = 222°$, in which quadrant does its terminal side lie? III

28. Identify the angles between 0° and 360° whose terminal sides are on $y = x$. 45°; 225°

29. Identify the angles between 0° and 360° whose terminal sides are on $y = -x$. 135°; 315°

30. **Thinking Critically** Two geometric objects are said to be *congruent* if they have the same size and shape. What would it mean to say that two angles are congruent? What is the relationship between coterminal and congruent angles? Congruent angles have the same measure. Coterminal angles have the same reference angle, but their angle measures can be different.

Ⓡ 31. Solve the quadratic equation $3x^2 - x = 8$. $\frac{1 \pm \sqrt{97}}{6}$

32. **Writing in Mathematics** Describe in your own words how to change from degrees-minutes-seconds to decimal degrees.

Ⓡ 33. Solve $3x^3 + x^2 + 15x + 5 = 0$ by factoring. $-\frac{1}{3}, \pm i\sqrt{5}$

34. *Horology* Horology is the science of measuring time or making timepieces. Through how many degrees does the minute hand of a clock rotate in 3 h 45 min? 81,000°

Ⓡ 35. Find the distance between points $P(3, -5)$ and $Q(-2, 3)$. $\sqrt{89}$

36. *Horology* Through how many degrees does the second hand of a clock rotate during a 93-min movie? 33,480°

37. Through how many degrees does a point on the equator rotate in 38 h? 570°

38. Through how many degrees does a point on latitude 20°N rotate in 38 h? 570°

Ⓒ 39. Find all angles t such that $3t$ is coterminal with 180° and t is between 0° and 360°. 60°, 180°, 300°

40. Find all angles t such that $4t$ is coterminal with 60° and t is between 0° and 360°. 15°, 105°, 195°, 285°

124 Chapter 3 Trigonometric Functions

Writing in Mathematics

32. Answers may vary. Students' answers should include the following ideas: To change from degrees-minutes-seconds to decimal degrees, use the proportions 1 minute is $\frac{1}{60}$ degree and 1 second is $\frac{1}{60}$ minute or $\frac{1}{3600}$ degree. Find the sum of the degrees plus $\frac{1}{60}$ times the minutes plus $\frac{1}{3600}$ times the seconds to obtain decimal degrees.

41. Find the measure in decimal degrees of the angle supplementary to 99°12′20″. 80.79°

42. Find the measure in decimal degrees of the angle complementary to 16°5′56″. 73.90°

43. *Horology* Through how many degrees does the second hand of a clock rotate in 2 h 23 min 20 s? 51,600°

44. Find the measure in degrees-minutes-seconds of an angle that is 11°5′40″ greater than its complement. 50°32′50″

45. *Entertainment* A certain 78-rpm phonograph record has a playing time of three minutes thirty-two and one-half seconds. Through how many degrees does it rotate during its playing time? 99,450°

46. *Horology* What is the measure in degrees of the smaller of the angles formed by the hands of a clock at 6:12? 114°

47. *Horology* What is the measure in degrees of the smaller of the angles formed by the hands of a clock at 3:15? 7.5°

Project

Hold a class forum to discuss what temperatures, seasons, and the lives of trees, flowers, birds, and insects would be like if the earth were inclined differently on its axis.

Review

Factor.

1. $125x^3 + y^3$ $(5x + y)(25x^2 - 5xy + y^2)$

2. $4x^2 - 12xy + 9y^2$ $(2x - 3y)^2$

What figures do each set of vertices represent? Draw the figure on a rectangular coordinate system and label the vertices.

3. $(0, 0), (a, 0), (a, a), (0, a)$

4. $(0, 0), (2a, 0), (0, 2b)$

5. Determine an equation of a line perpendicular to the line $2y = -x + 3$ and passing through the point $(4, 5)$. $y = 2x - 3$

6. Graph $f(x) = x^2 + 1$ and $g(x) = -x^2 + 9$ on the same set of axes. From the graph determine the solution set. $(-2, 5); (2, 5)$

7. Find a polynomial $P(x)$ with the given factors $x + 3i, x - 3i, 5x + 1$. $P(x) = 5x^3 + x^2 + 45x + 9$

8. The vertices of a rhombus *ABCD* are $(0, 0), (a, 0), (a + b, \sqrt{a^2 - b^2})$ and $(b, \sqrt{a^2 - b^2})$. Prove that the diagonals of a rhombus are perpendicular.

9. In which quadrant(s) does a point have a negative *x*-coordinate? A positive *x* and a negative *y*? Both coordinates positive? II, III; IV; I

10. The graph of a rational algebraic function has symmetry with respect to the line $x = 1$. Explain how the graphing process can be simplified. Graph the function for $x > 1$ and reflect it about $x = 1$.

Find the number of degrees in each interior angle of a regular

11. pentagon 108°

12. hexagon 120°

3.1 Angles in the Coordinate Plane **125**

Additional Answers

24.

25.

26.

Review

8. $m_{\overline{AC}} = \dfrac{\sqrt{a^2 - b^2} - 0}{a + b - 0} = \dfrac{\sqrt{a^2 - b^2}}{a + b}$;

$m_{\overline{BD}} = \dfrac{\sqrt{a^2 - b^2} - 0}{b - a} = \dfrac{\sqrt{a^2 - b^2}}{-(a - b)} =$

$-\sqrt{\dfrac{(a - b)(a + b)}{(a - b)(a - b)}} = -\sqrt{\dfrac{a + b}{a - b}} =$

$-\sqrt{\dfrac{(a + b)^2}{(a - b)(a + b)}} = -\dfrac{(a + b)}{\sqrt{a^2 - b^2}}$;

$m_{\overline{AC}} \cdot m_{\overline{BD}} = -1$

3.

square

4.

right triangle

6.

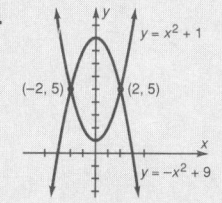

125

Ⓜ **Materials/Manipulatives**
circles of varying radii
globe or map of the world
string

Technology
scientific calculator
computer or programmable
  calculator

FOCUS

Eratosthenes was a librarian as well as a geographer, mathematician, poet, historian, and one of the most learned scholars of ancient time. He is known to many mathematics students for the "Sieve of Eratosthenes," a method for isolating prime numbers. Students may be interested in researching and demonstrating this method.

INSTRUCTION

Ⓜ • Use string to measure the radius of a large circle and then use that length to measure an arc of the same length on the circle. Emphasize that the arc corresponds to a central angle of 1 rad.
  • Students should be comfortable with the estimation that there are approximately 6 rad in a circle and 3 rad in a semicircle.

Technology Engineers sometimes use grads to measure angles. Since this unit of measure appears on some calculators, students may wish to research grads.

3.2 Angle Measures in Degrees and Radians

Objectives: To measure angles using degrees and radians
To convert between degree measure and radian measure
To measure arcs and sectors of circles

Focus

Can you locate Japan, the Persian Gulf, or the Pacific Ocean on a world map? A survey conducted jointly by the Gallup Organization of the United States and the Soviet Academy of Sciences showed that citizens of these two countries are far from expert in the field of geography.

There are signs that interest in geography is increasing. For example, the *National Geographic Society* sponsors a national geography contest and awards college scholarships to the top scoring students. A computer game that teaches geography is now very popular.

Ancient scholars were interested in geography. In fact, centuries before Columbus sailed across the Atlantic, the mathematician Eratosthenes wrote a geography text which mapped out the entire known world. He used knowledge of angle measurement to compute the circumference of the earth.

Measuring angles using degrees has deep roots in history and tradition. The exact origin of the 360° circle is not known, but it is clear that the use of the number 360 is arbitrary. There is another unit for measuring angles called a *radian* that is not arbitrary because it is related to the radius of the circle.

A **central angle** of a circle is an angle whose vertex is the center of the circle. When a central angle θ intercepts an arc that has the same length as the radius of the circle, the measure of that angle is one **radian,** abbreviated 1 rad. Note that the measure of an angle of 1 rad is independent of the size of the circle. Whenever the measure of an angle is given without specified units, assume that radian measure is being used.

θ = 1 rad

The circumference of a circle of radius r is $2\pi r$, so there are $\frac{2\pi r}{r}$ or 2π arcs of length r on the circle. Thus, an angle of one rotation or $360°$ has measure 2π rad. Since $360° = 2\pi$ rad, $180° = \pi$ rad, and $1° = \frac{\pi}{180}$ rad.

To convert from degrees to radians:

Multiply the number of degrees by $\frac{\pi}{180}$.

Example 1 Express each angle measure in radians. Give answers in terms of π.
  a. $135°$ **b.** $-90°$

  a. $135\left(\frac{\pi}{180}\right) = \frac{3\pi}{4}$ **b.** $-90\left(\frac{\pi}{180}\right) = -\frac{\pi}{2}$

Since π rad $= 180°$, 1 rad $= \frac{180}{\pi}$ degrees.

To convert from radians to degrees:

Multiply the number of radians by $\frac{180}{\pi}$.

Example 2 Express each angle measure in degrees. If necessary, round to the nearest tenth of a degree.
  a. $-\frac{8\pi}{3}$ **b.** $\frac{8}{3}$

  a. $-\frac{8\pi}{3} \cdot \frac{180}{\pi} = -480°$ **b.** $\frac{8}{3} \cdot \frac{180}{\pi} \approx 152.8°$

For estimating, remember that there are 2π, or about 6.3, rad in a complete rotation. One radian is approximately equal to $57.3°$.

Some calculators have functions that can be used to convert directly from one unit of angle measure to another. The instruction booklet that accompanies the calculator will explain the procedure.

The definition of radian measure relates the radius r of the circle to the length s of the arc intercepted by a central angle θ as follows:

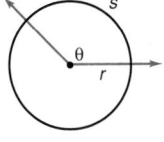

$$\theta = \frac{s}{r}$$

The number of radii in the arc is the measure of the angle in radians. This leads to the following formula for arc length.

For Example 3

1. Find the arc length to the nearest tenth of a centimeter of a circle of radius 4.5 cm that is intercepted by a central angle of 0.6π. 8.5 cm
2. Find the arc length to the nearest tenth of a centimeter of a circle of radius 7 cm that is intercepted by a central angle of 85°. 10.4 cm

Common Error Some students forget to change degrees to radians before using the formula for arc length. Remind them that the formula came from the definition of the *radian measure* of a central angle, and so is only meaningful for an angle measured in radians.

For Example 4

1. A pendulum swings through an angle of $\frac{1}{4}\pi$ rad, describing an arc 0.4 m long. Determine the length of the pendulum to the nearest tenth of a meter. 0.5 cm
2. A pendulum swings through an angle of 30°, describing an arc 1.2 m long. Determine the length of the pendulum to the nearest tenth of a meter. 2.3 m

Ⓜ **Modeling**

If students use a globe or map of the world to locate the places mentioned in the Focus, keep in mind that the present day name of Syene is Aswan.

For Example 5

Suppose that in the model described in Example 5, a third pole located in Nairobi, Kenya showed that the sun's rays made an angle of 25° with the pole. Find the distance from Syene to Nairobi to the nearest 100 km. 2700 km

The length s of the arc of a circle of radius r determined by central angle θ expressed in radians is given by $s = r\theta$.

Example 3 Determine to the nearest tenth of a centimeter the arc length of a circle of radius 24.5 cm that is intercepted by a central angle of 45°.

$$s = \frac{\pi}{4}(24.5) \qquad 45° = \frac{\pi}{4}$$
$$s = 19.2 \text{ cm} \qquad \text{To the nearest tenth}$$

Problems involving arc length have many real world applications.

Example 4 *Physics* A pendulum swings through an angle of 60°, describing an arc 5.0 m long. Determine the length of the pendulum to the nearest tenth of a meter.

Think of the pendulum as the radius of a circle.

$$s = r\theta$$
$$5.0 = \frac{r\pi}{3} \qquad 60° = \frac{\pi}{3}$$
$$r = \frac{15}{\pi}$$
$$\quad\, = 4.8 \text{ m} \qquad \text{To the nearest tenth of a meter}$$

The length of the pendulum is approximately 4.8 m.

Modeling

How did Eratosthenes compute the circumference of the earth?

Based on observations, Eratosthenes assumed that the earth is a sphere. He inferred that the earth is not only round, it is uniformly round. Thus, measurements made on a relatively small scale can be used to estimate much larger distances.

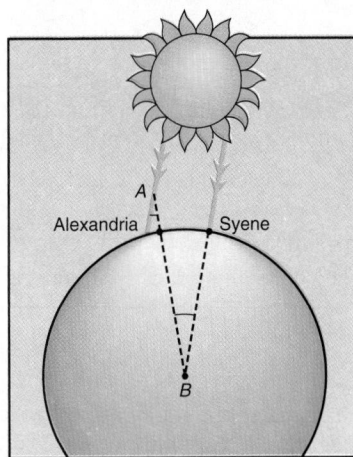

Eratosthenes knew that at noon on the first day of summer, the sun shone directly to the bottom of a well at Syene, a city in Egypt. Thus, the sun was directly overhead. At the same time and day in Alexandria, a city north of Syene, he used the shadow of a pole to calculate that the sun's rays made an angle of 7.2° with the pole, which is one-fiftieth of the measure of a full circle. He also knew that the measure of $\angle A$ is equal to the measure of $\angle B$. The drawing at the right is similar to the model that he must have used.

128   Chapter 3 Trigonometric Functions

Example 5 *Geography*   If Eratosthenes' estimate for the distance between Syene and Alexandria was 5000 stadia, describe how to estimate the circumference of the earth in stadia and in kilometers (1 stadium ≈ 0.157 km).

If the sun's rays are parallel, then ∠A and ∠B are congruent alternate interior angles of parallel lines. Therefore, ∠B is also one-fiftieth of a circle which is the circumference of the earth. Thus, the distance from Syene to Alexandria is one-fiftieth of the earth's circumference.

$$\frac{1}{50}C = 5000$$

$$C = 250{,}000 \text{ stadia}$$

$$C = (250{,}000)(0.157) \text{ km} = 39{,}250 \text{ km}$$

A sector of a circle is a region bounded by a central angle and an intercepted arc. Like arc length, the area A_s of a sector of a circle of radius r can be found using radians. A simple proportion gives a formula. If the radian measure of the central angle is θ, then

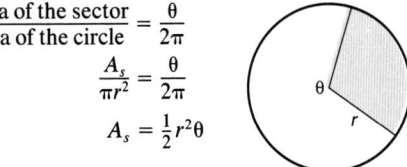

$$\frac{\text{area of the sector}}{\text{area of the circle}} = \frac{\theta}{2\pi}$$

$$\frac{A_s}{\pi r^2} = \frac{\theta}{2\pi}$$

$$A_s = \frac{1}{2}r^2\theta$$

Example 6   Determine to the nearest tenth of a square centimeter the area of the sector of a circle of radius 9.0 cm intercepted by a central angle of 120°.

$$A_s = \frac{1}{2}r^2\theta$$

$$A_s = \frac{1}{2}(9.0)^2\left(\frac{2\pi}{3}\right) \qquad 120° = \frac{2\pi}{3}$$

$$A_s = 84.8 \text{ cm}^2 \qquad \text{To the nearest tenth}$$

The area of the sector is approximately 84.8 cm².

Class Exercises

Express each angle measure in radians. Give answers in terms of π.

1. 30° $\frac{\pi}{6}$ **2.** −45° $-\frac{\pi}{4}$ **3.** 475° $\frac{95\pi}{36}$ **4.** 540° 3π

Express each angle measure in degrees. If necessary, round to the nearest tenth of 1 degree.

5. $\frac{2\pi}{3}$ 120°   **6.** $\frac{5\pi}{6}$ 150°   **7.** $\frac{2}{3}$ 38.2°   **8.** 5 286.5°

9. Determine the angle coterminal with $-\frac{7\pi}{4}$ that has radian measure between 0 and 2π rad. $\frac{\pi}{4}$

3.2 Angle Measures in Degrees and Radians   **129**

For Example 6
Determine the area to the nearest tenth of a square meter of the sector of a circle of radius 1.6 m intercepted by a central angle of $\frac{1}{4}\pi$.

1.0 m²

CLOSURE

Have students write a paragraph or two in their math journals which discusses converting degrees to radians and vice versa, and the procedures for measuring arcs and sectors of circles.

INDEPENDENT PRACTICE

Assignment Guide
Basic: 1–22, 31–35, 37–39, Project
Average: 1–6, 13–14, 16–41, Project
Enriched: 20, 22, 25–49, Project

Teacher's Resource Book
  Practice, page 17

Ⓡ Review
Exercises 19, 21, 31, 37, and 39 review the concepts of locating angles, using functions, graphing, and finding real solutions of a quadratic equation.

Project
This project is more effective if the students get actively involved by researching the exact latitude at which their school is located.

17.

Degrees	Radians	Degrees	Radians
0°	0	210°	$\frac{7\pi}{6}$
30°	$\frac{\pi}{6}$	225°	$\frac{5\pi}{4}$
45°	$\frac{\pi}{4}$	240°	$\frac{4\pi}{3}$
60°	$\frac{\pi}{3}$	270°	$\frac{3\pi}{2}$
90°	$\frac{\pi}{2}$	300°	$\frac{5\pi}{3}$
120°	$\frac{2\pi}{3}$	315°	$\frac{7\pi}{4}$
135°	$\frac{3\pi}{4}$	330°	$\frac{11\pi}{6}$
150°	$\frac{5\pi}{6}$	360°	2π
180°	π		

10. Determine the angle coterminal with -3π that has a radian measure between 0 and 2π rad. π

11. Determine the arc length of a circle of radius 6 cm intercepted by an angle of $\frac{1}{2}\pi$. 3π cm

12. Determine to the nearest tenth of a centimeter the arc length of a circle of radius 11.9 cm intercepted by an angle of 155°. 32.2 cm

13. Determine to the nearest tenth of a square inch the area of the sector of a circle of radius 10 in. intercepted by a central angle of $\frac{\pi}{8}$. 19.6 in.²

14. Determine to the nearest tenth of a square inch the area of the sector of a circle of radius 3.8 in. intercepted by a central angle of 42°. 5.3 in.²

15. *Geography* The radius of the earth is approximately 3960 mi. How many miles does a 48° longitudinal angle intercept at the equator? 3318 mi

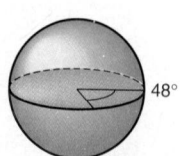

16. *Navigation* A nautical mile is the distance between two points on the equator whose longitudes differ by $\frac{1}{60}$ degree (1 minute). Assume that the radius of the earth is approximately 3960 mi, and show that a nautical mile is 1.15 times the length of a mile. $\left[\frac{1}{60} \cdot \frac{\pi}{180}\right] \cdot 3960 = 1.15$

17. Make a chart of corresponding degree and radian measures of familiar angles and illustrate those values on a circle.

Practice Exercises Use appropriate technology.

Express each angle measure in radians. Give answers in terms of π.

A 1. 120° $\frac{2\pi}{3}$ 2. $-80°$ $-\frac{4\pi}{9}$ 3. $-415°$ $-\frac{83\pi}{36}$ 4. 17° $\frac{17\pi}{180}$ 5. 25.5° $\frac{17\pi}{120}$ 6. $-48.1°$ $-\frac{481\pi}{1800}$

Express each angle measure in degrees.

7. $\frac{9\pi}{8}$ 202.5° 8. $-\frac{17\pi}{18}$ $-170°$ 9. $-\frac{14\pi}{9}$ $-280°$ 10. 3.1π 558°

11. 2.4π 432° 12. 3 171.9° 13. -7 $-401.1°$ 14. 1.42 81.4°

15. Determine to the nearest centimeter the arc length of a circle of radius 23 cm that is intercepted by a central angle of $\frac{\pi}{9}$. 8 cm

16. Determine to the nearest tenth of a centimeter the arc length of a circle of radius 117 cm that is intercepted by a central angle of $\frac{5\pi}{3}$. 612.6 cm

17. *Horology* A pendulum of length 2.4 m swings through an angle of 35°. How far does the tip of the pendulum travel? 1.5 m

18. *Horology* A pendulum of length 1.8 m swings through an angle of θ degrees. If its tip travels 2.6 m, what is the value of θ? 1.44 rad

Ⓡ 19. In what quadrant does the terminal side of an angle of 1.5 rad lie? I

20. *Horology* A pendulum of length 13 in. swings through an angle of 24°. How far does the tip of the pendulum travel? 5.4 in.

Ⓡ 21. Find a function $f(t)$ to express the degree measure of an angle whose radian measure is t. $f(t) = \frac{180t}{\pi}$

22. **Thinking Critically** Why do you think the number 360 was chosen for measuring angles? Name some other commonly used units of measure and discuss their origins. Answers may vary. Ex. yard, foot.

Express each angle measure in radians. If necessary, round answers to the nearest tenth of a radian.

B 23. 75°25′ 1.3   24. −42°50′ −0.7   25. 150°10′ 2.6   26. −117°35′ −2.1

27. Determine to the nearest tenth of a centimeter the arc length of a circle of radius 21.1 cm that is intercepted by a central angle of 67°. 24.7 cm

28. Determine to the nearest tenth of a foot the arc length of a circle of diameter 9.1 ft that is intercepted by a central angle of 194°. 15.4 ft

29. Determine to the nearest tenth of a centimeter the arc length of a circle of diameter 3.3 cm that is intercepted by a central angle of 24°. 0.7 cm

30. A wedged-shaped piece is cut from a pizza 10 in. in diameter so that the rounded edge of the crust measures 4.4 in. Determine the measure in degrees of the angle at the pointed end of the pie. 50.4°

Ⓡ 31. Solve $8 - \sqrt{x - 4} \geq 3$ for x. $4 \leq x \leq 29$

32. *Horology* The minute hand on a clock is 11.5 cm long. How far does its tip move between 4:00 and 4:15? 18.1 cm

33. Find to the nearest tenth of a square centimeter the area of the sector of a circle of radius 2.2 cm that is intercepted by a central angle of 14°. 0.6 cm²

34. Find to the nearest tenth of a square centimeter the area of the sector of a circle of radius 2.4 cm that is intercepted by a central angle of 300°. 15.1 cm²

35. The area of a circle is 36π m². Determine to the nearest square meter the area of the sector intercepted by a central angle of 50°. 15.7 cm²

36. The area of a circle is 50 cm². Determine to the nearest square centimeter the area of the sector intercepted by a central angle of 210°. 29.2 cm²

Ⓡ 37. Use a graphing utility to determine the number of real solutions of the function $f(x) = 3x^2 - 2x - 1$. 2

38. **Writing in Mathematics** Compare and contrast the definition of angle given in this chapter to the definition from elementary geometry, "An angle is the union of two noncollinear rays with a common endpoint."

Ⓡ 39. Determine the domain of the function $f(z) = \frac{z^2}{\sqrt{z^2 - 5}}$. $\{z \in R: |z| > \sqrt{5}\}$

C 40. *Mechanics* The wheel of a car has a 15-in. radius. Through what angle (in radians) does a point on the wheel rotate as the car travels 1 mi? 4224 rad

41. *Sports* A bicycle wheel has a diameter of 36 cm. Through what angle (in radians) does a point on the wheel rotate as the bicycle travels 1 km? 5555.6 rad

Writing in Mathematics
38. Answers may vary. One possibility follows: The definition of an angle as the union of two noncollinear rays with a common endpoint does not take into account the direction in which the angle is generated. If direction is important, the definition of this lesson is more useful.

LESSON FOLLOW-UP

Lesson Quiz

1. Express 35° in radians. Give the answer in terms of π. $\frac{7\pi}{36}$

2. Express 3.6π in degrees. 648°

3. Express 2.4 radians in degrees. Round the answer to the nearest tenth of a degree. 137.5°

4. Determine the arc length to the nearest tenth of a meter of a circle of radius 0.9 m that is intercepted by a central angle of 190°. 3.0 m

5. A pendulum swings through an angle of 25°, describing an arc 0.25 m long. Determine the length of the pendulum to the nearest hundredth of a meter. 0.57 m

6. Determine the area to the nearest tenth of a square meter of the sector of a circle of radius 1.9 m intercepted by a central angle of 115°. 3.6 m²

Additional Answers

37.

Construction   A large winch of diameter 1.1 m is used to lift heavy equipment as shown.

42. Find to the nearest tenth of a radian the angle through which the winch must turn in order to lift the equipment 2.5 m. 4.5 rad

43. To the nearest tenth of a meter how high is the equipment lifted when the winch rotates counterclockwise $\frac{15\pi}{8}$ rad? 3.2 m

44. Find all angles t such that $2t$ is coterminal with $\frac{5\pi}{6}$ and t is between 0 and 2π. $\frac{5\pi}{12}, \frac{17\pi}{12}$

45. *Geography*   San Francisco and Seattle are on the same meridian; that is, Seattle is due north of San Francisco. If the latitude of San Francisco is 37°47′ and that of Seattle is 47°37′, find the distance between the two cities. The radius of the earth is approximately 3960 mi. 679.3 mi

46. *Architecture*   An architect wishes to place six equally spaced lampposts around the edge of a semicircular plot as shown. The diameter of the semicircle is 24 m. What is the distance (around the semicircle) between any two lampposts? 7.5 m

47. An angle in standard position whose measure is $-\frac{7\pi}{6}$ undergoes $\frac{4}{3}$ counterclockwise rotations. Determine the measure of the angle between 0 and 2π that is coterminal with the resulting angle. $\frac{3\pi}{2}$

48. An angle in standard position whose measure is $\frac{3\pi}{8}$ undergoes $\frac{11}{3}$ clockwise rotations. Determine the measure of the angle between 0 and 2π that is coterminal with the resulting angle. $\frac{25\pi}{24}$

49. **Writing in Mathematics**   Explain why the formula $A_s = \frac{1}{2}r^2\theta$ for the area of a sector of a circle does *not* hold if θ is measured in degrees. Determine a formula for the area of a sector using degrees. In the proportion $\frac{A_s}{A_c} = \frac{\theta}{2\pi}$, θ is compared to 1 rotation expressed in *radians* (2π). $A = \frac{1}{2}r^2\theta\left(\frac{\pi}{180}\right) = \frac{\pi r^2\theta}{360}$.

Project

At noon on the first day of summer, the sun is directly overhead at latitude 23.5° north. Discuss how you can verify the circumference of the earth if you know the latitude of the point at which you are located. How would your measurements change for the first day of spring or fall when the sun is directly over the equator?

Challenge

1. Find two functions $f(x)$ and $g(x)$ such that $f(g(x)) = g(f(x))$.

2. Graph $f(x) = \llbracket|x|\rrbracket$ and $g(x) = |\llbracket x\rrbracket|$ on separate axes. Determine the points where $f(x) = g(x)$. $x \geq 0$

3. If $a \neq 0$, for what values of a and b does the following equation hold?

$$(a - b)(a + b) = b(a - b)$$ $a = b$

3.3 Applications: Angular and Linear Velocity

Objective: To solve problems involving angular velocity and linear velocity

Focus

In recent decades, automobile manufacturers have designed changes in transmissions to improve the mileage obtained by automobiles. The three-speed transmission has been replaced by the four-speed and five-speed transmissions found in today's cars. The use of more gears in transmissions produces more efficient performance in cars with smaller engines. More efficient engines, lighter-weight cars, and more aerodynamic body designs have all contributed to better gasoline mileage.

In Lesson 3.2, the formula for the length of a circular arc, $s = r\theta$, followed from the definition of radian measure. This formula can also be used to analyze the motion of a point along a circular path. Gears, tires, and ferris wheels are examples of circular objects that turn about axes through their centers and display *rotary motion*. Consider point P on the edge of a wheel with center O. As the wheel rotates, ray $\overrightarrow{OP}$ moves through an angle called the *angular displacement* θ of P.

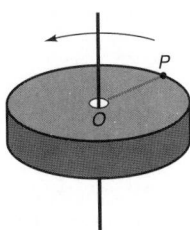

Example 1 *Mechanics* A wheel makes $1\frac{1}{4}$ rotations about its axis. Find the angular displacement in radians of a point P on the wheel.

Since $\overrightarrow{OP}$ moves through 2π rad for each rotation,

$$\theta = \frac{5}{4}(2\pi) = \frac{5\pi}{2}$$

Consider two points A and B on a record. As the record revolves, A travels a greater distance than B. Therefore, in some sense, A must be traveling faster than B. In order to study situations like this, a distinction is made between *angular velocity* and *linear velocity*.

Some students learn best if they are familiar with at least one lesson objective before they begin assembling information. Begin by posing a question such as "Which seat on a merry-go-round should a child choose for the fastest ride? for the slowest ride?" Students may be able to answer from experience. Note that this lesson will help them answer the question *and* understand why the answer is correct.

GUIDED PRACTICE

For Example 1

1. A gear makes 1.5 rotations about its axis. What is the angular displacement in radians of a point on the gear? $3\pi \approx 9.4$ rad

2. A circular knob is used to advance the paper in a typewriter. The knob makes 3.3 rotations about its axis. Find the angular displacement in radians of a point on the edge of the knob.
$6.6\pi \approx 20.7$ rad

For Example 2

1. Find the angular velocity of the tip of the minute hand of a watch in radians per second. 0.0017 rad/s

2. Find the angular velocity of the tip of the hour hand of a watch in radians per minute. 0.0087 rad/min

For Example 3

1. Find the angular velocity in radians per second of a point on a gear turning at the rate of 3.4 rpm. 0.36 rad/s

2. What is the angular velocity in radians per second of a notch on a wheel turning at a rate of 7600 rpm? 795.87 rad/s

---

The **angular velocity** ω of a point moving in a circular path is the angular displacement θ of the point per unit time t. Thus,

$$\omega = \frac{\theta}{t}$$

Angular velocity may be expressed in units such as revolutions per minute (rpm) or radians per second (rad/s).

Example 2 *Horology* Determine the angular velocity of the tip of the second hand of a clock in radians per second.

A second hand makes 1 revolution of 2π rad in 60 s.

Therefore, $\omega = \frac{\theta}{t} = \frac{2\pi}{60} \approx 0.1$ rad/s.

Many applications of angular velocity involve objects such as wheels, tires, and gears.

Example 3 *Mechanics* A wheel turns at the rate of 600 rpm. What is the angular velocity of the wheel in radians per second?

The rate of 600 rpm indicates that the wheel turns through $600(2\pi)$ rad in 1 min.

$$\omega = \frac{\theta}{t} = \frac{600(2\pi)}{60} \approx 63 \text{ rad/s}$$

On the record described earlier, *A* and *B* have the same angular displacements per unit of time. Thus, their angular velocities are the same. However, their *linear* velocities differ.

If an object moves along a circle of radius r at a constant rate, its **linear velocity** V is the distance s traveled along the circumference of the circle per unit of time t. Therefore,

$$V = \frac{s}{t} = \frac{r\theta}{t}$$

where θ is the angular displacement of the object in radians.

Example 4 *Horology* The second hand of a clock is 8.0 cm long. What is the linear velocity of the tip of this hand?

The tip of the hand travels 2π rad in 60 s.

$$V = \frac{r\theta}{t} = \frac{8.0(2\pi)}{60} \approx 0.84 \text{ cm/s}$$

134 Chapter 3 Trigonometric Functions

The word *radian* is not included in the answer to Example 4 because a radian is actually a ratio of two lengths and has no dimension. The word is sometimes retained to indicate that angle measure is involved.

There is a simple relationship between the angular velocity and the linear velocity of the same point.

> If a point travels in a circular path with radius r at a constant speed, linear velocity V, angular velocity ω, and angular displacement θ (measured in radians), then
> $$V = \frac{r\theta}{t} = r \cdot \frac{\theta}{t} = r\omega$$

Example 5 If the inner radius of a record is 0.50 cm, the outer radius is 15.0 cm, and it rotates at $33\frac{1}{3}$ rpm, compare the linear velocities of the points A and B.

$$\omega = \frac{\theta}{t} = \frac{\frac{100}{3}(2\pi)}{60} = \frac{10\pi}{9} \text{ rad/s} \qquad \textit{Angular velocity}$$

For point A: $V = r\omega = (15.0)\dfrac{10\pi}{9} \approx 52.4$ cm/s

For point B: $V = r\omega = (0.50)\dfrac{10\pi}{9} \approx 1.7$ cm/s

It is important to use consistent units of measure when working with problems of angular and linear velocity.

Example 6 *Sports* Hans rides a vehicle with large tires of radius 16 in. at 24 mph.
  a. Find the angular velocity of a tire in radians per minute.
  b. How many revolutions per minute does the tire make?

a. First, adjust the units of linear velocity to inches per minute.

$$V = \frac{24 \text{ mi}}{\text{h}} \cdot \frac{5280 \text{ ft}}{1 \text{ mi}} \cdot \frac{12 \text{ in}}{1 \text{ ft}} \cdot \frac{1 \text{ h}}{60 \text{ min}}$$
$$= 25{,}344 \text{ in./min}$$

Then, $\omega = \dfrac{V}{r} = \dfrac{25{,}344}{16} = 1584$ rad/min

Why is the answer in radians per minute?

b. To find the number of revolutions per minute, divide ω by 2π.

$$\frac{1584}{2\pi} \approx 252 \text{ rpm}$$

3.3 Applications: Angular and Linear Velocity   **135**

For Example 4
1. The second hand of a watch is 1.1 cm long. What is the linear velocity of the tip of this hand? 0.12 cm/s
2. A skater moves around the edge of a circular practice rink at the rate of 2 rpm. The rink has a radius of 4.1 m. What is the skater's velocity in meters per minute? 51.52 m/min

For Example 5
1. A gear rotates at 5 rps. Compare the linear velocities of two points 0.8 cm and 5.2 cm from the center of the gear. 25.1 cm/s; 163.4 cm/s
2. A merry-go-round at a playground spins at 1 rev/36 s. Compare the linear velocities of two children who are 2 ft and 4 ft from the center of the merry-go-round. 0.3 ft/s; 0.7 ft/s

For Example 6
A unicycle has a tire with radius 10 in. It is traveling at a speed of 5.5 mi/h.
1. Find the angular velocity of the tire in radians per second. 9.68 rad/s
2. How many revolutions per second does the tire make? 1.54 rps

Common Error Some students do not use unit labels effectively as a way of checking their answers. Encourage these students to use unit labels throughout the steps of solving problems like these.

Thinking Critically
The word *radian* is added to the answer in Example 6a to indicate that angular measurement is involved.

Students may be interested in researching the crankshift to drive shaft rpm for five-speed cars to which they have access to drive and comparing those ratios to the ratios stated in the model.

For Example 7

At what speeds is the third gear most efficient for the car described in Modeling? between 25.0 and 44.5 mi/h

CLOSURE

Have students write a paragraph in their math journals comparing and contrasting angular and linear velocity.

INDEPENDENT PRACTICE

Assignment Guide

Basic: 1–25, 28–29, 33, 35, Project
Average: 11–39, Project
Enriched: 21–49, Project

Teacher's Resource Book
Practice, page 18

Ⓡ Review

Exercises 7, 11, 18, 29, and 33 review the concepts of changing radians to degrees and vice versa, finding zeros of a polynomial, using coordinate geometry, and determining quadratic equations with two, one, or no real solutions.

Project

The act of creating models for this project greatly enlivens the discussion of the subject matter. However, be sure that students' models reflect an understanding for the *mathematical* concepts behind automotive design.

Modeling

Why does a car transmission have different gears?

To make the wheels of a car turn, the crankshaft and the drive shaft must also turn. The engine of a specific car runs most efficiently and uses less gas when the number of revolutions per minute of the crankshaft remains within 1800 and 3200 rpm. But to provide power and to make the wheels turn at different speeds, the drive shaft must turn at widely different speeds. The transmission gears make it possible for a given number of crankshaft revolutions to result in a wide range of drive shaft revolutions.

For a particular 5-speed car, the crankshaft–to–drive shaft rpm ratio is as follows: first gear, 3.5 to 1; second gear, 2 to 1; third gear, 1.4 to 1; fourth gear, 1 to 1; and fifth gear, 0.8 to 1. The tachometer monitors the rpm's of the crankshaft. At low speeds the drive shaft turns slowly in comparison to the crankshaft. At high speeds the opposite is true.

The drive shaft revolutions are converted to wheel revolutions at a fixed ratio. For this car, the drive shaft–to–wheel rpm ratio is 3.5 to 1 and each wheel has a circumference of approximately 6 ft.

Example 7 *Automotive Technology*   At what speeds is second gear most efficient for the car described above?

For second gear, the crankshaft–to–drive shaft rpm ratio is $2:1$. Thus, the number of revolutions per minute of the drive shaft is between $\frac{1800}{2}$ and $\frac{3200}{2}$ (900 to 1600 rpm).

The lowest speed can be determined as follows:

$$\frac{900 \text{ rev}}{\text{min}} \div (3.5) \cdot \frac{6 \text{ ft}}{\text{rev}} \cdot \frac{60 \text{ min}}{\text{h}} \cdot \frac{1 \text{ mi}}{5280 \text{ ft}} \approx 17.5 \text{ mph}$$

The highest speed can be determined as follows:

$$\frac{1600 \text{ rev}}{\text{min}} \div (3.5) \cdot \frac{6 \text{ ft}}{\text{rev}} \cdot \frac{60 \text{ min}}{\text{h}} \cdot \frac{1 \text{ mi}}{5280 \text{ ft}} \approx 31.2 \text{ mph}$$

Thus, in second gear, the car is most efficient between speeds of approximately 17.5 and 31.2 mph.

136   Chapter 3 Trigonometric Functions

Class Exercises

1. A wheel rotates 3.5 revolutions. Determine the angular displacement in radians of a point on the wheel. 7π

2. A gear rotates 0.45 revolution. Determine the angular displacement in radians of a point on the gear. 0.9π

Determine the angular velocity in radians per second of a wheel turning at the given number of revolutions per minute.

3. 100 10.5 rad/s   4. 350 36.7 rad/s   5. 192 20.1 rad/s   6. 188.8 19.8 rad/s

Determine the number of revolutions per minute of a wheel with the given angular velocity.

7. 33 rad/s 315.1 rpm   8. 52.8 rad/s 504.2 rpm   9. 88.2 rad/s 842.2 rpm

10. Determine the angular velocity in radians per second of a 45-rpm record. 4.71 rad/s

11. *Recreation* Determine the angular velocity in radians per second of a ferris wheel that takes 42 s to rotate once. 0.15 rad/s

12. *Recreation* Suppose that the ferris wheel of Exercise 11 has a diameter of 220 ft. Determine the linear velocity of a car on the rim of the wheel. 16.5 ft/s

13. *Geography* Assume that the earth is a sphere with radius 3960 mi. How fast is a point on the equator moving as the earth rotates about its axis? Express your answer in miles per hour. 1036.7 mi/h

Practice Exercises

 Use appropriate technology.

A 1. A wheel rotates 1.23 revolutions. Find the angular displacement in radians of a point on the wheel. 2.46π

2. *Home Economics* A bobbin on a sewing machine rotates 0.91 revolution. Find the angular displacement in radians of a point on the bobbin. 1.82π

Determine the angular velocity in radians per second of a wheel turning at the given number of revolutions per minute.

3. 124 12.99 rad/s   4. 36.5 3.82 rad/s   5. 1.5 0.16 rad/s   6. 78.6 8.23 rad/s

Ⓡ 7. Determine the radian measure of an angle of 76°. $\frac{19\pi}{45}$

Determine the number of revolutions per minute of a wheel with the given angular velocity.

8. 57 rad/s 544.31 rpm   9. 151 rad/s 1441.9 rpm   10. 300 deg/s 50 rpm

Ⓡ 11. Determine the degree measure of an angle of 2.5 rad. 143.2°

Determine the linear velocity V of a point rotating at angular velocity ω at a distance r from the axis of rotation.

12. $r = 15$ in., $\omega = 5\pi$ rad/s 75π in./s   13. $r = 1.3$ m, $\omega = 3.5\pi$ rad/s 4.55π m/s

14. $r = 22$ cm, $\omega = 8.5$ rad/s 187 cm/s   15. $r = 9.2$ cm, $\omega = 23$ rad/s 211.6 cm/s

16. $r = 1.4$ m, $\omega = 0.5$ rad/s 0.7 m/s   17. $r = 2.3$ m, $\omega = 14$ rad/s 32.2 m/s

3.3 Applications: Angular and Linear Velocity **137**

137

R 18. Use a graphing utility to estimate the zeros of the polynomial function
$f(x) = x^3 - 5x^2 + x + 1$. −0.35; 0.60; 4.74

Determine the linear velocity V of a point on a circle r units from the center
that moves through an angle θ in 1 min. Express your answers in centimeters
per second.

19. $r = 72$ cm, $\theta = 1.4\pi$ rad 1.68π cm/s   20. $r = 7.1$ cm, $\theta = 17$ rad 2 cm/s

21. $r = 1.2$ m, $\theta = 250°$ $\frac{25\pi}{9}$ cm/s   22. $r = 0.8$ m, $\theta = 1980°$ $\frac{44\pi}{3}$ cm/s

B 23. $r = 13$ m, $\theta = \frac{1}{4}\pi$ rad $\frac{65\pi}{12}$ cm/s   24. $r = 5$ m, $\theta = 56°$ $\frac{70\pi}{27}$ cm/s

25. *Engineering* If an engine is making 1000 rpm, what is the angular velocity
of the engine's crankshaft in radians per second? 104.7 rad/s

26. *Engineering* A flywheel mounted on an engine crankshaft has a radius of
6 in. If the engine is running at 2800 rpm, what is the linear velocity of a
point on the outer edge of the flywheel in feet per second? 146.6 ft/s

27. A point on a circle 16 cm from the center moves through an angle of 275°
in 1 min. What is the linear velocity of the point in centimeters per second? 1.28 cm/s

28. A wheel has diameter 16 in. What is the linear velocity of a point on the
edge of the wheel when it moves through an angle of 760° in 1 s? Express
your answer in inches per second. 106.1 in./s

R 29. The coordinates of two vertices of a square are $(0, -4)$ and $(-4, -4)$.
Find the vertices of the three possible squares. $(-4, 0), (0, 0); (-4, -8), (0, -8); (-2, -2), (-2, -6)$

30. *Sports* A skater is skating around the edge of a circular pond at a distance
of 6 m from the center. Her linear velocity is 7.3 m/s. Determine her
angular velocity in radians per second. How many times per minute does
she go around the pond? ω = 1.22 rad/s; 11.62 rpm

31. *Sports* A tennis court roller is 28 in. in diameter. It makes 1.5 revolutions
per second. Determine its angular velocity in radians per second. How fast
is it moving across the courts? ω = 9.42 rad/s; V = 131.9 in./s

32. *Recreation* A toy racing car is traveling
around a circular track that is 3.2 m in
diameter. Its linear velocity is 0.5 m/s.
What is its angular velocity? How many
times per minute does it go around
the track? ω = 0.31 rad/s; 2.98 rpm

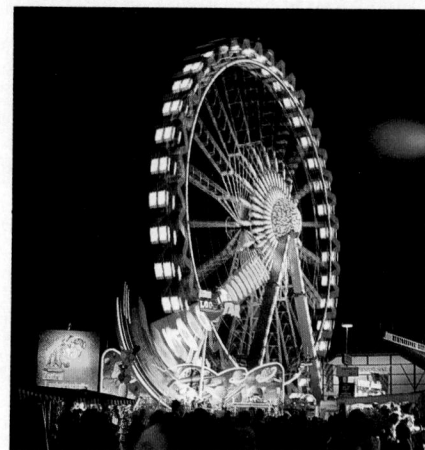

R 33. Provide an example of a quadratic equation
with one real solution; two real solutions;
no real solutions.

34. *Recreation* A ferris wheel 250 ft in
diameter makes one rotation every 45 s.
Determine the linear velocity of a car
on the rim of the wheel. 17.5 ft/s

138   Chapter 3 Trigonometric Functions

35. Thinking Critically   A large merry-go-round is four horses deep. What seat should a child choose for the fastest ride? For the slowest ride? Explain.

36. *Sports*   Explain how the principles of linear and angular velocity apply to playing crack the whip on skates.

37. Writing in Mathematics   Describe a situation in which you have experienced angular and linear velocity.

Automotive Technology   Use the information given in the model to answer the following questions.

38. If 2600 rpm is the most efficient use of the crankshaft, what gear is best for a speed of 35 mi/h? third

39. What is the range of speeds for the efficient use of fourth gear? 35.1 mi/h to 62.3 mi/h

C **40. Thinking Critically**   Explain why the expression $V = \dfrac{r\theta}{t}$ for linear velocity is only valid for θ measured in radians. Find the formula if θ is given in degrees.

41. *Physics*   A belt connects two pulleys. The larger has radius 40 cm and the smaller has radius 20 cm. The smaller pulley revolves at the rate of 48 rpm. Determine the linear velocity of the belt in centimeters per minute. What is the angular velocity of the larger pulley in radians per minute? $V = 1920\pi$ cm/min; 48π rad/min

42. Repeat Exercise 41 for pulleys with radii of 8 and 12 cm, with the smaller pulley rotating at a rate of 60 rpm. $V = 960\pi$ cm/min; $\omega = 80\pi$ rad/min

43. *Astronomy*   A space telescope travels about the earth in a circular orbit at a distance of 380 mi from the earth's surface. It makes one orbit every 95 min. Find its linear velocity in miles per hour. (The radius of the earth is approximately 3960 mi.) 17,223 mi/h

44. *Navigation*   A ship's radar rotating at 15 rpm shows a plane 29.74 mi away, directly northeast of the ship. On the next revolution of the radar, the plane is 29.12 mi away and still directly northeast of the ship. How fast is the plane moving? 0.155 mi/s or 558 mi/h

45. *Space Science*   A satellite placed in circular orbit over the equator in a west-east path and with speed set to make one rotation in 24 h is said to be synchronized with the earth. Such a satellite appears stationary to the observer below. Find the speed in miles per hour required for a synchronous satellite 250 mi above the equator. Assume that the diameter of the earth at the equator is 7920 mi. 1102 mi/h

3.3 Applications: Angular and Linear Velocity   **139**

Writing in Mathematics
37. Examples of angular and linear velocities will vary. Some common examples include amusement park rides, dancing, skating or running in a circle, gears, and wheels.

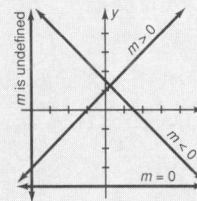
46. *Astronomy*   Approximate the linear speed of the earth in its orbit about the sun in miles per hour. Assume that the orbit of the earth about the sun is nearly a circle with radius 93,000,000 mi. 66,705 mi/h

47. *Sports*   As Yoshio and Hiroko are ice-skating, Yoshio spins his partner in a circle of diameter 1.8 m and then releases her. If Hiroko is moving about the circle at the rate of one rotation every 3 s, what is her linear velocity when Yoshio releases her? 1.9 m/s

Sports   The pedal and gear relationship of a bicycle is shown at the right. The radii of the gears are $r_1 = 5$ cm and $r_2 = 12$ cm. The radius of the wheel is $r_3 = 30$ cm.

48. How many rotations per minute of the pedal gear will produce a racing cyclist's speed of 60 km/h? 221.05 rpm

49. How many rotations per minute of the pedal gear will produce a touring cyclist's speed of 24 km/h? 88.42 rpm

Project

Research the crankshaft–to–drive shaft ratio for racing cars. Build a model to demonstrate why they often have as many as 10 or 15 gears.

Review

Solve each equation. Indicate any restriction on the solution set.

1. $5x^3 - 35x^2 - 60x = 0$ $0; \dfrac{7 \pm \sqrt{97}}{2}$

2. $36a = 3a^3$ $\pm 2\sqrt{3}, 0$

Graph using transformations.

3. $f(x) = (x - 2)^3 + 1$

4. $f(x) = -x^2 + 4$

5. Write the general form of a polynomial function.

Determine in which quadrant the terminal side of each angle θ lies.

6. $270° < \theta < 360°$ IV

7. $\dfrac{3\pi}{2} > \theta > \pi$ III

8. Solve the system of equations. Determine whether the system is consistent and independent, consistent and dependent, or inconsistent.
$$\begin{cases} 3x + 2y = 22 \\ 3x + y = 20 \\ x + y + 3z = 17 \end{cases}$$
(6, 2, 3); consistent and independent

9. Evaluate $P(x) = x^4 - 6x^2 - 18x + 6$ for $x = -3$. Is $x + 3$ a factor of $P(x)$? 87; not a factor

10. Draw the graphs of a line with a positive slope, a line with a negative slope, a line with slope 0, and a line whose slope is undefined.

Determine if the following functions are odd, even, or neither:

11. $g(x) = x^4 + x^2$ even

12. $h(x) = x^5 - x^3$ odd

Evaluate $g(f(x))$ and $f(g(x))$ for $x = a + b$.

13. $f(x) = x^2$, $g(x) = x + 1$ $a^2 + 2ab + b^2 + 1$; $a^2 + b^2 + 2ab + 2a + 2b + 1$

14. $f(x) = x^3$, $g(x) = 2x$ $2a^3 + 6a^2b + 6ab^2 + 2b^3$; $8a^3 + 24a^2b + 24ab^2 + 8b^3$

140   Chapter 3 Trigonometric Functions

3.4 Circular Functions

Objectives: To define the sine and cosine functions
To evaluate the sine and cosine functions of an angle given a point on its terminal side

Focus

In the spring of 1990, the space shuttle *Discovery* carried the Hubble Space Telescope into orbit. The 25,000-lb instrument, which is the size of a large tractor-trailer truck, orbits the earth every 95 min. At 380 mi from earth, it rides well above the gases that distort light from space. This vantage point enables the Hubble to detect objects just 1% as bright as can be seen with ground-based telescopes.

The telescope's faint-object camera can see stars seven times farther away than current telescopes can and will be used to help determine the age of the universe. A faint-object spectrograph will be used to study exploding stars called supernovas and perhaps provide clues to the speed at which the universe is slowing down.

These instruments would have seemed incredible to early astronomers such as Nicholas Copernicus, a sixteenth-century Polish scholar who spent 31 years observing the planets with only his eyes and making innumerable measurements with homemade instruments. Copernicus is credited with having had great influence on astronomy, as well as trigonometry. In fact, Copernicus used only sine and cosine functions in his trigonometric work.

The key trigonometric functions, *sine* and *cosine*, may be defined using the *unit circle*, a circle of radius 1 centered at the origin. From the distance formula, the equation of this circle is

$$x^2 + y^2 = 1$$

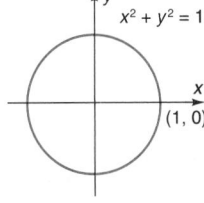

The unit circle is symmetric with respect to the *x*-axis, the *y*-axis, and the origin; these symmetries will prove to be very useful.

> The terminal side of an angle θ in standard position intersects the unit circle at a unique point $P(x, y)$.
>
> The *x*-value of this point is defined to be **cosine** θ.
> The *y*-value of this point is defined to be **sine** θ.

LESSON PLAN

Vocabulary
circular functions
cosine
reference triangle
sine
wrapping function

Technology
graphing calculator

FOCUS

Astronomers are convinced that what they can see through land-based telescopes represents only a small fraction of what they would like to see. A space telescope would greatly increase the amount of information available to scientists studying the origins and predicting the future of our universe. Although there have been many problems with the Hubble Space Telescope, it still represents a real step forward.

Historically, the interaction of mathematics and astronomy has been vital. Mathematics has helped to answer questions in astronomy, and those questions have prompted the development of important mathematics.

INSTRUCTION

- Review the concepts of symmetry with respect to the *x*-axis, *y*-axis, and origin and how these symmetries are evident in the unit circle.
- Ask students to find *y*-values corresponding to given *x*-values on the unit circle, and *x*-values corresponding to given *y*-values.
- Review the notion of similar triangles before introducing reference triangles.

Technology A graphing calculator may be used to graph the upper unit semicircle, $y = \sqrt{1 - x^2}$, and the lower unit semicircle, $y = -\sqrt{1 - x^2}$. The trace function may then be used to read values of the cosine and sine functions directly from the resulting circle. This may help students to see how the sine and cosine are related.

Alternative Learning Styles
Some students respond better to vivid imagery than to lengthy explanations. For example, ask them to imagine an ant walking counterclockwise around a unit circle on the coordinate plane. The ant's position can be described by giving the angle whose terminal side points to the ant. The position can also be given by a pair of coordinates (x, y). Point out that the two kinds of descriptions are evidently related and that those relationships are discussed in this lesson.

GUIDED PRACTICE

For Example 1
Use the definitions of the sine and cosine functions to find each value.

1. $\cos\left(-\dfrac{\pi}{2}\right)$ 0   2. $\sin\left(-\dfrac{\pi}{2}\right)$ −1

For Example 2
1. The terminal side of an angle θ in standard position passes through the point $P(3, 7)$. Draw the reference triangle and find the exact values of $\cos\theta$ and $\sin\theta$.

$$\cos\theta = \frac{3\sqrt{58}}{58}$$
$$\sin\theta = \frac{7\sqrt{58}}{58}$$

Since there is exactly one point $P(x, y)$ for any angle θ, each of the relations cosine $\theta = x$ and sine $\theta = y$ is a *function* of θ. They are abbreviated cos θ and sin θ.

Because they are defined using the unit circle, the cosine and sine functions are often called **circular functions.** Note that the values of x and y on the unit circle range between -1 and 1. This yields the two useful inequalities

$$-1 \le \cos\theta \le 1 \quad\text{and}\quad -1 \le \sin\theta \le 1$$

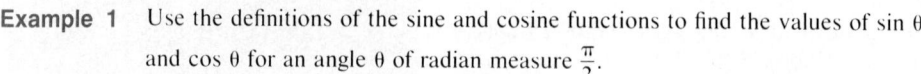

Example 1 Use the definitions of the sine and cosine functions to find the values of sin θ and cos θ for an angle θ of radian measure $\dfrac{\pi}{2}$.

The terminal side of an angle of radian measure $\dfrac{\pi}{2}$ is the positive y-axis, which intersects the unit circle at the point $P(0, 1)$. Therefore,

$$\cos\frac{\pi}{2} = 0 \quad\text{and}\quad \sin\frac{\pi}{2} = 1$$

For any angle θ, the values of cos θ and sin θ can be found if a point $Q(x, y)$ on the terminal side of θ is known, even if Q is not on the unit circle. A right triangle is formed when a perpendicular is drawn from Q to the x-axis. This triangle is called a **reference triangle.** In the figure, P and Q are corresponding vertices of similar triangles OPA and OQB. The point P is on the unit circle, and Q is on the circle of radius $r = \sqrt{x^2 + y^2}$. Since the lengths of corresponding sides of similar triangles are proportional, $\dfrac{x'}{1} = \dfrac{x}{r}$ and $\dfrac{y'}{1} = \dfrac{y}{r}$. Therefore,

$$\cos\theta = x' = \frac{x}{r} \quad\text{and}\quad \sin\theta = y' = \frac{y}{r}$$

Example 2 The terminal side of an angle θ in standard position passes through the point $P(2, 5)$. Draw the reference triangle and find the exact values of cos θ and sin θ.

$$r = \sqrt{x^2 + y^2} = \sqrt{4 + 25} = \sqrt{29}$$
$$\cos\theta = \frac{2}{\sqrt{29}} = \frac{2\sqrt{29}}{29}$$
$$\sin\theta = \frac{5}{\sqrt{29}} = \frac{5\sqrt{29}}{29}$$

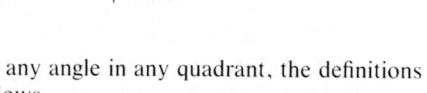

Note that θ could be the angle shown or any coterminal angle.

Since the relationships above apply to any angle in any quadrant, the definitions of cosine and sine are extended as follows.

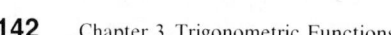

142   Chapter 3 Trigonometric Functions

Let θ be an angle in standard position, and let (x, y) be a point distinct from the origin on the terminal side of θ. Then,

$$\cos \theta = \frac{x}{r} \quad \text{and} \quad \sin \theta = \frac{y}{r} \quad \text{where } r = \sqrt{x^2 + y^2}$$

When you are asked to find the exact value of a function, express your answer as a whole number, fraction, or expression containing a radical. A decimal approximation is not usually an exact value.

Example 3 Find the exact values of $\cos \theta$ and $\sin \theta$ for angle θ in standard position with the given point on its terminal side. Draw the reference triangle.

  a. $P(-3, 4)$ **b.** $Q\left(-\frac{1}{2}, -2\right)$

a. $r = \sqrt{(-3)^2 + 4^2} = \sqrt{25} = 5$

$\cos \theta = \frac{-3}{5} = -\frac{3}{5} \quad \text{and} \quad \sin \theta = \frac{4}{5}$

b. $r = \sqrt{\left(-\frac{1}{2}\right)^2 + (-2)^2} = \frac{\sqrt{17}}{2}$

$\cos \theta = -\frac{1}{2} \cdot \frac{2}{\sqrt{17}} = -\frac{1}{\sqrt{17}} = -\frac{\sqrt{17}}{17}$

$\sin \theta = -2 \cdot \frac{2}{\sqrt{17}} = -\frac{4}{\sqrt{17}} = -\frac{4\sqrt{17}}{17}$

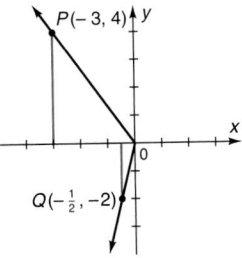

Since r, which is sometimes called the *radius vector*, is always positive, the signs of $\cos \theta$ and $\sin \theta$ are determined by the signs of x and y. These signs depend on the quadrant in which the terminal side of θ lies, as summarized below.

Quadrant	I	II	III	IV
$\cos \theta$	+	−	−	+
$\sin \theta$	+	+	−	−

II $(-, +)$ I $(+, +)$

III $(-, -)$ IV $(+, -)$

Example 4 State whether each value is positive, negative, or zero.

  a. $\cos 45°$ **b.** $\sin 3\pi$ **c.** $\sin \frac{5\pi}{4}$

A drawing can help you determine the answer.

a. $\cos 45° > 0$

b. $\sin 3\pi = 0$

c. $\sin \frac{5\pi}{4} < 0$

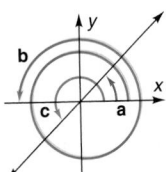

Since the values of $\cos \theta$ and $\sin \theta$ are the coordinates of a point on the unit circle, it is possible to use one of these values to find the other.

3.4 Circular Functions   **143**

---

2. The terminal side of an angle θ in standard position passes through the point $Q\left(2, \frac{1}{2}\right)$. Draw the reference triangle and find the values of $\cos \theta$ and $\sin \theta$.

$\cos \theta = \frac{4\sqrt{17}}{17}$

$\sin \theta = \frac{\sqrt{17}}{17}$

For Example 3
Find the exact values of $\cos \theta$ and $\sin \theta$ for angle θ in standard position with the given point on its terminal side. Draw the reference triangle.
1. $P(-6, 9)$

$\cos \theta = \frac{6\sqrt{117}}{117}$

$\sin \theta = \frac{9\sqrt{117}}{117}$

2. $Q\left(-1, -\frac{2}{5}\right)$

$\cos \theta = -\frac{5\sqrt{29}}{29}$

$\sin \theta = -\frac{2\sqrt{29}}{29}$

For Example 4
State whether each value is positive, negative, or zero.
1. $\cos 75°$ positive
2. $\sin(-75°)$ negative
3. $\cos 5\pi$ negative
4. $\sin(-3\pi)$ zero

1. Angle θ is in standard position with its terminal side in the second quadrant. Find the exact value of cos θ if sin θ is $\frac{8}{10}$. $-\frac{6}{10}$

2. Angle θ is in standard position with its terminal side in the fourth quadrant. Find the exact value of sin θ if cos θ is $\frac{4}{7}$. $-\frac{\sqrt{33}}{7}$

CLOSURE

Group students in pairs and have them explain to each other how to find exact values for the sine and cosine of an angle given a point on its terminal side.

INDEPENDENT PRACTICE

Assignment Guide

Basic: 1–27, 33–38
Average: 3, 10–40
Enriched: 20–49

Teacher's Resource Book
  Practice, page 19

Ⓡ **Review**

Exercises 3, 23, 33, 35, 37, and 39 review the concepts of converting degrees to radians, determining the equation of a line, one-to-one functions, evaluating functions, and linear velocity.

Example 5 Angle θ is in standard position with its terminal side in the third quadrant. Find the exact value of cos θ if sin θ = $-\frac{1}{2}$.

Since sin θ = $-\frac{1}{2}$, choose $y = -1$ and $r = 2$.

$$2^2 = x^2 + (-1)^2 \qquad r^2 = x^2 + y^2$$
$$4 = x^2 + 1$$
$$x^2 = 3$$
$$x = \sqrt{3} \quad \text{or} \quad x = -\sqrt{3}$$

Since θ is in the third quadrant, $x = -\sqrt{3}$ and cos θ = $-\frac{\sqrt{3}}{2}$.

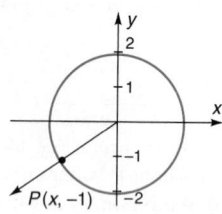

By definition, the set of angles in standard position is the domain of both the cosine function and the sine function. It is often useful to view these functions as having the set of real numbers as their domains. That goal is easily met by the agreement that cos *t* and sin *t* are the cosine and sine of an angle of measure *t* radians.

There is an interesting way to visualize the domain and range of the sine and cosine functions. Consider the unit circle with a number line tangent to it at the point (1, 0). If the positive half of the number line is wrapped around the unit circle, each point and corresponding number of the number line will touch the circle at just one point. Since the circumference of the circle is 2π, the number 2π will complete one wrap and will touch the unit circle at (1, 0). Values for the negative half of the real number line are found in exactly the same way, except the wrap is clockwise. This association is often referred to as the **wrapping function**. It associates with each real number *t* a unique point on the unit circle with coordinates $x = \cos t$ and $y = \sin t$.

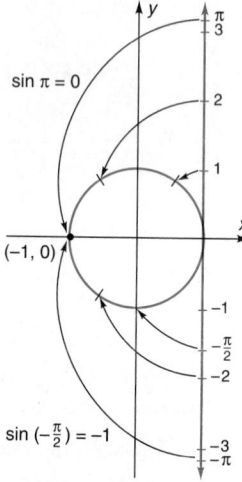

Class Exercises

1. Use the *definition* of the cosine and sine functions to find the value of cos π and sin π; of cos 180° and sin 180°. cos π = cos 180° = −1; sin π = sin 180° = 0

Find the exact value of cos θ and sin θ when the terminal side of an angle θ in standard position passes through the point given.

2. $Q(1, 6)$ $\frac{\sqrt{37}}{37}$; $\frac{6\sqrt{37}}{37}$ 3. $Q(-5, 12)$ $-\frac{5}{13}$; $\frac{12}{13}$

State whether each value is positive, negative, or zero.

4. cos $\frac{\pi}{3}$ + 5. sin $\frac{7\pi}{6}$ − 6. cos 270° 0 7. sin (−140°) −

8. Angle θ is in standard position with terminal side in the first quadrant. Find the exact value of sin θ if cos θ = $\frac{2}{5}$. $\frac{\sqrt{21}}{5}$

9. Angle θ is in standard position with terminal side in the fourth quadrant. Find the exact value of sin θ if cos θ = $\frac{\sqrt{2}}{2}$. $-\frac{\sqrt{2}}{2}$

10. **Thinking Critically** Why do coterminal angles have the same cosine and sine values? Coterminal angles have the same terminal side and sine, cosine can be evaluated using a point on the terminal side.

144 Chapter 3 Trigonometric Functions

Practice Exercises

A **1.** Use the *definition* of the cosine and sine functions to find the exact values of $\cos \frac{3\pi}{2}$ and $\sin \frac{3\pi}{2}$; $\cos 6\pi$ and $\sin 6\pi$. $\cos \frac{3\pi}{2} = 0$; $\sin \frac{3\pi}{2} = -1$; $\cos 6\pi = 1$; $\sin 6\pi = 0$

2. Use the *definition* of the cosine and sine functions to find the exact values of $\cos 225°$ and $\sin 225°$; $\cos 810°$ and $\sin 810°$. $-\frac{\sqrt{2}}{2}$; $-\frac{\sqrt{2}}{2}$; 0; 1

R **3.** Find the radian measure of an angle of $315°$. $\frac{7\pi}{4}$

Tell whether each of the following is positive, negative, or zero.

4. $\sin 3\pi$ 0   **5.** $\cos \frac{7\pi}{3}$ +   **6.** $\cos \frac{\pi}{9}$ +   **7.** $\sin \frac{15\pi}{16}$ +   **8.** $\sin 315°$ −   **9.** $\cos (-65°)$ +

Find the exact value of $\sin \theta$ and $\cos \theta$ if the given point lies on the terminal side of angle θ in standard position. Draw the reference triangle.

10. $Q(2, 5)$ **11.** $R(-1, 2)$ **12.** $S(3, -10)$ **13.** $T(-0.8, 5)$

14. $A(-1.3, -1)$ **15.** $B(-5, 0.5)$ **16.** $C(4, 4)$ **17.** $D(-1.1, -6)$

18. Angle θ is in standard position with terminal side in the second quadrant. Find the exact value of $\sin \theta$ if $\cos \theta = -\frac{1}{6}$. $\frac{\sqrt{35}}{6}$

19. Angle β is in standard position with terminal side in the third quadrant. Find the exact value of $\cos \beta$ if $\sin \beta = -\frac{3}{4}$. $-\frac{\sqrt{7}}{4}$

20. Thinking Critically A student answers a question on a precalculus quiz with the response "$\cos \theta = 1.05$." How do you know, even without knowing the value of θ, that this answer is incorrect? $|\cos \theta| \leq 1$ for all θ and $1.05 > 1$

21. *Architecture* A ramp to provide disabled people with access to a building is to be built so that the sine of the angle of inclination is $\frac{1}{2.5}$. If the ramp must reach a door that is 4 ft 3 in. above the sidewalk level, how long is the ramp? 10.625 ft

22. *Sports* Marishka jogs on a circular path around a lake. The radius of the path is 1 mi. Use a unit circle to draw a scale model of the path. If Marishka starts at the point $(1, 0)$, where will she be after 2.5π mi? Determine the value of $\sin 2.5\pi$ and $\cos 2.5\pi$. 1; 0

R **23.** Determine the equation of the line that coincides with the terminal side of an angle θ in standard position given that $P(3, 5)$ is on the terminal side of θ. $y = \frac{5}{3}x$

B **24.** Angle ϕ is in standard position with terminal side in the fourth quadrant. Find $\sin \phi$ if $\cos \phi = 0.8$. -0.6

Let θ be an angle in standard position. In which quadrant can θ lie under the given conditions?

25. $\sin \theta > 0$ I, II   **26.** $\cos \theta > 0$ I, IV

27. $\cos \theta < 0$ II, III   **28.** $\sin \theta < 0$ III, IV

29. $\sin \theta = \cos \theta$ I, III   **30.** $\sin \theta = -\cos \theta$ II, IV

31. $\sin \theta > 0$ and $\cos \theta > 0$ I   **32.** $\sin \theta < 0$ and $\cos \theta > 0$ IV

3.4 Circular Functions   **145**

145

Ⓡ **33. Thinking Critically** Is sin θ a one-to-one function? Why or why not?

34. Thinking Critically If cos θ = 1, what must be the value of sin θ? Why?

Ⓡ **35.** Let f(x) = x + 2π. If sin (k) = 0.19, what is the value of sin [f(k)]? 0.19

36. If cos θ = 0, what are the possible values of sin θ? Why?

Ⓡ **37.** Determine the equation of the line through the points P(π, sin π) and $Q\left(\frac{1}{2}\pi, \sin\frac{1}{2}\pi\right)$. $y = -\frac{2}{\pi}x + 2$

38. Writing in Mathematics Without referring to the text, write a definition of the cosine and sine functions. Include a sketch of the unit circle and show its relation to these functions.

Ⓡ **39.** *Automotive Technology* The wheel of a car has a radius of approximately 1 ft. The speedometer is set for wheels of this size. If a wheel with radius 1.2 ft is put on the car, at what speed will the car actually be going when the speedometer reads 45 mi/h? 54 mi/h

Ⓒ **40.** Use the definition of the cosine and sine functions and the fact that the line y = x makes an angle of $\frac{\pi}{4}$ with the positive x-axis to show that $\cos\frac{\pi}{4} = \frac{\sqrt{2}}{2}$ and $\sin\frac{\pi}{4} = \frac{\sqrt{2}}{2}$. P(1, 1) is on y = x; r = √2, thus $\cos\frac{\pi}{4} = \frac{1}{\sqrt{2}} = \frac{\sqrt{2}}{2}$ and $\sin\frac{\pi}{4} = \frac{1}{\sqrt{2}} = \frac{\sqrt{2}}{2}$

41. Given that $\cos\frac{\pi}{4} = \frac{\sqrt{2}}{2}$ and $\sin\frac{\pi}{4} = \frac{\sqrt{2}}{2}$, use the symmetry of the unit circle to find the cosine and sine values of $\frac{3\pi}{4}$, $\frac{5\pi}{4}$, and $\frac{7\pi}{4}$. $\left(-\frac{\sqrt{2}}{2}, \frac{\sqrt{2}}{2}\right); \left(-\frac{\sqrt{2}}{2}, -\frac{\sqrt{2}}{2}\right); \left(\frac{\sqrt{2}}{2}, -\frac{\sqrt{2}}{2}\right)$

42. Use the formula for arc length to verify that the length of the arc of a unit circle from 0 to the terminal side of the angle of radian measure t is t units. s = rθ; s = 1(t) = t

43. Let ⟦x⟧ be the greatest integer function. What are the possible values of ⟦sin θ⟧? Why? −1, 0, 1

Moving counterclockwise through the second quadrant, consider all angles θ.

44. How does the value of sin θ change? decreases from 1 to 0

45. How does the value of cos θ change? decreases from 0 to −1

Moving clockwise through the fourth quadrant, consider all angles φ.

46. How does the value of sin φ change? decreases from 0 to −1

47. How does the value of cos φ change? decreases from 1 to 0

Find the values of φ, where 0 ≤ φ < 2π, that make each equation true.

48. cos φ = sin φ $\frac{\pi}{4}; \frac{5\pi}{4}$

49. cos φ + sin φ = 0 $\frac{3\pi}{4}; \frac{7\pi}{4}$

Challenge

1. Graph the curves y = |x − 2| − 3, x = 0, and y = 0 on the same set of axes. Find the area of the region in quadrant IV bounded by the curves. 8.5

2. Find the sum of the following:
1 − 2 + 3 − 4 + 5 − 6 + 7 − 8 + 9 − 10 + · · · − 100 −50

3. Determine the value of a if the graphs of 2y + x + 5 = 0 and 5y + ax + 2 = 0 are to intersect at right angles. −10

146 Chapter 3 Trigonometric Functions

3.5 The Trigonometric Functions

Objectives: To define the trigonometric functions
To evaluate the trigonometric functions of angles

Focus

As early as 1500 B.C., Egyptians were computing shadow
lengths of sticks and building sundials. One form of sundial
was constructed on a vertical wall. A stick of length d was
attached perpendicular to the wall. The shadow of the stick
on the wall lengthened as the sun moved higher in the sky.
If a circle is drawn with center at the end of stick d and
just touching the wall, then the shadow on the wall is
tangent to the circle with radius d. This model may have
led to the trigonometric definition of the tangent of an
acute angle of a right triangle as the opposite side length
divided by the adjacent side length, or $\frac{s}{d}$. If the length of
d is 1 unit, the length of the shadow on the wall measured
in the same units will be the tangent of angle A. The word
tangent was first used by Thomas Fincke about 1583 A.D.

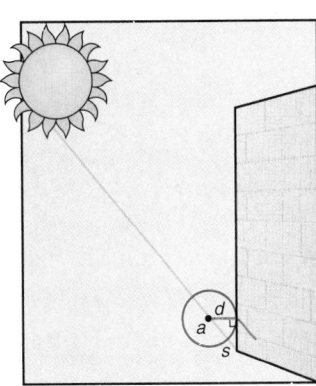

There are four other trigonometric functions closely related to the sine
and cosine functions. They are the *tangent, cotangent, secant,* and
cosecant functions. Let θ be an angle in standard position and let
$P(x, y)$ be a point distinct from the origin on the terminal side of θ. Let
$r = \sqrt{x^2 + y^2}$. The six trigonometric functions are defined as follows.

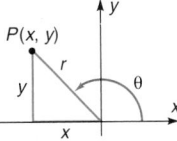

sine	$\sin \theta = \dfrac{y}{r}$	**cosecant**	$\csc \theta = \dfrac{r}{y}, \ y \neq 0$
cosine	$\cos \theta = \dfrac{x}{r}$	**secant**	$\sec \theta = \dfrac{r}{x}, \ x \neq 0$
tangent	$\tan \theta = \dfrac{y}{x}, \ x \neq 0$	**cotangent**	$\cot \theta = \dfrac{x}{y}, \ y \neq 0$

The six trigonometric functions form three pairs of **cofunctions:** sine and cosine,
tangent and cotangent, secant and cosecant. Observe that the definition of a
trigonometric function is equivalent to the definition of its cofunction with
x and y interchanged.

As with sine and cosine, the values of the other four functions depend only
on θ; they are independent of the choice of the point P. The domains of $\tan \theta$
and $\sec \theta$ are restricted to those values of θ for which $x \neq 0$; the domains of

3.5 The Trigonometric Functions **147**

Alternative Learning Styles

For some students, patterns are very helpful in learning. Spend some time discussing patterns in the definitions of the six trigonometric functions, especially those found in the cofunctions and the reciprocal functions.

GUIDED PRACTICE

For Example 1

The terminal side of an angle θ in standard position passes through the point *P*. Draw the reference triangle and evaluate the six trigonometric functions of θ.

1. $P(-1, 7)$

$\sin \theta = \dfrac{7\sqrt{2}}{10}$; $\cos \theta = -\dfrac{\sqrt{2}}{10}$

$\tan \theta = -7$; $\cot \theta = -\dfrac{1}{7}$

$\sec \theta = -5\sqrt{2}$; $\csc \theta = \dfrac{5\sqrt{2}}{7}$

2. $P(-4, -27)$

$\sin \theta = -\dfrac{27\sqrt{745}}{745}$; $\cos \theta = -\dfrac{4\sqrt{745}}{745}$

$\tan \theta = \dfrac{27}{4}$; $\cot \theta = \dfrac{4}{27}$

$\sec \theta = -\dfrac{\sqrt{745}}{4}$; $\csc \theta = -\dfrac{\sqrt{745}}{27}$

For Example 2

Analyze the domain of csc θ.

$\csc \theta = \dfrac{r}{y}, y \neq 0$; Therefore,

$D = \{\theta: \theta \neq k\pi, k \in Z\}$.

148

---

cot θ and csc θ are restricted to those values of θ for which $y \neq 0$. Since the tangent, cotangent, secant, and cosecant functions can be defined on the unit circle, they are also circular functions.

Example 1 The terminal side of an angle θ in standard position passes through the point $P(3, -4)$. Sketch the reference triangle and evaluate the six trigonometric functions of θ.

Since *P* has coordinates $(3, -4)$, $x = 3$, $y = -4$, and $r = \sqrt{3^2 + (-4)^2} = \sqrt{25} = 5$. Therefore,

$\sin \theta = \dfrac{-4}{5} = -\dfrac{4}{5}$ $\qquad \csc \theta = \dfrac{5}{-4} = -\dfrac{5}{4}$

$\cos \theta = \dfrac{3}{5}$ $\qquad \sec \theta = \dfrac{5}{3}$

$\tan \theta = \dfrac{-4}{3} = -\dfrac{4}{3}$ $\qquad \cot \theta = \dfrac{3}{-4} = -\dfrac{3}{4}$

The figure at the right shows that for a given angle, any two reference triangles are similar. The value of $\tan \theta$ is equal to $\dfrac{y}{x}$, and this ratio is the same for all reference triangles. For the angle in the example, $\dfrac{y}{x} = -\dfrac{4}{3}$. This method is used for all the trigonometric functions. If a point on the terminal side of an angle is known, the quadrant and reference triangle can be identified. Then the values of all the trigonometric functions can be determined.

Example 2 Analyze the domain of tan θ.

Let θ be an angle in standard position with $P(x, y)$ a point different from the origin on its terminal side. Then $\tan \theta = \dfrac{y}{x}$, and the values of θ are restricted to those for which *x* will always be nonzero. Since the *x*-value of a point is zero only on the *y*-axis, it follows that in radian measure, θ may take on any value except $\dfrac{\pi}{2}$ plus any integral multiple of π. Thus, the domain of $\tan \theta$ is $\left\{ \theta: \theta \neq \dfrac{\pi}{2} + k\pi, k \in Z \right\}$.

How would you express the domain of tan θ for θ in degrees?

One of the many relationships among the six trigonometric functions is that they form three pairs of *reciprocal functions* for all values of θ for which the denominators are nonzero:

$$\csc \theta = \dfrac{1}{\sin \theta} \qquad \sec \theta = \dfrac{1}{\cos \theta} \qquad \cot \theta = \dfrac{1}{\tan \theta}$$

148 Chapter 3 Trigonometric Functions

Thinking Critically

The domain of tan θ for θ in degrees may be expressed as $D = \{\theta: \theta \neq 90° + 180k, k \in Z\}$ since $\dfrac{\pi}{2}$ rad $= 90°$.

Example 3 Determine the value of $\sec \theta$ if $\cos \theta = \frac{1}{4}$.

Since $\sec \theta$ is the reciprocal of $\cos \theta$, $\sec \theta = 4$.

If you know the quadrant of an angle θ and the value of one of the trigonometric functions, it is possible to determine the value of the other five functions.

Example 4 Let θ be an angle in standard position with terminal side in quadrant II. If $\sin \theta = \frac{12}{13}$, evaluate $\cos \theta$, $\tan \theta$, $\csc \theta$, $\sec \theta$, and $\cot \theta$.

Draw the reference triangle.

Since $\sin \theta = \frac{12}{13}$, $y = 12$ and $r = 13$.

$$x = \pm\sqrt{13^2 - 12^2} = \pm 5$$

Since θ is in quadrant II, $x = -5$.

Hence, $\cos \theta = -\frac{5}{13}$, $\tan \theta = -\frac{12}{5}$, $\csc \theta = \frac{13}{12}$, $\sec \theta = -\frac{13}{5}$, and $\cot \theta = -\frac{5}{12}$.

Class Exercises

The terminal side of an angle θ in standard position passes through the point P. Draw the reference triangle and determine the values of the six trigonometric functions of θ.

1. $P(8, 6)$ **2.** $P(-2, 1)$ **3.** $P(-12, 5)$ **4.** $P\left(-\frac{1}{2}, -2\right)$

5. Complete the chart below.

Quadrant	$\sin \theta$	$\cos \theta$	$\tan \theta$	$\cot \theta$	$\sec \theta$	$\csc \theta$
I	+	+	+	+	+	+
II	+	−	−	−	−	+
III	−	−	+	+	−	−
IV	−	+	−	−	+	−

6. If $\sin \theta = \frac{1}{2}$, find the value of $\csc \theta$. 2 **7.** If $\cot \theta = \frac{7}{8}$, find the value of $\tan \theta$. $\frac{8}{7}$

Determine the exact values of the six trigonometric functions given that:

8. $\sin \theta = -\frac{1}{2}$ and θ is in quadrant IV **9.** $\sin \theta = \frac{\sqrt{3}}{2}$ and $\cos \theta = \frac{1}{2}$

10. $\sin \theta = 0$ and $\cos \theta = -1$

11. Thinking Critically Use the values found in Exercises 1 to 4 to evaluate the expression $(\sin \theta)^2 + (\cos \theta)^2$. Draw a tentative conclusion from these four examples. Give an algebraic or geometric reason to support your conclusion.

12. Analyze the domain of the function $\cot \theta$. $\{\theta \in \Re : \theta \neq k\pi, \ k \in \mathbb{Z}\}$

13. If $\sec \theta$ and $\cot \theta$ have opposite signs, in which quadrant(s) can θ lie? III or IV

14. If $\sec \theta$ and $\csc \theta$ have the same sign, in which quadrant(s) can θ lie? I or III

Additional Answers, Class Exercises

11. Students should conclude that $(\sin \theta)^2 + (\cos \theta)^2 = 1$. This is reasonable since sine and cosine of a given θ correspond to the y and x values of a point on the unit circle whose equation is $x^2 + y^2 = 1$.

For Example 3

1. Determine the value of $\sec \theta$ if $\cos \theta = 0.11$. 9.09

2. Determine the value of $\tan \theta$ if $\cot \theta = 0.4$. 2.5

Technology This is a good place to point out that calculators do not have keys for the secant, cosecant, and cotangent functions. In order to use a calculator to evaluate these functions, the reciprocal relationships must be used.

For Example 4

Determine the exact value of the other five trigonometric functions under the given conditions.

1. $\sin \theta = -\frac{6}{7}$ and θ is in quadrant IV.

$\cos \theta = \frac{\sqrt{13}}{7}$; $\tan \theta = -\frac{6\sqrt{13}}{13}$

$\cot \theta = -\frac{\sqrt{13}}{6}$; $\sec \theta = \frac{7\sqrt{13}}{13}$

$\csc \theta = -\frac{7}{6}$

2. $\cos \theta = -\frac{1}{9}$ and θ is in quadrant III.

$\sin \theta = -\frac{4\sqrt{5}}{9}$; $\tan \theta = 4\sqrt{5}$

$\cot \theta = \frac{\sqrt{5}}{20}$; $\sec \theta = -9$

$\csc \theta = -\frac{9\sqrt{5}}{20}$

CLOSURE

In their math journals, have students summarize the procedures for determining the exact values of the six trigonometric functions of θ given that θ is in standard position and given a point on the terminal side of θ.

Assignment Guide

Basic: 1–22, 33–37
Average: 7, 13, 16–40
Enriched: 16–17, 23–47

Teacher's Resource Book
   Practice, page 20

ⓡ Review

Exercises 7, 13, 33, 35, and 37 review the concepts of finding the area of a sector of a circle, slope of a line, one-to-one functions, evaluating functions, and linear velocity.

LESSON FOLLOW-UP

Test Yourself

Teacher's Resource Book
   Tests—Quiz, form A, page 9
   Tests—Quiz, form B, page 9

Lesson Quiz

1. The terminal side of an angle θ in standard position passes through the point $P(3, 8)$. Draw the reference triangle and determine the exact values of the six trigonometric functions of θ.

$\sin \theta = \dfrac{8\sqrt{73}}{73}$; $\cos \theta = \dfrac{3\sqrt{73}}{73}$

$\tan \theta = \dfrac{8}{3}$; $\cot \theta = \dfrac{3}{8}$

$\sec \theta = \dfrac{\sqrt{73}}{3}$; $\csc \theta = \dfrac{\sqrt{73}}{8}$

2. Determine the value of csc θ if $\sin \theta = 0.35$. 2.86
3. Determine the value of cot θ if $\tan \theta = -3.2$. −0.3125

Practice Exercises

The terminal side of an angle θ in standard position passes through the point P. Draw the reference triangle and determine the values of the six trigonometric functions of θ.

A 1. $P(1, -1)$ 2. $P(2, \sqrt{3})$ 3. $P(-4, 5)$ 4. $P(-7, -24)$ 5. $P(1, -2.5)$ 6. $P\left(\frac{1}{4}, \frac{1}{4}\right)$

ⓡ 7. What is the area of the sector of a circle of diameter 4.4 m that is determined by an angle of 40°? $\frac{4.84\pi}{9}$ m²

8. If $\cos \theta = \frac{2}{3}$, determine the exact value of sec θ. $\frac{3}{2}$

9. If $\csc \theta = -2.95$, evaluate sin θ. $-\frac{20}{59}$ 10. If $\tan \theta = 8$, evaluate cot θ. $\frac{1}{8}$
11. If $\sec \theta = 5.5$, evaluate cos θ. $\frac{2}{11}$ 12. If $\sin \theta = -0.7$, evaluate csc θ. $-\frac{10}{7}$

ⓡ 13. Determine the slope of the line through the points $P\left(\frac{\pi}{2}, \csc \frac{\pi}{2}\right)$ and $Q(-\pi, \sec(-\pi))$. $\frac{4}{3\pi}$

14. If cos θ and cot θ have the same sign, in which quadrant(s) can θ lie? I, II
15. If sin θ and sec θ have opposite signs, in which quadrant(s) can θ lie? II, IV
16. *Forestry* The shadow of a 3 ft vertical stick is 20 in. Nearby, the shadow of a tree is 15 ft long. How tall is the tree? 27 ft
17. *Surveying* A surveyor measures the angle of elevation, as shown, and finds that $\tan \theta = \frac{3}{20}$. If she is 467 ft from the building, how tall is the building? 70.05 ft

$\tan \theta = \frac{3}{20}$

467 ft

Find the exact values of the six trigonometric functions given that:

18. $\cos \theta = -\dfrac{2}{\sqrt{13}}$ and θ is in quadrant III 19. $\sin \theta = \dfrac{-4}{5}$ and θ is in quadrant IV

20. $\sec \beta = 3$ and β is in quadrant I 21. $\csc \phi = -1.6$ and ϕ is in quadrant III

B 22. $\sin \theta = \dfrac{2}{3}$ and $\cos \theta = -\dfrac{\sqrt{5}}{3}$ 23. $\sin \theta = -\dfrac{3\sqrt{13}}{13}$ and $\cos \theta = \dfrac{2\sqrt{13}}{13}$

24. $\sin \theta = 1$ and $\cos \theta = 0$ 25. $\sin \theta = -1$ and $\cos \theta = 0$

26. $\tan \theta = 2$ and θ is in quadrant I 27. $\cot \theta = \dfrac{1}{4}$ and θ is in quadrant III

28. $\cot \theta = 1.5$ and $\csc \theta < 0$ 29. $\tan \theta = -\dfrac{8}{15}$ and $\sec \theta < 0$

Analyze the domain of each function.

30. sec θ 31. csc θ $\{\theta: \theta \neq k\pi, k \in Z\}$ 32. sin θ $\mathscr{R}$

ⓡ 33. Use counterexamples to show that the functions sec θ and csc θ are not one-to-one. $\sec 0 = \sec 2\pi = 1$; $\csc \frac{\pi}{2} = \csc \frac{5\pi}{2} = 1$
34. **Thinking Critically** Let θ and β be coterminal angles. Explain why all six trigonometric functions must be equal for θ and β.

150   Chapter 3 Trigonometric Functions

Additional Answers

30. $\{\theta: \theta \neq \dfrac{2k+1}{2}\pi, k \in Z\}$

34. Trigonometric function values for a given angle can be found using a point on the terminal side of the angle. Coterminal angles have the same terminal side.

35. If $f(x) = \sqrt{x^2 - 1}$ and $g(x) = \frac{1}{x}$, evaluate $f(g(x))$ and $g(f(x))$.

36. Writing in Mathematics   Describe how to determine the sign of each of the six trigonometric functions of an angle if you are given one point on the terminal side of the angle.

37. *Recreation*   A merry-go-round makes one rotation every 2 min. What is the linear velocity of a seat located 10 ft from the center of the ride? 31.4 ft/min

C **38.** Find the range of the function sec θ.   **39.** Find the range of the function csc θ.
$\{y: |y| \geq 1\}$ $\{y: |y| \geq 1\}$

40. Use the fact that the line $y = x$ makes an angle of $\frac{\pi}{4}$ with the positive x-axis to find the exact values of the six trigonometric functions of $\theta = \frac{\pi}{4}$.

41. Let θ be an angle in quadrant IV. Use similar triangles to show that the definition of sec θ is independent of the choice of the point P on the terminal side of θ.

42. Show that the slope of the line through the terminal side of an angle θ is tan θ.

If $\sin \theta = \frac{1}{2}$ and $0 < \theta < \frac{\pi}{2}$, use the symmetry of the unit circle to find the exact values for each of the following:

43. $\sin (\theta + 2\pi)$ $\frac{1}{2}$ **44.** $\sin (-\theta)$ $-\frac{1}{2}$ **45.** $\sin (\theta + \pi)$ $-\frac{1}{2}$ **46.** $\sin (\theta - \pi)$ $-\frac{1}{2}$

47. Find the corresponding exact cosine values for θ and the related angles of Exercises 43 to 46. $\cos \theta = \frac{\sqrt{3}}{2}$; $\cos (\theta + 2\pi) = \frac{\sqrt{3}}{2}$; $\cos (-\theta) = \frac{\sqrt{3}}{2}$; $\cos (\theta + \pi) = -\frac{\sqrt{3}}{2}$; $\cos (\theta - \pi) = -\frac{\sqrt{3}}{2}$

Test Yourself

1. For a $\frac{5}{9}$ counterclockwise rotation, find the measure of the angle in degrees. 200°   3.1

2. Express 117°37′18″ in decimal degrees. 117.62°

3. Identify angles coterminal with a 612° angle. Find one whose measure is between 0° and 360°. $(612 + 360k)°$, $k \in Z$; 252°

4. Express $-120°$ in radians. $-\frac{2\pi}{3}$ **5.** Express $\frac{11\pi}{6}$ in degrees. 330°   3.2

6. Find the angular velocity ω in radians per second of a wheel turning at 500 rpm. 52.4 rad/s   3.3

7. Determine the linear velocity V of a point located 10 cm from the center of a wheel rotating at 16π rad/s. 502.7 rad/s

8. If $\sin \theta = -\frac{3}{5}$ and θ is in quadrant IV, find the exact value of $\cos \theta$. $\frac{4}{5}$ 3.4

9. The terminal side of an angle θ in standard position passes through the point $P(-2, 3)$. Draw the reference triangle and find the exact values of $\cos \theta$ and $\sin \theta$. $\cos \theta = -\frac{2\sqrt{13}}{13}$; $\sin \theta = \frac{3\sqrt{13}}{13}$

Find the exact values of the other five trigonometric functions for an angle in standard position lying in the given quadrant.

10. $\sin \theta = -\frac{4}{5}$, IV   **11.** $\csc \theta = \frac{13}{5}$, II   **12.** $\tan \theta = \frac{7}{24}$, III   3.5

---

4. Let θ be an angle in standard position with terminal side in quadrant II. If $\sin \theta = \frac{2}{5}$, evaluate the other five trigonometric functions of θ.

$\cos \theta = -\frac{\sqrt{21}}{5}$; $\tan \theta = -\frac{2\sqrt{21}}{21}$

$\cot \theta = -\frac{\sqrt{21}}{2}$; $\sec \theta = -\frac{5\sqrt{21}}{21}$

$\csc \theta = \frac{5}{2}$

5. If $\sin \theta = -1$ and $\cos \theta = 0$, find the exact values of csc θ, sec θ, tan θ, and cot θ.
tan θ is undefined; cot $\theta = 0$; csc $\theta = -1$; sec θ is undefined.

6. Suppose that $\cos \theta = 0.42$ and $0 \leq \theta < \frac{\pi}{2}$. Use the symmetry of the unit circle to find the exact values for each of the following:
a. $\cos (-\theta)$ 0.42
b. $\cos (\theta + \pi)$ -0.42
c. $\cos (\theta + 2\pi)$ 0.42

Alternative Assessment
Instruct the students to write an essay describing how the definition of a trigonometric function is related to the definition of its cofunction. Essays should include examples.

Enrichment
Analyze the domain of the function $f(\theta) = \sec 2\theta$.

$\sec \theta = \frac{r}{x}$, $x \neq 0$; Therefore,

$D_f = \{\theta: \theta \neq \frac{\pi}{4} + \frac{\pi}{2}k, k \in Z\}$ or $\{\theta: \theta \neq 45° + 90k, k \in Z\}$.

Additional Answers
Test Yourself
10. $\cos \theta = \frac{3}{5}$; $\tan \theta = -\frac{4}{3}$; $\cot \theta = -\frac{3}{4}$; $\sec \theta = \frac{5}{3}$; $\csc \theta = -\frac{5}{4}$

11. $\sin \theta = \frac{5}{13}$; $\cos \theta = -\frac{12}{13}$; $\tan \theta = -\frac{5}{12}$; $\cot \theta = -\frac{12}{5}$; $\sec \theta = -\frac{13}{12}$

12. $\sin \theta = -\frac{7}{25}$; $\cos \theta = -\frac{24}{25}$; $\cot \theta = \frac{24}{7}$; $\sec \theta = -\frac{25}{24}$; $\csc \theta = -\frac{25}{7}$

Writing in Mathematics
36. If $P(x, y)$ is on the terminal side of θ, the signs of cos θ and sec θ are determined from the sign of x; the signs of sin θ and csc θ are determined from the sign of y; the signs of tan θ and cot θ are determined from the signs of $\frac{y}{x}$.

LESSON PLAN

Vocabulary
quadrantal angle
reference angle

Ⓜ **Materials/Manipulatives**
clear glass of water
spoon

FOCUS

The bending of light rays at the boundary of two different media is called *refraction*. This phenomenon is familiar to most people, even though they may not be able to name or explain it. For example, most people have observed the fact that a spoon in a clear glass of water may appear "broken" at the water line. Refraction occurs whenever light rays pass from one medium to another, from air to water, from one kind of glass to another, from ice to air, and so on. For the purposes of this lesson, it is important for students to recognize that a mathematical description of refraction involves a trigonometric function. Students with an interest in physics may enjoy studying refraction and explaining concepts like the index of refraction to the group.

INSTRUCTION

Ⓜ • Use a spoon in a glass of water to illustrate the phenomenon of refraction.
• Point out that it would be simple to use a calculator to evaluate the trigonometric functions of any angle. However, hands-on computation of these values for selected angles, such as the quadrantal angles, gives insight into relationships that will be helpful later.

3.6 Functions of Special and Quadrantal Angles

Objective: *To find the six trigonometric functions of special angles and quadrantal angles*

Focus

Scientists are continually making discoveries about the intelligence and special abilities of dolphins. One remarkable trait is their ability to leap through hoops positioned above the surface of the water. Aiming for something in the air from under water is more complicated than it seems. A light ray passing from air to water changes direction when it enters the water; the angle i the light ray makes with the perpendicular in air is greater than the angle r that it makes with the perpendicular in water. Thus, to the dolphin under water, a target above the water may appear to be in a different spot from where it actually is.

The behavior of light rays passing from air to water was known for many centuries before scientists were able to find the mathematical relationship between the angles r and i. The key was found in trigonometry. If v_i is the velocity of light in air and v_r is its velocity in water, $\frac{\sin i}{\sin r} = \frac{v_i}{v_r}$. To use this and other similar formulas, you must be able to evaluate trigonometric functions.

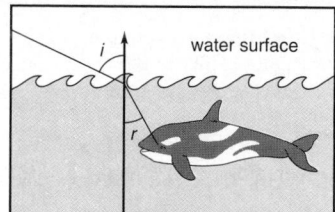

Values of the six trigonometric functions or any angle may be found using a calculator, computer, or tables. However, additional insights into the trigonometric functions can be gained by evaluating selected angles directly. Among these are the *quadrantal angles*.

> An angle whose terminal side lies on the x- or y-axis is called a **quadrantal angle.**

It is easy to find the point of intersection of the unit circle with the x- and y-axes as shown. To find the values of the trigonometric functions of quadrantal angles, use $r = 1$ and the coordinates of the point of intersection of the unit circle with the terminal side of the angle.

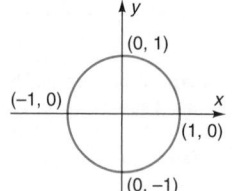

Example 1 Determine the exact values of the six trigonometric functions of each quadrantal angle.

a. $\frac{\pi}{2}$ **b.** 180°   **c.** 630°   **d.** 0

For each angle, use $r = 1$ and the coordinates of the point on the *x*- or *y*-axis.

a.
$\sin \frac{\pi}{2} = 1$ $\csc \frac{\pi}{2} = 1$

$\cos \frac{\pi}{2} = 0$ $\sec \frac{\pi}{2}$ is undefined.

$\tan \frac{\pi}{2}$ is undefined. $\cot \frac{\pi}{2} = 0$

b. $\sin 180° = 0$ $\csc 180°$ is undefined.
$\cos 180° = -1$ $\sec 180° = -1$
$\tan 180° = 0$ $\cot 180°$ is undefined.

c. $\sin 630° = -1$ $\csc 630° = -1$
$\cos 630° = 0$ $\sec 630°$ is undefined.
$\tan 630°$ is undefined. $\cot 630° = 0$

d. $\sin 0 = 0$ $\csc 0$ is undefined.
$\cos 0 = 1$ $\sec 0 = 1$
$\tan 0 = 0$ $\cot 0$ is undefined.

Two facts from geometry will help you compute the trigonometric values of angles with measures 45°, 30°, and 60°. First, recall that a 45°-45°-90° triangle has sides in the ratio $1:1:\sqrt{2}$. For any point on the terminal side of a 45° angle, the reference triangle is a 45°-45°-90° triangle. It is convenient to use a triangle with sides of lengths 1, 1, and $\sqrt{2}$.

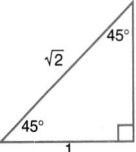

Example 2 Find the exact values of $\sin \theta$, $\cos \theta$, and $\tan \theta$ for $\theta = 45°$.

For a 45° angle, $x = 1$, $y = 1$ and $r = \sqrt{2}$.

$\sin 45° = \frac{1}{\sqrt{2}} = \frac{\sqrt{2}}{2}$

$\cos 45° = \frac{1}{\sqrt{2}} = \frac{\sqrt{2}}{2}$

$\tan 45° = \frac{1}{1} = 1$

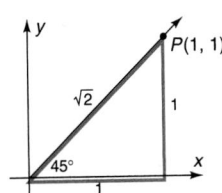

The second useful fact from geometry is that in a 30°-60°-90° triangle, the side opposite the 30° angle is half the length of the hypotenuse, and the side opposite the 60° angle is $\sqrt{3}$ times the length of the side opposite the 30° angle. Thus, the sides are in the ratio $1:\sqrt{3}:2$. For any point on the terminal side of either a 30° or a 60° angle, the reference triangle is a 30°-60°-90° triangle. Use one with a hypotenuse of length 2; the other two sides then have lengths of 1 and $\sqrt{3}$.

3.6 Functions of Special and Quadrantal Angles   **153**

Alternative Learning Styles

Global learners benefit from an overview of a lesson. Point out to students that this lesson will actually contain no new information. They already know everything they need to know to meet the lesson's objective. The main task is to recall and organize what they know, and to make some new connections.

GUIDED PRACTICE

For Example 1

Find the values of the six trigonometric functions of each angle.

1. $-\frac{1}{2}\pi$

$\sin \theta = -1$; $\cos \theta = 0$; $\tan \theta$ is undefined; $\cot \theta = 0$; $\sec \theta$ is undefined; $\csc \theta = -1$.

2. 540°

$\sin 540° = 0$; $\cos 540° = -1$; $\tan 540° = 0$; $\cot 540°$ is undefined; $\sec 540° = -1$; $\csc 540°$ is undefined.

For Example 2

Use a 45°-45°-90° reference triangle with hypotenuse of length $4\sqrt{2}$ to find the exact values of sin 45°, cos 45°, and tan 45°.

$\sin 45° = \frac{4}{4\sqrt{2}} = \frac{\sqrt{2}}{2}$;

$\cos 45° = \frac{4}{4\sqrt{2}} = \frac{\sqrt{2}}{2}$;

$\tan 45° = \frac{4}{4} = 1$

For Example 3

1. Use a 30°-60°-90° reference triangle with hypotenuse of length 12 to find the exact values of sin 60°, cos 60°, and tan 60°.

$\sin 60° = \dfrac{6\sqrt{3}}{12} = \dfrac{\sqrt{3}}{2}$;

$\cos 60° = \dfrac{6}{12} = \dfrac{1}{2}$;

$\tan 60° = \dfrac{6\sqrt{3}}{6} = \sqrt{3}$

2. Use a 30°-60°-90° reference triangle with hypotenuse of length 8 to find the exact values of sin 30°, cos 30°, and tan 30°.

$\sin 30° = \dfrac{4}{8} = \dfrac{1}{2}$;

$\cos 30° = \dfrac{4\sqrt{3}}{8} = \dfrac{\sqrt{3}}{2}$;

$\tan 30° = \dfrac{4}{4\sqrt{3}} = \dfrac{\sqrt{3}}{3}$

For Example 4

1. Find the exact values of sin 315°, cos 315°, and tan 315°.

$\sin 315° = -\dfrac{\sqrt{2}}{2}$; $\cos 315° = \dfrac{\sqrt{2}}{2}$;

$\tan 315° = -1$

2. Find the exact values of csc 315°, sec 315°, and cot 315°.

$\csc 315° = -\sqrt{2}$; $\sec 315° = \sqrt{2}$;

$\cot 315° = -1$

Example 3 Find the exact values of sin θ, cos θ, and tan θ for the given values of θ.
  a. 30°   **b.** 60°

a. 30° angle: $x = \sqrt{3},\ y = 1,\ r = 2$ **b.** 60° angle: $x = 1,\ y = \sqrt{3},\ r = 2$

$\sin 30° = \dfrac{1}{2}$

$\cos 30° = \dfrac{\sqrt{3}}{2}$

$\tan 30° = \dfrac{1}{\sqrt{3}} = \dfrac{\sqrt{3}}{3}$

$\sin 60° = \dfrac{\sqrt{3}}{2}$

$\cos 60° = \dfrac{1}{2}$

$\tan 60° = \dfrac{\sqrt{3}}{1} = \sqrt{3}$

The values found in Examples 2 and 3 are also those for angles of radian measure $\dfrac{\pi}{4}$, $\dfrac{\pi}{6}$, and $\dfrac{\pi}{3}$, respectively. Values of the secant, cosecant, and cotangent of these angles may be found directly from the reference triangles or by using the reciprocal relationships.

The symmetry of a circle with radius $\sqrt{2}$ centered at the origin is one tool for finding values of the trigonometric functions of integral multiples of 45° or $\dfrac{\pi}{4}$.

The symmetry of the circle and the values of the coordinates of P found in Example 2 give coordinates of points on the terminal sides of each of the angles.

Example 4 Find the exact values of sin θ, cos θ, and tan θ for each angle θ.
  a. 135°   **b.** 225°   **c.** $-\dfrac{\pi}{4}$

a. $\sin 135° = \dfrac{1}{\sqrt{2}} = \dfrac{\sqrt{2}}{2}$; $\cos 135° = \dfrac{-1}{\sqrt{2}} = -\dfrac{\sqrt{2}}{2}$;

$\tan 135° = \dfrac{-1}{1} = -1$

b. $\sin 225° = \dfrac{-1}{\sqrt{2}} = -\dfrac{\sqrt{2}}{2}$; $\cos 225° = \dfrac{-1}{\sqrt{2}} = -\dfrac{\sqrt{2}}{2}$;

$\tan 225° = \dfrac{-1}{-1} = 1$

c. $\sin\left(-\dfrac{\pi}{4}\right) = \dfrac{-1}{\sqrt{2}} = -\dfrac{\sqrt{2}}{2}$; $\cos\left(-\dfrac{\pi}{4}\right) = \dfrac{1}{\sqrt{2}} = \dfrac{\sqrt{2}}{2}$; $\tan\left(-\dfrac{\pi}{4}\right) = \dfrac{1}{-1} = -1$

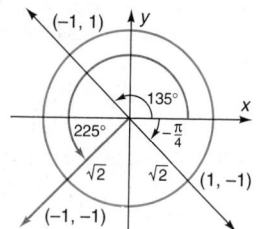

Is the circle displayed in Example 4 a unit circle?

Another tool useful for finding values of the trigonometric functions of certain angles is the *reference angle,* one of the angles of the reference triangle.

For an angle θ that is not a quadrantal angle, the **reference angle θ′** is the acute angle formed by the terminal side of θ and the x-axis.

Thinking Critically
The circle displayed in Example 4 has a radius of $\sqrt{2}$ units. Thus, it is not a unit circle.

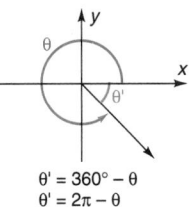

$\theta' = \theta$ $\theta' = 180° - \theta$ $\theta' = \theta - 180°$ $\theta' = 360° - \theta$

$\theta' = \pi - \theta$ $\theta' = \theta - \pi$ $\theta' = 2\pi - \theta$

To find the reference angle for an angle with negative measure, or for an angle greater than 360° (2π), first find a coterminal angle whose measure is between 0° and 360° (0 and 2π).

Example 5   Give the reference angle θ' for each angle θ in standard position.

       a. 135°   **b.** $-\dfrac{7\pi}{3}$

a. Since a 135° angle is in quadrant II, its reference angle $\theta' = 180° - 135° = 45°$.

b. Since $-\dfrac{7\pi}{3} = -2\pi - \dfrac{\pi}{3}$, this angle is

coterminal with the angle $\dfrac{5\pi}{3}$ in quadrant IV.

Thus, its reference angle $\theta' = 2\pi - \dfrac{5\pi}{3} = \dfrac{\pi}{3}$.

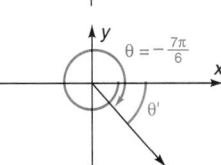

The absolute value of the trigonometric function of an angle θ is equal to that of its reference angle. Whether the trigonometric function of the angle is positive or negative is determined by the quadrant in which θ lies.

Example 6   Use the reference angle to find $\sin \theta$, $\cos \theta$, and $\tan \theta$ for each value of θ.

       a. 150°   **b.** 330°   **c.** $\dfrac{7\pi}{6}$

a. Since θ is in quadrant II, $\theta' = 180° - 150° = 30°$, sine is positive, and cosine and tangent are negative. Therefore,

$$\sin 150° = \dfrac{1}{2} \qquad \cos 150° = -\dfrac{\sqrt{3}}{2} \qquad \tan 150° = -\dfrac{\sqrt{3}}{3}$$

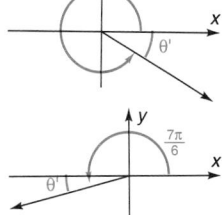

b. Since θ is in quadrant IV, $\theta' = 360° - 330° = 30°$, sine and tangent are negative, and cosine is positive. Therefore,

$$\sin 330° = -\dfrac{1}{2} \qquad \cos 330° = \dfrac{\sqrt{3}}{2} \qquad \tan 330° = -\dfrac{\sqrt{3}}{3}$$

c. Since θ is in quadrant III, $\theta' = \dfrac{7\pi}{6} - \pi = \dfrac{\pi}{6}$, sine and cosine are negative, and tangent is positive. Therefore,

$$\sin \dfrac{7\pi}{6} = -\dfrac{1}{2} \qquad \cos \dfrac{7\pi}{6} = -\dfrac{\sqrt{3}}{2} \qquad \tan \dfrac{7\pi}{6} = \dfrac{\sqrt{3}}{3}$$

For Example 5

Give the reference angle θ' for each angle in standard position.

1. $-\dfrac{1}{4}\pi$ $\theta' = \dfrac{\pi}{4}$

2. 110° $\theta' = 70°$

For Example 6

Use the reference angle to find values of $\sin \theta$, $\cos \theta$, and $\tan \theta$. Draw both θ and θ' in each case.

1. $\theta = -30°$

$\sin \theta = -0.5$; $\cos \theta = \dfrac{\sqrt{3}}{2}$;

$\tan \theta = -\dfrac{\sqrt{3}}{3}$

2. $\theta = \dfrac{2\pi}{3}$

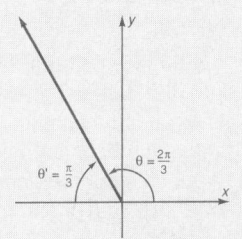

$\sin \dfrac{2\pi}{3} = \dfrac{\sqrt{3}}{2}$; $\cos \dfrac{2\pi}{3} = -\dfrac{1}{2}$;

$\tan \dfrac{2\pi}{3} = -\sqrt{3}$

1. If $0 \le \theta < 2\pi$, determine the values of θ for which $\sin \theta = \frac{1}{2}$.
   $\frac{\pi}{6}$ and $\frac{5\pi}{6}$

2. If $0 \le \theta < 2\pi$, determine the values of θ for which $\tan \theta = 1$.
   $\frac{\pi}{4}$ and $\frac{5\pi}{4}$

CLOSURE

Have students write an essay describing how to find the exact values of the six trigonometric functions of the special angles and quadrantal angles.

INDEPENDENT PRACTICE

Assignment Guide

Basic: 1–27, 35, 37, 39
Average: 9, 12–40
Enriched: 20–49

Teacher's Resource Book
  Practice, page 21

Ⓡ **Review**
Exercises 9, 19, 23, 35, 37, and 39 review concepts of determining exact values of trigonometric functions, solving quadratic equations, domain and range of a function, determining the equation of a line, and linear velocity.

Additional Answers
Class Exercises

1. $\sin \frac{3\pi}{2} = -1$; $\cos \frac{3\pi}{2} = 0$; $\tan \frac{3\pi}{2}$ is undefined; $\cot \frac{3\pi}{2} = 0$; $\sec \frac{3\pi}{2}$ is undefined; $\csc \frac{3\pi}{2} = -1$.

2. For any quadrantal angle, the terminal side of the angle lies on one of the axes. Therefore, the value of either x or y is equal to zero. When $x = 0$, the secant and tangent will be undefined; when $y = 0$, the cosecant and cotangent will be undefined.

4. $\sec 30° = \frac{2\sqrt{3}}{3}$; $\csc 30° = 2$; $\cot 30° = \sqrt{3}$; $\sec 60° = 2$; $\csc 60° = \frac{2\sqrt{3}}{3}$; $\cot 60° = \frac{\sqrt{3}}{3}$

The symmetry of a circle centered at the origin provides insight into the relationship between the trigonometric values of an angle and its reference angle. For example, study the figure for the angle θ in quadrant II. The angle θ and its reference angle θ' intersect the circle of radius r at $P(x, y)$ and $Q(x', y')$. By symmetry, $x = -x'$ and $y = y'$. Therefore,

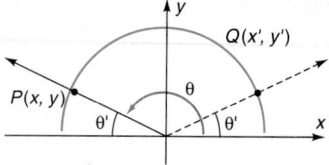

$$\cos \theta = \frac{x}{r} = -\frac{x'}{r} = -\cos \theta' \qquad \sin \theta = \frac{y}{r} = \frac{y'}{r} = \sin \theta' \qquad \tan \theta = \frac{y}{x} = -\frac{y'}{x'} = -\tan \theta'$$

Similar arguments can be used for angles in quadrants III and IV.

For any number k between -1 and 1, there are infinitely many angles θ for which $\sin \theta = k$. However, it is often important to determine the values of θ for which $\sin \theta = k$ on a restricted domain, such as $0 \le \theta < 2\pi$.

Example 7   If $0 \le \theta < 2\pi$, determine the values of θ for which $\sin \theta = -\frac{1}{2}$.

Since $\sin \frac{\pi}{6} = \frac{1}{2}$, consider angles which have $\frac{\pi}{6}$ as a reference angle. Since $\sin \theta < 0$, the angles must be in quadrants III and IV. From the figure, $\pi + \frac{\pi}{6} = \frac{7\pi}{6}$ and $2\pi - \frac{\pi}{6} = \frac{11\pi}{6}$. Thus, the values of θ for which $\sin \theta = -\frac{1}{2}$ are $\frac{7\pi}{6}$ and $\frac{11\pi}{6}$.

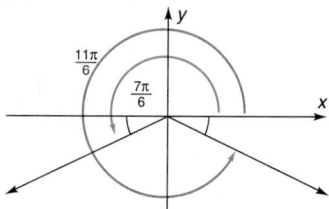

Class Exercises

1. Determine the exact values of the six trigonometric functions of an angle of radian measure $\frac{3\pi}{2}$.

2. **Thinking Critically**   Explain why for any quadrantal angle, some trigonometric values will be undefined.

3. Determine the exact values of $\sec 45°$, $\csc 45°$, and $\cot 45°$. $\sqrt{2}$; $\sqrt{2}$; 1

4. Determine the exact values of $\sec \theta$, $\csc \theta$, and $\cot \theta$ for $\theta = 30°$ and $60°$.

Determine the exact values of $\sec \theta$, $\csc \theta$, and $\cot \theta$ for the given values of θ.

5. $135°$ $-\sqrt{2}$; $\sqrt{2}$; -1 6. $225°$ $-\sqrt{2}$; $-\sqrt{2}$; 1   7. $-\frac{\pi}{4}$ $\sqrt{2}$; $-\sqrt{2}$; -1 8. $-\frac{\pi}{6}$ $\frac{2\sqrt{3}}{3}$; -2; $-\sqrt{3}$

Determine the reference angle θ' for each angle θ in standard position.

9. $174°$ $6°$ 10. $29°$ $29°$ 11. $\frac{5\pi}{6}$ $\frac{\pi}{6}$ 12. $\frac{13\pi}{12}$ $\frac{\pi}{12}$

Determine the exact values of the six trigonometric functions for each angle. Draw the reference angle in each case.

13. $150°$ 14. $315°$ 15. $\frac{2\pi}{3}$ 16. $-\frac{2\pi}{3}$

17. For $0 \le \theta < 2\pi$, determine the values of θ for which $\tan \theta = -1$. $\frac{3\pi}{4}$; $\frac{7\pi}{4}$

18. For $0 \le \theta < 2\pi$, determine the values of θ for which $\cos \theta = \frac{1}{2}$. $\frac{\pi}{3}$; $\frac{5\pi}{3}$

Practice Exercises

A 1. Determine the exact values of the six trigonometric functions of 2π.

2. Make a chart summarizing the exact values of the six trigonometric functions for the four quadrantal angles 0, $\frac{\pi}{2}$, π, and $\frac{3\pi}{2}$.

Determine the reference angle θ' for each angle θ in standard position.

3. $200°$ 20°
4. $300°$ 60°
5. $-\frac{5\pi}{8}$ $\frac{3\pi}{8}$
6. $\frac{3\pi}{5}$ $\frac{2\pi}{5}$
7. 1.3 1.3
8. -2.13 1.01

ℝ 9. If $\sin\theta = \frac{5}{7}$ and θ is in quadrant II, determine the exact value of $\cos\theta$. $-\frac{2\sqrt{6}}{7}$

Determine the exact values of the six trigonometric functions for each angle.
Draw the reference angle in each case.

10. $120°$
11. $390°$
12. $-60°$
13. $-135°$
14. $\frac{10\pi}{3}$
15. $\frac{-7\pi}{4}$
16. $\frac{-\pi}{3}$
17. $\frac{5\pi}{6}$

18. **Thinking Critically** Explain why the quadrantal angles are the *only* angles for which any trigonometric values are undefined.

ℝ 19. Solve the quadratic equation: $5t^2 - 1.2t - 6 = 0$ 1.22; -0.98

20. *Construction* The roof of a house is built at a $30°$ angle. The slant portion of the roof measures 17 ft. Use the ratios of a $30°$-$60°$-$90°$ right triangle to determine the height of the roof.   8.5 ft

21. *Design* A design for floor tiling uses tiles that are right triangles such that each leg measures 1 ft. Determine the area of a square formed from four such triangles.   2 ft²

22. **Writing in Mathematics** Explain in your own words a method for finding the reference angle for any angle β and describe its usefulness.

ℝ 23. Determine the domain of the function $F(t) = \frac{1}{1 + \sin t}$. $\left\{ t \in \mathcal{R} : t \neq \frac{3\pi}{2} + 2k\pi, \, k \in Z \right\}$

If $0 \le \theta < 2\pi$, determine the values of θ in radians that make each statement true.

B 24. $\cos\theta = -\frac{1}{2}$ $\frac{2\pi}{3}; \frac{4\pi}{3}$
25. $\cot\theta = 1$ $\frac{\pi}{4}; \frac{5\pi}{4}$
26. $\cot\theta = -1$ $\frac{3\pi}{4}; \frac{7\pi}{4}$
27. $\sin\theta = \frac{\sqrt{2}}{2}$ $\frac{\pi}{4}; \frac{3\pi}{4}$

28. $\sin\theta = -\frac{\sqrt{2}}{2}$ $\frac{5\pi}{4}; \frac{7\pi}{4}$
29. $\tan\theta = \frac{\sqrt{3}}{3}$ $\frac{\pi}{6}; \frac{7\pi}{6}$
30. $\sin\theta = -1$ $\frac{3\pi}{2}$
31. $\tan\theta = 0$ 0; π

32. $\sec\theta$ is undefined. $\frac{\pi}{2}; \frac{3\pi}{2}$
33. $\cot\theta$ is undefined.   0; π
34. $\tan\theta$ is undefined. $\frac{\pi}{2}; \frac{3\pi}{2}$

ℝ 35. Determine the range of the function $G(x) = 1 + \cos x$. $\{y \in \mathcal{R} : 0 \le y \le 2\}$

36. If $0 \le \theta < 360°$, for which values of θ is $\cos\theta = -\frac{\sqrt{2}}{2}$?   135°; 225°

ℝ 37. Determine the equation of the line through the point $P\left(\frac{\pi}{4}, \tan\frac{\pi}{4}\right)$ that is parallel to the line with equation $5x - 8y + 4.5 = 0$.

3.6 Functions of Special and Quadrantal Angles   **157**

Writing in Mathematics
22. One possible answer follows. The reference angle β' for an angle β is the acute angle formed by the terminal side of β and the x-axis. The reference angle may be used to find the values of the six trigonometric functions of β except for the signs, which are determined by the quadrant of β.

Alternative Assessment

Have students make a list of information from geometry that makes it possible to determine the values of the sine, cosine, and tangent of certain angles without using a calculator or table.

Enrichment

Describe the zeros of each function.

a. $f(t) = 1 + \cos t$ odd multiples of π

b. $g(t) = 2 + \sin t$ no zeros

c. $h(t) = 3 - 3 \cos t$
    even multiples of π

Additional Answers

37. $5x - 8y + 8 - \dfrac{5\pi}{4} = 0$

or $5x - 8y + 4.07 = 0$

46. $\sin\left(-\dfrac{\pi}{3}\right) = -\dfrac{\sqrt{3}}{2}; -\sin\dfrac{\pi}{3} = -\dfrac{\sqrt{3}}{2};$

$\sin\left(-\dfrac{\pi}{2}\right) = -1; -\sin\dfrac{\pi}{2} = -1$

Answers may vary.

48. $\sin\theta = \dfrac{-y}{r}; \sin\theta' = \dfrac{y}{r};$

$\sin\theta = -\sin\theta'$

$\cos\theta = \dfrac{-x}{r}; \cos\theta' = \dfrac{x}{r};$

$\cos\theta = -\cos\theta'$

$\tan\theta = \dfrac{y}{x}; \tan\theta' = \dfrac{y}{x};$

$\tan\theta = \tan\theta'$

Review

4.

38. Thinking Critically Compare the values of $\sin 2\theta$, $2 \sin \theta$, $(\sin\theta)^2$, and $\sin(\theta^2)$ for $\theta = \dfrac{\pi}{3}$. Does $\sin 2\theta = 2 \sin\theta$? Does $(\sin\theta)^2 = \sin(\theta^2)$? $\dfrac{\sqrt{3}}{2}; \sqrt{3}; \dfrac{3}{4}; 0.8897;$ no; no

Ⓡ 39. *Sports* The diameter of the wheel of an exercise bike is 20 in. If the pedal is turning at a rate of 4 turns per second, what is the linear velocity of a point of the circumference of the wheel in miles per hour? 14.3 mi/h

C 40. Suppose that θ is an angle in standard position and that $\sin\theta = \dfrac{2}{3}$. What is $\sin(\theta + 2\pi)$? $\sin(\theta + 4\pi)$? $\dfrac{2}{3}; \dfrac{2}{3}$

41. Suppose that θ is an angle in standard position in the first quadrant and that $\cos\theta = \dfrac{1}{3}$. What is $\cos(-\theta)$? $\dfrac{1}{3}$

42. Given $0 \le \theta < 4\pi$, find all values of θ for which $\sin\theta = -\dfrac{\sqrt{3}}{2}$ and $\cos\theta > 0$. $\dfrac{5\pi}{3}, \dfrac{11\pi}{3}$

43. Given $0 \le \theta < 4\pi$, find all values of θ for which $\tan\theta = -1$ and $\sin\theta < 0$. $\dfrac{7\pi}{4}, \dfrac{15\pi}{4}$

44. If $0° \le \theta < 360°$, determine values of θ for which $\sec\theta = \sqrt{2}$ and $\sin\theta = -\dfrac{\sqrt{2}}{2}$. 315°

45. If $0° \le \theta < 360°$, find all values of θ for which $\tan\theta = -\dfrac{\sqrt{3}}{3}$ and $\sec\theta = \dfrac{2\sqrt{3}}{3}$. 330°

46. Thinking Critically Use values found in this lesson to verify that $\sin(-\theta) = -\sin\theta$.

47. Thinking Critically Determine the relationship between $\cos\theta$ and $\cos(-\theta)$. $\cos\theta = \cos(-\theta)$

48. Thinking Critically Use the symmetry of a circle centered at the origin to show that for an angle θ in quadrant III with reference angle θ', $\sin\theta = -\sin\theta'$, $\cos\theta = -\cos\theta'$ and $\tan\theta = \tan\theta'$.

49. *Physics* The index of refraction k for a given liquid is given by $k = \dfrac{\sin i}{\sin r}$, where i is the angle at which the light strikes the surface of the liquid and r is the angle at which it travels after entering the liquid. Determine the index of refraction if the angle of incidence is 45° and the angle of refraction is 30°. $\sqrt{2}$ or 1.414

Review

Convert to decimal degrees, to the nearest tenth of a degree.

1. 66°33′45″ 66.6°

2. 72°42′30″ 72.7°

3. Round 3.141592654 to the nearest thousandth. 3.142

4. Graph the function $y = x^3 - x^2 - 9x + 4$ and approximate its real zeros. 3.3, 0.4, −2.8

5. Determine the angle in radians formed by the hands of a clock at 3:15 p.m. $\dfrac{\pi}{24}$

6. The measures of the angles of a four-sided figure can be represented by x, $3x$, $3x + 10$, and $4x + 20$. Find the measures of each angle. 30°, 90°, 100°, 140°

Given $f(x) = 3x - 1$ and $g(x) = 4x + 2$, determine:

7. $(g \circ f)\left(\dfrac{1}{2}\right)$ 4

8. $(f \circ g)(\sqrt{3})$ $12\sqrt{3} + 5$

158 Chapter 3 Trigonometric Functions

3.7 Evaluating Trigonometric Functions

Objectives: To find decimal approximations for the values of the six trigonometric functions
To find the measure of an angle for which the value of a trigonometric function is known

Focus

Since NASA was formed in 1958, it has launched hundreds of earth-orbiting satellites. These satellites are used for such diverse missions as collecting weather data, transmitting television signals, and measuring solar radiation.

Angle measurements and trigonometry are used extensively in space science, and specifically in modeling the orbits of satellites. Tracking stations require very accurate models of satellite motion in order to maintain communication links.

In applications of trigonometry, it is often necessary to find values such as sin 59.783°, cos 1°13'8", or tan 2.001. A scientific calculator is the tool most commonly used today for finding such values. Most calculators have at least two *modes*, degree and radian, for evaluating these functions. In order to obtain the correct results, a calculator must be in the appropriate mode. Also, it is important to know the *syntax*, or logic, employed by your calculator. For example, with some calculators, you can find sin 15° by first entering 15 and then using the sin key. With others, you must enter sin first and then enter 15.

You will find that a calculator gives decimal approximations for numbers such as π, $\sqrt{2}$, and $\sin \frac{\pi}{4}$. The situation in which the values are to be applied and the accuracy of the original data determine the number of decimal places to be used. Although the values of most trigonometric functions are approximations, it is customary to use the equals symbol. In this text, values of the trigonometric functions will be rounded to four decimal places, unless otherwise indicated. Some calculators display numbers with fixed decimal places, and these can be set to display four decimal places. Note that this is just what is displayed; the calculator uses as many digits as it can to actually do the calculations and retains all those digits in its memory.

3.7 Evaluating Trigonometric Functions **159**

LESSON PLAN

Technology
scientific calculator

FOCUS

The need for accurate mathematical models becomes apparent as you consider the number of satellites currently orbiting earth. This is not an area for trial and error methodology! Students with various interests may be motivated to research the use of earth-orbiting satellites in the fields of communication, meteorology, space science, or other areas of physics.

INSTRUCTION

- If all students are using the same kind of calculator, review briefly some of its features, such as logic, memory, fixed vs floating decimal places, radian and degree modes, parentheses, and inverse key.
- If students are using different kinds of calculators, it may be necessary to spend some time making sure that each student understands the logic and other features of his or her calculator. Grouping students according to kinds of calculator could be effective for this task. It would be advantageous if someone in each group brought his or her instruction manual.
- Remind students that if the input value is not labeled as degrees, then it is understood to be measured in radians. This is particularly important to remember for values like sin 3 and cos 1.1, which do not have the "flag" π.

Some students may better understand how to use a calculator to find an angle measure for a given trigonometric ratio if you begin with examples that do not require a calculator. For example, "Name an angle whose sine is 1." Once the task is clear, the calculator is a more effective tool for these students.

GUIDED PRACTICE

For Example 1

Find each value. Round answers to four decimal places.

1. cos 275°   0.0872
2. sin (-1.4π) 0.9511
3. tan 2 -2.1850

Common Error   When using a calculator to find trigonometric values, some students regularly use the wrong mode. This is where understanding helps identify errors. For example, with a calculator in degree mode, the value of sin $\frac{9\pi}{8}$ is given as 0.0616.

A student who can visualize this angle in standard position may realize that its sine should be negative and catch the error.

For Example 2

Find each value. Round answers to four decimal places.

1. sec 146° -1.2062
2. cot 39°52′   1.1974

Technology   Some students do not use or incorrectly use parentheses. Familiarity with the range of the trigonometric functions can help these students identify some of those errors. For example, to find csc 2 a student may enter sin 2^{-1} instead of (sin 2)$^{-1}$. The answer 0.4794 for sin 2^{-1} should be a clue, since $|\csc t| \geq 1$.

Example 1   Find each value. Round answers to four decimal places.

a. sin 250°   b. sin $\frac{\pi}{8}$ c. tan $(-95°)$

a. Place your calculator in degree mode.

sin 250° = -0.9396926208 *Use the* sin *key.*
$\quad\quad\quad$ = -0.9397 To four decimal places

b. Place the calculator in radian mode. Remember to use parentheses if necessary.

sin $\frac{\pi}{8}$ = 0.3826834324   *Use the* sin *and* π *keys.*
$\quad\quad$ = 0.3827   To four decimal places

c. Place the calculator in degree mode.

tan $(-95°)$ = 11.4300523   *Use the negative and* tan *keys.*
$\quad\quad\quad\quad$ = 11.4301   To four decimal places

Is -0.9397 *a reasonable answer for Example* 1a? *Why or why not? How do you know before evaluating* tan $(-95°)$ *that it is not negative?*

Most calculators give values of trigonometric functions for angles measured in decimal degrees rather than in degrees and minutes. For example, 36°50′25″ must be changed to decimal degrees by using a built-in calculator function or by performing the following calculation. The calculation will be done before or after using the sin key depending on the syntax of your calculator.

36°50′25″ = 36 + $\frac{50}{60}$ + $\frac{25}{3600}$ *Calculation-ready form*

Calculators usually have keys for the sine, cosine, and tangent functions; values of the other three functions are found using the respective reciprocal function. On some calculators the reciprocal key is labeled $\frac{1}{x}$. On others it is labeled x^{-1}. *Explain why these are equivalent.*

For a calculator such as a graphing calculator that uses syntax where the sin key is entered first, an appropriate keying sequence for csc 36° would be (sin 36)$^{-1}$. Always try to enter calculations in a single sequence so that you do not need to write down intermediate values. This will require planning ahead but the result will be that the calculator is doing the work, not you. For example, an input form for csc 36°50′25″ might be (sin (36 + 50/60 + 25/3600))$^{-1}$.

Example 2   Determine each value. Round answers to four decimal places.
a. cot 239°   b. csc 36°50′25″   c. sec 49.27°

a. cot 239° = 0.6009   To four decimal places

b. csc 36°50′25″ = 1.6678   To four decimal places

c. sec 49.27° = 1.5326   To four decimal places

160   Chapter 3 Trigonometric Functions

Thinking Critically
For Example 1a, -0.9397 is a reasonable answer because the absolute value of the sine function must be less than one. The tangent function is positive in quadrants I and III. Thus, tan $(-96°)$ is positive.

If the value of one of the trigonometric functions of an angle is known, a calculator can be used to determine one angle having that value. For example, consider sin θ = 0.5. Place the calculator in degree mode. Then use the second function, or inverse key, and the sin key to find the angle whose sine is 0.5, which is 30°. The label above the sin key may read sin⁻¹, which refers to the inverse function. But, a 30° angle is not the only angle that has a sine value of 0.5. From the definition of the sine function, an angle of 150° also has the sine value 0.5. In fact, all angles of the form (30 + 360k)° and (150 + 360k)°, k ∈ Z, have the same sine value.

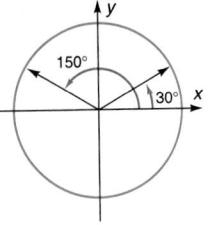

Example 3 Find values of θ, where 0° ≤ θ < 360°, to the nearest tenth of a degree.
  a. cos θ = 0.9266   **b.** sin θ = −0.6009

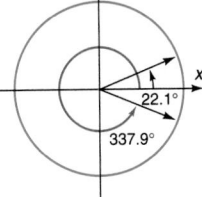

a. cos θ = 0.9266   *Place the calculator in degree mode.*
    θ = 22.1°   *Use the 2nd function and cos keys.*

There is also an angle in quadrant IV with the same cosine value. Using reference angles, θ = 360 − 22.1 = 337.9°. Thus, θ = 22.1° and 337.9°.

b. sin θ = −0.6009   *Place the calculator in degree mode.*
    θ = −36.9°   *Use the 2nd function and sin keys.*

An angle of −36.9° is in quadrant IV. This angle is coterminal with an angle of 360 − 36.9 = 323.1°, which is in the desired range. Since sine is negative, there is also an angle in quadrant III whose sine is −0.6009 and whose reference angle is 36.9°; θ = 180 + 36.9 = 216.9°. Thus, θ = 216.9° and 323.1°.

In Example 3, how can you check that 337.9° is a solution for part (a) *and that 216.9° is a solution for part* (b)?

When a calculator is in radian mode, the values given for the angles are in radians. Using 3.14 for π, angles with measures between 0 and 1.57 are in quadrant I, angles between 1.57 and 3.14 are in quadrant II, angles between 3.14 and 4.71 are in quadrant III, and angles between 4.71 and 6.28 are in quadrant IV.

Example 4 Find values of θ, where 0 ≤ θ < 2π, to the nearest hundredth of a radian.
  a. tan θ = 3.009   **b.** cot θ = −4.69

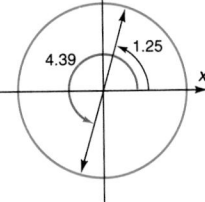

a. tan θ = 3.009   *Place the calculator in radian mode.*
    θ = 1.25 rad   *Use the 2nd function and tan keys.*

Recall that tangent is positive in quadrants I and III. 1.25 radians is in quadrant I. The desired angle in quadrant III is then π + 1.25 = 4.39. Thus, θ = 1.25 and 4.39.

3.7 Evaluating Trigonometric Functions   **161**

Thinking Critically
To check, find cos 337.9° in part (a) to see if it is approximately equal to 0.9266 and find sin 216.9° in part (b) to see if it is approximately equal to −0.6009.

INDEPENDENT PRACTICE

Assignment Guide

Basic: 1–28, 37–39, Project
Average: 9–39, Project
Enriched: 19–49, Project

Teacher's Resource Book
  Practice, page 22

ⓡ Review

Exercises 13, 21, 31, 37, and 39 review concepts of determining exact values for trigonometric functions of angles, solving absolute value equations, solving trigonometric equations, and solving quadratic equations.

Technology

- Class Exercise 19 emphasizes the fact that π is irrational. A calculator will distinguish between the key labeled π and a many-digit decimal approximation, even one that uses as many digits as the calculator displays.
- The Technology discussion on page 161 provides an illustration of the use of technology to support inductive reasoning.

LESSON FOLLOW-UP

Lesson Quiz

Determine each value. Round to four decimal places.
1. $\cos 22.5°$ 0.9239
2. $\tan(-3.08)$ 0.0617
3. $\sec 1.1$ 2.2046
4. $\sin 191°24'55''$ −0.1979
5. Determine the values of θ, where $0° \le \theta < 360°$, for which $\sin \theta = -0.4772$. Round the answer to the nearest tenth of a degree.
   208.5° and 331.5°
6. Determine the values of θ, where $0 \le \theta < 2\pi$, for which $\csc \theta = -1.3391$. Round the answer to the nearest hundredth of a radian.
   3.98 rad and 5.44 rad

---

b. $\cot \theta = -4.69$ *Place the calculator in radian mode.*

$\dfrac{1}{\tan \theta} = -4.69$ *Cotangent and tangent are reciprocal functions.*

$\tan \theta = \dfrac{1}{-4.69}$ *Calculation-ready form. Use the 2nd function, tan, negative, and reciprocal keys.*

$\theta = -0.21$ rad

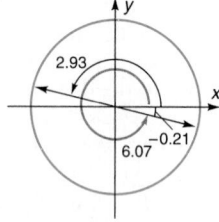

An angle of -0.21 in quadrant IV is coterminal with an angle of $2\pi - 0.21 = 6.07$ which is in the desired range. Since cotangent is negative in quadrant II, find an angle in the second quadrant with reference angle 0.21. The angle $\theta = \pi - 0.21 = 2.93$ is the other value for θ. Thus $\theta = 6.07$ and 2.93.

Modeling

Where and how far apart should satellite tracking stations be situated?

Satellite tracking stations must be close enough together so that continuous communication is maintained. As soon as the satellite loses contact with one station, the next station should pick it up. The stations

should be far enough apart so that undue expenses are avoided. Assuming that the communications waves travel in a straight line, the figure shows that the distance between stations will depend on the height of the satellite above the earth.

Example 5   *Space Science*   A satellite for collecting data is placed in a circular orbit 150 mi above the earth. As the satellite passes out of range (beyond the horizon) from the first station, it must be in contact with the second ground station. Determine the maximum distance possible between the two ground stations.

In this model, the earth is assumed to be a sphere with radius 3960 mi. Angle RBC is a right angle, since it is formed by a tangent and a radius. Using right triangle RBC,

$$\cos y = \frac{RB}{RC} = \frac{3960}{3960 + 150}$$
$$\cos y = 0.9635$$
$$y = 15.53° \text{ or } 0.2710 \text{ rad}$$

The distance s between station B and point T is determined using the relationship

$$s = ry = 3960(0.2710) = 1073 \text{ mi}$$

Thus, the two stations A and B can be at most 2(1073), or 2146, miles apart.

Class Exercises

Determine each value. Round to four decimal places.

1. $\sin 27°$ 0.4540   **2.** $\cos 36.24°$ 0.8065   **3.** $\tan \frac{\pi}{7}$ 0.4816   **4.** $\cot \frac{3\pi}{8}$ 0.4142

5. $\cos 67°50'$ 0.3773   **6.** $\sin 131°12'15''$ 0.7524 **7.** $\sin(-14°)$ −0.2419 **8.** $\tan\left(-\frac{2\pi}{15}\right)$ −0.4452

9. $\sec 22.9°$ 1.0856   **10.** $\csc \frac{5\pi}{16}$ 1.2027   **11.** $\sin 3.1$ 0.0416   **12.** $\cot(-1.06)$
−0.5604

Determine the value of θ, where $0° \le \theta < 360°$, to the nearest tenth of a degree.

13. $\sin \theta = 0.5758$ 35.2°; 144.8° **14.** $\tan \theta = -0.2699$ **15.** $\cos \theta = 0.2756$
164.9°; 344.9°   74.0°; 286.0°

Determine the value of θ, where $0 \le \theta < 2\pi$, to the nearest hundredth of a radian.

16. $\cos \theta = 0.2675$ 1.30; 4.98   **17.** $\sin \theta = -0.8183$ 4.10; 5.32 **18.** $\sec \theta = -1.015$ 2.97; 3.31

19. Thinking Critically If you find $\tan \frac{\pi}{2}$ on a calculator by using π, the
calculator will give an error message. However, if you find $\tan 1.5707963$,
the calculator gives a value. Explain. $\frac{\pi}{2} \ne 1.5707963$

Practice Exercises   Use appropriate technology.

Determine each value. Round to four decimal places.

A **1.** $\cos 163°$ −0.9563   **2.** $\sin(-15.8°)$ −0.2723   **3.** $\sin 127°5'10''$ 0.7977

4. $\tan(-76°26')$ −4.1441   **5.** $\sec 18°$ 1.0515   **6.** $\csc \frac{3\pi}{7}$ 1.0257

7. $\cot(-1.3\pi)$ −0.7265   **8.** $\cos \frac{12\pi}{13}$ −0.9709   **9.** $\tan 568°10'$ 0.5354

10. $\cot(-44.9°)$ −1.0035   **11.** $\sin -\frac{5\pi}{11}$ −0.9898   **12.** $\sec \frac{7\pi}{3}$ 2.000

Ⓡ **13.** Determine the exact value of $\sin 150°$; $\sec \frac{\pi}{2}$. $\frac{1}{2}$; undefined

Determine the value of θ, where $0° \le \theta < 360°$, to the nearest tenth of a degree.

14. $\sin \theta = 0.4067$ 24.0°; 156.0° **15.** $\cos \theta = -0.5023$ **16.** $\tan \theta = 2.9988$
120.2°; 239.8°   71.6°; 251.6°

Determine the value of each angle θ, where $0 \le \theta < 2\pi$, to the nearest hundredth
of a radian.

17. $\sin \theta = 0.8143$ 0.95; 2.19 **18.** $\cos \theta = 0.7838$ 0.67; 5.61 **19.** $\tan \theta = -0.2677$
2.88; 6.02

20. *Space Science* A satellite tracking station is located at point A. If a
satellite passes over the station in a circular orbit 200 mi above the earth,
how far can the station at A track the satellite before it moves below the
horizon? 1233 mi

Ⓡ **21.** Without using a calculator, find the values of θ between 0 and 2π that
satisfy the equation $\tan \theta = 1$. $\frac{\pi}{4}$; $\frac{5\pi}{4}$

22. *Navigation* From the top of a mountain 10,600 ft high (about 2 mi above
sea level) near the sea coast, how far out to sea might a person be able to
see on a clear day? about 126 mi

3.7 Evaluating Trigonometric Functions   **163**

Writing in Mathematics
38. Answers may vary. Students' answers might reflect the following: A calculator provides a
quick and accurate way to obtain values of the trigonometric functions for any input values.
Students can make mistakes by choosing the incorrect mode, by using an incorrect key-
stroking sequence, and by using incorrectly the additional steps required to obtain values
for secant, cosecant, and cotangent.

Alternative Assessment
A student uses a calculator to find an
angle whose sine is 0.1, and gives the
answer $\theta = 5.74$. Ask the students to
write a paragraph explaining how they
know, without using a calculator, that
this answer is incorrect. Students
should speculate as to what was the
most likely error that occurred.

Enrichment
Suppose you were asked to create a
table to be used to obtain the values
of the six trigonometric functions of
angles measured in degrees. Your
table would give sine, cosine, tangent,
cosecant, secant, and cotangent
values for every degree in a range
you specify. What is the least possible
number of degrees that this range
could be? Explain.
The range could be 90°, since the
trigonometric functions for any angle
can be computed using its reference
angle. Reference angles have measures
between 0° and 90°.

Determine the value of θ, where $0° \le \theta < 360°$, to the nearest tenth of a degree.

B **23.** $\sec \theta = 1.1111$ 25.8°; 334.2° **24.** $\cot \theta = -1.2222$
140.7°; 320.7° **25.** $\csc \theta = 2.5012$
23.6°; 156.4°

Determine the value of θ, where $0 \le \theta < 2\pi$, to the nearest hundredth of a radian.

26. $\csc \theta = 1.020$ 1.37; 1.77 **27.** $\cot \theta = 0.589$ 1.04; 4.18 **28.** $\sec \theta = -1.586$ 2.25; 4.03

29. An angle β in quadrant III satisfies the equation $\cos \beta = -0.4727$. What are the possible values of β to the nearest tenth of 1 degree? $(241.8 + 360k)°$, $k \in Z$

30. *Navigation* According to one definition, a *nautical mile* is the length of one minute of arc length on a meridian. Using this definition, the length of a nautical mile varies with latitude, because the earth is not a perfect sphere. A formula that approximates the length in feet is $6077 - 31 \cos 2\theta$, where θ is the latitude in degrees. Compare the lengths of a nautical mile in Omaha, Nebraska (latitude 41°15′42″ N) and Miami, Florida (latitude 25°46′37″ N). 6072.97 ft; 6057.73 ft

Ⓡ **31.** Solve: $|x - 2| < 3$ $-1 < x < 5$

Evaluate $(\tan \theta)^2 - (\sec \theta)^2$ for each value.

32. $42°$ -1 **33.** $-75.5°$ -1 **34.** $\dfrac{2\pi}{7}$ -1 **35.** 1.6π -1

36. **Thinking Critically** Use your answers to Exercises 32 to 35 to predict the value of $(\tan \theta)^2 - (\sec \theta)^2$ for arbitrary values of θ. Test your hypothesis using four new values for θ. Remember that round-off errors may occur when working with irrational numbers. $(\tan \theta)^2 - (\sec \theta)^2 = -1$

Ⓡ **37.** One positive integer is 3 less than another. Determine the integers if the sum of their squares is 117. 6; 9

38. **Writing in Mathematics** Describe some advantages of using a calculator to evaluate the trigonometric functions. Then suggest some ways students could make mistakes when they use calculators for this purpose.

Ⓡ **39.** Solve for θ, $0 \le \theta < 2\pi$, by factoring: $(\sin \theta)^2 - 2 \sin \theta + 1 = 0$ $\theta = \dfrac{\pi}{2}$

Physics The acceleration due to gravity is usually considered a constant, but it varies slightly with latitude. At sea level, it can be approximated by the formula

$$g = 9.78049[1 + 0.005288 (\sin \theta)^2 - 0.000006 (\sin 2\theta)^2] \text{ m/s}^2$$

where θ represents the latitude in degrees. Determine the acceleration due to gravity in each world city to five decimal places.

C **40.** New York City (lat. 40°45′06″ N) 9.80247 m/s² **41.** Montreal (lat. 45°30′33″ N) 9.80675 m/s²

42. Jerusalem (lat. 31°47′ N) 9.79479 m/s² **43.** Paris (lat. 48°50′14″ N) 9.80975 m/s²

44. *Physics* The formula for the behavior of light passing from air to water in Lesson 3.6 can be generalized to describe the behavior of light passing from any medium to another. If v_1 and θ_1 are the velocity of light and the angle the light ray makes with the vertical in the first medium, respectively, and v_2 and θ_2 the velocity and angle in the second medium, then $\dfrac{v_1}{v_2} = \dfrac{\sin \theta_1}{\sin \theta_2}$.
Suppose that $v_1 = 3.1 \times 10^8$ m/s, $\theta_1 = 44°$, and $\theta_2 = 29°$. Determine the velocity of light in the second medium. 2.16×10^8 m/s

164 Chapter 3 Trigonometric Functions

θ	-0.5	-0.25	-0.1	-0.01	-0.001	0.001	0.01	0.1	0.25
46. $\sin \theta$	-0.4794	-0.2474	-0.0998	-0.0100	-0.0010	0.0010	0.0100	0.0998	0.2474
$\dfrac{\sin \theta}{\theta}$	0.9589	0.9896	0.9983	1.0000	1.0000	1.0000	1.0000	0.9983	0.9896
47. $\dfrac{1 - \cos \theta}{\theta}$	-0.2448	-0.1244	-0.0500	-0.0050	-0.0005	0.0005	0.0050	0.0500	0.1244

45. *Physics*   If a projectile is fired from the origin at an angle θ with the horizontal and with initial velocity v_0, at time t it will be at point $P(x, y)$ where $x = (v_0 \cos \theta)t$ and $y = (v_0 \sin \theta)t - 16t^2$, with x and y measured in feet and t in seconds. Suppose that $\theta = 53°$ and $v_0 = 100$ ft/s. Plot the position of the projectile at time $t = 0, 1, 2, 3, 4, 5$, and 6. Describe its path.

46. The quotient $\frac{\sin \theta}{\theta}$, which occurs in calculus, is not defined when $\theta = 0$.

However, values of θ near 0 can be used to describe the behavior of the quotient as θ gets closer and closer to 0. Complete the chart below and use the information to make a statement about the behavior of $\frac{\sin \theta}{\theta}$ for θ near

zero. Remember to use *radians*.

θ	−0.5	−0.25	−0.1	−0.01	−0.001	0.001	0.01	0.1	0.25
$\sin \theta$									
$\frac{\sin \theta}{\theta}$									

47. Repeat Exercise 46 for the quotient $\frac{1 - \cos \theta}{\theta}$.

48. Using a square and hexagon, verify that the area A of a regular n-sided polygon circumscribed about a circle of radius 1 is given by the formula $A = n \tan \frac{180°}{n}$. Find the area for $n = 5, 10, 50, 100$, and 1000. Verify that as n gets larger and larger, the area gets closer and closer to π, the area of a circle of radius 1.

49. The area A of a regular n-sided polygon inscribed in a circle of radius 1 is given by the formula $A = \frac{n}{2} \sin \frac{360°}{n}$. Find the area for $n = 6, 10, 50, 100$, and 1000. Verify that as n gets larger and larger, the area gets closer and closer to π, which is the area of a circle of radius 1.

Project

Interview a professional in the telecommunications field. Gather information about how signals for television can be instantaneously transmitted half-way around the world.

Challenge

1. Solve for x: $|x - 2| \geq |x + 2|$ $x \leq 0$
2. Graph $(x - 3)^2 + (y + 1)^2 = 25$ and find the equation of the line tangent to the curve at the point $(7, 2)$. *Hint:* The tangent line is perpendicular to the line connecting the center of the circle to the point of tangency. $y = -\frac{4}{3}x + \frac{34}{3}$
3. If $f(x) = ax^2 - c$, show that the slope of the line connecting one x-intercept with the vertex is the negative of the slope of the line connecting the other x-intercept with the vertex.

Vocabulary
fundamental identities
odd-even identities
Pythagorean identities
ratio identities
reciprocal identities
trigonometric identity

Technology
scientific calculator

FOCUS

Both trainers and sports medicine specialists use tools of science and mathematics in daily practice. Computer models are used to analyze sports activities and help athletes make decisions that contribute to both safety and efficiency.

Physical anthropologists use similar tools to track the past. The footprints of dinosaurs have been analyzed for information about these ancient creatures. Their pace, stride, and step angles can be read from their footprints, and used, for example, to estimate their speed.

INSTRUCTION

- Have students recall some algebraic identities such as:

$$(a + b)(a - b) = a^2 - b^2$$
$$(\sqrt{x})^2 = x$$

Note that the first of these is true for all values of a and b, while the second is true for all values of x *for which the expression is defined*.

- Point out that most identities are discovered through *inductive reasoning*, and are then proved using *deductive reasoning*. Class Exercises 11 of Lesson 3.5, Practice Exercises 38 of Lesson 3.6, and 36 of Lesson 3.7 provided opportunities for students to discover trigonometric identities. In this lesson those identities are proven.

3.8 Fundamental Identities

Objective: To introduce and prove the reciprocal, ratio, Pythagorean, and odd-even identities

Focus

The measurement and analysis of angles sometimes occurs in unexpected situations. For example, kinetic analysts study the motion of runners using videotape and computer graphics. One such study focused on the *stride angle* of marathon runners, that is, the opening between the upper leading and the upper trailing leg. The study found that marathoners run most efficiently with a stride angle of approximately 100°.

Stress on the knees during running is measured by the *Q angle*. This is the angle formed by a line drawn down the center of the thigh through the knee and another line drawn from the bump on the top of the shinbone straight up the leg.

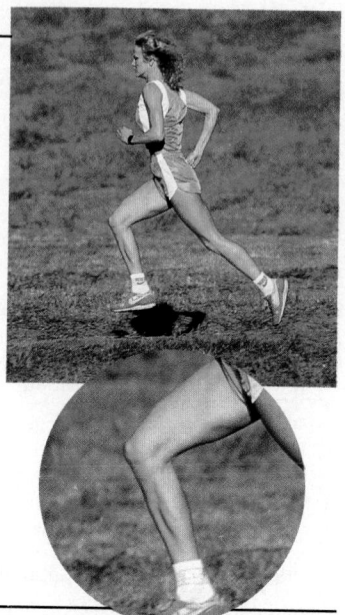

It would be a rare study of angles that did not invoke the tools of trigonometry. One of these tools is a collection of identities that can enable the user both to simplify complex expressions and to make more efficient use of available technology.

A **trigonometric identity** is a trigonometric equation that is true for all values of the variables for which the expressions in the equation are defined. Some examples of identities are the reciprocal identities which were introduced in Lesson 3.5.

$$\csc \theta = \frac{1}{\sin \theta} \qquad \sec \theta = \frac{1}{\cos \theta} \qquad \cot \theta = \frac{1}{\tan \theta}$$

These can be proved using the definitions of the six trigonometric functions.

Example 1 Use the definitions of $\cos \theta$ and $\sec \theta$ to prove that these functions are reciprocals of each other.

Given point $P(x, y)$ on the terminal side of θ,

$$\cos \theta = \frac{x}{r} \qquad \text{and} \qquad \sec \theta = \frac{r}{x}$$

Hence, $\qquad \dfrac{1}{\cos \theta} = \dfrac{1}{\frac{x}{r}} = \dfrac{r}{x} = \sec \theta \qquad$ and $\qquad \dfrac{1}{\sec \theta} = \dfrac{1}{\frac{r}{x}} = \dfrac{x}{r} = \cos \theta$

166 Chapter 3 Trigonometric Functions

The reciprocal identities hold only for those values of θ for which both sides of the equations are defined. Remember that it is this set of relations that enables you to use the calculator to evaluate csc θ, sec θ, and cot θ.

The reciprocal relations show that sec θ and csc θ may be *defined* in terms of cos θ and sin θ. Two **ratio identities** show that tan θ and cot θ may also be defined in these terms.

$$\tan \theta = \frac{\sin \theta}{\cos \theta}, \ \cos \theta \neq 0 \quad \text{and} \quad \cot \theta = \frac{\cos \theta}{\sin \theta}, \ \sin \theta \neq 0$$

Example 2 Prove the ratio identity $\tan \theta = \frac{\sin \theta}{\cos \theta}$, $\cos \theta \neq 0$.

Use the definitions of sine and cosine.

$$\frac{\sin \theta}{\cos \theta} = \frac{\frac{y}{r}}{\frac{x}{r}} = \frac{y}{x} = \tan \theta$$

In Lesson 3.4, cos θ and sin θ were introduced as the x- and y-coordinates of a point on the unit circle. Since the equation of the unit circle is $x^2 + y^2 = 1$, it follows by substitution that $(\cos \theta)^2 + (\sin \theta)^2 = 1$ for all θ. This relationship may also be proved algebraically as in Examples 1 and 2. The expressions $(\sin \theta)^2$ and $(\cos \theta)^2$ are usually written $\sin^2 \theta$ and $\cos^2 \theta$. The identity $\sin^2 \theta + \cos^2 \theta = 1$ is one of three identities called the **Pythagorean identities.** Since the other two can be derived readily from the first, the derivations are left as exercises.

$$\sin^2 \theta + \cos^2 \theta = 1 \qquad \tan^2 \theta + 1 = \sec^2 \theta \qquad 1 + \cot^2 \theta = \csc^2 \theta$$

Recall that a function f is *even* if $f(-x) = f(x)$ for all x in its domain. A function f is *odd* if $f(-x) = -f(x)$ for all x in its domain. Many functions are neither even nor odd, but all six trigonometric functions fall into one of these two categories. The functions sin θ, tan θ, csc θ, and cot θ are odd, while cos θ and sec θ are even.

Example 3 Prove that $\sin (-\theta) = -\sin \theta$ for all θ.

Let the terminal side of θ in standard position intersect a circle of radius r in a point $P(x, y)$. Then $\sin \theta = \frac{y}{r}$. By symmetry, the terminal side of $-\theta$ intersects the circle in $Q(x, -y)$, and so $\sin (-\theta) = \frac{-y}{r} = -\sin \theta$.

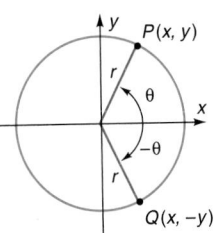

For an identity to be *proved*, it must be shown to be true for *all* values of the variable for which it is defined. An identity may be *verified* by substitution of one or more specific values. The process of verification may help a mathematician to discover an identity, but no amount of verification constitutes a proof.

Some students will find trigonometric identities more meaningful if they see examples first. Exercises in previous lessons have prepared the way for this, notably for the Pythagorean identities; for example, Practice Exercises 38 of Lesson 3.6 and 36 of Lesson 3.7.

For Example 1
Use the definition of sin θ and csc θ to prove that csc $\theta \cdot \sin \theta = 1$.
Given point $P(x, y)$ on the terminal side of θ, csc $\theta = \frac{r}{y}$, $y \neq 0$ and sin $\theta = \frac{y}{r}$. Hence, csc $\theta \cdot \sin \theta = \frac{r}{y} \cdot \frac{y}{r} = 1$.

For Example 2
Prove that sin $\theta \cdot \cot \theta = \cos \theta$.
Use the definitions of sine, cotangent, and cosine: sin $\theta = \frac{y}{r}$, cot $\theta = \frac{x}{y}$, $y \neq 0$, cos $\theta = \frac{x}{r}$. Hence, sin $\theta \cdot \cot \theta = \frac{y}{r} \cdot \frac{x}{y} = \frac{x}{r} = \cos \theta$.

For Example 3
Prove each identity.
1. cos $(-\theta)$ = cos θ
Let the terminal side of θ in standard position intersect a circle of radius r in a point $P(x, y)$. Then cos $\theta = \frac{x}{r}$. By symmetry, the terminal side of $-\theta$ intersect the circle in $Q(x, -y)$, and so cos $(-\theta) = \frac{x}{r} = \cos \theta$.

2. tan $(-\theta)$ = $-\tan \theta$
Let the terminal side of θ in standard position intersect a circle of radius r in a point $P(x, y)$. Then tan $\theta = \frac{y}{x}$. By symmetry, the terminal side of $-\theta$ intersects the circle in $Q(x, -y)$, and so tan $(-\theta)$ = $-\frac{y}{x} = -\tan \theta$, $x \neq 0$.

Use exact values to verify each identity for the given value of θ.

1. $\tan(-\theta) = -\tan\theta$; $\theta = \dfrac{\pi}{3}$

$$\tan\left(-\dfrac{\pi}{3}\right) \,\bigg|\, -\tan\dfrac{\pi}{3}$$

$$\tan\dfrac{5\pi}{3} \,\bigg|\, -\sqrt{3}$$

$$-\sqrt{3} = -\sqrt{3}$$

2. $1 + \tan^2\theta = \sec^2\theta$; $\theta = 150°$

$$1 + \tan^2\theta \,\bigg|\, \sec^2\theta$$

$$1 + \left(-\dfrac{\sqrt{3}}{3}\right)^2 \,\bigg|\, \left(\dfrac{2\sqrt{3}}{3}\right)^2$$

$$\dfrac{9}{9} + \dfrac{3}{9} \,\bigg|\, \dfrac{12}{9}$$

$$\dfrac{12}{9} = \dfrac{12}{9}$$

For Example 5

Simplify each expression by writing it in terms of sine and cosine.

1. $\cot\beta\sec\beta$

$$\cot\beta\sec\beta = \dfrac{\cos\beta}{\sin\beta} \cdot \dfrac{1}{\cos\beta}$$

$$= \dfrac{1}{\sin\beta}$$

2. $\dfrac{\sec^2\theta - 1}{\tan(-\theta)}$

$$\dfrac{\sec^2\theta - 1}{\tan(-\theta)} = \dfrac{\tan^2\theta}{-\tan\theta}$$

$$= \dfrac{-\tan\theta}{1}$$

$$= -\dfrac{\sin\theta}{\cos\theta}$$

CLOSURE

Have students explain in their math journals the difference between proving an identity and verifying an identity.

INDEPENDENT PRACTICE

Assignment Guide

Basic: 1–28
Average 11–38
Enriched: 19–46

Teacher's Resource Book
  Practice, page 23

Example 4 Use exact values to verify each identity for the given values of θ.

a. $\tan(-\theta) = -\tan\theta$; $\theta = 135°$ **b.** $1 + \cot^2\theta = \csc^2\theta$; $\theta = \dfrac{\pi}{3}$

a. $\tan(-135°) \,\bigg|\, -\tan 135°$
$\tan 225° \,\bigg|\, -(-1)$
$1 = 1$

b. $1 + \cot^2\theta \,\bigg|\, \csc^2\theta$
$1 + \left(\dfrac{\sqrt{3}}{3}\right)^2 \,\bigg|\, \left(\dfrac{2\sqrt{3}}{3}\right)^2$
$\dfrac{9}{9} + \dfrac{3}{9} \,\bigg|\, \dfrac{12}{9}$
$\dfrac{12}{9} = \dfrac{12}{9}$

The identities that have been discussed in this lesson are sometimes called the *fundamental identities*.

Fundamental Identities

Reciprocal identities	*Pythagorean identities*
$\csc\theta = \dfrac{1}{\sin\theta}$, $\sin\theta \neq 0$	$\sin^2\theta + \cos^2\theta = 1$
$\sec\theta = \dfrac{1}{\cos\theta}$, $\cos\theta \neq 0$	$1 + \cot^2\theta = \csc^2\theta$
$\cot\theta = \dfrac{1}{\tan\theta}$, $\tan\theta \neq 0$	$1 + \tan^2\theta = \sec^2\theta$

Ratio identities	*Odd-even identities*	
$\tan\theta = \dfrac{\sin\theta}{\cos\theta}$, $\cos\theta \neq 0$	$\sin(-\theta) = -\sin\theta$	$\csc(-\theta) = -\csc\theta$
$\cot\theta = \dfrac{\cos\theta}{\sin\theta}$, $\sin\theta \neq 0$	$\cos(-\theta) = \cos\theta$	$\sec(-\theta) = \sec\theta$
	$\tan(-\theta) = -\tan\theta$	$\cot(-\theta) = -\cot\theta$

The fundamental identities may be used to simplify trigonometric expressions and to convert expressions into forms that can be evaluated efficiently.

Example 5 Simplify each expression by writing it in terms of sine and cosine.

a. $\cot\theta\sin\theta$ **b.** $\dfrac{\sin^2\theta}{\sec^2\theta - 1}$

a. $\cot\theta\sin\theta = \dfrac{\cos\theta}{\sin\theta} \cdot \sin\theta = \cos\theta$ $\cot\theta = \dfrac{\cos\theta}{\sin\theta}$

b. $\dfrac{\sin^2\theta}{\sec^2\theta - 1} = \dfrac{\sin^2\theta}{\tan^2\theta}$ $\sec^2\theta - 1 = \tan^2\theta$

$= \dfrac{\sin^2\theta}{\dfrac{\sin^2\theta}{\cos^2\theta}}$ $\tan^2\theta = \dfrac{\sin^2\theta}{\cos^2\theta}$

$= \cos^2\theta$

Class Exercises

1. Use definitions to prove that csc θ and sin θ are reciprocal functions.

$\csc \theta = \frac{r}{y}$ and $\sin \theta = \frac{y}{r}$;

$\frac{1}{\sin \theta} = \frac{1}{\frac{y}{r}} = \frac{r}{y} = \csc \theta$

Use exact values to verify each identity for the given value of θ.

2. $\sin^2 \theta + \cos^2 \theta = 1$; $\theta = \frac{\pi}{4}$

$\left(\frac{\sqrt{2}}{2}\right)^2 + \left(\frac{\sqrt{2}}{2}\right)^2 = \frac{1}{2} + \frac{1}{2} = 1$

3. $\tan \theta = \frac{\sin \theta}{\cos \theta}$; $\theta = \frac{\pi}{3}$

$\sqrt{3} = \frac{\sqrt{3}}{2} \div \frac{1}{2}$

4. $\sin(-\theta) = -\sin \theta$; $\theta = 30°$

$-\frac{1}{2} = -\left(\frac{1}{2}\right)$

5. $1 + \tan^2 \theta = \sec^2 \theta$; $\theta = 135°$

$1 + (1)^2 = (-\sqrt{2})^2$

$1 + 1 = 2$

6. Prove that $\csc(-\theta) = -\csc \theta$ for all θ for which csc θ is defined.

$\csc(-\theta) = \frac{1}{\sin(-\theta)} = \frac{1}{-\sin \theta} = -\frac{1}{\sin} = -\csc \theta$

Use the fundamental identities to simplify these expressions.

7. $\sin \theta \csc \theta$ 1

8. $\sec^2 \theta - \tan^2 \theta$ 1

9. $\frac{\sin(-\theta)}{\sin \theta}$ -1

10. $\frac{\sin \theta}{\cos \theta \tan \theta}$ 1

Practice Exercises

$\cot \theta = \frac{x}{y}$ and $\tan \theta = \frac{x}{y}$;

A 1. Use definitions to prove that cot θ and tan θ are reciprocal functions.

$\cot \theta \cdot \tan \theta = \frac{y}{x} \cdot \frac{x}{y} = 1$

2. Use definitions to prove the ratio identity $\cot \theta = \frac{\cos \theta}{\sin \theta}$, $\sin \theta \neq 0$.

$\frac{\cos \theta}{\sin \theta} = \frac{\frac{x}{r}}{\frac{y}{r}} = \frac{x}{r} \cdot \frac{r}{y} = \frac{x}{y} = \cot \theta$

Use exact values to verify each identity for the given value of θ.

3. $1 + \cot^2 \theta = \csc^2 \theta$; $\theta = \frac{3\pi}{4}$

$1 + (-1)^2 = (\sqrt{2})^2$

$1 + 1 = 2$

4. $\cot \theta = \frac{\cos \theta}{\sin \theta}$; $\theta = \frac{5\pi}{6}$

$-\sqrt{3} = \frac{-\frac{\sqrt{3}}{2}}{\frac{1}{2}} = -\frac{\sqrt{3}}{2} \div \frac{1}{2} = -\frac{\sqrt{3}}{2} \cdot \frac{2}{1} = -\sqrt{3}$

5. $\cos(-\theta) = \cos \theta$; $\theta = -60°$

$\frac{1}{2} = \frac{1}{2}$

6. $\tan(-\theta) = -\tan \theta$; $\theta = 45°$

$-1 = -(1)$

7. $\sin^2 \theta + \cos^2 \theta = 1$; $\theta = \frac{\pi}{2}$

$1^2 + 0^2 = 1$

8. $\tan \theta = \frac{\sin \theta}{\cos \theta}$; $\theta = 180°$

$0 = \frac{0}{1}$

9. $\csc \theta = \frac{1}{\sin \theta}$; $\theta = 30°$

$2 = \frac{1}{\frac{1}{2}} = 1 \cdot \frac{2}{1} = 2$

10. $\cot \theta = \frac{1}{\tan \theta}$; $\theta = \frac{\pi}{3}$

$\frac{\sqrt{3}}{3} = \frac{1}{\sqrt{3}}$

Ⓡ 11. *Horology*   A pendulum of length 5 m swings through an arc of 0.5 rad. How far does the tip of the pendulum travel?   2.5 m

Use a scientific calculator to obtain values and verify each identity for the given θ. Remember that rounding errors may occur.

12. $\sin^2 \theta + \cos^2 \theta = 1$; $\theta = 46.7°$

13. $\sec^2 \theta = 1 + \tan^2 \theta$; $\theta = 239°$

14. $\tan \theta = \frac{\sin \theta}{\cos \theta}$; $\theta = \frac{7\pi}{8}$

15. $\cot \theta = \frac{\cos \theta}{\sin \theta}$; $\theta = 1.94$

16. $\sin(-\theta) = -\sin \theta$; $\theta = 1.3\pi$

17. $\cos(-\theta) = \cos \theta$; $\theta = 1.3$

18. $\tan(-\theta) = -\tan \theta$; θ $-29°$

19. $\sec(-\theta) = \sec \theta$; $\theta = -17.5°$

20. Simplify the expression $\frac{\tan \theta}{\tan(-\theta)}$. $\frac{\tan \theta}{-\tan \theta} = -1$

Ⓡ 21. *Physical Fitness*   Some scales measure only in kilograms. For a girl weighing 121 lb, the scale shows 55 kg. For a boy weighing 143 lb, the scale shows 65 kg. Determine the weight in pounds for a person weighing 60 kg. Write formulas to convert from kilograms to pounds and from pounds to kilograms.

132 lb; kg = 2.2 lb; lb = 0.45 kg

B 22. Simplify the expression $\frac{\cot^2 \beta - \csc^2 \beta}{\tan^2 \beta - \sec^2 \beta}$.   1

3.8 Fundamental Identities   **169**

Ⓡ **Review**

Exercises 11, 21, 23, 25, 27, and 40 review concepts of determining arc lengths of circles, determining and using formulas, and determining whether an algebraic function is odd or even.

Technology

The technology exercises on pages 169 to 170 address the fact that calculators often perform computations using even more decimal places than the display. Point out that computing each side of an equation in one step or using the calculator's memory can minimize the incidence of round-off errors.

LESSON FOLLOW-UP

Lesson Quiz

Tell whether each statement is true or false. If your answer is false, correct the underlined word or phrase.

1. The sine function is an <u>odd</u> function.   T

2. The secant function is the reciprocal of the <u>sine</u> function.

   F; cosine

3. For all θ, $\tan^2 \theta + 1 = \underline{\csc^2 \theta}$.

   F; $\sec^2 \theta$

4. For all θ for which tangent is defined, $\tan \theta \cdot \cos \theta = \underline{\sin \theta}$.   T

5. The cosine function is an <u>odd</u> function.   F; even

6. Write both the tangent and cotangent functions in terms of sine and cosine. Then use these relations to show that the tangent and cotangent are reciprocal functions.

$\tan \theta = \frac{\sin \theta}{\cos \theta}$ and $\cot \theta = \frac{\cos \theta}{\sin \theta}$;

$\tan \theta \cot \theta = \frac{\sin \theta}{\cos \theta} \cdot \frac{\cos \theta}{\sin \theta} = 1$.

Thus, tangent and cotangent are reciprocal functions.

Additional Answers

12. $(0.7278)^2 + (0.6858)^2 = 1$

13. $(-1.9416)^2 = 1 + (1.6643)^2 = 3.7698$

14. $-0.4142 = \frac{0.3827}{-0.9239}$

15. $-0.3869 = \frac{-0.3609}{0.9326}$

16. $0.8090 = -(-0.8090)$

17. $0.2675 = 0.2675$

18. $0.5543 = -(-0.5543)$

19. $1.0485 = 1.0485$

Alternative Assessment

Instruct students to use the sine and cosine functions and a unit circle to explain to at least one other student why it is always true that

$$(\sin \theta)^2 + (\cos \theta)^2 = 1$$

Enrichment

Simplify the expression and write it in terms of sine.

$$\frac{1}{\sec \theta + \tan \theta} + \frac{1}{\sec \theta - \tan \theta}$$

$$\frac{1}{\sec \theta + \tan \theta} + \frac{1}{\sec \theta - \tan \theta}$$

$$= \frac{\sec \theta - \tan \theta + \sec \theta + \tan \theta}{\sec^2 \theta - \tan^2 \theta}$$

$$= 2 \sec \theta = \frac{2}{\cos \theta} = \frac{2}{\sqrt{\cos^2 \theta}}$$

$$= \frac{2}{\sqrt{1 - \sin^2 \theta}} = \frac{2\sqrt{1 - \sin^2 \theta}}{1 - \sin^2 \theta}$$

Additional Answers

26. $\dfrac{\sin^2 \theta}{\sin^2 \theta} + \dfrac{\cos^2 \theta}{\sin^2 \theta} = \dfrac{1}{\sin^2 \theta}$
$1 + \cot^2 \theta = \csc^2 \theta$

27. $h(-x) = (-x)^2 + (-x) + 1 = x^2 - x + 1$; Therefore, $h(-x) \neq h(x)$.
$-h(x) = -(x^2 + x + 1) = -x^2 - x - 1$; Therefore, $h(-x) \neq -h(x)$.

Let $P(x, y)$ be on the terminal side of θ in standard position and let $r = \sqrt{x^2 + y^2}$.

28. $\left(\dfrac{y}{r}\right)^2 + \left(\dfrac{x}{r}\right)^2 = \dfrac{x^2 + y^2}{r^2} = \dfrac{r^2}{r^2} = 1$

29. $1 + \left(\dfrac{y}{x}\right)^2 = \dfrac{y^2}{y^2} + \dfrac{x^2}{y^2} = \dfrac{y^2 + x^2}{y^2} = \dfrac{r^2}{y^2} = \left(\dfrac{r}{y}\right)^2$

30. $\left(\dfrac{y}{x}\right)^2 + 1 = \dfrac{y^2}{x^2} + \dfrac{x^2}{x^2} = \dfrac{y^2 + x^2}{x^2} = \dfrac{r^2}{x^2} = \left(\dfrac{r}{x}\right)^2$

R 23. *Manufacturing*   A can for prepared food is to be 14 cm high and have a volume of 1500 cm³. Find the radius. *Hint*: $V = \pi r^2 h$. 5.84 cm

24. Thinking Critically   Criticize the following definition: "An even function is a function that is not odd." Some functions are neither odd nor even. Ex. $y = x + 2$

R 25. Show that the function $g(x) = x^3 - x$ is an odd function. $g(-x) = (-x)^3 - (-x) = -x^3 + x = -(x^3 - x) = -g(x)$

26. Derive the identity $1 + \cot^2 \theta = \csc^2 \theta$ from $\sin^2 \theta + \cos^2 \theta = 1$.

R 27. Show that the function $h(x) = x^2 + x + 1$ is neither even nor odd.

Prove the Pythagorean identities using the definitions and the methods of Examples 1 and 2.

28. $\sin^2 \theta + \cos^2 \theta = 1$ **29.** $1 + \cot^2 \theta = \csc^2 \theta$ **30.** $\tan^2 \theta + 1 = \sec^2 \theta$

Simplify each expression by writing it in terms of sine and cosine.

31. $\cos \beta \tan \beta$ sin β   **32.** $\sin \theta \cot \theta$ cos θ   **33.** $\tan \phi \csc \phi$ $\frac{1}{\cos \phi}$

Simplify each expression and write it in terms of cosine.

34. $(\csc^2 \theta - 1)(\sin^2 \theta)$ cos² θ   **35.** $(1 + \tan^2 \theta)(\sec^2 \theta)$ $\frac{1}{\cos^4 \theta}$ **36.** $\dfrac{1 - \sin^2 \phi}{\cos \phi}$ cos θ   **37.** $\dfrac{\sin^2 \theta}{\cos \theta} + \cos \theta$ $\frac{1}{\cos \theta}$

C 38. An angle β has terminal side in quadrant IV and $\cos \beta = 0.31$. Use the fundamental identities to find $\tan \beta$. −3.0669

39. An angle θ has terminal side in quadrant II and $\sin \theta = 0.81$. Use the fundamental identities to find $\tan \theta$. −1.3812

R 40. *Physics*   A ball is thrown vertically upward and its height is given by $h(t) = -16t^2 + 96t$. Determine the time (in seconds) it takes the ball to reach the ground. 6 s

41. Use the fundamental identities to find $\csc \theta$ given $\tan \theta = -5.5$ and $\sin \theta > 0$. 1.0164

42. Use the fundamental identities to find $\sin \phi$ and $\tan \phi$ given $\sec \phi = -\frac{5}{3}$ and $\tan \phi > 0$. $\sin \phi = -\frac{4}{5}$; $\tan \phi = \frac{4}{3}$

43. Express $\dfrac{1}{\csc \theta + \cot \theta} + \dfrac{1}{\csc \theta - \cot \theta}$ in terms of $\sin \theta$. $\frac{2}{\sin \theta}$

44. Express $1 + \dfrac{\cot \theta}{\csc \theta} - \sin^2 \theta$ in terms of $\cos \theta$. cos² θ + cos θ

45. Determine two values for θ such that $\sin \theta = \tan \theta$, $0 < \theta < 2\pi$. 0, π

46. Thinking Critically   Use the definitions and a scientific calculator to determine the value between 0 and π radians for which $\tan \theta$ approaches (gets close to) $\sec \theta$. Is there any value of θ for which $\tan \theta = \sec \theta$? Why or why not? no; As θ approaches $\frac{\pi}{2}$, tan θ approaches sec θ where both are undefined.

Review

Draw each angle in standard position.

1. 210°   **2.** −300°

3. Simplify $-6x^3y^{-1}$ if $x = 2$ and $y = -2$. 24

4. Give the angle in degrees formed by the hands of a clock at 1:00 p.m. 30°

170   Chapter 3 Trigonometric Functions

Review

1.   2.

170

3.9 Proving Trigonometric Identities

Objective: To use the fundamental identities to prove other trigonometric identities

Focus

Pythagoras, a Greek mathematician of the sixth century B.C., founded a religious, scientific, and philosophical fraternity. The group had a strict code of conduct which forbade eating lentils, picking up fallen objects, touching a white rooster, and letting swallows live under one's roof, to name a few!

The Pythagoreans believed that numbers were the essence of the universe, and that everything could be expressed using whole numbers and their ratios. Therefore, they were deeply disturbed by the discovery that certain ratios, such as the ratio of a diagonal to a side of a square, could not be expressed by whole numbers. They had difficulty accepting the existence of irrational numbers like $\sqrt{2}$.

Legend has it that Hippasus of Metapontum discovered the existence of irrational numbers. The Pythagoreans were at sea when he demonstrated his proof, and they threw Hippasus overboard for having produced a *counterexample* that contradicted their theories about numbers. Counterexamples are not usually that dangerous. In fact, they are valuable learning tools. A *hypothesis* can be proved using formal reasoning. A *counterexample* shows that the hypothesis is not valid.

In this lesson, some trigonometric equations will prove to be trigonometric identities. Counterexamples will be used to show that other equations, though true sometimes, are not identities.

An equation that is true for all values in the domain of the variable is called an identity. Trigonometry has many identities, and they can be useful when solving problems. In this lesson, the fundamental identities are used to prove other identities.

Proofs involving identities can be written in column form using a vertical line to separate the expressions to be proved equivalent. One approach to proving identities is to work with one side of the equation and attempt to show that it is equivalent to the other. You may *not* perform an operation such as multiplying, adding, or taking square roots on both sides of the equation.

3.9 Proving Trigonometric Identities **171**

LESSON PLAN
FOCUS

Work attributed to the Pythagoreans is generally understood to have been accomplished between 585 and 400 B.C. The Pythagoreans studied astronomy, music, arithmetic, and geometry. Their most familiar contribution was the *Pythagorean theorem*. Less commonly known is the fact that their study of number theory laid the ground work for number mysticism and some relationships discovered by the Pythagoreans were later used in astrology, magic, and the reading of horoscopes. The Pythagoreans were said to have been involved in politics, and Pythagoras himself was said to have been murdered for political reasons.

The notion of counterexample is the key to this Focus. Students should understand that one counterexample proves that a statement is false, even though no number of examples proves that it is true.

INSTRUCTION

- For practice, have students provide counterexamples to false algebraic hypotheses such as the following:

$$(a + b)^2 = a^2 + b^2$$
$$\sqrt{x^2} = x$$
$$\sqrt{a + b} = \sqrt{a} + \sqrt{b}$$
$$-x < x$$

- The Mersenne conjecture is another famous mathematical example of the role of counterexample. In the seventeenth century, Mersenne proposed that if p is a prime number, then $2^p - 1$ is also a prime number. In 1876 Eduard Lucas disproved the conjecture by showing that $2^{67} - 1$ is not prime.

- In contrast to an identity, a statement that is *false* for all values of the variable is called a *contradiction*. Some examples are $|x| < -3$ and $\cos \theta = 5$. Students are asked to give examples of contradictions in Practice Exercise 46.

171

Some students will better understand the potential usefulness of trigonometric identities if they recognize that they are related to familiar material. Begin by having students brainstorm around identities they have found useful in the past: $x + 0 = x$; $a \div a = 1$; $-(-y) = y$, and so on. This lesson will extend the notion of identities to trigonometry.

GUIDED PRACTICE

For Example 1
Prove:
$\csc \theta(\sin \theta + \cos \theta) = \cot \theta + 1$

$$= \frac{1}{\sin \theta}(\sin \theta + \cos \theta)$$

$$= \frac{\sin \theta}{\sin \theta} + \frac{\cos \theta}{\sin \theta}$$

$$= 1 + \cot \theta = \cot \theta + 1$$

Therefore,
$\csc \theta(\sin \theta + \cos \theta) = \cot \theta + 1$.

For Example 2
Prove:
$\sec x - \sin x \tan x = \cos x$

$$= \frac{1}{\cos x} - \sin x \cdot \frac{\sin x}{\cos x}$$

$$= \frac{1}{\cos x} - \frac{\sin^2 x}{\cos x}$$

$$= \frac{1 - \sin^2 x}{\cos x}$$

$$= \frac{\cos^2 x}{\cos x} = \cos x$$

Therefore, $\sec x - \sin x \tan x = \cos x$.

Example 1   Prove: $\sin \theta \sec \theta = \tan \theta$

$\sin \theta \sec \theta$	$\tan \theta$	
$\sin \theta \cdot \dfrac{1}{\cos \theta}$		*Reciprocal identity*
$\dfrac{\sin \theta}{\cos \theta}$		*Ratio identity*
$\tan \theta =$		Therefore, $\sin \theta \sec \theta = \tan \theta$.

The tools and techniques of algebra are often used to prove identities.

Example 2   Prove: $\tan \phi + \cot \phi = \csc \phi \sec \phi$

$\tan \phi + \cot \phi$	$\csc \phi \sec \phi$	
$\dfrac{\sin \phi}{\cos \phi} + \dfrac{\cos \phi}{\sin \phi}$		*Ratio identities*
$\dfrac{\sin^2 \phi + \cos^2 \phi}{\sin \phi \cos \phi}$		*LCD is $\sin \phi \cos \phi$.*
$\dfrac{1}{\sin \phi \cos \phi}$		*Pythagorean identity*
$\dfrac{1}{\sin \phi} \cdot \dfrac{1}{\cos \phi}$		*Reciprocal identities*
$\csc \phi \sec \phi =$		Therefore, $\tan \phi + \cot \phi = \csc \phi \sec \phi$.

The same techniques that are used to prove identities can also be used to simplify trigonometric expressions. For example,

$$\sqrt{4 - 4\sin^2 \theta} = \sqrt{4(1 - \sin^2 \theta)} = \sqrt{4\cos^2 \theta} = 2|\cos \theta|$$

Another useful approach to proving identities is to work with each side of the equation *independently*, replacing expressions with equivalent expressions. Once the right- and left-hand sides of the equation are shown to be equivalent, the identity is proved because two expressions that are equivalent to the same expression are equivalent to each other.

Example 3   Prove: $\dfrac{\cot \theta}{\sec \theta} = \csc \theta - \sin \theta$

$\dfrac{\cot \theta}{\sec \theta}$	$\csc \theta - \sin \theta$	
$\dfrac{\dfrac{\cos \theta}{\sin \theta}}{\dfrac{1}{\cos \theta}}$	$\dfrac{1}{\sin \theta} - \sin \theta$	
	$\dfrac{1 - \sin^2 \theta}{\sin \theta}$	
$\dfrac{\cos^2 \theta}{\sin \theta} = \dfrac{\cos^2 \theta}{\sin \theta}$		Therefore, $\dfrac{\cot \theta}{\sec \theta} = \csc \theta - \sin \theta$.

A *counterexample* is an example that shows that a statement is not an identity. While no number of examples proves an identity, just one counterexample proves that an equation is not an identity.

Example 4   Show that $\sin(\beta + \theta) = \sin\beta + \sin\theta$ is *not* an identity.

If either β or θ is zero, the equation is true. However, if $\beta = \frac{1}{2}\pi$ and $\theta = \frac{1}{2}\pi$, $\sin(\beta + \theta) = \sin\pi = 0$, while $\sin\beta + \sin\theta = \sin\frac{1}{2}\pi + \sin\frac{1}{2}\pi = 1 + 1 = 2$. Since $0 \neq 2$, $\sin(\beta + \theta) = \sin\beta + \sin\theta$ cannot be an identity.

Strategies for proving identities:
- Learn the basic identities so that they come to mind readily.
- Perform indicated algebraic operations such as adding fractions and factoring.
- Replace an expression equal to 1 with a Pythagorean identity.
- Multiply a fraction by 1 in a useful form. For example, if a denominator is $1 + \cos\theta$, multiplying the numerator and denominator by $1 - \cos\theta$ will give a denominator of $\sin^2\theta$.
- Write all expressions in terms of sines and cosines.

More can be added to the list, but specific suggestions are not as important as your willingness to try different approaches, recognize dead ends, and try again.

Example 5   Prove: $\dfrac{\sec\theta}{1 + \cos\theta} = \csc^2\theta\,(\sec\theta - 1)$

$$
\begin{array}{c|c}
\dfrac{\sec\theta}{1 + \cos\theta} & \csc^2\theta\,(\sec\theta - 1) \\[2mm]
\dfrac{\sec\theta}{1 + \cos\theta} \cdot \left(\dfrac{1 - \cos\theta}{1 - \cos\theta}\right) & \\[3mm]
\dfrac{\sec\theta - 1}{1 - \cos^2\theta} & \\[3mm]
\dfrac{\sec\theta - 1}{\sin^2\theta} & \\[3mm]
\csc^2\theta\,(\sec\theta - 1) = & \text{Therefore, } \dfrac{\sec\theta}{1 + \cos\theta} = \csc^2\theta\,(\sec\theta - 1).
\end{array}
$$

Class Exercises

Prove each identity.

1. $\tan\phi\,\csc\phi\,\cos\phi = 1$
2. $(\sec\phi + 1)(\sec\phi - 1) = \tan^2\phi$
3. $\cos\theta\,\csc\theta = \cot\theta$
4. $(1 + \tan\beta)(1 - \cot\beta) = \tan\beta - \cot\beta$
5. $\dfrac{1 - \cos^2 y}{\sin y} = \sin y$
6. $\sin^2\theta = 1 - \dfrac{1}{\sec^2\theta}$

3.9 Proving Trigonometric Identities   **173**

173

Assignment Guide
Basic: 1–28, 30–31
Average: 11–40
Enriched: 12, 22–50

Teacher's Resource Book
  Practice, pages 24

Ⓡ **Review**
Exercises 11, 13, 14, 23, and 31 review concepts of evaluating functions, angular and linear velocity, angle measure, and inverse functions.

LESSON FOLLOW-UP

Test Yourself

Teacher's Resource Book
  Tests—Quiz, form A, page 10
  Tests—Quiz, form B, page 10

Lesson Quiz
Prove each identity.

1. $\dfrac{\csc \theta}{\sec \theta} = \cot \theta$

$\dfrac{\csc \theta}{\sec \theta} = \dfrac{\frac{1}{\sin \theta}}{\frac{1}{\cos \theta}} = \dfrac{\cos \theta}{\sin \theta} = \cot \theta$

Therefore, $\dfrac{\csc \theta}{\sec \theta} = \cot \theta.$

2. $\dfrac{\cos \theta}{\sec \theta} + \dfrac{\sin \theta}{\csc \theta} = \sec^2 \theta - \tan^2 \theta$

$\left. \dfrac{\cos \theta}{\sec \theta} + \dfrac{\sin \theta}{\csc \theta} \right| \ \sec^2 \theta - \tan^2 \theta$

$\left. \dfrac{\cos \theta}{\frac{1}{\cos \theta}} + \dfrac{\sin \theta}{\frac{1}{\sin \theta}} \right| \ 1 + \tan^2 \theta - \tan^2 \theta$

$\left. \cos^2 \theta + \sin^2 \theta \right| \ 1$

$1 = 1$

Therefore,
$\dfrac{\cos \theta}{\sec \theta} + \dfrac{\sin \theta}{\csc \theta} = \sec^2 \theta - \tan^2 \theta.$

3. $\dfrac{\tan A + \cos A}{\sin A} = \sec A + \cot A$

$\dfrac{\tan A + \cos A}{\sin A} = \dfrac{\tan A}{\sin A} + \dfrac{\cos A}{\sin A}$

$= \dfrac{\frac{\sin A}{\cos A}}{\sin A} + \cot A$

$= \dfrac{1}{\cos A} + \cot A$

$= \sec A + \cot A$

Therefore,
$\dfrac{\tan A + \cos A}{\sin A} = \sec A + \cot A.$

Simplify each expression.

7. $\sqrt{25 \tan^2 \beta + 25}$ $5|\sec \beta|$

8. $(\sec \theta - \tan \theta)(\sin \theta + 1)$ $\cos \theta$

Find a counterexample to show that each statement is *not* an identity. Answers may vary.

9. $\cos (\theta + \phi) = \cos \theta + \cos \phi$
Let $\theta = \phi = 0$. $\cos (0 + 0) = 1$; $\cos 0 + \cos 0 = 2$

10. $\sin \theta + \cos \theta = 1$ Let $\theta = \dfrac{\pi}{4}$. $\dfrac{\sqrt{2}}{2} + \dfrac{\sqrt{2}}{2} \neq 1$

Practice Exercises

Prove each identity.

A 1. $\sin \theta \csc \theta = 1$ $\sin \theta \cdot \dfrac{1}{\sin \theta} = 1$

2. $\cot \theta \sec \theta \sin \theta = 1$ $\dfrac{\cos \theta}{\sin \theta} \cdot \dfrac{1}{\cos \theta} \cdot \sin \theta = 1$

3. $2 \sec^2 \theta = \dfrac{1}{1 - \sin \theta} + \dfrac{1}{1 + \sin \theta}$

4. $\dfrac{1 + \sin \theta}{\cos \theta} + \dfrac{\cos \theta}{1 + \sin \theta} = \dfrac{2}{\cos \theta}$

5. $(\csc \theta + 1)(\csc \theta - 1) = \cot^2 \theta$

6. $\cos^4 x - \sin^4 x = \cos^2 x - \sin^2 x$

7. $\csc^2 \theta = \cot^2 \theta + \sec^2 \theta - \tan^2 \theta$

8. $\dfrac{1 + \tan^2 x}{\sec x} = \sec x$

9. $\cos \phi (\sec \phi - \cos \phi) = \sin^2 \phi$

10. $\tan \theta - 1 = \dfrac{\sec \theta - \csc \theta}{\csc \theta}$

Ⓡ 11. If $f(x) = \cos x$ and $g(x) = \sqrt{1 + x}$, evaluate $f\left(g\left(-\frac{1}{4}\right)\right)$ 0.6479

12. **Writing in Mathematics** Choose an example from this lesson or its exercises and tell how using a trigonometric identity might allow more efficient use of technology. For example, you might show the steps needed to evaluate an expression in each of two equivalent forms.

Sports A horse trains by riding in a circle that is 0.8 mi in diameter. The horse runs two laps in 25 min.

Ⓡ 13. Determine the angular velocity of the horse. 0.50 rad/min

Ⓡ 14. Determine the linear velocity of the horse. 0.20 mi/min = 12.06 mi/h

Simplify each expression.

15. $\sqrt{64 - 64 \cos^2 \alpha}$ $8|\sin \alpha|$

16. $\tan \alpha \sec \alpha$ $\dfrac{\sin \alpha}{\cos^2 \alpha}$

17. $\sqrt{100 \csc^2 \theta - 100}$ $10|\cot \theta|$

18. $\sqrt[3]{\tan^2 \theta - \sec^2 \theta}$ -1

19. $\dfrac{\cos^2 \theta}{(1 - \sin^2 \theta)^2}$ $\sec^2 \theta$

20. $\dfrac{1 + \cot^2 \phi}{\cot^2 \phi}$ $\sec^2 \phi$

21. $\dfrac{\cos \theta}{1 - \sin \theta} - \dfrac{\cos \theta}{1 + \sin \theta}$ $2 \tan \theta$

22. $(1 - \tan^2 \beta)(\sec^2 \beta)$ $1 - \tan^4 \beta$

Ⓡ 23. *Horology* Find the angle between the hands of a clock at 4:24. $12°$ or $\dfrac{\pi}{15}$

Find a counterexample to show that each statement is *not* an identity. Answers may vary.

B 24. $\tan (\theta + \phi) = \tan \theta + \tan \phi$

25. $\cos (\theta - \beta) = \cos \theta - \cos \beta$

26. $\sin 2\theta = 2 \sin \theta$

27. $\frac{1}{2} \sec \phi = \sec \frac{1}{2} \phi$

28. $\sqrt{\sin^2 \theta} = \sin \theta$

29. $\sqrt{1 - \sin^2 \theta} = -\cos \theta$

30. **Thinking Critically** For what values of θ, where $0° \leq \theta < 360°$, is $\sqrt{1 - \cos^2 \theta} = \sin \theta$? For what values is it equal to $-\sin \theta$? $0° \leq \theta \leq 180°$; $180° \leq \theta < 360°$

Ⓡ 31. Find the inverse of the function $F(t) = \sqrt[3]{5t - 1}$. $F^{-1}(t) = \dfrac{t^3 + 1}{5}$

174 Chapter 3 Trigonometric Functions

Writing in Mathematics
12. Answers will vary. The identity in Practice Exercise 36 illustrates the claim that using trigonometric identities can help students to do other tasks more efficiently. To evaluate the right-hand side of this identity requires at least seven steps; the left-hand side can be evaluated in two steps.

32. Thinking Critically Find three values of k for which $\sin k\theta = k \sin \theta$ is an identity. Give a reason why each is valid. $k = 0$: $\sin 0\theta = 0 \sin \theta = 0$; $k = 1$: $\sin 1\theta = 1 \sin \theta$; $k = -1$: $\sin(-\theta) = -\sin \theta$

Prove each identity.

33. $\dfrac{1 - \cos \theta}{1 + \cos \theta} = (\csc \theta - \cot \theta)^2$

34. $\sec^2 x + \csc^2 x = \sec^2 x \csc^2 x$

35. $\sin^4 \alpha - \cos^4 \alpha = 1 - 2 \cos^2 \alpha$

36. $2 \tan \theta = \dfrac{\cos \theta}{\csc \theta + 1} + \dfrac{\cos \theta}{\csc \theta - 1}$

37. $\sec^4 \theta - 2 \sec^2 \theta \tan^2 \theta + \tan^4 \theta = 1$

38. $\cot^2 x + \cos^2 x + \sin^2 x = \csc^2 x$

39. $\dfrac{\cos y}{1 + \sin y} + \dfrac{1 + \sin y}{\cos y} = 2 \sec y$

40. $(\sin \beta + \cos \beta)^2 \tan \beta = \tan \beta + 2 \sin^2 \beta$

C **41.** $\dfrac{\cos \theta}{1 + \sin \theta} = \sec \theta - \tan \theta$

42. $\dfrac{1}{\csc \theta + \cot \theta} = \dfrac{1 - \cos \theta}{\sin \theta}$

43. For $0 < \theta < \frac{1}{2}\pi$, express $\cos \theta$, $\tan \theta$, $\csc \theta$, $\sec \theta$, and $\cot \theta$ in terms of $\sin \theta$.

44. Repeat Exercise 43 for $\frac{1}{2}\pi < \theta < \pi$.

45. Prove: $(\sec \beta + \tan \beta)^3 (\sec \beta - \tan \beta)^4 = \dfrac{1 - \sin \beta}{\cos \beta}$

46. Thinking Critically A statement that is false for all values of the variable involved is called a contradiction. One example of a contradiction is $\sin \theta = 2$. Explain why this is a contradiction, and give three additional contradictions involving the trigonometric functions.

47. Express $\tan \theta$ in terms of $\cos \theta$. $\pm\dfrac{\sqrt{1 - \cos^2 \theta}}{\cos \theta}$ **48.** Express $\sin \theta$ in terms of $\sec \theta$. $\pm\dfrac{\sqrt{\sec^2 \theta - 1}}{\sec \theta}$

49. Prove: $\sqrt{(3 \cos x + 4 \sin x)^2 + (4 \cos x - 3 \sin x)^2} = 5$

50. Use a scientific calculator to verify Exercise 49 for $x = \dfrac{\pi}{8}$.

Test Yourself

Determine the reference angle for the given angle θ in standard position.

1. $-110°$ $70°$ **2.** $325°$ $35°$ **3.** $\dfrac{4\pi}{5}$ $\dfrac{\pi}{5}$ **4.** $\dfrac{\pi}{10}$ $\dfrac{\pi}{10}$ 3.6

5. Determine the exact values of the six trigonometric functions of a $420°$ angle.

Determine each value to four decimal places.

6. $\sin 119°$ 0.8746 **7.** $\csc(-61.7°)$ -1.1357 **8.** $\tan \dfrac{3\pi}{10}$ 1.3764 **9.** $\cot\left(-\dfrac{\pi}{9}\right)$ 3.7
-2.7475

If $0° \le \theta < 360°$, determine θ to the nearest tenth of a degree.

10. $\cos \theta = -0.5152$ **11.** $\tan \theta = 1.0507$ **12.** $\csc \theta = 2.6363$
$121.0°$; $239.0°$ $46.4°$; $226.4°$ $22.3°$; $157.7°$

Verify each identity for the given angle measure.

13. $\sin^2\left(-\dfrac{\pi}{4}\right) + \cos^2\left(-\dfrac{\pi}{4}\right) = 1$

14. $\dfrac{\cot 240° \tan 240°}{\sin 240°} = \csc 240°$ 3.8

Prove each identity.

15. $\cos^2 \phi = 1 - \dfrac{1}{\csc^2 \phi}$

16. $\dfrac{\sec \theta}{\cos \theta} = 1 + \dfrac{\sin^2 \theta}{\cos^2 \theta}$ 3.9

3.9 Proving Trigonometric Identities   **175**

---

4. $\dfrac{1}{\sec \theta - 1} + \dfrac{1}{\sec \theta + 1} = \dfrac{2 \cos \theta}{\sin^2 \theta}$

$\dfrac{1}{\sec \theta - 1} + \dfrac{1}{\sec \theta + 1}$

$= \dfrac{\sec \theta + 1 + \sec \theta - 1}{\sec^2 \theta - 1}$

$= \dfrac{2 \sec \theta}{\tan^2 \theta} = \dfrac{\dfrac{2}{\cos \theta}}{\dfrac{\sin^2 \theta}{\cos^2 \theta}} = \dfrac{2 \cos \theta}{\sin^2 \theta}$

Therefore,

$\dfrac{1}{\sec \theta - 1} + \dfrac{1}{\sec \theta + 1} = \dfrac{2 \cos \theta}{\sin^2 \theta}$.

5. Find a counterexample to show that $\sin \theta = \sqrt{1 - \cos^2 \theta}$ is *not* an identity.

Let $\theta = \dfrac{3\pi}{2}$.

Then $\sin \theta = \sin \dfrac{3\pi}{2} = -1$.

$\sqrt{1 - \cos^2 \theta} = \sqrt{1 - \cos^2 \dfrac{3\pi}{2}} = 1$,

and $-1 \ne 1$. Therefore, $\sin \theta = \sqrt{1 - \cos^2 \theta}$ is not an identity.

Additional Answers, Test Yourself

5. $\sin 420° = \dfrac{\sqrt{3}}{2}$; $\cos 420° = \dfrac{1}{2}$; $\tan 420° = \sqrt{3}$; $\cot 420° = \dfrac{\sqrt{3}}{3}$; $\sec 420° = 2$;

$\csc 420° = \dfrac{2\sqrt{3}}{3}$

1.

Chapter 3   Summary and Review

Vocabulary

angle (120)
angular velocity (134)
central angle (126)
circular functions (142)
cofunctions (147)
cosecant (147)
cosine (141)
cotangent (147)
coterminal angles (122)
degrees (121)
fundamental identities (168)

initial side (120)
linear velocity (134)
negative angle (120)
odd-even identities (168)
positive angle (120)
Pythagorean identities (167)
quadrantal angle (152)
radian (126)
ratio identities (167)
reciprocal identities (168)

reference angle (154)
reference triangle (142)
secant (147)
sine (141)
standard position (120)
tangent (147)
terminal side (120)
trigonometric identity (166)
vertex (120)
wrapping function (144)

Angles in the Coordinate Plane   An angle is in standard position if its vertex is the   3.1
origin and its initial side lies on the positive x-axis.

1. Find the degree measure of the angle formed by a $\frac{1}{6}$ clockwise rotation. $-60°$
   Draw the angle in standard position.

2. Identify angles coterminal with a $-72°$ angle. Find one whose measure is
   between $0°$ and $360°$. $(-72 + 360k)°, \ k \in Z; \ 288°$

3. Express $72°15'46''$ in decimal degrees. $72.26°$

Angle Measures in Degrees and Radians   To convert from degrees to radians,   3.2
multiply the number of degrees by $\frac{\pi}{180°}$. To convert from radians to degrees, multiply
the number of radians by $\frac{180°}{\pi}$.

4. Express $-135°$ in radians. $-\frac{3\pi}{4}$ 5. Express $-\frac{13\pi}{4}$ in degrees. $-585°$

Applications: Angular and Linear Velocity   The formulas for angular velocity ω and   3.3
linear velocity V are:

$$\omega = \frac{\theta}{t} \quad \text{and} \quad V = \frac{r\theta}{t} = rw$$

6. Determine the number of revolutions per minute of a wheel whose angular
   velocity is 166 rad/s. 1585.2 rpm

7. A ferris wheel whose diameter is 200 ft takes 50 s to rotate once. Find its
   angular velocity in radians per second and the linear velocity of a car
   located at its rim. 0.13 rad/s; 12.57 ft/s

Circular Functions   The terminal side of an angle θ in standard position intersects   3.4
the unit circle in a unique point $P(x, y)$. The x-value of this point is cosine θ, and the
y-value is sine θ. If the circle has radius r, then $\cos \theta = \frac{x}{r}$ and $\sin \theta = \frac{y}{r}$.

8. If $\cos \theta = -\frac{7}{25}$ and θ is in quadrant II, determine the exact value of $\sin \theta$. $\frac{24}{25}$

176   Chapter 3 Trigonometric Functions

The Trigonometric Functions   The four additional trigonometric functions are:

3.5

$$\csc \theta = \frac{r}{y},\ y \neq 0 \qquad \sec \theta = \frac{r}{x},\ x \neq 0 \qquad \tan \theta = \frac{y}{x},\ x \neq 0 \qquad \cot \theta = \frac{x}{y},\ y \neq 0$$

9. Determine the exact values of $\sin \theta$, $\tan \theta$, $\csc \theta$, $\sec \theta$, and $\cot \theta$ if θ is an angle in standard position with terminal side in quadrant III and $\cos \theta = -\frac{8}{17}$.

Functions of Special Angles and Quadrantal Angles   An angle with measure 30°, 45°, or 60° or a multiple of these is a special angle. An angle whose terminal side lies on the x- or y-axis is a quadrantal angle. Reference angles are used to find the values of trigonometric functions for special angles that are not in the first quadrant.

3.6

10. Find the exact values of the trigonometric functions of $-90°$.

11. Find the exact values of the trigonometric functions of $\frac{5\pi}{3}$.

Evaluating Trigonometric Functions   A scientific calculator is frequently used to find values of trigonometric functions of an angle. It can also be used to find the measure of an angle if the value of one of the trigonometric functions of the angle is known.

3.7

12. Evaluate $\cos \frac{\pi}{7}$ and $\csc (-110.3°)$ to four decimal places. 0.9010; -1.0662

13. If $0° \leq \theta < 360°$ and $\tan \theta = -0.2701$, determine θ to the nearest tenth of a degree. 164.9°; 344.9°

Fundamental Identities   The ratio, reciprocal, Pythagorean, and odd-even identities comprise the fundamental trigonometric identities.

3.8

Reciprocal identities

$$\csc \theta = \frac{1}{\sin \theta},\ \sin \theta \neq 0$$

$$\sec \theta = \frac{1}{\cos \theta},\ \cos \theta \neq 0$$

$$\cot \theta = \frac{1}{\tan \theta},\ \tan \theta \neq 0$$

Pythagorean identities

$$\sin^2 \theta + \cos^2 \theta = 1$$

$$1 + \cot^2 \theta = \csc^2 \theta$$

$$1 + \tan^2 \theta = \sec^2 \theta$$

Ratio identities

$$\tan \theta = \frac{\sin \theta}{\cos \theta},\ \cos \theta \neq 0$$

$$\cot \theta = \frac{\cos \theta}{\sin \theta},\ \sin \theta \neq 0$$

Odd-even identities

$$\sin (-\theta) = -\sin \theta \qquad \tan (-\theta) = -\tan \theta$$

$$\csc (-\theta) = -\csc \theta \qquad \cot (-\theta) = -\cot \theta$$

$$\cos (-\theta) = \cos \theta \qquad \sec (-\theta) = \sec \theta$$

Verify each identity for the given angle measure.

14. $1 + \tan^2 210° = \sec^2 210°$

15. $\cot \frac{\pi}{4} = \dfrac{\cos \frac{\pi}{4}}{\sin \frac{\pi}{4}}$

Proving Trigonometric Identities   Trigonometric identities can be proved using algebraic manipulations and the fundamental identities.

3.9

Prove each identity.

16. $\dfrac{1 + \cot^2 \beta}{\csc \beta} = \csc \beta$

17. $\cos^2 \theta \tan \theta \cot \theta = 1 - \sin^2 \theta$

177

Chapter 3   Test

Additional Answers

8. $\sin \theta = \frac{24}{25}$; $\cos \theta = -\frac{7}{25}$;

$\tan \theta = -\frac{24}{7}$; $\csc \theta = \frac{25}{24}$;

$\sec \theta = -\frac{25}{7}$; $\cot \theta = -\frac{7}{24}$

12. $1 + \tan^2\left(-\frac{\pi}{3}\right) = \sec^2\left(-\frac{\pi}{3}\right)$

$1 + (-\sqrt{3})^2 = (2)^2$

$1 + 3 = 4$

$4 = 4$

13. $\sin(-315°) = -\sin(315°)$

$\frac{\sqrt{2}}{2} = -\left(-\frac{\sqrt{2}}{2}\right)$

14. $\frac{\sin \alpha}{\csc \alpha} + \frac{\cos \alpha}{\sec \alpha} = \frac{\sin \alpha}{\frac{1}{\sin \alpha}} + \frac{\cos \alpha}{\frac{1}{\cos \alpha}} =$

$\sin^2 \alpha + \cos^2 \alpha = 1$

15. $\frac{\csc^2 \alpha - 1}{\csc \alpha + 1} = \frac{1}{\sin \alpha} - 1$;

$\frac{\cot^2 \alpha}{\csc \alpha + 1} = \csc \alpha - 1$;

$\frac{\cot^2 \alpha(\csc \alpha - 1)}{(\csc \alpha + 1)(\csc \alpha - 1)} =$

$\frac{\cot^2 \alpha(\csc \alpha - 1)}{\csc^2 \alpha - 1} = \frac{\cot^2 \alpha(\csc \alpha - 1)}{\cot^2 \alpha} =$

$\csc \alpha - 1$

1. For an $\frac{11}{9}$ counterclockwise rotation, find the measure of the angle in degrees. 440°

2. Express 218°18′46″ in decimal degree form. 218.31°

3. Express $-\frac{7\pi}{5}$ in degrees. −252°

4. Express 315° in radians. $\frac{7\pi}{4}$

5. Find the angular velocity ω in radians per second of an object turning at 600 rpm. 63 rad/s

6. A point on a wheel 10 cm from the center moves through an angle of 315° in 1 min. Determine the linear velocity of the point in centimeters per second. 0.92 cm/s

7. If $\cos \theta = \frac{12}{13}$ and θ is in quadrant IV, determine the exact value of $\sin \theta$. $-\frac{5}{13}$

8. The terminal side of an angle θ in standard position passes through the point (−7, 24). Determine the exact values of the six trigonometric functions of θ.

9. Determine the exact value of tan 690°. $-\frac{\sqrt{3}}{3}$

10. Evaluate sin 62.2° to four decimal places. 0.8846

11. If $0° \le \theta < 360°$ and $\cot \theta = -1.4176$, determine θ to the nearest tenth of a degree. 144.8°; 324.8°

Verify each identity for the given angle measure.

12. $1 + \tan^2\left(-\frac{\pi}{6}\right) = \sec^2\left(-\frac{\pi}{6}\right)$ $\frac{4}{3} = \frac{4}{3}$

13. $\sin(-315°) = -\sin(315°)$ 0.7071 = 0.7071

Prove each identity.

14. $\frac{\sin \alpha}{\csc \alpha} + \frac{\cos \alpha}{\sec \alpha} = 1$

15. $\frac{\csc^2 \alpha - 1}{\csc \alpha + 1} = \frac{1}{\sin \alpha} - 1$

Challenge

One semicircular arc of the unit circle extends from π to 2π. Determine the exact coordinates of a point that separates that arc into two sections, the ratio of whose lengths is 1:5. How many points meet these criteria? $\left(-\frac{\sqrt{3}}{2}, -\frac{1}{2}\right)$; $\left(\frac{\sqrt{3}}{2}, -\frac{1}{2}\right)$; 2

Cumulative Review

Select the best choice for each question.

1. A wheel makes $2\frac{1}{2}$ rotations about its axis. Find the angular displacement in radians of a point P on the wheel. **3.3**
   E

   A. $\frac{5\pi}{2}$ **B.** $\frac{2\pi}{5}$ **C.** $\frac{3\pi}{14}$ **D.** $\frac{\pi}{3}$ **E.** 5π

2. Sin 180° = **3.6**
   B **A.** 1 **B.** 0 **C.** 0.5 **D.** −1 **E.** −0.5

3. Find the distance, to the nearest hundredth, from $P(1, -5)$ to the line that has slope $-\frac{2}{3}$ and passes through point $(8, -2)$. **2.8**
   C

   A. 3.61 **B.** 4.71 **C.** 6.38 **D.** 7.49
   E. none of these

4. Given $f(x) = 5x^2$, evaluate $f(-2)$. **1.4**
   D **A.** 100 **B.** −20 **C.** −100 **D.** 20
   E. none of these

5. Express 84°20′40″ in decimal degrees. **3.1**
   A

   A. 84.3444° **B.** 84.6666° **C.** 84.8333°
   D. 84.5° **E.** none of these

6. The reciprocal function of csc θ is **3.5**
   B **A.** cos θ **B.** sin θ **C.** $\frac{1}{\sin \theta}$ **D.** $\frac{1}{\cos \theta}$
   E. none of these

7. $1 + \tan^2 \theta =$ **3.8**
   C **A.** $\sin^2 \theta$ **B.** $\cot^2 \theta$ **C.** $\sec^2 \theta$
   D. $\cos^2 \theta$ **E.** none of these

8. Use your calculator to find the value of sin 280°. **3.7**
   E

   A. 0.9848 **B.** 0.0152 **C.** −0.0152
   D. 0.2365 **E.** −0.9848

9. A rotation of −220° terminates in which quadrant? **3.1**
   B

   A. I **B.** II **C.** III **D.** IV **E.** x−axis

10. Find an equation of the line in standard form that passes through the points $(4, 8)$ and $(-2, -4)$. **2.3**
    B

    A. $y + \frac{1}{2}x + 1 = 0$ **B.** $2x - y = 0$
    C. $y - 2x + 1 = 0$
    D. $y + 2x + 16 = 0$
    E. none of these

11. Find the value of cos θ of the angle in standard position that passes through point $(3, 4)$. **3.4**
    A

    A. $\frac{3}{5}$ **B.** $\frac{5}{3}$ **C.** $-\frac{3}{5}$ **D.** $-\frac{5}{3}$
    E. none of these

12. The ordered pair $x < 0$ and $y < 0$ represents a point in a coordinate plane. Name the quadrant that satisfies the given conditions. **1.3**
    C

    A. I **B.** II **C.** III **D.** IV
    E. none of these

13. Express 315° in radians. Give answer in terms of π. **3.2**
    B

    A. $\frac{2\pi}{5}$ **B.** $\frac{7\pi}{4}$ **C.** $\frac{5\pi}{2}$ **D.** $\frac{4\pi}{7}$
    E. none of these

14. The reference angle for 188° is **3.6**
    A **A.** 8° **B.** 82° **C.** 88° **D.** 16° **E.** 28°

15. Determine the number of real solutions of the quadratic equation $-4t = t^2 - 6$. **2.4**
    B

    A. 1 **B.** 2 **C.** 3 **D.** 4
    E. no solutions

16. The ratio identity for tan θ is **3.8**
    B **A.** cot θ **B.** $\frac{\sin \theta}{\cos \theta}$ **C.** csc θ **D.** $\frac{\cos \theta}{\sin \theta}$
    E. none of these

Summary

The graphs of the six trigonometric functions are analyzed and related to one another. Period, amplitude, and phase shift are introduced, and are used to graph transformations of the trigonometric curves. Addition of ordinates is used to graph sums of trigonometric and other functions. The inverse trigonometric functions are defined and analyzed, with some emphasis on geometric relationships. Application of sinusoidal functions to harmonic motion is studied.

Chapter Objectives

- To graph the sine and cosine functions
- To find the amplitude, period, and phase shift of a sine or cosine function from its equation
- To graph a sine or cosine function with given amplitude, period, and phase shift
- To analyze properties that determine the graphs of the tangent, cotangent, secant, and cosecant functions
- To graph the tangent, cotangent, secant, and cosecant functions
- To graph trigonometric functions that are the sums of two functions
- To define the inverse Sine and Cosine functions
- To evaluate expressions involving these functions
- To graph these functions
- To define and graph the inverse Tangent, Cotangent, Secant, and Cosecant functions
- To evaluate expressions involving these functions
- To rewrite trigonometric expressions as algebraic expressions
- To solve problems involving simple harmonic motion

4 Graphs and Inverses of Trigonometric Functions

Mathematical Power

Modeling   Most organisms show regular rhythmic behavior that seems to be related to environmental changes such as the length of daylight and darkness, the change of seasons, or the gravitational field of the moon. By studying graphical models, biologists have found answers to many interesting and important questions about living organisms. Although the exact nature of the internal "biological clock" is not yet fully understood, scientists believe that the environmental stimuli produce a series of chemical responses in the organism.

The fundamental unit of rhythmic behavior is a *cycle* which is measured in a length of time called a *period*. Many short-term rhythms, such as the rise and fall of body temperature or blood pressure, involve a period of about 24 h. These are called *circadian rhythms*, derived from the Latin phrase *circa diem*, meaning "about a day." Circadian rhythms model the active and rest phases of the behavior of most animals. Animals such as gray squirrels and chipmunks that are active by day and sleep during the night are called *diurnal*. Animals such as owls and bats that carry on their activities when it is dark are called *nocturnal*. Differences in patterns of activity result in less competition among species for available resources such as food.

When rhythmic behavior is represented graphically, the width of one full wave from crest to crest shows the duration of one complete period. Such periodic curves are generated by trigonometric functions.

Researchers have observed that in a controlled environment such as a windowless room or underground cave, where external cues such as lightness or darkness or temperature changes are absent, many internal rhythms of humans and other animals drift toward a 25-h period. It is believed that these rhythms are governed by a lunar cycle.

180

Features

Modeling

4.2 Solar waves	
4.5 Satellite tracking	
4.7 Simple harmonic motion	

This is the same cycle that affects the movement of the tides, and has a period of about 24 h 50 min. The figure below shows a circadian cycle and a lunar cycle graphed on the same set of axes. It illustrates the disconcerting fact that if a period of 24 h 50 min is more natural for humans, then we are literally hurrying ahead of ourselves by almost an hour each day.

The effects of any disruption in an organism's biological clock can be very visible. In one experiment, fiddler crabs were observed to exhibit a noticeable color change as night falls, clearly a circadian rhythm. Many other habits of this species, such as burrowing and feeding, respond to the changing of the tides and are thus called *circatidal*.

Perhaps you have experienced "jet lag," a feeling of fatigue that people get following a long, high-speed trip. This ill feeling demonstrates the strong tendency your body has to adhere to its own circadian rhythms.

Thinking Critically   Migration is an example of long-term rhythmic behavior. What other examples of long-term rhythmic behavior in living organisms can you give? What is the length of the period in each case?

Project   Over an extended period, chart the changes in your own rhythmic behavior, such as the times that you are fatigued, alert, hungry, or full. Make a graph of the data you collect and estimate the period. Speculate as to what might affect the particular cycle you are analyzing.

181

Mathematical Power

The use of mathematical models in the life sciences is quite extensive; in many instances, the most powerful descriptive tool is not a number but a picture. By displaying their experimental results visually, researchers can often recognize hidden patterns in masses of data.

The basic characteristic of periodic function is regularity—the graphs of these functions repeat in definite cycles. That so many complex behavioral and physiological processes of living organisms can be represented by such well-behaved functions is truly a remarkable fact.

To help students appreciate the influence of external stimulation on their behavior, have them suggest things they associate with the start of a new day—for example, the smell of breakfast cooking, the arrival of the daily newspaper, a TV or radio program, a factory whistle, and so on. Then ask them to imagine how their behavior might change if all of these cues were taken away. Interested students may enjoy reading *The Timing of Biological Clocks* by Arthur Winfree (Scientific American Library Series) which includes dramatic graphical representations of mathematical models.

Thinking Critically   Annual hibernation (dormancy during cold conditions) or estivation (dormancy during hot, dry conditions) are examples of long-term rhythmic behavior in animals. Flowering of plants or the shedding of leaves of some trees are botanical examples.

Review and Assessment

Student Text
- Test Yourself   213, 236
- Summary and Review   237–238
- Chapter Test   239

Teacher's Resource Book
- Tests   13–18
- Practice   25–31

Vocabulary
cycle
period
periodic

Technology
graphing utility

FOCUS

The Focus illustrates that mathematics is a tool for exploring a wide variety of ideas and human experiences. Students may be interested in the fact that the ability to recognize music has been found in other species. In one experiment pigeons learned to distinguish music of J. S. Bach from that of Stravinsky. Starlings can recognize a melody in different keys, and dolphins recognize octaves.

Richard Voss of IBM's Thomas J. Watson Research Center has found a simple mathematical relationship to describe how the notes of a musical piece rise and fall in relation to the piece as a whole. Students may wish to research his ideas about why music is so universally appealing.

INSTRUCTION

• Have students graph functions that are periodic over a given interval. They can then exchange graphs with others and use the notion of periodicity to expand the graph to a larger interval. In each case they should identify the period.

• Form cooperative learning groups and give each group a set of criteria such as the following and have the group graph the function that meets the criteria.

The function is periodic with period 4. The graph is symmetric with respect to the y-axis. The range of the function is $[-8, 4]$.

Objective: *To graph the sine and cosine functions*

Focus

Scientists are now using music as a tool for gaining insight into the workings of the human brain. Researchers have learned that the way our brains process music is closely related to perception, memory, and the range of sounds used for language. Most people have a sense of pitch that they use in conversation, as well as in listening to music. For example, if a person's voice is pitched higher than usual, it may be a signal that the person is under stress.

Scientists analyze musical sounds using mathematical functions whose graphs reflect the wavelike nature of the sounds. These equations can all be "built" from sine and cosine functions.

Since x and $x + 2\pi$ are coterminal angles, $\sin(x + 2\pi) = \sin x$ and $\cos(x + 2\pi) = \cos x$. Both of these functions are *periodic* with period 2π; it is the property of periodicity that makes them useful in representing wavelike phenomena such as sound.

> A function f is **periodic** if there is a positive real number h such that $f(x + h) = f(x)$ for every x in the domain of f. The smallest such positive number h is called the **period** of f; one **cycle** of the graph is completed in each period.

Example 1 Verify that the graph at the right represents a periodic function on $[-18, 18]$, and identify its period.

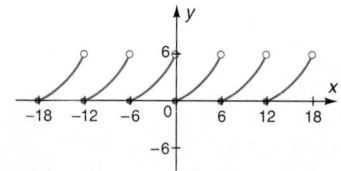

Since the graph repeats in cycles, the function is periodic. Its period is 6, since 6 is the smallest value of h such that $f(x + h) = f(x)$ for all x.

Knowing that a function is periodic simplifies the task of graphing it; once one cycle is graphed, the rest of the graph simply repeats that portion over and over.

For example, to graph $f(x) = \sin x$ over the interval $[-2\pi, 4\pi]$, make a table of selected values for $0 \le x \le 2\pi$. Plot the associated points. Connect the points with a smooth curve. Then use the periodicity of the sine function to extend the graph.

x	0	$\frac{\pi}{6}$	$\frac{\pi}{4}$	$\frac{\pi}{3}$	$\frac{\pi}{2}$	$\frac{3\pi}{4}$	π	$\frac{7\pi}{6}$	$\frac{5\pi}{4}$	$\frac{3\pi}{2}$	$\frac{7\pi}{4}$	2π
$\sin x$	0	0.5	0.71	0.87	1	0.71	0	-0.5	-0.71	-1	-0.71	0

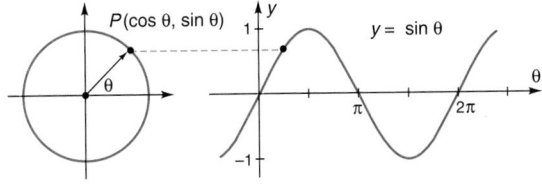

Examine the graph of $y = \sin \theta$, keeping in mind the definition of the sine in terms of the y-coordinate of a point P on the unit circle. Here θ is used instead of x to avoid confusion with the x-coordinate of P. Observe that as θ increases from 0 to 2π, $\sin \theta$ first increases from 0 to 1, then decreases from 1 to -1, and then increases from -1 to 0.

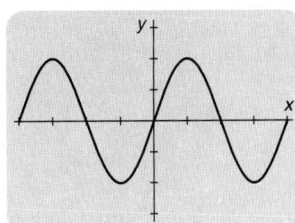

The sine function exhibits the following properties:

- Its period is 2π.
- For all x, $\sin(-x) = -\sin x$. It is an odd function.
- Its graph is symmetric with respect to the origin.
- Its domain is the set of all real numbers, $\mathcal{R}$.
- Its range is $[-1, 1]$; that is, $-1 \le \sin x \le 1$.
- Its zeros occur at multiples of π.

You can use a graphing utility to view the sine function. Since it completes one cycle in 2π rad, and its range varies between 1 and -1, you might set the viewing rectangle to $[-6.28, 6.28]$ by $[-1.5, 1.5]$. Your graphing utility may also have a special trigonometric setting. This feature sets the scale of the x-axis as a multiple of 2π or 360. Be sure that the equation you enter and the viewing rectangle are in the same unit of measure, that is, radians or degrees.

The graph of $y = \cos x$ may be constructed and analyzed in the same way as the graph of $y = \sin x$.

$[-2\pi, 2\pi]$ by $[-1.5, 1.5]$
x scl: $\frac{\pi}{2}$ y scl: 0.5

4.1 Graphs of the Sine and Cosine Functions   **183**

Technology A graphing utility may be used effectively to introduce the notion of dilation of graphs applied to the sine and cosine functions. Have the students use a graphing utility to obtain the graphs of $y = 3 \sin x$, $y = \frac{1}{4} \cos x$, and so on. Then ask them to describe the effect of each constant factor on the graphs. Recall the term *dilation* from Chapter 2 and apply it to this context.

Alternative Learning Styles
Many students learn new ideas best if these ideas are related to familiar material. Provide quick review of graphing techniques using a familiar function like $f(x) = x^2$.

GUIDED PRACTICE

For Example 1
Verify that the graph represents a periodic function on [0, 12] and identify its period. yes; period: 5

For Example 2

Graph function $y = \sin x$ on the interval $[-5\pi, 5\pi]$.

For Example 3

Graph the related basic function and the given function on the interval $[-2\pi, 2\pi]$.

1. $f(x) = \cos x - 2$

2. $g(x) = \cos\left(x - \frac{1}{2}\pi\right)$

Example 2 Make a table of values of $\cos x$ on the interval $[0, 2\pi]$. Then graph $y = \cos x$ on the interval $[-2\pi, 2\pi]$.

x	0	$\frac{\pi}{6}$	$\frac{\pi}{4}$	$\frac{\pi}{3}$	$\frac{\pi}{2}$	$\frac{3\pi}{4}$
$\cos x$	1	0.87	0.71	0.5	0	-0.71

x	π	$\frac{7\pi}{6}$	$\frac{5\pi}{4}$	$\frac{3\pi}{2}$	$\frac{7\pi}{4}$	2π
$\cos x$	-1	-0.87	-0.71	0	0.71	1

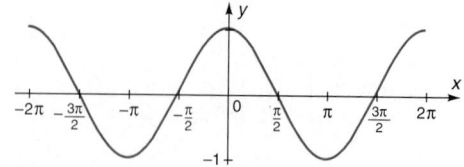

Observe that as x increases from 0 to π, $\cos x$ decreases from 1 to -1. As x increases from π to 2π, $\cos x$ increases from -1 to 1.

> **The cosine function exhibits the following properties:**
>
> - Its period is 2π.
> - For all x, $\cos(-x) = \cos x$. It is an even function.
> - Its graph is symmetric with respect to the y-axis.
> - Its domain is the set of all real numbers, $\mathcal{R}$.
> - Its range is $[-1, 1]$, that is, $-1 \le \cos x \le 1$.
> - Its zeros occur at odd multiples of $\frac{\pi}{2}$.

In Chapter 2, Lesson 2.2, you learned that transformations can be used to graph variations of certain basic functions. These same techniques can be used to graph variations of the basic sine and cosine functions. In Example 3 below, horizontal and vertical translations and reflections of $\sin x$ and $\cos x$ are discussed. Recall that the graph of $y = f(x - c) + d$ is a horizontal and vertical translation of the graph of $y = f(x)$. If c is positive, the shift is to the right; if c is negative, the shift is to the left; if d is positive, the shift is upward; if d is negative, the shift is downward.

Example 3 Graph the related basic function and the given function on the interval $[-2\pi, 2\pi]$.

  a. $f(x) = \sin x + 1.5$ **b.** $g(x) = -\cos x$ **c.** $h(x) = \sin\left(x + \frac{\pi}{2}\right)$

a. The graph of $y = \sin x + 1.5$ is a translation of the graph of $y = \sin x$ by an upward vertical shift of 1.5 units.

b. The graph of $y = -\cos x$ is a reflection of the graph of $y = \cos x$ in the x-axis.

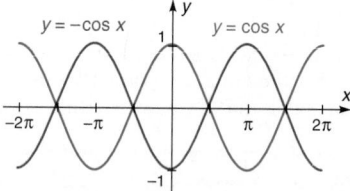

c. The graph of $y = \sin\left(x + \frac{\pi}{2}\right)$ is a translation of the graph of $y = \sin x$ by a horizontal shift of $\frac{\pi}{2}$ units to the left.

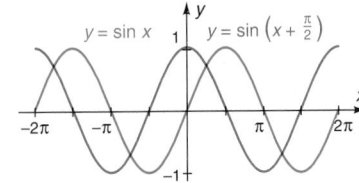

The graph of $y = \sin\left(x + \frac{\pi}{2}\right)$ in Example 3c coincides with the graph of $y = \cos x$. This suggests the identity $\cos x = \sin\left(x + \frac{\pi}{2}\right)$.

The graphs of functions such as $f(x) = 3 \sin x$ and $g(x) = \frac{1}{4} \cos x$ are easily obtained from the graphs of the basic sine and cosine functions. In each case, the y-values of the basic function are multiplied by a constant which serves to *dilate* (stretch or compress) the graph vertically. That is, the dilation stretches the basic graph away from the x-axis or compresses it toward the x-axis.

Example 4   Graph each function and the related basic function on $[-2\pi, 2\pi]$.

   a. $f(x) = 3 \sin x$ **b.** $g(x) = \frac{1}{4} \cos x$ **c.** $h(x) = -2.5 \cos x$

a. The range of f is $[-3, 3]$, with the same zeros as the sine function. Its graph is that of the sine function dilated vertically by a factor of 3.

b. The range of g is $\left[-\frac{1}{4}, \frac{1}{4}\right]$, and the graph of g is that of the cosine function dilated vertically by a factor of $\frac{1}{4}$.

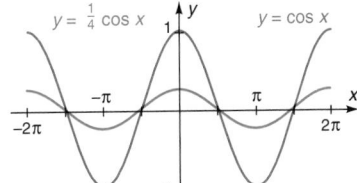

c. Since $-2.5 \cos x = 2.5\,(-\cos x)$, the graph is that of $-\cos x$, which was displayed in Example 3b, dilated vertically by a factor of 2.5.

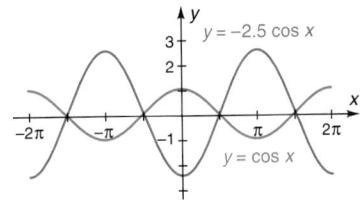

Examine the tables of values for $\sin x$ and $\cos x$ in Examples 1 and 2, and consider some of the cases where the function values are the same.

$$\sin \frac{\pi}{6} = \cos \frac{\pi}{3} = 0.5 \qquad \sin \frac{\pi}{3} = \cos \frac{\pi}{6} = 0.87 \qquad \sin \frac{\pi}{4} = \cos \frac{\pi}{4} = 0.71$$

Note that $\frac{\pi}{6} + \frac{\pi}{3} = \frac{\pi}{2}$ and $\frac{\pi}{4} + \frac{\pi}{4} = \frac{\pi}{2}$. This suggests an identity relating the cofunctions of complementary angles: The value of the sine of an acute angle is the same as the value of the cosine of the complement of that angle and the reverse.

Graph each function and the related basic function on the interval $[-2\pi, 2\pi]$.
1. $g(x) = -2 \sin x$

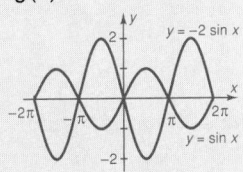

2. $h(x) = 0.5 \cos x$

Express each function in terms of its cofunction.

1. $\cos \dfrac{5\pi}{12}$ $\sin \dfrac{\pi}{12}$

2. $\sin \dfrac{11\pi}{7}$ $\cos \dfrac{15\pi}{14}$

For Example 6

On the same set of axes, graph $y = \cos x$ and $y = \cos(\pi - x)$.

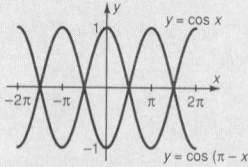

CLOSURE

Have students summarize in their math journals the properties of the sine and cosine functions. Then have them summarize the procedures for graphing each of these functions using the functions' properties and the fact that they are periodic functions.

INDEPENDENT PRACTICE

Assignment Guide

Basic: 1–29, 33–34, 43
Average: 3, 7, 11–14, 19–44
Enriched: 23–54

Teacher's Resource Book
  Practice, page 25

Ⓡ **Review**

Exercises 7, 11, 19, 29, 33, and 41 review concepts of graphing functions on a given interval, area of a sector of a circle, slope of perpendicular lines, and linear velocity.

Technology

The technology exercises on pages 187 to 189 emphasize analyzing the graphs and identifying relationships.

Example 5   Express each function in terms of its cofunction.

   a. $\sin \dfrac{\pi}{12}$ **b.** $\cos 40°$

   a. $\sin \dfrac{\pi}{12} = \cos\left(\dfrac{\pi}{2} - \dfrac{\pi}{12}\right) = \cos \dfrac{5\pi}{12}$ **b.** $\cos 40° = \sin(90° - 40°) = \sin 50°$

Indeed, the value of any trigonometric function of an angle θ is equal to the value of the cofunction of its complement $\dfrac{\pi}{2} - \theta$. You will be asked to prove the two *cofunction identities* in the exercises.

Cofunction Identities for Sine and Cosine

$$\sin \theta = \cos\left(\dfrac{\pi}{2} - \theta\right) \qquad \cos \theta = \sin\left(\dfrac{\pi}{2} - \theta\right)$$

In the next example, one of these identities is illustrated graphically.

Example 6   On the same set of axes, graph $y = \cos x$ and $y = \cos\left(\dfrac{\pi}{2} - x\right)$.

Since cosine is an even function,

$$\cos\left(\dfrac{\pi}{2} - x\right) = \cos\left[-\left(x - \dfrac{\pi}{2}\right)\right]$$

$$= \cos\left(x - \dfrac{\pi}{2}\right)$$

The graph is a translation of the basic cosine graph by a horizontal shift of $\dfrac{\pi}{2}$ units to the right. The result is identical to the graph of $\sin x$.

The graphs show that the relationship is not limited to values less than $\dfrac{\pi}{2}$. You are asked to graph $y = \sin\left(\dfrac{\pi}{2} - x\right)$ as an exercise.

Class Exercises

Tell whether or not each graph represents a periodic function on the given interval. If it does, identify the period.

1.

yes; 2

2.

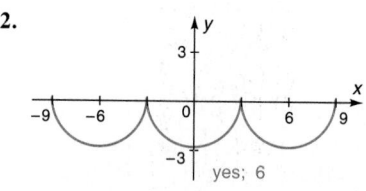

yes; 6

186   Chapter 4 Graphs and Inverses of Trigonometric Functions

Graph each function on the interval $[-2\pi, 2\pi]$. Explain how the graphs differ from $y = \sin x$ or $y = \cos x$.

3. $f(x) = \cos x + 2$ **4.** $G(x) = \sin (x - \pi)$ **5.** $g(x) = -\sin x$

6. $H(t) = \cos (t + \pi)$ **7.** $h(t) = 4 \cos t$ **8.** $F(x) = \frac{3}{4} \sin x$

9. For each function graphed in Exercises 3, 5, and 7, name an interval that represents one cycle, an interval in which the function is increasing, and an interval in which the function is decreasing.

10. For each function graphed in Exercises 4, 6, and 8, name an interval that represents one cycle, an interval in which the function is increasing, and an interval in which the function is decreasing.

11. What is the range of the function $h(t) = 4 \cos t$?

12. What is the range of the function $F(x) = \frac{3}{4} \sin x$?

13. Express $\sin \frac{\pi}{9}$ in terms of its cofunction.

14. Express $\cos 52°$ in terms of its cofunction.

15. Thinking Critically Explain an advantage, if any, of changing the viewing rectangle for the graph of $\sin x$ from $[0, 6.28]$ by $[-1.5, 1.5]$ to $[-10, 10]$ by $[-1.5, 1.5]$; from $[0, 6.28]$ by $[-1.5, 1.5]$ to $[0, 6.28]$ by $[-10, 10]$.

Practice Exercises Use appropriate technology.

Tell whether or not each graph represents a periodic function on the given interval. If it does, identify the period.

1.

2.

3.

4. Graph $y = \sin \left(\frac{\pi}{2} - x \right)$ on the interval $[-2\pi, 2\pi]$.

Graph each function on the interval $[-2\pi, 2\pi]$. For the trigonometric functions, explain how the graphs are transformations of $y = \sin x$ or $y = \cos x$.

5. $f(x) = \sin x - 0.5$ **6.** $g(t) = \cos (t - \pi)$

7. $r(x) = \sqrt{x} - 1$ **8.** $G(x) = \frac{1}{2} \cos x$

9. $k(x) = 10 \sin x$ **10.** $m(t) = 0.10 \sin t$

11. $h(t) = |t + 4|$ **12.** $F(t) = \sin (t + \pi)$

13. $g(z) = -4 \cos z$ **14.** $H(x) = -\frac{1}{3} \sin x$

4.1 Graphs of the Sine and Cosine Functions   **187**

LESSON FOLLOW-UP

Lesson Quiz

1. Verify that the graph represents a periodic function on $[-6, 6]$ and identify its period.

$f(x + 4) = f(x)$; period = 4

2. Graph the function $y = 3 \sin (x - \pi) - 1$ on the interval $[-2\pi, 2\pi]$. Explain how the graph is a transformation of the basic function.

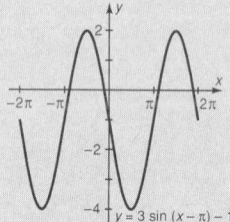

$y = 3 \sin (x - \pi) - 1$

The graph of $y = \sin x$ is dilated vertically by a factor of 3, shifted π units to the right, and translated down 1 unit.

3. Express $\sin \frac{3\pi}{8}$ in terms of its cofunction. $\cos \frac{\pi}{8}$

15. For each function graphed in Exercises 5, 9, and 13, name an interval that represents one cycle, an interval in which the function is increasing, and an interval in which the function is decreasing.

16. For each function graphed in Exercises 6, 10, and 14, name an interval that represents one cycle, an interval in which the function is increasing, and an interval in which the function is decreasing.

17. Use the graphs to determine which functions of Exercises 5 to 14 are even. 6, 8, 13

18. Use the graphs to determine which functions of Exercises 5 to 14 are odd. 9, 10, 12, 14

Ⓡ **19.** *Construction* A circular playground of radius 90 ft is divided into different parts. Find the area of the sector of the playground intercepted by a central angle of $\frac{5\pi}{9}$. 7068.58 ft²

Express each function in terms of its cofunction.

20. $\sin \frac{3\pi}{8}$ $\cos \frac{\pi}{8}$　**21.** $\sin \frac{6\pi}{13}$ $\cos \frac{\pi}{26}$　**22.** $\cos 37.5°$ $\sin 52.5°$　**23.** $\cos 82.3°$ $\sin 7.7°$

24. Prove the cofunction identity $\sin \theta = \cos \left(\frac{\pi}{2} - \theta\right)$ for $0 < \theta < \frac{\pi}{2}$.

25. Prove the cofunction identity $\cos \theta = \sin \left(\frac{\pi}{2} - \theta\right)$ for $0 < \theta < \frac{\pi}{2}$.

Find the range of each function.

B **26.** $f(x) = \sin x - 0.5$ $[-1.5, 0.5]$　　**27.** $G(x) = \frac{1}{2} \cos x$ $\left[-\frac{1}{2}, \frac{1}{2}\right]$

28. **Thinking Critically** Compare the graphs of the sine and cosine functions. List as many similarities and differences as you can.

Ⓡ **29.** *Architecture* The exterior of a house has decorative crossbeams that are placed perpendicular to one another. If one beam can be represented by the equation $x + 2y = 4$, determine the slope of a perpendicular crossbeam. 2

Graph each function. For the trigonometric functions, explain how the graphs are transformations of $y = \sin x$ or $y = \cos x$.

30. $F(t) = \sin \left(t - \frac{\pi}{4}\right) + 2$　　　　**31.** $G(x) = -\cos x + 3$

32. $H(x) = -\cos (x + 3)$　　　　　　Ⓡ **33.** $r(t) = \left|t - \frac{1}{2}\right| + \frac{1}{2}$

34. $f(x) = |\sin x|$　　　　　　　　**35.** $g(x) = |\cos x|$

36. $h(t) = 3 \sin (t) + 4$　　　　　　**37.** $w(\theta) = -\frac{1}{2} \cos (\theta) - 1$

38. Determine the range of $F(t) = 3 \sin t + 4$. [1, 7]

39. Determine the range of $w(\theta) = -\frac{1}{2} \cos \theta - 1$. $\left[-\frac{3}{2}, -\frac{1}{2}\right]$

40. Use the fact that cosine is an even function to graph $y = \cos (-x)$.

Ⓡ **41.** *Astronomy* The earth rotates on its axis once every 24 h. Determine the linear velocity of a point on the equator in miles per hour. Assume that the diameter of the earth is 7920 mi. 1036.73 mi/h

188　Chapter 4 Graphs and Inverses of Trigonometric Functions

28. Answers may vary. Some examples follow. Similarities: Ranges are the same, periods are the same, size of the intervals of increase and of decrease are the same, each demonstrates line and point symmetry; Differences: Intervals of a cycle are different, intervals of increase and of decrease are different, lines and points of symmetry are different.

42. Use the fact that sine is an odd function to graph $y = \sin(-x)$.

43. **Writing in Mathematics**   Describe at least three nonmathematical real world phenomena that are periodic or occur in cycles.

C 44. Explain how to express $\sin \dfrac{5\pi}{6}$ in terms of its cofunction.

45. Verify that the relationship between cofunctions presented in this lesson applies to the tangent and cotangent functions.

46. Verify that the relationship between cofunctions presented in this lesson applies to the secant and cosecant functions.

47. Prove that the period of the sine and cosine functions is 2π.

48. Determine the zeros of $f(x) = \sin\left(x + \dfrac{\pi}{4}\right)$. $k\pi - \frac{\pi}{4}$, $k \in Z$

49. Determine the zeros of $f(x) = \cos\left(x + \dfrac{\pi}{4}\right)$. $\frac{(4k+1)\pi}{4}$, $k \in Z$

50. Graph $y = \sin|x|$.   51. Graph $y = \cos|x|$.

Graph each function on the interval $[-2\pi, 2\pi]$.

52. $y = 3\cos x$ 53. $y = \sin 2x$ 54. $y = \sin x - 3$

Review

Prove each identity.

1. $\tan \theta \sec \theta = \dfrac{\sin \theta}{1 - \sin^2 \theta}$ 2. $\tan A = \dfrac{\sec A}{\csc A}$

Factor completely.

3. $x^4 - 13x^2 + 36$ $(x+2)(x-2)(x+3)(x-3)$ 4. $a^4b - c^2 + a^4 - c^2b$
$(a - \sqrt{c})(a + \sqrt{c})(a^2 + c)(b + 1)$

Given $f(x) = 3\sqrt{x+1}$ and $g(x) = 4x^2$, find the following:

5. $(f \circ g)(1)$ $3\sqrt{5}$ 6. $(g \circ f)(1)$ 72

7. $(f \circ g)(x)$ $3\sqrt{4x^2 + 1}$ 8. $(g \circ g)(x)$ $64x^4$

9. Find the linear velocity, in feet per second, of a point on the edge of one of the blades of a ceiling fan with a 4-ft diameter when it is spinning at a rate of 5 rps. 20π ft/s

Solve the given quadratic equation using an appropriate method:

10. $3x^2 + x - 2 = 0$ $\frac{2}{3}, -1$ 11. $x^2 + x - 20 = 0$ 4, −5

Convert to degrees, minutes, and seconds, to the nearest second.

12. $48.464°$ 48°27′50″   13. $15.73°$ 15°43′48″

Convert to decimal degrees, to the nearest tenth of a degree.

14. $189°45′10″$ 189.8°   15. $6°34′25″$ 6.6°

Simplify each expression.

16. $(1 - \cos x)^2 + (1 - \sin x)^2$ 17. $(\sec A + \cos A)^2$

18. $\sin^2 t - \sec^2 t + \tan^2 t + \cos^2 t + (\sin t)(\cos t)$ $\sin t \cos t$

Writing in Mathematics

43. Answers may vary. Some suggestions are daily temperature, number of leaves on a tree, tides, hair length of someone who gets regular haircuts.

Alternative Assessment

Ask students to give an example of one function built from the sine or cosine function for each technique listed below. Then have them graph the basic function and the new function on the same set of axes.

a. vertical translation
b. vertical dilation
c. reflection
d. horizontal translation

Enrichment

Describe a way to graph $y = |f(x)|$ using the graph of $y = f(x)$. Illustrate your description by graphing $y = |4 \sin x|$.

Sketch $y = f(x) = 4 \sin x$. Wherever $y < 0$, reflect the graph about the x-axis.

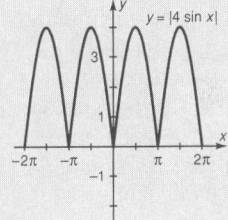

Additional Answers

44. $\sin \dfrac{5\pi}{6} = \cos\left(\dfrac{\pi}{2} - \dfrac{5\pi}{6}\right) =$
$\cos\left(-\dfrac{\pi}{3}\right) = \cos\dfrac{\pi}{3}$

45. $\tan\left(\dfrac{\pi}{2} - x\right) = \dfrac{\sin\left(\frac{\pi}{2} - x\right)}{\cos\left(\frac{\pi}{2} - x\right)} =$
$\dfrac{\cos x}{\sin x} = \cot x$;
$\cot\left(\dfrac{\pi}{2} - x\right) = \dfrac{\cos\left(\frac{\pi}{2} - x\right)}{\sin\left(\frac{\pi}{2} - x\right)} =$
$\dfrac{\sin x}{\cos x} = \tan x$

46. $\sec\left(\dfrac{\pi}{2} - x\right) = \dfrac{1}{\cos\left(\frac{\pi}{2} - x\right)} =$
$\dfrac{1}{\sin x} = \csc x$;
$\csc\left(\dfrac{\pi}{2} - x\right) = \dfrac{1}{\sin\left(\frac{\pi}{2} - x\right)} =$
$\dfrac{1}{\cos x} = \sec x$

47. For all x, $\cos(x + 2\pi) = \cos x$ and $\sin(x + 2\pi) = \sin x$. Since there is no number h, $0 < h < 2\pi$, for which $\cos(0 + h) = 1$ and $\sin(0 + h) = 0$, the conclusion is that the period of the sine and cosine is 2π.

4.2 Period, Amplitude, and Phase Shift

Objectives: To find the amplitude, period, and phase shift of a sine or cosine function from its equation
To graph a sine or cosine function with given amplitude, period, and phase shift

Focus

Solar astronomers have recently discovered that the entire surface of the sun is covered with waves of gases. Scientists believe that the waves are caused by the actions of millions of vibrations throughout the sun. These waves rise and fall in a regular cyclic pattern, and scientists can determine the size of the waves and the time it takes for a cycle to repeat itself. Like seismologists who study earthquakes, *helioseismologists* look to these waves and the vibrations that cause them for information about the sun's inner layers. This information may answer questions about particle physics as well as affect calculations of the age of the universe.

When studying wave phenomena, it is important to be able to determine the "height" of a wave. Any periodic function with a finite maximum and a finite minimum value has an *amplitude* defined as follows:

> Let f be a periodic function with maximum value M and minimum value m. The **amplitude** of f is $\frac{1}{2}(M - m)$.

The amplitude measures half the range of the function, or half the vertical spread.

Example 1 Assume that each graph represents a periodic function. Find its amplitude.

a.   b.   c.

a. Amplitude:
$\frac{1}{2}(2 - [-2]) = 2$

b. Amplitude:
$\frac{1}{2}(4 - 1) = 1.5$

c. Amplitude:
$\frac{1}{2}(15 - [-10]) = 12.5$

Note that if a periodic function does not have *both* a minimum and a maximum, it does not have an amplitude. In Example 1a, the amplitude of the periodic function *f* is equal to its maximum value. *Is this always the case?*

What is the amplitude of the function $f(x) = a \sin x$? Recall that the graph of $f(x) = a \sin x$ is the graph of the basic sine function *dilated vertically* by a factor of $|a|$. The graph illustrates that the maximum value of $f(x)$ is $|a|$; its minimum value is $-|a|$. The amplitude of $f(x)$ is thus $\frac{1}{2}[|a| - (-|a|)] = |a|$.

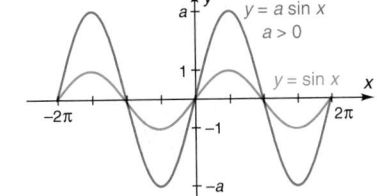

Similar reasoning shows that the amplitude of $g(x) = a \cos x$ is $|a|$.

The period of sin *x* and cos *x* is 2π. Horizontal dilation affects the period as vertical dilation affects the amplitude. The graph of $f(x) = \sin bx$ is the graph of the basic sine function *dilated horizontally* by a factor of $|b|$. When $|b| > 1$, the horizontal dilation is a compression, or movement toward the *y*-axis, so the period is correspondingly compressed. When $0 < |b| < 1$, the horizontal dilation is a stretch and the period is correspondingly stretched.

> Let $f(x) = a \sin bx$ and $g(x) = a \cos bx$. The **period** of both functions is $\frac{2\pi}{|b|}$, and the **amplitude** is $|a|$.

Example 2   Graph each function and determine its period.

   a. $F(x) = \sin 2x$ **b.** $G(x) = \cos \frac{1}{2}x$

a. The period of $\sin \theta$ is 2π, so the graph of $y = \sin \theta$ completes one cycle as θ varies from 0 to 2π. If $\theta = 2x$, the graph completes one cycle as $2x$ varies from 0 to 2π, or as *x* varies from 0 to π. Thus, the period of $\sin 2x$ is $\frac{2\pi}{2} = \pi$.

x	0	$\frac{\pi}{6}$	$\frac{\pi}{4}$	$\frac{\pi}{3}$	$\frac{\pi}{2}$	$\frac{2\pi}{3}$	$\frac{3\pi}{4}$	$\frac{5\pi}{6}$	π
$2x$	0	$\frac{\pi}{3}$	$\frac{\pi}{2}$	$\frac{2\pi}{3}$	π	$\frac{4\pi}{3}$	$\frac{3\pi}{2}$	$\frac{5\pi}{3}$	2π
$\sin 2x$	0	0.87	1	0.87	0	-0.87	-1	-0.87	0

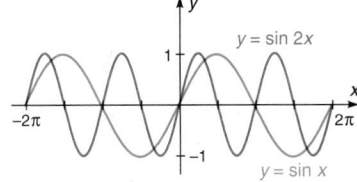

The graph of $\sin 2x$ is the graph of $\sin x$ moved toward the *y*-axis (compressed) horizontally by a factor of 2.

Technology   A graphing utility may be used effectively to introduce the notion of horizontal dilation. Have students use the utility to graph $y = \cos 2x$, $y = \cos \frac{1}{2}x$, $y = \sin 3x$, $y = \sin \frac{1}{3}x$, and several other related functions, each on the same set of axes as the basic function from which it was derived. Ask them to describe the effect that multiplying the input value *x* by various constants has on the graph of the basic function. Having students graph non-trigonometric equations such as $y = \sqrt{2x}$ and $y = |5x|$ (compared to the graphs of $y = \sqrt{x}$ and $y = |x|$) may also help them to understand horizontal dilation.

Alternative Learning Styles
Some students may find the amount of detailed information in this lesson discouraging. A bulletin board display summarizing information about amplitude, period, and phase shift for the simplest cases is beneficial.

GUIDED PRACTICE

For Example 1
Assume that the graph represents a periodic function and determine its amplitude.

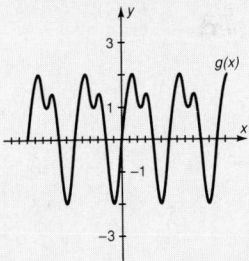

2

Thinking Critically
no; This is only true when there is no vertical shift in the graph.

Graph $f(x) = \sin \frac{1}{4}x$ and determine its period. 8π

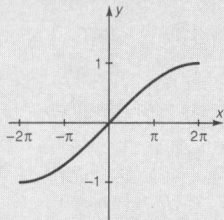

For Example 3

Find the amplitude and period of the function $f(x) = 2.5 \sin 3x$. Identify at least two zeros and a local maximum and minimum value. Then graph one cycle. 2.5; $\frac{2\pi}{3}$; zeros at $0, \frac{\pi}{3}, \frac{2\pi}{3}$,

maximums at $x = \frac{\pi}{6}, \frac{5\pi}{6}, \frac{9\pi}{6}$, etc;

minimums at $x = \frac{\pi}{2}, \frac{7\pi}{6}, \frac{11\pi}{6}$, etc.

b. The graph of $y = \cos \frac{1}{2}x$ completes one cycle as $\frac{1}{2}x$ varies from 0 to 2π, or as x varies from 0 to 4π. The period of $\cos \frac{1}{2}x$ is $\frac{2\pi}{\frac{1}{2}} = 4\pi$.

x	0	$\frac{\pi}{3}$	$\frac{\pi}{2}$	$\frac{2\pi}{3}$	π	$\frac{3\pi}{2}$	2π	$\frac{5\pi}{2}$	3π	$\frac{7\pi}{2}$	4π
$\frac{1}{2}x$	0	$\frac{\pi}{6}$	$\frac{\pi}{4}$	$\frac{\pi}{3}$	$\frac{\pi}{2}$	$\frac{3\pi}{4}$	π	$\frac{5\pi}{4}$	$\frac{3\pi}{2}$	$\frac{7\pi}{4}$	2π
$\cos \frac{1}{2}x$	1	0.87	0.71	0.5	0	-0.71	-1	-0.71	0	0.71	1

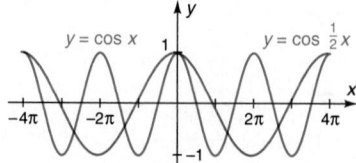

The graph of $\cos \frac{1}{2}x$ is the graph of $\cos x$ moved out from the y-axis (stretched) horizontally by a factor of 2. Thus, $\cos \frac{1}{2}x$ completes its cycle in a period twice as long as that of $\cos x$.

You can use the reasoning in Example 2 to find the periods of functions such as $f(x) = \sin 4x$ and $r(x) = \cos \frac{2}{3}x$. A graphing utility can be used to verify your response. Set the viewing rectangle to $[0, p]$ by $[-1.5, 1.5]$, where p is the period you have found. Then graph the function. If one complete cycle of the sine or cosine function appears, you are correct. If more or less than one cycle appears, adjust your answer accordingly and try again.

Knowing how to identify *zeros* and *local maximum and minimum* values of sine and cosine functions will help you graph these functions. Zeros are those points where the function crosses the x-axis. Since the sine function has zeros at every integral multiple of π, you can find zeros of $f(x) = \sin(bx + c)$ by setting $bx + c$ equal to these values and solving for x.

For example, to identify zeros of $f(x) = \sin\left(2x - \frac{\pi}{2}\right)$, set $2x - \frac{\pi}{2}$ equal to 0, π, $-\pi$, 2π, and so on. Solving these equations shows that $f(x)$ has zeros at $\frac{\pi}{4}$, $\frac{3\pi}{4}$, $-\frac{\pi}{4}$, $\frac{5\pi}{4}$, and so on. You may also set $2x - \frac{\pi}{2} = k\pi$, $k \in Z$, and solve this general equation to find all zeros of $f(x)$. *How would you find zeros of a function of the form $g(x) = \cos(bx + c)$?*

For a given cycle of the sine or cosine graphs, a local maximum occurs at the x-value at which the curve changes from rising to falling; a local minimum occurs at the x-value at which the graph changes from falling to rising. Notice that for the sine and cosine functions, local maxima occur when the function value is 1; local minima occur when the function value is -1. These facts can be used to locate local maximum and minimum values for functions related to the sine and cosine functions.

192   Chapter 4 Graphs and Inverses of Trigonometric Functions

Thinking Critically

Since the cosine function has zeros at every odd integral multiple of $\frac{\pi}{2}$, you can find zeros of a function of the form $g(x) = \cos(bx + c)$ by setting $bx + c$ equal to these values and solving for x.

Example 3 Find the amplitude and period of each function. Identify at least two zeros and a local maximum and minimum value. Then graph one cycle.

    a. $F(x) = 0.75 \cos 6x$ **b.** $G(x) = 3 \sin (-0.25x)$

a. The amplitude of F is 0.75. The period is $\frac{2\pi}{6} = \frac{\pi}{3}$. Since the basic cosine function has zeros at $\frac{\pi}{2}$ and $\frac{3\pi}{2}$, F will have zeros at $6x = \frac{\pi}{2}$ and $6x = \frac{3\pi}{2}$. Thus, zeros occur at $\frac{\pi}{12}$ and $\frac{\pi}{4}$. There are local maximums when $\cos 6x = 1$, which occurs when $6x = 0$ and when $6x = 2\pi$, that is, at $x = 0$ and $x = \frac{\pi}{3}$. There are local minimums when $\cos 6x = -1$, which occurs when $6x = \pi$, that is, at $x = \frac{\pi}{6}$. *How many cycles will this function have between 0 and 2π?*

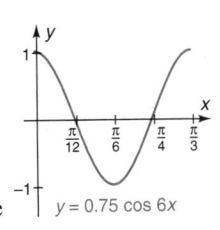
$y = 0.75 \cos 6x$

b. The amplitude of G is 3. The period is $\frac{2\pi}{|-0.25|} = 8\pi$. Since the basic sine function has zeros at -2π, $-\pi$, and 0 (among others), G will have zeros when $-0.25x = -2\pi$, $-0.25x = -\pi$, and $-0.25x = 0$, that is, at $x = 8\pi$, 4π, and 0. There are local maximums when $\sin(-0.25x) = 3$, which occurs at $x = 6\pi$. There are local minimums when $\sin(-0.25x) = -3$, which occurs at $x = 2\pi$.

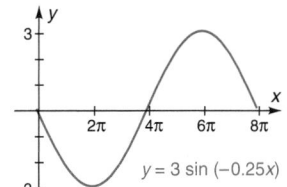
$y = 3 \sin (-0.25x)$

Recall that the graph of $y = f(x - c)$ is the graph of $y = f(x)$ shifted $|c|$ units right if $c > 0$, and shifted $|c|$ units left if $c < 0$. The **phase shift** of $f(x) = a \sin b(x - c)$ and $g(x) = a \cos b(x - c)$ is also determined by c. The basic function is shifted left if c is negative and right if c is positive.

Example 4 Determine the amplitude, period, and phase shift of $g(x) = 3 \sin \left(2x + \frac{\pi}{4}\right)$.

    Then graph one cycle of the function.

$g(x) = 3 \sin 2\left(x - \left(-\frac{\pi}{8}\right)\right)$ *Express in the form $a \sin b(x - c)$.*

The amplitude is $|a| = |3| = 3$; the period is $\frac{2\pi}{|b|} = \frac{2\pi}{2} = \pi$. Since $-\frac{\pi}{8} < 0$, the phase shift is $\frac{\pi}{8}$ units to the left. There is a local maximum at $\frac{\pi}{8}$ and a local minimum at $\frac{5\pi}{8}$.

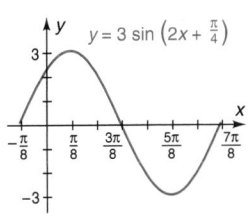
$y = 3 \sin \left(2x + \frac{\pi}{4}\right)$

Sinusoids are functions of the form $f(x) = a \sin b(x - c) + d$, where a, b, c, and d are real numbers. Since $\cos x = \sin \left(x + \frac{1}{2}\pi\right)$, any function of the form $f(x) = a \cos b(x - c) + d$ is also a sinusoid. When graphing sinusoidal functions, it may be helpful to first graph the related function $a \sin bx$ or $a \sin bx$. Then use the phase shift to graph the related function $a \sin b(x - c)$ or $a \cos b(x - c)$. Finally, use the vertical shift to obtain the desired graph.

4.2 Period, Amplitude, and Phase Shift   **193**

Technology Traditionally, identifying zeros of the basic sine and cosine functions is taught as a tool for graphing. Once the shape of the basic sine and cosine curves is known, identifying zeros of related functions is very useful for graphing those functions. Access to technology turns this relationship around. If a graphing utility is used, the graph (and the trace function) can be used to identify zeros. A similar observation can be made to locate local maximum and minimum values. Knowing these values can help with the graphing task, or knowing the graph can help find those values. Students should be able to use each kind of information to find the other.

For Example 4
Determine the amplitude, period, and phase shift of the function $f(x) = 2 \sin \left(\frac{1}{2}x - \pi\right)$. Then graph one cycle of the function. $2; 4\pi; 2\pi$ units right

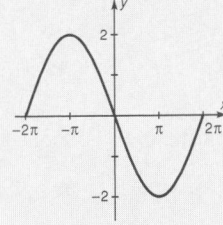

Thinking Critically

Since the period of the function $F(x) = 0.75 \cos 6x$ is $\frac{\pi}{3}$, the function will have six cycles on the interval $[0, 2\pi]$.

Example 5 Graph the function $g(x) = \frac{1}{2} \cos (4x - \pi) + 1$.

$$g(x) = \frac{1}{2} \cos 4\left(x - \frac{\pi}{4}\right) + 1 \qquad \textit{Express in the form } a \cos b(x - c) + d.$$

The amplitude is $\frac{1}{2}$ and the period is $\frac{2\pi}{4} = \frac{\pi}{2}$.
Graph the related function $y = \frac{1}{2} \cos 4x$.
Zeros of $\frac{1}{2} \cos 4x$ occur at $\frac{\pi}{8}$ and $\frac{3\pi}{8}$. There are local maximums at $x = 0$ and $x = \frac{\pi}{2}$, and a local minimum at $x = \frac{\pi}{4}$. The phase shift is $\frac{\pi}{4}$ units right. Graph the related function $\frac{1}{2} \cos 4\left(x - \frac{\pi}{4}\right)$. The vertical shift is one unit upward. Graph the desired function

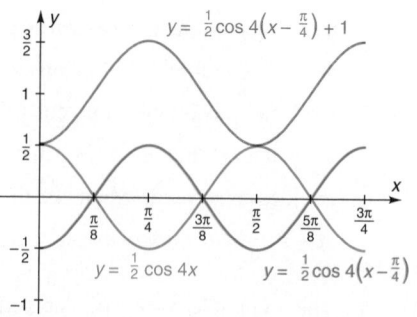

$g(x) = \frac{1}{2} \cos 4\left(x - \frac{\pi}{4}\right) + 1$. Note that $g(x)$ has no zeros. The local maximums are at $x = \frac{\pi}{4}, \frac{3\pi}{4}$, and so on. The local minimums are at $x = 0, \frac{\pi}{2}, \pi$, and so on.

Amplitude, Period, Phase Shift, and Vertical Shift of a Sinusoidal Function

The functions $f(x) = a \sin b(x - c) + d$ and

$g(x) = a \cos b(x - c) + d$ have amplitude $|a|$, period $\frac{2\pi}{|b|}$, phase shift $|c|$ (to the left if $c < 0$ and to the right if $c > 0$), and vertical shift $|d|$ (downward if $d < 0$ and upward if $d > 0$).

If you are given a sinusoidal graph, you can examine its characteristics to determine the function it represents.

Example 6 Determine the amplitude and period of the sinusoidal function whose graph is shown below. Then determine the function represented by the graph.

The amplitude is 2.5. The period is 3π. Use the form $y = a \sin b(x - c)$ with $a = 2.5$.
To find b, set $\frac{2\pi}{b} = 3\pi$; so $b = \frac{2}{3}$. There is no phase shift and no vertical shift, so $c = 0$ and $d = 0$. The function is $f(x) = 2.5 \sin \frac{2}{3}x$.

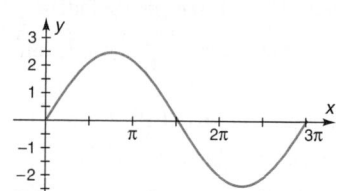

If you are given the amplitude, period, phase shift, and vertical shift of a sinusoidal function, you can express the function in general form.

194 Chapter 4 Graphs and Inverses of Trigonometric Functions

Example 7 Determine the sinusoidal functions with the characteristics listed below. Express your answers in the general form $f(x) = a \sin b(x - c) + d$ or $f(x) = a \cos b(x - c) + d$.

    a. sine: amplitude $\frac{1}{2}$; period π; translation one unit up

    b. cosine: amplitude 3; period $\frac{3\pi}{2}$; phase shift $\frac{\pi}{2}$ right

a. $a = \frac{1}{2}; \frac{2\pi}{b} = \pi, b = 2; c = 0; d = 1$ **b.** $a = 3; \frac{2\pi}{b} = \frac{3\pi}{2}, b = \frac{4}{3}; c = \frac{\pi}{2}; d = 0$

$\quad\quad f(x) = \frac{1}{2} \sin 2x + 1$ $f(x) = 3 \cos \frac{4}{3}\left(x - \frac{\pi}{2}\right)$

Modeling

How can you model the gaseous waves of the sun?

Measurements show that the waves peak and recede at regular intervals. This kind of activity can be modeled by a sine curve of the form $y = a \sin b(x - c) + d$. One difference in the data for the sun waves is that the independent variable does not represent degrees or radians, but time. The period is given in minutes.

Example 8 *Helioseismology* The sun's gaseous waves rise and then fall a total of 70 km. The period for this activity is 5 min. Determine an equation expressing this data, and then graph the function.

The equation will be of the form
$y = a \sin b(t + c)$.

The amplitude is one-half the total difference between maximum and minimum. Since the waves rise and then fall 70 km, $a = 35$ km.

The period is 5 min. Therefore, $\frac{2\pi}{b} = 5$ and $b = \frac{2\pi}{5}$.

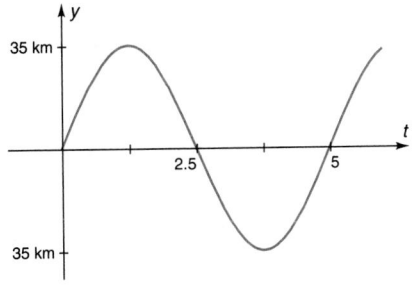

You may select any time as the starting point for the wave activity. Selecting $t = 0$ as the time midway between the lowest and highest wave positions yields $c = 0$ and the equation $y = 35 \sin \frac{2\pi}{5}t$.

For a sinusoidal function in which time is the independent variable, the period may be thought of as the time for one cycle. The **frequency**, which is the reciprocal of the period, is cycles per unit of time. For the example above, the frequency is 0.2 cycle per minute, or 12 cycles per hour.

4.2 Period, Amplitude, and Phase Shift   **195**

For Example 7
Determine a sinusoidal function with the given characteristics. Express your answers in the general form $f(x) = a \sin b(x - c) + d$ or $f(x) = a \cos b(x - c) + d$.

1. sine: amplitude $\frac{3}{2}$; period 3π; phase shift $\frac{\pi}{4}$ units left; translation 2 units down
$f(x) = \frac{3}{2} \sin \frac{2}{3}\left(x + \frac{\pi}{4}\right) - 2$

2. cosine: amplitude 2.5; period $\frac{2\pi}{3}$; phase shift π units right; translation 1 unit up
$f(x) = 2.5 \cos 3(x - \pi) + 1$

Modeling
Students may wish to research other motions, other than wave motions, which are periodic in nature and can be modeled by sine or cosine curves.

For Example 8
The displacement of the pendulum on a clock is 8 cm. It makes one complete cycle in 3 s. Determine an equation expressing this data, and then graph the function. $y = 8 \sin \frac{2\pi}{3}t$

195

Group students in pairs and have them explain to each other how to graph a sine or cosine function with a given amplitude, period, and phase shift.

INDEPENDENT PRACTICE

Assignment Guide
Basic: 1–25, 32–37, 39, Project
Average: 5, 15–46, Project
Enriched: 23–54, Project

Teacher's Resource Book
Practice, page 26

Ⓡ Review
Exercises 5, 15, 24, 25, 35, 37, and 39 review concepts of finding exact values of trigonometric functions, graphing functions, determining a function represented by a graph, determining whether a function is odd or even, and determining domain of a function.

Project
In their research of the planet Jupiter, students may discover that it is a source of radiation. This phenomenon may also be analyzed for cyclic behavior.

LESSON FOLLOW-UP

Lesson Quiz
1. Graph $f(x) = \sin 0.4x$ and determine its period.

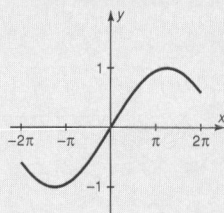

5π

Class Exercises

Assume that each graph represents a periodic function. Find its amplitude.

1.

5

2.
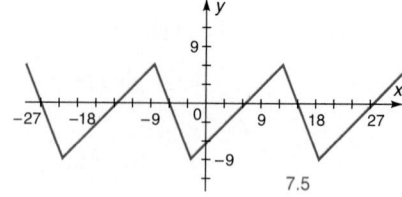
7.5

Determine the amplitude of each function.

3. $f(x) = 10 \sin x$ 10

4. $g(x) = -1.5 \cos \left(x + \frac{1}{2}\pi\right)$ 1.5

Determine the amplitude, period, and vertical shift of each function.

5. $r(t) = 0.7 \cos (3t) - 2$ 0.7; $\frac{2\pi}{3}$; 2 down

6. $h(x) = -100 \sin (0.1x) + 0.6$ 100; 20π; 0.6 up

7. $F(x) = \cos (-1.5x)$ 1; $\frac{4\pi}{3}$; 0

8. $G(t) = \pi \sin \left(-\frac{1}{4}t\right)$ π; 8π; 0

Determine the amplitude, period, phase shift, and vertical shift of each function. Then graph the function.

9. $f(x) = 5 \sin (3x - \pi)$

10. $g(x) = \frac{1}{4} \cos \left(\frac{1}{4}x - \frac{1}{2}\pi\right)$

11. $h(x) = -6 \sin (10x - 2\pi)$

12. $c(t) = \sqrt{2} \cos \left(-4t + \frac{\pi}{3}\right)$

13. **Writing in Mathematics**   Write a definition of *sinusoidal function*. Then compare your definition to one in a mathematics dictionary.

14. Use the definition of amplitude to prove that the amplitude of the function $f(x) = a \cos x$ is $|a|$.

Practice Exercises   Ⓛ Use appropriate technology.

Assume that each graph represents a periodic function. Find its amplitude.

A 1.

7.5

2.
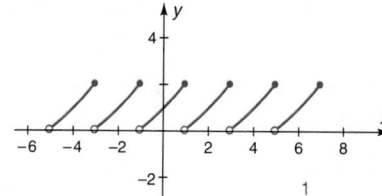
1

Determine the amplitude of each function.

3. $r(t) = 2000 \sin \left(\frac{1}{2}t\right)$ 2000

4. $s(t) = -\cos (t + 1)$ 1

Ⓡ 5. Find the exact value of $\sin t$ if $\cos t = \frac{6}{7}$ and t is in quadrant IV. $-\frac{\sqrt{13}}{7}$

Writing in Mathematics
13. A sinusoidal function is a function of the form $f(x) = a \sin b(x - c) + d$ or $f(x) = a \cos b(x - c) + d$, where a, b, c, and d are real numbers.

Graph each function and determine its period.

6. $f(x) = \sin 3x \quad \frac{2\pi}{3}$ **7.** $j(t) = \cos \frac{1}{4}t \quad 8\pi$ **8.** $r(\theta) = \sin(-12\theta) \quad \frac{\pi}{6}$ **9.** $g(x) = \cos 0.8x \quad \frac{5\pi}{2}$

Determine the period and amplitude of each function.

10. $h(x) = -0.9 \cos 9x \quad \frac{2\pi}{9}; \; 0.9$

11. $\beta(t) = 75 \sin 0.01t \quad 200\pi; \; 75$

12. $r(\theta) = -\sin \sqrt{2}\theta \quad \sqrt{2}\pi; \; 1$

13. $F(x) = 3\sqrt{3} \cos(-6.7x) \quad 0.299\pi; \; 3\sqrt{3}$

14. Graph a periodic function with amplitude 4 and period 6π.

Ⓡ **15.** Solve for x: $\quad 8 - \sqrt[3]{2x - 3} = 5 \quad 15$

16. Graph a periodic function with amplitude 10 and period $\frac{1}{2}\pi$.

17. Graph a periodic function with amplitude 6 and period $\frac{1}{4}\pi$.

18. How is the graph of $f(x) = 5 \cos(x - \pi)$ related to the graph of
$F(x) = \cos x$? vertical dilation of 5; horizontal shift π right

Determine a sinusoidal function with the given characteristics.

19. sine: amplitude 2; period 4π; phase shift $\frac{\pi}{2}$ to the right $f(x) = 2 \sin \frac{1}{2}\left(x - \frac{\pi}{2}\right)$

20. cosine: amplitude 1.25; period $\frac{5\pi}{2}$; translation one unit downward $f(x) = 1.25 \cos \frac{4}{5}x - 1$

Determine a function represented by each graph.

21.

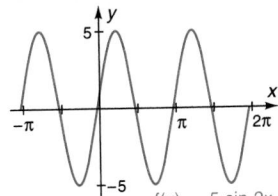

$f(x) = 5 \sin 2x$

22.

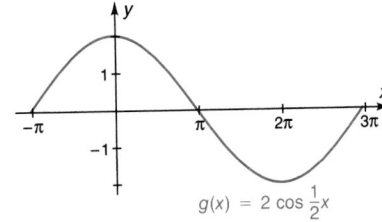

$g(x) = 2 \cos \frac{1}{2}x$

23.

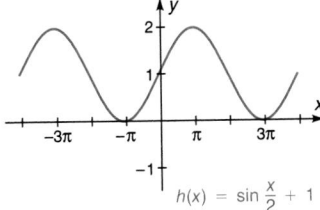

$h(x) = \sin \frac{x}{2} + 1$

Ⓡ **24.**

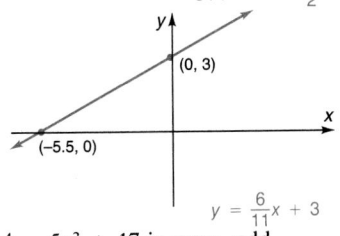

$y = \frac{6}{11}x + 3$

Ⓡ **25.** Determine whether the function $f(x) = x^6 - 3x^4 - 5x^2 + 17$ is even, odd,
or neither. even

Determine the amplitude, period, phase shift, and vertical shift of each
function. Then graph.

B **26.** $y = 2 \sin\left(2x - \frac{1}{2}\pi\right) - 1$

27. $y = 4 \cos(2x + 2\pi) + 2$

28. $y = \sin \frac{1}{4}(x - \pi)$

29. $y = 0.1 \cos(3x - 2\pi)$

30. $f(x) = 3 \cos\left(\frac{1}{3}x - \frac{\pi}{6}\right)$

31. $g(\theta) = \sqrt{2} \sin\left(\frac{1}{5}\theta - \frac{1}{5}\right)$

4.2 Period, Amplitude, and Phase Shift **197**

---

2. Find the amplitude and period of
$f(x) = 3.5 \cos 2x$. Identify at
least two zeros and a local maximum and minimum value. Then
graph one cycle. 3.5; π; $\pm\frac{\pi}{4}$, $\pm\frac{3\pi}{4}$;
etc; local maximums at 0, π, 2π, etc;
local minimums at $x = \frac{\pi}{2}$, $\frac{3\pi}{2}$, $\frac{5\pi}{2}$, etc.

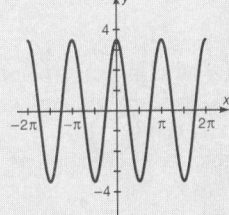

3. Determine the amplitude, period,
and phase shift of the function
$f(x) = -2 \cos\left(x + \frac{1}{4}\pi\right)$. Then
graph one cycle. 2; 2π; $\frac{\pi}{4}$ units left

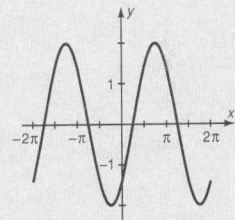

Determine a sinusoidal function with
the given characteristics.

4. cosine: amplitude 2.25; period $\frac{3\pi}{2}$;
phase shift π units left.
$f(x) = 2.25 \cos \frac{4}{3}(x + \pi)$

5. sine: amplitude 3; period 3π;
phase shift $\frac{\pi}{3}$ units right; translation 2 units downward.
$f(x) = 3 \sin \frac{2}{3}\left(x - \frac{\pi}{3}\right) - 2$

32. Determine the zeros and local maximum and minimum for the function of Exercise 27. Compare your answer with the graph.

33. Find zeros and local maximum and minimum for the function of Exercise 30. Compare your answer with the graph.

34. Writing in Mathematics Describe some real world motions that are sinusoidal.

R 35. Graph the function $F(x) = \begin{cases} x^2 + 1, & \text{if } x \le 4 \\ |x - 2|, & \text{if } x > 4 \end{cases}$

36. Thinking Critically Graph a periodic function that does not have a defined amplitude.

R 37. Determine the domain of the function $t(\theta) = \tan(\theta + \pi)$. $\left\{\theta: \theta \ne \left(\frac{2k+1}{2}\right)\pi, k \in Z\right\}$

38. *Acoustics* The sound wave for G below middle C can be described mathematically by the equation $y = \frac{1}{25} \sin 392\pi t$. Determine the amplitude and period of this function. If the frequency, or number of vibrations per second, is the reciprocal of the period, determine the frequency of G below middle C. $\frac{1}{25}$; $\frac{1}{196}$; 196

Determine a function represented by each graph.

R 39.

40.

41.

42.

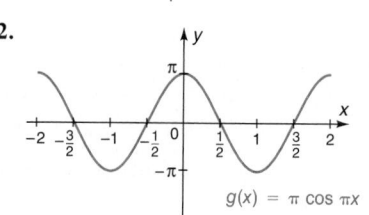

43. *Acoustics* The sound wave for A above middle C may be described by the function $f(x) = 0.001 \sin 880\pi t$. Determine the amplitude, period, and frequency of this function. 0.001; $\frac{1}{440}$; 440

44. *Electricity* The voltage V in an electrical circuit is represented by the function $V(t) = 10 \cos 120\pi t$, where t is time in seconds. Determine the amplitude and period of this function. 10; $\frac{1}{60}$

198   Chapter 4 Graphs and Inverses of Trigonometric Functions

Writing in Mathematics

34. Answers may vary. Some examples follow: Airflow during a respiratory cycle; wave motions when striking a tuning fork; voltage in an electrical current.

C 45. Graph the function $h(x) = x - [x]$ and determine its period.

46. Determine four unique sine or cosine functions with amplitude 2 and period 10π. Use a graphing utility to verify your answers.

47. Show that exactly one cycle of the graph $f(x) = a \sin b(x + c)$ is completed in the interval $\left[\dfrac{-c}{|b|}, \dfrac{2\pi - c}{|b|}\right]$.

48. Use a graphing utility to graph the following functions on the same coordinate system: $f(x) = \sin(2x)$, $g(x) = \sin\left(2x - \dfrac{\pi}{4}\right)$, and $h(x) = \sin\left(2x - \dfrac{\pi}{4}\right) + 2$.

49. *Physics*   A weight is hanging at rest from a spring. It is pulled down 16 cm, and then it is released. Assume that it moves uniformly between points 16 cm below and 16 cm above its resting position, and that it moves one-quarter cycle each second. Determine an equation that models its motion and draw its graph. $y = -16 \cos\left(\dfrac{\pi}{2}t\right)$

16 cm

5 kg

50. *Physics*   The displacement of the pendulum on a clock is 10 in. It makes one complete cycle in 4 s. Determine a sinusoidal function that represents its motion as a function of time. $y = 10 \sin\left(\dfrac{\pi}{2}t\right)$

Graph each function and determine the amplitude, period, vertical shift, and phase shift.

51. $G(t) = \cos(2t - 1) + 5$

52. $F(t) = 1 - 5 \sin(3t - \pi)$

53. $f(x) = |\sin x|$

54. $g(x) = |3 \cos(2x - 2\pi)|$

Project

Research the planet Jupiter. Determine whether it has gaseous waves like the sun. If so, do the waves rise and fall in a cyclic pattern?

Challenge

1. Charla is launching a hot air balloon. Her friend, Shine, has a video camera on the ground. He is following the balloon as it is rising to film the launching. The camera's tripod, which measures 4 ft, was placed 1000 ft from the launching pad. When the camera is pointed upward at an angle of 30°, how far up is the balloon, to the nearest foot? 581 ft

Simplify each of the following:

2. $\sin x \div \cos x \div \tan x \div \cot x \div \sec x \div \csc x$ $\sin^2 x$

3. $\dfrac{3(\sqrt{10} - \sqrt{2})}{2\sqrt{3} - \sqrt{5}}$ 3

4. Each side of triangle ABC is 16 units. Point D is the foot of the perpendicular dropped from A on $\overline{BC}$, and point E is the midpoint of $\overline{AD}$. Determine the distance from B to E. $4\sqrt{7}$

4.2 Period, Amplitude, and Phase Shift   **199**

FOCUS

Biology provides a wide range of examples of phenomena that can be described mathematically by periodic functions. Additional examples of rhythmic processes include the openings of oyster shells, food consumption of woodchucks, and oxygen consumption of chick embryos. The chapter opener on pages 180 and 181 gives a more detailed description of these phenomena. The concepts developed in this lesson will help students to analyze the data they collected for the project on page 181.

Scientists in the field of biological chronometry study the way organisms "keep time." They believe that biological rhythms should be considered a fundamental characteristic of life, along with metabolism, growth, and reproduction.

4.3 Graphing Other Trigonometric Functions

Objectives: To analyze properties that determine the graphs of the tangent, cotangent, secant, and cosecant functions
To graph the tangent, cotangent, secant, and cosecant functions

Focus

Biological processes which undergo regularly recurring changes are referred to as *rhythmic*. Biological rhythms have been described for thousands of organisms, including leaf movements in plants, color changes of Fiddler crabs, and openings of oyster shells. When researchers discovered that the leaf movements of plants are relatively independent of light and temperature, the existence of *biological clocks* was hypothesized, and the field of *biological chronometry* was born. Biological rhythms are described mathematically by periodic functions. The study of the periods and phases of these functions and how they change or do not change in response to various stimuli is fundamental to experiments in biological chronometry.

Resetting of a Fiddler Crab's Color-Change Rhythm

You have seen that the graphs of the sine and cosine functions are periodic. This lesson introduces the graphs of the following four periodic functions: tangent, cotangent, secant, and cosecant. Before trying to graph $\tan x$, $\cot x$, $\sec x$, and $\csc x$, recall that each is undefined at certain values of x, where the function is said to be *discontinuous*. The behavior of the graphs near those values must be examined carefully.

Focus first on $f(x) = \tan x$ near $x = \frac{\pi}{2}$, where tangent is undefined, and recall that $\tan x = \frac{\sin x}{\cos x}$. If x approaches $\frac{\pi}{2}$ but always remains less than $\frac{\pi}{2}$, then $\cos x$ approaches 0 and $\sin x$ approaches 1. In this case, the ratio of $\frac{\sin x}{\cos x}$ is positive and increases without bound. If x approaches $\frac{\pi}{2}$ but always remains larger than $\frac{\pi}{2}$, then $\cos x$ approaches 0 while remaining negative and $\sin x$ approaches 1. In this case, the ratio $\frac{\sin x}{\cos x}$ is negative and decreases without bound; that is, $\frac{\sin x}{\cos x}$ gets larger without bound in the negative direction.

200 Chapter 4 Graphs and Inverses of Trigonometric Functions

Calculator-generated values support these conclusions about the behavior of the tangent function near $x = \frac{\pi}{2}$. The tables below provide values of $\tan x$ as x approaches $\frac{\pi}{2}$, for $x < \frac{\pi}{2}$ and then for $x > \frac{\pi}{2}$. *What happens to the values of* $\tan x$ *in each case?*

x	1.5	1.57	1.5707	1.57079	1.570796	1.5707963
$\tan x$	14	1256	10,381	158,058	3,060,022	37,320,396

x	1.6	1.58	1.571	1.5708	1.570797	1.5707964
$\tan x$	−34	−109	−4,910	−272,242	−1,485,432	−13,660,269

The line $x = \frac{\pi}{2}$ is called a *vertical asymptote* of the graph. Note that the tangent function is undefined at all odd multiples of $\frac{\pi}{2}$, and the graph has vertical asymptotes at every line with equation $x = (2k + 1)\frac{\pi}{2}$, $k \in Z$.

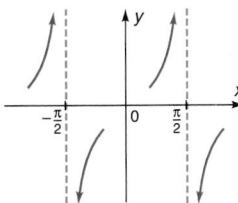

The definition of $\tan \theta$ can be used to show that the tangent is a periodic function with period π: If $P(x, y)$ is a point on the terminal side of θ, $\tan \theta = \frac{y}{x}$. Then $Q(-x, -y)$ is on the terminal side of $\theta + \pi$, so $\tan (\theta + \pi) = \frac{-y}{-x} = \frac{y}{x} = \tan \theta$.

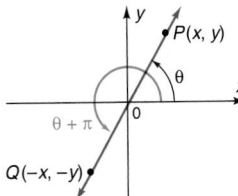

Since $\tan (-x) = -\tan x$, the tangent function is an odd function and its graph is symmetric about the origin. Since the period is π and tangent is symmetric about the origin, consider the interval $\left(-\frac{\pi}{2}, \frac{\pi}{2}\right)$. A table of values provides points that can be connected by a smooth curve.

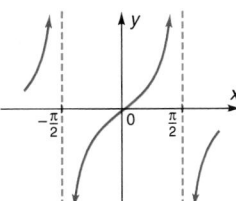

x	0	$\frac{\pi}{8}$	$\frac{\pi}{6}$	$\frac{\pi}{4}$	$\frac{\pi}{3}$
$\tan x$	0	0.4	0.6	1	1.7

x	$-\frac{\pi}{3}$	$-\frac{\pi}{4}$	$-\frac{\pi}{6}$	$-\frac{\pi}{8}$
$\tan x$	−1.7	−1	−0.6	−0.4

The periodic nature of tangent is used to extend the graph to other intervals. The graph shows that the range of $f(x) = \tan x$ is the set of all real numbers.

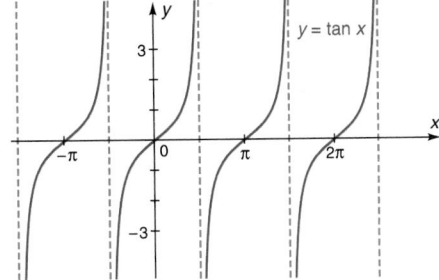

4.3 Graphing Other Trigonometric Functions **201**

Thinking Critically

As x approaches $\frac{\pi}{2}$ from the left, the values of the tangent function get larger and larger in the positive direction. As x approaches $\frac{\pi}{2}$ from the right, the values get larger and larger in the negative direction. Arrows on portions of the graph on either side of $\frac{\pi}{2}$ show the graph arbitrarily close to the vertical line $x = \frac{\pi}{2}$, increasing without bound on the left, decreasing without bound on the right. The line $x = \frac{\pi}{2}$ is a vertical asymptote of the graph.

GUIDED PRACTICE

For Example 1

Graph each function. Compare the graph to that of $y = \tan x$.

1. $f(x) = \tan \frac{1}{3}x$

The graph of h is a horizontal dilation of the graph of $f(x) = \tan x$ by a factor of $\frac{1}{3}$. The dilation moves the graph out from the y-axis and f has a period of 3π.

2. $g(x) = \tan 3x$

The graph of h is a horizontal dilation of the graph of $f(x) = \tan x$ by a factor of 3. The dilation moves the graph in toward the y-axis and g has a period of $\frac{\pi}{3}$.

A similar analysis can be used to graph $g(x) = \cot x$. Since $\cot x = \frac{\cos x}{\sin x}$, cotangent is undefined at every multiple of π and has vertical asymptotes with equations of the form $x = k\pi$, $k \in \mathbb{Z}$. The period of cotangent is π since $\cot (x + \pi) = \cot x$. Why? Since $\cot (-x) = -\cot x$, the cotangent is an odd function. Its graph is symmetric about the origin.

Consider x-values in the interval $(0, \pi)$ to determine one cycle. Then use this information and the periodic nature of the cotangent function to extend the graph.

x	$\frac{\pi}{8}$	$\frac{\pi}{6}$	$\frac{\pi}{4}$	$\frac{\pi}{3}$	$\frac{\pi}{2}$	$\frac{5\pi}{8}$	$\frac{2\pi}{3}$	$\frac{3\pi}{4}$	$\frac{7\pi}{8}$
$\cot x$	2.4	5.9	1	0.6	0	-0.4	-0.6	-1	-2.4

The range of the cotangent function is also the set of all real numbers.

When using a graphing utility to graph the cotangent function, you must often enter the reciprocal of the tangent function. Two possible ways to enter the cotangent function are $y = \frac{1}{\tan x}$ and $y = (\tan x)^{-1}$.

Related functions may be graphed as transformations of the tangent and cotangent functions.

Example 1 Graph the function $h(x) = \tan \frac{1}{2}x$. Compare the graph to that of $f(x) = \tan x$.

This function has a vertical asymptote when $\frac{1}{2}x = \frac{1}{2}\pi$, that is, when $x = \pi$, and also at any odd multiple of π. The graph of h is a horizontal dilation of the graph of $f(x) = \tan x$ by a factor of $\frac{1}{2}$. Since $\frac{1}{2} < 1$, the dilation moves the graph out from the y-axis and h has period 2π.

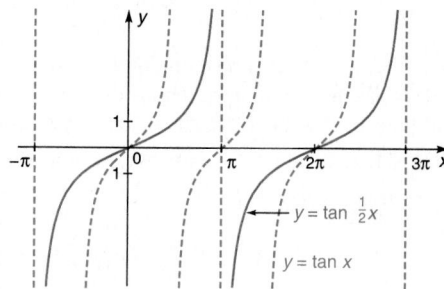

In Example 1, the horizontal dilation by a factor of $\frac{1}{2}$ causes $h(x)$ to have a period twice as long as that of $\tan x$. In general, the functions $y = \tan bx$ and $y = \cot bx$ have period $\frac{\pi}{|b|}$.

Since the tangent and cotangent functions have no maximum or minimum values, the concept of amplitude does not apply to these functions. However, constants in tangent and cotangent functions affect their graphs as with any function. For the general functions $f(x) = a \tan b(x - c) + d$ and $g(x) = a \cot b(x - c) + d$, the constant a vertically dilates the graph of $\tan x$ or $\cot x$.

202   Chapter 4 Graphs and Inverses of Trigonometric Functions

---

Thinking Critically

Since $\cot x$ is the reciprocal of the tangent function, which has period π, it follows that

$$\cot (x + \pi) = \frac{1}{\tan (x + \pi)} = \frac{1}{\tan x} = \cot x.$$

Both $f(x)$ and $g(x)$ have period $\frac{\pi}{|b|}$, phase shift $|c|$ (to the left if $c < 0$ or to the right if $c > 0$), and vertical shift $|d|$ (upward if $d > 0$ or downward if $d < 0$).

Example 2 Determine the period, phase shift, vertical shift, and the equations of two vertical asymptotes of the function $f(x) = 2 \tan \left(x - \frac{\pi}{6} \right) + 3$. Then graph the function using a graphing utility.

The period is $\frac{\pi}{|b|} = \frac{\pi}{1} = \pi$; the phase shift is $\frac{\pi}{6}$ to the right; the vertical shift is three units upward. Since the basic tangent function is undefined at $-\frac{\pi}{2}$ and $\frac{\pi}{2}$, f will have asymptotes at $x - \frac{\pi}{6} = -\frac{\pi}{2}$ and $x - \frac{\pi}{6} = \frac{\pi}{2}$.
Thus, vertical asymptotes will occur at

$$x = -\frac{\pi}{3} \quad \text{and} \quad x = \frac{2\pi}{3}$$

$[-\pi, \pi]$ by $[-3, 6]$
x scl: $\frac{\pi}{3}$ y scl: 1

To use a graphing utility, select a viewing rectangle of $[-\pi, \pi]$ by $[-3, 6]$. *Why?* Use a scale of $\frac{\pi}{3}$ on the x-axis and 1 on the y-axis. *Why?* To input this function, use appropriate parentheses, such as

$$y = 2 \tan (x - \pi \div 6) + 3$$

If you are given specific characteristics of a function or can obtain them from its graph, you can derive its equation.

Example 3 Derive an equation of the cotangent function with period $\frac{\pi}{2}$ and horizontal shift $\frac{\pi}{4}$ to the left. Then graph the function with a graphing utility.

Use the general form $f(x) = a \cot b(x - c)$. No vertical dilation is specified, so $a = 1$. To find b, set $\frac{\pi}{|b|} = \frac{\pi}{2}$. Thus, $|b| = 2$, and $b = \pm 2$. Choose $b = 2$ to avoid a reflection. Since there is a horizontal shift of $\frac{\pi}{4}$ to the left, set $c = -\frac{\pi}{4}$. Thus, the equation is

$$y = \cot 2\left(x + \frac{\pi}{4} \right)$$

$[-\frac{\pi}{2}, \frac{\pi}{2}]$ by $[-3, 3]$
x scl: $\frac{\pi}{4}$ y scl: 1

Is there more than one equation that possesses the above characteristics?

To input this function, use appropriate parentheses, such as

$$y = (\tan (2(x + \pi \div 4)))^{-1}$$

For Example 2
Determine the period, phase shift, vertical shift, and the equations of two vertical asymptotes of $f(x) = \cot (2x - \pi)$. Then graph the function using a graphing utility.

$\frac{\pi}{2}$; $\frac{\pi}{2}$ units right; asymptotes at $x = 0$ and $x = \frac{\pi}{2}$

For Example 3
Determine an equation for the function with the given characteristics. Then graph the function with a graphing utility.

tangent: period $\frac{\pi}{2}$; phase shift $\frac{\pi}{4}$ left;

$$y = \tan \left(2x + \frac{\pi}{2} \right)$$

Thinking Critically
The viewing rectangle is selected to show the period of the graph. A scale of $\frac{\pi}{3}$ is used on the x-axis to show the asymptotes; a scale of 1 is used on the y-axis to show the vertical shift.

There is only one equation with the given characteristics but there are many equivalent forms of the equation. For example, $y = \cot 2\left(x + \frac{\pi}{4} \right)$ may be expressed as $y = \cot \left(2x + \frac{\pi}{2} \right)$.

1. $f(x) = 4 \sec\left(\frac{1}{4}t\right)$

2. $g(t) = \frac{1}{2} \csc(3t)$

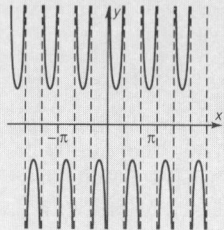

The analysis of the secant function proceeds from the fact that it is the reciprocal of the cosine function. Since $\sec x = \frac{1}{\cos x}$, $\sec x$ has vertical asymptotes at every line of the form $x = (2k + 1)\frac{\pi}{2}$, $k \in \mathbf{Z}$. *Why?* Secant is an even function, $\sec(-x) = \sec x$, and so its graph is symmetric about the y-axis. Because $-1 \le \cos x \le 1$, the range of $f(x) = \sec x$ is $(-\infty, -1] \cup [1, \infty)$. The period of the secant function is that of the cosine, 2π.

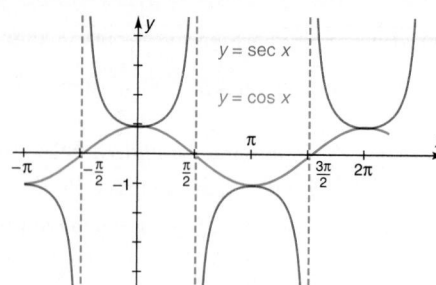

Since $\csc x = \frac{1}{\sin x}$, similar reasoning shows that the cosecant function has a vertical asymptote at every line with equation $x = k\pi$, $k \in \mathbf{Z}$, and has range $(-\infty, -1] \cup [1, \infty)$. Like the sine, it is an odd function, with graph symmetric about the origin. Its period is 2π.

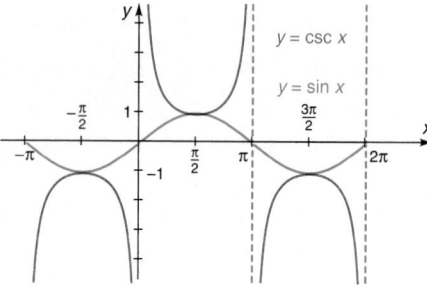

When using a graphing utility to graph the secant or cosecant functions, as with the cotangent function, you must usually enter the reciprocal function.

Related functions may be analyzed and graphed as transformations of the secant and cosecant.

Example 4 Graph the function $f(x) = -2 \sec \frac{1}{2}x$.

The factor -2 reflects the graph of the basic function in the x-axis and changes the range to $(-\infty, -2] \cup [2, \infty)$. The graph of this function completes one cycle as $\frac{1}{2}x$ varies between 0 and 2π, that is, as x varies between 0 and 4π.

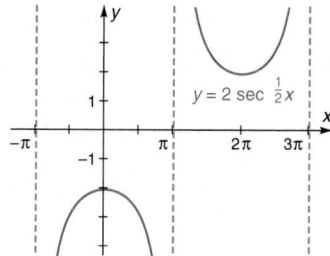

To use a graphing utility to graph $f(x) = -2 \sec \frac{1}{2}x$, use appropriate parentheses, such as $y = -2(\cos 0.5x)^{-1}$.

For the general functions $f(x) = a \sec b(x - c) + d$ and $g(x) = a \csc b(x - c) + d$, the constant a vertically dilates the graph of $\sec x$ or $\csc x$. Both $f(x)$ and $g(x)$ have period $\frac{2\pi}{|b|}$, phase shift $|c|$, and vertical shift $|d|$.

204   Chapter 4 Graphs and Inverses of Trigonometric Functions

Thinking Critically

The secant function is undefined at all odd multiples of $\frac{\pi}{2}$, and since $2k + 1$ is odd for all $k \in \mathbf{Z}$, $(2k + 1)\frac{\pi}{2}$ is an odd multiple of $\frac{\pi}{2}$, and the equations of the asymptotes of $f(x) = \sec x$ can be written in the form $x = (2k + 1)\frac{\pi}{2}$, $k \in \mathbf{Z}$.

Example 5 Find the period, phase shift, vertical shift, and the equations of two vertical asymptotes of the function $g(x) = \csc\left(4x + \dfrac{3\pi}{2}\right) - 1$. Then graph the function using a graphing utility.

Express g in general form:

$$\csc\left(4x + \frac{3\pi}{2}\right) - 1 = \csc 4\left(x - \left[-\frac{3\pi}{8}\right]\right) - 1$$

The period is $\dfrac{2\pi}{4} = \dfrac{\pi}{2}$. The phase shift is $\dfrac{3\pi}{8}$ to the left. The vertical shift is down one unit. There is one vertical asymptote where

$$4x + \frac{3\pi}{2} = \pi \qquad \text{that is, at} \qquad x = -\frac{\pi}{8}$$

Another asymptote occurs where

$$4x + \frac{3\pi}{2} = 2\pi \qquad \text{that is, at} \qquad x = \frac{\pi}{8}$$

To input this function, use appropriate parentheses, such as

$$y = (\sin(4x + 3\pi \div 2))^{-1} - 1$$

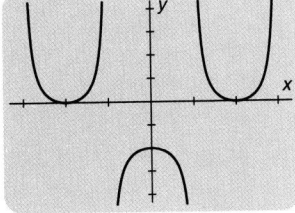

$\left[-\frac{3\pi}{8}, \frac{3\pi}{8}\right]$ by $[-4, 4]$
x scl: $\frac{\pi}{8}$ y scl: 1

Class Exercises

Determine the period of each function.

1. $f(x) = \tan 3x$ $\frac{\pi}{3}$ **2.** $g(x) = \cot(-2x)$ $\frac{\pi}{2}$ **3.** $F(t) = \sec\frac{1}{4}t$ 8π **4.** $G(\theta) = \csc(-7.2\theta)$ $\frac{5\pi}{18}$

Identify the vertical asymptotes of each function.

5. $y = \tan 2x$ **6.** $y = \sec\frac{1}{2}(x - \pi)$ **7.** $r(x) = \cot 3x$ **8.** $k(t) = \csc\frac{1}{4}t$

Determine the period, phase shift, and vertical shift for each function.

9. $f(x) = \cot 2(x - \pi) + 3$ **10.** $r(x) = \sec\left(x + \dfrac{3\pi}{4}\right) - 2$

Graph each function, showing vertical asymptotes.

11. $y = -\tan x$ **12.** $s(t) = \sec\frac{1}{4}t$

Practice Exercises   Use appropriate technology.

Determine the period of each function.

A   **1.** $y = \tan\frac{1}{4}x$ 4π **2.** $f(t) = \sec 0.2t$ 10π **3.** $G(x) = \csc 10x$ $\frac{\pi}{5}$

4. $h(\theta) = \cot 2\theta$ $\frac{\pi}{2}$ **Ⓡ 5.** $f(x) = \sin(3x - \pi)$ $\frac{2\pi}{3}$ **6.** $y = \sec(-3x)$ $\frac{2\pi}{3}$

Identify the vertical asymptotes of each function.

7. $y = \tan 0.3x$ $\frac{5}{3}(2k+1)\pi,\ k \in Z$ **8.** $y = \cot\frac{2}{3}t$ $\frac{3}{2}k\pi,\ k \in Z$

4.3 Graphing Other Trigonometric Functions   **205**

For Example 5

Determine the period, phase shift, vertical shift, and the equations of two vertical asymptotes of $F(x) = \sec(2x - \pi)$. Then graph the function using a graphing utility.

$\pi; \frac{\pi}{2}$ units right; 5 units up; asymptotes at $x = \pm\frac{\pi}{4}, x = \pm\frac{3\pi}{4}$, etc.

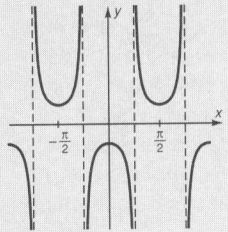

CLOSURE

Have students summarize in their math journals the properties of the graphs of the tangent, cotangent, secant, and cosecant functions. Then have them summarize how to use their personal graphing utility to graph cotangent, secant, and cosecant functions efficiently.

Additional Answers
Class Exercises

5. $\left(\dfrac{2k+1}{4}\right)\pi,\ k \in Z$

6. $2k\pi,\ k \in Z$

7. $\dfrac{k}{3}\pi,\ k \in Z$

8. $4k\pi,\ k \in Z$

9. $\frac{\pi}{2}; \pi$ right; 3 up

10. $2\pi; \dfrac{3\pi}{4}$ left; 2 down

11.

12.

Assignment Guide
Basic: 1–25, 31–35, 44
Average: 5, 9, 16–44
Enriched: 16, 26–55

Teacher's Resource Book
Practice, page 27

Ⓡ **Review**
Exercises 5, 9, 25, 31, 33, and 44
review concepts of period of sine
and cosine functions, linear velocity,
intervals on which sine functions increase and decrease, domain and
range of functions, and deriving a
function for given characteristics of
the function.

LESSON FOLLOW-UP

Lesson Quiz

1. Graph $h(x) = \cot \frac{1}{4}x$ and compare the graph to that of $f(x) = \cot x$.

The graph of h is a horizontal dilation
of the graph $f(x) = \cot x$ by a factor of $\frac{1}{4}$. The dilation moves the graph
out from the y-axis and has a period
of 8π.

Additional Answers

17. $\frac{\pi}{3}$; $\frac{\pi}{4}$ left; 0;
   Example: $x = -\frac{\pi}{12}, x = \frac{\pi}{4}$

18. 2π; π right; 1 up;
   Example: $x = \pi, x = 2\pi$

19. $\frac{\pi}{3}$; $\frac{\pi}{2}$ right; 1 down;
   Example: $x = \frac{\pi}{2}, x = \frac{5\pi}{6}$

20. $\frac{\pi}{3}$; $\frac{5\pi}{168}$ left; 6 up;
   Example: $x = -\frac{5\pi}{168}, x = \frac{23\pi}{168}$

Ⓡ **9.** *Music*   The frequencies of the sound waves produced by a piano range
from approximately 27 to 4139 vibrations per second. Determine the range
of the periods of these waves. $\left[\frac{1}{4139}\text{s}, \frac{1}{27}\text{s}\right]$

Graph each function, showing vertical asymptotes.

10. $y = \tan \frac{1}{4}x$ **11.** $y = \sec 2\theta$ **12.** $H(\theta) = -\tan \theta$

13. $f(t) = \csc \frac{2}{3}t$ **14.** $g(t) = \cot \frac{2}{5}t$ **15.** $y = 3 \sec x$

16. Writing in Mathematics   Construct a table of values for $y = \csc x$ near $x = \pi$.
Use values such that $x < \pi$ and $x > \pi$. Describe the behavior of the values of y.

For each function, determine the period, phase shift, vertical shift, and the
equations for two vertical asymptotes.

17. $y = \tan 3\left(x + \frac{\pi}{4}\right)$ **18.** $y = 4 \csc (x - \pi) + 1$

19. $y = 4 \cot \left(3x - \frac{3\pi}{2}\right) - 1$ **20.** $y = \csc \left(6x + \frac{5\pi}{28}\right) + 6$

Derive the equation for the function with the following characteristics:

21. $\tan x$: period, 2π; upward vertical shift of 2 units $f(x) = \tan \frac{1}{2}x + 2$

22. $\cot x$: period, π; phase shift of $\frac{\pi}{2}$ to the right $g(x) = \cot \left(x - \frac{\pi}{2}\right)$

Derive the equation and graph the function with the following characteristics:

23. $\tan x$: period, $\frac{\pi}{2}$; downward vertical shift of one unit $f(x) = \tan 2x - 1$

24. $\csc x$: period, 4π; phase shift of π to the left $g(x) = \csc \frac{1}{2}(x + \pi)$

Ⓡ **25.** *Recreation*   When a Ferris wheel is in motion, do all riders move at the
same linear velocity? Why or why not? yes; They are all the same distance from the center.

Determine the equation for each graph. Assume there are no vertical dilations.

Ⓑ **26.**

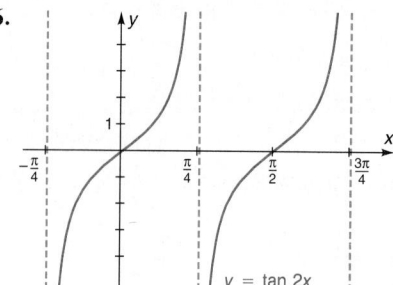

$y = \tan 2x$

27.

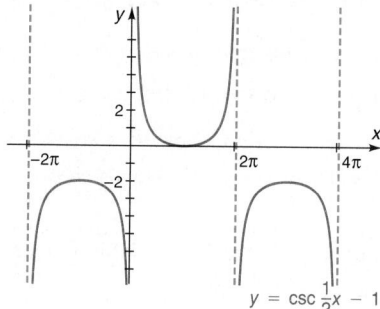

$y = \csc \frac{1}{2}x - 1$

Describe the intervals on which each function is (a) increasing and
(b) decreasing for $-2\pi \leq x \leq 2\pi$.

28. $y = \tan x$ **29.** $y = \sec x$ **30.** $y = -\tan x$ Ⓡ **31.** $y = \sin 2x$

32. Thinking Critically   Explain why the values of x, $\sin x$, and $\tan x$ are
almost the same for small positive values of x.

206   Chapter 4 Graphs and Inverses of Trigonometric Functions

Writing in Mathematics

16.

x	3.1	3.14	3.141	3.1415	3.14159	3.141592
$\csc x$	24.04964	627.88319	1687.3264	10,792.89	376,847.97	1,530,011.17

x	4	3.2	3.15	3.142	3.1416	3.141593
$\csc x$	-1.321349	-17.13087	-118.945	-2454.913	$-136,120.91$	$-2,886,836.028$

As x approaches π from above, the function values approach negative infinity. As x approaches π from below, the values approach positive infinity.

® 33. Determine the domain and range of the function $f(x) = \sqrt{3x} - 1$.

Graph each function, showing vertical asymptotes.

34. $y = -\tan \frac{1}{4}x$

35. $y = 4 \sec 2x$

36. $y = -3 \sec \left(x - \frac{1}{2}\pi\right)$

37. $f(x) = \cot \left(\frac{1}{3}x\right) + 2$

38. $g(x) = \csc \left(\frac{3}{4}x\right) - 1$

39. $y = \tan \left(x - \frac{\pi}{4}\right)$

Use a graphing utility to obtain each graph. Then state whether each function is odd, even, or neither.

40. $y = \tan \left(x - \frac{1}{2}\pi\right)$ odd

41. $y = \tan \left(x - \frac{1}{4}\pi\right)$ neither

42. $y = \cot (x) + 2$ neither

43. $y = \sec (x) + 3$ even

® 44. *Oceanography* At Skaket Bay on Cape Cod, the distance between high tide and low tide is 600 yd. The time period between two high tides is 12.5 h. Derive a sine function relating the position of the water to time, letting $t = 0$ be the time midway between low and high tide. $y = 300 \sin 0.16\pi t$

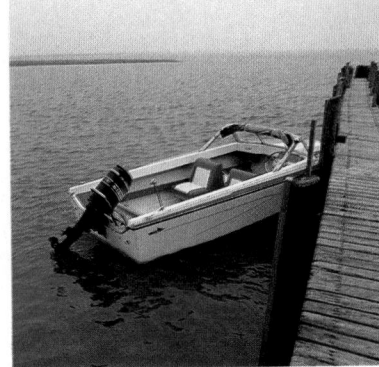

C 45. Determine the value(s) of k such that $\cot kx$ has vertical asymptotes at every integer. π

If F is any function with period 5, determine the period of each related function. Provide a reason for your answer in each case.

46. $y = F(x + 1)$

47. $y = F(x) + 5$

48. $y = F\left(\frac{1}{2}x\right)$

49. $y = F(3x)$

50. Determine the range of $y = \csc (t + 2\pi) + \csc (t + 4\pi)$. $(-\infty, -2] \cup [2, \infty)$

51. Determine the range of $y = \sec (t + 2\pi) + \sec (t + 4\pi)$. $(-\infty, -2] \cup [2, \infty)$

Graph each function over a two-period interval.

52. $y = \tan \left(2x - \frac{4\pi}{3}\right) + 1$

53. $y = 3 \cot (3x - \pi) - 1$

54. $y = 2 \csc \left(2x + \frac{4\pi}{3}\right) + 1$

55. $y = 3 \sec \left(3x + \frac{\pi}{3}\right) - 1$

Review

1. Divide $18x^3y^5 - 12x^4y^3 + 42x^3y^9$ by $6x^2y^3$. $3xy^2 - 2x^2 + 7xy^6$

2. How do the graphs of $f(x) = |x^2 - 2|$ and $f(x) = |x^2| - 2$ differ? In the second graph, the portion that falls below the x-axis may be reflected through the x-axis to obtain the first graph.

Determine the amplitude, period, phase shift, and vertical shift of the following:

3. $f(x) = 3 \cos 2\left(x - \frac{\pi}{6}\right) + 2$ 3; π; $\frac{\pi}{6}$ right; 2 up

4. $f(x) = 2 \sin 2\left(2x - \frac{\pi}{4}\right) - 1$ 2; $\frac{\pi}{2}$; $\frac{\pi}{8}$ right; 1 down

5. Through how many degrees does the minute hand of a clock rotate in 10 min? $-60°$

6. The sum of the squares of two consecutive even integers is 10 times the smaller number. Find the numbers. 2, 4

7. Determine the distance from the point $(-2, 3)$ to the line $2x - y = 2$. $\frac{9\sqrt{5}}{5}$

Determine the period, phase shift, vertical shift, and the equations for two vertical asymptotes. Then graph the function using a graphing utility.

2. $f(x) = \sec \left(x - \frac{1}{4}\pi\right) + 1.5$

2π; $\frac{\pi}{4}$ units right; 1.5 units up; asymptotes at $x = -\frac{\pi}{4}$ and $x = \frac{3\pi}{4}$

Determine the equation for the function with the given characteristics.

3. $\cot x$: period $\frac{\pi}{4}$; phase shift $\frac{\pi}{4}$ units right; vertical shift 3 units up $f(x) = \cot (4x - \pi) + 3$

4. $\sec x$: period $\frac{2\pi}{3}$; phase shift π units left; vertical shift 4 units down $f(x) = \sec 3(x + \pi) - 4$

Alternative Assessment

Have students write a paragraph describing how using more than one viewing rectangle on a graphing utility can enhance understanding of the behavior of periodic functions.

Enrichment

Determine an equation involving the cotangent function that has the same graph as that of $y = \tan x$, and another equation involving the cosecant function that has the same graph as that of $y = \sec x$. Answers may vary. Some examples follow.

$y = \cot \left(\frac{\pi}{2} - x\right)$; $y = \csc \left(\frac{\pi}{2} - x\right)$

Vocabulary
addition of ordinates

Ⓜ **Materials/Manipulatives**
compass
portable microphone or sound
  system
ruler
two speakers

Technology
graphing utility

FOCUS

Another example of constructive and
destructive interference is the effect
of two loudspeakers connected to
the same amplifier. If you stand at a
spot (point A in the diagram below)
which is equidistant from the two
speakers, the sound you hear would
be louder than if there were just one
speaker. The reason for this is that
the waves emitted from the speakers
arrive at point A in phase, and add
to each other. At point B the sound
is weaker than it would be if just one
speaker were used because a wave
from one speaker travels a half-
wavelength farther than a wave from
the other. The two waves arrive a
half-cycle out of phase and cancel
each other significantly.

4.4 Graphing by Addition of Ordinates

Objective: To graph trigonometric functions that are the sums of two
functions

Focus

Acoustics is the branch of physics that studies
sound and its transmission. Sound waves that are
produced at the same time from different sources
can combine to produce a phenomenon called
interference. Interference is said to be *constructive*
when the different waves are in phase, that is,
when the waves rise and fall simultaneously.
When constructive interference occurs, the
sounds combine to make a louder or more intense
sound. When sound waves are out of phase, the
result is *destructive* interference which may result
in occasional *dead spots* where the combined
waves cancel one another.

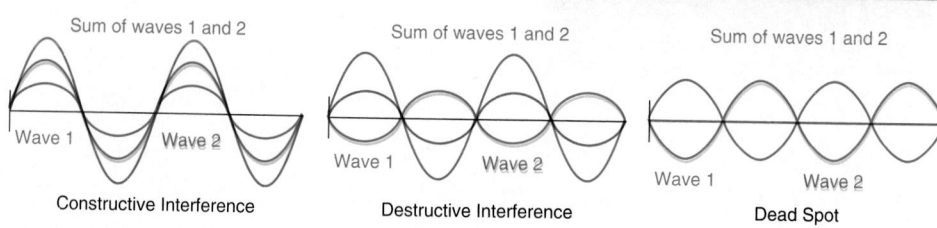

Constructive Interference   Destructive Interference   Dead Spot

Sound waves can be modeled using sinusoidal functions of the form
$y = a \sin b(x + c)$. Combinations of such trigonometric functions are very
important in the analysis of waves and in other applications. This lesson
focuses on graphing the sum of two or more trigonometric functions.

Recall that an ordinate is the y-value of an ordered pair (x, y). **Addition of
ordinates** is a technique used to obtain the graph of the sum $f + g$ of two
functions from the graphs of f and g. When one of the functions is constant,
addition of ordinates is simply a vertical translation. For example, if $f(x) = \sin x$
and $g(x) = 1$, then $(f + g)(x) = \sin x + 1$, and the graph of $f + g$ is that of
the sine function shifted up one unit.

In general, to graph a function that is the sum of two functions, first graph each
addend. Then *graphically add* the y-values of key points. Key points usually
occur at x-values where the corresponding y-values are easily found. A ruler or
compass is useful for measuring the vertical displacement of one graph and
then adding it to (or subtracting it from) the vertical displacement of the other.

208   Chapter 4 Graphs and Inverses of Trigonometric Functions

Example 1 Use addition of ordinates to graph $F(x) = x + \sin x$.

First graph $y = \sin x$ and $y = x$. Some key points are at $x = 0, \frac{\pi}{2}, \pi, \frac{3\pi}{2}$, and 2π since their sine values are easily found. For each key point, add the value of $\sin x$ to that of x to obtain points on the graph of $F(x)$. Then use those points to complete the curve.

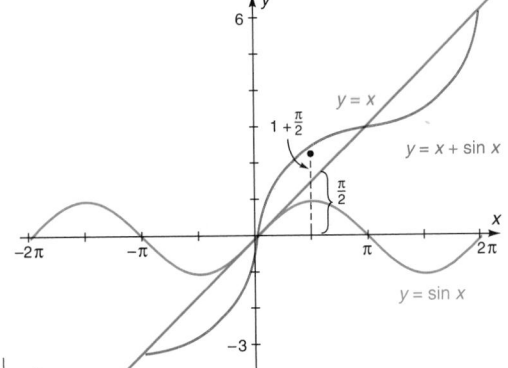

x	0	$\frac{\pi}{2}$	π	$\frac{3\pi}{2}$	2π
$\sin x$	0	1	0	-1	0
$x + \sin x$	0	2.57	3.14	3.71	6.28

Although the graph of $F(x)$ in Example 1 has a repeating pattern, it is not periodic; that is, there is no constant h for which $F(x + h) = F(x)$ for all x. In the next example, the sum of two periodic functions is a periodic function.

Example 2 Graph $f(x) = \sin x + \cos x$.

Since each addend function has period 2π, graph the sum function over the interval $[0, 2\pi]$ using key points from both: $0, \frac{\pi}{4}, \frac{\pi}{2}, \frac{3\pi}{4}, \pi, \frac{5\pi}{4}, \frac{3\pi}{2}, \frac{7\pi}{4}$, and 2π. The resulting graph has period 2π.

x	0	$\frac{\pi}{4}$	$\frac{\pi}{2}$	$\frac{3\pi}{4}$	π	$\frac{5\pi}{4}$	$\frac{3\pi}{2}$	$\frac{7\pi}{4}$	2π
$\sin x$	0	$\frac{\sqrt{2}}{2}$	1	$\frac{\sqrt{2}}{2}$	0	$-\frac{\sqrt{2}}{2}$	-1	$-\frac{\sqrt{2}}{2}$	0
$\cos x$	1	$\frac{\sqrt{2}}{2}$	0	$-\frac{\sqrt{2}}{2}$	-1	$-\frac{\sqrt{2}}{2}$	0	$\frac{\sqrt{2}}{2}$	1
$\sin x + \cos x$	1	$\sqrt{2}$	1	0	-1	$-\sqrt{2}$	-1	0	1

In Examples 1 and 2, key points are those where an addend function has a zero, a local maximum, or a local minimum. Points where the two functions intersect are also of interest.

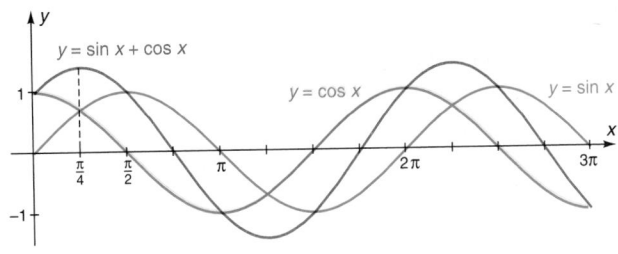

4.4 Graphing by Addition of Ordinates **209**

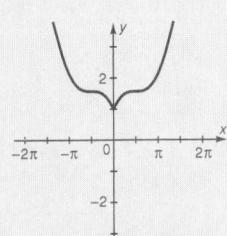

For Example 2
Graph each function.

1. $f(x) = 2 \sin x + 3 \cos x$

2. $f(x) = \sin x - 2 \cos x$

For Example 3
Determine the period of each function.

1. $f(x) = \sin x + \cos 2x$ 2π
2. $g(t) = \sin 1.6t - 2 \cos 0.4t$ 5π

For Example 4
Graph each function and describe its domain.

1. $G(x) = \dfrac{1}{x} + \cos 3x$

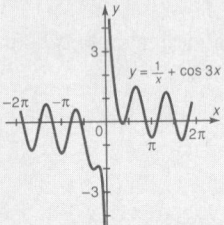

$D_G = \{x : x \neq 0\}$

2. $F(x) = \tan x + \csc x$

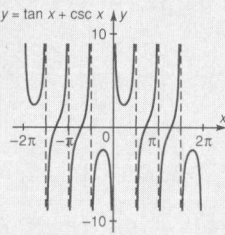

$D_F = \left\{x : x \neq \dfrac{k\pi}{2}, k \in Z\right\}$

Example 3   Determine the period of the function $F(t) = \sin \frac{1}{3}t + \cos \frac{1}{2}t$.

$F(t)$ is the sum of $g(t) = \sin \frac{1}{3}t$ and $h(t) = \cos \frac{1}{2}t$. The period of g is 6π, and the period of h is 4π. Thus, g completes one cycle in 6π and two cycles in 12π units. The function h completes one cycle in 4π, two in 8π, and three in 12π units. Thus, the entire pattern is completed between 0 and 12π, so F has period 12π.

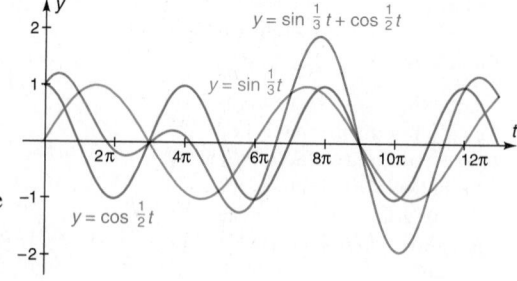

You can use a graphing utility with viewing rectangle $[-37.7, 37.7]$ by $[-2.1, 2.1]$ to verify that you have determined the correct period in Example 3. *Why was this viewing rectangle selected?*

Recall that the domain of the sum of two functions is the intersection of the domains of the addend functions.

Example 4   Graph $H(x) = \cos x - \tan x$ and describe the domain of H.

Begin by graphing $y = \cos x$ and $y = -\tan x$, and note that the domain of H excludes odd multiples of $\frac{\pi}{2}$ because the domain of $-\tan x$ excludes these values. Addition of ordinates gives the graph of H, which has period 2π.

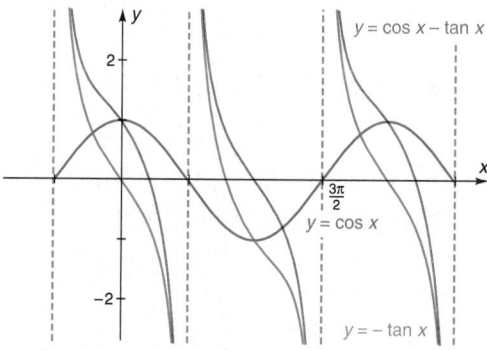

A graphing utility may be used to gain additional insight into the relationship between the graphs of addend functions and the graph of their sum.

Example 5   Use a graphing utility to graph $f(x) = \sin x$, $g(x) = -\cos 2x$, and $G(x) = \sin x - \cos 2x$ on the same set of axes.

Note that the period of f is 2π and the period of g is π, so you need an x-interval of at least 2π in order to view a complete cycle of G. Begin with a viewing rectangle $[-0.2, 8]$ by $[-2.1, 2.1]$ to get an overview of the graphs. *Why was the y-interval $[-2.1, 2.1]$ selected?*

The graph indicates that the minimum value of $G(x)$ is -1, so the range may be reset to y-values between -1.1 and 2.1 if desired. The graph also demonstrates that the period of G is 2π as predicted.

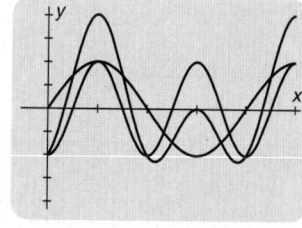

$[-0.2, 8]$ by $[-2.1, 2.1]$
x scl: $\frac{\pi}{2}$ y scl: 0.5

210   Chapter 4 Graphs and Inverses of Trigonometric Functions

Thinking Critically
The predicted period of F is 12π and $|12\pi| \approx 37.7$, and the potential minimum and maximum values of F are -2 and 2; thus, the viewing rectangle $[-37.7, 37.7]$ by $[-2, 2]$ was selected.

The maximum and minimum values of both f and g are 1 and -1, so the potential maximum and minimum values of G are 2 and -2. Setting the rectangle a little larger than what might actually appear gives a better overview than using $[-2, 2]$.

In Example 5, the zoom and trace features of the graphing calculator can be used to find zeros and values at points of intersection. They can also be used to identify y-values on the graphs of f, g, and G that correspond to a particular x-value. *How should the three values be related?* Although you have three curves on the screen, you may wish to view the graph of G separately by using the trace feature.

Insights into the behavior of functions may be gained by examining their graphs. For example, when the functions $y = \sin x$ and $y = \sin (x - \pi)$ are graphed on the same axes, addition of ordinates yields the sum of zero for every value of x. This leads to a new identity,

$$\sin (x - \pi) = -\sin x$$

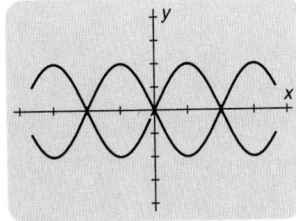

$[-2\pi, 2\pi]$ by $[-3, 3]$
x scl: $\frac{\pi}{2}$ y scl: 0.5

Class Exercises

Graph each function.

1. $y = \sin x + 3$

2. $y = \cos \frac{1}{4}x - 1.5$

Identify key points and then use addition of ordinates to graph each function on the given interval.

3. $y = x - \sin x$; $[0, \pi]$

4. $y = \sin x - 2 \cos x$; $[-2\pi, 2\pi]$

Determine the domain of each function.

5. $G(x) = \sin x + \cot x$ $\{x: x \neq k\pi, k \in Z\}$

6. $y = \sec x + \csc x$ $\left\{x: x \neq \frac{k\pi}{2}, k \in Z\right\}$

7. $f(x) = \dfrac{\sin x}{x}$ $\{x: x \neq 0\}$

8. $g(t) = \dfrac{\tan t}{t - 1}$ $\left\{t: t \neq 1, \text{ or } \frac{k\pi}{2}, k \text{ is odd}\right\}$

9. Thinking Critically If $H(x) = f(x) + g(x)$, where $f(x)$ has period $k\pi$ and $g(x)$ has period $n\pi$, for n, $k \in Z$ explain how to determine the period of H.

10. Thinking Critically Let $f(x) = \sin x - \tan x$ and $g(x) = \tan x$. Is the domain of $f + g$ equal to the domain of $\sin x$? Why or why not?

Practice Exercises   Use appropriate technology.

Determine the domain of each function.

A **1.** $y = \sec x + \dfrac{1}{x}$

2. $y = \tan \theta + \cot \theta$

Ⓡ **3.** $f(t) = \sqrt{t^2 - 21}$ all real numbers

4. $g(\phi) = \sec \phi - \csc \phi$

Graph each function.

5. $f(x) = \sec x + 3$

6. $g(x) = -\cot x + 4$

7. $h(t) = 1 - \sin t$

8. $r(t) = \cos 2t + \pi$

9. $y = x + \cos x$

10. $y = \sin x - x$

Ⓡ **11.** $y = 3 \cos \left(\frac{1}{2}x - \frac{1}{4}\pi\right)$

12. $y = \sin x + |x|$

4.4 Graphing by Addition of Ordinates   **211**

For Example 5
Use a graphing utility to graph $f(x) = \cos x$, $g(x) = -\sin 2x$, and $G(x) = \cos x - \sin 2x$ on the same set of axes.

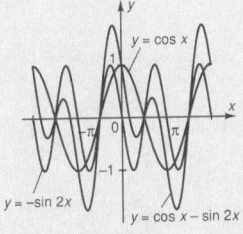

CLOSURE
Group students in pairs and have them summarize to each other the procedures for graphing by addition of ordinates.

INDEPENDENT PRACTICE
Assignment Guide
Basic: 1–23, 35–37, Project
Average: 9–12, 19–40, Project
Enriched: 26–51, Project

Teacher's Resource Book
  Practice, page 28

Ⓡ **Review**
Exercises 3, 11, 19, 21, 23, 35, and 37 review concepts associated with functions such as domain, graphing, proof by counterexample, problem-solving skills, and proving identities.

LESSON FOLLOW-UP
Test Yourself

Teacher's Resource Book
  Tests—Quiz, form A, page 13
  Tests—Quiz, form B, page 13

Thinking Critically
$G(x)$ should equal $f(x) + g(x)$ for every x.

Additional Answers, Class Exercises

Lesson Quiz

Graph each function.

1. $y = \tan x + 6$

2. $f(x) = \cos x - |x|$

3. $y = 5 \sin x - \cos x$

4. Determine the period of the function $G(t) = \sin 0.8t - 2 \cos 1.6t$.
2.5π

5. Describe the domain of $F(x) = \cot x - 3 \sec x$.
$D_F = \left\{ x : x \neq \dfrac{k\pi}{2}, k \in \mathbb{Z} \right\}$

Additional Answers

17. $0 + \cos 0 \neq 2\pi + \cos 2\pi$,
$1 \neq 2\pi + 1$

18. $\sin 0 - 0 \neq \sin 2\pi - 2\pi, 0 \neq -2\pi$

19. $3 \cos \left[\dfrac{1}{2}(0) - \dfrac{1}{4}\pi \right] \neq$

$3 \cos \left[\dfrac{1}{2}(2\pi) - \dfrac{1}{4}\pi \right]$,

$3 \cos \left(-\dfrac{1}{4}\pi \right) \neq 3 \cos \left(\dfrac{3}{4}\pi \right)$

20. $\sin 0 + |0| \neq \sin 2\pi + |2\pi|, 0 \neq 2\pi$

21. purse: $120; scarf: $40; book: $20

22. yes; The period of $f + g$ is the LCM of the periods of f and g, namely 2π, which is the period of f.

Refer to the graphs of Exercises 5 to 8 to determine the period of each of the following:

13. $f(x) = \sec x + 3$ 2π

14. $g(x) = -\cot x + 4$ π

15. $h(t) = 1 - \sin t$ 2π

16. $r(t) = \cos 2t + \pi$ π

Refer to the graphs of Exercises 9 to 12 to find a counterexample to prove that 2π is not the period of each of the following:

17. $y = x + \cos x$

18. $y = \sin x - x$

Ⓡ **19.** $y = 3 \cos \left(\dfrac{1}{2}x - \dfrac{1}{4}\pi \right)$

20. $y = \sin x + |x|$

Ⓡ **21.** *Consumerism* Kathleen spent $400 on her holiday shopping. She bought one purse for $6x$, four scarves for $2x$ each, and six books for x each. How much did each item cost?

22. **Thinking Critically** Let $f(x) = \cos x - \sin x$ and $g(x) = \sin x$. Is the period of $f + g$ equal to the period of f? Why or why not?

Ⓡ **23.** *Sports* Heidi swam 4 km farther than Gretchen. Together they swam 16 km. How far did each girl swim? Heidi: 10 km; Gretchen: 6 km

Graph each function and determine its period.

Ⓑ **24.** $y = \sin x + \sin 2x$ 2π

25. $y = \sin 2x + \cos x$ 2π

26. $y = \sin \dfrac{1}{2}x + \cos x$ 4π

27. $y = \cos \dfrac{1}{2}x + \sin x$ 4π

28. $f(t) = 2 \sin \dfrac{1}{2}t + \cos t$ 4π

29. $g(t) = \sin \dfrac{1}{2}t + 2 \cos \dfrac{1}{2}t$ 4π

30. $h(x) = 2 \sin \dfrac{1}{3}x + 3 \cos \dfrac{1}{2}x$ 12π

31. $F(x) = \sin \dfrac{1}{2}x + \cos \dfrac{1}{3}x$ 12π

Acoustics The equations for two different sound waves are $f(t) = 2 \sin 240\pi t$ and $g(t) = 0.8 \sin 300\pi t$.

32. Use a graphing utility to graph f, g, and $h(x) = f(x) + g(x)$.

33. Determine the periods of f, g, and h. $\dfrac{1}{120}; \dfrac{1}{150}; \dfrac{1}{30}$

34. *Oceanography* The graph of a tide function can be represented by the equation $y = 2 \sin \left(x - \dfrac{\pi}{2} \right) + \sin x$. Graph the function.

Ⓡ **35.** Prove the identity $\sin (t - \pi) = -\sin t$.

36. **Writing in Mathematics** Describe a method for setting the viewing rectangle when using a graphing utility to graph trigonometric functions and their sums.

Ⓡ **37.** *Electricity* The voltage V in an electrical circuit is represented by the function $V(t) = 12 \sin 100\pi t$. Determine the frequency of this function. 50

38. **Thinking Critically** Graph $y = \cos (t - \pi)$ on the same axes as the graph of $y = \cos t$. Describe the graph of $y = \cos t + \cos (t - \pi)$. To what identity does this lead? Prove the identity using the definition of cosine.

Writing in Mathematics

36. Let the horizontal dimensions be large enough to take in at least one period of the function. Let the vertical dimensions range from slightly below the anticipated minimum to slightly above the anticipated maximum. Try to include the origin in the graph if possible.

Graph the sum $F(x) = f(x) + g(x)$.

39.

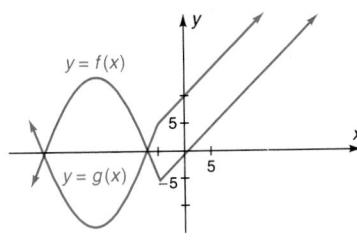

41. Thinking Critically What is the domain of $f(x) = \dfrac{1}{\sec x}$? How is this consistent with the fact that cosine and secant are reciprocal functions and the domain of cosine is all real numbers?

Graph each function over at least a one-period interval.

C 42. $y = 2 \cos x + \sin 2x + \sin \dfrac{x}{2}$

43. $f(x) = \cos x + \cos 2x + 2 \sin x$

44. $y = \sin \left(x + \dfrac{\pi}{2} \right) + \cos \left(x + \dfrac{\pi}{3} \right)$

45. $f(x) = \cos \left(x - \dfrac{\pi}{3} \right) + \sin \left(x - \dfrac{\pi}{4} \right)$

46. $y = \sin t + \tan t$

47. $y = 2 \sin x + \cot x$

Adapt the principles of addition of ordinates to sketch the graphs of the following products:

48. $y = x \cos x$ **49.** $y = x \sin x$ **50.** $y = |x| \sin x$ **51.** $y = |x| \cos x$

Project

Work with a partner to draw two sinusoidal graphs. Choose one of the graphs to represent the sum of two functions and the other to represent one of the addend functions. Then, independently, sketch the graph of the addend function. Will your answers necessarily be the same? Summarize your results.

Test Yourself

Graph each function over the interval $[-2\pi, 2\pi]$.

1. $f(x) = \cos x - 2$

2. $g(x) = \dfrac{1}{2} \sin x$ 4.1

Determine the amplitude, period, phase shift, and vertical shift of each function. Then graph.

3. $y = 3 \sin 2(x - \pi) - 1$

4. $y = -2 \cos (2x + \pi) + 0.5$ 4.2

Graph each function, showing vertical asymptotes.

5. $y = \tan \dfrac{1}{2}x$

6. $y = \sec 2x$ 4.3

7. $y = \cot \dfrac{1}{2}x + 3$

8. $y = 4 \csc \left(2x - \dfrac{1}{2}\pi \right)$

Graph each function and determine its period.

9. $f(x) = \cos 2x + \cos x$ 2π

10. $f(x) = 2 \cos x + \sin 2x$ 2π 4.4

4.4 Graphing by Addition of Ordinates   **213**

48.

49.

50.

51.

Vocabulary
inverse Cosine function
inverse Sine function
principal values

Technology
graphing utility

FOCUS

Basic laws that describe the motion of artificial satellites were discovered by Johannes Kepler (1571–1630). For example, what is now known as Kepler's third law may be used to determine the period of a satellite in an orbit of radius r about the earth:

$$T = 84\left(\frac{r}{r_e}\right)^{\frac{3}{2}}$$

where T is the period measured in minutes, and r_e is the radius of the earth. Since the radius of the earth is nearly 4000 mi, and most satellites orbit just a few hundred miles up, their period is usually close to 84 min.

INSTRUCTION

• Examples of functions that are one-to-one and others that are not one-to-one may help students to recall the ideas noted on page 214. One-to-one functions include linear functions like $f(x) = 2x - 1$, and the cubing function, $g(x) = x^3$. The absolute value function, $f(x) = |x|$, and the squaring function, $g(x) = x^2$, are not one-to-one.

• The squaring function is a good example of a familiar function which has an inverse *on a restricted domain*. For $g(x) = x^2$, $x \geq 0$, $g^{-1}(x) = \sqrt{x}$. For $g(x) = x^2$, $x \leq 0$, $g^{-1}(x) = -\sqrt{x}$. For this function, it is also easy to show that the graph of g^{-1} is the graph of g reflected about the line $y = x$.

4.5   The Inverse Sine and Cosine Functions

Objectives: To define the inverse Sine and Cosine functions
To evaluate expressions involving these functions
To graph these functions

Focus

Many different satellites have been placed into orbit around the earth. They are used to communicate between different parts of the world, to observe weather patterns, and to view outer space. Each of these satellites follows its own path through the sky. Most travel in regular elliptical orbits; that is, they are closer to the earth as they pass over one side and further away as they pass over the opposite side.

Scientists who use the transmitted information must know the position of the satellite at any given time. A function can be derived that will show the distance of the spacecraft above the earth for any given time. But how can you express time in terms of distance instead of distance in terms of time? How can you find the inverse of a trigonometric function?

Recall the following facts about the inverses of functions from Chapter 1:

• A function f that is not one-to-one has an inverse that is not a function. If the domain of f is restricted so that f is one-to-one, then the inverse of f is also a function.
• The graphs of a function and its inverse are symmetric about the line $y = x$.
• A function f has an inverse function f^{-1} if and only if $f(f^{-1}(x)) = x$ for all x in the domain of f^{-1}, and $f^{-1}(f(x)) =$ for all x in the domain of f.

These requirements apply to the six trigonometric functions, all of which are periodic and, hence, not one-to-one. However, on appropriately restricted domains, they do have inverse functions.

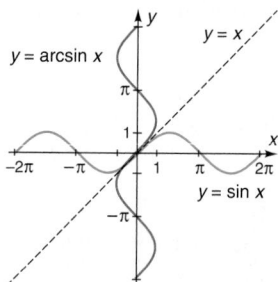

The function $y = \sin x$ has an inverse denoted by $y = \sin^{-1} x$ or $y = \arcsin x$ (read "arcsine"). Reflecting the graph of $y = \sin x$ in the line $y = x$ clearly shows that $y = \sin^{-1} x$ does not pass the vertical line test for functions.

214   Chapter 4 Graphs and Inverses of Trigonometric Functions

If the domain of the sine function is restricted to $\left[-\frac{\pi}{2}, \frac{\pi}{2}\right]$, the sine function takes on its full range of values from -1 to 1 *and* it is one-to-one. The sine function with this restricted domain is sometimes written $y = \text{Sin } x$. The inverse of $y = \text{Sin } x$ is called the **inverse Sine function,** written $y = \text{Sin}^{-1} x$ or $y = \text{Arcsin } x$, and is defined as follows:

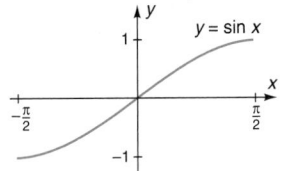

$$y = \text{Sin}^{-1} x \quad \text{if and only if} \quad \sin y = x \text{ and } -\frac{\pi}{2} \le y \le \frac{\pi}{2}$$

The domain of $y = \text{Sin}^{-1} x$ is $[-1, 1]$, and the range is $\left[-\frac{\pi}{2}, \frac{\pi}{2}\right]$. The values in the range of $\text{Sin}^{-1} x$ are called the **principal values** of $\sin^{-1} x$. The graph of the function $y = \text{Sin } x$ reflected in the line $y = x$ is the graph of the function $y = \text{Sin}^{-1} x$. When considering angles, the inverse function $y = \text{Sin}^{-1} x$ means y is the measure of the angle in the interval $\left[-\frac{\pi}{2}, \frac{\pi}{2}\right]$ whose sine is x.

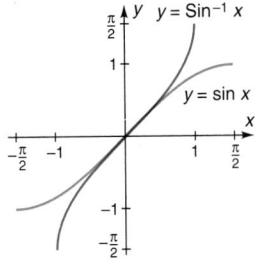

Example 1   Use the definition of the inverse Sine function to determine the exact value of each of the following:

     a. $\text{Sin}^{-1} 0$ **b.** $\text{Arcsin } 1$ **c.** $\text{Sin}^{-1} 1.5$

   a. $\text{Sin}^{-1} 0 = 0$, because $\sin 0 = 0$ and $0 \in \left[-\frac{\pi}{2}, \frac{\pi}{2}\right]$.

   b. $\text{Arcsin } 1 = \frac{\pi}{2}$, because $\sin \frac{\pi}{2} = 1$ and $\frac{\pi}{2} \in \left[-\frac{\pi}{2}, \frac{\pi}{2}\right]$.

   c. $\text{Sin}^{-1} 1.5$ is not defined, because there is no value of y in any interval for which $\text{Sin } y = 1.5$.

   Depending on your calculator, use the inv and sin keys or the $\sin^{-1}$ key to find $\text{Sin}^{-1} x$. Always be careful to note whether you are using radian or degree measure.

Example 2   Evaluate to four decimal places.   **a.** $\text{Sin}^{-1} 0.258$ **b.** $\text{Arcsin } (-0.91)$

   a. $\text{Sin}^{-1} 0.258 = 0.2610$ **b.** $\text{Arcsin } (-0.91) = -1.1433$

If you work Example 2a with the calculator in degree mode, the resulting display is the degree measure of the angle between $-90°$ and $90°$ whose sine is 0.258, that is, $15.0°$ (to the nearest tenth of a degree). Similarly, you can obtain $-65.5°$ for Example 2b.

In Chapter 3, an equation describing the angle of a light ray passing through air and water was introduced. The inverse Sine function can be used to solve that equation.

GUIDED PRACTICE

For Example 1

Use the definition of the inverse Sine function to determine the exact value of each of the following.

1. $\text{Sin}^{-1} (-1)$ $-\frac{\pi}{2}$

2. $\text{Arcsin } \frac{\sqrt{2}}{2}$ $\frac{\pi}{4}$

For Example 2

Evaluate to four decimal places.

1. $\text{Arcsin } 0.3240$ 0.3300

2. $\text{Sin}^{-1} 0.5681$ 0.6042

For Example 3

1. If a light ray makes an angle of 15° with the vertical in the air, determine the angle it makes with the vertical in the water. 11° to the nearest degree.

2. If a light ray makes an angle of 34° with the vertical in the water, determine the angle it makes with the vertical in the air. 48° to the nearest degree

For Example 4

Evaluate:

1. sin (Sin⁻¹ (0.6711)) 0.6711

2. Arcsin $\left(\sin \frac{5\pi}{4} \right)$ $-\frac{\pi}{4}$

Example 3 *Optics* When light travels from air to water, it is *refracted*; that is, the angle the light ray makes with the vertical changes as it passes from the air to the water. If i, called the angle of incidence, is the angle the light ray makes with the vertical in air, and r, the angle of refraction, is the angle in water, then the refraction is described by the equation $\frac{\sin i}{\sin r} = \frac{4}{3}$. If a light ray makes an angle of 30° with the vertical in the air, determine the angle it makes with the vertical in the water.

Since $i = 30°$ and $\sin 30° = \frac{1}{2}$, $\frac{\frac{1}{2}}{\sin r} = \frac{4}{3}$, and $\sin r = \frac{3}{8} = 0.375$. Then $r = \text{Sin}^{-1} 0.375 = 22°$, to the nearest degree.

From the definition of the inverse Sine function, sin (Arcsin x) = x, for all $x \in [-1, 1]$. For $x \in \left[-\frac{\pi}{2}, \frac{\pi}{2} \right]$, Arcsin (sin x) = x. For values of x outside the restricted interval, the relation Arcsin (sin x) = x does not hold.

Example 4 Evaluate: **a.** $\text{Sin}^{-1} \left(\sin \frac{\pi}{4} \right)$ **b.** sin (Arcsin 0.23) **c.** $\text{Arcsin} \left(\sin \frac{7\pi}{6} \right)$

a. $\text{Sin}^{-1} \left(\sin \frac{\pi}{4} \right) = \text{Sin}^{-1} \left(\frac{\sqrt{2}}{2} \right) = \frac{\pi}{4}$ **b.** sin (Arcsin 0.23) = 0.23

c. $\text{Arcsin} \left(\sin \frac{7\pi}{6} \right) = \text{Arcsin} \left(-\frac{1}{2} \right) = -\frac{\pi}{6}$ *Why is* $\text{Arcsin} \left(\sin \frac{7\pi}{6} \right) \neq \frac{7\pi}{6}$?

If the domain of the cosine function, $y = \cos x$, is restricted to $[0, \pi]$, the cosine function takes on its full range of values and is one-to-one. The cosine function with this restricted domain is written $y = \text{Cos } x$ and has an **inverse Cosine function,** $y = \text{Cos}^{-1} x$ or $y = \text{Arccos } x$ ("arccosine"), which is defined as follows:

| $y = \text{Cos}^{-1} x$ | if and only if | $\cos y = x$ and $0 \leq y \leq \pi$ |

The domain of $y = \text{Cos}^{-1} x$ is $[-1, 1]$ and the range is $[0, \pi]$. The values of the range of $\text{Cos}^{-1} x$ are called the principal values of $\cos^{-1} x$. The graph of $y = \text{Cos}^{-1} x$ is the reflection of $y = \text{Cos } x$ in the line $y = x$.

From the definition of the inverse Cosine function, cos ($\text{Cos}^{-1} x$) = x. When $x \in [0, \pi]$, it is also true that $\text{Cos}^{-1} (\cos x) = x$.

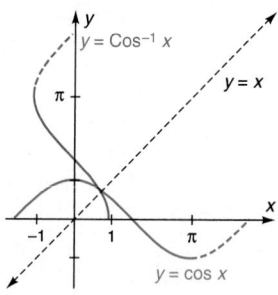

Thinking Critically

Since $\frac{7\pi}{6}$ is outside the interval $\left[-\frac{\pi}{2}, \frac{\pi}{2} \right]$, $\text{Arcsin} \left(\sin \frac{7\pi}{6} \right)$ cannot equal $\frac{7\pi}{6}$.

Example 5 Evaluate each expression, finding exact values where possible:

    a. $\text{Cos}^{-1} 1$ **b.** $\text{Arccos } 0$ **c.** $\text{Arccos } (-0.56)$

    d. $\text{Cos}^{-1}\left(\cos \frac{1}{2}\pi\right)$ **e.** $\cos (\text{Arccos } 0.5)$ **f.** $\text{Arccos}\left(\cos \frac{5\pi}{3}\right)$

  a. $\text{Cos}^{-1} 1 = 0$ since $\cos 0 = 1$ and $0 \in [0, \pi]$

  b. $\text{Arccos } 0 = \frac{1}{2}\pi$ since $\cos \frac{1}{2}\pi = 0$ and $\frac{1}{2}\pi \in [0, \pi]$

  c. $\text{Arccos } (-0.56) = 2.1652$ to four decimal places

  d. $\text{Cos}^{-1}\left(\cos \frac{1}{2}\pi\right) = \frac{1}{2}\pi$ since $\frac{1}{2}\pi \in [0, \pi]$

  e. $\cos (\text{Arccos } 0.5) = 0.5$

  f. $\text{Arccos}\left(\cos \frac{5\pi}{3}\right) = \text{Arccos}\left(\frac{1}{2}\right) = \frac{\pi}{3}$

Modeling

A communications technician is tracking the location of a satellite as it orbits the earth. How can she determine the optimum time for certain space observations?

The satellite has a maximum altitude that recurs at regular time intervals and a minimum altitude that also recurs at regular time intervals. The altitude y for any given time t can be modeled using the equation $y = a \sin b(t + c) + d$ or $y = a \cos b(t + c) + d$.

Example 6 *Space Science* A spacecraft orbits the earth every 90 min and varies in altitude from 150 to 1050 km. It is best able to make certain types of observations when it is at an altitude of 900 km or greater. Find the length of time during each orbit for which these observations are possible.

Derive a function that models the relationship between altitude and time for the given spacecraft. The amplitude is $(M - m) \div 2 = (1050 - 150) \div 2 = 450$. The period in minutes is 90. Therefore, $\frac{2\pi}{b} = 90$; $b = \frac{\pi}{45}$. The average altitude above the earth is $(M + m) \div 2 = (1050 + 150) \div 2 = 600$. Thus, $a = 450$, $b = \frac{\pi}{45}$, and $d = 600$. Assuming that $t = 0$ at the maximum altitude, an equation using cosine is

$$y = 450 \cos \frac{\pi}{45}t + 600$$

To determine time t for a given altitude, find the inverse.

$$\frac{y - 600}{450} = \cos \frac{\pi}{45}t$$ *Solve for cosine.*

$$\frac{\pi}{45}t = \text{Cos}^{-1}\left(\frac{y - 600}{450}\right)$$ *Express using the inverse cosine.*

$$t = \frac{45}{\pi}\text{Cos}^{-1}\left(\frac{y - 600}{450}\right)$$ *Solve for t.*

                        4.5 The Inverse Sine and Cosine Functions   **217**

For Example 7

Determine the exact value of each expression.

1. $\sin\left(\mathrm{Cos}^{-1}\left(\frac{5}{9}\right)\right)$ $\frac{2\sqrt{14}}{9}$

2. $\cos\left(\mathrm{Arcsin}\left(-\frac{3}{5}\right)\right)$ $\frac{4}{5}$

For Example 8

Graph each function.

1. $F(x) = \mathrm{Arcsin}\ x + 2$

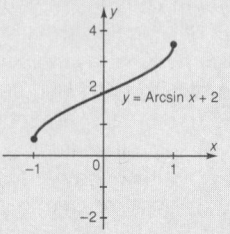

2. $G(x) = \mathrm{Cos}^{-1}(x - 1)$

To determine when the altitude will be greater than or equal to 900 km, substitute 900 for y.

$$t = \frac{45}{\pi} \mathrm{Cos}^{-1}\left(\frac{900 - 600}{450}\right) = 12$$

The altitude will be 900 km or greater for 12 min before and after it reaches its maximum point, that is, for 24 min in each orbit.

You can use reference triangles to evaluate expressions involving the Arcsine and Arccosine functions.

Example 7 Determine the exact value of each expression.

a. Let $\theta = \mathrm{Cos}^{-1}\frac{\sqrt{3}}{4}$, then $\cos\theta = \frac{\sqrt{3}}{4}$ and $\theta \in [0, \pi]$. Since $\cos\theta > 0$, θ is in quadrant I. By the Pythagorean theorem, $y = \sqrt{13}$, so

$$\sin\left(\mathrm{Cos}^{-1}\frac{\sqrt{3}}{4}\right) = \sin\theta = \frac{\sqrt{13}}{4}$$

b. Let $\theta = \mathrm{Arcsin}\ -\frac{2}{7}$, then $\sin\theta = -\frac{2}{7}$ and $\theta \in \left[-\frac{\pi}{2}, \frac{\pi}{2}\right]$. Since $\sin\theta < 0$, θ is in quadrant IV. By the Pythagorean theorem, $x = \sqrt{45}$, so

$$\cos\left(\mathrm{Arcsin}\ -\frac{2}{7}\right) = \cos\theta = \frac{\sqrt{45}}{7}$$

Other functions can be graphed as transformations of the graphs of the Arcsine and Arccosine functions.

Example 8 Graph each function:

      a. $f(x) = 2\ \mathrm{Cos}^{-1} x - 1$ **b.** $g(x) = -\mathrm{Arcsin}\ (x + 1)$

a. The graph of $y = \mathrm{Cos}^{-1} x$ is stretched vertically by a factor of 2 and shifted down one unit to obtain the graph of f.

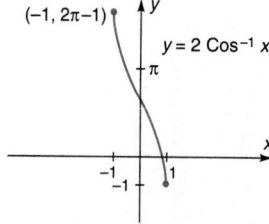

b. The graph of $y = \mathrm{Arcsin}\ x$ is reflected in the x-axis and shifted one unit left to obtain the graph of g.

Using a graphing utility or carefully applying graphing techniques can help you discover relationships between the inverse Sine and Cosine functions.

Example 9 Graph $y = \text{Cos}^{-1} x$ and $y = -\text{Sin}^{-1} x$ on the same axes. Suggest a relationship between the functions.

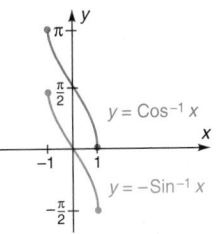

The vertical distance between the graphs for each x-value appears to be the same, indicating that the graph of $y = \text{Cos}^{-1} x$ is the graph of $y = -\text{Sin}^{-1} x$ translated $\frac{\pi}{2}$ units upward. This suggests that $\text{Cos}^{-1} x = -\text{Sin}^{-1} x + \frac{\pi}{2}$ or $\text{Sin}^{-1} x + \text{Cos}^{-1} x = \frac{\pi}{2}$.

The result in Example 9 can also be obtained by addition of ordinates. The graph of $y = \frac{\pi}{2} - \text{Sin}^{-1} x$ coincides with the graph of $y = \text{Cos}^{-1} x$.

Example 10 Estimate the solution of the equation $\text{Sin}^{-1} \frac{1}{2}x - \text{Cos}^{-1} x = 0$.

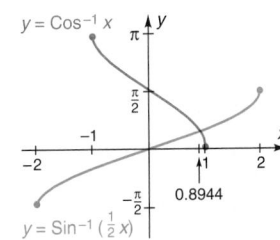

Since the given equation is equivalent to $\text{Sin}^{-1} \frac{1}{2}x = \text{Cos}^{-1} x$, use a graphing utility to find the x-value of the point of intersection of the graphs of $f(x) = \text{Sin}^{-1} \frac{1}{2}x$ and $g(x) = \text{Cos}^{-1} x$. Use the zoom and trace features to estimate $x = 0.8944$ to four decimal places.

Class Exercises

Use the definition of the inverse Sine function or inverse Cosine function to determine the exact value of each of the following:

1. $\text{Cos}^{-1} \frac{1}{2}$ **2.** $\text{Sin}^{-1} \frac{1}{2}$ **3.** $\text{Arcsin} \left(-\frac{\sqrt{2}}{2}\right)$ **4.** $\text{Arccos} \frac{\sqrt{3}}{2}$

Evaluate to four decimal places.

5. $\text{Sin}^{-1} 0.55$ **6.** $\text{Cos}^{-1} 0.33$ **7.** $\text{Arccos} (-0.87)$ **8.** $\text{Arcsin} (-0.481)$

Evaluate to the nearest tenth of a degree.

9. $\text{Arcsin} \, 0.6983$ **10.** $\text{Arccos} (-0.233)$ **11.** $\text{Cos}^{-1} (-0.473)$ **12.** $\text{Sin}^{-1} (-0.7276)$

Determine the exact value of each expression.

13. $\cos (\text{Arccos} \, 0.87)$ **14.** $\sin (\text{Sin}^{-1} 0.3)$ **15.** $\text{Arcsin} \left(\sin \frac{\pi}{3}\right)$

16. $\text{Arccos} \left(\cos \frac{7\pi}{4}\right)$ **17.** $\sin \left(\text{Arccos} \frac{1}{2}\right)$ **18.** $\cos \left(\text{Sin}^{-1} \left(-\frac{\sqrt{3}}{2}\right)\right)$

Graph each function.

19. $f(x) = 2 \, \text{Sin}^{-1} x + 1$ **20.** $f(x) = \text{Cos}^{-1} (x + 2)$

4.5 The Inverse Sine and Cosine Functions   **219**

Additional Answers, Class Exercises

19.

20.

For Example 9
Graph $y = \text{Sin}^{-1} x$ and $y = -\text{Cos}^{-1} x$ on the same axes. Then use the graph to suggest a relationship between the functions.

$-\text{Cos}^{-1} x = \text{Sin}^{-1} x - \frac{\pi}{2}$

or

$-\text{Sin}^{-1} x = \text{Cos}^{-1} x - \frac{\pi}{2}$

For Example 10
Use a graphing utility to estimate the solution of each equation.

1. $\text{Sin}^{-1} x = 3 \, \text{Cos}^{-1} x$
$x = 0.9239$ to four decimal places

2. $\text{Sin}^{-1} x = \frac{1}{2} \text{Cos}^{-1} x$
$x = 0.5000$ to four decimal places

CLOSURE

Group students in groups of three or four and have them take turns presenting the main points of the lesson to each other.

INDEPENDENT PRACTICE

Assignment Guide
Basic: 1–26, 33, 37, Project
Average: 7, 9, 13–14, 17–40, Project
Enriched: 23–50, Project

Teacher's Resource Book
Practice, page 29

Ⓡ **Review**
Exercises 7, 9, 19, 25, 33, and 37 review concepts of evaluating trigonometric functions to four decimal places, determining the equation of a line, linear velocity, graphing, and inverse of an algebraic function.

LESSON FOLLOW-UP

Lesson Quiz

1. Use the definition of the inverse Sine function to determine the exact value of $\text{Sin}^{-1}\left(-\dfrac{\sqrt{2}}{2}\right)$. $-\dfrac{\pi}{4}$

2. Evaluate Arccos 0.8916 to four decimal places. 0.4699

Evaluate.

3. $\sin(\text{Sin}^{-1} 0.2385)$ 0.2385

4. $\text{Arccos}\left(\cos\left(\dfrac{3\pi}{4}\right)\right)$ $\dfrac{3\pi}{4}$

5. $\cos\left(\text{Arcsin}\left(\dfrac{2}{7}\right)\right)$ $\dfrac{\sqrt{45}}{7}$

6. Graph $y = 5 \text{ Arcsin } x - 2$.

$y = 5 \text{ Arcsin } x - 2$

Additional Answers

Class Exercises

21. $D = \{x: -2 \le x \le 2\}$;
$R = \{y: -\pi \le y \le \pi\}$

Practice Exercises

13. $D = \left\{x: -\dfrac{1}{3} \le x \le \dfrac{1}{3}\right\}$;
$R = \{g(x): 1 \le g(x) \le \pi + 1\}$

14. Since $\sin(\text{Arcsin } x) = x$, if $-1 \le x \le 1$, the results could be verified by taking the sine and seeing if it is equal to the value given in the original exercise.

20.

21.

21. State the domain and range of the function $f(x) = 2 \text{ Sin}^{-1}\left(\dfrac{1}{2}x\right)$.

Practice Exercises

 Use appropriate technology.

Use the definition of the inverse Sine function or inverse Cosine function to determine the exact value of each of the following:

A 1. $\text{Arccos } \dfrac{1}{2}$ $\dfrac{\pi}{3}$ 2. $\text{Cos}^{-1} \dfrac{\sqrt{2}}{2}$ $\dfrac{\pi}{4}$ 3. $\text{Sin}^{-1} \dfrac{\sqrt{3}}{2}$ $\dfrac{\pi}{3}$ 4. $\text{Arcsin } -\dfrac{1}{2}$ $-\dfrac{\pi}{6}$

Evaluate to four decimal places.

5. $\text{Sin}^{-1} 0.841$ 0.9991   6. $\text{Arcsin }(-0.022)$ -0.0220 Ⓡ 7. $\tan 26.7$ 282.6799

8. $\text{Sin}^{-1} \dfrac{3}{8}$ 0.3844   Ⓡ 9. $\sin 2.4 + \cos 3.9$ -0.0505 10. $\text{Arccos } \dfrac{1}{4}$ 1.3181

Evaluate to the nearest tenth of a degree.

11. $\text{Cos}^{-1} 0.4726$ 61.8°   12. $\text{Sin}^{-1} 0.8320$ 56.3°

13. **Thinking Critically** State the domain and range of the function $g(x) = \text{Arccos }(3x) + 1$.

14. **Thinking Critically** Provide a strategy for verifying your answers to Exercises 5 and 6. Explain why your strategy works.

Evaluate.

15. $\text{Arcsin }(\sin 0.67\pi)$ 16. $\text{Arccos }(\cos 0.35)$ 17. $\cos\left(\text{Sin}^{-1} \dfrac{\sqrt{2}}{2}\right)$ $\dfrac{\sqrt{2}}{2}$ 18. $\sin\left(\text{Arcsin } \dfrac{1}{2}\right)$ $\dfrac{1}{2}$
      0.67π   0.35

Ⓡ 19. Determine the equation of the line through the points $P(1, \text{Cos}^{-1} 1)$ and $Q(0.8, \text{Sin}^{-1} 0.8)$. $y = -4.64x + 4.64$

Graph.

20. $f(x) = \text{Arcsin } x + 1$ 21. $f(x) = 2 \text{ Cos}^{-1} x$

22. *Optics* A light ray passing from air to water forms an angle of 45° with the perpendicular in air. What angle does the ray form with the perpendicular in water? 32°

B 23. **Thinking Critically** Find two intervals different from $[0, \pi]$ on which the Cosine function could be defined. Justify your answer.

24. **Thinking Critically** Find two intervals different from $\left[-\dfrac{\pi}{2}, \dfrac{\pi}{2}\right]$ on which the Sine function could be defined. Justify your answer.

Ⓡ 25. *Sports* The radius of the wheel of an exercise bike is 10 in. If the pedal is turning 3 times per second, determine the linear velocity of a point on the circumference of the wheel in miles per hour. 10.71 mi/h

26. **Thinking Critically** Describe the relationship between periodic and one-to-one functions. Can a function be both periodic and one-to-one?

27. *Optics* A light ray passing from air to water forms an angle of 29° with the perpendicular in water. What angle does the ray form with the perpendicular in the air? 40°

220   Chapter 4 Graphs and Inverses of Trigonometric Functions

23. Answers may vary. Example: $[\pi, 2\pi]$, $[-\pi, 0]$; These intervals will give all possible values of the cosine once and only once.

26. Since a periodic function repeats, it contains points with different abscissas but the same ordinate. It can never be one-to-one in its entirety, because a given ordinate would result in a variety of abscissas. If the domain were limited to preserve one-to-one characteristics, the function would lose its periodic characteristics.

Determine the exact value of each expression.

28. $\mathrm{Arccos}\left(\sin\frac{4\pi}{3}\right)$ $\frac{5\pi}{6}$ **29.** $\mathrm{Arcsin}\left(\cos\frac{\pi}{2}\right)$ 0 **30.** $\cos\left(\mathrm{Sin}^{-1}\frac{2}{5}\right)$ $\frac{\sqrt{21}}{5}$ **31.** $\sin\left(\mathrm{Arccos}\left(-\frac{1}{3}\right)\right)$ $\frac{2\sqrt{2}}{3}$

Graph.

32. $y = -2\,\mathrm{Cos}^{-1}(x-1)$ ℝ **33.** $y = 4\sin\left(x+\frac{1}{4}\pi\right)$ **34.** $y = \frac{1}{2}\,\mathrm{Arcsin}(x+1) - 2$

Use a graphing utility to estimate the solution of each equation to four decimal places.

35. $\mathrm{Sin}^{-1}x = 2\,\mathrm{Cos}^{-1}x$ 0.8660 **36.** $\mathrm{Sin}^{-1}2x = \mathrm{Cos}^{-1}x$ 0.4472

ℝ **37.** Determine the inverse of the function $g(x) = 5x^3 - 12$. $\frac{\sqrt[3]{25x+300}}{5}$

Space Science A satellite orbits the earth every 70 min and varies in altitude between 950 km and 1150 km.

38. Determine an equation that expresses altitude y in terms of time t.

39. Determine an equation that expresses time in terms of altitude.

40. If $t = 0$ is the time of maximum altitude, determine the first time after $t = 0$ for which the satellite has an altitude of 1020 km. 20.89 min

C **41.** Evaluate $\sin\left(\mathrm{Arccos}\frac{\sqrt{2}}{2} + \pi\right)$. $-\frac{\sqrt{2}}{2}$

42. Determine the domain of $f(x) = \mathrm{Sin}^{-1}x + \mathrm{Cos}^{-1}x$. $[-1, 1]$

43. Solve the equation $\mathrm{Sin}^2\theta - 6\,\mathrm{Sin}\,\theta + 5 = 0$. $\frac{\pi}{2}$

44. Solve the equation $2\,\mathrm{Sin}^2\theta + 7\,\mathrm{Sin}\,\theta - 4 = 0$. $\frac{\pi}{6}$

45. Solve the equation $\mathrm{Sin}^{-1}x - \mathrm{Cos}^{-1}x = 0$. $\frac{\sqrt{2}}{2}$

46. Prove that the inverse Sine is an odd function.

47. Find a counterexample to show that Arccosine is not an even function.

48. Determine a general form for the values of $\arcsin\frac{\sqrt{3}}{2}$.

49. Graph the function $F(x) = \mathrm{Sin}^{-1}x + \mathrm{Cos}^{-1}x$. Then use the graph to suggest an identity relating $\mathrm{Sin}^{-1}x$ and $\mathrm{Cos}^{-1}x$.

50. For which values of x is $\mathrm{Arcsin}\,x \geq \mathrm{Arccos}\,x$? $\frac{\sqrt{2}}{2} \leq x \leq 1$

Project

Research the actual orbiting times and altitudes for different satellites. Determine why different satellites are given different kinds of orbits. Are there some satellites that stay in a fixed position over the earth? How is that possible?

Challenge

1. A circular grass plot 24 ft in diameter is cut by a straight gravel path 6 ft wide, one edge of which passes through the center of the plot. Determine the number of square feet in the remaining grass area. $120\pi - 36\sqrt{3}$ ft²

2. If the side of one square is the diagonal of a second square, what is the ratio of the area of the second square to that of the first? $\frac{1}{2}$

4.5 The Inverse Sine and Cosine Functions **221**

32.   **33.**   **34.**

Vocabulary
Arccosecant
Arccotangent
Arcsecant
Arctangent
inverse Cosecant
inverse Cotangent
inverse Secant
inverse Tangent

Technology
graphing utility
scientific calculator

FOCUS

Students may be interested in researching the uses of spectroscopy
in the fields of criminology, archaeology, and environmental science.

4.6 Other Inverse Trigonometric Functions

Objectives: To define and graph the inverse Tangent, Cotangent, Secant,
and Cosecant functions
To evaluate expressions involving these functions
To rewrite trigonometric expressions as algebraic expressions

Focus

Infrared spectroscopy is one method chemists use
to identify substances. If a definitive identification
of a substance is needed, some of it is inserted
into the laser beam of an *infrared
spectrophotometer*. The resulting image, or
spectrogram, is as unique as a fingerprint. It can
be analyzed for clues to the chemical composition
of the substance or compared directly with the
spectrograms of known substances. Certain
wavelengths of light cause different molecular
bonds to stretch or bend. The record of all the
stretches is contained in a complicated curve that
is transformed mathematically into a second curve
which can easily be interpreted by the trained
chemist. This procedure is similar to finding the
inverse of a function.

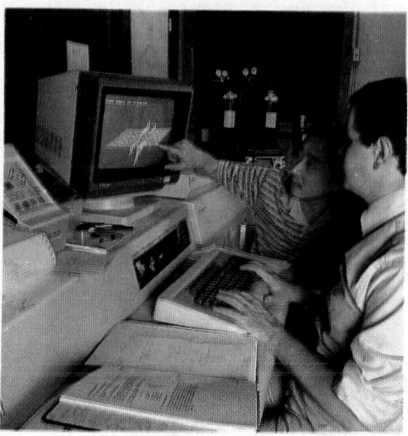

In Lesson 4.5, inverse functions of the Cosine and Sine functions
were introduced. If the domains of the tangent, cotangent, secant,
and cosecant functions are appropriately restricted, then these
functions have inverses that are also functions.

Restricting the domain of the tangent function to $\left(-\frac{\pi}{2}, \frac{\pi}{2}\right)$ results in
a one-to-one function and maintains the full range of function values.
This new function is written $y = \mathrm{Tan}\, x$. The **inverse Tangent**, or
Arctangent, function is written as $y = \mathrm{Tan}^{-1} x$, or $y = \mathrm{Arctan}\, x$,
and is defined as

$$y = \mathrm{Tan}^{-1} x \quad \text{if and only if} \quad \tan y = x \text{ and } -\frac{\pi}{2} < y < \frac{\pi}{2}$$

The domain of $y = \mathrm{Tan}^{-1} x$ is the set of all real numbers, and
the range is $\left(-\frac{\pi}{2}, \frac{\pi}{2}\right)$. The function may be read, "y is the
angle whose tangent value is x." The values of the range of
$\mathrm{Tan}^{-1} x$ are called the *principal values* of $\tan^{-1} x$. Its graph is
the reflection of $y = \mathrm{Tan}\, x$ in the line $y = x$.

In order to define the remaining three inverse trigonometric functions, the domains of the trigonometric functions are restricted, and the resulting functions are named using capital letters: $y = \text{Cot } x$, $y = \text{Sec } x$, and $y = \text{Csc } x$. The restricted domain of each trigonometric function becomes the range of its corresponding inverse function.

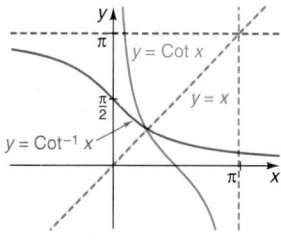

If $y = \cot x$ and x is restricted to $(0, \pi)$, the resulting one-to-one function is written $y = \text{Cot } x$. The **inverse Cotangent**, or **Arccotangent**, function is defined as

$\qquad y = \text{Cot}^{-1} x$ if and only if $\cot y = x$ and $0 < y < \pi$

The domain of $y = \text{Cot}^{-1} x$ is $\{x: x \in R\}$, and the range is $\{y: 0 < y < \pi\}$.

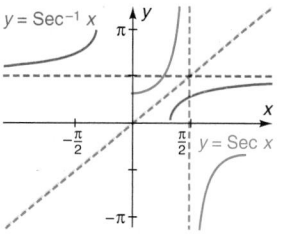

If $y = \sec x$ and x is restricted to $[0, \pi]$ with $x \neq \frac{\pi}{2}$, the resulting one-to-one function is written $y = \text{Sec } x$. The **inverse Secant**, or **Arcsecant**, function is defined as

$\qquad y = \text{Sec}^{-1} x$ if and only if $\sec y = x$ and $0 \leq y \leq \pi$, $y \neq \frac{\pi}{2}$

The domain of $y = \text{Sec}^{-1} x$ is $\{x: |x| \geq 1\}$, and the range is $\left\{y: 0 \leq y \leq \pi, y \neq \frac{\pi}{2}\right\}$.

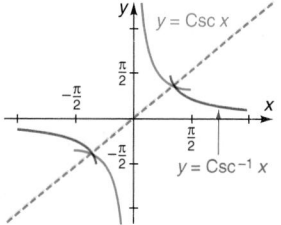

If $y = \csc x$ and x is restricted to $\left[-\frac{\pi}{2}, \frac{\pi}{2}\right]$ with $x \neq 0$, the resulting one-to-one function is written $y = \text{Csc } x$. The **inverse Cosecant**, or **Arccosecant**, function is defined as

$y = \text{Csc}^{-1} x$ if and only if $\csc y = x$ and $-\frac{\pi}{2} \leq y \leq \frac{\pi}{2}$, $y \neq 0$

The domain of $y = \text{Csc}^{-1} x$ is $\{x: |x| \geq 1\}$, and the range is $\left\{y: -\frac{\pi}{2} \leq y \leq \frac{\pi}{2}, y \neq 0\right\}$.

As in the cases of $\text{Sin}^{-1} x$ and $\text{Cos}^{-1} x$, the values of the ranges of $\text{Cot}^{-1} x$, $\text{Sec}^{-1} x$, and $\text{Csc}^{-1} x$ are called the principal values, respectively, of $\cot^{-1} x$, $\sec^{-1} x$, and $\csc^{-1} x$.

Example 1   Use the definition of each inverse trigonometric function to determine the exact value of each of the following:

     a. Arctan 1   **b.** $\text{Csc}^{-1} \dfrac{2\sqrt{3}}{3}$

   a. $\text{Arctan } 1 = \dfrac{\pi}{4}$ since $\tan \dfrac{\pi}{4} = 1$ and $-\dfrac{\pi}{2} < \dfrac{\pi}{4} < \dfrac{\pi}{2}$

   b. $\text{Csc}^{-1} \dfrac{2\sqrt{3}}{3} = \dfrac{\pi}{3}$ since $\csc \dfrac{\pi}{3} = \dfrac{2\sqrt{3}}{3}$ and $-\dfrac{\pi}{2} \leq \dfrac{\pi}{3} \leq \dfrac{\pi}{2}$

Use the inv and tan keys or the $\tan^{-1}$ key to find values of the inverse Tangent function. Since calculators do not have keys for the inverse Secant, Cosecant, and Cotangent functions, you must apply your knowledge of reciprocal relationships to evaluate these functions.

4.6 Other Inverse Trigonometric Functions   **223**

Use the definition of each inverse trigonometric function to determine the exact value of each of the following expressions.

1. Arctan $\dfrac{\sqrt{3}}{3}$ $\dfrac{\pi}{6}$

2. Arcsec -1 π

For Example 2

Evaluate to four decimal places.
1. $\text{Tan}^{-1}\,1.54$ 0.9949
2. Arccsc -3.86 -0.2621

For Example 3

Evaluate each expression to the nearest tenth of a degree.
1. Arctan 2.55   68.6°
2. $\text{Sec}^{-1}\,-8.66$ 96.6°

For Example 4

Determine the exact value of each expression.

1. Arctan $\left(\tan\dfrac{5\pi}{4}\right)$ $\dfrac{\pi}{4}$

2. $\sec(\text{Sec}^{-1}\,4.32)$ 4.32

Common Error   Students often forget that an expression such as $\text{Tan}^{-1}\,(\tan x) = x$ only for x in the range of the inverse Tangent. One way to help them remember this is to consistently use sentences such as "The Arctangent of a number x is the number between $-\dfrac{1}{2}\pi$ and $\dfrac{1}{2}\pi$ whose tangent is x."

Example 2   Evaluate to four decimal places: **a.** $\text{Sec}^{-1}\,2.71$ **b.** Arccot (-5.1)

a. Let $y = \text{Sec}^{-1}\,2.71$ **b.** Let $y = \text{Arccot}\,(-5.1)$

$y = \text{Cos}^{-1}\left(\dfrac{1}{2.71}\right)$ $y = \text{Tan}^{-1}\left(\dfrac{1}{-5.1}\right)$ *Reciprocal functions*

$y = 1.1929$ $y = -0.1936$ To four decimal places

Yet -0.1936 is not in the range of the inverse Cotangent function. The cotangent function has period π, so $-0.1936 + \pi = 2.9480$ also has a cotangent of -5.1. Since $0 < 2.9480 < \pi$, Arccot $(-5.1) = 2.9480$ to four decimal places.

Remember that $\text{Sec}^{-1}\,x = \text{Cos}^{-1}\dfrac{1}{x}$ and that $\text{Csc}^{-1}\,x = \text{Sin}^{-1}\dfrac{1}{x}$. For the inverse Cotangent, remember that a number whose cotangent is x is equal to a number whose tangent is $\dfrac{1}{x}$, but it may be necessary to use the π-periodicity of the cotangent function to find a number in the appropriate range.

Example 3   Evaluate to the nearest tenth of a degree.
   a. Arcsec (-1.433) **b.** $\text{Cot}^{-1}\,4.317$

a. With the calculator in degree mode, evaluate $\text{Cos}^{-1}\left(\dfrac{1}{-1.433}\right)$. Thus, Arcsec $(-1.433) = 134.3°$.

b. With the calculator in degree mode, evaluate $\text{Tan}^{-1}\left(\dfrac{1}{4.317}\right)$. This gives a value of 13.0°, which is in the appropriate range. Thus, $\text{Cot}^{-1}\,4.317 = 13.0°$.

From their definitions, the inverse trigonometric functions listed below have the following special relationships with their corresponding functions.

For all x, $\tan(\text{Tan}^{-1}\,x) = x$ and $\cot(\text{Cot}^{-1}\,x) = x$.

For all x, where $|x| \geq 1$, $\sec(\text{Sec}^{-1}\,x) = x$ and $\csc(\text{Csc}^{-1}\,x) = x$.

$\text{Tan}^{-1}\,(\tan x) = x$ for $x \in \left(-\dfrac{\pi}{2}, \dfrac{\pi}{2}\right)$ $\text{Cot}^{-1}\,(\cot x) = x$ for $x \in (0, \pi)$

$\text{Sec}^{-1}\,(\sec x) = x$ for $x \in [0, \pi]$, $x \neq \dfrac{\pi}{2}$

$\text{Csc}^{-1}\,(\csc x) = x$ for $x \in \left[-\dfrac{\pi}{2}, \dfrac{\pi}{2}\right]$, $x \neq 0$

Example 4   Determine the exact value of each expression:

   a. $\tan(\text{Tan}^{-1}\,0.08\pi)$ **b.** $\text{Arcsec}\left(\sec\left(-\dfrac{\pi}{4}\right)\right)$

a. $\tan(\text{Tan}^{-1}\,0.08\pi) = 0.08\pi$

b. Since $-\dfrac{\pi}{4}$ is not in the range of Arcsecant, compute the value of $\sec\left(-\dfrac{\pi}{4}\right)$ to obtain $\text{Arcsec}\left(\sec\left(-\dfrac{\pi}{4}\right)\right) = \text{Arcsec}\,(\sqrt{2}) = \dfrac{\pi}{4}$.

224   Chapter 4 Graphs and Inverses of Trigonometric Functions

Knowledge of the principal values of the inverses of trigonometric functions will help you find the exact values of expressions such as $\tan\left(\text{Sin}^{-1}\frac{3}{7}\right)$ and $\text{Sin}^{-1}\left(\cos\frac{2\pi}{5}\right)$ that occur in calculus. Drawing the reference triangle will help you evaluate these expressions.

Example 5 Find the exact value of $\tan\left(\text{Sin}^{-1}\frac{3}{7}\right)$.

Let $\theta = \text{Sin}^{-1}\frac{3}{7}$. The task is to find $\tan\theta$, where θ is the angle in $\left[-\frac{\pi}{2}, \frac{\pi}{2}\right]$ whose sine is $\frac{3}{7}$. Since the principal values of the inverse sine function are in the first and fourth quadrants, and since $\sin\theta > 0$, θ is in quadrant I.

Draw an angle θ in quadrant I. From the definition of the sine function, there is a point $P(x, y)$ on the terminal side of θ for which $y = 3$ and the distance r from P to the origin is 7. Then, using the Pythagorean theorem, $x = \sqrt{7^2 - 3^2} = 2\sqrt{10}$. Therefore,

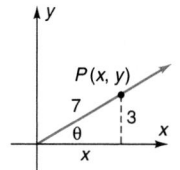

$$\tan\theta = \frac{y}{x} = \frac{3}{2\sqrt{10}} = \frac{3\sqrt{10}}{20}.$$

Transformations of the graphs of each of the inverse trigonometric functions can be done using methods similar to those used in the previous lesson.

Example 6 Graph $f(x) = 1 - \text{Arctan } x$.

The graph of f is the graph of $y = \text{Arctan } x$ reflected about the x-axis and then translated one unit upward.

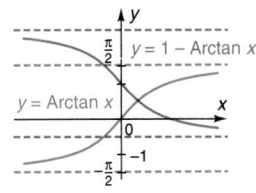

The definitions of the trigonometric functions and the trigonometric identities make it possible to rewrite trigonometric equations as algebraic equations. The relationships between trigonometric and algebraic expressions are useful in calculus.

Example 7 Rewrite $y = \sin(\text{Cos}^{-1} t)$ as an algebraic equation.

Let $\theta = \text{Cos}^{-1} t$. Then $\cos\theta = t$ and θ is in $[0, \pi]$. Since the sine function is nonnegative over $[0, \pi]$, $\sin\theta = \sqrt{1 - t^2}$. Therefore,

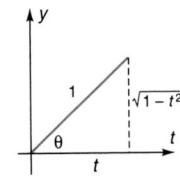

$$\sin(\text{Cos}^{-1} t) = \sin\theta = \sqrt{1 - t^2}$$

Thus, $y = \sqrt{1 - t^2}$.

Geometric representations of the definitions of the trigonometric functions can be helpful when finding algebraic equations.

For Example 5
Determine the exact value of each expression.

1. $\cot\left(\text{Cos}^{-1}\frac{5}{12}\right)$ $\frac{5\sqrt{119}}{119}$

2. $\sin\left(\text{Cot}^{-1}\frac{\sqrt{2}}{2}\right)$ $\frac{\sqrt{6}}{3}$

For Example 6
Graph each function.
1. $F(x) = \text{Tan}^{-1} x + 2$

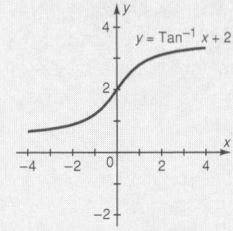

2. $G(x) = 2 \text{ Arcsec } x$

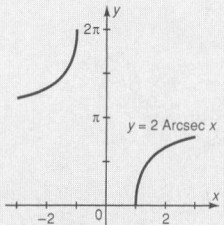

For Example 7
Rewrite each of the following as an algebraic equation.

1. $y = \cos(\text{Csc}^{-1} t)$ $y = \frac{1}{t}\sqrt{t^2 - 1}$

2. $y = \sin(\text{Sec}^{-1} t)$ $y = \frac{1}{t}\sqrt{t^2 - 1}$

Example 8   Rewrite $y = \sec (\text{Tan}^{-1} t)$ as an algebraic equation.

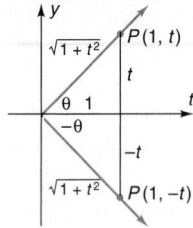

Let $\theta = \text{Tan}^{-1} t$. Then $\tan \theta = t$ and θ is in $\left(-\frac{1}{2}\pi, \frac{1}{2}\pi\right)$. Thus, θ lies in either quadrant I or quadrant IV. Since $P(1, t)$ is on the terminal side of θ, $r = \sqrt{1 + t^2}$. Then,

$$\sec (\text{Tan}^{-1} t) = \sec \theta = \frac{\sqrt{1 + t^2}}{1} = \sqrt{1 + t^2}$$

Therefore, $y = \sqrt{1 + t^2}$.

In Examples 6 and 7, the relationships involving trigonometric functions and their inverses were expressed independently of the trigonometric functions. This follows from the fact that the trigonometric functions were originally defined as simple algebraic ratios.

Class Exercises

1. $\text{Tan}^{-1} (-1)$ $-\frac{\pi}{4}$ 2. $\text{Arctan } 0$ 0 3. $\text{Csc}^{-1} 2$ $\frac{\pi}{6}$ 4. $\text{Arcsec } \frac{2\sqrt{3}}{3}$ $\frac{\pi}{6}$

Evaluate to four decimal places.

5. $\text{Arcsec } 10.9$ 1.4789 6. $\text{Arccsc } (-2.35)$ -0.4395 7. $\text{Cot}^{-1} 0.56$ 1.0603

Evaluate to the nearest tenth of a degree.

8. $\text{Arctan } (-8.456)$ $-83.3°$ 9. $\text{Csc}^{-1} 1.857$ $32.6°$ 10. $\text{Arcsec } 1.222$ $35.1°$

Use reference triangles to determine the exact value of each expression.

11. $\tan \left(\text{Sin}^{-1} \frac{2}{5}\right)$ $\frac{2\sqrt{21}}{21}$ 12. $\cos \left(\text{Sin}^{-1} \frac{2}{7}\right)$ $\frac{3\sqrt{5}}{7}$ 13. $\sec \left(\text{Sin}^{-1} \left(-\frac{7}{25}\right)\right)$ $\frac{25}{24}$ 14. $\csc (\text{Tan}^{-1} \sqrt{2})$ $\frac{\sqrt{6}}{2}$

Rewrite each of the following as an algebraic equation:

15. $y = \cos (\text{Sec}^{-1} t)$ $y = \frac{1}{t}$ 16. $y = \sec (\text{Sin}^{-1} t)$ $y = \frac{\sqrt{1 - t^2}}{1 - t^2}$

17. Graph $h(t) = \text{Tan}^{-1} t - 1$.

18. **Thinking Critically** Why is the range of the inverse Tangent function $\left(-\frac{1}{2}\pi, \frac{1}{2}\pi\right)$ rather than $\left[-\frac{1}{2}\pi, \frac{1}{2}\pi\right]$? tangent is not defined at $\pm\frac{1}{2}\pi$

Practice Exercises   Use appropriate technology.

Use the definition of the inverse trigonometric functions to determine the exact value of each of the following:

A 1. $\text{Arctan } 1$ $\frac{\pi}{4}$ 2. $\text{Csc}^{-1} 1$ $\frac{\pi}{2}$ 3. $\text{Csc}^{-1} \sqrt{2}$ $\frac{\pi}{4}$

Evaluate to four decimal places.

4. $\text{Tan}^{-1} 23.1$ 1.5275 5. $\text{Arcsec } 9.7$ 1.4675 6. $\text{Arccot } 7.36$ 0.1350 7. $\text{Csc}^{-1} 15$ 0.0667

Evaluate to the nearest tenth of a degree.

8. $\text{Arctan } 1.556$ $57.3°$ Ⓡ 9. $\text{Cos}^{-1} 0.477$ $61.5°$ 10. $\text{Arccsc } (-1.5)$ $-41.8°$ 11. $\text{Arcsec } (-4.5)$ $102.8°$

23.

24.

25.

Determine the exact value of each expression.

12. Arctan (tan π) 0

13. Tan^{-1} (tan 0.8) 0.8

14. cot (Arccot 0.6) 0.6

Ⓡ 15. $\sin\left(\text{Cos}^{-1}\dfrac{\sqrt{2}}{2}\right)$ $\dfrac{\sqrt{2}}{2}$

Use reference triangles to determine the exact value of each expression.

16. $\tan\left(\text{Cos}^{-1}\dfrac{3}{4}\right)$ $\dfrac{\sqrt{7}}{3}$

17. $\sin\left(\text{Tan}^{-1}\left(-\dfrac{3}{2}\right)\right)$ $-\dfrac{3\sqrt{13}}{13}$

18. $\csc\left(\text{Cos}^{-1}\dfrac{2}{9}\right)$ $\dfrac{9\sqrt{77}}{77}$

Ⓡ 19. *Finance* Maria invests $3000 at 8% interest, compounded quarterly. How much money is in her account at the end of 4 years? $4118.35

Rewrite each of the following as an algebraic expression:

20. tan $(\text{Sin}^{-1}\ t)$ $\dfrac{t\sqrt{1-t^2}}{1-t^2}$

21. sin $(\text{Tan}^{-1}\ t)$ $\dfrac{t\sqrt{1+t^2}}{1+t^2}$

22. sec $(\text{Sin}^{-1}\ t)$ $\dfrac{\sqrt{1-t^2}}{1-t^2}$

Graph.

B 23. $y = 3 + \text{Tan}^{-1} x$

24. $h(t) = -\text{Arctan}\ t$

25. $g(t) = \text{Arctan}\ (t + 3)$

26. $y = \text{Sec}^{-1} x - 2$

Ⓡ 27. $f(x) = |\cos x + 1|$

28. $f(x) = |\text{Csc}^{-1} x|$

29. Determine an interval other than $\left(-\dfrac{\pi}{2}, \dfrac{\pi}{2}\right)$ on which the tangent function is one-to-one and takes on its full range of values. $\left(\dfrac{\pi}{2}, \dfrac{3\pi}{2}\right)$

30. Graph $H(x) = \text{Tan}^{-1} x + \text{Cot}^{-1} x$ and use the graph to suggest an identity relating the inverse Tangent and inverse Cotangent functions.

31. Thinking Critically The inverse Secant function can be defined as follows:

$$y = \text{Sec}^{-1} x \text{ if and only if sec } y = x \text{ and } \begin{cases} 0 \le y < \dfrac{\pi}{2}, & \text{if } x \ge 1 \\ \pi \le y < \dfrac{3\pi}{2}, & \text{if } x \le -1 \end{cases}$$

Verify that the secant function is one-to-one for the given values, and graph the function.

32. *Sports* A runner on a circular track naturally leans away from the perpendicular. The angle of incline θ satisfies the relationship $\tan\theta = \dfrac{v}{gR}$, where R is the radius of the track, v the speed of the runner, and g the acceleration due to gravity. Determine the angle of incline for a runner on a track of radius 55 m running at 6.7 m/s. Use 9.8 m/s² for g. 0.7122°

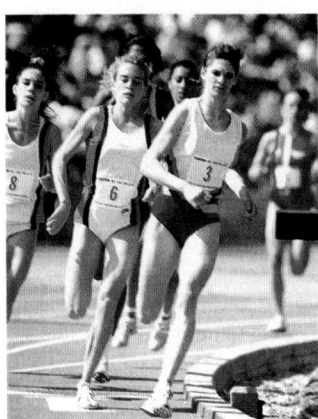

Ⓡ 33. *Physiology* Using physics, it can be shown that the force on the hip joint of a person standing erect on one foot (for example, when walking slowly) is nearly $2\frac{1}{2}$ times the weight of the person. To find the force, first find the value of the force angle θ that satisfies the equations $F \sin\theta = 2.31W$ and $F \cos\theta = 0.52W$, where F is the force on the hip and W is the person's weight. Find the value of θ in degrees. 77.3°

26.

27.

28.

Lesson Quiz

1. Use the definition of the inverse Tangent function to evaluate Arctan $-\dfrac{\sqrt{3}}{3}$. $-\dfrac{\pi}{6}$

2. Evaluate Arccot 2.453 to four decimal places. 0.3871

3. Evaluate Sec^{-1} 5.41 to the nearest tenth of a degree. 79.3°

Find the exact value of each expression.

4. Arctan $\left(\tan\dfrac{7\pi}{4}\right)$ $-\dfrac{\pi}{4}$

5. sec (Arcsec −2.08) −2.08

6. Graph $y = \text{Arctan } x - 4$

Additional Answers

30.

$\text{Tan}^{-1} x + \text{Cot}^{-1} x = \dfrac{\pi}{2}$

31.

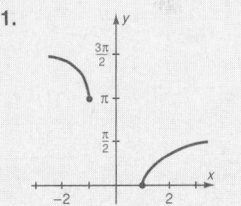

Given $x = 2$, $y = \dfrac{\pi}{3}$; given $y = \dfrac{\pi}{3}$; $x = 2$.

Given $x = -2$, $y = \dfrac{4\pi}{3}$; given $y = \dfrac{4\pi}{3}$, $x = -2$.

34. **Writing in Mathematics** Write a paragraph explaining the relationship of one-to-oneness and the existence of inverse functions. Use three or more examples in your explanation, at least one of which is trigonometric.

Ⓡ 35. Graph the function $f(x) = x^2 + \sin x$.

Using calculus, it can be shown that the area beneath the curve $y = \dfrac{1}{x^2 + 1}$ and bounded by the x-axis and the vertical lines $x = a$ and $x = b \ (a < b)$ is given by $A = \text{Tan}^{-1} b - \text{Tan}^{-1} a$.

36. Determine the area between the lines $x = -1$ and $x = 1$. $\dfrac{\pi}{2}$

37. Determine the area between the lines $x = 1$ and $x = \sqrt{3}$. $\dfrac{\pi}{12}$

Rewrite each of the following as an algebraic equation.

38. $y = \tan (\text{Cos}^{-1} u)$ 39. $y = \cos (\text{Arctan } u)$ 40. $y = \sin (\text{Sec}^{-1} t)$

Ⓡ 41. Given $f(x) = x^2 - 8x + 12$. Determine the inverse of the function. Then determine the domain and range of the function and its inverse.

Ⓒ 42. Determine the domain of the function $F(x) = \text{Sin}^{-1} x + \text{Csc}^{-1} x$. $[-1, 1]$

43. Use reference triangles to verify that $\text{Sec}^{-1} 2 = \text{Tan}^{-1} \sqrt{3}$.

44. Prove that $\sin (\text{Arccsc } v) = \dfrac{1}{v}$.

45. *Physics* A person of weight W wearing leather shoes and standing on an oak board inclined at an angle θ will slide down the board when the force of gravity parallel to the board is greater than the force of friction. This will occur when $W \sin \theta > 0.6 W \cos \theta$. Estimate the maximum angle θ for which the person will not slide down the board. 31°

Determine an expression for Z that will make each statement true.

46. $\tan^{-1} \dfrac{5}{x} = \sin^{-1} Z$ 47. $\text{Sin}^{-1} \left(\dfrac{x}{\sqrt{49 + x^2}} \right) = \text{Cos}^{-1} Z$

Define an inverse function for each function, and state its domain and range. Verify that for the range of the inverse function, the original function is one-to-one.

48. $f(t) = \tan t - 1$ 49. $g(t) = 1 - \cos t$

Rewrite each of the following as an algebraic expression:

50. $\tan \left(\text{Sin}^{-1} \left(\dfrac{z}{\sqrt{z^2 + 3}} \right) \right)$ $\dfrac{\sqrt{3}}{3} z$ 51. $\csc \left(\text{Tan}^{-1} \left(\dfrac{\sqrt{25 - v^2}}{v} \right) \right)$ $\dfrac{5\sqrt{25 - v^2}}{25 - v^2}$

Review

Solve each of the following equations for x. If a solution occurs more than once, state its multiplicity.

1. $18x^4 - 24x^3 + 8x^2 = 0$ 0 (mult. 2), $\frac{2}{3}$ (mult. 2)   2. $x^2 - 10x + 25 = -1$ $5 \pm i$

3. Use a graphing utility to determine the values of x, $0 < x < 2\pi$, such that $|\sin x| = \sin |x|$. $(0, \pi]$

4.7 Modeling: Simple Harmonic Motion

Objective: To solve problems involving simple harmonic motion

Focus

In the sixteenth century, a young man observed that suspended church lamps swinging through various arc lengths always took the same amount of time for one complete swing. The young man was an Italian astronomer, mathematician, and physicist named Galileo (1564–1642) who later used his knowledge of swinging objects to develop a pendulum clock.

Galileo's experiments with pendulums required some ingenuity. To begin the swinging of the pendulum, he let a candle burn through a stringlike fiber. He used his own pulse rate as a timing device. Neglecting air resistance and friction, he developed a mathematical model from his experiments. A pendulum swinging through a small arc is an example of *simple harmonic motion*, a back-and-forth motion which takes the same amount of time for each complete cycle.

Motion that repeats itself in equal intervals of time is called *periodic* or *harmonic*. The graphs of these motions are *sinusoidal*. Because these motions are dependent upon *time*, the independent variable is *t*.

Modeling

How is simple harmonic motion modeled?

Simple harmonic motion can be described mathematically by the *sinusoidal functions* $f(x) = a \sin b(t - c) + d$ or $f(x) = a \cos b(t - c) + d$. In this case, $|a|$ is the *amplitude* of the motion, or the maximum displacement. The *period* of the motion is $\frac{2\pi}{|b|}$, which is the time required for one complete cycle. The **frequency** is the number of cycles per unit time, and is therefore equal to $\frac{|b|}{2\pi}$.

Example 1 *Mechanics*   Determine an equation to model the data that might have resulted from Galileo's pendulum experiments.

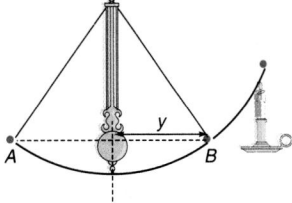

For the movement of a pendulum, recording times and corresponding displacement distances from a vertical reference line provides data that can be graphed and interpreted. Duplicating Galileo's pendulum experiments with modern instruments results in the following data.

LESSON PLAN

Vocabulary
amplitude
frequency
period
simple harmonic motion

Ⓜ **Materials/Manipulatives**
pendulum
weight suspended from a spring

Technology
graphing utility

FOCUS

Galileo went to the University of Pisa to study medicine, but instead became a professor of mathematics. Much of what he taught would now be called astronomy, physics, or engineering rather than mathematics.

He was a practical thinker who believed that principles of science must come from observation and experimentation. He is sometimes called the originator of the scientific method. Although not its inventor, Galileo was one of the first to construct a telescope. He invented a microscope, and designed the first pendulum clock. It was Robert Hooke and Christian Huygens, however, who did most of the basic work with the pendulum.

- Have students time the motion of a simple pendulum to see that it does take the same amount of time for each swing, no matter how wide the arc. Have them guess what affects the time of the swings (the length of the pendulum).
- Use a weight suspended on a spring to model simple harmonic motion. Be sure to point out that friction causes the maximum displacement to change over time. In the mathematical model, when friction is ignored the maximum displacement is considered constant, and so a sine or cosine curve is a good description of the motion.

Alternative Learning Styles

The two activities suggested above can be good motivators for students who are concrete learners. A model of a ferris wheel would also be a useful learning tool for this lesson.

GUIDED PRACTICE

Modeling

When discussing the motion of a pendulum, students may realize that the lengths of the swings decrease and eventually dwindle to nothing. The sinusoidal graph that models harmonic motion is simply a tool for analyzing pendulum motion over a specific time interval and does not tell the whole story. Like any model, it has its limitations.

For Example 1

Determine an equation to model the sinusoidal function whose graph is shown below.

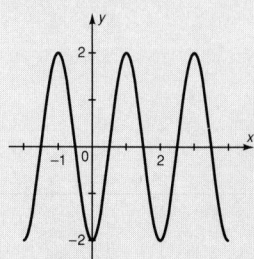

$y = -2 \cos \pi t$

230

Time	0	0.5	1.0	1.5	2.0	2.5	3.0	3.5	4.0	4.5
Displacement	0	1.4	2.5	3.0	2.7	1.8	0.4	−1.0	−2.3	−2.9

The graphical representation of the data shows the sinusoidal nature of the relationship between time and displacement.

The graph for the harmonic motion indicates that the equation $y = 3 \sin t$ is a reasonable trigonometric model.

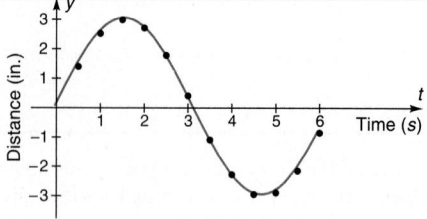

Many real world phenomena such as sound waves, tides, and even the motion of a person seated on a ferris wheel can be modeled using sinusoidal functions.

Example 2 *Entertainment* A person is seated on a ferris wheel of radius 100 ft that makes one rotation every 30 s. The center of the wheel is 105 ft above the ground. Find and graph a function to represent the person's height above the ground at any time t of a 2-min ride. Assume uniform speed from the beginning to the end of the ride and that the person is at the level of the center of the wheel and headed up when the ride begins.

Let y be the person's height above or below the plane of the center of the ferris wheel. Then y will vary between -100 and 100 ft. At the beginning of the ride, $t = 0$ and $y = 0$. At $t = 7.5$, $y = 100$; at $t = 15$, $y = 0$; and so on.

t	y
0	0
7.5	100
15	0
22.5	−100
30	0

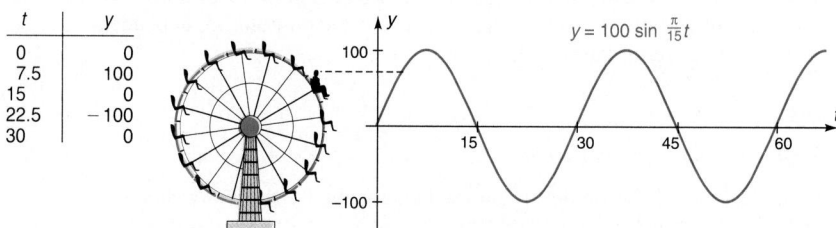

The sine curve above has amplitude 100 and period 30. So $a = 100$ and $b = \dfrac{2\pi}{30} = \dfrac{\pi}{15}$. Thus the equation is $y = 100 \sin \dfrac{\pi}{15} t$. Because the center of the wheel is 105 ft above the ground, the graph is translated 105 units upward, $d = 105$, and the person's height can be modeled by the function $h(t) = 100 \sin \dfrac{\pi}{15} t + 105$.

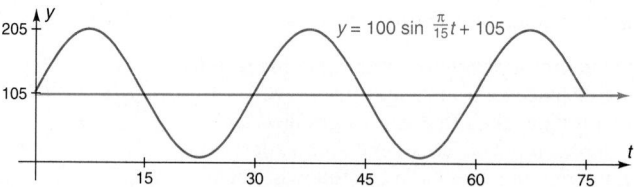

Simple harmonic motion occurs when an object is shifted from its rest position, and the force exerted to return it to rest is proportional to the shift. A classic example of this kind of motion is the motion of a weight moving up and down at the end of a spring. The stiffer the spring, the faster the movement of the weight, and hence the smaller the period; the farther the weight is pulled down or compressed, the greater the amplitude. If the effect of friction is ignored, the weight may be assumed to move in the same way indefinitely with a constant displacement, and this movement may be described by a sinusoidal function.

Example 3 *Mechanics* A weight is at rest hanging from a spring. It is compressed 15 cm and released. Every 8 s, the weight moves back and forth between the point 15 cm below its rest position and the point 15 cm above it. Ignoring the effect of friction, determine an equation of the function and graph it.

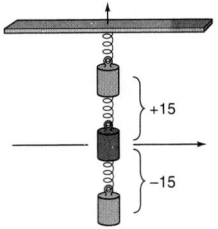

Let y be the distance of the center of the weight from its resting position. Then y varies between 15 and -15 every 8 s, and so the amplitude is 15 and the period is 8. When $t = 0$, $y = 15$, so use the cosine function to model this motion with $a = 15$. Because the period is 8, $b = \frac{2\pi}{8} = \frac{\pi}{4}$.

Since $c = 0$ and $d = 0$, the equation of this function is $y = 15 \cos \frac{\pi}{4}t$.

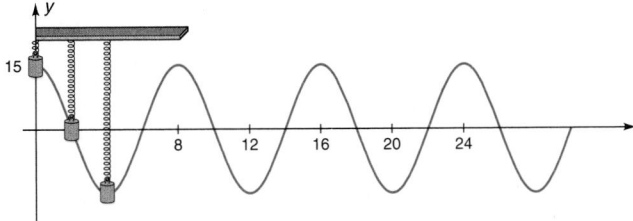

How did the starting position of the weight lead to the choice of the cosine function with $a = 15$? What choice would you have made if the starting position were -15? At rest and headed up? At rest and headed down?

It is possible for simple harmonic motion to start at any point in its cycle. The graphs of sinusoidal functions may be shifted left or right as needed to describe the motion; the constant c in the equations $y = a \sin b(t - c) + d$ and $y = a \cos b(t - c) + d$ indicates such a horizontal shift.

Example 4 *Mechanics* Suppose the weight described in Example 3 were at $y = 7.5$ and rising when $t = 0$. Find and graph an equation for the position of the weight.

$y = 15 \sin \frac{\pi}{4}(t - c)$ *From Example 3,* $a = 15$ *and* $b = \frac{\pi}{4}$

$7.5 = 15 \sin \frac{\pi}{4}(0 - c)$ $y = 7.5$ *when* $t = 0$

$\frac{1}{2} = \sin \left(-\frac{\pi}{4}c \right)$

For Example 2
How would the function of Example 2 change if it made one rotation every 20 s?

$h(t) = 100 \sin \frac{\pi}{10}t + 105$

Technology   Students should be able to relate the graphs of the sinusoidal functions, obtained using a graphing utility, to the physical situation they describe. Also, they should be able to predict changes in the graphs and verify them using technology.

For Example 3
1. What is the equation of the function of Example 3 if the weight were compressed 24 cm and then released? $y = 24 \cos \frac{\pi}{4}t$

2. What is the equation of the function of Example 3 if the weight moved back and forth once every 10 s? $y = 15 \cos \frac{\pi}{5}t$

For Example 4
1. What is the equation of the function of Example 4 if the weight were at $y = 7.5$ and falling when $t = 0$? $y = -15 \sin \frac{\pi}{4}\left(t - \frac{2}{3}\right)$

2. What is the equation of the function of Example 4 if the weight were at $y = -7.5$ and rising when $t = 0$? $y = 15 \sin \frac{\pi}{4}\left(t - \frac{2}{3}\right)$

Thinking Critically
The graph of the basic cosine function suggests its choice. At $t = 0$, $\cos t$ is at its maximum, 1, and headed down. If the starting position were -15, choose the cosine function with $a = -15$ (or $y = -\cos x$ with $a = 15$). If it were at rest and headed up, choose the sine function, since $\sin 0 = 0$ and the sine function increases on $\left[0, \frac{1}{2}\pi\right]$. If it were at rest and headed down, choose $y = -\sin x$. In both cases, $a = 15$.

1. The sound created when a tuning fork is struck is described mathematically by the equation $y = 3 \sin 400\pi t$, where t is measured in seconds. Determine the amplitude, period, and frequency of this sound. $3; \frac{1}{200}$ s; 200 cycles/s

2. An alternating current of electricity is described mathematically by the equation $f(t) = 0.6 \sin 400t$, where t is measured in seconds. Determine the amplitude, period, and frequency of this current.
$0.6; \frac{\pi}{200}$ s; $\frac{200}{\pi}$ cycles/s

CLOSURE

Group students in pairs and have them interview a physics teacher or student who is familiar with the study of harmonic motion. Have them ask that person to give examples of harmonic motion, and then prepare a detailed oral report about one new example. Encourage students to use models or pictures to illustrate the motion as appropriate.

INDEPENDENT PRACTICE

Assignment Guide
Basic: 1–18, 21, 23–25, 31, Project
Average: 10–32, Project
Enriched: 18–40, Project

Teacher's Resource Book
   Practice, page 31

ℝ Review
Exercises 11, 15, 21, 24, 29, and 31 review concepts of simplifying expressions, graphing, determining equations of lines, deriving inverse functions, determining distance between two points, and verifying one-to-oneness of a function.

Project
The project involving pendulum motion is an excellent opportunity for cooperative learning. It is also an opportunity for cross-curricular learning and may be coordinated with similar subject matter that the students are learning in their science courses.

232

$$\sin^{-1}\frac{1}{2} = -\frac{\pi}{4}c$$
$$\frac{\pi}{6} = -\frac{\pi}{4}c$$
$$c = -\frac{2}{3}$$
$$y = 15 \sin\frac{\pi}{4}\left(t + \frac{2}{3}\right) \qquad \textit{Substitute.}$$

[–2, 10] by [–20, 20]
x scl: 1   y scl: 5

A graphing utility confirms that this graph is rising at $t = 0$. A cosine function could also have been used to express the given relationship.

Alternating current can be described by sinusoidal functions.

Example 5   *Electricity*   The alternating electric current in most homes and businesses is described by the function $c(t) = 10\sqrt{2} \sin 120\pi t$, where $c(t)$ amperes is the current at time t seconds. Find the amplitude, period, and frequency of this current.

Using the equation $y = a \sin b(t - c) + d$, you can see that c and d are both 0. The amplitude is $10\sqrt{2}$, the period is $\frac{2\pi}{120\pi}$ or $\frac{1}{60}$ s, and the frequency is 60 cycles/s.

Class Exercises

Mechanics   The harmonic motion of a weight suspended from a spring is described by each equation, where y is the directed distance in centimeters of the weight from its rest position at t seconds. Find the amplitude, period, and frequency of each.

1. $y = 3 \cos 0.21t$ $3; \frac{19\pi}{2}; \frac{2}{19\pi}$ 2. $y = 10 \sin 3t$ $10; \frac{2\pi}{3}; \frac{3}{2\pi}$ 3. $y = 12 \sin \pi(2t + 6)$
   $12; 1; 1$

Mechanics   A weight suspended from a spring is moved to an initial position and released. Describe its motion using a sinusoidal function of the form $y = a \sin bt$ or $y = a \cos bt$. Assume that $b = \frac{1}{4}\pi$ and that the starting position is:

4. 7 cm below the rest position $y = -7 \cos\frac{\pi}{4}t$ 5. 5.2 cm above the rest position
   $y = 5.2 \cos\frac{\pi}{4}t$

Acoustics   An oscilloscope converts sound waves into electrical impulses and displays them on a screen. The sound of a tuning fork is displayed as a sinusoidal curve. Determine the amplitude, the period, and the frequency of the sound wave with the given display. Determine an equation for each function.

6. t 7; 10; $\frac{1}{10}$
$y = 7 \sin 0.2\pi t + 1$

7. t

232   Chapter 4 Graphs and Inverses of Trigonometric Functions

---

Additional Answers, Class Exercises

7. 6; 24; $\frac{1}{24}$; $y = -6 \sin\frac{\pi}{12}t$

12. He would be sure that the only force involved would be the force of gravity. If he held the pendulum bob, he might give it an initial force in releasing it.

Electricity   An alternating current is described by each sinusoidal function, where $c(t)$ is the current measured in amperes at t seconds. Determine the amplitude, period, and frequency of each.

8. $c(t) = 10 \sin 30\pi t$ 10; $\frac{1}{15}$; 15

9. $c(t) = 0.8 \sin 650t$ 0.8; $\frac{\pi}{325}$; $\frac{325}{\pi}$

10. *Acoustics*   The frequency of the musical tone A above middle C is 440 cycles/s. Determine the period of the vibration of a piano string playing A above middle C. $\frac{1}{440}$

11. Thinking Critically   Using the form $y = a \cos b(t - c) + d$, determine an equation to describe the motion in Example 4 of this lesson. $y = 15 \cos \frac{\pi}{4}\left(t - \frac{4}{3}\right)$

12. Thinking Critically   Refer to the Focus and explain why Galileo used the candle burning through the fiber in his experiments with pendulums.

Practice Exercises   Use appropriate technology.

Electricity   An alternating current is described by each sinusoidal function, where $c(t)$ is the current measured in amperes at t seconds. Find the amplitude, period, and frequency of each.

A **1.** $c(t) = 30 \sin 120\pi t$ 30; $\frac{1}{60}$; 60

2. $c(t) = 40 \cos 250t$ 40; $\frac{\pi}{125}$; $\frac{125}{\pi}$

3. $c(t) = 24 \sin(t + 4)$ 24; 2π; $\frac{1}{2\pi}$

4. $c(t) = 18 \cos\left(120\pi t + \frac{\pi}{2}\right)$ 18; $\frac{1}{60}$; 60

Electricity   The *voltage E* in an electrical circuit is also described by a sinusoidal function. Determine the amplitude, period, and frequency for each function. The voltage E is measured in volts, and time t is measured in seconds.

5. $E = 5 \cos 120\pi t$ 5; $\frac{1}{60}$; 60

6. $E = 110 \sin 377t$ 110; $\frac{2\pi}{377}$; $\frac{377}{2\pi}$

7. $E = 3.8 \cos 40\pi t$ 3.8; $\frac{1}{20}$; 20

8. $E = 8 \cos 332t$ 8; $\frac{\pi}{166}$; $\frac{166}{\pi}$

9. *Acoustics*   The amplitude of a sound wave produced by middle C is 1.5, and the frequency is 264 cycles/s. Determine an equation for a sinusoidal function describing this sound. $y = 1.5 \sin 528\pi t$

10. *Acoustics*   The amplitude of a sound wave produced by the note E above middle C is 0.8, and the frequency is 330 cycles/s. Determine an equation for a sinusoidal function representing this sound. $y = 0.8 \sin 660\pi t$

Ⓡ **11.** Simplify: $3x^5 - 2x^3y^2 - 3x^2y^3 - 2y + x$ when $x = 2$ and $y = -3$ 284

12. Thinking Critically   Compare and contrast the definitions of the terms *period and amplitude* given in Lesson 4.2 with those presented in this lesson.

Acoustics   An oscilloscope converts sound waves into electrical impulses and displays them on a screen. The sound of a tuning fork is displayed as a sinusoidal curve. Determine the amplitude, the period, and the frequency of the sound wave with the given display. Determine an equation for each function.

13.

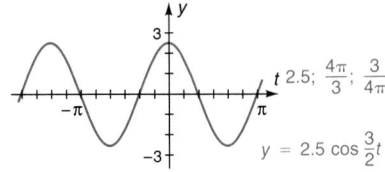

2.5; $\frac{4\pi}{3}$; $\frac{3}{4\pi}$

$y = 2.5 \cos \frac{3}{2}t$

14.

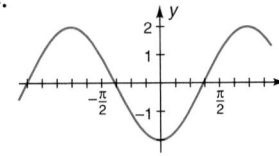

4.7 Modeling: Simple Harmonic Motion   **233**

Additional Answers
12. In this lesson amplitude refers to the maximum displacement of the object exhibiting simple harmonic motion. In Lesson 2 amplitude refers to the maximum displacement of a sinusoidal curve from its line of horizontal symmetry. Similarly, the period of an object in simple harmonic motion is the time required for a complete cycle. For a sine or cosine curve, the period is the size of an interval of the domain that yields a complete cycle.

14. 2; $\frac{3\pi}{2}$; $\frac{2}{3\pi}$; $y = -2 \cos \frac{4}{3}t$

15.

16.

17.

18.

$y = -110 \cos \frac{2\pi}{35}t + 114$

19.

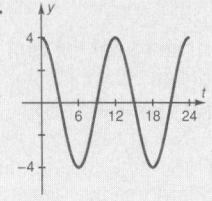

$y = 4 \cos \frac{\pi}{6}t$

22.

Ⓡ **15.** Determine the equation of the line through the point $P(7, -1.5)$ that is perpendicular to the line $3x - 2.7y + 5.9 = 0$. Graph the two lines.

16. *Mechanics*   A weight suspended from a spring is set into oscillating motion by compressing it to a point 3 cm above its rest position and releasing it. It takes 1.2 s for the weight to complete one cycle. Determine an equation to describe the position of the weight at time t seconds, letting position 0 represent its rest position. Graph the equation. $y = 3 \cos \frac{5\pi}{3}t$

17. *Mechanics*   A weight suspended from a spring is set into oscillating motion by pulling it to a point 10.4 cm below its rest position and releasing it. It takes 4 s for the weight to complete one cycle. Determine an equation that describes the position of the weight at time t seconds; let position 0 represent its rest position. Graph the equation. $y = -10.4 \cos \frac{\pi}{2}t$

18. A person is seated on a ferris wheel of radius 110 ft that makes one rotation every 35 s. The center of the wheel is 114 ft above the ground. Determine and graph an equation to represent the person's height at any time t of a 3-min ride. Assume that the ride begins at the bottom of the wheel.

Ⓑ **19.** *Oceanography*   The highest tides in the world are found in the Bay of Fundy in Nova Scotia. The motion of these tides is simple harmonic motion, and so can be described by a sinusoidal function. At high tide the water is approximately 4 m above sea level, and at low tide 4 m below; the time between high tides is approximately 12 h. Determine and graph an equation describing the motion of the tides. Assume that it is high tide at $t = 0$ h.

20. *Oceanography*   How many meters does the tide in the Bay of Fundy drop 1 h after high tide? Refer to Exercise 19.   0.54 m

Ⓡ **21.** Derive the inverse function of the function found in Exercise 19. $y = \frac{6}{\pi} \text{Cos}^{-1}\left(\frac{t}{4}\right)$

22. *Oceanography*   High tide in a bay is 2.6 m above sea level, and low tide is 2.6 m below sea level. The time between high tides is $12\frac{1}{4}$ h. Use a sinusoidal function to describe the motion of the tides, assuming that it is low tide at $t = 0$ hours. Graph the function. $y = -2.6 \cos 0.16\pi t$

23. **Writing in Mathematics**   Keep a journal for a week in which you describe all the examples of simple harmonic motion you see, hear, or read about. Occurrences that are "nearly" simple harmonic (such as a bouncing ball whose amplitude decreases with time) are acceptable.

Ⓡ **24.** Graph the sinusoidal function $y = 3 \sin (x - 1.5\pi)$ and its reflection about the x-axis and about the line $y = x$. Which of the reflected graphs represents a sinusoidal function?   reflection about the x-axis

Mechanics   The horizontal distance d of the tip of a pendulum from its vertical position at rest can be represented by a sinusoidal function. Determine an equation of motion for the tip of a pendulum satisfying the given conditions. Assume that the pendulum is at rest at time $t = 0$.

25. maximum displacement 12 cm; one cycle in 2 s $y = 12 \sin \pi t$

26. maximum displacement 7.5 in.; one cycle in 3.1 s $y = 7.5 \sin 0.65\pi t$

27. maximum displacement 6 in.; $\frac{1}{4}$ cycle/s $y = 6 \sin \frac{\pi}{2}t$

28. maximum displacement 5 cm; 1.5 cycles/s $y = 5 \sin 1.3\pi t$

234   Chapter 4 Graphs and Inverses of Trigonometric Functions

Writing in Mathematics
23. Answers may vary. Some examples follow: pendulums, tides, weights, pistons, ferris wheels, buoys and other floating objects when wave motion is present, yo-yos, bouncing balls, pedals on a bike, some exercise equipment.

29. Determine the distance between the points P and Q on the plane which have coordinates $P(1, \text{Sin}^{-1}\ 1)$ and $Q(-1, \text{Tan}^{-1}\ (-1))$. 3.1

30. *Electricity*   The usual 110-V household alternating current varies from -155 to $+155$ V with a frequency of 60 cycles/s. Determine an equation that describes the variation in voltage. $v(t) = 155 \sin 120\pi t$

31. Verify that the function f is one-to-one and find its inverse if $f(x) = 5(x - 7.1)^3$.

32. *Mechanics*   A weight suspended from a spring is oscillating in simple harmonic motion. It completes 5 cycles of its motion every second. If the distance from the highest point to the lowest point of the oscillation is 80 cm, determine an equation that models the motion of the mass. Assume that the weight is at its highest point at $t = 0$. $y = 40 \cos 10\pi t$

C 33. *Astronomy*   Delta Cephei is a star whose brightness increases and decreases in a way that can be described by a sinusoidal function. Its brightness averages 4.0. It changes up to 4.35 and down to 3.65; the time between maximum brightness is 5.4 days. Determine an equation describing Delta Cephei's brightness as a function of time, assuming that its brightness is 4 at day 0. $y = 0.35 \sin 0.37\pi t + 4$

34. *Astronomy*   Another star whose brightness varies sinusoidally has a period of 11 days. Its average brightness is 3.6, and the variation ranges from 3.9 to 3.3. Determine an equation to describe this variation as a function of time. $y = 0.3 \sin 0.18\pi t + 3.6$

35. *Mechanics*   A 6-lb weight hanging from the end of a spring is pulled 10 cm below its resting position and released; it takes 0.9 s to complete a cycle. Determine an equation for the motion of the weight, assuming that it is 5 cm below its resting position and rising at $t = 0$. $y = 10 \sin \frac{20\pi}{9}\left(t - \frac{3}{40}\right)$

36. Repeat Exercise 35, assuming that the weight is 5 cm below its resting position and falling at $t = 0$. $y = 10 \sin \frac{20\pi}{9}\left(t - \frac{3}{8}\right)$

37. *Physics*   A wheel is turning counterclockwise at a constant speed. A light attached to the rim of the wheel sends a horizontal light beam onto a wall. As the wheel turns, the light beam moves up and down the wall as shown. Suppose that the wheel has radius 2, turns at a rate of 3 rad/s, and starts with the light source at $(2, 0)$. Determine an equation expressing the y-coordinate of the light beam in terms of time t seconds. $y = 2 \sin 3t$

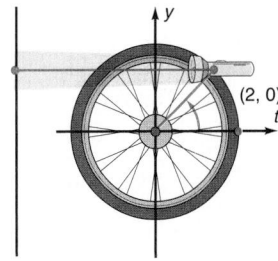

38. *Engineering*   The crankshaft-piston combination in an automobile is similar to a wheel-piston device. One end of a shaft is attached to a piston that moves up and down. The other end is attached to a wheel by means of a horizontal arm that slides back and forth over a peg on the rim of the wheel. Suppose that the wheel has radius 4 ft, the vertical shaft is 10 ft long, and the wheel rotates counterclockwise at a rate of 2 rad/s. Determine an equation for the vertical distance from the piston to the wheel center in terms of time t seconds; assume that when $t = 0$ the peg is at $(-4, 0)$. $y = -4 \sin 2t + 10$

4.7 Modeling: Simple Harmonic Motion **235**

39. *Marine Studies*   A buoy bobs up and down in simple harmonic motion as waves pass it. A particular buoy moves a total of 4.2 ft from its highest point to its lowest point and returns to its highest point every 12 s. Find an equation of motion for the buoy; assume that it is at its highest point at $t = 0$. $y = 2.1 \cos \frac{\pi}{6} t$

40. *Transportation*   As Alan drives into his garage at night, a tiny stone becomes wedged between the treads in one of his tires. As he drives to work the next morning at a steady 35 mi/h, the distance of the stone from the pavement varies sinusoidally with the distance he travels. Assume that his wheel has a radius of 12 in. and that at $t = 0$ the stone is at the bottom. Determine the equation that most closely models the distance of the stone from the pavement. When is the first time that the stone will be 9 in. from the pavement? $y = -12 \cos 616t + 12; \; 0.002$ s

Project

Work with a partner to find a function that models the time of one period of a pendulum swing in terms of the length of the pendulum. For the pendulum, use a string of length 30 cm with a weight attached to one end. Record the amount of time in seconds required for the pendulum to swing through 30 periods, and then divide by 30 to find an average time for one period. Repeat the experiment for string lengths that are multiples of 10 cm long up to 80 cm. Graph ordered pairs of the form (length of pendulum, time for one period) and connect the points with a curve. Compare your results with another team and draw a conclusion.

Test Yourself

Use the definition of inverse Sine function or inverse Cosine function to determine the exact value of each of the following:

1. $\text{Cos}^{-1} \dfrac{\sqrt{3}}{2}$ $\frac{\pi}{6}$ **2.** $\text{Arcsin} \left(-\dfrac{1}{2}\right)$ $-\frac{\pi}{6}$ **3.** $\text{Arccos} \left(-\dfrac{\sqrt{2}}{2}\right)$ $\frac{3\pi}{4}$ 4.5

Graph each function.

4. $y = \text{Arcsin } x - 2$ **5.** $y = \text{Cos}^{-1} (x - 2)$

6. *Optics*   A light ray passing from air to water forms a 60° angle with the perpendicular in air. What angle does the ray form with the perpendicular in water?   40.5°

Use the definition of the inverse trigonometric functions to determine the exact value of each of the following:

7. $\text{Arctan } (-1)$ $-\frac{\pi}{4}$ **8.** $\text{Cot}^{-1} \sqrt{3}$ $\frac{\pi}{6}$ **9.** $\text{Csc}^{-1} 2$ $\frac{\pi}{6}$ 4.6

10. Graph $y = \text{Arcsec } x + 1$.

11. Rewrite $y = \cos (\text{Tan}^{-1} t)$ as an algebraic equation. $y = \dfrac{\sqrt{1 + t^2}}{1 + t^2}$

12. *Mechanics*   A weight suspended from a spring moves up and down between points 12 cm above and 12 cm below the rest position every 10 s. Determine an equation of the function and graph it. $y = 12 \cos \frac{\pi}{5} t$ 4.7

Chapter 4   Summary and Review

Vocabulary

addition of ordinates (208)
amplitude (190)
cycle (182)
frequency (195)
inverse Cosecant (223)
inverse Cosine (216)

inverse Cotangent (223)
inverse Secant (223)
inverse Sine (215)
inverse Tangent (222)
period (182)
periodic function (182)

phase shift (193)
principal values (215)
simple harmonic motion (229)
sinusoids (193)
vertical shift (194)

Graphs of the Sine and Cosine Functions   The sine and cosine functions are periodic   4.1
with period 2π. The sine is an odd function, and the cosine is an even function.

Graph each function over the interval $[-2\pi, 2\pi]$. Explain how the graphs are
transformations of $y = \sin x$ or $y = \cos x$.

1. $f(x) = \sin\left(x - \frac{\pi}{3}\right) + 1$

2. $g(x) = 3 \cos\left(x + \frac{\pi}{4}\right)$

Period, Amplitude, and Phase Shift   The general functions $f(x) = a \sin b(x - c) + d$ 4.2
and $g(x) = a \cos b(x - c) + d$ have amplitude $|a|$, period $\frac{2\pi}{|b|}$, phase shift $|c|$ (to the
right if $c > 0$ and to the left if $c < 0$), and vertical shift $|d|$ (downward if $d < 0$ and
upward if $d > 0$).

Determine the amplitude, period, phase shift, and vertical shift of each function.
Then graph the function.

3. $y = 2 \cos\left(x + \frac{\pi}{6}\right) - 3$

4. $y = 3 \sin\left(2x - \frac{\pi}{2}\right) + 2$

Graphing Other Trigonometric Functions   The general functions $f(x) =$ 4.3
$a \tan b(x - c) + d$ and $g(x) = a \cot b(x - c) + d$ have period $\frac{\pi}{|b|}$, phase shift $|c|$ (to
the right if $c > 0$ and to the left if $c < 0$), and vertical shift $|d|$. The general functions
$h(x) = a \sec b(x - c) + d$ and $k(x) = a \csc b(x - c) + d$ have period $\frac{2\pi}{|b|}$, phase
shift $|c|$ (to the right if $c > 0$ and to the left if $c < 0$), and vertical shift $|d|$.

For each function, determine the period, phase shift, vertical shift, and the
equations for two vertical asymptotes. Then graph the function.

5. $f(x) = \tan 2\left(x - \frac{1}{4}\pi\right) + 1$

6. $f(t) = 3 \csc (t - \pi) - 2$

7. $f(x) = 2 \sec\left(2x - \frac{\pi}{3}\right) + 1$

8. $g(x) = \cot 2x + 3$

Graphing by Addition of Ordinates   This is a technique for obtaining the graph of   4.4
the sum $f + g$ of two functions by adding the respective y-values for each x-value.

Graph each function.

9. $g(t) = \cos t + t$

10. $h(x) = \cos \frac{1}{2}x + \sin \frac{1}{2}x$

Summary and Review   **237**

237

Additional Answers

17.

18.

23.

24.

27.

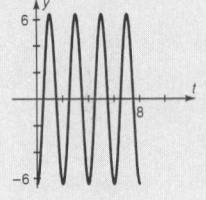

The Inverse Sine and Cosine Functions   The sine function with domain restricted to   4.5
$\left[-\frac{\pi}{2}, \frac{\pi}{2}\right]$ is written $y = \text{Sin } x$, and the cosine function with domain restricted
to $[0, \pi]$ is written $y = \text{Cos } x$. The inverse Sine function, $y = \text{Sin}^{-1} x$, has domain
$[-1, 1]$ and range $\left[-\frac{\pi}{2}, \frac{\pi}{2}\right]$. The inverse Cosine function, $y = \text{Cos}^{-1} x$, has domain
$[-1, 1]$ and range $[0, \pi]$.

Determine the exact value of each.

11. $\text{Arcsin}\left(-\frac{1}{2}\right)$ $-\frac{\pi}{6}$

12. $\text{Cos}^{-1}\frac{\sqrt{3}}{2}$ $\frac{\pi}{6}$

13. $\sin\left(\text{Arcsin}\frac{\pi}{6}\right)$ $\frac{\pi}{6}$

14. $\text{Arccos}\left(\cos\frac{5\pi}{3}\right)$ $\frac{\pi}{3}$

Evaluate to four decimal places.

15. $\text{Arccos}(-0.75)$ 2.4189

16. $\text{Sin}^{-1} 0.37$ 0.3790

Graph each function.

17. $f(x) = \text{Sin}^{-1} x + 2$

18. $f(x) = 3 \text{ Arccos } x$

Other Inverse Trigonometric Functions   When the domains of the other trigonometric   4.6
functions are restricted to make them one-to-one, they are written $y = \text{Tan } x$,
$y = \text{Cot } x$, $y = \text{Sec } x$, and $y = \text{Csc } x$. The inverse Tangent function, $y = \text{Tan}^{-1} x$,
has domain $\{x: x \in R\}$ and range $\left\{y: -\frac{1}{2}\pi < y < \frac{1}{2}\pi\right\}$; the inverse Cotangent
function, $y = \text{Cot}^{-1} x$, has domain $\{x: x \in R\}$ and range $\{y: 0 < y < \pi\}$;
the inverse Secant function, $y = \text{Sec}^{-1} x$ has domain $\{x: |x| \geq 1\}$ and range
$\left\{y: 0 \leq y \leq \pi, y \neq \frac{1}{2}\pi\right\}$; the inverse Cosecant function, $y = \text{Csc}^{-1} x$, has domain
$\{x: |x| \geq 1\}$ and range $\left\{y: -\frac{1}{2}\pi \leq y \leq \frac{1}{2}\pi, y \neq 0\right\}$.

The definitions of the trigonometric functions and the trigonometric identities make
it possible to rewrite trigonometric equations as algebraic equations.

Evaluate to four decimal places.

19. $\text{Sec}^{-1} 4.5$ 1.3467   **20.** $\text{Arccos}(-0.52)$ 2.1176   **21.** $\text{Arctan } 7$ 1.4289   **22.** $\text{Cot}^{-1}(0.37)$ 1.2164

Graph.

23. $h(t) = \text{Tan}^{-1} t + 1$

24. $g(x) = \text{Arcsec }(x - 2)$

25. Find the exact value of $\tan\left(\text{Sin}^{-1}\frac{5}{12}\right)$. $\frac{5\sqrt{119}}{119}$

26. Rewrite $y = \sec(\text{Cot}^{-1} t)$ as an algebraic equation. $y = \frac{\sqrt{t^2 + 1}}{t}$

Application: Harmonic Motion   Sinusoidal equations of the form $y = a \sin b(t - c) + d$ 4.7
and $y = a \cos b(t - c) + d$ can be used to model simple harmonic motion.

27. *Mechanics*   A weight suspended from a spring is set into oscillating
motion by pulling it to a point 6.4 cm below its resting position and then
releasing it. It takes 2 s for the weight to complete one cycle. Determine an
equation describing the position of the weight at time t seconds, letting 0
represent its rest position. Graph the equation. $y = -6.4 \cos \pi t$

238   Chapter 4 Graphs and Inverses of Trigonometric Functions

Chapter 4 Test

For each function, determine (where applicable) the amplitude, period, phase shift, vertical shift, and the equations for two vertical asymptotes. Then graph the function.

1. $f(x) = 3 \cos \frac{1}{4}x$

2. $g(x) = \sin(3x - \pi) - 1$

3. $G(x) = \tan\left(2x - \frac{\pi}{3}\right) + 2$

4. $F(x) = 2 \sec\left(x - \frac{\pi}{3}\right)$

5. Graph the function $g(x) = 2 \sin x + \cos 2x$ over the interval $[-2\pi, 2\pi]$.

Determine the equation for each graph.

6.

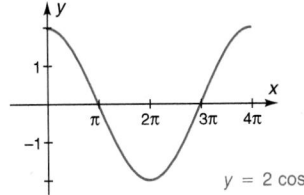

$y = 2 \cos \frac{1}{2}x$

7.

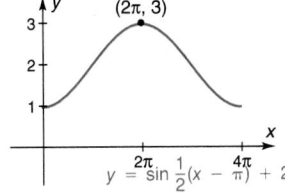

$(2\pi, 3)$

$y = \sin \frac{1}{2}(x - \pi) + 2$

Use the definition of the inverse functions to determine the exact value of each of the following:

8. $\operatorname{Arcsin} \frac{\sqrt{2}}{2}$ $\frac{\pi}{4}$

9. $\operatorname{Arccos}\left(-\frac{\sqrt{2}}{2}\right)$ $\frac{3\pi}{4}$

10. $\operatorname{Tan}^{-1} \frac{\sqrt{3}}{3}$ $\frac{\pi}{6}$

11. $\operatorname{Csc}^{-1} \sqrt{2}$ $\frac{\pi}{4}$

12. Graph the equation $y = \operatorname{Arccos} x + 2$.

13. Find the exact value of $\tan\left(\operatorname{Cos}^{-1} \frac{8}{17}\right)$. $\frac{15}{8}$

14. A weight suspended from a spring is set into oscillating motion by compressing it to a point 5.6 cm above its resting position and releasing it. It takes 3 s for the weight to complete one cycle. Determine an equation that describes the position of the weight at time t seconds, letting 0 represent the rest position. Graph the equation. $y = 5.6 \cos \frac{2\pi}{3}t$

Challenge

The curve at the right is a graphical model of a simple harmonic motion. Derive an equation for the graph. $y = 7 \cos \frac{\pi}{10}t - 2$

1.

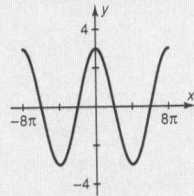

$3; 8\pi; 0; 0$

2.

$1; \frac{2\pi}{3}; \frac{\pi}{3}$ right;
1 down

3.

Amplitude does not apply; $\frac{\pi}{2}; \frac{\pi}{6}$ right;
2 up

4.

Amplitude does not apply; $2\pi, \frac{\pi}{3}$ right; 0

5.

12.

14.

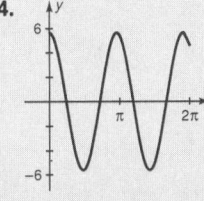

239

Cumulative Review

In each item you are to compare a quantity in Column 1 with a quantity in Column 2. Write the letter of the correct answer from these choices:

A. The quantity in Column 1 is greater than the quantity in Column 2.
B. The quantity in Column 2 is greater than the quantity in Column 1.
C. The quantity in Column 1 is equal to the quantity in Column 2.
D. The relationship cannot be determined from the given information.

Notes: Information centered over both columns refers to one or both of the quantities being compared. A symbol that appears in both columns has the same meaning in each column. All variables represent real numbers. Most figures are not drawn to scale.

	Column 1	Column 2	
	$f(x) = 3x^2 - 4x + 1$		
1. $f(2)$ B		$f(-1)$	1.4
	The sum of		
2. all natural C numbers		all whole numbers	1.2
	$f(x) = |x|$		
3. 6 C		-6	1.7
	$\dfrac{45 \text{ min}}{4} = \dfrac{1 \text{ h } 15 \text{ min}}{x}$		
4. x A		6	1.3
5. $[\![-7]\!]$ C		-7	1.7
	$f(x) = 3x^4 + x^2 - 4$		
6. $f(-x)$ C		$f(x)$	2.1
7. $\cos \dfrac{2\pi}{3}$ B		$\sin \dfrac{2\pi}{3}$	3.5
8. $\dfrac{\pi}{6}$ C		$\text{Sin}^{-1} \dfrac{1}{2}$	4.5
	$4x^2 - 12x + 9 = 0$		
9. x C		$\dfrac{3}{2}$	2.4

	Column 1	Column 2	
10. $\dfrac{\sin \theta}{\cos \theta}$ D		$\dfrac{\cos \theta}{\sin \theta}$	3.8
	$f(x) = 3 \sin 4x$		
11. period C		$\dfrac{\pi}{2}$	4.2
	$3x = 5 - 6y$		
12. slope of line C		$-\dfrac{1}{2}$	2.3
13. 0 A		$\cos 540°$	3.6
14. $\sec (\text{Tan}^{-1} 1)$ C		$\sqrt{2}$	4.6
	$f(x) = -2x + 3 \qquad g(x) = x^2 - 2$		
15. $f(-2)$ A		$g(\sqrt{5})$	1.4
	$\cos \theta = \dfrac{1}{3}$		
16. $\sec \theta$ A		$\tan \theta$	3.5
	$f(x) = \dfrac{x-2}{x+2} \qquad g(x) = \sqrt{x^2 + 1}$		
17. $f(g(0))$ B		$g(f(0))$	1.5
18. $\sin 60°$ C		$\cos 30°$	3.5
	amplitude		
19. $f(x) = 2 \sin 3x$ B	$g(x) = 4 \cos 2x$		4.2

20. Express the function $\sin \frac{\pi}{8}$ in terms of its cofunction. $\cos \frac{3\pi}{8}$ 4.1

34.

21. Determine the range of the cotangent function. the set of all real numbers   4.3

22. For the pair of functions, $f(x) = 4x - 12$ and $g(x) = \frac{1}{4}x + 3$, find the line in which g is a reflection of f. $y = x$ 2.2

23. Determine the angular velocity in radians per second of a wheel turning at 240 rpm. 25   3.3

37.

24. For all x, $\sin(-x) = -\sin x$. Is this function odd, even, or neither? odd   4.1

25. Determine the period of the function $F(t) = \sin \frac{1}{2}t + \cos \frac{1}{3}t$. 12π 4.4

26. Identify at least two zeros for the function $F(x) = 0.5 \cos 3x$. $\frac{\pi}{6}, \frac{\pi}{2}$ 4.2

27. Given the point $(4, -5)$, determine a point that satisfies symmetry with respect to the y-axis. $(-4, -5)$ 2.1

28. Sec θ and cot θ have opposite signs in which quadrant(s)? III, IV   3.5

29. Determine $\sin\left(\text{Cos}^{-1} \frac{\sqrt{5}}{6}\right)$. $\frac{\sqrt{31}}{6}$ 4.5

30. Determine the x- and y-intercepts of the quadratic function $f(x) = 5x^2 - 20x$.   2.5
x-intercepts: (0, 0), (4, 0); y-intercept: (0, 0)

31. A $\frac{4}{9}$ clockwise rotation would terminate in which quadrant and yield what angle measurement? III, $-160°$ 3.1

32. Find the value of $\cos \theta$ if $\sin \theta = -\frac{2}{3}$ and angle θ is in standard position with terminal side in the fourth quadrant. $\frac{\sqrt{5}}{3}$ 3.4

33. Solve for x: $4x^3 + 8x^2 - 3x - 6 = 0$ $\pm \frac{\sqrt{3}}{2}, -2$ 2.6

34. Graph and determine the period of the function $F(x) = \sin \frac{1}{2}x$. 4π 4.2

35. Use the definition of inverse Sine function to determine the exact value of $\text{Sin}^{-1} 2$. not defined   4.5

36. Determine the arc length of a circle of radius 10 cm intercepted by an angle of $\frac{2\pi}{3}$, to the nearest tenth. 20.9 cm   3.2

37. Graph the function $f(x) = \frac{1}{3} \cos x$.   4.1

38. Determine the sinusoidal function of sine with amplitude $\frac{2}{3}$, period π, translation 2 units up. $f(x) = \frac{2}{3} \sin 2x + 2$ 4.2

39. Determine the distance between the points $(-3.2, 6.8)$ and $(-8.3, -5.2)$. $d = 13.04$ 2.7

40. The values of the sine function are always between ___?___. -1 and 1 inclusive   4.1

41. Determine the equation of the horizontal line that passes through point $(-8, 3)$. $y = 3$ 2.3

42. Determine the angle coterminal with $-\frac{7\pi}{2}$ that has a radian measure between 0 and 2π. $\frac{\pi}{2}$ 3.1

Cumulative Review   **241**

Summary

Triangles, both right and oblique, are solved using the trigonometric functions, the law of sines and the law of cosines. Areas of sectors and segments of circles as well as areas of triangles are determined. Heron's formula is introduced and used for finding areas. Applications include using triangle solutions in geographic models and in estimating inaccessible distances.

Chapter Objectives

- To solve a right triangle given the measures of one angle and one side or the measures of two sides
- To solve an isosceles triangle by dividing it into congruent right triangles
- To introduce and prove the law of sines
- To use the law of sines to solve a triangle when the measures of two angles and one side are given
- To use the law of sines to solve a triangle when two sides and an angle opposite one of them is given
- To introduce and prove the law of cosines
- To use the law of cosines to solve a triangle when the measures of two sides and the included angle are given or when the measures of three sides are given
- To find the area of a triangle given the measures of two sides and the included angle or one side and two angles
- To use Heron's formula to find the area of a triangle given the lengths of three sides
- To find the area of the segment of a circle

5 Applications of Trigonometry

Mathematical Power

Modeling   Have you ever tried sailing a toy boat or dropping a stick into a river and then watching as it moved downstream? Or, while swimming or sitting in a rowboat, did you notice that the speed at which the river flows seems to vary at different places across the width? Usually, for a straight stretch of river, the flow will be fastest in the middle and then taper off to almost nothing near the banks.

There are many factors that can influence how a river flows. In order to construct a mathematical model, you must first decide what assumptions can be made that will simplify the situation but still yield a useful result. Consider an example in which the banks are 40 m apart and river flow is 3 m/s at the middle. To simplify the problem, suppose that the river is straight without any obstacles such as sand bars and that the banks are parallel. Also assume that the flow tapers off *symmetrically* to 0 m/s at the banks.

To model this situation, you must try to find a mathematical function that will fit the known facts. If the model is a good one, it may help you to make new predictions about the situation. For example, you may be able to use it to estimate the volume of water flow.

Features

Modeling

To create a model, represent the velocity of the flow as $V = f(x)$. Then $f(0) = f(40) = 0$ and $f(20) = 3$. Moreover, $f(x)$ is symmetric about $x = 20$ and $0 \leq f(x) \leq 3$ for $0 \leq x \leq 40$. Each of the three models below fits the conditions.

Model I   This model assumes that the river's flow increases and decreases at a constant rate from each bank to the middle. The function used is linear.

$$V = \begin{cases} \frac{3}{20}x, & 0 \leq x \leq 20 \\ -\frac{3}{20}x + 6, & 20 < x \leq 40 \end{cases}$$

Model II   This model also reflects the desired symmetry but uses a parabolic curve defined by a quadratic function.

$$V = \frac{3x(40 - x)}{400}, \qquad 0 \leq x \leq 40$$

Model III   A sine curve also fits the conditions of the problem.

$$V = 3 \sin \frac{\pi}{40}x, \qquad 0 \leq x \leq 40$$

The functions used in Model II and Model III suggest that the river's flow drops off gradually from the center to the edges, in contrast to the steep decline reflected in Model I. Many other models are also possible. The particular model that you choose to work with will depend on how the model is to be used.

Thinking Critically   Suppose you are the captain of a ship sailing on the river described above. What instructions would you give the crew for traveling upstream? For traveling downstream? What other factors that were omitted could influence a river's flow?

Project   Do research to obtain some basic facts about the flow of a river in your state. Adapt one of the models described above to fit the information you gather. Be sure to list the assumptions or simplifications you are using and explain why you think the choice of a model is reasonable. Discuss ways in which the model could be applied.

243

Mathematical Power
In the context of a problem about river flow, this lesson illustrates several important steps in the modeling process; moreover, it serves to remind students that the sine, cosine, and tangent are *functions,* with graphs and defining equations, which can be used in modeling just as linear or quadratic functions are used.

As the discussion points out, real world situations almost always require simplification, but this must be done in a way that retains the elements that are important for the model-maker's purposes. Because experimental data about river speed at different distances from the banks is *not* available, certain reasonable assumptions about the flow are made. Be sure students understand that the assumption of symmetry does not necessarily imply a constant rate of change in speed and, so, this assumption must be noted specifically in Model I.

As part of the lesson summary, explain that finding a satisfactory curve to model information depends on mathematical experience and a certain amount of imagination. The more familiar students become with a wide range of functions, the more possibilities they will have to choose from. Also, a simple model that serves its purpose is preferable to a complex model that is difficult to work with.

Thinking Critically   One possibility is to travel downstream in the middle of the river and upstream near the banks, if possible. Possible factors that might influence a river's flow include prevailing winds and other weather conditions, seasonal currents and tides, and widening or narrowing of the river bed.

Vocabulary
angle of depression
angle of elevation

Ⓜ **Materials/Manipulatives**
compass
globe or map with latitudes labeled
protractor
straightedge

Technology
scientific calculator
Geometric Supposer

FOCUS

Have students research Aristarchus and his attempt to find distances from the earth to the moon and to the sun using ratios, Fibonacci and his work with application of trigonometry to surveying, and Euclid and his early development of the law of cosines. This may provide students with an appreciation of the development of trigonometry from applications like the one in the Focus.

INSTRUCTION

• Students should be able to determine the six right triangle ratios regardless of how the triangle is labeled or its orientation.

Ⓜ • A transparency of a table similar to the one for Class Exercises 5 to 8 may help students organize their work.

• If it is available, students can use the Geometric Supposer to measure sides and angles of right triangles and to determine the six trigonometric functions for the acute angle. Then have them use a calculator to compare results.

• Encourage students to draw diagrams before starting the computations.

5.1 Solving Right Triangles

Objectives: *To solve a right triangle given the measures of one angle and one side or the measures of two sides*
To solve an isosceles triangle by dividing it into congruent right triangles

Focus

The boundary between Wyoming and Montana is the 45th parallel of latitude. Measuring latitude is a way of locating places on the earth in relation to the equator. At the equator, the circumference of the earth is about 40,212 km. Many other circles lie in planes which may be considered parallel to the equatorial plane because they intersect neither the equatorial plane nor each other. The position of these parallels of latitude is given by an angle whose vertex is at the center of the earth. One segment of the angle is a radius at the equator, and the other connects the center to the parallel of latitude.

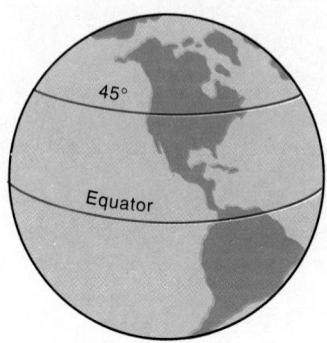

The circles of latitude decrease in size as they get farther from the equator. A function can be found which expresses the length of any parallel in terms of the latitude of the parallel. The function provides a method for working with right triangles.

In Chapter 3, you learned to find the values of the trigonometric functions of any angle θ given a point $P(x, y)$ distinct from the origin on its terminal side, with $r = \sqrt{x^2 + y^2}$. In this chapter, trigonometric functions will be presented in terms of the ratios of lengths of sides of right triangles.

A triangle is said to be **solved** when the lengths of all its sides and the measures of all its angles are known. The trigonometric functions of an acute angle are used to solve right triangles. In labeling triangles, capital letters are usually used to represent the angles themselves or their measures. Lowercase letters refer to the sides opposite their respective angles or to their measures. The Greek letters α (alpha), β (beta), γ (gamma), and θ (theta) are also used to represent angles.

Right triangle ABC with acute angle A can be used to express the trigonometric functions of θ as ratios in terms of the lengths of the sides of the triangle, where

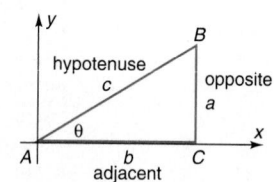

$$a = \text{length of leg opposite } \theta$$
$$b = \text{length of leg adjacent to } \theta$$
$$c = \sqrt{a^2 + b^2} = \text{hypotenuse}$$

244   Chapter 5 Applications of Trigonometry

Trigonometric Functions	Right Triangle Ratios ($0° < \theta < 90°$)
$\sin \theta = \dfrac{y}{r}$	$\sin \theta = \dfrac{a}{c} = \dfrac{\text{length of leg opposite } \theta}{\text{length of hypotenuse}}$
$\cos \theta = \dfrac{x}{r}$	$\cos \theta = \dfrac{b}{c} = \dfrac{\text{length of leg adjacent to } \theta}{\text{length of hypotenuse}}$
$\tan \theta = \dfrac{y}{x}$	$\tan \theta = \dfrac{a}{b} = \dfrac{\text{length of leg opposite } \theta}{\text{length of leg adjacent to } \theta}$
$\csc \theta = \dfrac{r}{y}$	$\csc \theta = \dfrac{c}{a} = \dfrac{\text{length of hypotenuse}}{\text{length of leg opposite } \theta}$
$\sec \theta = \dfrac{r}{x}$	$\sec \theta = \dfrac{c}{b} = \dfrac{\text{length of hypotenuse}}{\text{length of leg adjacent to } \theta}$
$\cot \theta = \dfrac{x}{y}$	$\cot \theta = \dfrac{b}{a} = \dfrac{\text{length of leg adjacent to } \theta}{\text{length of leg opposite } \theta}$

Example 1 Solve right triangle ABC if $b = 18$, $\angle A = 37°$, and $\angle C = 90°$. Determine a and c to the nearest unit.

To find c, use $\cos 37°$.

$$\cos 37° = \frac{18}{c} \qquad \cos A = \frac{b}{c}$$

$$c = \frac{18}{\cos 37°} \qquad \textit{Calculation-ready form}$$

$$c = 23 \qquad \textit{To the nearest unit}$$

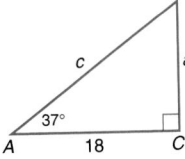

To find a, use $\tan 37°$.

$$\tan 37° = \frac{a}{18} \qquad \tan A = \frac{a}{b}$$

$$a = 18 \tan 37°$$

$$a = 14 \qquad \textit{To the nearest unit}$$

$$\angle B = 90° - 37° = 53° \qquad \textit{Angles A and B are complementary.}$$

When the lengths of two sides of a right triangle are known, the Pythagorean theorem can be used to determine the length of the third side. The angles can be determined by using the trigonometric functions.

Example 2 Solve right triangle ABC if $c = 8.65$, $a = 5.74$, and $\angle C = 90°$. Determine b to the nearest hundredth and angle measures to the nearest tenth of a degree.

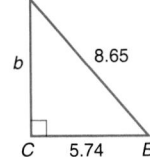

$$(5.74)^2 + b^2 = (8.65)^2 \qquad \textit{Use the Pythagorean theorem.}$$

$$b^2 = (8.65)^2 - (5.74)^2$$

$$b = \sqrt{(8.65)^2 - (5.74)^2} \qquad \textit{Calculation-ready form}$$

$$b = 6.47$$

5.1 Solving Right Triangles   **245**

Technology It may be necessary
to review inverse function keys and
their operation on the calculator.
Students should consult the owners'
manuals for their particular
calculators.

For Example 3

1. Solve isosceles triangle *ABC* if
   $a = c = 12.4$, $\overline{BD}$ is the altitude,
   and $\angle C = 56°$. Find *AC* to the
   nearest tenth. $\angle A = 56°$, $\angle B = 68°$,
   AC = 13.9
2. Solve isosceles triangle *KLM* if
   $k = m = 19.8$, $\overline{LN}$ is the altitude,
   and $\angle K = 38°$. Determine *KM* to
   the nearest tenth. $\angle M = 38°$,
   $\angle L = 104°$, *KM* = 31.2

For Example 4

A security camera in a bank mounted
on a wall 10 ft from the floor is aimed
at a spot on the floor 22 ft away.
Determine the angle of depression
from the security camera to the spot
on the floor. The angle of depression is
approximately 24°.

$$\cos B = \frac{5.74}{8.65}$$

$\angle B = 48.4°$ To the nearest tenth

$\angle A = 90° - 48.4° = 41.6°$ *Angles A and B are complementary.*

Note that a calculator retains many more digits than it displays. Although
you must round to the required number of digits to answer specific parts
of certain exercises, you should retain full values in your calculator until you
have completed an entire exercise.

An isosceles triangle with the altitude drawn from its vertex angle consists of
two congruent right triangles. If sufficient information is available to solve one
of the right triangles, the original isosceles triangle may also be solved.

Example 3   Solve isosceles triangle *ABC* if $a = c = 6.0$, $\overline{BD}$ is
the altitude, and $\angle C = 40°$. Determine *AC* to the
nearest tenth.

$\angle A = \angle C = 40°$ *Base angles of an isosceles triangle are equal.*

$\angle B = 180° - (\angle A + \angle C)$ *The sum of the measures of the angles in a triangle is 180°*
$\angle B = 180° - (40° + 40°)$
$\angle B = 100°$

$$\cos 40° = \frac{DC}{6}$$

$DC = 6 \cos 40°$
$DC = 4.596$ *Retain the full value of DC in your calculator.*

$AC = 2(DC) = 9.2$ *The altitude to the base of an isosceles triangle bisects the base.*

Many applications of right triangle trigonometry involve two special
angles. The **angle of depression** is the acute angle measured from a
horizontal line down to the line of sight. The **angle of elevation** is the
acute angle measured from a horizontal line up to the line of sight.
Note that the angle of depression is equal to the angle of elevation.

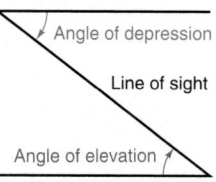

Example 4   *Security*   A heat sensor security light is positioned 8 ft above street level and
illuminates a front walk all the way to the curb, which is a distance of 40 ft.
Determine the angle of depression from the security light to the curb.

Since the angle of depression α equals the angle of
elevation β, find $\angle \beta$.

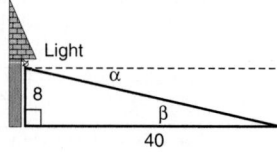

$\tan \beta = \frac{8}{40} = 0.2$

$\angle \beta = 11°$ To the nearest degree

The angle of depression is approximately 11°.

246   Chapter 5 Applications of Trigonometry

Modeling

What is the length of a parallel of the earth at any given latitude?

The radius of the earth, denoted R, is approximately 6400 km. Angle B represents the latitude angle. Let r be the radius of the circle around the earth at latitude B. Then

$$\cos B = \frac{r}{R}$$
$$r = R \cos B$$

The length of the parallel at latitude B is given by

$$C = 2\pi r$$
$$C = 2\pi R \cos B \qquad \textit{Substitute } R \cos B \textit{ for } r.$$

Example 5 *Geography* Determine the length of the 30th parallel that passes through Austin, Texas, to the nearest whole number.

$$C = 2\pi R \cos B$$
$$C = 2\pi(6400) \cos 30°$$
$$C = 34{,}825 \qquad \text{To the nearest whole number}$$

The length of the 30th parallel is approximately 34,825 km.

Class Exercises

Solve each right triangle ABC. Express answers to the nearest unit or degree.

1.
$\angle B = 55°;\ b = 26;\ c = 31$

2.
$\angle A = 75°;\ b = 3;\ c = 12$

3.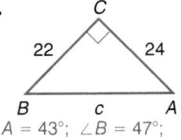
$\angle A = 43°;\ \angle B = 47°;\ c = 33$

4.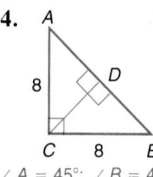
$\angle A = 45°;\ \angle B = 45°;\ c = 11$

Complete the table below using right triangle ABC. Express answers to the nearest tenth of a unit or degree.

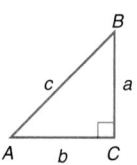

	a	b	c	$\angle A$	$\angle B$
5.	56	16	58.2	74.1°	15.9°
6.	96.4	37	103.2	69°	21°
7.	202.7	365.6	418	29°	61°
8.	26.9	10.9	29	68°	22°

9. Thinking Critically For right triangle ABC, with side b fixed and both a and c getting longer, which trigonometric functions of $\angle A$ have function values that get larger? Stay fixed? Get smaller? sec, tan; none; cos, cot

10. The angle of elevation of the top of Twin Towers from a distance of 200 ft from the base is 80°. Find the height of the Twin Towers. 1134 ft

5.1 Solving Right Triangles **247**

For Example 5
1. Determine the length of the 43rd parallel to the nearest whole number. 29,409 km
2. Determine the length of the 29th parallel. 35,171 km

Common Error Some students may have calculators in radian mode instead of degree mode. Remind those students to check the mode before beginning any calculations.

CLOSURE

Group students in pairs and have them summarize to each other the procedures for solving a right triangle and for solving an isosceles triangle.

Practice Exercises   Use appropriate technology.

Solve each triangle *ABC*. Express answers to the nearest unit or degree.

A 1.

$\angle B = 71°$; $a = 4$; $c = 13$

2.

$\angle A = 12°$; $b = 28$; $c = 29$

3.
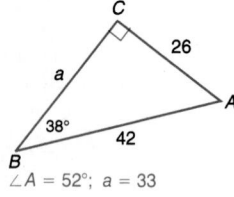
$\angle A = 52°$; $a = 33$

4.

$\angle A = 54°$; $\angle B = 36°$; $c = 26$

5.
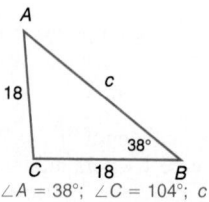
$\angle A = 38°$; $\angle C = 104°$; $c = 28$

6.

$\angle A = 56°$; $\angle B = 56°$; $c = 11$

Solve each right triangle *ABC* with $\angle C = 90°$ using the given information. Express answers to the nearest tenth of a unit or degree.

7. $\angle B = 70°$, $a = 36$

8. $b = 47$, $\angle A = 56°$

9. $\angle B = 32°$, $c = 340$

10. $c = 100$, $\angle A = 35°$
   $\angle B = 55°$; $a = 57.4$; $b = 81.9$

11. $b = 7$, $c = 25$
   $\angle A = 73.7°$; $\angle B = 16.3°$; $a = 24$

12. $a = 29$, $b = 46$
   $\angle A = 32.2°$; $\angle B = 57.8°$; $c = 54.4$

® 13. If $f(x) = 3x$ and $g(x) = \sin x$, find $(f \cdot g)(x)$ when $x = 2.5$. 4.5

14. *Construction*   A homeowner is to construct a ramp to his front door to make it wheelchair-accessible. How long is the ramp if the door is 4 ft above ground level and the angle of elevation is 20°? 11.7 ft

15. *Entertainment*   For a laser light show at an amusement park, the laser beam directed from the top of a 30-ft building is to reflect from an object that is 100 ft away from a point directly below the location of the laser. What is the angle of depression from the laser to the reflecting object? 16.7°

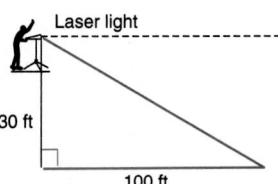

16. **Thinking Critically**   Two right triangles with congruent hypotenuses are placed together so that the hypotenuse of the first triangle coincides with the hypotenuse of the second triangle. Under what conditions will the resulting quadrilateral be a rectangle? A square? A trapezoid?

17. *Construction*   A backyard storage shed has been found to be leaning and making a 6° angle with the vertical. How much has the top of this shed moved off the vertical if it were originally 10 ft high? 1 ft

18. **Writing in Mathematics**   Explain how the definitions of the trigonometric functions as stated for an acute angle of a right triangle compare with those used for an angle in standard position.

® 19. If $f(x) = x^2$ and $g(x) = \cos x$, find $(f \cdot g)(-3)$. –8.9

20. **Thinking Critically**   Which of the six trigonometric functions can have function values greater than 1? Why?

248   Chapter 5 Applications of Trigonometry

Writing in Mathematics
18. The hypotenuse of the triangle would be the radius r, the adjacent side would be x, and the opposite side would be y. Thus, $\sin \theta = \frac{y}{r}$, $\cos \theta = \frac{x}{r}$, and $\tan \theta = \frac{y}{x}$.

B **21.** *Construction*   During construction of a house, one side of the door
frame is supported by a brace 4 ft long. One end of the brace makes
an angle of 48° with the floor. To the nearest tenth of a foot, how high
from the floor is the end of the brace attached to the door frame? 3 ft

22. Determine the length of the 45th parallel. 28,434 km

23. Determine the parallel which is one-half the length of the equator. 60th parallel

24. *Construction*   An 80-ft rope is attached to the top of a vertical pole
standing in the center of a circus tent. The other end of the rope is attached
to a stake 60 ft from the base of the pole. Determine the angle of elevation
of the rope. 41°

Ⓡ **25.** Determine the measures of the angle, its complement, and its supplement if
four times the supplement equals nine times the complement. 18°; 72°; 162°

26. **Thinking Critically**   Two right triangles with one congruent leg are placed
together so that the congruent legs are coincident. Under what conditions
will the resulting figure be a parallelogram? An isosceles triangle?

Ⓡ **27.** Use the following information to determine all the angles
in the figure: $\angle BCD = 115°$, $\angle ADC = 53°$, $\angle DAB = 62°$.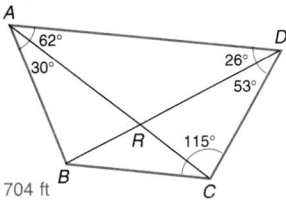

28. *Surveying*   An observer on the twelfth floor of a
building determines that the angle of depression of the
foot of a building across the street is 54.6° and the angle
of elevation of the top of the same building is 82.3°. If the
street is 80 ft wide, find the height of the observed building. 704 ft

Ⓡ **29.** If $h(x) = x^2 + 3$, graph $h^{-1}(x)$.

30. *Surveying*   A surveyor observes that the top
of a building makes an angle of 37.2° with the
road. From another location 400 ft away the
angle of elevation is 20°. How far is the base
of the building from the first observation point
on the road? 191.8 ft

31. Each side of a regular hexagon is 32.6 cm long. What is the radius of the
inscribed circle? 28.2 cm

32. Each side of a regular pentagon is 48.6 in. long. What is the radius of the
inscribed circle? 33.4 in.

33. *Surveying*   A pilot of a small plane was flying over an oil spill at an
altitude of 10,000 ft. He found that the near edge of the spill had an angle
of depression of 58° and the far edge of the spill had an angle of depression
of 44°. What is the width of the spill? 16,604 ft

34. *Engineering*   A security camera in a bank is mounted on the wall 6.2 ft
above the level of the counter and 9.4 ft behind the front edge of the
counter. What is the angle of depression of the camera if it is to be aimed
2 ft beyond the front edge of the counter? 28.5°

Ⓡ **35.** Graph $f(x) = 2 \cos \frac{1}{2}x + 2$.

36. Determine the parallel of latitude of the earth that has length 38,000 km, to
the nearest degree. 19th parallel

5.1 Solving Right Triangles   **249**

29.

35.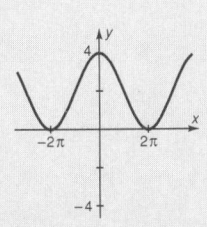

C 37. *Construction* A painter wishes to rent a ladder to paint the gable of a house that is 60 ft tall at its peak. The ladder must reach a point 6 ft from the peak. For safety reasons the ladder must be placed at a 74° angle. How long should the ladder be? 56 ft

38. *Mechanics* Two pulleys have diameters of 16 and 22 cm, respectively, and their centers are 38 cm apart. If the two pulleys are to be belted together, what must the length of the belt be? 136 cm

39. *Mechanics* Two pulleys have diameters of 24 and 28 in., respectively, and their centers are 42 in. apart. If the two pulleys are to be belted together, what must the length of the belt be? 166 in.

40. How much longer would the belt have to be if the belt were crossed in Exercise 38? 9 cm

41. How much shorter is the belt in Exercise 39 than it would have to be if the belt were crossed? 14 in.

42. *Photography* A camera is on a tripod 10 ft from a group of people. If the camera lens has angles of depression and elevation of 20° and is at a height of 5 ft from the floor, will both the feet and head of a man 6 ft tall be seen by the lens? no

43. *Photography* A camera is on a tripod 9 ft from a group of people. If the camera lens has angles of depression and elevation of 25° and is at a height 3 ft from the floor, will both the feet and head of a man 6 ft 6 in. tall be seen by the lens? yes

44. *Aviation* A plane approaching an airport is being tracked by two devices on the ground that are 746 ft apart. The angle of elevation from the first device is 17.4°, and from the second it is 15.5°. Determine the height of the plane. 1798 ft

15.5°
17.4°
746 ft

> **Project**

Find the degree of latitude for the city or town in which you live. Find the length of the parallel on which you live. How long would it take to fly half way around the parallel on which you live at 1150 km/h? How long would it take to fly to the same point if you flew over the north pole? Assume that the circumference of the earth over the poles is the same as at the equator.

Review

Determine the amplitude and period of each function.

1. $f(x) = \sin 4\left(x - \frac{\pi}{4}\right)$ 1; $\frac{\pi}{2}$

2. $g(\theta) = 3 \cos \frac{1}{3}(3\theta - 6\pi)$ 3; 2π

3. Determine the equation of the line passing through $(-3, 5)$ and $(-6, -8)$.
   $y = \frac{13}{3}x + 18$

Determine whether each statement is true or false.

4. For $-2\pi \le x \le 2\pi$, $\sin x = \cos x$ when $x = \frac{\pi}{4}, \frac{5\pi}{4}, -\frac{3\pi}{4}, -\frac{7\pi}{4}$. true

5. All trigonometric functions are continuous functions. false

Objectives: To introduce and prove the law of sines
To use the law of sines to solve a triangle when the measures of two angles and one side are given

Focus

The figure at the right shows a tree that is leaning at a dangerous angle. The owner of the house must know whether the tree will hit the house if it falls. Using the information given in the figure and the skills developed in this lesson, you can determine the height of the tree and ascertain whether it will reach the house if it falls.

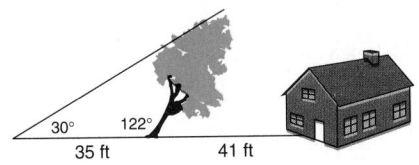

30° 122°
35 ft   41 ft

If the tree described above were standing straight, making a right angle with the ground, you would be able to solve the triangle using the trigonometric ratios. In this lesson, you will learn how to solve **oblique** (nonright) triangles whenever the measures of any two angles and a side are given.

Law of Sines

For any $\triangle ABC$, where a, b, and c are the lengths of the sides opposite the angles with measures A, B, and C, respectively,

$$\frac{\sin A}{a} = \frac{\sin B}{b} = \frac{\sin C}{c}$$

To prove the law of sines, two cases must be considered: acute and obtuse.

Case 1:   Triangle ABC is acute.

Proof: Draw the altitude h from B to side $\overline{AC}$ and label the intersection point D. In right triangles ABD and CBD,

$\sin A = \dfrac{h}{c}$ and $\sin C = \dfrac{h}{a}$

$h = c \sin A$ $h = a \sin C$

$c \sin A = a \sin C$ *Substitution*

$\dfrac{\sin A}{a} = \dfrac{\sin C}{c}$ *Divide both sides by ac.*

Similarly, draw altitude h_1 from A to side BC. Then

$\sin C = \dfrac{h_1}{b}$ and $\sin B = \dfrac{h_1}{c}$

$h_1 = b \sin C$ $h_1 = c \sin B$

5.2 The Law of Sines   **251**

LESSON PLAN

Vocabulary
law of sines

Technology
scientific calculator
Geometric Supposer

FOCUS

Applications involving oblique triangles are not difficult to find. Their use in teaching the law of sines and law of cosines helps to legitimize these topics for the students.

INSTRUCTION

• Stress that students should set up problems in calculation-ready form before using a scientific calculator.
• Encourage students to draw diagrams before starting the computations.
• Students may use the Geometric Supposer to measure sides and angles of oblique triangles, then compute the ratios $\dfrac{\sin A}{a}$, $\dfrac{\sin B}{b}$, and $\dfrac{\sin C}{c}$. They can then use a calculator to compare results.

Alternative Learning Styles
Some students need justification for solving oblique triangles. Ask them to help compile a list of situations where oblique triangles and the law of sines would be useful.

For Example 1

1. Solve $\triangle ABC$ if $\angle A = 38°$, $\angle B = 64°$, and $c = 81$. Express answers to the nearest unit.
$\angle A = 38°$, $\angle B = 64°$, $\angle C = 78°$, $a = 51$, $b = 74$, and $c = 81$

2. Solve $\triangle PQR$ if $\angle Q = 72°$, $\angle R = 44°$, and $p = 114$. Express answers to the nearest unit.
$\angle P = 64°$, $\angle Q = 72°$, $\angle R = 44°$, $p = 114$, $q = 121$, and $r = 88$

For Example 2

1. Solve $\triangle ABC$ if $\angle A = 56°$, $\angle B = 74°$, and $b = 78.2$. Express the lengths of the sides to the nearest tenth of a unit.
$\angle A = 56°$, $\angle B = 74°$, $\angle C = 50°$, $a = 67.4$, $b = 78.2$, and $c = 62.3$

2. Solve $\triangle DEF$ if $\angle E = 108°$, $\angle F = 28°$, and $e = 146.8$. Express the lengths of the sides to the nearest tenth of a unit.
$\angle D = 44°$, $\angle E = 108°$, $\angle F = 28°$, $d = 107.2$, $e = 146.8$, and $f = 72.5$

Common Error Students will sometimes use an incorrect ratio when using the law of sines. Stress that the side and the angle must be opposite each other and that in each ratio the side and the angle are named by the same letter.

$$b \sin C = c \sin B \qquad \textit{Substitution}$$
$$\frac{\sin C}{c} = \frac{\sin B}{b} \qquad \textit{Divide both sides by bc.}$$

Therefore, $\qquad \dfrac{\sin A}{a} = \dfrac{\sin B}{b} = \dfrac{\sin C}{c} \qquad \textit{Transitive property}$

You will be asked to prove the obtuse case in Exercise 37.

In practice, pairs of these ratios are used to solve certain oblique triangles.

$$\frac{\sin A}{a} = \frac{\sin B}{b} \qquad \frac{\sin A}{a} = \frac{\sin C}{c} \qquad \frac{\sin B}{b} = \frac{\sin C}{c}$$

If the measures of two angles and the included side of a triangle are given, then the law of sines can be used to solve the triangle.

Example 1 Solve $\triangle ABC$ if $\angle A = 42°$, $\angle B = 57°$, and $c = 67$. Express answers to the nearest unit.

$$\angle C = 180° - (57° + 42°) = 81°$$

To find a:

$$\frac{\sin A}{a} = \frac{\sin C}{c}$$
$$\frac{\sin 42°}{a} = \frac{\sin 81°}{67}$$
$$67 \sin 42° = a \sin 81°$$
$$\frac{67 \sin 42°}{\sin 81°} = a$$
$$45 = a$$

To find b:

$$\frac{\sin B}{b} = \frac{\sin C}{c}$$
$$\frac{\sin 57°}{b} = \frac{\sin 81°}{67}$$
$$67 \sin 57° = b \sin 81°$$
$$\frac{67 \sin 57°}{\sin 81°} = b \qquad \textit{Calculation-ready form}$$
$$57 = b$$

Therefore, $\angle A = 42°$, $\angle B = 57°$, $\angle C = 81°$, $a = 45$, $b = 57$, and $c = 67$.

The law of sines can also be used to solve a triangle if the measures of two angles and a side opposite one of the angles are given.

Example 2 Solve $\triangle ABC$ if $\angle A = 23°$, $\angle B = 87°$, and $b = 47.5$. Express lengths to the nearest tenth of a unit.

$$\angle C = 180° - (23° + 87°) = 70°$$

To find a:

$$\frac{\sin A}{a} = \frac{\sin B}{b}$$
$$\frac{\sin 23°}{a} = \frac{\sin 87°}{47.5}$$
$$\frac{47.5 \sin 23°}{\sin 87°} = a$$
$$18.6 = a$$

To find c:

$$\frac{\sin B}{b} = \frac{\sin C}{c}$$
$$\frac{\sin 87°}{47.5} = \frac{\sin 70°}{c}$$
$$\frac{47.5 \sin 70°}{\sin 87°} = c$$
$$44.7 = c$$

Therefore, $\angle A = 23°$, $\angle B = 87°$, $\angle C = 70°$, $a = 18.6$, $b = 47.5$, and $c = 44.7$.

Oblique triangles serve as models for many real world occurrences.

252 Chapter 5 Applications of Trigonometry

Example 3 *Navigation* A ship is moving in a straight line toward the Point Cove lighthouse. The measure of the angle of elevation from the bridge of the ship to the lighthouse beacon is 25°. Later, from a point 600 ft closer, the angle of elevation is 47°. To the nearest foot, how high is the beacon above the level of the bridge?

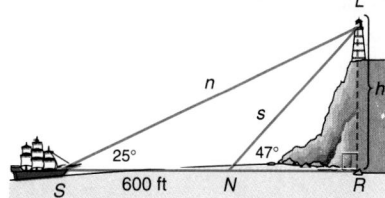

$\angle SNL = 180° - 47° = 133°$ $\angle SNL$ and $\angle LNR$ are supplementary.
$\angle SLN = 180° - (133° + 25°) = 22°$

$$\frac{\sin 22°}{600} = \frac{\sin 133°}{n}$$ Use the law of sines.

$$n = \frac{600 \sin 133°}{\sin 22°} = 1171$$ Retain the full value of n in your calculator.

$$\sin S = \frac{h}{n}$$ Definition of sine using $\triangle SLR$

$n \sin 25° = h$ Use the value of n retained in your calculator.
$\qquad h = 1171 \sin 25° = 495$ To the nearest foot

The beacon is 495 ft above the level of the bridge of the ship.

Class Exercises

Solve each triangle for the indicated side or angle.

1.
x = 25°

2.
b = 24

3.
b = 15.2

4.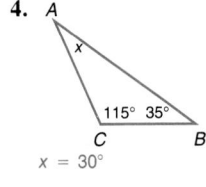
x = 30°

Solve each triangle *ABC*. Express answers to the nearest unit.

5. $\angle A = 65°$, $\angle B = 85°$, $b = 100$
6. $\angle B = 49°$, $\angle C = 61°$, $c = 100$
7. $\angle A = 120°$, $\angle C = 20°$, $b = 50$
8. $\angle C = 137°$, $\angle B = 21°$, $a = 83$
9. $\angle A = 57°$, $\angle B = 42°$, $a = 56.8$
$\angle C = 81°$; $b = 45$; $c = 67$
10. $\angle B = 29°$, $\angle C = 51°$, $c = 72.4$
$\angle A = 100°$; $a = 92$; $b = 45$

11. **Thinking Critically** For right triangle *ABC* with right angle at *C*, does the law of sines hold? If so, what does *c* equal? If not, why is the law invalid?
yes; $c = \dfrac{a}{\sin A} = \dfrac{b}{\sin B}$ $= \sqrt{a^2 + b^2}$

12. *Surveying* Two surveyors located at points *A* and *B* sight the marker at *M*. Their lines of sight to the marker make angles of 82° and 44°, respectively. The distance from *A* to *M* is 100 yd. Determine the distance between the surveyors. 116 yd

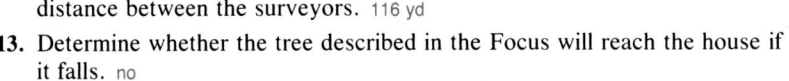

13. Determine whether the tree described in the Focus will reach the house if it falls. no

5.2 The Law of Sines **253**

For Example 3
The navigator of a hot air balloon traveling at a fixed altitude determines that the angle of depression to the landing site straight ahead is 15°. A half hour later, from a point 2 mi closer, the angle of depression is 68°. At what altitude is the balloon traveling? Express your answer to the nearest thousandth of a unit. 0.601 mi

CLOSURE
Have students summarize in their math journals how and when to use the law of sines to solve a triangle.

INDEPENDENT PRACTICE
Assignment Guide
Basic: 1–25, 29, 31–33
Average: 10–37, 42
Enriched: 19–47

Teacher's Resource Book
Practice, page 33

Ⓡ **Review**
Exercises 19, 25, 29, 31, and 33 review the concepts of even and odd functions, graphing absolute value equations, angle of depression, and trigonometric function values for acute angles.

Additional Answers
Class Exercises
5. $\angle C = 30°$; $a = 91$; $c = 50$
6. $\angle A = 70°$; $a = 107$; $b = 86$
7. $\angle B = 40°$; $a = 67$; $c = 27$
8. $\angle A = 22°$; $b = 79$; $c = 151$

Lesson Quiz

Solve each triangle *ABC*. Express answers to the nearest unit.

1. $\angle A = 24°$, $\angle B = 39°$, $c = 102$.
$\angle A = 24°$, $\angle B = 39°$, $\angle C = 117°$,
$a = 47$, $b = 72$, and $c = 102$

2. $\angle B = 48°$, $\angle C = 82°$, $c = 29.4$.
$\angle A = 50°$, $\angle B = 48°$, $\angle C = 82°$,
$a = 23$, $b = 22$, and $c = 29.4$

3. A surveyor determines that the angle of elevation of the top of a building is 57°. From a spot 200 ft closer, the angle of elevation is 65°. Determine the height of the building to the nearest foot. 1092 ft

Additional Answers
11. $\angle C = 52°$; $a = 60$; $c = 58$
12. $\angle A = 56°$; $a = 159$; $b = 188$
13. $\angle C = 84°$; $b = 33$; $c = 55$
14. $\angle A = 99°$; $a = 16$; $b = 5$
15. $\angle B = 30°$; $a = 31$; $c = 8$
16. $\angle A = 27°$; $b = 151$; $c = 230$
22. A triangle with the given angles may have sides of any length.

Solve each triangle for the indicated side.

A 1.

2.

3.

4.

5.

6.

7.

8.

9.
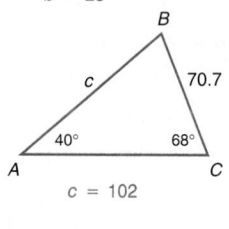

10. A triangular field has two angles that measure 35° and 74°, respectively. The side opposite the 74° angle measures 126.5 m. Determine the measure of the third angle and the lengths of the missing sides to the nearest unit. 71°; side opp. 35° = 75; side opp. 71° = 124

Solve each triangle *ABC*. Express answers to the nearest unit.

11. $\angle A = 55°$, $\angle B = 73°$, $b = 70$
12. $\angle B = 78°$, $\angle C = 46°$, $c = 138$
13. $\angle A = 59°$, $\angle B = 37°$, $a = 47.6$
14. $\angle B = 17°$, $\angle C = 64°$, $c = 14.9$
15. $\angle A = 140°$, $\angle C = 10°$, $b = 24$
16. $\angle C = 117°$, $\angle B = 36°$, $a = 117$
17. $\angle A = 102°$, $\angle B = 46°$, $c = 89.4$
$\angle C = 32°$; $a = 165$; $b = 121$
18. $\angle B = 151°$, $\angle C = 19°$, $b = 412.6$
$\angle A = 10°$; $a = 148$; $c = 277$

Ⓡ 19. Is the function $f(x) = 2x^3 + 4x$ even or odd? Explain. odd

20. *Surveying* A vacant lot shaped like a triangle is between two streets that intersect at an angle that measures 75°. The longest side, which is 140 ft long, is opposite that angle. Determine the length of the shortest side if the angle opposite that side measures 28°. 68 ft

21. Writing in Mathematics Explain the law of sines in your own words.

Thinking Critically Explain why the information does not determine a unique triangle.

B 22. Triangle *ABC* with $\angle A = 50°$, $\angle B = 70°$, and $\angle C = 60°$
23. Triangle *RST* with $\angle R = 100°$, $\angle S = 60°$, and $\angle T = 30°$ not a triangle

254 Chapter 5 Applications of Trigonometry

Writing in Mathematics
21. Answers may vary. Example: "For each angle in a given triangle, the ratio of the sine of the angle to the length of the side opposite that angle is the same."

24. *Construction* A 92-ft path cuts diagonally from Elm St. to Spruce St. It makes an angle of 68° with Spruce St. and 34° with Elm St. Determine the distance that is saved by using the path. 48 ft

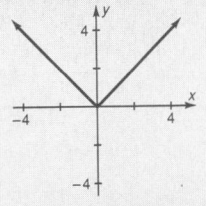

Ⓡ 25. Graph: $y = |x|$

26. The longer diagonal of a parallelogram makes angles of 38° and 44° with the sides, and its length is 15 in. Determine the length of the shorter side of the parallelogram. 9 in.

27. A bystander watches a window washer on the side of a building at a 76° angle of elevation. Later, he notices that the window washer is at a 49° angle of elevation when viewed from the same spot. How far down the building has the window washer moved if the bystander stands 20 ft from the building? 57 ft

28. *Landscaping* A tree trimmer wants to determine the height of a tree before cutting it down to be sure that the tree will not fall on a nearby building. It is determined that the angle of elevation to the top of the tree is 29° from one point on a level path. From a point 50 ft closer, the angle of elevation is 34°. Determine the height of the tree. 156 ft

Ⓡ 29. *Aeronautics* The angle of depression from a medical emergency helicopter to its landing space is 56°. If the helicopter is flying at 1000 ft, find the distance from the helicopter to the landing space. 1206 ft

30. *Surveying* Two surveyors sight a hot air balloon coming straight at the first surveyor who is 100 yd in front of the second. The angle of elevation from the first surveyor to the balloon is 75°, while the angle of elevation from the second surveyor to the balloon is 54°. If the balloon is traveling at a fixed altitude, determine its height above the ground. 218 yd

Ⓡ 31. *Aeronautics* The angle of depression from a police helicopter to a car on a straight highway below is 42°. If the helicopter is flying at 2000 ft, determine its distance to the car. 2989 ft

32. **Thinking Critically** If sin P = sin R in triangle PQR, then what may be said about triangle PQR? an isosceles triangle with right ∠Q

Ⓡ 33. Determine the six trigonometric functions for α if $\tan \alpha = \frac{5}{6}$ and $0 < \alpha < \frac{\pi}{2}$.

34. Show that $\frac{r + s}{s} = \frac{\sin R + \sin S}{\sin S}$ for any triangle RST.

35. Show that $\frac{r - s}{s} = \frac{\sin R - \sin S}{\sin S}$ for any triangle RST.

36. Show that $\frac{r - s}{r + s} = \frac{\sin R - \sin S}{\sin R + \sin S}$ for any triangle RST.

37. Prove the law of sines for obtuse triangles (Case 2). *Hint:* Draw a diagram.

38. **Thinking Critically** Show that if triangle ABC is inscribed in a semicircle, the diameter of the circle is equal to the ratio
$\frac{a}{\sin A} = \frac{b}{\sin B} = \frac{c}{\sin C}$.

39. Prove that for any triangle ABC, $a \sin B - b \sin A = 0$.

5.2 The Law of Sines **255**

38. Since △ABC is inscribed in a semicircle, ∠B is a right angle. b = diameter; law of sines says $\frac{\sin A}{a} = \frac{\sin B}{b} = \frac{\sin C}{c}$; since sin B = 1, then $\frac{\sin A}{a} = \frac{1}{b} = \frac{\sin C}{c}$ or $b = \frac{a}{\sin A} = \frac{c}{\sin C} = \frac{b}{\sin B}$.

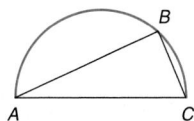

40. In any triangle having sides r, s, and t, it is true that $r + s > t$. Use the law of sines to show that $\sin R + \sin S > \sin (R + S)$.

C 41. Three gears are arranged as shown. Determine the measure of angle θ correct to the nearest degree.

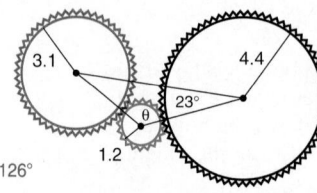

42. Three gears are arranged as shown. Determine the measure of angle θ correct to the nearest degree.

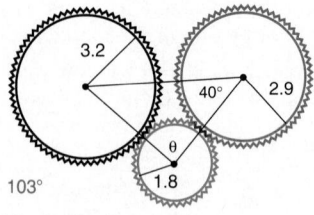

43. An 8-ft loading ramp that makes an angle of 20° with the horizontal is to be replaced by a ramp whose angle with the horizontal is 15°. Determine the length of the new ramp. 10.6 ft

44. Find the perimeter of the piece of land with the indicated measurements. 675 m

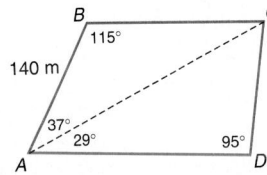

45. Find the perimeter of the piece of land with the indicated measurements. 1148 ft

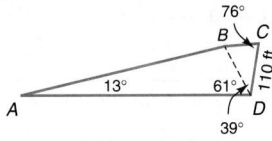

46. Points M and N are on the same side of a river and are 270 ft apart. A tree is at point K on the opposite side of the river. $\angle NMK$ measures 42° and $\angle MNK$ measures 28°. Determine the distance from M to K. 135 ft

47. Points A and B are on the same side of a river and 375 m apart. Point C is located on the opposite side of the river from A and B. In triangle ABC, $\angle B = 61°$ and $\angle C = 56°$. Determine the distance between A and C. 396 m

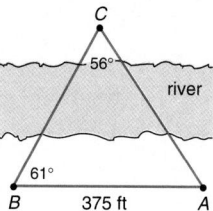

Challenge

1. Jacqueline has 160 ft of fencing for the vegetable garden she is going to make. She cannot decide on whether to have a rectangular garden or a circular one. If she wants to use all of the fencing, which type of garden will have more area with which to work? Why? circular

2. Find the radius of a circle whose circumference is n units and whose area is n square units, with $n > 0$.

256   Chapter 5 Applications of Trigonometry

5.3 The Ambiguous Case

Objective: To use the law of sines to solve a triangle when two sides and an angle opposite one of them are given

Focus

A power shovel is used to pick up and move earth at construction and demolition sites. The arm and the beam of a particular power shovel are attached at a point that is 65 ft from its base. The distance from this point to the bottom of the shovel is 25 ft. If the bottom of the shovel touches the ground at a right angle, then a unique triangle will be formed by the beam, the shovel arm, and the ground (top figure). If the angle θ between the beam and the ground is too large, there is no triangle and the shovel does not touch the ground (middle figure). If θ is small enough to allow the shovel to touch the ground at two points, two triangles are determined (bottom figure). Then the power shovel can be used to perform the task of moving earth from one point to another.

Solving an oblique triangle when the measures of two sides and an angle opposite one of them are given may not always result in exactly one solution. Two triangles, one triangle, or no triangle may be drawn from the given information. When two triangles result, the situation is called the **ambiguous case.**

Example 1 Solve $\triangle ABC$ if $\angle A = 29.5°$, $a = 12.9$, and $b = 8.7$. Express answers to the nearest tenth.

$$\frac{\sin 29.5°}{12.9} = \frac{\sin B}{8.7} \qquad \frac{\sin A}{a} = \frac{\sin B}{b}$$

$$\frac{8.7 \sin 29.5°}{12.9} = \sin B$$

$$\sin^{-1}(8.7 \sin 29.5 \div 12.9) = \angle B \qquad \textit{Calculation-ready form}$$

$$19.4° = \angle B$$

$$\angle C = 180° - (29.5° + 19.4°) = 131.1°$$

$$\frac{\sin 29.5°}{12.9} = \frac{\sin 131.1°}{c} \qquad \frac{\sin A}{a} = \frac{\sin C}{c}$$

$$\frac{12.9 \sin 131.1°}{\sin 29.5} = c \qquad \textit{Calculation-ready form}$$

$$19.7 = c$$

Therefore, $\angle A = 29.5°$, $\angle B = 19.4°$, $\angle C = 131.1°$, $a = 12.9$, $b = 8.7$, and $c = 19.7$.

LESSON PLAN

Vocabulary
ambiguous case

Ⓜ **Materials/Manipulatives**
compass
protractor
straightedge

Technology
scientific calculator

FOCUS

The description of the workings of a power shovel serves to give a vivid illustration of the different cases that arise when dealing with the law of sines. Use such visual imagery to relate the concepts of the lesson.

INSTRUCTION

Ⓜ Give students the measures of two sides of a triangle and the measure of the angle opposite one of them. Ask them to construct as many non-congruent triangles as possible with the given data using only a straightedge and compass.

Alternative Learning Styles

Ⓜ Some students benefit from a constructive geometric view of why some given conditions result in the ambiguous case. Have students use a compass and straightedge to construct triangles from given conditions. Choose angles and sides that will result in no triangle, one triangle, and two triangles.

For Example 1

1. Solve △ABC if ∠A = 37.4°, a = 11.6, and b = 9.4. Express lengths to the nearest tenth and angle measures to the nearest tenth of a degree.
∠A = 37.4°, ∠B = 29.5°, ∠C = 113.1°, a = 11.6, b = 9.4, and c = 17.6

2. Solve △KLM if ∠M = 65.5°, m = 37.4, and ℓ = 28.6. Express lengths to the nearest tenth and angle measures to the nearest tenth of a degree.
∠K = 70.4°, ∠L = 44.1°, ∠M = 65.5°, k = 38.7, ℓ = 28.6, and m = 37.4

For Example 2

1. Solve △ABC if ∠A = 35.18°, c = 17.8, and a = 11.46. Express lengths to the nearest hundredth and angle measures to the nearest hundredth of a degree.
∠A = 35.18°, ∠B = 81.33°, ∠C = 63.49°, a = 11.46, b = 19.66, and c = 17.28 or ∠A = 35.18°, ∠B = 28.31°, ∠C = 116.51°, a = 11.46, b = 9.43, and c = 17.28

2. Solve △PQR if ∠Q = 51.24°, p = 29.43, and q = 25.54. Express lengths to the nearest hundredth and angle measures to the nearest hundredth of a degree.
∠P = 63.97°, ∠Q = 51.24°, ∠R = 64.79°, p = 29.43, q = 25.54, and r = 29.63 or ∠P = 116.03°, ∠Q = 51.24°, ∠R = 12.73°, p = 29.43, q = 25.54, and r = 7.22

In Example 1, the length of a is greater than the length of b. Whenever $a \geq b$ and a is the side opposite the given angle, there will be one triangle to solve.

It is possible to define two completely different triangles when the measures of two sides and the angle opposite one of them are related in a particular way. If the altitude of the triangle, $b \sin A$, is less than a which is in turn less than b ($b \sin A < a < b$), then two distinct triangles satisfy the given conditions.

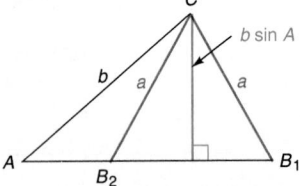

Example 2 Solve △ABC if ∠A = 57.25°, b = 32.48, and a = 30.72. Express answers to the nearest hundredth.

$$\frac{\sin 57.25°}{30.72} = \frac{\sin B}{32.48}$$ Use the law of sines.

$$\frac{32.48 \sin 57.25°}{30.72} = \sin B$$

$$\sin^{-1}(32.48 \sin 57.25 \div 30.72) = \angle B$$ Calculation-ready form

∠B = 62.78° or ∠B = 180° − 62.78° = 117.22°

There are two possible solutions to △ABC, as shown below.

∠C = 180° − (57.25° + 62.78°) = 59.97°

∠C = 180° − (57.25° + 117.22°) = 5.53°

To determine the measure of c in each triangle, use the law of sines.

$$\frac{\sin A}{a} = \frac{\sin C}{c}$$

$$\frac{\sin 57.25°}{30.72} = \frac{\sin 59.97°}{c}$$

$$c = \frac{30.72 \sin 59.97°}{\sin 57.25°}$$

$$c = 31.62$$

$$\frac{\sin A}{a} = \frac{\sin C}{c}$$

$$\frac{\sin 57.25°}{30.72°} = \frac{\sin 5.53}{c}$$

$$c = \frac{30.72 \sin 5.53°}{\sin 57.25°}$$

$$c = 3.52$$

Therefore, one solution is ∠A = 57.25°, ∠B = 62.78°, ∠C = 59.97°, a = 30.72, b = 32.48, and c = 31.62. The other solution is ∠A = 57.25°, ∠B = 117.22°, ∠C = 5.53°, a = 30.72, b = 32.48, and c = 3.52.

Sometimes the given information does not define a triangle.

Example 3 Solve △ABC if ∠A = 72.6°, a = 13.7, and b = 23.2.

$$\frac{\sin 72.6°}{13.7} = \frac{\sin B}{23.2} \qquad \frac{\sin A}{a} = \frac{\sin B}{b}$$

$$\frac{23.2 \sin 72.6°}{13.7} = \sin B \qquad \textit{Calculation-ready form}$$

$$1.6 = \sin B$$

The values of the sine function are always between −1 and 1, inclusive. Therefore, no triangle exists that satisfies the given information.

As stated above, there may be *zero*, *one*, or *two* solutions to a triangle when two sides and an angle opposite one of them are given. A summary of all the possibilities follows.

If ∠A is an acute angle and a < b, then there are three possibilities:

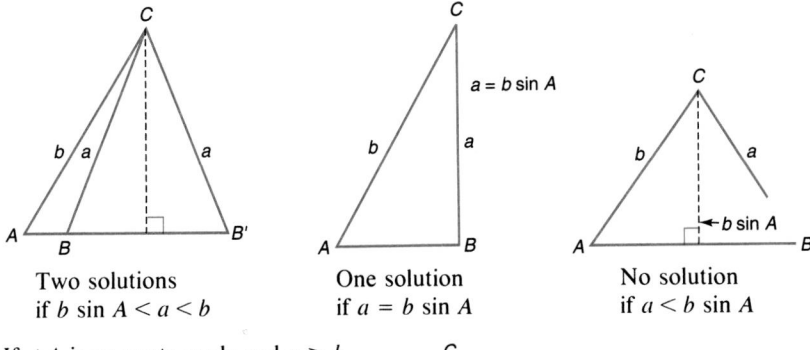

| Two solutions if $b \sin A < a < b$ | One solution if $a = b \sin A$ | No solution if $a < b \sin A$ |

If ∠A is an acute angle and a ≥ b, then there is exactly one solution:

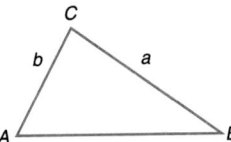

If ∠A is an obtuse or right angle, then there are two different possibilities:

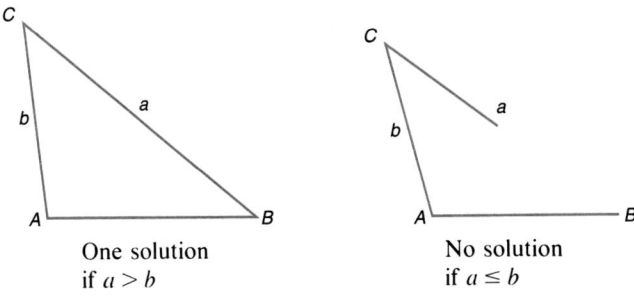

One solution if a > b   No solution if a ≤ b

For Example 3
1. Solve △ABC if ∠A = 71.4°, a = 45.3, and b = 51.4.
   No triangle exists.
2. Solve △DEF if ∠E = 57.85°, e = 67.23, and d = 92.89.
   No triangle exists.

For Example 4
Determine the number of solutions in each case.
1. ∠A = 29°, b = 31, a = 23
   two solutions
2. ∠A = 85°, b = 56, a = 48
   no solution
3. ∠A = 132°, b = 96, a = 105
   one solution
4. ∠R = 141°, r = 36, s = 66
   no solution

CLOSURE
Group students in pairs and have them summarize the lesson to each other. Make sure that they understand the conditions that will lead to the different numbers of solutions.

Example 4 Determine the number of solutions in each case.

    a. $\angle A = 52°$ **b.** $\angle A = 121°$ **c.** $\angle A = 28°$
        $b = 11$ $a = 37.4$ $b = 49$
        $a = 15$ $b = 45.2$ $a = 35$

a.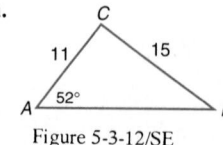

Figure 5-3-12/SE

One solution,
since A is acute
and $a \geq b$

b.

No solution,
since A is obtuse
and $a < b$

c.

Two solutions,
since A is acute
and $b \sin A < a < b$

Class Exercises

Determine the number of solutions in each case.

1. $\angle A = 71°$, $a = 43$, $b = 52$ none
2. $\angle A = 33°$, $b = 13$, $a = 17$ one
3. $\angle B = 92°$, $b = 64$, $c = 85$ none
4. $\angle A = 108°$, $a = 37.5$, $b = 32.3$ one
5. $\angle B = 62°$, $b = 85.8$, $c = 61.7$ one
6. $\angle C = 47°$, $c = 53.3$, $b = 64.1$ two
7. $\angle B = 98°$, $b = 16.3$, $c = 11.9$ one
8. $\angle C = 119°$, $b = 83.5$, $c = 64.8$ none
9. $\angle C = 35°$, $a = 54.3$, $c = 54.3$ one
10. $\angle C = 90°$, $b = 42$, $c = 42$ none
11. $\angle A = 102°$, $a = 84.6$, $b = 93.7$ none
12. $\angle B = 14°$, $a = 11.7$, $b = 5.6$ two

Solve each triangle. If no triangle exists, tell why. If two triangles exist, give
both solutions.

13. Triangle *PQR* with $\angle Q = 71°$, $q = 38.2$, and $r = 39.6$ $\angle R = 78.6°$; $\angle P = 30.4°$; $p = 20.4$ or $\angle R = 101.4°$; $\angle P = 7.6°$; $p = 5.3$
14. Triangle *WXY* with $\angle Y = 52°$, $y = 57.4$, and $w = 83.2$ no solution; $\angle Y$ is acute and $w \sin Y > y$
15. Triangle *ABC* with $\angle A = 48°$, $a = 46.2$, and $c = 62.3$ no solution; $\angle A$ is acute and $c \sin A > a$
16. Triangle *LMN* with $\angle L = 100°$, $\ell = 75.2$, and $m = 64.3$ $\angle M = 57°$; $\angle N = 23°$; $m = 29.8$
17. Triangle *RST* with $\angle S = 37°$, $s = 17.8$, and $t = 26.9$ $\angle R = 78°$; $\angle T = 65°$; $r = 28.9$
18. Triangle *HIJ* with $\angle J = 97°$, $j = 27.2$, and $h = 52.8$ no solution; $\angle J$ is obtuse and $h > j$

19. **Thinking Critically** When $\angle A$ is acute and $a = b$, a triangle is constructible.
   When $\angle A$ is obtuse and $a \leq b$, a triangle cannot be constructed. Why is
   this so?

20. *Engineering* A monument 21 ft long is to be
   placed across a triangular lot formed by two
   streets, Elm and Oak. The angle between the
   streets is 35°, and the monument must be 12 ft
   from the corner along Elm Street. What is the
   least distance that the monument could be from
   the corner along Oak Street? 30 ft

Additional Answers, Class Exercises
19. If $a = b$, then $\triangle ABC$ is an isosceles triangle with $\angle A = \angle B$. But $\angle A > 90°$, and a
   triangle can have at most one obtuse angle. Therefore, no triangle can be constructed.

Practice Exercises Use appropriate technology.

Determine the number of solutions in each case.

A **1.** $\angle A = 126°$, $a = 4$, $b = 3$ one
    2. $\angle A = 119°$, $a = 4$, $b = 3$ one

3. $\angle T = 93°$, $t = 16$, $r = 19$ none
    4. $\angle T = 101°$, $t = 26$, $r = 31$ none

5. $\angle H = 61°$, $h = 14$, $g = 15.3$ two
    6. $\angle H = 78°$, $h = 21.2$, $f = 24.7$ none

7. $\angle M = 50°$, $m = 13.4$, $k = 17.5$ none
    8. $\angle M = 82°$, $m = 28.0$, $k = 28.3$ none

9. $\angle Q = 46°$, $q = 46$, $r = 15$ one
    10. $\angle Q = 86°$, $q = 94$, $r = 86$ one

11. $\angle D = 49°$, $d = 21.5$, $f = 23.9$ two
    12. $\angle D = 62°$, $d = 47.1$, $f = 51.3$ two

Ⓡ **13.** Determine the period of $f(x) = 3 \sin 2x$. π

Solve each triangle. If no triangle exists, tell why. If two triangles exist, give both solutions.

14. Triangle ABC with $\angle A = 49°$, $a = 22$, and $b = 24$

15. Triangle DEF with $\angle D = 53°$, $d = 35$, and $e = 41$

16. Triangle RST with $\angle R = 67°$, $r = 62$, and $t = 56$ $\angle S = 57°$; $\angle T = 56°$; $s = 56$

17. Triangle PQR with $\angle P = 75°$, $p = 41$, and $r = 38$ $\angle Q = 41°$; $\angle R = 64°$; $q = 28$

18. Triangle GHI with $\angle H = 29.4°$, $h = 8.7$, and $g = 13.3$

19. Triangle KLM with $\angle L = 44.2°$, $l = 19.3$, and $m = 23.6$

20. Triangle ABC with $\angle C = 57.6°$, $c = 27.7$, and $a = 41.5$ none; $\sin A = 1.26$

Ⓡ **21.** Determine the amplitude of $f(x) = 3 \cos \frac{1}{2}x$. 3

B **22.** **Thinking Critically** Construct a triangle that illustrates the ambiguous case (two solutions). What conditions would produce a right triangle?

A carpenter is building a slanted wall as shown at the right. The slant height is 31 ft, and the wall makes an angle of 50° with the horizontal.

23. Will a 26-ft beam be long enough to serve as a perpendicular support? yes

24. If the beam is too long, by how much should it be cut, to the nearest foot? 2 ft

25. One angle of a triangle measures 47°, the adjacent side is 32 cm, and the opposite side is 35 cm. Determine the measure of the third side. 48 cm

26. One angle of a triangle measures 29°, the adjacent side is 62 ft, and the opposite side is 69 ft. Determine the measure of the third side. 116 ft

Ⓡ **27.** Use transformations of $y = x^2$ to graph $y = (x - 2)^2 + 3$.

28. Two noncongruent triangles have $\angle A = 62°$, $a = 16.6$, and $b = 17.3$. Solve the triangle with the greater perimeter. $\angle B = 67°$; $\angle C = 51°$; $c = 14.6$

29. Two noncongruent triangles have $\angle B = 48°$, $b = 17.8$, and $c = 22.4$. Solve the triangle with the smaller perimeter. $\angle A = 21°$; $\angle C = 111°$; $a = 8.6$

30. Two noncongruent triangles have $\angle B = 39°$, $c = 15.3$, and $b = 12.5$. Solve the triangle with the smaller area. $\angle A = 11°$; $\angle C = 130°$; $a = 3.8$

5.3 The Ambiguous Case   **261**

Additional Answers
Practice Exercises

14. two solutions:
  $\angle B = 55°$; $\angle C = 76°$; $c = 28$ or
  $\angle B = 125°$; $\angle C = 6°$; $c = 3$

15. two solutions:
  $\angle E = 69°$; $\angle F = 58°$; $f = 37$ or
  $\angle E = 111°$; $\angle F = 16°$; $f = 12$

18. two solutions:
  $\angle G = 48.6°$; $\angle I = 102°$; $i = 17.3$ or
  $\angle G = 131.4°$; $\angle I = 19.2°$; $i = 5.8$

19. two solutions:
  $\angle K = 77.3°$; $\angle M = 58.5°$; $k = 27.0$ or
  $\angle K = 14.3°$; $\angle M = 121.5°$; $k = 6.8$

22.

A right triangle can only occur if the ratio of the two known sides is equal to the sine of the known angle.

27.

31. Two noncongruent triangles have $\angle A = 43°$, $c = 17.1$, and $a = 13.4$. Solve the triangle with the greater area. $\angle B = 77°$; $\angle C = 60°$; $b = 19.1$

32. **Writing in Mathematics** Write a short paragraph describing the contributions to trigonometry of Johann Muller, who was more generally known as "Regiomontanus."

33. *Advertising* A tall sign is erected along an interstate highway. Two braces are attached to the sign as shown at a height 32 ft from the top of the sign. If the braces make angles of 49° with the horizontal and are each 8 ft long, determine the distance from the top of the sign to the ground. 38 ft

34. **Writing in Mathematics** There are always two angles, one acute and one obtuse, that have the same sine. Sometimes there are two triangles, sometimes not. Explain.

35. *Surveying* Two stakes A and B are 600 ft apart on the same side of a canyon opposite a tree at C. If the angle between the lines of sight AB and AC is 81° and the angle between BA and BC is 37°, how far is it from A to C? 409 ft

36. *Surveying* A broadcast antenna is located at the top of a building 1000 ft tall. From a point on the same horizontal plane as the base of the building, the angles of elevation of the top and bottom of the antenna are 65.8° and 62.6°, respectively. How tall is the antenna? 153 ft

37. *Surveying* From the top of a 100-ft lighthouse on top of a hill, a ship is observed on fire at an angle of depression measuring 17.6°. If the angle of depression to the ship from the base of the lighthouse measures 15.4°, how many feet is it from the ship to the base of the lighthouse? 2483 ft

38. *Engineering* Two steel braces are attached to a building to support a perch for two television personalities who will broadcast the 4th of July parade. The braces are attached to the building 15 ft apart vertically and at angles of 65° and 35°. How long is the longer brace? 13.8 ft

39. *Engineering* The top and bottom of a 5-ft-high snowplow are to be attached to two steel braces of different lengths that meet at an angle of 44°. If the length of one of the braces is 4.2 ft, at what angle does the shorter brace meet the blade? 100°

40. Prove for acute triangle ABC that $c = a \cos B + b \cos A$.

41. Prove for obtuse triangle ABC with obtuse angle B that $c = b \cos A + a \cos B$.

42. Let D be a point on side c opposite $\angle C$ of triangle ABC such that $\overline{CD}$ bisects $\angle C$. Use the law of sines to prove that $\dfrac{AD}{DB} = \dfrac{b}{a}$.

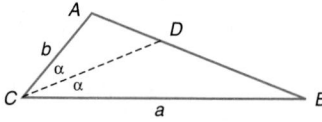

Writing in Mathematics

32. Answers may vary. Regiomontanus was a fifteenth century German mathematician and astronomer. He is generally credited with leading the revival and advancement of the study of trigonometry in Europe.

34. If $\angle A$ is acute, then $b \sin A < a < b$, so $\angle B$ can be acute or obtuse.

43. Writing in Mathematics Determine the meaning of one Astronomical Unit and describe how you would use this unit to find the distances from Earth to Mars on the date when the angle between the lines from Earth to Mars and Earth to Sun is 59.5°. The mean distance from Mars to the Sun is 1.524 A.U.

44. Suppose that A and B are two angles of a triangle and a and b are the lengths of the opposite sides. Show that if $B = 2A$, then $\cos A = \dfrac{b}{2a}$.

45. If P is the center of the circle of radius r inscribed in triangle ABC, prove that the area K of the triangle is rs, where $s = \dfrac{a + b + c}{2}$.

46. *Programming* Write a program to find the length of a side when two angles of a triangle and the side opposite one of them are given.

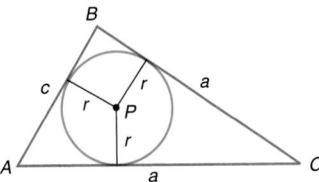

Test Yourself

Solve each right triangle ABC with $\angle C = 90°$ using the given information. Express answers to the nearest tenth of a unit or degree.

1. $\angle B = 68°$, $a = 37$ $\angle A = 22°$; $b = 91.6$; $c = 98.8$ **2.** $b = 6$, $c = 37$ $\angle A = 80.7°$; $\angle B = 9.3°$; $a = 36.5$ **5.1**

3. $\angle A = 31°$, $c = 312$ $\angle B = 59°$; $a = 160.7$; $b = 267.4$ **4.** $a = 14$, $b = 9$ $\angle A = 57.3°$; $\angle B = 32.7°$; $c = 16.6$

5. Solve isosceles triangle ABC if the base is 18 cm long and the vertex angle has a measure of 64°. Determine the measure of each leg to the nearest tenth of a centimeter. 17.0 cm

6. A cliff is 125 ft high. The angle of depression of a ship from the top of the cliff is 14.6°. Determine the distance of the ship from the foot of the cliff. 480 ft

7. A 95-ft extension ladder rests on top of a hook and ladder truck with its base 14 ft from the ground. When the angle of elevation of the ladder is 78°, how high up the building will it reach? 107 ft

Solve each triangle ABC. Express answers to the nearest unit.

8. $\angle A = 54°$, $\angle B = 72°$, $a = 32$ $\angle C = 54°$; $b = 38$; $c = 32$ **9.** $\angle A = 118°$, $\angle B = 25°$, $c = 37$ $\angle C = 37°$; $a = 54$; $b = 26$ **5.2**

10. A surveyor makes measurements of a triangular field as shown. Determine the distance from M to N. 210 ft

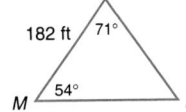

Determine the possible number of triangles in each case.

11. $\angle A = 42°$, $a = 18$, $b = 24$ two   **12.** $\angle Q = 25°$, $q = 10$, $p = 7$ one   **5.3**

Solve each triangle. If no triangle exists, tell why. If two triangles exist, give both solutions.

13. $\angle A = 40°$, $a = 75$, $b = 85$ $\angle B = 46.8°$; $\angle C = 93.2°$; $c = 116.5$ or $\angle B = 133.2°$; $\angle C = 6.8°$; $c = 13.8$ **14.** $\angle A = 87°$, $a = 47$, $b = 50$ no solution; $a < b \sin A$

5.3 The Ambiguous Case   **263**

Writing in Mathematics

43. One astronomical unit is the distance from the Earth to the Sun, about 149.6 million km. You can solve the triangle whose vertices are the Earth, the Sun, and Mars by using the law of sines. Let $\angle E = 59.5°$, $e = 1.524$, and $m = 1$. Then side s, representing the distance from the Earth to Mars, is determined to be 1.765 A.U.

Vocabulary
heading
triangulation

Ⓜ Materials/Manipulatives
overhead projector

Technology
scientific calculator

FOCUS

Invite discussion as to some of
the methods that might be used to
measure the unknown distances
described in the Focus, and some of
the problems that these methods
might present.

INSTRUCTION

- Point out that when the included
  angle is a right angle, the law of
  cosines reduces to the Pythagorean
  theorem.
- Use a diagram to help demonstrate
  the fact that the law of cosines is
  actually the generalized Pythagorean theorem. Point out that the term
  $-2ab \cos C$ is the correction factor
  and that $2ab \cos C$ is positive or
  negative dependent upon whether
  angle C is acute or obtuse.

5.4 The Law of Cosines

Objectives: *To introduce and prove the law of cosines*
To use the law of cosines to solve a triangle when the measures
of two sides and the included angle are given or when the
measures of three sides are given

Focus

The search for sources of energy is an ongoing
process. Oil companies explore and drill beneath
land and sea. They must often calculate distances
that cannot be directly measured. A petroleum
company may engage a team of surveyors to
determine the distance between an oil drilling
platform and an oil pumping station. The surveyors
use triangulation, which is a way of calculating
distances and angles. A region is divided into a
network of connected or overlapping triangles. The
lengths of the side or sides of a triangle are used
along with angle measurements and trigonometric
formulas to compute parts of the triangles that
cannot be measured directly.

If the measures of two angles and one side of a triangle or two sides and the
angle opposite one of them are known, then the law of sines can be used to
solve the triangle. If the measures of the three sides or two sides and the
included angle are known, another formula called the *law of cosines* is used.

To prove the law of cosines, two cases of oblique triangles must be considered.
In one triangle the included angle is acute, and in the other the included angle
is obtuse.

Triangle ABC is acute. Draw h, the altitude from B to side b, and
label the intersection point D. Let x represent the measure of $\overline{DC}$,
and $b - x$ the measure of $\overline{AD}$.

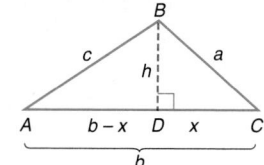

Apply the Pythagorean theorem to $\triangle BDA$.

$$
\begin{aligned}
c^2 &= (b - x)^2 + h^2 \\
&= b^2 - 2bx + x^2 + h^2 \\
&= b^2 - 2bx + a^2 && \text{In } \triangle BCD, a^2 = x^2 + h^2. \\
&= b^2 - 2b(a \cos C) + a^2 && \text{Since } \cos C = \tfrac{x}{a}, x = a \cos C. \\
&= a^2 + b^2 - 2ab \cos C
\end{aligned}
$$

You can derive expressions for a^2 and b^2 in a similar manner. In Exercise 43,
you will be asked to prove the case of an included angle that is obtuse.

264   Chapter 5 Applications of Trigonometry

Law of Cosines

For any triangle ABC, where a, b, and c are the lengths of the sides opposite the angles with measures A, B, and C, respectively,

$$a^2 = b^2 + c^2 - 2bc \cos A$$
$$b^2 = a^2 + c^2 - 2ac \cos B$$
$$c^2 = a^2 + b^2 - 2ab \cos C$$

Modeling

How can a team of surveyors determine the distance between an oil drilling platform and a pumping station?

When oil was discovered in the North Sea, an oil company built an offshore drilling platform at point A and a pumping station at point B. To determine the inaccessible distance between A and B, a team of surveyors used **triangulation.** They located two points, D and C, and measured the distance between them along the shoreline. They then measured the four angles $\angle ADC$, $\angle BDC$, $\angle DCA$, and $\angle DCB$. Using the law of sines on triangle ADC, they were able to find the length AD from

$$\frac{\sin \angle DCA}{AD} = \frac{\sin \angle DAC}{DC}$$

Similarly, they determined DB using the law of sines on triangle DBC.

$$\frac{\sin \angle DCB}{DB} = \frac{\sin \angle DBC}{DC}$$

Since $\angle ADB = \angle ADC - \angle BDC$, the surveyors knew two sides and the included angle on $\triangle ABD$. They then calculated AB using the law of cosines.

Example 1 *Surveying* Determine the distance between the oil drilling platform and the pumping station if $\angle ADC = 109°$, $\angle BDC = 42°$, $\angle DCA = 37°$, and $\angle DCB = 98°$, and the distance between points D and C on the shoreline is 1040 m.

Use the law of sines on triangle ADC.

$$\frac{\sin 37°}{AD} = \frac{\sin 34°}{1040}$$

$$AD = \frac{1040 \sin 37°}{\sin 34°} \qquad \textit{Calculation-ready form}$$

$$AD = 1119 \text{ m}$$

5.4 The Law of Cosines   **265**

Alternative Learning Styles

Ⓜ Many students need a more visual presentation to understand what conditions determine a triangle. Use two pencils of different lengths to represent adjacent sides of a triangle on an overhead projector. Show that many different angles may be constructed having these two adjacent sides. Once a third side or an angle between them is fixed, a particular triangle is determined. Showing this to students will help them understand the relationships between the two sides and the included angle in the law of cosines.

GUIDED PRACTICE

Modeling
When discussing the original question regarding how distances might be measured at sea, ask students to think of methods different from the one covered in the example. Have them speculate as to the difficulties that each method presents.

For Example 1
Determine the distance between P and Q in the figure if $\angle PSR = 115°$, $\angle QSR = 51°$, $\angle SRP = 46°$, $\angle SRQ = 102°$, and $SR = 1260$ ft.

2914 ft

For Example 2

1. Solve the oblique triangle ABC if $\angle C = 96.4°$, $a = 5.8$, and $b = 8.3$.
   $\angle A = 32.8°$, $\angle B = 50.8°$, $\angle C = 96.4°$, $a = 5.8$, $b = 8.3$, and $c = 10.6$

2. Solve the oblique triangle RST if $\angle S = 75.8°$, $r = 51.9$, and $t = 36.2$.
   $\angle R = 65.0°$, $\angle S = 75.8°$, $\angle T = 39.2°$, $r = 51.9$, $s = 55.5$, and $t = 36.2$

For Example 3

1. Solve triangle PQR if $p = 17.2$, $q = 15.4$, and $r = 13.6$. Express angle measure to the nearest degree.
   $\angle P = 72°$, $\angle Q = 59°$, and $\angle R = 49°$

2. Solve triangle RST if $r = 27.8$, $s = 31.3$, and $t = 23.5$. Express angle measure to the nearest degree.
   $\angle R = 59°$, $\angle S = 75°$, and $\angle T = 46°$

For Example 4

Two airplanes leave an airport at the same time. The heading of the first is 150° and the heading of the second is 260°. If the planes travel at the rates of 680 mi/h and 560 mi/h, respectively, how far apart are they after 2 h? 2036 mi

Use the law of sines on triangle DBC.

$$\frac{\sin 98°}{DB} = \frac{\sin 40°}{1040}$$

$$DB = \frac{1040 \sin 98°}{\sin 40°} \quad \textit{Calculation-ready form}$$

$$DB = 1602 \text{ m} \quad \textit{Retain the full value of AD in your calculator.}$$

$$\angle ADB = 109° - 42° = 67°$$

Now use the law of cosines on triangle ADB to find AB.

$$(AB)^2 = (AD)^2 + (DB)^2 - 2(AD)(DB) \cos \angle ADB$$

$$AB = \sqrt{1119^2 + 1602^2 - 2(1119)(1602) \cos 67°}$$

$$AB = 1555 \text{ m} \quad \text{To the nearest meter}$$

The distance between the platform and the pumping station is 1555 m.

The given information sometimes dictates that you use either the law of sines or the law of cosines. At other times, you will have to choose which law to use.

Example 2   Solve the oblique triangle ABC if $\angle C = 100.5°$, $a = 1.2$, and $b = 2.6$.

Use the law of cosines to find side c.

$$c^2 = a^2 + b^2 - 2ab \cos C$$

$$c = \sqrt{1.2^2 + 2.6^2 - 2(1.2)(2.6) \cos 100.5°}$$

$$c = 3.1 \quad \textit{Retain the full value of c in your calculator.}$$

You can use either the law of cosines or the law of sines to find $\angle A$.

$$\frac{\sin 100.5°}{3.1} = \frac{\sin A}{1.2} \qquad \frac{\sin C}{c} = \frac{\sin A}{a}$$

$$\frac{1.2 \sin 100.5°}{3.1} = \sin A$$

$$\sin^{-1}(1.2 \sin 100.5° \div 3.1) = \angle A$$

$$22.4° = \angle A$$

$$\angle B = 180° - (100.5° + 22.4°) = 57.1°$$

Therefore, $\angle A = 22.4°$, $\angle B = 57.1°$, $\angle C = 100.5°$, $a = 1.2$, $b = 2.6$, and $c = 3.1$.

If you solve $a^2 = b^2 + c^2 - 2bc \cos A$ for $\cos A$, you obtain an expression for $\cos A$ in terms of a, b, and c, the three sides of the triangle.

$$a^2 = b^2 + c^2 - 2bc \cos A$$

$$2bc \cos A = b^2 + c^2 - a^2$$

$$\cos A = \frac{b^2 + c^2 - a^2}{2bc}$$

Similarly, you can show that $\cos B = \dfrac{a^2 + c^2 - b^2}{2ac}$ and $\cos C = \dfrac{a^2 + b^2 - c^2}{2ab}$.

If the lengths of all three sides of a triangle are given, you can solve it using this form of the law of cosines.

Example 3 Solve triangle ABC if $a = 14.3$, $b = 10.6$, and $c = 8.4$. Express angle measures to the nearest degree.

To find $\angle A$:

$\cos A = \dfrac{b^2 + c^2 - a^2}{2bc}$

$\cos A = \dfrac{(10.6)^2 + (8.4)^2 - (14.3)^2}{2(10.6)(8.4)}$

$\angle A = 97°$

To find $\angle B$:

$\cos B = \dfrac{a^2 + c^2 - b^2}{2ac}$

$\cos B = \dfrac{(14.3)^2 + (8.4)^2 - (10.6)^2}{2(14.3)(8.4)}$

$\angle B = 47°$

$\angle C = 180° - (97° + 47°) = 36°$

Would you obtain a different answer if you solved for $\angle C$ before solving for $\angle A$ in Example 3?

One important application of the law of cosines is to find distances and angles in navigation. Navigators often use the term **heading**. The heading is the angle made in the clockwise direction from the north. The heading in the figure is 318°.

Example 4 *Aviation* Two airplanes leave an airport at the same time. The heading of the first is 120° and the heading of the second is 320°. If the planes travel at the rates of 700 and 600 mi/h, respectively, how far apart are they after 1 h?

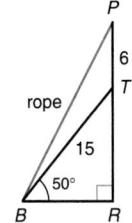

$\beta = 360° - 320° = 40°$
$\alpha = 120° + \beta = 160°$

$d = \sqrt{(600)^2 + (700)^2 - 2(600)(700)\cos 160°} = 1280$

Therefore, the planes are 1280 mi apart after 1 h.

Engineers also use the law of cosines in their work.

Example 5 *Engineering* A rope is attached to a 6-ft pole mounted to the top of a piece of inclined climbing equipment at a school for mountain climbers. The length of the inclined plane from bottom to top is 15 ft, and it is inclined at an angle of 50°. How long must the rope be if it is to touch the ground so that climbers may use it to climb up the structure?

$\angle BTR = 180° - (50° + 90°) = 40°$
$\angle BTP = 180° - 40° = 140°$ *Supplement of $\angle BTR$*

$t = \sqrt{(15)^2 + (6)^2 - 2(6)(15)\cos 140°}$
$t = 20$

Therefore, the rope should be approximately 20 ft long.

5.4 The Law of Cosines   **267**

For Example 5
An 18-ft brace attached to a vertical pole makes an angle of 65° with the pole. Another brace is to be attached to the pole at a point 4 ft above the first. How long must the second brace be if it is to meet the ground at the same place as the first brace? 20 ft

Common Error Some students use the law of sines when the law of cosines should be used. Remind these students that an angle and the side opposite it must be known in order to use the law of sines.

CLOSURE
Have students summarize in their math journals the procedures for solving an oblique triangle by using the law of cosines.

INDEPENDENT PRACTICE
Assignment Guide
Basic: 1–21, 23, Project
Average: 7–11, 15, 19–34, Project
Enriched: 22, 24–44, Project

Teacher's Resource Book
Practice, page 35

ℝ **Review**
Exercises 11, 13, 15, 19, and 23 review concepts of determining slope of a line, evaluating composite functions, graphing sinusoidals, restricting the domain of a function, and finding asymptotes.

Thinking Critically
The answers would be the same if $\angle C$ were solved for before solving for $\angle A$ since a unique triangle is determined by any of three given sides.

Technology

A short program for using the law of cosines may be written and saved in a calculator for use in exercises like the one in Example 3.

Project

A class forum is more effective when it is well organized. Designate students to take charge of certain tasks such as leading the discussion, recording the events, and presenting the facts.

LESSON FOLLOW-UP

Lesson Quiz

1. Determine the distance from A to B if $\angle ADC = 104°$, $\angle BDC = 68°$, $\angle DCA = 55°$, $\angle DCB = 94°$, and $DC = 980$ ft.

980 ft

1887 ft

2. Solve the oblique triangle RST if $R = 67.6°$, $s = 44.2$, and $t = 38.7$. $\angle R = 67.6°$, $\angle S = 61.9°$, $\angle T = 50.5°$, $r = 46.3$, $s = 44.2$, and $t = 38.7$

3. Solve triangle ABC if $a = 15.6$, $b = 9.8$, and $c = 7.4$. Express angle measures to the nearest degree. $\angle A = 130°$, $\angle B = 29°$, $\angle C = 21°$, $a = 15.6$, $b = 9.8$, and $c = 7.4$

4. Two airplanes leave an airport at the same time. The heading of the first is 80° and the heading of the second is 190°. If the planes travel at the rates of 500 mi/h and 540 mi/h, respectively, how far apart are they after 1 h? 852 mi

The following table indicates which law to use when solving triangles:

Given Information	Appropriate Law
Three sides	Law of cosines
Two sides and the included angle	Law of cosines
Two sides and an angle opposite one side (ambiguous case)	Law of sines
One side and two angles	Law of sines

Class Exercises

Solve each triangle. Express lengths to the nearest unit and angles to the nearest degree.

1. $\angle C = 130°$, $a = 8$, and $b = 9$
2. $\angle R = 48°$, $p = 12$, and $q = 17$
3. $\angle R = 63°$, $s = 25$, $t = 35$
4. $k = 12$, $l = 9$, and $m = 20$
5. $\angle C = 67°$, $a = 27$, $b = 43$
   $\angle A = 37°$; $\angle B = 76°$; $c = 41$
6. $P = 108°$, $q = 54$, and $r = 66$
   $\angle Q = 32°$; $\angle R = 40°$; $p = 97$
7. Determine the measure of the largest angle in triangle DEF if $d = 17.6$, $e = 15.3$, and $f = 31.5$. $\angle F = 146°$
8. Determine the measure of the smallest angle in triangle PQR if $r = 41.3$, $q = 37.7$, and $p = 5.8$. $\angle P = 7°$
9. *Surveying*   A triangular field is 102.4 yd on one side and 113.2 yd on another. The measure of the angle between them is 63.6°. Determine the length of the third side. 114.0 yd
10. *Sports*   An adjustable steel brace with two arms is used to support a basketball backboard on a garage roof. If the backboard is 46 in. high and the brace arms attached at the top and bottom are 58 and 52 in., respectively, determine the angle between the two braces. 49°
11. In a parallelogram, two adjacent sides meet at an angle of 38°. They are 7 and 11 ft long. Determine the length of the longer diagonal. 17 ft
12. *Surveying*   A surveyor wishes to measure the width of a building. The distances from A and B to the surveyor at C are 400 and 520 ft, respectively. The measure of the angle at C is 76°. Determine the width of the building. 574 ft

A   B
400 ft   76°   520 ft
          C
          surveyor

13. **Writing in Mathematics**   A person with a working calculator and the ability to measure distances, but with no means to measure angles, needs to determine the angle measures of some irregularly shaped polygons. Would the law of sines or cosines be more useful? Explain. Write a word problem for such a situation and provide a complete solution.

Writing in Mathematics

13. Law of cosines would be more useful since law of sines requires at least one angle. Examples may vary.

Practice Exercises 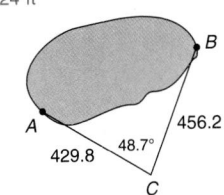 Use appropriate technology.

Solve each triangle. Express lengths to the nearest unit and angles to the nearest degree.

A 1. $\angle C = 79°$, $a = 25$, and $b = 29$
   2. $\angle C = 47°$, $a = 15$, and $b = 21$
   3. $\angle A = 42°$, $b = 12$, and $c = 19$
   4. $\angle A = 84°$, $b = 5$, and $c = 7$
   5. $\angle P = 34°$, $q = 71$, and $r = 85$
   6. $\angle S = 59°$, $r = 112$, and $t = 95$
   7. $a = 15$, $b = 17$, and $c = 29$
   8. $a = 105$, $b = 76$, and $c = 41$
   9. $\angle K = 56°$, $\ell = 3.4$, and $m = 4.2$
   10. $\angle D = 81°$, $e = 2.1$, and $f = 1.7$

Ⓡ 11. Determine the slope of a line that passes through $(-9, 4)$ and $(6, -7)$. $-\frac{11}{15}$

12. The sides of a parallelogram are 24.6 and 38.2, and the measure of one angle is 143°. Determine the length of the longer diagonal. 59.7

Ⓡ 13. Evaluate $g(f(-4))$ if $f(x) = -x^2 + 3$ and $g(x) = 5x - 2$. -67

14. *Surveying* A triangular lot is 506.8 ft on one side and 602.5 ft on another. The measure of the angle between them is 57.4°. Determine the length of the third side. 539.3 ft

Ⓡ 15. Graph $y = 3\cos\left(x - \frac{\pi}{4}\right)$.

16. In a parallelogram, two adjacent sides meet at an angle of 108°. The sides are 17 and 23 ft long. Determine the length of the shorter diagonal. 24 ft

17. *Surveying* A bridge is to be built across a lake from point A to point B. A surveyor at C determines that the distances from C to B and C to A are 456.2 and 429.8 ft, respectively. He also measures the angle between sides CA and CB to be 48.7°. Determine the length of the bridge to the nearest tenth. 366.1 ft

18. An isosceles triangle with congruent sides of length 18 in. has a vertex angle of 72°. Determine the length of the third side. 21 in.

Ⓡ 19. What restrictions on the domain of $f(x) = \sin x$ will make $f^{-1}(x)$ a function? $-\frac{\pi}{2} \le x \le \frac{\pi}{2}$

20. **Thinking Critically** In what type of triangle does $\dfrac{a}{\cos A} = \dfrac{b}{\cos B}$?

B 21. *Surveying* To approximate the distance from two points R and T on opposite sides of a small lake, a man walks 600 ft from R to P, then turns 35° to face T, and walks 870 ft to T. Find RT. 512 ft

22. *Surveying* To approximate the straight line distance from a point D to a point E on opposite sides of a small hill, a woman walks 720 ft from D to F, then turns 47° to face E, and walks 940 ft to E. Find DE. 692 ft

Ⓡ 23. Determine the first asymptote such that $x > 0$ for the function $f(x) = \tan\frac{1}{2}x$. $x = \pi$

24. *Aviation* An airplane leaves an airport at 10:00 a.m. with a heading of 180° and a speed of 650 mi/h. At 1:00 p.m. the pilot changes the heading to 200°. Determine how far the plane is from the airport at 3:00 p.m. 3203 mi

25. *Aviation* An airplane leaves an airport at 9:00 p.m. with a heading of 270° and a speed of 610 mi/h. At 10:00 p.m. the pilot changes the heading to 310°. Determine how far the plane is from the airport at 1:00 a.m. 2331 mi

26. One end of a 9.3-ft pole is 13.6 ft from an observer's eyes, and the other end is 17.4 ft from the observer's eyes. Through what angle does the observer see the pole? 32°

27. One end of a 7.8-ft sign is 15.7 ft from an observer's eyes, and the other end is 11.2 ft from the observer's eyes. Through what angle does the observer see the sign? 28°

28. *Navigation*   Two ships leave a port at the same time. The heading of the first ship is 73°, and the heading of the second is 115°. If the ships travel at the rate of 12 knots (1 knot = 1 nautical mile per hour) and 15 knots, respectively, determine how far apart they are after 2 h. 20 nautical mi

29. *Aviation*   Two planes leave an airport at the same time. The heading of the first plane is 350°, and the heading of the second is 49°. If the planes travel at the rate of 420 and 510 mi/h, respectively, how far apart are they after 3 h? 1394 mi

30. *Engineering*   A telephone pole has two guy wires attached at the same points. One is of length 40 ft and makes an angle of 43° with the ground. The other guy wire is of length 52 ft. Determine the measure of the angle the second guy wire makes with the ground. 32°

31. *Sports*   Tee Ball is similar to baseball, but the field is a diamond 40 ft square. The "pitcher's mound" is positioned 25 ft from homeplate. Determine the distance from the pitcher's mound to third base. 28 ft

32. *Aviation*   Two planes take off from the same airport at the same time. One flies at a heading of 343° at an average speed of 512.4 mi/h, while the other flies on at a heading of 47° at an average speed of 320.6 mi/h. How far apart are the planes after 2 h? 941 mi

33. *Surveying*   A builder must know the distance across a small lake between two points *A* and *B*. A surveyor is hired to measure the distances from *C* to *A* and from *C* to *B* and finds them to be 700 and 612 yd, respectively. The measure of ∠*ACB* is 79°. Determine the distance from *A* to *B*. 837 yd

34. *Surveying*   An environmentalist group must determine the width of a protected bog area. Two stakes are positioned on opposite sides of the bog at *P* and *Q*. The distances from *P* and *Q* to *R*, a point on high ground, are determined to be 982 and 876 ft, respectively. The measure of angle *R* is 138°. Determine the width of the bog from *P* to *Q*. 1735 ft

C **35.** *Physics*   If two forces act at a point, the magnitude of their sum (the resultant force) is the length of the diagonal of a parallelogram that includes the common point. The lengths of the adjacent sides are the magnitudes of the two respective forces. If forces of 220 and 180 lb act at an angle of 46° to each other, determine the magnitude of their sum. 369 lb

36. *Physics*   If forces of 175.6 and 193.8 lb act on an object with resultant force 347.2 lb, determine the angle that the resultant force makes with the lesser force. 21°

37. *Aviation*   A pilot intends to fly a distance of 175 mi from Chicago to Indianapolis. She begins 21° off her course and proceeds 70 mi before discovering her error. After correcting her course, how much farther must she fly to get to Indianapolis? 112 mi

38. *Aviation*   A plane leaves an airport and travels at a heading of 85° at 615 mi/h. Another plane leaves the same airport 20 min later and travels at a heading of 113° at 645 mi/h. How far apart are they 30 min after the second plane leaves? 273.5 mi

Law of Tangents   Another formula, called the law of tangents, that can be used to solve triangles when the measures of two sides and the included angle are known is

$$\frac{a-b}{a+b} = \frac{\tan\frac{1}{2}(A-B)}{\tan\frac{1}{2}(A+B)}$$

39. Use the law of tangents to find, to the nearest degree, the measures of the other two angles of a triangle if $a = 28$, $b = 26$, and $\angle C = 46°$. $\angle A = 72°$; $\angle B = 62°$

40. In $\triangle ABC$, find the measures of sides b and c if their sum is 88, and $\angle B = 30°$ and $\angle C = 52°$. $b = 34$; $c = 54$

41. Show that for any triangle ABC, $1 + \cos B = \dfrac{(a+c+b)(a+c-b)}{2ac}$.

42. Show that for any triangle ABC, $1 - \cos C = \dfrac{(c-a+b)(c+a-b)}{2ab}$.

43. Derive the law of cosines for the case in which $\angle C$ is an obtuse angle. *Hint*: Recall that $\cos(180° - C) = -\cos C$.

44. In Example 1, determine the corrected distance between the platform and the pumping station if the surveyors made an error of 2° measuring $\angle DCA$. 1525 m

Project

Hold a class forum to discuss how the distance between a platform and a pumping station could be computed if surveyors did not know trigonometry.

Challenge

1. Show that $4\cos^2\theta - 4\cos^4\theta + \cos^2(2\theta) = \sin^2(-\theta) + \cos^2(-\theta)$.

2. The area of a rectangular strawberry patch is 700 ft². The longer side of the rectangular patch is against the barn and does not require fencing. The cost of the fencing for the remaining three sides is $225 at $3 per foot. Find the dimensions of each possible garden to the nearest tenth.

5.4 The Law of Cosines   **271**

Vocabulary
Heron's formula
segment

Ⓜ **Materials/Manipulatives**
square tiles

Technology
scientific calculators

FOCUS

The presentation of Heron's accomplishments can be very motivational because he dealt with both the theoretical and the practical. Have students research other individuals who showed this variety.

INSTRUCTION

Encourage students to draw diagrams before starting the calculations.

Ⓜ **Alternative Learning Styles**
Some students do not have a well-developed concept of area. Using examples like covering a floor with 9-in. tiles and then covering the same floor with 12-in. tiles helps to fix the concept for them. Repeat the idea by having them cover a triangle with square tiles and estimate the area.

5.5 The Area of a Triangle

Objectives: To find the area of a triangle given the measures of two sides and the included angle or one side and two angles
To use Heron's formula to find the area of a triangle given the lengths of three sides
To find the area of a segment of a circle

Focus

Approximately 2000 years ago, a mathematician and inventor named Heron lived in Alexandria, Egypt. He was knowledgeable about the practical achievements of the Egyptians, and about the theoretical mathematics of the Greeks. Because he was interested in both theoretical and applied mathematics, Heron presented formulas for finding exact answers, as well as methods for making approximations. He invented a number of devices operated by water or steam, including a fire engine and siphon. The formula for finding the area of a triangle when three sides are known bears his name— Heron's formula.

When you know enough parts to determine a unique triangle, you can also determine the area of the triangle. The method used to find the area depends upon the given information.

Recall that the area of a triangle is equal to one-half the product of the base and the height. Assume that sides b and c are given along with acute $\angle A$. Let K represent the area of the triangle, and h the altitude from B to side AC. Then

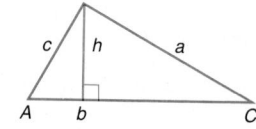

$$K = \tfrac{1}{2}bh$$

But $\qquad\qquad h = c \sin A \qquad$ $\sin A = \frac{h}{c}$

So $\qquad\qquad K = \tfrac{1}{2}bc \sin A \qquad$ *Substitute $c \sin A$ for h.*

By similar methods and appropriate choices for altitudes, you can derive two other forms for the area that involve the sine of $\angle B$ or $\angle C$. The proof of the case in which one angle is obtuse is left as an exercise.

272 Chapter 5 Applications of Trigonometry

The area K of triangle ABC is given by any one of these formulas:

$$K = \tfrac{1}{2}bc \sin A \qquad K = \tfrac{1}{2}ac \sin B \qquad K = \tfrac{1}{2}ab \sin C$$

Example 1 Determine the area of $\triangle DEF$ if $\angle E = 49.6°$, $d = 17.4$ in., and $f = 19.7$ in. Express your answer to the nearest square inch.

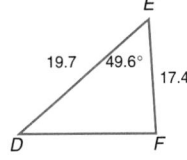

$K = \tfrac{1}{2}df \sin E$

$K = \tfrac{1}{2}(17.4)(19.7) \sin 49.6°$ *Calculation-ready form*

$K = 131$ in.²   To the nearest square inch

The preceding formula can be used along with the law of sines to derive another formula for the area of a triangle. This formula allows you to find the area of a triangle if two angles and one side are known.

Assume that $\angle A$, $\angle C$, and b are known. Then,

$$\angle B = 180° - (\angle A + \angle C)$$

The law of sines gives

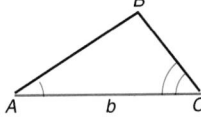

$$a = \frac{b \sin A}{\sin B}$$

$K = \tfrac{1}{2}ab \sin C$

$K = \dfrac{(b \sin A)(b \sin C)}{2 \sin B} = \dfrac{b^2 \sin A \sin C}{2 \sin B}$ *Substitute* $\frac{b \sin A}{\sin B}$ *for a.*

This formula or the following equivalent forms may be used to find the area of a triangle when two angles and one side are known:

$$K = \frac{a^2 \sin B \sin C}{2 \sin A} \qquad \text{and} \qquad K = \frac{c^2 \sin A \sin B}{2 \sin C}$$

Example 2 Determine the area of $\triangle PQR$ if $\angle P = 51.7°$, $\angle Q = 41.5°$, and $p = 156.3$ cm. Express your answer to the nearest square centimeter.

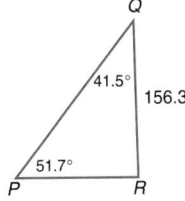

$\angle R = 180° - (51.7° + 41.5°) = 86.8°$

$K = \dfrac{p^2 \sin R \sin Q}{2 \sin P}$

$K = \dfrac{156.3^2(\sin 86.8°)(\sin 41.5°)}{2 \sin 51.7°}$ *Calculation-ready form*

$K = 10{,}297$ cm²

5.5 The Area of a Triangle   **273**

GUIDED PRACTICE

For Example 1

Determine the area of each triangle. Express your answer to the nearest square unit.

1. $\angle B = 56.4°$, $a = 21.5$ in., $c = 24.7$ in.
   221 in.²
2. $\angle R = 112.9°$, $p = 87.4$ ft, $q = 76.1$ ft
   3063 ft²

For Example 2

Determine the area of each triangle. Express your answer to the nearest square unit.

1. $\angle D = 56.9°$, $\angle E = 71.4°$, $d = 46.7$ cm
   968 cm²
2. $\angle S = 29.5°$, $\angle T = 85.4°$, $t = 123.4$ in.
   3412 in.²

For Example 3

Determine the area of each triangle. Express your answer to the nearest square unit.

1. $p = 31.3$ ft, $q = 27.4$ ft, $r = 24.8$ ft
326 ft²

2. $a = 45.9$ m, $b = 49.1$ m, $c = 41.5$ m
884 m²

For Example 4

A triangular sign with side measures of 11, 13, and 16 in. requires a brace perpendicular to the longest side from the opposite vertex. Determine the length of the brace to the nearest tenth of an inch. 8.9 in.

When the lengths of three sides of a triangle are known, you can use the law of cosines to determine the measure of an angle. Then you can apply one of the above formulas to find the area of the triangle. However, Heron's formula often involves fewer calculations.

Heron's Formula

If a, b, and c are the measures of the sides of a triangle, then the area K of the triangle is given by

$$K = \sqrt{s(s - a)(s - b)(s - c)} \qquad \text{where } s = \frac{a + b + c}{2}$$

The quantity s is called the **semiperimeter** of the triangle.

Example 3   Determine the area of $\triangle RST$ if $r = 15.2$ cm, $s = 22.7$ cm, and $t = 8.9$ cm. Express you answer to the nearest square centimeter.

$$s = \frac{15.2 + 22.7 + 8.9}{2} = 23.4$$

$K = \sqrt{23.4(23.4 - 15.2)(23.4 - 22.7)(23.4 - 8.9)}$ *Calculation-ready form*
$K = 44$ cm²

If three sides of a triangle are known, Heron's formula can be used to find the length of an altitude. A builder who knows the lengths of both sides of the gable of a house and the width of the house can determine the length of the vertical brace needed to support the gable.

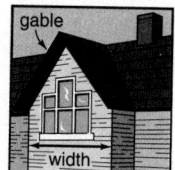

Example 4   *Construction*   The gable on the end of a house has side measures of 12 and 16 ft, respectively. The width of the house is 22 ft. Find the minimum length of board that the builder must purchase for the brace which extends from the peak of the gable to the level of the roof line.

$$s = \frac{12 + 16 + 22}{2} = 25$$

$K = \sqrt{25(25 - 12)(25 - 16)(25 - 22)}$ *Calculation-ready form*
$K = 94$ *Retain the full value in the calculator.*

$94 = \frac{1}{2}(22)h$ *Use $K = \frac{1}{2}bh$.*

$\frac{2(94)}{22} = h$ *Calculation-ready form*

$8.5 = h$

The builder should purchase a 9-ft board since boards are sold by the foot.

In Chapter 3, Lesson 3.2, the formula for the area of a sector of a circle was introduced. Using radians, the formula is

$$A_s = \tfrac{1}{2}r^2\theta$$

where θ is the measure of the central angle that intercepts the arc.

A **segment of a circle** is the region bounded by a minor arc and the chord of the arc. The area of the segment may be found by subtracting the area of triangle AOB from the area of sector AOB.

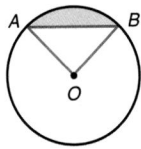

Example 5 Determine the area A of the segment in the circle with center Q shown at the right below if $\angle Q = 80°$ and $QR = 10$ in.

$A = \tfrac{1}{2}r^2\theta\left(\dfrac{\pi}{180}\right)$ θ in degrees

$A = \dfrac{80}{360}(\pi)(10)^2$ Calculation-ready form

$A = 70$ in.²   Retain A in your calculator.

$K = \tfrac{1}{2}pr\sin Q$ Find the area K of △PQR.

$K = \tfrac{1}{2}(10)(10)\sin 80°$ Calculation-ready form

$K = 49$ in.²   Retain K in your calculator.

Thus, the approximate area of the segment is $70 - 49 = 21$ in.²

The relationships between the lengths of the sides of a 30°-60°-90° triangle are reviewed in the figure at the right. You can see that the area of an equilateral triangle in terms of its side s is

$$A = \dfrac{s^2\sqrt{3}}{4}$$

Example 6 A circular traffic sign has a red equilateral triangle with 24-in. sides inscribed in it. Determine the area of the nonred parts.

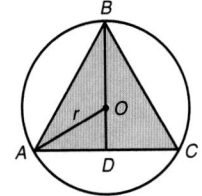

$OD = \dfrac{12}{\sqrt{3}} = 4\sqrt{3}$ Since AD = 12 and △ADO is a 30°-60°-90° right triangle.

$r = 2(4\sqrt{3}) = 8\sqrt{3}$

Area of circle: $\pi(8\sqrt{3})^2 = 192\pi$ $A = \pi r^2$

Area of equilateral triangle: $\dfrac{(24)^2\sqrt{3}}{4} = 144\sqrt{3}$ $A = \dfrac{s^2\sqrt{3}}{4}$

Area of nonred parts: $192\pi - 144\sqrt{3}$ in.²

5.5 The Area of a Triangle   **275**

For Example 5

1. Determine the area of the segment in the circle with center B shown below if $\angle B = 85°$ and $AB = 30$ in.

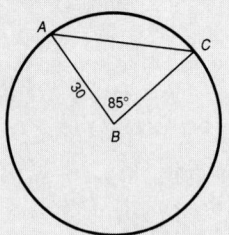

219 in.²

2. Determine the area of the segment in the circle with center S shown below if $\angle S = 140°$ and $RS = 18.6$ cm.

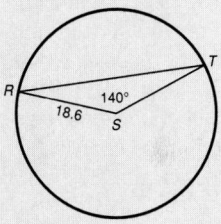

311 cm²

For Example 6

A circular traffic sign has a green square with 16-in. sides inscribed in the circle. Determine the exact area of the nongreen parts.
$(128\pi - 256)$ in.²

Group students in pairs and have them summarize for each other the procedures for determining the area of a triangle and the area of a segment of a circle using the methods presented in this lesson.

INDEPENDENT PRACTICE

Assignment Guide
Basic: 1–28, 43
Average: 9, 13, 18–44
Enriched: 25–53

Teacher's Resource Book
  Practice, page 36

® Review
Exercises 9, 13, 19, 21, and 23 review the concepts of finding the area of a sector of a circle, determining whether an equation is an identity, evaluating functions, determining amplitude, and simplifying trigonometric expressions.

LESSON FOLLOW-UP

Test Yourself

Teacher's Resource Book
  Tests—Quiz, form A, page 18
  Tests—Quiz, form B, page 18

Class Exercises

Determine the area of each triangle using the given information. Give answers to the nearest square unit.

1. $\angle T = 51.7°$, $r = 9.4$, $s = 13.1$ 48
2. $\angle M = 62.5°$, $k = 17.7$, $l = 18.3$ 144
3. $r = 7.4$, $s = 9.3$, $t = 14.5$ 30
4. $x = 8.7$, $y = 11.6$, $w = 19.2$ 31
5. $\angle A = 54°$, $\angle B = 49°$, $b = 12$ 75
6. $\angle D = 62°$, $\angle F = 55°$, $d = 21$ 182

In triangle ABC, find the length of the altitude to side BC to the nearest tenth.

7. $a = 17.3$, $b = 12.7$, $c = 6.5$ 3.9
8. $a = 25.4$, $b = 33.4$, $c = 51.5$ 28.4

Determine the area of the segment of a circle given arc degree measure PR and radius r.

9. $PR = 75°$, $r = 15$ 39
10. $PR = 112°$, $r = 14$ 101

11. **Thinking Critically**   What is the effect upon the area of a sector of a circle if the length of its arc is tripled? The area is tripled.

12. The adjacent sides of a parallelogram are 20 and 25 cm, and one angle measures 80°. Determine the area of the parallelogram. 492 cm²

13. An isosceles trapezoid has two base angles that measure 45°. The lengths of the bases are 12 in. and 16 in. The sides measure 9 in. each. Find its area. 89 in.²

Practice Exercises   Use appropriate technology.

Use the given information to determine the area of each triangle. Express your answers to the nearest square unit.

A 1. $\angle J = 40°$, $k = 15$, $l = 23$ 111
2. $\angle P = 50°$, $q = 19$, $r = 28$ 204
3. $\angle E = 55°$, $\angle F = 48°$, $f = 34$ 621
4. $\angle B = 63°$, $\angle C = 54°$, $c = 48$ 1130
5. $r = 25$, $s = 31$, $t = 50$ 313
6. $p = 37$, $q = 42$, $r = 73$ 550
7. $\angle H = 104.5°$, $g = 67.2$, $i = 77.6$ 2524
8. $\angle L = 96.4°$, $k = 52.3$, $m = 76.9$ 1998

® 9. Determine the area of the sector of a circle with arc measure 1.8 rad and radius 5 to the nearest square unit. 22.5

Determine the area of the segment of a circle with the given arc measure and radius.

10.
1139
11.
235
12.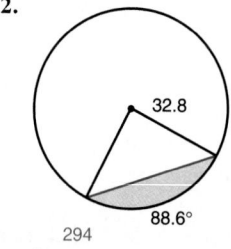
294

® 13. Determine whether $\sin \alpha \cos \alpha \cot \alpha = 2 \cos \alpha$ is an identity using a graphing utility. not an identity

276   Chapter 5 Applications of Trigonometry

Determine the length of the altitude to side *RS* to the nearest tenth of a unit.

14. $r = 25.4$, $s = 29.3$, $t = 48.6$ 12.5   **15.** $r = 12.5$, $s = 13.6$, $t = 20.1$ 8.3

16. $r = 12.5$, $s = 10.1$, $t = 18.3$ 6.6   **17.** $r = 13.4$, $s = 12.1$, $t = 19.9$ 8.0

18. Writing in Mathematics   Describe how you would find the measure of the third side of a triangle if two sides and the area of the triangle are known. Is this always possible? Why or why not?

19. Find $f(x) = \sec^{-1}(x)$ if $x = 1.5$ rad. 0.8 rad

20. A DO NOT PASS sign is an isosceles triangle with side measures of 22, 22, and 16 in., respectively. Determine the area of the sign. 164 in.²

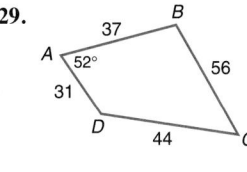
22 in.
DO NOT PASS 16 in.
22 in.

21. Determine the amplitude of $f(x) = \sin x + \cos x$. $\sqrt{2}$

22. The adjacent sides of a parallelogram are 18 and 26 cm long, and one angle measures 70°. Determine the area of the parallelogram. 439.2 cm²

23. Simplify $\cos A \cot A + \sin A$. csc A

24. Thinking Critically   What is the effect upon the area of a sector of a circle if the length of its arc is doubled and the length of the radius is tripled? The area is 18 times larger.

B 25. Thinking Critically   The adjacent sides of a parallelogram have lengths c and d, and the included angle θ is acute. Express the area of the parallelogram in terms of c, d, and θ. $A = cd \sin \theta$

26. *Surveying*   Determine the area of a triangular parcel of land if two adjacent sides have measures of 212 and 278 ft, respectively, and the angle between them is 83°. 29,248.35 ft²

27. *Manufacturing*   A toy roof support has the shape of an equilateral triangle and an area of 163 in.² Determine the perimeter. 58.2 in.

Determine the area of the given polygons.

28.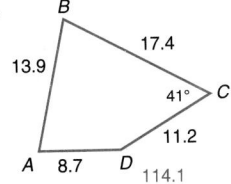
B
17.4
13.9
41° C
11.2
A 8.7 D 114.1

29.
A
37
B
52°
31
56
D 44 C
1115

30. Determine the area of a regular hexagon which is inscribed in a circle with radius 6.92 ft. 124.41 ft²

31. Determine the area of the regular pentagon which is inscribed in a circle with radius 8.76 ft. 182.45 ft²

32. Determine the area of a regular octagon which is inscribed in a circle with radius 6.34 in. 114.05 in.²

33. Determine the lateral surface area of the cone formed by bringing together the two sides of a circular sector that has arc degree measure 190° and is cut from a circular piece of tin of radius 14 cm. *Hint*: Lateral surface area of a cone $= \pi r \ell$ where ℓ is the slant height. 324.98 cm²

5.5 The Area of a Triangle   **277**

34. Determine the lateral surface area of the cone formed by bringing together the two sides of a circular sector that has arc degree measure 230° and is cut from a circular piece of tin of radius 18 in. 650.3 in.²

35. *Manufacturing*   A cone-shaped tent is made from a circular piece of fabric 12 ft in diameter, with a sector of central angle 140° removed. Determine the surface area of the tent. 69 ft²

36. *Manufacturing*   A cone-shaped tent is made from a circular piece of fabric 11 ft in radius with a sector of central angle 96° removed. Determine the surface area of the tent. 279 ft²

37. Determine the sum of the three segments formed by inscribing an equilateral triangle in a circle of radius 20 cm. 737 cm²

38. Determine the sum of the four segments formed by inscribing a square in a circle of radius 10 in. 114 in.²

39. Determine the area of the shaded region. The vertices of the triangle are the centers of the arcs. 4

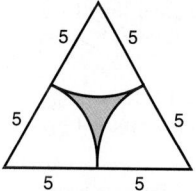

40. Determine the area of the shaded region. The vertices of the square are the centers of the arcs. 21

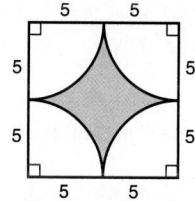

41. In the semicircle of radius 5, the length of chord *CB* is 6. Determine the area of the shaded region. 15

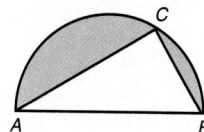

42. In the semicircle of radius 13, the length of chord *AB* is 10. Determine the area of the shaded region. 145

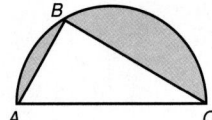

43. **Writing in Mathematics**   Describe why it is possible for two triangles to have identical areas but quite different perimeters. Provide an example.

C 44. *Programming*   Write an algorithm for a program to find the area of a triangle using Heron's formula.

45. Determine the area of a regular pentagon with sides of measure 47.84 in. 3937.60 in.²

46. *Surveying*   The shortest side of a triangular piece of property with area 218,000 ft² is on a straight river and requires no fence. How much fence is needed to construct fences on the remaining two sides if the angles at the vertices of the property are 41°, 64°, and 75°? 1631 ft

47. *Surveying*   A lot in the shape of a quadrilateral has two sides of length 18.2 and 20.1 yd, respectively, perpendicular to each other. The other two sides have lengths of 19.6 and 20.8 yd. Determine the area of the lot. 385.7 yd²

278   Chapter 5 Applications of Trigonometry

48. Determine the area of the shaded region formed by the semicircles inscribed in the square. **51**

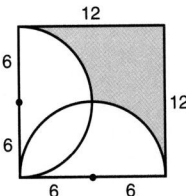

49. Determine the area of the shaded region. The cross is equilateral. **26**

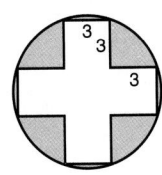

50. Determine the area of the shaded region. The cross is equilateral. **71**

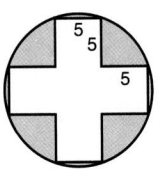

51. Determine the area of the shaded region. Points *P* and *Q* are the centers for the arcs. **37**

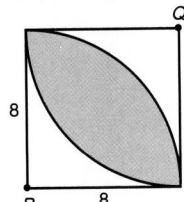

52. Determine the area of the shaded region. Points *P* and *Q* are the centers for the arcs. **43**

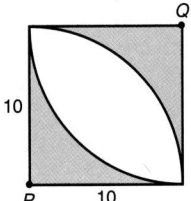

53. Determine the area of the shaded region. Triangle *ABC* is equilateral and point *O* is the center for the circumscribed circle. **88**

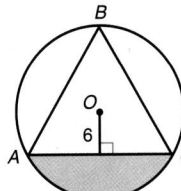

Test Yourself

Solve each triangle. Express lengths to the nearest unit and angles to the nearest degree.

1. $a = 10$, $b = 12$, $c = 14$

2. $a = 15$, $b = 13$, $c = 9$ 5.4

3. $a = 54$, $b = 32$, $\angle C = 48°$
$\angle A = 96°$; $\angle B = 36°$; $c = 40$

4. $b = 18$, $c = 20$, $\angle A = 13°$
$\angle B = 54°$; $\angle C = 113°$; $a = 5$ 5.5

5. Determine the area of $\triangle ABC$ if $\angle A = 35.6°$, $b = 27.8$ cm, and $c = 16.4$ cm. Express your answer to the nearest square centimeter. **133 cm²**

6. The sides of a parallelogram are 9 and 12 cm long, and the measure of the included angle is 30°. Determine the area of the parallelogram. **54 cm²**

7. Determine the area of the segment of the circle with arc degree measure 60° and radius 28 cm. **71 cm²**

Chapter 5 Summary and Review

Vocabulary

ambiguous case (257)
angle of depression (246)
angle of elevation (246)
heading (267)

Heron's formula (274)
law of cosines (264)
law of sines (251)
oblique triangles (251)

segment of a circle (275)
semiperimeter (274)
solving triangles (244)
triangulation (265)

Solving Right Triangles Right triangle trigonometry can be used to find lengths of missing sides and measures of missing angles. For an acute angle θ in right triangle ABC, the trigonometric functions are as follows:

5.1

$$\sin \theta = \frac{a}{c} = \frac{\text{length of leg opposite } \theta}{\text{length of hypotenuse}}$$

$$\cos \theta = \frac{b}{c} = \frac{\text{length of leg adjacent to } \theta}{\text{length of hypotenuse}}$$

$$\tan \theta = \frac{a}{b} = \frac{\text{length of leg opposite } \theta}{\text{length of leg adjacent to } \theta}$$

$$\cot \theta = \frac{b}{a} = \frac{\text{length of leg adjacent to } \theta}{\text{length of leg opposite } \theta}$$

$$\sec \theta = \frac{c}{b} = \frac{\text{length of hypotenuse}}{\text{length of leg adjacent to } \theta}$$

$$\csc \theta = \frac{c}{a} = \frac{\text{length of hypotenuse}}{\text{length of leg opposite } \theta}$$

Solve each right triangle ABC with $\angle C = 90°$.

1. $\angle B = 54°$, $a = 168$
$\angle A = 36°$; $b = 231$; $c = 286$

2. $a = 14.8$, $b = 23.5$
$\angle A = 32.2°$; $\angle B = 57.8°$; $c = 27.8$

3. Each side of a regular pentagon is 36.8 cm long. Determine the radius of an inscribed circle. 25.3 cm

4. A cartographer needs to know how high the mapping satellite is when it photographs the central plains region. He asks two observers in the region to take angle of elevation measurements at the same time of day. The angles reported are 37° and 31°. If the observers are 54 mi apart, how high is the satellite? 18 mi

The Law of Sines The law of sines can be used to solve triangles when two angles and one side are given.

5.2

$$\frac{\sin A}{a} = \frac{\sin B}{b} = \frac{\sin C}{c}$$

5. Solve $\triangle ABC$ if $\angle A = 67°$, $\angle B = 52°$, and $a = 36$. Express the lengths of the sides to the nearest unit. $b = 31$; $c = 34$; $\angle C = 61°$

6. The angles of elevation of the top of a building from two points on ground level are 56° and 72°. The distance between the two points is 48 ft. Determine the height of the building. 137 ft

The Ambiguous Case   When the measures of two sides and an angle opposite one of them are given, *two* triangles, *one* triangle, or *no* triangle may be determined.

5.3

Determine the possible number of triangles in each case.

7. $\angle A = 51°$, $a = 26$, $c = 17$ one

8. $\angle A = 42°$, $a = 28$, $b = 36$ two

9. $\angle A = 63°$, $a = 11$, $c = 15$ none

10. $\angle A = 110°$, $a = 20$, $b = 19$ one

11. $\angle A = 88°$, $a = 13$, $c = 13$ two

12. $\angle A = 131°$, $a = 8$, $b = 8$ none

The Law of Cosines   The law of cosines can be used to solve triangles when two sides and the included angle or three sides are given.

5.4

$$a^2 = b^2 + c^2 - 2bc \cos A \qquad \cos A = \frac{b^2 + c^2 - a^2}{2bc}$$

$$b^2 = a^2 + c^2 - 2ac \cos B \qquad \cos B = \frac{a^2 + c^2 - b^2}{2ac}$$

$$c^2 = a^2 + b^2 - 2ab \cos C \qquad \cos C = \frac{a^2 + b^2 - c^2}{2ab}$$

13. Solve triangle ABC if $a = 27$ cm, $b = 32$ cm, and $c = 18$ cm. $\angle A = 57°$; $\angle B = 88°$; $\angle C = 35°$

14. Solve triangle XYZ if $\angle X = 67°$, $y = 10$, and $z = 22$. $\angle Y = 27.0°$; $\angle Z = 86.0°$; $x = 20.3$

15. Two airplanes leave an airport at the same time. The heading of the first is 60° and the heading of the second is 130°. If the airplanes travel at the rates of 420 and 510 mi/h, how far apart are they after 1 h?   538 mi

The Area of a Triangle   The following formulas can be used to find the area of a triangle when two sides and the included angle are given.

5.5

$$K = \tfrac{1}{2}ab \sin C \qquad K = \tfrac{1}{2}bc \sin A \qquad K = \tfrac{1}{2}ac \sin B$$

The following formulas can also be used when two angles and the included side are given.

$$K = \frac{a^2 \sin B \sin C}{2 \sin A} \qquad K = \frac{b^2 \sin A \sin C}{2 \sin B} \qquad K = \frac{c^2 \sin A \sin B}{2 \sin C}$$

Determine the area of $\triangle ABC$ to the nearest unit.

16. $\angle C = 67°$, $a = 42$, $b = 38$ 735

17. $\angle B = 120°$, $\angle C = 30°$, $a = 18$ 140

18. $\angle B = 55°$, $a = 31$, $c = 29$ 368

19. $\angle B = 68°$, $\angle C = 74°$, $a = 16$ 185

When three sides of a triangle are given, Heron's formula can be used to find the area of the triangle and the altitude.

$$K = \sqrt{s(s - a)(s - b)(s - c)} \qquad \text{where } s = \frac{a + b + c}{2}$$

20. Determine the area and the altitude to side DE of $\triangle DEF$, to the nearest unit, if $d = 18$, $e = 26$, and $f = 34$.   231; 13.6

The area of a segment of a circle can be found by subtracting the area of a triangle from the area of a sector.

21. Determine the area of a segment of a circle with arc degree measure 92° and radius of 36 in.   393 in.²

Chapter 5   Test

Solve each triangle. Express lengths to the nearest unit and angles to the nearest degree.

1. $\angle B = 68°$, $\angle C = 90°$, $a = 42$

2. $\angle A = 41°$, $\angle B = 61°$, $c = 35$

3. $\angle B = 45°$, $\angle C = 48°$, $a = 96$
   $\angle A = 87°$; $b = 68$; $c = 71$

4. $a = 12$, $b = 13$, $c = 15$
   $\angle A = 50°$; $\angle B = 56°$; $\angle C = 74°$

5. Solve isosceles triangle *ABC* if $a = c = 14.6$ cm and $\angle C = 52°$. Express *AC* to the nearest tenth of a unit. $\angle A = 52°$; $\angle B = 76°$; $b = 18.0$

6. A cliff near a lake is 154 ft high. The angle of depression of a boat from the top of the cliff is 37°. Find the distance of the boat from the foot of the cliff. 204 ft

Determine the possible number of triangles in each case.

7. $\angle A = 54°$, $a = 26$, $b = 19$ one

8. $\angle P = 38°$, $p = 16$, $q = 23$ two

9. The angles of elevation of the top of a building from two observers 158 ft apart are 32° and 47°. Find the distance of each observer from the top of the building. 446 ft; 323 ft

10. Determine the measure of the smallest angle of a triangle if the lengths of the sides are 9, 12, and 16. 34°

11. To approximate the distance from two points *A* and *B* on opposite sides of a small lake, a surveyor walks 320 ft from *A* to *C*, then turns 38° to face *B*, and walks 560 ft to *B*. Find *AB*. 365 ft

12. Determine the area of $\triangle ABC$ to the nearest square inch if $\angle A = 150°$, $b = 14$ in., and $c = 27$ in. 95 in.²

13. Determine the area of a triangular lot to the nearest square foot if the sides have lengths of 98, 125, and 164 ft. 6111 ft²

14. Determine the sum of the four segments formed by inscribing a square in a circle of radius 14 cm. 224 cm²

Challenge

A trapezoid with congruent diagonals has bases 20 and 30 cm long. The diagonals intersect at an angle of measure 45°. Determine the area of the trapezoid to the nearest square centimeter. 259 cm²

Cumulative Review

Select the best choice for each question.

1. Determine the number of real   2.4
B   solutions of the quadratic equation
$3x^2 - 8x - 1 = 0$.
   A. 1   **B.** 2   **C.** none   **D.** 3   **E.** 4

2. Evaluate $\text{Sec}^{-1}\, 8.2$ to the nearest   4.6
A   tenth of a degree.
   A. 83.0°   **B.** 82.9°   **C.** 7.1°
   D. 97.0°   **E.** none of these

3. Given $\dfrac{\text{length of leg opposite } \theta}{\text{length of leg adjacent to } \theta}$,   5.1
D   you are naming
   A. $\sin \theta$ **B.** $\csc \theta$ **C.** $\cos \theta$
   D. $\tan \theta$ **E.** $\cot \theta$

4. Determine the area of triangle RST 5.5
E   if $r = 12.4$ cm, $s = 21.2$ cm and
$t = 7.6$ cm. Express your answer to
the nearest square centimeter.
   A. 376 cm²   **B.** 1376 cm²   **C.** 736 cm²
   D. 1736 cm²   **E.** no solution

5. Correspondence between the   1.4
A   elements of the domain and the range
of a relation is called a
   A. mapping   **B.** heading   **C.** function
   D. relation   **E.** none of these

6. Determine the angle measures, to   5.4
C   the nearest degree, of triangle ABC if
$a = 36.2$, $b = 84.3$, and $c = 103.1$.
   A. 36°, 50°, 94°   **B.** 58°, 80°, 42°
   C. 19°, 50°, 111°   **D.** 40°, 60°, 80°
   E. none of these

7. As θ increases from 0 to π, which   4.1
D   of these functions decreases from 1 to
-1?
   A. $\sin \theta$ **B.** $\tan \theta$ **C.** $\csc \theta$
   D. $\cos \theta$ **E.** $\cot \theta$

8. Determine the number of   5.3
E   solutions possible if $\angle A$ in triangle ABC
is an obtuse angle, and if $a \le b$.
   A. 1   **B.** 2   **C.** 3   **D.** 4   **E.** none

9. A sundae costs \$2.25 at Ted's Ice   1.1
B   Cream Palace. Each additional topping
costs 75 cents. The linear equation that
models the cost of the sundae in terms
of the number of toppings is
   A. $y = 2.25x + 0.75$
   B. $y = 0.75x + 2.25$
   C. $y = 0.5x + 2.25$
   D. $y = 2.25x + 0.5$ **E.** none

10. Find the area of the triangle DEF,   5.5
D   if $\angle E = 42°$, $d = 15.2$ in., and
$f = 17.2$ in. Express your answer to
the nearest square inches.
   A. 9 in.²   **B.** 875 in.²   **C.** 358 in.²
   D. 87 in.²   **E.** 36 in.²

11. Express 38.405° in degrees-   3.1
B   minutes-seconds.
   A. 83°18′24″   **B.** 38°24′18″
   C. 24°38′18″   **D.** 18°24′38″
   E. none

12. Which equation can be defined as   4.5
C   an inverse of $y = \sin x$?
   A. $y = \cos x$ **B.** $y = \arccos x$
   C. $y = \arcsin x$ **D.** $y = \arctan x$
   E. none of these

13. Determine the value of $\sin \theta$ for   3.4
D   the angle in standard position that
passes through point $(-3, -4)$.
   A. $\frac{5}{4}$ **B.** $\frac{4}{5}$ **C.** $-\frac{5}{4}$ **D.** $-\frac{4}{5}$ **E.** none

14. How many cycles will the function   4.2
E $F(x) = 2 \cos \frac{1}{4}x$ have from 0 to 2π?
   A. 4   **B.** 3   **C.** 2   **D.** 1
   E. none of these

15. Determine the number of solutions   5.3
A   that satisfy triangle ABC if $\angle A = 84°$,
$b = 28.64$, and $a = 43.68$.
   A. 1   **B.** 2   **C.** 3   **D.** none

Summary

The sum and difference identities and double-angle and half-angle identities are developed and used. Identities are also verified with the aid of a graphing utility. Trigonometric equations and inequalities are solved both algebraically and graphically. Solution methods are also explored for trigonometric equations and inequalities in quadratic form.

Chapter Objectives

- To develop and use formulas for the trigonometric functions of a sum or difference of two angle measures
- To determine whether an equation is an identity using a graphing utility
- To develop and use the double-angle identities
- To develop and use the half-angle identities
- To develop and use the product/sum identities
- To solve trigonometric equations and inequalities
- To solve trigonometric equations and inequalities in quadratic form

6 Trigonometric Identities and Equations

Mathematical Power

Modeling   Navigation is the science of determining a vessel's location and course. Methods of navigation have evolved over many centuries. The sophisticated systems used today make use of advanced technology such as radar, satellite transmissions, and shipboard computers that can plot a course at the touch of a button. But before such state-of-the-art equipment was developed, navigators relied only on their charts of the seas, some simple devices like the compass and the sextant, and a little mathematical knowledge. The ability to use these tools to plot courses manually was an essential skill for navigators in the past, and it remains an important skill for contemporary navigators—even those with high-tech systems at their disposal.

One of the oldest and simplest method for navigating the seas is called *dead reckoning*. This involves estimating a ship's location by keeping track of the speed and direction that it has traveled from its last known location, or *fix*. The direction is usually given as a compass heading, measured in degrees between 0° and 360°. Each of the angle measures on a compass represents a direction; 0° or 360° represents north, 90° represents east, 180° represents south, and 270° represents west. The speed of a vessel is usually given in nautical miles per hour, or *knots*.

Because it does not take into account such factors as current and steering error, dead reckoning is a relatively inaccurate system of navigation. A navigator must therefore use *piloting* to determine a new fix periodically, and then dead reckoning to navigate between fixes. To determine a fix at sea, a navigator uses landmarks and aids to navigation (such as buoys, or knolls). Using a *pelorus*, a hand compass, a navigator can find the *bearing*, or direction, from the vessel to several landmarks. The navigator can then plot lines on the ship's charts to represent those bearings. The point of intersection of the lines gives the fix of the vessel. If this fix differs from the estimated fix found through

Features

Modeling

dead reckoning, the navigator can use trigonometry to determine the course that is necessary to correct the error.

You may be curious to know how a navigator would determine a fix if no landmarks are in sight. If a ship is not outfitted with any of the sophisticated equipment mentioned earlier, its navigator must use the sun, moon, and stars to determine a fix. This practice is called *celestial navigation* and is somewhat more complex than piloting; it requires knowledge of astronomy and spherical trigonometry.

Thinking Critically Suppose you are in a sailing vessel and you are using dead reckoning to navigate between two points. After 5 h you use piloting to determine a fix and find that although your direction is still correct, you are 5 mi short of your estimated position. What factors do you think might have led to these results?

Project Research the navigational device called the *sextant* and learn how it is used. Give a presentation to the class and be sure to demonstrate the geometric and trigonometric principles behind its function.

285

Mathematical Power

This discussion of navigation is a good opportunity to show students that mathematical modeling is far from a new concept and is in no way dependent on computers and other technology. The use of mathematics to solve problems is in fact an integral part of the development of human achievement. Looking at a problem from an historical perspective can be a great motivator for students; they can be challenged with questions like, "How would you accomplish this task if you did not have modern technology at your disposal?" Such an approach is one way of generating interest in the trigonometric identities.

When researching the sextant, students will find that it is constructed from two mirrors and operates according to a simple rule of reflection: If an object is seen by repeated reflection in two mirrors, the angle between the object and its image is twice the angle between the mirrors. Encourage students to try to demonstrate this principle geometrically. You may want to review this discussion when you reach Lesson 11.7, which includes a model on curved reflectors.

Thinking Critically Answers may vary. Students should consider the likely possibilities that the vessel was sailing directly into a 5-knot current, or that the vessel's speed was underestimated by 5 knots.

Review and Assessment

Student Text

Teacher's Resource Book

6.1 Sum and Difference Identities

Objective: *To develop and use formulas for the trigonometric functions of a sum or difference of two angle measures*

Focus

Recall that the measure of an exterior angle θ of a triangle is equal to the sum of the measures of the two nonadjacent interior angles: $\theta = \alpha + \beta$. If you know the values of $\sin \alpha$ and $\sin \beta$, can you determine $\sin \theta$ by adding these two values? Does $\sin 90° = \sin 30° + \sin 60°$? Since $\sin 90° = 1$, $\sin 30° = \frac{1}{2}$, and $\sin 60° = \frac{\sqrt{3}}{2}$, you can see that the answer is no.

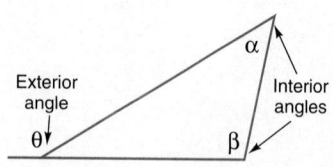

Throughout the ages, certain tasks in surveying, astronomy, navigation, and mathematics itself required formulas for finding the sine or cosine of the sum or difference of two angles. Ptolemy of Alexandria computed and tabulated trigonometric tables as early as 150 A.D. However, problems such as finding $\sin (\alpha + \beta)$ sometimes arose when only the values of the sine or cosine of α and β were known and trigonometric tables were not readily available. Therefore, using chords of circles, Ptolemy developed the equivalent of our present-day formulas for $\sin (\alpha + \beta)$ and $\sin (\alpha - \beta)$.

In previous chapters, the identities you studied involved only one angle. In this lesson, you will become acquainted with identities equivalent to those developed by Ptolemy that involve more than one angle. The first of these identities is an identity for the cosine of the difference of two angles.

To derive the identity for $\cos (\alpha - \beta)$, place α and β in standard position on the unit circle as shown. Points A and B are on the terminal sides of angles α and β, respectively. Let $\overline{AB}$ be the chord connecting A and B. The measure of $\angle BOA$ is $\alpha - \beta$. Use the law of cosines to find AB.

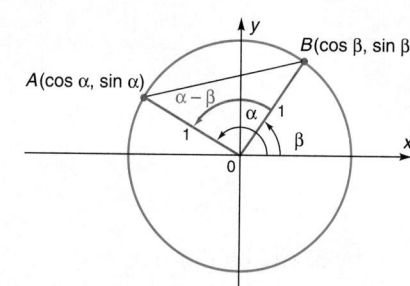

$$(AB)^2 = 1^2 + 1^2 - 2(1)(1) \cos (\alpha - \beta)$$
$$= 2 - 2 \cos (\alpha - \beta)$$

Therefore, $AB = \sqrt{2 - 2 \cos (\alpha - \beta)}$.

Also, from the distance formula,

$$AB = \sqrt{(\cos \alpha - \cos \beta)^2 + (\sin \alpha - \sin \beta)^2}$$
$$= \sqrt{\cos^2 \alpha - 2 \cos \alpha \cos \beta + \cos^2 \beta + \sin^2 \alpha - 2 \sin \alpha \sin \beta + \sin^2 \beta}$$
$$= \sqrt{1 + 1 - 2 \cos \alpha \cos \beta - 2 \sin \alpha \sin \beta} = \sqrt{2 - 2 \cos \alpha \cos \beta - 2 \sin \alpha \sin \beta}$$

Then the two representations of *AB* must be equal.

$$\sqrt{2 - 2\cos(\alpha - \beta)} = \sqrt{2 - 2\cos\alpha\cos\beta - 2\sin\alpha\sin\beta}$$
$$2 - 2\cos(\alpha - \beta) = 2 - 2\cos\alpha\cos\beta - 2\sin\alpha\sin\beta$$
$$-2\cos(\alpha - \beta) = -2(\cos\alpha\cos\beta + \sin\alpha\sin\beta)$$
$$\cos(\alpha - \beta) = \cos\alpha\cos\beta + \sin\alpha\sin\beta \qquad \textit{Difference identity for cosine}$$

In the diagram, $\alpha > \beta$, so $\alpha - \beta$ is positive. The identity also holds when $\alpha - \beta$ is negative. You will be asked to show that this is so in the exercises. Thus, the identity holds for any real values of α and β.

The *sum identity for cosine* follows from the *difference identity for cosine*. You will be asked to prove this identity in the exercises.

Difference Identity for Cosine

$$\cos(\alpha - \beta) = \cos\alpha\cos\beta + \sin\alpha\sin\beta$$

Sum Identity for Cosine

$$\cos(\alpha + \beta) = \cos\alpha\cos\beta - \sin\alpha\sin\beta$$

The sum and difference identities for cosine can be used to find exact values of some trigonometric functions.

Example 1 Find the exact value of $\cos\dfrac{\pi}{12}$.

Since $\dfrac{\pi}{12} = \dfrac{\pi}{3} - \dfrac{\pi}{4}$, let $\alpha = \dfrac{\pi}{3}$ and $\beta = \dfrac{\pi}{4}$.

$$\cos\dfrac{\pi}{12} = \cos\left(\dfrac{\pi}{3} - \dfrac{\pi}{4}\right)$$
$$= \cos\dfrac{\pi}{3}\cos\dfrac{\pi}{4} + \sin\dfrac{\pi}{3}\sin\dfrac{\pi}{4}$$
$$= \dfrac{1}{2}\left(\dfrac{\sqrt{2}}{2}\right) + \left(\dfrac{\sqrt{3}}{2}\right)\left(\dfrac{\sqrt{2}}{2}\right) = \dfrac{\sqrt{2} + \sqrt{6}}{4}$$

The *difference and sum identities for sine* also involve two angles.

Difference Identity for Sine

$$\sin(\alpha - \beta) = \sin\alpha\cos\beta - \cos\alpha\sin\beta$$

Sum Identity for Sine

$$\sin(\alpha + \beta) = \sin\alpha\cos\beta + \cos\alpha\sin\beta$$

To prove the sum identity for sine, recall the cofunction identities $\sin x = \cos\left(\dfrac{\pi}{2} - x\right)$ and $\cos x = \sin\left(\dfrac{\pi}{2} - x\right)$.

6.1 Sum and Difference Identities   **287**

GUIDED PRACTICE

For Example 1

1. Find the exact value of $\cos\dfrac{5\pi}{12}$.

$$\dfrac{-\sqrt{2} + \sqrt{6}}{4}$$

2. Find the exact value of $\cos 105°$.

$$\dfrac{-\sqrt{6} + \sqrt{2}}{4}$$

Common Error Some students interchange the sine and cosine function values for the special angles 30° and 60°. Have them review the work they did with special angles in Lesson 3.6.

$$\sin x = \cos \left(\frac{\pi}{2} - x\right) \qquad \textit{Start with the cofunction identity.}$$

$$\sin (\alpha + \beta) = \cos \left[\frac{\pi}{2} - (\alpha + \beta)\right] \qquad \textit{Let } x = \alpha + \beta.$$

$$\sin (\alpha + \beta) = \cos \left[\left(\frac{\pi}{2} - \alpha\right) - \beta\right]$$

$$\sin (\alpha + \beta) = \cos \left(\frac{\pi}{2} - \alpha\right) \cos \beta + \sin \left(\frac{\pi}{2} - \alpha\right)\sin \beta \qquad \textit{Use the cofunction identities.}$$

$$\sin (\alpha + \beta) = \sin \alpha \cos \beta + \cos \alpha \sin \beta$$

Given exact values of trigonometric functions, you can find exact values of trigonometric functions of sums and differences of angle measures. Note that it is not necessary to find the angle measures.

Example 2   Find exact values for $\sin (\alpha - \beta)$ and $\cos (\alpha - \beta)$ given that $\tan \alpha = \frac{3}{4}$, $\sec \beta = \frac{13}{5}$, and neither α nor β is in quadrant I.

First find $\sin \alpha$, $\cos \alpha$, $\sin \beta$, and $\cos \beta$, and then use the difference identities. To find $\sin \alpha$ and $\cos \alpha$, note that since $\tan \alpha = \frac{3}{4}$, α must be in quadrant III. *Why?*

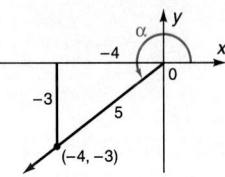

$$r = \sqrt{(-4)^2 + (-3)^2} = 5 \qquad \textit{Since } x = -4 \textit{ and } y = -3.$$

Thus, $\sin \alpha = -\frac{3}{5}$ and $\cos \alpha = -\frac{4}{5}$.

Since $\cos \beta = \dfrac{1}{\sec \beta}$, $\cos \beta = \frac{5}{13}$.

To find $\sin \beta$, note that $\sec \beta = \frac{13}{5}$, and β is in quadrant IV. *Why?* Use $x = 5$ and $r = 13$, and find y.

$$y = \pm\sqrt{13^2 - 5^2} = \pm 12$$

Since β is in quadrant IV, $y = -12$. Thus, $\sin \beta = -\frac{12}{13}$.

Then, $\sin (\alpha - \beta) = \left(-\frac{3}{5}\right)\left(\frac{5}{13}\right) - \left(-\frac{4}{5}\right)\left(-\frac{12}{13}\right) = \left(-\frac{15}{65}\right) - \left(\frac{48}{65}\right) = -\frac{63}{65}$ and

$\cos (\alpha - \beta) = \left(-\frac{4}{5}\right)\left(\frac{5}{13}\right) + \left(-\frac{3}{5}\right)\left(-\frac{12}{13}\right) = \left(-\frac{20}{65}\right) + \left(\frac{36}{65}\right) = \frac{16}{65}$.

The *difference and sum identities for tangent* follow from the difference and sum identities for sine and cosine. You will be asked to prove these identities in the exercises.

Difference Identity for Tangent

$$\tan (\alpha - \beta) = \frac{\tan \alpha - \tan \beta}{1 + \tan \alpha \tan \beta}$$

Sum Identity for Tangent

$$\tan (\alpha + \beta) = \frac{\tan \alpha + \tan \beta}{1 - \tan \alpha \tan \beta}$$

---

288   Chapter 6 Trigonometric Identities and Equations

Sum and difference identities can be used in the solution of real world problems.

Example 3 *Security* A video security monitor is to be mounted 10 ft above the floor on the back wall of a store. It will scan through an angle θ in a vertical plane along the aisle. The aisle begins 5 ft from the back wall and is 40 ft long. Through what angle θ must the monitor rotate?

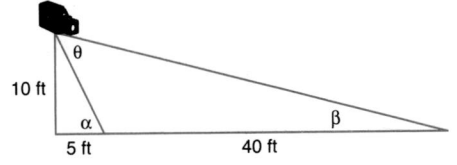

10 ft

5 ft   40 ft

$$\tan \alpha = \frac{10}{5} = 2 \qquad \tan \beta = \frac{10}{45} = \frac{2}{9}$$

$\alpha = \beta + \theta$ *The measure of an exterior angle is equal to the sum of*
$\theta = \alpha - \beta$ *the measures of the two nonadjacent interior angles.*

$$\tan \theta = \tan (\alpha - \beta) = \frac{\tan \alpha - \tan \beta}{1 + \tan \alpha \tan \beta} = \frac{2 - \frac{2}{9}}{1 + (2)\left(\frac{2}{9}\right)} = \frac{16}{13}$$

$$\theta = 50.91°$$

The monitor should rotate through an angle of 50.91°.

The sum and difference identities can be used to prove other identities.

Example 4 Prove each identity.

    a. $\tan \left(\frac{\pi}{4} - \alpha\right) = \frac{1 - \tan \alpha}{1 + \tan \alpha}$ **b.** $-\cos \beta = \cos (\pi + \beta)$

a.

$$\tan \left(\frac{\pi}{4} - \alpha\right) \;\Big|\; \frac{1 - \tan \alpha}{1 + \tan \alpha}$$

$$\frac{\tan \frac{\pi}{4} - \tan \alpha}{1 + \tan \frac{\pi}{4} \tan \alpha}$$

$$\frac{1 - \tan \alpha}{1 + (1) \tan \alpha}$$

$$\frac{1 - \tan \alpha}{1 + \tan \alpha} =$$

b.

$$-\cos \beta \;\Big|\; \cos (\pi + \beta)$$
$$\cos \pi \cos \beta - \sin \pi \sin \beta$$
$$(-1) \cos \beta - (0) \sin \beta$$
$$= -\cos \beta$$

Class Exercises

Express each in terms of the sine, cosine, or tangent of one angle.

1. $\cos \frac{\pi}{4} \cos \frac{\pi}{3} - \sin \frac{\pi}{4} \sin \frac{\pi}{3}$ $\cos \frac{7\pi}{12}$ **2.** $\sin \frac{\pi}{4} \cos \frac{\pi}{3} + \cos \frac{\pi}{4} \sin \frac{\pi}{3}$ $\sin \frac{7\pi}{12}$

3. $\sin 75° \cos 35° - \cos 75° \sin 35°$ $\sin 40°$ **4.** $\cos 112° \cos 42° + \sin 112° \sin 42°$ $\cos 70°$

5. $\dfrac{\tan \frac{7\pi}{9} + \tan \frac{\pi}{9}}{1 - \tan \frac{7\pi}{9} \tan \frac{\pi}{9}}$ $\tan \frac{8\pi}{9}$ **6.** $\dfrac{\tan \frac{5\pi}{8} - \tan \frac{3\pi}{8}}{1 + \tan \frac{5\pi}{8} \tan \frac{3\pi}{8}}$ $\tan \frac{\pi}{4}$

6.1 Sum and Difference Identities   **289**

For Example 3
A spotlight fastened to the floor 8 ft from a wall is focused on a painting with bottom edge 6 ft from the floor. What is the measure of angle θ if the painting is 5 ft high? $\theta = 17.1°$

5 ft

6 ft

8 ft

For Example 4
Prove each identity.

1. $\cos \left(\alpha - \frac{\pi}{4}\right) = \dfrac{\sqrt{2}(\cos \alpha + \sin \alpha)}{2}$

$\cos \left(\alpha - \frac{\pi}{4}\right) = \cos \alpha \cos \frac{\pi}{4} +$

$\sin \alpha \sin \frac{\pi}{4} = \cos \alpha \left(\dfrac{1}{\sqrt{2}}\right) +$

$\sin \alpha \left(\dfrac{1}{\sqrt{2}}\right) = \dfrac{\cos \alpha + \sin \alpha}{\sqrt{2}} =$

$\dfrac{\sqrt{2}(\cos \alpha + \sin \alpha)}{2}$

2. $\tan \left(\theta + \frac{\pi}{4}\right) = \dfrac{\tan \theta + 1}{1 - \tan \theta}$

$\tan \left(\theta + \frac{\pi}{4}\right) = \dfrac{\tan \theta + \tan \frac{\pi}{4}}{1 - \tan \theta \tan \frac{\pi}{4}} =$

$\dfrac{\tan \theta + 1}{1 - \tan \theta}$

Common Error Some students work on both sides of the identity to be proved rather than on just one side. Use an erroneous proof to show why this procedure is flawed. Encourage students to show a chain of equivalent statements converting one side to the other.

CLOSURE

Have students write the identities presented in this lesson in their math journals in different forms, such as those shown in the Alternative Learning Styles commentary. Pair students to compare identities and check for accuracy.

Assignment Guide
Basic: 1–35
Average: 1–35 odd, 37–57
Enriched: 15–47 odd, 48–67

Teacher's Resource Book
  Practice, page 37

ℝ **Review**
Exercises 7, 15, 29, 37, 46, and 48
review concepts such as finding areas and distances, finding equations of lines, using third degree equations, and finding inverse functions.

LESSON FOLLOW-UP

Lesson Quiz
Find the exact value of each expression.

1. $\sin \frac{7\pi}{12}$ $\frac{\sqrt{2}+\sqrt{6}}{4}$

2. $\tan -\frac{11}{12}$ $2-\sqrt{3}$

Find the exact value for each function given that $\sin \alpha = \frac{7}{25}$, $\sec \beta = -\frac{5}{3}$, $\frac{\pi}{2} < \alpha < \pi$, and $\pi < \beta < \frac{3\pi}{2}$.

3. $\cos(\alpha + \beta)$ $\frac{4}{5}$

4. $\sin(\beta - \alpha)$ $\frac{117}{125}$

5. $\tan(\alpha - \beta)$ $-\frac{117}{44}$

6. Determine the measure of θ in the diagram. 28.41°

7. Prove the identity:
$$\sin\left(\theta - \frac{\pi}{6}\right) = \frac{\sqrt{3}\sin\theta - \cos\theta}{2}$$
$\sin\left(\theta - \frac{\pi}{6}\right) = \sin\theta\cos\frac{\pi}{6} -$
$\sin\frac{\pi}{6}\cos\theta = \frac{\sqrt{3}}{2}\sin\theta -$
$\frac{1}{2}\cos\theta = \frac{\sqrt{3}\sin\theta - \cos\theta}{2}$

Tell whether each of the following statements is true or false.

7. $\cos 105° = \cos 45° + \cos 60°$ false

8. $\sin\frac{13\pi}{12} = \sin\pi\cos\frac{\pi}{12} + \cos\pi\sin\frac{\pi}{12}$ true

Use a sum or difference identity for sine or cosine to find an exact value for each trigonometric expression.

9. $\sin\frac{11\pi}{12}$ $\frac{\sqrt{6}-\sqrt{2}}{4}$

10. $\cos\frac{7\pi}{12}$ $\frac{\sqrt{2}-\sqrt{6}}{4}$

11. $\tan\frac{13\pi}{12}$ $2-\sqrt{3}$

12. $\cos 195°$ $\frac{-\sqrt{6}-\sqrt{2}}{4}$

13. $\sin 285°$ $\frac{-\sqrt{6}-\sqrt{2}}{4}$

14. $\tan 255°$ $2+\sqrt{3}$

Find the exact value for each given $\cos\alpha = \frac{4}{5}$, $\sin\beta = -\frac{5}{13}$, $0 \le \alpha \le \frac{\pi}{2}$, and $\pi \le \beta \le \frac{3\pi}{2}$.

15. $\cos(\alpha - \beta)$ $-\frac{63}{65}$

16. $\sin(\alpha - \beta)$ $-\frac{16}{65}$

17. $\sin(\alpha + \beta)$ $-\frac{56}{65}$

18. $\cos(\alpha + \beta)$ $-\frac{33}{65}$

19. $\tan(\alpha - \beta)$ $\frac{16}{63}$

20. $\tan(\alpha + \beta)$ $\frac{56}{33}$

Practice Exercises   📈 Use appropriate technology.

Express each in terms of the sine, cosine, or tangent of one angle.

A **1.** $\sin\frac{\pi}{3}\cos\frac{5\pi}{6} + \cos\frac{\pi}{3}\sin\frac{5\pi}{6}$ $\sin\frac{7\pi}{6}$

2. $\cos\frac{\pi}{3}\cos\frac{5\pi}{6} - \sin\frac{\pi}{3}\sin\frac{5\pi}{6}$ $\cos\frac{7\pi}{6}$

3. $\cos\frac{5\pi}{12}\cos\frac{7\pi}{8} - \sin\frac{5\pi}{12}\sin\frac{7\pi}{8}$ $\cos\frac{31\pi}{24}$

4. $\sin\frac{5\pi}{8}\cos\frac{\pi}{6} + \cos\frac{5\pi}{8}\sin\frac{\pi}{6}$ $\sin\frac{19\pi}{24}$

5. $\frac{\tan 40° + \tan 17°}{1 - \tan 40°\tan 17°}$ $\tan 57°$

6. $\frac{\tan 25° - \tan 24°}{1 + \tan 25°\tan 24°}$ $\tan 1°$

ℝ **7.** *Landscaping*   Find the area of a triangular flower garden with sides 21 ft, 23 ft, and 24 ft, to the nearest square foot. 220 ft²

Tell whether each of the following statements is true or false.

8. $\cos 62° = \cos(20° + 42°)$ true

9. $\cos(-10°) = \cos 10° - \cos 20°$ false

10. $\tan 110° = \frac{\tan 100° + \tan 10°}{1 + \tan 100°\tan 10°}$ false

11. $\tan 60° = \frac{\tan 75° - \tan 15°}{1 + \tan 15°\tan 75°}$ true

12. $\sin 75° = \sin 45° + \sin 30°$ false

13. $\sin 100° = \sin 85°\cos 15° - \cos 85°\sin 15°$ false

14. $\sin 60° = \sin 70°\cos 10° - \cos 70°\sin 10°$ true

ℝ **15.** *Surveying*   The south end of Kelly Pond is 6.5 mi from the intersection of Arnold Avenue and Lynn Lane, and the north end is 4.1 mi from the intersection. If the two roads are straight and intersect at an angle of 68°, what is the distance from the north end to the south end of the pond, to the nearest tenth of a mile? 6.3 mi

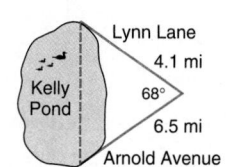

Use a sum or difference identity to find an exact value for each trigonometric expression.

16. $\sin\frac{5\pi}{12}$ $\frac{\sqrt{6}+\sqrt{2}}{4}$

17. $\cos\frac{7\pi}{12}$ $\frac{\sqrt{2}-\sqrt{6}}{4}$

18. $\tan\frac{11\pi}{12}$ $-2+\sqrt{3}$

19. $\sin 375°$ $\frac{-\sqrt{2}+\sqrt{6}}{4}$

20. $\cos 15°$ $\frac{\sqrt{2}+\sqrt{6}}{4}$

21. $\tan 405°$ 1

290   Chapter 6 Trigonometric Identities and Equations

Find the exact value for each trigonometric expression given $\sin \alpha = \frac{4}{5}$, $\sin \beta = \frac{12}{13}$, $0 \le \alpha \le \frac{\pi}{2}$, and $\frac{\pi}{2} \le \beta \le \pi$.

22. $\cos(\alpha - \beta)$ $\frac{33}{65}$

23. $\sin(\alpha - \beta)$ $-\frac{56}{65}$

24. $\tan(\alpha - \beta)$ $-\frac{56}{33}$

25. $\cos(\alpha + \beta)$ $-\frac{63}{65}$

26. $\sin(\alpha + \beta)$ $\frac{16}{65}$

27. $\tan(\alpha + \beta)$ $-\frac{16}{63}$

28. **Thinking Critically** Determine angle θ in Example 3 of this lesson without using a sum or difference identity. 50.91°

Ⓡ 29. Find the equation of a line that passes through the origin and is parallel to the line $2x - 7y = 42$. $2x - 7y = 0$

30. **Thinking Critically** How can you use the difference identities to determine whether sine and cosine are odd or even functions?

Find the exact value for each given that $\cot \alpha = -\frac{8}{15}$, $\sin \beta = -\frac{7}{25}$, and neither α nor β in standard position terminates in quadrant IV.

Ⓑ 31. $\cos(\alpha - \beta)$ $\frac{87}{425}$

32. $\sin(\alpha - \beta)$ $-\frac{416}{425}$

33. $\tan(\alpha - \beta)$ $-\frac{416}{87}$

34. $\cos(\alpha + \beta)$ $\frac{297}{425}$

35. $\sin(\alpha + \beta)$ $-\frac{304}{425}$

36. $\tan(\alpha + \beta)$ $-\frac{304}{297}$

Ⓡ 37. **Writing in Mathematics** Given line ℓ crosses the positive x-axis, write a paragraph to describe why the slope m of line ℓ is equal to the tangent of the angle θ between ℓ and the positive x-axis.

38. **Thinking Critically** Let θ be the acute angle formed by the intersection of lines j and k, which form angles α and β, respectively, with the x-axis. Let m_1 be the slope of j, and m_2 the slope of k. Show that $\tan \theta = \frac{m_2 - m_1}{1 + m_1 m_2}$. (Refer to Exercise 37.)

Use a sum or difference identity to find an exact value for each.

39. $\sin(-285°)$ $\frac{\sqrt{2} + \sqrt{6}}{4}$

40. $\cos(-165°)$ $\frac{-\sqrt{6} - \sqrt{2}}{4}$

41. $\tan(-105°)$ $2 + \sqrt{3}$

42. $\cos\left(-\frac{23\pi}{12}\right)$ $\frac{\sqrt{6} + \sqrt{2}}{4}$

43. $\sin\left(-\frac{11\pi}{12}\right)$ $\frac{-\sqrt{6} + \sqrt{2}}{4}$

44. $\tan\left(-\frac{17\pi}{12}\right)$ $-2 - \sqrt{3}$

45. *Security* Referring to Example 3 in the lesson, how will θ change if the monitor is lowered to 8 ft above the ground? decreases by 3°

Ⓡ 46. *Irrigation* A drainage ditch is 2 m longer than it is wide and 2 m wider than it is deep. Find the dimensions of the ditch if its water capacity is 15 m³. $d = 1$ m, $w = 3$ m, $\ell = 5$ m

47. *Forestry* A watch tower is located 50 ft from the ground in a forest. The ranger is searching for a wounded animal on a straight path that is 1000 ft long and begins 100 ft from the base of the tower. Through what angle θ must he rotate his light to search the entire length of the path? 24°

Ⓡ 48. *Cryptography* A simple cipher takes a number and codes it using the function $f(x) = 3x + 5$. Find the inverse of this function and determine whether the inverse is also a function. $f^{-1}(x) = \frac{x - 5}{3}$; function

49. *Aviation* A jet plane flying at an altitude of 12 km has a radar unit that detects objects on the ground up to 13 km from the plane in one direction and up to 20 km from the plane in the opposite direction. Find the exact value of the sine of the angle θ through which the radar unit detects objects. $\frac{99}{\sqrt{10,642}}$

6.1 Sum and Difference Identities   **291**

Writing in Mathematics
37. The slope m of line ℓ can be found by computing the change in y over the change in x between the point of intersection of the line and the x-axis and any other point on the line. Then $m = \frac{y}{x}$. But $\tan \theta = \frac{y}{x}$; therefore, $m = \tan \theta$.

50. Prove the sum identity for cosine: $\cos(\alpha + \beta) = \cos\alpha\cos\beta - \sin\alpha\sin\beta$

51. Prove the difference identity for sine: $\sin(\alpha - \beta) = \sin\alpha\cos\beta - \cos\alpha\sin\beta$

52. Prove the sum identity for tangent: $\tan(\alpha + \beta) = \dfrac{\tan\alpha + \tan\beta}{1 - \tan\alpha\tan\beta}$

53. Prove the difference identity for tangent: $\tan(\alpha - \beta) = \dfrac{\tan\alpha - \tan\beta}{1 + \tan\alpha\tan\beta}$

54. Prove that the difference identity for cosine holds when $\alpha - \beta$ is negative. *Hint:* Recall the identity $\cos(-x) = \cos x$.

Prove each identity.

C 55. $\cos\left(\dfrac{\pi}{4} + \theta\right) = \dfrac{\sqrt{2}(\cos\theta - \sin\theta)}{2}$

56. $\sin\left(\dfrac{2\pi}{3} - \theta\right) = \dfrac{\sqrt{3}\cos\theta + \sin\theta}{2}$

57. $\tan\left(\theta + \dfrac{\pi}{6}\right) = \dfrac{\sqrt{3}\tan\theta + 1}{\sqrt{3} - \tan\theta}$

58. $\tan\left(\dfrac{5\pi}{4} - \theta\right) = \dfrac{1 - \tan\theta}{1 + \tan\theta}$

59. $\dfrac{\sin(\alpha + \beta)}{\cos\alpha\cos\beta} = \tan\alpha + \tan\beta$

60. $\sin(\alpha + \beta) + \sin(\alpha - \beta) = 2\sin\alpha\cos\beta$

61. $\sin(\alpha + \beta) - \sin(\alpha - \beta) = 2\cos\alpha\sin\beta$

62. $\sin(\alpha + \beta)\sin(\alpha - \beta) = \sin^2\alpha - \sin^2\beta$

63. $\cos(\alpha + \beta)\cos(\alpha - \beta) = \cos^2\alpha - \sin^2\beta$

64. $\cos(\alpha + \beta)\cos\beta + \sin(\alpha + \beta)\sin\beta = \cos\alpha$

65. $\sin(\alpha - \beta)\cos\beta + \cos(\alpha - \beta)\sin\beta = \sin\alpha$

66. $\cot(\alpha + \beta) = \dfrac{\cot\alpha\cot\beta - 1}{\cot\alpha + \cot\beta}$

67. $\cot(\alpha - \beta) = \dfrac{\cot\alpha\cot\beta + 1}{\cot\beta - \cot\alpha}$

Review

For what values of x, $-2\pi \leq x \leq 2\pi$, is the function undefined?

1. $y = \csc x$ $-2\pi, -\pi, 0, \pi, 2\pi$

2. $y = 5\sin x$ none

3. $y = \tan\dfrac{x}{2}$ $\pm\pi$

4. $y = \sec 2x$ $-\dfrac{3\pi}{4}, -\dfrac{\pi}{4}, \dfrac{\pi}{4}, \dfrac{3\pi}{4}$

5. In a 30°-60°-90° triangle, if d represents the length of the hypotenuse, then the side opposite the 30° angle is $\dfrac{d}{2}$. How could the side opposite the 60° angle be represented? $\dfrac{\sqrt{3}}{2}d$

6. A ladder 25 ft long is placed up against a treehouse at an angle of 51° with the ground. How high is the treehouse?   19.4 ft

7. Find the area of a circle if its circumference is 26π. 169π

8. If the measure of one acute angle in a right triangle is 42°, what is the measure of the other acute angle?   48°

292   Chapter 6 Trigonometric Identities and Equations

6.2 Verifying Identities Graphically

Objective: *To determine whether an equation is an identity using a graphing utility*

Focus

Air traffic controllers observe radar screens and communicate with aircraft to ensure that two planes do not occupy the same airspace at the same time. A scope shows the locations of the planes radially around the control tower, but the controller may have to track a plane's altitude manually. Sometimes a plane contains equipment that transmits a signal to the control tower that identifies itself and its altitude. The resulting electronic picture on the controller's scope provides instantaneous information that can be used to verify that the plane is not dangerously near another plane in the vicinity.

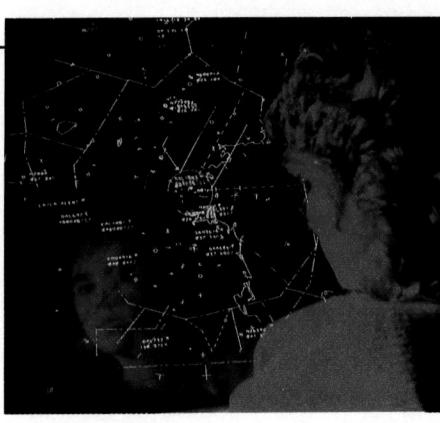

A graphing utility also provides instantaneous information concerning spatial relationships, for example, relationships represented by mathematical curves.

To determine whether an equation might be an identity, use a graphing utility to graph both sides on the same set of axes. If the graphs coincide, you can be reasonably certain that the original equation is an identity. However, this method of verification is not a proof that the equation is an identity.

Example 1   Use a graphing utility to determine whether $1 - \sin^2 \theta = \cos^2 \theta$ appears to be an identity.

Graph $y = 1 - \sin^2 \theta$ and $y = \cos^2 \theta$ on the same set of axes. The graphs appear to coincide. This suggests that $1 - \sin^2 \theta = \cos^2 \theta$ is an identity. The zoom-trig feature quickly provides an appropriate viewing rectangle.

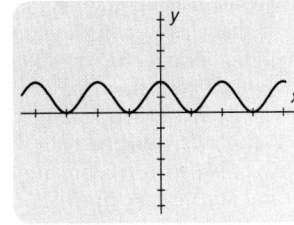

$[-2\pi, 2\pi]$ by $[-3, 3]$
x scl: $\frac{\pi}{2}$ y scl: 0.5

If you have correctly entered both sides of the equation on the utility and the graphs do not coincide, then the equation is not an identity.

Technology
graphing utility

FOCUS

Students should be able to see the advantages of using advanced technology to facilitate work such as controlling air traffic. Discuss the recent technology development that students employ and its impact on their lives. Some students may wish to investigate the trigonometric concepts used to locate planes on a scope and to find the altitude of a plane.

INSTRUCTION

- This lesson provides students with many opportunities to practice using their graphing utilities. Before proceeding to the text examples, some students may need help setting range values. Students should consult their owner's manual for inputting range specifications. Remind students to set a large range initially to be sure to include the graphs of both functions or relations on the screen.
- Point out the use of the zoom feature in the paragraph following Example 3.

Alternative Learning Styles
Some students may find it helpful to verify graphs that are generated by graphing utilities by making their own graphs. Provide a relatively simple equation such as $\sin^2 x + \cos^2 x = 1$. Have students plot about 10 points over the interval $-2\pi \leq x \leq 2\pi$ for each function: $y = \sin^2 x + \cos^2 x$ and $y = 1$.

GUIDED PRACTICE

For Example 1

Use a graphing utility to determine whether the given statement appears to be an identity.

1. $\dfrac{\sin \alpha}{\cos \alpha} = \tan \alpha$ yes

2. $3 \cos^2 \beta + 3 \sin^2 \beta = 3$ yes

For Example 2

Use a graphing utility to determine whether the given statement appears to be an identity.

1. $\cos^2 \alpha + 2 = 2 \sin^2 \alpha$ no

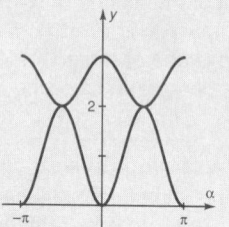

2. $\tan^2 \beta + \sec^2 \beta = 1$ no

Example 2 Use a graphing utility to determine whether $\sin^2 \beta - 1 = \cos^2 \beta$ appears to be an identity.

Graph $y = \sin^2 \beta - 1$ and $y = \cos^2 \beta$ on the same set of axes. The graphs do not coincide. Therefore, $\sin^2 \beta - 1 = \cos^2 \beta$ is not an identity.

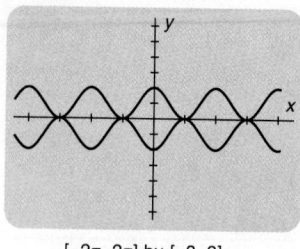

$[-2\pi, 2\pi]$ by $[-3, 3]$
x scl: $\frac{\pi}{2}$ y scl: 0.5

Graph each side of an equation separately as well as together. Knowing the shape of each side will prevent you from drawing erroneous conclusions.

Example 3 Use a graphing utility to determine whether $\operatorname{Sin}^{-1} x = \operatorname{Cos}^{-1} x + \frac{\pi}{2}$ appears to be an identity.

Graph $y = \operatorname{Sin}^{-1} x$ and $y = \operatorname{Cos}^{-1} x + \frac{\pi}{2}$ on the same set of axes. The graph is shown below at the left with a viewing rectangle of $[-1, 1]$, scale 0.5, by $[-2, 5]$, scale 1. Since your graphing utility will draw one continuous curve, you may be tempted to assume that the equation is an identity. If you graph each side individually, you will see that there are two *distinct* curves that intersect at $\left(1, \frac{\pi}{2}\right)$.

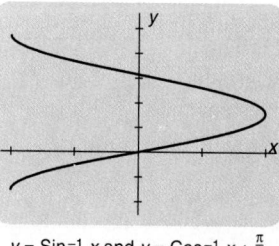

$y = \operatorname{Sin}^{-1} x$ and $y = \operatorname{Cos}^{-1} x + \frac{\pi}{2}$

$y = \operatorname{Sin}^{-1} x$

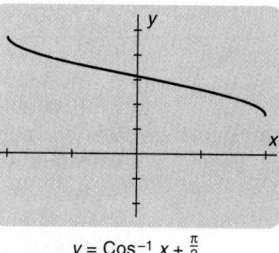

$y = \operatorname{Cos}^{-1} x + \frac{\pi}{2}$

When using a graphing utility, you may need to use different viewing rectangles to completely determine the graph. When the two functions $y = \cos x$ and $y = 1.01 \cos x$ are graphed on a standard trigonometric setting, they appear to coincide. However, when you zoom in, you can see that the graphs are different.

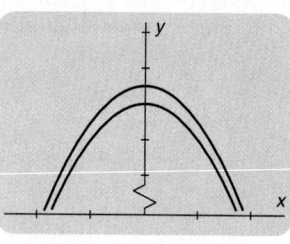

$[-2\pi, 2\pi]$ by $[-3, 3]$
x scl: $\frac{\pi}{2}$ y scl: 1

$[-0.5, 0.5]$ by $[0.95, 1.05]$
x scl: 0.2 y scl: 0.02

294 Chapter 6 Trigonometric Identities and Equations

Class Exercises

Use a graphing utility to determine whether each equation appears to be an identity.

1. $\sin \alpha \sec \alpha = \tan \alpha$ yes **2.** $\cos \alpha \csc \alpha = \cot \alpha$ yes **3.** $\sin^2 \beta + \cos^2 \beta = 1$ yes

4. $\sin^2 \beta = 1 - \cos^2 \beta$ yes **5.** $\cos (\pi - x) = \cos x$ no **6.** $\sin (\pi - x) = -\sin x$ no

7. $\cos \left(\dfrac{\pi}{2} + \theta\right) = \cos \theta$ no **8.** $\sin \left(\dfrac{\pi}{2} + \theta\right) = -\sin \theta$ no

9. $\cos^2 x (\tan^2 x + 1) = 1$ yes **10.** $\sin x (\cos x - \sin x) = \cos^2 x$ no

11. Thinking Critically How can a graphing utility be used to graph secant, cosecant, and cotangent? Graph $y = \dfrac{1}{\cos x}$, $y = \dfrac{1}{\sin x}$, $y = \dfrac{1}{\tan x}$.

Practice Exercises   Use appropriate technology.

Use a graphing utility to determine whether each equation appears to be an identity.

A **1.** $\tan x = \dfrac{\sin x}{\cos x}$ yes **2.** $\cot \alpha = \dfrac{\cos \alpha}{\sin \alpha}$ yes

3. $\sin \left(\dfrac{3\pi}{2} - \beta\right) = -\cos \beta$ yes **4.** $\tan \left(\dfrac{3\pi}{2} + \alpha\right) = -\cot \alpha$ yes

5. $\sec (\pi + \theta) = \csc \theta$ no **6.** $\csc (\beta - \pi) = \sec \beta$ no

7. $\dfrac{\sin x}{1 + \cos x} = \dfrac{1 - \sin x}{\cos x}$ no **8.** $\dfrac{\sin \theta}{1 + \cos \theta} = \csc \theta - \cot \theta$ yes

9. $\dfrac{\cot \alpha \tan \alpha}{\sin \alpha} = -\csc \alpha$ no **10.** $\dfrac{\sin \beta \csc \beta}{\tan \beta} = -\cot \beta$ no

11. $\cos x \cot x + \sin x = \csc x$ yes **12.** $\sin x \tan x + \cos x = \sec x$ yes

13. $\cos \beta = \cos \beta - 0.002$ no **14.** $\sin \alpha = \sin \alpha + 0.01$ no

15. $\tan \theta = 0.99 \tan \theta$ no **16.** $\cot \theta = 1.03 \cot \theta$ no

17. $\sec^4 \alpha - \tan^4 \alpha = \sec^2 \alpha + \tan^2 \alpha$ yes **18.** $\sec^2 \beta + \tan^2 \beta + 1 = \dfrac{2}{\cos^2 \beta}$ yes

Ⓡ **19.** *Sports* Antonio bowled 150, 165, 141, and 168 in four games. What must he bowl in the fifth game to have an average of 160? 176

20. Writing in Mathematics Explain in your own words how a graphing utility can be used to show the difference between a trigonometric equation that is an identity and one that is not.

Ⓡ **21.** *Consumerism* A moving company charges $300 for the use of a truck and $80 per hour for labor. Find the cost of a move that requires 8 h of labor. $940

Ⓡ **22.** *Engineering* A 19.9-ft walkway between two department stores is higher at one end than the other. The sine of the angle of elevation is 0.1299. Determine the distance between the two buildings. 19.7 ft

B **23. Thinking Critically** Find a trigonometric equation that would be an identity on the interval $0 \le x \le 2\pi$ but would not be an identity on any other interval. ex: $\sin \left\lVert \dfrac{x}{2\pi} \right\rVert = 0$

6.2 Verifying Identities Graphically **295**

Writing in Mathematics
20. Answers may vary. Students' answers should include the idea that the graphs of the functions or relations on both sides of the equation should coincide.

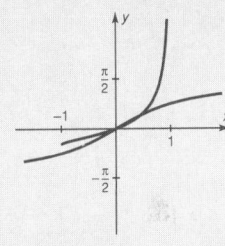
295

LESSON FOLLOW-UP

Lesson Quiz

Use a graphing utility to determine whether the given statement appears to be an identity.

1. $1 - 2\cos^2 x = \cos 2x$ no

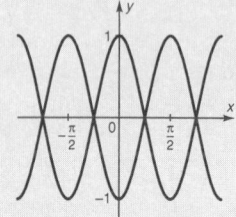

2. $\sec^2 \beta - 1 = \tan^2 \beta$ yes

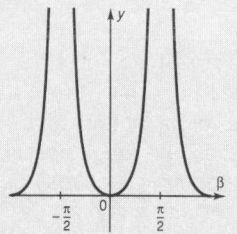

3. $\sin^2 (\alpha + \pi) = -\cos^2 \left(\alpha + \frac{\pi}{2}\right)$
no

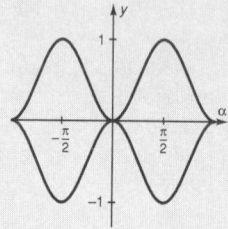

Alternative Assessment

Have students discuss and compare advantages and disadvantages of using a graphing utility rather than plotting points manually to show whether or not the statement $\cos^2 x = 1 - 1.01 \sin^2 x$ is true.

Use a graphing utility to determine whether each equation appears to be an identity.

24. $\dfrac{\cos x}{\cos x + \sin x} = \dfrac{\cot x}{1 + \cot x}$ yes

25. $\dfrac{\cos x}{\csc x + 1} + \dfrac{\cos x}{\csc x - 1} = 2 \tan x$ yes

26. $\sec \beta + \tan \beta = \dfrac{\cos \beta}{\sin \beta - 1}$ no

27. $\cos \beta - 1 = \dfrac{\sin \beta}{\csc \beta + \cot \beta}$ no

28. $\dfrac{\sin \theta}{\tan \theta} + \dfrac{\cos \theta}{\cot \theta} = \cos \theta + \sin \theta$ yes

29. $\csc \theta - \sin \theta = \cos^2 \theta \csc \theta$ yes

30. $\sqrt{x} = -\sqrt{x}$ no

31. $(\sqrt{x})^2 = (-\sqrt{x})^2$ yes

32. $(\sqrt{x})^2 = -(\sqrt{x})^2$ no

33. $-(\sqrt{x})^2 = (-\sqrt{x})^2$ no

34. $-\text{Cos}^{-1} \beta - \dfrac{\pi}{2} = -\text{Sin}^{-1} \beta$ no

35. $\text{Sin}^{-1} \beta - \dfrac{\pi}{2} = \text{Cos}^{-1} \beta$ no

36. $\cot \alpha - \sin \alpha = (\cos^2 \alpha + \cos \alpha - 1)(\csc \alpha)$ yes

® **37.** *Sports* Find the distance from second base to home plate on a baseball field given that the four bases are vertices of a square and that the distance between bases is 90 ft. 127.3 ft

® **38.** *Physics* The voltage V in a certain electrical circuit can be represented by the formula $V = 8 \cos 80\pi t$, where t is measured in seconds. Find the amplitude, period, and frequency. $8; \frac{1}{40}; 40$

Use a graphing utility to determine whether each equation appears to be an identity.

C **39.** $\dfrac{1}{1 + \cos \beta} - \dfrac{1}{1 - \cos \beta} = \dfrac{2}{\sec \beta - \cos \beta}$ no

40. $\dfrac{1}{1 - \sin \beta} - \dfrac{1}{1 + \sin \beta} = \dfrac{2}{\tan \beta \cos \beta}$ no

41. $\sin^2 x (2 + \tan^2 x) = \sec^2 x - \cos^2 x$ yes

42. $\sin^2 x (2 + \tan^2 x) = \sin^2 x + \tan^2 x$ yes

43. $\dfrac{2 \cos \theta \sin \theta}{1 - \cos \theta - \sin \theta} = -1 - \cos \theta - \sin \theta$ yes

44. $\dfrac{\sin \alpha + \cos \alpha - 1}{2 \sin \alpha \cos \alpha} = \dfrac{1}{\cos \alpha + \sin \alpha + 1}$ yes

45. $\dfrac{\sin \beta}{\cos \beta + 1} = \dfrac{\cos \beta + \sin \beta - 1}{1 + \cos \beta - \sin \beta}$ yes

46. $\dfrac{\cos^2 x}{\sin x - \sin^3 x + \cos^2 x} = \cos x + 1$ no

47. $\dfrac{\csc x + 1}{\csc x - 1} - \dfrac{\sec x - \tan x}{\sec x + \tan x} = 4 \tan x \sec x$ yes

48. $\dfrac{\cos \theta + 1}{\cos \theta - 1} + \dfrac{1 - \sec \theta}{1 + \sec \theta} = -2 \cot^2 \theta - \csc^2 \theta$ yes

Challenge

1. In an obtuse isosceles triangle, the two equal sides are s. Show that an altitude from the vertex must be less than $\dfrac{s}{\sqrt{2}}$.

2. Derive an identity for $\sec (\alpha \pm \beta)$ in terms of the functions secant and tangent only. $\dfrac{(\sec \alpha)(\sec \beta)}{1 \mp (\tan \alpha)(\tan \beta)}$

3. The volume of a cone with radius r and height h is to remain constant. Find the new height of the cone if the radius is increased n times. $\dfrac{h}{n^2}$

296 Chapter 6 Trigonometric Identities and Equations

Additional Answers, Challenge

1. The vertex angle must be obtuse because a triangle can have no more than one obtuse angle. Thus, the sum of the base angles must be less than 90°, and since they are equal, each must be less than 45°. Therefore, the sine of the base angle must be less than $\sin 45°$ or $\dfrac{1}{\sqrt{2}}$. Then, $\dfrac{a}{s} < \dfrac{1}{\sqrt{2}}$ and $a < \dfrac{s}{\sqrt{2}}$.

6.3 Double-Angle and Half-Angle Identities

Objectives: *To develop and use the double-angle identities*
To develop and use the half-angle identities

Focus

Projectile motion refers to the movement of an object projected into the air at or near the earth's surface. Galileo and his colleagues were the first people to accurately describe projectile motion. They demonstrated that the horizontal and vertical components of the motion can be analyzed separately. In particular, the horizontal distance that a projectile travels depends, in part, on its *launch angle*, the angle that the path of the projectile initially makes with the ground.

Problems involving projectile motion occur in sports such as baseball and football. A baseball player wishes to increase the distance he can bat the ball. A football player strives to achieve a long kick or a long "hang" time. Projectile motion is also illustrated in nature, for example, by frogs and locusts. Each of these creatures jumps at a launch angle that is determined to a large extent by its anatomical structure.

Using trigonometric functions of double angles, you can model all the above motions with the same set of equations. These equations can be derived using *double-angle identities*.

The double-angle identities follow from the sum identities.

$$\sin(\alpha + \beta) = \sin\alpha\cos\beta + \cos\beta\sin\alpha \qquad \textit{Sum identity for sine}$$
$$\sin(\alpha + \alpha) = \sin\alpha\cos\alpha + \cos\alpha\sin\alpha \qquad \textit{Let } \alpha = \beta.$$
$$\sin 2\alpha = 2\sin\alpha\cos\alpha$$

$$\cos(\alpha + \beta) = \cos\alpha\cos\beta - \sin\alpha\sin\beta \qquad \textit{Sum identity for cosine}$$
$$\cos(\alpha + \alpha) = \cos\alpha\cos\alpha - \sin\alpha\sin\alpha \qquad \textit{Let } \alpha = \beta.$$
$$\cos 2\alpha = \cos^2\alpha - \sin^2\alpha$$

$$\tan(\alpha + \beta) = \frac{\tan\alpha + \tan\beta}{1 - \tan\alpha\tan\beta} \qquad \textit{Sum identity for tangent}$$

$$\tan(\alpha + \alpha) = \frac{\tan\alpha + \tan\alpha}{1 - \tan\alpha\tan\alpha} \qquad \textit{Let } \alpha = \beta.$$

$$\tan 2\alpha = \frac{2\tan\alpha}{1 - \tan^2\alpha} \qquad \tan\alpha \neq \pm 1$$

6.3 Double-Angle and Half-Angle Identities **297**

LESSON PLAN

Vocabulary
double-angle identities
half-angle identities

Technology
graphing utility

FOCUS

Discuss students' experiences with launch angles in sports such as basketball, football, soccer, golf, javelin throwing, and tennis. Ask questions like, "At what approximate angle does the ball or javelin obtain a maximum distance?"

Students may wish to research the advances in trigonometry made by Johann Müller (1436–1476). Müller, also known as Regiomontanus, wrote the first European exposition of plane and spherical trigonometry as a subject in its own right and independent of astronomy.

INSTRUCTION

Students should know how to perform basic algebraic manipulations, particularly substitution, to derive the double-angle identities from the sum identities developed in Lesson 6.1 and the half-angle identities from the double-angle identities.

GUIDED PRACTICE

For Example 1

Given $\sin \theta = -\frac{12}{13}$ and $\pi < \theta < \frac{3\pi}{2}$, determine the exact values of each expression.

1. $\cos 2\theta$ $-\frac{119}{169}$

2. $\sin 2\theta$ $\frac{120}{169}$

3. $\tan 2\theta$ $-\frac{120}{119}$

There are two alternate forms of the identity for $\cos 2\alpha$. You will be asked to prove them in the exercises.

Double-Angle Identities	
$\sin 2\alpha = 2 \sin \alpha \cos \alpha$	$\cos 2\alpha = \cos^2 \alpha - \sin^2 \alpha$
$\tan 2\alpha = \dfrac{2 \tan \alpha}{1 - \tan^2 \alpha},\ \tan \alpha \neq \pm 1$	$\cos 2\alpha = 2 \cos^2 \alpha - 1$
	$\cos 2\alpha = 1 - 2 \sin^2 \alpha$

Example 1 Given $\cos \theta = -\frac{5}{13}$ and $\frac{\pi}{2} < \theta < \pi$, determine the exact values of:

   a. $\sin 2\theta$ **b.** $\cos 2\theta$ **c.** $\tan 2\theta$

Find $\sin \theta$ and $\tan \theta$, and then use the double-angle identities. Since $\cos \theta = -\frac{5}{13}$ and θ is in quadrant II, use $x = -5$ and $r = 13$ to find y.

$$y = \sqrt{13^2 - (-5)^2} = 12$$

Thus, $\sin \theta = \frac{12}{13}$ and $\tan \theta = -\frac{12}{5}$.

a. $\sin 2\theta = 2 \sin \theta \cos \theta$

$= 2\left(\frac{12}{13}\right)\left(-\frac{5}{13}\right) = -\frac{120}{169}$

b. $\cos 2\theta = \cos^2 \theta - \sin^2 \theta$

$= \left(-\frac{5}{13}\right)^2 - \left(\frac{12}{13}\right)^2 = -\frac{119}{169}$

c. $\tan 2\theta = \dfrac{2 \tan \theta}{1 - \tan^2 \theta} = \dfrac{2\left(-\frac{12}{5}\right)}{1 - \left(-\frac{12}{5}\right)^2} = \dfrac{120}{119}$

Modeling

A college athlete is studying the offensive strategy used in a recent soccer game. How can she increase the distance she can kick the ball?

By using basic principles of physics, the student finds that the horizontal distance x traveled by a projectile such as a soccer ball can be modeled using the equation

$$x = \frac{2v^2 \sin \theta \cos \theta}{g}$$

where $g = 9.8$ m/s^2, v is the initial velocity, and θ is the measure of the launch angle.

298   Chapter 6 Trigonometric Identities and Equations

Using the double-angle identity $\sin 2\theta = 2 \sin \theta \cos \theta$ to simplify the equation,

$$x = \frac{v^2 \sin 2\theta}{g}$$

When creating a model, you must make certain assumptions. This model assumes the following: (1) Air resistance can be neglected, (2) the earth is flat rather than curved over the small distance traveled by the projectile, (3) the direction in which the earth's gravity accelerates the projectile remains virtually the same over this small distance, and (4) the projectile is in the same vertical plane for the duration of its flight.

Example 2   *Sports*   The soccer player determines that she consistently kicks the ball at an angle of 30° with an initial velocity of 25 m/s.
   a. How far is the ball from the soccer player when it hits the ground?
   b. How can the soccer player maximize the horizontal distance that the ball travels before returning to the ground? Assume that she is already kicking the ball as hard as she can.

   a. The soccer ball travels $\dfrac{25^2 \sin 2(30°)}{9.8} = 55.2$ m.

   b. The maximum value of the sine function occurs when the angle measures 90°. If the measure of the launch angle θ is 45°, then 2θ will be 90°. Thus, for a given initial velocity, a launch angle of 45° will maximize the horizontal distance traveled by a projectile.

Is it appropriate to ignore air resistance when calculating the distance traveled by a light object such as a locust?

The *half-angle identities,* which are used in calculus, can be readily derived from the double-angle identities. Derivations for the half-angle identities for sine and cosine follow. You will be asked to derive the tangent identities in the exercises.

Half-Angle Identities

$$\sin \frac{\alpha}{2} = \pm \sqrt{\frac{1 - \cos \alpha}{2}} \qquad \tan \frac{\alpha}{2} = \pm \sqrt{\frac{1 - \cos \alpha}{1 + \cos \alpha}}, \cos \alpha \neq -1$$

$$\cos \frac{\alpha}{2} = \pm \sqrt{\frac{1 + \cos \alpha}{2}} \qquad \tan \frac{\alpha}{2} = \frac{1 - \cos \alpha}{\sin \alpha}, \sin \alpha \neq 0$$

$$\tan \frac{\alpha}{2} = \frac{\sin \alpha}{1 + \cos \alpha}, \cos \alpha \neq -1$$

To derive the half-angle identities for sine and cosine, set θ equal to $\frac{\alpha}{2}$ in the double-angle identities for cosine. Neither $\sin \frac{\alpha}{2}$ nor $\cos \frac{\alpha}{2}$ has two values. The

6.3 Double-Angle and Half-Angle Identities   **299**

Modeling
Students may wish to research the use of physics in sports to see how knowledge of trigonometry can be used by trainers and athletes to give them a winning edge over the competition.

For Example 2
A punter for a professional football team consistently kicks the football at an angle of 42° with an initial velocity of 25 m/s.
1. How far is the ball from the punter when it first hits the ground? 63.4 m
2. How much farther does the ball travel from the punter if the angle is increased to 44°? about 0.3 m farther

For Example 3

If sec $\alpha = 2$ and tan $\alpha < 0$, find the exact values of each expression.

1. cos $\frac{\alpha}{2}$ $\quad -\frac{\sqrt{3}}{2}$

2. tan $\frac{\alpha}{2}$ $\quad -\frac{\sqrt{3}}{3}$

3. sin $\frac{\alpha}{2}$ $\quad \frac{1}{2}$

Common Error · Students often have difficulty determining the quadrants of angles and the proper signs of trigonometric expressions when using the half-angle identities.

values of $\sin\frac{\alpha}{2}$, $\cos\frac{\alpha}{2}$, and $\tan\frac{\alpha}{2}$ are positive or negative depending on the quadrant in which $\frac{\alpha}{2}$ lies.

$$\cos 2\left(\frac{\alpha}{2}\right) = 1 - 2\sin^2\left(\frac{\alpha}{2}\right) \qquad \cos 2\left(\frac{\alpha}{2}\right) = 2\cos^2\left(\frac{\alpha}{2}\right) - 1$$

$$\cos\alpha = 1 - 2\sin^2\left(\frac{\alpha}{2}\right) \qquad \cos\alpha = 2\cos^2\left(\frac{\alpha}{2}\right) - 1$$

$$2\sin^2\left(\frac{\alpha}{2}\right) = 1 - \cos\alpha \qquad 2\cos^2\left(\frac{\alpha}{2}\right) = 1 + \cos\alpha$$

$$\sin^2\left(\frac{\alpha}{2}\right) = \frac{1 - \cos\alpha}{2} \qquad \cos^2\left(\frac{\alpha}{2}\right) = \frac{1 + \cos\alpha}{2}$$

$$\sin\frac{\alpha}{2} = \pm\sqrt{\frac{1 - \cos\alpha}{2}} \qquad \cos\frac{\alpha}{2} = \pm\sqrt{\frac{1 + \cos\alpha}{2}}$$

If α is known to be in a particular quadrant, then $\frac{\alpha}{2}$ will be in one of two quadrants. For example, if α is in the third quadrant and $n \in Z$, then

$$\pi + 2\pi n < \alpha < \frac{3\pi}{2} + 2\pi n$$

Therefore, $\qquad \frac{\pi}{2} + \pi n < \frac{\alpha}{2} < \frac{3\pi}{4} + \pi n$

If $n = 0$, then $\frac{\pi}{2} < \frac{\alpha}{2} < \frac{3\pi}{4}$. Thus $\frac{\alpha}{2}$ is in the second quadrant. If $n = 1$, then $\frac{3\pi}{2} < \frac{\alpha}{2} < \frac{7\pi}{4}$. Thus $\frac{\alpha}{2}$ is in the fourth quadrant. For all other integral values of n, $\frac{\alpha}{2}$ will be in either the second or the fourth quadrant. For simplicity, it will usually be assumed that $0 \leq \alpha < 2\pi$.

Example 3 If $\tan\alpha = \frac{5}{12}$ and $\sin\alpha < 0$, find the exact values of each of the following. Assume that $0 \leq \alpha < 2\pi$.

a. $\sin\frac{\alpha}{2}$ $\qquad$ **b.** $\cos\frac{\alpha}{2}$ $\qquad$ **c.** $\tan\frac{\alpha}{2}$

Find $\sin\alpha$ and $\cos\alpha$, and then use the half-angle identities. The terminal side of α is in quadrant III.

Why? Since $\tan\alpha = \frac{5}{12}$, let $x = -12$ and $y = -5$. Then solve for r.

$$r = \sqrt{(-12)^2 + (-5)^2} = 13$$

Thus, $\sin\alpha = -\frac{5}{13}$ and $\cos\alpha = -\frac{12}{13}$.

The terminal side of $\frac{\alpha}{2}$ is in quadrant II: $\pi \leq \alpha \leq \frac{3\pi}{2}$ and $\frac{\pi}{2} \leq \frac{\alpha}{2} \leq \frac{3\pi}{4}$. In quadrant II, sine is positive and cosine is negative.

300 Chapter 6 Trigonometric Identities and Equations

a. $\sin \dfrac{\alpha}{2} = +\sqrt{\dfrac{1 - \left(-\frac{12}{13}\right)}{2}}$

$\qquad = \sqrt{\dfrac{13 + 12}{26}}$

$\qquad = \dfrac{5}{\sqrt{26}}$

$\qquad = \dfrac{5\sqrt{26}}{26}$

b. $\cos \dfrac{\alpha}{2} = -\sqrt{\dfrac{1 + \left(-\frac{12}{13}\right)}{2}}$

$\qquad = -\sqrt{\dfrac{13 - 12}{26}}$

$\qquad = -\dfrac{1}{\sqrt{26}}$

$\qquad = -\dfrac{\sqrt{26}}{26}$

c. $\tan \dfrac{\alpha}{2} = \dfrac{-\frac{5}{13}}{1 + \left(-\frac{12}{13}\right)} = \dfrac{-5}{13 - 12} = -5$

In Example 3, suppose that $2\pi \le \alpha < 4\pi$. *How would the three answers change? Which answer would not change? Why not?*

The double-angle and half-angle identities may be used to prove other identities.

Example 4 Prove each identity.

$\qquad$ **a.** $\tan \theta = \dfrac{1 - \cos 2\theta}{\sin 2\theta}$ $\qquad$ **b.** $\cos \alpha = \cos^2 \dfrac{\alpha}{2} - \sin^2 \dfrac{\alpha}{2}$

a. $\tan \theta$ $\quad\Bigg|\quad$ $\dfrac{1 - \cos 2\theta}{\sin 2\theta}$

$\qquad\qquad\qquad \dfrac{1 - (\cos^2 \theta - \sin^2 \theta)}{2 \sin \theta \cos \theta}$ $\qquad \cos 2\theta = \cos^2 \theta - \sin^2 \theta$
$\qquad\qquad\qquad\qquad\qquad\qquad\qquad\qquad\quad \sin 2\theta = 2 \sin \theta \cos \theta$

$\qquad\qquad\qquad \dfrac{(1 - \cos^2 \theta) + \sin^2 \theta}{2 \sin \theta \cos \theta}$

$\qquad\qquad\qquad \dfrac{\sin^2 \theta + \sin^2 \theta}{2 \sin \theta \cos \theta}$ $\qquad 1 - \cos^2 \theta = \sin^2 \theta$

$\qquad\qquad\qquad \dfrac{2 \sin^2 \theta}{2 \sin \theta \cos \theta}$

$\qquad\qquad\qquad \dfrac{\sin \theta}{\cos \theta}$

$\qquad\quad = \tan \theta$

b. $\cos \alpha$ $\quad\Bigg|\quad$ $\cos^2 \dfrac{\alpha}{2} - \sin^2 \dfrac{\alpha}{2}$

$\qquad\qquad\qquad \left(\pm\sqrt{\dfrac{1 + \cos \alpha}{2}}\right)^2 - \left(\pm\sqrt{\dfrac{1 - \cos \alpha}{2}}\right)^2$

$\qquad\qquad\qquad \dfrac{1 + \cos \alpha}{2} - \dfrac{1 - \cos \alpha}{2}$

$\qquad\qquad\qquad \dfrac{2 \cos \alpha}{2}$

$\qquad\quad = \cos \alpha$

6.3 Double-Angle and Half-Angle Identities **301**

Prove each identity.

1. $\dfrac{\sin 2\theta}{2 \sin^2 \theta} = \cot \theta$

$\dfrac{\sin 2\theta}{2 \sin^2 \theta} = \dfrac{2 \sin \theta \cos \theta}{2 \sin \theta \sin \theta} = \dfrac{\cos \theta}{\sin \theta} = \cot \theta$

2. $\left(\sin \dfrac{x}{2} + \cos \dfrac{x}{2}\right)^2 = 1 + \sin x$

$\left(\sin \dfrac{x}{2} + \cos \dfrac{x}{2}\right)^2 = \left(\sin \dfrac{x}{2}\right)^2 +$

$2 \sin \dfrac{x}{2} \cos \dfrac{x}{2} + \left(\cos \dfrac{x}{2}\right)^2 =$

$\left(\sin \dfrac{x}{2}\right)^2 + \sin x + \left(\cos \dfrac{x}{2}\right)^2 =$

$1 + \sin x$

CLOSURE

Have students record in their math journals the procedures they use to find exact values of trigonometric expressions from given conditions such as those found in Examples 1 and 3. Procedures may include first drawing a unit circle with the given angle and its double-angle or half-angle.

301

Assignment Guide
Basic: 1–24, 29, 33
Average: 1–27 odd, 28–50, Project
Enriched: 15–43 odd, 44–58, Project

Teacher's Resource Book
Practice, page 39

ⓇReview
Exercises 21, 23, 25, 44, and 46 review concepts such as direct and inverse variation, the distance and midpoint formulas, and quadratic solutions.

Project
You may want to extend the project by addressing other examples that show the use of angles in sports. You can have the students find these examples in the school's athletic program.

LESSON FOLLOW-UP

Test Yourself

Teacher's Resource Book
Test—Quiz form A, page 21
Test—Quiz form B, page 21

Additional Answers
Class Exercises
12. $\sin 3\theta = \sin (2\theta + \theta) =$
$\sin 2\theta \cos \theta + \cos 2\theta \sin \theta =$
$2 \sin \theta \cos \theta \cos \theta +$
$(1 - 2 \sin^2 \theta) \sin \theta =$
$2 \sin \theta \cos^2 \theta + \sin \theta - 2 \sin^3 \theta =$
$2 \sin \theta (1 - \sin^2 \theta) + \sin \theta -$
$2 \sin^3 \theta = 2 \sin \theta - 2 \sin^3 \theta +$
$\sin \theta - 2 \sin^3 \theta = 3 \sin \theta -$
$4 \sin^3 \theta$

13. $\tan^2 \left(\frac{\alpha}{2} \right) = \left(\frac{1 - \cos \alpha}{\sin \alpha} \right)^2 =$
$\frac{(1 - \cos \alpha)^2}{\sin^2 \alpha}$

14. $\sin 2(30°) = \sin 2(60°) = \frac{\sqrt{3}}{2}$

Class Exercises

Use the double-angle identities to find the exact value of each.

1. Given $\cos \alpha = -\frac{12}{13}$ and $\frac{\pi}{2} \le \alpha \le \pi$, find $\cos 2\alpha$. $\frac{119}{169}$

2. Given $\cos \alpha = -\frac{3}{5}$ and $\frac{\pi}{2} \le \alpha \le \pi$, find $\sin 2\alpha$. $-\frac{24}{25}$

3. Given $\sin \alpha = -\frac{3}{5}$ and $\pi \le \alpha \le \frac{3\pi}{2}$, find $\sin 2\alpha$. $\frac{24}{25}$

4. Given $\sin \alpha = -\frac{3}{5}$ and $\frac{3\pi}{2} \le \alpha \le 2\pi$, find $\cos 2\alpha$. $\frac{7}{25}$

5. Given $\cos \beta = \frac{4}{5}$ and $\frac{3\pi}{2} \le \beta \le 2\pi$, find $\tan 2\beta$. $-\frac{24}{7}$

6. Given $\tan \beta = -\frac{5}{12}$ and $\frac{\pi}{2} \le \beta \le \pi$, find $\tan 2\beta$. $-\frac{120}{119}$

Use the half-angle identities to find the exact value of each.

7. Given $\cos \beta = \frac{3}{5}$ and $\frac{3\pi}{2} \le \beta \le 2\pi$, find $\sin \frac{\beta}{2}$. $\frac{\sqrt{5}}{5}$

8. Given $\cos \beta = -\frac{3}{5}$ and $\pi \le \beta \le \frac{3\pi}{2}$, find $\cos \frac{\beta}{2}$. $-\frac{\sqrt{5}}{5}$

9. Given $\cos \theta = \frac{\sqrt{3}}{3}$ and $0 \le \theta \le \frac{\pi}{2}$, find $\tan \frac{\theta}{2}$. $\frac{\sqrt{6} - \sqrt{2}}{2}$

10. Given $\sin \theta = \frac{4}{5}$ and θ lies in the second quadrant, find $\sin \frac{\theta}{2}$. $\frac{2\sqrt{5}}{5}$

11. Given $\sin \theta = -\frac{2}{5}$ and θ lies in the third quadrant, find $\tan \frac{\theta}{2}$. $\frac{-5 - \sqrt{21}}{2}$

Prove each identity.

12. $\sin 3\theta = 3 \sin \theta - 4 \sin^3 \theta$
13. $\tan^2 \left(\frac{\alpha}{2} \right) = \frac{(1 - \cos \alpha)^2}{\sin^2 \alpha}$

14. **Thinking Critically**   Why do footballs kicked from ground level with launch angles of 30° and 60° at the same initial speed have the same range?

Practice Exercises

Use appropriate technology.

Use double-angle or half-angle identities to find the exact value of each.

A 1. $\sin \frac{5\pi}{12}$ 2. $\cos \frac{\pi}{8}$ 3. $\cos \frac{7\pi}{8}$ 4. $\sin \frac{7\pi}{12}$ 5. $\tan \frac{11\pi}{8}$ 6. $\tan \frac{11\pi}{12}$

7. Given $\sin \theta = -\frac{5}{6}$ and $\frac{3\pi}{2} \le \theta \le 2\pi$, find $\cos 2\theta$. $-\frac{7}{18}$

8. Given $\cos \theta = -\frac{4}{5}$ and $\pi \le \theta \le \frac{3\pi}{2}$, find $\sin 2\theta$. $\frac{24}{25}$

9. Given $\sin \alpha = -\frac{12}{13}$ and $\frac{3\pi}{2} \le \alpha \le 2\pi$, find $\sin 2\alpha$. $-\frac{120}{169}$

302   Chapter 6 Trigonometric Identities and Equations

Practice Exercises
1. $\frac{\sqrt{2 + \sqrt{3}}}{2}$ 2. $\frac{\sqrt{2 + \sqrt{2}}}{2}$ 3. $-\frac{\sqrt{2 + \sqrt{2}}}{2}$ 4. $\frac{\sqrt{2 + \sqrt{3}}}{2}$ 5. $\sqrt{2} + 1$
6. $-2 + \sqrt{3}$

10. Given $\cos \alpha = -\dfrac{5}{13}$ and $\dfrac{\pi}{2} \le \alpha \le \pi$, find $\tan 2\alpha$. $\dfrac{120}{119}$

11. Given $\cos \beta = -\dfrac{3}{5}$ and $\dfrac{\pi}{2} \le \beta \le \pi$, find $\sin \dfrac{\beta}{2}$. $\dfrac{2\sqrt{5}}{5}$

12. Given $\sin \beta = -\dfrac{3}{5}$ and $\dfrac{3\pi}{2} \le \beta \le 2\pi$, find $\cos \dfrac{\beta}{2}$. $-\dfrac{3\sqrt{10}}{10}$

13. Given $\cos \theta = -\dfrac{3}{5}$ and $\pi \le \theta \le \dfrac{3\pi}{2}$, find $\tan \dfrac{\theta}{2}$. -2

14. Given $\sin \theta = -\dfrac{8}{17}$ and $\pi \le \theta \le \dfrac{3\pi}{2}$, find $\tan \dfrac{\theta}{2}$. -4

15. Given $\tan \alpha = -\dfrac{5}{12}$ and $\dfrac{3\pi}{2} \le \alpha \le 2\pi$, find $\tan \dfrac{\alpha}{2}$. $-\dfrac{1}{5}$

16. Given $\tan \alpha = -\dfrac{3}{4}$ and $\dfrac{\pi}{2} \le \alpha \le \pi$, find $\tan \dfrac{\alpha}{2}$. 3

17. Given $\sin \alpha = -\dfrac{\sqrt{2}}{2}$ and α lies in the fourth quadrant, find $\cos \dfrac{\alpha}{2}$. $-\dfrac{\sqrt{2+\sqrt{2}}}{2}$

18. Given $\tan \beta = \sqrt{3}$ and β lies in the first quadrant, find $\sin \dfrac{\beta}{2}$. $+\dfrac{1}{2}$

19. Given $\cos \theta = -\dfrac{4}{5}$ and $\tan \theta > 0$, find $\sin \dfrac{\theta}{2}$. $+\dfrac{3\sqrt{10}}{10}$

20. Given $\tan \alpha = -1$ and $\cos \theta < 0$, find $\tan \dfrac{\alpha}{2}$. $\sqrt{2}+1$

Ⓡ 21. If N varies directly as P, determine the constant of variation given that N is 7.5 when P is 12. $\dfrac{5}{8}$

22. **Thinking Critically**   Determine two different radical expressions for $\sin 15°$. Then show that the two expressions are equal. *Hint:* You can write $15°$ both as a half-angle measure and as a difference of two angle measures.

Ⓡ 23. If T varies inversely as D, determine the constant of variation given that T is 123 when D is 11. 1353

24. *Sports*   Find the horizontal distance traveled by a football kicked at a launch angle of $45°$ with an initial velocity of 70 ft/s. (Use $g = 32$ ft/s².) 153.125 ft

Ⓡ 25. Find the distance between the points $(6, -3)$ and $(-12, -5)$. $2\sqrt{82}$

26. *Sports*   Find the horizontal distance traveled by a soccer ball kicked at a launch angle of $35°$ with an initial velocity of 30 m/s. 86.3 m

Physics   A plane traveling at the speed of sound (approximately 742.82 mi/h at 32°F at sea level) is said to be traveling at Mach 1. When the speed of a plane is greater than that of sound, listeners may hear a sonic boom created by sound waves that form a cone with vertex angle β. The Mach number is defined to be $M = \dfrac{\text{speed of plane}}{\text{speed of sound}}$. If $M > 1$, $\sin \left(\dfrac{\beta}{2} \right) = \dfrac{1}{M}$.

27. Given $\beta = \dfrac{\pi}{6}$, find the Mach number to the nearest tenth. 3.9

28. Given $\beta = \dfrac{\pi}{5}$, find the Mach number to the nearest tenth. 3.2

6.3 Double-Angle and Half-Angle Identities   **303**

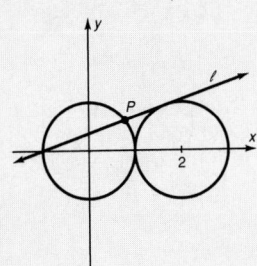

33. $\cos 2\beta = \cos^2 \beta - \sin^2 \beta =$
$\cos^2 \beta - (1 - \cos^2 \beta) = 2\cos^2 \beta - 1$

34. $\cos 2\beta = \cos^2 \beta - \sin^2 \beta =$
$(1 - \sin^2 \beta) - \sin^2 \beta = 1 - 2\sin^2 \beta$

35. $\tan \dfrac{\alpha}{2} = \dfrac{\sin \frac{\alpha}{2}}{\cos \frac{\alpha}{2}} = \dfrac{\pm\sqrt{\frac{1-\cos\alpha}{2}}}{\pm\sqrt{\frac{1+\cos\alpha}{2}}} =$
$\pm\sqrt{\dfrac{1-\cos\alpha}{1+\cos\alpha}}$

36. $\tan \dfrac{\alpha}{2} = \pm\sqrt{\dfrac{1-\cos\alpha}{1+\cos\alpha}} \cdot \sqrt{\dfrac{1+\cos\alpha}{1+\cos\alpha}} =$
$\pm\sqrt{\dfrac{1-\cos^2\alpha}{(1+\cos\alpha)^2}} = \dfrac{\pm\sqrt{\sin^2\alpha}}{1+\cos\alpha} =$
$\dfrac{\sin\alpha}{1+\cos\alpha}$

37. $\tan \dfrac{\beta}{2} = \pm\sqrt{\dfrac{1-\cos\beta}{1+\cos\beta}} \cdot \sqrt{\dfrac{1-\cos\beta}{1-\cos\beta}} =$
$\pm\sqrt{\dfrac{(1-\cos\beta)^2}{1-\cos^2\beta}} = \dfrac{1-\cos\beta}{\pm\sqrt{\sin^2\beta}} =$
$\dfrac{1-\cos\beta}{\sin\beta}$

38. $\cos 3\theta = \cos(2\theta + \theta) =$
$\cos 2\theta \cos \theta - \sin 2\theta \sin \theta =$
$(2\cos^2 \theta - 1)\cos\theta -$
$2\sin\theta\cos\theta\sin\theta = 2\cos^3\theta -$
$\cos\theta - 2\sin^2\theta\cos\theta = 2\cos^3\theta -$
$\cos\theta - 2(1 - \cos^2\theta)\cos\theta =$
$2\cos^3\theta - \cos\theta - 2\cos\theta +$
$2\cos^3\theta = 4\cos^3\theta - 3\cos\theta$

39. $\tan 3\theta = \tan(2\theta + \theta) =$
$\dfrac{\tan 2\theta + \tan\theta}{1 - \tan 2\theta \tan\theta} =$
$\dfrac{\frac{2\tan\theta}{1-\tan^2\theta} + \tan\theta}{1 - \frac{2\tan\theta}{1-\tan^2\theta}(\tan\theta)} \cdot \dfrac{1-\tan^2\theta}{1-\tan^2\theta} =$
$\dfrac{2\tan\theta + \tan\theta(1 - \tan^2\theta)}{(1 - \tan^2\theta) - 2\tan^2\theta} =$
$\dfrac{2\tan\theta + \tan\theta - \tan^3\theta}{1 - \tan^2\theta - 2\tan^2\theta} =$
$\dfrac{3\tan\theta - \tan^3\theta}{1 - 3\tan^2\theta}$

Use a graphing utility to determine whether each equation appears to be an identity.

B 29. $\sin \dfrac{\alpha}{2} \cos \dfrac{\alpha}{2} = \dfrac{\sin\alpha}{2}$ yes

30. $2\sin^2 3\beta = 2 - 2\cos^2 3\beta$ yes

31. $\sin \dfrac{\alpha}{2} = \dfrac{\sin\alpha}{1+\cos\alpha}$ no

32. $\tan \dfrac{\beta}{2} = \dfrac{1+\cos\beta}{\sin\beta}$ no

Prove each identity.

33. $\cos 2\beta = 2\cos^2 \beta - 1$

34. $\cos 2\beta = 1 - 2\sin^2 \beta$

35. $\tan \dfrac{\alpha}{2} = \pm\sqrt{\dfrac{1-\cos\alpha}{1+\cos\alpha}}$

36. $\tan \dfrac{\alpha}{2} = \dfrac{\sin\alpha}{1+\cos\alpha}$

37. $\tan \dfrac{\beta}{2} = \dfrac{1-\cos\beta}{\sin\beta}$

38. $\cos 3\theta = 4\cos^3 \theta - 3\cos\theta$

39. $\tan 3\theta = \dfrac{3\tan\theta - \tan^3 \theta}{1 - 3\tan^2 \theta}$

40. $\cos^4 \beta - \sin^4 \beta = 2\cos^2 \beta - 1$

41. $\sin 4\alpha = 2\sin 2\alpha \cos 2\alpha$

42. $\sin 8\alpha = 2\sin 4\alpha \cos 4\alpha$

43. **Thinking Critically** Develop a double-angle identity for cotangent, and note its restrictions.

44. Given that the value of the discriminant for a particular quadratic equation is negative, what is the nature of its solutions? complex

45. *Sports* The maximum height h reached by a projectile is given by $h = \dfrac{v^2 \sin^2 \theta}{2g}$. Determine the maximum height reached by a football kicked at a launch angle of 50° with an initial velocity of 65 ft/s. (Use $g = 32$ ft/s².) 38.7 ft

46. What is the midpoint of the line segment determined by the two points with coordinates $(\cos\alpha, \sin\alpha)$ and $(\cos\beta, \sin\beta)$?

47. *Sports* The total time t of flight of a projectile is given by $t = \dfrac{2v\sin\theta}{g}$.
Find the "hang" time (time aloft) for the football discussed in Exercise 45. 3.1 s

48. *Nature* A salmon jumps out of the water at an angle of 70° with an initial velocity of 6 m/s. How high does it jump? 1.6 m

49. *Nature* How long will the salmon described in Exercise 48 be out of the water? 1.2 s

Prove each identity.

C 50. $\cot 2\alpha - \cot\alpha = -\csc 2\alpha$

51. $2\cot 2\alpha = 2\cot\alpha - \sec\alpha\csc\alpha$

52. $\sec 2\alpha = \dfrac{\cot\alpha + \tan\alpha}{\cot\alpha - \tan\alpha}$

53. $\cot\alpha - \tan\alpha = \dfrac{2\cos 2\alpha}{\sin 2\alpha}$

Find the exact value of each trigonometric expression.

54. Given $\cot 2\theta = -\dfrac{3}{4}$ and $0 \le \theta \le \dfrac{\pi}{2}$, find $\cos\theta$. $\dfrac{\sqrt{5}}{5}$

55. Given $\tan 2\theta = \dfrac{3}{4}$ and $0 \le \theta \le \dfrac{\pi}{2}$, find $\sin\theta$. $\dfrac{\sqrt{10}}{10}$

304 Chapter 6 Trigonometric Identities and Equations

---

40. $\cos^4 \beta - \sin^4 \beta = (\cos^2 \beta + \sin^2 \beta)(\cos^2 \beta - \sin^2 \beta) = 1[\cos^2 \beta - (1 - \cos^2 \beta)] =$
$\cos^2 \beta - 1 + \cos^2 \beta = 2\cos^2 \beta - 1$

41. $\sin 4\alpha = \sin 2(2\alpha) = 2\sin 2\alpha \cos 2\alpha$

42. $\sin 8\alpha = \sin 2(4\alpha) = 2\sin 4\alpha \cos 4\alpha$

43. $\cot 2\alpha = \dfrac{1}{\tan 2\alpha} = \dfrac{1 - \tan^2 \alpha}{2\tan\alpha} = \dfrac{\cot^2 \alpha - 1}{2\cot\alpha}, \alpha \neq n\pi, n \in Z$

56. Given $\tan 2\beta = -\dfrac{3}{4}$ and $\dfrac{\pi}{2} \le \beta \le \pi$, find $\tan \beta$. $-\dfrac{1}{3}$

57. Given $\cot 2\beta = \dfrac{\sqrt{3}}{3}$ and $\dfrac{\pi}{2} \le \beta \le \pi$, find $\cot \beta$. $-\dfrac{\sqrt{3}}{3}$

58. Use the half-angle formula for cosine and the fact that $\cos \dfrac{\pi}{4} = \dfrac{\sqrt{2}}{2}$ to find the exact value of $\cos \dfrac{\pi}{8}$ and $\cos \dfrac{\pi}{16}$. Then use the pattern from these results to guess the exact value of
$$\sqrt{2 + \sqrt{2 + \sqrt{2 + \cdots}}}.$$

Project

Determine whether a baseball hit with an initial velocity of 115 ft/s at a launch angle of 45° will clear a 4-ft fence 400 ft from home plate. (Assume that the ball is hit when its height is 4 ft from the ground). yes

Test Yourself

Use a sum or difference identity to find the exact value for each.

1. $\tan \dfrac{5\pi}{12}$ $2 + \sqrt{3}$

2. $\cos 105°$ $\dfrac{\sqrt{2} - \sqrt{6}}{4}$

6.1

Determine the exact value for each trigonometric expression given $\sin \alpha = \dfrac{5}{13}$, $\sin \beta = -\dfrac{3}{5}$, $\dfrac{\pi}{2} \le \alpha \le \pi$, and $\dfrac{3\pi}{2} \le \beta \le 2\pi$.

3. $\sin (\alpha - \beta)$ $-\dfrac{16}{65}$

4. $\cos (\alpha + \beta)$ $-\dfrac{33}{65}$

Use a graphing utility to determine whether each equation appears to be an identity.

5. $\tan (\alpha - \pi) = \tan \alpha$ yes

6. $\tan \left(\dfrac{3\pi}{4} + \alpha\right) = \dfrac{\tan \alpha - 1}{\tan \alpha + 1}$ yes

6.2

7. $\sin \left(\dfrac{\pi}{2} + \beta\right) = -\cos \beta$ no

8. $\cos \left(\beta - \dfrac{\pi}{6}\right) = \dfrac{\sqrt{3} \cos \beta + \sin \beta}{2}$ yes

Use double-angle or half-angle identities to find the exact value of each.

9. Given $\cos \beta = -\dfrac{3}{5}$ and $\pi \le \beta \le \dfrac{3\pi}{2}$, find $\cos 2\beta$. $-\dfrac{7}{25}$

6.3

10. Given $\cos \theta = \dfrac{8}{17}$ and $0 \le \theta \le \dfrac{\pi}{2}$, find $\cos \dfrac{\theta}{2}$. $\dfrac{5\sqrt{34}}{34}$

Prove each identity.

11. $\cos 2\alpha = \dfrac{\cot \alpha - \tan \alpha}{\cot \alpha + \tan \alpha}$

12. $\cot \dfrac{\alpha}{2} = \dfrac{\sin \alpha}{1 - \cos \alpha}$

6.3 Double-Angle and Half-Angle Identities   **305**

FOCUS

Discuss the advantages of converting an expression involving sums to one involving products (or vice versa). Have students provide examples to support their thinking. For example, factoring the numerator of the following rational expression greatly simplifies it.

$$\frac{x^2 + 2x + 1}{x + 1} = \frac{(x + 1)(x + 1)}{x + 1} = x + 1,$$
$$x \neq -1$$

INSTRUCTION

- Students should see that though lengthy, the product/sum identities are derived simply by adding or subtracting the sum and difference identities for sine or cosine.
- Students should understand how both forms of identities are derived and applied, though they need not be expected to memorize them.
- Encourage the practice of recording identities on index cards for easy reference.

6.4 Product/Sum Identities

Objective: *To develop and use product/sum identities*

Focus

When you study calculus, you will be asked to simplify expressions of the form $\frac{f(x + h) - f(x)}{h}$, $h \neq 0$. For example, if a function is defined by $f(x) = x^2 + 2x + 3$, then

$$\frac{f(x + h) - f(x)}{h} = \frac{[(x + h)^2 + 2(x + h) + 3] - [x^2 + 2x + 3]}{h}$$

$$= \frac{x^2 + 2hx + h^2 + 2x + 2h + 3 - x^2 - 2x - 3}{h}$$

$$= \frac{2hx + h^2 + 2h}{h} = 2x + h + 2$$

When functions other than polynomial functions are involved, the simplification is more complicated. If $f(x) = \sin x$, then $\frac{f(x + h) - f(x)}{h} = \frac{\sin(x + h) - \sin x}{h}$. To simplify this, it is useful to express a trigonometric sum as a product.

In algebra, the distributive property serves as a connector between the operations of addition and multiplication. A sum may be written as a product and a product as a sum. For example, the sum $x^2y + xz$ may be written as the product $x(xy + z)$. The product/sum identities serve a similar purpose in trigonometry.

Product/Sum Identities
$2 \cos \alpha \cos \beta = \cos(\alpha - \beta) + \cos(\alpha + \beta)$
$2 \sin \alpha \sin \beta = \cos(\alpha - \beta) - \cos(\alpha + \beta)$
$2 \sin \alpha \cos \beta = \sin(\alpha + \beta) + \sin(\alpha - \beta)$
$2 \cos \alpha \sin \beta = \sin(\alpha + \beta) - \sin(\alpha - \beta)$

Each of the product/sum identities may be derived by adding or subtracting the sum and difference identities for sine or cosine.

$$\sin \alpha \cos \beta + \cos \alpha \sin \beta = \sin(\alpha + \beta)$$
$$\underline{\sin \alpha \cos \beta - \cos \alpha \sin \beta = \sin(\alpha - \beta)}$$
$$2 \sin \alpha \cos \beta = \sin(\alpha + \beta) + \sin(\alpha - \beta) \quad \textit{Add.}$$

$$\sin \alpha \cos \beta + \cos \alpha \sin \beta = \sin(\alpha + \beta)$$
$$\underline{\sin \alpha \cos \beta - \cos \alpha \sin \beta = \sin(\alpha - \beta)}$$
$$2 \cos \alpha \sin \beta = \sin(\alpha + \beta) - \sin(\alpha - \beta) \quad \textit{Subtract.}$$

306   Chapter 6 Trigonometric Identities and Equations

You will be asked to derive the other two product/sum identities in the exercises.

Example 1   Express $2 \cos \frac{7\pi}{12} \cos \frac{\pi}{3}$ as a sum.

$$2 \cos \alpha \cos \beta = \cos(\alpha - \beta) + \cos(\alpha + \beta)$$

$$2 \cos \frac{7\pi}{12} \cos \frac{\pi}{3} = \cos\left(\frac{7\pi}{12} - \frac{\pi}{3}\right) + \cos\left(\frac{7\pi}{12} + \frac{\pi}{3}\right)$$

$$= \cos \frac{3\pi}{12} + \cos \frac{11\pi}{12} = \cos \frac{\pi}{4} + \cos \frac{11\pi}{12}$$

You can also use the product/sum identities to express sums or differences as products.

Example 2   Express $\sin 55° + \sin 37°$ as a product.

Use $2 \sin \alpha \cos \beta = \sin(\alpha + \beta) + \sin(\alpha - \beta)$.

Let $\alpha + \beta = 55°$ and $\alpha - \beta = 37°$.

$$\begin{array}{ll} \alpha + \beta = 55 & 46 + \beta = 55 \\ \underline{\alpha - \beta = 37} & \beta = 9 \\ \quad 2\alpha = 92 \quad \text{\textit{Add.}} & \\ \quad\ \ \alpha = 46 & \end{array}$$

Thus, $\sin 55° + \sin 37° = 2 \sin 46° \cos 9°$.

There is an alternate form for the product/sum identities that is often easier to apply. You can derive these alternate identities by letting $x = \alpha + \beta$ and $y = \alpha - \beta$. Add the equations to solve for α and subtract them to solve for β.

$$\begin{array}{ll} x = \alpha + \beta & x = \alpha + \beta \\ \underline{y = \alpha - \beta} & \underline{y = \alpha - \beta} \\ x + y = 2\alpha & x - y = 2\beta \\ \dfrac{x + y}{2} = \alpha & \dfrac{x - y}{2} = \beta \end{array}$$

Substitute into the product/sum identities to obtain the alternate forms.

Product/Sum Identities—Alternate Forms

$$\cos x + \cos y = 2 \cos\left(\frac{x + y}{2}\right) \cos\left(\frac{x - y}{2}\right)$$

$$\cos x - \cos y = -2 \sin\left(\frac{x + y}{2}\right) \sin\left(\frac{x - y}{2}\right)$$

$$\sin x + \sin y = 2 \sin\left(\frac{x + y}{2}\right) \cos\left(\frac{x - y}{2}\right)$$

$$\sin x - \sin y = 2 \cos\left(\frac{x + y}{2}\right) \sin\left(\frac{x - y}{2}\right)$$

GUIDED PRACTICE

For Example 1
Express each product as a sum or difference.

1. $2 \sin \frac{11\pi}{12} \sin \frac{\pi}{4}$ $\cos \frac{2\pi}{3} - \cos \frac{7\pi}{6}$

2. $2 \cos \frac{5\pi}{8} \sin \frac{\pi}{6}$ $\sin \frac{19\pi}{24} - \sin \frac{11\pi}{24}$

For Example 2
Express each difference as a product.

1. $\cos 75° - \cos 25°$
   $-2 \sin 50° \sin 25°$

2. $\sin 87° - \sin 49°$ $2 \cos 58° \sin 19°$

For Example 3
Express each sum as a product.

1. $\cos \frac{\pi}{6} + \cos \frac{\pi}{3}$ $2 \cos \frac{\pi}{4} \cos \frac{\pi}{12}$

2. $\sin \frac{7\pi}{12} + \sin \frac{3\pi}{4}$ $2 \sin \frac{2\pi}{3} \cos \frac{\pi}{12}$

Prove the identity.

$$\frac{\sin 7\theta + \sin 5\theta}{\cos 7\theta + \cos 5\theta} = \tan 6\theta$$

$$\frac{\sin 7\theta + \sin 5\theta}{\cos 7\theta + \cos 5\theta} =$$

$$\frac{\sin(6\theta + \theta) + \sin(6\theta - \theta)}{\cos(6\theta + \theta) + \cos(6\theta - \theta)} =$$

$$\frac{2\sin 6\theta \cos\theta}{2\cos 6\theta \cos\theta} = \frac{\sin 6\theta}{\cos 6\theta} = \tan 6\theta$$

CLOSURE

Have students describe in their own words how the product/sum identities in both forms can be derived. Ask which form of identities would be used to convert a product to a sum and which would be used to convert a sum to a product.

INDEPENDENT PRACTICE

Assignment Guide

Basic: 1–25
Average: 1–25 odd, 26–38
Enriched: 1–35 odd, 36–47

Teacher's Resource Book
   Practice, page 40

® Review

Exercises 9, 19, 25, and 34 to 37 review concepts such as radical notation, sample groups, angular velocity, and trigonometric identities.

Additional Answers

Class Exercises

5. $2\cos\frac{19\pi}{24}\cos\frac{\pi}{24}$

6. $2\sin\frac{23\pi}{24}\sin\frac{7\pi}{24}$

7. $2\sin\frac{47\pi}{24}\cos\frac{19\pi}{24}$

8. $2\cos\frac{\pi}{4}\sin\frac{\pi}{12}$

9. $-2\sin 47.5° \sin 19.5°$

10. $2\sin 68° \cos 31°$

11. Use $\sin(\alpha + \beta) + \sin(\alpha - \beta) =$
$2\sin\alpha\cos\beta$
Let $x = \alpha + \beta$ and $y = \alpha - \beta$.
Then $\alpha = \frac{x + y}{2}$ and $\beta = \frac{x - y}{2}$.
Therefore, $\sin x + \sin y =$
$2\sin\left(\frac{x + y}{2}\right)\cos\left(\frac{x - y}{2}\right)$.

Example 3 Express $\cos 81° - \cos 49°$ as a product.

Use $\cos x - \cos y = -2\sin\left(\frac{x + y}{2}\right)\sin\left(\frac{x - y}{2}\right)$.

$$\cos 81° - \cos 49° = -2\sin\left(\frac{81° + 49°}{2}\right)\sin\left(\frac{81° - 49°}{2}\right)$$

$$= -2\sin 65° \sin 16°$$

The product/sum identities can be used to prove other identities.

Example 4 Prove $\dfrac{\cos 3\alpha - \cos\alpha}{\sin 3\alpha + \sin\alpha} = -\tan\alpha$.

$$\left.\begin{array}{c|c}
\dfrac{\cos 3\alpha - \cos\alpha}{\sin 3\alpha + \sin\alpha} & -\tan\alpha \\[2ex]
\dfrac{-2\sin\left(\frac{3\alpha + \alpha}{2}\right)\sin\left(\frac{3\alpha - \alpha}{2}\right)}{2\sin\left(\frac{3\alpha + \alpha}{2}\right)\cos\left(\frac{3\alpha - \alpha}{2}\right)} & \\[3ex]
\dfrac{-2\sin 2\alpha \sin\alpha}{2\sin 2\alpha \cos\alpha} & \\[2ex]
\dfrac{-\sin\alpha}{\cos\alpha} & \\[2ex]
-\tan\alpha & =
\end{array}\right.$$

Class Exercises

Express each product as a sum or difference.

1. $2\sin\frac{\pi}{6}\sin\frac{\pi}{4}$

2. $2\sin\frac{\pi}{4}\cos\frac{\pi}{6}$

3. $2\cos 77° \sin 29°$

4. $2\cos 85° \cos 29°$

Express each sum or difference as a product.

5. $\cos\frac{3\pi}{4} + \cos\frac{5\pi}{6}$

6. $\cos\frac{2\pi}{3} - \cos\frac{5\pi}{4}$

7. $\sin\frac{7\pi}{6} + \sin\frac{11\pi}{4}$

8. $\sin\frac{\pi}{3} - \sin\frac{\pi}{6}$

9. $\cos 67° - \cos 28°$

10. $\sin 99° + \sin 37°$

Prove each identity.

11. $\sin x + \sin y = 2\sin\left(\frac{x + y}{2}\right)\cos\left(\frac{x - y}{2}\right)$

12. $\dfrac{\sin 5\alpha + \sin 3\alpha}{\cos 5\alpha + \cos 3\alpha} = \tan 4\alpha$

308 Chapter 6 Trigonometric Identities and Equations

---

12. $\dfrac{\sin 5\alpha + \sin 3\alpha}{\cos 5\alpha + \cos 3\alpha} = \dfrac{\sin(4\alpha + \alpha) + \sin(4\alpha - \alpha)}{\cos(4\alpha + \alpha) + \cos(4\alpha - \alpha)} = \dfrac{2\sin 4\alpha \cos\alpha}{2\cos 4\alpha \cos\alpha} = \tan 4\alpha$

Practice Exercises ⌂ Use appropriate technology.

Express each product as a sum or difference.

A **1.** $2 \cos \frac{3\pi}{7} \cos \frac{\pi}{7}$ $\cos \frac{2\pi}{7} + \cos \frac{4\pi}{7}$

2. $2 \cos \frac{7\pi}{11} \cos \frac{3\pi}{11}$ $\cos \frac{4\pi}{11} + \cos \frac{10\pi}{11}$

3. $2 \sin \frac{7\pi}{12} \sin \frac{5\pi}{12}$ $\cos \frac{\pi}{6} - \cos \pi$

4. $2 \sin \frac{8\pi}{13} \sin \frac{3\pi}{13}$ $\cos \frac{5\pi}{13} - \cos \frac{11\pi}{13}$

5. $2 \sin 87° \cos 31°$ $\sin 118° + \sin 56°$

6. $2 \sin 94° \cos 47°$ $\sin 141° + \sin 47°$

7. $2 \cos 111° \sin 59°$ $\sin 170° - \sin 52°$

8. $2 \cos 85° \sin 19°$ $\sin 104° - \sin 66°$

Ⓡ **9.** Evaluate: $\sqrt[3]{4a^2b^{11}} \sqrt[6]{2a^2b^8}$ $ab^5\sqrt[6]{32}$

Express each sum or difference as a product.

10. $\cos \frac{7\pi}{8} + \cos \frac{3\pi}{8}$

11. $\cos \frac{5\pi}{11} + \cos \frac{3\pi}{11}$

12. $\cos \frac{5\pi}{6} - \cos \frac{\pi}{6}$

13. $\sin 13 + \sin 4$

14. $\sin 7 + \sin 2$

15. $\cos 74° - \cos 25°$

16. $\cos 62° - \cos 43°$

17. $\sin 3.2 - \sin 1.7$

18. $\sin 5.6 - \sin 3.4$

Ⓡ **19.** *Medicine*   In an experimental group, 70 subjects are given medication X and 49 are given medication Y. Among these, 10 subjects are administered both medications. How many subjects are in the experimental group? 109

20. Writing in Mathematics   Explain why $\cos \frac{5\pi}{6} + \cos \frac{\pi}{6} \neq \cos \pi$.

Geography   Latitude and longitude can be used to determine the great-circle distance between city A and city B in the Northern Hemisphere using the formula $\cos d = \cos \theta \cos a \cos b + \sin a \sin b$, where θ is the positive longitudinal difference between cities A and B; a is the latitude of city A; b is the latitude of city B; and d is the degree measure of the great-circle arc between A and B ($0° < d \leq 180°$). Find the degree measure, to the nearest tenth of a degree, of the great-circle arc between the given cities. Assume that the earth is spherical.

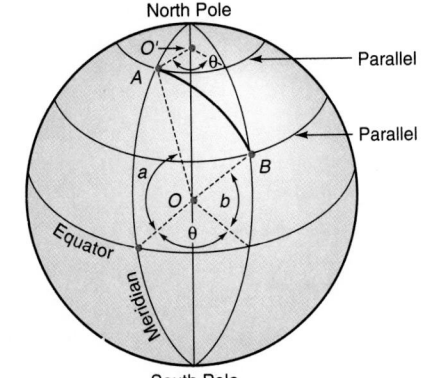

21. Los Angeles (latitude 34.1°; longitude 118.3°) Boston (latitude 42.4°; longitude 71.1°) 37.4°

22. New York City (latitude 40.8°; longitude 74°) Miami (latitude 25.8°; longitude 80.2°) 15.9°

B **23.** *Music*   The equation of a sound wave produced by a certain musical instrument is $f(x) = 0.02 \sin 660\pi x + 0.02 \sin 1320\pi x$. Express the equation of this sound wave as a product. $0.04 \sin 990\pi x \cos 330\pi x$

24. Thinking Critically   Use the addition formulas to express $\cos \left(\theta + \frac{n\pi}{2} \right)$, where n is an integer, in terms of $\sin \theta$ and $\cos \theta$. On what does the sign of your answer depend?

LESSON FOLLOW-UP

Lesson Quiz

Express each product as a sum and each sum as a product.

1. $2 \cos 56° \cos 18°$
$\cos 38° + \cos 74°$

2. $\sin 225° \sin 300°$
$\frac{1}{2}(\cos 75° - \cos 525°)$

3. $\sin \frac{7\pi}{4} + \sin \frac{3\pi}{8}$ $2 \sin \frac{17\pi}{16} \cos \frac{11\pi}{16}$

4. $\sin \frac{5\pi}{12} - \sin \frac{11\pi}{6}$ $-2 \sin \frac{17\pi}{24} \cos \frac{9\pi}{8}$

5. Prove the identity.

$$\tan 2\theta = \frac{\cos 3\theta - \cos \theta}{\sin \theta - \sin 3\theta}$$

$$\frac{\cos 3\theta - \cos \theta}{\sin \theta - \sin 3\theta} =$$

$$\frac{\cos (2\theta + \theta) - \cos (2\theta - \theta)}{\sin (2\theta - \theta) + \sin (2\theta + \theta)} =$$

$$\frac{-2 \sin 2\theta \sin \theta}{-2 \cos 2\theta \sin \theta} = \frac{\sin 2\theta}{\cos 2\theta} = \tan 2\theta$$

Additional Answers

10. $2 \cos \frac{5\pi}{8} \cos \frac{\pi}{4}$

11. $2 \cos \frac{4\pi}{11} \cos \frac{\pi}{11}$

12. $-2 \sin \frac{\pi}{2} \sin \frac{\pi}{3}$

13. $2 \sin 8.5 \cos 4.5$

14. $2 \sin 4.5 \cos 2.5$

15. $-2 \sin 49.5° \sin 24.5°$

16. $-2 \sin 52.5° \sin 9.5°$

17. $2 \cos 2.45 \sin 0.75$

18. $2 \cos 4.5 \sin 1.1$

24. $\cos \left(\theta + \frac{n\pi}{2} \right) = \cos \theta \cos \frac{n\pi}{2} -$

$\sin \theta \sin \frac{n\pi}{2}$; The expression equals

$\pm\cos \theta$ if n is even and $\pm\sin \theta$ if n is odd. If n is divisible by 4 the expression equals $\cos \theta$; if n is even but not divisible by 4, it equals $-\cos \theta$. If $(n - 1)$ is divisible by 4, the expression equals $-\sin \theta$; if $(n - 1)$ is even but not divisible by 4, it equals $\sin \theta$.

25. *Physics*   A car is traveling at a speed of 30 mi/h. Find the angular velocity of a tire in revolutions per minute if the radius of the tire rim is 6 in. and there are 4 in. of tire between the road surface and the rim. 504 rpm

Prove each identity.

26. $2 \cos \alpha \cos \beta = \cos (\alpha - \beta) + \cos (\alpha + \beta)$

27. $2 \sin \alpha \sin \beta = \cos (\alpha - \beta) - \cos (\alpha + \beta)$

28. $\cos x - \cos y = -2 \sin \left(\frac{x + y}{2}\right) \sin \left(\frac{x - y}{2}\right)$ *Hint*: Use Exercise 27.

29. $\sin x - \sin y = 2 \cos \left(\frac{x + y}{2}\right) \sin \left(\frac{x - y}{2}\right)$

30. $\cot \alpha = \frac{\cos 4\alpha + \cos 2\alpha}{\sin 4\alpha - \sin 2\alpha}$

31. $\cot \theta = \frac{\sin 5\theta + \sin 3\theta}{\cos 3\theta - \cos 5\theta}$

32. $\tan 2\beta = \frac{\cos \beta - \cos 3\beta}{\sin 3\beta - \sin \beta}$

33. $\cot 5\beta = \frac{\sin 2\beta - \sin 8\beta}{\cos 8\beta - \cos 2\beta}$

Use a graphing utility to determine whether each equation appears to be an identity.

34. $\tan \beta = \frac{\sin 5\beta - \sin 3\beta}{\cos 5\beta + \cos 3\beta}$ yes

35. $\cot \alpha - \tan \alpha = \frac{2 \cos 2\alpha}{\sin 2\alpha}$ yes

36. $\tan \theta = \frac{\sin 3\theta - \sin \theta}{\cos 3\theta + \cos \theta}$ yes

37. $\cot 3\theta = \frac{\cos 4\theta + \cos 2\theta}{\sin 4\theta + \sin 2\theta}$ yes

Simplify each expression.

38. $\frac{\sin (x + h) - \sin x}{h}$

39. $\frac{\sin (x + h) + \sin x}{h}$

40. $\frac{\cos (x + h) - \cos x}{h}$

41. $\frac{\cos (x + h) + \cos x}{h}$

42. $\frac{\tan (x + h) - \tan x}{h}$

43. $\frac{\tan (x + h) + \tan x}{h}$

Prove each identity.

44. $\cos (x + y) \cos (x - y) = \cos^2 y - \sin^2 x$

45. $\sin (x + y) \cos (x - y) = \sin x \cos x + \sin y \cos y$

46. $\sin^2 x - \sin^2 y = \sin (x + y) \sin (x - y)$

47. $\cos^2 x - \cos^2 y = -\sin (x + y) \sin (x - y)$

Review

Determine whether the following statements are true or false. If the statement is false, give an example to show why it is false.

1. A function f is a periodic function if and only if there exists some number a such that $f(x) = f(x + a)$. true

2. All trigonometric functions are continuous functions. false; tan, sec

3. Simplify: $-5\frac{2}{3} \div 3\frac{1}{3}$ $-\frac{17}{10}$

31. $\frac{\sin 5\theta + \sin 3\theta}{\cos 3\theta - \sin 5\theta} = \frac{2 \sin \left(\frac{5\theta + 3\theta}{2}\right) \cos \left(\frac{5\theta - 3\theta}{2}\right)}{-2 \sin\left(\frac{3\theta + 5\theta}{2}\right) \sin \left(\frac{3\theta - 5\theta}{2}\right)} = \frac{2 \sin 4\theta \cos \theta}{-2 \sin 4\theta \sin (-\theta)} = \cot \theta$

6.5 Solving Trigonometric Equations and Inequalities

Objective: To solve trigonometric equations and inequalities

Focus

Orbiting spacecraft with on-board sensors are frequently used to map the surface of the earth. However, distortions are introduced because of the earth's spherical shape. The sensors can accurately measure the angle a spacecraft makes with a point on the ground, but they cannot accurately measure the distance from the spacecraft to the point.

 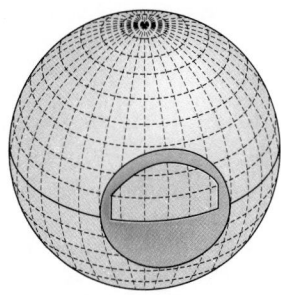

One reason for this is that all ground points are interpreted to lie in the same plane, not on a curved surface. As shown in the figures, a wide band on a sphere will appear distorted when viewed from a distance above the sphere. Fortunately, the distorted information can be corrected by a computer using trigonometric principles.

The computer that corrects distortions in satellite photos does so by solving thousands of *trigonometric equations*. There are two types of trigonometric equations—identities and conditional equations. Trigonometric equations that are true for all values of a variable for which the equation is defined are *identities*. You have worked with identities in earlier chapters and in the first four lessons of this chapter. Equations that are true for at least one value of the variable, but not all values, are called *conditional equations*. For example, the equation $1 + \sin x = 2$ is a conditional equation since it is true for some values of x such as $-\frac{3\pi}{2}$, $\frac{\pi}{2}$, and $\frac{5\pi}{2}$, but is false for $x = 0$ and $x = \pi$.

Many conditional trigonometric equations can be solved by combining algebraic techniques with trigonometric identifies. Several of these techniques will be demonstrated in this lesson and the next. The first technique is factoring.

LESSON PLAN

Vocabulary
conditional equation

Technology
graphing utility

FOCUS

There are many instances where modern technology employs the principles of trigonometry. The Fourier series, developed by J. B. Fourier (1768–1830), states that any function can be represented by a series of the form:

$$f(x) = \frac{1}{2}a_0 + a_1 \cos x$$
$$+ a_2 \cos 2x + \cdots$$
$$+ a_n \cos nx + \cdots$$
$$+ b_1 \sin x + b_2 \sin 2x + \cdots$$
$$+ b_n \sin nx + \cdots$$

This series is now used in the theory of heat, holography, and electric signals in communications.

INSTRUCTION

Remind students that when using a graphing utility, they should first set the unit of measure in both the mode and the range according to that given in the directive.

Alternative Learning Styles
Many students may benefit from a visual representation of conditional equations they have solved using algebraic techniques. Encourage them to use a graphing utility to graph these equations and to check that their solutions are approximately equal to the x-intercepts of their graphs.

Solve each conditional equation
for x, where $0 \leq x < 2\pi$.
1. $\sin 2x = 2 \sin x$ $0, \pi$

2. $\cos^2 x - \sin^2 x = 0$ $\dfrac{\pi}{4}, \dfrac{3\pi}{4}, \dfrac{5\pi}{4}, \dfrac{7\pi}{4}$

For Example 2
Solve each conditional equation
for x, where $0 \leq x < 2\pi$.

3. $\cos^2 x - 3 \sin x + 3 = 0$ $\dfrac{\pi}{2}$

4. $4 \tan^2 x = 3 \sec^2 x$ $\dfrac{\pi}{3}, \dfrac{2\pi}{3}, \dfrac{4\pi}{3}, \dfrac{5\pi}{3}$

Common Error   Some students do
not check extraneous solutions introduced when two sides of an equation are squared. Make sure that a
check is included as part of the solution process.

Example 1   Solve $\sin 2x = -\cos x$, where $0 \leq x < 2\pi$.

$$\sin 2x = -\cos x$$
$$\sin 2x + \cos x = 0$$
$$2 \sin x \cos x + \cos x = 0 \qquad \text{\small $\sin 2x = 2 \sin x \cos x$}$$
$$\cos x \, (2 \sin x + 1) = 0 \qquad \text{\small \textit{Factor.}}$$

$$\cos x = 0 \qquad \text{or} \qquad 2 \sin x + 1 = 0$$
$$\cos x = 0 \qquad \text{or} \qquad \sin x = -\tfrac{1}{2}$$
$$x = \frac{\pi}{2}, \frac{3\pi}{2} \quad \text{or} \qquad x = \frac{7\pi}{6}, \frac{11\pi}{6}$$

Thus, the solution set is $\left\{ \dfrac{\pi}{2}, \dfrac{7\pi}{6}, \dfrac{3\pi}{2}, \dfrac{11\pi}{6} \right\}$.

If the restriction $0 \leq x < 2\pi$ is omitted from Example 1, then the number of
solutions is infinite. Then the general solution set is

$$\left\{ x : x = \frac{\pi}{2} + 2n\pi, \; x = \frac{7\pi}{6} + 2n\pi, \; x = \frac{3\pi}{2} + 2n\pi, \; \text{or} \; x = \frac{11\pi}{6} + 2n\pi; \; n \in Z \right\}$$

The addend $2n\pi$ is determined by the period of the function. If the function
had been tangent instead of sine or cosine, then $n\pi$ would be added. *Why?*

A second technique for solving trigonometric equations is to express the terms
using only one trigonometric function. This technique may be combined with
other techniques, such as factoring. When both sides of an equation are squared,
extraneous solutions are sometimes introduced. So check for any potential
solutions that satisfy the squared equation but not the original equation.

Example 2   Solve $\sin x + \cos x = 1$, where $0 \leq x < 2\pi$.

$$\sin x + \cos x = 1$$
$$\sin x = 1 - \cos x$$
$$\sin^2 x = (1 - \cos x)^2 \qquad \text{\small \textit{Square both sides.}}$$
$$\sin^2 x = 1 - 2 \cos x + \cos^2 x$$
$$1 - \cos^2 x = 1 - 2 \cos x + \cos^2 x \qquad \text{\small $\sin^2 x = 1 - \cos^2 x$}$$
$$2 \cos^2 x - 2 \cos x = 0$$
$$2 \cos x \, (\cos x - 1) = 0$$
$$2 \cos x = 0 \qquad \text{or} \quad \cos x - 1 = 0$$
$$\cos x = 0 \qquad \text{or} \qquad \cos x = 1$$
$$x = \frac{\pi}{2}, \frac{3\pi}{2} \quad \text{or} \qquad x = 0$$

Check

$$\sin \frac{\pi}{2} + \cos \frac{\pi}{2} = 1 \qquad \sin \frac{3\pi}{2} + \cos \frac{3\pi}{2} = 1 \qquad \sin 0 + \cos 0 = 1$$
$$1 + 0 = 1 \qquad\qquad -1 + 0 \neq 1 \qquad\qquad 0 + 1 = 1$$

$\dfrac{\pi}{2}$ is a solution $\qquad$ $\dfrac{3\pi}{2}$ is not a solution $\qquad$ 0 is a solution

Thus, the solution set is $\left\{ 0, \dfrac{\pi}{2} \right\}$.

The period of a function affects the number of solutions over a fixed interval.

Example 3   Solve $\sin 3x = 1$, where $0 \le x < 2\pi$.

Since $0 \le x < 2\pi$, $0 \le 3x < 6\pi$. Thus, you must find all solutions to the equation in the expanded interval.

$$3x = \frac{\pi}{2} \qquad 3x = \frac{5\pi}{2} \qquad 3x = \frac{9\pi}{2}$$

$$x = \frac{\pi}{6} \qquad x = \frac{5\pi}{6} \qquad x = \frac{9\pi}{6} = \frac{3\pi}{2}$$

The solution set is $\left\{ \frac{\pi}{6}, \frac{5\pi}{6}, \frac{3\pi}{2} \right\}$.

The equations considered in the preceding examples had exact solutions. However, solutions to most trigonometric equations must be approximated.

Example 4   Find, to the nearest hundredth of a radian, the solutions to $6 \sin x - 1 = 3 \sin x + 1$.

$$6 \sin x - 1 = 3 \sin x + 1$$
$$3 \sin x = 2$$
$$\sin x = \frac{2}{3}$$
$$x = 0.73 + 2n\pi \text{ and } x = 2.41 + 2n\pi; \ n \in Z$$

Graphing utilities can also be used to solve trigonometric equations. Express the equation in function-form, that is, in the form $f(x) = 0$. Graph the function. The zeros of the function are the solutions of the related equation. Use the zoom and trace features to obtain the desired degree of accuracy. Be sure to use radian or degree mode as needed and to select an appropriate viewing window. After obtaining an approximate solution, it is important to check the solution in the original equation.

Example 5   Use a graphing utility to solve each equation.

    a. $2 + \sec x = 0$, where $0° \le x < 360°$ **b.** $2 \sin x - x = \frac{\pi}{2}$

a. Graph $y = 2 + \sec x$, using degree mode.

From the graph, the solutions appear to be $120°$ and $240°$. The cursor location obtained with the trace command gives only close approximations of $120°$ and $240°$. Therefore, it is important to check these solutions in the original equation.

$$2 + \sec 120° = 0 \qquad 2 + \sec 240° = 0$$
$$0 = 0 \qquad\qquad\qquad 0 = 0$$

[0, 360] by [−20, 20]
x scl: 60   y scl: 5

6.5 Solving Trigonometric Equations and Inequalities   **313**

For Example 3
Solve each conditional equation for x, where $0 \le x < 2\pi$.

1. $\sin 2x = -\frac{\sqrt{3}}{2}$ $\frac{2\pi}{3}, \frac{5\pi}{6}, \frac{5\pi}{3}, \frac{11\pi}{6}$

2. $\cos 3x = \frac{\sqrt{2}}{2}$

   $\frac{\pi}{12}, \frac{7\pi}{12}, \frac{3\pi}{4}, \frac{5\pi}{4}, \frac{17\pi}{12}, \frac{23\pi}{12}$

Common Error Some students fail to consider solutions of x outside the interval $0 \le x < 2\pi$. Remind them to represent all possible solutions when no domain is given in the directive.

For Example 4
Find the solutions to the nearest hundredth of a radian.

1. $5 \cos x + 2 = 2 \cos x + 1$
   $1.91 + 2n\pi$ and $4.37 + 2n\pi$ for $n \in Z$

2. $\csc^2 x + 8 \csc x + 15 = 0$
   $-0.20 + 2n\pi$, $3.34 + 2n\pi$, $-0.34 + 2n\pi$, and $3.48 + 2n\pi$ for $n \in Z$

For Example 5
Use a graphing utility to solve each equation.

1. $3 + \csc x = 0$,
   where $0° < x < 360°$

   199.5°, 340.5°

2. $4 \cos x = x + \frac{\pi}{4}$,
   where $0 < x < 2\pi$

   1.08

b. Express the equation as $2 \sin x - x - \frac{\pi}{2} = 0$.

Then graph the function $y = 2 \sin x - x - \frac{\pi}{2}$, using radian mode. Use the zoom and trace features to obtain $x = -2.60$, to the nearest hundredth. Check -2.60 in the original equation.

$$2 \sin x - x = \frac{\pi}{2}$$
$$2 \sin (-2.60) - (-2.60) = 1.57$$
$$1.57 = 1.57$$

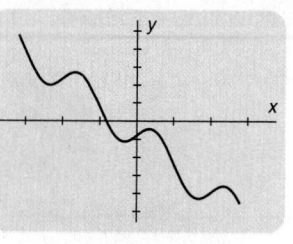

[−10, 10] by [−10, 10]
x scl: π   y scl: 2

You can adapt the techniques for solving trigonometric equations to trigonometric inequalities.

Example 6 Solve $\cos x < x$ where $-3\pi \le x \le 3\pi$, to the nearest hundredth of a radian.

Express $\cos x = x$ in function-form as $\cos x - x = 0$.

Select $[-3\pi, 3\pi]$ by $[-10, 10]$ for the viewing rectangle. The graph intersects the x-axis near $x = 1$. Use the zoom and trace features to obtain $x = 0.74$, to the nearest hundredth. Looking at the graph, you can see that $\cos x - x < 0$ for all values of x to the right of 0.74. Thus, the solution set is $\{x: x > 0.74\}$.

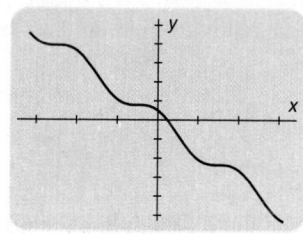

[−10, 10] by [−10, 10]
x scl: π   y scl: 2

Class Exercises

Solve each equation, where $0 \le x < 2\pi$. If the equation does not have an exact solution, round to the nearest hundredth of a radian.

1. $2 \cos x + \sqrt{3} = 0$ $\frac{5\pi}{6}, \frac{7\pi}{6}$
2. $\sqrt{3} \sec x + 2 = 0$ $\frac{5\pi}{6}, \frac{7\pi}{6}$
3. $\sin 2x = -1$ $\frac{3\pi}{4}, \frac{7\pi}{4}$
4. $\tan 2x = 1$ $\frac{\pi}{8}, \frac{5\pi}{8}, \frac{9\pi}{8}, \frac{13\pi}{8}$
5. $4 \cos x + 2 = \cos x + 1$ 1.91, 4.37
6. $4 \tan x + 3 = 3 \tan x + 5$
7. $\sin 2x \cos x - \cos 2x \sin x = -\frac{\sqrt{3}}{2}$ $\frac{4\pi}{3}, \frac{5\pi}{3}$
8. $\sin 2x \sin x + \cos 2x \cos x = 1$ 0

Solve each inequality, where $0 \le x < 2\pi$.

9. $\sin x < 0$
$\pi < x < 2\pi$
10. $\tan x > 1$
$\frac{\pi}{4} < x < \frac{\pi}{2}, \frac{5\pi}{4} < x < \frac{3\pi}{2}$
11. $\sin x - \cos x < 0$
$0 \le x < \frac{\pi}{4}, \frac{\pi}{2} < x < \frac{5\pi}{4}, \frac{3\pi}{2} < x < 2\pi$
12. $\sin 2x > 0$
$0 < x < \frac{\pi}{2}, \pi < x < \frac{3\pi}{2}$

Practice Exercises Use appropriate technology.

Solve each equation, where $0 \le x < 2\pi$. If the equation does not have an exact solution, round to the nearest hundredth of a radian.

A **1.** $2 \cos x - 1 = 0$ $\frac{\pi}{3}, \frac{5\pi}{3}$
2. $2 \cos x - \sqrt{3} = 0$ $\frac{\pi}{6}, \frac{11\pi}{6}$
3. $\sin x - \frac{1}{2} = 0$ $\frac{\pi}{6}, \frac{5\pi}{6}$
4. $\sin x - \frac{\sqrt{3}}{2} = 0$ $\frac{\pi}{3}, \frac{2\pi}{3}$

314   Chapter 6 Trigonometric Identities and Equations

5. $\sqrt{2}\sec x = 2$ $\frac{\pi}{4}, \frac{7\pi}{4}$

6. $\sqrt{2}\csc x = 2$ $\frac{\pi}{4}, \frac{3\pi}{4}$

7. $1 + \sqrt{3}\tan x = 0$ $\frac{5\pi}{6}, \frac{11\pi}{6}$

8. $1 - \sqrt{3}\tan x = 0$ $\frac{\pi}{6}, \frac{7\pi}{6}$

9. $5\cos x + 11 = 4\cos x + 12$ 0

10. $16\sin x + 20 = 15\sin x + 19$ $\frac{3\pi}{2}$

11. $9\sin x - 1 = \sin x + 2$ $0.38, 2.76$

12. $20\cos x - 49 = 12\cos x - 60$ no solution

13. $3\tan x \sin x + \sin x = 0$ $0, 2.82, \pi, 5.96$

14. $\sec^2 x \cos x + \cos x - 2 = 0$ 0

15. $\sin 2x = \cos x$ $\frac{\pi}{6}, \frac{\pi}{2}, \frac{5\pi}{6}, \frac{3\pi}{2}$

16. $\sin 2x = -2\cos x$ $\frac{\pi}{2}, \frac{3\pi}{2}$

17. Solve triangle ABC given $a = 23$, $\angle B = 33°$, and $\angle C = 89°$. $\angle A = 58°$; $b = 14.8$; $c = 27.1$

18. *Robotics*   The angle with measure θ formed by the "elbow" of a robot arm can be represented by the formula $1.4\cos\theta + 1.25\cos 2\theta = 0$. Find θ, where $0° \le \theta \le 90°$. $61.3°$

19. Determine the amplitude, period, phase shift, and vertical shift for $y = 3\sin(2x + 2\pi) - 1$. $3; \pi; \pi$ left; 1 down

20. **Writing in Mathematics**   Explain why you should not divide both sides of the equation $\cos x \cot x = \cos x$ by the factor $\cos x$ when solving it.

Solve each inequality, where $0 \le x < 2\pi$.

21. $\cos x < 0$ $\frac{\pi}{2} < x < \frac{3\pi}{2}$

22. $\sin x > 0$ $0 < x < \pi$

23. $\sin x > \frac{\sqrt{3}}{2}$ $\frac{\pi}{3} < x < \frac{2\pi}{3}$

24. $\cos x < -\frac{\sqrt{3}}{2}$ $\frac{5\pi}{6} < x < \frac{7\pi}{6}$

25. Is the function $f(x) = x^5 + 2x^3 + 2x + 1$ even, odd, or neither? Explain your answer.

26. **Thinking Critically**   Why are you asked to solve equations on the interval $0 \le x < 2\pi$ instead of $0 \le x \le 2\pi$? 2π is coterminal with 0

Solve each equation, where $0 \le x < 2\pi$. If the equation does not have an exact solution, round to the nearest hundredth of a radian.

27. $\cos 3x = 1$ $0, \frac{2\pi}{3}, \frac{4\pi}{3}$

28. $\tan 3x = 2$

29. $\csc 2x = 2$ $\frac{\pi}{12}, \frac{5\pi}{12}, \frac{13\pi}{12}, \frac{17\pi}{12}$

30. $\sec 2x = -2$

31. $\cot 2x = 4$

32. $\tan 2x = -4$

33. *Aviation*   A jet plane took off at a rate of 300 ft/s and climbed in a straight path for 5.3 min. What was the angle of elevation of its path given that its final altitude was 15,000 ft? $9.05°$

34. **Thinking Critically**   Why does the equation $3\cos 2x = -7\sin x$ have only two solutions on the interval $0 \le x < 2\pi$ even though $3\cos 2x = -4\sin x + 1$ has three solutions on the same interval?

Solve each equation for all values of x.

35. $\sec x - 1 = \tan x$

36. $\sin 2x = 2\cos x$

37. $\sin 2x = \sin x$

38. $\cos x = \sec x$

39. $\tan x = \cot x$

40. $\sin 4x = \sin 2x$

41. $\cos 2x + \cos 4x = 0$ $\frac{\pi}{6} + n\pi, \frac{\pi}{2} + n\pi, \frac{5\pi}{6} + n\pi, n \in Z$

42. $\cos 2x \cos x + \sin 2x \sin x = \frac{1}{2}$ $\frac{\pi}{3} + 2n\pi, \frac{5\pi}{3} + 2n\pi, n \in Z$

43. $\cos 2x \cos x - \sin 2x \sin x = \frac{1}{2}$ $\frac{\pi}{9} + \frac{2n\pi}{3}, \frac{5\pi}{9} + \frac{2n\pi}{3}, n \in Z$

6.5 Solving Trigonometric Equations and Inequalities   **315**

---

4. $\tan 3x = \sqrt{3}$
$\frac{\pi}{9}, \frac{4\pi}{9}, \frac{7\pi}{9}, \frac{10\pi}{9}, \frac{13\pi}{9}, \frac{16\pi}{9}$

Find the solutions to the nearest hundredth of a radian.

5. $7\sin 2x + 2 = 10\sin 2x + 1$
$0.34 + 2n\pi, 2.8 + 2n\pi$ for $n \in Z$

6. $\csc^2 x - 15\csc x + 1 = 0$
$0.07 + 2n\pi, 3.07 + 2n\pi$ for $n \in Z$

Use a graphing utility to solve each equation.

7. $4 - \sec x = 0$, where $0° < x < 360°$

$75.5°, 284.5°$

8. $3\sin x = x + \frac{\pi}{6}$, where $0 < x < 2\pi$

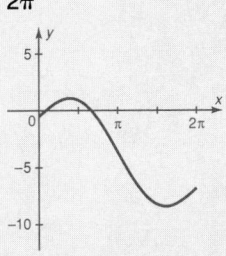

$0.27, 2.09$

Additional Answers

25. neither; $f(-x) \ne f(x)$; $f(-x) \ne -f(x)$

28. $0.37, 1.42, 2.46, 3.51, 4.56, 5.61$

30. $\frac{\pi}{3}, \frac{2\pi}{3}, \frac{4\pi}{3}, \frac{5\pi}{3}$

31. $0.12, 1.69, 3.26, 4.83$

32. $0.91, 2.48, 4.05, 5.62$

35. $2n\pi, n \in Z$

36. $\frac{\pi}{2} + n\pi, n \in Z$

37. $n\pi, \frac{\pi}{3} + 2n\pi, \frac{5\pi}{3} + 2n\pi, n \in Z$

38. $n\pi, n \in Z$

39. $\left(\frac{2n-1}{4}\right)\pi, n \in Z$

40. $\frac{n\pi}{2}, \frac{\pi}{6} + n\pi, \frac{5\pi}{6} + n\pi, n \in Z$

Writing in Mathematics

20. The solution $x = \frac{\pi}{2}$ would be omitted if both sides of the equation were first divided by $\cos x$.

44. *Electricity*   An electric generator produces an alternating current that can be described by the equation $C(t) = 20 \sin 45\pi \,(t - 0.1)$. Find the smallest positive value of t for which the current is 10 amperes. 0.0148

Ⓡ 45. Find the equation of the line that passes through the point (4, 3) and is tangent to the circle $x^2 + y^2 = 25$. 4x + 3y = 25

46. *Space Exploration*   Suppose that scientists want to check the accuracy of the sensors on the spacecraft discussed in the Focus. A spacecraft at E has located point S on the ground. Angle α determined by $\overline{ES}$ and $\overline{EB}$ is 28°. Angle β determined by $\overline{BS}$ and $\overline{BE}$ is 46°. To test the sensors, the scientists must calculate angle θ, the angle formed by the line segment to the horizon $\overline{DE}$ and the line segment $\overline{BE}$ to the center of the earth. This value of θ should equal the observed angle.

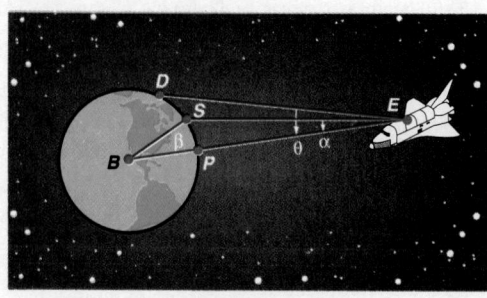

Angles α, β, and θ are related by the equation $\tan \alpha = \dfrac{\sin \theta \sin \beta}{1 - \sin \theta \cos \beta}$. Find θ. 29.2°

Ⓒ 47. *Physics*   An object is suspended on two connected springs whose vertical positions are represented by $y_1 = 1.6 \sin 2t$ and $y_2 = 4.6 \sin t$. The vertical position of the object is $y = y_1 + y_2$, or $y = 1.6 \sin 2t + 4.6 \sin t$. Find the first two values of t for which the object is at position $y = 0$. 0, π

Solve each equation, where $0 \le x < 2\pi$.

48. $\tan 4x - 1 = 0$

49. $\cos 2x \sin 3x = 0$

Solve each inequality for all values of x in the interval $[0, 2\pi]$.

50. $\tan x - 2 \le 0$

51. $\sqrt{3} \cot x - 1 \le 0$

52. $|\sin x| \le \dfrac{\sqrt{3}}{2}$

53. $|\cos x| \le \dfrac{\sqrt{3}}{2}$

54. $|\cos x| > \dfrac{3}{2}$

55. $\cos 3x + \cos x < 0$

56. $\sin 3x + \sin x < 0$

57. $\sin x \cos x \tan x < 0$

58. $\sin x \cos x \tan x \ge 0$

Challenge

1. Find the equation of the line that passes through the intersection points of the curves $y = \sin x$ and $y = \frac{1}{2} \sec x$ on the interval $0 \le x \le 2\pi$. $y = -\dfrac{\sqrt{2}}{\pi}x + \dfrac{3\sqrt{2}}{4}$

The new athletic director at Central High School was faced with the following problem. The initial basketball court maintenance fee is $500 and the one coach receives a salary of $750 for the season. The scorekeeper, timer, and statistician cost $220 per game played.

2. Determine the linear equation that represents the cost c of the basketball season in terms of the number of games g played. c = 1250 + 220g

3. The athletic department has budgeted $5000 for the basketball team. Determine the maximum number of games the team can play and stay within the budget. 17

6.6 Solving Trigonometric Equations and Inequalities in Quadratic Form

Objective: To solve trigonometric equations and inequalities in quadratic form

Focus

Although almost every species serves as food for some other species, predators and prey coexist over long periods of time. This fact is explained in part by the fact that prey have developed defenses such as poisonous chemicals, shells, or skins. Prey populations also use camouflage to avoid detection. In response to such defensive measures, predators have developed counterdefenses of their own, for example, stronger jaws and teeth, powerful digestive enzymes, and improved eyesight. Predator-prey relationships are important in establishing a stable natural population.

Eventually a prey population grows so large that its members become relatively easy for predators to find. Then more prey are eaten than are replaced by new births. As the prey's death rate becomes larger than its birthrate, its population diminishes. In response to the smaller prey population, some predators starve, causing a corresponding drop in the predator population. When a sufficiently small number of predators are left, the prey are again able to reproduce and survive in large numbers. The entire process then repeats itself.

Scientists A. J. Lotka and Vito Volterra have been modeling the predator-prey interactions of pairs of species since the 1920s. Periodic functions are sometimes used to represent the relative changes in predator-prey populations such as hawks and sparrows, wolves and caribou, foxes and rabbits, and even pitcher plants and flies.

Trigonometric equations that represent predator-prey interactions are often in quadratic form $ax^2 + bx + c = 0$ with the variable x replaced by a trigonometric expression. Algebraic techniques such as factoring can sometimes be used to solve such equations.

318

Alternative Learning Styles

- Some students may benefit from a review of the techniques for factoring quadratic expressions. Elicit from students several quadratic expressions using variables. For example:

  $x^2 + 3x + 1$ and $2y^2 - y - 15$

- Demonstrate how to factor each factorable expression. Then in the original expressions replace each variable with a trigonometric expression such as sin x and repeat the factoring procedures.

- You may wish to keep a list of several basic factoring forms on a side board for students' use.

GUIDED PRACTICE

For Example 1
Solve.

1. $2 \sin^2 x - \sin x - 1 = 0$

$\frac{\pi}{2} + 2n\pi, \frac{7\pi}{6} + 2n\pi, \frac{11\pi}{6} + 2n\pi, n \in Z$

2. $\tan^2 x - 2 \tan x + 1 = 0$

$\frac{\pi}{4} + n\pi, n \in Z$

For Example 2
Solve for x to the nearest hundredth of a radian, where $0 < x < 2\pi$.

1. $8 \sin^2 x - 5 \sin x - 1 = 0$
0.90, 2.24, 3.30, 6.12

2. $\sec^2 x + 14 \sec x + 7 = 0$
1.65, 4.63

Common Error Some students do not include all possible angle solutions, or they include angles not contained within the interval given in the directive. Have them closely analyze their answers after rereading the original question.

Example 1   Solve $2 \cos^2 x + 3 \cos x - 2 = 0$.

$$2 \cos^2 x + 3 \cos x - 2 = 0$$
$$(2 \cos x - 1)(\cos x + 2) = 0 \qquad \textit{Factor.}$$
$$2 \cos x - 1 = 0 \quad \text{or} \quad \cos x + 2 = 0$$
$$\cos x = \tfrac{1}{2} \quad \text{or} \quad \cos x = -2$$

$x = \dfrac{\pi}{3} + 2n\pi, \ n \in Z$ 　　*Since $-1 \leq \cos x \leq 1$ for all values of x, $\cos x = -2$*

or 　　　　　　　　　　　　　　*has no solution.*

$x = \dfrac{5\pi}{3} + 2n\pi, \ n \in Z$

Trigonometric equations in quadratic form $ax^2 + bx + c = 0$ are not always factorable. However, you can solve them with the quadratic formula $x = \dfrac{-b \pm \sqrt{b^2 - 4ac}}{2a}$.

Example 2   Solve $2 \sin^2 x = 1 + 2 \sin x$ to the nearest hundredth of a radian, where $0 \leq x < 2\pi$.

$$2 \sin^2 x = 1 + 2 \sin x$$
$$2 \sin^2 x - 2 \sin x - 1 = 0 \qquad a = 2, \ b = -2, \ c = -1$$
$$\sin x = \frac{-(-2) \pm \sqrt{(-2)^2 - 4(2)(-1)}}{2(2)} \qquad \textit{Quadratic formula}$$
$$\sin x = \frac{2 \pm \sqrt{4 + 8}}{4}$$
$$\sin x = \frac{2 \pm \sqrt{12}}{4} = \frac{2 \pm 2\sqrt{3}}{4}$$
$$\sin x = \frac{1 + \sqrt{3}}{2} = 1.3660 \qquad \textit{Reject.}$$

or

$$\sin x = \frac{1 - \sqrt{3}}{2} = -0.3660$$

$x = -0.3747$ 　　*This calculator result is a fourth-quadrant value but is not in the domain.*

$x = \pi + 0.3747 = 3.52$ 　　*Third-quadrant value*

or

$x = 2\pi - 0.3747 = 5.91$ 　　*Fourth-quadrant value*

Why is $\sin x = 1.3660$ rejected?

You can also use a graphing utility to solve quadratic trigonometric equations. Use the amplitude and period to help you select an appropriate viewing rectangle. When you use the zoom feature of a graphing utility to find an apparent zero, you may find that the graph does not in fact intersect the x-axis, so that there is no zero there.

318   Chapter 6 Trigonometric Identities and Equations

Example 3   Use a graphing utility to solve $10 \sin^2 x = 11 \sin x - 0.9$ to the nearest hundredth of a radian, where $-\pi \le x \le 2\pi$.

Express the equation in function-form as $10 \sin^2 x - 11 \sin x + 0.9 = 0$.
The graph appears to intersect the x-axis at three points in the interval $[-\pi, 2\pi]$.

$[-\pi, 2\pi]$ by $[-4, 25]$
x scl: $\frac{\pi}{2}$ y scl: 5

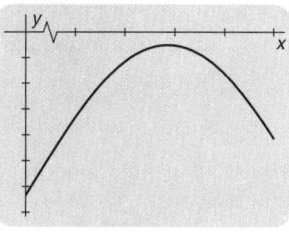

$[1, 2]$ by $[-1.4, 0]$
x scl: 0.2 y scl: 0.2

Use the zoom and trace features to verify this assumption and to obtain your answers to the nearest hundredth. Zooming in on the first point yields 0.09. Zooming in on the third point yields 3.05. However, when you zoom in on the middle point as shown at the right above, you find that the graph does not intersect the x-axis.

Modeling

An environmentalist is studying the populations of rabbits and foxes in the same region over a certain time period. How can she determine the size of each population at a given time?

The graphs below model the respective populations. Notice that both populations are increasing at the start of the study. As the fox population reaches a certain level, the rabbit population begins to decline. The decline in rabbit population then leads to a later decline in the fox population to a level where the complete cycle begins again. If all other factors remain unchanged, the two populations are likely to continue this periodic rise and fall.

6.6 Solving Trigonometric Equations and Inequalities in Quadratic Form   **319**

For Example 4

The birth rate of a particular insect is determined from the function $f(t) = 0.8 \sin^2 t - 3 \sin t + 3$, and the death rate is represented by $f(t) = -0.4 \sin t + \cos t + 3$. Determine all values of t, to the nearest hundredth of a radian, for which the birth rate equals the death rate.

$2.73 + 2n\pi, 5.95 + 2n\pi, n \in Z$

For Example 5

Solve each inequality to the nearest hundredth of a radian.

1. $3 \cos^2 x > 2x - 1$ $\{x: x < 0.97\}$

2. $\sin^2 x < x^2 - 3$
$\{x: x < -1.96 \text{ or } x > 1.96\}$

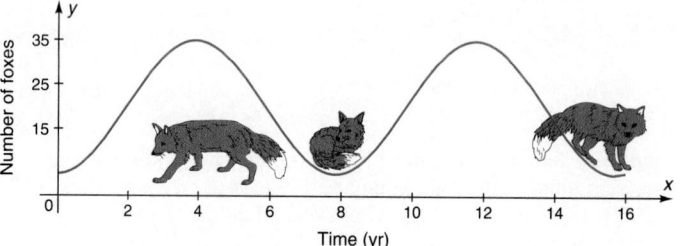

This model does not utilize information about changes in the food supply, other predators in the region, or the complex environment surrounding these two populations.

Environmentalists are often interested in the birth and death rates that influence the population size of a given species.

Example 4   *Biology*   The birthrate for a bird species is represented by $f(t) = 0.9 \cos^2 t + 2 \cos t + 2$, and the death rate by $f(t) = -0.7 \cos 2t + 2$. Determine all the values of t, to the nearest hundredth of a radian, for which the birthrate equals the death rate.

Use a graphing utility to graph

$y = 0.9 \cos^2 t + 2 \cos t + 2$ and $y = -0.7 \cos 2t + 2$

The graphs intersect at $1.30 + 2n\pi$ and $4.98 + 2n\pi$, $n \in Z$.

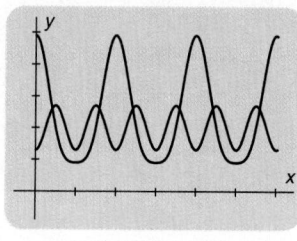

[0, 19] by [−1, 6]
x scl: $\frac{\pi}{2}$ y scl: 1

The techniques developed above can also be applied to trigonometric inequalities in quadratic form.

Example 5   Solve $2 \sin^2 x > x + 1$ on the interval $-2\pi \le 0 < 2\pi$, to the nearest hundredth of a radian.

Express $2 \sin^2 x > x + 1$ in function-form as $2 \sin^2 x - x - 1 > 0$. Then use a graphing utility to graph $y = 2 \sin^2 x - x - 1$.

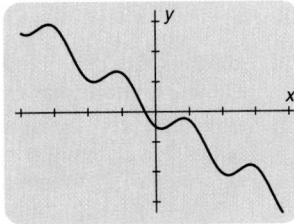

The graph intersects the x-axis between -1 and 0. Use the zoom and trace features to obtain $x = -0.51$, to the nearest hundredth.

Looking at the graph, you can see that $2 \sin^2 x - x - 1 > 0$ for all values of x to the left of -0.51. Thus, the solution set is $\{x: x < -0.51\}$.

$[-2\pi, 2\pi]$ by $[-6, 6]$
x scl: $\frac{\pi}{2}$ y scl: 2

Class Exercises

Solve each trigonometric equation, where $0 \le x < 2\pi$. If the equation does not have an exact solution, round to the nearest hundredth of a radian.

1. $4 \sin^2 x - 3 = 0$ $\frac{\pi}{3}, \frac{2\pi}{3}, \frac{4\pi}{3}, \frac{5\pi}{3}$ **2.** $4 \cos^2 x - 3 = 0$ $\frac{\pi}{6}, \frac{5\pi}{6}, \frac{7\pi}{6}, \frac{11\pi}{6}$

3. $2 \cos^2 x + 3 \cos x + 1 = 0$ $\frac{2\pi}{3}, \pi, \frac{4\pi}{3}$ **4.** $2 \sin^2 x + 3 \sin x + 1 = 0$ $\frac{7\pi}{6}, \frac{3\pi}{2}, \frac{11\pi}{6}$

5. $2 \cos^2 x - 3 \sin x - 3 = 0$ $\frac{7\pi}{6}, \frac{3\pi}{2}, \frac{11\pi}{6}$ **6.** $2 \sin^2 x - \cos x - 1 = 0$ $\frac{\pi}{3}, \pi, \frac{5\pi}{3}$

7. $2 \tan^2 x - 3 \sec x + 3 = 0$ 0   **8.** $2 \tan x - 2 \cot x = -3$ 0.46, 2.03, 3.60, 5.17

9. $\sin^2 x + \cos x = 0$ 2.24, 4.05   **10.** $\cos^2 x + \sin x = 0$ 3.81, 5.62

Solve each trigonometric inequality, where $0 \le x < 2\pi$.

$0 \le x \le \frac{\pi}{6}$ or $\frac{5\pi}{6} \le x \le 2\pi$

11. $2 \sin^2 x - \cos x - 1 \ge 0$ $\frac{\pi}{3} \le x \le \frac{5\pi}{3}$ **12.** $2 \cos^2 x - 3 \sin x \ge 0$

13. $\sin^2 x - \sin x \le 0$ $0 \le x \le \pi$ **14.** $2 - 2 \sin^2 x + 3 \cos x + 1 \ge 0$

$\frac{2\pi}{3} \ge x \ge 0, \ x = \pi, \ 2\pi > x \ge \frac{4\pi}{3}$

Practice Exercises   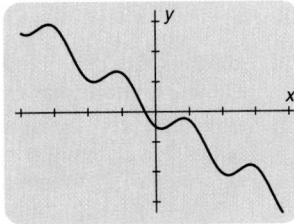 Use appropriate technology.

Solve each trigonometric equation, where $0 \le x < 2\pi$. If the equation does not have an exact solution, round to the nearest hundredth of a radian.

A 1. $\sin^2 x - \sin x - 2 = 0$ $\frac{3\pi}{2}$ **2.** $\cos^2 x - \cos x - 2 = 0$

3. $4 \cos^2 x = 1$ $\frac{\pi}{3}, \frac{2\pi}{3}, \frac{4\pi}{3}, \frac{5\pi}{3}$ **4.** $4 \sin^2 x = 1$

5. $2 \sin^2 x - 5 \sin x - 3 = 0$ $\frac{7\pi}{6}, \frac{11\pi}{6}$ **6.** $2 \cos^2 x + 3 \cos x - 2 = 0$

7. $\sec^2 x - 2 \sec x = 0$ $\frac{\pi}{3}, \frac{5\pi}{3}$ **8.** $\tan^2 x - \sec x = 1$

9. $2 \cos^2 2x + \cos 2x - 1 = 0$ **10.** $2 \sin^2 2x + \sin 2x - 1 = 0$

11. $\sin^2 \frac{x}{2} = \cos x$ 1.23, 5.05   **12.** $\cos^2 \frac{x}{2} = \cos x$ 0

13. $\cos 2x - \sin x = 0$ $\frac{\pi}{6}, \frac{5\pi}{6}, \frac{3\pi}{2}$ **14.** $\cos 2x - \sin x = 1$ 0, π, $\frac{7\pi}{6}, \frac{11\pi}{6}$

R 15. *Physics*   Find the linear velocity V of a point located 14 in. from the center of a disk rotating at 8π rad/s. 112π in./s

Additional Answers, Practice Exercises

2. π **4.** $\frac{\pi}{6}, \frac{5\pi}{6}, \frac{7\pi}{6}, \frac{11\pi}{6}$ **6.** $\frac{\pi}{3}, \frac{5\pi}{3}$

8. $\pi, \frac{\pi}{3}, \frac{5\pi}{3}$ **9.** $\frac{\pi}{6}, \frac{5\pi}{6}, \frac{7\pi}{6}, \frac{11\pi}{6}, \frac{\pi}{2}, \frac{3\pi}{2}$ **10.** $\frac{\pi}{12}, \frac{5\pi}{12}, \frac{3\pi}{4}, \frac{13\pi}{12}, \frac{17\pi}{12}, \frac{7\pi}{4}$

CLOSURE

Pair students and have them discuss the procedures for solving trigonometric equations in quadratic form using algebraic techniques and using a graphing utility, and then compare the advantages and disadvantages of each method.

INDEPENDENT PRACTICE

Assignment Guide

Basic: 1–26
Average: 1–31 odd, 32–38, Project
Enriched: 9–37 odd, 38–48, Project

Teacher's Resource Book
   Practice, page 42

R Review
Exercises 15, 21, 33, 37, and 38 review concepts such as finding linear velocity solving mixture problems, analyzing graphs and domains of trigonometric functions, and proving trigonometric identities studied in previous lessons.

Project

To enhance the project, have students investigate drastic changes in the populations of various species. This may involve sudden population growth, such as that of the white-tailed deer. It also may involve sudden population decline, such as that being experienced by many species in the Amazon forests. Have the students speculate as to reasons for these changes.

Solve each trigonometric inequality, where $0 \leq x < 2\pi$. If the equation does not have an exact solution, round to the nearest hundredth of a radian.

16. $2 \cos^2 x - 1 \leq 0$

17. $2 \sin^2 x + 1 \geq 0$ all real x

18. $\sin^2 x \leq x$ $x \geq 0$

19. $\cos^2 x \geq x$ $0 \leq x \leq 0.64$

20. **Thinking Critically** Provide an example of a trigonometric equation in quadratic form that has exponents other than the numbers 1 and 2. ex: $\sin^6 x + 5 \sin^3 x + 6 = 0$

Ⓡ 21. *Pharmacology* A pharmacist has 50 ml of a 6% alcohol solution. If he needs to have a more concentrated solution, how much water should be evaporated so that the remaining solution is 10% alcohol? 20 ml

Solve each trigonometric equation for all values of x. If the equation does not have an exact solution, round to the nearest hundredth of a radian.

B 22. $3 \cot^2 x - 1 = 0$

23. $3 \sec^2 x - 4 = 0$

24. $\cos^2 x + \cos 2x = -\frac{1}{2}$

25. $\cos^2 x + \cos 2x = -1$

26. $\sin^2 x + \sin x + 1 = 0$

27. $\cos^2 x + \cos x + 1 = 0$

28. $8 \tan^2 x - 3 = 7 \tan 2x + 21$

29. $12 \cot^2 x - 6 = 2 \cot 2x - 9$

30. $\csc^2 x = -7 \csc x - 10$

31. $\sec^2 x = -10 \sec x - 16$

32. **Writing in Mathematics** Discuss the information that can be obtained by graphing the sum of the functions that represent the birth and death rates for a specific species.

Ⓡ 33. How do the domains of the sine and cosine functions differ from those of the other four trigonometric functions?

Physics The acceleration of an object due to gravity g at a particular place can be expressed as a function of the object's latitude and its elevation above sea level as follows: $g = 980.616 - 2.5928 \cos 2\alpha + 0.0069 \cos^2 2\alpha - 0.000003086h$, where α is the latitude (north or south) in degrees, h is the elevation above sea level in centimeters, and g is in centimeters per second per second.

Determine the acceleration due to gravity at each of the following:

34. At sea level on the equator. 978.0301 cm/s²

35. At sea level at a latitude of 42° N. 980.3451 cm/s²

36. At an elevation of 2000 m and a latitude of 42° N. 980.2833 cm/s²

Ⓡ 37. Prove: $\dfrac{\cos 5\alpha}{\sin 5\alpha} = \dfrac{\sin 8\alpha - \sin 2\alpha}{\cos 2\alpha - \cos 8\alpha}$

Ⓡ 38. Find the exact value of $\cos \frac{\alpha}{2}$ if $\cos \alpha = \frac{3}{5}$ and α lies in the fourth quadrant. $-\frac{2\sqrt{5}}{5}$

Solve each trigonometric inequality, where $0 \leq x < 2\pi$. If possible, express the solution in terms of π. Otherwise round to the nearest hundredth of a radian.

C 39. $2 \sin^2 x + 3 \sin x - 2 \geq 0$ $\frac{\pi}{6} \leq x \leq \frac{5\pi}{6}$

40. $2 \sin^2 x + \sin x + 3 \leq 0$ no solution

41. $2 \cos^2 x + \cos x + 3 \geq 0$ all real x

42. $2 \cos^2 x + 3 \cos x - 2 \leq 0$ $\frac{\pi}{3} \leq x \leq \frac{5\pi}{3}$

43. $\sin^3 x \geq 0$ $0 \leq x \leq \pi$

44. $\cos^3 x \leq 0$ $\frac{\pi}{2} \leq x \leq \frac{3\pi}{2}$

322   Chapter 6 Trigonometric Identities and Equations

Writing in Mathematics

32. By graphing the difference of the functions that represent the birth rates and death rates, you can easily see the points for which the birth rate equals the death rate by finding the x-intercepts.

Solve each equation to the nearest hundredth of a radian, where $0 \leq x < 2\pi$.

45. $8 \tan^2 3x - 17 \tan 3x + 3 = 0$

46. $5 \sin^2 (2x + 1) + 2 \sin (2x + 1) - 1 = 0$

47. $3 \cos^2 (2x - 1) + 12 \cos (2x - 1) - 3 = 0$ 1.17, 2.98, 4.31, 6.12

48. Thinking Critically Find two trigonometric equations that have graphs that appear to intersect at a particular point but in fact do not intersect. At least one of the equations should be quadratic. Use the zoom feature on your graphing utility to show that the graphs do not intersect.

Project

Describe the effects on both the predator and prey populations if some of a specific species of prey are removed from one part of the world and transported to another. Is there more than one possible outcome? What happened when rabbits were transported to Australia?

Test Yourself

Express each product as a sum or difference.

1. $2 \cos \frac{5\pi}{12} \cos \frac{6\pi}{12}$ $\cos \frac{\pi}{12} + \cos \frac{11\pi}{12}$

2. $2 \sin \frac{7\pi}{13} \sin \frac{6\pi}{13}$ $\cos \frac{\pi}{13} - \cos \pi$ 6.4

Express each sum or difference as a product.

3. $\sin 7.2 - \sin 3.5$ $2 \cos 5.35 \sin 1.85$

4. $\cos \frac{5\pi}{6} + \cos \frac{\pi}{6}$ $2 \cos \frac{\pi}{2} \cos \frac{\pi}{3}$

Solve each equation, where $0 \leq x < 2\pi$. If the equation does not have an exact solution, round to the nearest hundredth of a radian.

5. $2 \cos^2 x + \cos x = 2$ 0.67, 5.61

6. $1 - \sqrt{3} \cot x = 0$ $\frac{\pi}{3}, \frac{4\pi}{3}$ 6.5

7. $5 \cos x - 2 = \cos x + 1$ 0.72, 5.56

8. $\cos 2x = \frac{1}{2}$ $\frac{\pi}{6}, \frac{5\pi}{6}, \frac{7\pi}{6}, \frac{11\pi}{6}$

Solve each trigonometric equation or inequality, where $0 \leq x < 2\pi$. If there is no exact solution, round to the nearest hundredth of a radian.

9. $2 \sin^2 x - 9 \sin x - 5 = 0$ $\frac{7\pi}{6}, \frac{11\pi}{6}$

10. $2 \cos^3 x + 3 \cos x - 3 = 0$ 0.75, 5.54 6.6

11. $2 \cos^2 x > x - 2$ $0 \leq x \leq 3.62$

12. $3 \sin^2 x > x - 1$ $0 \leq x < 2.39$

6.6 Solving Trigonometric Equations and Inequalities in Quadratic Form **323**

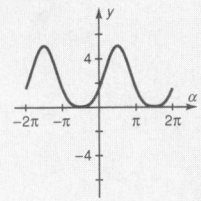
323

Chapter 6   Summary and Review

Vocabulary

difference identity for cosine (287)

difference identity for sine (287)

difference identity for tangent (288)

double-angle identities (298)

half-angle identities (299)

product/sum identities (306)

sum identity for cosine (287)

sum identity for sine (287)

sum identity for tangent (288)

Sum and Difference Identities

$$\cos(\alpha + \beta) = \cos\alpha\cos\beta - \sin\alpha\sin\beta$$

$$\cos(\alpha - \beta) = \cos\alpha\cos\beta + \sin\alpha\sin\beta$$

$$\sin(\alpha + \beta) = \sin\alpha\cos\beta + \cos\alpha\sin\beta$$

$$\sin(\alpha - \beta) = \sin\alpha\cos\beta - \cos\alpha\sin\beta$$

$$\tan(\alpha + \beta) = \frac{\tan\alpha + \tan\beta}{1 - \tan\alpha\tan\beta}$$

$$\tan(\alpha - \beta) = \frac{\tan\alpha - \tan\beta}{1 + \tan\alpha\tan\beta}$$

6.1

Use a sum or difference identity to find the exact value for each trigonometric function.

1. $\sin\dfrac{17\pi}{12}$ $\dfrac{-\sqrt{6} - \sqrt{2}}{4}$

2. $\tan 345°$ $-2 + \sqrt{3}$

Find the exact value for each trigonometric expression given that $\sin\alpha = -\dfrac{7}{25}$, $\tan\beta = \dfrac{3}{4}$, $\pi \le \alpha \le \dfrac{3\pi}{2}$, and $0 \le \beta \le \dfrac{\pi}{2}$.

3. $\cos(\alpha - \beta)$ $-\dfrac{117}{125}$

4. $\sin(\alpha + \beta)$ $-\dfrac{4}{5}$

5. Prove: $\sin\left(\dfrac{3\pi}{2} + \alpha\right) = -\cos\alpha$

Verifying Identities Graphically   If the graphs of the two sides of an equation appear to be identical, it is likely that the equation is an identity. If the graphs are not the same, the equation is not an identity.

6.2

Use a graphing utility to determine whether each equation appears to be an identity.

6. $\dfrac{\sin\alpha}{1 + \sec\alpha} = \dfrac{\sin\alpha\,\cos\alpha}{\cos\alpha + 1}$ yes

7. $(1 - \cos\beta)^2 = (\sin\beta - \tan\beta)^2$ no

Double-Angle and Half-Angle Identities

6.3

$$\sin 2\alpha = 2\sin\alpha\cos\alpha$$

$$\sin\frac{\alpha}{2} = \pm\sqrt{\frac{1 - \cos\alpha}{2}}$$

$$\tan 2\alpha = \frac{2\tan\alpha}{1 - \tan^2\alpha},\ \tan\alpha \ne \pm 1$$

$$\cos\frac{\alpha}{2} = \pm\sqrt{\frac{1 + \cos\alpha}{2}}$$

$$\cos 2\alpha = \cos^2 \alpha - \sin^2 \alpha \qquad\qquad \tan \frac{\alpha}{2} = \pm\sqrt{\frac{1 - \cos \alpha}{1 + \cos \alpha}},\ \cos \alpha \neq -1$$

$$\cos 2\alpha = 2\cos^2 \alpha - 1 \qquad\qquad\qquad \tan \frac{\alpha}{2} = \frac{1 - \cos \alpha}{\sin \alpha},\ \sin \alpha \neq 0$$

$$\cos 2\alpha = 1 - 2\sin^2 \alpha \qquad\qquad\qquad \tan \frac{\alpha}{2} = \frac{\sin \alpha}{1 + \cos \alpha},\ \cos \alpha \neq -1$$

Use double-angle or half-angle identities to find the exact value of each trigonometric expression.

8. Given $\sin \alpha = -\frac{24}{25}$ and $\frac{3\pi}{2} \leq \alpha \leq 2\pi$, find $\sin 2\alpha$. $-\frac{336}{625}$

9. Given $\tan \alpha = \frac{4}{3}$ and $\pi \leq \alpha \leq \frac{3\pi}{2}$, find $\tan \frac{\alpha}{2}$. -2

10. Prove: $\tan \frac{\beta}{2} = \csc \beta - \cot \beta$

Product/Sum Identities $\qquad\qquad\qquad\qquad\qquad\qquad\qquad\qquad\qquad$ 6.4

$$2\cos \alpha \cos \beta = \cos (\alpha - \beta) + \cos (\alpha + \beta)$$
$$2\sin \alpha \sin \beta = \cos (\alpha - \beta) - \cos (\alpha + \beta)$$
$$2\sin \alpha \cos \beta = \sin (\alpha + \beta) + \sin (\alpha - \beta)$$
$$2\cos \alpha \sin \beta = \sin (\alpha + \beta) - \sin (\alpha - \beta)$$

There are also alternate forms for the product/sum identities.

Express each product as a sum or difference.

11. $2 \sin \frac{\pi}{3} \sin \frac{\pi}{4}$ $\cos \frac{\pi}{12} - \cos \frac{7\pi}{12}$ $\qquad\qquad$ 12. $2 \sin 75° \cos 105°$ $\sin 180° - \sin 30°$

Express each sum or difference as a product.

13. $\sin \frac{17\pi}{6} + \sin \frac{7\pi}{6}$ $2 \sin 2\pi \cos \frac{5\pi}{6}$ $\qquad\qquad$ 14. $\cos 7.6 - \cos 1.5$ $-2 \sin 4.55 \sin 3.05$

15. Prove: $\dfrac{\cos 2\alpha}{\cos 6\alpha} = \dfrac{\sin 2\alpha + \sin 6\alpha}{\sin 10\alpha - \sin 2\alpha}$

Solving Trigonometric Equations and Inequalities Many trigonometric equations and $\quad$ 6.5
inequalities can be solved using algebraic techniques combined with trigonometric identities.

Solve each trigonometric equation or inequality, where $0 \leq x < 2\pi$.

16. $11 \csc x + 15 = 9 \csc x + 19$ $\frac{\pi}{6}, \frac{5\pi}{6}$ $\qquad\qquad$ 17. $1 - 2 \cos x > 0$ $\frac{\pi}{3} < x < \frac{5\pi}{3}$

Solving Trigonometric Equations and Inequalities in Quadratic Form Trigonometric $\quad$ 6.6
equations and inequalities in quadratic form can be solved using factoring, the
quadratic formula, or graphing.

Solve each trigonometric equation or inequality to the nearest hundredth of a
radian, where $0 \leq x < 2\pi$.

18. $5 \sin^2 x - \sin x - 5 = 0$ 4.27, 5.15 $\qquad\qquad$ 19. $\cos^2 x > x - 1$ $0 \leq x < 1.16$

Summary and Review **325**

Chapter 6 Test

Use a sum or difference identity to find the exact value for each trigonometric expression.

1. $\sin \dfrac{7\pi}{12}$ $\dfrac{\sqrt{6}+\sqrt{2}}{4}$

2. $\cos \dfrac{11\pi}{12}$ $\dfrac{-\sqrt{6}-\sqrt{2}}{4}$

3. $\tan 315°$ -1

4. Find the exact value of $\sin(\alpha + \beta)$ given that $\sin \alpha = \dfrac{3}{5}$, $\cos \beta = -\dfrac{12}{13}$,

$\dfrac{\pi}{2} \le \alpha \le \pi$, and $\pi \le \beta \le \dfrac{3\pi}{2}$. $-\dfrac{16}{65}$

Use a graphing utility to determine whether each trigonometric expression appears to be an identity.

5. $\tan(\alpha + \pi) = \cot \alpha$ no

6. $\dfrac{\cos \alpha}{\sec \alpha} - \dfrac{\cot \alpha}{\tan \alpha} = -\cos^2 \alpha \cot^2 \alpha$ yes

Use double-angle or half-angle identities to find the exact value of each trigonometric expression.

7. If $\tan \theta = -\dfrac{12}{5}$ and $\dfrac{3\pi}{2} \le \theta \le 2\pi$, find $\tan \dfrac{\theta}{2}$. $-\dfrac{2}{3}$

8. If $\sin \alpha = \dfrac{7}{25}$ and $\dfrac{\pi}{2} \le \alpha \le \pi$, find $\sin 2\alpha$. $-\dfrac{336}{625}$

9. Prove: $\tan 2\beta = \dfrac{\sin 3\beta + \sin \beta}{\cos \beta + \cos 3\beta}$

10. Express $2\cos 6x \cos x$ as a sum. $\cos 5x + \cos 7x$

11. Express $\sin 92° - \sin 11°$ as a product. $2\cos 51.5° \sin 40.5°$

Solve each trigonometric equation or inequality, where $0 \le x < 2\pi$. If there is no exact solution, round to the nearest hundredth.

12. $12 \tan x - 8 = 10 \tan x - 10$ $\dfrac{3\pi}{4}, \dfrac{7\pi}{4}$

13. $2\sin^2 x + \sin x - 2 = 0$ 0.90, 2.24

14. $3\sin^2 x < x - 4$ $5.47 < x < 6.28$

Challenge

How many solutions does $5\sin^2(3x + 1) + 2\sin(3x + 1) - 1 = 0$ have on the interval $0 \le x < 2\pi$? 12

Cumulative Review

1. Determine the length of the 40° parallel that passes through Philadelphia, Pennsylvania, to the nearest whole number. 30,804 km 5.1

2. Rewrite as an algebraic expression: $y = \sin(\text{Sec}^{-1} t)$ $\frac{\sqrt{t^2 - 1}}{t}$ 4.6

3. Evaluate: $\sin 630°$ −1 3.4

4. Can the number line be expressed as $(-\infty, \infty)$? yes 1.7

5. Determine the semiperimeter of triangle ABC, where $a = 18$, $b = 6$, and $c = 24$. 24 5.5

6. Use a sum or difference identity to find an exact value for the trigonometric expression $\sin 195°$. $\frac{\sqrt{2} - \sqrt{6}}{4}$ 6.1

7. What is the number and nature of solutions of a quadratic equation if the discriminant $b^2 - 4ac < 0$? 2, imaginary 2.4

8. Use the law of cosines to find $\angle B$, to the nearest degree, in triangle ABC if $a = 16$, $c = 24$, and $b = 8$. 49° 5.3

9. Define an angle of elevation. The acute angle measured from a horizontal line up to the line of sight. 5.1

10. The angle of elevation of the top of a church steeple from its base is 70°. If the base is 10-ft square, what is the height of the steeple? 13.7 ft. 5.1

11. Express $2 \cos x \cos 5x$ in terms of sums. cos 4x + cos 6x 6.4

12. Find the domain of the function $f(x) = \frac{x}{x^2 - 16}$. $D = \{x: x \neq \pm 4\}$ 1.4

13. Use a graphing utility to determine whether the equation $1 + \tan^2 \theta = \sec^2 \theta$ appears to be an identity. yes 6.2

14. As θ increases from π to 2π, $\cos \theta$ increases from __?__. −1 to 1 4.1

15. Find the value of $\cos \theta$ if $\sin \theta = -\frac{4}{9}$ and θ is in standard position with terminal side in quadrant III. $-\frac{\sqrt{65}}{9}$ 3.4

16. Use the double-angle formula to express $\frac{\tan 3x}{1 - \tan^2 3x}$ as a single function. $\frac{1}{2}$ tan 6x 6.3

17. Graph: $h(x) = \tan \frac{2}{3}x$. 4.3

18. $\cos \theta = \frac{\text{length of adjacent side to } \theta}{\underline{\quad ? \quad}}$ length of the hypotenuse 5.1

19. Determine the number of revolutions per minute of a wheel with an angular velocity of 48.2 rad/s. 460.28 rpm 3.3

20. If $\sin x = \frac{3}{5}$ and $\cos x < 0$, find $\sin 2x$. $-\frac{24}{25}$ 6.3

21. If three sides of a triangle are known, Heron's formula can be used to find the length of an __?__. altitude 5.5

22. The point where the parabola intersects the axis of symmetry is called the __?__. vertex 2.5

23. Solve $\tan^2 \theta + 3 \tan \theta - 18 = 0$, where $0 \leq \theta \leq 2\pi$, to the nearest hundredth of a radian. 1.25, 1.74, 4.39, 4.88 6.6

Cumulative Review **327**

Summary

Synthetic substitution, synthetic division, the factor theorem, and the remainder theorem are presented and used. Considerable material involving integral, rational, real, and complex zeros of polynomials is introduced. Graphs of polynomial and rational functions are analyzed and radical equations are solved graphically. Concepts involving the graphs of continuous and noncontinuous functions are explored. Methods of decomposing partial fractions are also studied.

Chapter Objectives

- To evaluate a polynomial for a given value of the variable using synthetic substitution
- To divide polynomials by first degree binomials using synthetic division
- To prove and apply the remainder and factor theorems
- To graph polynomial functions
- To identify equations of polynomial functions from their graphs
- To determine the rational zeros of a polynomial function
- To state and apply the fundamental theorem of algebra
- To apply theorems about the zeros of polynomial functions
- To approximate zeros of polynomial functions
- To determine asymptotes and points of discontinuity of rational functions
- To graph rational functions
- To graph radical functions
- To solve radical equations
- To decompose a fraction into a sum of partial fractions

7 Polynomial Functions

Mathematical Power

Modeling   Human learning and memory are quite remarkable. Think about what happens when you are asked to name members of a certain group—for example, flowers, ice cream flavors, last year's movies, or famous scientists. The items that you mention would probably occur in blocks or partial lists, with distinct pauses between the blocks. For example, when naming flowers, you might start out by saying

> rose, daisy, tulip, carnation

Then, after a pause, you could continue by listing

> orchid, marigold, violet

Then another pause while you think and come up with

> daffodil, petunia, snapdragon, zinnia

No doubt you began by mentioning the flowers with which you are most familiar; then, as you had to mentally search for less common items, the pauses occurred. And, while thinking, you may have been forming subgroups in your mind to help you—flowers in the garden, flowers used at weddings, and so on.

Psychologists who have studied this behavior call the pause, or time between one block of words and another, the *interresponse time*. Moreover, based on extensive research, they have defined a function to model the length of each pause and the number of words in each partial list. For each time interval t,

328

Features

Modeling

7.3 Manufacturing
7.6 Architecture

$f(t)$ = average number of words that occur in succession before an interresponse of time t or longer

If you plot t on the horizontal axis and $f(t)$ on the vertical axis, the graph will look like the one shown. The best-fitting curve for the graph is a *third degree polynomial*:

$$f(t) = At^3 + Bt^2 + Ct + D$$

Finding a polynomial that accurately represents a set of data is a particularly useful step in the modeling process. Once the polynomial is found, its graph can be closely analyzed to reveal various qualities of the real world situation that gave rise to the original data set.

Thinking Critically   Can you describe a situation in which the type of memory model described above might be useful?

Project   Conduct your own experiments to approximate interresponse times for different types of lists. Ask several people to give verbal lists for categories you select. You might try using one easy category, such as vegetables or television programs, and one category that is more difficult, such as famous mathematicians or bird species. Record values for interresponse times using a stopwatch if one is available. Determine if there is any clear pattern present in the data you find and if your results are consistent with the ideas in the introduction. How might you explain inconsistencies? What other conclusions can you draw?

329

In order to find mathematical models to describe the data collected in many real world situations, functions of degree greater than 2 must be considered. For any finite set of data points, there are methods to determine the degree and equation of a polynomial function whose graph contains those points. Graphing utilities are extremely useful for finding the polynomial of best fit for a data set. Point out that, unlike linear or quadratic functions, higher order polynomials of the same degree can have many different shapes.

Explain that in the memory example, each coefficient (A, B, C, D) and each exponent would have a meaning that relates to the actual data in the experiment. Caution students they cannot assume that arbitrary points on the graph of the polynomial will correspond to interresponse times; only for actual data points is the correspondence necessarily true. Be sure students understand the meaning of $f(t)$. Note that the definition implies that the pause between words in the same block is generally shorter than the pause between one block and the next.

Thinking Critically   Answers may vary. One situation in which the memory model might be used is in designing a memory game or game show.

Review and Assessment

Student Text
- Test Yourself   355, 379
- Summary and Review   380–381
- Chapter Test   382

Teacher's Resource Book
- Tests   25–28
- Practice   43–50

Vocabulary

depressed polynomial
factor theorem
remainder theorem
synthetic division
synthetic substitution

Technology

graphing utility
symbolic manipulator

FOCUS

Have students research what is meant by NP-complete problems. This may provide students with an appreciation of the algorithms presented in this chapter.

INSTRUCTION

- Draw a graph of a polynomial function such as $p(x) = x^2 + x - 10$ on the chalkboard or overhead projector. State that $(1, p(1))$, $(2, p(2))$, and so on are coordinates for points on the graph. Have students graph $p(x)$ on a graphing utility and use the trace function to read out coordinates for points on the graph. Point out that the second value is the function value.

- Discuss how the division algorithm for numbers can be applied to polynomials.

- Point out that dividing a polynomial by a linear factor such as $x + 2$ is the same as evaluating the polynomial at $x = -2$.

- Note that the answers to Examples 3 and 4 are written in the form: dividend = (divisor)(quotient) + remainder. Using this form will help to prepare students for the factor theorem.

7.1 Synthetic Division and the Remainder and Factor Theorems

Objectives: To evaluate a polynomial for a given value of the variable using synthetic substitution

To divide polynomials by first degree binomials using synthetic division

To prove and apply the remainder and factor theorems

Focus

Computer programmers assess the running time for an algorithm. Some programs, with loops that repeat over and over, can take many hours to run. The *complexity function* measures the cost, in terms of the time and storage required, as a function of the size n of the input problem.

Algorithms can have running times proportional to functions such as $f(n) = n$, $f(n) = \log n$, $f(n) = n^2$, $f(n) = n^3$, and $f(n) = 2^n$. The function $f(n) = n$ represents an algorithm for which time is directly proportional to the number of instructions in the program, whereas $f(n) = 2^n$ represents an algorithm with exponential running time. As n increases, the time associated with an exponential function will be greater than those of linear or quadratic functions.

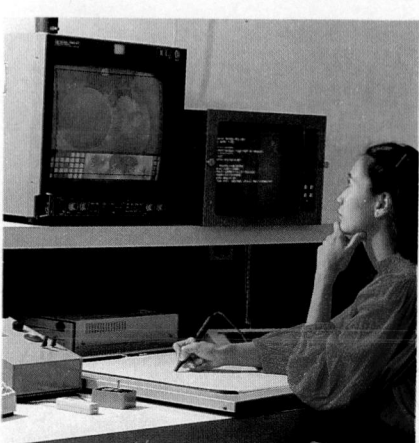

Recall that a *polynomial function* of degree n is a function of the form

$$f(x) = a_n x^n + a_{n-1} x^{n-1} + \cdots + a_1 x + a_0 \qquad a_n \neq 0$$

where n is a nonnegative integer and $a_n, a_{n-1}, \ldots, a_0$ are real numbers. The degree of a polynomial is the degree of the term of highest degree. The *zeros* of a function are the values of x for which $f(x) = 0$.

In Chapter 1, functions were evaluated by replacing the variable with a given value and performing the indicated operations. Another procedure for evaluating polynomials is performed by expressing the polynomial in *nested form*. The polynomial function $f(x) = 5x^2 + 3x + 7$ in nested form is $f(x) = (5x + 3)x + 7$. To express a polynomial in nested form, arrange the terms in descending order, group variables together, and factor out x. Repeat the process as many times as possible. The procedure is demonstrated below.

$$
\begin{aligned}
g(x) &= 3x^4 + x^3 - 4x^2 - 6x + 9 \\
&= (3x^3 + x^2 - 4x - 6)x + 9 \\
&= ((3x^2 + x - 4)x - 6)x + 9 \\
&= (((3x + 1)x - 4)x - 6)x + 9
\end{aligned}
$$

330   Chapter 7 Polynomial Functions

Example 1 Evaluate $g(x) = 3x^4 + x^3 - 4x^2 - 6x + 9$ for $x = 2$ by using substitution and then by using the nested form.

Substitution

$f(2) = 3(2)^4 + (2)^3 - 4(2)^2 - 6(2) + 9 = 37$

Nested form

$f(2) = (((3 \cdot 2 + 1)2 - 4)2 - 6)2 + 9$
$\quad\quad = (((7)2 - 4)2 - 6)2 + 9 \quad\quad 3 \times 2 + 1 = 7$
$\quad\quad = ((10)2 - 6)2 + 9 \quad\quad\quad 7 \times 2 - 4 = 10$
$\quad\quad = (14)2 + 9 \quad\quad\quad\quad\quad 10 \times 2 - 6 = 14$
$\quad\quad = 37 \quad\quad\quad\quad\quad\quad\quad 14 \times 2 + 9 = 37$

Notice that evaluating a function in nested form proceeds through a repetition of the following steps: Multiply and then add (or subtract). To begin, multiply the first coefficient of the polynomial by the value for x, then add the next coefficient. This method is called **synthetic substitution** and can be written in schematic form as follows:

Bring down the 3, multiply it by 2, and then write 6 under 1. Add $6 + 1$, write 7, and then repeat the process.

$2 \times 7 = 14$; $14 - 4 = 10$; write 10
$2 \times 10 = 20$; $20 - 6 = 14$; write 14
$2 \times 14 = 28$; $28 + 9 = 37$; write 37

Value for x   *Coefficients*

$$\begin{array}{r|rrrrr} 2 & 3 & 1 & -4 & -6 & 9 \\ & & 6 & 14 & 20 & 28 \\ \hline & 3 & 7 & 10 & 14 & 37 \end{array}$$

The last number in the bottom row is equal to $f(2)$.

Example 2 Evaluate $f(x) = 3x^5 + 4x^3 - 7x^2 + 1$ for $x = -1$ using synthetic substitution.

$$\begin{array}{r|rrrrrr} -1 & 3 & 0 & 4 & -7 & 0 & 1 \\ & & -3 & 3 & -7 & 14 & -14 \\ \hline & 3 & -3 & 7 & -14 & 14 & -13 \end{array}$$ *Insert zeros for missing coefficients.*

Thus, $f(-1) = -13$.

Synthetic substitution can be used to divide polynomials. When a larger number is divided by a smaller number, the result is a unique quotient and a remainder, which may be zero. For example, $911 \div 25 = 36$ with a remainder of 11. Dividing polynomials is similar to dividing numbers. When you divide a polynomial by another polynomial of lower degree, the result is a unique quotient and a remainder, which may be zero. To obtain the original number, or polynomial, multiply the quotient by the original divisor and add the remainder.

	Dividend	=	Divisor	·	Quotient	+	Remainder
For example,	911	=	25	·	36	+	11

	Polynomial	=	Divisor	·	Quotient	+	Remainder
	$P(x)$	=	$(x - a)$	·	$Q(x)$	+	R
For example,	$x^2 + 3x - 2$	=	$(x + 4)$	·	$(x - 1)$	+	2

Long division with polynomials is demonstrated at the top of the next page.

7.1 Synthetic Division and the Remainder and Factor Theorems **331**

GUIDED PRACTICE

For Example 1
Evaluate each function using two different methods.
1. $f(x) = 4x^2 + 3x - 9$
   for $x = 11$ 508
2. $g(x) = -5x^3 + 4x^2 - 7x + 10$
   for $x = 7$ -1558

For Example 2
Use synthetic substitution to evaluate each function.
1. $f(x) = 4x^5 + 3x^4 + x^2 - 7x + 9$
   for $x = -3$ -690
2. $g(x) = -5x^4 + 11x^3 - 6x^2 - 8$
   for $x = -0.2$ -8.336

Technology When using a calculator to do the multiplication and addition in the synthetic substitution process, students will find it easier to use 0.2 rather than $\frac{1}{5}$ when evaluating at $x = \frac{1}{5}$.

For example, dividing $f(x) = 3x^4 - x^2 + 2x - 5$ by $x + 3$ yields

$$
\begin{array}{r}
3x^3 - 9x^2 + 26x - 76 \\
x + 3 \overline{)3x^4 \quad\quad - x^2 + 2x - 5} \\
\underline{3x^4 + 9x^3} \\
-9x^3 - x^2 \\
\underline{-9x^3 - 27x^2} \\
26x^2 + 2x \\
\underline{26x^2 + 78x} \\
-76x - 5 \\
\underline{-76x - 228} \\
223
\end{array}
$$

Thus, $3x^4 - x^2 + 2x - 5 = (x + 3)(3x^3 - 9x^2 + 26x - 76) + 223$.

Using synthetic substitution to evaluate $f(-3)$ yields the same coefficients.

$$
\begin{array}{r|rrrrr}
-3 & 3 & 0 & -1 & +2 & -5 \\
   &   & -9 & 27 & -78 & 228 \\
\hline
   & 3 & -9 & 26 & -76 & 223
\end{array}
$$

Since synthetic substitution determines the coefficients of the quotient as well as the remainder, synthetic substitution is also called **synthetic division.** Note that the degree of the quotient polynomial is one less than the degree of the dividend.

Notice that the remainder of $f(x)$ when divided by $x + 3$ is equal to the value of the polynomial when $x = -3$.

Remainder Theorem

When polynomial $P(x)$ is divided by $x - a$, the remainder is $P(a)$.

Proof: $P(x) = (x - a) \cdot Q(x) + R$ *Division algorithm*
$P(a) = (a - a) \cdot Q(a) + R$ *Substitution*
$P(a) = R$

It is important to pay close attention to positive and negative signs when performing synthetic division. Remember that the procedure used to evaluate for $x = 2$ is the same as that used to divide by $x - 2$.

Example 3   Divide $2x^3 - 3x^2 + 4$ by $x + 2$ using synthetic division and then express the polynomial as a product of a divisor and a quotient with a remainder.

$$
\begin{array}{r|rrrr}
-2 & 2 & -3 & 0 & 4 \\
   &   & -4 & 14 & -28 \\
\hline
   & 2 & -7 & 14 & -24
\end{array}
$$
$a = -2$ *since* $x + 2 = x - (-2)$

Thus, $(2x^3 - 3x^2 + 4) = (x + 2)(2x^2 - 7x + 14) - 24$.

Synthetic division is applicable to the division of polynomials with leading coefficient 1. In the following example, the divisor $2x - 3$ is replaced by the divisor $x - \frac{3}{2}$. After dividing, the quotient is divided by a factor of 2 and the original divisor is restored.

332   Chapter 7 Polynomial Functions

Example 4   Divide $8x^4 - 16x^3 + 16x^2 - 27x + 18$ by $2x - 3$.

$$\frac{3}{2} \bigg| \begin{array}{ccccc} 8 & -16 & 16 & -27 & 18 \\ & 12 & -6 & 15 & -18 \\ \hline 8 & -4 & 10 & -12 & 0 \end{array} \qquad 2x - 3 = 2\left(x - \frac{3}{2}\right)$$

Thus, $8x^4 - 16x^3 + 16x^2 - 27x + 18 = \left(x - \frac{3}{2}\right)(8x^3 - 4x^2 + 10x - 12)$

$$= \left(x - \frac{3}{2}\right)(2)(4x^3 - 2x^2 + 5x - 6)$$

$$= (2x - 3)(4x^3 - 2x^2 + 5x - 6)$$

Therefore, $(8x^4 - 16x^3 + 16x^2 - 27x + 18) \div (2x - 3) = 4x^3 - 2x^2 + 5x - 6$.

A theorem that has implications for graphing polynomial functions is the *factor theorem*. Recall that if $P(x) = 0$ is a polynomial equation and $P(a) = 0$, then a is a *solution* of the polynomial equation.

Factor Theorem

A number a is a solution of the polynomial equation $f(x) = 0$ if and only if $x - a$ is a factor of $f(x)$.

Since the theorem is in if-and-only-if form, there are two statements to prove.

- If a is a solution of the polynomial equation $f(x) = 0$, then $x - a$ is a factor of $f(x)$.

  Proof: $f(a) = 0$ because a is a solution of $f(x) = 0$. By the remainder theorem, $f(a)$ is the remainder when $f(x)$ is divided by $x - a$. Thus, $f(x) = (x - a)Q(x) + 0$ and $x - a$ is a factor of $f(x)$.

- If $x - a$ is a factor of $f(x)$, then a is a solution of $f(x) = 0$.

  Proof: If $x - a$ is a factor of $f(x)$, then $f(x) = (x - a)Q(x)$, where $Q(x)$ is a polynomial with degree one less than the degree of $f(x)$. $f(a) = (a - a)Q(a) = (0)[Q(a)] = 0$. Thus, a is a solution of $f(x) = 0$.

Example 5   Determine whether $x - 5$ is a factor of $x^4 - 3x^3 + 7x^2 - 60x - 125$.

$$5 \bigg| \begin{array}{ccccc} 1 & -3 & 7 & -60 & -125 \\ & 5 & 10 & 85 & 125 \\ \hline 1 & 2 & 17 & 25 & 0 \end{array}$$

Since the remainder is zero, $f(5) = 0$ and $x - 5$ is a factor of $f(x)$.

If the remainder is zero when dividing a polynomial $P(x)$ by $x - a$, the quotient polynomial $Q(x)$ is called the **depressed polynomial.** In Example 5, $f(x) = (x - 5)(x^3 + 2x^2 + 17x + 25) + 0$. Thus, the depressed polynomial is $x^3 + 2x^2 + 17x + 25$. *Why is a zero of the depressed polynomial a zero of the original function?*

7.1 Synthetic Division and the Remainder and Factor Theorems   **333**

For Example 4
1. Divide $(12x^4 - 23x^3 + 31x^2 - 23x + 6)$ by $(3x - 2)$.
   $4x^3 - 5x^2 + 7x - 3$
2. Divide $(15x^4 - x^3 - 11x^2 + 17x + 9)$ by $(5x + 3)$.
   $3x^3 - 2x^2 - x + 4$, R = -3

For Example 5
Use the factor theorem to determine whether the second polynomial is a factor of the first polynomial.
1. $f(x) = x^4 - 4x^3 + 3x^2 - 3x - 36$; $x - 4$ yes
2. $g(x) = 3x^5 + 21x^4 - 5x^3 - 35x^2 - x - 2$; $x + 7$ no

Technology Ask students to devise a way on their graphing utility to answer the questions in Example 5 without using synthetic division. One possible method is to graph $f(x)$ and $g(x)$; check that $f(4)$ is about 0 and $g(-7)$ is about 5 and not 0.

Thinking Critically
A zero of the depressed polynomial makes one factor of the original equation equal to zero, and thus is a zero of the original equation.

Determine k so that the second polynomial is a factor of the first polynomial.

1. $f(x) = x^4 + 6x^3 + 12x^2 + k - 10; x + 1$ 3
2. $g(x) = x^5 - 5x^4 + 7x^3 + kx^2 - 4x + 20; x - 5$ −35

CLOSURE

Using their own words, have students describe how to determine whether a linear expression is a factor of a polynomial.

INDEPENDENT PRACTICE

Assignment Guide

Basic: 1–16, 18, 21–24, 29–32
Average: 1–31 odd, 33–40, 43, 45, 48, 51
Enriched: 29–62

Teacher's Resource Book
  Practice, page 43

Ⓡ **Review**
Exercises 5, 17, 19, 21, and 43 review concepts such as finding areas of triangles, using long division to divide polynomials, factoring, and graphing.

Technology Although there are no specific exercises in this lesson that require the use of a calculator, many of them may be expedited by using a calculator.

Additional Answers

Class Exercises

14. $Q(x) = (x - 5)(x + 3)(x + 1) = x^3 - x^2 - 17x - 15; P(x) = k[Q(x)]$ for any real k, so y-int is $(0, -15k)$, $k \in \mathcal{R}$

Example 6   Determine k so that $g(x) = 2x^3 + 5x^2 + kx - 16$ has $x - 2$ as a factor.

$$\underline{2\,\rfloor}\ \begin{array}{cccc} 2 & 5 & k & -16 \\ & 4 & 18 & 2k + 36 \\ \hline 2 & 9 & (k + 18) & (2k + 20) \end{array}$$

For $x - 2$ to be a factor of $g(x)$, the remainder must be zero. Solving $2k + 20 = 0$ yields $k = -10$. Thus, $g(x) = 2x^3 + 5x^2 - 10x - 16$.

Summary: If in polynomial $P(x)$, $P(a) = 0$, then
  $x = a$ is a zero of $P(x)$.
  $x = a$ is a solution of the equation $P(x) = 0$.
  $x - a$ is a factor of $P(x)$.

Class Exercises

Express each polynomial in nested form and then evaluate for the given value.

1. $g(x) = -5x^5 - 4x^2 + 7x - 8; x = -2$
   $g(x) = ((-5x^3 - 4)x + 7)x - 8;\ 122$

2. $f(x) = 7x^4 + 5x^3 - 13; x = -3$
   $f(x) = (7x + 5)x^3 - 13;\ 419$

Use synthetic substitution to evaluate each function for the given value.

3. $g(x) = 6x^3 + x^2 - 19x + 5; x = \frac{3}{2}$ −1

4. $f(x) = 9x^3 - 3x^2 + 10x - 15; x = \frac{2}{3}$ −7

Use the remainder theorem and synthetic division to find the indicated value.

5. $h(x) = 2x^4 + 11x^3 + 9x^2 - x - 4; x = -2$ −22

6. $p(x) = 4x^3 + 8x^2 - 3x + 7; x = -5$ −278

Divide, using synthetic division. Then express the polynomial as a product of a divisor and a quotient with a remainder.

7. $(2x^3 - 3x^2 + 2x - 4) \div (x - 2)$

8. $(x^5 - 5x^2) \div (x + 3)$

9. $(4x^5 - 7x^3 + 9x^2 - 4x - 1) \div (2x + 1)$

Use the factor theorem and synthetic division to determine whether the first polynomial is a factor of the second.

10. $x - 3; 4x^5 - 3x^3 - 7x^2 + 12$ no

11. $x - 6; 8x^5 + 5x^4 - 11x - 18$ no

12. **Writing in Mathematics**   Describe how you can use synthetic division to find the quotient: $[x^4 + 2x^3 - 7x^2 - 8x + 12] \div [(x - 1)(x + 3)]$.

13. Determine K so that $f(x) = x^4 + 3x^3 - 5x^2 + Kx - 24$ has $x - 2$ as a factor. 2

14. **Thinking Critically**   If $P(x)$ is a polynomial of degree 3 and $P(5)$, $P(-3)$, and $P(-1)$ are all zero, determine the y-intercept of the graph of $P(x)$.

Practice Exercises   Use appropriate technology.

Express each polynomial function in nested form.

A 1. $f(x) = 3x^3 - 4x^2 + 7$ $(3x - 4)x^2 + 7$

2. $g(x) = -x^3 - 2x^2 - 3x - 4$ $((-x - 2)x - 3)x - 4$

3. $h(x) = 2x^5 + 3x^4 - 11x^3 - 15x^2 + 2x + 6$
   $((((2x + 3)x - 11)x - 15)x + 2)x + 6$

4. $h(x) = 2x^4 - 12x^3 + 27x^2 - 57x + 19$
   $(((2x - 12)x + 27)x - 57)x + 19$

Ⓡ 5. *Landscaping*   Determine the area of a triangular flower garden with sides 12 ft, 20 ft, and 21 ft, to the nearest ten square feet. 120 ft²

Writing in Mathematics
12. First divide the original equation by $x - 1$, then divide the quotient by $x + 3$.

Use the factor theorem and synthetic division to determine whether the first polynomial is a factor of the second.

6. $x + 1$; $x^4 - x^3 - 2x^2 + 7x + 7$ yes

7. $x - 3$; $x^5 - 6x^4 + 14x^3 - 17x^2 + 10x - 12$ yes

8. $x - 5$; $x^5 - 3x^4 - 13x^3 + 19x^2 - 17x + 15$ no

9. $x + 11$; $x^4 + 4x^3 - 7x + 99$ no

10. $2x + 3$; $2x^4 + 5x^3 + 3x^2 + 8x + 12$ yes

11. $5x - 2$; $20x^4 - 8x^3 + 25x^2 + 50x - 16$ no

Use synthetic substitution to evaluate each function.

12. $g(-1)$ when $g(x) = -x^3 - 2x^2 - 3x - 4$ -2

13. $g(-3)$ when $g(x) = x^4 + 3x^3 - 5x^2 + 9$ -36

14. $h\left(-\frac{1}{3}\right)$ when $h(x) = 6x^3 - x^2 - 7x + 1$ 3

15. $h(-0.7)$ when $h(x) = 2x^3 + 3x^2 - 7x + 1$ 6.684

16. **Writing in Mathematics**   Describe the relationship between the solutions of the polynomial equation $P(x) = 0$ and the factors of $P(x)$.

Ⓡ 17. Divide $(x^3 + 3x^2 - 5x + 4)$ by $2x - 3$. Do *not* use synthetic division.

18. **Thinking Critically**   When would a fourth degree polynomial function $P(x)$ expressed as a product of four linear factors *not* have four distinct solutions for the equation $P(x) = 0$? when two of the factors differ by at most a constant multiple

Ⓡ 19. Factor $x^3 + 5x^2 + 6x$ completely. $x(x + 3)(x + 2)$

20. **Writing in Mathematics**   Explain the meaning of the remainder theorem.

Ⓡ 21. Graph the function $g(x) = -2x^2 - 4x + 1$.

22. **Writing in Mathematics**   Explain the meaning of the factor theorem.

Divide, using synthetic division. Then express the polynomial as a product of a divisor and a quotient with a remainder.

23. $(x^3 - 4x^2 + 7x - 1) \div (x - 2)$

24. $(6x^3 - x^2 - 7x + 5) \div (x - 3)$

25. $(x^4 + 3x^3 - 5x^2 + 9) \div (x + 3)$

26. $(x^4 + 3x^3 - 5x^2 + 9) \div (x + 4)$

27. $(x^4 - 2x^3 + x - 8) \div (x - 1)$

28. $(x^4 + 2x^2 - 10) \div (x + 1)$

Divide, using synthetic division.

B 29. $(4x^4 - 2x^2 - 1) \div (2x - 1)$

30. $(2x^3 + 3x^2 + 4) \div (2x + 1)$

31. $(9x^3 - 7x^2 + 6x + 2) \div (3x + 2)$

32. $(6x^3 - 9x^2 - 12x - 6) \div (3x + 4)$

33. $\left(x^3 + \frac{1}{6}x^2 - \frac{5}{12}x + \frac{1}{12}\right) \div \left(x - \frac{1}{2}\right)$

34. $(3x^3 + ax^2 + a^2x + 2a^3) \div (x - a)$

Determine k so that the given function has the given binomial factor.

35. $f(x) = x^3 - x^2 + kx - 12$; $x - 3$ -2

36. $g(x) = x^3 - 4x^2 - kx - 16$; $x + 3$ $\frac{79}{3}$

37. $p(x) = 3x^3 + kx^2 - 19x + 6$; $x + 3$ 2

38. $h(x) = 2x^3 + 5x^2 + kx - 16$; $x - 2$ -10

39. *Computer Technology*   Two similar computer programs have different running times: $f(n) = n^2$ and $g(n) = 10n$. Which one would you choose for $n = 4$? For $n = 12$? $f(n)$; $g(n)$

40. *Engineering*   The cubic equation $x^3 - 0.2562x^2 + 0.1140x - 0.1020 = 0$ is used in working with reinforced concrete. The quantity x is the distance from the upper surface of a beam to the "neutral plane." Is it correct that x is 0.472 to three decimal places? Why or why not? yes; $f(0.472) \approx -0.0001$

Writing in Mathematics
16. If a zero of $P(x)$ is a, then $x - a$ is a factor of $P(x)$.
20. If a polynomial is divided by a linear expression, the remainder is the polynomial evaluated at the zero of the linear expression.
22. A given number is a solution to a polynomial equal to 0 if the linear expression with the number as a zero is a factor of the polynomial. Also, if the expression is a factor of the polynomial, then the zero of the expression is a zero of the polynomial.

LESSON FOLLOW-UP

Lesson Quiz

1. Evaluate $f(x) = -7x^5 + 5x^3 - x^2 + 3x - 6$ for $x = -4$. 6814

2. Divide $g(x) = 12x^4 + 7x^3 - 5x^2 - 3x - 6$ by $x + 6$ using synthetic division, and then express the polynomial as a product of a divisor and a quotient with a remainder. $(x + 6)(12x^3 - 65x^2 + 385x - 2313)$, R = 13,872

3. Determine whether $x - 11$ is a factor of $h(x) = x^5 - 11x^4 - 3x^3 + 40x - 77$. no

4. Determine k so that $x + 5$ is a factor of $f(x) = x^4 + kx^2 + 37x + 10$. -18

Additional Answers

17. $\frac{x^2}{2} + \frac{9}{4}x + \frac{7}{8}$, R $= \frac{53}{8}$

21.

23. $(x - 2)(x^2 - 2x + 3)$, R = 5
24. $(x - 3)(6x^2 + 17x + 44)$, R = 137
25. $(x + 3)(x^3 - 5x + 15)$, R = -36
26. $(x + 4)(x^3 - x^2 - x + 4)$, R = -7
27. $(x - 1)(x^3 - x^2 - x)$, R = -8
28. $(x + 1)(x^3 - x^2 + 3x - 3)$, R = -7
29. $2x^3 + x^2 - \frac{1}{2}x - \frac{1}{4}$, R = $-\frac{5}{4}$
30. $x^2 + x - \frac{1}{2}$, R = $\frac{9}{2}$
31. $3x^2 - \frac{13}{3}x + \frac{44}{9}$, R = $-\frac{70}{9}$
32. $2x^2 - \frac{17}{3}x + \frac{32}{9}$, R = $-\frac{182}{9}$
33. $x^2 + \frac{2}{3}x - \frac{1}{12}$, R = $\frac{1}{24}$
34. $3x^2 + 4ax + 5a^2$, R = $7a^3$

Alternative Assessment

Write an essay describing how to determine whether a linear factor $(x - a)$ is a factor of a polynomial. Include the significance of a factor to the graph of the polynomial and provide an example of a polynomial, its factors, and its graph.

Enrichment

Investigate whether synthetic division is valid in base systems other than ten. Give examples for several bases to support your answer.

Additional Answers

43.

49. There are n solutions.
50. Since $S(x) = -P(x)$, their graphs are reflections in the x-axis.

Computer Technology   The time in minutes needed to run a computer program is given by the following functions.

41. $f(n) = 2n^2 + 3n$, where n is the number of times that a particular loop is repeated. How long will it take to run a program that has 10 loops? 3 h 50 min

42. $f(n) = n^3 + n^2$, where n is the number of repetitions of a loop. If only 11 h of computer time are available, how many times can the loop be repeated? 8 times

 43. Graph $h(x) = \tan(x + \pi) - 2$.

Determine the value of k in each function for the given condition.

44. $g(x) = x^4 - kx^2 - 2x - 5; g(2) = -5$ 3   45. $p(x) = x^4 + kx^3 + 2x + k; p(1) = 9$ 3

46. $f(x) = x^4 - 2x^3 + kx^2 - x + 5; f(-2) = 51$ 3

47. $s(x) = x^4 + kx^3 + x + k + 5: s(-2) = 65$ $-\frac{46}{7}$

48. **Writing in Mathematics**   Use a graphing utility to graph the functions $f(x) = x - 3$, $g(x) = (x - 3)^2$, $h(x) = (x - 3)^3$, and $p(x) = (x - 3)^4$. Compare the behaviors of the graphs near $x = 3$.

49. **Thinking Critically**   If a polynomial function of degree n can be expressed as the product of n distinct linear factors, then what may be said about the number of distinct solutions to the equation $P(x) = 0$?

50. **Thinking Critically**   If $P(x) = (x + 5)(x + 4)(x - 1)$ and $S(x) = (x + 5)(1 - x)(x + 4)$, how do the graphs of $P(x)$ and $S(x)$ differ?

C 51. Express $f(x) = x^3 - 3x^2 - x + 3$ as a product of linear factors. $(x + 1)(x - 1)(x - 3)$

52. Express $g(x) = x^3 + 3x^2 - x - 3$ as a product of linear factors. $(x - 1)(x + 1)(x + 3)$

53. Divide $2x^4 - 12x^3 + 27x^2 - 54x + 81$ by $(x - 3)^2$. $2x^2 + 9$

54. Divide $x^4 + 2x^3 - 7x^2 - 8x + 12$ by $[(x + 3)(x - 1)]$. $x^2 - 4$

55. Find b such that when $bx^2 - bx + 4$ is divided by $x + 1$, the remainder is zero. -2

56. Find K such that when $Kx^3 - 17x^2 - 4Kx + 5$ is divided by $x - 5$, the remainder is zero. 4

57. For what value of d does $x^2 + dx + 4$ yield the same remainder when divided by either $x - 1$ or $x + 1$? 0

58. For what value of b does $x^2 + bx + 4$ yield the same remainder when divided by either $x - 1$ or $x - 3$? -4

59. If $f(x) = x^4 + Bx^3 + Bx + 4$ and $f(1) = 30$, find $f(-1)$. -20

60. If $g(x) = x^4 + Ax^3 + Ax + 4$ and $g(2) = 6$, find $g(-2)$. 34

61. If $p(x) = 3x^3 + 2x^2 + Kx + M$, $p(-3) = -41$, and $p(2) = 29$, find K and M. -5; 7

62. **Writing in Mathematics**   Describe a method that can be used to find the linear factors common to $6x^3 + 11x^2 - x - 6$ and $6x^3 + 25x^2 + 34x + 15$.

Review

1. Express $625x^2 - 16$ as the product of three binomials. $(25x + 4)(5x + 2)(5x - 2)$

2. A rocket on a launch pad casts a shadow that is 166 m when the sun is at an angle of $63°$. Determine the height of the rocket. 325.79 m

---

Writing in Mathematics

48. The graphs meet at $x = 3$ and approximate one another very near $x = 3$.
62. Answers may vary. Graph both polynomials and look for common zeros.

7.2 Graphs of Polynomial Functions

Objectives: To graph polynomial functions
To identify equations of polynomial functions from their graphs

Focus

An interesting chapter in the history of mathematics concerns the efforts to solve polynomial equations. The ancient Greeks solved problems involving squares using geometric constructions. With the algebraic notation introduced by Arabian mathematicians, a general solution for the quadratic equation was developed. You know this solution as the quadratic formula. Later, Italian mathematicians found general solutions to third and fourth degree equations by devising formulas in terms of coefficients and radicals. Two brilliant young mathematicians named Niels Henrik Abel and Evariste Galois, who were ages 18 and 16, respectively, tried to find a formula to solve the fifth degree equation, $ax^5 + bx^4 + cx^3 + dx^2 + ex + f = 0$. They were not successful, and Abel later proved that there are no general formulas for equations of degree above 4. The solutions of polynomial equations are the same as the zeros of polynomial functions, and graphs are often helpful in locating them.

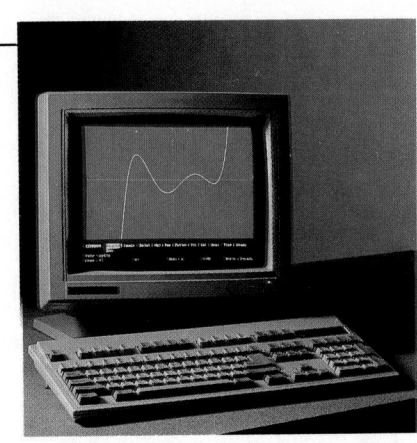

The graphs of polynomial functions have certain fundamental shapes that you should recognize. Many polynomial functions are sums, differences, products, or translations of basic polynomial functions of the form $f(x) = ax^n$.

Quadratic function

Cubic function

Quartic function

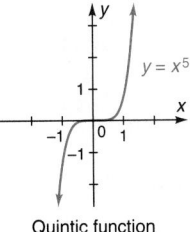

Quintic function

A turning point is a point on a graph such that the value of the function is a relative maximum or a relative minimum. *Relative extrema* consist of relative maximum and relative minimum values of the function. The graph of a polynomial of degree n can have as many as $n - 1$ relative extrema. For example, $f(x) = x^5$ has no relative extrema. Below are examples of other quintic polynomials.

7.2 Graphs of Polynomial Functions **337**

INSTRUCTION

- On the overhead projector or chalkboard draw a curve having two or more relative extrema and two or more zeros, one of which has multiplicity two. Label the zeros and intercepts. Ask students, "What is the polynomial function of this curve?" Some students may make attempts to answer this question; many will be confounded. Discuss various aspects of the curve. Tell students that at the end of the lesson, everyone in the class should be able to write the function of the curve. Then after working through the lesson, test your hypothesis.

- Encourage students to record in their math journals a list of the components of a polynomial function that they should be able to identify on a graph or use to sketch a graph.

- Students should be able to sketch a graph of a polynomial function of any degree if it is expressed as a product of linear factors or if it can be factored easily into linear factors; otherwise, they need the help of a graphing utility.

Alternative Learning Style

Students may be motivated by real world applications of polynomial graphs. Economics is an area where data points are generated and then fitted with a curve. Direct students to the library or to an economics teacher to find out about some polynomials that are used in economics. Have students work in small groups and, using the concepts taught in this lesson, discuss and sketch graphs of these polynomials.

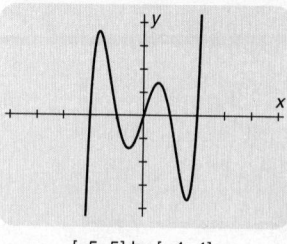

[-5, 5] by [-4, 4]

$$f(x) = x^5 - 5x^3 + 4x$$
$$= x(x - 2)(x - 1)(x + 1)(x + 2)$$
Four relative extrema

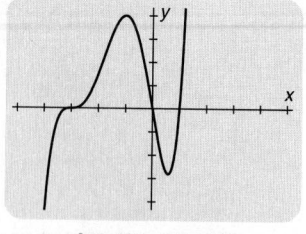

[-5, 5] by [-16, 16]
x scl: 1   y scl: 4

$$f(x) = x^5 + 8x^4 + 18x^3 - 27x$$
$$= x(x - 1)(x + 3)^3$$
Two relative extrema

Example 1 Graph $f(x) = (x - 3)(x + 2)(x - 1)$.

The function can be entered in a graphing utility in factored form. Zeros are -2, 1, and 3. The y-intercept is $(0, 6)$. For $f(x) > 0$, the graph is above the x-axis. For $f(x) < 0$, the graph is below the x-axis.

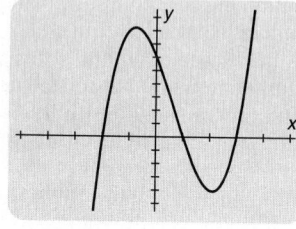

[-5, 5] by [-5, 9]

The graph of a function of the form $f(x) = ax^n$ with n an even number will rise at both the left and right if a is positive, and it will fall at both the left and right if a is negative. *Why?* If n is odd, the graph will rise at the left and fall at the right or the reverse. The coefficient of the term of highest degree of a polynomial is called the **leading coefficient.** It always determines whether the function rises or falls at the left and right. *Why?*

Recall that a function is even if $f(-x) = f(x)$ and odd if $f(-x) = -f(x)$. An even function is symmetric with respect to the y-axis. An odd function is symmetric with respect to the origin.

Example 2 Graph the function $f(x) = x^4 - x^2$ using a graphing utility. Determine whether it is even or odd. Describe the behavior of the function for $-1 \leq x \leq 1$.

Since $f(-x) = (-x)^4 - (-x)^2 = x^4 - x^2 = f(x)$, $f(x)$ is even. Factoring yields $f(x) = x^2(x - 1)(x + 1)$. Thus, f has zeros at -1, 0, and 1. The graph rises at the left and right, crosses the x-axis at -1 and 1, and touches the x-axis at 0. The graph dips below the x-axis for $-1 < x < 0$ and $0 < x < 1$ because for these values $x^2 > x^4$. Set the viewing rectangle to $[-2, 2]$ by $[-1, 1]$ to observe the behavior of the graph between $x = -1$ and $x = 1$.

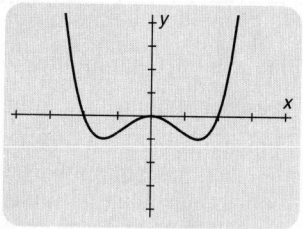

[-2, 2] by [-1, 1]
x scl: 0.5   y scl: 0.25

338   Chapter 7 Polynomial Functions

Thinking Critically
Since the leading coefficient is positive, the graph approaches ∞ as x approaches ∞, and it approaches $-\infty$ as x approaches $-\infty$.

There are several reasons why it is important to analyze a function as you use a graphing utility. First, you might make a keying mistake. Knowing the basic shape of a graph will help you realize when a graph is not the correct representation of a function. Second, the standard viewing rectangle may not display the behavior of the function clearly for certain values, as in Example 2 above. When this happens, you should change the viewing rectangle.

You can often identify equations of polynomial functions from their graphs.

Example 3 Determine an equation for the polynomial graph shown at the right.

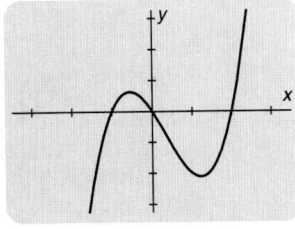

[−3, 3] by [−3, 3]

The graph has the shape of the cubic function with a positive leading coefficient. Zeros occur at −1, 0, and 2. Thus, $f(x) = x(x + 1)(x - 2) = x^3 - x^2 - 2x$.

A polynomial function will have a zero that is a real number at each point at which it crosses the x-axis.

Example 4 Indicate the shape of the graph of a polynomial function of degree 5, with positive leading coefficient, and five distinct real zeros.

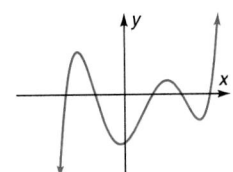

The graph will cross the x-axis 5 times. The graph will fall at the left and rise at the right. *Why?* The general shape is shown at the right.

Recall that the graph of $y = f(x - a) + b$ is a horizontal and vertical translation of the graph of $y = f(x)$.

Example 5 Graph each function without using a graphing utility.
    a. $f(x) = x^3$ **b.** $g(x) = x^3 + 2$ **c.** $h(x) = (x - 2)^3$

a. $f(x)$ represents the graph of the basic function.

b. $g(x)$ represents a translation of the graph of the basic cubic function up 2 units.

c. $h(x)$ represents a translation of the graph of the basic cubic function 2 units to the right.

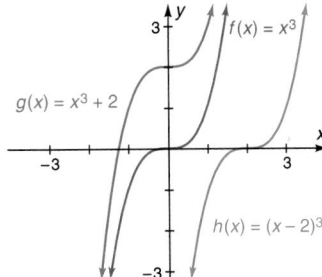

Note that if $(x - r)$ is a factor k times, then r is a zero of *multiplicity k*.

7.2 Graphs of Polynomial Functions   **339**

For Example 1
Graph $f(x) = (x - 2)(x - 1)(x + 3)$.

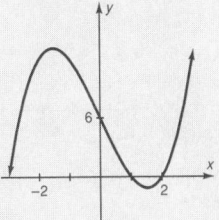

For Example 2
Graph $f(x) = x^5 + x^3$ using a graphing utility and determine whether the function is even, odd, or neither.

odd

For Example 3
Determine an equation for the polynomial graph pictured below.

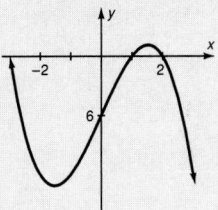

$f(x) = -1(x - 1)(x + 3)(x - 2)$

For Example 4

Indicate the shape of the graph of an even polynomial function of degree 4 with a negative leading coefficient and two distinct real zeros.
Answers may vary.

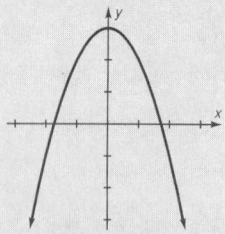

For Example 5

Graph each function without using a graphing utility.

1. $f(x) = x^4$

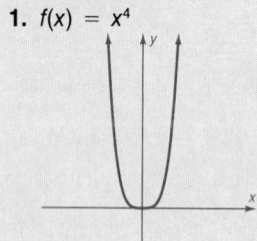

2. $g(x) = (x + 1)^4 - 2$

For Example 6

Use a graphing utility to determine the real zeros and the number of relative extrema. Then express the function as a product of linear factors.

$f(x) = x^4 + x^3 - 11x^2 - 9x + 18$
zeros at 1, 3, -2, -3; 3 relative extrema;
$f(x) = (x - 1)(x - 3)(x + 2)(x + 3)$

CLOSURE

Have students identify and describe the components of a polynomial function that are used to graph the function.

340

If $n = 1$, the graph will cross the x-axis at $x = r$.

If n is odd and greater than 1, the graph will intersect the x-axis at $x = r$ and flatten out as it passes through that point.

If n is even, the graph will be tangent to the x-axis at $x = r$ and will not cross the x-axis at that point.

Multiplicity 1 at r

Multiplicity 3 at r

Multiplicity 2 at r

Example 6 Use a graphing utility to graph the function $f(x) = x^4 + 3x^3 - 4x$. Determine each real zero and the number of relative extrema. Then express the function as a product of linear factors.

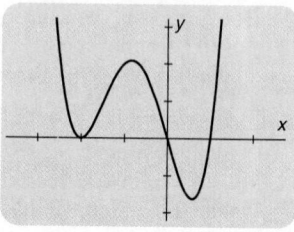

[−3, 2] by [−2, 3]

The shape of the graph and the trace feature reveal the following zeros: -2 (multiplicity 2), 0, and 1. The graph has three relative extrema. It can be expressed as $f(x) = x(x - 1)(x + 2)^2$.

Class Exercises

Determine the maximum number of relative extrema for each polynomial function.

1. $f(x) = x^5 + 7x^3 - 6x + 2$ 4
2. $f(x) = -x^4 - x^3 + 4x - 9$ 3

Determine an equation for each polynomial graph.

3.

Degree 3 $y = (x + 1)(x - 6)^2$

4.

Degree 6
$y = -(x - 1)^3(x + 6)(x + 3)(x - 7)$

Graph each polynomial function. Identify the zeros.

5. $f(x) = (x - 2)^2(x - 3)(x + 1)^3$
6. $g(x) = (x + 5)(x + 2)^2(x - 3)^2$
7. $h(x) = -x^3 + x^2 + 6x$
   $f(x)$ is the graph of $g(x)$ shifted down 2 units.
8. $p(x) = x^4 - 2x^3 - 3x^2$
9. **Thinking Critically** Compare the graphs of $f(x) = x^4 - 2$ and $g(x) = x^4$.
10. **Thinking Critically** Compare the graphs of $f(x) = -x^5$ and $g(x) = x^5$.
    $f(x)$ is the reflection of $g(x)$ in the y-axis.

Practice Exercises   Use appropriate technology.

Determine the maximum number of relative extrema for each polynomial function.

A 1. $f(x) = x^4 - 2x^2 + 5x - 1$ 3
2. $f(x) = x^4 + 3x^2 - 7x + 6$ 3

340   Chapter 7 Polynomial Functions

3. $g(x) = -x^5 + 5x^4 - 3x + 2$ 4

4. $g(x) = -x^5 - 6x^3 + 4x - 9$ 4

5. $h(x) = 2x^5 - 9x^2$ 4

6. $h(x) = 3x^4 - 5x$ 3

Graph each polynomial function. Identify the zeros.

7. $f(x) = (x - 4)^2$ 4 (mult. 2)

8. $f(x) = (x + 5)^2$ −5 (mult. 2)

9. $g(x) = x(x - 2)(x + 1)$ 0, 2, −1

10. $g(x) = (x + 6)^2(x - 3)$ −6 (mult. 2), 3

11. $f(x) = (x - 1)^3(x + 4)^2(x - 2)$
1 (mult. 3); −4 (mult. 2); 2

12. $f(x) = (x + 3)^2(x - 2)^3(x + 5)$
−3 (mult. 2); 2 (mult. 3); −5

13. Determine the domain of the function $\dfrac{1}{\sqrt{x^2}}$. all real x, $x \neq 0$

Graph each function and determine whether it is even, odd, or neither.

14. $f(x) = x^6 - x^2$ even

15. $f(x) = x^6 - x^4$ even

16. $f(x) = x^5 - x^3$ odd

17. $f(x) = x^6 - x^4 - x^2 + 2$ even

18. $f(x) = x^4 - 4x^2 + 3$ even

19. $f(x) = x^5 - 2x^3 - 5$ neither

20. Thinking Critically What is the minimum number of relative extrema that a fourth degree polynomial can have? Why? 1

21. Use a graphing utility to determine the solutions of $\sin x = 2 \cos x$, $0 \le x \le 2\pi$. 1.11; 4.24

22. Indicate the shape of the graph of a polynomial function of degree 4, with negative coefficient of x^4 and four distinct real zeros.

Manufacturing The cost of manufacturing a certain pen is $1500 for start-up expenses and 35¢ a pen. The pens are sold for 65¢ each.

23. Determine a function $f(x)$ that shows the relationship between the number of pens manufactured and the manufacturing cost. Determine another function $g(x)$ that shows the relationship between pens sold and dollar sales.

24. Graph the lines for the two functions derived in Exercise 23. Why is the point of intersection called the break even? At that point, cost = revenue.

Determine an equation for each polynomial graph.

25.

Degree 5 $f(x) = (x - 8)^2(x + 3)^3$

26.

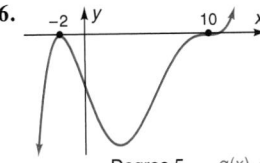

Degree 5 $g(x) = (x + 2)^2(x - 10)^3$

Without using a graphing utility, draw a quick graph of each function.

27. $f(x) = x^5 - 3$

28. $f(x) = -(x + 3)^2$

29. $f(x) = (x + 1)^4$

30. *Demographics* The graph at the right shows the population of a town in thousands over a period of 5 years. Determine two relative extrema on the graph and determine the approximate population at each.
(2 years, 150,000), (4 years, 80,000)

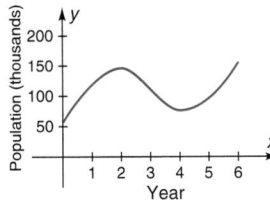

7.2 Graphs of Polynomial Functions   **341**

INDEPENDENT PRACTICE

Assignment Guide

Basic: 1–20, 25–35 odd

Average: 1–19 odd, 22–38

Enriched: 1–37 odd, 40–51

Teacher's Resource Book
Practice, page 44

Ⓡ Review

Exercises 13, 21, 31, 39, and 47 review concepts such as finding the domain of a function, solving trigonometric equations, using the law of cosines, evaluating functions, and finding measures of angles.

LESSON FOLLOW-UP

Lesson Quiz

Graph each function. Find the zeros of the function and the number of relative extrema of each.

1. $f(x) = (x + 4)^2(x + 2)^2$
zeros at −2(mult. 2), −4(mult. 2);
3 relative extrema

2. $g(x) = x^3 - x^2 - 6x$
zeros at −2, 0, 3; 2 relative extrema

3. Determine an equation for the polynomial graph pictured below.

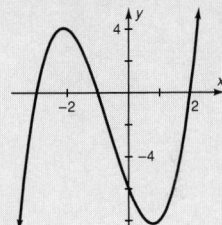

4. Determine whether the function $f(x) = x^5 + x^3 - 3x + 5$ is even, odd, or neither. neither

Additional Answers

48.

49.

50.

51.

® 31. If cos ß = 0.5678, determine the possible values for sin ß. 0.8231; −0.8231

Use a graphing utility to graph each function. Determine each zero and the number of relative extrema. Then express the function as a product of linear factors.

32. $f(x) = x^3 − 3x^2 − 4x + 12$ **33.** $f(x) = x^4 + 6x^3 + 9x^2$

34. $f(x) = x^4 + 5x^3 + 9x^2 + 7x + 2$ **35.** $f(x) = x^4 − 3x^2 + 2x$

36. $f(x) = x^5 − x^4 − 12x^3$ **37.** $f(x) = x^5 + 5x^4 − 5x^3 − 25x^2 + 4x + 20$

38. *Space Science* A small spherical satellite is being designed to have a volume between 20 m³ and 30 m³. The formula for the volume of a sphere is $\frac{4}{3}\pi r^3$. Use a graphing calculator to graph this function. Determine the range of values for the radius that will give the desired volume. Express your answer to the nearest tenth of a meter. $1.7 \le r \le 1.9$ m

® 39. In triangle *ABC*, $\angle A = 25°$, b = 10, c = 15. Find *a*. 7.3

40. *Business* Calculators sold for *x* dollars are projected to have a profit in thousands defined by the function $f(x) = −(x − 5)^2 + 8$. Graph the function and determine the relative maximum. What price will give the maximum profit, and what is the profit at that price? $5; $8000

41. Writing in Mathematics Describe some differences between fourth degree and fifth degree polynomials.

C 42. Determine an equation of a cubic polynomial whose only real zeros are −5 and 2. $f(x) = (x + 5)^2(x − 2)$ or $f(x) = (x − 2)^2(x + 5)$

43. Indicate the shape of a polynomial function of degree 4 with negative coefficient of x^4 and only one real zero at 3 of multiplicity 2 and the complex zeros ±i.

44. Determine an equation for the graph you drew in Exercise 43. $f(x) = −(x − 3)^2(x^2 + 1)$

45. Determine an equation of a cubic polynomial *P* with zeros −2, 1, and 3, and $P(0) = 12$. $P(x) = 2(x + 2)(x − 1)(x − 3)$

46. Determine an equation of a cubic polynomial *Q* with zeros 1, 2, and 3, and $P(0) = −6$. $Q(x) = (x − 1)(x − 2)(x − 3)$

® 47. An angle in standard position whose measure is $−\frac{4\pi}{3}$ undergoes $\frac{5}{3}$ clockwise rotations. Determine the measure of the angle between 0 and 2π that is coterminal with the resulting angle. $\frac{4\pi}{3}$

Graph each function and determine whether it is even, odd, or neither.

48. $p(x) = |x^4 − x^2 − 6|$ even   **49.** $q(x) = |x^4 − x^2 − 2|$ even

50. $t(x) = −|3x^3 − x^2 − 6x + 2|$ neither   **51.** $n(x) = −|2x^3 − 5x|$ even

Challenge

Determine the smallest integral value for *n* which the following is consistently accurate to one decimal place. Determine the value of the sum at that value for *n*.

$$1 − \frac{1}{2} + \frac{1}{3} − \frac{1}{4} + \frac{1}{5} − \cdots \pm \frac{1}{n}$$ n = 75; series = .6997692

342   Chapter 7 Polynomial Functions

Writing in Mathematics
41. Answers may vary. Fourth degree polynomials may have 1 or 3 relative extrema and may be even but never odd; fifth degree polynomials may have 0, 2, or 4 relative extrema and may be odd but never even.

7.3 Integral and Rational Zeros of Polynomial Functions

Objective: *To determine the rational zeros of a polynomial function*

Focus

Worldwide competition in manufacturing requires a highly skilled work force capable of using mathematics to model and solve day-to-day manufacturing problems. Many companies encourage employees to improve the efficiency and the quality of their work. An increasing number of workers and supervisors are expected to use mathematics to solve work-related problems which were formerly solved by trial and error or referred to the engineering staff.

Manufacturing processes that involve computations of area or volume often lead to models involving second and third degree polynomials. Recall that if a number a is a solution of the polynomial equation $P(x) = 0$, then a is a zero of the polynomial function $P(x)$. There are different types of zeros. Integral and rational zeros will be examined in this lesson. Integral zeros are zeros that are integers.

The zeros of the polynomial function
$P(x) = x^2 + 5x + 6$ can be found by
solving the equation $x^2 + 5x + 6 = 0$.
The zeros of $P(x)$ are the integers -3 and -2.

$$x^2 + 5x + 6 = 0$$
$$(x + 3)(x + 2) = 0$$
$$x + 3 = 0 \quad \text{or} \quad x + 2 = 0$$
$$x = -3 \quad \text{or} \quad x = -2$$

Note that the quadratic equation above has a leading coefficient of 1. To factor the polynomial, you select numbers that are factors of the constant term 6. This procedure can sometimes be used to determine zeros of polynomials in general, as stated in the following theorem.

Integral Zeros Theorem

If an integer a is a zero of a polynomial function with integral coefficients and a leading coefficient of 1, then a is a factor of the constant term of the polynomial.

The integer 2 is an integral zero of $f(x) = x^3 + 4x^2 - 7x - 10$ since $f(2) = 0$. Note that 2 is a factor of the constant term 10. The theorem does not give the integral zeros, but it does limit the number of choices.

LESSON PLAN

Vocabulary
integral zeros theorem
rational zeros theorem

Technology
graphing utility
symbolic manipulator

FOCUS

Have students investigate the use of and need for mathematics in the workplace. Students may interview family members, neighbors, or employees of companies in your area. They should be sure to inquire about how the application of mathematics in each job has developed or changed over time. In class compile a list of these applications for display and discussion.

INSTRUCTION

- Give students the following function:

  $$f(x) = 4x^3 + 8x^2 - x - 2$$

  Discuss how they might find the zeros of this function without the use of a graphing utility. Note that in this lesson, there are two theorems that will facilitate the use of synthetic division to find zeros of functions.
- Point out the shorthand method of dividing synthetically, used in each example.
- Encourage students to carefully read the proof of the rational zeros theorem and to explain it using their own words.

Alternative Learning Styles

Some students better retain what they learn through the use of visual aids. The following activity may help these students to see and understand the relationships between the graph of a polynomial function, its zeros, and its equation.

- Display the graphs of polynomials on a screen for all students to see:

$$f(x) = x^3 + x^2 - 8x - 12$$
$$g(x) = x^3 + 7x^2 + 2x - 40$$

- Pair students to work together to identify the zeros of each function.
- Have them try to find relationships between the zeros and the coefficients in each equation.
- Repeat this activity for polynomials with a leading integral coefficient not equal to 1.

GUIDED PRACTICE

For Example 1

Determine the integral zeros of each function.

1. $f(x) = x^3 - 4x^2 + x + 6$ $-1, 2, 3$

2. $g(x) = x^3 - 7x^2 + 11x - 5$
  1 (mult. 2), 5

Common Error In Exercise 2 some students may think that there must be three different zeros. Remind these students that a zero may have a multiplicity of two or more.

Example 1   Determine the integral zeros of $f(x) = x^3 - 6x^2 + 3x + 10$.

Since an integral zero must be a factor of the constant term, list the possible factors of 10: $\pm 1, \pm 2, \pm 5, \pm 10$. A graphing utility indicates that zeros occur near -1, 2, and 5. You can use synthetic division to check that these are the zeros of the function. It is convenient to write the coefficients of the polynomial just once and then perform the addition steps mentally.

[-10, 10] by [-12, 12]
x scl: 2   y scl: 2

	1	-6	3	10	Coefficients of $f(x)$
-1	1	-7	10	0	-1 is a zero of $f(x)$.
2	1	-4	-5	0	2 is a zero of $f(x)$.
5	1	-1	-2	0	5 is a zero of $f(x)$.

Thus, the integral zeros are -1, 2, and 5.

Sometimes zeros are rational numbers. For example, $\frac{5}{4}$ is a rational zero of $f(x) = 4x^3 + 7x^2 - 43x + 35$ since $\frac{5}{4}$ is a rational number and $f\left(\frac{5}{4}\right) = 0$. Note that the numerator 5 is a factor of the constant term 35 and the denominator 4 is a factor of the leading coefficient 4. This relationship is generalized in the *rational zeros theorem*, which provides rational number choices for zeros.

Rational Zeros Theorem

Let $f(x) = a_n x^n + a_{n-1}x^{n-1} + a_{n-2}x^{n-2} + \cdots + a_1 x + a_0, a_0 \neq 0$, be a polynomial function in standard form that has integral coefficients.

Then if the nonzero rational number $\frac{p}{q}$ in lowest terms is a zero of $p(x)$, p must be a factor of the constant term a_0 and q must be a factor of the leading coefficient a_n.

Proof: Let $\frac{p}{q}$, in lowest terms, be a zero of the integral polynomial

$$f(x) = a_n x^n + a_{n-1}x^{n-1} + a_{n-2}x^{n-2} + \cdots + a_1 x + a_0, \text{ where } \frac{p}{q} \neq 0$$

$$a_n\left(\frac{p}{q}\right)^n + a_{n-1}\left(\frac{p}{q}\right)^{n-1} + a_{n-2}\left(\frac{p}{q}\right)^{n-2} + \cdots + a_1\left(\frac{p}{q}\right) + a_0 = 0 \quad \text{Since } f\left(\frac{p}{q}\right) = 0.$$

$$a_n\left(\frac{p^n}{q^n}\right) + a_{n-1}\left(\frac{p^{n-1}}{q^{n-1}}\right) + a_{n-2}\left(\frac{p^{n-2}}{q^{n-2}}\right) + \cdots + a_1\left(\frac{p}{q}\right) + a_0 = 0$$

$$a_n p^n + a_{n-1}p^{n-1}q + a_{n-2}p^{n-2}q^2 + \cdots + a_1 pq^{n-1} + a_0 q^n = 0 \quad \text{Multiply by } q^n.$$

Then, $a_0 q^n = -(a_n p^n + a_{n-1}p^{n-1}q + a_{n-2}p^{n-2}q^2 + \cdots + a_1 pq^{n-1})$

and $a_n p^n = -(a_{n-1}p^{n-1}q + a_{n-2}p^{n-2}q^2 + \cdots + a_1 pq^{n-1} + a_0 q^n)$

Dividing the first equation by p and the second equation by q yields

$$\frac{a_0 q^n}{p} = -(a_n p^{n-1} + a_{n-1}p^{n-2}q + a_{n-2}p^{n-3}q^2 + \cdots + a_1 q^{n-1})$$

and $$\frac{a_n p^n}{q} = -(a_{n-1}p^{n-1} + a_{n-2}p^{n-2}q + \cdots + a_1 pq^{n-2} + a_0 q^{n-1})$$

344   Chapter 7 Polynomial Functions

Since p, q, and all the coefficients are integers, the right sides of the equations are integers. Therefore, the left sides of the equations are also integers. Since p and q are relatively prime, p is not a factor of q^n. Therefore, p is a factor of a_0. Similarly, q is not a factor of p^n and is therefore a factor of a_n.

You can use the rational zeros theorem and synthetic division to find zeros of polynomial functions. To narrow down the possible number of rational zeros, use a graphing utility.

Example 2 Determine the rational zeros of $f(x) = 12x^3 - 16x^2 - 5x + 3$.

Determine a list of possible rational zeros using the rational zeros theorem. The factors of the constant term 3 are ± 1, ± 3, and the factors of the leading coefficient 12 are ± 1, ± 2, ± 3, ± 4, ± 6, ± 12.

Possible zeros include ± 1, ± 3, $\pm\frac{1}{2}$, $\pm\frac{1}{3}$, $\pm\frac{1}{4}$, $\pm\frac{1}{6}$, $\pm\frac{1}{12}$, $\pm\frac{3}{2}$, and $\pm\frac{3}{4}$. Use a graphing utility to narrow down the possible number of rational zeros. Since the possible rational zeros range from -3 to 3, set the viewing rectangle to $[-3, 3]$ by $[-8, 6]$. Zeros appear near $-\frac{1}{2}$ and $\frac{3}{2}$ and at either $\frac{1}{4}$ or $\frac{1}{3}$.

	12	-16	-5	3	Coefficients of $f(x)$
$-\frac{1}{2}$	12	-22	-6	0	$-\frac{1}{2}$ is a zero of $f(x)$.
$\frac{1}{4}$	12	-13	$-\frac{33}{4}$	$\frac{15}{16}$	
$\frac{1}{3}$	12	-12	-9	0	$-\frac{1}{3}$ is a zero of $f(x)$.
$\frac{3}{2}$	12	2	-2	0	$-\frac{3}{2}$ is a zero of $f(x)$.

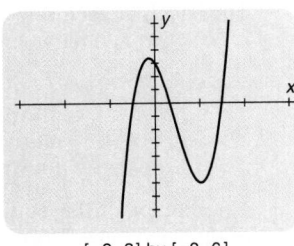
$[-3, 3]$ by $[-8, 6]$

Thus, the zeros are the rational numbers $-\frac{1}{2}$, $\frac{1}{3}$, and $\frac{3}{2}$.

Some polynomials have irrational zeros. First find any rational zeros. Then solve the depressed polynomial to determine any irrational zeros.

Example 3 Determine the zeros of $f(x) = x^3 + 3x^2 - 2x - 6$.

Since a rational zero must be a factor of the constant term, list the possible factors of -6: ± 1, ± 2, ± 3, ± 6. Use a graphing utility to narrow down the possibilities. A zero appears to occur near -3. Use synthetic division to check that -3 is a zero.

	1	3	-2	-6
-3	1	0	-2	0

$[-6, 6]$ by $[-8, 6]$

Thus, $f(x) = (x + 3)(x^2 - 2)$. Factor $x^2 - 2$ to determine additional zeros of $f(x)$. Since $x^2 - 2 = (x - \sqrt{2})(x + \sqrt{2})$, the irrational numbers $\sqrt{2}$ and $-\sqrt{2}$ are zeros of $f(x)$.
Thus, the zeros are -3, $\sqrt{2}$, and $-\sqrt{2}$.

7.3 Integral and Rational Zeros of Polynomial Functions   **345**

Modeling

How can a box-making machine supervisor determine the dimensions of boxes of different volumes?

A box-making machine supervisor may be asked to change the dimensions of the boxes being made to create boxes of slightly larger volume from the same piece of cardboard. Such a problem will require the supervisor to solve the polynomial equation which models the relationship of box volume to box dimensions. In general, the volume for a rectangular box is determined by multiplying length by width by height, $V = \ell wh$.

Example 4   *Manufacturing*   A firm must make open-top boxes having volume 64 in.³ There is a large supply of square cardboard sheets that measure 10 in. by 10 in. Each box is to be made by cutting small squares from each corner of the sheet and folding up the sides. What size square should be cut from each corner to produce a box with volume 64 in.³?

Let x represent the side of each square cut from the sheet. Then x represents the depth of the box. The length of each side of the box is $10 - 2x$, and the volume V is

$$V(x) = x(10 - 2x)(10 - 2x)$$
$$64 = x(10 - 2x)(10 - 2x)$$
$$0 = 4x^3 - 40x^2 + 100x - 64$$
$$0 = x^3 - 10x^2 + 25x - 16$$

The solution of this equation corresponds to the zeros of the polynomial $V(x) = x^3 - 10x^2 + 25x - 16$. Although the possible solutions range from -16 to 16, you should only be interested in positive values. *Why?*

 A graphing utility indicates that a zero occurs near 1. Use synthetic division to check that 1 is a zero of the function.

1	1	-10	25	-16
	1	-9	16	0

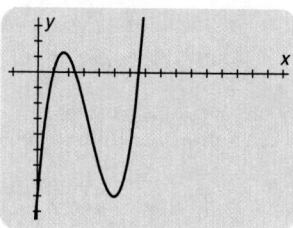

[−1, 16] by [−18, 6]
x scl: 1   y scl: 2

The remaining zeros of the polynomial are found by solving the depressed equation.

$x^2 - 9x + 16 = 0$ *The depressed equation cannot be factored.*

$x = \dfrac{9 \pm \sqrt{(-9)^2 - 4(1)(16)}}{2(1)}$ *Use the quadratic formula.*

$x = 2.44$ and $x = 6.56$ To the nearest hundredth.

The zeros of $V(x)$ are 1, 2.44, and 6.56. Since volume must be positive, 6.56 must be rejected as a possible solution. *Why?* The values $x = 1$ and $x = 2.44$ represent the two possible solutions to the problem. If $x = 1$, the dimensions will be 1 in. by 8 in. by 8 in. If $x = 2.44$, the dimensions will be 2.44 in. by 5.12 in. by 5.12 in.

346   Chapter 7 Polynomial Functions

Class Exercises

Determine the possible integral zeros of each polynomial.

1. $p(x) = x^4 - 7x^3 - 3x^2 + 2x + 12$
±1; ±2; ±3; ±4; ±6; ±12

2. $f(x) = x^4 + 5x^3 + 4x^2 - x - 18$
±1; ±2; ±3; ±6; ±9; ±18

Determine the possible rational zeros of each polynomial.

3. $h(x) = -4x^5 + 17x^3 - 5x^2 + 6x - 9$

4. $g(x) = 6x^4 - 3x^3 + x^2 - 10x + 15$

Determine the zeros of each polynomial.

5. $p(x) = x^3 - 28x + 48$ −6, 2, 4

6. $f(x) = x^4 - 7x^2 - 6x$ −2, −1, 0, 3

7. $g(x) = 6x^3 - 31x^2 + 16x + 9$ 1, $\frac{9}{2}$, $-\frac{1}{3}$

8. $h(x) = 6x^3 - 5x^2 - 18x - 7$ −1, $-\frac{1}{2}$, $\frac{7}{3}$

9. $f(x) = x^3 - 9x^2 + 12x - 4$ 1, $4 \pm 2\sqrt{3}$

10. $g(x) = x^4 + 3x^3 - 9x^2 - 15x + 20$
−4, 1, ±√5

11. Thinking Critically Under what conditions will a polynomial of degree 5 have fewer than five distinct zeros? Provide an example.

12. Writing in Mathematics Describe the relationship between the zeros of $p(x) = x^4 + 2x^3 - 13x^2 - 14x + 24$ and $q(x) = -x^4 - 2x^3 + 13x^2 + 14x - 24$ and discuss why this relationship exists.

Practice Exercises   Use appropriate technology.

Determine the possible integral zeros of each polynomial.

A **1.** $f(x) = x^3 + 5x^2 - 3x + 6$ ±1; ±2; ±3; ±6

2. $g(x) = x^3 - 7x^2 + 2x - 8$ ±1; ±2; ±4; ±8

3. $g(x) = x^4 - 5x^2 + x - 10$ ±1; ±2; ±5; ±10

4. $f(x) = 10x^4 + 7x^2 - x + 15$

Ⓡ **5.** Express $-315°$ in radians. $-\frac{7\pi}{4}$

Determine the possible rational zeros of each polynomial.

6. $h(x) = 5x^4 - 11x^3 + x - 9$

7. $p(x) = 7x^4 - 13x^3 - x - 25$

8. $p(x) = -2x^3 + 5x^2 - 6x + 18$

9. $h(x) = -3x^3 + 3x^2 - 8x + 20$

10. *Manufacturing* If the manufacturer in Example 4 cuts a 2.5-in. square from each corner, how much will the volume of the box differ from the 64 in.³? 1.5 in.³

Ⓣ **11.** Determine the period and amplitude of $f(x) = 2 \sin 3x$. $\frac{2\pi}{3} = 120°$; 2

Determine the zeros of each polynomial.

12. $f(x) = x^3 + 6x^2 + 11x + 6$ −1; −2; −3

13. $g(x) = x^3 - 6x^2 + 11x - 6$ 1; 2; 3

14. $m(x) = x^3 + x^2 - 3x - 3$ −1; ±1.73

15. $f(x) = x^3 - x^2 - 5x + 5$ 1; ±2.24

16. $p(x) = x^4 - 7x^2 - 6x$ 0; −1; −2; 3

17. $h(x) = x^4 - x^3 - 10x^2 + 4x + 24$
2; −2 (mult. 2); 3

18. Thinking Critically Why does Exercise 17 include only three distinct zeros?
(x + 2) is a factor of multiplicity 2.

Ⓡ **19.** Verify the identity $1 + \tan^2 \theta = \sec^2 \theta$ for $\theta = -60°$.

20. Prove the integral zeros theorem for the general cubic polynomial.

Find the rational zeros of each polynomial.

B **21.** $p(x) = 10x^3 - 17x^2 - 5x + 12$ $-\frac{4}{5}$; 1; $\frac{3}{2}$

22. $h(x) = 25x^3 - 25x^2 - 26x + 24$ −1; $\frac{4}{5}$; $\frac{6}{5}$

23. $g(x) = 18x^3 + 3x^2 - 7x - 2$ $-\frac{1}{2}$; $-\frac{1}{3}$; $\frac{2}{3}$

24. $f(x) = -6x^3 + 11x^2 + 3x - 2$ $-\frac{1}{2}$; $\frac{1}{3}$; 2

25. $n(x) = 2x^4 + 5x^3 - 11x^2 - 20x + 12$
−3; −2; $\frac{1}{2}$; 2

26. $m(x) = 2x^4 + 5x^3 - 5x - 2$
−2; −1; $-\frac{1}{2}$; 1

7.3 Integral and Rational Zeros of Polynomial Functions **347**

Writing in Mathematics
12. The zeros are identical. Since $p(x) = -q(x)$, if $p(a) = 0$, then $q(a) = -p(a) = 0$.

Exercises 5, 11, 19, 29, and 31 review concepts of radian measure, period and amplitude of trigonometric functions, trigonometric identities, coordinate geometry proofs, and solving trigonometric equations.

Project

The Project presents a good opportunity for hands-on learning. This may help students who are "visual learners."

Technology

Exercise 43 requires the use of a calculator.

LESSON FOLLOW-UP

Lesson Quiz

1. Find the integral zeros for $f(x) = x^3 - 6x^2 + 32$. -2, 4 (mult. 2)

2. Find the rational zeros for $g(x) = 12x^3 + 4x^2 - 3x - 1$. $-\frac{1}{2}$, $-\frac{1}{3}$, $\frac{1}{2}$

3. Find all zeros of $h(x) = x^3 + x^2 - 3x - 3$. $-\sqrt{3}$, -1, $\sqrt{3}$

Alternative Assessment

Write a word problem whose solution involves finding the zeros of a polynomial function of degree 3 or greater. Include a strategy for solving the problem and a complete solution.

Enrichment

Show that $x - a$ is a factor of $x^n - a^n$, where n is a positive integer. Since $a^n - a^n = 0$, a is a zero of $x^n - a^n$ for all n. Therefore, $x - a$ is a factor of $x^n - a^n$.

Additional Answers

27. 1-in. or 2-in. squares; $1 \times 8 \times 6$ in., $2 \times 6 \times 4$ in.

28. It is possible when they are constant multiples of each other, or if they have different nonintegral zeros.

30. Answers may vary. Example:
$p(x) = (x + 1)(x + 5)(x + 4)$,
$q(x) = (x + 1)(x + 5)(x - 4)$

36. -3, $-\frac{5 \pm \sqrt{17}}{2}$

---

27. *Manufacturing*   A company wishes to make boxes with volume 48 in.³ from sheets of cardboard 8 in. by 10 in. by cutting squares from each corner. What size squares should they cut? What are the dimensions of the boxes?

28. **Thinking Critically**   Under what conditions is it possible for two polynomial functions to have the same integral zeros but different graphs?

① **29.** Show that $(-3, 9)$, $(-11, 2)$, and $(-3, 2)$ are the vertices of a right triangle.

30. **Thinking Critically**   Determine the equations for two different third degree polynomials that have exactly two zeros in common.

① **31.** Solve: $\csc^2 x = 3$, $0 \le x < 2\pi$ 0.62; 2.53; 3.76; 5.67

32. How long is the edge of a cube if, after a slice 1 in. thick is cut from one side, the volume of the remaining figure is 100 in.³? 5 in.

33. The dimensions of a rectangular box are given by three consecutive integers, and its volume is 1716 cm³. Determine the dimensions of the box. $11 \times 12 \times 13$ cm

34. *Physics*   Under certain conditions, the velocity of an object as a function of time is given by $v(t) = 2t^3 - 17t^2 + 38t - 15$. Find all t such that $v(t) = 0$. $\frac{1}{2}$; 3; 5

35. *Physics*   Under certain conditions, the velocity of an object as a function of time is given by $v(t) = 3t^3 + 11t^2 + 5t - 3$. Find all t such that $v(t) = 0$. $\frac{1}{3}$

Determine the zeros of each polynomial.

C **36.** $p(x) = x^3 + 8x^2 + 17x + 6$ **37.** $h(x) = 2x^3 - 17x^2 + 11x + 15$ $\frac{3}{2}$; $\frac{7 \pm \sqrt{69}}{2}$

38. $f(x) = 2x^3 - 15x^2 + 14x + 11$ $-\frac{1}{2}$; $4 \pm \sqrt{5}$ **39.** $g(x) = x^4 + 3x^2 - 4$ -1, 1, $2i$, $-2i$

40. If $f(x) = x^3 - 2cx^2 + 5cx - 5$, find c so that the graph of f contains $(3, -1)$. $\frac{23}{3}$

41. If $g(x) = cx^3 - x^2 - 2cx - 5$, find c so that the graph of g contains $(2, 15)$. 6

42. *Manufacturing*   The cost of producing x gallons of a solvent is given by $C(x) = x^3 - 5x^2 - 22x + 80$. How many gallons can be produced for $96? 8 gal

43. If $p(x) = 4 \sin^4 x - 12 \sin x \cos^2 x - 7 \cos^2 x + 9 \sin x + 5$, find all zeros of $p(x)$ over the interval $0 \le x \le 2\pi$. $\frac{\pi}{6}$

44. *Engineering*   The deflection y of a beam at a horizontal distance x from one end is given by $y = 0.25(x^4 - 2L^2x^2 + L^3x)$, where L is the length of the beam. For what values of x is the deflection zero? $x = 0$, L, $-\frac{L \pm L\sqrt{5}}{2}$

Project

Develop a mathematical model that can be used to maximize the volume of a box that can be constructed by cutting squares from the corners of a rectangular piece of cardboard of given dimensions. Present your model to the class.

Review

Simplify and write with positive exponents.

1. $5x^6y^{-5} \frac{5x^6z}{y^5}$ **2.** $-\frac{12r^{-2}}{s^{-2}t^{-4}} - \frac{12t^4}{r^2s^2}$ **3.** $\left(\frac{14m^{-2}n}{7p^{-6}q}\right)^{-1} \frac{m^2q}{2np^6}$

29.

$\overline{AB}$ and $\overline{BC}$ are perpendicular.
$AB = 8$; $BC = 7$; $AC = 113$;
$(AB)^2 + (BC)^2 = (AC)^2$

7.4 The Fundamental Theorem of Algebra

Objective: *To state and apply the fundamental theorem of algebra*

Focus

Carl Friedrich Gauss is heralded as the greatest mathematician of the nineteenth century. He was a child prodigy who taught himself to read and to make mathematical calculations before the age of 3. At the age of 10, he developed the formula $\frac{n(n + 1)}{2}$ for the sum of the first n positive integers.

Gauss's interests in mathematics were extraordinarily diverse. He contributed to the applied fields of astronomy, geodesy, and electricity, and to the abstract fields of differential geometry, number theory, and Euclidian and non-Euclidian geometry. At the age of 20, he proved the fundamental theorem of algebra.

Unless otherwise stated, the polynomials in this text are understood to have real coefficients. However, there are a number of theorems in this chapter for which the coefficients are specified. For example, restricting the coefficients of a polynomial to the set of rational numbers leads to theorems that could not be stated about the zeros of the polynomial if the coefficients were not so specified. Conversely, a theorem stated for a polynomial with a certain set of coefficients, such as the rationals, will also be true when the coefficients belong to a subset of the specified set, such as the integers. Recall the ordering of subsets of numbers: integers $\subset$ rationals $\subset$ reals $\subset$ complex numbers.

The following theorem, stated for polynomials with complex coefficients, is also true for polynomials with real, rational, or integral coefficients. Note that restricting the set of coefficients does not change the set of possible zeros. For example, a polynomial with integral coefficients may have complex zeros.

Fundamental Theorem of Algebra

Every polynomial function of positive degree with complex coefficients has at least one complex zero.

The proof of this theorem is beyond the scope of this text.

Recall that a complex number is a number of the form $a + bi$, where a and b are real numbers. The symbol $\sqrt{-1}$ is represented by i; and $i^2 = -1$, $i^3 = -i$, and $i^4 = 1$. For example, $\sqrt{-16} = i\sqrt{16} = 4i$ and $\sqrt{-6} = i\sqrt{6}$.

LESSON PLAN

Vocabulary
fundamental theorem of algebra
complex conjugate theorem
conjugate radical theorem

Technology
graphing utility
symbolic manipulator

FOCUS

In 1799 Gauss obtained his doctorate from the University of Helmstedt, Germany, with a thesis entitled "New Demonstration of the Theorem that Every Rational Integral Algebraic Function in one Variable can be Resolved into Real Factors of First or Second Degree." In this thesis Gauss used graphs of curves to show that any polynomial of positive degree has at least one complex root, or zero. He then proved that the polynomial can be factored into real linear and quadratic factors. Gauss wrote three more proofs of this theorem, the fourth proof written fifty years after the first.

Encourage students to read further about the discoveries of Gauss in a history of mathematics book.

Given the two complex numbers $a + bi$ and $c + di$, then

Addition: $(a + bi) + (c + di) = (a + c) + (b + d)i$

Subtraction: $(a + bi) - (c + di) = (a - c) + (b - d)i$

Multiplication: $(a + bi)(c + di) = (ac - bd) + (ad + bc)i$

Division: $\dfrac{a + bi}{c + di} = \dfrac{a + bi}{c + di} \cdot \dfrac{c - di}{c - di}$ *Multiply by 1 using complex conjugate.*

$$= \frac{(ac + bd) + (bc - ad)i}{c^2 + d^2} = \frac{(ac + bd)}{c^2 + d^2} + \frac{(bc - ad)}{c^2 + d^2}i$$

The complex number $4i$ is a zero of $P(x) = x^4 - x^3 + 15x^2 - 16x - 16$ because $P(4i) = 0$. This is confirmed below using synthetic division.

$$
\begin{array}{r|rrrrr}
4i & 1 & -1 & 15 & -16 & -16 \\
   &   & 4i & -16 - 4i & 16 - 4i & 16 \\
\hline
   & 1 & -1 + 4i & -1 - 4i & -4i & 0
\end{array}
$$

The fundamental theorem of algebra leads to another theorem.

> If $P(x) = a_n x^n + a_{n-1} x^{n-1} + \cdots + a_1 x + a_0, a_n \neq 0$, is a polynomial of positive degree with complex coefficients, then $P(x)$ has n linear factors.

Proof: From the fundamental theorem of algebra, there exists a complex number r_1 such that $P(r_1) = 0$. By the factor theorem, which also applies to polynomial equations with complex coefficients, $(x - r_1)$ is a factor of P. Thus,
$$P(x) = (x - r_1)Q_1(x)$$
where $Q_1(x)$ is the quotient obtained when $P(x)$ is divided by $(x - r_1)$. Note that since the degree of P is n, the degree of $Q_1(x)$ is $n - 1$. Repeating the argument on $Q_1(x)$ will result in a $Q_2(x)$ such that
$$Q_1(x) = (x - r_2)Q_2(x).$$
So, $\qquad\qquad P(x) = (x - r_1)(x - r_2)Q_2(x)$

and the degree of $Q_2(x)$ is $n - 2$. Continuing in the same pattern n times,
$$P(x) = (x - r_1)(x - r_2)(x - r_3) \cdots (x - r_n)Q_n(x)$$
and each r_i is a complex zero of P. Because there are n factors of the form $(x - r_i)$, the polynomial $Q_n(x)$ must be a constant. That constant is a_n.

Therefore, $P(x) = a_n(x - r_1)(x - r_2)(x - r_3) \cdots (x - r_n)$, where each r_i is a complex zero of P.

A consequence of the above theorem is that a polynomial function of degree n cannot have more than n zeros.

> *Corollary* If $P(x)$ is a polynomial function with complex coefficients and degree n, then P has exactly n zeros.

Note that having n complex zeros does not necessarily mean having n distinct zeros. Whenever a zero of a polynomial function occurs a maximum of k times, then $(x - r)$ is a factor k times and r has *multiplicity* k. In the complex number $a + bi$, b may equal 0; thus, all real numbers are also complex numbers.

Example 1   Express $x^3 - 5x^2 + 3x + 9$ as a product of linear factors.

Since a rational zero must be a factor of the constant term, the possible zeros are $\pm 1, \pm 3, \pm 9$. Use a graphing utility to narrow down the possibilities. A zero appears near -1. Use synthetic division to verify -1 is a zero.

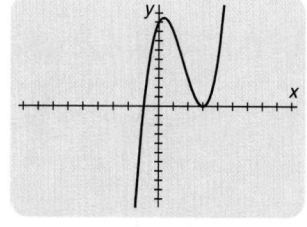

[−9, 9] by [−10, 10]

Thus, $P(x) = (x + 1)(x^2 - 6x + 9)$. Since the depressed polynomial $(x^2 - 6x + 9) = (x - 3)^2$, its zeros are -1 and 3 (multiplicity 2).

$$P(x) = x^3 - 5x^2 + 3x + 9 = (x + 1)(x - 3)^2.$$

The complex conjugate theorem is used to find zeros of real polynomials.

Complex Conjugate Theorem

If a complex number, $a + bi$, is a zero of a polynomial function with real coefficients, then its conjugate, $a - bi$, is also a zero of the polynomial.

Proof: Let $a + bi$ be a complex number with $b \neq 0$; let $f(x)$ be a polynomial function for which $f(a + bi) = 0$. By the factor theorem, $x - (a + bi)$ is a factor of $f(x)$.

It is necessary to show that $x - (a - bi)$ is also a factor of $f(x)$; that is, $[x - (a + bi)][x - (a - bi)]$ is a factor of $f(x)$. Thus,

$$f(x) = [x - (a + bi)][x - (a - bi)]Q(x) + (cx + d) \quad \textit{Why does } R = cx + d?$$
$$= [x^2 - 2ax + a^2 + b^2]Q(x) + (cx + d)$$

Since $0 = f(a + bi)$,

$$0 = [(a + bi)^2 - 2a(a + bi) + a^2 + b^2]Q(a + bi) + c(a + bi) + d$$
$$= [a^2 + 2abi - b^2 - 2a^2 - 2abi + a^2 + b^2]Q(a + bi) + c(a + bi) + d$$
$$= [0][Q(a + bi)] + c(a + bi) + d]$$

Thus, $c(a + bi) + d = 0$, $ac + cbi + d = 0$ and $(ac + d) + cbi = 0$. Since $b \neq 0$, $c = 0$. If $c = 0$, then d must also be 0.

Therefore, $f(x) = [x - (a + bi)][x - (a - bi)]Q(x) + 0$ and $x - (a - bi)$ is a factor of $f(x)$. Thus, $f(a - bi) = 0$.

7.4 The Fundamental Theorem of Algebra   **351**

GUIDED PRACTICE

For Example 1

Express each polynomial as a product of linear factors.

1. $x^3 + 5x^2 - 22x - 56$
   $(x + 2)(x + 7)(x - 4)$
2. $2x^3 + x^2 - 40x - 75$
   $(2x + 5)(x + 3)(x - 5)$

Example 2   Determine all zeros of $P(x) = x^4 - 6x^3 + 10x^2 + 2x - 15$ given that $2 + i$ is a zero.

By the complex conjugate theorem $2 - i$ is also a zero of the polynomial. Use the coefficients of the depressed polynomial and synthetic division.

$$
\begin{array}{r|cccc}
2 - i & 1 & -4 + i & 1 - 2i & 6 - 3i \\
 & & 2 - i & -4 + 2i & -6 + 3i \\
\hline
 & 1 & -2 & -3 & 0
\end{array}
$$

The new depressed polynomial is a quadratic which can be factored or solved by applying the quadratic formula.

$$x^2 - 2x - 3 = (x + 1)(x - 3)$$

Therefore, the zeros are $-1, 3, 2 + i,$ and $2 - i.$

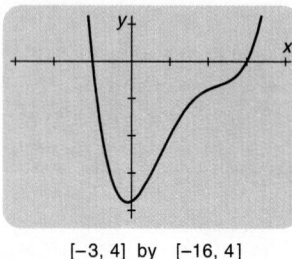

Example 2 can also be done using a graphing utility to first find the integral zeros. Observing the graph at the right, you can see that -1 and 3 appear to be zeros. Synthetic division will verify that they are zeros. Since $2 + i$ is a zero, $2 - i$ is also a zero. Thus, you again obtain the zeros $-1, 3, 2 + i,$ and $2 - i.$

[−3, 4] by [−16, 4]
x scl: 1   y scl: 4

If you are given the zeros of a polynomial, you can determine a polynomial function with those zeros.

Example 3   Determine a polynomial function with real coefficients of lowest degree and leading coefficient of 1 that has $1 + 5i$ and 2 as zeros.

Since real coefficients are desired, $1 - 5i$ must also be a zero.

$$
\begin{aligned}
P(x) &= [x - 2][(x - (1 - 5i)][(x - (1 + 5i)] \\
&= (x - 2)(x^2 - 2x + 26) \\
&= x^3 - 4x^2 + 30x - 52
\end{aligned}
$$

A theorem similar to the complex conjugate theorem concerning conjugate radicals is stated below. Its proof is left as an exercise.

> **Conjugate Radical Theorem**
>
> If $a + \sqrt{b}$ is a zero of a polynomial function with rational coefficients, where a and b are rational, but $\sqrt{b}$ is irrational, then the conjugate number $a - \sqrt{b}$ is also a zero of the polynomial.

352   Chapter 7 Polynomial Functions

Example 4 Determine a polynomial function of lowest degree with rational coefficients that has $1 + \sqrt{2}$ and 0 as zeros.

By the conjugate radical theorem, if $1 + \sqrt{2}$ is a zero, $1 - \sqrt{2}$ is also a zero.

$$P(x) = [x - 0][x - (1 + \sqrt{2})][x - (1 - \sqrt{2})]$$
$$= x[x^2 - (1 - \sqrt{2})x - (1 + \sqrt{2})x + (1 - 2)]$$
$$= x^3 - 2x^2 - x$$

Class Exercises

Express each polynomial as a product of linear factors.

1. $p(x) = x^3 + 2x^2 - 5x - 6$ $(x + 1)(x + 3)(x - 2)$ **2.** $f(x) = x^3 - 2x^2 - 15x + 36$ $(x + 4)(x - 3)^2$

3. $g(x) = x^4 + 2x^3 - 3x^2 - 4x + 4$ **4.** $h(x) = x^4 - 4x^3 - 3x^2 + 10x + 8$
$(x + 2)^2(x - 1)^2$ $(x + 1)^2(x - 4)(x - 2)$

Determine the zeros of each polynomial.

5. $p(x) = x^5 + x^3 - 2x^2 - 12x - 8$ -1 (mult. 2); 2; $\pm 2i$

6. $t(x) = x^4 - 5x^3 + 11x^2 + 11x - 78$ -2; 3; $2 \pm 3i$

7. $f(x) = 8x^5 - 12x^4 + 6x^3 - 5x^2 + 3$ $-\frac{1}{2}$; 1 (mult. 2); $\pm\frac{i\sqrt{3}}{2}$

Determine all remaining zeros of each polynomial given one of the zeros.

8. $p(x) = 9x^4 - 42x^3 + 79x^2 - 40x + 6$; $2 + i\sqrt{2}$ $2 - i\sqrt{2}$; $\frac{1}{3}$ (mult. 2)

9. $t(x) = 4x^4 - 46x^3 + 135x^2 - 138x + 54$; $5 + \sqrt{7}$ $5 - \sqrt{7}$; $\frac{3 \pm i\sqrt{3}}{4}$

Determine a polynomial function of lowest degree with rational coefficients that has the given zeros.

10. $1 + \sqrt{3}$ $f(x) = x^2 - 2x - 2$ **11.** $3 + i\sqrt{5}$ and $3 - i\sqrt{5}$, each with multiplicity 2.
$f(x) = x^4 - 12x^3 + 64x^2 - 168x + 196$

12. Thinking Critically Is it possible to have a polynomial function with rational coefficients that has only $3 + \sqrt{7}$ as a zero? If so, describe; if not, tell why not.

Practice Exercises

Express each polynomial as a product of linear factors.
$(x - 3)(x + 2)(x + 5)$
A **1.** $p(x) = x^3 - 3x^2 - 10x + 24$ $(x - 4)(x - 2)(x + 3)$ **2.** $t(x) = x^3 + 4x^2 - 11x - 30$

3. $f(x) = x^4 - 3x^3 - 13x^2 + 51x - 36$ **4.** $g(x) = x^4 - 4x^3 - 16x^2 + 16x + 48$

5. $h(x) = 2x^4 - 15x^3 + 42x^2 - 52x + 24$ **6.** $n(x) = 3x^4 + 14x^3 + 12x^2 - 24x - 32$
$(x - 2)^3(2x - 3)$ $(x + 2)^3(3x - 4)$

Determine the zeros of each polynomial.

7. $p(x) = x^3 - 8x - 8$ -2; $1 \pm \sqrt{5}$ **8.** $t(x) = x^3 + 2x^2 - 5x - 6$ -3; -1; 2

9. $f(x) = x^4 + x^3 - x^2 + x - 2$ -2; 1; $\pm i$ **10.** $g(x) = x^4 - x^3 + x^2 - 3x - 6$ -1; 2; $\pm i\sqrt{3}$

11. $h(x) = x^3 + 3x^2 - 5x - 39$ 3; $-3 \pm 2i$ **12.** $n(x) = x^3 - 6x^2 + 13x - 10$ 2; $2 \pm i$

Ⓡ **13.** Given that $\sin x = -\frac{4}{7}$, and $\cos x < 0$, determine $\cos 3x$. $-\frac{15\sqrt{33}}{343} = -0.2512$

7.4 The Fundamental Theorem of Algebra **353**

For Example 4
Determine a polynomial of lowest degree with rational coefficients that the given numbers as zeros.
1. $-3 + \sqrt{3}$ and 0
$x^3 + 6x^2 + 6x$
2. $2 - \sqrt{7}$, -1
$x^3 - 3x^2 - 7x - 3$
3. $\sqrt{2}$, $5 + \sqrt{5}$
$x^4 - 10x^3 + 18x^2 + 20x - 40$

CLOSURE

Have students describe how they would find the zeros of the function:

$$f(x) = x^3 - 2x^2 + 5x - 10$$

INDEPENDENT PRACTICE

Assignment Guide
Basic: 1–18, 19–31 odd
Average: 1–15 odd, 17–34, 48
Enriched: 1–33 odd, 35–49

Teacher's Resource Book
Practice, page 46

Ⓡ **Review**
Exercises 13, 19, 31, 33, and 40 review concepts of determining values of trigonometric functions, and using trigonometric identities, volume formulas for cylinders and cones, and systems of equations.

Additional Answers

Class Exercises
12. no; To have rational coefficients, the polynomial must also have $3 - \sqrt{7}$ as a zero.

Practice Exercises
3. $(x - 3)^2(x - 1)(x + 4)$
4. $(x - 2)(x + 2)^2(x - 6)$

LESSON FOLLOW-UP

Test Yourself

Teacher's Resource Book
  Tests—Quiz, form A, page 25
  Tests—Quiz, form B, page 25

Lesson Quiz

1. Factor $p(x) = x^3 - 4x^2 - 15x + 18$ as a product of linear factors. $(x - 6)(x - 1)(x + 3)$

2. Find the zeros of $f(x) = 6x^3 - 25x^2 - 2x + 56$. $-\frac{4}{3}, \frac{7}{2}, 2$

3. Find the remaining zeros of $p(x) = x^4 - 3x^3 + 18x^2 - 48x + 32$ given that $4i$ is a zero. $-4i, 1, 2$

4. Find a polynomial of lowest degree with real coefficients and a leading coefficient of 1 that has $7 - 4i$ as a zero. $f(x) = x^2 - 14x + 65$

Additional Answers

17. Answers may vary. Some examples follow. The zeros may have different multiplicities. The signs of the leading coefficients may be different.

18. Answers may vary. Some examples follow. One graph may rise from the left; the other may fall from the left. If a zero has a real odd multiplicity, its graph will cross the x-axis at that zero; if a zero has a real even multiplicity, its graph will have a relative extrema at that point.

33. $\sin y + \cos y \tan y = \sin y + \cos y \frac{\sin y}{\cos y} = \sin y + \sin y = 2 \sin y$

39. $x^8 - 28x^7 + 294x^6 - 1232x^5 - 99x^4 + 14{,}420x^3 - 21{,}560x^2 - 37{,}800x + 72{,}900$

Determine another zero for a polynomial function that has each of the following as a zero.

14. i $-i$

15. $3 + 2i$ $3 - 2i$

16. $-2 - \sqrt{2}$ $-2 + \sqrt{2}$

17. **Thinking Critically** Two different polynomial functions with real coefficients have the same set of zeros. How is this possible?

18. **Thinking Critically** How are the graphs of the polynomial functions in Exercise 17 alike and how are they different?

Ⓡ 19. *Construction* A water storage tank is to be constructed in the shape of a right circular cylinder 15 ft high. Find the radius that gives a volume of 240π ft³. 4 ft

Determine a polynomial function of lowest degree with rational coefficients that has the following zeros.

20. $\sqrt{3}$ $f(x) = x^2 - 3$

21. $1 - \sqrt{5}$ $f(x) = x^2 - 2x - 4$

22. $2 + \sqrt{2}$ $f(x) = x^2 - 4x + 2$

Determine all remaining zeros of each polynomial given one of the zeros.

B 23. $p(x) = 3x^4 - 16x^3 + 24x^2 + 44x - 39$; $3 + 2i$ $3 - 2i$, $\frac{1 \pm \sqrt{10}}{3}$

24. $t(x) = x^4 + 2x^3 - 4x - 4$; $-1 + i$ $-1 - i$, $\pm\sqrt{2}$

25. $f(x) = x^4 + 4x^3 + 4x - 1$; $-2 + \sqrt{5}$ $-2 - \sqrt{5}$; $\pm i$

26. $g(x) = 2x^4 - 22x^3 + 65x^2 - 24x - 3$; $3 - \sqrt{6}$ $3 + \sqrt{6}$, $\frac{5 \pm 3\sqrt{3}}{2}$

27. $p(x) = 2x^6 - x^5 - 2x^3 - 6x^2 - x - 4$; i i, $-i$ (mult. 2), $\frac{1 \pm \sqrt{33}}{4}$

28. $n(x) = x^6 + x^5 - 4x^4 + 2x^3 - 11x^2 + x - 6$; $-i$ $-i$, i (mult. 2), -3, 2

Derive a polynomial function of lowest degree with rational coefficients that has the following zeros.

29. $1 + \sqrt{5}$ and 0 $f(x) = x^3 - 2x^2 - 4x$

30. $1 - \sqrt{3}$ and 2 $f(x) = x^3 - 4x^2 + 2x + 4$

Ⓡ 31. *Construction* A storage shelter in the shape of a right circular cone has a height of 12 m and volume 350 m³. Determine the radius of the base to the nearest tenth of a meter. 5.3 m

32. *Ecology* A pond is stocked with 100 bass. The number of bass in the pond after t years is given by the equation $f(t) = -t^2 + 25t + 100$. When does the size of the school exceed 200? $5 < t < 20$

Ⓡ 33. Prove the identity $\sin y + \cos y \tan y = 2 \sin y$.

34. *Demography* The population in thousands of a city during 6 years is described by the function $f(t) = t^3 - 15t + 100$, $0 < t < 6$. To the nearest tenth of a year, when was the population at its lowest; and to the nearest hundred, what was the population at that time? 2.2y; 77,600

Determine a polynomial of lowest degree with real coefficients that has the given zeros.

35. $4 + 3i$ $x^2 - 8x + 25$ 36. $3 - 4i$ $x^2 - 6x + 25$ 37. $5 - i\sqrt{2}$ and -5 $x^3 - 5x^2 - 23x + 135$ 38. $2 - i\sqrt{5}$ and -2 $x^3 - 2x^2 + x + 18$

C 39. $7 - i\sqrt{5}$ (multiplicity 2) and $\sqrt{5}$ (multiplicity 2)

354   Chapter 7 Polynomial Functions

R 40. Solve the system of equations algebraically: $\begin{cases} y = x^3 \\ y = 7x + 6 \end{cases}$ $(-1, -1), (3, 27), (-2, -8)$

41. Determine the equation of the third degree polynomial, $p(x)$, that crosses the x-axis at $x = -1$ and $x = 2$ and has a y-intercept of 6. $p(x) = x^3 - 4x^2 + x + 6$

42. Express in factored form a polynomial function of degree 10 and leading coefficient 3 that has no zero except the complex number $\sqrt{3}$. $p(x) = 3(x - \sqrt{3})^{10}$

43. Express in factored form a polynomial function of degree 12 and leading coefficient 2 that has no zero except the complex number $\sqrt{2}$. $p(x) = 2(x - \sqrt{2})^{12}$

44. **Writing in Mathematics**   Explain whether or not a polynomial function of degree n with real coefficients must intersect the x-axis in n different points.

45. **Thinking Critically**   If $p(x)$ and $t(x)$ are two polynomial functions of degree 9 with real coefficients whose graphs intersect in at least 10 points. Should the graphs coincide? Why or why not?

If $p(x) = x^3 + x^2 - x - 1$, $q(x) = 11 - x$, and $r(x) = 44x^3 + 12x^2 - 11x - 6$ determine the solutions to the following equations:

46. $p(x) = q(x)$ $2, -\dfrac{3 \pm i\sqrt{15}}{2}$

47. $p(x) = r(x)$ $0.55, 0.40 \pm 0.22i$

48. Prove the conjugate radical theorem. The proof is similar to the proof of the complex conjugate theorem.

49. **Thinking Critically**   If a polynomial has a total of five solutions, determine the possible combinations of real and imaginary solutions. all real; 1 real, 4 imaginary; 3 real, 2 imaginary

Test Yourself

1. Evaluate $f(x) = 3x^3 + 2x^2 - 6x + 4$ when $x = -5$ using synthetic substitution. -291 7.1

2. Divide $(2x^3 - 3x^2 + 5)$ by $(x + 3)$ using synthetic division. $2x^2 - 9x + 27$ R $= -76$

3. Use the factor theorem to determine whether $x - 2$ is a factor of $h(x)$ when $h(x) = x^4 + 3x^3 - 7x^2 - 45x - 80$. not a factor

4. Determine k so that $f(x) = 2x^3 - 5x^2 + kx - 20$ has $x + 2$ as a factor. -28

Without using a graphing utility, draw each function.

5. $f(x) = x^3 - 3$

6. $g(x) = (x - 1)^4$ 7.2

Graph each polynomial function. Determine the zeros and the number of relative extrema.

7. $f(x) = x^3 + 4x^2 - 5x$ $-5, 0, 1; 2$

8. $h(x) = x^4 + x^3 - 12x^2 - 28x - 16$ $-2, -1, 4; 3$

9. Determine the integral zeros of $f(x) = x^3 + 7x^2 - x - 7$. $-7, -1, 1$ 7.3

10. Determine the rational zeros of $f(x) = 12x^3 - 17x^2 + 3x + 2$. $-\dfrac{1}{4}, \dfrac{2}{3}, 1$

11. Express $p(x) = x^3 - 3x^2 - 10x + 24$ as a product of linear factors. $(x + 3)(x - 2)(x - 4)$ 7.4

12. Determine the zeros of $f(x) = (x + 3)^2(x - 4)^3(x + 2)$ and state the multiplicity of each. -3 (mult. 2); 4 (mult. 3); -2 (mult. 1)

13. Determine the zeros of $f(x) = x^4 - 2x^3 - 4x^2 - 8x - 32$. $-2, 4, 2i, -2i$

14. Determine a polynomial function of lowest degree with real coefficients that has $2 - 3i$ and 4 as zeros. $p(x) = x^3 - 8x^2 + 29x - 52$

7.4 The Fundamental Theorem of Algebra   **355**

Writing in Mathematics
44. A polynomial function of degree n has n distinct zeros if each has a multiplicity of 1; otherwise the function has fewer than n distinct zeros. This function may have one distinct zero with multiplicity n. So, the graph of the function can intersect the x-axis in 1 to n different points.

Vocabulary

Descartes' rule of signs
intermediate value theorem
location theorem
lower bound
sum and products of zeros theorem
upper bound
upper and lower bound theorem

Technology

graphing utility
symbolic manipulator

FOCUS

Encourage students to look in biology, physics, and economics textbooks for examples of polynomial functions. Collect and display them in your classroom. This will help students to make connections between mathematics and other subject areas.

INSTRUCTION

- The polynomial functions presented in this lesson have rational or irrational zeros that are not easily found using algebraic methods. Discuss Descartes' rule of signs, the location theorem, and the upper and lower bound theorem, which help to find intervals containing these zeros.
- Before solving Example 2, discuss how to find two consecutive integers between which a real zero is located. Suggestions should include evaluating the function at consecutive integers using trial-and-error with substitution or with synthetic division and checking for different signs in the evaluated values.
- Students that do not have a graphing utility should not be expected to find decimal zeros of functions such as in Example 2. However, they should be able to locate each zero between two integers.

7.5	**Descartes' Rule, the Intermediate Value Theorem, and Sum and Product of Zeros**

Objectives: To apply theorems about the zeros of polynomial functions
To approximate zeros of polynomial functions

Focus

Scientific, industrial, and business problems often require determining the minimum or maximum of a function. Physicists look for the minimum amount of energy required to determine the arrangement of crystals. Astronomers seek maximum visibility. Automobile manufacturers minimize air resistance and noise. Power plant operators minimize the quantity of pollutants. Businesses often wish to maximize profits and minimize costs.

This effort to maximize or minimize is frequently accomplished through research using polynomial functions. In calculus, finding maximum and minimum values of a function depends on finding the zeros of a related function.

There are several theorems that will increase your understanding of the relationship between a polynomial function and its zeros. The first of these theorems is Descartes' rule of signs, which is stated without proof.

> **Descartes' Rule of Signs**
>
> The number of *positive* real zeros of a polynomial function $P(x)$, with real coefficients, is equal to the number of variations in sign of the terms of $P(x)$ or is less than this number by a multiple of 2.
>
> The number of *negative* real zeros is equal to the number of variations in sign of the terms of $P(-x)$ or is less than this number by a multiple of 2.

The number of variations in sign is determined by arranging the terms of the polynomial in descending order of the powers of the variable and counting the number of pairs of consecutive terms with different signs. Note that Descartes' rule of signs does not guarantee the number of real zeros but merely places an upper limit on the number of zeros.

356   Chapter 7 Polynomial Functions

Example 1 Determine the possible number of positive and negative real zeros of the polynomial $P(x) = x^3 - 5x^2 + 4x + 12$.

$$P(x) = x^3 - 5x^2 + 4x + 12$$
$$P(-x) = (-x)^3 - 5(-x)^2 + 4(-x) + 12$$
$$= -x^3 - 5x^2 - 4x + 12$$

There are two changes in sign in $P(x)$, so there are either two or zero positive real zeros. There is one change in sign in $P(-x)$, so there is one negative real zero.

Real zeros that are integers can be determined from the graph of a polynomial function as demonstrated in an earlier lesson. The following theorems are useful in locating real zeros and other values of polynomials.

Location Theorem

If $P(x)$ is a polynomial function with real coefficients, and a and b are real numbers such that $P(a)$ is positive and $P(b)$ is negative, then $P(x)$ has at least one zero between a and b.

The location theorem is a special case of a more general theorem called the intermediate value theorem. The proof will be provided in a calculus course.

Intermediate Value Theorem

If $P(x)$ is a polynomial function such that $a < b$ and $P(a) \neq P(b)$, then $P(x)$ takes on every value between $P(a)$ and $P(b)$ in the interval $[a, b]$.

If $P(a) > 0$ and $P(b) < 0$, does the location theorem guarantee that there is only one zero between a and b?

The polynomial function $P(x) = x^3 + x - 1$ has a zero between 0 and 1 since $P(0) = -1$ and $P(1) = 1$. To determine the value of this real zero of $P(x)$, use a graphing utility with appropriate viewing rectangles. Repeated use of the zoom and trace features allows you to find real zeros to the desired degree of accuracy.

Example 2 Graph $f(x) = x^3 + x - 1$ using a graphing utility and locate the real zero correct to the nearest hundredth.

Since there is a real zero between 0 and 1, an appropriate viewing rectangle might be $[-2, 2]$ by $[-10, 10]$. Looking at the graph, you can see that the graph crosses

7.5 Descartes' Rule, the Intermediate Value Theorem, and Sum and Product of Zeros **357**

Thinking Critically
No, there may be many zeros between a and b.

Graph the given polynomial function using a graphing utility and find the real zeros correct to the nearest hundredth.

1. $p(x) = x^3 + 15x + 7$

−0.46

2. $f(x) = x^4 + 3x^3 + 15x − 7$

0.45, −4.03

Technology When graphing the polynomial functions with a graphing calculator, it will be necessary to use both the zoom and trace features to approximate the real zeros correct to the nearest hundredth.

For Example 3

Determine the sum and product of the zeros of each polynomial.

1. $f(x) = x^4 + x^3 + 3x^2 + 9x − 54$
sum: −1; product: −54

2. $g(x) = 2x^4 − 9x^3 + 14x^2 − 5x$
sum: $\frac{9}{2}$; product: 0

---

the x-axis to the right of 0.5. Evaluate $f(0.6)$ and $f(0.7)$ to obtain $f(0.6) = -0.184$ and $f(0.7) = 0.043$. Thus, by the location theorem, the real zero is between 0.6 and 0.7. Using the zoom and trace features several times indicates that the real zero is 0.68, correct to the nearest hundredth, which is shown below on the right.

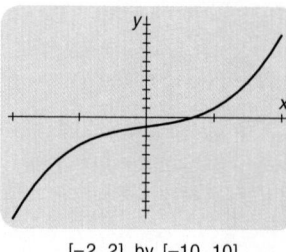

[−2, 2] by [−10, 10]

[0.6, 0.7] by [−0.2, 0.05]
x scl: 0.02   y scl: 0.05

The following theorem states several further relationships between the zeros and the coefficients of a polynomial.

Sum and Product of Zeros Theorem

In the polynomial $f(x) = a_n x^n + a_{n-1} x^{n-1}, + \cdots + a_1 x + a_0$, with $a_n \neq 0$, the sum of the zeros is equal to $-\dfrac{a_{n-1}}{a_n}$, and the product of the zeros is equal to $\dfrac{a_0}{a_n}$ for n even and $-\dfrac{a_0}{a_n}$ for n odd.

Example 3 Determine the sum and product of the zeros for each of the following.

a. $f(x) = 4x^4 − 3x^3 + 2x^2 − x + 6$ **b.** $g(x) = 3x^5 − 2x^3 + x^2 − x + 4$

a. $a_n = 4$, $a_{n-1} = -3$, $a_0 = 6$, n is even

Sum of the zeros: $-\left(\dfrac{-3}{4}\right) = \dfrac{3}{4}$ Product of the zeros: $\dfrac{6}{4} = \dfrac{3}{2}$

b. $a_n = 3$, $a_{n-1} = 0$, $a_0 = 4$, n is odd

Sum of the zeros: $-\left(\dfrac{0}{3}\right) = 0$ Product of the zeros: $-\dfrac{4}{3}$

Note that in part (b) above, there is no x^4 term. However, this term must be considered when finding the sum of the roots. The coefficient of x^4 is 0.

The graphing utility offers a useful, straightforward method of determining the zeros of a polynomial. However, there are several algorithms that can be used in programming a computer or calculator to make accurate approximations of zeros. One of the easiest of these algorithms is the bisection method. This method is based on the location theorem. A function is repeatedly evaluated at the midpoint of an interval over which the polynomial shows a change in sign.

358   Chapter 7 Polynomial Functions

You can use the bisection method and synthetic substitution to find the zeros of a polynomial. For example, if $f(x) = x^3 - x^2 + x - 2$, a change in signs indicates a zero between 1 and 2. Synthetic substitution on smaller and smaller intervals proceeds as follows:

	1	-1	$+1$	-2	
1	1	0	1	-1	
2	1	1	3	4	Bisect the interval [1, 2].
1.5	1	0.5	1.75	0.625	Bisect the interval [1, 1.5].
1.25	1	0.25	1.3125	-0.3594	Bisect the interval [1.25, 1.5].
1.375	1	0.375	1.5156	0.0840	1.375 is a good approximation.

Thus, $a = 1.375$ is a reasonably good approximation of a zero. But this algorithm can be easily included in a computer or calculator program to find a zero to any desired degree of accuracy.

Why was the interval [1, 1.5] bisected instead of the interval [1.5, 2]?

It is often useful to know that the zeros of a polynomial are within certain bounds. An **upper bound** for the real zeros of a polynomial function is a number greater than or equal to the greatest real zero of the function. Similarly, a **lower bound** is a number less than or equal to the least real zero of the function. The following theorem can help you locate the zeros of a polynomial function:

Upper and Lower Bound Theorem

Let $P(x)$, a polynomial function with positive leading coefficient, be divided by $x - c$.

- If $c > 0$ and all the coefficients in the quotient and remainder are nonnegative, then c is an upper bound of the zeros.
- If $c < 0$ and the coefficients in the quotient and remainder alternate in sign, then c is a lower bound of the zeros.

It should be noted that this theorem has several restrictions. It will only give a negative lower bound and a positive upper bound. Secondly, the theorem is not an "if and only if" statement. That is, if synthetic substitution does not indicate a bound, you cannot be absolutely sure that the number is not a bound. Therefore, the method does not always give you the least upper bound or the greatest lower bound. In practice, a graphing utility is often the most useful tool for finding upper and lower bounds.

Example 4   Determine the least integral upper bound and greatest integral lower bound for the zeros of the function $f(x) = x^5 + 5x^4 - 3x^3 - 29x^2 + 2x + 23$.

A graphing utility shows a lower bound near -4 and an upper bound near 3. Use synthetic division to test $-6, -5, -4$.

7.5 Descartes' Rule, the Intermediate Value Theorem, and Sum and Product of Zeros   **359**

Sketch one possible graph that satisfies the following conditions:
- The leading coefficient is negative.
- $P(x)$ is a fifth degree polynomial.
- $P(x)$ has two distinct negative real zeros, one with multiplicity 2, and one positive real zero with multiplicity 2.
- The greatest integral lower bound is -4; the least integral upper bound is 3. Answers may vary.

CLOSURE

Have students write a paragraph explaining how to find the number of real zeros of a polynomial function and locate each between two consecutive integers without the use of a graphing calculator.

	1	5	-3	-29	2	23
-6	1	-1	3	-47	284	-1681
-5	1	0	-3	-14	72	-337
-4	1	1	-7	-1	6	-1

The test shows that -6 is a lower bound. However, the function remains negative for x-values up to -4. Thus, the greatest integral lower bound for zeros of the function is -4.

The graph shows an upper bound near 2. Test 2 and 3.

	1	5	-3	-29	2	23
2	1	7	11	-7	-12	-1
3	1	8	21	34	104	335

[-5, 4] by [-25, 25]
x scl: 1 y scl: 5

Synthetic division shows that 3 is an upper bound for the zeros. Since some of the coefficients in the row associated with 2 are negative, 2 is not an upper bound. By the location theorem, there is a zero between 2 and 3. Thus, 3 is the least integral upper bound for the zeros of the function.

Example 5 Sketch one possible graph of $P(x)$ that satisfies the following conditions:
- $P(x)$ is a fourth degree polynomial with leading coefficient 1.
- $P(x)$ has two distinct negative real zeros and one positive real zero with multiplicity 2.
- The greatest integral lower bound for the zeros of $P(x)$ is -5.
- The least integral upper bound is 4.

Such a graph will rise to the left and the right and cross the negative x-axis twice between -5 and 0 and be tangent to the positive x-axis once between 0 and 4. One possible graph is shown at the right.

Why is it necessary to specify that the leading coefficient is 1? How would the graph change if the leading coefficient were -2?

Sketch another graph satisfying the conditions of Example 5 with a substantially different shape.

Class Exercises

Determine the possible number of positive and negative real zeros of each polynomial.

1. $p(x) = x^3 + 5x + 12$ none; one

2. $p(x) = x^3 - 5x - 12$ one; two or zero

3. $f(x) = x^4 + x^2 + x + 3$ none; two or zero

4. $f(x) = x^4 - x^3 + x - 7$ three or one; one

360   Chapter 7 Polynomial Functions

Thinking Critically

If the leading coefficient were negative, the upper and lower bound theorem could not be applied.

Answers may vary. Check students' graphs.

Locate the real zeros of each polynomial between consecutive integers.

5. $p(x) = x^4 - 20x^2 - 21x - 22$

6. $p(x) = x^4 - 3x^3 + 2x + 12$ none

7. $f(x) = x^5 - x^4 + 2x^2 - x + 4$ -1 and -2

8. $f(x) = x^4 - 3x^2 - 6x - 2$ 2 and 3; 0 and -1

Determine the least integral upper bound and the greatest integral lower bound for the zeros of each polynomial.

9. $f(x) = x^4 - 2x^3 + 4x - 4$ 2; -2

10. $f(x) = x^4 + 3x - 13$ 2; -3

Use a graphing utility and the location theorem to determine all zeros of each polynomial, correct to the nearest hundredth.

11. $p(x) = x^3 - 9x^2 + 23x - 15$ 1; 3; 5

12. $p(x) = x^4 - x^3 - 7x^2 + x + 6$ -2; -1; 1; 3

Determine the sum and product of the zeros of each polynomial.

13. $f(x) = 3x^4 - 3x^3 + 2x - 1$ 1; $-\frac{1}{3}$

14. $f(x) = 4x^3 - 2x^2 + x$ $\frac{1}{2}$; 0

Practice Exercises   ⬡ Use appropriate technology.

Determine the possible number of positive and negative real zeros of each polynomial.

4, 2, or no pos., 1 neg.

A **1.** $p(x) = x^4 - 3x^2 + 6$ 2 or no pos., 2 or no neg.

2. $g(x) = 8x^5 - 12x^4 + 6x^3 - 5x^2 + 3$

3. $f(x) = x^4 - 15x^2 + 10x + 24$ 2 or no pos., 2 or no neg.

4. $h(x) = 7x^5 + 13x^4 - 8x^3 - 4x - 5$ 1 pos., 2 or no neg.

Locate the real zeros of each polynomial between consecutive integers.

5. $f(x) = 2x^3 + 3x - 24$ 2 and 3

6. $f(x) = 3x^3 + 4x - 18$ 1 and 2

7. $g(x) = 2x^4 - 3x^2 + 20x - 65$ -3 and -2, 2 and 3

8. $g(x) = 2x^4 - 5x^2 + 16x - 50$ -3 and -2, 2 and 3

Ⓡ **9.** *Surveying* Find, to the nearest square foot, the area of a triangular lot if two sides measure 166 ft and 222 ft, and the angle between them is 74.8°. 17,781 ft²

Determine the least integral upper bound and the greatest integral lower bound for the zeros of each polynomial.

10. $p(x) = x^3 + 2x^2 + 8x + 3$ 1; -3

11. $p(x) = 3x^3 + x^2 - 9x + 4$ 2; -3

12. $f(x) = x^6 + x^4 - 7x^2 + 6$ 2; -2

13. $f(x) = 5x^6 + 16x^3 - 20$ 1; -2

14. $g(x) = 2x^5 - 5x^2 + 8$ 2; -2

15. $f(x) = x^3 - 3x^2 + 5x - 4$ 3; -1

16. Writing in Mathematics Let $P(x)$ be a polynomial function with real coefficients and $P(a) > 0$ and $P(b) < 0$. Describe several possibilities for the behavior of P between a and b.

Ⓡ **17.** Solve $2 \sin^2 x - 3 \sin x + 1 = 0$ for x, $0° \leq x < 360°$. 30°, 90°, 150°

Determine the sum and product of the zeros for each of the following:

18. $p(x) = 2x^4 - 3x^2 + 3x - 2$ 0; -1

19. $p(x) = 3x^5 - 4x^4 + x^3 - 5x^2 + 15$ $\frac{4}{3}$; -5

Sketch a graph for a polynomial function satisfying the given conditions.

20. A cubic with one negative real zero and two positive distinct real zeros, a greatest integral lower bound of -4, and a least integral upper bound of 5.

21. A fourth degree polynomial with no real zeros.

7.5 Descartes' Rule, the Intermediate Value Theorem, and Sum and Product of Zeros **361**

INDEPENDENT PRACTICE

Assignment Guide

Basic: 1–28
Average: 18–40, 42
Enriched: 25–33 odd, 34–52

Teacher's Resource Book
  Practice, page 47

Ⓡ **Review**
Exercises 9, 17, 25, 35, and 47 review concepts such as finding the area of a triangle, solving trigonometric equations, finding angular velocity, evaluating trigonometric functions, and proving trigonometric identities.

Technology Exercises 26 to 33, 40 to 43, and 52 require the use of a graphing utility with both trace and zoom features. Exercise 49 requires the use of a programmable calculator or a computer.

Additional Answers
Class Exercises
5. between -4 and -5 and between 5 and 6

Practice Exercises
20.

21.
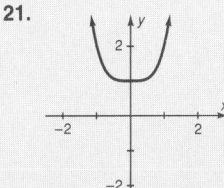

Writing in Mathematics
16. Answers may vary. The graph of $P(x)$ will cross the x-axis between $x = a$ and $x = b$ if it is a linear function or a third degree function, in which case it may flatten as it approaches the zero from both the right and the left. If the function has two zeros between a and b, one must have multiplicity of 2; if the function has three zeros between a and b, each can have multiplicity of 1.

Lesson Quiz

1. Find the possible number of positive and negative real zeros of the function $f(x) = x^4 - 8x^2 + 12$.
   2 or 0 positive; 2 or 0 negative

2. Locate the real zeros of $p(x) = x^3 + 9x - 4$ between consecutive integers. between 0 and 1

3. Determine the sum and product of the zeros for the polynomial function $g(x) = x^3 - 3x^2 - 46x + 48$. sum: 3; product: −48

4. Find the least integral upper bound and the greatest integral lower bound for the zeros of $g(x) = x^4 - x^3 - 6x - 9$. 3; −2

5. Use a graphing utility to find all zeros of $r(x) = x^3 + x - 5$. Write any irrational zeros correct to the nearest hundredth.

1.52

6. Sketch one possible graph that satisfies the following conditions. $f(x)$ is a third degree polynomial. $f(x)$ has one negative root and one positive root with multiplicity 2. The leading coefficient is positive. The greatest integral lower bound is −2; the least integral upper bound is 1.

22. A fourth degree polynomial with a negative leading coefficient, a negative real zero with multiplicity 2, and a positive real zero with multiplicity 2.

23. A fifth degree polynomial with one positive zero with multiplicity 5 and a least integral upper bound of 5.

24. **Thinking Critically** For a polynomial function $f(x)$, $f(3) = 1$ and $f(4) = 1$. What can you say about the zeros of the function between 3 and 4?

ⓡ 25. *Sports* A hammer thrower whirls a hammer on a 1-m chain in a circle. If the hammer moves at 1.75 revolutions per second, determine its velocity when the thrower releases it. 11.0 m/s

Use a graphing utility and the location theorem to determine all real zeros of each polynomial, correct to the nearest tenth.

Ⓑ 26. $p(x) = 3x^3 + 8x^2 - 1$ −2.6; −0.4; 0.3
27. $p(x) = 4x^3 + 14x^2 + 10x - 3$ −2.2; −1.5; 0.2
28. $f(x) = 6x^3 + 4x^2 + 9x + 6$ −0.7
29. $f(x) = 8x^3 - 14x^2 + 2x + 3$ −0.4; 0.8; 1.4
30. $g(x) = x^4 - 2x^3 - 12x^2 - 15x$ 0; 5
31. $g(x) = x^4 - 3x^3 - 11x^2 + 21x$ 0; −3; 4.4; 1.6
32. $h(x) = 6x^4 - 13x^3 + 2x^2 - 4x + 15$ 1.5; 1.7
33. $h(x) = 24x^4 - 8x^3 - 44x^2 + 7x + 12$
   −0.5; 0.7; −1.1; 1.3

34. **Thinking Critically** A polynomial function has function values $p(2) = 12$, $p(3) = -6$, and $p(4) = 3$. What may be said about the graph of $p(x)$?
   It crosses the x-axis between 2 and 3 and between 3 and 4.

ⓡ 35. Determine the exact value of $\sin(\alpha - \beta)$ if $\sin \alpha = \frac{4}{5}$, $\tan \beta = \frac{12}{5}$, $0° < \alpha < 90°$, and $0° < \beta < 90°$. $-\frac{16}{65}$

Given $P(x)$ is a polynomial such that $P(3) = 4$ and $P(4) = -1$:

36. What does the location theorem tell you about $P(x)$?

37. What does the intermediate value theorem tell you about $P(x)$?

38. Show that a polynomial function has no real zeros if all the terms are of even degree and all the coefficients are positive. *Hint*: the constant term has even degree 0.

39. *Business* During the summer, an average of 30,000 people per day take the boat ride around the island of Manhattan in New York. The price per ticket is $18. It is estimated that for every drop in price of $1 per ticket, an additional 3,000 people will take the boat ride. Determine the ticket price that will generate the greatest revenue. $14

Use a graphing utility to determine the indicated zero of each polynomial, correct to the nearest tenth.

40. The negative zero of $p(x) = x^3 + 2x + 47$ −3.4
41. The positive zero of $p(x) = x^3 + 3x^2 - 10$ 1.5
42. The positive zero of $p(x) = 2x^3 - 9x^2 - 17x - 10$ 6.0
43. The negative zero of $p(x) = 5x^3 - 8x^2 - 11x + 15$ −1.4

362   Chapter 7 Polynomial Functions

Additional Answers

22.

23.

C **44.** Determine the dimensions, correct to the nearest hundredth, of a rectangular solid with volume 43 ft³ if the dimensions form an arithmetic sequence with common difference 2. 1.88 × 3.88 × 5.88 ft

45. *Construction* The width of the strongest beam which can be cut from a log 10 in. in diameter is given by the positive irrational solution of the equation $x^3 - 100x^2 + 425 = 0$. Determine the width correct to the nearest hundredth. 2.08 in.

46. *Manufacturing* The dimensions of a rectangular box are 5, 6, and 7 cm. By what constant amount k should the dimensions of each side be increased if the volume of the box is to be doubled? 1.5 cm

Ⓡ **47.** Prove $\sin(\alpha + \beta) + \sin(\alpha - \beta) = 2\sin\alpha\cos\beta$.

There is a method for locating the zero of a polynomial called *linear interpolation* that is more efficient than the bisection method. Given an interval $[x_1, x_2]$ on which there is a change in sign, this method uses the slope formula, $\dfrac{y_2 - y_1}{x_2 - x_1} = \dfrac{y_1 - 0}{x_1 - x}$, to locate a new x-value. The value of x found using this method is not simply in the center of the interval but is closer to the end of the interval that is closer to being a zero. Like the bisection method, this method may be repeated to achieve greater accuracy.

48. Use the interpolation method to find a zero for the polynomial $f(x) = x^3 - x^2 - 3x + 1$. Let $x_1 = 2.1$ and $x_2 = 2.2$. Verify that $f(x)$ has a sign change between x_1 and x_2. Then use interpolation to find a closer approximation to a zero between x_1 and x_2. $f(x_1) = -0.449$; $f(x_2) = 0.208$; 2.17

49. *Programming* Write a program to approximate a zero of a polynomial using linear interpolation. Input the degree and coefficients of the polynomial, and two values, $x = a$ and $x = b$, such that a zero is known to be in (a, b). Repeat the process using the interval (a, c) or (c, b), depending upon which contains the zero. Output each approximation c, and stop when the absolute value of $f(c)$ is less than 0.00001.

50. Use the intermediate value theorem to prove the location theorem.

Consider the polynomial, $p(x) = 2x^4 - 3x^3 - 2x^2 - x + 6$.

51. Determine the number and nature of the zeros.

52. Determine any real zeros correct to three decimal places. 1.5; 1.521

Challenge

1. In the following addition problem, complete the statement with the digits 0 to 6, using each digit only once.

$$\underline{?}\ \underline{?} + \underline{?}\ \underline{?} = \underline{?}\ \underline{?}\ \underline{?} \quad 42 + 63 = 105$$

2. Determine the value of b in the cubic function $f(x) = 4bx^3 + bx^2 - \dfrac{6}{b}x$ if the zeros are $\left\{\dfrac{1}{b}, -\dfrac{3}{2b}, 2 - b\right\}$. 2

3. Solve for x: $(x^2 - 2x + 1)^{-1} - (2 - x)(x - 3)^{-1} = 1$ 2; −1

7.5 Descartes' Rule, the Intermediate Value Theorem, and Sum and Product of Zeros **363**

363

Alternative Assessment

Have students work in pairs and give them the following instructions: Write three polynomial functions, exchange them with your partner, and find all the zeros of each function. Try to find the zeros first using algebraic methods; then together check your results with a graphing utility.

Enrichment

Find the equation of the polynomial whose zeros are twice those of the polynomial $P(x) = x^3 + 3x^2 - 3x - 9$. $f(x) = x^3 + 6x^2 - 12x - 72$. The coefficients of $P(x)$ are multiplied by successive powers of 2 to form $f(x)$.

Additional Answers

24. There will be either zero or an even number of zeros between 3 and 4.

36. $P(x)$ has an odd number of zeros between 3 and 4.

37. $P(x)$ will take on every value between $P(3)$ and $P(4)$ in the interval $[3, 4]$.

38. Answers may vary. Example: $f(x) = ax^4 + bx^2 + c$ with a, b, and $c > 0$; By Descartes' rule of signs, there are no positive zeros and no negative zeros.

47. $\sin(\alpha + \beta) + \sin(\alpha - \beta) = \sin\alpha\cos\beta + \cos\alpha\sin\beta + \sin\alpha\cos\beta - \cos\alpha\sin\beta = 2\sin\alpha\cos\beta$

50. By the intermediate value theorem, a polynomial $P(x)$ on the interval $[a, b]$ will take on every value k between $P(a)$ and $P(b)$. If $P(a) > 0$ and $P(b) < 0$, then there must be a value c on the interval $[a, b]$ for which $P(c) = 0$.

51. 4 zeros; 2 or 0 positive rational zeros; 2 or 0 negative rational zeros

Vocabulary
continuous
horizontal asymptote
rational function
slant asymptote
vertical asymptote

Technology
graphing utility
symbolic manipulator

FOCUS

A discussion about architecture can be a lively introduction to the subject matter of this lesson. Invite students to comment on their own ideas about architecture, design, and construction. Ask them to speculate as to the mathematical concepts that come into play in these pursuits. Encourage them to find mathematical applications in architecture that go beyond simple geometry.

INSTRUCTION

- Drawing many graphs and pointing out the behavior of a graph near points of discontinuity is important. Ask students to describe the behavior of the graph as x gets large without bound, as x gets small without bound, and as x approaches any point of discontinuity from the left and the right.
- Have students test the asymptote rules for several rational functions.

7.6 Rational Functions

Objectives: To determine asymptotes and points of discontinuity
To graph rational functions

Focus

An architect is planning an unusual office building in a cylindrical shape. The building is to be constructed on a square plot of land. Zoning regulations restrict the total number of square feet of office space that can be built on the site. The architect uses a variety of mathematical equations and graphs to display the possible size of the building. Computer-assisted graphing is an indispensable tool in planning such projects.

Before graphing utilities were invented, a great deal of time and analysis was required to graph complicated functions. However, the calculator or computer screen may display the graph as a number of curves going in varied directions. It takes mathematical understanding and analysis to know exactly what the graph is telling you about the function.

A function $f(x)$ is said to be continuous at point $(a, f(a))$ if it is defined at the point and passes through it without a break; that is, you can draw the graph through $(a, f(a))$ without lifting your pencil from the paper. A function is continuous on an interval (a, b) if it is continuous for every point in the interval. A function is said to be continuous if it is continuous for every point in its domain. A point of discontinuity is represented by a break in the graph. With a graphing utility, use the integer zoom-in feature to clearly observe a break in the graph. With the trace feature, no y value will be given at the break.

Example 1 Graph the function $g(x) = \dfrac{x^2 - 9}{x + 3}$ and determine any points of discontinuity.

Expressing $\dfrac{x^2 - 9}{x + 3}$ as $\dfrac{(x + 3)(x - 3)}{x + 3}$, you obtain $g(x) = x - 3$. Except at $x = -3$, the graph is a straight line. However, the function is not defined for $x = -3$, which is a point of discontinuity.

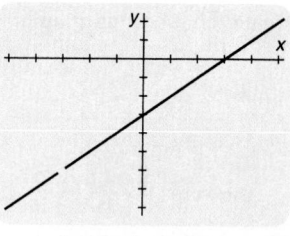

[−5, 5] by [−8, 2]

364 Chapter 7 Polynomial Functions

There are three basic kinds of discontinuity: *point, jump,* and *infinite.* The graph in Example 1 exhibited point discontinuity. In Chapter 1, you studied the greatest integer function and piecewise functions, which can exhibit jump discontinuities. In Chapter 4, you graphed functions such as the tangent and cotangent, which exhibit infinite discontinuities.

Now consider the function $P(x) = \frac{1}{x^2}$. When x is close to 0, $P(x)$ becomes very large. Note that the function is not defined for $x = 0$. The y-axis is a **vertical asymptote;** $P(x)$ increases without bound as x approaches 0. Using arrow notation, this is written $P(x) \to \infty$ as $x \to 0$. Similarly, when $P(x)$ is close to zero, $|x|$ increases without bound; $P(x) \to 0$ as $x \to \infty$ and $P(x) \to 0$ as $x \to -\infty$. The x-axis is a **horizontal asymptote.**

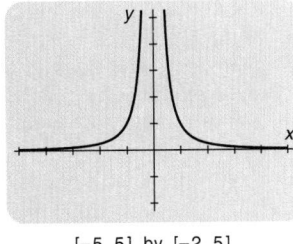

[−5, 5] by [−2, 5]

A **rational function** is a quotient of two polynomials. It is of the form $\frac{f(x)}{g(x)}$, where $g(x) \neq 0$. The graphs of rational functions frequently display infinite and point discontinuities.

 A graphing utility set for standard viewing will often show vertical but not horizontal asymptotes. However, you can confirm that a function approaches a particular value using the trace feature. The graph of the function $f(x) = \frac{1}{x} + 1$ is shown below. There is a vertical asymptote at $x = 0$ and a horizontal asymptote at $f(x) = 1$.

You can see that the value of the function approaches 1 on the positive and negative sides of the x-axis. As x increases without bound in the positive ($+\infty$) or in the negative direction ($-\infty$), the value of the function approaches 1. This value is said to be the *limit* of $f(x)$ as x gets large without bound. The value of the function never equals 1, but the limit is 1. This relationship can be expressed using limit notation.

[−5, 5] by [−4, 4]

$$\lim_{x \to \infty} f(x) = 1 \qquad \lim_{x \to -\infty} f(x) = 1$$

The function $f(x) = \frac{1}{x - 2}$ has a vertical asymptote at $x = 2$.

In limit notation, this is expressed as follows:

$$\lim_{x \to 2^+} f(x) = \infty \qquad \lim_{x \to 2^-} f(x) = -\infty$$

$\uparrow$ $\uparrow$

x approaches 2   *x approaches 2*
from the right   *from the left*

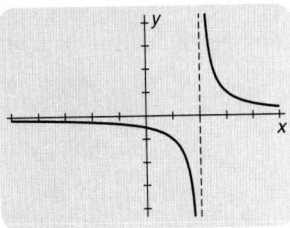

[−5, 5] by [−4, 4]

Recall that intercepts are points at which a graph crosses the x- or y-axes.

GUIDED PRACTICE
For Example 1
Graph $\frac{x^2 - 16}{x + 4}$ and determine any points of discontinuity.

$x = -4$

For Example 2

Determine the intercepts and asymptotes for the function $f(x) = \dfrac{4x + 3}{x - 5}$.

asymptotes: $x = 5$, $y = 4$; x-int: $\left(-\dfrac{3}{4}, 0\right)$; y-int: $\left(0, -\dfrac{3}{5}\right)$

Common Error Students may interchange x- and y-intercepts.

For Example 3

Graph $\dfrac{x^2 - 2x - 3}{x^2 - 5x - 6}$ and determine the vertical and horizontal asymptotes.

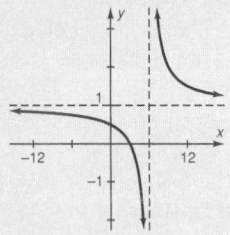

$x = 6$; $y = 1$

Common Error Students may interchange the horizontal and vertical asymptotes.

Example 2 Graph the function $f(x) = \dfrac{3x - 5}{x + 1}$. Determine its intercepts and asymptotes.

To find the x-intercept, let $f(x) = 0$ and solve for x: $x = \dfrac{5}{3}$. To find the y-intercept, let $x = 0$ and solve for y: $y = -5$. The denominator of the function equals 0 when $x = -1$. Use a graphing utility to find the limit of the function as $x \to \infty$, as $x \to -\infty$, and as x approaches any point of discontinuity from the right and from the left. You can see a vertical asymptote at $x = -1$ and a horizontal asymptote at $y = 3$.

$$\lim_{x \to -1^-} f(x) = \infty \qquad \lim_{x \to -1^+} f(x) = -\infty$$

$$\lim_{x \to \infty} f(x) = 3 \qquad \lim_{x \to -\infty} f(x) = 3$$

[-10, 10] by [-10, 10]

Division demonstrates why $f(x) = 3$ is a horizontal asymptote. This form of $f(x)$ shows that as x becomes very large, $\dfrac{8}{x + 1}$ becomes very small, and the value of the function approaches 3.

$$\begin{array}{r} 3 \\ x + 1 \overline{) 3x - 5} \\ 3x + 3 \\ \hline -8 \end{array}$$

$$f(x) = 3 - \dfrac{8}{x + 1}$$

The following chart summarizes rules that will help you determine asymptotes.

Asymptote Rules

Let $\dfrac{f(x)}{g(x)}$ be a rational function where $f(x)$ is a polynomial of degree n and $g(x)$ is a polynomial of degree m.

If $g(a) = 0$ and $f(a) \neq 0$, then $x = a$ is a *vertical asymptote*.

Three possible conditions determine a *horizontal asymptote*:

- If $n < m$, then $y = 0$ is a horizontal asymptote.
- If $n > m$, then there is no horizontal asymptote.
- If $n = m$, then $y = c$ is a horizontal asymptote, where c is the quotient of the leading coefficients of f and g.

Example 3 Graph the function $f(x) = \dfrac{x^2 - x - 2}{x^2 - x - 6}$. Find the vertical and horizontal asymptotes.

Since $f(x) = \dfrac{x^2 - x - 2}{x^2 - x - 6} = \dfrac{(x + 1)(x - 2)}{(x - 3)(x + 2)}$, vertical asymptotes occur at $x = 3$ and at $x = -2$. *Why?* The degree of the numerator is the same as the degree of the denominator. Thus, by the asymptote rules, $y = \dfrac{1}{1} = 1$ is a horizontal asymptote.

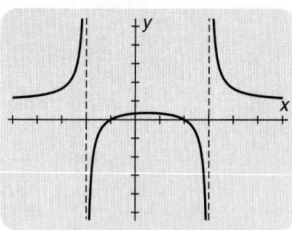

[-5, 6] by [-5, 5]

366 Chapter 7 Polynomial Functions

Thinking Critically

If $x = 3$ or $x = -2$, there would be division by zero.

Modeling

How can an architect determine the dimensions for a cylindrical office building?
In a right circular cylinder, the area of the circular base is found by using πr^2.
For an office building in the shape of a cylinder, total floor space is equal to
the area of each floor multiplied by the number of floors, $\pi r^2 n$.

Example 4 *Architecture* An office building is being constructed in the shape of a cylinder.
Zoning restrictions permit the building to have 100,000 ft^2 of floor space.
  a. Determine the number of stories for a building that will use most of a
square plot of land with 100 ft on each side and will approach the
maximum allowable floor space.
  b. Derive an equation and graph that will show the possible dimensions and
number of stories for any 100,000-ft^2 building in this shape.

a. The equation for total floor space is $S = \pi r^2 n$, where n is the number of floors.
If the building is to use the entire plot, the radius of the cylinder is 50 ft. Thus,

$$100{,}000 = \pi r^2 n$$
$$100{,}000 = \pi (50)^2 n$$
$$12.7 \approx n$$

Since 100,000 ft^2 is a maximum, 12.7 must be rounded down to 12 stories.

b. Solving the equation given above for n yields

$$n = \frac{100{,}000}{\pi r^2}$$

The graph of this function is shown at the right. As
the radius increases along the x-axis, the number of
stories decreases.

*Are all (r, n) ordered pairs reasonable choices?
Explain.*

[−2, 120] by [−2, 80]
x scl: 10   y scl: 10

The graphs of some functions exhibit **slant asymptotes** which occur when the
function values approach a straight line that is neither vertical nor horizontal.

Example 5 Graph the function $f(x) = \dfrac{2x^2 - 3x}{x + 1}$. Determine its asymptotes.

Setting $2x^2 - 3x = 0$, shows zeros at $(0, 0)$ and $\left(\frac{3}{2}, 0\right)$.
There is a vertical asymptote at $x = -1$.

$$\lim_{x \to -1^+} f(x) = \infty \qquad \lim_{x \to -1^-} f(x) = -\infty$$

The equation of the slant asymptote can be found by
dividing and then rewriting the function.

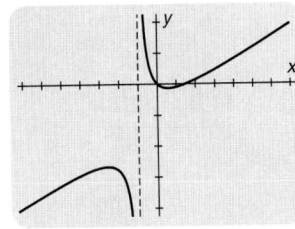

[−7, 7] by [−20, 10]
x scl: 1   y scl: 5

7.6 Rational Functions **367**

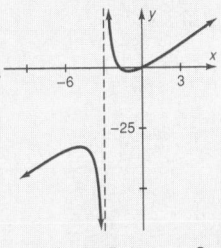

Thinking Critically
no; If r were very small, then n would be very large, and the building might not be safe.

INDEPENDENT PRACTICE

Assignment Guide

Basic: 1–37
Average: 7–37 odd, 39–45
Enriched: 21–23, 27–41 odd, 42–57

Teacher's Resource Book
Practice, page 48

Additional Answers

Class Exercises

9.

$y = 1; x = -1, y = 0$

10.

$y = 1; x = 1, y = 0$

11.

$x = -\frac{3}{4}, y = 3;$
$x = -1, y = 4$

12.

$x = -\frac{2}{3},$
$y = 1;$
$x = 2,$
$y = -3$

13.

$x = \pm 1,$
$y = -\frac{1}{3};$
$x = -3$
$y = x - 3$

14.

$x = 0,$
$x = 2,$
$y = 0;$
$x = 1,$
$y = x - 1$

368

$$\begin{array}{r} 2x - 5 \\ x + 1 \overline{\smash{)}2x^2 - 3x} \\ \underline{2x^2 + 2x} \\ -5x \\ \underline{-5x - 5} \\ 5 \end{array}$$

$f(x) = 2x - 5 + \dfrac{5}{x + 1}$

As x increases, $\dfrac{5}{x + 1}$ decreases and $f(x)$ approaches $2x - 5$. Thus, the line $y = 2x - 5$ is a slant asymptote.

The graph of a rational function of the form $\dfrac{f(x)}{g(x)}$ will have a slant asymptote when the degree of f is one more than the degree of g.

Class Exercises

Determine the points of discontinuity for each function.

1. $f(x) = \dfrac{1}{x + 7}$ -7 **2.** $g(x) = -\dfrac{3}{x - 4}$ 4 **3.** $h(x) = \dfrac{x^2 - 25}{x + 5}$ -5 **4.** $p(x) = \dfrac{x^2 - 36}{x - 6}$ 6

5. $f(x) = \begin{cases} -2x, & \text{if } x < 2 \\ x^2, & \text{if } x \geq 2 \end{cases}$ 2
6. $g(x) = \begin{cases} -x + 2, & \text{if } x \geq 4 \\ x + 5, & \text{if } x < 4 \end{cases}$ 4

7. $f(x) = [\![x + 1]\!]$ $\{n: n \in Z\}$
8. $f(x) = [\![2x - 1]\!]$ $\frac{n}{2}$, where $n \in Z$

Graph each function. Determine any intercepts and asymptotes.

9. $f(x) = \dfrac{1}{x + 1}$ **10.** $g(x) = \dfrac{1}{1 - x}$ **11.** $f(x) = \dfrac{4x + 3}{x + 1}$

12. $g(x) = -\dfrac{3x + 2}{x - 2}$ **13.** $f(x) = \dfrac{x^2 - 1}{x + 3}$ **14.** $f(x) = \dfrac{x^2 - 2x}{x - 1}$

15. Thinking Critically How does the limit as x gets large for the family of functions $f(x) = \dfrac{A}{Bx + C}$ compare to the family of functions $g(x) = \dfrac{Ax}{Bx + C}$, where A, B, and C are constants? $f(x) \to 0$; $g(x) \to \frac{A}{B}$

Practice Exercises

 Use appropriate technology.

Determine the points of discontinuity for each function.

A **1.** $h(x) = \dfrac{1}{x - 9}$ 9 **2.** $p(x) = \dfrac{1}{x + 8}$ -8 **3.** $n(x) = \dfrac{1}{x + 2}$ -2 **4.** $m(x) = \dfrac{6}{x - 4}$ 4

5. $h(x) = \dfrac{x^2 - 16}{x - 4}$ 4 **6.** $p(x) = \dfrac{x^2 - 36}{x + 6}$ -6 **7.** $n(x) = [\![x + 5]\!]$ all integers **8.** $m(x) = [\![2x - 5]\!]$ $\frac{n}{2}$, $n \in Z$

9. $t(x) = \begin{cases} x, & \text{if } x \geq 1 \\ x + 2, & \text{if } x < 1 \end{cases}$ 1
10. $s(x) = \begin{cases} x + 1, & \text{if } x \geq 4 \\ 2x - 1, & \text{if } x < 4 \end{cases}$ 4

Graph each function.

11. $\dfrac{x^2 - 49}{x + 7}$ **12.** $\dfrac{x^2 - 25}{x - 5}$ **13.** $\dfrac{3x^2 - 27}{x + 3}$ **14.** $\dfrac{4x^2 - 64}{x - 4}$

R **15.** Express 30° in radians. $\frac{\pi}{6}$

16. Thinking Critically Is $f(x) = \dfrac{x^2 - 100}{x + 10}$ a rational function? Why or why not?

368   Chapter 7 Polynomial Functions

Practice Exercises

11.

12.

13.

14.

17. **Thinking Critically**   Is $f(x) = \dfrac{1}{x^2 + 3}$ a rational function? Why or why not?

Architecture   A storage building is to be constructed in the shape of a right circular cone and have the capacity of 5000 ft³.

18. Derive a function to show the height as a function of the radius. $P(r) = \dfrac{15{,}000}{\pi r^2}$

19. Graph the function and indicate a useful viewing rectangle. $40 < P < 60;\ 0 < r < 20$

20. Determine the height, to the nearest whole number, if the radius is to be 10 ft.   48 ft

Ⓡ 21. Determine the principal value of x if $\tan^{-1} 1 = x$.   45° or $\dfrac{\pi}{4}$

Chemistry   Boyle's law states that at a given temperature the product of pressure times volume is constant for a particular gas. Assume that $pv = 350$ for a certain gas.

22. Graph the function with v as the independent variable, and a viewing rectangle that shows positive values. $0 < p < 350;\ 0 < v < 350$

23. Find p when $v = 25$.   14

24. *Architecture*   Using the information given in the model and in Example 4, find the number of stories the building can have if an area of 3500 ft² of the plot must remain for a park and the building must have 80,000 ft² of floor space.   12

Ⓡ 25. Find the area of a sector of a circle of radius 10 m with central angle of 40°.   35 m²

Graph each function. Determine any intercepts and asymptotes.

B 26. $f(x) = \dfrac{1}{x}$ 27. $g(x) = -\dfrac{2}{x}$ 28. $h(x) = -\dfrac{1}{x^2}$ 29. $j(x) = \dfrac{1}{(x-2)^2}$

30. $m(x) = \dfrac{4x+3}{x+2}$ 31. $n(x) = \dfrac{6x+5}{x+3}$ 32. $f(x) = \dfrac{5-2x}{x-6}$ 33. $g(x) = \dfrac{3-4x}{x-5}$

34. $f(x) = \dfrac{2x^2-1}{x+2}$ 35. $m(x) = \dfrac{x^2-4x}{x+1}$ 36. $j(x) = \dfrac{3x^2-2x}{x-3}$ 37. $g(x) = \dfrac{4x^2-5}{x-2}$

38. $t(x) = \dfrac{(x+2)^2}{(x-1)(x+3)}$ 39. $f(x) = \dfrac{(x-4)^2}{(x+1)(x-6)}$

40. $f(x) = \dfrac{(x+2)(x-3)}{(x+1)(x-2)}$ 41. $g(x) = \dfrac{(x+1)(x-7)}{(x-2)(x+8)}$

42. *Physics*   A relationship between power P, current I, and resistance R, is given by the equation $R = \dfrac{P}{I^2}$. Indicate any asymptotes. Explain the effect a change in current has on the resistance.

Ⓡ 43. Express $\cot(x+y)$ in terms of $\cot x$ and $\cot y$. $\dfrac{\cot x\ \cot y - 1}{\cot x + \cot y}$

44. **Thinking Critically**   What can be said about the horizontal and vertical asymptotes of the rational function $f(x) = \dfrac{ax+b}{cx+d}$ when a, b, c, and d are constants with $c \neq 0$ and $ad \neq bc$?

45. **Writing in Mathematics**   Describe the similarities and differences of the horizontal and vertical asymptotes for $f(x) = \dfrac{x+5}{x-2}$ and $g(x) = \dfrac{x+5}{2-x}$.

7.6 Rational Functions   **369**

Ⓡ **Review**

Exercises 15, 21, 25, 43, and 53 review concepts such as expressing angle measures using radians, solving trigonometric functions, finding the area of a sector, and using trigonometric identities.

LESSON FOLLOW-UP

Lesson Quiz

1. Determine any points of discontinuity for $f(x) = \dfrac{9}{x-7}$. $x = 7$

2. Graph $g(x) = \dfrac{x+3}{x-5}$ and determine the asymptotes and intercepts.

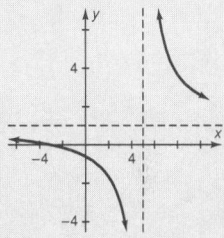

asymptotes: $y = 1;\ x = 5$;
x-int: $(-3, 0)$; y-int: $\left(0, -\dfrac{3}{5}\right)$;

3. Determine the vertical and horizontal asymptotes of $h(x) = \dfrac{x^2+4x+3}{x^2-6x+8}$.

$x = 2,\ x = 4;\ y = 1$

4. Sketch the graph of $t(x) = \dfrac{x^2+6}{x-3}$ and determine its asymptotes.

$x = 3$; slant asymptote, $y = x + 3$

Writing in Mathematics

45. The vertical asymptote, $x = 2$, is the same. The horizontal asymptote for $f(x)$ is $y = 1$, and for $g(x)$ is $y = -1$.

Graph each function. Determine any intercepts and asymptotes.

C **46.** $m(x) = \dfrac{8 + x}{|x|}$ **47.** $n(x) = \dfrac{10 + x}{|x|}$

48. The rational function $r(x) = \dfrac{x - \dfrac{7x^3}{60}}{1 + \dfrac{x^2}{20}}$ is called a Padé approximation for
$y = \sin x$. Compare $\sin x$ and $r(x)$ for $x = 0.2, 0.7, 1, 2, 3$.

Find the limits as x approaches any point of discontinuity from the right and from the left.

49. $f(x) = \begin{cases} 2x, & \text{if } x \geq 4 \\ x^2, & \text{if } x < 4 \end{cases}$ 8, 16   **50.** $g(x) = \begin{cases} 3x, & \text{if } x \geq 3 \\ x^2, & \text{if } x < 3 \end{cases}$ none

51. $h(x) = \begin{cases} x + 5, & \text{if } x > 3 \\ 3x, & \text{if } \leq 3 \end{cases}$ 8, 9   **52.** $p(x) = \begin{cases} x + 7, & \text{if } x \geq 2 \\ 2x, & \text{if } x < 2 \end{cases}$ 9, 4

Ⓡ **53.** Determine the exact solutions to $\dfrac{\sec x}{1 + \sec x} = \dfrac{\sec^2 x}{2 + \sec x}$. 45°, 315° $\left(\dfrac{\pi}{4}, \dfrac{7\pi}{4}\right)$

54. Show that the rational function $f(x) = \dfrac{x^{12}}{x^{14} + 2}$ has a horizontal asymptote. $12 < 14$; $y = 0$ is a horiz. asymp.

55. Draw a graph of $P(x)$ such that $P(x)$ has a vertical asymptote at $x = 1$, an oblique asymptote at $y = x + 2$, and a y-intercept of -5.

56. Determine an equation for the graph you drew in Exercise 55. $p(x) = \dfrac{x^2 - 3x + 5}{x - 1}$

57. Is there only one graph that will fit the criteria of Exercise 55? Explain your answer.

Project

Estimate the total number of square feet in your school. Compare your estimate with those of other students. Now assume that a new square-shaped school is being planned with the same total number of square feet as your school but with a different number of floors. Determine an equation and draw a graph that gives the number of floors as a function of the side of the square.

Review

1. An archeologist discovers a standing totem pole. The pole casts an 11-ft shadow when the sun is at an angle of 57°. What is the height of the totem pole? 16.94 ft

2. In a 45°-45°-90° triangle, if s represents the length of each congruent side, how could the hypotenuse be represented? $s\sqrt{2}$

Translate each situation into a variation equation using k as a constant.

3. y varies directly as x. $y = kx$ 4. y varies inversely as x. $xy = k$

5. y varies jointly as x and z. $y = kxz$ 6. y varies directly as the square of x. $y = kx^2$

370   Chapter 7 Polynomial Functions

48.

	0.2	0.7	1	2	3
$\sin x$	0.1987	0.6442	0.8415	0.9093	0.1411
$r(x)$	0.1995	0.6442	0.8413	0.8889	-0.1034

7.7 Radical Functions

Objectives: To graph radical functions
To solve radical equations

Focus

The sphere is a common shape found in nature and in many aspects of daily life. The earth, sun, moon, and the planets are spheres. Satellites, basketballs, and tiny ball-bearings are also spherical in shape.

The polynomial function $V = \frac{4}{3}\pi r^3$ represents the formula for the volume of a sphere. The volume of a sphere increases as its radius increases and is directly proportional to the cube of the radius. However, you may wish to express the radius as a function of the volume. In this case, you must solve the equation for r,

$r = \sqrt[3]{\dfrac{3V}{4\pi}}$. This equation is the inverse of the original formula and is called a *radical equation*.

A **radical equation** is an equation that has a variable in the radicand. You can use the same methods for transforming the graphs of radical functions as you use for polynomial functions.

Example 1   Graph $g(x) = \sqrt{x} + 2$ and $h(x) = \sqrt{x - 2}$ on the same set of axes as $f(x) = \sqrt{x}$. Describe the graphs of $g(x)$ and $h(x)$ in terms of $f(x)$.

The graph of $g(x)$ is the graph of $f(x)$ translated up 2 units.

The graph of $h(x)$ is the graph of $f(x)$ translated 2 units to the right.

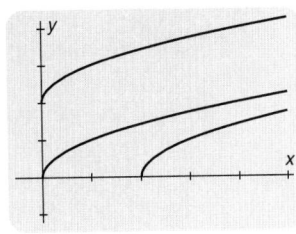

[-1, 5] by [-1, 4]

Notice in Example 1 that $f(x)$ takes on only positive values because the square root of a negative number is not a real number.

LESSON PLAN

Vocabulary
radical equation

Technology
graphing utility
symbolic manipulator

FOCUS
Direct students to various subject areas such as geometry, engineering, banking, astronomy, and physics that use functions or formulas that can be converted into radical equations. For example, the formula for finding the volume of a cube can be converted to a radical equation for finding the length of a side, $s = \sqrt[3]{V}$.

INSTRUCTION
- Use the equations in Example 2 to demonstrate on a graphing utility why extraneous solutions can be introduced when a radical equation is squared.
- Students should be able to solve radical equations such as in Example 2 without the use of a graphing utility. However, encourage them to use calculators for lengthy computations involving radicals and the quadratic formula.
- Encourage students to check their results on a graphing utility by checking that the zeros on the graph are the same as the solutions found algebraically.

Alternative Learning Styles
Many students would benefit from visual representations of radical equations or functions. Have students graph several radical equations to become more familiar with the general shape of their graphs. Sample equations may include $y = \sqrt{x}$ and $y = \sqrt{x - 2}$. Have students compare these graphs to those of $y = x^2$ and $y = (x - 2)^2$.

For Example 1

Graph on the same axes. Describe $g(x)$ in terms of $f(x)$.

1. $f(x) = \sqrt{x}$; $g(x) = -\sqrt{x}$

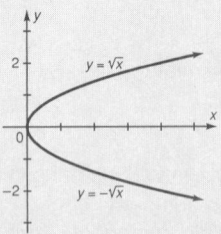

The graph of $g(x)$ is a reflection of the graph of $f(x)$ in the x-axis.

2. $f(x) = \sqrt[3]{x}$; $g(x) = \sqrt[3]{x+1} - 1$

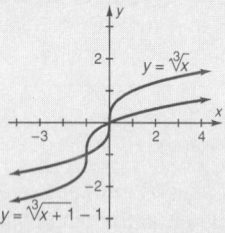

The graph of $g(x)$ is a translation of the graph of $f(x)$, 1 unit to the left and 1 unit down.

For Example 2

Solve and check each equation.

1. $\sqrt{x - 10} - x = -12$
$x = 11$ (reject); $x = 14$

2. $\sqrt{5 - x} = x + 2$
$x = \dfrac{-5 + \sqrt{29}}{2} = 0.19$;

$x = \dfrac{-5 - \sqrt{29}}{2} = -5.19$ (reject)

For Example 3

Solve and check each equation.

1. $\sqrt{x + 4} + \sqrt{5x} = 8$ 5
2. $\sqrt{2x}\,\sqrt{x + 3} = \sqrt{8}$ 1

To solve a radical equation that has only one variable in the radicand, isolate that term on one side of the equation. Then, if the index is 2, square both sides of the equation. However, this new equation may have solutions that are not solutions of the original equation. Therefore, it is important to check solutions in the original equation to rule out any *extraneous solutions*.

Example 2   Solve and check the equation $\sqrt{x + 6} + x = 14$.

$$\sqrt{x + 6} + x = 14$$

$\sqrt{x + 6} = 14 - x$	*Isolate the radical.*
$x + 6 = 196 - 28x + x^2$	*Square both sides.*
$x^2 - 29x + 190 = 0$	*Simplify.*
$(x - 19)(x - 10) = 0$	*Factor.*
$x = 19$ or $x = 10$	*Possible solutions*

Check:

$$\sqrt{x + 6} + x = 14 \qquad\qquad \sqrt{x + 6} + x = 14$$
$$\sqrt{19 + 6} + 19 \overset{?}{=} 14 \qquad \sqrt{10 + 6} + 10 \overset{?}{=} 14$$
$$24 \neq 14 \qquad\qquad\qquad\qquad 14 = 14$$

The solution is 10.

The graphing utility makes it clear that the equation derived by squaring both sides of an equation may be different from the original equation, except for a common solution. The graph at the right shows the functions related to the original and the squared equations from Example 2:

$$y = \sqrt{x + 6} + x - 14 \quad \text{and} \quad y = x^2 - 29x + 190$$

They are very different from each other but they both have 10 as zeros.

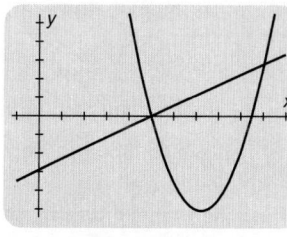

[−2, 22] by [−20, 20]
x scl: 2 y scl: 4

A radical equation may contain two radical expressions with indexes of 2. To solve such an equation, rewrite it with one of these terms isolated on one side of the equal sign and square both sides. If a variable remains in a radicand, you must repeat the isolation process.

Example 3   Solve and check the equation $\sqrt{x - 8} - \sqrt{x} = -2$.

$$\sqrt{x - 8} - \sqrt{x} = -2$$

$\sqrt{x - 8} = \sqrt{x} - 2$	*Isolate one radical.*
$x - 8 = x - 4\sqrt{x} + 4$	*Square both sides.*
$-12 = 4\sqrt{x}$	
$-3 = \sqrt{x}$	*Isolate the radical.*
$9 = x$	*Square both sides.*

Check:

$$\sqrt{x - 8} - \sqrt{x} = -2$$
$$\sqrt{9 - 8} - \sqrt{9} \overset{?}{=} -2$$
$$-2 = -2$$

372   Chapter 7 Polynomial Functions

Radical equations with indexes greater than 2 can be solved using similar techniques. Isolate the term containing the radical, and then raise each side of the equation to a power equal to the index of the radical.

Example 4 Solve and check the equation $\sqrt[3]{3y + 2} - 2 = 0$.

$$\sqrt[3]{3y + 2} - 2 = 0$$
$$\sqrt[3]{3y + 2} = 2 \qquad \textit{Isolate the radical.}$$
$$3y + 2 = 8 \qquad \textit{Cube both sides.}$$
$$y = 2$$

Check:
$$\sqrt[3]{3y + 2} - 2 \overset{?}{=} 0$$
$$\sqrt[3]{3(2) + 2} - 2 \overset{?}{=} 0$$
$$0 = 0$$

A graphing utility makes it possible to quickly determine approximate solutions to radical equations that are time-consuming to solve algebraically. Most graphing utilities have a square root key to use when the index of a radical is 2. When using a graphing utility to graph radical equations with other indexes, you must convert the index to a fractional or decimal exponent and use parentheses as needed.

Example 5 Use a graphing utility to find the zeros of each equation to the nearest hundredth. Check each solution by substituting into the original equation.

a. $\sqrt{x + 2} + \sqrt{x + 5} = x^2 + \sqrt{\dfrac{x}{3}}$ **b.** $\sqrt[3]{x^2 - 3x + 7} = 2x$

a. The related function is

$$f(x) = \sqrt{x + 2} + \sqrt{x + 5} - x^2 - \sqrt{\dfrac{x}{3}}$$

Use the zoom and trace features to determine a zero at $x = 1.95$. Substitute into the original equation.

$$\sqrt{1.95 + 2} + \sqrt{1.95 + 5} \overset{?}{=} 1.95^2 + \sqrt{\dfrac{1.95}{3}}$$
$$4.62 \approx 4.61$$

Thus, $x = 1.95$ is a good approximation.

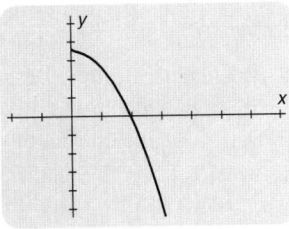

[−2, 7] by [−5, 5]

b. The related function is

$$f(x) = \sqrt[3]{x^2 - 3x + 7} - 2x$$

Use the zoom and trace features to obtain $x = 0.86$. Substituting into the original equation yields

$$\sqrt[3]{0.86^2 - 3(0.86) + 7} \overset{?}{=} 2(0.86)$$
$$1.73 \approx 1.72$$

Thus, $x = 0.86$ is a good approximation.

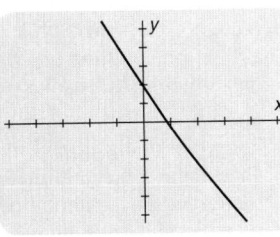

[−5, 5] by [−5, 5]

7.7 Radical Functions   **373**

For Example 4
Solve and check each equation.
1. $\sqrt[3]{2x - 5} + 6 = 11$ 65
2. $4\sqrt[3]{x^2 + 9} - 12 = 0$ $\pm 3\sqrt{2}$

Technology Direct students to familiarize themselves with the methods described in their calculator manuals for evaluating radicals with indices other than 2.

For Example 5
Use a graphing utility to solve each equation to the nearest hundredth.
1. $\sqrt[3]{x + 4} + x = \sqrt{x + 2}$

−0.22

2. $\sqrt[3]{x^2 - x + 8} + 1 = 2\sqrt{x}$

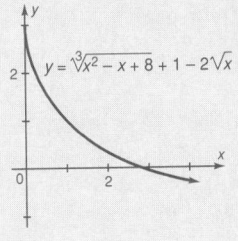

2.82

Have students describe an algebraic procedure for solving an equation involving one or more radicals.

INDEPENDENT PRACTICE

Assignment Guide
Basic: 1–24
Average: 1–15 odd, 16–30
Enriched: 1–19 odd, 20–37

Teacher's Resource Book
Practice, page 49

® Review
Exercises 9, 17, 21, 25, and 34 review concepts such as finding slope and *y*-intercepts, domains of functions, volume formulas, determining the period, amplitude, and zeros of a function, and graphing using addition of ordinates.

Additional Answers

Class Exercises
1.

Practice Exercises
1.

2.
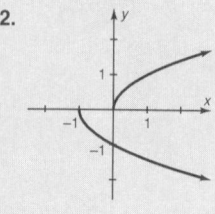

Class Exercises

Graph on the same axes and explain the transformations.

1. $f(x) = \sqrt[3]{x}$, $g(x) = \sqrt[3]{x} + 2$, $h(x) = \sqrt[3]{x} - 4$

Solve and check each equation algebraically.

2. $\sqrt{x + 1} = 5$ 24
3. $\sqrt{x - 3} = 2$ 7
4. $\sqrt{x + 2} = x - 4$ 7
5. $\sqrt{x + 10} = x - 2$ 6
6. $\sqrt{3x} - \sqrt{x + 6} = 0$ 3
7. $\sqrt{4x - 10} = 3\sqrt{x - 5}$ 7

Use a graphing utility to solve each equation.

8. $3 = \sqrt{x + 2}$ 7
9. $-1 = \sqrt{x^2 - 3}$ no sol.
10. $\sqrt{x + 1} - \sqrt{x} = x^3$ 0.77
11. $10 = \sqrt[3]{(x + 2)^2}$ –33.6, 29.6
12. $\sqrt{2x + 1} = \dfrac{1}{\sqrt{x - 3}}$ 3.14
13. $\sqrt{x + 3} = x^4 - \sqrt[3]{x} + 1$ –0.27, 1.21

Practice Exercises ⟨⟩ Use appropriate technology.

Graph on the same axes. Describe $g(x)$ in terms of $f(x)$.

A **1.** $f(x) = \sqrt{x}$, $g(x) = \sqrt{x - 2} + 3$
2. $f(x) = \sqrt{x}$, $g(x) = -\sqrt{x + 1}$

Use a graphing utility to solve each equation.

3. $\sqrt[4]{(x + 3)^3} = \dfrac{x}{2}$ 23.1
4. $\sqrt[3]{(x - 1)^5} = x + 1$ 3.4
5. $2 = \sqrt{x - 1} + \dfrac{x}{2}$ 2
6. $-1 = \sqrt{x - 5} - \dfrac{x}{3}$ 6, 9
7. $0 = \sqrt{x^3 - 2}$ 1.26
8. $0 = \sqrt[3]{x^4 - 3}$ 1.3

® **9.** Determine the slope and the *y*-intercept of the equation $3x - 4y = 13$. $\dfrac{3}{4}$; $-\dfrac{13}{4}$

Solve and check each equation algebraically.

10. $\sqrt{x - 1} = 2x - 8$ 5
11. $\sqrt{x + 5} = x - 7$ 11
12. $\sqrt{2}(\sqrt{x + 3}) = x - 1$ 5
13. $\sqrt{x + 2} = 3\sqrt{2}$ 16
14. $\sqrt[3]{2x} = \sqrt[3]{5x}$ 0
15. $2\sqrt[3]{2x} - 4 = 0$ 4

16. Thinking Critically Describe how the domains of radical functions differ from the domains of polynomial functions.

® **17.** Determine the domain of the function $f(x) = \sin x + \tan x$. $x \neq k\left(\dfrac{\pi}{2}\right)$, $k \in Z$

B **18.** *Manufacturing* Spherical submarines are used for underwater research. In order to hold a two-person team and equipment, the sphere must have a volume of at least 2000 ft³, but to withstand deep sea pressure it must not be greater than 5000 ft³. Determine an equation that expresses the radius of the sphere as a function of the volume. Graph the equation and find the minimum and maximum for the radius. $f(v) = \sqrt[3]{\dfrac{3v}{4\pi}}$; 7.8 ft; 10.6 ft

19. *Manufacturing* A company makes ice cream cones with heights of 5 in., but the radii vary. Determine a radical function that expresses the radius as a function of volume. Graph the function and determine the radius that will give a volume of 12 in³. $f(V) = \sqrt{\dfrac{3V}{5\pi}}$; 1.5 in.

374   Chapter 7 Polynomial Functions

---

16. The domains of radical functions are limited to those values for which the radicand is positive. A negative radicand yields a value that is not a real number. The domain of any polynomial is the set of real numbers since no real number will yield a value that is not a real number.

20. *Surveying* Certain crops are planted in circular areas for irrigation purposes. Derive and graph an equation expressing the radius as a function of the area of a circle. If it is most efficient to plant a certain crop in an area of at least 200,000 ft² but not more than 300,000 ft², determine the minimum and maximum values for the radius. $f(A) = \sqrt{\dfrac{A}{\pi}}$; 252 ft; 309 ft

21. Express the formula for the volume of a sphere in terms of the diameter. $V = \dfrac{\pi d^3}{6}$

Solve and check each equation algebraically.

22. $\sqrt{x + 1} = \sqrt{\dfrac{x}{2}} + 1$ 0, 8   **23.** $\sqrt{x - 1} + 1 = \sqrt{x + 6}$ 10   **24.** $\sqrt{x + 10} = 5 - \sqrt{3 - x}$ −1, −6

25. Find the period and amplitude of the function, $f(x) = \sin x + \cos x$, and then determine the zeros of the associated equation on the interval $0 \le x < 2\pi$. 2π; 1.4; 5.5; 2.4

26. *Sociology* The function $f(x) = x^2 + 3x$ represents the growth of membership in a club during a 10-month interval. Determine a function $g(x)$ that expresses time as a function of membership. $g(x) = -\dfrac{3 + \sqrt{9 + 4x}}{2}$

Use a graphing utility to solve each equation.

27. $\sqrt{x + 3} = x^3 - 5$ 1.9   **28.** $\sqrt[4]{(x + 3)^3} = 2x + \sqrt{x}$ 0.9   **29.** $\sqrt{x - 1} = \sqrt[3]{\dfrac{x}{5}}$ 1.4

For Exercises 30 to 33, $f(x) = \sqrt{x}$, $g(x) = -2x^2$, $h(x) = \sqrt[3]{x + 1}$.

30. Determine $h^{-1}(x)$. $h^{-1}(x) = x^3 - 1$

31. Determine all values of x for which $f(x) = h(x)$. 2.15

32. Determine all values of x for which $g(x) = h(f(x))$. none

33. Determine all values of x for which $f^{-1}(x) = h(x)$. −0.78, 1.13

34. Graph $y = \sin x + \cos x + \sin 2x$ over a one-period interval.

Solve each equation algebraically.

35. $\sqrt{x} - 6 = \sqrt[4]{x}$ 81   **36.** $-1 + \sqrt{x^2 + c} = x$ $\dfrac{c - 1}{2}$ **37.** $\sqrt{2y + d} = \sqrt{y + e}$ $e - d$

Challenge

1. Determine the smallest integral value for n which makes the following inequality true:

$$1 + \frac{1}{2} + \frac{1}{3} + \frac{1}{4} + \frac{1}{5} + \cdots + \frac{1}{n} > 4 \quad 31$$

2. Determine which fractions in the series $\dfrac{1}{2}, \dfrac{1}{3}, \dfrac{1}{4}, \ldots, \dfrac{1}{20}$ are repeating decimals. Discover a pattern to predict which fractions in the interval $\dfrac{1}{21}, \dfrac{1}{22}, \dfrac{1}{23}, \ldots, \dfrac{1}{100}$ will also be repeating. $\dfrac{1}{3}, \dfrac{1}{6}, \dfrac{1}{9}, \dfrac{1}{12}, \dfrac{1}{15}, \dfrac{1}{18}, \dfrac{1}{3n}, n \in Z$

3. Determine two values for b which satisfy the equation:

$$\sqrt[\frac{1}{b+3}]{\sqrt[\frac{1}{b-2}]{\sqrt[\frac{1}{b-1}]{\sqrt[\frac{1}{b}]{2}}}} = 4^{12} \quad 1, -4$$

7.7 Radical Functions   **375**

Additional Answers

19.

20.

34.

375

FOCUS

Some time after 1629 Pierre de Fermat developed a theorem for finding the area under a curve that became the basis for integral calculus. When the curves are rational functions, the techniques for integrating, or finding the area under the curve, are more easily applied if the function can be expressed as a sum of fractions whose numerators are constants.

Encourage interested students to research the history of integral calculus.

INSTRUCTION

- To understand the process of decomposing fractions, have students follow the text carefully to work through adding two fractions and then decomposing the result back into the original two fractions, or partial fractions.
- For Example 4, review how polynomials can be factored using a graphing utility and then using synthetic division.

Alternative Learning Styles
Some students may find it helpful to decompose numerical fractions as a means of reviewing concepts underlying the decomposition of rational expressions. For example: $\frac{4}{5} + \frac{2}{7} =$

$\frac{4 \cdot 7 + 2 \cdot 5}{5 \cdot 7} = \frac{28 + 10}{35} = \frac{38}{35}, \frac{38}{35} =$

$\frac{38}{5 \cdot 7}, \frac{38}{5 \cdot 7} = \frac{A}{5} + \frac{B}{7}$; multiplying by 35 yields the equation $38 = 7A + 5B$. Using trial-and-error, we obtain $A = 4$ and $B = 2$, so $\frac{38}{35} = \frac{4}{5} + \frac{2}{7}$. Note that there is no need to use trial-and-error with rational expressions.

376

7.8 Partial Fractions

Objective: *To decompose a fraction into a sum of partial fractions*

Focus

Occasionally, doing something is easier than undoing it. Riding 2 mi down a hill on your bike is great fun. Pedaling back up is hard work. It is easier to tie a knot than to untie one. It is easier to stitch than "unstitch" in needlepoint, but removing a mistake is worth the effort.

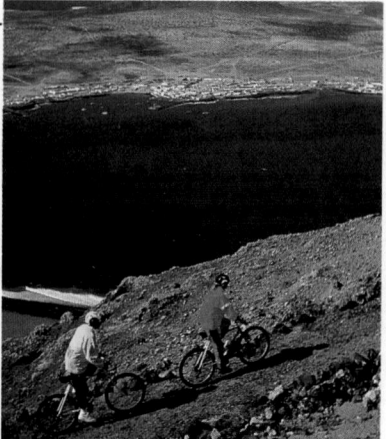

Similar situations arise in mathematics. For example, multiplication is often easier than division. You are quite familiar with adding fractions by finding a common denominator. In this lesson, you will learn how to "undo" this procedure by decomposing an algebraic fraction into the sum of several *partial fractions*. This process will be helpful to you in calculus.

To add or subtract fractions, you must first find a common denominator.

$$\frac{2}{x-3} + \frac{5}{x+1} = \frac{2(x+1) + 5(x-3)}{(x-3)(x+1)} = \frac{2x+2+5x-15}{(x-3)(x+1)} = \frac{7x-13}{x^2-2x-3}$$

The decomposition of a fraction into **partial fractions** reverses the process shown above. This lesson addresses the decomposition of fractions with denominators that can be factored into linear factors and in which the degree of the numerator is less than the degree of the denominator.

The first step in decomposing into partial fractions is to factor the denominator.

$$\frac{7x-13}{x^2-2x-3} = \frac{7x-13}{(x-3)(x+1)}$$

Express as two fractions using A and B for the numerators.

$$\frac{7x-13}{(x-3)(x+1)} = \frac{A}{(x-3)} + \frac{B}{(x+1)}$$

Multiply by the least common denominator.

$$7x - 13 = A(x+1) + B(x-3)$$

Eliminate B by letting $x = 3$: $7(3) - 13 = 4A$
$$A = 2$$

Eliminate A by letting $x = -1$: $7(-1) - 13 = -4B$
$$B = 5$$

Substituting the values for A and B yields the original fractions.

$$\frac{7x-13}{(x-3)(x+1)} = \frac{2}{x-3} + \frac{5}{x+1}$$

Example 1 Decompose $\dfrac{x-6}{x^2-2x}$ into partial fractions.

$$\frac{x-6}{x(x-2)} = \frac{A}{x} + \frac{B}{x-2} \qquad x^2-2x = x(x-2)$$

$$x - 6 = A(x-2) + Bx \qquad \textit{Multiply by the LCD.}$$

Let $x = 0$: $-6 = -2A$ Let $x = 2$: $2 - 6 = 2B$
$ 3 = A$ $ B = -2$

$$\frac{x-6}{x^2-2x} = \frac{3}{x} - \frac{2}{x-2} \qquad \textit{Substitute.}$$

Follow the same procedure to decompose a fraction into partial fractions when the denominator must be factored into three nonrepeating linear factors.

Example 2 Decompose $\dfrac{4x^2+13x-12}{x^3+x^2-6x}$ into partial fractions.

$$\frac{4x^2+13x-12}{x(x-2)(x+3)} = \frac{A}{x} + \frac{B}{x-2} + \frac{C}{x+3} \qquad x^3+x^2-6x = x(x-2)(x+3)$$

$$4x^2 + 13x - 12 = A(x-2)(x+3) + Bx(x+3) + Cx(x-2)$$

Let $x = 0$: $-12 = -6A$ Let $x = 2$: $30 = 10B$ Let $x = -3$: $-15 = 15C$
$ A = 2$ $ B = 3$ $ C = -1$

$$\frac{4x^2+13x-12}{x^3+x^2-6x} = \frac{2}{x} + \frac{3}{x-2} - \frac{1}{x+3} \qquad \textit{Substitute.}$$

Note that in Examples 1 and 2, the linear factors of the denominator are nonrepeating. However, in partial fraction decomposition, you may find that a linear factor $(x-a)$ is repeated n times. If $(x-a)^n$ is a factor of the denominator, then the partial fraction decomposition must include

$$\frac{A_1}{x-a} + \frac{A_2}{(x-a)^2} + \cdots + \frac{A_n}{(x-a)^n}$$

Example 3 Decompose $\dfrac{3x^2+4x+5}{(x+2)(x-1)^2}$ into partial fractions.

$$\frac{3x^2+4x+5}{(x+2)(x-1)^2} = \frac{A}{x+2} + \frac{B}{x-1} + \frac{C}{(x-1)^2}$$

$$3x^2 + 4x + 5 = A(x-1)^2 + B(x+2)(x-1) + C(x+2)$$

Let $x = 1$: $12 = 3C$ Let $x = -2$: $9 = 9A$
$ C = 4$ $ A = 1$

To solve for B, let $x = 0$ and substitute $5 = 1 + (-2B) + 8$
the values obtained for A and C. $ B = 2$

$$\frac{3x^2+4x+5}{(x+2)(x-1)^2} = \frac{1}{x+2} + \frac{2}{x-1} + \frac{4}{(x-1)^2} \qquad \textit{Substitute.}$$

7.8 Partial Fractions **377**

GUIDED PRACTICE

For Example 1

Decompose into partial fractions.

1. $\dfrac{2x-12}{x^2-3x}$ $\dfrac{4}{x} - \dfrac{2}{x-3}$

2. $\dfrac{2x-8}{x^2-4x+3}$ $\dfrac{3}{x-1} - \dfrac{1}{x-3}$

For Example 2

Decompose into partial fractions.

1. $\dfrac{-6x^2+11x+15}{x^3-2x^2-15x}$

   $-\dfrac{1}{x} - \dfrac{2}{x-5} + \dfrac{3}{x+3}$

2. $\dfrac{8}{x^3-6x^2+8x}$ $\dfrac{1}{x} + \dfrac{1}{x-4} - \dfrac{2}{x-2}$

For Example 3

Decompose into partial fractions.

1. $\dfrac{-2x^2+14x-15}{(x-1)(x-2)^2}$

   $\dfrac{1}{x-2} + \dfrac{5}{(x-2)^2} - \dfrac{3}{x-1}$

2. $\dfrac{3x^2+16x+14}{(x+3)^3}$

   $\dfrac{3}{x+3} + \dfrac{2}{(x+3)^2} - \dfrac{7}{(x+3)^3}$

For Example 4

Decompose into partial fractions.

1. $\dfrac{-21x-34}{x^3+7x^2+8x-16}$

   $\dfrac{2}{x+2} - \dfrac{3}{x-1} + \dfrac{1}{x+4}$

2. $\dfrac{7x^2+x}{x^3-3x^2-9x-5}$

   $\dfrac{5}{x-5} + \dfrac{2}{x+1} - \dfrac{1}{(x+1)^2}$

Technology   If students have access to a symbolic manipulator, they may use it to find factors of the denominator of the rational expression.

CLOSURE

Have students describe in their own words the procedures for decomposing a fraction into partial fractions.

INDEPENDENT PRACTICE

Assignment Guide
Basic: 1–14, 15–23 odd
Average: 1–9 odd, 10–26
Enriched: 1–13 odd, 14–30

Teacher's Resource Book
Practice, page 50

® Review
Exercises 11, 13, 14, and 24 review concepts such as graphing functions, determining whether functions are odd or even, finding the minimum of a function, and solving trigonometric equations.

LESSON FOLLOW-UP

Test Yourself
Teacher's Resource Book
Tests—Quiz, form A, page 26
Tests—Quiz, form B, page 26

Lesson Quiz
Decompose into partial fractions.

1. $\dfrac{5x + 8}{x^2 + 5x + 4}$ $\dfrac{1}{x+1} + \dfrac{4}{x+4}$

2. $\dfrac{4x^2 - 2x - 24}{x^3 + 2x^2 - 8x}$ $\dfrac{3}{x} - \dfrac{1}{x-2} + \dfrac{2}{x+4}$

3. $\dfrac{3x^2 + 3x + 7}{(x+3)^2(x-2)}$
$\dfrac{2}{x+3} - \dfrac{5}{(x+3)^2} + \dfrac{1}{x-2}$

Additional Answers
Practice Exercises

6. $\dfrac{3}{x} - \dfrac{2}{x-2} + \dfrac{1}{x-1}$

7. $\dfrac{1}{x-1} - \dfrac{3}{x+1} + \dfrac{2}{x+2}$

8. $\dfrac{3}{x-1} + \dfrac{1}{x-2} + \dfrac{2}{x-3}$

9. $\dfrac{5}{x+1} - \dfrac{2}{x-2} + \dfrac{1}{(x-2)^2}$

You can use a graphing utility to help identify the zeros of a polynomial of degree greater than 2. After factoring the depressed polynomial, you can decompose the fraction.

Example 4 Decompose $\dfrac{4x^2 - 9x - 37}{x^3 + 2x^2 - 11x - 12}$ into partial fractions.

A graphing utility indicates that there appears to be a zero in the denominator at -1. Synthetic division shows that -1 is a zero. The depressed polynomial is $x^2 + x - 12$, which may be factored into $(x + 4)(x - 3)$. Therefore,

$$\frac{4x^2 - 9x - 37}{(x+1)(x+4)(x-3)} = \frac{A}{x+1} + \frac{B}{x+4} + \frac{C}{x-3} \qquad x^3 + 2x^2 - 11x - 12 = (x+1)(x+4)(x-3)$$

$$4x^2 - 9x - 37 = A(x+4)(x-3) + B(x+1)(x-3) + C(x+1)(x+4)$$

Let $x = -1$: $-24 = -12A$ Let $x = -4$: $63 = 21B$ Let $x = 3$: $-28 = 28C$
$A = 2$ $B = 3$ $C = -1$

$$\frac{4x^2 - 9x - 37}{x^3 + 2x^2 - 11x - 12} = \frac{2}{x+1} + \frac{3}{x+4} - \frac{1}{x-3}$$

Class Exercises

6. $\dfrac{2}{x+1} + \dfrac{3}{x+2} + \dfrac{4}{x+3}$

Decompose into partial fractions.

1. $\dfrac{3x + 4}{x(x+2)}$ $\dfrac{2}{x} + \dfrac{1}{x+2}$

2. $\dfrac{-x + 5}{(x-1)(x+1)}$ $\dfrac{2}{x-1} - \dfrac{3}{x+1}$

3. $\dfrac{4x + 7}{x^2 + x - 6}$ $\dfrac{1}{x+3} + \dfrac{3}{x-2}$

4. $\dfrac{6x^2 + 11x - 24}{x(x-3)(x+4)}$ $\dfrac{2}{x} + \dfrac{3}{x-3} + \dfrac{1}{x+4}$

5. $\dfrac{2x^2 - 6x - 4}{x^3 - 4x}$ $\dfrac{1}{x} - \dfrac{1}{x-2} + \dfrac{2}{x+2}$

6. $\dfrac{9x^2 + 34x + 29}{x^3 + 6x^2 + 11x + 6}$

7. $\dfrac{4x^2 + 4x - 2}{(x+1)^2(x-1)}$
$\dfrac{1}{(x+1)^2} + \dfrac{\frac{5}{2}}{x+1} + \dfrac{\frac{3}{2}}{x-1}$

8. $\dfrac{4x^2 - 4x - 4}{(x-1)^2(x+1)}$
$\dfrac{-2}{(x-1)^2} + \dfrac{3}{x-1} + \dfrac{1}{x+1}$

9. $\dfrac{3x^2 + 14x + 12}{(x+2)^2(x+1)}$
$\dfrac{4}{(x+2)^2} + \dfrac{2}{x+2} + \dfrac{1}{x+1}$

Practice Exercises Use appropriate technology.

Decompose into partial fractions.

A 1. $\dfrac{5x - 3}{x(x-1)}$ $\dfrac{3}{x} + \dfrac{2}{x-1}$

2. $\dfrac{x - 11}{x^2 - 2x - 3}$ $\dfrac{-2}{x-3} + \dfrac{3}{x+1}$

3. $\dfrac{3x - 3}{x^2 - 4x - 5}$ $\dfrac{2}{x-5} + \dfrac{1}{x+1}$

4. $\dfrac{-2x^2 - x + 6}{x^3 - 5x^2 + 6x}$ $\dfrac{1}{x} - \dfrac{5}{x-3} + \dfrac{2}{x-2}$

5. $\dfrac{5x^2 + 9x + 3}{x(x+1)^2}$ $\dfrac{3}{x} + \dfrac{1}{(x+1)^2} + \dfrac{2}{x+1}$

6. $\dfrac{2x^2 - 9x + 6}{x(x-2)(x-1)}$

7. $\dfrac{6}{x^3 + 2x^2 - x - 2}$

8. $\dfrac{6x^2 - 25x + 25}{x^3 - 6x^2 + 11x - 6}$

9. $\dfrac{3x^2 - 17x + 25}{(x+1)(x-2)^2}$

10. **Thinking Critically** How can you use a graphing utility to check whether you have correctly determined a decomposition into partial fractions?

® 11. Graph the function $x^5 - 2x^3 - 4x$ and determine whether it is even, odd, or neither. odd

12. **Writing in Mathematics** Explain how a graphing utility can be used to help you determine factors for decomposition into partial fractions.

® 13. Solve $\sin x = 2 \sin x$ on the interval $0 \le x < 2\pi$. $0, \pi$

378 Chapter 7 Polynomial Functions

Writing in Mathematics

12. Use the graphing utility to graph the denominator of a rational expression. Find its zeros and use them to write linear factors. These linear factors become the denominators of the partial fractions.

14. *Business* The owner of a business determines his profit by the function

$p(x) = \dfrac{x^2}{6} - 5x - 90$, $x > 0$, where x is the number of units produced.

Graph the function and determine the minimum number of units that must be produced to earn a profit. 43 units

Decompose into partial fractions.

B 15. $\dfrac{3x^2 - 15x + 16}{(x + 1)(x + 2)^2}$

16. $\dfrac{3x^2 - x + 4}{x^3 - x^2 - x + 1}$

17. $\dfrac{x^2 - 11x + 18}{x^3 + 6x^2 + 9x}$

18. $\dfrac{17x^2 - 11x - 22}{6x^3 + 23x^2 - 6x - 8}$

19. $\dfrac{-5x^2 - 16x + 1}{6x^3 + x^2 - 10x + 3}$

20. $\dfrac{6x^2 - 4x + 2}{4x^3 - 4x^2 + x}$

21. $\dfrac{-3x^3 + 12x^2 - 10x + 4}{x^4 - 3x^3 + 3x^2 - x}$

22. $\dfrac{3x + 2}{x^3 + x^2}$

23. $\dfrac{x^3 - 2x^2 + 4x - 2}{x^4 - 3x^3 + 3x^2 - x}$

24. Graph $f(x) = x^5 - 4$ without using a graphing utility.

Determine an algebraic function that can be decomposed into the following.

C 25. $\dfrac{2}{x - 3} + \dfrac{3}{x + 2} + \dfrac{3}{(x + 2)^2}$ $\dfrac{5x^2 + 8x - 19}{x^3 + x^2 - 8x - 12}$

26. $\dfrac{2}{x - 1} - \dfrac{3}{(x - 1)^2} + \dfrac{1}{(x - 1)^3}$ $\dfrac{2x^2 - 7x + 6}{x^3 - 3x^2 + 3x - 1}$

If the denominator has a nonrepeating quadratic factor that cannot be factored, the partial fraction decomposition will include a factor of the form

$\dfrac{Ax + B}{ax^2 + bx + c}$. Decompose into partial fractions.

27. $\dfrac{2x^2 + x + 1}{(x^2 + 1)(x - 1)}$ $\dfrac{1}{x^2 + 1} + \dfrac{2}{x - 1}$

28. $\dfrac{3x^2 + 7x + 4}{(x^2 + 2x + 2)(x + 2)}$

29. $\dfrac{-3x - 9}{(x^2 + 2)(x^2 - 1)}$

30. Thinking Critically If the denominator has a repeating quadratic factor, then the partial fraction decomposition will include a term of what form?

$\dfrac{Ax + B}{(ax^2 + bx + c)^2}$

Test Yourself

1. Determine the possible number of positive and negative real zeros of the polynomial $p(x) = 2x^4 - 6x^3 - x^2 - x + 5$. 0 or 2 pos., 0 or 2 neg. 7.5

2. Locate the real zeros of $h(x) = x^3 - 5x^2 + 1$ between consecutive integers. −1 and 0, 0 and 1, 4 and 5

3. Use a graphing utility and the location theorem to determine all zeros of $f(x) = x^4 - 3x^2 - 6x - 2$ to the nearest hundredth. −0.41, 2.41

4. Determine any points of discontinuity for $f(x) = \dfrac{6}{x - 8}$. 8   7.6

5. Graph the function $f(x) = \dfrac{2x - 3}{x + 2}$. Determine any intercepts or asymptotes.

6. Solve and check the equation $\sqrt{3 - x} = x + 9$ algebraically. −6   7.7

7. Use a graphing utility to solve the equation $3 = \sqrt{x + 2} + \dfrac{x}{2}$. 2

Decompose into partial fractions.

8. $\dfrac{6x - 2}{2x^2 - 3x - 2}$ $\dfrac{2}{2x + 1} + \dfrac{2}{x - 2}$

9. $\dfrac{-2x^2 + x + 1}{x^3 + 2x^2 + x}$ $\dfrac{1}{x} - \dfrac{3}{x + 1} + \dfrac{2}{(x + 1)^2}$ 7.8

7.8 Partial Fractions **379**

Test Yourself

5.

x-int: $\left(\dfrac{3}{2}, 0\right)$; y-int: $\left(0, -\dfrac{3}{2}\right)$

asymptotes: $x = -2$; $y = 2$

Additional Answers

14.

15. $\dfrac{34}{x + 1} - \dfrac{31}{x + 2} - \dfrac{58}{(x + 2)^2}$

16. $\dfrac{2}{x + 1} + \dfrac{3}{(x - 1)^2} + \dfrac{1}{x - 1}$

17. $\dfrac{2}{x} - \dfrac{1}{x + 3} - \dfrac{20}{(x + 3)^2}$

18. $\dfrac{3}{x + 4} - \dfrac{2}{3x - 2} + \dfrac{1}{2x + 1}$

19. $-\dfrac{2}{x - 1} + \dfrac{2}{3x - 1} + \dfrac{1}{2x + 3}$

20. $\dfrac{2}{x} + \dfrac{3}{(2x - 1)^2} - \dfrac{1}{2x - 1}$

21. $-\dfrac{4}{x} + \dfrac{1}{x - 1} + \dfrac{2}{(x - 1)^2} + \dfrac{3}{(x - 1)^3}$

22. $\dfrac{1}{x} + \dfrac{2}{x^2} - \dfrac{1}{x + 1}$

23. $\dfrac{2}{x} - \dfrac{1}{x - 1} + \dfrac{2}{(x - 1)^2} + \dfrac{1}{(x - 1)^3}$

24.

28. $\dfrac{2x + 1}{x^2 + 2x + 2} + \dfrac{1}{x + 2}$

29. $\dfrac{x + 3}{x^2 + 2} - \dfrac{2}{x - 1} + \dfrac{1}{x + 1}$

379

Chapter 7   Summary and Review

Vocabulary

asymptote rules (366)
complex conjugate theorem (351)
conjugate radical theorem (352)
depressed polynomial (333)
Descartes' rule of signs (356)
factor theorem (333)
fundamental theorem of algebra (349)
horizontal asymptote (365)
integral zeros theorem (343)
intermediate value theorem (357)
leading coefficient (338)
location theorem (357)

partial fractions (376)
radical equation (371)
rational function (365)
rational zeros theorem (344)
remainder theorem (332)
slant asymptotes (367)
sum and product of zeros (358)
synthetic division (332)
synthetic substitution (331)
upper and lower bound theorem (359)
vertical asymptote (365)

Synthetic Division and the Remainder and Factor Theorems   Synthetic division is a   7.1
method for dividing a polynomial in one variable by a binomial of the form $x - a$
where a can be any number. The remainder theorem states that if a polynomial $P(x)$
is divided by $x - a$, the remainder is $P(a)$. The factor theorem states that $x - a$ is a
factor of the polynomial $P(x)$ if and only if $P(a) = 0$.

1. Evaluate $g(x) = 2x^3 - 3x^2 - x + 7$ when $x = 4$ using synthetic substitution. 83

2. Divide $(4x^3 - 2x + 5)$ by $(x + 2)$ using synthetic division. $4x^2 - 8x + 14$, R = -23

3. Evaluate $f(x) = 5x^4 - 2x^3 - 3x^2 + 2x - 5$ for $x = -3$ using the remainder
   theorem. 421

4. Use the factor theorem to determine whether $x + 3$ is a factor of $t(x)$ when
   $t(x) = x^4 - 4x^3 - 5x^2 + x + 9$. not a factor

5. Determine k so that $g(x) = x^3 - x^2 + kx + 24$ has $x + 4$ as a factor. -14

Graphs of Polynomial Functions   The properties of a   7.2
polynomial function can be observed in its graph. Real
zeros occur at the x-intercepts. A polynomial of
degree n can have at most $n - 1$ relative extrema.

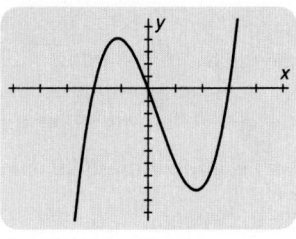

$y = x^3 - x^2 - 6x$

6. Determine an equation for the graph at the right.

7. Graph the function $f(x) = x(x - 2)^2(x + 1)$.

[−5, 5] by [−10, 5]

Integral and Rational Zeros of Polynomial Functions   The integral zeros theorem and   7.3
the rational zeros theorem are helpful when you must find zeros of polynomial
functions or solutions to polynomial equations.

8. Determine the rational zeros of $r(x) = x^3 - 2x^2 - 14x - 5$. 5

9. Determine all zeros of $f(x) = 4x^3 - 4x^2 - 23x + 30$. 2; 1.5; -2.5

The Fundamental Theorem of Algebra The fundamental theorem of algebra and the complex conjugate theorem are helpful in finding complex zeros of polynomial functions or solutions to polynomial equations. If $P(x)$ is a polynomial of positive degree n with complex coefficients, then $P(x)$ has n linear factors. If $P(x)$ is a polynomial with complex coefficients and degree n, then P has exactly n zeros.

7.4

10. Express $h(x) = x^3 + 6x^2 + 5x - 12$ as a product of linear factors. $(x - 1)(x + 3)(x + 4)$

11. Determine all zeros of $g(x) = x^4 - 4x^3 + 4x^2 - 36x - 45$. $-1;\ 5;\ \pm 3i$

12. Determine the zeros of $f(x) = (x + 6)^2(x - 1)^3(x^2 + 4)$; state their multiplicities. -6 (mult. 2); 1 (mult. 3); $\pm 2i$

13. Determine all the zeros of $p(x) = x^5 - x^4 - x^3 + x^2 - 2x + 2$ given $p(i) = 0$. $1;\ \pm\sqrt{2};\ \pm i$

14. Determine a polynomial of lowest degree with real coefficients that has $1 - i$ and -3 as zeros. $x^3 + x^2 - 4x + 6$

Descartes' Rule, the Intermediate Value, and Sum and Product of Zeros Descartes' rule of signs, the location theorem, and the upper and lower bound theorem can be useful in finding zeros of polynomial functions. In the equation, $a_n x^n + a_{n-1}x^{n-1} + \cdots + a_1 x + a_0 = 0$, with $a_n \neq 0$, the sum of the zeros is equal to $-\dfrac{a_{n-1}}{a_n}$, and the product of the zeros is equal to $\dfrac{a_0}{a_n}$ for n even and $-\dfrac{a_0}{a_n}$ for n odd.

7.5

15. How many positive and negative zeros are possible for $p(x) = x^4 + 3x^3 - x^2 - 1$? 1 pos.; 1 neg.

16. Locate the real zeros of $g(x) = x^3 - 4x - 6$ between consecutive integers. 2 and 3

17. Determine all zeros of $f(x) = x^4 + 5x^3 + 6x^2 + 5x + 1$ to the nearest tenth. $-0.3;\ -3.7$

18. Find the sum and product of the zeros for $f(x) = 4x^4 - 2x^3 + 3x^2 - 2x + 12$. $\frac{1}{2};\ 3$

Rational Functions A function f is continuous at point $(a,\ f(a))$ if it is defined at the point and if it passes through the point without a break; that is, it is possible to trace the graph through the point without lifting the pencil from the paper. To understand and interpret the graph of a rational function, determine its intercepts and asymptotes.

7.6

19. Determine any points of discontinuity for the function $f(x) = \dfrac{5}{x + 12}$. -12

20. Graph $f(x) = \dfrac{4x}{x - 3}$. Determine any intercepts and asymptotes.

Radical Functions Radical equations can be solved algebraically by raising both sides of the equation to a power that will eliminate the radical. All solutions of the derived equation should be checked in the original equation. Many radical equations can also be solved using a graphing utility.

7.7

21. Solve and check the equation $\sqrt{x + 3} - 1 = x - 4$ algebraically. 6

22. Use a graphing utility to solve to the nearest hundredth:
    $\sqrt{x - 1} + \sqrt{x + 3} = x^3 - 2x^2$. 2.55

Partial Fractions An algebraic fraction in which the degree of the numerator is less than the degree of the denominator can sometimes be decomposed into a sum of partial fractions. The first step is to factor the denominator.

7.8

Decompose into partial fractions.

23. $\dfrac{x - 17}{x^2 + x - 12}$ $\dfrac{3}{x + 4} - \dfrac{2}{x - 3}$

24. $\dfrac{3x + 8}{x^2 + 4x + 4}$ $\dfrac{3}{x + 2} + \dfrac{2}{(x + 2)^2}$

$(0, 0);\ x = = 4$

Chapter 7   Test

1. Evaluate $p(x) = -3x^3 + 4x^2 + 2x - 8$ when $x = -3$. 103

2. Divide $(3x^3 - 4x^2 - 6)$ by $(x - 3)$ using synthetic division. $3x^2 + 5x + 15$, $R = 39$

3. Evaluate $g(x) = 4x^4 + 5x^3 - 2x^2 - x + 6$ for $x = 2$ using the remainder theorem. 100

4. Use the factor theorem to determine whether $x + 2$ is a factor of $h(x)$ when $h(x) = x^5 - 2x^3 - x^2 + 3x - 4$. not a factor

5. Determine k so that $f(x) = x^3 - 11x^2 + kx - 6$ has $x - 3$ as a factor. $k = 26$

6. Graph $f(x) = (x - 1)^2(x + 2)^2$.

7. Determine an equation of a cubic polynomial whose only zero is 3. $f(x) = (x - 3)^3$

8. Determine the zeros of $t(x) = 3x^3 - x^2 - 22x + 24$. $-3, 2, \dfrac{4}{3}$

9. Find the rational zeros of $f(x) = x^3 - 3x^2 - 3x - 4$. 4

10. Express $g(x) = x^3 + 4x^2 - 11x - 30$ as a product of linear factors. $(x + 2)(x - 3)(x + 5)$

11. Determine all zeros of $g(x) = x^4 + 3x^2 - 4$ given that $2i$ is one zero. ± 1; $-2i$

12. Determine a polynomial of lowest degree with real coefficients that has $2 - i$ and 2 as zeros. $p(x) = x^3 - 6x^2 + 13x - 10$

13. Determine the possible number of positive and negative zeros of the polynomial $g(x) = x^3 - 7x^2 + x - 1$. 1 or 3 pos., no neg.

14. Locate the real zeros of $h(x) = x^3 - x^2 - 5$ between consecutive integers. 2 and 3

15. Find all zeros of $t(x) = x^4 - 2x^3 - 5x^2 - 3$. Express irrational zeros correct to the nearest tenth. -1.7; 3.5

16. Determine any points of discontinuity for $f(x) = \dfrac{3}{x - 14}$. 14

17. Graph $f(x) = \dfrac{x + 8}{x - 5}$. Determine any intercepts or asymptotes.

18. Solve and check $\sqrt{4 - x} = x + 6$ algebraically. -3.3

19. Use a graphing utility to solve $\sqrt[3]{x - 3} + x = \sqrt{x + 1}$. 2.6

Decompose into partial fractions.

20. $\dfrac{5x + 7}{x^2 + 2x - 3}$ $\dfrac{2}{x + 3} + \dfrac{3}{x - 1}$

21. $\dfrac{x^2 + 6x + 2}{x^3 + 2x^2 + x}$ $\dfrac{2}{x} - \dfrac{1}{x + 1} + \dfrac{3}{(x + 1)^2}$

Challenge

Show that when 1 is added to the product of four consecutive integers, the result is a perfect square.

Cumulative Review

Select the best choice for each question.

1. Determine the number of relative   7.2
A extrema of $f(x) = x^5 + x^3 - 2x^2 - 6x$.
   A. 2   **B.** 4   **C.** 4   **D.** 1   **E.** none

2. Evaluate $\text{Sin}^{-1} 0.325$, in radians,   4.5
B to four decimal places.
   A. 5.6142   **B.** 0.3310   **C.** 1.7629
   D. 7.1629   **E.** 3.4726

3. Solve $5 \tan x + 3 = 2 \tan x - 6$ 6.5
D to the nearest hundredth of a radian,
   where $0 \le x < 2\pi$.
   A. 18.92; 50.31   **B.** 1.29; 6.32
   C. 1.03; 6.11   **D.** 1.89; 5.03
   E. none of these

4. The altitude to the base of an   5.1
C isosceles triangle bisects the
   A. hypotenuse   **B.** adjacent side
   C. base   **D.** base angle
   E. none of these

5. Find the quadrant or axis in which   3.1
B the terminal side of an angle of $\frac{12}{5}$
   counterclockwise rotation lies.
   A. I   **B.** II   **C.** III   **D.** IV   **E.** x-axis

6. Determine k so that $g(x) =$ 7.1
A $x^3 + 6x^2 + kx - 12$ has $x + 3$ as a factor.
   A. 5   **B.** 8   **C.** 2   **D.** 3
   E. none of these

7. Determine the rational zeros of   7.3
C $f(x) = 24x^3 + 50x^2 - 29x - 10$.
   A. $\frac{2}{5}, 4, -\frac{3}{2}$ **B.** $\frac{5}{2}, \frac{1}{4}, -\frac{2}{3}$
   C. $-\frac{5}{2}, -\frac{1}{4}, \frac{2}{3}$ **D.** $-\frac{2}{5}, -\frac{1}{4}, \frac{2}{3}$
   E. none

8. A polynomial function will have a   7.2
B zero that is a real number at each point
   at which it crosses the
   A. y-axis   **B.** x-axis
   C. origin   **D.** both x- and y-axis
   E. none of these

9. Determine the slope and   2.3
A y-intercept of the line passing through
   points $(-6, -2)$ and $(-5, -4)$.
   A. $m = -2$, $b = -14$
   B. $m = 2$, $b = 14$
   C. $m = \frac{1}{2}$, $b = 7$
   D. $m = -\frac{1}{2}$, $b = -7$
   E. none of these

10. Find the area of triangle RST if   5.5
B $r = 12$, $t = 8$, and $\angle S = 30°$.
   A. 36   **B.** 24   **C.** 96   **D.** 56   **E.** 48

11. The zeros of the sine function   4.1
A occur at multiples of
   A. π **B.** $\frac{\pi}{2}$ **C.** 2π **D.** $\frac{\pi}{4}$ **E.** $\frac{3\pi}{2}$

12. Determine the possible number of   7.5
C positive and negative real zeros of the
   polynomial $P(x) = x^3 - 4x^2 - 5x + 18$.
   A. 1   **B.** 2   **C.** 3   **D.** 4   **E.** none

13. Express in terms of one angle: 6.1
C $\sin 35° \cos 55° + \cos 35° \sin 55°$
   A. $\cos 90°$ **B.** $\sin 15°$ **C.** $\sin 90°$
   D. $\cos 15°$ **E.** none of these

14. The law of sines can be used to   5.4
D solve a triangle when the given
   information is

   I. 3 sides
   II. 2 sides and an included angle
   III. 1 side and 2 angles

   A. I only   **B.** I and II   **C.** II and III
   D. III only   **E.** I and III

15. Determine a polynomial function   7.4
D with real coefficients of lowest degree
   and leading coefficient of 1 that has
   $1 + 3i$ and 4 as zeros.
   A. $P(x) = x^2 - 4$
   B. $P(x) = x^3 - 4x^2 + 40$
   C. $P(x) = x^3 - 10x^2 - 4x + 10$
   D. $P(x) = x^3 - 6x^2 + 18x - 40$

Cumulative Review   **383**

Summary

Solving linear and nonlinear systems of equations in two variables is introduced using techniques of substitution and graphing. Then solving inequalities in one variable and in two variables using graphical methods is discussed. Various methods for solving quadratic, polynomial, and rational inequalities are presented. Linear programming and its applications round out the chapter.

Chapter Objectives

- To solve linear systems of equations in two variables
- To solve nonlinear systems of equations in two variables
- To solve linear inequalities in one variable algebraically and graphically
- To solve absolute value inequalities
- To graph linear inequalities in two variables
- To solve quadratic inequalities
- To solve polynomial inequalities and graph the solutions
- To solve rational inequalities and graph the solutions
- To solve systems of inequalities in two variables graphically
- To solve optimization problems involving systems of linear inequalities
- To apply linear programming

8 Inequalities and Linear Programming

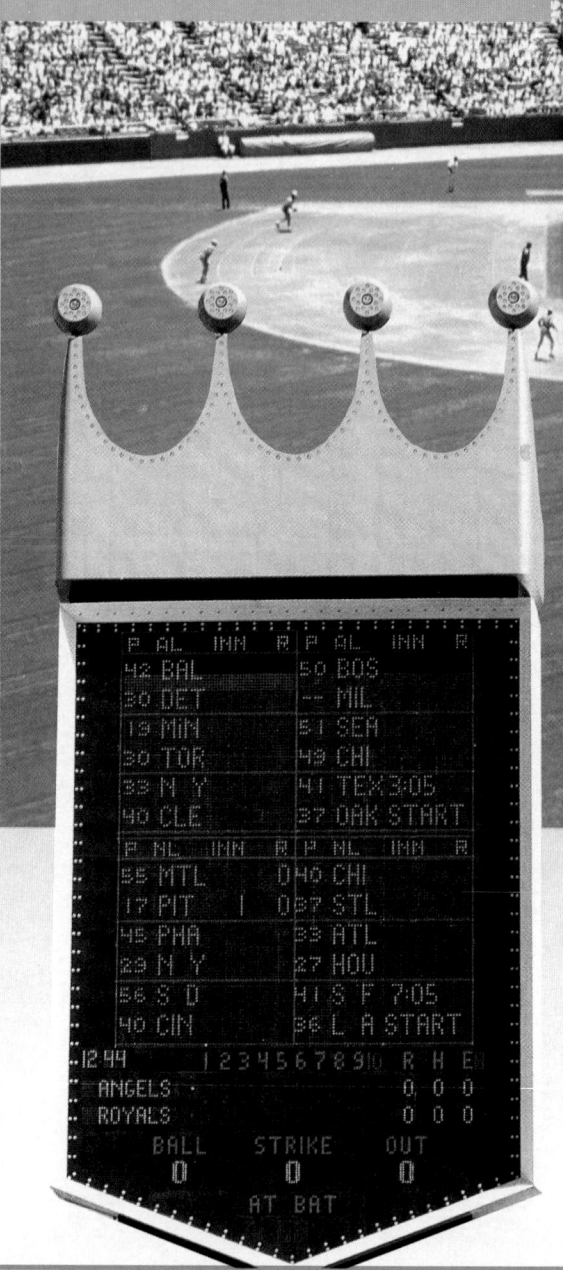

Mathematical Power

Modeling Before the umpire can yell "Play ball," at the ball park, someone has to figure out a game schedule. This is a fact that most people take for granted, but it is no simple task. To cope with the many factors that are involved, mathematics comes into play.

Consider a simplified model of the major league schedule in 1991. There were 14 American League (AL) teams and 12 National League (NL) teams. Each league was divided equally into an East and West division. The length of the regular season, that is, before the league playoffs or World Series, was 162 games for each team. During the regular season in major league baseball, teams in both divisions of the same league play each other, but teams in different leagues do not. For the National League in 1991, this meant that a team played each of the other five teams in its own division and each of the six teams in the other division for a total of 162 games. Let

x = number of times an NL team plays another team in its own division
y = number of times an NL team plays another team in the other division

Then, from what was stated above,

$$5x + 6y = 162$$

Since it is desirable that a team play more games against each of the teams in its own division, the above equation is restricted by the inequality $x > y$. Also, x and y must be positive integers.

Features

Modeling
8.5 Geometric probability
8.6 Linear programming

Projects   417, 424
Challenge   400, 417
Review   392, 405, 424

The only ordered pairs that satisfy all the restrictions are (18, 12), (24, 7), and (30, 2). The most equitable schedule has a National League team playing 18 games against each of the teams in its own division and 12 games against each of the teams outside its division.

Now consider some of the other conditions or restrictions that might be placed on the variables when making up the schedule. The cost of traveling from one city to another dictates that teams play each other in series of several games. However, to ensure fair competition, no team should have to play too many consecutive games away from its own field. In addition, scheduling games between division rivals toward the end of the season makes for a more exciting finish. The list of conditions goes on and on— from minimizing the number of air miles each team must travel to maximizing the revenues the league will receive.

Baseball scheduling is an example of a problem that can be solved using techniques of *linear programming*. Representing relationships among the many variables as a system of equations and inequalities makes them manageable.

Thinking Critically In 1961, when the American League grew from 8 to 10 teams (no divisions), the regular season was changed from 154 to 162 games. Suggest a mathematical reason why this was done.

Project Construct a scheduling model for a specific sports league. Use your own knowledge from participating in a sports league, such as soccer or bowling, obtain the data from someone else, or refer to published accounts of professional sports competitions. Be sure to explain all variables and restrictions that you use.

385

Mathematical Power

Many problems involve finding the best way to accomplish a given objective under certain conditions. If these conditions and the objective are described by linear equations and/or inequalities, then the problem is a *linear programming* problem. Petroleum refineries, faced with mixture problems in blending gasolines, were the first industrial users of linear programming.

Most real world linear programming problems involve a large number of variables and are solved on high-speed computers using methods such as the *simplex algorithm*. This method was developed by American mathematician George B. Dantzig in the late 1940s to solve some complex problems in allocating supplies for the U.S. Air Force. In 1984 a researcher at Bell Labs, Narendra Karmakar, devised an alternative algorithm that has proved superior for some problems.

When discussing the baseball model, ask students which of the ordered pairs (18, 12), (24, 7), and (30, 2) would be the best choice to solve the scheduling problem. Have them defend their responses.

Thinking Critically In 1961 each team had to play each of the other 9 teams. In order for a team to play the same number of games against each of its opponents, the total number of games in the season had to be a multiple of 9. The number 154 is not a multiple of 9, but 162 is.

Review and Assessment

Student Text

Teacher's Resource Book

Vocabulary
consistent system
dependent system
inconsistent system
independent system
linear system
solution of a system

Ⓜ **Materials/Manipulatives**
transparencies

Technology
graphing utility
symbolic manipulator

FOCUS

Zeno was one of the Pythagoreans, probably best known for his mathematical paradoxes involving motion and infinitesimals. A paradox is a statement that, whether asserted or denied, leads to a contradiction. Students may be interested in researching Zeno's paradox of the tortoise and Achilles, which leads to the concept of a limit.

INSTRUCTION

• When discussing Example 1, remind students that if the result of the simplification, after substitution, is an equation of the form $0 = c$, $c \neq 0$, then the system of linear equations is inconsistent. If the result is an equation of the form $0 = 0$, then the system is consistent and dependent.

• Before doing Example 2, point out that when solving an equation for one of its variables, coefficients should be left in rational form to help reduce rounding errors.

Ⓜ • Transparencies may effectively be used to present graphic solutions of linear systems of equations.

8.1 Systems of Equations

Objectives: To solve linear systems of equations in two variables
To solve nonlinear systems of equations in two variables

Focus

No doubt in your childhood you heard Aesop's fable of the tortoise and the hare. But did you know that this story was transformed into a math problem in which the warrior Achilles is trying to catch the tortoise? Suppose the tortoise moves at a rate of 100 yards a minute and has a head start of 1000 yards. If Achilles is 10 times faster than the tortoise, when and where will he overtake it? An equation can be determined for each participant that represents the location as a function of time. The solution to this *system of equations* is an ordered pair that represents the time and location where Achilles catches the tortoise.

A model for a real world problem may give rise to a set of equations called a *system*. A **solution** of a system of equations in two variables is any ordered pair that satisfies all the equations in the system. In the coordinate plane, this solution is represented by a point that is common to the graphs of all the equations in the system.

A linear equation is an equation in which the variables appear only in the first degree. A system of equations consisting entirely of linear equations is called a **linear system.** A linear system of equations in two variables that has *at least one* solution is called a **consistent system.** A consistent system may be either **independent,** having *exactly one* solution, or **dependent,** having *infinitely many* solutions. A linear system with no solution is called an **inconsistent system.**

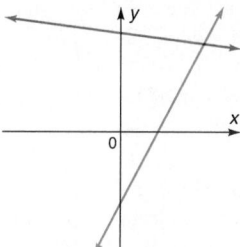

One solution
Intersecting lines
Different slopes
Consistent and independent

Infinite number of solutions
Coincidental lines
Same slope
Consistent and dependent

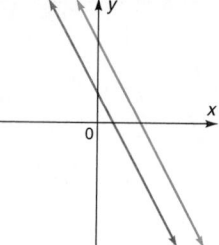

No solution
Parallel lines
Same slope
Inconsistent

386   Chapter 8 Inequalities and Linear Programming

One method for solving systems of linear equations is by substitution. To use the substitution method, solve either equation for one of its variables. Substitute for that variable in the other equation, obtaining an equation in one variable. Solve the equation in one variable. Then substitute in either equation to find the other variable. Check the solution in both original equations.

Example 1   Solve each linear system by substitution.

a. $\begin{cases} x + 4y = -0.5 + 4x \\ 2x + 3y = 0.5x + 2y + 1 \end{cases}$ b. $\begin{cases} 5x = 10y \\ 3x - 6y = 7 \end{cases}$

a. $x + 4y = -0.5 + 4x$ *Solve the first equation for y.*
$\quad\quad 4y = 3x - 0.5$
$\quad\quad\ y = 0.75x - 0.125$

$\quad\quad\quad\quad\quad 2x + 3y = 0.5x + 2y + 1$ *Use the second equation.*
$\quad\quad\quad\quad\quad\quad 1.5x + y = 1$ *Simplify.*
$\quad 1.5x + (0.75x - 0.125) = 1$ *Substitute for y.*
$\quad\quad\quad\quad\quad\quad 2.25x = 1.125$ *Solve for x.*
$\quad\quad\quad\quad\quad\quad\quad\quad x = 0.5$

$y = 0.75(0.5) - 0.125$ *Substitute 0.5 for x in the first equation.*
$y = 0.25$

The solution is $(0.5, 0.25)$. Check this solution in both original equations.

b. $5x = 10y$ *Solve the first equation for x.*
$\ \ x = 2y$

$\quad 3x - 6y = 7$ *Use the second equation.*
$3(2y) - 6y = 7$ *Substitute for x.*
$\ \ 6y - 6y = 7$
$\quad\quad\quad 0 = 7$ *Contradiction*

No solution; the system is inconsistent. *Explain how expressing both equations in the slope-intercept form shows that the graphs of the equations will not intersect.*

Sometimes the addition method, which was reviewed in Lesson 1.1, is the most convenient method for solving a system of linear equations.

Example 2   Solve using the addition method: $\begin{cases} \frac{4}{3}x - 5y = 7\frac{1}{3} \\ 2x - 3y = 2 \end{cases}$

$\quad 4x - 15y = 22$ *Multiply both sides of the first equation by 3.*
$\underline{-4x + 6y = -4}$ *Multiply both sides of the second equation by -2.*
$\quad\quad -9y = 18$ *Add the equations.*
$\quad\quad\quad\ y = -2$

$\quad\quad 2x - 3y = 2$ *Use the original second equation.*
$2x - 3(-2) = 2$ *Substitute -2 for y.*
$\quad\quad\quad\ x = -2$ *Solve for x.*

The solution is $(-2, -2)$. This should be checked in the original first equation.

Alternative Learning Styles
Using familiar experiences provides motivation for many students. Have students discuss situations where they have encountered the problem of finding the intersection of two or more graphs.

GUIDED PRACTICE

For Example 1
Solve each linear system by substitution.

1. $\begin{cases} 0.2x + 0.4y + 1 = -0.5x - 2 \\ -0.6x + 0.5y = 0.1x + 0.9y + 3 \end{cases}$
infinite number of solutions since it is consistent and dependent; $0.7x + 0.4y = -3$

2. $\begin{cases} \dfrac{x}{2} - \dfrac{y}{3} = 0 \\ \dfrac{x}{6} - \dfrac{y}{18} = \dfrac{1}{2} \end{cases}$
$(6, 9)$

Common Error   Some students may solve the first equation for y without multiplying both sides of the equation by the LCM, and thus obtain a fraction for y. Those students may then incorrectly simplify the complex fraction that results when that expression for y is substituted in the second equation. Have these students review simplifying complex fractions.

For Example 2
Solve each linear system using the addition method.

1. $\begin{cases} \dfrac{5}{2}x - 3y = \dfrac{3}{2} \\ 4x - 5y = 3 \end{cases}$
$(-3, -3)$

2. $\begin{cases} 2x + 3y + 1 = 0 \\ 0.6x - 0.2y + 3.6 = 0 \end{cases}$
$(-5, 3)$

Thinking Critically
By expressing both equations in the slope-intercept form, you can determine at a glance whether or not the slopes are the same. If the slopes are the same but the y-intercepts are not equal, the graphs of the equations will not intersect.

Solve each system graphically.

1. $\begin{cases} 4x - 2y = -17 \\ 4x + 20 = -12x + 8y \end{cases}$

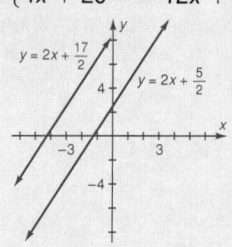

$y = 2x + \frac{17}{2}$ $y = 2x + \frac{5}{2}$

no solution; The lines are parallel.

2. $\begin{cases} 4x + 3y = 0 \\ \dfrac{7x}{4} - \dfrac{3y}{8} = \dfrac{27}{5} \end{cases}$

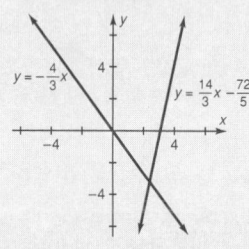

$y = -\frac{4}{3}x$ $y = \frac{14}{3}x - \frac{72}{5}$

$(2.4, -3.2)$

Technology After solving for y, students should determine the y-intercept and use this value to help determine a minimum or maximum value of y for the viewing rectangle.

For Example 4

Solve and graph each system.

1. $\begin{cases} y - \sqrt{x} = 0 \\ y = 2x - 3 \end{cases}$
$(2.25, 1.5)$

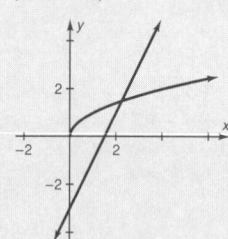

Solving a system of linear equations *algebraically* means using the substitution or addition method to solve the system. Systems of linear equations in two variables can also be solved by graphing the equations on the same set of axes and determining the point of intersection, if any. Most graphing utilities have a trace feature with which to pinpoint the x and y values of the point of intersection. Remember to solve each equation for y.

Example 3 Solve each linear system graphically.

a. $\begin{cases} 0.3x - 1.1 = 0.2y \\ 0.1x = 0.4y + 0.7 \end{cases}$ **b.** $\begin{cases} 7y + 5x = -21 \\ 8.82y = -6.30x - 26.46 \end{cases}$

a. $0.3x - 1.1 = 0.2y$
$\qquad y = (0.3x - 1.1)/0.2$

$0.1x = 0.4y + 0.7$
$\qquad y = (0.1x - 0.7)/0.4$

The point of intersection is $(3, -1)$.

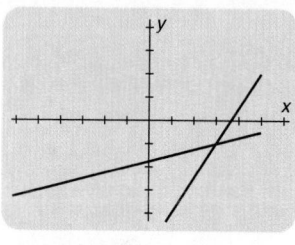

$[-6, 6]$ by $[-4, 4]$

b. $7y + 5x = -21$
$\qquad y = (-5x - 21)/7$

$8.82y = (-6.30x - 26.46)$
$\qquad y = (-6.30x - 26.46)/8.8$

The lines coincide. Therefore, the system is consistent and dependent.

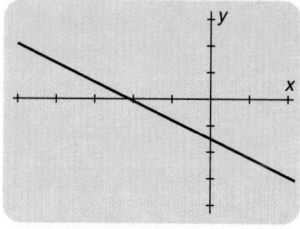

$[-10, 4]$ by $[-8, 6]$
x scl: 2 y scl: 2

Use the zoom feature to obtain more accurate approximations. Check approximated values of the variables in the original system to be certain of the exact solutions. Some utilities are equipped with an integer zoom command that will display integral x-values.

A system of equations in which one or more of the equations is nonlinear is called a *nonlinear* system. Nonlinear systems can often be solved by the same methods as linear systems. Consistent nonlinear systems may have more than one solution.

Example 4 Solve using substitution and graph the system: $\begin{cases} y + 7 = 12x - 3x^2 \\ 13 = 9x - y \end{cases}$

$\quad y = 9x - 13$ $\qquad\qquad$ *Solve the linear equation for y.*

$(9x - 13) + 7 = 12x - 3x^2$ $\quad$ *Substitute for y in the other equation.*
$\quad 3x^2 - 3x - 6 = 0$ $\qquad$ *Solve for x.*
$\qquad x^2 - x - 2 = 0$
$(x + 1)(x - 2) = 0$ $\qquad$ *Factor.*
$\quad x = -1$ or $x = 2$

388   Chapter 8 Inequalities and Linear Programming

Substitute these values for x in one of the original equations and solve for y.

$$13 = 9(-1) - y \qquad 13 = 9(2) - y$$
$$22 = -y \qquad\qquad -5 = -y$$
$$y = -22 \qquad\qquad y = 5$$

The solutions are $(-1, -22)$ and $(2, 5)$.

To graph, solve each equation for y.

$$y = -3x^2 + 12x - 7$$
$$y = 9x - 13$$

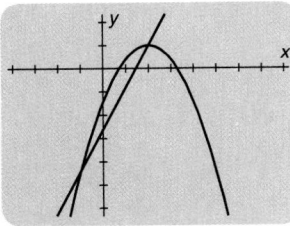

[-4, 8] by [-30, 10]
x scl: 1   y scl: 5

The solutions found algebraically correspond to the points of intersection of the graphs.

Nonlinear systems of equations are often used to model real world problems.

Example 5 *Construction* An animal trainer has 600 ft of fencing and wants to build an L-shaped pen with a total area of 6800 ft². The pen is to be comprised of two juxtaposed rectangles of equal dimensions as shown in the diagram. Find the dimensions of the rectangles.

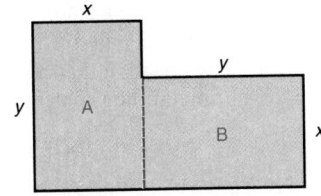

Let x represent the width of a rectangle and y represent the length. The perimeter of the part of the pen determined by rectangle A is $2x + y + (y - x)$ and by rectangle B is $2y + x$.

$$2x + y + (y - x) + 2y + x = 600 \qquad \textit{Perimeter of the pen}$$
$$2x + 4y = 600$$

$$2xy = 6800 \qquad \textit{Area of the pen}$$

$$\begin{cases} 2x + 4y = 600 \\ 2xy = 6800 \end{cases} \qquad \textit{Solve the system of equations by substitution.}$$

$$x = 300 - 2y \qquad \textit{Solve the first equation for x.}$$

$$2(300 - 2y)y = 6800 \qquad\qquad \textit{Substitute for x in the second equation.}$$
$$600y - 4y^2 = 6800$$
$$y^2 - 150y + 1700 = 0$$
$$y = \frac{150 \pm \sqrt{150^2 - 4(1700)}}{2} \qquad \textit{Quadratic formula}$$
$$y = 12.35 \quad \text{or} \quad y = 137.65 \qquad \textit{To the nearest hundredth}$$

$$2x(12.35) = 6800 \qquad 2x(137.65) = 6800 \qquad \textit{Substitute for y in the second equation.}$$
$$x = \frac{6800}{2(12.35)} \qquad\qquad x = \frac{6800}{2(137.65)}$$
$$x = 275.30 \qquad\qquad x = 24.70 \qquad \textit{To two decimal places}$$

Since one wall of the pen was represented by $y - x$, y must be greater than x and the dimensions 12.35 ft by 275.30 ft must be rejected. Thus, the dimensions of the rectangles should be 24.70 ft by 137.65 ft.

Common Error Some students will accept the apparent solution $(1, -1)$. Remind these students that when solving an equation in which it is necessary to square a quantity, extraneous roots may be found, and stress that all possible answers should be checked in the original equations. Have students graph $y = -\sqrt{x}$ to see the solution $(1, -1)$.

2. $\begin{cases} x^2 + y^2 = 25 \\ x + y = 1 \end{cases}$

Technology To solve this system graphically, students should notice that the equation $x^2 + y^2 = 25$ is not a function. On some graphing utilities, students must graph $y = \sqrt{25 - x^2}$ and $y = -\sqrt{25 - x^2}$.

For Example 5
A problem similar to the following was solved by the Babylonians around 1800 B.C. Writings on tablets dating back to this time period illustrate the algebraic nature of Babylonian geometry.

The sum of the areas of two squares is 185. The length of the side of one square is 7 more than $\frac{1}{2}$ the length of the side of the second square. Find the sides of the squares.
The lengths of the sides of the squares are 8 and 11.

CLOSURE

Have students summarize in their math journals the procedures for solving algebraically both linear and nonlinear systems of equations in two variables. Then have them repeat the process for solving such systems graphically.

INDEPENDENT PRACTICE

Assignment Guide

Basic: 1–20, 25–27, 36–37
Average: 7–8, 15–37
Enriched: 8, 20, 23–45

Teacher's Resource Book
Practice, page 51

Ⓡ **Review**

Exercises 13, 15, 17, 24, 25, 36, and 37 review concepts of graphing absolute value functions, solving trigonometric equations, determining field properties, determining maximum and minimum points, solving triangles, and determining the equations of a line.

Additional Answers

Class Exercises

3.

4.

8.

Class Exercises

Solve each system algebraically.

1. $\begin{cases} 2x + 3y = -10 \\ x + 2y = -1 \end{cases}$ $(-17, 8)$

2. $\begin{cases} 5x - 4y = 22 \\ 5x - 2y = 8 \end{cases}$ $(-1.2, -7)$

Solve each linear system graphically.

3. $\begin{cases} 3x + 4y = 1 \\ -5x + 2y = 7 \end{cases}$ $(-1, 1)$

4. $\begin{cases} x + 4y = -5 \\ 8x - y = -7 \end{cases}$ $(-1, -1)$

Solve each nonlinear system of equations.

5. $\begin{cases} x^2 = y - 1 \\ y - 3 = x \end{cases}$ $(-1, 2), (2, 5)$

6. $\begin{cases} y - x^2 = 4x \\ 2y + x = 1 \end{cases}$ $(-4.61, 2.81),$ $(0.11, 0.45)$

7. **Thinking Critically** Suppose you are using a graphing utility to solve a linear system of equations and the trace function approximates the point of intersection as $x = -1.4$ and $y = 2.2$. What steps would you take to determine the exact solution?

8. Determine the equation that models each participant's location as a function of time in the problem presented in the Focus. Solve by graphing.

Practice Exercises Use appropriate technology.

Solve each linear system algebraically.

A 1. $\begin{cases} 2y + x = 3 \\ 3x + y = -11 \end{cases}$ $(-5, 4)$

2. $\begin{cases} 5y + 2x = 10 \\ 2x - 3y = 13 \end{cases}$ $\left(\frac{95}{16}, -\frac{3}{8}\right)$

3. $\begin{cases} 6x + 10y = 21 \\ 2x - 5y = -4 \end{cases}$ $\left(\frac{13}{10}, \frac{33}{25}\right)$

4. $\begin{cases} 4x - 3y = -9 \\ 12x + 3y = -8 \end{cases}$ $\left(-\frac{17}{16}, \frac{19}{12}\right)$

5. $\begin{cases} -y + 2x = 5 \\ 3x + 6y = 20 \end{cases}$ $\left(\frac{10}{3}, \frac{5}{3}\right)$

6. $\begin{cases} 4x + 2y = 1 \\ 5y - x = 32 \end{cases}$ $\left(-\frac{59}{22}, \frac{129}{22}\right)$

Solve and graph each system.

7. $\begin{cases} x^2 + y = 6 \\ y - 5 = x \end{cases}$ $\left(\frac{-1 + \sqrt{5}}{2}, \frac{9 + \sqrt{5}}{2}\right),$ $\left(\frac{-1 - \sqrt{5}}{2}, \frac{9 - \sqrt{5}}{2}\right)$

8. $\begin{cases} -4x + y = 4 \\ x^2 + y = 10x \end{cases}$ $(3 + \sqrt{5}, 16 + 4\sqrt{5})$ $(3 - \sqrt{5}, 16 - 4\sqrt{5})$

Solve each system graphically.

9. $\begin{cases} 5x + 4y = 2 \\ -5x - 2y = 4 \end{cases}$ $(-2, 3)$

10. $\begin{cases} y = (x - 1)^2 - 4 \\ x + y = -1 \end{cases}$ $(-1, 0), (2, -3)$

11. $\begin{cases} x^2 + 2x - 5 = y \\ y + 7 = 3x \end{cases}$ no solution

12. *Finance* At the beginning of last year, the Sanchez family invested $5000. Part of the money was in a certificate of deposit paying 8% and part was in a bond paying 12%. Assuming simple interest, the total interest they received was $472. If the amount invested in a certificate of deposit is $400 less than twice the amount invested in the bond, determine how much money they invested in each type of investment.

Ⓡ 13. Determine the field properties that are satisfied by the set of rational numbers under the operation of multiplication. closure, assoc., comm., mult. ident., inv.

390 Chapter 8 Inequalities and Linear Programming

7. Use zoom and trace. Then check results in the equations. Note: Sometimes there is no "exact" solution in decimal form.

390

14. **Thinking Critically** A linear system of two equations is solved by substitution and results in the equation $0 = 0$. Explain why this system cannot have a unique solution. The two equations are equivalent. This system consists of two coincidental lines.

Ⓡ 15. Graph: $f(x) = |x + 2| - 1$

16. *Aviation* A plane flew 1750 km in 6 h with a tail wind of constant velocity. It then flew back 540 km in 3 h with a head wind of the same velocity. Find the speed of the plane and the speed of the wind.

Ⓡ 17. Solve $\sin^2 x + 2 \sin x = 0$ for all values of x, $0 \le x \le 2\pi$. $0, \pi, 2\pi$

18. *Construction* A carpenter is building a square room with a square adjacent foyer according to the floor plan shown at the right. If the total area is to be 3284 ft^2 and the perimeter is to be 256 ft, find the lengths of each side of the figure. $x = 50$ ft, $y = 28$ ft or $x = 52.4$ ft, $y = 23.2$ ft

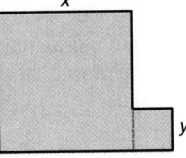

19. **Writing in Mathematics** Describe some of the pitfalls of using a graphing utility to solve linear and nonlinear systems of equations.

Solve each linear system by substitution.

B 20. $\begin{cases} 0.2x + 0.3y = 0.1 \\ 0.6x + 0.4y = 3.7 \end{cases}$ $(10.7, -6.8)$

21. $\begin{cases} 0.3x - 0.4y = -3.5 \\ 0.2x + 0.1y = 2.5 \end{cases}$ $\left(\frac{65}{11}, \frac{145}{11}\right)$

22. $\begin{cases} \dfrac{x}{7} + \dfrac{3y}{14} = 2 \\ \dfrac{7x}{15} - \dfrac{4y}{5} = -\dfrac{8}{3} \end{cases}$ $\left(\frac{24}{5}, \frac{92}{15}\right)$

23. $\begin{cases} \dfrac{x}{2} + \dfrac{3y}{4} = 6 \\ \dfrac{2x}{3} - \dfrac{y}{9} = 8 \end{cases}$ $(12, 0)$

Ⓡ 24. Determine the coordinates of the maximum or minimum point of the graph of the function $f(x) = -x^2 + 6x - 9$. maximum: (3, 0)

Ⓡ 25. Given triangle ABC with $a = 4$ ft, $b = 7$ ft, and $\angle C = 40°$, solve the triangle. $c = 4.7$ ft; $\angle A = 33°$; $\angle B = 107°$

Solve each system of equations.

26. $\begin{cases} x^2 + y^2 = 4 \\ x^2 + y = 4 \end{cases}$ $(\pm 2, 0)$ $(\pm\sqrt{3}, 1)$

27. $\begin{cases} y - |x| = 3 \\ y^2 - 9 = 0 \end{cases}$ $(0, 3)$

28. $\begin{cases} 7x - 2y = -22 \\ 4x - 5y = -28 \end{cases}$ $(-2, 4)$

Solve each system graphically.

29. $\begin{cases} -2y + 8x = 3 \\ -x + \dfrac{1}{4}y = 1 \end{cases}$ no solution

30. $\begin{cases} 5x = 2 - 4y \\ -3x + 10 = -2y \end{cases}$ $(2, -2)$

31. $\begin{cases} y = 2 \cos x \\ 3y = 4x - 3 \end{cases}$ $(1.24, 0.65)$

32. $\begin{cases} y = \sqrt{x + 5} \\ 3x^2 + 30x + 43 = 8y \end{cases}$ $(-1, 2)$

33. **Thinking Critically** How would you express the solution to the following system of equations? $\begin{cases} y = \sin x \\ y = \cos x \end{cases}$

34. *Finance* Shelby receives a windfall of $45,000. He deposits $20,000 in a savings account and invests the rest in a mutual fund that yields $1\frac{1}{4}$% higher interest than the savings account. Assuming simple interest, determine the interest rate for the mutual fund if he earns $4025 from the total interest on both investments. 9.5%

8.1 Systems of Equations **391**

---

35. *Manufacturing* A box is made from a 60 in. by 80 in. piece of cardboard by cutting equal squares from the corners and folding up the sides. The volume of the box is five times greater than the volume of a cube with one side equal to the height of the box. What is the volume of the box? 21,277.30 in.³

(R) 36. Determine the equation of a line perpendicular to the line with equation $2x - 3y = 10$ and passing through the origin. $3x + 2y = 0$

(R) 37. Determine the equation of a line perpendicular to the line shown and passing through the point $(2, 2)$. $y = \frac{1}{3}x + \frac{4}{3}$

C 38. Use a graphing utility to determine the point(s) of intersection of the graphs of $xy = 1$ and $y = x^2 - 5x + 4$. $(4, 0.25)$

39. If $xy = p$ and $x + y = q$, find x and y in terms of p and q.

Solve each system. $\left(\dfrac{q \pm \sqrt{q^2 - 4p}}{2}, \dfrac{q \mp \sqrt{q^2 - 4p}}{2} \right)$

40. $\begin{cases} xy = 1 \\ y = \text{Sin}^{-1} x \end{cases}$ $(0.9, 1.1), (-0.9, -1.1)$

41. $\begin{cases} y = \tan x \\ y = \cos x, \ 0 \le x \le \pi \end{cases}$ $(0.79\pi, -0.78)$, $(0.21\pi, 0.78)$

42. *Pharmaceuticals* A pharmacist needs to mix a 50 fluid ounce solution containing 54% glucose. The pharmacist has on hand a 30% solution and a 90% solution. Determine how many ounces of each solution are mixed.

43. *Traffic Control* The number of vehicles entering an intersection is equal to the number leaving. Using this fact, determine values for a, b, and c, in terms of d.

44. **Thinking Critically** Solve the system $y = \cos x$ and $y = -0.5x^2 + 1$ graphically. What conclusions can you draw about using a graph to solve systems of equations?

45. Solve the system by substitution.
$$\begin{cases} 4 - 6x - 7y = 0 \\ 12 + 11x - 4z = 0 \\ x - y - z = 0 \end{cases} \quad (-4, 4, -8)$$

Review

Using a dashed line, graph $x = -5$, $x = 5$, $y = 9$, and $y = -9$ on the same set of axes. Then graph the following equations using the dashed lines as a boundary for their length unless otherwise noted.

1. $\dfrac{x^2}{9} + \dfrac{y^2}{16} = 1$

2. $y = -|-x| - 4$

3. $(x + 2)^2 + (y - 4)^2 = 1$

4. $(x - 2)^2 + (y - 4)^2 = 1$

5. $y = 4(x - 2)^2 + 5$

6. $y = 4(x + 2)^2 + 5$

7. $y = x - 3$ for $3 \le x \le 5$

8. $y = x + 3$ for $-5 \le x \le -3$

Graph the following equations on the same set of axes.

9. $y = \frac{3}{4} \cos 8x, \ x \ge 0$

10. $y = \frac{3}{4} \cos 4x, \ x \le 0$

392 Chapter 8 Inequalities and Linear Programming

8.2 Linear Inequalities

Objectives: *To solve linear inequalities in one variable algebraically and graphically*
To solve absolute value inequalities
To graph linear inequalities in two variables

Focus

For railroads to run safely, warning lights must work correctly. In the first illustration at the right a train is approaching the station. If the station is clear on one side or the other, then the light for the clear side will show green and a switch will send the train to that side. If *A or B* shows green, then the train may proceed.

In the second illustration, the lights warn the train about two roads that the tracks will cross. If both roads are clear, then both lights will show green. If *A and B* show green, then the train may proceed without stopping.

To solve inequalities, you will work with rules like the ones that the train follows. You will have to look carefully at how many conditions are given and how they are related to one another.

Previous chapters have primarily involved equations. But many real world problems are better modeled by *inequalities*. An important property of the real number system that pertains to inequalities is the trichotomy property.

Recall

Trichotomy Property

If *a* and *b* are two real numbers, then exactly one of the following statements is true:

$$a < b \qquad a = b \qquad a > b$$

The solution of an inequality is the set of all values that make the inequality true. Two inequalities are *equivalent* if they have the same solution set. The solution of an inequality can be described by using interval notation or by drawing a graph.

Vocabulary
addition property
boundary
closed half-plane
conjunction
disjunction
half-plane
multiplication property
open half-plane
transitive property
trichotomy property

Ⓜ **Materials/Manipulatives**
transparencies

Technology
graphing utility

FOCUS

A Frenchman by the name of Jean Damery is in the *Guiness Book of World Records* for having built the smallest model railroad. The scale is 1:1000. Draw on students' experiences with model railroading to reinforce the concepts of "and" and "or" presented in the Focus.

INSTRUCTION

- If students have had some set theory, review the concepts of intersection (conjunction) and union (disjunction) before discussing the Focus and the introductory material in the chapter.
- An inequality of the form $a < x < b$, can be difficult for some students to grasp. One way to help them understand its meaning is to have them look at the inequality as a "sandwich" where *x* is between *a* and *b*.

Ⓜ **Alternative Learning Styles**
The use of transparencies can provide a visually oriented review of the set concepts of union and intersection using Venn diagrams and may be helpful for many students in understanding the solution of a linear inequality written in interval notation.

GUIDED PRACTICE

For Example 1

Solve each inequality. Express the solution in interval notation and graph its solution on the number line.

1. $\dfrac{3x + 2}{10} < -\dfrac{2}{5}$ $(-\infty, -2)$

2. $-1 \le \dfrac{5x - 1}{3} < 2$ $\left[-\dfrac{2}{5}, \dfrac{7}{5}\right)$

3. $\dfrac{x}{2} - 2 \le 0$ or $\dfrac{x}{2} - 2 > 5$

$(-\infty, 4] \cup (14, \infty)$

Common Error When solving a disjunction, some students may try to write the solution as a conjunction such as $14 < x \le 4$. Point out that 14 is not less than or equal to 4 and therefore this inequality does not make sense.

Inequality	Interval	Graph
$a < x < b$	(a, b)	
$a \le x \le b$	$[a, b]$	
$a \le x < b$	$[a, b)$	
$a < x \le b$	$(a, b]$	
$x > a$	(a, ∞)	
$x \ge a$	$[a, \infty)$	
$x < a$	$(-\infty, a)$	
$x \le a$	$(-\infty, a]$	

A *linear inequality in one variable* is an inequality in which the variable appears only in the first degree. To solve a linear inequality, use the properties of inequality to isolate the variable. The properties listed below are stated for $<$ but are true if the symbol $<$ is replaced by $\le$, $>$, or $\ge$. Remember that $a > 0$ means a is positive, whereas $a \ge 0$ means a is nonnegative. Likewise, $a < 0$ means a is negative, whereas $a \le 0$ means a is nonpositive.

Properties of Inequality

Given that a, b, and c are real numbers.

Addition Property	If $a < b$, then $a + c < b + c$.
Multiplication Property	If $a < b$ and $c > 0$, then $ac < bc$.
	If $a < b$ and $c < 0$, then $ac > bc$.
Transitive Property	If $a < b$ and $b < c$, then $a < c$.

In a compound inequality, two conditions are given. When the first *and* second conditions must both be satisfied, the resulting statement is called a **conjunction.** The solution of a conjunction is the *intersection* of the sets satisfying each condition. When the first *or* the second condition must be satisfied, the resulting statement is called a **disjunction.** The solution of a disjunction is the *union* of the sets satisfying each condition.

Conjunction

$-3 < x < 3$
$x > -3$ *and* $x < 3$

The solution is the set of numbers greater than -3 *and* less than 3.

Disjunction

$x < -2$ or $x > 2$

The solution is the set of numbers less than -2 *or* greater than 2.

Example 1 Solve each inequality. Express the solution in interval notation and draw its graph on the number line.

a. $\dfrac{3-5x}{2} < \dfrac{5}{4}$ b. $3 \le 4x - 1 < 7$ c. $2x - 3 \ge 2$ or $2x - 3 < -4$

a. $\dfrac{3-5x}{2} < \dfrac{5}{4}$

$6 - 10x < 5$ *Multiply both sides by the LCD.*

$-10x < -1$

$x > \dfrac{1}{10}$ *If $a < b$ and $c < 0$, then $ac > bc$.*

Interval notation: $\left(\dfrac{1}{10}, \infty\right)$

b. $3 \le 4x - 1 < 7$ *Conjunction*

Solution 1	*Solution 2*	
$3 \le 4x - 1 < 7$	$4x - 1 \ge 3$ and	$4x - 1 < 7$
$4 \le \quad 4x \quad < 8$	$4x \ge 4$ and	$4x < 8$
$1 \le \quad x \quad < 2$	$x \ge 1$ and	$x < 2$

Interval notation: $[1, 2)$

c. $2x - 3 \ge 2$ or $2x - 3 < -4$ *Disjunction*

$x \ge \dfrac{5}{2}$ or $x < -\dfrac{1}{2}$

Interval notation: $\left(-\infty, -\dfrac{1}{2}\right) \cup \left[\dfrac{5}{2}, \infty\right)$

Many real world problems using inequalities involve absolute value. Absolute value inequalities can be solved by interpreting absolute value as a distance.

$|x| < a$ represents the set of all real numbers whose distance from zero is less than a units. From the graph it can be seen that $|x| < a$ means that $x > -a$ and $x < a$, that is, $-a < x < a$.

$|x| > a$ represents the set of all real numbers whose distance from zero is greater than a units. From the graph it can be seen that $|x| > a$ means that $x < -a$ or $x > a$.

Example 2 Solve each inequality. Express the solution in interval notation and draw its graph on the number line.
a. $|2x + 1| \le 3$ b. $|2x + 1| > 3$

a. $|2x + 1| \le 3$

$-3 \le 2x + 1 \le 3$ *If $|x| < a$, then $-a < x < a$.*

$-4 \le 2x \quad\quad \le 2$

$-2 \le \quad x \quad \le 1$

Interval: $[-2, 1]$

For Example 2
Solve each inequality. Express the solution in interval notation and graph its solution on the number line.

1. $|6 - 4x| \le 2$ [1, 2]

Common Error When solving an inequality by working on both sides at the same time, some students may forget to reverse one or both of the inequality signs. Remind these students that when both sides of an inequality are divided by a negative number, the direction of each inequality sign must be reversed.

2. $\left|\dfrac{x-1}{4}\right| > 1$ $(-\infty, -3) \cup (5, \infty)$

Graph each inequality in the coordinate plane.

1. $-3x + 5y \geq 2$

2. $x \geq -3$

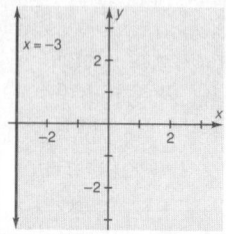

b. $|2x + 1| > 3$

$2x + 1 < -3$ or $2x + 1 > 3$ *If $|x| > a$, then $x < -a$ or $x > a$.*

$\quad 2x < -4$ or $\qquad 2x > 2$

$\qquad x < -2$ or $\qquad\quad x > 1$

Interval: $(-\infty, -2) \cup (1, \infty)$

Describe the union of the two solution sets in parts (a) and (b).

Thus far in the lesson you have worked with linear inequalities in one variable. The solution is graphed on the number line. Inequalities may have two variables. Then the solution is a set of ordered pairs and is graphed on the coordinate plane.

A *linear inequality in two variables* is an inequality of the form $y < mx + b$, where m and b are real numbers. A linear inequality in two variables may also use any of the relations $>$, $\leq$, or $\geq$.

The graph of a linear equation corresponding to a linear inequality in two variables divides the plane into two regions, each of which is called a **half-plane.** The set of all points (x, y) which satisfy the inequality lies in one of the half-planes. The line that is the graph of the equation is the **boundary** of the half-plane. If the relation is $\leq$ or $\geq$, the points on the boundary are included in the solution and the solution is a **closed half-plane** indicated on the graph by a solid line. If the relation is $<$ or $>$, the points on the boundary are not included in the solution and the solution is an **open half-plane** indicated by a dashed line.

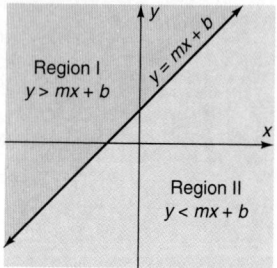

To graph a linear inequality in two variables, solve for y. Then graph the corresponding equation. Use a test point to determine which half-plane satisfies the inequality. Shade the half-plane.

Example 3   Graph each inequality in the coordinate plane.   **a.** $3x - y > 4$ **b.** $y \leq -2$

a. $3x - y > 4$

$\qquad -y > -3x + 4$ *Solve for y.*

$\qquad\quad y < 3x - 4$

$\qquad\quad y = 3x - 4$ *Corresponding equation*

Since the relation is $<$, draw a dashed line. Choose a test point in either region, such as $(0, 0)$.

$\qquad y < 3x - 4$

$\qquad 0 \underset{\cdot}{\_?\_} 3(0) - 4$

$\qquad 0 > -4$

Since $(0, 0)$ does not satisfy the inequality, shade the open half-plane below the line $y = 3x - 4$.

b. $y \leq -2$

Since the relation is $\leq$, draw a solid line. Shade the closed half-plane below the line $y = -2$.

396   Chapter 8 Inequalities and Linear Programming

Thinking Critically

The union of the solution sets in parts *a* and *b* may be expressed $(-\infty, -2) \cup [-2, 1] \cup (1, \infty) = (-\infty, \infty)$ or $\{x: x \in \mathcal{R}\}$.

If you are asked to graph an inequality such as $x \leq 2$, be sure that it is specified whether the graph is to be on a number line or in the coordinate plane. The context of a problem will determine which is appropriate.

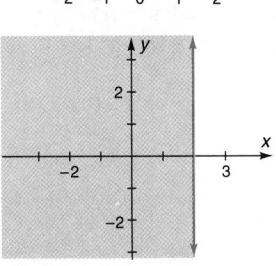

One variable
$x \leq 2$

Two variables
$x \leq 2$

 When a linear inequality in two variables is solved for y, the half-plane which represents its graph can be determined by inspection. This is particularly important if you are using a graphing utility to determine the graph of an inequality. Many graphing utilities cannot graph an inequality, but they can graph its corresponding equation. You then must use inspection to determine whether the line is solid or dashed and which half-plane is to be shaded. Since many graphing utilities require you to input a function in the form $y = f(x)$, the set of rules below can be used to determine which region should be shaded.

$y < mx + b$ Open half-plane *below* the line $y = mx + b$
$y \leq mx + b$ Closed half-plane *below* the line $y = mx + b$
$y > mx + b$ Open half-plane *above* the line $y = mx + b$
$y \geq mx + b$ Closed half-plane *above* the line $y = mx + b$

Real world consumer problems can often be modeled using inequalities.

Example 4 *Budgeting* The Lucas family owns an air conditioner and a 16-in. window fan. The electric company informed them that it costs 15.75¢ per hour to run the air conditioner and 2.1¢ per hour to run the fan. The Lucas family wants to keep its cooling costs under $15 per month. Determine a set of values for the number of hours they can run each piece of equipment per month and keep within their budget. Round answers to the nearest tenth.

Let x represent the number of hours the air conditioner is used, and y the number of hours the fan is used. Then the cost of cooling the house is $15.75x + 2.1y$. Since $\$15 = 1500¢$, solve the inequality $15.75x + 2.1y < 1500$.

$15.75x + 2.1y < 1500$ *Solve by graphing.*
$2.1y < -15.75x + 1500$ *Solve for y.*
$y < (-15.75x + 1500)/2.1$ *Input form*
$y < -7.5x + 714.3$ To the nearest tenth

Since the relation is $<$, the solution is an open half-plane below the line $y = -7.5x + 714.3$.

Neither the air conditioner nor the fan can be run a negative number of hours; therefore the solution must be restricted to the first quadrant.

If the Lucas family did not run the fan at all, what is the maximum number of hours they could run the air conditioner during the month?

8.2 Linear Inequalities   **397**

For Example 4
A trial lawyer charges $150 for an initial consultation plus $125 for each additional hour or part thereof to represent a person in court for a civil action. Alternatively, the lawyer will charge a flat fee of $1875 which includes the initial consultation. Determine the number of court hours the trial would have to take for the hourly rate to exceed the flat fee. The trial would have to take more than 13.8 h.

Thinking Critically
The maximum number of hours the air conditioner could run is about 95 h.

397

Solve each inequality graphically.

1. $y \geq |x - 5|$

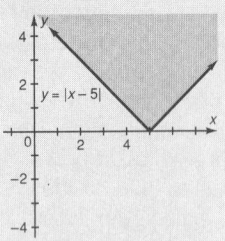

2. $y < |2x - 3|$

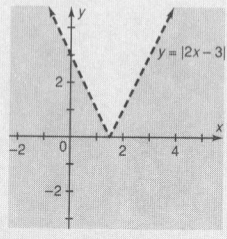

CLOSURE

Group students in pairs and have them summarize to each other the procedures for graphing linear inequalities in one and two variables.

INDEPENDENT PRACTICE

Assignment Guide
Basic: 1–20, 25, 30–31, 33–35
Average: 7–8, 10–15, 19–35
Enriched: 19–20, 23–47

Teacher's Resource Book
  Practice, page 52

Ⓡ Review

Exercises 7, 15, 25, 31, and 33 review concepts of graphing, including quadratic functions, absolute value equations, sinusoidals, axis of symmetry, vertex, and intercepts, and using coordinate geometry.

An absolute value inequality in two variables is solved in a similar manner to a linear inequality in two variables. Graph the absolute value function and use a test point to determine if the region above or below the graph should be shaded.

Example 5 Solve $y \leq -|2x + 3|$ graphically.

Graph $y = -|2x + 3|$ using solid lines.

By inspection the region is on or below the graph of $y = -|2x + 3|$.

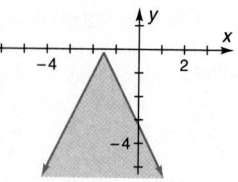

Class Exercises

Express each sentence as an inequality.

1. The cost c of a new calculator is more than \$10 but less than \$20. $10 < c < 20$

2. It took Matty at least $\frac{1}{2}$ hour to finish his homework t, but he never worked more than 2 hours. $\frac{1}{2} \leq t \leq 2$

3. Cars must parallel park a distance d at least 15 ft from a fire hydrant. $d \geq 15$

4. A certain strain of bacteria will die if the temperature t drops below 65°F or rises above 98°F. $t < 65$ or $t > 98$

Solve each inequality. Express the solution in interval notation and draw its graph on the number line.

5. $5x + 3 \leq -7x + 4$ 6. $-4 < 2x + 5 \leq 9$ 7. $|2 - 3x| > 11$ 8. $|2x| + 1 < 2$

Graph each inequality in the coordinate plane.

9. $-x + 3y > 6$ 10. $4x - 5y \leq -5$ 11. $|10 - 3x| \geq y$ 12. $y > |1 - 2x|$

13. **Thinking Critically** The formula for converting from °C to °F is $F = \frac{9}{5}C + 32$. How could you use a graph of this equation in the coordinate plane to determine the values of C for which F is greater than 68°?

Practice Exercises   Use appropriate technology.

Solve each inequality. Express the solution in interval notation and draw its graph on the number line.

A 1. $-1 \leq 3x - 4 \leq 8$ 2. $-4 < 2x - 8 \leq 12$ 3. $|x + 1| < 5$

4. $|x - 2| \geq 2$ 5. $|6 - 2x| \geq 4$ 6. $|1.5x - 9| > 0$

Ⓡ 7. Graph: $f(x) = 2x^2 - 4x$

8. **Thinking Critically** If $a < b$, does it follow that $a^2 < b^2$? Explain your answer.

Graph each inequality in the coordinate plane.

9. $3x + y < 4$ 10. $-2x + 4y \geq 8$ 11. $3x - 2y \leq 12$

12. $7x > 32 - 5y$ 13. $y \leq |2x + 1|$ 14. $y < -|x - 5|$

398   Chapter 8 Inequalities and Linear Programming

15. For the function $f(x) = 2x - 3x^2 - 7$, give the axis of symmetry, vertex, and x- and y-intercepts.

16. *Consumerism*   The cost of renting a car is \$12 per day plus \$0.20 per mile. If the car is rented for only one day, determine the mileage for which the cost of renting the car would be less than \$40. less than 140 mi

17. *Physics*   Given that the volume of a gas is constant, the pressure exerted by the gas decreases by 10 lb/in.³ for each drop in temperature of 1°F. If the initial pressure is 120 lb/in.³ at a temperature of 78°F, determine the temperatures for which the pressure will be between 80 and 90 lb/in.³

18. *Consumerism*   A tool rental company offers the following rates. To rent a steamer by the hour to remove wallpaper, there is an initial charge of \$15 per day or part thereof, plus \$3 per hour. They also offer a flat rate of \$42 for the day. Determine how many hours you would have to use the steamer for the flat rate to be less expensive than the hourly rate. more than 9 h

19. **Writing in Mathematics**   List five real world examples of compound inequalities like the ones listed in Class Exercises 1 to 4.

20. **Thinking Critically**   Construct an inequality in which the original relation is >, but the graph is the open half-plane below the boundary. ex: $-y > x + 1$

Solve each inequality. Express the solution in interval notation and draw its graph on the number line.

B 21. $-2 < \dfrac{x + 5}{4} < 5$

22. $0 \le \dfrac{3 - 2x}{4} \le 1$

23. $\dfrac{|5 - 3x|}{4} > 0$

24. $4|x + 2| + 3 < 0$

Ⓡ 25. Graph $y = 3 \sin 2x$ from -2π to 2π.

Solve each inequality. Give the solution as an inequality and in interval notation.

26. $3x - 2 < 0$ $x < \dfrac{2}{3}; \left(-\infty, \dfrac{2}{3}\right)$

27. $4x + 1 \le 3$ $x \le \dfrac{1}{2}; \left(-\infty, \dfrac{1}{2}\right]$

Graph each inequality in the coordinate plane.

28. $0.25y - 0.32x > 1.8$

29. $|y| \le 3$

30. **Thinking Critically**   Use inequalities to describe the set of points in each of quadrants I, II, III, and IV.

Ⓡ 31. Using coordinate geometry, show that $P(3, -1)$, $Q(7, 7)$, and $R(9, 1)$ are vertices of an isosceles triangle. $PR = QR = 2\sqrt{10}; PQ = 4\sqrt{5}$

32. *Business*   A 1-lb loaf of bread that costs a baker \$1.25 to make sells for \$1.59. In any one week he makes a profit of between \$50 and \$75 on the bread. How many loaves of bread does he normally sell in one week?

Ⓡ 33. Graph: $y = |x + 2|$

34. *Budgeting*   The cost of buying a school lunch is 85¢ per day. If a student has a yearly budget of \$92 for food, determine the number of days he should bring his lunch to make sure he does not exceed his budget. Assume that there are 180 school days per year and that lunch brought from home is not deducted from his budget. at least 72 days

8.2 Linear Inequalities   **399**

Writing in Mathematics

19. Answers may vary. Examples: Water remains in a liquid state at temperatures t above 32°F and below 212°F; The speed limit on a major highway is 55 mi/h.

35. Writing in Mathematics Write a poem or limerick that could be used by your classmates to help them remember when to draw a solid line and when to draw a dashed line when graphing an inequality.

Solve each inequality. State the solution as an inequality and in interval notation.

C **36.** $2x - 3 < x - 5 < 3x + 3$ $-4 < x < -2;$ $(-4, -2)$

37. $4x + 1 < 5x - 2 < 6x - 5$ $x > 3;$ $(3, \infty)$

38. $|x + 3| > 2x - 1$ $x < 4; (-\infty, 4)$

39. $|6 - 2x| \leq 4x + 1$ $x \geq \frac{5}{6}; \left[\frac{5}{6}, \infty\right)$

Graph each inequality in the coordinate plane.

40. $-5 \leq x + 2y \leq 9$

41. $12 > 3x - y > -6$

42. $-3 \leq 2x + y < 6$

43. $8 > y - 2x > -4$

44. *Grading* To receive a grade of C in a course, a student must have at least a 75 average on all five exams but less than an 80 average. If the student's scores on the first four tests were 60, 90, 82, and 78, determine the grades on the fifth test that will result in an overall grade of C. All scores are based on 100. [65, 90)

45. *Conservation* For a particular brand of tire, for each 1 lb of pressure the tire is underinflated, the gas mileage decreases by 3 mi/gal. For a given car the tire pressure is 32 lb/in.^{2} and the gas mileage at that rate is 27 mi/gal. What values of the tire pressure would cause the gas mileage to be less than 18 mi/gal? less than 29 lb/in.^{2}

46. Find all values of x such that the distance from three times x minus four to two times x plus three is always less than ten. $-3 < x < 17$

47. *Sports* Going into the last day of the season a baseball player has collected 224 hits in 564 at bats. How many consecutive hits does he need to have a final average of .400 or more? at least 3 hits

Challenge

1. The inequality $y + x > \sqrt{x^2}$ is true if and only if ___?___ . $y > 0$ or $y > -2x$

2. A certain number is squared by adding 1. Express the number in radical form and then approximate it to four decimal places. $\frac{1 \pm \sqrt{5}}{2}$; -0.6180 or 1.6180

3. A Mersenne number is a positive integer of the form $2^p - 1$, where p is a prime number. For how many one-digit values of p is $2^p - 1$ itself a prime number? Name them. 4; 2, 3, 5, 7

4. If $f(x) = x^m$ and m is a whole number, what additional restriction on m will guarantee that $f^{-1}(x)$ is a function? m is odd.

5. If the solutions of $x^2 + mx = 6$ are squared, the sum of those squares is 13. What is the value of m^2? 1

6. If x is the product of any three positive consecutive even integers, then what is the largest number guaranteed to be an integral factor of x? 48

7. If $g(x) = 5^x$, express $g(x) + g(x + 1)$ in terms of $g(x)$. $6g(x)$

8. What is the maximum number of slices of pizza that can be produced by eight straight cuts in one pie? 37

400   Chapter 8 Inequalities and Linear Programming

Writing in Mathematics

35. Answers may vary. Example: "If you see a greater or less than sign, draw the graph with a broken line. If the sign also includes 'equal to,' only a solid line will do."

8.3 Quadratic Inequalities

Objective: *To solve quadratic inequalities*

Focus

Have you ever wondered how a company sets the prices for its products? This is one of the tasks of a marketing strategist. Prices may be based on factors such as the perceived demand for the product, the strength of the competitors in the marketplace, and the state of the economy.

In any business venture a primary goal is to maximize profit. In Chapter 2, quadratic equations were used to model profit functions and then solved for their maximum values. But in planning a marketing strategy, it is often better to determine a range of values for the desired profit. Thus real world problems are often modeled by inequalities.

A *quadratic inequality in one variable* is an inequality of the form $ax^2 + bx + c < 0$, where a, b, and c are real numbers and $a \neq 0$. If you graph $y = ax^2 + bx + c$, then $y < 0$ when the graph is below the x-axis. The solution of the inequality will be in the intervals on the x-axis corresponding to the part of the graph that is below the x-axis. Therefore, to solve $ax^2 + bx + c < 0$, graph $f(x) = ax^2 + bx + c$ and determine where the graph is *below* the x-axis. Similarly, the intervals where the graph is *above* the x-axis give the solution of the inequality $ax^2 + bx + c > 0$.

Example 1 Solve each inequality with the aid of a graph. State the solution as an inequality, in interval notation, and graph it on the number line.
    a. $x^2 - 4x - 5 \leq 0$ **b.** $x^2 - 4x - 5 > 0$

[−5, 9] by [−10, 5]

Graph $f(x) = x^2 - 4x - 5$.
The y-intercept is $(0, -5)$.
The x-intercepts are $(-1, 0)$ and $(5, 0)$.

a. The inequality $x^2 - 4x - 5 \leq 0$ is satisfied for all values of x such that the graph of f is *on or below* the x-axis.

    Inequality: $-1 \leq x \leq 5$
    Interval: $[-1, 5]$

b. The inequality $x^2 - 4x - 5 > 0$ is satisfied for all values of x such that the graph of f is *above* the x-axis.

    Inequality: $x < -1$ or $x > 5$
    Interval: $(-\infty, -1) \cup (5, \infty)$

LESSON PLAN

Vocabulary
quadratic inequality in two variables

Ⓜ **Materials/Manipulatives**
transparencies

Technology
graphing utility

FOCUS

The Focus provides an excellent opportunity to relate mathematics to certain career goals that students may have.

INSTRUCTION

- The use of transparencies is encouraged for those students who may need to review graphs of quadratic functions of the form $ax^2 + bx + c$, $a \neq 0$ for $a < 0$ and $a > 0$, as well as the formula for finding the minimum or maximum point of a parabola.
- To help students strengthen the connection between the algebraic and graphical solution of a quadratic inequality, have them verify all algebraic solutions graphically.
- To help students quickly decide whether a solution is between two critical values or less than or greater than the values, emphasize the use of test points.

Alternative Learning Styles
Some students need a more global view of how to determine the solution of a quadratic inequality before doing individual problems. The use of transparencies along with Practice Exercise 36 is encouraged.

For Example 1

Solve each inequality with the aid of a graph. State the solution as an inequality, in interval notation, and graph it on the number line.

1. $-2x^2 + 4x + 9 \geq 0$

$-1.3 \leq x \leq 3.3$; $[-1.3, 3.3]$

Technology Have students adjust the scale as well as the viewing rectangle to make the graph easier to read.

2. $3x^2 - 2x + 1 > 0$

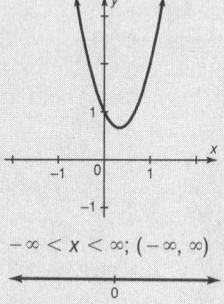

$-\infty < x < \infty$; $(-\infty, \infty)$

For Example 2

Solve each inequality algebraically. State the solution as an inequality, in interval notation, and graph it on the number line.

1. $-4x^2 + 3x + 7 < 0$
$x < -1$ or $x > 1.75$;
$(-\infty, -1)$ or $(1.75, \infty)$

2. $15x^2 + 60x < 0$
$-4 < x < 0$; $(-4, 0)$

In Example 1, since the x-intercepts of $f(x) = x^2 - 4x - 5$ are $(-1, 0)$ and $(5, 0)$, the zeros of this function are -1 and 5. Notice that the values of the function change sign only when the graph passes through a zero of the function. Therefore, the zeros of a function determine the endpoints of the solution intervals of a quadratic inequality. One way to solve a quadratic inequality algebraically is to find the zeros of the related function. Set up intervals on the number line by graphing the zeros. Then determine whether the function is positive or negative in each interval. When the function is negative, $f(x) < 0$. When the function is positive, $f(x) > 0$.

Example 2 Solve $6x^2 + 10x - 5 \geq 0$ algebraically. State the solution as an inequality, in interval notation, and graph it on the number line.

Determine the zeros of $f(x) = 6x^2 + 10x - 5$.

$x = \dfrac{-10 \pm \sqrt{10^2 - 4(6)(-5)}}{2(6)}$ *Use the quadratic formula.*

$x = -2.07$ or $x = 0.40$ To the nearest hundredth

Test points in each interval determined by zeros.

$f(-3) = 6(-3)^2 + 10(-3) - 5 = 19$ *Positive, so $f(x) > 0$*
$f(0) = 6(0)^2 + 10(0) - 5 = -5$ *Negative, so $f(x) < 0$*
$f(1) = 6(1)^2 + 10(1) - 5 = 11$ *Positive, so $f(x) > 0$*

Since the original relation was $\geq$, the endpoints are included in the solution intervals.

Inequality: $x \leq -2.07$ or $x \geq 0.40$
Interval: $(-\infty, -2.07] \cup [0.40, \infty)$

When the related function of a quadratic inequality has no real zeros, the inequality must either be true for all real values of the variable or false for all values of the variable. Simply test one value to determine if the solution is the set of real numbers or the empty set.

Example 1 showed how graphical methods can help solve an inequality in one variable. You can extend this method by graphing each side of an inequality as a separate function of x. Then use the graphs to determine the intervals on the x-axis that satisfy the conditions of the inequality.

Example 3   *Economics*   A kitchenware maker produces a peppermill that costs $3.00 to manufacture and will sell for at least $5.00. Market research shows that at $5.00 each, 5000 peppermills can be sold each month. It further shows that for each dollar the price is increased, the number that can be sold each month decreases by 450 units. Determine graphically the range of the selling price for which the monthly profit will be at least $14,000. Assume that all the peppermills manufactured are sold.

402   Chapter 8 Inequalities and Linear Programming

Let x represent the number of $1 increases. The price of each peppermill is $5 + x$. The profit on each peppermill is the price minus the cost.

Price $-$ cost $= (5 + x) - 3 = x + 2$

The number of peppermills sold each month is equal to 5000 minus 450 times the number of $1 increases, or $5000 - 450x$.

The monthly profit $P(x)$ is equal to the profit per peppermill times the number of peppermills sold per month.

$$P(x) = (x + 2)(5000 - 450x) = -450x^2 + 4100x + 10,000$$

To determine the prices for which the profit function is greater than $14,000, solve the following inequality:

$$P(x) \geq 14,000$$
$$-450x^2 + 4100x + 10,000 \geq 14,000$$

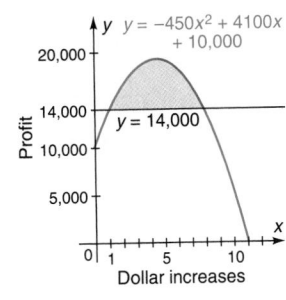

Graph the functions represented by each side of the inequality. The shaded region indicates the area of desired profits. The range of integer x-values for the region is $2 \leq x \leq 8$. Since the x-values represent $1 increases over the $5 selling price, the range of desired prices is $7 \leq x \leq 13$. The price of the peppermills should be between $7 and $13. *What price yields the greatest profit?*

A **quadratic inequality in two variables** is an inequality of the form $y > ax^2 + bx + c$, where a, b, and c are real numbers and $a \neq 0$. To solve such an inequality, graph the function $f(x) = ax^2 + bx + c$. Draw a smooth curve if the relation is $\geq$ or $\leq$, or a dashed curve if the relation is $>$ or $<$. To determine the solution set, test a convenient point in the plane. If the point satisfies the original inequality, shade the region that contains the point. If it does not, shade the region that does not contain the point.

Example 4   Graph $y < 2x^2 - 12x + 7$ in the coordinate plane.

Graph the function $f(x) = 2x^2 - 12x + 7$. Use a dashed curve.

Axis of symmetry: $x = 3$ since $x = \dfrac{-(-12)}{2(2)} = 3$

Vertex: $(3, -11)$ since $f(3) = 2(3)^2 - 12(3) + 7 = -11$

y-intercept: $(0, 7)$

Test the point $(0, 0)$. Since the point $(0, 0)$ satisfies the original inequality, shade the region "outside" the parabola.

Class Exercises

Represent each set on a number line.

1. $\{x: 0 \leq x < 2 \text{ or } 4 \leq x \leq 7\}$

2. $\{x: x > -4 \text{ and } x < 5\}$

3. $(-4, 5] \cup [7, 12)$

4. $[0, 5] \cap (2, 6]$

8.3 Quadratic Inequalities   **403**

For Example 3
The National Collegiate A.A. Men's Rules state that the height of the basket on a regulation basketball court must be 10 ft (upper edge). For a particular throw the height s of a basketball at any time t, in seconds, can be determined by the equation $s = -16t^2 + 40t + 6$. Determine for what values of t, to the nearest tenth of a second, the ball is higher than the basket. Express the answer in interval (0.1, 2.4)   2.4)

For Example 4
Graph the inequality in the coordinate plane.
$4 - y \geq 5x^2 - 2x$

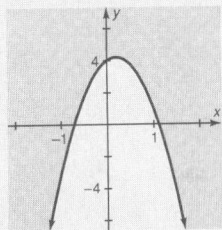

Common Error   Some students may forget to reverse the direction of the inequality sign when solving for y. Remind these students that both sides of the inequality must be multiplied by -1 in order to solve for y.

CLOSURE
Have students summarize the lesson in their math journals.

Additional Answers

1.

2.

3.

4.

403

Assignment Guide
Basic: 1–23, 28, 36
Average: 9, 11, 16–38
Enriched: 10, 21–22, 24–27, 29–47

Teacher's Resource Book
  Practice, page 53

® **Review**

Exercises 9, 11, 23, and 28 review concepts of graphing absolute value functions, using sum or difference identities, solving triangles, and using the factor theorem.

LESSON FOLLOW-UP

Lesson Quiz

1. Solve the inequality $-x^2 - 4x + 5 \le 0$ with the aid of a graph. State the solution as an inequality, in interval notation, and graph it on the number line.

$(-\infty, -5] \cup [1, \infty)$

Solve each inequality with the aid of a graph.

5. $x^2 + 6x + 9 \le 0$ $x = -3$ 6. $4x^2 + 8x > 0$ $x > 0, x < -2$ 7. $-x^2 + 2x + 15 \le 0$
    $x \le -3$ or $x \ge 5$

Solve each inequality algebraically.

8. $9t^2 - 24t + 15 \ge 0$ $(-\infty, 1] \cup \left[\frac{5}{3}, \infty\right)$ 9. $2x^2 + x - 4 < 0$ $(-1.7, 1.2)$

Graph each inequality in the coordinate plane.

10. $y \ge x^2 + 4x + 8$ 11. $y - 4 < x^2 - 5x$

12. *Space Science*   The height of a rocket s launched vertically into the air at any time t, in seconds, can be determined by the equation $s = -16t^2 + 320t$. Determine the values of t for which the height of the rocket is less than 1200 ft. $0 \le t < 5$ or $t > 15$

Practice Exercises   Use appropriate technology.

Solve each inequality with the aid of a graph. Round approximate answers to the nearest hundredth.

A 1. $x^2 - 4x + 3 \ge 0$ $x \ge 3$ or $x \le 1$ 2. $x^2 - 8x + 16 \le 0$ $x = 4$
  3. $x^2 + 2x < 0$ $-2 < x < 0$ 4. $2x^2 - 10x > 0$ $x < 0$ or $x > 5$
  5. $2x^2 - 19x + 24 < 0$ $\frac{3}{2} < x < 8$ 6. $-3x^2 - 2x + 1 > 0$ $-1 < x < \frac{1}{3}$
  7. $2x^2 - x - 20 \ge 0$ $x \le -2.92$ or $x \ge 3.42$ 8. $3x^2 + 12x + 9 \le 0$ $-3 \le x \le -1$

® 9. Graph: $y = |x + 2| - 1$

10. **Thinking Critically**   Describe the graph of $f(x) = ax^2 + bx + c$ if the corresponding inequality $ax^2 + bx + c > 0$, $a \ne 0$, is true for all values of x.

® 11. Express $2 \cos \frac{\pi}{6} \sin \frac{\pi}{9}$ as a sum or difference. $\sin \frac{5\pi}{18} - \sin \frac{\pi}{18}$

Solve each inequality algebraically.

12. $x^2 - 6x + 8 \ge 0$ 13. $x^2 + 7x - 8 < 0$ 14. $3t^2 - 27 < 0$
15. $-5x^2 + 125 \ge 0$ 16. $t^2 + 4t - 6 < 0$ 17. $2x^2 + 2x - 5 \ge 0$
  $-5 \le x \le 5$ $-2 - \sqrt{10} < t < -2 + \sqrt{10}$ $x \le \frac{-1 - \sqrt{11}}{2}$ or $x \ge \frac{-1 + \sqrt{11}}{2}$
Graph each inequality in the coordinate plane.
18. $y \le 16 - x^2$ 19. $y > (16 - x)^2$

20. *Physics*   A small metal ball is dropped from the roof of a building. The height of the ball s at any time t, in seconds, is given by the equation $s = -16t^2 + 70t$. Determine the values of t for which the height of the ball will be less than 25 ft. $0 \le t < 0.4$ or $t > 4$

21. **Thinking Critically**   Analyze the inequality $x^2 + 9 < 0$. Determine for what values of x it is true, if any. Justify your answer.

22. *Aviation*   A plane flies due north at 300 mi/h for 3 h then due west at 250 mi/h. If x represents the number of hours the plane is flying due west, determine for what values of x the plane will be more than 3700 mi from its original point. $x > 14.36$ h

® 23. Solve triangle ABC if $a = 4$, $b = 2$, and $\angle A = 140°$. $\angle B = 19°$; $\angle C = 21°$; $c = 2.23$

Additional Answers, Class Exercises

10.   11.

Solve each inequality with the aid of a graph. Round approximate answers to the nearest hundredth.

B 24. $2x^2 - 9x + 9 \geq 0$ $x \geq 3 \text{ or } x \leq \frac{3}{2}$

25. $4x^2 + 8x + 3 < 0$ $-\frac{3}{2} < x < -\frac{1}{2}$

26. $6x^2 + 19x < -15$ $-\frac{5}{3} < x < -\frac{3}{2}$

27. $-2x^2 < 11x + 14$ $x < -\frac{7}{2} \text{ or } x > -2$

28. Solve: $x^3 - 2x^2 - 11x + 12 = 0$ 1, -3, 4

Solve each inequality algebraically.

29. $4x^2 - 7x \leq -3$ $\frac{3}{4} \leq x \leq 1$

30. $-12x^2 + 5x \leq -2$ $x \leq -\frac{1}{4} \text{ or } x \geq \frac{2}{3}$

31. $-4t^2 \geq -4t - 7$ $\frac{1 - 2\sqrt{2}}{2} \leq t \leq \frac{1 + 2\sqrt{2}}{2}$

32. $-24 \leq x^2 - 12x$ $x \leq 6 - 2\sqrt{3} \text{ or } x \geq 6 + 2\sqrt{3}$

Graph each inequality in the coordinate plane.

33. $y > 3(x - 2)^2 - 4$

34. $3x^2 - y - 2 \geq -6x$

35. $x - x^2 > 4y$

36. **Thinking Critically** Given a quadratic inequality $ax^2 + bx + c < 0$ with two real zeros z_1 and z_2, $z_1 < z_2$, determine the values of x for which the inequality is true if $a < 0$; $a > 0$.

37. *Construction* The function $W = 90x^2 - 135x$ gives the weight, in pounds, of a steel beam in terms of the width, in inches, of its cross-sectional area. Determine the values of x for which the beam will weigh less than 180 lb.

38. *Forestry* The area of the base of a tree is a function of the radius of the base, $A = \pi r^2$. Determine the values for r for which the area will be greater than 10 ft². more than 1.78 ft

C Solve each inequality with the aid of a graph.

39. $x + 1 \leq x^2 \leq x + 5$

40. $x^2 \leq |x - 5| \leq 6$

41. $x - 4 < -x^2 - 6x < x$

42. The solution of a quadratic inequality where the leading coefficient is positive is the interval $(-3, -2)$. Write an inequality satisfying these conditions. ex: $(x^2 + 5x + 6) < 0$

43. The solution of a quadratic inequality where the leading coefficient is negative is the interval $(-\infty, 0.5) \cup (4.5, \infty)$. Write an inequality with this solution. ex: $-4x^2 + 20x - 9 < 0$

44. The solution of the quadratic inequality $ax^2 + bx + c < 0$, $a < 0$, is $\{x: x \text{ is a real number}\}$. Write two different inequalities which satisfy these conditions. ex: $-x^2 + 3x - 3 < 0$, $-x^2 + 4x - 5 < 0$

45. The solution of the quadratic inequality $ax^2 + bx + c < 0$, $a < 0$, is $\{x: x \neq 0\}$. Write two different inequalities which satisfy these conditions. ex: $-2x^2 < 0$, $-3x^2 < 0$

Solve each inequality.

46. $x^2 + 2 < x^4 - 2$ $x < -1.6 \text{ or } x > 1.6$

47. $-x^4 + 5 \leq x^2 + 3$ $x \leq -1 \text{ or } x \geq 1$

Review

1. Quadrant I of the rectangular coordinate plane can be represented as $\{(x, y): x > 0 \text{ and } y > 0\}$. Using similar set notation, represent the other three quadrants in the rectangular coordinate system.
$\{(x, y): x > 0 \text{ and } y < 0\}$; $\{(x, y): x < 0 \text{ and } y > 0\}$; $\{(x, y): x < 0 \text{ and } y < 0\}$

2. Find the distance between the points $(-2, 4)$ and $(6, -2)$. 10

8.3 Quadratic Inequalities **405**

2. The height of an object at any time t, in seconds, thrown vertically into the air can be determined by the equation $s = -16t^2 + 40t$. Determine the values of t for which the height of the object is at least 9 ft.
$0.25 \leq t \leq 2.25$

3. Graph the inequality $y - 2 < 3x^2 + 4x$ in the coordinate plane.

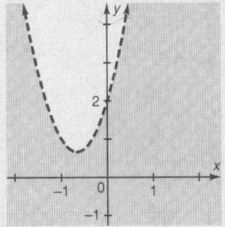

Alternative Assessment

Ask students to write a paragraph in which they describe a strategy for solving a quadratic inequality algebraically and discuss any difficulties they are having in finding a solution.

Enrichment

Solve the quadratic inequality $x^2 - 6x + 9 \leq -x^2 + 6x - 4$ by graphing the related function for each side.

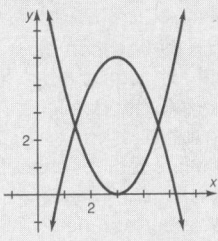

$1.4 \leq x \leq 4.6$

Additional Answers

33.

34.

35.

406

LESSON PLAN

Ⓜ Materials/Manipulatives
cardboard
compass
scissors
transparencies

Technology
graphing utility
symbolic manipulator

FOCUS

The Focus provides an opportunity
for cross-curricular learning. Have
students who are familiar with the
Mach numbers from their studies of
physics explain to the class what the
numbers represent.

INSTRUCTION

• Have students draw a circle with a
radius of 2 in. on cardboard, cut it
out, and make a small notch on
the circle. Then have them place
this notch on a line and trace one
arc of a cycloid by putting dots in
the notch as they move the circle
along the line, rotating it in a
clockwise direction.

• When discussing the location principle, stress that although a polynomial function can change signs
only when its graph passes
through a zero this does not imply
that a polynomial function must
change signs at a zero of the
graph. (See Guided Practice for
Example 1.)

Alternative Learning Styles
Constructing a physical model can
be helpful to many students in understanding mathematical ideas.
Having students construct a cycloid
as described above is encouraged.

8.4 Solving Polynomial and Rational Inequalities

Objectives: *To solve polynomial inequalities and graph the solutions*
To solve rational inequalities and graph the solutions

Focus

"Strange as it may sound, the power of mathematics
rests on its evasion of all unnecessary thought and on its
wonderful savings of mental operations."

The above quote is attributed to Ernst Mach, an
Austrian physicist of the nineteenth century. You may
have heard the term "Mach number" associated with the
speed of supersonic jets. Mach's philosophy on the
purpose of mathematics has great relevance today. With
the development of calculators and computers,
mathematicians need not burden themselves with tedious
mental calculations; they are
free to explore concepts
more deeply than ever before. As you have seen and
will continue to see, the use of graphing utilities and
other technology allows you to solve equations and
inequalities that otherwise would have been quite
inaccessible.

A *polynomial inequality* of degree *n in one variable* is an inequality of the form
$a_n x^n + a_{n-1} x^{n-1} + \cdots + a_1 x + a_0 < 0$, $a_n \neq 0$, where $a_n, a_{n-1}, \ldots, a_1, a_0$
are real numbers. Polynomial inequalities may also involve any of the relations
$>$, $\leq$, or $\geq$. One method for solving a polynomial inequality is to analyze the
graph of the corresponding polynomial function. Determine the intervals that
are bounded by the zeros of the function, that is, the points where the graph
crosses the *x*-axis. Decide whether they satisfy the inequality. A *sign chart* will
help you organize your results. The trace feature of a graphing utility will
be useful for determining the zeros.

Example 1 Solve $6x^3 - 10x^2 < 24x$.

$6x^3 - 10x^2 < 24x$
$6x^3 - 10x^2 - 24x < 0$ *Write in standard form.*

Graph the corresponding function

$$f(x) = 6x^3 - 10x^2 - 24x$$

The zeros are -1.3, 0, and 3.

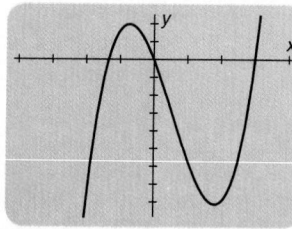

[−4, 4] by [−40, 10]
x scl: 1   *y* scl: 5

Since the relation was $<$, the points on the graph that are below the x-axis satisfy the inequality, while the points that are above the x-axis do not.

The solution for the inequality $6x^3 - 10x^3 < 24x$ is $(-\infty, -1.3) \cup (0, 3)$.

The algebraic interpretation of the solution of polynomial inequalities is based on the location theorem. The location theorem states that if f is a continuous function on the closed interval $[a, b]$ and if $f(a)$ and $f(b)$ have different signs, then $f(x)$ has at least one zero in the open interval (a, b). It follows that if there is an interval in which there is no zero of the function, the function must be positive or negative throughout that interval. Therefore, any polynomial function will change signs only when its graph passes through a zero of the function.

Polynomial inequalities can be solved algebraically using the steps listed below.

> **To solve a polynomial inequality:**
> 1. Write the inequality in standard form.
> 2. Find the zeros of the corresponding polynomial function.
> 3. Reading from left to right on the number line, set up intervals so that the endpoints are at the zeros.
> 4. Choose a test point in each interval, and substitute this value into the function to determine its sign.

Example 2 Solve the inequality $x^3 + 4x^2 < x + 4$ algebraically.

$$x^3 + 4x^2 - x - 4 < 0 \qquad \textit{Write in standard form.}$$
$$x^2(x + 4) - 1(x + 4) = 0 \qquad \textit{Factor the corresponding equation.}$$
$$(x^2 - 1)(x + 4) = 0$$
$$(x - 1)(x + 1)(x + 4) = 0$$
$$x = -4 \quad \text{or} \quad x = -1 \quad \text{or} \quad x = 1$$

The zeros of the corresponding function are -4, -1, and 1.

Determine the sign of $f(x) = x^3 + 4x^2 - x - 4$ for a point in each interval.

The inequality $x^3 + 4x^2 - x - 4 < 0$ is satisfied on the intervals $(-\infty, -4)$ and $(-1, 1)$.

A *polynomial inequality in two variables* is an inequality of the form $y < a_n x^n + a_{n-1} x^{n-1} + \cdots + a_1 x + a_0$, $a_n \neq 0$, where $a_n, a_{n-1}, \ldots, a_1, a_0$ are real numbers. Polynomial inequalities may also involve any of the relations $>$, $\leq$, or $\geq$. To solve a polynomial inequality in two variables, graph the

8.4 Solving Polynomial and Rational Inequalities   **407**

For Example 1
Solve each inequality with the aid of a graph.
1. $2x^3 - 4x^2 \geq 0$

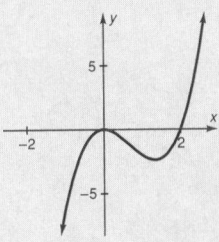

$\{0\} \cup [2, \infty)$

Common Error Some students may think that the curve must change signs at each critical value. Point out that when a zero of the function is of an even multiplicity, the graph will not cross the x-axis at that zero.

2. $x^5 - 2x^2 + 3 \leq 0$

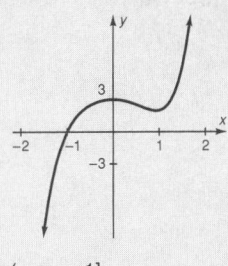

$(-\infty, -1]$

For Example 2
Solve each inequality algebraically.
1. $x^4 - 5x^2 - 36 < 0$ $(-3, 3)$
2. $2x^3 - 5x^2 - 3x \geq 0$
   $[-0.5, 0] \cup [3, \infty)$

Graph each inequality in the coordinate plane.

1. $y \geq x^4 - 3x^2$

2. $y > 3x^3 - 5x + 1$

For Example 4

Solve the inequality with the aid of a graph.

$$\frac{x^2 - 4}{x^2 - 2} < 0$$

$(-2, -1.4) \cup (1.4, 2)$

corresponding polynomial function and determine whether the region above or below the function satisfies the inequality. If you are using a graphing utility, you may need to use inspection to determine the shaded region and whether to use a solid or dashed curve.

Example 3 Graph the inequality $y < 3x^3 - 4x^2 + x$ in the coordinate plane.

Graph the corresponding function $f(x) = 3x^3 - 4x^2 + x$.

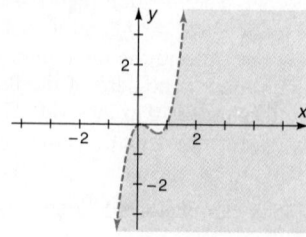

[−4, 5] by [−3, 3]

Since the relation is $<$, represent the function with a dashed curve. Use the point $(0, 1)$ as a test point.

$$1 \underline{\ ?\ } 3(0)^3 - 4(0)^2 + 0$$
$$1 > 0$$

Since $(0, 1)$ does not satisfy the inequality, shade the region below the function.

The graphical and algebraic methods for solving polynomial inequalities can also be used to solve rational inequalities. To find the intervals to be tested, find the real zeros of both the numerator and denominator of the corresponding rational function.

Example 4 Solve the inequality $\frac{x^4 - 5}{x^2 - 3} > 0$ with the aid of a graph.

Graph the corresponding rational function $f(x) = \frac{x^4 - 5}{x^2 - 3}$.

The real zeros of the denominator are $\sqrt{3}$ and $-\sqrt{3}$, or about 1.7 and −1.7. These are the vertical asymptotes of the graph. The real zeros of the numerator are $\sqrt[4]{5}$ and $-\sqrt[4]{5}$ or about 1.5 and −1.5.

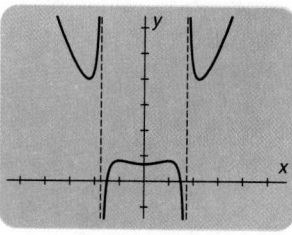

[−5, 5] by [−3, 18]
x scl: 1   y scl: 3

The graph of the function $f(x) = \frac{x^4 - 5}{x^2 - 3}$ gives the solution to the inequality. Since the relation is $>$, the points on the graph above the x-axis satisfy the inequality.

$$\begin{array}{ccccc} + & - & + & - & + \\ & -1.7 & -1.5 & 1.5 & 1.7 \end{array}$$

The solution is $(-\infty, -1.7) \cup (-1.5, 1.5) \cup (1.7, \infty)$.

Using graphing utilities enables you to solve complicated inequalities, such as those involving radical expressions, that would otherwise be very difficult to solve. If an inequality is in a form $f(x) < g(x)$, it is often best to graph both sides of the inequality. You can then determine where the graph of $f(x)$ is below the graph of $g(x)$. To input a radical expression like $\sqrt[3]{4 - x^2}$, use rational exponents; for example, $(4 - x^2) \wedge (1/3)$ is a possible input form.

Example 5 Solve the inequality $\sqrt[3]{4 - x^2} \geq x^2 - 3$ with the aid of a graph.

Let $f(x) = \sqrt[3]{4 - x^2}$ and let $g(x) = x^2 - 3$. Graph both functions on the same set of axes. The trace feature shows the points where the two graphs intersect to be about $(-1.9, 0.68)$ and $(1.9, 0.68)$.

Since the relation is $\geq$, the solution to the inequality is given by the region in which the graph of $f(x) = \sqrt[3]{4 - x^2}$ is *above* the graph of $g(x) = x^2 - 3$ and the points of intersection of the two graphs. In interval notation the solution is $[-1.9, 1.9]$.

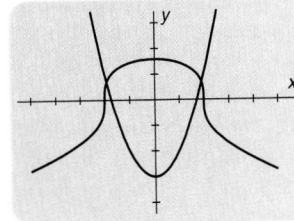

$[-5, 5]$ by $[-4, 3]$

Class Exercises

Solve each polynomial inequality algebraically.

1. $25x^3 - 4x \leq 0$ $(-\infty, -0.4] \cup [0, 0.4]$

2. $3x^3 + 24x^2 < -48x$ $(-\infty, -4) \cup (-4, 0)$

3. $x^4 + x^2 \geq 12$ $(-\infty, -1.73] \cup [1.73, \infty)$

4. $x^5 - 5x^3 > -4x$ $(-2, -1) \cup (0, 1) \cup (2, \infty)$

Solve each inequality with the aid of a graph.

5. $2x^3 + 2x^2 + 3 < 0$

6. $\dfrac{x^2 - 5}{x^3 - 20} \geq 0$

7. $x^3 - 6 \geq \sqrt{x^3} + 2$

Graph each inequality in the coordinate plane.

8. $y > x^4 - x^2 - 6$

9. $y \leq 2 - x - x^3$

10. *Recreation* A domed tent is in the shape of a hemisphere. Determine the values of the radius for which the volume of the tent will be greater than 120 ft³. $r \geq 3.86$ ft

11. *Shipping* A certain shipper will only accept containers in the shape of a cube whose volume is less than 250 ft³. Determine the range of values of the length of the side of a container that would meet this shipper's criteria. $0 < x < 6.3$ ft

Practice Exercises

 Use appropriate technology.

Solve each inequality algebraically. $[0, 2] \cup [9, \infty)$

A **1.** $x^3 - 4x^2 + 4x < 0$ $(-\infty, 0)$

2. $x^3 - 11x^2 \geq -18x$

3. $x^3 - 3x^2 < 0$ $(-\infty, 0) \cup (0, 3)$

4. $x^4 - 25x^2 \geq 0$ $(-\infty, -5] \cup [0] \cup [5, \infty)$

5. $x^3 - 3x^2 + 84 \leq 28x$ $(-\infty, -5.3] \cup [3, 5.3]$

6. $5x^3 + 6x^2 > 10x + 12$ $(-1.4, -1.2) \cup (1.4, \infty)$

8.4 Solving Polynomial and Rational Inequalities **409**

For Example 5
Solve the inequality with the aid of a graph.
$x^2 - 2 \leq \sqrt[3]{3 - x^2}$

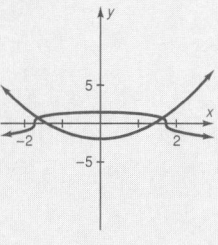

$[-1.6, 1.6]$

CLOSURE
Group students in pairs and have them summarize to each other how to solve polynomial and rational inequalities with the aid of graphs.

INDEPENDENT PRACTICE

Assignment Guide
Basic: 1–21, 25, 31–32, 34
Average: 10–34
Enriched: 14, 16, 23–44

Teacher's Resource Book
  Practice, page 54

Ⓡ **Review**
Exercises 11, 15, 17, 19, 31, and 33 review concepts of solving absolute value inequalities, graphing functions, and using coordinate proofs.

Additional Answers
Class Exercises

5.

$(-\infty, -1.6)$

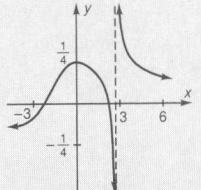
6.

$(-2.2, 2.2) \cup (2.7, \infty)$

7.

$[2.3, \infty)$

8.

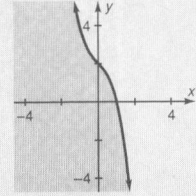
9.

409

Test Yourself

Tests—Quiz, form A, page 29
Tests—Quiz, form B, page 29

Additional Answers

7.

$(-\infty, -3) \cup$
$(-1.3, 1)$

8.

$(-1.6, 1.8)$

9.

$\{-3\} \cup [6, \infty)$

10.

$(-2.4, 1) \cup$
$(2.4, \infty)$

20. $(-\infty, -5) \cup (-1.4, 1.4)$

38. $\left(-2\pi, -\dfrac{3\pi}{2}\right) \cup \left(-\pi, -\dfrac{\pi}{2}\right) \cup$
$\left(\dfrac{\pi}{2}, \pi\right) \cup \left(\dfrac{3\pi}{2}, 2\pi\right)$

39. $[-2\pi, -1.8\pi] \cup \left[-\dfrac{\pi}{2}, 0.2\pi\right] \cup$
$\left[\dfrac{3\pi}{2}, 2\pi\right]$

40. $(-\pi, 1) \cup (\pi, 2\pi)$

41. Answers may vary. The number of intervals would increase. In addition, the length of the intervals in Exercise 40 would increase.

Solve each inequality with the aid of a graph.

7. $3x^3 + 10x^2 - x - 12 < 0$

8. $\sqrt{x + 4} > 0.25x^4$

9. $x^3 - 27x - 54 \geq 0$

10. $\dfrac{x^3 - 1}{x^2 - 6} > 0$

Ⓡ **11.** Solve: $|x - 5| \geq 3$ $(-\infty, 2] \cup [8, \infty)$

Graph each inequality in the coordinate plane.

12. $y \leq x^3 - 3x^2 - 5x + 12$

13. $6x^3 - 11x^2 - 4x + 4 \leq y$

14. Writing in Mathematics Write a story problem which involves determining when the volume of a cube is less than or greater than a given value. Give a complete solution to the problem.

Ⓡ **15.** Graph: $f(x) = x^3 + 1$

16. Thinking Critically Analyze the inequality $x^3 + 8 \leq 0$. Determine for what values of x it is true, if any. Justify your answer.

Ⓡ **17.** Graph: $f(x) = \sqrt{x - 1}$

18. *Construction* A storage shed is built in the shape of a rectangular solid with volume $V = 2x^3 - 27x^2 + 90$. Determine for what values of x the volume of the shed will be less than 53 ft³. (1.2 ft, 2.0 ft) ∪ (13.2 ft, 13.4 ft)

Ⓡ **19.** Using coordinate geometry, prove that the diagonals of a rectangle bisect each other.

Solve each inequality algebraically.

$(-\infty, 1.26] \cup [1.91, \infty)$

Ⓑ **20.** $x^3 + 5x^2 - 2x - 10 < 0$

21. $x^6 - 9x^3 + 14 \geq 0$

22. $2x^4 + x^3 + 6x + 3 > 0$
$(-\infty, -1.4) \cup (-0.5, \infty)$

23. $x^5 + x^4 - 16x - 16 \leq 0$
$(-\infty, -2] \cup [-1, 2]$

Solve each inequality with the aid of a graph.

24. $x^3 - 4x^2 - 5x < 4 - 3x^2$

25. $x^3 - 3x + 1 \geq \sqrt[3]{4x^2 + x}$

26. $12 - 5x \leq 22x^2 - 8x^3$

27. $\dfrac{(x + 3)^3}{x^4 - 10} \leq 0$

Graph each inequality in the coordinate plane.

28. $y < x^4 - 3x^3 - 2x^2 + 3x + 8$

29. $y \geq x^4 - 3x^3 + x^2 + 6x - 5$

30. Thinking Critically Determine the values of a and b that would make the inequality $ax^4 + bx^2 \leq 0$ true for all values of x. $a \leq 0$ and $b \leq 0$

Ⓡ **31.** Graph from $-\pi$ to π: $y = 2 \sin 3x$

32. *Construction* A 3-ft-high fence encloses an area that is four times longer than it is wide. Determine the values of the width for which the volume of this space is greater than 240 ft³. greater than 4.5 ft

Ⓡ **33.** Graph: $f(x) = 2|x| + 3$

Solve each inequality with the aid of a graph.

Ⓒ **34.** $|x^3| > 4x^2$

35. $0 \geq -2|x^3 - 4x + 5|$

36. $-|1 - x^3| < \sqrt[3]{x^4 - 25}$

37. $\dfrac{-x^2 + 25}{x^2 - 3x + 5} \geq |x|$

410 Chapter 8 Inequalities and Linear Programming

Writing in Mathematics

14. Answers may vary. One example follows: A certain delivery company will only accept packages in the shape of a cube. The minimum volume a package may have is 1 ft³. If customers are charged $20 for packages up to a volume of 8 ft³, determine the range of lengths ℓ of a $20 package.

Solve each inequality, where $-2\pi \le x \le 2\pi$.

38. $\dfrac{x}{\cos x \sin x} < 0$

39. $\sqrt{\cos x} \ge \sqrt[3]{\sin x}$

40. $\dfrac{\sin x}{\cos^2 x} < \dfrac{x^2 - 9}{x^3 - 1}$

41. Thinking Critically For Exercises 38 to 40, determine the effect that eliminating the restriction on the domain would have on the solution of each inequality.

42. *Construction* A rectangular pool is surrounded by a cement path of uniform width. Determine the possible widths of the sidewalk if the area of the pool must be at least 600 ft² and at most 900 ft². [2.3, 5]

40 ft
sidewalk
30 ft
pool

43. *Sports* A piece of stage scenery is in the shape of a rectangle connected to a semicircle as shown below. The area of the piece is 190 ft². Determine the values of the radius for which the height of the piece will be less than 15 ft. 7.04 ft $< r <$ 11 ft

44. *Construction* A hemispheric dome is to be constructed on the top of a building with a square base and a height twice the length of the side of the base. Determine the values of the length of the side of the base for which the volume of the building with the dome will be greater than 852 ft³. Length must be greater than 7.2 ft.

Test Yourself

8.1

Solve the system of equations algebraically:

1. $\begin{cases} 2x + 3y = 0 \\ 7x - 2 = 6y + 9 \end{cases}$ $\left(1, -\frac{2}{3}\right)$

2. $\begin{cases} \dfrac{x}{2} + \dfrac{y}{3} = 5 \\ \dfrac{3x}{2} - \dfrac{2y}{9} = 4 \end{cases}$ (4, 9)

3. Solve the system of equations graphically: $\begin{cases} x - y = 4 \\ x^2 - 2(2x - 1) = y \end{cases}$

8.2, 8.3, 8.4

Solve each inequality.

4. $|2x - 4| \ge 7$ $(-\infty, -1.5] \cup [5.5, \infty)$

5. $x^2 + 200 < 33x$ (8, 25)

6. $x^4 - 5x^2 + 4 > 0$
$(-\infty, -2) \cup (-1, 1) \cup (2, \infty)$

7. $\dfrac{x^2 + 9x - 14}{x^3 + 2} \le 0$ $(-1.3, 1.4)$

8.2, 8.3, 8.4

Graph each inequality in the coordinate plane.

8. $4 \le 2x - 3y$

9. $y < 4x^2 - 4x - 3$

10. $x^4 - x > y$

11. $y \le x^4 - 1$

8.4 Solving Polynomial and Rational Inequalities **411**

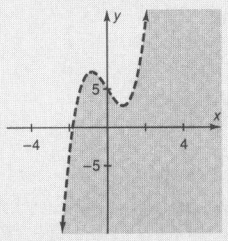

Vocabulary
feasible region
unbounded region
vertices

Ⓜ **Materials/Manipulatives**
cardboard
compass
metric ruler
quarters

Technology
graphing utility
symbolic manipulator

FOCUS

The Focus provides some excellent examples of how probability is applied in certain professions.

INSTRUCTION

• Point out that when solving real world applications graphically, it may be necessary to restrict x and y to the first quadrant. In these cases the inequalities $x \geq 0$ and $y \geq 0$ should be included in the set of inequalities which describe the problem.

• For the problem in Example 3 of Guided Practice, have students construct a circle of radius 6 cm on cardboard. Have them perform the experiment of trying to pitch the quarter onto the circle. Then have them compute the empirical probability of winning by finding the ratio of the number of times the coin landed completely in the circle to the number of times it was tossed.

• When assigning Practice Exercises 36 to 41, suggest that students may find using a test point to determine the region of intersection more efficient than trying to shade the regions.

8.5 Systems of Inequalities

Objective: *To solve systems of inequalities in two variables graphically*

Focus

Probability theory is one of the most widely applied topics in mathematics. Government agencies and large companies use probability formulas and techniques to help them plan more efficiently. While such formulas can be very complex, they are based on simple concepts that are used in everyday decision making. Probability is used by insurance companies establishing new rates, by urban planners selecting the site for a new mall, and by transportation experts setting up schedules for buses, trains, and planes.

Later in this course, you will learn some of the interesting formulas of probability. But there are methods available for solving certain probability problems that require no more knowledge of probability than its definition. One such method is *geometric probability*, in which the probability problem is represented as a system of inequalities.

A linear system of inequalities in two variables can be solved graphically. The solution to the system of inequalities is the intersection of the half-planes generated by each inequality in the system. This intersection is called the **feasible region** of the system and any "corners" of this region are called **vertices.**

Example 1 Solve the linear system of inequalities graphically: $\begin{cases} 2x - 3y \leq 9 \\ 4x - 2y > -2 \\ y \leq 3 \end{cases}$

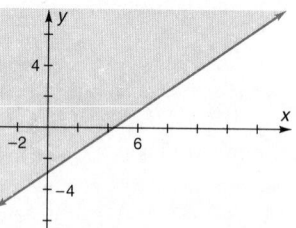

Graph each inequality on the same set of axes.

$$2x - 3y \leq 9$$
$$-3y \leq -2x + 9$$
$$y \geq \tfrac{2}{3}x - 3 \qquad \textit{If a < b and c < 0, then ac > bc}$$

Draw a solid line and shade the closed half-plane above the line $y = \tfrac{2}{3}x - 3$. This region is shaded in red.

412 Chapter 8 Inequalities and Linear Programming

$$4x - 2y > -2$$
$$-2y > -4x - 2$$
$$y < 2x + 1$$

On the same axes, draw a dashed line and shade the open half-plane below the line $y = 2x + 1$. This region is shaded in blue. The solution of the first two inequalities is the red and blue region.

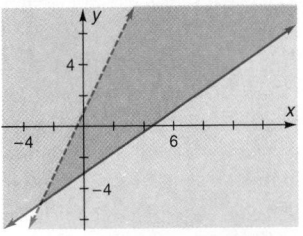

$$y \leq 3$$

Draw a solid line and shade the open half-plane below the line $y = 3$. This region is shaded gray. The triple-shaded region represents the solution of the entire system. The points on the lines $y = \frac{2}{3}x - 3$ and $y = 3$ are included, but the points on the line $y = 2x + 1$ are not included. Notice that the feasible region is bounded and the vertices are $(-3, -5)$, $(1, 3)$, and $(9, 3)$.

 If you are using a graphing utility to graph a system of inequalities, you may need to use inspection to determine the region to be shaded and the nature of the lines on the graph. Also, be sure to set the viewing rectangle so that all the vertices of the region can be seen.

The feasible region in Example 1 is bounded and forms a convex polygon. Such regions are important in both geometric probability and linear programming problems. A feasible region that is not closed is called **unbounded.** If the shaded portions of the inequalities do not intersect, then the solution to the system is the empty set.

Systems in which not all the inequalities are linear can also be solved by graphing.

Example 2 Solve the system of inequalities graphically: $\begin{cases} -x^2 + 4x > y + 5 \\ 2x + 3y \geq 14 \end{cases}$

Graph each inequality on the same set of axes.

$$-x^2 + 4x > y + 5$$
$$-x^2 + 4x - 5 > y$$

Draw a dashed curve and shade the region below the parabola.

$$2x + 3y \geq 14$$
$$3y \geq -2x + 14$$
$$y \geq -\frac{2}{3}x + \frac{14}{3}$$

Draw a solid line and shade the region above the line.

Since the regions do not intersect, the system of inequalities has no solution.

Systems of inequalities can be used for a variety of applications such as finance and manufacturing and to model probability problems.

8.5 Systems of Inequalities **413**

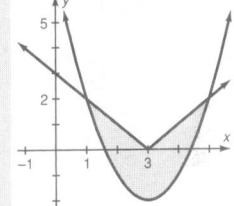

Review some simple examples of probability problems before introducing the concept of geometric probability.

For Example 3

A game at a county fair consists of pitching quarters onto a board with painted circles. You win only if the coin lands completely inside a circle. If the coin touches the edge of the circle or lands outside, you lose. Each painted circle has a radius of 6 cm and a quarter has a radius of 1.3 cm. Assume that where the quarter lands cannot be controlled. Determine the probability to the nearest hundredth of winning for a given painted circle.

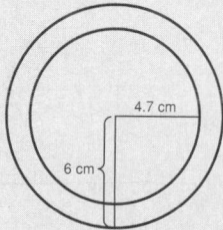

Consider where the center of the coin must land for it to be completely inside the circle. The center of the coin must land so that it is more than 1.3 cm from the edge of the circle in any direction. Therefore, in order to win, the center of the coin must be anywhere within a circle that is concentric with the painted circle and which has a radius of (6 − 1.3) or 4.7 cm.

$$\frac{\text{Area of small circle}}{\text{Area of painted circle}} = \frac{\pi(4.7)^2}{\pi(6)^2} = 0.61$$

CLOSURE

Have students summarize in their math journals procedures for solving systems of inequalities graphically in two variables.

Modeling

How can train schedules be established and reviewed to ensure that the timing of different trains will be adequate to the number of travelers?

Systems of inequalities and geometric probability can help in planning and decision making. The probability of a certain event occurring is defined as the number of possible "favorable" outcomes divided by the total number of possible outcomes.

Consider the following situation. A dart is thrown at a rectangular target with a circle painted in the middle as shown in the diagram. Throws that miss the rectangle entirely are not considered. *If it is impossible to control where on the rectangle the dart will land, what is the probability that it will land in the circle?*

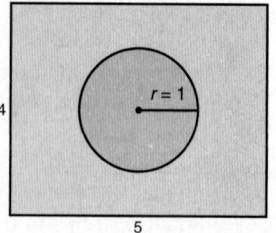

This problem can be solved using *geometric probability*. The number of possible favorable outcomes, called the *event*, is the set of all points in the circle. The total number of possible outcomes, called the *sample space*, is the set of all points in the rectangle. Thus, the probability that the dart will land in the circle is simply the area of the circle divided by the area of the rectangle.

Area of the circle: $\pi(1)^2 = \pi$ Area of rectangle: $5 \cdot 4 = 20$ Probability: $\frac{\pi}{20} \approx 0.16$

Geometric probability can be used to solve problems about scheduling trains as well as problems in traffic safety, mobile communications, and time management.

Example 3 *Transportation*   Hector Cruz is a transportation planner for the Jefferson County rapid transit system. He has arranged it so that a northbound train leaves the central station every 8 min and a southbound train every 12 min. Now he is studying the flow of crowds and wants to know, for any random moment, the probability that the next train will be southbound.

Make a graph to model the information. Let the x-axis represent the time that may elapse before the departure of a southbound train. Let the y-axis represent the time that may elapse before the departure of a northbound train. The origin represents the point at which the wait for the next train begins.

A point such as (7, 3) represents the situation in which a southbound train leaves after 7 min and a northbound train leaves after 3 min. Since the wait will not be longer than 8 min for a northbound train or 12 min for a southbound train, the total number of possible outcomes is the set of all points in the shaded rectangle on the graph. Then, the sample space is given by the system:

$$\begin{cases} x \geq 0 \\ y \geq 0 \\ x \leq 12 \\ y \leq 8 \end{cases}$$

414   Chapter 8 Inequalities and Linear Programming

For the next train to be southbound, the x-coordinate must be less than the y-coordinate, so $y > x$. Graph $y = x$ and shade the region above the line. Thus, the number of favorable outcomes is the set of all points in the shaded triangle on the graph.

To determine the probability that the next train will be southbound, divide the area of the shaded region by the area of the rectangle.

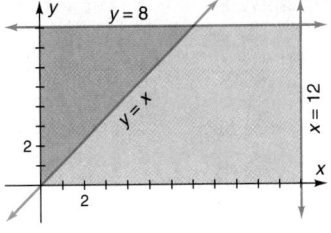

Area of rectangle: $8 \cdot 12 = 96$

Area of shaded region: $\frac{1}{2} \cdot 8 \cdot 8 = 32$ Probability: $\frac{32}{96} = \frac{1}{3}$

Class Exercises

Solve each linear system of inequalities graphically.

1. $\begin{cases} 3x + 4y < 8 \\ x \geq 0, y \geq 0 \end{cases}$
2. $\begin{cases} x - 2y < 0 \\ 2x + y > 3 \end{cases}$
3. $\begin{cases} -x + 3y > 6 \\ 4x - 5y \leq -5 \end{cases}$
4. $\begin{cases} x < -y + 1 \\ y \leq 4x - 4 \end{cases}$

5. $\begin{cases} y + 5x - 2 \geq 0 \\ -6 > y - 3x \end{cases}$
6. $\begin{cases} |x| \leq 6 \\ |y| > 3.5 \end{cases}$
7. $\begin{cases} x^2 - 2x \geq y \\ x^2 + 2x > y \end{cases}$
8. $\begin{cases} 0.25x^2 - 3 < y \\ |x| \geq 4 \end{cases}$

9. *Design* A table top is to be made from 54 tiles. Roses and day lilies are to be painted on the tiles. A rose fits on one tile but a day lily requires three tiles. Not every tile needs to be decorated. Determine a set of values for the number of roses and day lilies that can be painted on this table.

Practice Exercises   Use appropriate technology.

Solve each system of linear inequalities graphically.

A 1. $\begin{cases} x + y < 3 \\ 2x - y \geq 2 \end{cases}$
2. $\begin{cases} x + y \leq -2 \\ -2x + y > 1 \end{cases}$
3. $\begin{cases} 3x + y < 5 \\ 4x - 2y > 4 \end{cases}$

4. $\begin{cases} x - y < 0 \\ 2x + y > 3 \end{cases}$
5. $\begin{cases} 5x - 2y \leq 10 \\ x \geq -4 \end{cases}$
6. $\begin{cases} 3x - 7y < 0 \\ y \leq -2 \end{cases}$

7. $\begin{cases} y \geq 2x - 3 \\ y < -5x + 1 \end{cases}$
8. $\begin{cases} y \leq -5x \\ y > 2x + 1 \end{cases}$
9. $\begin{cases} 3x + y < 4 \\ 3x - 2y \leq 12 \end{cases}$

10. **Thinking Critically**   Construct an inequality in which the original relation is $>$, but the graph is the open half-plane below the boundary. ex: $2x - y > 12$

R 11. Solve: $|x - 3| < 4$ $(-1, 7)$

Solve each system of inequalities graphically.

12. $\begin{cases} y \leq -3x^2 - 5x + 12 \\ 0.1x + 0.15y > 1.8 \end{cases}$
13. $\begin{cases} x^3 \geq y \\ |y| \leq 8 \end{cases}$

14. $\begin{cases} y < 2(x - 2)^2 - 1 \\ y < -2(x + 2)^2 + 1 \end{cases}$
15. $\begin{cases} y \geq x^2 + 10x + 22 \\ y \leq -x^2 - 10x - 28 \end{cases}$

8.5 Systems of Inequalities   **415**

INDEPENDENT PRACTICE

Assignment Guide
Basic: 1–20, 29, 33, Project
Average: 10–11, 16–35, Project
Enriched: 24–45, Project

Teacher's Resource Book
  Practice, page 55

R **Review**
Exercises 11, 16, 17, 31, and 33 review concepts of solving absolute value inequalities, solving quadratic equations, the distance formula, coordinate proofs, and solving inverse trigonometric functions.

Additional Answers
Class Exercises

1.

2.

3.

4.

5.
6.
7.
8.

Project

This is a good opportunity for cross-curricular learning. Have students read about meteors and research the effects a meteor would have if it fell to earth.

LESSON FOLLOW-UP

Lesson Quiz

Solve each system of inequalities graphically.

1. $\begin{cases} 3x + 4y \le 12 \\ 5x + 2y \le 10 \end{cases}$

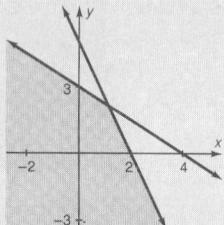

2. $\begin{cases} y - 4 \le x^2 + 2x \\ |y| \ge 2 \end{cases}$

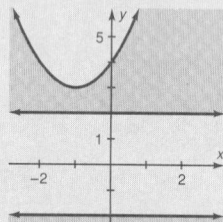

3. Darts are thrown at a rectangular dart board with a triangle painted in the center. Assume that where the darts land cannot be controlled and darts landing outside the rectangle are discounted. Find the probability to the nearest hundredth that a dart will not land inside the triangle.

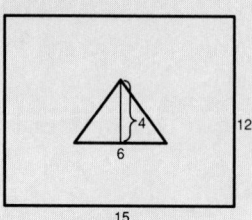

$$\frac{\text{Area outside of triangle}}{\text{Area of the rectangle}} =$$

$$\frac{(12)(15) - \frac{1}{2}(6)(4)}{(12)(15)} = 0.93$$

Ⓡ 16. Solve $x^4 - 3x^2 - 54 = 0$ by factoring. $x = \pm 3; x = \pm i\sqrt{6}$

Ⓡ 17. Determine the distance from the origin to the line $2x + 3y = -6$. 1.7

18. *Energy* An electric clock costs 25.8¢ per month to operate. A battery clock costs, on the average, 15¢ per month (assuming one battery needs to be replaced every 6 months.) Determine a set of values for the number of each type of clock that should be purchased to keep the cost of running the clocks less than $1.50 per month.

19. *Nutrition* A medium Delicious apple has 96 calories and a medium Anjou pear has 122 calories. Matty eats a midmorning snack several times a week. He eats either a Delicious apple on an Anjou pear. If he wants to keep the total calories for his midmorning snack at less than 500 calories per week, determine a set of values for the number of apples and pears he can eat each week.

20. *Transportation* Suppose that in the situation described in Example 3, the transportation planner is studying the effect of changes in the constraints. What is the probability that a train running in either direction will leave within the next 5 min? $\frac{25}{96}$

Solve each system of linear inequalities graphically.

Ⓑ 21. $\begin{cases} 5x - 2y \le 10 \\ |x| < 2 \end{cases}$ 22. $\begin{cases} 3x - 7y > 21 \\ |y| < 4 \end{cases}$ 23. $\begin{cases} 2x - y \ge 5 \\ x \le 4 \\ y > 0 \end{cases}$ 24. $\begin{cases} x < y \\ x \ge -2 \\ |y| < 3 \end{cases}$

25. $\begin{cases} 4x + y > 0 \\ 3x - 2y \ge 0 \\ x > 0, y \ge 0 \end{cases}$ 26. $\begin{cases} x + 3y > 0 \\ 3x - 4y > -12 \\ x \ge 0, y > 0 \end{cases}$ 27. $\begin{cases} y < x^2 \\ y < x^3 \\ y > x^4 \end{cases}$ 28. $\begin{cases} y \le \cos x \\ |x| \le \pi \\ |y| \le 1 \end{cases}$

Determine a system of inequalities that defines the shaded region.

29.

ex: $\begin{cases} x + y \le 5 \\ 3x + 2y \le 12 \\ x \ge 0 \\ y \ge 0 \end{cases}$

30.

ex: $\begin{cases} 2x - y \le 8 \\ y < 4 \\ x \ge 0 \\ y \ge 0 \end{cases}$

Ⓡ 31. Using coordinate geometry, prove that the length of the median to the hypotenuse of any right triangle is one-half the length of the hypotenuse.

32. *Construction* A patio is to be made of red and natural-colored patio blocks. The red blocks cost $1.70 each and the natural blocks cost $1.50 each. If the number of natural blocks must be less than one-third the number of red blocks, determine a set of values for the number of each color block that can be purchased if the budget for the patio is $400.

Ⓡ 33. Determine x to the nearest degree, if $\tan x = 1.428$, $0° \le x < 360°$. 55°, 235°

Additional Answers

31.

$$PS = \sqrt{(a - 0)^2 + (b - 0)^2} = \sqrt{a^2 + b^2};$$
$$QR = \sqrt{(2a - 0)^2 + (0 - 2b)^2} = 2\sqrt{a^2 + b^2};$$
$$PS = \frac{1}{2}QR$$

$R(0, 2b)$ $S(a, b)$ $P(0, 0)$ $Q(2a, 0)$

34. Thinking Critically Create a system of inequalities that results in a region that is a polygon but is not convex. ex: $y - |x| \leq 2, |x| \leq 2$

35. *Transportation* Suppose that in the situation described in Example 3, no trains leave in the first 2 min. What is the probability that the next train will be southbound? $\frac{3}{10}$

Solve each system of inequalities.

C **36.** $\begin{cases} |x + 3y| < 6 \\ |2x - y| > 3 \end{cases}$ **37.** $\begin{cases} |5x - y| \geq 2 \\ |4x - 5y| < 20 \end{cases}$ **38.** $\begin{cases} y > x^2 - 1 \\ y < \cos x \end{cases}$

39. $\begin{cases} y \geq x^2 - 2x \\ y \leq \sin x \end{cases}$ **40.** $\begin{cases} y \leq \sqrt{x} \\ y \geq -\sqrt{x} \end{cases}$ **41.** $\begin{cases} x < y^2 \\ x > -y^2 \end{cases}$

42. Thinking Critically In the situation described in Example 3, what happens to the probability that the next train will be southbound as more and more time passes? Describe what happens to the graphs of the sample space and the event space.

43. *Energy* When on vacation, the Baskins leave one lamp with a 100-W bulb on a timer and one lamp with a 60-W bulb on another timer. The 100-W bulb costs 1.3¢ per hour and the 60-W bulb costs 0.8¢ per hour to run. The lamp with the 100-W bulb is to be left on at least 50 h longer than the other lamp. If they want the cost of the lights to be less than $8 for the month, determine a set of values for the number of hours each lamp can be on.

44. *Design* A tile floor 10 by 12 ft is to consist of rectangular- and triangular-shaped tiles. Two triangular-shaped tiles cover the same area as one rectangular tile. Each rectangular tile is 1 ft². The rectangular tiles cost $1.75, and the triangular tiles cost $0.95. For design purposes at least half the total area must be covered by triangular tiles. If the budget for the floor is $250, determine a set of values for the number of each shape tile that should be purchased.

45. *Time Management* The photocopying machine in a school office is made available to teachers each day between the hours of 3:00 and 4:00 p.m. Mr. Grim and Ms. Grump each have 10 min of copying to do each day. If they each enter the office at points in the available hour, what is the probability that one of them will have to wait while the other finishes copying? $\frac{11}{36}$

Project

A meteor is going to fall to earth and there is no way of telling where it will land. Find the probability that it will land in the ocean, in your country, in your state, and in your town.

Challenge

Find a system of three linear inequalities that fit these criteria:
a. The only solution is (3, 2).
b. No boundary is horizontal or vertical. Answers may vary.

44. $T \geq 120, R \geq 0, R \geq -\frac{1}{2}T + 120, R \leq -\frac{19}{35}T + \frac{1000}{7}$, where T and R represent the number of triangular-shaped and rectangular-shaped tiles, respectively, and T is an even integer.

Alternative Assessment
Group students in small groups and ask each group to describe a situation, create a corresponding word problem that can be solved by using geometric probability, and include a complete solution.

Enrichment
Graph the system of inequalities
$$\begin{cases} 4x + 3y \leq 60 \\ 9 < y < 16 \end{cases}$$

Then determine the probability to the nearest hundredth that a point chosen at random on this grid will be in the feasible region.

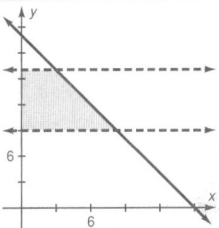

Vertices of the feasible region: (0, 9), (8.25, 9), (3, 16), (0, 16). The feasible region can be divided into a rectangle and triangle.
Area of rectangle: (3)(7) = 21
Area of triangle: $\frac{1}{2}$(5.25)(7) = 18.375
$\frac{\text{Area of feasible region}}{\text{Area of grid}} = \frac{21 + 18.375}{(21)(15)} = 0.125$

Additional Answers
43. $S \geq 0, H \geq 0, S \leq H - 50,$
$S < -\frac{13}{8}H + 1000$, where S and H represent the time in hours a 60-W bulb and a 100-W bulb, respectively, are left on.

Vocabulary
constraints
feasible region
linear program
objective function
optimization problems

Ⓜ **Materials/Manipulatives**
transparencies

Technology
graphing utility
symbolic manipulator

FOCUS

The discussion of the Berlin airlift provides an opportunity for cross-curricular learning. Invite discussion about other historical references to the use of mathematical models.

INSTRUCTION

Ⓜ Use transparencies to help students visualize the graphical representation for determining the point at which a maximum or minimum value of the objective function occurs (discussed before Example 3), and have students use a graphing utility to draw the family of lines for different values of P. Have students start with $P = 30$ and increase the value of P by 10 until $P = 150$.

Technology If students use a graphing utility to graph a system of linear inequalities, remind them that the coordinates of the vertices they read from the graph may only be approximate. Since exact values for the coordinates of the vertices are needed to determine the maximum or minimum value of the function, the points of intersection of the boundary lines should be found algebraically.

8.6 Linear Programming

Objective: *To solve optimization problems involving systems of linear inequalities*

Focus

Following the end of World War II, the city of West Berlin, located deep in the Russian sector of Germany, was occupied by Britain, France, and the United States. On June 24, 1948, the Russians blocked all land routes through East Germany to Berlin in hopes of forcing the Western forces out of Berlin. In response to this blockade an airlift was planned. Researchers for the United States Air Force were faced with the problem of supplying food, clothing, fuel, and other necessities to the 2 million people in West Berlin.

The Berlin airlift, a problem which involved dozens of variables, was an early real world problem in which the method of *linear programming* was applied. There were limits on the numbers of planes and crew members available, as well as the amount of fuel, possible flight times, and other factors. These limits are the constraints within which a solution must be found. If, for example, there are only 100 planes available, then a solution must not call for 200 planes.

A mathematical model consisting of a linear function to be *optimized* (maximized or minimized) and a set of inequalities representing the restrictions on resources is called a **linear program.** In a linear program, the function to be maximized or minimized is called the **objective function.** This function might represent amounts of money earned or spent, goods manufactured or delivered, or any of a variety of other quantities. The linear inequalities are called **constraints,** and the solution of the system of linear inequalities is called the **feasible region.** If a linear program has a solution, it will occur at a **vertex** of the feasible region. If there are multiple solutions, at least one of them will occur at a vertex.

> **To solve a linear program:**
> - Solve the system of linear inequalities.
> - Determine the coordinates of the vertices of the feasible region. That is, solve the system of equations consisting of the lines whose intersection is the vertex.
> - Evaluate the objective function to be optimized at each vertex.
> - Identify the maximum or minimum value of the objective function.

418 Chapter 8 Inequalities and Linear Programming

Example 1 Determine the values of x and y that will maximize the objective function $P = 20x + 30y$ under the constraints:

$$\begin{cases} x + 2y \leq 8 \\ 3x + 2y \leq 12 \\ x \geq 0, y \geq 0 \end{cases}$$

Graph the system of linear inequalities. Determine the vertices.

$A(0, 0)$	*From the graph.*
$B(4, 0)$	*x-intercept of $3x + 2y = 12$*
$D(0, 4)$	*y-intercept of $x + 2y = 8$*

To determine the vertex at C, solve the system:

$$\begin{cases} x + 2y = 8 \\ 3x + 2y = 12 \end{cases}$$

$-2x = -4$	*Subtract the second equation from the first.*
$x = 2$	
$2 + 2y = 8$	*Substitute 2 for x in the first equation.*
$2y = 6$	*Solve for y.*
$y = 3$	The remaining vertex is $C(2, 3)$.

Vertex	$P = 20x + 30y$	*Evaluate $P = 20x + 30y$ at each vertex.*
$A(0, 0)$	$P = 20(0) + 30(0) = 0$	
$B(4, 0)$	$P = 20(4) + 30(0) = 80$	
$C(2, 3)$	$P = 20(2) + 30(3) = 130$	
$D(0, 4)$	$P = 20(0) + 30(4) = 120$	

The maximum value of P is 130 and occurs at the point $(2, 3)$. *Does the objective function $P = 20x + 30y$ have a minimum in the feasible region?*

A linear program may also be used to minimize the objective function. Note that if two vertices of the feasible region are both solutions to a linear program, every point on the line segment connecting the two vertices will also be a solution. *Why?*

Example 2 Determine the value of x and y that will minimize the objective function $C = 5x + 15y$ under the constraints:

$$\begin{cases} 10x + 30y \geq 90 \\ 200x + 100y \geq 800 \\ x \geq 0, y \geq 0 \end{cases}$$

Graph the linear system of inequalities. Determine the vertices.

$G(9, 0)$	*x-intercept of $10x + 30y = 90$*
$E(0, 8)$	*y-intercept of $200x + 100y = 800$*
$F(3, 2)$	*Solution of the system* $\begin{cases} 10x + 30y = 90 \\ 200x + 100y = 800 \end{cases}$

Thinking Critically
The objective function has a minimum, 0, in the feasible region because this region is bounded.

If two vertices of the feasible region are both solutions, all points on the line segment connecting the two vertices will also minimize the objective function and are therefore solutions.

Alternative Learning Styles
Many students benefit from having a general problem-solving strategy written on a side board for easy reference. Use the strategy detailed in the lesson.

GUIDED PRACTICE

For Example 1
Determine the values of x and y that will maximize the function $P = 300x + 150y$ under the constraints:

$$\begin{cases} 8x + 10y \leq 80 \\ 12x + 5y \leq 60 \\ x \geq 0 \\ y \geq 0 \end{cases}$$

$P(2.5, 6) = 1650$ maximum

Common Error Students may incorrectly solve the system of linear inequalities. Have students use a graphing utility to check their solution.

For Example 2
Determine the values of x and y that will minimize the function $C = 7x + 3y$ under the constraints:

$$\begin{cases} 4x + 3y \leq 75 \\ x + 3y \geq 30 \\ x \geq 0 \\ y \geq 0 \end{cases}$$

$C(0, 10) = 30$ minimum

Modeling

This example serves to introduce the modeling capabilities of linear programming. A more in-depth treatment of linear programming models is given in the next lesson.

For Example 3

The ALLMUSIC Record Company makes demonstration records (demos) of new songs on cassettes and compact disks. Each cassette takes 20 min to record and 10 min to test and label. A compact disk takes 30 min to record and 20 min to test and label. The recording studio is available 12 h per day. The machinery for testing and labeling is available 7 h per day. The company makes $3 profit on each cassette and $5 on each CD. Determine the number of each type of demo the company should make to maximize the daily profit.

$$\text{Constraints:} \begin{cases} 20x + 30y \le 720 \\ 10x + 20y \le 420 \\ x \ge 0 \\ y \ge 0 \end{cases}$$

Profit: $P = 3x + 5y$

$P = 3(18) + 5(12) = \$114$ profit;
The company should produce 18 cassettes and 12 CDs per day.

Vertex	$C = 5x + 15y$	
$G(9, 0)$	$C = 5(9) + 15(0) = 45$	
$F(3, 2)$	$C = 5(3) + 15(2) = 45$	
$E(0, 8)$	$C = 5(0) + 15(8) = 120$	

Evaluate the objective function at each vertex.

The minimum value of C is 45 and occurs at $(9, 0)$ and $(3, 2)$. Therefore, all points on the line segment connecting these two vertices will also yield a minimum value of C.

The feasible region for the linear program in Example 1 is a convex polygon. The objective function has both a minimum and a maximum on the region, the minimum being 0. The feasible region in Example 2 is *unbounded* as x and y increase in a positive direction. The objective function has a minimum on this region but no maximum.

Modeling

How can linear programming be used to maximize the amount of supplies delivered in a single day?

The technique of linear programming was devised to model problems in determining allocation of resources to maximize productivity or profit or minimize waste or cost. This technique, which can involve linear equations and inequalities in many variables, was developed during World War II by the United States Air Force. The type of problems that are solved using linear programming are called **optimization problems.**

A simple linear program involves linear systems of equations and inequalities such as those presented in the first two examples. The system of inequalities, or constraints, represents the limitations on the resources available in the problem situation. The objective function represents some factor such as cost or profit which is to be minimized or maximized. The diagram at the right gives a graphical representation of how this was done in Example 1. The objective function

$$P = 20x + 30y$$

when solved for y is

$$y = -\frac{2}{3}x + \frac{P}{30}$$

This can be thought of as the "family" of parallel lines with slope $-\frac{2}{3}$ and y-intercept $\frac{P}{30}$. The maximum of the objective function over the feasible region is represented by the last vertex that is intercepted by one of these lines as they move "up" the region. *How would you determine the minimum value?*

Consider the following problem concerning the Berlin airlift which utilizes the optimization capabilities of linear programming.

420 Chapter 8 Inequalities and Linear Programming

Thinking Critically
To determine the minimum value, locate the first vertex intercepted by one of these lines.

Example 3 *Relief* A total of 44 planes was available on a given day during the airlift. Some planes were large and some were small. The large planes required four-person crews and the small planes required two-person crews, selected from a total of 128 crew members. A large plane could carry 30,000 ft³ of cargo and a small plane could carry 20,000 ft³. How many planes of each type are needed to maximize the cargo space?

Let x represent the number of large planes, and y the number of small planes. Make a table to organize the data.

	Large	Small	Limits
Number of planes	x	y	44
Number of crew	4	2	128
Volume of cargo	30,000	20,000	

Thus the problem is to maximize the objective function $V = 30,000x + 20,000y$ subject to the following constraints:

$$\begin{cases} x + y \le 44 \\ 4x + 2y \le 128 \\ x \ge 0, y \ge 0 \end{cases}$$

Graph the feasible region and find the vertices.

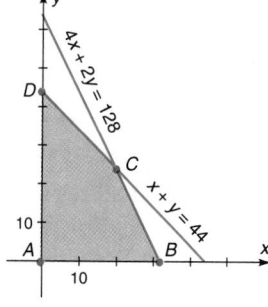

$A(0, 0)$	*Origin*
$D(0, 44)$	*y-intercept of $x + y = 44$*
$B(32, 0)$	*x-intercept of $4x + 2y = 128$*
$C(20, 24)$	*Solution of the system:* $\begin{cases} x + y = 44 \\ 4x + 2y = 128 \end{cases}$

Evaluate $V = 30,000x + 20,000y$ at each vertex.

$A(0, 0)$	$V = 30,000(0) + 20,000(0) = 0$
$B(32, 0)$	$V = 30,000(32) + 20,000(0) = 960,000$
$C(20, 24)$	$V = 30,000(20) + 20,000(24) = 1,080,000$
$D(0, 44)$	$V = 30,000(0) + 20,000(44) = 880,000$

The maximum volume of cargo that can be airlifted under the given constraints will be achieved by using 20 large planes and 24 small planes.

If you are using a graphing utility to solve a linear program, remember that once the equations of the constraints are graphed, you may have to use inspection to determine the feasible region. You can then use the zoom and trace features to determine the coordinates of the vertices.

8.6 Linear Programming **421**

Lesson Quiz

1. Determine the values of x and y that will minimize the objective function $C = 3x + 5y$ under the constraints:

$$\begin{cases} 7x + 6y \geq 42 \\ 5x + 10y \geq 50 \\ \qquad x \geq 0 \\ \qquad y \geq 0 \end{cases}$$

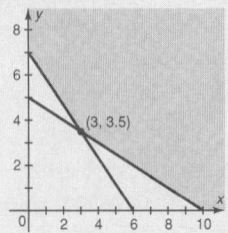

$C(3, 3.5) = 26.5$ minimum

2. Determine the values of x and y that will maximize the objective function $P = 5x + 2y$ under the constraints:

$$\begin{cases} 30x + 20y \leq 600 \\ 40x + 10y \leq 500 \\ \qquad x \geq 0 \\ \qquad y \geq 0 \end{cases}$$

$P(8, 18) = 76$ maximum

Class Exercises

The graph of a system of linear inequalities for a linear program and the objective function to be maximized are given. Draw the family of lines representing each objective function. Determine the maximum value of the objective function from the graph.

1. $P = 5x + 3y$

$P(6, 0) = 30$ maximum

2. $P = 20x + 40y$

$P(7, 8) = 460$ maximum

The graph of a system of linear inequalities for a linear program and the objective function to be minimized are given. Draw the family of lines representing each objective function. Determine the minimum value of the objective function from the graph.

3. $C = 2x + 2y$

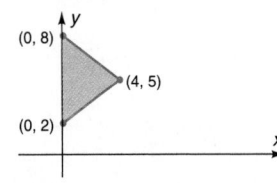

$C(0, 2) = 4$ minimum

4. $C = 300x + 400y$

$C(2, 3) = 1800$ minimum

5. Determine the values of x and y that will maximize the function $P = 300x + 200y$ under the constraints at the right. **(5, 2)**

$$\begin{cases} 20x + 10y \leq 120 \\ 100x + 200y \leq 900 \\ x \geq 0, y \geq 0 \end{cases}$$

Practice Exercises

Use appropriate technology.

Determine the values of x and y that will optimize (maximize or minimize) the objective function under the given constraints.

A 1. Maximize $P = 2x + 3y$
$$\begin{cases} x + y \leq 10 \ \textbf{(2, 8)} \\ x \leq 6 \\ y \leq 8 \\ x \geq 0, y \geq 0 \end{cases}$$

2. Maximize $P = 6x + 4y$
$$\begin{cases} x + y \leq 8 \ \textbf{(4, 4)} \\ x \leq 4 \\ y \leq 7 \\ x \geq 0, y \geq 0 \end{cases}$$

3. Maximize $P = 20x + 10y$
$$\begin{cases} x + y \leq 6 \ \textbf{(6, 0)} \\ x + y \geq 1 \\ x \geq 0, y \geq 0 \end{cases}$$

4. Maximize $P = 30x + 20y$
$$\begin{cases} x + y \leq 7 \ \textbf{(7, 0)} \\ x + y \geq 2 \\ x \geq 0, y \geq 0 \end{cases}$$

5. Minimize $C = 4x + 12y$
$$\begin{cases} 3x + 2y \geq 12 \ \textbf{(4, 0)} \\ y \leq 6 \\ x \leq 4 \end{cases}$$

6. Minimize $C = 40x + 60y$
$$\begin{cases} x + y \geq 3 \ \textbf{(3, 0)} \\ x \leq 3 \\ y \leq 3 \end{cases}$$

422 Chapter 8 Inequalities and Linear Programming

Additional Answers, Class Exercises

1.

2.

3.

4.

7. Minimize $C = 60x + 75y$

$$\begin{cases} 2x + y \geq 48 & \text{(18, 12)} \\ x + 2y \geq 42 \\ x \geq 4 \\ y \geq 6 \end{cases}$$

8. Minimize $C = 10,000x + 20,000y$

$$\begin{cases} 5x + y \geq 10 & \text{(4, 2)} \\ x + y \geq 6 \\ x + 4y \geq 12 \\ x \geq 0, y \geq 0 \end{cases}$$

Ⓡ **9.** Express $\cos 78° + \cos 10°$ as a product. 2 cos 44° cos 34°

10. Thinking Critically   Given the graph of the solution of the linear system of inequalities for a linear program, determine the minimum value of $P = ax + by$, $a > 0$ and $b > 0$. 0

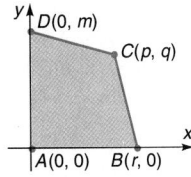
$D(0, m)$, $C(p, q)$, $A(0, 0)$ $B(r, 0)$

11. *Manufacturing*   A manufacturer of coats produces floor length and three-quarter length coats. Information about the manufacturer's resources is summarized in the table below. Determine the maximum profit that can be made with the available resources. $176

	Floor	Three-quarter	Limits
Number made	x	y	
Cutting time per coat	2 h	1 h	40 h
Sewing time per coat	1 h	1 h	32 h
Profit per coat	$7	$5	

12. Thinking Critically   In Example 3, why were the inequalities $x \geq 0$ and $y \geq 0$ included in the constraints? There cannot be a negative number of planes.

Ⓡ **13.** Solve $3 \cos^2 x + 8 \cos x + 1 = 0$ for x between 0 and 2π. 1.7, 4.58

14. *Business*   A baker makes bran muffins and corn muffins which are sold by the box. The baker can sell at most 20 boxes of bran muffins and 15 boxes of corn muffins per day. It takes 1 h to make a box of bran muffins and 1 h to make a box of corn muffins. The baker has 30 h per week to bake muffins. The profit on a box of bran muffins is $1.25. The profit on the corn muffins is $1.35 per box. Determine how many boxes of each he should bake to maximize his profit. 15 boxes of bran; 15 boxes of corn

Determine the values of x and y that will optimize the objective function under the given constraints. Calculate the optimum value of the objective function.

Ⓑ **15.** Maximize $P = 0.06x + 0.1y$

$$\begin{cases} 2x + 2y \geq 4 & \text{(0, 4); 0.4} \\ 3x + 2y \leq 12 \\ 2x + 3y \leq 12 \\ x \geq 0, y \geq 0 \end{cases}$$

16. Maximize $P = 40x + 60y$

$$\begin{cases} 10y \leq 10x + 30 & \text{(1.5, 4.5); 330} \\ 10y \geq -10x - 20 \\ 20x + 20y \leq 120 \\ y \geq 0 \end{cases}$$

17. Minimize $C = 80x + 120y$

$$\begin{cases} 0.2x + 0.1y \geq 1.6 & \text{(10, 2); 1040} \\ 0.01x + 0.01y \geq 0.12 \\ x + 2y \geq 14 \\ x \geq 0, y \geq 0 \end{cases}$$

18. Minimize $C = 100x + 70y$

$$\begin{cases} 80x + 90y \leq 720 & \text{(0, 6); 420} \\ 80x + 90y \geq 540 \\ x \geq 0, y \geq 0 \end{cases}$$

Ⓡ **19.** Solve $4x^4 - 4x^2 - 3 = 0$ by factoring. Give solutions to the nearest hundredth. $x = \pm0.71i, \pm1.22$

3. Jon tie-dyes silk scarfs. He makes square and rectangular scarfs. A square scarf requires 1 oz of dye and a rectangular scarf requires 4 oz of dye. It takes 2 h to make either type of scarf. He makes $3 profit on each square scarf and $4 on each rectangular scarf. This week he has 16 oz of dye on hand and can work 20 h. Assuming he can sell all the scarfs he makes, determine how many of each type he should make to maximize his profit.

Constraints: $\begin{cases} x + 4y \leq 16 \\ 2x + 2y \leq 20 \\ x \geq 0 \\ y \geq 0 \end{cases}$

Profit: $P = 3x + 4y$

(8, 2)

He should make 8 square and 2 rectangular scarfs.

20. **Thinking Critically** Given a linear program, describe the graph of a solution of a linear system of equations for which there is no minimum value of the linear objective function.

Ⓡ 21. Determine the circumference of a circle if its area is 49π. 14π

22. *Manufacturing* A company makes two types of window cleaners, Cleanit and Super Cleanit. The formula for a 16-oz bottle of Cleanit is 8 oz ammonia and 8 oz distilled water. The formula for a 16-oz bottle of Super Cleanit is 12 oz ammonia and 4 oz distilled water. The profit on a bottle of Cleanit is $1 and on Super Cleanit $1.25. If the manufacturer has on hand 1200 oz ammonia and 800 oz distilled water, how many bottles of each type of cleaner should be produced to maximize the profit?

Ⓡ 23. Give the amplitude and period of $f(x) = -2 \cos 2\left(2x - \dfrac{\pi}{3}\right)$. $2; \dfrac{\pi}{2}$

For the feasible region shown, determine an objective function that has a:

24. Maximum at B 25. Minimum at C, if $(0, 0)$ is excluded
ex: $C = 2x + 3y$ ex: $C = 9y - 2x$

Given the linear program with objective function $P = ax + by$, subject to the constraints at the right, determine conditions on a and b so that a maximum will occur at the following points:

$$\begin{cases} x + 3y \le 15 \\ 2x + y \le 10 \\ x \ge 0, y \ge 0 \end{cases}$$

C 26. The intersection of the lines $x + 3y = 15$ and $2x + y = 10$ $\dfrac{1}{3} < \dfrac{a}{b} < 2$

27. The y-intercept of $x + 3y = 15$ $b > 0$ and   28. Both points in Exercise 26 and 27 $a = \dfrac{b}{3}$
$a < \dfrac{b}{3}$

29. The x-intercept of $2x + y = 10$ 30. Both points in Exercises 26 and 29
$a > 0$ and $a > 2b$ $a = 2b$

31. **Writing in Mathematics** Write a paragraph describing a situation in which your community could use linear programming to allocate limited resources.

32. *Cooking* A recipe for bouillabaisse requires 2 qt stock for 8 servings and a chef cannot make more than 240 servings per day. A recipe for gumbo calls for 3 qt stock for 8 servings and the chef cannot make more than 160 servings per day. The chef has 96 qt stock available. If the profit on one serving of bouillabaisse is $2.50 and the profit on one serving of gumbo is $3.75, find the amount of each that the chef should make in order to maximize profit.

Project

Suppose you are in charge of the portion of the airlift described in Example 3. Changing one constraint at a time, use linear programming to determine different ways of increasing the volume of cargo that you can ship.

Review   yes; no; A mirror aligned with the y-axis shows line symmetry, but a mirror cannot show an odd function's point symmetry.

1. Could you use a mirror to demonstrate that the graph of a trigonometric function represents an even function? An odd function? Explain.

2. Determine whether the inverse of the quadratic function $f(x) = 3x^2 - 2$ is also a function.   no

424   Chapter 8 Inequalities and Linear Programming

Applications of Linear Programming

Objective: To apply linear programming

Focus

The busiest airport in the world is O'Hare Airport in Chicago, Illinois. Each year more than 56 million people pass through O'Hare. Personnel to assist with security, baggage handling, food service, and other factors must be assigned in such a way as to maximize efficiency. The available work force and the budget allocated to run the airport are just two of the variables that are taken into consideration. Airports are among the many businesses that use linear programming to solve their resource allocation problems.

Like many other mathematical models, linear programming is a tool for solving real world problems. The mathematics provides critical information on which a decision may be based, but the decision maker still has the responsibility of interpreting that information. For example, consider the situation in which a linear program has more than one optimal solution; that is, when the objective function is parallel to one side of the feasible region. The most efficient solution to the real world problem may be any of a number of points and it is up to the decision maker to choose among them. In some situations, only integral solutions are possible.

Graphing utilities may be helpful in determining the feasible region for a linear program. However, most utilities will only graph the corresponding equations for the inequalities listed in the constraints. You must understand how to graph inequalities in order to determine the region itself.

Example 1 *Budgeting* Flywithus Airlines is updating its security system at a major airport. The budget for new metal detectors is $75,000. The airline has a maximum of 18 security guards available for each shift. There are two types of metal detectors available. Unit *A* costs $5000, requires one security guard, and can process 300 people per hour. Unit *B* costs $7500, requires two security guards, and can process 500 people per hour. Since unit *B* has a better reliability record, the purchasing agent has mandated that at least four units must be type *B*. Determine the number of units of each type that should be purchased to maximize the number of people processed.

8.7 Applications of Linear Programming **425**

For Example 1

A company manufactures two types of tennis balls: one for clay courts and one for grass courts. A gross of clay court balls requires 3 h on the assembly line and 1 h on the packing machine. A gross of grass court balls requires 1 h on the assembly line and 1 h on the packing machine. To meet a specific order, the company must produce at least 20 gross of grass court balls. A gross of clay court balls sells for $75 wholesale and a gross of grass court balls sells for $62 wholesale. If the assembly line operates at most 120 h per week and the packing machine operates at most 80 h per week, determine how many gross of each type of tennis ball should be manufactured to maximize the company's revenue.

Constraints: $\begin{cases} 3x + y \le 120 \\ x + y \le 80 \\ y \ge 20 \\ x \ge 0 \end{cases}$

$P = 75x + 62y$

clay court: 20 gross;
grass court: 60 gross

Common Error Students may forget to include the constraint $y \ge 20$. Have these students write two lines for the number of gross of tennis balls, one for each type, and include the limit in the table.

Let x represent the number of type A units purchased, and let y represent the number of type B units purchased. Make a table to organize the data.

	Unit A	Unit B	Limits
Number of units	x	y	
Security guards	1	2	18
Cost	$5000	$7500	$75,000
People processed	300	500	
Minimum required	0	4	

Since the airline wants to maximize the number of people processed, the objective function is $P = 300x + 500y$, with constraints:

$\begin{cases} x + 2y \le 18 & \text{\textit{Number of security guards}} \\ 5000x + 7500y \le 75,000 & \text{\textit{Cost}} \\ y \ge 4 & \text{\textit{Minimum number of B units}} \\ x \ge 0 \end{cases}$

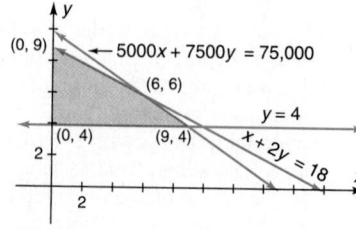

Determine the feasible region and find the coordinates of the vertices. Substitute each vertex in the objective function to determine the maximum value.

(0, 4)	$P = 300(0) + 500(4) = 2000$	
(9, 4)	$P = 300(9) + 500(4) = 4700$	
(6, 6)	$P = 300(6) + 500(6) = 4800$	*Maximum*
(0, 9)	$P = 300(0) + 500(9) = 4500$	

To maximize the number of people processed through security each hour, the airline should purchase six A units and six B units.

Linear programming is very useful in business for identifying ways to maximize profit and minimize cost.

Example 2 *Nutrition* A nutritionist is requested to devise a formula for a base for an instant breakfast meal. The breakfast must contain at least 12 g protein and 8 g carbohydrates. A tablespoon of protein powder made from soybeans has 5 g protein and 2 g carbohydrates. A tablespoon of protein powder made from milk solids has 2 g protein and 4 g carbohydrates. Soybean protein powder costs $0.70 per tablespoon, whereas milk protein powder costs $0.30 per tablespoon. Determine the number of tablespoons of each type of protein powder that should be used as the base for this breakfast to meet the given requirements and minimize the cost.

Let x represent the number of tablespoons of soybean protein powder, and let y represent the number of tablespoons of milk protein powder. Make a table to organize the given information.

	Soybean	Milk	Requirements
Number of tablespoons	x	y	
Protein	5 g	2 g	12 g
Carbohydrates	2 g	4 g	8 g
Cost	$0.70	$0.30	

Since cost is to be minimized, the objective function is
$C = 0.70x + 0.30y$, with constraints:

$$\begin{cases} 5x + 2y \geq 12 & Protein \\ 2x + 4y \geq 8 & Carbohydrates \\ x \geq 0, y \geq 0 \end{cases}$$

Determine the feasible region and find the coordinates of the vertices. Notice that the feasible region is unbounded.

Test each vertex in the objective function to determine the minimum value.

(0, 6)	$C = 0.70(0) + 0.30(6) = 1.80$	
(2, 1)	$C = 0.70(2) + 0.30(1) = 1.70$	*Minimum*
(4, 0)	$C = 0.70(4) + 0.30(0) = 2.80$	

Therefore, the nutritionist should make a base consisting of 2 tablespoons of soybean protein powder and 1 tablespoon of milk protein powder.

Class Exercises

For each exercise set up a table to organize the given formation. Write the objective function and the constraints. Do not solve.

1. *Manufacturing*   A manufacturer of hand-finished decorator waste baskets makes two different types of waste baskets. The first type is teak and requires 2 oz stain and 1 oz high-gloss finish. The second type is mahogany and requires 1 oz stain and 2 oz high-gloss finish. The manufacturer makes a profit of $5 on each basket. On a given shift the manufacturer has available 6 oz stain and 6 oz high-gloss finish. With these resources determine how many of each type of basket she should produce to maximize profit.

2. *Purchasing*   A supermarket wants to purchase automatic hand-held price labelers. The first type can label 7 items per minute and costs $5. The second type can label 10 items per minute and costs $6. The manufacturer can supply at most 60 of type A and 45 of type B of these labelers. The supermarket wants to limit its costs to $420. Determine how many of each type of labeler that should be purchased to maximize the number of items that can be processed.

3. *Business*   A nut company produces two types of mixtures, regular and deluxe. The company is donating bags of the two types of mixtures to be used for a school picnic. A bag of the regular mix has 4 oz of peanuts, 1 oz of cashews, and 5 oz of almonds. A bag of the deluxe mix has 3 oz of peanuts, 1 oz of cashews, and 5 oz of almonds. Overall, the company promised to supply at least 27 oz of peanuts, 8 oz of cashews, and 30 oz of almonds. The regular mix costs the company $2 a bag, whereas the deluxe mix costs them $7 a bag. Determine the number of bags of each type of mix the company should donate to minimize the cost.

8.7 Applications of Linear Programming   **427**

For Example 2
A company makes two types of cat food. The first cost $0.35 per can, provides 15 units of vitamin A, and contains 80 calories. The second type costs $0.28 per can, provides 30 units of vitamin A, and contains 60 calories. The veterinarian recommends that Hallie get at least 900 units of vitamin A per month and at least 2400 calories. Determine how many cans of each type of cat food should be purchased to minimize the cost if Hallie's owner can store no more than 50 cans of food.

Constraints: $\begin{cases} x + y \leq 50 \\ 15x + 30y \geq 900 \\ 80x + 60y \geq 2400 \\ x \geq 0 \\ y \geq 0 \end{cases}$

$C = 0.35x + 0.28y$

12 cans @ $0.35 per can;
24 cans @ $0.28 per can

CLOSURE
Group students in pairs and have them summarize the lesson to each other.

INDEPENDENT PRACTICE
Assignment Guide
Basic: 1–15, 17, 19–20
Average: 7–9, 11, 13–26
Enriched: 8, 13–18, 20–34

Teacher's Resource Book
   Practice, page 57

LESSON FOLLOW-UP

Test Yourself

Teacher's Resource Book
  Tests—Quiz, form A, page 30
  Tests—Quiz, form B, page 30

Additional Answers
8. Answers may vary.
9.

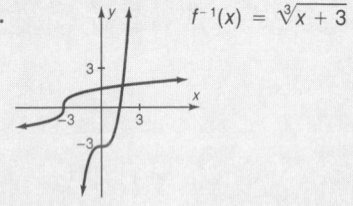

$f^{-1}(x) = \sqrt[3]{x + 3}$

---

4. *Nutrition*   A company makes two types of salad dressing, regular and light. The regular has 6 mg fat and 2 mg sodium per serving, whereas the light has 2 mg fat and 6 mg sodium per serving. The regular dressing costs 3¢ per serving to make and the light costs 2¢ per serving. A diet research facility wants to run tests on the effect of fat and sodium on the amount of weight their patients lose. They request that the company send them individual one-serving packets of dressing so that the total fat content is at least 26 mg and the total sodium content is at least 14 mg. Determine the number of packets of each type of dressing the company should send to meet these requirements and minimize the cost.

Practice Exercises   Use appropriate technology.

Solve each linear program in the Class Exercises.

A **1.** Exercise 1
      2 of each
2. Exercise 2
      30 type A; 45 type B
3. Exercise 3
      10 regular,
      0 deluxe
4. Exercise 4
      4 regular,
      1 light

5. *Delivery*   A delivery service has a fleet of trucks. Each truck can accommodate a maximum weight of 3500 lb and 400 ft³ of merchandise. A small refrigerator weighs 35 lb and occupies 3 ft³ of space. A 21-in. television set weighs 25 lb and occupies 5 ft³ of space. The service gets a fee of $10 for each refrigerator it delivers and $8 for each television set. Determine how many of each item that should be loaded into each truck to maximize the revenue for the truck.   75 televisions; 35 refrigerators

6. *Manufacturing*   A model maker agrees to produce at least five prototypes of a new puzzle. The puzzle can be produced in plastic or metal. It takes 2 h to produce the plastic model and 3 h to produce the metal model. The model maker has at most 18 h to devote to this project. The plastic model costs $7 to produce, and the metal model costs $5 to produce. Find how many of each prototype he should make to minimize his cost.   0 plastic, 5 metal

® **7.** Find any maximum or minimum values of $f(x) = 3x^2 - 6x + 4$.   maximum at (1, 1)

8. Thinking Critically   A manufacturer makes two products. Each product requires time on an assembly line and time to be hand packed. The manufacturer's goal is to maximize revenue. After setting up and solving a linear program, he determines he should make zero units of the second product. Describe a set of conditions that would lead to such a solution.

® **9.** Determine the inverse function for $f(x) = x^3 - 3$. Graph both functions on the same set of axes.

10. *Manufacturing*   A manufacturer makes two types of picnic tables, deluxe and standard. The deluxe table takes 6 h to build and 1 h to finish. The standard table takes 4 h to build and 2 h to finish. The manufacturer can devote at most 120 h per week to building and 40 h per week to finishing. The profit on each deluxe table is $30, and on each standard table $36. Find how many of each type of table that should be produced to maximize the profit.   10 deluxe; 15 standard

® 11. Solve the triangle: $\angle A = 28°$, $a = 35$, $b = 49$

12. *Gardening*   A garden nursery has 70 acres of planting fields. The nursery wants to grow marigolds and impatiens. It costs the nursery $60 per acre to grow the marigolds and $30 per acre to grow the impatiens. The budget for planting is $1800. It takes 3 days to plant an acre of marigolds and 4 days to plant an acre of impatiens. The nursery has a maximum of 120 days to plant the flowers. The marigolds will bring a profit of $180 per acre, and the impatiens will bring a profit of $100 per acre. Find how many acres of field that should be devoted to each type of flower to maximize the profit.
24 acres of marigolds; 12 acres of impatiens

13. **Writing in Mathematics**   Suppose a linear programming problem yields more than one maximum for the objective function. What factors would you consider when interpreting the results?

14. **Thinking Critically**   Suppose a linear programming problem has the objective function $F = 5x + 2y$ with constraints at the right. Explain which constraints have an effect on the feasible region.
$$\begin{cases} 4x + 3y \le 15 \\ x - y \ge -6 \\ x \ge 0, y \ge 0 \end{cases}$$

® 15. A circular gear with a 10-in. radius is turning at a rate of 6 revolutions per second. Determine the linear velocity, in inches per second, of a point on the circumference of the gear. 377 in./s

B 16. *Pet Care*   A dog food manufacturer uses a beef mixture and a liver mixture. One ounce of the beef mixture provides 12 units of vitamin A, 8 units of vitamin B_1, and 10 units of vitamin C. This mixture costs 20¢ per ounce to make. One ounce of the liver mixture provides 8 units of vitamin A, 12 units of vitamin B_1, and 10 units of vitamin C. This mixture costs 22¢ per ounce to make. The final mixture must contain at least 110 units of vitamin A and 120 units each of vitamins B_1 and C. Find how many ounces of each mixture the manufacturer should use to minimize his cost.
6 oz beef; 6 oz liver

® 17. Graph $y = 2 \cos 4x$ from $-\pi$ to π.

18. *Finance*   An investor has $48,000 to invest. Her financial adviser suggests she invest in Tax-Free Bonds and Treasury Bills. In particular, she is advised to invest at least three times as much in Tax-Free Bonds as in Treasury Bills. On a given day the Tax-Free Bonds are yielding 6% and the Treasury Bills are yielding 10%. Determine how much she should invest in each security to maximize her return. $36,000 Bonds; $12,000 Treasury Bills

® 19. Given $f(x) = x^2 - 2$ and $g(x) = 3x + 4$, evaluate $(g \circ f)(-2)$. 10

20. **Thinking Critically**   Given a linear program with three constraints, construct the graph of a feasible region in which one of the constraints is not included in the region. Interpret the meaning of the excluded constraint in relation to the other constraints.

21. *Gardening*   A gardener can purchase two types of fertilizer. A 50-lb bag of Growsome fertilizer has 5 units of nitrogen, 15 units of phosphorus, and 5 units of potash and costs $12. A 50-lb bag of Growalot has 10 units of nitrogen, 10 units of phosphorus, and 30 units of potash and costs $16. For a given crop the farmer must make sure that it does not receive more than 100 units of nitrogen and does receive less than 120 units each of phosphorus and potash. Determine how many bags of each type of fertilizer the gardener should purchase to minimize his costs.

8.7 Applications of Linear Programming   **429**

Writing in Mathematics
13. Students should consider factors that have not been included in the original design of the problem.

Lesson Quiz

A company makes two types of calculators, scientific and graphing. The scientific requires 20 min on the assembly line and 20 min to test. The graphing calculator requires 30 min on the assembly line and 10 min to test. The profit on each calculator is $12. If the assembly line can operate at most 12 h per day and the testing machine can operate at most 8 h per day, determine how many of each type of calculator the company should manufacture to maximize its profit.

1. Set up a table to organize the information.

	Scientific	Graphing	Limits
Number	x	y	
Assembly	20	30	720 min
Testing	20	10	480 min
Profit	12	12	

2. Write the objective function and the constraints for Problem 1.

$$\text{Constraints:} \begin{cases} 20x + 30y \le 720 \\ 20x + 10y \le 480 \\ x \ge 0 \\ y \ge 0 \end{cases}$$

$P = 12x + 12y$

3. Graph the constraints and determine the vertices of the feasible region.

4. Determine the number of each type of calculator the company should produce to maximize its profit. State the maximum profit. scientific: 18; graphing: 12; maximum profit: $360

Use the graph at the right to answer Exercises 22 to 24.

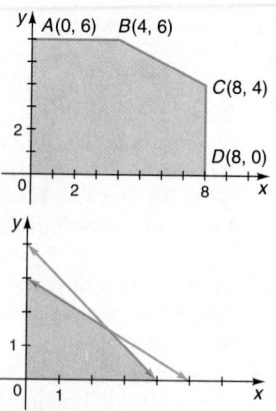

22. Determine the constraints that will give the feasible region shown. $0 \le y \le 6; 0 \le x \le 8; x + 2y \le 16$

23. Determine an objective function that will give a maximum at point B. $C = ax + by$ where $0 < a < \dfrac{b}{2}$

24. Determine an objective function that will give a maximum at points B and C. $C = ax + by$ where $a = \dfrac{b}{2}; b > 0$

25. Writing in Mathematics Write a problem to fit a linear program with the feasible region shown at the right with optimal point $(0, 3)$.

Ⓡ **26.** Simplify: $-x^3y^{-2}z^3 + x^{-2}z^2$ if $x = -2, y = 2,$ and $z = 3$ $\dfrac{225}{4}$

Ⓒ **27.** *Manufacturing* A design company makes two types of fabric. Each fabric must go through three processes to be completed. Fabric A requires 0.1 min in process I, 0.1 min in process II, and 0.1 min in process III. Fabric B requires 0.1 min in process I, 0.4 min in process II, and 0.5 min in process III. The profit on a yard of fabric A is $20, and the profit on a yard of fabric B is $24. The manufacturer's schedule allows for 240 min per day on process I, 720 min per day on process II, and 160 min per day on process III. Determine the number of yards of each type of fabric to be made in order to maximize profit. 1600 yd of A; 0 yd of B

28. *Manufacturing* PartiesPlus makes centerpieces for parties. During a given week it limits its production to three products: a wedding scene, a bridal shower display, and a golden anniversary memento. Lauren designs and cuts out the patterns, Jacques assembles them, and Paul finishes them. Lauren and Paul can each work 40 h per week. Jacques can work 44 h per week. The wedding scene requires 2 h to design and cut, 1 h to assemble, and 2 h to finish. The profit on this centerpiece is $20. The bridal shower display requires 1 h to design and cut, 2 h to assemble, and 2 h to finish. The profit on this item is $20. The anniversary memento requires 3 h to design and cut, 4 h to assemble, and 2 h to finish. The company only makes the golden anniversary memento by special order. If there are exactly six requests for the golden anniversary memento, determine how many of each type of the other centerpieces the company should make to maximize its profit. 8 wedding; 6 bridal shower

29. *Manufacturing* A company is experimenting with a new dry cement mix. In order for the cement to set properly, the company has determined that the mix must contain at least 90 oz sand, 60 oz dirt, 100 oz filler, and 50 oz dry antifreeze per bag. The company has available two products which they want to mix together to make the new product. Product I has 25 oz sand, 10 oz dirt, 35 oz filler, and 5 oz dry antifreeze and costs $1.20 per oz. Product II has 10 oz sand, 10 oz dirt, 20 oz filler, and 25 oz dry antifreeze and costs $1.60 per oz. Determine how many ounces of each product the company should use to keep the cost of the new cement to a minimum. 5 oz product I; 1 oz product II

430 Chapter 8 Inequalities and Linear Programming

Writing in Mathematics

25. The problem should involve finding a maximum, since in this feasible region (0, 0) will always be the minimum. Have students write the constraints first and then try to make up a problem using the constraints.

30. *Agriculture*   For crop rotation, a farmer determines that at least one-sixth of the fields must lie fallow for one planting season. It costs the farmer $20 per acre to till the fallow fields and $80 per acre to till and plant crops in the rest of the fields. If the cash reserve for planting for the year is $1600, determine the maximum number of acres that can be farmed without borrowing money.   19

31. **Thinking Critically**   Suppose after seeing the results of the linear program in Exercise 27 an executive is unsatisfied with the profit earned by the company. How could the constraints be modified to increase the profit?

32. *Delivery*   WeDeliver accepts three types of packages; letters, jiffy mailers, and boxes under 3 ft³. The company makes a profit of $8, $3, and $1, respectively, on these deliveries. There are 118 h per week available for deliveries uptown and 120 h per week available for deliveries downtown. It takes 7 h to deliver letters uptown and 10 h to deliver letters downtown. It takes 6 h to deliver jiffy mailers uptown and 5 h to deliver jiffy mailers downtown. This week one box was delivered uptown, which took 4 h. Determine the number of letters and jiffy mailers the company should deliver to maximize its profit for this week.   12 letters; 0 jiffy mailers

33. *Entertainment*   A multiplex movie theater is being built with a new concept in ticket sales. They intend to have reserved and open seating in each theater. From the market survey it has been determined that there must be at least 8 and at most 16 reserved seats in each theater and at least 80 but not more than 120 open seats with the ratio of reserved to open seating not to exceed one-twelfth. If a ticket for a reserved seat costs more than a ticket for an open seat, determine how many reserved and open seats the theater should contain to maximize revenue.   10 reserved; 120 open

34. **Thinking Critically**   A watch company finds that to minimize costs it should produce 20 wrist watches and 27 pocket watches per week. However, it also finds that to maximize revenue it should produce 32 wrist watches and 28 pocket watches per week. How can the company go about determining the best weekly production quota for each type of watch?

Test Yourself

1. Solve the system of inequalities: $\begin{cases} y - 7 \le -2(x - 5)^2 \\ |x - 4.5| < y \\ 8 > x + y \end{cases}$ 8.5

2. Maximize the function $P = 5x + 4y$, with constraints at the right: $\begin{cases} x + y \le 5 \quad (3, 2) \\ 2x + y \le 8 \\ 2x + 3y \le 12 \\ x \ge 0, y \ge 0 \end{cases}$ 8.6   8.7

3. *Gardening*   Mr. McGregor grows peppers and onions. It takes 1 m² of land to grow 1 bushel of peppers and costs $1.00. It takes 6 m² of land to grow a bushel of onions and costs $3.00. His profit on a bushel of peppers is $2.00, and his profit on a bushel of onions is $5.00. If he has 24 m² of land available and $15.00 to spend, how many bushels of each vegetable should he grow in order to maximize his profit?   15 bushels of peppers; 0 bushels of onions

8.7 Applications of Linear Programming   **431**

5. $\left(\frac{4}{3}, 2\right]$

6. $\left(\frac{5}{3}, \frac{13}{3}\right)$

7.

8.

9. $\left(-\frac{7}{2}, 1\right)$

10. $(-0.79, 2.12)$

11. $x > 1$ or $x < -\frac{2}{3}$

12. $\left(1, \frac{5}{2}\right)$

13.

14.

Chapter 8   Summary and Review

Vocabulary

boundary of a half-plane (396)
closed half-plane (396)
conjunction (394)
consistent system (386)
constraint (418)
dependent system (386)
disjunction (394)
feasible region (418)
half-plane (396)
inconsistent system (386)
independent system (386)

linear program (418)
linear system of equations (386)
objective function (418)
open half-plane (396)
optimization problem (420)
quadratic inequality
  in two variables (403)
solution of a system (386)
unbounded (413)
vertex of a region (418)

Systems of Equations   To solve a system by substitution, solve one of the equations for one variable in terms of the other. Substitute for that variable in the other equation and solve. To solve a system graphically, graph both equations on the same set of axes and determine the point or points of intersection.

8.1

Solve each system of equations.

1. $\begin{cases} 5 - 3y = 2x \\ 5y = 21 + 3x \end{cases}$ $(-2, 3)$

2. $\begin{cases} -2x + 5y = -6 \\ y = 4 + x - x^2 \end{cases}$ $\begin{matrix}(-2, -2); \\ (2.6, -0.16)\end{matrix}$

3. $\begin{cases} 3x - 7y = 1 \\ 2x = 3y - 1 \end{cases}$ $(-2, -1)$

4. $\begin{cases} y = x^2 \\ 2x = y - 3 \end{cases}$ $(3, 9); (-1, 1)$

Linear Inequalities   Linear inequalities in one varible can be solved algebraically by using the rules for working with inequalities to isolate the variable. The graph of a linear inequality in two variables can be an open or closed half-plane.

8.2

Solve each inequality and graph the solution on a number line.

5. $-2 < 3x - 6 \le 0$

6. $|3x - 9| < 4$

Graph each inequality.

7. $6y - 10x \ge -5$

8. $|5x - 1| < y + 19$

Quadratic Inequalities   Quadratic inequalities in one variable can be solved algebraically or graphically. The solution to a quadratic inequality may be either a conjunction or a disjunction.

8.3

Solve each inequality and graph the solution on a number line.

9. $7 > 5x + 2x^2$

10. $3x^2 - 4x - 5 \le 0$

11. $3x^2 - x - 2 > 0$

12. $2x^2 + 5 < 7x$

Graph each inequality in the coordinate plane.

13. $5x + y \le 6 - 4x^2$

14. $y > -3x + 2x^2 - 2$

432   Chapter 8 Inequalities and Linear Programming

Polynomial and Rational Inequalities A polynomial inequality of degree n in one variable is an inequality of the form $a_n x^n + a_{n-1} x^{n-1} + \cdots + a_1 x + a_0 < 0$, $a_n \neq 0$, where $a_n, a_{n-1}, \ldots, a_1, a_0$ are real numbers. Polynomial and rational inequalities in one variable can be solved algebraically or with the aid of a graph. To solve a polynomial inequality, find the zeros of the polynomial. Then test points from each of the intervals determined by the zeros. To solve a polynomial inequality in two variables, graph the corresponding equation and test a point in one of the regions.

8.4

Solve each inequality.

15. $3 > 5x^2 + 2x^3$ $(-\infty, -2.2) \cup (-1, 0.7)$

16. $0.2x^4 - 2x^2 + 1 < \sqrt[5]{x^4 + 5}$ $(-3.3, 3.3)$

17. $\dfrac{9x + 3}{x^3 - 8x^2} \leq 0$ $\left[-\dfrac{1}{3}, 0\right) \cup (0, 8)$

18. $\dfrac{4x - 2}{x^2 - 3x} > 0$ $\left(0, \dfrac{1}{2}\right) \cup (3, \infty)$

Graph each inequality in the coordinate plane.

19. $y > x^4 - x^3 + x^2 - 3x - 6$

20. $y \leq 2x^5 + x^3 - 8x - 4$

Systems of Inequalities To solve systems of inequalities, graph them on the same set of axes and determine the intersection of the graphs.

8.5

Solve each system.

21. $\begin{cases} -3y - 4 < -5x \\ -7x + 12y \geq 10 \end{cases}$

22. $\begin{cases} 4x + y > 25 \\ x^2 + y \leq 36 \end{cases}$

23. $\begin{cases} 2x + y < 1 \\ 3x < y + 1 \end{cases}$

24. $\begin{cases} y > x - 5 \\ y < x^2 - 1 \end{cases}$

25. *Hardware* A pound of common nails costs \$3.50 and a pound of finishing nails costs \$4.50. Determine a set of values for the number of pounds of each you can buy if you have \$24.00 to spend.

Linear Programming To solve a linear program, first graph all the constraints on the same set of axes. The intersections of the constraints determine the feasible region. Evaluate the objective function for each vertex of the feasible region to find the maximum or minimum.

8.6

26. If the cost of producing a certain commodity is represented by the function $C = 4x + 3y$, find the minimum cost with the constraints at the right.

$\begin{cases} 2x + y \geq 4 \quad 10 \\ 3x + 3y \geq 9 \\ x \geq 0, y \geq 0 \end{cases}$

Applications of Linear Programming Linear programming is used for solving optimization problems in business and industry. It is important to analyze the results in a linear program for infeasibility or alternate optimal solutions.

8.7

27. *Craftsmanship* Poppa Gippetto makes marionette puppets. Each human figure requires 2 ft² of plywood, 3 oz of paint, and takes 3 h to make. Each equine figure requires 5 ft² of plywood, 2 oz of paint, and takes 4 h to make. Gippetto has 100 oz of paint and 122 ft² of plywood. He and his apprentice can devote 120 h a week to the work. If each equine figure sells for \$5.00 and each human figure sells for \$1.00, how many of each type of figure should he make in a week to maximize revenue? 24 equine figures; 0 human figures

Summary and Review **433**

19.

20.

21.

22.

23.

24.

25.

$\begin{cases} 3.5x + 4.5y \leq 24 \\ x \geq 0 \\ y \geq 0 \end{cases}$

Chapter 8 Test

Solve each system of equations.

1. $\begin{cases} 5x - 3y = 1 \\ 2x + 4 = -y \end{cases}$ $(-1, -2)$

2. $\begin{cases} x^2 + 4y = 36 \\ x + 2y = 6 \end{cases}$ $(6, 0); (-4, 5)$

Solve each inequality and graph the solution on a number line.

3. $6 \le 3|2x + 1|$

4. $-10x + 3 < 8x^2$

5. $x^3 - 5x^2 \le -16$

Graph each inequality.

6. $3x - 2y < 1$

7. $y \le 5 - 6x - 3x^2$

8. $y > x^3 + 3.5$

Solve each system of inequalities graphically.

9. $\begin{cases} y > -2x \\ y - 2x < 8 \\ x \le 1 \end{cases}$

10. $\begin{cases} y \ge |3x - 3| \\ y \le -2(x - 1)^2 + 7 \end{cases}$

11. The profit earned by a certain company is determined by the function
$P = x + 2y$. Find the maximum profit with the constraints given below.

$\begin{cases} 2x + 3y \le 15 \quad 8\frac{1}{3} \\ 2x - 3y \ge 5 \\ x \ge 1 \\ y \ge 0 \end{cases}$

12. The cost of manufacturing a certain product is determined by the function
$C = 5x + 2y$. Find the minimum cost with the constraints given below.

$\begin{cases} y \ge 9 - 2x \quad 18 \\ y + x \ge 6 \\ x \ge 0 \\ y \ge 0 \end{cases}$

Challenge

The graph at right shows the feasible region for a linear
programming problem. Find three objective functions such that
each will yield a different maximum.
ex: 1. $P = x + y$; max: 13
    2. $P = x + 4y$; max: 29
    3. $P = -x + y$; max: 2

Cumulative Review

In each item you are to compare a quantity in Column 1 with a quantity in Column 2. Write the letter of the correct answer from these choices:

A. The quantity in Column 1 is greater than the quantity in Column 2.
B. The quantity in Column 2 is greater than the quantity in Column 1.
C. The quantity in Column 1 is equal to the quantity in Column 2.
D. The relationship cannot be determined from the given information.

Notes: Information centered over both columns refers to one or both of the quantities being compared. A symbol that appears in both columns has the same meaning in each column. All variables represent real numbers. Most figures are not drawn to scale.

	Column 1	Column 2	
1.	$\cos 30°$	$\cos 330°$	3.2
C			

The value of the slope

	Column 1	Column 2	
2.	$-2x + y = 4$	$y = -2x + 5$	2.3
A			

Triangle ABC—number of solutions

3.	$a = b \sin A$	$b \sin A < a < b$	5.3
B			

$\sin \theta$

4.	$P(-3, 4)$	$P(5, -2)$	3.4
A			
5.	$\sin (-x)$	$-\sin x$	4.1
C			

$x^2 - 3x > 18$ and $x > 0$

6.	x	4	8.3
A			

$$3x - 2y = -9$$
$$2x + y = 1$$

7.	x	y	8.1
B			

$$f(x) = x^2$$
$$g(x) = 2x + 1$$

8.	$(f \circ g)(x)$	$(g \circ f)(x)$	1.5
D			

$$x^3 + x^2 - 4x - 4 = 0$$

9.	x	$-1, \pm 2$	2.6
C			

$$f(x) = x^4 - 2x^3 + 5x - 6$$

10.	$f(-1)$	-14	7.1
A			

$$f(x) = 5x^4 + 4x^3 - x + 2$$

11.	Sum of the zeros	Product of the zeros	7.5
B			

12.	$\text{Cos}^{-1} \frac{1}{2}$	$\frac{\pi}{6}$	4.5
A			

$$f(x) = 5x - 3$$

13.	$f^{-1}(-8)$	-1	1.6
C			

$$2x^2 + 5x = 12$$

14.	discriminant	110	2.4
A			

Period

15.	$F(x) = \sin 3x$	$G(x) = \cos \frac{1}{3}x$	4.2
B			

$$f(x) = [x]$$

16.	$f(3.8)$	3	1.7
C			

distance from $P(2, 3)$ to the line $y = 2x + 1$

17.	0.76	0.89	2.8
B			
18.	$\sin (-1080°)$	$\cos (-900°)$	3.6
A			

Cumulative Review   **435**

19. Evaluate $f(x) = 2x^5 - 7x^3 + 5x^2$ for $x = -1$ using synthetic substitution. 10   7.1

20. Since $\tan(-x) = -\tan x$, is the tangent function an odd function, an even function, or neither? odd   4.3

21. Solve the linear system: $\begin{cases} 3x = 6y \\ 2x - 4y = 5 \end{cases}$ no solution, inconsistent   8.1

22. Use the horizontal line test to determine if $h^{-1}(x)$ is a function when $h(x) = x^2 + 5$. not a function   1.6

23. Solve the linear system of inequalities graphically: $\begin{cases} 3x - 4y \le 12 \\ 6x - 2y > -8 \\ y \le 2 \end{cases}$ 8.5

24. Express $x^3 - 5x^2 - 8x + 48$ as a product of linear factors. $P(x) = (x + 3)(x - 4)^2$ 7.4

25. Determine the reference angle for $-210°$. 30°   3.4

26. In triangle ABC, if $a = 12$, $c = 20$, and $\angle B = 60°$, find b to the nearest hundredth. 17.44   5.4

27. Solve the inequality $-4 \le 3x + 2 \le 11$. Express the solution in interval notation and draw its graph on a number line. $[-2, 3]$ 8.2

28. Determine the integral zeros of $f(x) = x^3 - 3x^2 - 6x + 8$. $-2, 4, 1$ 7.3

29. Determine the value of x and y that will maximize the objective function $C = 2x + 8y$ under the constraints: $\begin{cases} 20x + 40y \le 80 \\ 100x + 50y \le 200 \\ x \ge 0, \ y \ge 0 \end{cases}$ (0, 2)   8.6

30. Determine if the lines are parallel, perpendicular, or neither: $4x + 5y = 20$; $-5x + 4y = 10$ perpendicular   2.3

31. Solve $x^2 - 2x - 8 \le 0$. State the solution in interval notation and graph it on a number line. $[-2, 4]$ 8.3

32. Find the amplitude and period of $F(x) = 2\cos\frac{3}{4}x$. $2; \frac{8\pi}{3}$ 4.2

33. Determine the sum and product of the zeros of $f(x) = x^4 - 2x^3 - 13x^2 - 26x + 24$. $2; 24$ 7.5

34. Solve $6\cos^2\theta + 5\cos\theta - 4 = 0$, where $0° \le \theta \le 360°$. 60°; 300°   6.6

35. Find the area of triangle PQR if $\angle P = 54.6°$, $\angle Q = 38.2°$, and $p = 165.2$ cm. Express your answer to the nearest square centimeter. $10{,}340 \text{ cm}^2$ 5.5

36. Express $62°20'40''$ in decimal degrees. 62.34°   3.1

37. Find the exact value of $\cos\frac{5\pi}{6}$. $-\frac{\sqrt{3}}{2}$ 6.1

38. Solve: $8x^3 - 2x^2 < 3x$ $(-\infty, -0.5) \cup (0, 0.75)$ 8.4

39. Simplify: $\sin^2\theta \cot\theta \tan\theta$ $\sin^2\theta$ 3.9

40. An angle whose terminal side lies on the x- or y-axis is called a $\underline{\ ?\ }$. quadrantal angle   3.6

41. Find a quadratic equation in standard form with real coefficients that has the solutions $-2 + 5i$ and $-2 - 5i$. $x^2 + 4x + 29 = 0$ 2.4

42. Determine the value of $\sec\theta$ if $\cos\theta = \frac{1}{3}$. 3   3.5

43. Simplify: $(\sec x - 1)(\sec x + 1)$ $\tan^2 x$ 3.9

44. In right triangle ABC, $b = 12.2$, $\angle A = 32°$, and $\angle C = 90°$. Determine a to the nearest tenth. 7.6   5.1

45. Navigators often use the term *heading*. The heading is the angle made in the clockwise direction from the $\underline{\ ?\ }$. north   5.4

46. Determine the inverse function of $y = \frac{3}{4}x$. $y = \frac{4}{3}x$ 1.6

47. Determine the asymptotes of the function $f(x) = \dfrac{3x^2 - 4x}{x + 1}$. $x = -1$; slant asymptote: $y = 3x - 7$ 7.6

48. If $0 \le \theta < 2\pi$, determine the values of θ for which $\sin \theta = -\frac{3}{4}$. Round answers to four decimal places. 3.9897; 5.4351   3.7

49. Express $\cos 20° + \cos 4°$ as a product. $2 \cos 12° \cos 8°$ 6.4

50. In triangle ABC, if $\angle A = 38°$, $\angle C = 16°$, and $c = 18$, find a to the nearest hundredth. 40.21   5.2

51. Solve and check the equation $\sqrt{2x - 3} + 5 = 4$. no solution   7.7

52. Express $\cos^4 x - \sin^4 x$ as a single function. $\cos 2x$ 6.3

53. Express $330°$ in radians. Give answer in terms of π. $\frac{11\pi}{6}$ 3.2

54. Solve: $x^2 - 6x - 7 \le 0$. $-1 \le x \le 7$ 8.3

55. Solve triangle DEF for d if $\angle D = 58°$, $\angle E = 80°$, and $e = 42$. Express your answer to the nearest unit. 36   5.2

56. Simplify: $\dfrac{2 \tan 40°}{1 - \tan^2 40°}$. $\tan 80°$ 6.3

57. A civil engineer designing a stretch of a highway using the coordinate plane, marks off the points $P(2, 1)$, $Q(-3, 2)$, and $R(-8, 3)$. Determine if the points are collinear. yes   2.7

58. Given $f(x) = \dfrac{1}{x - 2}$ and $g(x) = 3x$, find $(f + g)(3)$. 10   1.5

59. Determine the angular velocity in radians per second of a wheel turning at 160 rpm. 16.8 rad/s   3.3

60. Determine the zeros of $p(x) = x^3 - 7x + 6$. $-3, 2, 1$ 7.3

61. Determine the exact value of $\text{Tan}^{-1}\sqrt{3}$. $\frac{\sqrt{\pi}}{3}$ 60°   4.6

62. Solve $8 \cos \theta + 5 = 2 \cos \theta - 3$, where $0 \le \theta < 2\pi$, to the nearest hundredth of a radian. no solution   6.5

Determine if each statement is always true, sometimes true, or never true.

63. The zeros of a function f are the values of x for which $f(x) = 0$. always   7.1

64. $\sin 90° = \sin 30° + \sin 60°$ never   6.1

65. A linear equation is an equation in which the variables appear only in the second degree. never   8.1

66. The sum of the measures of the angles in a triangle is $180°$. always   5.1

CHAPTER OVERVIEW

Summary

The first lesson involves simplifying and evaluating expressions with rational exponents. Problems with entering rational exponents on a calculator or computer are examined. Exponential equations are graphed using transformations and also using graphing utilities. Logarithmic functions are defined, analyzed, and graphed. Properties of logarithms are presented and methods of solving logarithmic and exponential equations are explored. Applications are stressed throughout each lesson, and the final lesson is devoted to a variety of specific applications of exponential growth and decay models.

Chapter Objectives

- To simplify and evaluate expressions with rational exponents
- To graph exponential functions
- To solve simple exponential equations
- To graph logarithmic functions
- To evaluate logarithms
- To express logarithms in expanded form and in condensed form
- To solve equations involving logarithms
- To use logarithms to solve exponential equations
- To use a graphing utility to solve exponential and logarithmic equations and inequalities
- To solve real world problems using exponential and logarithmic equations

Mathematical Power

Modeling   Did you ever wonder how you might look 20 or even 50 years from now? Mathematicians and biologists have been working together to create models of the changes in people's physical characteristics over time. These models give rise to some important questions. How do growth rates of different parts of the body compare? Do these growth rates vary at different stages of life? If the growth rates were constant, this would imply that an adult is an enlarged, but proportional or similar, version of a baby. Of course, simple observation reveals that this is *not* the case.

For example, data collected on the relationship of arm length compared with total body height shows that at birth the arm is about one-third as long as the body. As individuals reach adulthood, the arm length is then about two-fifths body height. Obviously, these findings do not support a theory of consistent proportional growth. However, scientists still believe some orderly law must govern the relationship of arm length to height.

To gain further insight into the growth process, a team of researchers made various graphical models. First, they plotted their information using a standard scale. Since they knew that the growth they were studying was not proportional, they were not surprised to find that their graph was a curve rather than a straight line. Still, the actual relationship was not clear.

As you will learn in this chapter, *logarithmic* and *exponential functions* are used extensively in models of growth. The researchers therefore decided to try displaying the same data on a *log-log* scale, that is, a scale in which each axis is marked off evenly in orders of magnitude: 1, 10, 100, 1000, and so on. When the data is plotted on a log-log scale, it seems to give rise to two distinct straight lines.

438

Features

Modeling

One line fits early development, that is, development before 9 months of age, and has a slope of 1.2. The other line fits later development and has a slope of 1.0. The growth before 9 months is known as *allometric growth*: arm length increases relatively faster than height.

Using properties of logarithms that you will learn in this chapter, it can be shown that the relationship of arm length a and height h is given by the equation

$$a = bh^s$$

This equation or model is called a *power curve*. As with linear models, the values of s and b can be found with techniques of curve fitting.

Thinking Critically   How might law enforcement authorities or archaeologists use models of human growth and change in their work? Can you think of other professions where the models could be applied? What other factors could be used with the model to make more accurate predictions?

Project   Investigate other growth relationships such as head size in relation to body height, or brain and heart weights in relation to age in years. Use graphs to help you display and analyze your findings. Identify any allometric and isometric relationships you find.

439

Mathematical Power

Logarithms were once regarded as an aid for computation. However, since scientific calculators are now readily available, the most important modern usage of logarithms is in equations that model real world phenomena.

Human growth is a very complex process. The series of photographs on these pages are all of the same woman, at different ages in her life. The final photo is actually a computer-generated representation that has been artificially "aged." Old photos and background information were used to make the changes in the computer image. This technique is used to help locate missing persons. It is also used in archaeology to reconstruct original features from skeletons found in excavations.

After introducing logarithms, have students examine log-log paper and emphasize the difference between linear and logarithmic scales. Logarithmic scales are often used to model data with a very wide range of values. Students may already be familiar with examples of logarithmic scales such as decibel levels, which measure sound intensity, *pH* factors, which measure acidity, or the Richter scale, which measures earthquake intensity.

Thinking Critically   Answers may vary. Authorities might use such models to get an updated picture of a fugitive or kidnapped person. These models could guide archaeologists with skeletal reconstruction. They might also be useful to plastic surgeons or movie makeup artists. Specific family characteristics might influence predictions.

Review and Assessment

Student Text

Teacher's Resource Book

Ⓜ Materials/Manipulatives
ruler
stopwatch
string
weight

Technology
scientific calculator
symbolic manipulator

FOCUS

Atomic clocks are used to determine Coordinated Universal Time (CUT). These clocks use the natural vibrations of atoms to keep time and are more accurate than pendulum clocks. Even more precise are cesium beam clocks. You may wish to have students research how cesium beam clocks work.

INSTRUCTION

Ⓜ • Have students make a pendulum with the string and weight. Using the stopwatch, have them time the swing for strings of different length. Ask the students to draw a conclusion about how the length of the string affects the period of the pendulum.
• Students should be able to state in their own words each of the properties for integer exponents recalled on page 440.

Alternative Learning Styles
Many students need an overall view of the lesson before approaching specific problems. Discuss the need to simplify expressions and review simplifying expressions with integral exponents.

9.1 Rational Exponents

Objective: To simplify and evaluate expressions with rational exponents

Focus

The pendulum clock was invented in 1656 by Christian Huygens of the Netherlands. Huygens observed that the pendulum is a useful component for a clock since the time it takes a pendulum of a given length to complete each swing is constant. This time interval is called the *period* of the pendulum. A practical advantage is that even as the pendulum slows down, the clock continues to keep very nearly correct time since the period is practically independent of the amplitude of the swings. The *Standard Seconds Pendulum*, which is about 39 in. long, has a period of 2 s.

A pendulum clock can be made to run faster by shortening the pendulum and slower by lengthening it. The formula $T = 2\pi L^{\frac{1}{2}} g^{-\frac{1}{2}}$ has been devised to determine the approximate relationship between the period and the length of a given pendulum. Though the formula is relatively simple, it requires an understanding of rational exponents.

The importance of integer exponents is evident in the study of quadratic and polynomial functions, sequences and series, conic sections, and many other topics in mathematics. However, as the example of Huygens' pendulum clock makes clear, an understanding of noninteger exponents is also important. The availability of such exponents makes it possible to analyze and understand a great many relationships more easily, from such diverse areas as finance, physics, biology, archaeology, and demographics. To define *rational exponent*, it is desirable to review the following properties of integer exponents.

Recall
Properties of Integer Exponents

$$a^m \cdot a^n = a^{m+n} \qquad \left(\frac{a}{b}\right)^n = \frac{a^n}{b^n},\ b \neq 0 \qquad a^0 = 1,\ a \neq 0$$
$$(a^n)^m = a^{nm}$$
$$(ab)^n = a^n b^n \qquad \frac{a^m}{a^n} = a^{m-n},\ a \neq 0 \qquad a^{-n} = \frac{1}{a^n},\ a \neq 0$$

Suppose that the properties of integer exponents hold for rational exponents. Then, if n is a positive integer,

$$\left(a^{\frac{1}{n}}\right)^n = a^{\frac{1}{n} \cdot n} = a^1 = a$$

Thus, if the exponent properties hold for rational exponents, then $a^{\frac{1}{n}}$ is an nth root of a. Recall that the *principal nth root* of a, symbolized $\sqrt[n]{a}$, is defined as follows.

- If n is odd, then $\sqrt[n]{a}$ is the nth root of a. *Example:* $\sqrt[3]{-8} = -2$
- If n is even and $a \geq 0$, then $\sqrt[n]{a}$ is the *nonnegative* nth root of a. *Example:* $\sqrt[4]{81} = 3$
- If n is even and $a < 0$, then $\sqrt[n]{a}$ is not a real number. *Example:* $\sqrt{-9} = 3i$

So, both $a^{\frac{1}{n}}$ and $\sqrt[n]{a}$ may represent the principal root of a, provided rational exponents are defined as follows.

If m is an integer, n is a positive integer, and $\sqrt[n]{a}$ is a real number,

then $\qquad a^{\frac{1}{n}} = \sqrt[n]{a} \qquad$ and $\qquad a^{\frac{m}{n}} = (\sqrt[n]{a})^m$

It can be shown that $(\sqrt[n]{a})^m = \sqrt[n]{a^m}$. You are asked to do so in Exercise 54 at the end of the lesson. Thus, $a^{\frac{m}{n}}$ is equal to both $\sqrt[n]{a^m}$ and $(\sqrt[n]{a})^m$. *Suppose that $\sqrt[n]{a}$ is not a real number. What can you conclude about a and n?*

Example 1 Express each exponential expression in radical form and evaluate.

  a. $144^{\frac{1}{2}}$ **b.** $16^{\frac{3}{4}}$ **c.** $(-125)^{\frac{2}{3}}$ **d.** $100^{-\frac{1}{2}}$

  a. $144^{\frac{1}{2}} = \sqrt{144} = 12$ $\qquad\qquad$ **b.** $16^{\frac{3}{4}} = (\sqrt[4]{16})^3 = 8$

  c. $(-125)^{\frac{2}{3}} = (\sqrt[3]{-125})^2 = 25$ $\qquad$ **d.** $100^{-\frac{1}{2}} = \dfrac{1}{100^{\frac{1}{2}}} = \dfrac{1}{\sqrt{100}} = \dfrac{1}{10}$

To use a calculator or computer to evaluate an exponential expression, use the exponentiation key, which is usually labeled x^y, y^x, or $\char"02C6$. To evaluate an exponential expression such as $16^{\frac{3}{4}}$, you could use an input form such as $16^{\wedge}(3 \div 4)$. However, if this technique is used for an expression with a negative radicand, an error message may result. For example, you may receive such a message if you use the input form $(-125)^{\wedge}(2 \div 3)$ for Example 1c. *Why are parentheses needed for -125?* To avoid this problem, enter the expression in another form such as $(-125)^{\wedge}2^{\wedge}(1 \div 3)$ or $(-125)^{\wedge}(1 \div 3)^{\wedge}2$.

In general, if you are using a calculator to evaluate an expression entered in the form $a^{\wedge}(m \div n)$, an error message may result if $a < 0$ and n is odd, unless $\dfrac{m}{n}$ is an odd integer or the reciprocal of an odd integer. In this case, it is necessary to enter such an expression in another form, perhaps as $a^{\wedge}m^{\wedge}(1 \div n)$ or $a^{\wedge}(1 \div n)^{\wedge}m$. Of course an error message will also be displayed if $a < 0$ and n is even, but in this case the error message is correct. *Why?*

For Example 1

Express each in radical form and evaluate.

1. $(-32)^{\frac{3}{5}}$ $\quad \sqrt[5]{(-32)^3} = -8$

2. $(343)^{-\frac{2}{3}}$ $\quad \dfrac{1}{\sqrt[3]{343^2}} = \dfrac{1}{49}$

Thinking Critically

If $\sqrt[n]{a}$ is not a real number, you can conclude that $a < 0$ and n is even.

Parentheses are needed for -125 to obtain a positive rather than a negative answer.

The ERROR message is correct because the nth root of a negative number is not defined when n is even.

Express each radical in exponential form and evaluate using a calculator. Round approximate answers to the nearest hundredth.

1. $\sqrt[5]{132^7}$ $132^{\frac{7}{5}} = 930.69$

2. $\sqrt{-122^3}$ $(-122)^{\frac{3}{2}}$ not a real number

Common Error Some students may forget to insert parentheses around the -122 when entering the value. Have these students determine if the answer is real or imaginary before inputting the data.

3. $-\dfrac{\sqrt{0.09}}{\sqrt[3]{\pi^2}}$ $\dfrac{(0.09)^{\frac{1}{2}}}{\pi^{\frac{2}{3}}} = 0.14$

For Example 3

Simplify each expression.

1. $(2x^{\frac{3}{4}}y^{-\frac{1}{2}})^8$ $\dfrac{256x^6}{y^4}$

2. $\sqrt[3]{x^2(x^{\frac{1}{2}} - x^{\frac{3}{2}})}$ $(x - x^3)^{\frac{1}{3}}$

Common Error Some students will try to take the cube root of each term. Have these students review the rules for simplifying radicals.

Calculators are useful for finding the decimal approximation of a radical when the radical is irrational. To use a calculator or computer to evaluate a radical, first express it in exponential form.

Example 2 Express each radical in exponential form and evaluate using a calculator. Round approximate answers to the nearest hundredth.

a. $\sqrt[3]{64^2}$ b. $\sqrt[8]{120^6}$ c. $\sqrt[5]{-7}$ d. $\sqrt[3]{(-225)^2}$

a. $\sqrt[3]{64^2} = 64^{\frac{2}{3}} = 16$ b. $\sqrt[8]{120^6} = 120^{\frac{6}{8}} = 120^{\frac{3}{4}} \approx 36.26$

c. $\sqrt[5]{-7} = (-7)^{\frac{1}{5}} \approx -1.48$ d. $\sqrt[3]{(-225)^2} = (-225)^{\frac{2}{3}} = [(-225)^2]^{\frac{1}{3}}$ or

$$\left[(-225)^{\frac{1}{3}}\right]^2 \approx 36.99$$

The properties of exponents extend to rational exponents and can be used to simplify operations on exponential expressions. It is often preferable to use rational exponents instead of radicals. A *simplified* expression will be understood to be one in which no radicals appear and in which all exponents are positive. Assume that all variables represent *positive* real numbers, unless otherwise specified.

Example 3 Simplify each expression.

a. $\left(2x^{\frac{4}{7}}y^{\frac{1}{5}}\right)\left(5x^{\frac{3}{14}}y^{\frac{2}{5}}\right)$ b. $\left(\dfrac{4x^2z^{-4}}{9y^3}\right)^{-\frac{1}{2}}$

c. $\sqrt[3]{\sqrt[4]{x^{36}y^{-5}}}$ d. $\sqrt[3]{64x} + 5\sqrt[3]{8x} - \left(\sqrt[3]{\dfrac{1}{27x}}\right)^{-1}$

a. $\left(2x^{\frac{4}{7}}y^{\frac{1}{5}}\right)\left(5x^{\frac{3}{14}}y^{\frac{2}{5}}\right) = 10x^{\frac{4}{7}+\frac{3}{14}}y^{\frac{1}{5}+\frac{2}{5}} = 10x^{\frac{8}{14}+\frac{3}{14}}y^{\frac{3}{5}} = 10x^{\frac{11}{14}}y^{\frac{3}{5}}$

b. Recall that $\left(\dfrac{a}{b}\right)^{-n} = \left(\dfrac{b}{a}\right)^n$, $a, b \neq 0$.

Therefore, $\left(\dfrac{4x^2z^{-4}}{9y^3}\right)^{-\frac{1}{2}} = \left(\dfrac{9y^3}{4x^2z^{-4}}\right)^{\frac{1}{2}} = \dfrac{9^{\frac{1}{2}}y^{\frac{3}{2}}}{4^{\frac{1}{2}}x^1z^{-2}} = \dfrac{3y^{\frac{3}{2}}}{2xz^{-2}} = \dfrac{3y^{\frac{3}{2}}z^2}{2x}$

c. $\sqrt[3]{\sqrt[4]{x^{36}y^{-5}}} = \left[(x^{36}y^{-5})^{\frac{1}{4}}\right]^{\frac{1}{3}} = (x^{36}y^{-5})^{\frac{1}{12}} = x^3y^{-\frac{5}{12}} = \dfrac{x^3}{y^{\frac{5}{12}}}$

d. $\sqrt[3]{64x} + 5\sqrt[3]{8x} - \left(\sqrt[3]{\dfrac{1}{27x}}\right)^{-1} = (64x)^{\frac{1}{3}} + 5(8x)^{\frac{1}{3}} - \left(\dfrac{1}{27x}\right)^{-\frac{1}{3}} = 64^{\frac{1}{3}}x^{\frac{1}{3}} + 5 \cdot 8^{\frac{1}{3}}x^{\frac{1}{3}} - 27^{\frac{1}{3}}x^{\frac{1}{3}}$

$$= 4x^{\frac{1}{3}} + 5 \cdot 2x^{\frac{1}{3}} - 3x^{\frac{1}{3}} = 4x^{\frac{1}{3}} + 10x^{\frac{1}{3}} - 3x^{\frac{1}{3}} = 11x^{\frac{1}{3}}$$

In the Focus, one application of rational exponents was introduced, the pendulum clock. The time T, in seconds, that it takes a pendulum to make one complete swing is called the period of the pendulum and can be calculated approximately using the formula $T = 2\pi L^{\frac{1}{2}}g^{-\frac{1}{2}}$, where L is the length of the pendulum and g is the acceleration that a falling body undergoes due to gravity. At sea level the value of g is about 9.80 m/s².

442 Chapter 9 Exponential and Logarithmic Functions

Example 4 A clock has a pendulum of length 99.5 cm. Determine the period of the pendulum to the nearest tenth of a second.

99.5 cm = 0.995 m   *Convert to meters.*

$T = 2\pi L^{\frac{1}{2}}g^{-\frac{1}{2}} = 2\pi(0.995)^{\frac{1}{2}}(9.80)^{-\frac{1}{2}} = 2.00206591 \approx 2.0$ s

Class Exercises

Evaluate each expression. If necessary, use a calculator to round your answer to the nearest hundredth.

1. $\sqrt[3]{27^4}$ 81
2. $\sqrt[5]{-32^2}$ -4
3. $\dfrac{1}{\sqrt[3]{343^2}}$ 0.02
4. $\dfrac{1}{\sqrt{49^3}}$ 0.27

Simplify each expression.

5. $\left(2x^{\frac{5}{7}}\right)\left(3x^{-\frac{2}{7}}\right)$ $6x^{\frac{3}{7}}$
6. $(64x^{-12}y^{16})^{-\frac{1}{4}}$ $\dfrac{x^3}{2.83y^4}$
7. $(2x^4y^8)^{\frac{1}{2}}$ $\sqrt{2}x^2y^4$
8. $(16x^4)(32y^2)^{\frac{1}{3}}$ $32\sqrt[3]{4}x^4y^{\frac{2}{3}}$

9. $\sqrt[10]{(81x^{20}y^{10})^5}$ $9x^{10}y^5$
10. $(16x)^{\frac{1}{2}} + \left(\dfrac{4}{x}\right)^{-\frac{1}{2}} - (x^2)^{\frac{1}{4}}$ $\dfrac{7x^{\frac{1}{2}}}{2}$
11. $\sqrt[5]{\sqrt[3]{\dfrac{x^{15}}{y^{-16}}}}$ $xy^{\frac{16}{15}}$
12. $\sqrt{\sqrt[3]{128x^{-6}y^{-1}}}$ $\dfrac{2^{\frac{7}{6}}}{xy^{\frac{1}{6}}}$

13. *Mechanics* The frequency of a piston that moves with simple harmonic motion is given by the formula $f = \dfrac{1}{2\pi} \cdot \left(\dfrac{g}{A}\right)^{\frac{1}{2}}$. Determine the frequency to the nearest hundredth, given that the maximum displacement A is 0.12 m and g is 9.8 m/sec². 1.43 s

14. *Engineering* The compression ratio of an engine R is 220 : 45. The efficiency of this engine can be approximated by the formula $E = 100 - \dfrac{100}{R^{\frac{2}{5}}}$. Determine the value of E to the nearest tenth. 47.0

Practice Exercises

 Use appropriate technology.

Express each exponential expression in radical form and evaluate.

A **1.** $169^{\frac{1}{2}}$ 13
2. $(-27)^{\frac{2}{3}}$ 9
3. $36^{-\frac{1}{2}}$ $\frac{1}{6}$
4. $16^{-\frac{1}{4}}$ $\frac{1}{2}$

Evaluate each expression.

5. $\sqrt[3]{-216^2}$ -36
6. $\sqrt[4]{625^3}$ 125
7. $\dfrac{1}{\sqrt{100^5}}$ $\frac{1}{100,000}$
8. $\dfrac{1}{\sqrt[7]{-128^4}}$ $-\frac{1}{16}$

Simplify each expression.

9. $\left(2x^{\frac{1}{3}}y^{\frac{1}{2}}\right)\left(3x^{\frac{2}{3}}y^{\frac{1}{2}}\right)$ $6xy$
10. $(64x^3y^6z^{-1})^{\frac{1}{3}}$ $\dfrac{4xy^2}{z^{\frac{1}{3}}}$
11. $\left(\dfrac{8x^3y^{-6}}{z^{-3}}\right)^{\frac{1}{3}}$ $\dfrac{2xz}{y^2}$
12. $\left(\dfrac{y^{-5}z^{10}}{32x^5}\right)^{-\frac{1}{5}}$ $\dfrac{2xy}{z^2}$

13. $\sqrt[8]{x^{16}y^{-8}}$ $\dfrac{x^2}{y}$
14. $\sqrt{\sqrt{16x^4y^{-8}}}$ $\dfrac{2x}{y^2}$
15. $(27y^2)^{\frac{1}{3}} - \left(\dfrac{1}{8y^2}\right)^{-\frac{1}{3}}$ $y^{\frac{2}{3}}$
16. $(4x^4y^2)^{\frac{1}{2}} - 3(x^8y^4)^{\frac{1}{4}}$ $-x^2y$

Ⓡ **17.** The volume of a suitcase is represented by $h^3 + 12h^2 + 35h$. If the depth of the suitcase is h and the length is $h + 7$, find its width. $h + 5$

18. Thinking Critically Explain why $\left(\dfrac{a}{b}\right)^{-n} = \left(\dfrac{b}{a}\right)^n$, $a, b \neq 0$; n is an integer.

9.1 Rational Exponents **443**

Additional Answers, Practice Exercises

18. $\left(\dfrac{a}{b}\right)^{-n} = \dfrac{1}{\left(\dfrac{a}{b}\right)^n} = \dfrac{1}{\dfrac{a^n}{b^n}} = \dfrac{b^n}{a^n} = \left(\dfrac{b}{a}\right)^n$

For Example 4
1. A clock has a pendulum of length 112.4 cm. Determine the period of the pendulum to the nearest tenth of a second. 2.1 s
2. A clock has a pendulum of length 2.4 m. Determine the period of the pendulum to the nearest second. 3 s

CLOSURE

Group students in pairs and have them summarize the properties of rational exponents for each other.

INDEPENDENT PRACTICE

Assignment Guide
Basic: 1–24, 31–35
Average: 15–43
Enriched: 18, 24–30, 32, 34, 36–54

Teacher's Resource Book
  Practice, page 58

Ⓡ **Review**
Exercises 17, 19, 31, 33, and 35 review concepts of factoring, graphing, finding zeros of a polynomial, and solving inequalities.

LESSON FOLLOW-UP

Lesson Quiz
1. Evaluate $\sqrt[3]{216^2}$ 36
2. Evaluate $\sqrt[5]{(-34)^3}$ using a calculator and round to the nearest tenth. -8.3

Simplify each expression.
3. $(3x^{\frac{3}{5}})(5x^{-\frac{7}{10}})$ $\dfrac{15}{x^{\frac{1}{10}}}$
4. $\sqrt[3]{\sqrt{64x^{-12}y^6}}$ $\dfrac{2y}{x^2}$
5. A clock has a pendulum of length 72.8 cm. Determine the period of the pendulum to the nearest tenth of a second. 1.7 s

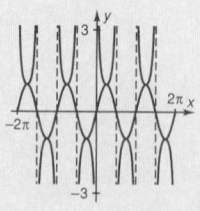
Ⓡ **19.** Graph the function $f(x) = x^2 + 3x - 10$.

Express each radical in exponential form and evaluate it using a calculator. Round approximate answers to the nearest hundredth.

20. $\sqrt[6]{6^2}$ 2.05   **21.** $(\sqrt{17})^3$ 70.09   **22.** $\sqrt[3]{-129}$ −5.05   **23.** $\sqrt[5]{-218}$ −2.94

24. *Mechanics*   Determine the period of a pendulum whose length is 3 m, given that $g = 9.8$ m/s².   3.48 s

Simplify each expression.

B **25.** $\left(\dfrac{x^{\frac{4}{3}}y^{\frac{1}{3}}}{y^{\frac{5}{6}}z^{\frac{1}{3}}}\right)^{-\frac{3}{4}}$ $\dfrac{y^{\frac{3}{8}}z^{\frac{1}{4}}}{x}$ **26.** $\sqrt[5]{x\left(x^{\frac{2}{3}} + x^{-\frac{2}{3}}\right)}$ $\left(x^{\frac{5}{3}} + x^{\frac{1}{3}}\right)^{\frac{1}{5}}$ **27.** $\sqrt[5]{\sqrt{x^{-20}y^{40}z^{-4}}}$ $\dfrac{y^4}{x^2z^{\frac{2}{5}}}$

28. $\sqrt[4]{\sqrt[3]{\dfrac{x^9}{y^{15}z^{-12}}}}$ $\dfrac{x^{\frac{3}{4}}z}{y^{\frac{5}{4}}}$ **29.** $\left(x^{\frac{3}{5}}y^{\frac{1}{10}}z^{-\frac{1}{5}}\right)^{-\frac{5}{2}}$ $\dfrac{z^{\frac{1}{2}}}{x^{\frac{3}{2}}y^{\frac{1}{4}}}$ **30.** $\left(\dfrac{z^{-16}}{16x^4y^4}\right)^{-\frac{1}{4}}$ $2xyz^4$

Ⓡ **31.** On the same set of axes, graph $y = \sin 2x$ and $y = \csc 2x$ from -2π to 2π.

32. Thinking Critically   Use the properties of rational exponents to show that $\sqrt[n]{\sqrt[p]{a}} = \sqrt[np]{a}$.

Ⓡ **33.** Find the zeros of $f(x) = x^3 - 3x$.   0, $\pm\sqrt{3}$

34. Writing in Mathematics   Discuss advantages and disadvantages of finding the root of a number using a calculator, first for the case when the root is written as a radical and then when the root is written as a rational exponent.

Ⓡ **35.** Solve and graph the solution on the number line: $|5x - 4| \ge 24$

Evaluate each expression to the nearest hundredth using a calculator.

36. $\sqrt[3]{0.032^2}$ 0.10   **37.** $\sqrt[3]{(-0.032)^2}$ 0.10   **38.** $(-119)^{-\frac{4}{5}}$ 0.02

39. $(1417)^{-\frac{1}{2}}$ 0.03   **40.** $\left(\dfrac{1}{\sqrt{2}}\right)^{-\frac{2}{3}}$ 1.26   **41.** $\sqrt[3]{(-235)^{-\frac{1}{5}}}$ −0.69

42. *Geometry*   The radius of a spherical balloon is given by the formula $r = \left(\dfrac{3V}{4\pi}\right)^{\frac{1}{3}}$, where V is the volume of the balloon. Determine, to the nearest tenth, the radius of a balloon whose volume is 125 in.³   3.10 in.

43. *Banking*   The total amount of money in a bank account paying compound interest can be determined by the formula $A = P\left(1 + \dfrac{r}{n}\right)^{nt}$, where P is the principal (amount deposited), r is the annual rate of interest expressed as a decimal, n is the number of times the interest is compounded in one year, and t is the time in years. Determine the total amount of money in an account at the end of 4 months if the original sum deposited was $2550, the interest rate is 8%, compounded 4 times a year, and no money is deposited or withdrawn. $2618.23

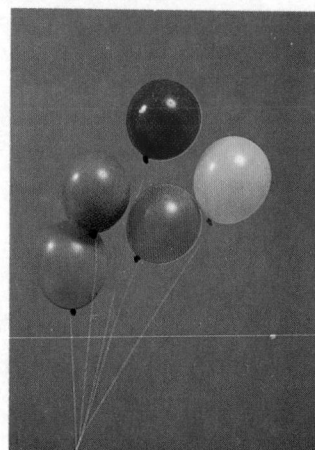

Writing in Mathematics

34. Answers may vary. For square roots and cube roots either form is easy to enter. For other roots the expression must be entered in rational exponent form.

Simplify each expression.

44. $\left(\dfrac{(xy)^{-2}(yz)^{-3}}{(xz)^3(zw)^{-2}}\right)^{-\frac{1}{2}}$ $\dfrac{x^{\frac{5}{2}}y^{\frac{5}{2}}z^2}{w}$

45. $\sqrt{\left(x^{\frac{5}{7}}y^{\frac{3}{14}}\right)^{-7}\left(x^{\frac{2}{3}}\right)^6}$ $\dfrac{1}{x^{\frac{1}{2}}y^{\frac{3}{4}}}$

46. $\dfrac{(x^{2n+2})(\sqrt[3]{x^2})}{x^{2n+3}}$ $\dfrac{1}{x^{\frac{1}{3}}}$

47. $\sqrt{\sqrt[m+1]{\sqrt[m+1]{\dfrac{1}{y^2}}}}$ $|y|$

48. Express as a single fraction: $x^{-\frac{1}{3}}y^{\frac{1}{3}} - x^{\frac{2}{3}}y^{-\frac{2}{3}}$ $\dfrac{y - x}{x^{\frac{1}{3}}y^{\frac{2}{3}}}$

Simplify.

49. $(\sqrt[n]{(-x)^n})^2$ x^2

50. $(\sqrt[n]{(-x)^n})^3$ n even: x^3; n odd: $-x^3$

51. *Physics* For an object falling with no air resistance, its final velocity can be determined by the formula $v = \left(\dfrac{2g}{s^{-1}} + \dfrac{1}{v_0^{-2}}\right)^{\frac{1}{2}}$, where the acceleration due to gravity g is 32 ft/s^2. If the distance fallen by the object, s, is 292 ft, and the initial velocity, v_0, is 27 ft/s, determine the final velocity v to the nearest integer. 139.3 ft/s

52. Thinking Critically Given $a^{\frac{m}{n}}$, where m is an integer, n is a positive integer, and m and n are relatively prime (have no common factors), determine for what values of m and n, m/n will be an odd integer or the reciprocal of an odd integer.

53. The mass of an object increases as the velocity at which it travels according to the equation $m_v = \dfrac{m_0}{\sqrt{1 - \left(\dfrac{v}{c}\right)^2}}$ where m_v is the mass at velocity v, m_0 is the mass of the object at rest, v is the velocity in miles per second, and c is the velocity of light, approximately 186,300 mi/s. Find, to the nearest 100 mi/s, the velocity at which m_v is twice the mass at rest. 161,300 mi/s

54. Show that if $\sqrt[n]{a}$ is a real number, m is an integer, and n is a positive integer, $(\sqrt[n]{a})^m = \sqrt[n]{a^m}$. Remember to consider both the case when n is even and the case when n is odd.

Review

Express each number in scientific notation.

1. 0.00000000005 5×10^{-11}

2. 0.00764 7.64×10^{-3}

3. 65930 6.593×10^4

4. 17,000,000,000 1.7×10^{10}

5. Are the systems $\begin{cases} 3a + 2b = 8 \\ 7a + 3b = 17 \end{cases}$ and $\begin{cases} a + b = 3 \\ -5a + b = -9 \\ 2a + 2b = 6 \end{cases}$ equivalent? Yes

Evaluate for $x = -2.5$.

6. x^3 -15.625

7. $-x^3$ 15.625

8. $\sqrt{x^2}$ 2.5

9. $-\sqrt{x^2}$ -2.5

9.1 Rational Exponents **445**

Objectives: *To graph exponential functions*
To solve simple exponential equations

Focus

In 1798 Thomas Malthus, a British economist, published his theory concerning population growth. In a famous essay, Malthus pessimistically claimed that because the world's population increases at a much faster rate than its supply of food and other resources, the eventual result must be widespread famine. However, the predicted worldwide food shortage has failed to occur. Malthus failed to foresee important improvements in the efficiency of production of food and goods, especially in developed areas. For this reason, his model is not now considered to be useful for predicting the actual growth of populations. Still, certain aspects of his theory are used as a basis for contemporary population studies.

The Malthusian population model postulates that, over time, an unchecked population grows very rapidly. It applies to populations of all kinds, from human beings to the cells in a bacteria culture. In mathematical terms, most population growth is modeled by *exponential functions*.

To understand the way in which a population increases exponentially over time, consider a simpler population than the one analyzed by Malthus. Suppose you have a single-celled organism that reproduces by dividing every hour. After one hour you would have 2 cells, after two hours 2^2, or 4 cells, after three hours 2^3, or 8 cells, and so on. Then after *x* hours you would have 2^x cells. *How many cells would you have at the end of a day?*

A function that can be expressed in the form $f(x) = b^x$, $b > 0$ and $b \neq 1$, is called an **exponential function.** Its domain is the set of real numbers, its range the set of positive real numbers. Note that since *x* can be any real number, it is possible for an expression to have irrational exponents. The properties of exponents hold for such expressions. Using a calculator, you can approximate the value of b^x when *x* is irrational.

446   Chapter 9 Exponential and Logarithmic Functions

Thinking Critically
At the end of a day you would have 16,777,216 cells.

Example 1   Graph $h(x) = 2^x$ and $k(x) = 5^x$ on the same axes. For each function, find the domain, range, and x- and y-intercepts. Determine whether each function is increasing or decreasing and whether each function is one-to-one.

x	$h(x) = 2^x$	$k(x) = 5^x$
-3	0.125	0.008
$-\sqrt{2}$	0.3752	0.1027
-2	0.25	0.04
-1	0.5	0.2
0	1	1
1	2	5
$\sqrt{3}$	3.3220	16.2425
2	4	25
3	8	125

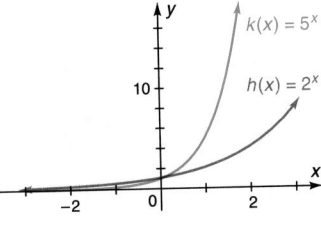

For both functions, the domain is $\{x : x \in \mathcal{R}\}$ and the range is $\{y : y > 0\}$. The y-intercept is 1 for both functions. Neither function has an x-intercept. Both $h(x)$ and $k(x)$ are increasing functions and are therefore one-to-one.

The basic form of the graph of an exponential function $f(x) = b^x$ when $b > 1$, is shown at the right. The point $(0, 1)$ is common to all such graphs, but the value of b determines their "steepness." Notice the behavior of the curve as the interval along the x-axis extends indefinitely to the left, that is, as "x approaches $-\infty$ (negative infinity)." The distance between the curve and the x-axis approaches 0. Therefore, the exponential function is *asymptotic* to the x-axis. Also, since b^x approaches ∞ (positive infinity) as x approaches ∞, the range of the exponential function is $\{y : y > 0\}$.

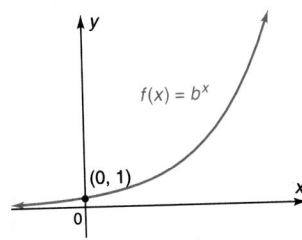

Recall that if $g(x) = f(-x)$, then the graph of $g(x)$ is the reflection of the graph of $f(x)$ in the y-axis. For the exponential function $f(x) = b^x$, $f(-x) = b^{-x} = \frac{1}{b^x} = \left(\frac{1}{b}\right)^x$. Therefore, the graph of $g(x) = \left(\frac{1}{b}\right)^x$ is the reflection of the graph of $f(x) = b^x$ in the y-axis.

Example 2   Graph $n(x) = \left(\frac{1}{2}\right)^x$ and $m(x) = \left(\frac{1}{5}\right)^x$ on the same axes. For each function, find the domain, range, and x- and y-intercepts. Determine whether each function is increasing or decreasing and whether each is one-to-one.

$n(x) = \left(\frac{1}{2}\right)^x = 2^{-x}$

Therefore, the graph of $n(x) = 2^{-x}$ is the reflection of the graph of $f(x) = 2^x$ in the y-axis.

$m(x) = \left(\frac{1}{5}\right)^x = 5^{-x}$

Therefore, the graph of $m(x) = 5^{-x}$ is the reflection of the graph of $g(x) = 5^x$ in the y-axis.

9.2 Exponential Functions   **447**

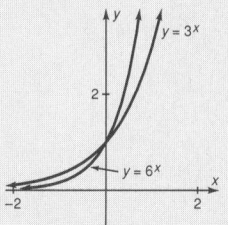

For Example 2

Graph $m(x) = \left(\frac{1}{4}\right)^x$ and $n(x) = \left(\frac{1}{10}\right)^x$ on the same set of axes. For each function find the domain, range, and x- and y-intercepts. Determine whether each function is increasing or decreasing, and whether each is one-to-one.

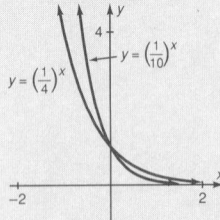

domain: $\{x: x \in \mathcal{R}\}$ for both functions; range: $\{y: y > 0\}$ for both functions; y-intercept: (0, 1) for both functions; no x-intercepts for either function; Since both functions are decreasing, they are one-to-one.

For Example 3

Graph each function using transformations. Determine the equation of the asymptote of each function.

1. $f(x) = -e^x - 3$

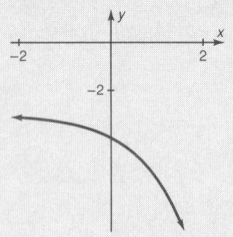

$y = -3$

2. $g(x) = e^x + 3$

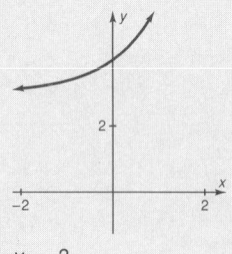

$y = 3$

The domain of both functions is $\{x: x \in R\}$ and the range of both functions is $\{y: y > 0\}$. The y-intercept is 1 for both functions. Neither function has an x-intercept. Both $n(x)$ and $m(x)$ are decreasing functions and are therefore one-to-one. Both functions are asymptotic to the x-axis.

Examples 1 and 2 illustrate that, in general, any exponential function $f(x) = c^x$ is one-to-one.

The graph of an exponential function, like the graphs of other functions, can be reflected, dilated, or translated. You have already seen how the value of the base b influences the graph of an exponential function. It will be helpful to choose a function with a specific base and analyze various transformations of the graph of that function.

One base that is widely used in the study of exponential functions is the number e. This constant is the base of natural logarithms. It appears in a wide variety of applications including archaeology, chemistry, space science, business, and engineering. The value of e is defined as the number that the expression $\left(1 + \frac{1}{n}\right)^n$ approaches as n approaches infinity. Thus, if you substitute larger and larger values for n into the expression, you will get closer and closer approximations for the value of e. The value of e to 16 decimal places is $e \approx 2.7182818284590452$. The function $f(x) = e^x$ is called the **natural exponential function.**

Example 3 Graph each function using transformations. Determine the equation of the asymptote of each function.
  a. $f(x) = e^x$ **b.** $g(x) = e^x + 2$ **c.** $m(x) = -e^x$

a. $f(x) = e^x$

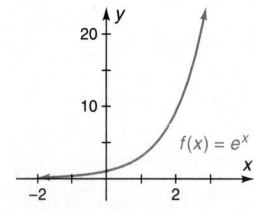

Natural exponential function
Asymptote: $y = 0$

b. $g(x) = e^x + 2$

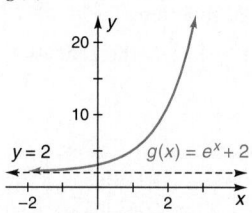

Translation (vertical shift up 2 units)
Asymptote: $y = 2$

c. $m(x) = -e^x$

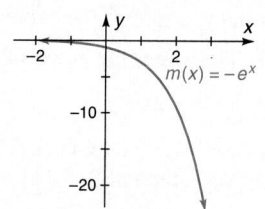

Reflection in the x-axis
Asymptote: $y = 0$

Recall that for any one-to-one function f, $f(m) = f(p)$ if and only if $m = p$. Since exponential functions are one-to-one, $b^m = b^p$ if and only if $m = p$. Therefore, some equations such as $4^x = 2^{x+1}$ can be solved by expressing both sides of the equation in terms of the same base. Equations that contain one or more exponential expressions are called **exponential equations.** Some exponential equations can be solved by using algebraic techniques such as factoring.

448   Chapter 9 Exponential and Logarithmic Functions

Example 4 Solve each exponential equation. **a.** $25^x = \sqrt{5}$ **b.** $2xe^x - 4e^x = 0$

a. $(5^2)^x = 5^{\frac{1}{2}}$ *Express in terms*
$\quad 5^{2x} = 5^{\frac{1}{2}}$ *of the same base.*
$\quad 2x = \frac{1}{2}$
$\quad\quad x = \frac{1}{4}$

b. $(2x - 4)e^x = 0$ *Factor.*
$\quad 2x - 4 = 0$ or $e^x = 0$
$\quad\quad 2x = 4$ *There is no value of*
$\quad\quad\quad x = 2$ *x for which $e^x = 0$.*

Modeling

How can you use an exponential function to predict population?

For a single-celled organism, population growth is modeled by an exponential function. The growth of a bacteria culture is a simplified example of exponential growth since it models only the birthrate of the culture and not its death rate. To find a more precise model, you need to consider many factors contributing to the life span of the organism. The improved model for predicting population growth will be an exponential function with a constant base that is chosen specifically for a particular problem under consideration.

Consider a community with an initial population P. Suppose the rate of increase in population of the community for each year is represented by r, where $0 < r < 1$. Then after 1 year the population of the community will be $P + rP$ or $P(1 + r)$. After 2 years the population will be $P(1 + r) + rP(1 + r)$ or $P(1 + r)^2$. After 3 years the population will be $P(1 + r)^3$. In general, the population of the community after t years will be $P(1 + r)^t$.

Example 5 *Demographics* The bar graph at the right shows the population of the United States for the last 4 census years. Use the data in the graph to determine a model for predicting population growth. Use the model to estimate the population in 1975.

To determine the rate of increase r, first find the increase in population from 1960 to 1970.

1970 population − 1960 population = increase in population over 10 years
$\quad 203{,}000{,}000 - 179{,}000{,}000 \quad = 24{,}000{,}000$

The average increase in population per year is $24{,}000{,}000 \div 10 = 2{,}400{,}000$.

$$r = \frac{2{,}400{,}000}{179{,}000{,}000} \approx 0.013 \text{ or } 1.3\%$$ *Express this increase as a percent.*

Substitute the initial population and the rate into the formula to obtain the model.

$\quad P = 179{,}000{,}000(1 + 0.013)^t \quad P = (1 + r)^t$

$\quad P = 179{,}000{,}000(1 + 0.013)^{15} \approx 217{,}000{,}000$ *In 1975, $t = 15$.*

The United States population in 1975 was approximately 217 million.

9.2 Exponential Functions **449**

For Example 4
Solve each exponential equation.
1. $4^{3x+1} = 32 \quad \frac{1}{2}$
2. $x^2e^{3x} = 4e^{3x} \quad \pm 2$

Modeling
Studying population growth is an essential part in urban planning. Schooling and housing are just two of the many areas that are affected by these studies.

For Example 5
Using the graph in Example 5, determine a model for predicting population growth in the 1980s using 1970 and 1980 data. Use the model to predict the population in the year 1982.
$P = 203{,}000{,}000(1 + 0.011)^t; t = 12$
The United States population in 1982 was approximately 231,000,000.

Common Error Some students may forget to divide the difference between the 1980 and 1970 populations by 10. Remind the students that given populations are for a 10-year period and therefore they must determine the average yearly difference.

CLOSURE
Have students write a letter to non-precalculus students, explaining the procedures for graphing exponential functions and for solving simple exponential equations.

INDEPENDENT PRACTICE
Assignment Guide
Basic: 1–22, 29, 35–37, 39, Project
Average: 9–13, 18–39, Project
Enriched: 10, 12, 18–22, 25–28, 30–34, 36, 38, 40–48, Project

Teacher's Resource Book
Practice, page 59

450

 Review

Exercises 9, 11, 13, 29, 35, 37, and 39 review concepts of determining maximum values, simplifying exponential expressions, evaluating radical expressions, solving systems graphically, and finding inverse functions.

Additional Answers
Class Exercises

1.

2.

3.

4.

5.

6.
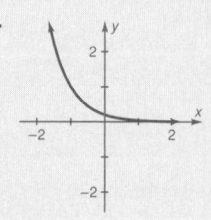

The model presented above is effective for predicting population growth, but it is not without flaws. For example, the value of r reflects the increase in population from 1960 to 1970, but this increase is not constant for every decade. In later lessons, you will learn about more reliable models for population growth, models that use base e.

Class Exercises

Graph each function. State whether it is increasing or decreasing.

1. $f(x) = 4^x$ increasing
2. $g(x) = e^x - 1$ increasing
3. $f(x) = 2^{-x}$ decreasing

4. $m(x) = 10^x + 2$ increasing
5. $H(x) = \left(\frac{1}{3}\right)^x$ decreasing
6. $g(x) = \left(\frac{1}{5}\right)^{x+1}$ decreasing

Solve each exponential equation.

7. $9^{4x} = 3^5$ $\frac{5}{8}$
8. $(\sqrt{3})^x = 243$ 10
9. $\left(\frac{1}{64}\right)^x = 2^{3x+5}$ $\frac{-5}{9}$
10. $xe^{2x} = 5e^{2x}$ 5

11. *Demographics*   Use the equation in Example 5 to predict the United States population in 1990. Then, check the accuracy of the prediction against the actual 1990 population.   264,000,000

12. *Atmospheric Pressure*   An approximate rule for determining atmospheric pressure, P in grams per square centimeter at altitudes less than 80 km, is $P = 1035(1 - r)^h$, where h is the altitude in kilometers and r is the rate of decrease in pressure in grams per square centimeter per kilometer. Determine the atmospheric pressure at an altitude of 25 km given that the rate of drop in pressure is 11.2% per kilometer.   53.1 g/cm²

Practice Exercises   Use appropriate technology.

Graph each function. Find the domain, range, and x- and y-intercepts. Determine whether the function is increasing or decreasing and whether it is one-to-one.

A **1.** $f(x) = 3^x$
2. $g(x) = 6^x$
3. $f(x) = \left(\frac{1}{10}\right)^x$
4. $f(x) = \left(\frac{1}{6}\right)^x$

5. $g(x) = e^x + 1$
6. $h(x) = 3^{-x}$
7. $H(x) = e^{x-3}$
8. $f(x) = \left(\frac{1}{2}\right)^x - 3$

Ⓡ **9.** Determine the maximum value of $f(x) = 6x - 5x^2$. $\frac{9}{5}$

10. **Thinking Critically**   Explain why the exponential function $y = b^x$ is not defined for $b < 0$.

Ⓡ **11.** Simplify and write with positive exponents: $(e^{-2}\sqrt[3]{e})^{\frac{1}{2}}$ $\frac{1}{e^{\frac{5}{6}}}$

12. **Writing in Mathematics**   Describe the changes in the graph of $y = b^x$, $b > 1$, as b increases.

Ⓡ **13.** Evaluate $\sqrt[5]{\sqrt[3]{17.2}}$ to the nearest tenth.   1.2

Solve each exponential equation.

14. $4^{x+2} = 8$ $-\frac{1}{2}$
15. $7^t = \sqrt{7^3}$ $\frac{3}{2}$
16. $xe^x = 0$ 0
17. $e^x - 9xe^x = 0$ $\frac{1}{9}$

450   Chapter 9 Exponential and Logarithmic Functions

Writing in Mathematics
12. As b increases, the graph of $f(x) = b^x$ gets closer to the y-axis for $x > 0$ and closer to the x-axis for $x < 0$.

18. The population of a bacteria colony is given by $P = P_0(1 + r)^t$, where P_0 is the initial population, r is the rate of increase in the number of bacteria per day, and t is the number of elapsed days. Find the bacteria population after 5 days given that the initial number of bacteria is 200 and the rate of increase is 12% per day. 352

19. *Consumer Awareness* An automobile that originally cost $12,000 depreciates at the rate of 20% per year. Find the value of the car in 6 years. Use the formula $A = A_0(1 + r)^t$, where A_0 is the original cost of the car, r is the rate of increase (a negative number) in the car's value, and t is the time in years. $3145.73

20. *Demographics* The model for population growth for a certain city is $P(t) = 3000e^{0.03t}$, where P is the population at the end of time t, in years. Determine the population for this city at the end of 5 years. 3486

21. *Atmospheric Pressure* A rule for approximating atmospheric pressure for altitudes less than 80 km is $P = 1035\left(\frac{1}{2}\right)^{\frac{h}{5.8}}$, where P is measured in grams per square centimeter and h is the altitude in kilometers. Determine the atmospheric pressure at an altitude of 62 km. 0.63 g/cm²

22. *Demographics* Create a model for predicting the population of the United States using the data from the graph of Example 5. Use the 1960 and 1980 populations to determine r. Use the model to predict the United States population in the year 2000. 302,000,000

Graph each function using transformations. Determine the equation of the asymptote of each graph.

B 23. $f(x) = 2^{x+1} + 3$ 24. $g(x) = 3e^x$ 25. $g(x) = 4^{x-1} + 2$

26. $f(x) = -e^x + 3$ 27. $g(x) = 7^x - 2$ 28. $f(x) = \left(\frac{2}{3}\right)^x + 1$

Ⓡ 29. Solve the system graphically: $\begin{cases} 4x + 2y \le 16 \\ 2x + 3y \le 12 \end{cases}$

Solve each exponential equation.

30. $x^2e^{2x} - 3xe^{2x} - 4e^{2x} = 0$ 4, −1   31. $6x^2e^{3x} + xe^{3x} = 2e^{3x}$ $\frac{1}{2}$, $-\frac{2}{3}$

32. $e^{4x-1} = 1$ $\frac{1}{4}$ 33. $e^{-2x}(e^{3x+6} - e^{2x}) = 0$ −6

34. *Cost of Living* In 1985, the annual cost of tuition at a certain college was $10,000. In 1990 the cost was $15,000. Determine an exponential model for predicting the cost of tuition at the college. Use the model to predict the tuition in the year 1995. $T = 10,000(1 + 0.1)^t$; $T = $25,937.42

Ⓡ 35. Evaluate: $\sqrt[4]{(-2)^4}$ 2

36. **Thinking Critically** Compare the polynomial function $P(x) = 1 + x + \frac{1}{2}x^2 + \frac{1}{6}x^3$ with the natural exponential function $f(x) = e^x$. What do you notice?

Ⓡ 37. Find the inverse function of $f(x) = x^3 + 1$. $f^{-1}(x) = \sqrt[3]{x - 1}$

9.2 Exponential Functions   **451**

LESSON FOLLOW-UP

Lesson Quiz

1. Graph $f(x) = 3^x$ and $g(x) = \left(\frac{1}{3}\right)^x$ on the same set of axes. For each function find the domain, range, and x- and y-intercepts. Determine whether each function is increasing or decreasing and whether each is one-to-one. Determine the asymptote for each function.

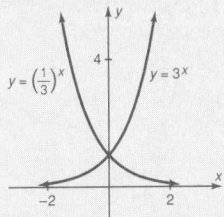

domain: $\{x: x \in \mathcal{R}\}$ for both functions; range: $\{y: y > 0\}$ for both functions; y-intercept: (0, 1) for both functions; no x-intercepts for either function; $f(x)$ is increasing and $g(x)$ is decreasing, so both functions are one-to-one; asymptote: $y = 0$ for both functions.

2. Graph $f(x) = e^x - 1$ and determine the equation of its asymptote.

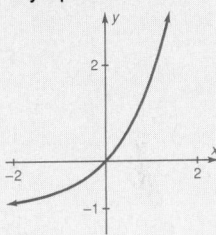

$y = -1$

Solve each exponential equation.

3. $9^{2x+1} = \sqrt{3}$ $-\frac{3}{8}$

4. $2xe^{2x} + x^2e^{2x} = 0$ 0, −2

5. Using the table below, write a model for predicting population growth. Use the model to predict the population in the year 1986.

Metro City

Year	Population
1970	105,000
1980	120,000

$P = 105,000(1 + 0.014)^t$
The Metro City population in 1986 was approximately 131,000.

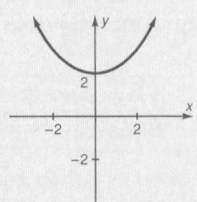
38. *Space Science* The power output P, in watts, of a satellite's radioisotope power supply is modeled by the exponential equation $P = 50e^{-\frac{t}{250}}$, where t is the time in days. How much power will be available at the end of 2 years? P = 2.7 W

⊞ **39.** Find the value of k that makes $16x^2 - kx + 9 = 0$ a perfect square trinomial. 24

Graph each pair of functions on the same axes and compare them.

C **40.** $f(x) = e^x$, $g(x) = e^{3x}$ **41.** $f(x) = 4^x$, $g(x) = 4^{2x}$

42. A dilation of $f(x) = 2^x$ by a factor of 8 is equivalent to a horizontal shift of $f(x)$. Determine the equation of this horizontal shift. $g(x) = 2^{x+3}$

43. A horizontal shift of 4 units to the left of $g(x) = 3^{-x}$ is equivalent to a dilation of $g(x)$. Determine the equation of this dilation. $f(x) = 3^{-x-4}$

Simplify and graph each function.

44. $f(x) = \dfrac{e^{2x} - 3e^x}{3e^x}$ $f(x) = \frac{1}{3}e^x - 1$ **45.** $g(x) = e^{2x}(e^{-x+1} - 2e^{-2x})$ $g(x) = e^{x+1} - 2$

46. *Engineering* The curve formed by suspending wire or cable from two fixed points is called a *catenary*. A model of this curve is the sum of two natural exponential functions. Graph this function, $f(x) = e^{\frac{1}{2}x} + e^{-\frac{1}{2}x}$.

47. *Physics* The half-life of a radioisotope is the time required for half of the isotope to decay. Find an equation for the amount of a radioisotope that remains after t days given that the initial amount is 6 kg and the half-life is 1 day. How much of the substance remains after 3 days? $A = 6\left(\frac{1}{2}\right)^t$; 0.75 kg

48. A certain country doubled in population over the course of 40 years. Use a calculator and trial and error to find the approximate annual rate of increase in the population. 1.75%

Project

Find the world's population in ancient times and also during the Middle Ages. Use the information to create a model for predicting the world's population. Use the model to predict the current world population and compare it with the actual population.

Challenge

1. How many of the first 100 positive integers are divisible by the numbers 2, 3, 4, and 5? 1

2. What is the number of factors when $x^{13} - x$ is factored completely into polynomials and monomials with real integral coefficients? 67

9.3 Logarithmic Functions

Objectives: To graph logarithmic functions
To evaluate logarithms

Focus

The intensity of sound waves that can be heard by the human ear can vary from the barely audible, measured at 10^{-16} W/cm², to the threshold of pain, measured at 10^{-4} W/cm². Thus, the loudest sound that you can hear is one trillion times as great as the softest. These sound intensities involve measurements over a very wide range of numbers. To simplify the scale of measurement, it is convenient to define a new unit of loudness based on the

logarithms of the measured intensities. The loudness, or magnitude, of a sound is defined as the logarithm of the ratio of the sound's intensity to the number 10^{-16}, the intensity of the barely audible sound mentioned above. This basic unit of loudness is called the *bel*, in honor of Alexander Graham Bell. Since this unit is really too large for practical use, the more common unit is the *decibel*, a unit that is one-tenth as large.

The measurement of sound using decibels illustrates the point that, for some applications, it is more convenient to work with the logarithm of a measured quantity (or the ratio of two such quantities) than to work with the quantity itself. In this lesson, logarithmic functions are studied in detail.

Since the exponential function $f(x) = b^x$ is one-to-one, it has an inverse function. The inverse function of an exponential function is called the **logarithmic function.**

> For all positive real numbers x and b, $b > 0$ and $b \neq 1$,
>
> $$y = \log_b x \quad \text{if and only if} \quad x = b^y$$

The expression $\log_b x$ is read "the logarithm of x to the base b." Because $f(x) = \log_b x$ is the inverse of the exponential function $g(x) = b^x$, the range of $g(x)$ is the domain of $f(x)$ and the domain of $g(x)$ is the range of $f(x)$. Therefore, the domain of the logarithmic function $f(x)$ is $\{x: x > 0\}$ and the range is $\{y: y \in R\}$.

LESSON PLAN

Vocabulary
change-of-base formula
common logarithmic function
logarithmic equation
logarithmic function
natural logarithmic function

ⓜ Materials/Manipulatives
transparencies

Technology
graphing utility
symbolic manipulator

FOCUS

The use of a Richter scale, which is used to measure the magnitude of an earthquake, is another example where logarithms can simplify the scale of measurement. You may wish to have students research the history of the Richter scale.

INSTRUCTION

ⓜ • Use transparencies to emphasize the general shape of the graph of a logarithmic function. Then have students focus on the effect the value of the base has on the graph.
• When finding the y-intercept of a logarithmic function, remind students that $b^0 = 1$.

Alternative Learning Styles
Some students need a kinesthetic approach to graphing. Have them trace the general shape of a logarithmic function in the air with their hand. Repeat this exercise throughout the lesson before having them graph each function on paper.

For Example 1

Express each logarithmic equation as an exponential equation and solve for the variable.

1. $\log_{\sqrt{5}} 5\sqrt{5} = y$

$(\sqrt{5})^y = 5\sqrt{5}$ or $5^{\frac{y}{2}} = 5^{\frac{3}{2}}, y = 3$

2. $\log_b \dfrac{1}{216} = -3$

$b^{-3} = \dfrac{1}{216}; b^{-3} = 6^{-3}, b = 6$

Common Error When expressing the fraction $\dfrac{1}{216}$ as a power of 6, some students may forget to use a negative exponent. Remind these students that when a factor is moved from the denominator to the numerator of a fraction, or vice versa, the sign of the exponent of that factor changes.

For Example 2

Graph each logarithmic function. Find the domain, range, x- and y-intercepts, and asymptote of each function. Determine whether each function is increasing or decreasing.

1. $f(x) = \log_4 x$

$D = \{x: x > 0\}; R = \{y: y \in \mathcal{R}\};$ x-int: (1, 0); no y-int; asymptote: $x = 0$; increasing

---

An equation that contains a logarithmic expression is called a **logarithmic equation.** Such equations can often be expressed in exponential form since $y = \log_b x$ is equivalent to $x = b^y$. Often a logarithmic equation can be more readily solved if it is expressed in exponential form.

Example 1 Express each logarithmic equation as an exponential equation and solve for the variable.

    a. $\log_7 x = 2$ **b.** $\log_2 \dfrac{1}{16} = y$ **c.** $\log_b 81 = 4$

a. $\log_7 x = 2$ **b.** $\log_2 \dfrac{1}{16} = y$ **c.** $\log_b 81 = 4$
    $7^2 = x$ $2^y = \dfrac{1}{16}$ $b^4 = 81$
    $49 = x$ $2^y = 2^{-4}$ $b^4 = 3^4$
                     $y = -4$ $b = 3$

Since the logarithmic function $f(x) = \log_b x$ and the exponential function $g(x) = b^x$ are inverses, their graphs are symmetric with respect to the line $y = x$.

To construct a table of values for a logarithmic function, express the function in exponential form, choose values for y and find the corresponding values of x.

For b > 1

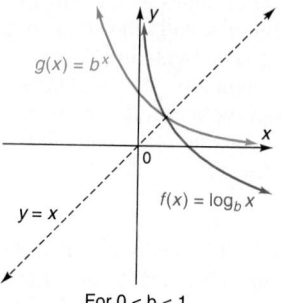

For 0 < b < 1

Example 2 Graph each logarithmic function. Find the domain, range, x- and y-intercepts, and asymptote and whether the function is increasing or decreasing.
    a. $f(x) = \log_2 x$ **b.** $g(x) = \log_{\frac{1}{2}} x$

a.

x	f(x)
0.125	−3
0.25	−2
0.5	−1
1	0
2	1
4	2
8	3
16	4

The function is increasing over its domain, $\{x: x > 0\}$. The range is $\{y: y \in R\}$ and y-axis is the asymptote. There is no y-intercept. The x-intercept is 1.

b.

x	g(x)
0.125	3
0.25	2
0.5	1
1	0
2	−1
4	−2
8	−3
16	−4

The function is decreasing over its domain, $\{x: x > 0\}$. The range is $\{y: y \in R\}$ and the y-axis is the asymptote. There is no y-intercept. The x-intercept is 1.

454   Chapter 9 Exponential and Logarithmic Functions

From Example 2 you can see that the graph of the logarithmic function is asymptotic to the y-axis and is increasing for $b > 1$ and decreasing for $0 < b < 1$. The point $(1, 0)$ is common to the graphs of all basic logarithmic functions.

Although the base of a logarithmic function can be any positive real number except 1, two numbers, 10 and e, are particularly useful choices. A logarithmic function with base 10 is called a **common logarithmic function** and is denoted $f(x) = \log x$ (without a subscript). Common logarithms have been historically useful for evaluating complicated logarithmic expressions with the help of tables. A logarithmic function with base e, denoted $g(x) = \ln x$, is called a **natural logarithmic function.** As with the natural exponential function, natural logarithms figure prominently in many applications in science and finance.

The properties of the basic logarithmic function can be used to find the asymptotes and intercepts of other logarithmic functions. The asymptote of the basic logarithmic function $f(x) = \log_b x$ is the y-axis, that is, the line $x = 0$. The asymptote of a logarithmic function of the form $h(x) = \log_b (ax + c)$ is the line with equation $ax + c = 0$. To find the x-intercept, let $y = 0$ in the equation $y = \log (ax + c)$. To find the y-intercept, let $x = 0$ in $y = \log (ax + c)$.

Example 3 Graph each function. Give the asymptotes and x- and y-intercepts. State the domain and range and whether the function is increasing or decreasing.
  a. $h(x) = \log (3x + 10)$ **b.** $g(x) = -2 \ln x + 2$

a. $h(x) = \log (3x + 10)$

Asymptote: $x = -\frac{10}{3}$ *Let $3x + 10 = 0$ to find the asymptote.*

$y = \log (3x + 10)$ *Let $y = 0$ to find the x-intercept.*
$0 = \log (3x + 10)$
$3x + 10 = 10^0$ *$y = \log_b x$ if and only if $x = b^y$*
$3x + 10 = 1$ *$10^0 = 1$*
$x = -3$ The x-intercept is -3.

$y = \log [3(0) + 10]$ *Let $x = 0$ to find the y-intercept.*
$10^y = 10$
$y = 1$ The y-intercept is 1.

Domain: $\{x: x > -\frac{10}{3}\}$ Range: $\{y: y \in \mathcal{R}\}$ The function is increasing.

b. $g(x) = -2 \ln x + 2$

Asymptote: $x = 0$ y-axis

$y = -2 \ln x + 2$ *Let $y = 0$ to find the x-intercept.*
$0 = -2 \ln x + 2$
$-2 = -2 \ln x$
$1 = \ln x$
$x = e^1 \approx 2.718$ The x-intercept is 2.718.

Since the asymptote is the y-axis, there is no y-intercept.

Domain: $\{x: x > 0\}$ Range: $\{y: y \in \mathcal{R}\}$ The function is decreasing.

9.3 Logarithmic Functions   **455**

2. $g(x) = \log_{\frac{1}{4}} x$

$D = \{x: x > 0\}$; $R = \{y: y \in \mathcal{R}\}$; x-int: $(1, 0)$; no y-int; asymptote: $x = 0$; decreasing

For Example 3
Graph each function. Find the domain, range, x- and y-intercepts, and asymptote of each function. Determine whether the function is increasing or decreasing.
1. $f(x) = \log 100x - 4$

$D = \{x: x > 0\}$; $R = \{y: y \in \mathcal{R}\}$; x-int: $(100, 0)$; no y-int; asymptote: $x = 0$; increasing

Common Error When finding the y-intercept, some students may forget to bring the constant to the other side. Have these students move the constant before writing the logarithmic equation in exponential form.

2. $h(x) = \ln(4x + 8)$

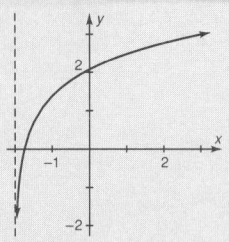

In the past, tables were used for evaluating logarithms, but now calculators are preferred. Scientific calculators have keys for evaluating both common logarithms and natural logarithms. In this book, values of logarithms will be given to four decimal places unless otherwise specified. The values are really approximations. However, for simplicity, the equality symbol (=) is used rather than the approximate equality symbol (≈).

Example 4   Find each logarithm to four decimal places.
   a. log 510   **b.** log 0.03   **c.** ln 70.5

   a. log 510 = 2.7076   **b.** log 0.03 = -1.5229 **c.** ln 70.5 = 4.2556

To evaluate and graph a logarithm with a base other than 10 or e, the *change-of-base* formula can be used. You are asked to prove this formula in Exercise 48.

Change-of-Base Formula

$$\log_b x = \frac{\log_a x}{\log_a b}$$

Example 5   Find the value of $\log_3 4$ to four decimal places.

$$\log_3 4 = \frac{\log 4}{\log 3} = 1.2619$$

Either the natural or common logarithm may be used in the change-of-base formula to graph any function. This strategy is especially useful when using a graphing utility. For example, the function $f(x) = \log_2 x$ is the same as the function $f(x) = \dfrac{\ln x}{\ln 2}$, which may then be input into a calculator or computer.

Example 6   Graph each function using the change-of-base formula and a graphing utility.
   a. $f(x) = \log_5 x$ **b.** $g(x) = \log_{\frac{1}{4}}(x - 3)$

   a. $f(x) = \log_5 x$

   $\log_5 x = \dfrac{\ln x}{\ln 5}$ *Input form*

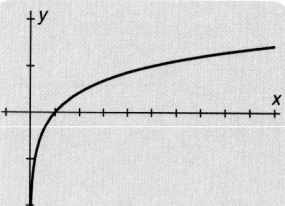

   b. $g(x) = \log_{\frac{1}{4}}(x - 3)$

   $\log_{\frac{1}{4}}(x - 3) = \dfrac{\log(x - 3)}{\log 0.25}$

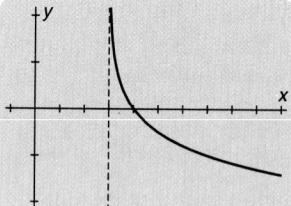

Logarithms are used to model a wide variety of problems. For example, the formula mentioned in the Focus for the magnitude of sound D, in decibels (db), is $D(x) = 10 \log \frac{I}{I_0}$, where I is the intensity of the sound and I_0 is the intensity of the threshold of hearing. The intensity of the threshold of human hearing, or the faintest audible sound, is 10^{-16} W/cm^2.

Example 7 Determine the magnitude or loudness of each sound to the nearest decibel.
 a. Threshold of hearing, $I = 10^{-16}$ **b.** Whisper, $I = 3.16 \times 10^{-15}$
 c. Subway train, $I = 5.01 \times 10^{-7}$

 a. $D(10^{-16}) = 10 \log \frac{10^{-16}}{10^{-16}} = 10 \log 1 = 10 \cdot 0 = 0$ db

 b. $D(3.16 \times 10^{-15}) = 10 \log \frac{3.16 \times 10^{-15}}{10^{-16}} \approx 15$ db

 A whisper is usually between 10 and 20 decibels.

 c. $D(5.01 \times 10^{-7}) = 10 \log \frac{5.01 \times 10^{-7}}{10^{-16}} \approx 97$ db

 The sound of a subway train is usually between 90 and 100 decibels.

Another application of logarithms is the Richter Scale, which is used to measure the magnitude of an earthquake. It is based on the equation $M(x) = \log \frac{x}{x_0}$, where x_0 is the magnitude of a zero-level earthquake with a seismographic reading of 0.001 mm and x is the seismographic reading of the earthquake.

Class Exercises

Solve for x to the nearest hundredth.
 1. $\log 0.00325 = x$ **2.** $\ln 4255 = x$ **3.** $\ln x = -2.22$ **4.** $\log x = 4.0005$
 -2.49 8.36 0.11 $10{,}011.52$

Express each logarithmic equation as an exponential equation and solve.
 5. $\log 10^{0.3} = y$ **6.** $\log_b 36 = 2$ **7.** $\ln 1 = y$ **8.** $\log_6 x = -3$
 $10^y = 10^{0.3}; y = 0.3$ $b^2 = 36; b = 6$ $e^y = 1; y = 0$ $6^{-3} = x; x = \frac{1}{216}$

Without graphing, determine whether each function is an increasing or decreasing function.
 9. $f(x) = \log_7 x$ **10.** $g(x) = \log_{\frac{1}{10}} x$ **11.** $h(x) = \log_{\sqrt{5}} x$ **12.** $m(x) = \ln x$
 increasing   decreasing   increasing   increasing

Graph each logarithmic function by finding its asymptote and x- and y-intercepts. State the domain and range and whether the function is increasing or decreasing.
 13. $f(x) = \log (x + 10)$ **14.** $g(x) = \ln (x - e)$

 15. *Acoustics*   Determine the magnitude of ordinary conversation to the nearest decibel given that the intensity is $I = 10^{-10}$ W/cm^2. 60 db

 16. *Seismology*   Determine the value of a reading on the Richter Scale for an earthquake with a seismographic reading of 0.2 mm. 2.3

For Example 6
Graph each function using the change-of-base formula and a graphing utility.
 1. $f(x) = \log_{\sqrt{3}} (x + 1)$

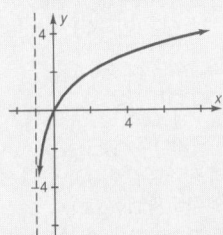

 2. $g(x) = \log_{\frac{1}{10}} x - 3$

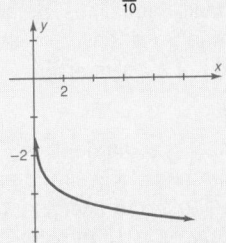

Technology Emphasize the need for the appropriate use of parentheses when entering a function.

For Example 7
The Richter scale is used to measure the magnitude of an earthquake. It is based on the equation

$$M(x) = \log \frac{x}{x_0}$$

where x_0 is the magnitude of a zero-level earthquake with a seismographic reading of 0.001 mm and x is the seismographic reading of the earthquake. Determine the value of the Richter scale to the nearest tenth for an earthquake whose seismographic reading is 50 mm. 4.7

CLOSURE

Group students in pairs and have them explain to each other how to graph logarithmic functions using a graphing utility.

Additional Answers, Class Exercises
13.

$D = \{x: x > -10\}$;
$R = \{y: y \in \mathcal{R}\}$;
x-int: $(-9, 0)$;
y-int: $(0, 1)$;
asymptote: $x = -10$;
increasing

14.

$D = \{x: x > e\}$;
$R = \{y: y \in \mathcal{R}\}$;
x-int: $(e + 1, 0)$;
no y-int;
asymptote: $x = e$;
increasing

Assignment Guide

Basic: 1–22, 25, 28, 33, 35, 37,
   Project
Average: 11–12, 15–39, Project
Enriched: 12, 20–22, 26–48, Project

Teacher's Resource Book
   Practice, page 60

Ⓡ Review

Exercises 11, 15, 19, 25, 33, and 35
review concepts of finding inverse
functions, evaluating radical expressions, dividing polynomials, solving
systems of linear inequalities, determining equivalent functions, and determining zeros of a polynomial.

Project

You may want to give students a
start on their projects by giving them
bits of information about decibel
levels. For example, a jet airplane
registers 140 decibels on takeoff and
a ringing telephone registers about
70 decibels.

LESSON FOLLOW-UP

Test Yourself

Teacher's Resource Book
   Tests—Quiz, form A, page 41
   Tests—Quiz, form B, page 41

Additional Answers

9.

10.

Practice Exercises   Use appropriate technology.

Find each logarithm to four decimal places.

A **1.** log 170 2.2304   **2.** log 179,000 5.2529   **3.** ln 16 2.7726   **4.** $\log_5 3$ 0.6826

Express each logarithmic equation as an exponential equation and solve.

5. $\log_5 625 = y$ **6.** $\log_{32} x = -\frac{3}{5}$ **7.** $\log_b \frac{1}{4} = \frac{1}{2}$ **8.** $\ln e^4 = y$
   $5^y = 625; y = 4$ $32^{-\frac{3}{5}} = x; x = \frac{1}{8}$ $b^{\frac{1}{2}} = \frac{1}{4}; b = \frac{1}{16}$ $e^y = e^4; y = 4$

Graph each logarithmic function.

9. $f(x) = \log_3 x$ **10.** $g(x) = \log_5 x$

Ⓡ **11.** Find the inverse function of the function $y = 4x^2$. State any restrictions on
   the domain, if necessary. $y = \frac{\sqrt{x}}{2}$; D: {x: x ≥ 0}

12. Thinking Critically   The value of $\log_2 15$ is directly proportional to the
   value of log 15. Analyze this statement in terms of the change-of-base
   formula to determine the constant of proportionality. $\frac{1}{\log 2} \approx 3.32$

Graph each function. Find the domain, range, x- and y-intercepts, and asymptote
of each function, and determine whether the function is increasing or decreasing.

13. $f(x) = \log (2x + 9)$ **14.** $h(x) = \log (x + 0.1)$

Ⓡ **15.** Evaluate: $\frac{\sqrt[3]{8^2}}{\sqrt[4]{16^{-2}}}$ 16

Graph each function using the change-of-base formula and a graphing utility.

16. $f(x) = \log_4 x$ **17.** $g(x) = \log_{15} x$ **18.** $h(x) = \log_3 (x + 1)$

Ⓡ **19.** Find the remainder when $x^4 - 3$ is divided by $x^3 - 2$. $2x - 3$

20. *Acoustics*   Determine the magnitude of thunder to the
   nearest decibel given that the intensity is 0.0001 W/cm². 120 db

21. *Electricity*   The time t, in seconds, at which the
   current in a circuit is I amperes is given by the
   formula $t = -\log_2 I$. Determine after how many
   seconds the current will be 0.2 amp. 2.3 s

22. *Chemistry*   The pH of a solution is given by the
   formula pH $= -\log [H^+]$, where $[H^+]$ is the hydrogen
   ion concentration in moles per liter. Determine the
   pH of milk if the hydrogen ion concentration is
   2.0×10^{-7} moles per liter. 7

Graph each function.

B **23.** $f(x) = 2 \ln (e - x)$ **24.** $g(x) = \ln (ex) + 2$

Ⓡ **25.** Solve the system of linear inequalities: $\begin{cases} x + y \le 5 \\ 3x + y \le 9 \\ x \ge 0, \ y \ge 0 \end{cases}$

Graph each function. Find the domain, range, x- and y-intercepts, and asymptote
of each function, and determine whether the function is increasing or decreasing.

26. $f(x) = \log (5x + 6) - 3$ **27.** $h(x) = -2 \ln (x + e^2)$

458   Chapter 9 Exponential and Logarithmic Functions

16.

17.

18.

28. Thinking Critically Compare the graphs of $f(x) = -\log_2 x$ and $g(x) = \log_{\frac{1}{2}} x$ and the graphs of $h(x) = -\log_4 x$ and $m(x) = \log_{\frac{1}{4}} x$. State a general conclusion.

Graph each function using the conclusion of Exercise 28.

29. $f(x) = \log_{\frac{1}{e}} x$

30. $g(x) = \log_{\frac{1}{10}} x$

31. $h(x) = \log_{\frac{1}{\sqrt{5}}} (3 - x)$

32. *Banking* The rate at which a sum of money would have to be invested to double in a given number of years, t, is $r = \dfrac{\ln 2}{t}$, assuming continuous compounding. Determine the rate at which a sum of money would have to be invested to double in 7 years. 9.9%

Ⓡ 33. Are $f(x) = x + 3$ and $g(x) = \dfrac{x^2 - 4x - 21}{x - 7}$ equivalent functions?
no; 7 is not in the domain of g.

34. *Seismology* If the magnitude of an earthquake is 3 on the Richter Scale, determine how many times more intense it is compared with a zero-level earthquake. 1000 times

Ⓡ 35. Find the zeros of $P(x) = 2x^4 - 7x^2 - 15$ to the nearest tenth. $\pm 2.2, \pm 1.2i$

36. *Chemistry* The pH of a solution is given by the formula $\text{pH} = -\log [H^+]$, where $[H^+]$ is the hydrogen ion concentration in moles per liter. Find the value of $[H^+]$ for the substances in the table.

Substance	pH	
Acid rain	4.52	3.02×10^{-5}
Pure water	7	1×10^{-7}
Sea water	8.5	3.16×10^{-9}

37. Writing in Mathematics You are asked to graph the function $g(x) = \log_3 (x - 2) + 3$. Describe at least two different techniques for sketching this graph. Explain the advantages and disadvantages of each technique.

The ancient Greeks classified the brightness of stars by *magnitude;* that is, they referred to stars of the first magnitude, second magnitude, and so on. The modern measure of brightness involves comparing two stars in terms of their *brightness ratio r*. The brightness of two stars can also be compared by finding the difference d in their magnitude. For example, the magnitude difference for a second magnitude star and fifth magnitude star is $5 - 2$, or 3. The numbers d and r are approximately related by the equation $d = 2.5 \log r$.

38. Find the brightness ratio for two stars of the first and seventh magnitude, respectively. 251.2

39. The brightness ratio of two stars is 100. The magnitude of the brighter star is 8. Find the magnitude of the other star. 3

Find the equation of each function from its graph. In each case, a logarithmic function has been translated from its basic position.

C **40.**
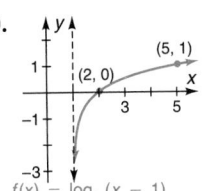
$f(x) = \log_4 (x - 1)$

41.
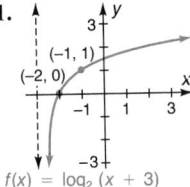
$f(x) = \log_2 (x + 3)$

42.
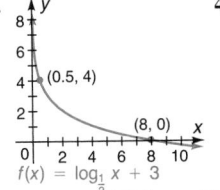
$f(x) = \log_{\frac{1}{2}} x + 3$

43.

$f(x) = \log x - 5$

9.3 Logarithmic Functions **459**

Writing in Mathematics
37. The logarithmic function $g(x)$ can be graphed by finding its asymptote and x- and y-intercepts or as a translation of the basic curve $f(x) = \log_3 x$.

459

44. *Seismology*   Given that the intensity of one earthquake is 200 times the intensity of another, determine the difference in their magnitude. 2.3

45. *Radioactive Decay*   The formula $t = 2350 (\ln 200 - \ln x)$ can be used to determine the number of years t it would take 200 mg of radium to decompose so that only x milligrams remain. Graph the function and determine from the graph the number of years it would take to have less than 20 mg radium remaining. approx. 5411 years

46. The decibel level in the working area immediately surrounding a shipyard riveter is about 98 db. Find the decibel level of two riveters working together, that is, the decibel level at twice the intensity of sound for one riveter. 101 db or 3 db louder

47. On the Richter Scale, the San Francisco earthquake of 1906 and 1989 measured about 7.1 and 7.9, respectively. Compare the magnitudes of the observed seismographic readings.

48. Prove the change-of-base formula $\log_b x = \dfrac{\log_a x}{\log_a b}$. *Hint*: Let $\log_b x = p$, $\log_a x = q$, and $\log_a b = r$. Then use the definition of $f(x) = \log_b x$, the rules for exponents, and the fact that for any real number M, $M \neq 0$, $M \neq 1$, $M^u = M^v$ if and only if $u = v$.

Project

Make a table with three columns headed *Intensity, Decibel Level,* and *Common Sound.* Then find the decibel level for each of the given intensity levels and a common sound from everyday life that is an example of each decibel level.

Intensity levels (W/cm²): 10^{-16}, 10^{-15}, 10^{-14}, 10^{-13}, 10^{-12}, 10^{-11}, 10^{-10}, 10^{-9}, 10^{-8}, 10^{-7}, 10^{-6}, 10^{-5}, 10^{-4}

Test Yourself

Evaluate each expression.

1. $\sqrt[3]{-343^2}$ -49

2. $0.1^{-\frac{5}{4}}$ 17.8

9.1

Simplify each expression.

3. $\left(\dfrac{16xy^4}{81x^5}\right)^{\frac{1}{4}}$ $\dfrac{2y}{3x}$

4. $\left(x^{\frac{3}{4}}y^{-\frac{2}{3}}z^{\frac{5}{2}}\right)^{-\frac{2}{9}}$ $\dfrac{y^{\frac{4}{27}}}{x^{\frac{1}{6}}z^{\frac{5}{9}}}$

Solve each equation.

5. $4^{3x} = 2\sqrt{2}$ $\frac{1}{4}$

6. $\log_3 \dfrac{1}{\sqrt{27}} = x$ $-\frac{3}{2}$

9.2, 9.3

Graph each function. Determine the domain, range, intercepts, and asymptotes.

7. $f(x) = 3^{x+1} + 1$

8. $g(x) = -\ln x + 2.5$

9.2, 9.3

9. *Demographics*   In the 1970 census the population of the Greater Chicago area was listed as 7,778,948. By 1980 the population had grown to 7,937,326. Use this data to construct a model for predicting the population growth of the city and estimate Chicago's population in the year 2001. 8,285,213

460   Chapter 9 Exponential and Logarithmic Functions

9.4 Properties of Logarithms

Objectives: To express logarithms in expanded form and in condensed form
To solve equations involving logarithms

Focus

In predicting weather patterns, meteorologists must keep track of many conditions, such as temperature, precipitation, and atmospheric pressure. Atmospheric pressure is a result of the force of gravity on the atmosphere, which weighs about 5.7×10^{15} tons. One instrument used to measure atmospheric pressure is the mercury barometer, which gives the pressure in a unit called a millibar (mb). The pressure of the earth's atmosphere at sea level at 0°C is 1013 mb. The earth's atmosphere becomes less dense with increasing altitude; atmospheric pressure is a function of altitude. Like other phenomena that can vary over a wide range, atmospheric pressure is measured using a logarithmic scale.

The study of meteorology and other physical phenomena can lead to equations involving logarithms. Such equations can often be simplified and solved using properties of logarithms.

Since a logarithmic function is the inverse of an exponential function, the properties of logarithms can be derived from the properties of exponents. By definition, $y = \log_b x$ if and only $b^y = x$.

Properties of Logarithms

If M, N, and b are positive real numbers, $b \neq 1$, and r is any real number, then

$$\log_b MN = \log_b M + \log_b N$$
$$\log_b \frac{M}{N} = \log_b M - \log_b N$$
$$\log_b M^r = r \log_b M$$

The expression on the right side of each equation above is said to be the *expanded form* of the logarithm on the left side. The properties of logarithms can be derived from the properties of exponents by using simple substitutions.

9.4 Properties of Logarithms **461**

For Example 1

Using the definition of a logarithm and the properties of exponents, derive the property $\log_b \dfrac{M}{N} = \log_b M - \log_b N$.

Let $\log_b M = u$ and $\log_b N = v$. Then $b^u = M$ and $b^v = N$.

$\dfrac{M}{N} = \dfrac{b^u}{b^v}$ Divide.

$\dfrac{M}{N} = b^{u-v}$ $\dfrac{a^m}{a^n} = a^{m-n}$

$\log_b \dfrac{M}{N} = \log_b b^{u-v}$ Take the log of both sides.

$\log_b b^{u-v} = u - v$ $\log_b b^r = r$

$\log_b \dfrac{M}{N} = \log_b M - \log_b N$ Substitute.

For Example 2

Express each logarithm in expanded form.

1. $\log_3 \dfrac{\sqrt[4]{x^3}}{y^2}$ $\dfrac{3}{4} \log_3 x - 2 \log_3 y$

2. $\log (x - y)^3 y^{-2}$
$3 \log (x - y) - 2 \log y$

Common Error Some students may write $\log (x - y)$ as $\log \dfrac{x}{y}$. Have these students substitute values in each expression to verify that the quantities are not equivalent.

For Example 3

Express each as a single logarithm.

1. $\dfrac{1}{2} \log y + 3 \log (x + y)$
$\log \sqrt{y}(x + y)^3$

2. $\dfrac{3}{4} \ln 16y - 2 \ln x + \dfrac{1}{4} \ln y$ $\ln \dfrac{8y}{x^2}$

Common Error Some students may write $\dfrac{3}{4} \ln 16y$ as $\ln 16 y^{\frac{3}{4}}$. Remind these students to enclose the expression $16y$ in parentheses.

Example 1   Using the definition of a logarithm and the properties of exponents, derive:
   a. $\log_b b^r = r$ **b.** $\log_b MN = \log_b M + \log_b N$

a. Let $\log_b b^r = A$. Then

$b^A = b^r$ *$y = \log_b x$ if and only if $b^y = x$*
$A = r$ *Since the exponential function is one-to-one, $b^m = b^n$ if and only if $m = n$.*
$\log_b b^r = r$ *Substitution*

b. Let $w = \log_b M$ and $v = \log_b N$. Then

$b^w = M$ and $b^v = N$ *$y = \log_b x$ if and only if $b^y = x$*
$MN = b^w \cdot b^v$ *Multiply.*
$MN = b^{w+v}$ *$a^m \cdot a^n = a^{m+n}$*
$\log_b MN = w + v$ *$y = \log_b x$ if and only if $b^y = x$*
$\log_b MN = \log_b M + \log_b N$ *Substitution*

You are asked to prove the remaining logarithm properties in the exercises. To express a logarithm in expanded form, use the properties of logarithms.

Example 2   Express each logarithm in expanded form.   **a.** $\log_b \sqrt[3]{2x^2 y^5}$ **b.** $\ln \dfrac{(x + y)^{\frac{1}{2}}}{x^4 y}$

a. $\log_b \sqrt[3]{2x^2 y^5} = \log_b (2x^2 y^5)^{\frac{1}{3}}$ $\sqrt[3]{a} = a^{\frac{1}{3}}$

$\qquad\qquad\quad = \dfrac{1}{3} \log_b (2x^2 y^5)$ $\log_b M^r = r \log_b M$

$\qquad\qquad\quad = \dfrac{1}{3} [\log_b 2 + \log_b x^2 + \log_b y^5]$ $\log_b MN = \log_b M + \log_b N$

$\qquad\qquad\quad = \dfrac{1}{3} [\log_b 2 + 2 \log_b x + 5 \log_b y]$

b. $\ln \dfrac{(x + y)^{\frac{1}{2}}}{x^4 y} = \ln (x + y)^{\frac{1}{2}} - \ln x^4 y$ $\log_b \dfrac{M}{N} = \log_b M - \log_b N$

$\qquad\qquad\quad = \dfrac{1}{2} \ln (x + y) - (4 \ln x + \ln y)$

$\qquad\qquad\quad = \dfrac{1}{2} \ln (x + y) - 4 \ln x - \ln y$ *Can $\ln (x + y)$ be expanded further? Explain.*

A logarithmic expression can sometimes be simplified by rewriting it as a single logarithm, called *condensed form*. Before combining expressions, be sure that they have the same base.

Example 3   Express in condensed form.
   a. $4 \log 3x - 3 \log y + 5 \log 3z$ **b.** $\dfrac{1}{3} \ln x^2 - \dfrac{1}{2} \ln y^3$

a. $4 \log 3x - 3 \log y + 5 \log 3z = \log (3x)^4 - \log y^3 + \log (3z)^5$

$\qquad\qquad\qquad\qquad = \log \dfrac{81x^4}{y^3} + \log 243z^5 = \log \dfrac{19{,}683x^4 z^5}{y^3}$

b. $\dfrac{1}{3} \ln x^2 - \dfrac{1}{2} \ln y^3 = \ln \sqrt[3]{x^2} - \ln \sqrt{y^3} = \ln \dfrac{\sqrt[3]{x^2}}{\sqrt{y^3}}$

462   Chapter 9 Exponential and Logarithmic Functions

Thinking Critically
The parentheses indicate that $x + y$ is a single term, and thus $\ln (x + y)$ cannot be expanded further.

Some logarithmic equations can be solved by expressing them in equivalent exponential form. First, simplify the logarithmic equation by condensing the logarithmic expressions, if possible.

Example 4 Determine the domain of the logarithmic equation $\log_3 (5x - 12) + \log_3 x = 2$. Then solve by expressing the equation in equivalent exponential form.

$\log_3 (5x - 12) + \log_3 x = 2$

$5x - 12 > 0 \quad$ and $\quad x > 0 \qquad$ *$\log_b M$ is defined if and only if $M > 0$.*

$\qquad x > \frac{12}{5} \quad$ and $\quad x > 0$

Therefore, the domain is $\left\{ x\colon x > \frac{12}{5} \right\}$.

$\log_3 (5x - 12) + \log_3 x = 2 \qquad$ *Express the equation in condensed form.*
$\qquad \log_3 (5x - 12)(x) = 2 \qquad$ *$\log_b MN = \log_b M + \log_b N$*
$\qquad \log_3 (5x^2 - 12x) = 2$
$\qquad\qquad 5x^2 - 12x = 3^2 \qquad$ *$y = \log_b x$ if and only if $b^y = x$*
$\qquad 5x^2 - 12x - 9 = 0$
$\qquad (5x + 3)(x - 3) = 0$
$\qquad\qquad x = -\frac{3}{5} \quad$ or $\quad x = 3$

Since 3 is in the domain of the function but $-\frac{3}{5}$ is not, 3 is the only solution.

It is often useful to convert a logarithmic equation to an appropriate exponential form. Once this is done, you can use the exponentiation keys on a calculator, such as e^x, x^y, or $\char94$, to evaluate the calculation-ready expression.

Example 5 A formula for determining the height at which a certain atmospheric pressure occurs is $h = \dfrac{-(\ln P - \ln 14.7)}{0.21}$. Here P is the atmospheric pressure in pounds per square inch and h is the height in miles. Determine the atmospheric pressure at the midpoint of the mesosphere to the nearest hundredth of a millibar given that 1 mb = 0.0145 lb/in.²

$h = \dfrac{-(\ln P - \ln 14.7)}{0.21}$

$-0.21h = \ln P - \ln 14.7$

$-0.21h = \ln \dfrac{P}{14.7} \qquad$ *$\log_b \frac{M}{N} = \log_b M - \log_b N$*

$e^{-0.21h} = \dfrac{P}{14.7} \qquad$ *$\ln x = y$ if and only if $e^y = x$*

$P = 14.7 e^{-0.21h}$

Regions of the Atmosphere	
Troposphere	Sea level–7 mi
Stratosphere	7 mi–30 mi
Mesosphere	30 mi–50 mi
Thermosphere	50 mi–400 mi
Exosphere	Over 400 mi

The midpoint of the mesosphere occurs at $\dfrac{30 + 50}{2} = 40$ mi. Therefore,

$P = 14.7 e^{(-0.21)(40)} = 0.0033055497$ lb/in.²

$P = 0.0033055497$ lb/in.² $\cdot \dfrac{1 \text{ mb}}{0.0145 \text{ lb/in.}^2} = 0.23$ mb $\qquad$ To the nearest hundredth

9.4 Properties of Logarithms **463**

For Example 4
Determine the domain of each logarithmic equation. Then solve by expressing the equation in equivalent exponential form.
1. $\log_5 (x + 3) - \log_5 (x - 2) = 1$
$\quad D = \{x\colon x > 2\}; x = 3\frac{1}{4}$
2. $3 \log_2 x + 2 \log_2 x = 5$
$\quad D = \{x\colon x > 0\}; x = 2$

For Example 5
Using the information in Example 5, determine the atmospheric pressure at the midpoint of the thermosphere.
3×10^{-18} mb

Have students summarize in their math journals the new math connections they made in this lesson.

INDEPENDENT PRACTICE

Assignment Guide
Basic: 1–20, 27–29
Average: 11–15, 19–36
Enriched: 12, 14, 23–26, 28, 30–45

Teacher's Resource Book
 Practice, page 61

Ⓡ Review

Exercises 11, 13, 15, 19, 27, and 29 review concepts of graphing exponential and logarithmic functions, solving quadratic inequalities, evaluating composite functions and inverse trigonometric functions, and describing logarithmic functions.

Additional Answers

Class Exercises
1. $b^0 = 1$, where $b > 0$
2. $b^1 = b$, where $b \in \mathcal{R}$

Practice Exercises

11.

12. They are not equivalent.
$\log \frac{x}{2} = \log x - \log 2 \neq \frac{\log x}{\log 2}$

13.

Class Exercises

Using the definition of a logarithm, explain why each of the properties of logarithms is true.

1. $\log_b 1 = 0$

2. $\log_b b = 1$

Express each in condensed form.

3. $\log x + 4 \log x^2 - 3 \log x^3$ 0

4. $2 \ln \sqrt{y} - \frac{1}{2} \ln y^4 + \ln 2y$ ln 2

Express each in expanded form, if possible.

5. $\log_b x^3 \sqrt{y}$
$3 \log_b x + \frac{1}{2} \log_b y$

6. $\log_b \frac{x^2}{\sqrt[5]{yz}}$
$2 \log_b x - \frac{1}{5} \log_b y - \frac{1}{5} \log_b z$

7. $\ln \frac{\sqrt{x^3}}{\sqrt[4]{y}}$
$\frac{3}{2} \ln x - \frac{1}{4} \ln y$

8. $\log_b (x - y)$
$\log_b (x - y)$

Determine the domain of each logarithmic equation. Then solve by writing the equation in equivalent exponential form.

9. $\log_6 (x + 5) + \log_6 x = 1$ $\{x : x > 0\}$; 1

10. $\log_4 (x + 1) - \log_4 x = 2$ $\{x : x > 0\}$; $\frac{1}{15}$

11. *Chemistry* The pH value of a solution is given by the formula pH = $-\log [H^+]$ where $[H^+]$ is the hydrogen ion concentration in moles per liter. Solve the equation for $[H^+]$ and determine the hydrogen ion concentration for a solution with a pH of -7. 10^7

Practice Exercises

Using the definition of a logarithm and the properties of exponents, derive each of the following properties of logarithms.

A 1. $\log_b M^r = r \log_b M$

2. $\log_b \frac{M}{N} = \log_b M - \log_b N$

Express each logarithm in expanded form.

3. $\log_b \frac{xy^2}{z}$
$\log_b x + 2 \log_b y - \log_b z$

4. $\log_b \frac{x^3}{\sqrt[4]{y}}$
$3 \log_b x - \frac{1}{4} \log_b y$

5. $\log_b \sqrt[5]{x^2 y}$
$\frac{1}{5}[2 \log_b x + \log_b y]$

6. $\log_b \sqrt{\frac{y^4}{4x^2}}$
$\frac{1}{2}[4 \log_b y - \log_b 4 - 2 \log_b x]$

Express each in condensed form.

7. $3 \log x + \log 3 - 3 \log y$ $\log \frac{3x^3}{y^3}$

8. $\frac{1}{4} \log x^2 - 2 \log y + \log 4$ $\log \frac{4\sqrt{x}}{y^2}$

9. $0.5 \ln 9x + 3 \ln 3x + 2 \ln y^2$ $\ln 81x^{\frac{7}{2}}y^4$

10. $\frac{2}{3} \log_3 x^3 - \log_3 \frac{3}{4}y^4 - \log_3 10$ $\log_3 \frac{2x^2}{15y^4}$

Ⓡ 11. Graph the function $f(x) = 3^x$.

12. Thinking Critically Analyze the logarithmic expressions $\log \frac{x}{2}$ and $\frac{\log x}{\log 2}$ and determine whether they are equivalent. Justify your answer.

Ⓡ 13. Graph $h(x) = \log_3 x$.

14. Writing in Mathematics Write a sentence expressing why the equation $b^{\log_b M} = M$ is true.

Ⓡ 15. Solve and write the solution in interval form: $2x^2 - 5x - 12 \leq 0$ [−1.5, 4]

464 Chapter 9 Exponential and Logarithmic Functions

Writing in Mathematics
14. The expression $\log_b M$ is the exponent that b is raised to in order to get M.

Determine the domain of each logarithmic equation. Then solve by transforming the equation to equivalent exponential form.

16. $\log_3 (x + 8) + \log_3 x = 2$
{x: x > 0}; 1

17. $\log_2 (x + 3) - \log_2 (x + 1) = 3$
{x: x > -1}; $-\frac{5}{7}$

18. *Electricity*   An electrical circuit has both a resistance R and a capacitance C. If the switch is closed, the charge q at time t can be found using the formula $\ln q - \ln q_0 = -\frac{t}{RC}$. Solve for q. $q_0 e^{-\frac{t}{RC}}$

Ⓡ 19. Given $f(x) = 2x$ and $g(x) = x^3 - 1$, evaluate $(f \circ g)(x)$. $2x^3 - 2$

20. Prove that $\log_b \frac{1}{N} = -\log_b N$. Then use a graphing utility to compare the graphs of $f(x) = \log_4 \frac{1}{x}$ and $g(x) = -\log_4 x$.
$\log_b \frac{1}{N} = \log_b N^{-1} = -\log_b N$, or
$\log_b 1 - \log_b N = 0 - \log_b N = -\log_b N$

Express each logarithm in expanded form.

B 21. $\log \left(\frac{gmM}{d^2} \right)$
$\log g + \log m + \log M - 2 \log d$

22. $\log [P(1 + r)^t]$
$\log P + t \log (1 + r)$

Express each in condensed form and simplify.

23. $\frac{1}{4}(\log_b x - \log_b y)$ $\log_b \sqrt[4]{\frac{x}{y}}$

24. $3 \log (x + y) - (\log x + \log y)$ $\log \frac{(x + y)^3}{xy}$

25. $3 \ln e + 4 \ln e^2 - 2 \ln e$ 9

26. $3 \log 0.1 + 4 \log 0.01 - 2 \log 0.001$ -5

Ⓡ 27. Evaluate: $\operatorname{Csc}^{-1} 1.4663$ 43°

28. **Thinking Critically**   Using a graphing utility, find a pattern for the graphs of the function $h(x) = \log x + \log x^a$ for integral values of a. *Hint*: Compare this function to $f(x) = \log x$.

Ⓡ 29. Determine the domain, range, asymptote, and intercepts of $f(x) = \log_2 (x + 1)$. Determine whether the function is increasing or decreasing. Graph the function.

Determine the domain of each logarithmic equation. Then solve by expressing the equation in equivalent exponential form.

30. $\log_5 (6x - 7) + \log_5 x = 1$

31. $2 \log_2 x - \log_2 (2x - 2) = 1$

32. $5 \log_3 x - 2 \log_3 x = -3$

33. $2 \log_2 4x - \log_2 (3x + 1) = 1$

34. *Banking*   The formula $t = \frac{\ln A - \ln P}{r}$ can be used to determine the number of years t that a current certificate of deposit must be invested at the First National Bank to accumulate an amount of money A. The amount invested is P and r is the continuously compounded annual interest rate. Determine, to the nearest dollar, the amount that must be invested for 2 years at 8.25% to grow to $4246. $3600

35. *Space Satellites*   The number of days left in the power output of a satellite can be determined from the formula $\ln P = \ln 50 - \frac{t}{250}$, where P is the power output in watts and t is the number of days left. Find the number of full days left in the power supply if the power output is 18.2 W.   252 days

9.4 Properties of Logarithms   **465**

1. Express $\ln \frac{x^3 \sqrt{y}}{vz}$ in expanded form.
   $3 \ln x + \frac{1}{2} \ln y - \ln v - \ln z$

2. Express $4 \log (x - y) - 2 \log (3y)$ in condensed form.
   $\log \frac{(x - y)^4}{9y^2}$

3. Determine the domain of the logarithmic equation $\log_2 (3x + 10) + \log_2 x = 3$, and solve.
   $D = \{x: x > 0\}$;
   $x = -4$ (reject); $x = \frac{2}{3}$

4. The formula $t = \frac{\ln A - \ln P}{r}$ can be used to determine the number of years t that a current certificate of deposit at Second City Bank, paying interest compounded continuously, was invested, where A is the amount of money accumulated after t years, P is the amount invested, and r is the interest rate. Determine the amount, to the nearest dollar, that was invested for $3\frac{1}{2}$ years at 7% and yielded $12,281. $P = 9612

Additional Answers

28. As a increases, the graph of $h(x)$ gets "steeper." The same is true for negative values of a, but the graph will be decreasing instead of increasing.

29.
$D = \{x: x > -1\}$; $R = \{y: y \in \mathcal{R}\}$; x-int: 0; y-int: 0; asymptote: $x = -1$; increasing

30. $\left\{x: x > \frac{7}{6}\right\}$; $\frac{5}{3}$

31. $\{x: x > 1\}$; 2

32. $\{x: x > 0\}$; $\frac{1}{3}$

33. $\{x: x > 0\}$; 0.59

Alternative Assessment

Have students research the history of logarithms and prepare for pre-sentation a report which includes a discussion of how the invention of the scientific calculator has affected the use of logarithms. Have students illustrate their discussion by using specific examples.

Enrichment

Using a graphing utility, graph $f(x) = 4 \log x$ and $g(x) = \log x^4$ on the same set of axes. Explain the results.

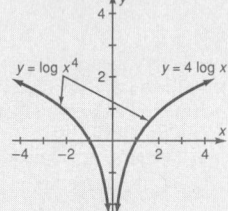

When both functions are defined over the same domain, $\{x: x > 0\}$, the graphs will coincide.

Additional Answers

37. $D = \{x: x > 2\}; \frac{20}{9}$

38. $D = \{x: x > 0\}; 0.001$

39. $D = \{x: x > 5\}; 5.25$

40. $D = \{x: x > 0\}; 1$

36. *Physics*   The absorption of light by sea water is modeled by the equation $\ln I = \ln I_0 - 0.014d$, where I_0 is the intensity of the light in the atmosphere and I is the intensity at a depth of d cm. Find at what depth the intensity of the light in the water will be 50% of the light in the atmosphere. 49.5 cm

Determine the domain of each logarithmic equation. Then solve by writing the equation in equivalent exponential form. Use the change-of-base formula if necessary.

C **37.** $\log_{0.1} (x - 2) + \log x = 1$

38. $\log_{100} x^2 - \log x^3 = 6$

39. $2 \log_4 (x - 5) - 3 \log_4 (x - 5) = 1$

40. $\log_b x = \ln x, b > 0, b \neq 1, b \neq e$

Use a graphing utility to solve each equation.

41. $x^2 - 4x + 4 = \log_2 x$ 1.3; 3.3

42. $x^3 + 5 = \ln x$ no solutions

43. *Chemistry*   The pOH of a solution is the hydroxyl ion concentration and can be determined by the formula pOH $= -\log [OH^-]$. The pH of a solution is given by the formula pH $= -\log [H^+]$. The relationship between pH and pOH is given by the equation pH $+$ pOH $= 14$. Find $[H^+]$, the concentration of the hydrogen ion. $\frac{10^{-14}}{[OH^-]}$

44. *Meteorology*   The thermopause is the boundary between the thermosphere and the exosphere. Determine the ratio of atmospheric pressure at the thermopause, to the atmospheric pressure at sea level. Refer to the Focus and Example 5. 3.3×10^{-37}

45. The graph of a basic function can be dilated, translated, or reflected in the x-axis as illustrated in the table below.

Basic Function	Transformed Function
$f(x) = x^2$	$g(x) = a(x - h)^2 + k$
$f(x) = \sin x$	$g(x) = a \sin (x - h) + k$

Here the value of $|a|$ determines the vertical dilation of the curve. If $a < 0$, the curve is reflected in the x-axis. The value of h determines the horizontal translation, or shift. The value of k determines the vertical shift. Apply the above principles to the basic logarithmic function $f(x) = \log_b x$ and find the values of a, h, and k for the functions $g(x) = -2 \ln x + 2$ and $h(x) = \log (3x + 10)$ of Example 3 in Lesson 9.3. $g(x): a = -2, h = 0, k = 2$
$h(x): a = 1, h = -\frac{10}{3}, k = \log 3$

Review

Simplify each expression:

1. $(\sin x - \cos x)^2$ $1 - \sin 2x$

2. $(\csc \theta + \cot \theta)(\csc \theta - \cot \theta)$ 1

3. Find the inverse function of $f(x) = x^2 - 14$. Restrict the domain of f if necessary. $f^{-1}(x) = +\sqrt{x + 14}; x \geq -14$

9.5 Exponential Equations and Inequalities

Objectives: *To use logarithms to solve exponential equations*
To use a graphing utility to solve exponential and logarithmic
equations and inequalities

Focus

Exponential equations have applications in finance. The *compound interest formula* for determining the interest earnings on a savings account is one such application. An essential variable in the formula is the number of times a year the interest is compounded. You are probably familiar with accounts in which the interest is said to be compounded quarterly, monthly, or daily. As you will see in this lesson, it is even possible for

interest to be compounded *continuously*. In that case, interest earnings can be calculated for any given moment in time. The modification of the compound interest formula that allows for continuous compounding involves the number e and provides a vivid illustration of how the natural exponential function can be used as a powerful modeling tool.

In Lesson 9.2, you solved some simple exponential equations by expressing both sides of the equation in terms of the same base. A more general technique for solving such equations is to take the logarithm of both sides of the equation. For this reason it is important to be adept at evaluating logarithms.

Compare the logarithms of 260, 26,000, and 0.26.

$$\log 260 = \log (2.6 \times 10^2) = \log 2.6 + \log 10^2 = 0.4150 + 2 = 2.4150$$
$$\log 26{,}000 = \log (2.6 \times 10^4) = \log 2.6 + \log 10^4 = 0.4150 + 4 = 4.4150$$
$$\log 0.26 = \log (2.6 \times 10^{-1}) = \log 2.6 + \log 10^{-1} = 0.4150 - 1 = -0.5850$$

These examples illustrate that any common logarithm can be thought of as the sum of an integer, which is called the **characteristic,** and a nonnegative decimal less than 1, called the **mantissa.** In the above examples, 0.4150 is the mantissa for all three logarithms. *Why?* The characteristics are 2, 4, and −1, respectively. Note that the characteristic represents the exponent of 10 when the original number is expressed in scientific notation.

A calculator can be used to find x when $\log x$ or $\ln x$ is known. Since the logarithmic function is the inverse of the exponential function, use the exponential keys to find 10^x or e^x, respectively.

Thinking Critically
Using the properties of logarithms and scientific notation, all three numbers contain log 2.6 as an addend.

LESSON PLAN

Vocabulary
compound interest formula
continuous compound interest
    formula

Ⓜ **Materials/Manipulatives**
newspaper ads showing interest
    rates for certificates of deposit

Technology
graphing utility
symbolic manipulator

FOCUS

Financial applications can be very motivational for students, particularly when the effort is made to show how the applications are relevant to their own lives. Illustrate the power of exponential growth with a model of interest earnings over a period of many years.

INSTRUCTION

• Review the value of e before discussing the Modeling in this lesson.
• Remind students that the value of e can be found on some calculators using the e^x key with an exponent of 1.

Ⓜ **Alternative Learning Styles**
For some students the motivation to learn a mathematical concept comes from using information or situations from their daily lives in the problems discussed. Ask students where they have used or seen interest rates in their own experience before discussing the compound or continuous compound interest formula.

Example 1 Solve for x to the nearest hundredth.
  a. $\log x = 3.2274$ **b.** $\log x = -1.3545$
  c. $\ln x = 2.0855$ **d.** $\ln x = 0.0362$

a. $\log x = 3.2274$ **b.** $\log x = -1.3545$ **c.** $\ln x = 2.0855$ **d.** $\ln x = 0.0362$
$x = 10^{3.2274}$ $x = 10^{-1.3545}$ $x = e^{2.0855}$ $x = e^{0.0362}$
$x = 1688.11$ $x = 0.04$ $x = 8.05$ $x = 1.04$

Logarithms are especially useful for solving exponential equations in which both sides of the equation cannot be written in terms of the same base. This method of solution relies on the fact that $\log_b M = \log_b N$ if and only if $M = N$.

> **To solve an exponential equation:**
> - Isolate the exponential expression.
> - Take the logarithm of both sides of the equation.
> - Verify all answers by substitution in the original equation.

Logarithmic inequalities are solved in a similar manner. Recall that when multiplying or dividing an inequality by a negative number, the inequality must be reversed. Therefore, determine whether a logarithmic expression is positive or negative before multiplying or dividing by that expression.

 To check a logarithmic equation or inequality, use a graphing utility and determine the x-intercept.

Example 2 Solve each exponential equation or inequality for x to the nearest hundredth.
  a. $4^{2x-1} - 27 = 0$ **b.** $5^{3x-1} - 7^{4x} > 0$ **c.** $\dfrac{e^x}{e^x - 1} = 5$ **d.** $3e^{-x} - e^x = -2$

a.
$$4^{2x-1} - 27 = 0$$
$$4^{2x-1} = 27 \qquad \textit{Isolate the exponential expression.}$$
$$\log 4^{2x-1} = \log 27 \qquad \textit{Take the logarithm of both sides.}$$
$$(2x - 1) \log 4 = \log 27 \qquad \log_b M^r = r \log_b M$$
$$2x \log 4 - \log 4 = \log 27$$
$$2x \log 4 = \log 27 + \log 4$$
$$x = \frac{\log 27 + \log 4}{2 \log 4} = 1.69 \qquad \text{To the nearest hundredth}$$

b.
$$5^{3x-1} - 7^{4x} > 0$$
$$5^{3x-1} > 7^{4x}$$
$$(3x - 1) \log 5 > 4x \log 7 \qquad \textit{If } a > b, \textit{ then } \log a > \log b.$$
$$3x \log 5 -- \log 5 > 4x \log 7$$
$$3x \log 5 - 4x \log 7 > \log 5$$
$$x(3 \log 5 - 4 \log 7) > \log 5$$
$$x < \frac{\log 5}{3 \log 5 - 4 \log 7} \qquad \textit{Reverse the inequality since } 3 \log 5 - 4 \log 7 \textit{ is negative.}$$
$$x < -0.55 \qquad \textbf{To the nearest hundredth}$$

c. $\dfrac{e^x}{e^x - 1} = 5$

$\quad\quad e^x = 5e^x - 5 \quad\quad$ *Simplify.*

$\quad -4e^x = -5$

$\quad\quad\quad e^x = \dfrac{5}{4} \quad\quad\quad$ *Isolate e^x.*

$\quad x\ln e = \ln\dfrac{5}{4} \quad\quad$ *Take the natural logarithm of both sides.*

$\quad\quad\quad x = \ln\dfrac{5}{4} = 0.22 \quad$ To the nearest hundredth

d.
$\quad\quad 3e^{-x} - e^x = -2 \quad\quad$ *To eliminate negative exponents,*

$\quad\quad\quad 3 - e^{2x} = -2e^x \quad\quad$ *multiply both sides by e^x.*

$\quad e^{2x} - 2e^x - 3 = 0 \quad\quad$ *Quadratic in e^x*

$(e^x - 3)(e^x + 1) = 0 \quad\quad$ *Factor.*

$\quad\quad e^x = 3 \quad$ or $\quad e^x = -1 \quad$ *Reject -1 since $e^x > 0$ for all real values of x.*

$\quad\quad\quad\quad x = \ln 3 = 1.10 \quad$ To the nearest hundredth

 Not all exponential or logarithmic equations and inequalities can be solved using algebraic techniques. In such cases, a graphing utility can be used to find the solutions. The technique of graphing each side of the equation and determining the points of intersection can be used. Alternately, express the equation in function-form and graph.

Example 3 Solve each using a graphing utility. **a.** $e^x = x^2$ **b.** $\log x < x - 2$

a. $e^x = x^2$

Graph the functions $f(x) = e^x$ and $g(x) = x^2$.
The zoom and trace features show that the graphs
intersect at $x = -0.703$, to the nearest thousandth.
Check -0.703 in the original equation.

$\quad\quad e^x = x^2$

$e^{-0.703} = (-0.703)^2$

$\quad 0.495 \approx 0.494$

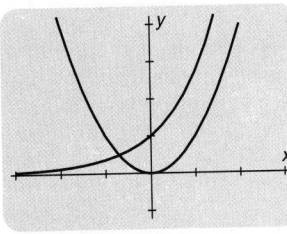

[–3, 3] by [–1, 4]

b. $\log x < x - 2$

Express the equation in function form as
$\log x - x + 2 = 0$. Then graph the function $g(x) = \log x - x + 2$. The zoom and trace features show
that the graph intersects the x-axis at $x = 0.010$ and
at $x = 2.376$, to the nearest thousandth. Since $\log x - x + 2 < 0$, the solution is values of x for which
the graph is *below* the x-axis. Thus, $0 < x < 0.010$
and $x > 2.376$.

[–1, 4] by [–3, 2]

 A graphing utility can also be used to solve exponential and logarithmic inequalities in two variables. Use the graphing utility to graph the corresponding functions, and then use inspection to determine the region to be shaded and whether the curve should be solid or dashed.

9.5 Exponential Equations and Inequalities **469**

For Example 3
Solve each using a graphing utility.

1. $e^x = x^2 - 1$

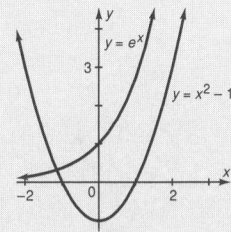

$x = -1.15$

2. $x > \log x - 2$

$x > 0$

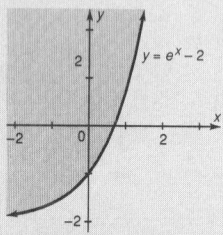
Example 4 Solve the inequality $y < 3 \log 2x$ by graphing.

Graph the function $f(x) = 3 \log 2x$. Use a dashed curve. Then shade the region *below* that curve. With a graphing calculator determine the region to be shaded by inspection.

[−2, 10] by [−2, 5]
x scl: 2   y scl: 1

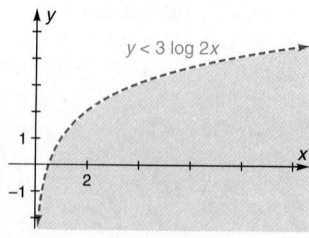

Exponential equations are often encountered in applications in which a quantity increases by a constant ratio during each of a sequence of constant time intervals. The compound interest earned on an investment increases with the passage of time so that the total value of the investment is an exponential function of the number of years that the interest is allowed to grow.

Compound Interest Formula

$$A = P\left(1 + \frac{r}{n}\right)^{nt}$$

In this formula, A is the total value of the investment after t years, P is the principal invested, r is the rate of interest, and n is the number of times the interest is compounded per year.

Example 5   *Finance*   The Iglesias family wants to give the youngest daughter $20,000 when she is ready for college. They now have $11,500 to invest. Determine how many years it will take them to achieve their goal given that they invest this amount at 8.3% compounded monthly.

$$A = P\left(1 + \frac{r}{n}\right)^{nt}$$ *Solve the compound interest formula for t.*

$$20{,}000 = 11{,}500\left(1 + \frac{0.083}{12}\right)^{12t}$$ *A = $20,000, P = $11,500, r = 0.083, n = 12*

$$\frac{20{,}000}{11{,}500} = \left(1 + \frac{0.083}{12}\right)^{12t}$$ *Isolate the exponential expression.*

$$\log 20{,}000 - \log 11{,}500 = 12t \log\left(1 + \frac{0.083}{12}\right)$$ *Take the logarithm of both sides.*

$$\frac{\log 20{,}000 - \log 11{,}500}{12 \log\left(1 + \frac{0.083}{12}\right)} = t$$ *Calculation-ready form*

$$7 = t$$ To the nearest year

If it is assumed that the Iglesias family does not add to or withdraw money from this account, the family will have the $20,000 at the end of 7 years.

Modeling

How can you determine the earnings on an account when the interest is compounded continuously?

To illustrate the effect that n, the number of times a year the interest is compounded, has on the compound interest formula, choose fixed values for the other variables and let $n = m$. Consider a hypothetical situation in which $1 is deposited in a bank account paying 100% interest for 1 year. Using a calculator, determine A for $m = 4, 8, 12, 100, 365, 10,000, 100,000$, and $1,000,000$, rounded to five decimal places.

$$A = 1\left(1 + \frac{1}{m}\right)^{m(1)} = \left(1 + \frac{1}{m}\right)^{m} \qquad P = 1, r = 1, t = 1, n = m$$

m	4	8	12	100	365	10,000	100,000	1,000,000
A	2.44141	2.56578	2.61304	2.70481	2.71457	2.71815	2.71827	2.71828

Notice that as the number of times that the interest is compounded in a year increases, the value of A gets closer and closer to e. So as m gets very large, the value of A approaches e as a limit. To determine a formula for continuously compounded interest, substitute $m = \frac{n}{r}$ in the compound interest formula.

$$A = P\left(1 + \frac{r}{n}\right)^{nt} = P\left(1 + \frac{1}{m}\right)^{m(rt)} \qquad m = \frac{n}{r}$$

$$A = Pe^{rt} \qquad\qquad \left(1 + \frac{1}{m}\right)^{m} \text{ approaches } e \text{ when } m \text{ approaches infinity.}$$

Continuous Compound Interest Formula

$$A = Pe^{rt}$$

Example 6 *Finance* Mrs. Johnson received a bonus equivalent to 10% of her yearly salary and has decided to deposit it in a savings account in which interest is compounded continuously. Her salary is $38,500 per year and the account pays $7\frac{1}{2}\%$ interest. How long will it take for her deposit to double in value?

$A = Pe^{rt}$ *Use the continuous compound interest formula.*

$7700 = 3850e^{0.075t}$ $P = 0.1(38,500) = 3850, \ A = 2(3850) = 7700, \ r = 0.075$

$2 = e^{0.075t}$

$\ln 2 = \ln e^{0.075t}$ *Take the logarithm of both sides.*

$\ln 2 = 0.075t \ln e$ $\ln b^r = r \ln b$

$\ln 2 = 0.075t$ $\ln e = 1$

$t = \dfrac{\ln 2}{0.075} = 9$ *To the nearest year*

Can you derive a general formula to determine the time it will take for a given investment to double?

9.5 Exponential Equations and Inequalities   **471**

Modeling

Examining the hypothetical interest model to arrive at an approximation for e can be an effective method for demonstrating the natural applicability of that number. Similar hypothetical simulations can be done with a cell division model.

For Example 6

A sum of money invested at a fixed interest rate, compounded continuously, tripled in 19 years. Determine the interest rate at which the money was invested. $r = 5.8\%$

Ask each student to write you a letter, telling you which ideas in the lesson were easy to understand and which were difficult to understand, and explaining why.

INDEPENDENT PRACTICE

Assignment Guide
Basic: 1–22, 31, 33–35, 37, Project
Average: 12–38, Project
Enriched: 16, 18, 20–30, 32, 34, 36 38–48, Project

Teacher's Resource Book
   Practice, page 62

Ⓡ **Review**
Exercises 15, 17, 19, 31, 33, 35, and 37 review concepts of evaluating exponential functions, using the factor theorem, describing a trigonometric function, graphing logarithmic functions, solving logarithmic equations, solving absolute value inequalities, and finding zeros of polynomials.

Project
After completing the Project, students should see the importance of factors other than high interest rates when deciding when and where to invest money.

Additional Answers
Class Exercises
1. Express both sides as a power of 5.
2. Take the log or ln of both sides.
3. Use the property $a^0 = 1$.
4. Take the ln of both sides.

Class Exercises

Determine the simplest method of solution for each exponential equation. Justify your answer.

1. $5^{3x} = 25^{2x+3}$ **2.** $5^{3x} = 17^{2x+3}$ **3.** $e^{4x} = 1$ **4.** $e^{4x} = 7.42$

Solve each exponential equation or inequality for x. Round answers to the nearest hundredth. Check using a graphing utility.

5. $6^{4x-1} - 51 = 0$ 0.80 **6.** $7e^{4x} \geq 32$ $x \geq 0.38$ **7.** $4^{2x-1} = 5^{x+2}$ 3.96

8. $e^x - 6e^{-x} - 5 = 0$ 1.79 **9.** $\dfrac{5^x + 1}{5^x} < 2$ $x > 0$ **10.** $\dfrac{2^x}{2^x - 4} = 2$ 3

11. *Food Service* The number of salads an apprentice salad chef can prepare per day after t days of training is modeled by the learning curve $S = 120 - 120e^{-0.5t}$. Determine how many days of training the apprentice should receive to be able to prepare 50 salads per day. 1 day

12. *Depreciation* One method used to determine the value of an item after t years is to use the depreciation formula $V = V_0(1 - r)^t$, where V is the final value of the item, V_0 is the original value, and r is the rate of depreciation. Determine in how many years a \$12,000 truck will be worth less than \$2000 if it depreciates at a rate of 22% per year.
8 years

Practice Exercises

 Use appropriate technology.

Solve for x to the nearest hundredth.

A **1.** $\ln x = 6.5555$ 703.10 **2.** $\ln 20.0855 = x$ 3.00 **3.** $\log 522.7353 = x$ 2.72 **4.** $\log x = 2.3010$ 199.99

Solve each exponential equation or inequality for x. Round answers to the nearest hundredth. Check using a graphing utility.

5. $7^{2x} = 123$ 1.24 **6.** $6^{3x-1} \leq 92$ $x \leq 1.17$ **7.** $8^{3x+2} - 57 = 0$ −0.02

8. $4^{3x} = 6^{2x+5}$ 15.57 **9.** $\dfrac{3^x}{3^x - 1} = 2$ 0.63 **10.** $\dfrac{4^x}{4^x - 5} = 3$ 1.45

11. $e^x + 4 - 45e^{-x} \geq 0$ $x \geq 1.61$ **12.** $e^x - 7 - 18e^{-x} = 0$ 2.20

Solve each using a graphing utility.

13. $e^{-x} = 1 + \log x$ 0.44 **14.** $\ln x \leq x^3 - 2$ $0 \leq x \leq 0.1$ or $x \geq 1.3$

Ⓡ **15.** If $f(x) = 6^x$, find $f(x + 1) - f(x)$ in terms of $f(x)$. $5f(x)$

16. Thinking Critically Analyze the exponential equation $b^x - c = 0$. Determine for what values of c this equation has a solution. Test your conclusion. $c > 0$

Ⓡ **17.** Determine whether $x - 3$ is a factor of $x^3 - 2x^2 + 7x - 30 = 0$. yes

Thinking Critically
A general formula might be $2P = Pe^{rt}$.

18. *Banking* The Whites inherited $3500, which they want to save for their daughter's college tuition. They purchase a certificate of deposit paying 8.25% interest compounded continuously. Determine after how many years their investment will be worth $5000. 4 years

19. Determine the period, amplitude, and phase shift of the graph of $y = 3 \cos (2x - \pi)$. period: π, amplitude: 3, phase shift: $\frac{\pi}{2}$ to the left

20. *Cooking* The temperature T of a loaf of bread t minutes after being removed from the oven can be modeled by the equation $T = T_R + 105e^{-0.19t}$, where T_R is the room temperature. Determine how many minutes it will take a loaf of bread to cool down to 90°F at a room temperature of 75°F. 10 min

21. *Investment* The Krafts invest $3000 at 7.2% compounded continuously. Determine after how many years their investment will be worth a minimum of $10,000. 17 years

22. *Sound Amplification* The power output P_0 of an amplifier is given by the formula $P_0 = P_i e^{\frac{D}{10}}$, where P_i is the power input and D is the decibel voltage gain. Determine the decibel voltage gain for an amplifier with a power output of 40 W and an input of 27 W. 3.9 db

Solve each exponential equation or inequality for x. Round answers to the nearest hundredth. Check using a graphing utility.

B 23. $2(15^{3x-1}) - 142 = 0$ 0.86   24. $3(16^{-2x+1}) - 0.71 = 0$ 0.76   25. $4(6^{2x-1}) - 3^{4x+5} = 0$ −7.27

26. $3(7^{4x-1}) = 4(2^{7x+3})$ 27. $6e^x = -7 + 3e^{-x}$ −1.10   28. $\dfrac{e^{2x}}{e^{2x} - 3} \geq -6$ 1.47 $x \leq 0.47$ or $x > 0.55$

Solve each inequality by graphing.

29. $y < -e^x + 5$ 30. $y \geq -5 \log (x - 2)$

R 31. Graph: $y = \log_2 x$

32. *Finance* Charlene wants to purchase a car in 3 years. She needs a down payment of about $4000. Determine the continuously compounded interest rate at which she would have to deposit $3200 so that she will have the money she needs at the end of 3 years. 7.44%

R 33. Solve the logarithmic equation $\log_2 (x + 2) + \log_2 x = 3$. 2

34. **Thinking Critically** Analyze the equation $\dfrac{e^x}{e^x + a} = n, a > 0$, and determine the values of n for which it has a solution. $0 < n < 1$

R 35. Solve for x: $1 \leq |x - 2| \leq 7$ $-5 \leq x \leq 1$ or $3 \leq x \leq 9$

36. *Investment* Determine how many years it will take for a sum of money to double in value when it is invested at 8.2% interest compounded every 3 months. 8.5 years

R 37. Find all the zeros of $f(x) = x^3 - 5x^2 + 7x + 13$. $-1, 3 \pm 2i$

38. *Investment* At the age of 25, Coris invests $2000 in an Individual Retirement Account (IRA) that is allowed to accumulate interest tax-free until she retires. Pat, who is 35, also invests $2000 in an IRA. Pat and Coris each earn 8% annually compounded continuously, and each withdraws the funds from the account at age 65. To the nearest hundred, how much more money does Coris collect than Pat? $27,000

9.5 Exponential Equations and Inequalities   **473**

473

Solve each exponential equation for x to the nearest tenth. Check using a graphing utility.

C 39. $(2^{2x+3})^2 - (3^{2x-1})^3 = 0$ 1.95

40. $\dfrac{e^{2x-3}}{10^x} = 7$ -16.3

Solve each inequality using a graphing utility.

41. $\sin x > 0.01e^x$

42. $10(\log x)^2 \leq \cos^2 x$

Solve each exponential equation for x in terms of a. Give your answer in simplest form.

43. $e^{ax} + 15a^2e^{-ax} = 8a$ $\dfrac{\ln 5a}{a}$ or $\dfrac{\ln 3a}{a}$

44. $4^{5x-a} = 3^{a-4x}$ 0.22a

45. *Finance* The Jacksons want to take a second mortgage of \$35,000 on their home. The bank offers 5-, 7-, 10-, 15-, and 20-year mortgages. On their income they can afford monthly payments of \$620 for this second mortgage. Monthly payments on the mortgage are computed using the

formula $M = \dfrac{P\left(\frac{r}{12}\right)}{1 - \left(1 + \frac{r}{12}\right)^{-12t}}$, where P is the initial value of the mortgage

and r is the annual interest rate. Determine the number of years t they should take this mortgage for if the annual current rate of interest is 11.8%. 7, 10, 15 or 20 years

46. Thinking Critically Discuss the advantages and disadvantages of the five choices for the length of a mortgage in Exercise 45.

47. *Investments* Find a formula to determine the amount of time, in years, it will take an investment to increase 150% if it pays interest at a fixed rate compounded n times a year. Then determine the time for the investment to increase 150% if it pays interest at a fixed rate compounded continuously. $t = \dfrac{\log 1.5}{n \log\left(1 + \frac{r}{n}\right)}$; $t = \dfrac{\ln 1.5}{r}$

48. Thinking Critically People sometimes select one bank over another based on the frequency at which the bank compounds. Does the frequency of compounding make a significant difference in the annual interest received? Consider an investment of \$1000 at 12% compounded semiannually, quarterly, daily, and continuously.

Project

Gather information from at least six savings institutions on potential interest earnings. Included in your data should be interest rates, intervals of compounding, early withdrawal penalties, incentives for large deposits, and any other pertinent factors. Then write a proposal on what you consider to be the best course of action to take when making a short-term investment of \$100,000. Answers may vary.

Challenge

A square has a side of 10 cm with a possible measurement error of ±0.1 cm. What is the possible error in square centimeters of the area of the square? ±2.01 cm²

474   Chapter 9 Exponential and Logarithmic Functions

Exponential Growth and Decay Models

Objective: *To solve real world problems using exponential and logarithmic equations*

Focus

In his *Notebook,* Mark Twain provides a clear example of how a mathematical model, if interpreted incorrectly, can yield an erroneous result. Twain describes a winding section of the Mississippi River that stretches from Cairo, Illinois, to New Orleans, Louisiana. He notes that historical records show that 176 years prior to his writing, the stretch of river measured 1215 mi. By 1722, due to course changes in the river, both natural and man-made, the stretch measured only 1180 mi. Consequently, he reasons that

the length of the stretch at the time of his writing is only 973 mi. Since the river had shortened 242 mi in 176 years, Twain finally concludes that its length is shrinking at a rate of a little more than a mile and a third per year. He then predicts that in 742 years the Mississippi River will be only a mile and three quarters long and that Cairo and New Orleans will be joined and governed under one mayor!

Mark Twain's strained reasoning is intended to be comical, but it helps to introduce the problem of taking a model too literally. For example, a simple exponential model may be used to predict population growth or decay. Careful analysis of other factors in the real world situation may then lead to a *modified* model of growth or decay.

Phenomena such as population growth, demand for a product, the spread of epidemics, information dissemination, and economic growth can all be modeled using an **exponential growth curve.** This curve is the graph of an equation of the form $y = Ab^t$, where $b > 1$ and $A > 0$. Based on this equation, the current population of a community can be expressed as an exponential function of time. The function has as its rule the equation $P = P_0 e^{rt}$, which can be used to model population growth. In the equation, P is the population after t years, P_0 is the original population, and r is the annual growth rate of the population.

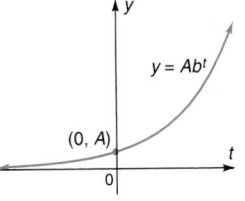

9.6 Exponential Growth and Decay Models **475**

LESSON PLAN

Vocabulary
exponential decay curve
exponential growth curve
modified decay curve
modified growth curve

Ⓜ **Materials/Manipulatives**
room thermometer
thermometer for liquids

Technology
graphing utility
symbolic manipulator

FOCUS

Encourage students to discuss the Focus to determine the flaw in the logic. Have them search for other examples of erroneous reasoning used for the purpose of wit. You may also want to ask students to determine from the information exactly what year Twain wrote the story. The answer is 1872.

INSTRUCTION

Ⓜ After discussing Newton's law of cooling, have students collect data using a cup of hot liquid and write a model of the cooling curve for that liquid. Then have them test the model by predicting the temperature at different times and comparing the results to the experimental results.

Alternative Learning Styles
Some students need to discuss concrete examples before discussing the theoretical mathematics. Have students discuss experiments from biology, chemistry, or physics in which exponential growth or decay was explored.

For Example 1

The population of a culture of bacteria grew exponentially from 200 to 2300 in 18 h.

1. Find the average growth rate of the population of this culture and determine an equation of the population growth curve for this culture.
$r = 0.1356859464 \approx 14\%$;
$p = 200e^{0.14t}$

2. Assuming a constant growth rate, predict the population to the nearest hundredth at the end of the day. approximately 5800

Example 1 The population in Raleigh-Durham, North Carolina, grew from 560,774 in 1980 to 665,400 in 1987.

  a. Using these statistics, find the average growth rate of the population in Raleigh-Durham and determine an equation of the population growth curve for this region. Graph the equation.

  b. Assuming a constant growth rate, predict the population for Raleigh-Durham in 1995 to the nearest ten thousand.

a.
$$P = P_0 e^{rt} \qquad \textit{Solve for r.}$$
$$665,400 = 560,774e^{7r}$$
$$e^{7r} = \frac{665,400}{560,774}$$
$$\ln e^{7r} = \ln 665,400 - \ln 560,774$$
$$7r = \ln 665,400 - \ln 560,744 \qquad \ln e^x = x$$
$$r = \frac{\ln 665,400 - \ln 560,744}{7}$$
$$r = 0.0244386273 \approx 2.4\%$$

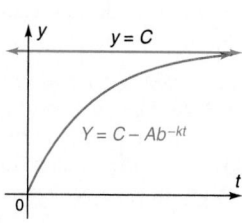

The average growth rate of the population between 1980 and 1987 was 2.4% per year. The equation of the population growth curve is $P = 560,774 \, e^{0.024t}$.

b. $P = 560,774 \, e^{0.024t}$
$P = 560,774 \, e^{0.024(15)}$
$P = 803,773.8691$

If the growth rate is constant, the population in Raleigh-Durham in 1995 will be approximately 800,000.

An exponential growth curve may be modified to model a situation in which early growth is rapid but later growth begins to level off due to a number of factors. For example, suppose you develop a model for predicting the growth of a culture of bacteria under ideal conditions. Then you learn that as the population becomes very large, the individual organisms begin to compete with each other for available nutrients. The population growth will then begin to decline dramatically. You must modify your growth model to account for the new data. A **modified growth curve** is the graph of an equation of the form $y = C - Ab^{-kt}$, where $b > 1$ and $A > 0$.

Example 2 *Health Care* A measles outbreak on many college campuses has necessitated the vaccination of incoming freshmen. To make students aware of this situation, information is printed in newspapers and broadcast on radio and television news. A survey of a sample of the population shows that the number of people N who will have heard the information after t months can be modeled by the equation $N = N_f(1 - e^{-0.16t})$, where N_f is the fixed population. Graph this information dissemination curve for a region with an incoming freshmen population of 20,000 students and determine the number of students, to the nearest thousand, who have heard the information after 6 months, 8 months, and 1 year.

476   Chapter 9 Exponential and Logarithmic Functions

$N = N_f(1 - e^{-0.16t})$ $N_f = 20,000$

$N = 20,000(1 - e^{(-0.16)6}) = 12,342.14228$ $t = 6$

$N = 20,000(1 - e^{(-0.16)8}) = 14,439.25399$ $t = 8$

$N = 20,000(1 - e^{(-0.16)12}) = 17,067.86076$ $t = 12$

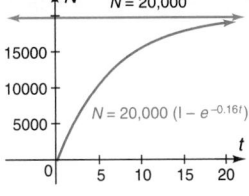

To the nearest thousand, 12,000 students have the information after 6 months, 14,000 have the information after 8 months, and 17,000 have the information after 1 year.

Just as an exponential growth curve models a rapid expansion in the amount of a substance, an exponential decay curve is characterized by a sharp decline in the amount of a substance.

Depreciation, carbon dating of fossils, and the power supply of a satellite are examples of phenomena that can be modeled using an exponential decay curve. An **exponential decay curve** is the graph of an equation of the form $y = Ab^{-t}$, where $b > 1$ and $A > 0$.

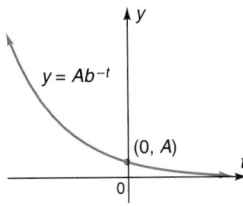

Fossils are specimens of plants or animals that have been partly preserved from some past geological period. When alive, these creatures, like all living organisms, have cells that contain a known percent of the radioisotope carbon-14. When the organism dies, the amount of carbon-14 it contains decreases exponentially. The *half-life* of a radioisotope (or of any other decaying substance) is the time required for one-half of the initial quantity to decay. The half-life of a radioisotope is an unchanging physical characteristic of the isotope, so it can be used to determine the age of a fossil. An equation for determining the age of a fossil using carbon-14 dating is $A = A_0\left(\frac{1}{2}\right)^{\frac{t}{5570}}$ or $A = A_0(2)^{-\frac{t}{5570}}$, where A is the current level of carbon-14, A_0 is the original amount of carbon-14, t is age of the fossil in years, and 5570 is the half-life of carbon-14 in years.

Example 3   *Archaeology*   Cocoa beans, used to make cocoa and chocolate, were known to the Mayans in the sixteenth century. Determine the age of a cocoa bean fossil that has 87 mg of carbon-14 if it originally contained 90 mg of carbon-14.

$$A = A_0(2)^{-\frac{t}{5570}}$$
$$87 = 90(2)^{-\frac{t}{5570}} \qquad A = 87 \text{ mg and } A_0 = 90$$
$$\frac{87}{90} = 2^{-\frac{t}{5570}}$$
$$\log\frac{87}{90} = \log(2)^{-\frac{t}{5570}} \qquad \textit{Take the logarithm of both sides.}$$
$$\log 87 - \log 90 = \log(2)^{-\frac{t}{5570}} \qquad \log_b\frac{M}{N} = \log_b M - \log_b N$$
$$\log 87 - \log 90 = -\frac{t}{5570}\log 2 \qquad \log_b N^r = r\log_b N$$
$$t = \frac{-5570(\log 87 - \log 90)}{\log 2} \qquad \textit{Calculation-ready form}$$
$$t = 272.4264747 \approx 270 \qquad \text{The fossil is approximately 270 years old.}$$

9.6 Exponential Growth and Decay Models   **477**

For Example 2
A new discount clothing store has opened on the main street of a town of 8200 people. The store has no budget to advertise. Previous experience in other towns has shown that the number of people who will have heard of this store by word-of-mouth, after t weeks, can be modeled by the equation $N = N_f(1 - e^{-0.09t})$, where N_f is the fixed population. Graph this information dissemination curve and determine the number of people, to the nearest hundred, who will have heard of this store after 1 mo, 6 wk, and 3 mo.

1 mo: 2500; 6 wk: 3400; 3 mo: 5400

Technology   To determine the values of N for specific values of t, have students use the zoom-integer and trace functions.

For Example 3
A fossil found at an archeological dig has 74 mg of carbon-14. If it originally contained 150 mg, use the carbon-14 dating formula to determine its age. approximately 5678 years old

Newton's law of cooling states that the final temperature of an object that is warmer than the air around it can be determined by the formula $T_f = T_r + (T_0 - T_r)e^{-rt}$, where T_f is the final temperature of the object after t minutes, T_r is the temperature of the surrounding air, T_0 is the original temperature of the object, and r is the rate at which the object is cooling. Newton's law of cooling is an example of a **modified decay curve.**

Example 4   *Restaurant Management*   Letendre's restaurant is famous for its vegetable soup. The chef wants the soup to be served to the customer at a temperature of no less than 160°F. It has been determined that the cooling rate for this soup is 0.21°F per minute. When the soup is removed from the pot, it is 212°F. If the room temperature in the restaurant is 68°, determine in how many minutes the soup must be served to meet the chef's request.

$$T_f = T_r + (T_0 - T_r)e^{-rt} \qquad T_f = 160, \ T_r = 68°, \ T_0 = 212°, \ and \ r = 0.21$$
$$160 = 68 + (212 - 68)e^{-0.21t}$$
$$92 = 144e^{-.021t}$$
$$\frac{92}{144} = e^{-0.21t} \qquad \text{Isolate the exponential expression.}$$
$$\ln 92 - \ln 144 = -0.21t \qquad \text{Take the natural logarithm of both sides.}$$
$$\frac{\ln 92 - \ln 144}{-0.21} = t \qquad \text{Calculation-ready form}$$
$$t = 2.13345106$$

The soup should be served within 2 min of being removed from the pot.

Class Exercises

Determine whether each equation represents an exponential growth or an exponential decay curve. Use a graphing utility to justify your answer.

1. $y = 100e^{-0.2t}$ **decay**
2. $y = 50 - 50e^{-0.17t}$ **growth**
3. $y = 50e^{0.07t}$ **growth**
4. $y = 100 + 100e^{-0.31t}$ **decay**

5. *Electricity*   The power supply of a satellite decreases exponentially over the time it is being used. The equation for determining the power supply P, in watts, after t days is $P = 50e^{-\frac{t}{250}}$. Determine the number of days it will take for the power supply to be less than 30 W. 128 days

6. *Technical Education*   The number of disk drives D a trainee can assemble per day after t days of training can be modeled by the equation $D = 50 - 50e^{-0.09t}$. Determine the number of days of training a person would need to be able to assemble 18 disk drives per day. 5 days

Practice Exercises   🔄 Use appropriate technology.

Graph each exponential equation and determine whether it represents a growth curve or decay curve.

A 1. $y = 2e^{0.21t}$ **growth**
2. $y = 2e^{-0.21t}$ **decay**
3. $y = 5(2)^t$ **growth**
4. $y = 4 - 4(2)^{-t}$ **growth**

Additional Answers, Practice Exercises

5. *Bacteria Growth*   The number of bacteria, N, in a culture after t minutes is given by the equation $N = N_0 e^{0.06t}$ where N_0 is the original number of bacteria in the culture. Given that there are originally 100 bacteria in the culture, determine in how many minutes, to the nearest minute, there will be a minimum of 200 bacteria. 12 min

6. *Population Growth*   In Colorado Springs, Colorado, the population in 1987 was 389,910. In 1995 it is expected to grow to 524,000. Find the average growth rate of the population in Colorado Springs between 1987 and 1995. Then determine an equation for the population growth. Estimate the population in 1999 to the nearest thousand. Graph the equation of the population growth. The model for population growth is $P = P_0 e^{rt}$, where P is the population after t years, P_0 is the original population, and r is the rate of growth of the population per year.

Ⓡ 7. Solve $3^{2x+1} = 2^{5x-2}$ for x to the nearest tenth. 2.0

8. *Spread of Rumors*   A school has a population of 300 students. A rumor is spread by word of mouth. The model for the number of people N who will have heard the rumor after t days is $N = 300 - 300e^{-0.12t}$. Determine how many days it will take for a minimum of 200 students to have heard the rumor. 9 days

9. *Carbon-14 Dating*   A fossil containing 20 mg of carbon-14 originally had 45 mg. Determine the age of the fossil to the nearest year. 6516 years

10. *Food Service*   The cooling model for coffee served in a mug is $T_f = T_r + (T_0 - T_r)e^{-0.30t}$. Given that the original temperature of the coffee is 155°F and the room temperature is 75°F, determine after how many minutes the coffee will be 110°F. 3 min

Ⓡ 11. Determine whether $x = -2$ is a solution of $x^4 - 2x^3 + x - 1 = 0$. no

12. **Thinking Critically**   Interpret the meaning of the value of the population growth curve $P = P_0 e^{rt}$ when $t = 0$.

Ⓡ 13. Graph: $f(x) = \log_4 (x + 1)$

14. **Writing in Mathematics**   Write a word problem that can be solved using the population growth model $P = P_0 e^{0.03t}$.

15. *Sales*   The model for predicting the sales S of a new brand of sweatshirt after t years is $S = 50{,}000 - 50{,}000e^{-rt}$, where r is the rate of growth of sales. Determine the growth rate of sales to the nearest tenth of a percent if 4000 sweatshirts were sold in the first 2 years. 4.2%

16. *Light Intensity*   The intensity of light at a depth of d meters in the ocean from a light source of intensity I_0 is $I = I_0 e^{-1.4d}$. Determine at what depth the intensity of the light in the ocean is one-third of the intensity of the light source at the surface. 0.78 m

Ⓡ 17. Graph: $f(x) = |x + 1| - 3$

18. *Education*   To meet the standards of a new client, a secretarial school must ensure that the minimum typing speed of its new graduates is increased by 50% from the previous standard of 55 wpm. Given that the formula for number of words per minute typed W after t weeks of training is $W = 90 - 90e^{-0.11t}$, determine the minimum number of weeks of training the students should receive. 23 weeks

9.6 Exponential Growth and Decay Models   **479**

Writing in Mathematics
14. Answers may vary. In the statement of the problem students should provide values for two of the three variables, P, P_0, and t.

R 19. Determine the amplitude and period of the function $f(x) = 2 \cos 4\pi x$. $2; \frac{1}{2}$

20. Thinking Critically Interpret the meaning of the information dissemination model $N = N_f - N_f e^{-kt}$ when t gets very large.

R 21. Find a variation equation using k as a constant for y varies inversely as x. $xy = k$

22. *Optics* The percentage of light P that can pass through a substance is modeled by the equation $P = 10^{-kd}$, where d is the thickness of the substance and k is a constant that depends on the substance. Graph this function for a substance with a constant of 0.3. Determine the thickness of the substance, given that 57% of the light passes through it. Determine the thickness given that 30% of the light passes through it.

B 23. *Population Decline* In the Yukon territory in Canada the population declined from 23,153 in 1981 to 22,200 in 1983. Determine the rate of decline using the equation $P = P_0 e^{rt}$. If the rate of decline stays constant, determine in how many years the population will be four-fifths of the population recorded in 1983. $r = -2.1\%$; 13 years

24. *Manufacturing* The number of calculators N a worker can assemble per day after t days of training is given by the equation $N = 80 - 80e^{-0.09t}$. To function effectively on the job, a worker must be able to assemble 70 calculators per day. Determine the minimum number of weeks of training a worker should be given to function effectively. 4

25. *Medicine* A model for the concentration C (in milligrams) of a drug in the bloodstream of a patient t hours after being administered is $C = 5e^{-0.4t}$. Graph this equation and determine in how many hours there will be 2.25 mg of the drug in the patient's bloodstream. In how many hours will there be 0.5 mg?

26. *Food Service* The internal temperature of a turkey is 180°F when it is removed from the oven. Using Newton's law of cooling and a cooling rate of 0.04°F/min, determine after how many minutes the temperature of the turkey will be 120°F at a room temperature of 68°F. Determine the number of minutes for a temperature of 35°F in the refrigerator. 19 min; 13 min

R 27. *Investment* A sum of money is invested at 8.2% compounded continuously. Determine after how many years there will be a 150% increase in the original investment. 12 years

C 28. *Biology* A culture of 500 bacteria has grown exponentially to 2000 bacteria in 40 h. After 40 h the growth levels off and the total number of bacteria approaches 2200 as the number of hours gets large. Determine the modified growth model for this culture. $P = 2200 - 500e^{-0.023t}$

29. *Food Technology* A loaf of bread is removed from the oven when its temperature is 180°F. After 10 min of standing at a room temperature of 82°F, the temperature of the bread is 150°F. Use Newton's law of cooling to determine the cooling model for this bread. $T_t = 82 - 98e^{-0.037t}$

30. *Information Dissemination*   In a school with a population of 4000 students, information about a school dance is posted on bulletin boards and listed in the school newspaper. After 20 days, 2900 students know about the dance. Use the information model $N = N_f - N_f e^{-kt}$, where N_f is the total population and t is the time in days, to determine the number of students who have not heard about the dance after 30 days. 569

31. **Writing in Mathematics**   Use data from geography to create an erroneous model like Mark Twain's Mississippi River model presented in the Focus.

32. *Marine Biology*   The age of a young whale is related to its length by the equation $A = e^{\frac{L-13}{k}}$, where A is the whale's age in years and L is its length in feet. A 3.5-year-old whale is 22.78 ft. Determine the value of k in the equation and find the length of a 4.5-year-old whale. 7.8; 24.73 ft

33. *Archaeology*   One formula used for carbon-14 dating is $A = A_0 2^{-\frac{t}{5570}}$. Write an equivalent formula using base e. $A = A_0 e^{-\frac{0.693t}{5570}}$

34. In a certain electric circuit, the current is given by the formula $I = \frac{E}{R}\left(1 - e^{-\frac{Rt}{L}}\right)$, where E is the voltage, R is the resistance in ohms, L is the inductance in henrys, and t is the elapsed time in seconds. The values of R and L are constant. Predict how the right side of the formula behaves as the value of t becomes very great. Approaches $\frac{E}{R}$ as a limit.

Project

Make a table of the major components of radioactive waste and list their half-lives. Find out what quantities of various materials such as cover soil, cement, and salt are required to reduce the radiation to acceptable levels.

Test Yourself

1. Express $\log \frac{x^5 y^2}{\sqrt{z}}$ in expanded form. $5 \log x + 2 \log y - \frac{1}{2} \log z$ 9.4

2. Express $2 \ln 3x - 4 \ln y + 3 \ln z^2$ in condensed form. $\ln \frac{9x^2 z^6}{y^4}$

Determine the domain of each equation and solve for x.

3. $\ln 3x = 4 \ln 2 + \ln 3$ $\{x : x > 0\}$; 16

4. $\log x + \log (4x - 9) = 2$ $\left\{x : x > \frac{9}{4}\right\}; \frac{25}{4}$

Solve each exponential equation for x. Round your answers to the nearest hundredth. Check using a graphing utility.   9.5

5. $3^{4x-1} - 5^{2x} = 0$ 0.93

6. $\frac{e^x}{e^x - 1} = -6$ −0.15

7. *Finance*   Tak invests $7500 at 11.5% interest. Determine in how many years his investment will be worth $13,220, given that the interest is compounded quarterly. 5 years

8. *Biology*   A bacteria culture has an initial population of 25,000. After 14 h the population has grown to 46,000. Use the formula $P = P_0 e^{rt}$, where t is measured in hours, to find the rate of growth r for the culture and then predict the population after 24 h. 0.0436; 71,185   9.6

9.6 Exponential Growth and Decay Models   **481**

Writing in Mathematics
31. Answers may vary. A worked out solution should accompany each model.

3.

$D = \{x: x \in \mathcal{R}\};$
$R = \{y: y \leq 1\};$
x-int: (0, 0);
y-int: (0, 0)

4.

$D = \{x: x \in \mathcal{R}\};$
$R = \{y: y > 0\};$
no x-int;
y-int: $\left(0, \frac{1}{4}\right)$

7.

$D = \{x: x > -3\};$
$R = \{y: y \in \mathcal{R}\};$
x-int: (−2, 0);
y-int: (0, −1.10);
asymptote:
$x = -3$

8.

$D = \{x: x > 0\};$
$R = \{y: y \in \mathcal{R}\};$
x-int: (0.04, 0);
no y-int;
asymptote: $x = 0$

Chapter 9 Summary and Review

Vocabulary

change-of-base formula (456)
characteristic (467)
common logarithmic
  function (455)
compound interest
  formula (470)
continuous compound
  interest formula (471)

exponential decay
  curve (477)
exponential equation (448)
exponential function (446)
exponential growth
  curve (475)
logarithmic equation (454)
logarithmic function (453)

mantissa (467)
modified decay curve (478)
modified growth curve (476)
natural exponential
  function (448)
natural logarithmic
  function (455)
rational exponents (441)

Rational Exponents   The properties of integer exponents are extended to rational   9.1
exponents. An expression is said to be simplified when it is written with all positive
rational exponents and with no radicals.

Simplify each expression.

1. $\left(x^{\frac{1}{2}}y^{-2}z^{\frac{7}{8}}\right)^{-4}\left(x^{-6}y^{4}z^{\frac{1}{4}}\right)^{2}\dfrac{y^{16}}{x^{14}z^{3}}$

2. $\sqrt[v]{(0.001xy^{3})^{-2}}\ \dfrac{10}{x^{\frac{1}{3}}y}$

Exponential Functions   An exponential function is a function of the form $f(x) = b^{x}$,   9.2
$b > 0$ and $b \neq 1$. The number e, the base of the natural logarithm, is the value that
the expression $\left(1 + \dfrac{1}{n}\right)^{n}$ approaches as n approaches infinity.

Graph each function. State the domain, range, and x- and y-intercepts.

3. $f(x) = -e^{x} + 1$

4. $g(x) = \left(\dfrac{1}{2}\right)^{x+2}$

Solve each exponential equation.

5. $0.125^{x-2} = \sqrt{2}$ 1.83

6. $3xe^{x} - 27e^{x} = 0$ 9

Logarithmic Functions   The inverse of an exponential function is a logarithmic   9.3
function. For all positive real numbers x and b, $b \neq 1$, $y = \log_{b} x$ if and only if
$x = b^{y}$. Base 10 and base e, where $e \approx 2.71828182$, are the two bases used most
frequently for logarithmic functions.

Graph each function. State the domain, range, intercepts, and asymptotes.

7. $g(x) = -\ln(x + 3)$

8. $f(x) = \log_{\frac{1}{2}} x - 4.5$

Evaluating Logarithms   A calculator can be used to evaluate logarithms. To
evaluate a logarithm with a base other than 10 or e, use the change-of-base formula:
$\log_{b} x = \dfrac{\log_{a} x}{\log_{a} b}$.

Find each logarithm to four decimal places.

9. $\log 0.36$ −0.4437

10. $\log_{7} 2$ 0.3562

Properties of Logarithms If M, N, and b are positive real numbers, $b \neq 1$, and r is any real number, then

$$\log_b MN = \log_b M + \log_b N \qquad \log_b \frac{M}{N} = \log_b M - \log_b N \qquad \log_b M^r = r \log_b M$$

11. Express $\ln \dfrac{x^6 \sqrt{y}}{2z^2}$ in expanded form. $6 \ln x + \frac{1}{2} \ln y - \ln 2 - 2 \ln z$

12. Express $2 \log 2x - \left(\frac{1}{3} \log y^4 - \log 5 \right)$ in condensed form. $\log \dfrac{20x^2}{y^{\frac{4}{3}}}$

13. Solve $\log_3 (x + 1) + \log_3 (x - 7) = 2$ for x. 8

Exponential Equations To solve an exponential equation:

9.5

- Isolate the exponential expression.
- Take the logarithm of both sides of the equation.
- Verify all answers by substitution in the original equation.

In financial applications of exponential functions, the compound interest formula $A = P\left(1 + \dfrac{r}{n}\right)^{nt}$ is used. For interest that is compounded continuously, the formula is modified to $A = Pe^{rt}$.

Solve each exponential equation for x to three decimal places.

14. $6^x = 216^{x+2}$ -3

15. $2^{10x+2} = 512^{3x}$ 0.118

16. $4^{x+2} = 5^{x+7}$ -38.063

17. $12^{x^2} = 16^{3x}$ 0 or 3.347

18. *Finance* Mr. Herrera invests \$9000 in an account that earns 11.5% interest compounded monthly. How long will it take for his investment to triple? 10 years

Exponential Growth and Decay Models An equation of the form $y = Ab^t$, where $b > 1$ and $A > 0$, models exponential growth. An equation of the form $y = Ab^{-t}$, where $b > 1$ and $A > 0$, models exponential decay.

9.6

19. *Archaeology* A skull is found to contain 78 mg of carbon-14. It originally contained 145 mg. Use carbon-14 dating to determine the age of the skull to the nearest hundred years. The half-life of carbon-14 is 5570 years. 5000 y

20. *Information Dissemination* A rumor of a corporate merger starts in a large office building. The number of people N who will have heard this rumor after t weeks can be estimated using the equation $N = N_f - N_f e^{-0.15t}$, where N_f is the fixed population. Given that there are 4500 employees in the building, determine after how many weeks 75% of the building's population will have heard the information. 9 weeks

21. *Physics* A carton of orange juice with a temperature of 85°F is placed in a refrigerator. If the temperature in the refrigerator is 38°F, the orange juice will cool to a temperature of 75°F in 10 min. Use the formula $T_f = T_r + (T_0 - T_r)e^{-rt}$ to determine the rate of cooling r to the nearest thousandth. 0.024

22. Determine whether the equation represents exponential growth or exponential decay: $y = 200e^{0.6t}$ exponential growth

Chapter 9   Test

Additional Answers

3.

$D = \{x: x \in \mathcal{R}\}$;
$R = \{y: y > 3\}$;
no x-int;
y-int: (0, 5);
asymptote: $y = 3$

4.

$D = \left\{x: x > \dfrac{5}{3}\right\}$;
$R = \{y: y \in \mathcal{R}\}$;
x-int: (1.67, 0);
no y-int;

asymptote: $x = \dfrac{5}{3}$

Simplify each expression.

1. $\dfrac{x^{\frac{5}{4}}y^{-\frac{1}{2}}}{x^{\frac{3}{2}}y^{-\frac{1}{4}}} \dfrac{1}{x^{\frac{1}{4}}y^{\frac{1}{4}}}$

2. $(-0.125x^6y^4)^{\frac{1}{3}} \cdot (0.0625x^4y^{-1})^{\frac{1}{2}}$
$\qquad -0.125x^4y^{\frac{5}{6}}$

Graph each function and state the domain, range, intercepts, and asymptotes of each.

3. $f(x) = 2e^{-x} + 3$

4. $g(x) = -\log(3x - 5) - 5$

5. Solve for x: $\left(\dfrac{1}{6}\right)^{x-7} = 216^{x+2} \dfrac{1}{4}$

6. Express $\log \dfrac{y^2}{3}$ in expanded form. $2\log y - \log 3$

7. Express $0.25 \ln x^2y - 0.5 \ln z + 2 \ln 5$ in condensed form. $\ln \dfrac{25\sqrt[4]{x^2y}}{\sqrt{z}}$

Solve for x to the nearest hundredth.

8. $\log_x 6 = 3.5$ 1.67

9. $\ln 200 - \ln x = 2$ 27.07

10. $3^{4x} \geq 27$ $x \geq 0.75$

11. $-8e^x + 2xe^x = 0$ 4

12. Solve using a graphing utility: $\ln x \geq x^2 - 3$ $0 < x \leq 1.9$

13. *Finance*   Sara deposits $1700 in a savings account that pays 7.75% interest compounded quarterly. How much more would she earn on her deposit in 56 years if the interest were compounded continuously? $5302.02

14. *Biology*   A colony of single-celled organisms has an initial population of 3500. After 24 hours the population triples. Use the formula $P = P_0e^{rt}$, where t measured in hours, to find the rate of growth r for this organism, and predict the number of cells in the population if it continues to grow at this rate for another 144 hours. $r = 0.046$; 7,948,694

15. *Physics*   A bottle of spring water with an initial temperature of 72°F is placed in a freezer with a temperature of 28°F. After 15 min, the temperature of the water drops to 50°F. Use the formula $T_f = T_r + (T_0 - T_r)e^{-rt}$ to find the rate of cooling r and determine how long it will take the water to reach a temperature of 32°F. 0.046; 52 min

Challenge

Using only the information below, determine a method for finding the natural logarithm of at least five numbers between 4 and 20.

$\ln 2 = 0.6931$ Let $A = 2$ and $B = 3$.
$\ln 3 = 1.0986$ $\ln A^nB^p = n \ln A + p \ln B$

Cumulative Review

Select the best choice for each question.

1. Solve for x: $9^x = 3^{3x-1}$ 9.2
A
   A. 1   **B.** 3   **C.** 9   **D.** -1
   E. none of these

2. Solve for x: $|4x - 1| \le 5$ 8.2
B
   A. $x = 1$ or $x = \frac{3}{2}$ **B.** $-1 \le x \le \frac{3}{2}$

   C. $x = -1$ or $x = \frac{3}{2}$ **D.** $-1 \ge x \ge \frac{3}{2}$
   E. none of these

3. Determine the length of the 60th   5.1
E
   parallel that passes through Oslo,
   Norway, to the nearest whole number.
   A. 36,048   **B.** 24,206   **C.** 12,659
   D. 6000   **E.** none of these

4. Determine the characteristic and   9.5
C
   the mantissa for log $= 2.6385$.
   A. characteristic $= 6385$
       mantissa $= 2$
   B. characteristic $= -8$
       mantissa $= -0.6385$
   C. characteristic $= 2$
       mantissa $= 0.6385$
   D. characteristic $= 8$
       mantissa $= 0.6385$
   E. none of these

5. Name the three basic kinds of   7.6
A
   discontinuity.
   A. point, jump, infinite
   B. point, jump, finite
   C. point, skip, infinite
   D. point, skip, finite
   E. none of these

6. Evaluate: $(64)^{-\frac{1}{2}}$ 9.1
C
   A. 8   **B.** -8 **C.** $\frac{1}{8}$ **D.** $-\frac{1}{8}$
   E. none of these

7. Use a trigonometric identity to   6.1
B
   find the value of cos 285°.
   A. $\frac{\sqrt{2} - \sqrt{6}}{4}$ **B.** $\frac{\sqrt{6} - \sqrt{2}}{4}$ **C.** $\frac{1}{2}$
   D. $-\frac{1}{2}$ **E.** none of these

8. Express in expanded form: 9.4
A
   $\log_b \sqrt[3]{4x^5y^7}$
   A. $\frac{1}{3}[\log_b 4 + 5 \log_b x + 7 \log_b y]$

   B. $-\frac{1}{3}[\log_b 4 + 5 \log_b x + 7 \log_b y]$

   C. $3[4 \log_b + 5 \log_b x + 7 \log_b y]$
   D. $1[4 \log_b + 5 \log_b x + 7 \log_b y]$
   E. none of these

9. A linear system of equations in   8.1
A
   two variables that has at least one
   solution is called
   A. consistent   **B.** inconsistent
   C. quadratic   **D.** singular
   E. none of these

10. Solve and check: $\sqrt{x - 5} -$ 7.7
E
   $\sqrt{x} = 2$
   A. $\frac{81}{16}$ **B.** $\frac{16}{81}$ **C.** $\frac{9}{4}$ **D.** $\frac{4}{9}$
   E. no solution

11. Find an angle which satisfies   4.1
B
   $\cot \theta = \tan 25°$.
   A. 155°   **B.** 65°   **C.** 25°   **D.** 225°
   E. none of these

12. Find the amplitude and period of   4.2
B
   the function $F(x) = 0.2 \cos 4x$.
   A. amplitude $= 0.2$; period $= 4\pi$
   B. amplitude $= 0.2$; period $= \frac{\pi}{2}$

   C. amplitude $= -0.2$; period $= -\frac{\pi}{2}$

   D. amplitude $= 2$; period $= \pi$
   E. none of these

13. Express the logarithmic equation   9.3
D
   as an exponential equation and

   solve: $\log_2 \frac{1}{32} = x$

   A. $32^x = \frac{1}{2}$, $x = 5$

   B. $\frac{1}{2}^x = 32$, $x = 5$ **C.** $2^{32} = \frac{1}{x}$

   D. $2^x = \frac{1}{32}$, $x = -5$ **E.** none of these

10 Polar Coordinates and Complex Numbers

Summary

The polar coordinate system is introduced as a way of locating points in a plane. Elementary graphing in the polar coordinate system is discussed and symmetry·is used as a tool for graphing. The complex number system is reviewed and the polar form of complex numbers is introduced. Algorithms for multiplying and dividing complex numbers are presented, and a geometric perspective on certain products is given. DeMoivre's theorem is introduced and then extended to include the complex roots theorem. The use of complex numbers to model alternating electrical currents is discussed.

Chapter Objectives

* To use polar coordinates
* To convert rectangular coordinates to polar coordinates and polar coordinates to rectangular coordinates
* To graph polar equations
* To graph special curves in polar coordinates
* To express complex numbers in polar form
* To determine products and quotients of complex numbers in polar form
* To use DeMoivre's theorem to evaluate powers of complex numbers
* To determine the roots of complex numbers

Mathematical Power

Modeling   In this course you worked with models from many diverse fields of study—from seismology to psychology. But all the models you have studied have had one thing in common. They have all dealt with structured, measurable phenomena. You might be curious to know that mathematics also provides tools for analyzing phenomena that are seemingly random in nature, such as drifting clouds, flickering flames, or turbulent seas. To model these and other "irregular" phenomena, irregular geometric forms called *fractals* were developed.

Fractals have certain unique properties that make them suitable for modeling seemingly chaotic behavior. One of these properties is *self-similarity*. That is, if you enlarge or magnify a portion of the shape, that portion will still appear to have the same structure as the original shape. For example, if you examine a large portion of some continental coastline, it will appear irregular with many coves and promontories. Then if you choose a portion and "zoom in" on it, more details appear and the image continues to possess the irregularities of the original coastline. The traditional shapes of geometry—triangles, circles, squares—lose their structure when magnified and become featureless lines when viewed on a large enough scale.

Another important property of fractals is that they have nonintegral, or fractional, dimensions. In geometry, a line is a one-dimensional object, a plane is a two-dimensional object, and a solid is a three-dimensional object. In the world of fractals, a jagged line is given a dimension between 1 and 2; the specific value depends on just how jagged the line is. So, for example, the fractal dimension of the coastline of Great Britain has

486

Features

Modeling

been determined to be about 1.25. A more jagged coastline would have a dimension closer to 2. Fractal objects such as a crumpled paper ball or the branches of a tree would have dimensions between 2 and 3.

Much of the pioneering work in fractal geometry was done by a Polish-born scientist named Benoit Mandelbrot, who developed the fractal image called the *Mandelbrot set*, shown below. This set is constructed from a repeated, or iterated, process based on *complex numbers* of the form $c = a + bi$ that are graphed in the complex plane.

Fractal geometry is a good example of how a system that uses imaginary numbers can have some very real applications. Fractals are used in the study of fluid dynamics, geology, and cell biology. Fractals are also used extensively in contemporary computer-generated art. Many of the planet landscapes and special effects that you see in state-of-the-art science fiction films are generated with fractal images.

Thinking Critically   Think of a country or state with a border that is perfectly smooth. Would successive magnifications of a portion of the border reveal any hidden details? What do you think the fractal dimension of this border is?

Project   Research examples and applications of fractals other than those mentioned in this discussion, and include the dimensions if possible. You may wish to give a visual presentation of the various fractals and their applications. Discuss other seemingly irregular natural phenomena that might be modeled using fractal geometry.

487

Mathematical Power

Fractal geometry is one of the most exciting areas of contemporary mathematical research, and new discoveries are met with great interest by a wide variety of professionals including physicists, earth scientists, biologists, graphic artists, and movie makers. Fractals are now understood to be related to another developing area of mathematics, *chaos theory,* where the order in seeming disorder is studied.

Though Mandelbrot's first comprehensive publication of fractal theory took place in 1975, mathematicians had explored some of the basic ideas (including fractal dimension) between 1875 and 1925, but did not recognize their significance. Moreover, the creation of fractal pictures was a nearly impossible task until computer-generated graphics became available. Point out that since the computer uses a set of algorithms to generate the fractal curves, these pictures serve as a test of the reasonableness of the mathematical theory (or model) that produced the algorithm.

To help students understand the concept, suggest they think of fractal dimension as a type of ratio of the length of a fractal curve on one photo to its length on successive enlargements; this ratio is regular and constant.

Thinking Critically   Enlargements would *not* reveal any hidden structure—there are no "ins and outs" for a smooth curve. Students should intuitively understand that in this case the fractal dimension is simply 1.

Vocabulary
polar axis
polar coordinates
polar coordinate system
pole
$r\theta$-plane

Ⓜ Materials/Manipulatives
overhead projector
maps
transparencies

Technology
scientific calculator

FOCUS

A polar coordinate frame is a natural choice for analyzing uniform circular motion. With the radius r constant, only the single variable θ is needed to describe the motion, which is sometimes written $\theta(t)$ to emphasize time dependence.

Students may be interested in researching three-dimensional extensions of the polar coordinate system such as cylindrical and spherical polar coordinates which are also useful in the study of motion.

10.1 Polar Coordinates

Objectives: To use polar coordinates
To convert rectangular coordinates to polar coordinates and polar coordinates to rectangular coordinates

Focus

Since ancient times, scholars have studied *uniform circular motion,* that is, motion in a circle at a constant speed. Plato, for example, commented on the motion of the stars and planets. In our own era, scientists study both the motion of electrons around the nucleus of an atom and the nearly circular paths of orbiting spacecraft. To facilitate the study of circular motion, scientists can employ *polar coordinates* as a system of reference. This system is often easier to work with than the more familiar framework of rectangular coordinates, particularly to describe motion using a function of one variable. An example is the use of t to represent the time for an object to move along a circular arc.

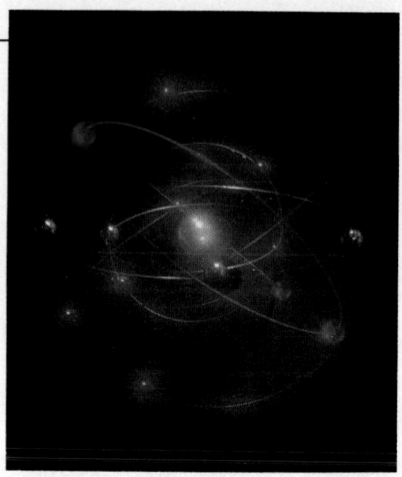

As pointed out in the Focus, the **polar coordinate system** is an alternative to the Cartesian system of rectangular coordinates for locating points in a plane. It consists of a fixed point O, called the **pole,** or origin, and a fixed ray $\overrightarrow{OA}$, called the **polar axis,** with O its initial point. Any convenient unit can be chosen to define a scale along the polar axis.

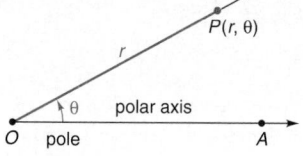

The **polar coordinates** of a point P in the polar coordinate system consist of an ordered pair (r, θ). The directed distance from the pole to P is r, and the measure of the angle from the polar axis to $\overrightarrow{OP}$ is θ. The polar coordinates of the pole O are $(0, \theta)$, where θ may assume any real value. Angle θ can be measured in degrees or radians. Both r and θ can be either positive or negative. When θ is positive, the **polar angle** is obtained by rotating $\overrightarrow{OP}$ counterclockwise from the polar axis, and when θ is negative, the rotation is clockwise. When r is positive, the **polar distance** is measured from O along the terminal side of the angle θ, and when r is negative, it is measured from O on the ray opposite the terminal side of θ. A plane is called an **$r\theta$-plane** when polar coordinates (r, θ) are used to identify its points.

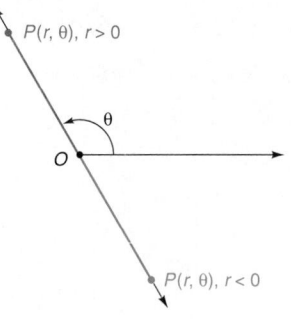

488   Chapter 10 Polar Coordinates and Complex Numbers

Example 1   Graph each point on the $r\theta$-plane.

a. $P\left(2, \dfrac{\pi}{3}\right)$ **b.** $Q\left(2, -\dfrac{\pi}{3}\right)$ **c.** $R\left(-2, \dfrac{\pi}{3}\right)$ **d.** $S\left(-2, -\dfrac{\pi}{3}\right)$

a.

b.

c.

d.

Note that rotations of θ and $\theta + 2n\pi$, $n \in Z$, produce angles with the same terminal sides, so the same point can be represented by infinitely many different pairs of polar coordinates. The fact that r may be positive or negative also generates different coordinates for the same point. However, if $r > 0$ and $0 \le \theta < 2\pi$, then, except for the pole, any point is represented by exactly one pair of polar coordinates.

Example 2   Plot the point P with polar coordinates $\left(1, \dfrac{2\pi}{3}\right)$ and find three other polar representations of this point.

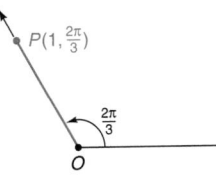

The point is graphed at the right. Three other possible representations are $\left(1, -\dfrac{4\pi}{3}\right)$, $\left(-1, \dfrac{5\pi}{3}\right)$, and $\left(-1, -\dfrac{\pi}{3}\right)$.

Why do the polar coordinates $(0, \theta)$ represent the origin (pole) no matter what the value of θ?

An equation with polar coordinates is called a **polar equation.** A **polar graph** is a graph of the set of all points (r, θ) that satisfy a given polar equation. You will study techniques for graphing specific polar equations in the next lesson. However, the two most basic graphs, $r = c$ and $\theta = k$, where c and k are constants, are shown in Example 3.

Example 3   Graph each polar equation.

a. $r = 3$ **b.** $\theta = \dfrac{\pi}{3}$

a. The points whose directed distance from the origin is 3 all lie on the circle with center at the origin and radius 3

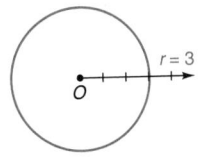

b. For $r > 0$, the points $P(r, \theta)$ for which $\theta = \dfrac{\pi}{3}$ lie on the terminal side of the angle in standard position with radian measure $\dfrac{\pi}{3}$. For $r < 0$, the points lie on the opposite ray. Thus, the graph of $\theta = \dfrac{\pi}{3}$ is the line through the origin that forms an angle of $\dfrac{\pi}{3}$ with the polar axis.

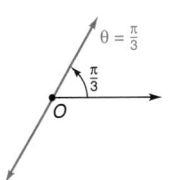

10.1 Polar Coordinates   **489**

Thinking Critically
Since the polar distance is 0, it is not measured along the terminal side nor on the ray opposite the terminal side of θ and thus $(0, \theta)$ represents the origin no matter what the value of θ is.

INSTRUCTION

Ⓜ • Use transparencies to demonstrate the relationships of the cartesian and polar coordinate systems. Stress that these systems are just two approaches to locating points on a plane.

Ⓜ • Discuss the problem of locating points on a map. Most modern local maps contain labeled grids with a key indicating the location of various places in terms of the grid. Longitude and latitude lines serve the same purpose on world or U.S. maps. Most students are probably familiar with locating points relative to a fixed point, using descriptions such as "6 blocks southeast of city hall."

• Some students may be interested in investigating three-dimensional coordinate systems after they discuss how they might extend either the rectangular or polar coordinate system to locate points in three-space.

Alternative Learning Styles

Ⓜ Discussing a variety of ways to locate places on a map helps students whose learning style is concrete.

GUIDED PRACTICE

For Example 1

Graph the point $P\left(4, \dfrac{3\pi}{4}\right)$ on the $r\theta$-plane.

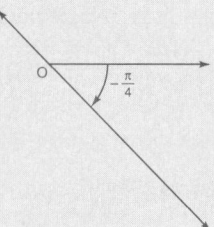
Superimpose a rectangular coordinate system on a polar coordinate system, letting the two origins coincide and the positive x-axis coincide with the polar axis. For any point P, a correspondence can be established between its polar coordinates (r, θ) and its rectangular coordinates (x, y). By definition of the sine and cosine functions, $x = r \cos \theta$ and $y = r \sin \theta$, where $r = \sqrt{x^2 + y^2}$ and $\tan \theta = \dfrac{y}{x}$. This is the case $r > 0$. You are asked in the exercises to show that the same relationships hold for the case $r < 0$.

The rectangular coordinates (x, y) and polar coordinates (r, θ) of a point P are related as follows:

$$x = r \cos \theta \qquad y = r \sin \theta$$
$$\tan \theta = \dfrac{y}{x} \qquad x^2 + y^2 = r^2$$

Example 4 Find the rectangular coordinates of each point with the given polar coordinates. Round to the nearest hundredth if necessary.

  a. $P\left(4, \dfrac{3\pi}{4}\right)$ **b.** $Q(-1, 2.03)$

a. $x = 4 \cos \dfrac{3\pi}{4} = 4\left(-\dfrac{\sqrt{2}}{2}\right) = -2\sqrt{2}$

$y = 4 \sin \dfrac{3\pi}{4} = 4\left(\dfrac{\sqrt{2}}{2}\right) = 2\sqrt{2}$

The rectangular coordinates of P are $(-2\sqrt{2}, 2\sqrt{2})$.

b. $x = -\cos 2.03 = -(-0.44) = 0.44$

$y = -\sin 2.03 = -0.90$

The rectangular coordinates of Q are $(0.44, -0.90)$.

In Example 4, note that Q could have been labeled with the polar coordinates $(1, 2.03 + \pi) \approx (1, 5.17)$ but its rectangular coordinates would always be the same: $x = \cos 5.17 = 0.44$ and $y = \sin 5.17 = -0.90$. For a given point, its rectangular coordinates are unique; its polar coordinates are not.

To convert from rectangular to polar coordinates, use the Pythagorean theorem and the Arctangent function. The principal values of the inverse tangent relation are between $-\dfrac{\pi}{2}$ and $\dfrac{\pi}{2}$, so $\theta = \text{Arctan } \dfrac{y}{x}$, if the point is in the first or fourth quadrants. If it is in the second or third quadrants, add π radians to Arctan $\dfrac{y}{x}$. *Why?*

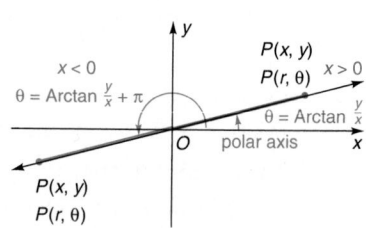

Thinking Critically

Since the period of the tangent function is π, π radians must be added to Arctan $\dfrac{y}{x}$ when θ is in the second or third quadrants.

Polar coordinates (r, θ) of point P with rectangular coordinates (x, y) can be determined as follows:

$$r = \sqrt{x^2 + y^2}$$
$$\theta = \text{Arctan}\,\frac{y}{x}, \text{ if } x > 0 \qquad \theta = \text{Arctan}\left(\frac{y}{x}\right) + \pi, \text{ if } x < 0$$

Example 5 Find polar coordinates of point A with rectangular coordinates $(-\sqrt{3}, 1)$.

$$r = \sqrt{(-\sqrt{3})^2 + 1^2} = \sqrt{3 + 1} = 2$$

Since $x < 0$,

$$\theta = \text{Arctan}\left(-\frac{1}{\sqrt{3}}\right) + \pi = -\frac{\pi}{6} + \pi = \frac{5\pi}{6}$$

Polar coordinates of A are $\left(2, \frac{5\pi}{6}\right)$.

 Many calculators have built-in functions for converting from rectangular to polar coordinates and the reverse. Since methods vary from model to model, consult the owner's manual for details. The relationship between polar and rectangular coordinates can also be used to convert equations from rectangular to polar form or from polar to rectangular form.

Example 6 Convert each of the following:
      a. $x = 3$ to a polar equation
      b. $r = 4 \sin \theta$ to a rectangular equation

a. $x = 3$
     $r \cos \theta = 3$ *Replace x with r cos θ.*
     $r = \dfrac{3}{\cos \theta}$
     $r = 3 \sec \theta$

b. $r = 4 \sin \theta$
     $r^2 = 4r \sin \theta$ *Multiply both sides by r.*
  $x^2 + y^2 = 4y$ *Replace r² with x² + y² and r sin θ with y.*

Class Exercises

Graph each point on the $r\theta$-plane and find three additional polar representations.

1. $P(1, \pi)$ **2.** $Q\left(-1.5, \frac{2\pi}{3}\right)$ **3.** $R\left(10, -\frac{5\pi}{8}\right)$

Graph each polar equation.

4. $r = 5$ **5.** $r = -9$ **6.** $\theta = -\frac{7\pi}{5}$

Find the rectangular coordinates of each point with the given polar coordinates.

7. $\left(5, \frac{\pi}{6}\right)$ $\left(\frac{5\sqrt{3}}{2}, \frac{5}{2}\right)$ **8.** $\left(-2.2, \frac{5\pi}{3}\right)$ $(-1.1, 1.9053)$ **9.** $\left(1, -\frac{\pi}{2}\right)$ $(0, -1)$

10.1 Polar Coordinates   **491**

Technology Many scientific calculators have built-in functions for converting between polar and rectangular coordinates. Directions for entering one pair of coordinates and displaying the other, however, vary from model to model. Encourage students to use the owner's manual in order to take advantage of their calculators' capabilities.

For Example 5

Find polar coordinates for the point with rectangular coordinates $P(10, -10)$. Round to the nearest hundredth if necessary.

Answers may vary. $\left(10\sqrt{2}, \frac{7\pi}{4}\right)$

For Example 6

1. Convert $y = -1$ to a polar equation.
$r = -\csc \theta$

2. Convert $r = 5 \cos \theta$ to a rectangular equation.
$x^2 - 5x + y^2 = 0$

CLOSURE

Have students write you a letter explaining the new concepts they learned in this lesson.

INDEPENDENT PRACTICE

Assignment Guide

Basic: 1–25
Average: 7–8, 15, 23–44
Enriched: 31–55

Teacher's Resource Book
   Practice, page 64

Ⓡ **Review**
Exercises 7, 15, 31, 33, and 39 review concepts of graphing, determining distance between points, representing cost as a linear function, using natural logarithms, and determining percentages.

Additional Answers

4.

5.

6.

Lesson Quiz

1. Graph $Q\left(-\dfrac{1}{2}, \dfrac{\pi}{6}\right)$ on the $r\theta$-plane.

2. Plot the point with polar coordinates $\left(8, -\dfrac{\pi}{3}\right)$ and give three additional polar representations of this point.

Answers may vary.
$\left(8, \dfrac{5\pi}{3}\right), \left(-8, \dfrac{2\pi}{3}\right), \left(-8, -\dfrac{4\pi}{3}\right)$

Graph each equation on the $r\theta$-plane.

3. $r = 9$

4. $\theta = -\dfrac{\pi}{5}$

Find a pair of polar coordinates with the given rectangular coordinates.

10. $(3, -3)$ $\left(4.24, \dfrac{7\pi}{4}\right)$ 11. $(4, -4\sqrt{3})$ $\left(8, \dfrac{5\pi}{3}\right)$ 12. $(10, 3)$ $(10.44, 0.2915)$

Convert each polar equation to rectangular form.

13. $r = 5$ $x^2 + y^2 = 25$ 14. $r \cos \theta = 7$ $x = 7$ 15. $\theta = \pi$ $y = 0$

Convert each rectangular equation to polar form.

16. $x = 15$ $r \cos \theta = 15$ 17. $y = -2.5$ $r \sin \theta = -2.5$ 18. $x^2 + y^2 = \sqrt{3}$ $r = \sqrt[4]{3}$

19. **Thinking Critically** Show that if P is a point with polar coordinates (r, θ) and $r < 0$, then the corresponding rectangular coordinates of point P are (x, y) with $x = r \cos \theta$ and $y = r \sin \theta$.

Practice Exercises   Use appropriate technology.

Graph each point on the $r\theta$-plane.

A 1. $P\left(3, \dfrac{\pi}{6}\right)$ 2. $Q(-2, -135°)$ 3. $R(-2, 120°)$

 4. $S\left(1.5, -\dfrac{\pi}{3}\right)$ 5. $T\left(-1, -\dfrac{5\pi}{4}\right)$ 6. $W(0, 150°)$

Ⓡ 7. Graph $2x - 3y + 3 = 0$ on the xy-plane.

 8. **Thinking Critically** Graph on the xy-plane points P, S, and T from Practice Exercises 1, 4, and 5. Explain why a given pair of coordinates names different points in the two systems.

Plot each point with the given polar coordinates. Then find three additional polar representations for each point with the given polar coordinates.

 9. $\left(-7, \dfrac{\pi}{6}\right)$ 10. $\left(2.8, \dfrac{7\pi}{3}\right)$ 11. $\left(29, -\dfrac{8\pi}{3}\right)$

12. $(11, 16°)$ 13. $(-6, -200°)$ 14. $\left(-5, -\dfrac{3\pi}{4}\right)$

Ⓡ 15. Find the distance between $P(1, -3.6)$ and $Q(-4, 0)$ on the xy-plane. 6.16

Graph each polar equation.

16. $r = 6$ 17. $r = -5$ 18. $\theta = 2$

19. $\theta = -1$ 20. $\theta = 17\pi$ 21. $\theta = -5\pi$

Find the rectangular coordinates of each point with the given polar coordinates. Round to the nearest hundredth if necessary.

22. $\left(10, -\dfrac{\pi}{4}\right)$ 23. $\left(-9, \dfrac{5\pi}{6}\right)$ 24. $(2, 1.67)$ 25. $(1, 1)$
  $(5\sqrt{2}, -5\sqrt{2})$ $\left(\dfrac{9\sqrt{3}}{2}, -\dfrac{9}{2}\right)$ $(-0.20, 1.99)$ $(0.54, 0.84)$

Find polar coordinates of each point with the given rectangular coordinates.

B 26. $(5, -5)$ $\left(5\sqrt{2}, -\dfrac{\pi}{4}\right)$ 27. $(0, 9)$ $\left(9, \dfrac{\pi}{2}\right)$ 28. $(-4, 4\sqrt{3})$ $\left(8, \dfrac{2\pi}{3}\right)$ 29. $\left(-\dfrac{1}{2}, \dfrac{\sqrt{3}}{2}\right)$ $\left(1, \dfrac{2\pi}{3}\right)$

30. **Writing in Mathematics** Rectangular and polar coordinates are two ways of describing the locations of points relative to a fixed point. Choose a landmark and describe two ways of giving its location relative to your school or home.

492   Chapter 10 Polar Coordinates and Complex Numbers

Writing in Mathematics
30. Answers may vary. The gas station is 3 blocks north and 4 blocks west of school. It is also about 5 blocks northwest of school as the crow flies.

31. *Business*   A private detective charges a $500 retainer fee plus $250 per day for his services. Write a linear function that represents the cost in hiring him and find the total cost for a job requiring 9 days to complete. $c = 500 + 250d;$ 2750

32. Find two polar equations for the line through the pole that is perpendicular to the polar axis. $\theta = \frac{\pi}{2}, \theta = -\frac{\pi}{2}$

33. *Geology*   A fossil that originally contained 120 mg of carbon-14 now contains 100 mg. Determine the approximate age of the fossil to the nearest 100 years given that carbon-14 has a half-life of 5570 years.   1500 years

34. Find two polar equations for the circle with center at the pole and radius $\sqrt{3}$. $r = \sqrt{3}, r = -\sqrt{3}$

Convert each polar equation to rectangular form.

35. $r = \sqrt{5}$ **36.** $r = 2 \csc \theta$ **37.** $r = -\sec \theta$ **38.** $r = -6 \sin \theta$
$x^2 + y^2 = 5$ $y = 2$ $x = -1$ $x^2 + y^2 + 6y = 0$

39. *Pharmacology*   How much water should be evaporated from 50 ml of a 6% alcohol solution so that the remaining solution is 10% alcohol?   20 ml

40. *Physics*   The radiation pattern of a certain antenna can be represented by $r = 60(1 + \sin \theta)$. Convert the equation to rectangular form.
$x^2 + y^2 = 60\sqrt{x^2 + y^2} + 60y$

Convert each rectangular equation to polar form.

41. $x^2 = 12$ **42.** $x^2 + y^2 = 7$ **43.** $3x - 2y = 1$ **44.** $x - 3y = 1$

C 45. $2x^2 + 2y^2 + 5x = 0$ $2r^2 + 5r \cos \theta = 0$ **46.** $3x^2 + 3y^2 - 2x = 0$ $3r^2 - 2r \cos \theta = 0$

47. $x^2 + (y - 2)^2 - 4 = 0$ $r^2 - 4r \sin \theta = 0$ **48.** $(x - 5)^2 + y^2 - 25 = 0$ $r^2 - 10r \cos \theta = 0$

Convert each polar equation to rectangular form. $3\sqrt{x^2 + y^2} + y = 1$ $4\sqrt{x^2 + y^2} - x = 1$

49. $r = 7 \tan \theta \sec \theta$ **50.** $r = 2 \csc \theta \cot \theta$ **51.** $r = \dfrac{1}{3 + \sin \theta}$ **52.** $r = \dfrac{1}{4 - \cos \theta}$
$x^2 = 7y$ $y^2 = 2x$

53. Given that $P_1(r_1, \theta_1)$ and $P_2(r_2, \theta_2)$ are two points in the $r\theta$-plane and r_1 and r_2 are positive, use the law of cosines to derive the following *distance formula for polar coordinates*:

$$P_1P_2 = \sqrt{r_1^2 + r_2^2 - 2r_1r_2 \cos(\theta_2 - \theta_1)}$$

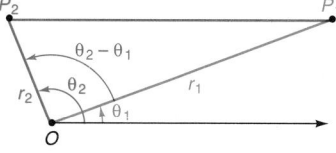

54. Use the formula you derived in Exercise 53 to find the distance between $P\left(3.1, \frac{\pi}{2}\right)$ and $Q\left(2, -\frac{\pi}{4}\right)$.   4.73

55. **Thinking Critically**   Show that the distance formula for polar coordinates in Exercise 53 need not be restricted to positive values of the polar distances. *Hint:* Assume that $r_2 < 0$. Relabel P_2 so that its polar distance is positive, apply the distance formula, and use an identity for $\cos(\theta_2 + \pi)$.

Review

1. A survey was done to determine the demand for a bumper sticker with a new slogan. The demand curve was found to be linear. The demand was 10 stickers for $5.00 and 20 stickers for $8.00. Determine the equation for this product and the number of stickers that could be sold at $11.00. $y = \frac{10}{3}x - \frac{20}{3}$; 30

2. Which field properties hold for the set of all squares of positive integers under multiplication?   clos., assoc., commut., ident.

10.1 Polar Coordinates   **493**

---

5. Find the rectangular coordinates of point $P\left(-8, \frac{\pi}{4}\right)$. $(-4\sqrt{2}, -4\sqrt{2})$

6. Find the polar coordinates of the point $Q(-6, 6)$. Round to the nearest hundredth if necessary.
$\left(6\sqrt{2}, \frac{3\pi}{4}\right)$

7. Convert $y = -7$ to a polar equation. $r = -7 \csc \theta$

8. Convert $r = 9 \sin \theta$ to a rectangular equation.
$x^2 + y^2 - 9y = 0$

Alternative Assessment
Tell students that the ordered pairs $(1, -1)$ and $\left(\sqrt{2}, \frac{3\pi}{4}\right)$ can be used to identify the same point on a coordinate plane. Then have the students explain what each coordinate indicates about the location of the point.

Enrichment
Show that the polar equation for the hyperbola with rectangular equation $x^2 - y^2 = 25$ is $r^2 = 25 \sec 2\theta$.
$(r \cos \theta)^2 - (r \sin \theta)^2 = 25$, $r^2 \cos^2 \theta - r^2 \sin^2 \theta = 25$, $r^2(\cos^2 \theta - \sin^2 \theta) = 25$, $r^2 \cos 2\theta = 25$, $r^2 = \dfrac{25}{\cos 2\theta} = 25 \sec 2\theta$

Additional Answers
41. $r^2 \cos^2 \theta = 12$
42. $r = \sqrt{7}$
43. $3r \cos \theta - 2r \sin \theta = 1$
44. $r \cos \theta - 3r \sin \theta = 1$
53. $(P_1P_2)^2 = r_1^2 + r_2^2 - 2r_1r_2 \cos(\theta_2 - \theta_1)$, so $P_1P_2 = \sqrt{r_1^2 + r_2^2 - 2r_1r_2 \cos(\theta_2 - \theta_1)}$
55. $(P_1P_2)^2 = r_1^2 + (-r_2)^2 + 2r_1r_2 \cos(\theta_2 + \pi - \theta_1)$, so $P_1P_2 = \sqrt{r_1^2 + r_2^2 - 2r_1r_2 \cos(\theta_2 - \theta_1)}$

Vocabulary
cardioid
lemniscate
limaçon
polar grid
rose
spiral of Archimedes

Ⓜ **Materials/Manipulatives**
polar graph paper
transparencies

Technology
graphing utility
symbolic manipulator

FOCUS

Karl von Frisch, a German scientist, became interested in studying bees when he read a report that bees were thought to be colorblind. He questioned that conclusion and spent 45 years studying bees, observing, experimenting, and documenting information. When trying to attract bees to an experimental spot, von Frisch observed that once one bee had found a good food source, many other bees would arrive, and almost without exception, these would be members of the same hive. The scientist conjectured that the bees must have a way of communicating information about the location of the food, and he was led to the discovery of the bees' dance.

Students may be interested in reading von Frisch's book, *The Dancing Bees,* which is an interesting and readable account of his studies.

10.2 Graphs of Polar Equations

Objectives: To graph polar equations
To graph special curves in polar coordinates

Focus

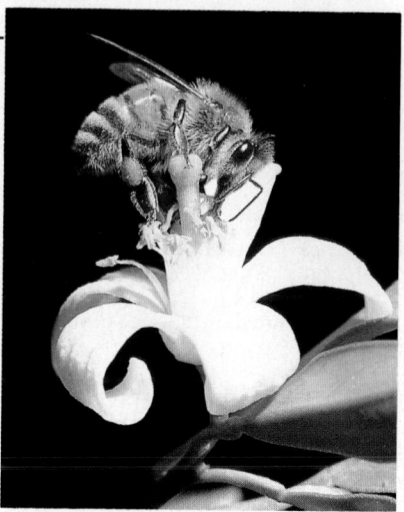

When a honeybee finds a rich source of food, it performs special movements called *dancing* to communicate its discovery to members of its hive. Other bees imitate the dancer and then go out to seek the nectar or pollen. The odor of the nectar or pollen on the first bee's body tells the others the kind of food that is available. How do they know where to look?

Studies and experiments have convinced scientists that the dance itself communicates the location of the food very efficiently. The dancing bee uses the orientation of its body to indicate the horizontal angle between the sun and the feeding place. The kind of dance, "circling" or "wagging," and the tempo of the wagging movements indicate the distance to the food.

Although there are variations among different strains of bees in the details of communication, almost all give the direction and distance of the food from the hive. If you think of the beehive as a fixed point or pole, you will realize that the bees communicate in a kind of polar coordinate system.

In the previous lesson, two simple polar graphs were identified. The graph of an equation of the form $r = c$ is a circle with radius $|c|$ and with its center at the pole; the graph of $\theta = k$ is a line through the pole. In this lesson, other polar graphs are explored and some techniques for graphing in the polar coordinate system are suggested.

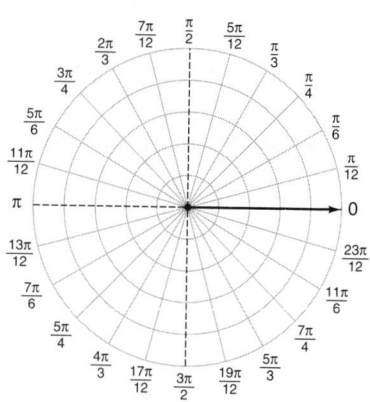

The most straightforward graphing technique is to make a table of values that satisfy the equation, graph the associated points, and join them with a smooth curve. A calculator and a **polar grid,** like the one shown at the right, will aid you in this process. The polar grid consists of lines through the pole and concentric circles centered at the pole. It is used as a guide for easy location of points.

494   Chapter 10 Polar Coordinates and Complex Numbers

Example 1 Graph $r = 6 \cos \theta$. Use a table of values for θ between 0 and 2π.

θ	0	$\frac{\pi}{6}$	$\frac{\pi}{4}$	$\frac{\pi}{3}$	$\frac{\pi}{2}$	$\frac{2\pi}{3}$	$\frac{3\pi}{4}$	$\frac{5\pi}{6}$	π	$\frac{7\pi}{6}$	$\frac{5\pi}{4}$	$\frac{3\pi}{2}$	$\frac{7\pi}{4}$	2π
$6 \cos \theta$	6	5.2	4.2	3	0	-3	-4.2	-5.2	-6	-5.2	-4.2	0	4.2	6

The graph appears to be that of a circle of radius 3 with center on the polar axis and tangent to the line $\theta = \frac{\pi}{2}$ at the pole. Notice that the graph is traced *twice* (in the counterclockwise direction) as θ ranges between 0 and 2π.

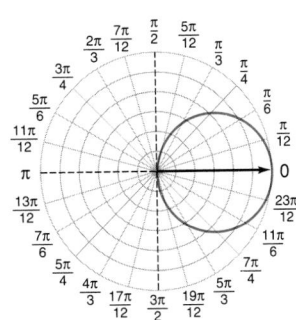

A graphing utility can be used to draw graphs of polar equations. This may be done using the equations $x = r \cos \theta$ and $y = r \sin \theta$ that allow you to change from polar to rectangular coordinates. For the polar equation of Example 1, choose the utility's *parametric mode* and enter the equations

$$x = 6 \cos t \cos t$$
$$y = 6 \cos t \sin t$$

Many utilities use t rather than θ. Here, the variable t is called a *parameter,* that is, a third variable that is related to both x and y in a pair of **parametric equations.** (Parametric equations are discussed in greater detail in Chapter 12.) At the right is the graph of $r = 6 \cos \theta$ as generated by a graphing utility. The zoom-square feature will help you obtain a graph that looks "circular."

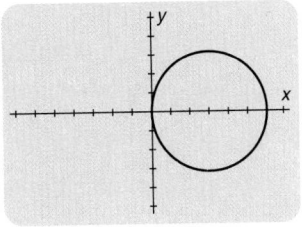

[−7.5, 7.5] by [−5, 5]
T min: 0   T max: 2π T step: $\frac{\pi}{30}$

In general, to graph the polar graph $r = f(\theta)$ using a graphing utility, enter the equations

$$x = f(t) \cos t$$
$$y = f(t) \sin t$$

while in the utility's parametric mode. Some graphing utilities have a polar mode that allows you to enter the polar equation $r = f(t)$ directly.

What is the graph of $r = a \cos \theta$? A little experimentation shows that the graph is a circle of radius $\frac{1}{2}|a|$ with center on the polar axis or its extension and tangent to the line $\theta = \frac{1}{2}\pi$ at the pole. If $a > 0$, the circle is to the right of the pole, and if $a < 0$, the circle is to the left of the pole.

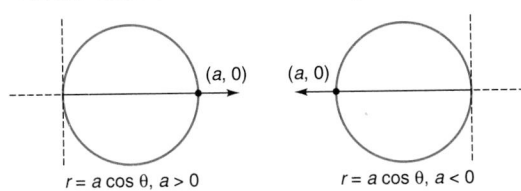

$r = a \cos \theta, a > 0$ $r = a \cos \theta, a < 0$

10.2 Graphs of Polar Equations   **495**

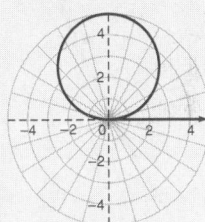

Technology Note that some computer graphing utilities have a polar plot mode in which students can graph polar equations directly. Usually these are limited to polar *functions* of the form $r = f(\theta)$ or $r = f(t)$.

Point out that graphing calculators can also be used to graph polar functions. The TI-81, for example, has a parametric mode which can be used for polar graphing, but instead of graphing $r = f(t)$ directly, one must graph $x = f(t) \cos t$ and $y = f(t) \sin t$.

Also point out that programs can be written to facilitate polar graphing. You may wish to refer students to "Computer Assisted Polar Graphing" in the March 1987 edition of *Mathematics Teacher*.

For Example 2

Graph $r = 4\theta$ for $\theta > 0$.

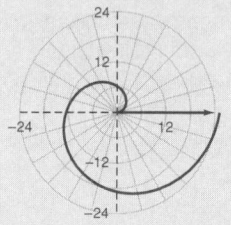

As you may suspect, the graph of $r = a \sin \theta$ is similar to the graph of $r = a \cos \theta$. It is a circle of radius $\frac{1}{2}|a|$ with center on the line $\theta = \frac{1}{2}\pi$ or its extension, and tangent to the polar axis at the pole. If $a > 0$, the circle is above the polar axis, and if $a < 0$, the circle is below the polar axis.

In Example 1 and related graphs, the variable θ is introduced in terms of the sine and cosine functions. Because both sine and cosine have periods of 2π, you need to examine only those values of θ between 0 and 2π. In the next example, you must also consider values greater than 2π since the function is not periodic.

Example 2 Graph $r = \theta$ for $\theta \geq 0$.

Two methods are shown, graphing from a table of values and using a graphing utility.

Method 1: Graphing points from a table of values shows that the function has a spiral shape.

θ	0	$\frac{\pi}{4}$	$\frac{\pi}{2}$	$\frac{3\pi}{4}$	π	$\frac{3\pi}{2}$	2π	$\frac{9\pi}{4}$	$\frac{5\pi}{2}$	3π	$\frac{7\pi}{2}$	4π
r	0	0.79	1.57	2.36	3.14	4.71	6.28	7.07	7.85	9.42	11.00	12.57

Method 2: Using a graphing utility, enter the parametric equations $x = t \cos t$, $y = t \sin t$.

Graphs using both methods are shown below.

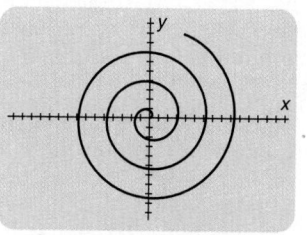

[−30, 30] by [−20, 20]
x scl: 2   y scl: 2
T min: 0   T max: 20   T step: 0.1

The graph of the function in Example 2 is called a **Spiral of Archimedes.**

As with rectangular graphs, recognition of certain kinds of *symmetry* can make polar graphs easier to draw. Three important types are symmetry with respect to the pole, the polar axis, and the line $\theta = \frac{1}{2}\pi$. There are simple tests for each type of symmetry. These tests are summarized at the top of the following page together with graphs that illustrate the three types of symmetry.

If an equation fails to pass a given test, its graph may still have the indicated symmetry. However, the graph of any equation that satisfies the test must have the symmetry.

496   Chapter 10 Polar Coordinates and Complex Numbers

Tests for Symmetry in Polar Graphs

If an equation is equivalent to the one formed by making the given substitutions, then its graph has the indicated symmetry:

Replace r by $-r$	Symmetry with respect to the pole
Replace θ by $-\theta$	Symmetry with respect to the polar axis
Replace θ by $\pi - \theta$ or (r, θ) by $(-r, -\theta)$	Symmetry with respect to the line $\theta = \frac{1}{2}\pi$

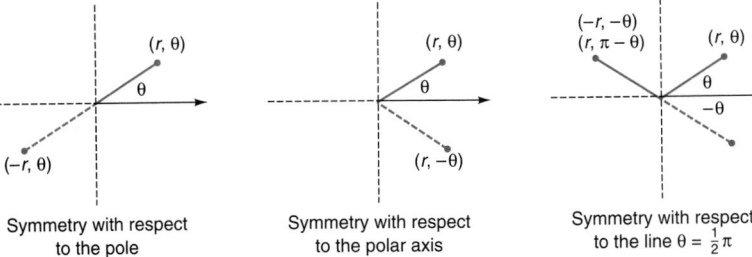

Symmetry with respect to the pole

Symmetry with respect to the polar axis

Symmetry with respect to the line $\theta = \frac{1}{2}\pi$

The test for symmetry can be used to verify that the graph of $r = 6 \cos \theta$ of Example 1 has the symmetry that its sketch suggests. The graph appears to be symmetric with respect to the polar axis.

Since $\cos \theta = \cos(-\theta)$, the equation $r = 6 \cos(-\theta)$ is equivalent to $r = 6 \cos \theta$. Therefore, the graph *is* symmetric with respect to the polar axis.

Symmetry is useful in graphing an important group of polar graphs called **limaçons.** (*Limaçon* is the French word for *snail*.)

Example 3 Use the tests for symmetry to identify the kinds of symmetry of the graph of $r = 2 + 4 \cos \theta$. Then graph the equation.

θ	0	$\frac{\pi}{6}$	$\frac{\pi}{4}$	$\frac{\pi}{3}$	$\frac{\pi}{2}$	$\frac{5\pi}{9}$	$\frac{2\pi}{3}$	$\frac{3\pi}{4}$	π
$2 + 4 \cos \theta$	6	5.46	4.83	4	2	1.30	0	-0.83	-2

As in Example 1, $f(-\theta) = f(\theta)$, so the graph is symmetric with respect to the polar axis. As θ varies from 0 to π, the red curve represents the table of values. Symmetry is then used to complete the graph.

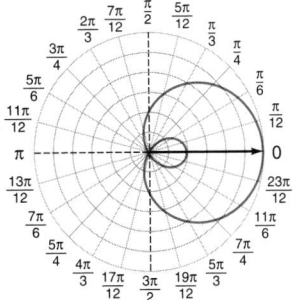

Limaçons are the graphs of equations of the form $r = a + b \cos \theta$ and $r = a + b \sin \theta$. A special case of the limaçon occurs when $a = b$, that is, when its equation is $r = a + a \cos \theta$ or $r = a + a \sin \theta$. The resulting graph is called a **cardioid** because of its heartlike shape.

10.2 Graphs of Polar Equations   **497**

For Example 3
Use the tests for symmetry to identify the kind of symmetry possessed by the graph of the equation $r = 5 + 10 \cos \theta$. Then graph the equation. The graph is symmetric with respect to the polar axis.

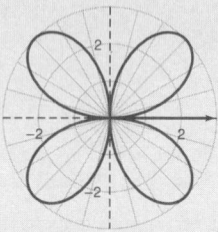
Example 4   Graph $r = 2 + 2 \sin \theta$.

Since $\sin (\pi - \theta) = \sin \theta$, the graph is symmetric with respect to the line $\theta = \frac{1}{2}\pi$.

θ	0	$\frac{\pi}{6}$	$\frac{\pi}{4}$	$\frac{\pi}{3}$	$\frac{\pi}{2}$	$\frac{2\pi}{3}$	$\frac{3\pi}{4}$	$\frac{5\pi}{6}$	π	$\frac{7\pi}{6}$	$\frac{5\pi}{4}$	$\frac{3\pi}{2}$	$\frac{7\pi}{4}$	2π
$2 + 2 \sin \theta$	2	3	3.4	3.7	4	3.7	3.4	3	2	1	0.6	0	0.6	2

Notice that a limaçon whose equation involves the sine function is symmetric with respect to a vertical line, while one whose equation involves the cosine is symmetric with respect to a horizontal line. Compare these curves with the circles $r = a \cos \theta$ and $r = a \sin \theta$.

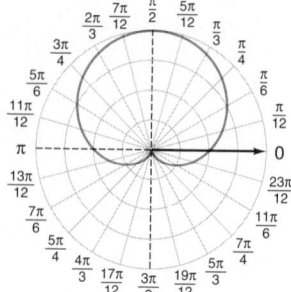

When you draw a polar graph, it can be helpful to identify the zeros and the maximum values of $|r|$. This is done in Example 5.

Example 5   Graph $r = 3 \cos 2\theta$.

The graph is symmetric with respect to the polar axis, since $3 \cos 2(-\theta) = 3 \cos 2\theta$. To see that it is also symmetric with respect to the line $\theta = \frac{1}{2}\pi$, note that

$$3 \cos 2 (\pi - \theta) = 3 \cos (2\pi - 2\theta) = 3 \cos (-2\theta) = 3 \cos 2\theta$$

In the interval $[0, 2\pi]$, r equals 0 when the curve goes through the pole, that is, when $\theta = \frac{\pi}{4}, \frac{3\pi}{4}, \frac{5\pi}{4}, \frac{7\pi}{4}$. The maximum value of $|r|$ is 3, at $\theta = 0, \frac{\pi}{2}, \pi$, and $\frac{3\pi}{2}$.

As θ ranges from 0 to $\frac{\pi}{4}$, r decreases from 3 to 0.	As θ ranges from $\frac{\pi}{4}$ to $\frac{\pi}{2}$, r decreases from 0 to -3.	As θ ranges from $\frac{\pi}{2}$ to $\frac{3\pi}{4}$, r increases from -3 to 0.	As θ ranges from $\frac{3\pi}{4}$ to π, r increases from 0 to 3.
			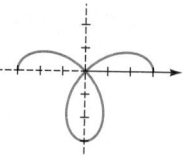

Use symmetry to complete the graph.

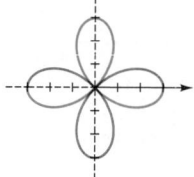

498   Chapter 10 Polar Coordinates and Complex Numbers

A graphing utility will not only verify the accuracy of the graph in Example 5 but will also generate the graph along the path just described. Use the parametric equations $x = 3 \cos 2t \cos t$, $y = 3 \cos 2t \sin t$. Choose a convenient viewing rectangle that does not greatly distort the shape of the graph. One such choice is $[-5, 6]$ by $[-3, 4]$.

Graphs of equations of the form $r = a \cos n\theta$ and $r = a \sin n\theta$, where $a \neq 0$ and n is a nonzero integer, are called **roses** or *rose curves*. The following examples illustrate the relationship between n and the number of rose petals.

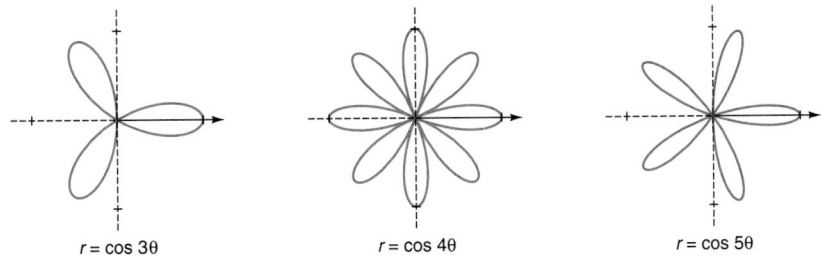

$r = \cos 3\theta$ $r = \cos 4\theta$ $r = \cos 5\theta$

If n is odd, the rose has n leaves or petals; each is traced twice as θ ranges from 0 to 2π. If n is even, the rose has $2n$ leaves, each of which is traced once as θ ranges from 0 to 2π.

In each of Examples 1 through 5, r is a function of θ. Thus, to each value of θ there corresponds exactly one value of r. However, it is sometimes necessary to graph a polar equation in which r is not a function of θ.

Example 6 Graph $r^2 = 4 \cos 2\theta$.

Because r^2 must be greater than zero, the only valid values of θ are those for which $\cos 2\theta \geq 0$. In the interval $[0, 2\pi]$, this eliminates $\frac{\pi}{4} < \theta < \frac{3\pi}{4}$ and

$\frac{5\pi}{4} < \theta < \frac{7\pi}{4}$ shown as the shaded regions in the graph at the left below. (To see this, it may be helpful to graph $y = \cos 2x$.)

The graph of $r^2 = 4 \cos 2\theta$ is symmetric with respect to the polar axis, the line $\theta = \frac{1}{2}\pi$ and the pole. The value $r = 0$ occurs when θ is an odd multiple of $\frac{1}{4}\pi$; $|r|$ reaches its maximum of 2 when $\theta = 0$ and $\theta = \pi$.

Graphing points in the interval $\left[0, \frac{1}{4}\pi\right]$ gives the curve at the left below, which may be extended by symmetry to complete the graph as shown at the right below.

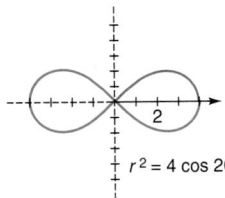

$r^2 = 4 \cos 2\theta$

10.2 Graphs of Polar Equations   **499**

For Example 6
Graph $r^2 = 4 \sin 2\theta$.

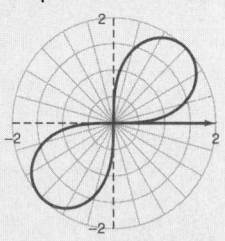

For Example 7
Transform the polar equation $r = 7 \csc \theta$ to rectangular form and then graph.
$r \sin \theta = 7$
$\quad y = 7$

$r = 7 \csc \theta$

For Example 8

Graph $x^2 + y^2 - 6y = 0$.

$r = 6 \sin \theta$

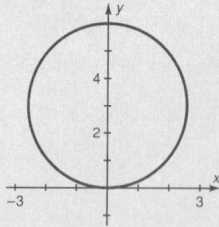

CLOSURE

Have students make two lists: one consisting of the lesson concepts they found easy to understand and the other consisting of the concepts they found difficult to understand. Then have them give reasons for their choices.

INDEPENDENT PRACTICE

Assignment Guide

Basic: 1–25, 33, 35–37, 41
Average: 13, 17–45
Enriched: 19, 27–32, 34–54

Teacher's Resource Book
  Practice, page 65

Ⓡ **Review**

Exercises 13, 17, 33, 35, and 39 review concepts of plotting polar coordinates, verifying identities, and using problem-solving skills.

Technology Encourage the use of a graphing utility for Exercises 1 to 9 to observe the symmetry predicted by the tests. A graphing utility could be used effectively for Exercises 49 to 54.

Graphs of equations of the form $r^2 = a^2 \sin 2\theta$ or $r^2 = a^2 \cos 2\theta$ are called **lemniscates**. This term comes from the Greek word for *ribbon*.

Sometimes transforming an equation from polar to rectangular form makes the task of graphing the equation much simpler.

Example 7 Transform the polar equation $r = 8 \sec \theta$ to rectangular form and graph.

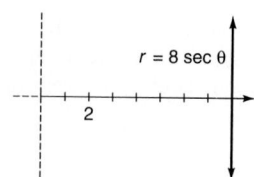

Since $\sec \theta = \dfrac{1}{\cos \theta}$, the equation may be expressed as

$r = \dfrac{8}{\cos \theta}$, which is equivalent to $r \cos \theta = 8$. In rectangular

form, this is the equation $x = 8$, which is a vertical line.

Transforming from rectangular to polar form may simplify an equation.

Example 8 Graph the equation $(x^2 + y^2)^2 = 50xy$.

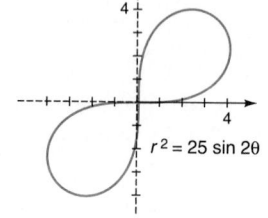

$$(x^2 + y^2)^2 = 50xy \qquad \textit{Transform the equation.}$$
$$(r^2)^2 = 50(r \cos \theta)(r \sin \theta)$$
$$r^4 = 50r^2 \cos \theta \sin \theta$$
$$r^4 - 50r^2 \cos \theta \sin \theta = 0$$
$$r^2(r^2 - 50 \cos \theta \sin \theta) = 0 \qquad \textit{Factor.}$$
$$r^2 = 0 \quad \text{or} \quad r^2 - 50 \cos \theta \sin \theta = 0$$
$$r = 0 \qquad\qquad\qquad r^2 = 25 \cdot 2 \cos \theta \sin \theta$$
$$\qquad\qquad\qquad r^2 = 25 \sin 2\theta \qquad \textit{2 sin θ cos θ = sin 2θ}$$

You may recognize that $r^2 = 25 \sin 2\theta$ is a lemniscate. In the interval $[0, 2\pi]$, θ has real values only in $\left[0, \dfrac{\pi}{2}\right]$ and $\left[\pi, \dfrac{3\pi}{2}\right]$. The graph is symmetric with respect to the origin and about the line $\theta = \frac{1}{4}\pi$. If you consider the values of θ for which $|r|$ reaches its maximum value, this line of symmetry should not surprise you.

Class Exercises

1. Test the functions $r = c$ and $\theta = k$, where c and k are constants, for symmetry.

Identify the kinds of symmetry the graph of each polar equation possesses.

2. $r = 24 \cos 6\theta$ polar axis **3.** $r = 5 - \sin 2\theta$ none **4.** $r = 2\theta$ line $\theta = \dfrac{\pi}{2}$

5. $r = 4 \sec \theta$ polar axis **6.** $r = \dfrac{4}{1 - \cos \theta}$ polar axis **7.** $r^2 = 16 \sin 2\theta$ pole

8. Identify the admissible values of θ for the lemniscate $r^2 = 16 \sin 2\theta$. $0 \le \theta \le \dfrac{\pi}{2}, \pi \le \theta \le \dfrac{3\pi}{2}$

9. What is the maximum value of $|r|$ for the lemniscate $r^2 = 16 \sin 2\theta$? At what value(s) of θ does it occur? $4; \dfrac{\pi}{4}, \dfrac{5\pi}{4}$

Without drawing, identify the graph of each of the following.

10. $r = 6.1$ **11.** $\theta = 2.7\pi$ **12.** $r = 3 \cos \theta$

13. $r = 8(1 + \sin \theta)$ **14.** $r = 4 - 2 \cos \theta$ **15.** $r = \pi \sin 12\theta$

16. $r = 5 - 5 \cos \theta$ **17.** $r = 25 \cos 7\theta$ **18.** $r^2 = 10 \sin 2\theta$

500 Chapter 10 Polar Coordinates and Complex Numbers

Additional Answers, Class Exercises

10. circle with center at the pole **11.** line through the pole **12.** circle with center on polar axis
13. cardioid **14.** limaçon **15.** rose with 24 leaves
16. cardioid **17.** rose with 7 leaves **18.** lemniscate

19. Test the function $r = e^{-\theta}$ for symmetry. no symmetry

20. Convert the equation $r = \dfrac{2}{\sin \theta + 1}$ to rectangular form and graph. $y = -\dfrac{x^2}{4} + 1$

Practice Exercises   Use appropriate technology.

Identify the kinds of symmetry the graph of each polar equation possesses.

A **1.** $r = 22$ pole, polar axis, $\theta = \frac{\pi}{2}$ **2.** $r = 3 \cos \theta$ polar axis   **3.** $r = -6 \sin \theta$ $\theta = \frac{\pi}{2}$

4. $r = 8 \sec \theta$ polar axis   **5.** $r = \frac{1}{2}\theta$ $\theta = \frac{\pi}{2}$ **6.** $r = 4 \sin 5\theta$ $\theta = \frac{\pi}{2}$

7. $\theta = \frac{1}{4}\pi$ pole   **8.** $r^2 = 36 \cos 2\theta$ pole, polar axis, $\theta = \frac{\pi}{2}$ **9.** $r^2 = 9 \sin 2\theta$ pole

Use the techniques of this lesson to graph each equation.

10. $r = 12 \cos \theta$ **11.** $r = -4 \sin \theta$ **12.** $r = 15 \sin \theta$

Ⓡ **13.** $\theta = -\frac{1}{4}\pi$ **14.** $r = 5(1 + \cos \theta)$ **15.** $r = 2 - 4 \cos \theta$

16. $r = 4 \cos 3\theta$ Ⓡ **17.** $r = -8$ **18.** $r = 8 \sin 2\theta$

19. Writing in Mathematics   Suppose you were asked which has a simpler equation, a circle or a straight line. Answer this question in light of the ideas of this lesson.

Transform each polar equation to rectangular form and graph.

20. $r \cos \theta = 9$ **21.** $r \sin \theta = -2$ **22.** $r = -3 \csc \theta$

23. $r = 2\sqrt{7} \sec \theta$ **24.** $r \sec \theta = 2$ **25.** $r \csc \theta = \sqrt{11}$

Graph each polar equation.

B **26.** $r = 4 + 3 \cos \theta$ **27.** $r = 6 + 3 \cos \theta$ **28.** $r^2 = 16 \cos 2\theta$

29. $r^2 = 16 \sin 2\theta$ **30.** $r = 2\theta$ **31.** $r = 2 + 3 \sin \theta$

32. Convert the equation $r = \dfrac{1}{1 - \sin \theta}$ to rectangular form and graph.

Ⓡ **33.** Use an appropriate addition identity to show that $\sin (\pi - \theta) = \sin \theta$. (This is the relationship used in Example 4.)

34. Use symmetry to graph $r = \theta$, allowing θ to be both positive and negative.

Ⓡ **35.** *Packaging*   An open rectangular box is to be constructed from a piece of cardboard by cutting out squares of the same size from the four corners and turning up the sides. If the original piece of cardboard is 24 in. by 30 in. long and the volume is to be 1040 in.³, what is the length of the side of each cutout square? 2 in.

36. Thinking Critically   Explain why any polar equation that can be thought of as a function of $\sin \theta$ will have a graph that is symmetric with respect to the line $\theta = \frac{1}{2}\pi$. *Hint:* An equation of this type can be expressed as $r = f(\sin \theta)$, for example, $r = 2 - 4 \sin \theta$.

37. *Astronomy*   The path of a certain comet can be approximated by the equation $r = \dfrac{2}{1 - \sin \theta}$. Use the techniques of this lesson to graph its path.

Writing in Mathematics
19. The answer to the question depends on the coordinate system in which you are working. In the rectangular coordinate system a line has the simpler equation. In the polar coordinate system a circle, particularly a circle with center at the pole, has the simpler equation.

LESSON FOLLOW-UP

Lesson Quiz
1. Graph $r = 3 \cos \theta$.

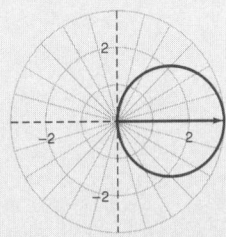

Identify the kind of symmetry possessed by the graph of each polar equation.
2. $r = 8 + 8 \cos \theta$
polar axis symmetry
3. $r = 5\theta$ pole symmetry
4. Write a polar equation whose graph would be a cardioid.
Answers may vary. Students' equations should be of the form $r = a + a \cos \theta$ or $r = a + a \sin \theta$.
5. Graph $r = 5 \sin 2\theta$.

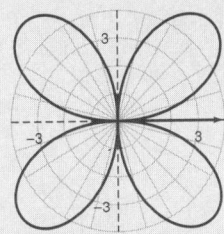

6. Transform the polar equation $r = \dfrac{3}{1 - \sin \theta}$ to rectangular form and graph. $y = \dfrac{x^2}{6} - \dfrac{3}{2}$

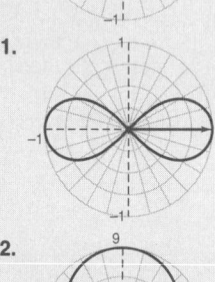
38. Use the techniques of this lesson to graph $r = \dfrac{2}{\cos \theta}$.

Ⓡ 39. *Chemistry*   How many liters of a 30% salt solution must be added to 12 L of a 70% salt solution to obtain a 55% salt solution? 7.2 L

Express each equation in polar form and graph.

40. $y = (x^2 + y^2)^{\frac{3}{2}}$ $r^2 = \sin \theta$

41. $(x^2 + y^2)^2 = x^2 - y^2$ $r^2 = \cos 2\theta$

42. Graph $r = 5 + 4 \sin \theta$.

43. Graph $r = 10 + 4 \sin \theta$.

Determine a polar equation for each graph.

C 44.   45.   46.   47.

  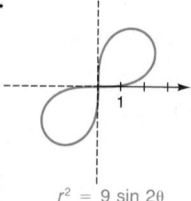

$r = 4 \sin \theta$ $r = 1 + \cos \theta$ $r = 4 \sin 3\theta$ $r^2 = 9 \sin 2\theta$

48. **Thinking Critically**   The limaçons that are graphs of $r = a + b \cos \theta$, for a and b positive numbers, may be categorized according to the relative sizes of a and b. Use examples to help describe the differences among the shapes of the limaçons under the following four conditions, and determine the effects of the numbers a and b on their graphs:

   a. $a < b$ **b.** $a = b$ **c.** $b < a < 2b$ **d.** $a \geq 2b$
    with loop inside   cardioid   dented or dimpled   closer to a circle

Graph each of the following pairs of equations.

49. $r = 2 \cos \theta$

   $r = 2 \cos \left(\theta - \dfrac{\pi}{4} \right)$

50. $r = 2 + 4 \sin \theta$

   $r = 2 + 4 \sin \left(\theta - \dfrac{\pi}{3} \right)$

51. **Thinking Critically**   In rectangular coordinates, the graph of $y = f(x - h)$ is the graph of $y = f(x)$ translated horizontally. Determine how the graph of $r = f(\theta - \beta)$ is related to the graph $r = f(\theta)$ by examining the graphs for Exercises 49 and 50.

52. Show that the polar equation $r = a \cos \theta + b \sin \theta$ represents a circle and identify its center and radius. *Hint:* Transform to rectangular form.

53. Graph the equations $r = \sqrt{2} \cos \theta$ and $r = \sin 2\theta$. Then determine the points of intersection of the curves. $P_1\left(1, \frac{\pi}{4}\right)$, $P_2(0, 0)$, $P_3\left(-1, \frac{3\pi}{4}\right)$

54. **Thinking Critically**   Find the common solutions of $r = 5 \cos \theta$ and $r = 5 \sin \theta$ algebraically. Then graph the equations on the same coordinate plane. Why does the algebraic solution of the polar equations not identify all points of intersection of the graphs of the two equations?

Challenge

Three circles of radius 2, radius 1, and radius $\frac{1}{2}$ are externally tangent. Their centers are connected to form a triangle. Determine the area of the triangle. $A \approx 1.87$

   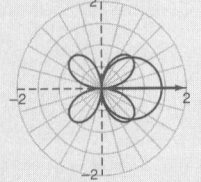

Polar Form of Complex Numbers

Objective: *To express complex numbers in polar form*

Focus

The history of complex numbers is one of a long struggle for recognition. The sixteenth century mathematician Geronimo Cardan, while working on a solution to the general cubic equation, recognized the necessity of postulating the existence of the square root of a negative number. He declared that he was able to do this only by "putting aside the mental tortures involved" concluding, nevertheless, that complex numbers were essentially useless. In the seventeenth century, René Descartes introduced the terms "real" and "imaginary" to distinguish between the two major subsets of the set of complex numbers, thereby also indicating his opinion of their relative significance. In the late seventeenth century, Gottfried Leibniz, one of the creators of calculus, reflected the most informed mathematical opinion of his time when he referred to "that amphibian between being and non-being, . . . the imaginary root of negative unity." Nor did his great contemporary and rival, Sir Isaac Newton, believe that complex numbers were especially significant.

Today the situation has completely changed; scientists and mathematicians consider complex numbers to be an indispensable tool for understanding many branches of pure and applied mathematics. Examples include the two related fields of hydrodynamics and aerodynamics and the construction of some kinds of maps. In electricity, complex numbers greatly simplify the algebra of alternating currents. In the relatively new area of fractal geometry, complex numbers provide a key to the creation of certain kinds of computer generated designs. Fractal geometry was used to assist in the generation of landscapes for the film *Star Trek II: The Wrath of Kahn* by Lucasfilm and the Moons of Endor in George Lucas's *Return of the Jedi*. No longer does anyone seriously question the existence or usefulness of the square root of -1.

Complex numbers were discussed as solutions of quadratic equations in Chapter 2 and as zeros of polynomials in Chapter 7. This lesson focuses on the geometric interpretation of complex numbers as points on the plane. Both rectangular and polar coordinates may then be used to represent complex numbers. Each of these representations is valuable for understanding and ease of computation.

10.3 Polar Form of Complex Numbers **503**

LESSON PLAN

Vocabulary
absolute value
argument
complex plane
imaginary axis
modulus
polar form
r cis θ
real axis
rectangular form

Technology
graphing utility

FOCUS

Fractal geometry is an area of great interest to today's mathematicians, computer scientists, artists, and applied scientists. Geometric figures classified as fractals have two properties: self-similarity and fractional dimension. A figure is said to be self-similar if its appearance remains basically the same when viewed under a microscope. The sketch below illustrates a self-similar tree with three branches at every fork.

The notion of fractional dimension is not as simple to describe. However, since students are familiar with the notions of two-dimensional and three-dimensional figures, it suffices to say that a figure with dimension 2.5 lies somewhere between a plane figure and a solid. The fractional dimension measures the roughness or irregularity of the fractal.

504

INSTRUCTION

- Have students discuss their experiences with complex numbers before introducing the new material. In the discussion note that identifying complex numbers with points on the plane was a very important step historically, and is an important connection for many applications of complex numbers. For example, it is the key to the role of complex numbers in fractal geometry and it is another example of a valuable *mathematical connection* (Curriculum Standard 4).
- Point out that the complex numbers form the first set of numbers that is not ordered.

Technology Complex numbers can be manipulated algebraically and graphed using certain graphing utilities.

Alternative Learning Styles
The Focus provides a humanizing anecdote that many students can enjoy. Encourage them to appreciate the irony in this part of the history of mathematics.

GUIDED PRACTICE

For Example 1
Graph the numbers $6 - 1.5i$ and $10i$ on the complex plane.

For Example 2
Find the modulus of each complex number.

1. $4 + \frac{1}{2}i$ $\quad \frac{\sqrt{65}}{2}$

2. $\sqrt{5}i$ $\quad \sqrt{5}$

Recall that every complex number may be expressed in the form $a + bi$ where a and b are real numbers and $i = \sqrt{-1}$. The arithmetic of complex numbers is an extension of the arithmetic of real numbers, with the added feature that $i^2 = (\sqrt{-1})^2 = -1$. For example,

$$(2 - 3i) + (0.5 + i) = 2.5 - 2i$$

$$(6 + 2i)\left(-\frac{1}{2} + i\right) = -3 + 6i - i + 2i^2 = -3 + 5i - 2 = -5 + 5i$$

Just as the real numbers are associated with points on the real number line, the complex numbers can be associated with points on the plane. Each complex number $a + bi$ is represented by the point P with rectangular coordinates (a, b). The real part corresponds to the horizontal axis, the imaginary part to the vertical axis. The plane is then referred to as the **complex plane,** the horizontal axis as the **real axis,** and the vertical axis as the **imaginary axis.**

Example 1 Graph each number on the complex plane.

    a. $2 + 3i$ **b.** $-\sqrt{3} + i$ **c.** $-2i$ **d.** 4.5

The given numbers correspond to the points $A(2, 3)$, $B(-\sqrt{3}, 1)$, $C(0, -2)$, and $D(4.5, 0)$.

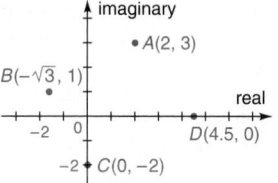

Every real number corresponds to a point on the real axis, and every pure imaginary number to a point on the imaginary axis.

The point P representing the complex number $a + bi$ can be given rectangular coordinates (a, b) or polar coordinates (r, θ). If $r > 0$, then $a = r \cos \theta$ and $b = r \sin \theta$, where $r = \sqrt{a^2 + b^2}$ and θ is an angle with (a, b) on its terminal side. The complex number $a + bi$ may then be written as $a + bi = r \cos \theta + (r \sin \theta)i = r(\cos \theta + i \sin \theta)$.

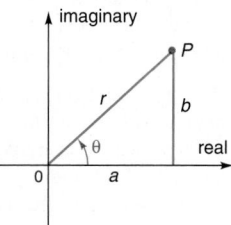

In this representation, r is called the **modulus** or **absolute value** of $a + bi$ and is represented by $|a + bi|$. Thus, $r = |a + bi| = \sqrt{a^2 + b^2}$. Notice that r gives the distance of P from the origin or pole and is by assumption nonnegative. The angle θ is called the **argument** of $a + bi$.

Example 2 Find the modulus of each complex number.

    a. $3 - i$ **b.** $-\frac{i}{2}$

a. $|3 - i| = \sqrt{3^2 + (-1)^2} = \sqrt{9 + 1} = \sqrt{10}$

b. $\left|-\frac{i}{2}\right| = \sqrt{0^2 + \left(-\frac{1}{2}\right)^2} = \sqrt{\frac{1}{4}} = \frac{1}{2}$

As a general rule, complex numbers cannot be *ordered;* for example, it is not usually meaningful to speak of $2 - 3i$ as being larger or smaller than $5 + 2i$. Two exceptions to the rule are the set of real numbers and the set of pure imaginary numbers, both of which can be ordered. However, it is meaningful to compare the absolute values of two complex numbers, since these are real numbers. *What is the geometric meaning of the statement* $|a + bi| < |c + di|$?

The expression $r(\cos \theta + i \sin \theta)$ is often abbreviated r **cis** θ. It is called the **polar form** or *trigonometric form* of the complex number, whereas $a + bi$ is called the **rectangular form**. If the polar form of a complex number is known, finding the rectangular form is a simple application of the relationships $x = r \cos \theta$ and $y = r \sin \theta$.

Example 3 Express each complex number in rectangular form.

$$\textbf{a. } z = 7\left(\cos \frac{\pi}{4} + i \sin \frac{\pi}{4}\right) \qquad \textbf{b. } w = 8 \text{ cis } \frac{\pi}{6}$$

a. $z = 7\left(\cos \frac{\pi}{4} + i \sin \frac{\pi}{4}\right) = 7\left(\frac{\sqrt{2}}{2} + \frac{i\sqrt{2}}{2}\right) = \frac{7\sqrt{2}}{2} + \frac{7\sqrt{2}}{2}i$

b. $w = 8 \text{ cis } \frac{\pi}{6} = 8\left(\cos \frac{\pi}{6} + i \sin \frac{\pi}{6}\right) = 8\left(\frac{\sqrt{3}}{2} + \frac{i}{2}\right) = 4\sqrt{3} + 4i$

Like the polar coordinates of a point, the polar form of a complex number is not unique. However, the modulus r is always taken to be nonnegative. It is customary, though not required, to use a value in the interval $[0, 2\pi)$ for the argument.

Example 4 Express each complex number in polar form.

$$\textbf{a. } z = 2 - 2i \qquad \textbf{b. } w = -1 + i\sqrt{3} \qquad \textbf{c. } 2(\cos \pi - i \sin \pi)$$

a. $r = |z| = |2 - 2i| = \sqrt{2^2 + (-2)^2} = \sqrt{8} = 2\sqrt{2}$

Since θ lies in quadrant IV and $\tan \theta = \frac{y}{x} = -1$, $\theta = \frac{7\pi}{4}$.

Therefore, the polar form is $z = 2\sqrt{2}\left(\cos \frac{7\pi}{4} + i \sin \frac{7\pi}{4}\right)$.

b. $r = |w| = |-1 + i\sqrt{3}| = \sqrt{(-1)^2 + (\sqrt{3})^2} = \sqrt{1 + 3} = \sqrt{4} = 2$

Since θ lies in quadrant II and $\tan \theta = -\sqrt{3}$, $\theta = \frac{2\pi}{3}$.

Thus, the polar form is $w = 2\left(\cos \frac{2\pi}{3} + i \sin \frac{2\pi}{3}\right)$.

c. To change $2(\cos \pi - i \sin \pi)$ to polar form, it is necessary to change the expression inside the parentheses to a sum. This can be done by using the fact that $\cos(-\pi) = \cos(\pi)$ and $\sin(-\pi) = -\sin(\pi)$.

$$2(\cos \pi - i \sin \pi) = 2[\cos(-\pi) + i \sin(-\pi)]$$

Examining the special case of real numbers provides additional insight into polar form.

Thinking Critically
The complex number $a + bi$ is a shorter distance from the origin than the number $c + di$.

For Example 5
Describe the polar form, in degrees, of a pure imaginary number *bi*.
$bi = |b|(\cos \theta + i \sin \theta)$ where $\theta = 90°$ if $b > 0$, 270° if $b < 0$, and may have any value if $b = 0$.

CLOSURE

Have students summarize the lesson in their math journals.

INDEPENDENT PRACTICE

Assignment Guide
Basic: 1–23, 28–31, 35–37
Average: 7, 11, 14–41
Enriched: 23–52

Teacher's Resource Book
  Practice, page 66

Ⓡ **Review**
Exercises 7, 11, 29, 31, 35, and 37 review concepts of verifying field properties for complex numbers, using exponential functions to solve interest problems, and graphing polar equations.

Additional Answers
Class Exercises

1.

2.

3.

Example 5 Describe the polar form of a real number *a*.

As a complex number, *a* may be expressed in rectangular form as $a + 0i$. Its modulus is then $\sqrt{a^2 + 0^2} = \sqrt{a^2} = |a|$. Any real number is located on the real axis (horizontal axis).

To find the argument, consider the three cases $a < 0$, $a = 0$, and $a > 0$. The graph shows that for $a > 0$, $\theta = 0$, and for $a < 0$, $\theta = \pi$. As with polar coordinates, for $a = 0$, the angle θ may take on any value. Thus,

$$a = |a|(\cos \theta + i \sin \theta)$$

where $\theta = 0$ if $a > 0$, $\theta = \pi$ if $a < 0$, and θ may have any value if $a = 0$.

In the next lesson, you will see that the relative ease of multiplying and dividing complex numbers in polar form makes it worth the effort to find the modulus and argument required to express them in this form.

Class Exercises

Graph each number in the complex plane.

1. $4 - i$
2. $\sqrt{5}$
3. $-8i$
4. $2\left(\cos \dfrac{\pi}{2} + i \sin \dfrac{\pi}{2}\right)$
5. $3.5 \operatorname{cis} 75°$
6. $-\pi$

Find the modulus of each complex number.

7. $-7 + 10i$ $\sqrt{149}$
8. $9 \cos\left(-\dfrac{\pi}{4}\right) + 9i \sin\left(-\dfrac{\pi}{4}\right)$ 9

Express each complex number in rectangular form.

9. $2.1\left(\cos \dfrac{5\pi}{6} + i \sin \dfrac{5\pi}{6}\right)$ $-1.82 + 1.05i$
10. $\sqrt{7} \operatorname{cis} 2.1$ $-1.34 + 2.28i$

Express each complex number in polar form.

11. $-10 + 10i$
$10\sqrt{2}\left(\cos \dfrac{3\pi}{4} + i \sin \dfrac{3\pi}{4}\right)$
12. $-3\sqrt{3} + 3i$
$6\left(\cos \dfrac{5\pi}{6} + i \sin \dfrac{5\pi}{6}\right)$
13. $5.2i$
$5.2\left(\cos \dfrac{\pi}{2} + i \sin \dfrac{\pi}{2}\right)$
14. 1999
$1999(\cos 0 + i \sin 0)$

Practice Exercises

Graph each number on the complex plane.

A 1. $3 + 0.5i$
2. $i\sqrt{10}$
3. 3.2
4. $-4i$
5. $4 \operatorname{cis} 1.5$
6. $3\left(\cos \dfrac{\pi}{8} + i \sin \dfrac{\pi}{8}\right)$

Ⓡ 7. Identify the additive identity for the complex numbers. $0 + 0i$

Compute the modulus of each complex number.

8. $8 - 1.1i$ 8.08
9. $3 \operatorname{cis} \dfrac{\pi}{4}$ 3
10. $\dfrac{\sqrt{3}}{2}i$ $\dfrac{\sqrt{3}}{2}$

Ⓡ 11. Identify the multiplicative identity for the set of complex numbers. $1 + 0i$

506   Chapter 10 Polar Coordinates and Complex Numbers

Express each complex number in rectangular form.

12. $6\left(\cos\dfrac{3\pi}{8} + i\sin\dfrac{3\pi}{8}\right)$ **13.** $\text{cis}\left(-\dfrac{\pi}{6}\right)$ **14.** $2\sqrt{2}\,\text{cis }1.9$

15. $\text{cis}\,(-135°)$ **16.** $\cos 15° + i\sin 15°$ **17.** $1.2\,\text{cis }1.2$

Express each complex number in polar form.

18. $9 - 9i$ **19.** $3 + 4i$ **20.** $1 + i\sqrt{3}$

21. $-8i$ **22.** 9.5 **23.** $2.2(\sqrt{5} - i)$

In some situations, it is desirable to select an argument of a complex number from the interval $(-\pi, \pi)$. Express each complex number in polar form using an argument in this interval.

24. $-1 - i$ **25.** $6 - 3i$ **26.** $-2i\sqrt{5}$ **27.** $\sqrt{2} - i\sqrt{2}$

28. Thinking Critically Given that $r\,\text{cis }\alpha$ and $r\,\text{cis }\beta$ are two representations of the same number, what is the relationship between α and β? α and β differ by a multiple of 2π.

29. Show that the complex numbers are closed under addition and multiplication.

30. Thinking Critically Suppose that a complex number $z = a + bi$ also happens to be a real number. Explain why its absolute value (modulus) as a complex number coincides with its absolute value as a real number.

31. *Business* Solve $1400 = 1000e^{0.09t}$ for t to determine how many years it will take $1000, deposited at 9% interest compounded continuously, to grow to $1400. 3.739 years

32. Thinking Critically Recall that the conjugate of the complex number $a + bi$ is the complex number $a - bi$. Find the geometric relationship between the points on the complex plane that represent a complex number and its conjugate. They are symmetric with respect to the real axis.

33. Show that for a and b not both zero, the multiplicative inverse of $a + bi$ is $\dfrac{a - bi}{a^2 + b^2}$.

34. Use the formula from Exercise 33 above to find the multiplicative inverse of $w = 2 + i$. $\dfrac{2}{5} - \dfrac{1}{5}i$

35. *Physics* The path of a certain comet can be approximated by the equation $r = \dfrac{3}{1 - \sin\theta}$. Sketch the graph of its path. Is its path a circle, a parabola, an ellipse, or a hyperbola? parabola

36. Writing in Mathematics Explain how to find the polar form of a complex number $a + bi$.

37. *Radioactive Decay* Ricky found 30 mg of an isotope in a specimen. After 10 h, only 20 mg of the isotope remained. Determine the approximate half-life of the isotope. 17.1 h

38. Give an example of a complex number $z = a + bi$ satisfying each of the following criteria:
  a. The imaginary part of z is 2 and $|z| = 12$. $2\sqrt{35} + 2i$
  b. The real part of z is -3 and $|z| = 21$. $-3 + 12\sqrt{3}i$
  c. Its graph lies on the line $y = -x$ and on the circle $x^2 + y^2 = 36$. $-3\sqrt{2} + 3\sqrt{2}i$ and $3\sqrt{2} - 3\sqrt{2}i$

10.3 Polar Form of Complex Numbers   **507**

508

---

39. **Writing in Mathematics** Describe the polar form of a pure imaginary number, that is, a number of the form $0 + bi$.

Graph the set of complex numbers $z = a + bi$ satisfying each condition.

C **40.** $|z| = 4$ **41.** $|z| < 7$

42. $|z + 1| < 3$ **43.** $|z - (2 + i)| \leq 5$

44. The imaginary part of z is -2.

45. The real part of z and the imaginary part of z are equal.

Let $\bar{z}$ represent the complex conjugate of z, so that if $z = a + bi$, $\bar{z} = a - bi$.

46. Show that for two complex numbers z and w, $\overline{(z + w)} = \bar{z} + \bar{w}$.

47. Show that for two complex numbers z and w, $\overline{zw} = \bar{z} \cdot \bar{w}$.

48. Show that the sum of a complex number and its conjugate is always a real number.

49. Show that the product of a complex number and its conjugate is always a real number.

50. Given the complex number $z = r(\cos\theta + i\sin\theta)$, find the polar form of $\bar{z}$. Give a reason. *Hint:* Look at the graphs of z and its conjugate.

Test Yourself

Find the rectangular coordinates of each point with the given polar coordinates.

1. $\left(\sqrt{2}, \frac{5\pi}{6}\right)$ $\left(-\frac{\sqrt{6}}{2}, \frac{\sqrt{2}}{2}\right)$ **2.** $\left(2, -\frac{\pi}{3}\right)$ $(1, -\sqrt{3})$ 10.1

Find the polar coordinates of each point with the given rectangular coordinates.

3. $(5, -4)$ $(\sqrt{41}, 5.61)$ **4.** $(-1, \sqrt{3})$ $\left(2, \frac{2\pi}{3}\right)$

Convert each polar equation to rectangular form.

5. $r\sin\theta = 8$ $y = 8$ **6.** $r = 6$ $x^2 + y^2 = 36$

Convert each rectangular equation to polar form.

7. $x = -\sqrt{5}$ $r\cos\theta = -\sqrt{5}$ **8.** $x^2 + y^2 = \sqrt{7}$ $r^2 = \sqrt{7}$

Use the tests for symmetry to identify the kinds of symmetry the graph of each polar equation possesses.

9. $r^2 = 25\sin 2\theta$ **10.** $r = 4\theta$ **11.** $r = 12\cos 6\theta$ 10.2
  pole $\theta = \frac{\pi}{2}$ polar axis

Graph each polar equation.

12. $r = 4\cos\theta$ **13.** $r = 3 + 3\sin\theta$ **14.** $r = 3\sin 3\theta$

Express each complex number in rectangular form.

15. $2\left(\cos\frac{7\pi}{6} + i\sin\frac{7\pi}{6}\right)$ $-\sqrt{3} - i$ **16.** $\sqrt{3} \text{ cis } \frac{2\pi}{3}$ $-\frac{\sqrt{3}}{2} + \frac{3}{2}i$ 10.3

Express each complex number in polar form.

17. $-8 + 8i$ $8\sqrt{2}\left(\cos\frac{3\pi}{4} + i\sin\frac{3\pi}{4}\right)$ **18.** $1.9i$ $1.9\left(\cos\frac{\pi}{2} + i\sin\frac{\pi}{2}\right)$

508   Chapter 10 Polar Coordinates and Complex Numbers

Additional Answers

46. $\overline{z + w} = \overline{(a + bi) + (c + di)} = \overline{(a + c) + (b + d)i} = (a + c) - (b + d)i = (a - bi) + (c - di) = \bar{z} + \bar{w}$

47. $\overline{zw} = \overline{(a + bi) \cdot (c + di)} = \overline{(ac - bd) + (bc + ad)i} = (ac - bd) - (bc + ad)i$; $\bar{z} \cdot \bar{w} = (a - bi) \cdot (c - di) = (ac - bd) - (bc + ad)i$

48. $z + \bar{z} = a + bi + a - bi = 2a$, which is a real number

49. $z \cdot \bar{z} = (a + bi) \cdot (a + bi) = a^2 + b^2$, which is a real number

50. $\bar{z} = r[\cos(-\theta) + i\sin(-\theta)]$

10.4 Products and Quotients of Complex Numbers in Polar Form

Objective: To determine products and quotients of complex numbers in polar form

Focus

Often, new mathematics is developed as a direct result of an attempt to solve a real world problem. Sometimes, though, a mathematical concept is developed years before anyone finds an application for it. The arithmetic of complex numbers is a case in point.

In the 1890s, decades after the properties of complex numbers had been fully developed, Charles P. Steinmetz, a General Electric engineer, was looking for a way of analyzing and understanding alternating current. The model that already existed for understanding direct current was the familiar arithmetic of real numbers. Steinmetz believed that alternating current, which changes its magnitude and direction continuously, required a different model. The model that met his needs turned out to be the arithmetic of complex numbers.

Recall that one way to find the product of two complex numbers in rectangular form is to treat the numbers as though they were binomials. For example,

$$(2 - 7i)(10 + 5i) = 2(10) + 2(5i) + (-7i)10 + (-7i)5i$$
$$= 20 + 10i - 70i + 35$$
$$= 55 - 60i$$

You can also multiply complex numbers in their polar forms, although at first glance that process may seem quite cumbersome. Consider the following example:

$$\left(2 \operatorname{cis} \frac{\pi}{3}\right)\left(5 \operatorname{cis} \frac{\pi}{4}\right) = 10\left(\cos \frac{\pi}{3} + i \sin \frac{\pi}{3}\right)\left(\cos \frac{\pi}{4} + i \sin \frac{\pi}{4}\right)$$

$$= 10\left(\cos \frac{\pi}{3} \cos \frac{\pi}{4} + i \cos \frac{\pi}{3} \sin \frac{\pi}{4} + i \sin \frac{\pi}{3} \cos \frac{\pi}{4} + i^2 \sin \frac{\pi}{3} \sin \frac{\pi}{4}\right)$$

$$= 10\left[\left(\cos \frac{\pi}{3} \cos \frac{\pi}{4} - \sin \frac{\pi}{3} \sin \frac{\pi}{4}\right) + i\left(\sin \frac{\pi}{4} \cos \frac{\pi}{3} + \cos \frac{\pi}{4} \sin \frac{\pi}{3}\right)\right]$$

Note that the last two expressions in parentheses are the sum identities for $\cos\left(\frac{\pi}{3} + \frac{\pi}{4}\right)$ and $\sin\left(\frac{\pi}{3} + \frac{\pi}{4}\right)$. Therefore,

$$\left(2 \operatorname{cis} \frac{\pi}{3}\right)\left(5 \operatorname{cis} \frac{\pi}{4}\right) = 10\left[\cos\left(\frac{\pi}{3} + \frac{\pi}{4}\right) + i \sin\left(\frac{\pi}{3} + \frac{\pi}{4}\right)\right] = 10 \operatorname{cis}\left(\frac{7\pi}{12}\right)$$

10.4 Products and Quotients of Complex Numbers in Polar Form **509**

LESSON PLAN

Technology
scientific calculator

FOCUS

Point out that since alternating current makes transmitting power over long distances easy and economical, nearly all large scale electronic power distribution systems use it. Have students discuss how alternating current is part of many life processes as well; for example, the beating of the heart induces alternating current in surrounding tissues. An *electrocardiogram* studies the current for information about the heart's health and an *electroencephalogram* studies similar alternating current in the brain. Both the electrocardiogram and the electroencephalogram are valuable diagnostic tools.

INSTRUCTION

• When discussing the procedure for multiplying complex numbers in polar form, an ideal situation would be to begin with the example $\left(2 \operatorname{cis} \frac{\pi}{3}\right)\left(5 \operatorname{cis} \frac{\pi}{4}\right)$ with the entire class and review the sum identities. Then have small groups of students work different exercises modeled after the example, and have a volunteer from each group record the exercise and answer on the board. Next have students form a conjecture about the product $(r_1 \operatorname{cis} \theta_1)(r_2 \operatorname{cis} \theta_2)$ and finally have them prove the conjecture.

• Note that similar strategies could be used for dividing two complex numbers.

Alternative Learning Styles

Students who learn in a global way benefit from an overview of a lesson before they encounter details. These students may benefit from hearing at the outset that in this lesson they will see that multiplying and dividing complex numbers in polar form is actually easier than working with those numbers in rectangular form. Those same students will also learn more effectively if several exercises are worked before the theorems on multiplying and dividing complex numbers are proven.

GUIDED PRACTICE

For Example 1

Find each product. Express your answers in rectangular form.

1. $5\left(\cos \frac{\pi}{8} + i \sin \frac{\pi}{8}\right) \cdot 3.1\left(\cos \frac{2\pi}{3} + i \sin \frac{2\pi}{3}\right)$ $15.5 \cos \frac{19\pi}{24} + i \sin \frac{19\pi}{24} = -12.3 + 9.4i$

2. $\left(5 \operatorname{cis} \frac{\pi}{6}\right)\left(\sqrt{2} \operatorname{cis} \frac{\pi}{2}\right)$ $5\sqrt{2} \operatorname{cis} \frac{2\pi}{3}$;

$5\sqrt{2}\left(-0.5 + \frac{\sqrt{3}}{2}i\right) = -3.54 + 6.12i$

For Example 2

1. Interpret geometrically the result of multiplying a complex number by $\frac{1}{2}$. The graph of the product is located at half the distance from the origin as the distance of the graph of the original number.

2. Interpret geometrically the result of multiplying a complex number by $\frac{1}{2}i$. The graph of the product is the graph of the original number rotated $\frac{\pi}{2}$ counterclockwise about the pole and located at half the distance from the pole as the original number.

It thus appears that you can always obtain the product of two complex numbers in polar form by multiplying their moduli and adding their arguments. Is this true? That is, is the equation $z_1 z_2 = r_1 r_2[\cos(\theta_1 + \theta_2) + i \sin(\theta_1 + \theta_2)]$ an identity? The sum identities for sine and cosine are the keys to answering this question. Recall the identities $\sin(\alpha + \beta) = \sin \alpha \cos \beta + \cos \alpha \sin \beta$ and $\cos(\alpha + \beta) = \cos \alpha \cos \beta - \sin \alpha \sin \beta$. For two complex numbers $z_1 = r_1 \operatorname{cis} \theta_1$ and $z_2 = r_2 \operatorname{cis} \theta_2$,

$$z_1 z_2 = r_1(\cos \theta_1 + i \sin \theta_1) \cdot r_2(\cos \theta_2 + i \sin \theta_2)$$
$$= r_1 r_2(\cos \theta_1 \cos \theta_2 + i \cos \theta_1 \sin \theta_2 + i \sin \theta_1 \cos \theta_2 + i^2 \sin \theta_1 \sin \theta_2)$$
$$= r_1 r_2[(\cos \theta_1 \cos \theta_2 - \sin \theta_1 \sin \theta_2) + i(\sin \theta_1 \cos \theta_2 + \cos \theta_1 \sin \theta_2)]$$
$$= r_1 r_2[\cos(\theta_1 + \theta_2) + i \sin(\theta_1 + \theta_2)] \quad \text{or} \quad r_1 r_2 \operatorname{cis}(\theta_1 + \theta_2)$$

The above result has now been proved and may be formally stated as follows:

> If $z_1 = r_1(\cos \theta_1 + i \sin \theta_1)$ and $z_2 = r_2(\cos \theta_2 + i \sin \theta_2)$ are complex numbers in polar form, then their product is
> $$z_1 z_2 = r_1 r_2[(\cos(\theta_1 + \theta_2) + i \sin(\theta_1 + \theta_2)]$$

Example 1   Find the product of $z = \frac{1}{2}\left(\cos \frac{2\pi}{3} + i \sin \frac{2\pi}{3}\right)$ and $w = \sqrt{2}\left[\cos\left(-\frac{\pi}{6}\right) + i \sin\left(-\frac{\pi}{6}\right)\right]$. Express the answer in rectangular form. Then draw a diagram that shows the two numbers and their product.

$$zw = \frac{\sqrt{2}}{2}\left[\cos\left(\frac{2\pi}{3} - \frac{\pi}{6}\right) + i \sin\left(\frac{2\pi}{3} - \frac{\pi}{6}\right)\right]$$
$$= \frac{\sqrt{2}}{2}\left(\cos \frac{\pi}{2} + i \sin \frac{\pi}{2}\right)$$
$$= \frac{i\sqrt{2}}{2} \qquad \cos \frac{\pi}{2} = 0$$

Example 2 provides further insight into the geometric significance of the product of two complex numbers.

Example 2   Interpret geometrically the multiplication of a complex number by i.

The polar form of i is $1\left(\cos \frac{\pi}{2} + i \sin \frac{\pi}{2}\right)$. Therefore, if $z = r(\cos \theta + i \sin \theta)$ is any complex number,

$$zi = r\left[\cos\left(\theta + \frac{\pi}{2}\right) + i \sin\left(\theta + \frac{\pi}{2}\right)\right]$$

This product has the same modulus as z and an argument that is greater by $\frac{\pi}{2}$. Thus, the graph of the product is the graph of z rotated $\frac{\pi}{2}$ counterclockwise about the pole.

A calculator may be used to evaluate the trigonometric functions when finding the product of two complex numbers in polar form.

Example 3 Find the product of $u = 5\left(\cos\frac{\pi}{5} + i\sin\frac{\pi}{5}\right)$ and $v = 3\left(\cos\frac{\pi}{10} + i\sin\frac{\pi}{10}\right)$.

$$uv = 3 \cdot 5\left[\cos\left(\frac{\pi}{5} + \frac{\pi}{10}\right) + i\sin\left(\frac{\pi}{5} + \frac{\pi}{10}\right)\right] = 15\left(\cos\frac{3\pi}{10} + i\sin\frac{3\pi}{10}\right)$$

To express the product in rectangular form, use a calculator.

$$uv = 15(0.5878 + 0.8090i) \approx 8.82 + 12.14i$$

Modeling

In direct electrical current, a constant voltage E, working against a resistance R, produces a constant current I. These three real numbers are related by the equation E = IR. How can an electrical engineer model the corresponding relationship for alternating current?

In the alternating current model developed by the engineer Charles Steinmetz, voltage is represented by a complex number V and the alternating current by the complex number I. In alternating current, the impedance in a circuit is represented by a complex number Z. The components of Z may be resistance (represented by the real number R), capacitance (represented by the real number X_C), and inductance (represented by the real number X_L). The impedance Z is then given by

$$Z = R + (X_L - X_C)i$$

The voltage in the alternating current circuit may be determined using

$$V = IZ$$

with operations on complex numbers replacing the real number operations used in the model for direct current. The magnitude of the voltage in the circuit at any time is the real part of V at that time.

Example 4 *Electricity* In an alternating current circuit, the current at a given time is represented by $I = 1 + i\sqrt{3}$ amps and the impedance is represented by $z = 1 - i$ ohms. What is the voltage across this circuit at that time?

In polar form, $I = 2\operatorname{cis}\frac{\pi}{3}$ and $Z = \sqrt{2}\operatorname{cis}\frac{7\pi}{4}$.

$V = 2\sqrt{2}\operatorname{cis}\left(\frac{\pi}{3} + \frac{7\pi}{4}\right)$ *Apply the relationship V = IZ.*

$\quad = 2\sqrt{2}\operatorname{cis}\frac{25\pi}{12} = 2\sqrt{2}\left(\cos\frac{25\pi}{12} + i\sin\frac{25\pi}{12}\right)$, or $2.73 + 0.73i$ volts

The magnitude of the voltage in the circuit is represented by the real part of V. At the given time, it is 2.73 V.

10.4 Products and Quotients of Complex Numbers in Polar Form   **511**

For Example 3
Find each product. Express your answers in rectangular form.
1. (18 cis 4)[1.7 cis (−1.1)]
   30.6 cis 2.9 = −29.71 + 7.32i
2. (4 cis 63°)(7 cis 48°)
   28 cis 111° = −10.03 + 26.14i

Modeling
You may want to familiarize students with the definitions of alternating current and direct current. Point out that battery operated devices use direct current while most household appliances use alternating current.

For Example 4
1. In an alternating current circuit, the current at a given time is represented by $I = 2 + 0.5i$ amps and the impedance is represented by $z = -1.5 + 0.5i$ ohms. What is the voltage across this circuit at that time? $\frac{1}{4}(\sqrt{170}$
   cis 3.0648) = −3.25 + 0.25i; At the given time, the voltage is 3.25 V.
2. In an alternating current circuit, the current at a given time is represented by $I = 4 + 5i$ amps and the impedance is represented by $z = 6 - 2.1i$ ohms. What is the voltage across this circuit at that time?
   $\sqrt{41}(\sqrt{40.41}$ cis 6.8426) = 34.50 + 21.6i; At the given time, the voltage is 34.50 V.

Find the value of each quotient.

1. $\dfrac{2 - 1.3i}{1 + 10i}$

$-\dfrac{11}{101} - \dfrac{21.3i}{101} = -0.1089 - 0.2109i$

2. $\dfrac{\sqrt{2} - 9i}{-8 + i}$

$\dfrac{-8\sqrt{2} - 9}{65} + \dfrac{72 - \sqrt{2}}{65}i =$
$-0.3125 + 1.0859i$

For Example 6

Find the product zw and the quotient $z \div w$ for each pair of complex numbers. Express the answers in polar form. Then convert your answers back to rectangular form.

1. $z = 2 - 2i$ and $w = -\dfrac{1}{2} - \dfrac{1}{2}i$

$zw = 2(\cos 3\pi + i \sin 3\pi)$
$\quad = -2$

$\dfrac{z}{w} = 4\left(\cos \dfrac{\pi}{2} + i \sin \dfrac{\pi}{2}\right)$
$\quad = 4i$

2. $z = 6 - i$ and $w = -4 + \dfrac{1}{4}i$

$zw = 24.3785(\cos 9.1972 +$
$\quad\quad i \sin 9.1972)$
$\quad = -23.75 + 5.5i$

$\dfrac{z}{w} = 1.5177 (\cos 3.0389 + i \sin 3.0389)$
$\quad = -1.5097 + 0.1556i$

You may ask how the rules for multiplying complex numbers in polar form can be applied to division. First consider the quotient of two complex numbers in rectangular form. Recall that the product of a nonzero complex number and its conjugate is a nonzero real number:

$$(a + bi)(a - bi) = a^2 - (bi)^2 = a^2 - b^2i^2 = a^2 + b^2$$

To divide complex numbers, express the quotient in fraction form and simplify by multiplying the numerator and denominator by the conjugate of the denominator.

Example 5 Find the value of the quotient $\dfrac{4 + 3i}{2 - 5i}$.

$$\dfrac{4 + 3i}{2 - 5i} = \dfrac{4 + 3i}{2 - 5i} \cdot \dfrac{2 + 5i}{2 + 5i} = \dfrac{-7 + 26i}{4 + 25} = \dfrac{-7}{29} + \dfrac{26i}{29} \qquad \text{\textit{The conjugate of } 2 - 5i \text{ \textit{is} } 2 + 5i.}$$

The strategy of Example 5 may be used to find the multiplicative inverse of any nonzero complex number. To find the multiplicative inverse of $a + bi$, where at least one of a and b is nonzero, use the conjugate $a - bi$.

$$\dfrac{1}{a + bi} = \dfrac{1}{a + bi} \cdot \dfrac{a - bi}{a - bi} = \dfrac{a - bi}{a^2 + b^2}$$

In other words, if z is a nonzero complex number with a complex conjugate $\bar{z}$, then the multiplicative inverse of z is $\dfrac{\bar{z}}{|z|^2}$.

The following generalization indicates how to divide complex numbers that are expressed in polar form. Its proof is left as an exercise.

> If $z_1 = r_1(\cos \theta_1 + i \sin \theta_1)$ and $z_2 = r_2(\cos \theta_2 + i \sin \theta_2)$ are complex numbers in polar form, then the quotient $\dfrac{z_1}{z_2}$, $z_2 \neq 0$, is given by
>
> $$\dfrac{z_1}{z_2} = \dfrac{r_1}{r_2}[\cos (\theta_1 - \theta_2) + i \sin (\theta_1 - \theta_2)]$$

Informally speaking, you may say that to divide one complex number in polar form by another, find the quotient of their moduli and the difference of their arguments. When complex numbers are given in rectangular form, it is often useful to change them to polar form before finding products and quotients.

Example 6 Find the product zw and the quotient $z \div w$ of the complex numbers $z = \sqrt{3} + i$ and $w = 1 - i\sqrt{3}$. Express the answers in polar form. Then convert your answers back to rectangular form.

$$z = 2\left(\cos \dfrac{\pi}{6} + i \sin \dfrac{\pi}{6}\right) \qquad \text{and} \qquad w = 2\left(\cos \dfrac{5\pi}{3} + i \sin \dfrac{5\pi}{3}\right)$$

$$zw = 4\left(\cos \dfrac{11\pi}{6} + i \sin \dfrac{11\pi}{6}\right) = 2\sqrt{3} - 2i \qquad \dfrac{\pi}{6} + \dfrac{5\pi}{3} = \dfrac{11\pi}{6}$$

$$\dfrac{z}{w} = \cos \left(-\dfrac{3\pi}{2}\right) + i \sin \left(-\dfrac{3\pi}{2}\right) = 0 + i = i \qquad \dfrac{\pi}{6} - \dfrac{5\pi}{3} = -\dfrac{3\pi}{2}$$

512 Chapter 10 Polar Coordinates and Complex Numbers

Class Exercises

Find each product. Express your answers in rectangular form.

1. $(3 - i)(7 + 5i)$ $26 + 8i$

2. $\left(\frac{1}{4} + 6i\right)(-12 + 4.8i)$ $-31.8 - 70.8i$

3. $(8 - 1.1i)(10 - 9i)$ $70.1 - 83i$

4. $(\sqrt{3} + 3i)(\sqrt{3} - 3i)$ $12 + 0i$

Find each product. Express your answers first in polar form and then in rectangular form.

5. $\left(3 \operatorname{cis} \frac{\pi}{4}\right)\left(\sqrt{5} \operatorname{cis} \frac{\pi}{2}\right)$

6. $\left[\frac{7}{6} \operatorname{cis} \frac{5\pi}{8}\right]\left[\frac{4}{9} \operatorname{cis}\left(-\frac{2\pi}{3}\right)\right]$

7. $8\left(\cos \frac{\pi}{4} + i \sin \frac{\pi}{4}\right) \cdot 15\left(\cos \frac{\pi}{6} + i \sin \frac{\pi}{6}\right)$

8. $21(\cos 100° + i \sin 100°) \cdot 0.4(\cos 12° + i \sin 12°)$

Find each quotient. Express your answers in rectangular form.

9. $\frac{6 - 7i}{2 + i}$ $1 - 4i$

10. $\frac{-5}{10 + 0.5i}$ $-0.4988 + 0.0249i$

11. $\frac{7 + 19i}{-i}$ $-19 + 7i$

12. Find the multiplicative inverse of the complex number $9 - 4i$. $\frac{9}{97} + \frac{4i}{97}$

Find each quotient. Express your answers first in polar form and then in rectangular form.

$7\left(\cos \frac{\pi}{4} + i \sin \frac{\pi}{4}\right)$; $4.950 + 4.950i$

13. $21\left(\cos \frac{\pi}{2} + i \sin \frac{\pi}{2}\right) \div 3\left(\cos \frac{\pi}{4} + i \sin \frac{\pi}{4}\right)$

14. $\left(13.7 \operatorname{cis} \frac{5\pi}{8}\right) \div \left(\operatorname{cis} \frac{\pi}{12}\right)$ $13.7 \operatorname{cis} \frac{13\pi}{24}$; $-1.788 + 13.583i$

15. $2.8(\cos 190° + i \sin 190°) \div 0.6(\cos 22° + i \sin 22°)$ $4.67(\cos 168° + i \sin 168°)$; $-4.568 + 0.971i$

Practice Exercises   🔄 Use appropriate technology.

Find each product. Express answers in rectangular form.

A **1.** $(2 + 3i)(6 + i)$ $9 + 20i$

2. $(8 - 5i)(-15 + 0.3i)$ $-118.5 + 77.4i$

3. $\left(22 \operatorname{cis} \frac{\pi}{4}\right)\left[5 \operatorname{cis}\left(-\frac{\pi}{2}\right)\right]$ $77.782 - 77.782i$

4. $4\left(\cos \frac{\pi}{3} + i \sin \frac{\pi}{3}\right) \cdot 25\left(\cos \frac{\pi}{5} + i \sin \frac{\pi}{5}\right)$ $-10.45 + 99.45i$

Draw a diagram to show the two numbers and their product.

5. $3(\cos 65° + i \sin 65°)$ and $1.7(\cos 29° + i \sin 29°)$ $5.1(\cos 94° + i \sin 94°)$

6. $\frac{1}{3} \operatorname{cis} \frac{3\pi}{10}$ and $\frac{9}{4} \operatorname{cis} \frac{\pi}{5}$ $\frac{3}{4} \operatorname{cis} \frac{\pi}{2}$

Ⓡ **7.** Find a quadratic equation with solutions 9 and 1.5. $x^2 - 10.5x + 13.5 = 0$

Find each quotient. Express answers in rectangular form.

8. $\frac{5 + i}{8 - i}$ $\frac{3}{5} + \frac{1}{5}i$

9. $\frac{-50}{1 + 13i}$ $-\frac{5}{17} + \frac{65}{17}i$

10. $\frac{2.6 - 9i}{i}$ $-9 - 2.6i$

Ⓡ **11.** Find a quadratic equation with $1 - 7i$ as one of its roots. $x^2 - 2x + 50 = 0$

Find the multiplicative inverse of each complex number.

12. $5 - 14i$ $\frac{5}{221} + \frac{14i}{221}$

13. $\sqrt{2} + i\sqrt{2}$ $\frac{\sqrt{2}}{4} - \frac{\sqrt{2}}{4}i$

14. $0 - 0.6i$ $\frac{5}{3}i$

15. $3 + \pi i$ $\frac{3}{9 + \pi^2} - \frac{\pi}{9 + \pi^2}i$

10.4 Products and Quotients of Complex Numbers in Polar Form   **513**

CLOSURE

Ask students to write you a letter summarizing the procedure for multiplying and dividing complex numbers in polar form.

INDEPENDENT PRACTICE

Assignment Guide

Basic: 1–23, 28–29, 33, 36, Project
Average: 7, 11, 17–41, Project
Enriched: 24–28, 30–32, 34–52, Project

Teacher's Resource Book
Practice, page 67

Ⓡ **Review**
Exercises 7, 11, 29, 33, and 37 review the concepts of determining a quadratic equation given its roots, determining slope of a line, determining exponential growth, and graphing rational fractions.

Project

The project provides an opportunity for cross-curricular learning and can be linked to subject matter being taught in the students physical science classes.

Additional Answers
Practice Exercises

5.

6.

513

Lesson Quiz

1. Find the product of the complex numbers $3\left(\cos\dfrac{\pi}{5} + i\sin\dfrac{\pi}{5}\right)$ and $2.1\left(\cos\dfrac{3\pi}{10} + i\sin\dfrac{3\pi}{10}\right)$. Express your answer in rectangular form. $6.3\left(\cos\dfrac{\pi}{2} + i\sin\dfrac{\pi}{2}\right); 6.3i$

2. Give a geometric interpretation of the result of multiplying a complex number by $2i$. The graph of the product is the graph of the original number rotated $\dfrac{\pi}{2}$ counterclockwise about the pole and at twice the distance from the pole as the original number.

3. In an alternating current circuit, the current at a given time is represented by $I = 4 + 0.5i$ amps and the impedance is represented by $z = -1.1 + i$ ohms. What is the voltage across this circuit at that time? 4.90 V

4. Find the value of the quotient $\dfrac{8 - 2.1i}{17 + 4i}$. $\dfrac{127.6}{305} - \dfrac{67.7}{305}i = 0.4184 - 0.2220i$

5. Find the quotient $5\operatorname{cis}\dfrac{3\pi}{8} \div 3\operatorname{cis}\dfrac{\pi}{3}$. Express the answer in rectangular form. $\dfrac{5}{3}\operatorname{cis}\dfrac{\pi}{24}$; $1.6524 + 0.2175i$

Additional Answers

16. $\dfrac{4}{3}\operatorname{cis}\left(-\dfrac{\pi}{6}\right); \dfrac{2\sqrt{3}}{3} - \dfrac{2}{3}i$

17. $\dfrac{9}{5}\operatorname{cis}\dfrac{5\pi}{8}$; $-0.69 + 1.66i$

24. rotation π counterclockwise

25. rotation $\dfrac{3\pi}{2}$ counterclockwise

26. distance from origin doubled and rotation $\dfrac{\pi}{2}$ counterclockwise

28. $(r\operatorname{cis}\theta)^2 = r^2\operatorname{cis}2\theta$

30. $17.89\operatorname{cis}(0.464)$; $16 + 8i$

31. $14\operatorname{cis}\dfrac{3\pi}{2}$; $-14i$

32. $2\operatorname{cis}0$; 2

Find each quotient. Express answers first in polar and then in rectangular form.

16. $16\left(\cos\dfrac{2\pi}{3} + i\sin\dfrac{2\pi}{3}\right) \div 12\left(\cos\dfrac{5\pi}{6} + i\sin\dfrac{5\pi}{6}\right)$

17. $\left(27\operatorname{cis}\dfrac{9\pi}{8}\right) \div \left[15\operatorname{cis}\left(-\dfrac{3\pi}{2}\right)\right]$

18. $5(\cos 250° + i\sin 250°) \div 0.2(\cos 44° + i\sin 44°)$ $25(\cos 206° + i\sin 206°); -22.470 - 10.959i$

19. $[12\operatorname{cis}(-100°)] \div [2\operatorname{cis}(-145°)]$ $6\operatorname{cis}45°; 4.24 + 4.24i$

20. *Electricity* Calculate the complex number representation of the voltage across an electrical circuit if the current is represented by $3 + 7i$ and the impedance is represented by $5.5 - 2i$. $30.5 + 32.5i$

21. *Electricity* Calculate the complex number representation of the voltage across an electrical circuit if the current is represented by $4 - 5i$ and the impedance is represented by $6 + 3i$. $39 - 18i$

Electricity The magnitude of the voltage across an alternating current circuit is the real part of the complex number that represents it.

22. What is the magnitude of the voltage in Exercise 20? 30.5 V

23. What is the magnitude of the voltage in Exercise 21? 39 V

Provide a geometric interpretation of the result of multiplying any complex number by the given number.

B 24. -1 25. $-i$ 26. $2i$

27. Interpret geometrically the result of dividing a complex number by i. rotation $\dfrac{3\pi}{2}$ counterclockwise

28. **Thinking Critically** Examine several examples and formulate a hypothesis about a formula for the square of a complex number in polar form.

Ⓡ 29. Find the slope of the line joining the points representing $2 - 3i$ and $-\sqrt{2} + i$ on the complex plane. $-4 + 2\sqrt{2}$

Give the polar and rectangular form of each product or quotient.

30. $(6 - 2i) \cdot (2 + 2i)$ 31. $(7 + 0i) \cdot (-2i)$ 32. $(8 + 2i) \div (4 + i)$

Ⓡ 33. *Biology* There were initially 1000 bacteria in a culture, and there were 6000 bacteria 2 h later. Express the number of bacteria present at any time t as an exponential function. Under ideal growth conditions how many bacteria would be present after $2\dfrac{1}{2}$ h? 9391

34. *Electricity* The voltage across an alternating current circuit is represented by $8\operatorname{cis}\dfrac{\pi}{9}$, and the impedance is represented by $6 + 3i$. Find a representation of the current, expressing the answer in polar form. $1.19\operatorname{cis}(-0.1146)$

35. *Electricity* The voltage in a circuit is $12\operatorname{cis}0.14\pi$, and the impedance is $3 - 2i$. Find the current, expressing the answer in polar form. $3.33\operatorname{cis}(1.0278)$

36. **Writing in Mathematics** Describe how the formulas given in the lesson can make multiplying and dividing complex numbers less complicated.

Ⓡ 37. Graph the rational function $f(x) = \dfrac{x - 2}{x - 9}$.

38. Verify that one of the square roots of i is $\dfrac{1}{2}(\sqrt{2} + \sqrt{2}i)$, and use this fact to find the second square root of i.

514   Chapter 10 Polar Coordinates and Complex Numbers

Writing in Mathematics

36. The formulas provide a means of changing products and quotients to simple products and quotients involving sums and differences. This is particularly useful if the complex numbers are already in polar form.

Physics A wheel of radius 4 cm is rotating counterclockwise about an axis through its center at 30 revolutions per second. A point P on the rim is on the positive x-axis when the wheel begins to move. The position $s(t)$ of P at any time t (in seconds) is given by the equation $s(t) = 4 \text{ cis } \pi t$. Find $s(t)$ when:

39. $t = 0.75$ s 4 cis $(0.75\pi) = -2\sqrt{2} + 2\sqrt{2}i$ **40.** $t = 3.15$ s 4 cis $(3.15\pi) = -3.5640 - 1.816i$

41. *Programming* Write a program that will multiply or divide two complex numbers of the form $a + bi$ and $c + di$. The program should allow the user to input the values of a, b, c, and d and output the product or quotient of the number in polar form or rectangular form, as specified by the user.

Find each product or quotient. Express answers in polar form.

C **42.** $2(\cos 50° - i \sin 50°) \cdot 6(\cos 35° - i \sin 35°)$ 12(cos 275° + i sin 275°)

43. $\sqrt{5}\left(\cos \frac{1}{4}\pi + i \sin \frac{1}{2}\pi\right) \cdot 3\left(\cos \frac{1}{2}\pi + i \sin \frac{1}{4}\pi\right)$ $\frac{3\sqrt{15}}{2}$[cos (2.5261) + i sin (2.5261)]

44. $3\left[\sin \frac{\pi}{4} + i \cos \frac{\pi}{4}\right] \div 12\left[\cos \frac{2\pi}{3} + i \sin \left(-\frac{2\pi}{3}\right)\right]$ $\frac{1}{4}\left(\cos \frac{11\pi}{12} + i \sin \frac{11\pi}{12}\right)$

45. $(3 \cos 250° + 4i \sin 250°) \div (10 \cos 50° + i \sin 50°)$ 0.6019[cos (247.935°) + i sin (247.935°)]

46. Show that the multiplicative inverse of the nonzero complex number $z = r(\cos \theta + i \sin \theta)$ is $\frac{1}{r}[\cos(-\theta) + i \sin(-\theta)]$.

47. Suppose $z_1 = r_1 \text{ cis } \theta_1$ and $z_2 = r_2 \text{ cis } \theta_2$ are complex numbers in polar form. Prove their quotient is given by $\frac{z_1}{z_2} = \frac{r_1}{r_2}[\cos(\theta_1 - \theta_2) + i \sin(\theta_1 - \theta_2)]$.

In advanced mathematics, complex numbers are used as the domain and range of complex functions. A very important function in the theory of *fractals* and *chaos* is the squaring function: $f(z) = z^2$. Compute each value of f.

48. $f(1 + i)$ 2i **49.** $f\left[\frac{1}{2}\left(\text{cis } \frac{1}{4}\pi\right)\right]$ $\frac{1}{4}i$ **50.** $f(\sqrt{5} - 8i)$ $-59 - 16\sqrt{5}i$

51. *Euler's formula*, $e^{x+yi} = e^x(\cos y + i \sin y)$, is used to define the value of the exponential function with complex domain and range. Find the value of $e^{2+\pi i}$. $-e^2$

52. Let $a + bi$ and $c + di$ be two complex numbers. Use Euler's formula (Exercise 51) to show that the exponential function for complex numbers behaves like the exponential function for real numbers in the sense that $e^{a+bi}e^{c+di} = e^{(a+bi)+(c+di)}$.

<hr>

Project

Research and compare direct and alternating electrical currents. Why do we use alternating current in our homes today? Answers may vary.

Review

1. James can rake the yard in 7 h and Tony can do it in 5 h. If they rake the yard together, will they be able to attend the baseball game starting in three hours? $2\frac{11}{12}$ h; yes

2. Express $\log x^2 y^3$ in terms of $\log x$ and $\log y$. 2 log x + 3 log y

Vocabulary
DeMoivre's theorem

Ⓜ **Materials/Manipulatives**
chambered nautilus
phonograph record
pine cone

Technology
symbolic manipulator

FOCUS

One reason spirals occur frequently in living things is due to differences in rates of growth. Living things grow in such a way that the faster growing surface lies on the outside, and the slower growing surface is on the inside.

The grooves on a phonograph record form an *Archimedean spiral.* The spiral found in the shell of the chambered nautilus is called a *logarithmic spiral.* Interested students may wish to investigate the difference between these two kinds of spirals, now or when they study arithmetic and geometric sequences. These sequences give a mathematical description of the difference between an Archimedean and a logarithmic spiral.

Students may also be interested in investigating the *Frazer spiral,* which is actually an optical illusion.

10.5   Powers of Complex Numbers

Objective: To use DeMoivre's theorem to evaluate powers of complex numbers

Focus

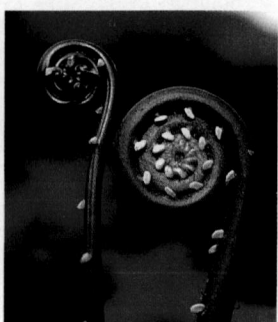

Of all the eye-catching forms that occur in nature, among the most intriguing is that of the *spiral.* There are no more beautiful embodiments of this pattern than the equiangular spirals found in such diverse objects as seashells, pine cones, wild sheep horns, cat claws, and even galaxies. Equiangular spirals have also been observed in growing ferns, dying plants, and the paths of insects around lights.

An **equiangular spiral** has the property that all radii from its center intersect the spiral at exactly the same angle. In contrast to the somewhat evenly spaced Spiral of Archimedes, the equiangular spiral expands rapidly at an ever-increasing rate. Some equiangular spirals can be modeled using powers of complex numbers.

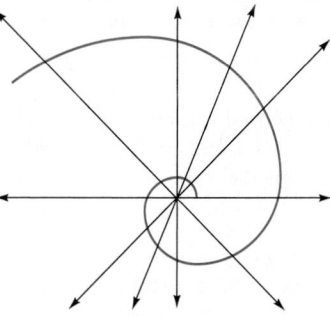

You can compute positive integral powers of complex numbers using repeated applications of the multiplication theorem you studied in the last lesson. For example, if $z = r(\cos \theta + i \sin \theta)$, then

$$z^2 = [r(\cos \theta + i \sin \theta)] \cdot [r(\cos \theta + i \sin \theta)]$$
$$= r^2(\cos 2\theta + i \sin 2\theta)$$

$$z^3 = z \cdot z^2 = [r(\cos \theta + i \sin \theta)] \cdot [r^2(\cos 2\theta + i \sin 2\theta)]$$
$$= r^3(\cos 3\theta + i \sin 3\theta)$$

$$z^4 = z \cdot z^3 = [r(\cos \theta + i \sin \theta)] \cdot [r^3(\cos 3\theta + i \sin 3\theta)]$$
$$= r^4(\cos 4\theta + i \sin 4\theta)$$

Is it true that z^5 will equal $r^5(\cos 5\theta + i \sin 5\theta)$ and that the pattern will continue? The French mathematician Abraham DeMoivre proved the following theorem for finding any power of a complex number expressed in polar form.

DeMoivre's Theorem

If $z = r(\cos \theta + i \sin \theta)$ is a complex number in polar form, then for any integer n,

$$z^n = r^n(\cos n\theta + i \sin n\theta)$$

Example 1   Evaluate each power. Express the answer in rectangular form.

a. $\left[5\left(\cos \dfrac{4\pi}{9} + i \sin \dfrac{4\pi}{9}\right)\right]^3$ **b.** $\left[-\left(\cos \dfrac{2\pi}{5} + i \sin \dfrac{2\pi}{5}\right)\right]^5$

a. $\left[5\left(\cos \dfrac{4\pi}{9} + i \sin \dfrac{4\pi}{9}\right)\right]^3 = 5^3\left[\cos \left(3 \cdot \dfrac{4\pi}{9}\right) + i \sin \left(3 \cdot \dfrac{4\pi}{9}\right)\right]$

$= 125\left(\cos \dfrac{4\pi}{3} + i \sin \dfrac{4\pi}{3}\right)$

$= -\dfrac{125}{2} - \dfrac{125\sqrt{3}}{2} i$

b. $\left[-\left(\cos \dfrac{2\pi}{5} + i \sin \dfrac{2\pi}{5}\right)\right]^5 = [-1]^5\left[\cos \left(5 \cdot \dfrac{2\pi}{5}\right) + i \sin \left(5 \cdot \dfrac{2\pi}{5}\right)\right]$

$= -(\cos 2\pi + i \sin 2\pi) = -1$

Recall that raising a binomial to a large exponent can be a tedious process. For example, $\left(\dfrac{\sqrt{3}}{2} + i\right)^7$, when expanded, has eight terms. However, DeMoivre's theorem simplifies the procedure for evaluating an integral power of a complex number.

Example 2   Evaluate z^7 for $z = \left(\dfrac{\sqrt{3}}{2} + \dfrac{i}{2}\right)$. Express the answer in rectangular form.

Since $x = \dfrac{\sqrt{3}}{2}$ and $y = \dfrac{1}{2}$, $r = \sqrt{\left(\dfrac{\sqrt{3}}{2}\right)^2 + \left(\dfrac{1}{2}\right)^2} = 1$ and $\theta = \dfrac{\pi}{6}$.

Thus, in polar form, $z = \cos \dfrac{\pi}{6} + i \sin \dfrac{\pi}{6}$.

By DeMoivre's theorem, $z^7 = \cos \dfrac{7\pi}{6} + i \sin \dfrac{7\pi}{6} = -\dfrac{\sqrt{3}}{2} - \dfrac{i}{2}$.

Modeling

How can a researcher studying the growth of chambered nautilus shells model the shape of these shells?

The chambered nautilus shell is one of the most interesting examples of an equiangular spiral. As the nautilus outgrows its shell, an additional larger chamber is added to the shell and the nautilus moves into this larger chamber. As the shell gets larger, the radius gets larger but the angle of intersection of the outer shell with the radius remains the same.

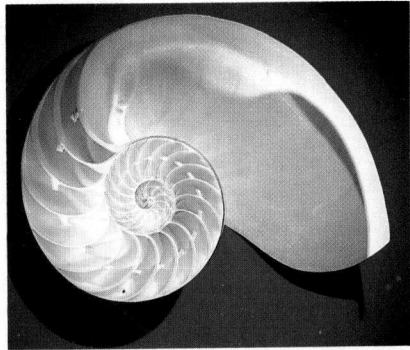

10.5 Powers of Complex Numbers   **517**

For Example 2

Evaluate each power. Express the answer in rectangular form.

1. $(5 - 5i)^5$

$12{,}500 \sqrt{2} \operatorname{cis} \frac{35\pi}{4} =$
$-12{,}500 + 12{,}500i$

2. $(6 + 2.4i)^5$

$z = \sqrt{41.76}(\cos 0.3805 + i \sin 0.3805)$
$z^5 = 11{,}269.41(\cos 1.9025 + i \sin 1.9025)$
$= -3669.93 + 10{,}655.10i$

Modeling

You may wish to return to this discussion of the chambered nautilus when you discuss Fibonacci sequences in Chapter 13.

For Example 3

Compute z^8 and z^9 for $z = 1 + i$. Do they appear to lie on the wall of the shell as shown by the graph?
$z^8 = 16$; $z^9 = 16 + 16i$; yes

For Example 4

1. Evaluate z^5 for $z = 1.1(\cos \pi - i \sin \pi)$.
$1.61051 \operatorname{cis}(-5\pi) = -1.61051$

2. Evaluate z^6 for $z = \sqrt{5}(\cos 145° - i \sin 145°)$.
$(\sqrt{5})^6 [\cos 6(-145°) + i \sin 6(-145°)] = 125[\cos(-870°) + i \sin(-870°)]$; $-\frac{125}{2}\sqrt{3} - \frac{125}{2}i$

As you have observed throughout this book, mathematical modeling may involve the use of a variety of functions or graphs. Sometimes, however, a real world situation can be modeled using just numbers and operations on these numbers. For example, the growth of the spiral of the chambered nautilus shell can be modeled by the powers of the complex number $z = 1 + i$.

Example 3   *Biology*   A nautilus shell has been traced on a section of a complex plane. One radius of the shell has been drawn to the point $(1, 1)$ on the shell, which represents the complex number $z = 1 + i$.

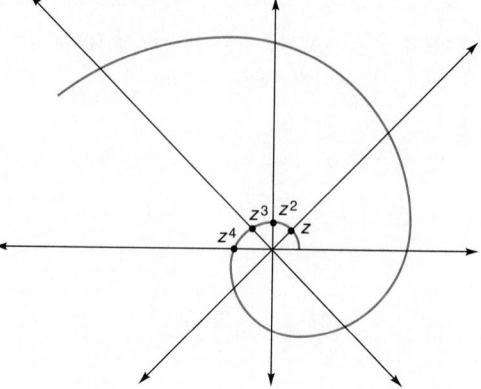

   a. Compute z^2, z^3, z^4.

   b. Refer to the graph to determine whether these points seem to lie on the wall of the shell.

a. Since $x = 1$ and $y = 1$, $r = \sqrt{2}$ and $\theta = \frac{\pi}{4}$. Therefore,

$$z = \sqrt{2}\left(\cos \frac{\pi}{4} + i \sin \frac{\pi}{4}\right)$$

$$z^2 = 2\left(\cos \frac{\pi}{2} + i \sin \frac{\pi}{2}\right) = 2(0 + i) = 2i$$

$$z^3 = 2\sqrt{2}\left(\cos \frac{3\pi}{4} + i \sin \frac{3\pi}{4}\right) = 2\sqrt{2}\left(-\frac{\sqrt{2}}{2} + \frac{i\sqrt{2}}{2}\right) = -2 + 2i$$

$$z^4 = 4(\cos \pi + i \sin \pi) = 4(-1 + 0) = -4$$

b. Yes, z^2, z^3, z^4 do seem to represent points on the sketch of the shell.

Note that a complex number must be in *polar form*, $r(\cos \theta + i \sin \theta)$, before DeMoivre's theorem can be applied.

Example 4   Evaluate z^4 for $z = 2(\cos 40° - i \sin 40°)$.

The negative sign before the expression $i \sin 40°$ should alert you to the fact that the given complex number is not in polar form. In this case, the identities $\sin(-\theta) = -\sin \theta$ and $\cos(-\theta) = \cos \theta$ make it easy to rewrite z as $2[\cos(-40°) + i \sin(-40°)]$.

$$z^4 = 2^4[\cos 4(-40°) + i \sin 4(-40°)] \qquad \text{Apply DeMoivre's theorem.}$$
$$= 16[\cos(-160°) + i \sin(-160°)] \qquad \text{Use a calculator.}$$
$$\approx -15.0351 - 5.4723i$$

The examples in this lesson have focused on positive integral powers of complex numbers. Can DeMoivre's theorem be extended to zero and negative integral powers of complex numbers? The following discussion shows that it can.

518   Chapter 10 Polar Coordinates and Complex Numbers

Recall that for any nonzero real number k, $k^0 = 1$ and $k^{-n} = \frac{1}{k^n}$ for any positive integer n. For example, $17^0 = 1$, and $2^{-5} = \frac{1}{2^5} = \frac{1}{32}$. These definitions can be extended to complex numbers:

> For any nonzero complex number z, $z^0 = 1$ and $z^{-n} = \frac{1}{z^n}$ for every positive integer n.

First verify DeMoivre's theorem when $n = 0$.

If $\qquad z = r(\cos \theta + i \sin \theta) \qquad$ and $\qquad r \neq 0$

then $\qquad z^0 = r^0[\cos (0 \cdot \theta) + i \sin (0 \cdot \theta)]$
$\qquad\qquad = 1(\cos 0 + i \sin 0) = 1(1 + 0) = 1$

Since by definition $z^0 = 1$, the theorem holds for $n = 0$.

To see that DeMoivre's theorem also holds for negative integral powers, observe that when n is a positive integer, $z^n = r^n(\cos n\theta + i \sin n\theta)$ and so

$$z^{-n} = \frac{1}{z^n}$$
$$= 1 \div z^n$$
$$= 1(\cos 0 + i \sin 0) \div r^n(\cos n\theta + i \sin n\theta) \qquad \textit{Polar form}$$
$$= \frac{1}{r^n}[\cos (0 - n\theta) + i \sin (0 - n\theta)]$$
$$= r^{-n}[\cos (-n\theta) + i \sin (-n\theta)]$$

Thus, $z^{-n} = [r(\cos \theta + i \sin \theta)]^{-n} = r^{-n}[\cos (-n\theta) + i \sin (-n\theta)]$, and DeMoivre's theorem holds for exponents that are negative integers.

Example 5   Use DeMoivre's theorem to evaluate each power. Express answers in rectangular form.

   a. $\left[4\left(\cos \frac{\pi}{4} + i \sin \frac{\pi}{4}\right)\right]^{-3}$ **b.** $(3 + 4i)^{-5}$

a. $\left[4\left(\cos \frac{\pi}{4} + i \sin \frac{\pi}{4}\right)\right]^{-3} = 4^{-3}\left[\cos \left(-3 \cdot \frac{\pi}{4}\right) + i \sin \left(-3 \cdot \frac{\pi}{4}\right)\right]$
$$\qquad\qquad = \frac{1}{64}\left(-\frac{\sqrt{2}}{2} - \frac{\sqrt{2}}{2} i\right) = -\frac{\sqrt{2}}{128} - \frac{\sqrt{2}}{128} i$$

b. To apply DeMoivre's theorem, convert $3 + 4i$ to polar form: $r = \sqrt{3^2 + 4^2} = 5$

Since $x > 0$, $y > 0$, and $\tan \theta = \frac{4}{3}$, $\tan^{-1} \frac{4}{3} \approx 0.9273$.

Therefore, $\qquad 3 + 4i = 5 \text{ cis } 0.9273$.

and $\qquad (3 + 4i)^{-5} = (5 \text{ cis } 0.9273)^{-5}$
$$\qquad\qquad = 5^{-5} \text{ cis } [-5(0.9273)]$$
$$\qquad\qquad = 0.000320 \text{ cis } (-4.64)$$
$$\qquad\qquad = -0.000024 + 0.000319i \qquad \textit{In rectangular form}$$

For Example 5
Use DeMoivre's theorem to evaluate each power. Express answers in rectangular form.

1. $\left[10\left(\text{cis } \frac{\pi}{3}\right)\right]^{-2}$

$\frac{1}{100}\left[\cos\left(-\frac{2\pi}{3}\right) + i \sin \left(-\frac{2\pi}{3}\right)\right]$;

$-\frac{1}{200} - \frac{\sqrt{3}}{200}i$

2. $\left[6\left(\text{cis } \frac{2\pi}{3}\right)\right]^{-5}$

$\frac{1}{7776}\left[\cos\left(-\frac{10\pi}{3}\right) + i \sin \left(-\frac{10\pi}{3}\right)\right]$;

$-\frac{1}{15,552} + \frac{\sqrt{3}}{15,552}i$

CLOSURE

Have students summarize the procedures for using DeMoivre's theorem to evaluate powers of complex numbers and expressing results in rectangular form in their math journals.

INDEPENDENT PRACTICE

Assignment Guide
Basic: 1–21, 37, Project
Average: 7, 15, 18–37, Project
Enriched: 18, 25–36, 38–45, Project

Teacher's Resource Book
   Practice, page 68

ⓡ **Review**
Exercises 7, 15, 19, and 35 review concepts of finding area, solving and graphing polynomial inequalities, finding zeros of a polynomial, determining decibel level of a sound, and determining compound interest.

Project
Students should notice that as successive points are graphed, a spiral pattern results.

LESSON FOLLOW-UP

Lesson Quiz
Use DeMoivre's theorem to evaluate each power. Express answers in rectangular form.

1. $[\sqrt{3}\,(\cos 1.1\pi + i \sin 1.1\pi)]^4$
$9(\cos 4.4\pi + i \sin 4.4\pi); 2.7812 + 8.5595i$

2. $(-3 + 3i)^7$
$\left[\sqrt{18}\left(\cos\frac{3\pi}{4} + i \sin\frac{3\pi}{4}\right)\right]^7 =$
$17{,}496\sqrt{2}\left(\cos\frac{21\pi}{4} + i \sin\frac{21\pi}{4}\right);$
$-17{,}496 - 17{,}496i$

3. $\left[8\left(\cos\frac{\pi}{6} - i \sin\frac{\pi}{6}\right)\right]^3$
$\left[8\left(\cos\left(-\frac{\pi}{6}\right) + i \sin\left(-\frac{\pi}{6}\right)\right)\right]^3 =$
$512\left[\cos\left(-\frac{\pi}{2}\right) + i \sin\left(-\frac{\pi}{2}\right)\right]; -512i$

4. $\sqrt{3}\left[\cos\left(-\frac{\pi}{4}\right) + i \sin\left(-\frac{\pi}{4}\right)\right]^6$
$27\left[\cos\left(-\frac{3\pi}{2}\right) + i \sin\left(-\frac{3\pi}{2}\right)\right]; 27i$

5. $\left[4\left(\text{cis}\frac{2\pi}{3}\right)\right]^{-2}$
$\frac{1}{16}\left[\cos\left(-\frac{4\pi}{3}\right) + i \sin\left(-\frac{4\pi}{3}\right)\right];$
$-\frac{1}{32} + \frac{\sqrt{3}}{32}i$

Additional Answers
Class Exercises

9. $(3i)^5 = 243i; 1 \div 243i = -\frac{1}{243}i$

10. $\left(-\frac{1}{2} + \frac{i\sqrt{3}}{2}\right)^3 = \left(\text{cis}\frac{2\pi}{3}\right)^3 = 1 + 0i = 1$

Practice Exercises
3. $9.24 \times 10^{-4} + (3.83 \times 10^{-4})i$

15.

20. $-1 + i = \sqrt{2}\,\text{cis}\frac{3\pi}{4}; (-1 + i)^{10} = \left(\sqrt{2}\,\text{cis}\frac{3\pi}{4}\right)^{10} = 2^5\,\text{cis}\frac{15\pi}{2} = 32\,\text{cis}\frac{3\pi}{2} = -32i$

Class Exercises

Use DeMoivre's theorem to evaluate each power. Express answers in rectangular form.

1. $\left[6\left(\cos\frac{\pi}{4} + i \sin\frac{\pi}{4}\right)\right]^3$ $-152.735 + 152.735i$

2. $\left[\frac{1}{2}\,\text{cis}\frac{\pi}{8}\right]^{-3}$ $3.061 - 7.391i$

3. $\left[\sqrt{5}\left(\cos\frac{2\pi}{3} + i \sin\frac{2\pi}{3}\right)\right]^{-4}$ $-0.02 - 0.035i$

4. $[3\,\text{cis}\,1.6\pi]^5$ $243 + 0i$

5. $(-\sqrt{2} + i\sqrt{2})^4$ $-16 + 0i$

6. $(1 - i)^9$ $16 - 16i$

7. $(1 - 8i)^0$ $1 + 0i$

8. $(3i)^{-5}$ $0 - \frac{1}{243}i$

9. Verify your result in Exercise 8 by computing $(3i)^5$ algebraically and then finding the value of $1 \div (3i)^5$.

10. Use DeMoivre's theorem to show that $-\frac{1}{2} + \frac{i\sqrt{3}}{2}$ is a cube root of 1.

Practice Exercises
Use appropriate technology.

Use DeMoivre's theorem to evaluate each power. Express answers in rectangular form.

A. $\left\{5\left[\cos\left(-\frac{\pi}{4}\right) + i \sin\left(-\frac{\pi}{4}\right)\right]\right\}^4$ $-625 + 0i$

2. $[\sqrt{3}\,\text{cis}\,2.3\pi]^6$ $21.843 - 15.870i$

3. $\left[10\left(\cos\frac{5\pi}{8} + i \sin\frac{5\pi}{8}\right)\right]^{-3}$

4. $\left(\sqrt{7}\,\text{cis}\frac{\pi}{9}\right)^{-1}$ $0.355 - 0.129i$

5. $\left(\sqrt{11}\,\text{cis}\frac{\pi}{11}\right)^0$ $1 + 0i$

6. $\left(3\,\text{cis}\frac{\pi}{6}\right)^{-2}$ $0.056 - 0.096i$

7. *Landscaping* Find the area of a triangular flower garden with sides measuring 18 ft, 21 ft, and 25 ft, to the nearest ten square feet. $190\ \text{ft}^2$

Use DeMoivre's theorem to evaluate each power. Express answers in rectangular form.

8. $(5 - 5i)^3$ $-250 - 250i$

9. $(2 + 2i)^5$ $-128 - 128i$

10. $(-2i)^{-3}$ $0 - \frac{1}{8}i$

11. $(3 + i\sqrt{3})^{-2}$ $\frac{1}{24} - \frac{\sqrt{3}}{24}i$

12. $(3 - 5i)^6$ $39{,}104.15 + 3958.47i$

13. $(2 - 8i)^{-4}$ $1.204 \times 10^{-4} - 1.795 \times 10^{-4}i$

14. Verify your result in Exercise 10 by computing $(-2i)^3$ algebraically and then finding the value of $1 \div (-2i)^3$. $(-2i)^3 = 8i; 1 \div 8i = -\frac{1}{8}i$

15. Solve the inequality $x^3 - 6x^2 + 8x > 0$ and graph the solution set. $\{x: 0 < x < 2 \text{ or } x > 4\}$

16. *Biology* Using $z = 1 + i$, compute z^5, z^6, and z^7. Graph these points on a complex plane. Do they appear to extend the spiral discussed in Example 3? $-4 - 4i; -8i; 8 - 8i;$ yes

17. Find the zeros of the polynomial $f(x) = -x^2 + 2x - 3$. $1 + \sqrt{2}i, 1 - \sqrt{2}i$

18. **Writing in Mathematics** Describe how graphs can be useful for mathematical modeling.

19. *Acoustics* The decibel level of a sound is defined to be $D = 10 \log\frac{I}{10^{-16}}$, where I is the sound intensity measured in watts per square meter (W/m²). Find the decibel level of a sound with intensity 5×10^{-10} W/m². 66.99

20. Use DeMoivre's theorem to show that $-1 + i$ is a tenth root of $-32i$.

Use DeMoivre's theorem to evaluate each power.

21. $\dfrac{\left(2\,\text{cis}\frac{1}{4}\pi\right)^7}{\left[3\,\text{cis}\left(-\frac{1}{4}\pi\right)\right]^5}$ $0.527\,\text{cis}\,3\pi$

22. $\dfrac{\left(\frac{1}{2}\,\text{cis}\,10°\right)^4}{(-5\,\text{cis}\,25°)^2}$ $\frac{1}{400}\,\text{cis}\,(-10°)$

23. $\left(\text{cis}\frac{2\pi}{3}\right)^{-2} \div \left(0.1\,\text{cis}\frac{\pi}{6}\right)^3$ $1000\,\text{cis}\frac{\pi}{6}$

Writing in Mathematics
18. Graphs are important tools for mathematical modeling. Graphs sketched from known values can help predict the behavior of a function for unknown values. Graphs can help identify patterns as well. Examining a graph can help a scientist recognize that a new situation is very much like an already solved problem, and so point out other available tools and methods of solution.

$$2.7557[\cos(4.7766) + i \sin(4.7766)]$$

24. $\left(\dfrac{1.2 \text{ cis } 65°}{0.6 \text{ cis } 34°}\right)^5$ 32 cis 155° **25.** $\left(\cos\dfrac{\pi}{4} + i \sin\dfrac{\pi}{2}\right)^5$ **26.** $\left(\cos\dfrac{\pi}{2} - i \sin\dfrac{\pi}{4}\right)^3$ $\dfrac{\sqrt{2}}{4}i$

27. $\left[3\left(\cos\dfrac{\pi}{3} - i \sin\dfrac{\pi}{3}\right)\right]^3$ -27 **28.** $\left\{2\left[\cos\dfrac{\pi}{4} + i \sin\left(-\dfrac{\pi}{4}\right)\right]\right\}^4$ -16

Use DeMoivre's theorem to evaluate each power. Express answers in rectangular form.

29. $\dfrac{(\sqrt{3} + i)^2}{(-1 + i\sqrt{3})^4}$ **30.** $\dfrac{(-0.5 + i\sqrt{3})^3}{(6 - 6i)^5}$ **31.** $\dfrac{(1 - i)^{-2}(1 + i\sqrt{3})^3}{(5 + 5i)^2}$ **32.** $\dfrac{(1 - i)^7}{(1 + i)^7}$

33. *Programming* Write a program that will evaluate $(a + bi)^n$, where n is an integer. The program should allow the user to input a, b, and n and use DeMoivre's theorem to evaluate the expression.

34. Show that 4, 4 cis $\dfrac{2\pi}{3}$, and 4 cis $\dfrac{4\pi}{3}$ are cube roots of 64.

Ⓡ **35.** *Economics* How long will it take money to double if it is invested at 11% compounded annually? Compounded monthly? 6.64 years; 6.33 years

36. Thinking Critically Explain why a real number can have nonreal roots, but a nonreal number cannot have real roots. *Hint:* Think about the field properties of the real numbers.

Predict the geometric behavior of the pattern z, z^2, z^4, z^8, z^{16}, z^{32}, ... in the following cases. *Hint:* Create some examples and then plot them.

C **37.** Complex numbers z with modulus less than 1

38. Complex numbers z with modulus greater than 1

39. Complex numbers z with modulus equal to 1

Use DeMoivre's theorem to derive an identify for each expression in terms of $\sin\theta$, $\cos\theta$, or both. *Hint:* Expand $(\cos\theta + i \sin\theta)^2$ and $(\cos\theta + i \sin\theta)^3$ in two ways.

40. $\cos 2\theta$ $\cos^2\theta - \sin^2\theta$ **41.** $\sin 2\theta$ $2\cos\theta \sin\theta$ **42.** $\cos 3\theta$ $4\cos^3\theta - 3\cos\theta$ **43.** $\sin 3\theta$ $3\sin\theta - 4\sin^3\theta$

44. Use DeMoivre's theorem to show $r^{\frac{1}{n}} \text{cis} \dfrac{\theta}{n}$ is always an nth root of $z = r \text{ cis } \theta$.

45. Use the conclusion of Exercise 44 to find one cube root of $8i$. Express your answer in rectangular form. $\sqrt{3} + i$

Project

Write a program for a computer or a calculator to compute and graph z^n for $n = -2, -1, 0, 1, 2, 3, 4, 5,$ and 6. Run the program for $z = 1 - i$. Run the program again several times with different values of z. Describe the pattern that results each time. Compare your results with those of others.

Challenge

1. Determine all possible values of b if the following points are collinear: (2, 1), $(-2b, 5)$, and $(b^2 - 11, b)$ ± 3

2. The product of two 2-digit numbers is 1176. Their average is 49. Find the two numbers. 84, 14

Vocabulary
complex roots theorem

FOCUS

Forensic chemists also make use of the *Fourier transform* (and so of complex numbers) in their work. Infrared spectroscopy is one method they use to identify unknown substances. If a definitive identification of a substance is needed, some of it is inserted into the laser beam of an infrared spectrophotometer. Like fingerprints, the resulting image or spectrogram is unique. It can be analyzed for clues to the chemical composition of the substance, or it can be compared directly to the spectrograms of known substances. Certain wavelengths of light cause different molecular bonds to stretch or bend. The record of all the stretches is contained in a complicated curve that is transformed mathematically into a second curve, which can easily be interpreted by the trained chemist. The crucial mathematical transformation is accomplished through the Fourier transform.

10.6 Roots of Complex Numbers

Objective: To determine the roots of complex numbers

Focus

A *synthetic organic chemist* designs new chemical compounds that are often synthetic versions of natural substances. During World War II, more than a thousand scientists worked on the challenge of developing large quantities of penicillin. They determined its chemical structure and attempted to synthesize that structure. Thirty-one years after its discovery, chemist John Sheehan found the key to its synthesis. His technique is now used to make 3000 metric tons of penicillin each year.

Nuclear magnetic resonance (NMR) is an important tool for today's synthetic organic chemist. It enables the chemist to determine whether a newly synthesized compound is structurally identical to a known compound. The recent application of a mathematical technique called a *Fourier transform* has significantly improved both the efficiency and the sensitivity of NMR. The Fourier transform is a sophisticated technique that involves multiplication by a complex function, that is, by a function whose domain and range are the set of complex numbers. The computation of powers and roots of complex numbers may also be required.

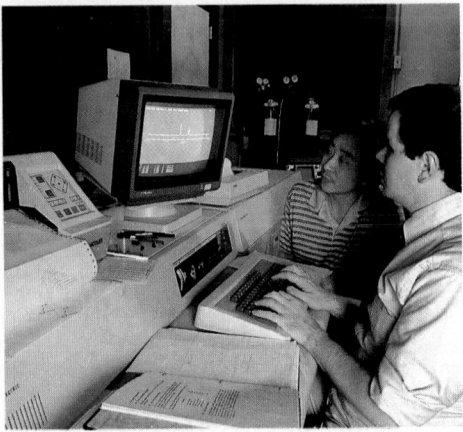

You are familiar with the concepts of square root, cube root, and higher roots from the arithmetic of real numbers. Recall that for real numbers a and b and for any positive integer n, b is said to be an nth root of a if and only if $b^n = a$. For example, 2 is a fifth root of 32 because $2^5 = 32$, and -5 is a cube root of -125 because $(-5)^3 = -125$. This definition can be extended to the complex number system.

> For complex numbers r and z and for any positive integer n, r is an nth root of z if and only if $r^n = z$.

For example, $3i$ is a fourth root of 81 because $(3i)^4 = 81$, and $\sqrt{3} + i$ is a cube root of $8i$ because $(\sqrt{3} + i)^3 = \left(2 \operatorname{cis} \frac{\pi}{6}\right)^3 = 8 \operatorname{cis} \frac{\pi}{2} = 8i$.

522   Chapter 10 Polar Coordinates and Complex Numbers

Note that finding an nth root of a complex number c is equivalent to finding a solution of the equation $x^n = c$. Recall that the fundamental theorem of algebra guarantees the existence of at least one solution. In fact, there are exactly n distinct complex nth roots of any complex number. DeMoivre's theorem is a natural tool for verifying that a given number is an nth root of another. It is also useful for determining all the nth roots of a complex number.

Example 1 Find the four fourth roots of $81 \operatorname{cis} \frac{2\pi}{3}$.

Let w represent a fourth root, and suppose that in polar form $w = r \operatorname{cis} \theta$. Then $w^4 = (r \operatorname{cis} \theta)^4 = r^4 \operatorname{cis} 4\theta$. Thus,

$$r^4 \operatorname{cis} 4\theta = 81 \operatorname{cis} \frac{2\pi}{3}$$

This implies that $r^4 = 81$, and that 4θ is a number with the same cosine and sine as $\frac{2\pi}{3}$. Since r is a positive real number, it is the positive real fourth root of 81, that is, $r = 3$. The value of 4θ, on the other hand, is not a unique number. Both sine and cosine are periodic with period 2π, so

$$4\theta = \frac{2\pi}{3} + 2k\pi$$

where $2k\pi$ is any integral multiple of 2π. Solve the equation $4\theta = \frac{2\pi}{3} + 2k\pi$ for various integral values of k.

For $k = 0$, $4\theta = \frac{2\pi}{3}$, so $\theta = \frac{\pi}{6}$.

For $k = 1$, $4\theta = \frac{2\pi}{3} + 2\pi = \frac{8\pi}{3}$, so $\theta = \frac{2\pi}{3}$.

For $k = 2$, $4\theta = \frac{2\pi}{3} + 4\pi = \frac{14\pi}{3}$, so $\theta = \frac{7\pi}{6}$.

For $k = 3$, $4\theta = \frac{2\pi}{3} + 6\pi = \frac{20\pi}{3}$, so $\theta = \frac{5\pi}{3}$.

Thus, the four distinct roots are $r_1 = 3 \operatorname{cis} \frac{\pi}{6}$, $r_2 = 3 \operatorname{cis} \frac{2\pi}{3}$, $r_3 = 3 \operatorname{cis} \frac{7\pi}{6}$, and $r_4 = 3 \operatorname{cis} \frac{5\pi}{3}$. A corollary of the fundamental theorem of algebra guarantees that there are no others. *What would happen if you substituted additional integral values for k?*

The reasoning used in Example 1 can be used to find the nth roots of any complex number z. This corollary to DeMoivre's theorem is summarized in the *complex roots theorem.*

Complex Roots Theorem

For any positive integer n and any complex number $z = r \operatorname{cis} \theta$, the n distinct nth roots of z are the complex numbers $\sqrt[n]{r} \operatorname{cis} \frac{\theta + 2k\pi}{n}$ for $k = 0, 1, 2, \ldots, n - 1$.

Thinking Critically
Additional values of k would give roots that have already been identified.

- Review the notions of the *real nth roots* of a real number before discussing handling the material of this lesson. For example, be sure that students understand that -2 is a square root of 4, even though by convention we write $\sqrt{4} = 2$. Point out that the radical symbol for even roots denotes *by agreement* the principal or positive real nth root.
- Have students work several exercises like the one in Example 1 before presenting the complex roots theorem. Have them work in small groups to try to summarize and generalize the results of those exercises since verbalizing patterns that occur is an important part of problem solving.
- Similarly, have students graph several sets of nth roots for various complex numbers and have them try to generalize the geometric visualization of the roots before discussing the paragraph above Example 3 in the textbook.
- Point out that the symbol $\sqrt[n]{r}$ in the complex roots theorem denotes the positive real nth root of the positive number r.

Alternative Learning Styles
Some students find it easier to understand new concepts through the use of analogies and metaphors. These students might find it helpful to think of the complex roots theorem as reversing the action of DeMoivre's theorem. For example, a given output of DeMoivre's theorem, the complex roots theorem allows you to find all possible input numbers from which it could have come.

GUIDED PRACTICE

For Example 1
1. Find the three cube roots of $125 \operatorname{cis} \frac{\pi}{4}$.

   $5 \operatorname{cis} \frac{\pi}{12}$, $5 \operatorname{cis} \frac{3\pi}{4}$, $5 \operatorname{cis} \frac{17\pi}{12}$

2. Find the four fourth roots of 16.
   $2, -2, 2i, -2i$

For Example 2

1. Find the cube roots of $1000i$.

$10 \text{ cis } \frac{\pi}{6}$, $10 \text{ cis } \frac{5\pi}{6}$, $10 \text{ cis } \frac{3\pi}{2}$

2. Find the fifth roots of $-3 + 3i$.

$\sqrt[10]{18} \text{ cis } \frac{3\pi}{20}$, $\sqrt[10]{18} \text{ cis } \frac{11\pi}{20}$,

$\sqrt[10]{18} \text{ cis } \frac{19\pi}{20}$, $\sqrt[10]{18} \text{ cis } \frac{27\pi}{20}$,

$\sqrt[10]{18} \text{ cis } \frac{7\pi}{4}$

For Example 3

Graph the five fifth roots of 32.

For Example 4

Find the three cube roots of 1 and locate them on the complex plane.

$1, -\frac{1}{2} + \frac{\sqrt{3}}{2}i, -\frac{1}{2} - \frac{\sqrt{3}}{2}i$

In the complex roots theorem, note that $\sqrt[n]{r}$ is the positive real nth root of the positive number r.

Example 2   Find the five fifth roots of $-32i$.

In polar form, $-32i = 32 \text{ cis } \frac{3\pi}{2}$. Therefore, by the complex roots theorem, the fifth roots of $-32i$ are

For $k = 0$: $r_1 = 2 \text{ cis } \frac{1}{5}\left(\frac{3\pi}{2}\right) = 2 \text{ cis } \frac{3\pi}{10}$

For $k = 1$: $r_2 = 2 \text{ cis } \frac{1}{5}\left(\frac{3\pi}{2} + 2\pi\right) = 2 \text{ cis } \frac{1}{5}\left(\frac{7\pi}{2}\right) = 2 \text{ cis } \frac{7\pi}{10}$

For $k = 2$: $r_3 = 2 \text{ cis } \frac{1}{5}\left(\frac{3\pi}{2} + 4\pi\right) = 2 \text{ cis } \frac{1}{5}\left(\frac{11\pi}{2}\right) = 2 \text{ cis } \frac{11\pi}{10}$

For $k = 3$: $r_4 = 2 \text{ cis } \frac{1}{5}\left(\frac{3\pi}{2} + 6\pi\right) = 2 \text{ cis } \frac{1}{5}\left(\frac{15\pi}{2}\right) = 2 \text{ cis } \frac{3\pi}{2}$, or $-2i$

For $k = 4$: $r_5 = 2 \text{ cis } \frac{1}{5}\left(\frac{3\pi}{2} + 8\pi\right) = 2 \text{ cis } \frac{1}{5}\left(\frac{19\pi}{2}\right) = 2 \text{ cis } \frac{19\pi}{10}$

In general, the n nth roots of $z = r \text{ cis } \theta$ are located on the circle with its center at the origin and radius $\sqrt[n]{r}$ (the positive real nth root of r). The complex roots theorem provides the reason for this phenomenon. Each of the roots has modulus $\sqrt[n]{r}$. Since the difference between the arguments of successive roots is $\frac{2\pi}{n}$, the roots are equally spaced about the circle.

Example 3   Graph the four fourth roots of 81.

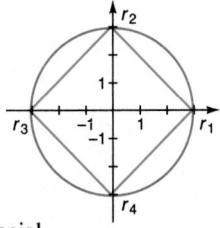

Construct a circle of radius $81^{\frac{1}{4}} = 3$ with center at the origin. Since $3^4 = 81$, one fourth root of 81 is $3 = 3(1 + 0i)$. Then separate the circle into four arcs of equal length to locate the other three roots of 81. The four roots are $3 + 0i$, $0 + 3i$, $-3 + 0i$, and $0 - 3i$.

The various nth roots of 1, often referred to as *roots of unity*, are of special interest. Since in polar form $1 = 1 \text{ cis } 0$, and for any n, $\sqrt[n]{1} = 1$, the nth roots of unity are of the form

$$\text{cis } \frac{2k\pi}{n} \qquad \text{for } k = 0, 1, 2, \ldots, n - 1$$

Example 4   Find the five fifth roots of 1 and locate them on the complex plane.

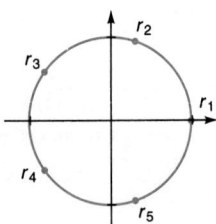

The five fifth roots of 1 are located on the circle of radius 1 equally spaced $\frac{2\pi}{5}$ radians apart. Since one of these roots is $1 + 0i = \text{cis } 0$, the other four may be located easily. In polar form, they are $\text{cis } \frac{2\pi}{5}$, $\text{cis } \frac{4\pi}{5}$, $\text{cis } \frac{6\pi}{5}$, and $\text{cis } \frac{8\pi}{5}$. In rectangular form, they are $0.31 + 0.95i$, $-0.81 + 0.59i$, $-0.81 - 0.59i$, and $0.31 - 0.95i$ rounded to the nearest hundredth.

The roots of unity can be used to obtain the roots of other real numbers.

Example 5   Use the cube roots of unity to find the cube roots of 125.

The three cube roots of unity are $\text{cis } 0 = 1$, $\text{cis } \frac{2\pi}{3} = -\frac{1}{2} + \frac{\sqrt{3}}{2}i$, and $\text{cis } \frac{4\pi}{3} = -\frac{1}{2} - \frac{\sqrt{3}}{2}i$. Multiply each of these cube roots of unity by $\sqrt[3]{125} = 5$ to obtain the cube roots of 125: $r_1 = 5$, $r_2 = -\frac{5}{2} + \frac{5\sqrt{3}}{2}i$, and $r_3 = -\frac{5}{2} - \frac{5\sqrt{3}}{2}i$.

The complex roots theorem provides a connection between the roots of a complex number and the zeros of a polynomial.

Example 6   Factor the polynomial $p(x) = x^3 + 10$ into linear factors with complex coefficients.

Linear factors of this polynomial are of the form $x - r$, where r is a cube root of -10. *Why?* Therefore, it is sufficient to find the cube roots of -10. Since $-10 = 10 \text{ cis } \pi$, the roots are:

$$r_1 = \sqrt[3]{10} \text{ cis } \frac{\pi}{3} = \sqrt[3]{10}\left(\frac{1}{2} + \frac{i\sqrt{3}}{2}\right)$$

$$r_2 = \sqrt[3]{10} \text{ cis } \frac{\pi + 2\pi}{3} = \sqrt[3]{10} \text{ cis } \pi = -\sqrt[3]{10}$$

$$r_3 = \sqrt[3]{10} \text{ cis } \frac{\pi + 4\pi}{3} = \sqrt[3]{10} \text{ cis } \frac{5\pi}{3} = \sqrt[3]{10}\left(\frac{1}{2} - \frac{i\sqrt{3}}{2}\right)$$

Therefore, the desired factorizaton is

$$x^3 + 10 = (x + \sqrt[3]{10})\left[x - \left(\frac{\sqrt[3]{10}}{2} + \frac{i\sqrt[3]{10}\sqrt{3}}{2}\right)\right]\left[x - \left(\frac{\sqrt[3]{10}}{2} - \frac{i\sqrt[3]{10}\sqrt{3}}{2}\right)\right]$$

Class Exercises

Find the indicated roots of each complex number and locate them on the complex plane.

1. three cube roots of -8

2. four fourth roots of $16i$

3. five fifth rooths of $\text{cis } \frac{\pi}{4}$

4. three cube roots of $216 \text{ cis } \frac{\pi}{3}$

5. two square roots of $49 \text{ cis } \frac{2\pi}{5}$

6. six sixth roots of $10 \text{ cis } \frac{\pi}{3}$

Graph the indicated roots.

7. three cube roots of 1000

8. five fifth roots of -1

9. four fourth roots of 81

10. three cube roots of -12

11. Factor the polynomial $x^5 - 4$ into linear factors.

12. Find the four fourth roots of 256. $4, 4i, -4, -4i$

13. **Thinking Critically**   Restate the complex roots theorem for θ in degrees.
    If $z = r \text{ cis } \theta$ with θ measured in degrees, then $\sqrt[n]{z} = \sqrt[n]{r} \text{ cis } \frac{(\theta + 360k)}{n}$, $k = 0, 1, \ldots, n - 1$

Thinking Critically
Cube roots of -10 are zeros of the polynomial as determined by the factor theorem.

For Example 5

1. Use the cube roots of unity to find the cube roots of 216.
   $6, -3 + 3i\sqrt{3}, -3 - 3i\sqrt{3}$

2. Use the cube roots of unity to find the fifth roots of 243.
   $3, 0.93 + 2.85i, 0.93 - 2.85i, -2.43 + 1.76i, -2.43 - 1.76i$

For Example 6

Factor each polynomial into linear factors with complex coefficients.

1. $x^3 - 125$
   $(x - 5)\left[x - \left(-\frac{5}{2} + \frac{5\sqrt{3}}{2}i\right)\right]\left[x - \left(-\frac{5}{2} - \frac{5\sqrt{3}}{2}i\right)\right]$

2. $x^5 + 243i$
   $[x - (-3i)][x - (2.85 - 0.93i)][x - (-2.85 - 0.93i)][x - (-1.76 + 2.43i)][x - (1.76 + 2.43i)]$

CLOSURE

Have students write you a letter identifying the parts of the lesson that they found difficult and those they found easy. Then have them give reasons for their choices.

Additional Answers

Class Exercises

1. $2 \text{ cis } \frac{\pi}{3}, -2, 2 \text{ cis } \frac{5\pi}{3}$

2. $2 \text{ cis } \frac{\pi}{8}, 2 \text{ cis } \frac{5\pi}{8}, 2 \text{ cis } \frac{9\pi}{8}, 2 \text{ cis } \frac{13\pi}{8}$

3. $\text{cis } \frac{\pi}{20}, \text{cis } \frac{9\pi}{20}, \text{cis } \frac{17\pi}{20}, \text{cis } \frac{5\pi}{4}, \text{cis } \frac{33\pi}{20}$

4. $6 \text{ cis } \frac{\pi}{9}, 6 \text{ cis } \frac{7\pi}{9}, 6 \text{ cis } \frac{13\pi}{9}$

5. $7 \text{ cis } \frac{\pi}{5}, 7 \text{ cis } \frac{6\pi}{5}$

6. $\sqrt[6]{10} \text{ cis } \frac{\pi}{18}, \sqrt[6]{10} \text{ cis } \frac{7\pi}{18}, \sqrt[6]{10} \text{ cis } \frac{13\pi}{18}, \sqrt[6]{10} \text{ cis } \frac{19\pi}{18}, \sqrt[6]{10} \text{ cis } \frac{25\pi}{18}, \sqrt[6]{10} \text{ cis } \frac{31\pi}{18}$

11. $(x - \sqrt[5]{4}) \cdot \left(x - \sqrt[5]{4} \text{ cis } \frac{2\pi}{5}\right) \cdot \left(x - \sqrt[5]{4} \text{ cis } \frac{4\pi}{5}\right) \cdot \left(x - \sqrt[5]{4} \text{ cis } \frac{6\pi}{5}\right) \cdot \left(x - \sqrt[5]{4} \text{ cis } \frac{8\pi}{5}\right)$

Assignment Guide
Basic: 1–21, 25, 35–37
Average: 11, 15–38
Enriched: 22–32, 34–47

Teacher's Resource Book
  Practice, page 69

® **Review**
Exercises 11, 15, 21, 25, and 33 review concepts of problem solving, finding powers of complex numbers, solving quadratic equations, factoring the sum or difference of two cubes, solving polynomial equations, and factoring quadratic polynomials.

LESSON FOLLOW-UP

Test Yourself

Teacher's Resource Book
  Tests—Quiz, form A, page 46
  Tests—Quiz, form B, page 46

Lesson Quiz

1. Find the four fourth roots of
   $625 \text{ cis } \frac{3\pi}{8}$. $5 \text{ cis } \frac{3\pi}{32}$, $5 \text{ cis } \frac{35\pi}{32}$,

   $5 \text{ cis } \frac{19\pi}{32}$, $5 \text{ cis } \frac{51\pi}{32}$

2. Find the three cube roots of
   $-4 + 4i$. $1.26 + 1.26i$, $-1.72 + 0.46i$, $0.46 - 1.72i$

3. Find and graph the four fourth roots of unity. $1, -1, i, -i$

Practice Exercises

Find the indicated roots of each complex number and locate them on the complex plane.

A 1. three cube roots of -125

   2. five fifth roots of $32i$

   3. four fourth roots of cis $\frac{\pi}{4}$

   4. three cube roots of $729 \text{ cis } \frac{\pi}{5}$

   5. two square roots of $36 \text{ cis } \frac{\pi}{8}$

   6. eight eighth roots of $10 \text{ cis } \frac{\pi}{3}$

   7. three cube roots of $5 + 5i$

   8. six sixth roots of $\sqrt{3} - i$

   9. three cube roots of $1 - i$

   10. four fourth roots of $-1 - i\sqrt{3}$

® 11. *Packaging* Ninety-six pears were packed in boxes so that the number of boxes was four less than twice the number of pears in each box. How many boxes were used? 12

12. Find the four fourth roots of unity. $1, i, -1, -i$

Use the results of Exercise 12 to compute the four fourth roots of each number.

13. 81 $3, -3, 3i, -3i$

14. 2401 $7, -7, 7i, -7i$

® 15. Verify the results of Exercise 13 by raising each of the roots you found to the fourth power. $3^4 = 81; (-3)^4 = 81; (3i)^4 = 81; (-3i)^4 = 81$

16. Find the six sixth roots of unity and use them to find the six sixth roots of 64.

Graph the indicated roots.

17. three cube roots of -64

18. four fourth roots of 0.0001

19. five fifth roots of $\frac{1}{32}$

20. eight eighth roots of 130

® 21. Find the six sixth roots of unity by factoring $x^6 - 1$ and using the quadratic formula. Verify that your answers agree with the results of Exercise 16.

Find all solutions of each equation.

B 22. $x^4 + 625 = 0$ 23. $x^3 - 52 = 0$ 24. $x^6 - 25x = 0$ **®** 25. $x^4 - 13x^2 + 42 = 0$

26. $x^3 + 2 = 2i$ 27. $x^5 - i\sqrt{3} = 1$ 28. $81x^4 = i$ 29. $256x^4 = -i$

Factor each polynomial into linear factors with complex coefficients.

30. $f(x) = x^4 + 24$ 31. $g(x) = x^3 - i$ 32. $h(x) = x^3 - 27i$

® 33. $p(x) = 6x^2 - 11x + 10$ 34. $p(x) = x^3 - 20$ 35. $f(x) = x^4 - 16i$

36. **Writing in Mathematics** Explain why the complex roots theorem is simply another way of stating DeMoivre's theorem.

37. *Programming* Write a program that will compute the n nth roots of a complex number $a + bi$. The program should allow the user to input a, b, and n and output all n roots in rectangular form.

526 Chapter 10 Polar Coordinates and Complex Numbers

Writing in Mathematics

36. The complex roots theorem looks at the relationship stated in DeMoivre's theorem from the opposite direction. DeMoivre's theorem starts with a complex number and examines raising it to an integral power. The complex roots theorem starts with a number that is an integral power of a complex number, and looks for the original number.

Find the indicated roots and express them in rectangular form.

38. $(1 + i)^{\frac{2}{3}}$ **39.** $(1 + i\sqrt{3})^{\frac{2}{3}}$ **40.** $(-2 + 2i\sqrt{3})^{\frac{3}{4}}$

41. Thinking Critically   For a positive real number x, $\sqrt{x}$ is defined as the positive real number whose square is x. Extend this definition to negative real numbers by setting $\sqrt{y} = i\sqrt{|y|}$ for real numbers $y < 0$. For instance, $\sqrt{-4} = 2i$, and so on. Show by example that for this extended definition, it is *not* always true that $\sqrt{ab} = \sqrt{a}\sqrt{b}$.

42. Find and graph the three cube roots of 27 on the complex plane. Show that these three points determine an equilateral triangle on the plane.

43. Find and graph the four fourth roots of 16 cis $\frac{\pi}{4}$ on the plane. Show that these points are the vertices of a square.

44. Find the five fifth roots of unity and let w be the one of smallest *positive* argument. Compute w^1, w^2, w^3, w^4, w^5. What do you observe?

45. Repeat the preceding exercise for the six sixth roots of unity, this time computing w^1, w^2, w^3, w^4, w^5, w^6.

46. Thinking Critically   Generalize the results of the two preceding exercises and test your hypothesis using the seven seventh roots of unity.

47. Thinking Critically   Make a table of the nth roots of unity for $n = 2, 3, 4, 5, 6$. Based on these examples, state a hypothesis about the sum of the nth roots of unity for any n.

Test Yourself

Find each product or quotient. Express answers first in polar form and then in rectangular form.

         10.4

1. $2\left(\cos\frac{\pi}{3} + i\sin\frac{\pi}{3}\right) \cdot 12\left(\cos\frac{\pi}{4} + i\sin\frac{\pi}{4}\right)$ $24\left(\cos\frac{7\pi}{12} + i\sin\frac{7\pi}{12}\right); \ -6.21 + 23.18i$

2. $24\left(\cos\frac{\pi}{2} + i\sin\frac{\pi}{2}\right) \div 3\left(\cos\frac{\pi}{5} + i\sin\frac{\pi}{5}\right)$ $8\left(\cos\frac{3\pi}{10} + i\sin\frac{3\pi}{10}\right); \ 4.70 + 6.47i$

3. $\left[\frac{2}{3}\text{ cis }\frac{3\pi}{8}\right]\left[\frac{1}{6}\text{ cis }\left(-\frac{\pi}{4}\right)\right]$ $\frac{1}{9}$ cis $\frac{\pi}{8}$; $0.10 + 0.04i$ **4.** $\left(12.2\text{ cis }\frac{7\pi}{6}\right) \div \left(\text{cis }\frac{\pi}{12}\right)$ $\begin{matrix} 12.2 \text{ cis } \frac{13\pi}{12}; \\ -11.78 - 3.16i \end{matrix}$

Use DeMoivre's theorem to evaluate each power. Express answers in rectangular form.

5. $\left(4\text{ cis }\frac{\pi}{8}\right)^3$ $24.49 + 59.13i$ **6.** $\left(\sqrt{5}\text{ cis }\frac{\pi}{9}\right)^{-1}$ $0.4202 - 0.1530i$ **7.** $\left(\sqrt{7}\text{ cis }\frac{\pi}{13}\right)^0$ 1 10.5

8. $(2 + 3i)^4$ $-119 - 120i$ **9.** $(-3i)^{-2}$ $-\frac{1}{9}$ **10.** $(3 + i\sqrt{3})^3$ $41.57i$

Find the indicated roots of each complex number.

11. three cube roots of 343 cis $\left(-\frac{\pi}{3}\right)$ **12.** four fourth roots of $\frac{i}{16}$ 10.6

13. Factor the polynomial $p(x) = x^4 - 256i$ into linear factors.
$$\left(x - 4\text{ cis }\frac{\pi}{8}\right)\left(x - 4\text{ cis }\frac{5\pi}{8}\right)\left(x - 4\text{ cis }\frac{9\pi}{8}\right)\left(x - 4\text{ cis }\frac{13\pi}{8}\right)$$

10.6 Roots of Complex Numbers   **527**

46. If w is the nth root of unity of smallest positive argument, then the n nth roots of unity are w^1, w^2, ..., w^n. Therefore, the seven roots of unity are 1, cis $\frac{2\pi}{7}$, cis $\frac{4\pi}{7}$, cis $\frac{6\pi}{7}$, cis $\frac{8\pi}{7}$, cis $\frac{10\pi}{7}$, and cis $\frac{12\pi}{7}$.

---

4. Use the fourth roots of unity to find the fourth roots of 81.
$3, -3, 3i, -3i$

5. Factor the polynomial $p(x) = x^3 + 16$ into linear factors with complex coefficients.
$$[x + \sqrt[3]{16}]\left[x - \left(\frac{\sqrt[3]{16}}{2} + \frac{i\sqrt[3]{16}\sqrt{3}}{2}\right)\right]\left[x - \left(\frac{\sqrt[3]{16}}{2} - \frac{i\sqrt[3]{16}\sqrt{3}}{2}\right)\right]$$

Alternative Assessment
Ask students to suppose that they have found all six sixth roots of a complex number. Then have them write a paragraph describing how DeMoivre's theorem could be used to check the results and why this method works.

Enrichment
Find all roots of $x^6 + 6x^3 - 16 = 0$.
$\sqrt[3]{2}, -\frac{\sqrt[3]{2}}{2} + \frac{\sqrt[6]{108}}{2}i, -\frac{\sqrt[3]{2}}{2} - \frac{\sqrt[6]{108}}{2}i,$
$-2, 1 + i\sqrt{3}, 1 - i\sqrt{3}$

Additional Answers

38. $-i\sqrt[3]{2}, \frac{\sqrt[3]{2}\sqrt{3}}{2} + \frac{\sqrt[3]{2}}{2}i, -\frac{\sqrt[3]{2}\sqrt{3}}{2} + \frac{\sqrt[3]{2}}{2}i$

39. $1.216 + 1.020i, -1.492 + 0.543i,$
$0.276 - 1.563i$

40. $2\sqrt{2}, -2\sqrt{2}, 2\sqrt{2}i, -2\sqrt{2}i$

41. Let $a < 0$ and $b < 0$. Then $ab > 0$ and $ab = |a||b|$. Hence, $\sqrt{ab} = \sqrt{|a||b|} = \sqrt{|a|}\sqrt{|b|}$. But $\sqrt{a}\sqrt{b} = (i\sqrt{|a|})(i\sqrt{|b|}) = i^2\sqrt{|a||b|} = -\sqrt{|a|}\sqrt{|b|}$. Therefore, $\sqrt{ab} \neq \sqrt{a}\sqrt{b}$.

44. 1, cis $\frac{2\pi}{5}$, cis $\frac{4\pi}{5}$, cis $\frac{6\pi}{5}$, cis $\frac{8\pi}{5}$;
$w^1 = $ cis $\frac{2\pi}{5}$, $w^2 = $ cis $\frac{4\pi}{5}$, $w^3 = $ cis $\frac{6\pi}{5}$, $w^4 = $ cis $\frac{8\pi}{5}$, $w^5 = 1$; The terms w^1, w^2, w^3, w^4, and w^5 are the five fifth roots.

45. 1, cis $\frac{\pi}{3}$, cis $\frac{2\pi}{3}$, cis π, cis $\frac{4\pi}{3}$, cis $\frac{5\pi}{3}$;
$w^1 = $ cis $\frac{\pi}{3}$, $w^2 = $ cis $\frac{2\pi}{3}$, $w^3 = $ cis π, $w^4 = $ cis $\frac{4\pi}{3}$, $w^5 = $ cis $\frac{5\pi}{3}$, $w^6 = 1$

527

Additional Answers

1.

Vocabulary

absolute value (504)	polar coordinate system (488)
argument (504)	polar distance (488)
cardioid (497)	polar equation (489)
complex plane (504)	polar form (505)
complex roots theorem (523)	polar graph (489)
DeMoivre's theorem (517)	polar grid (494)
equiangular spiral (516)	pole (488)
imaginary axis (504)	$r\theta$-plane (488)
lemniscate (500)	real axis (504)
limaçon (497)	rectangular form (505)
modulus (504)	rose (499)
parametric equations (495)	Spiral of Archimedes (496)
polar angle (488)	tests for symmetry in polar graphs (497)
polar axis (488)	
polar coordinates (488)	

Polar Coordinates   A point on a plane has rectangular coordinates of the form   10.1
(x, y) and polar coordinates of the form (r, θ). To convert from polar to rectangular coordinates, use the formulas $x = r \cos \theta$ and $y = r \sin \theta$. To convert from rectangular to polar coordinates, use $r = \sqrt{x^2 + y^2}$, $\theta = \text{Arctan} \frac{y}{x}$ if $x > 0$, and $\theta = \text{Arctan} \frac{y}{x} + \pi$ if $x < 0$.

1. Graph the point $\left(-4, \frac{5\pi}{6}\right)$ on the $r\theta$-plane.

2. Find the rectangular coordinates of the point with polar coordinates $\left(2, \frac{7\pi}{4}\right)$. ($\sqrt{2}, -\sqrt{2}$)

3. Find the polar coordinates of the point with rectangular coordinates $(-3, -4)$. (5, 4.0689)

Graphs of Polar Equations   There are tests to determine symmetry of polar graphs   10.2
with respect to the pole, the polar axis, and the line $\theta = \frac{\pi}{2}$. Special curves include
the following. In all cases, $a \neq 0$, $b \neq 0$.

Cardioid	$r = a + a \cos \theta$ or $r = a + a \sin \theta$
Circle	$r = a \cos \theta$ or $r = a \sin \theta$
Limaçon	$r = a + b \cos \theta$ or $r = a + b \sin \theta$
Lemniscate	$r^2 = a^2 \cos 2\theta$ or $r^2 = a^2 \sin 2\theta$
Rose	$r = a \cos n\theta$ or $r = a \sin n\theta$, n an integer, $n \neq -1, 0, 1$
Spiral of Archimedes	$r = a\theta$

Use the tests for symmetry to identify the kinds of symmetry the graph of each
polar equation possesses.

4. $r^2 = 49 \cos 2\theta$
pole, polar axis, $\theta = \frac{\pi}{2}$

5. $r = 2 + 4 \sin \theta$
$\theta = \frac{\pi}{2}$

6. $r = -3\theta$
not symmetric

Graph each polar equation.

7. $r = 1 - 2 \sin \theta$ **8.** $r = 3 + 3 \cos \theta$ **9.** $r = -2\theta$

7.
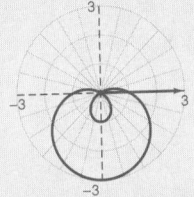

Polar Form of Complex Numbers   The polar form of a complex number $a + bi$ is   **10.3**
$r(\cos \theta + i \sin \theta)$, or r cis θ, where $r = \sqrt{a^2 + b^2}$ and $\tan \theta = \dfrac{b}{a}$, $a \neq 0$. The
rectangular form of a complex number can be determined using the relationships
$x = r \cos \theta$ and $y = r \sin \theta$.

Express each complex number in rectangular form.

8.

10. cis $\dfrac{5\pi}{6}$ $-\dfrac{\sqrt{3}}{2} + \dfrac{1}{2}i$ **11.** cis $(-45°)$ $\dfrac{\sqrt{2}}{2} - \dfrac{\sqrt{2}}{2}i$ **12.** $2\left(\cos \dfrac{\pi}{4} + i \sin \dfrac{\pi}{4}\right)$
                                                                              $\sqrt{2} + \backslash$

Express each complex number in polar form.

13. $6 + 2i$ $2\sqrt{10}$ cis 0.32175 **14.** $-i$ cis $\dfrac{3\pi}{2}$ **15.** $\sqrt{5}$ $\sqrt{5}$ cis 0

9.

Products and Quotients of Complex Numbers in Polar Form   The product and   **10.4**
quotient of two complex numbers $z_1 = r_1 (\cos \theta_1 + i \sin \theta_1)$ and
$z_2 = r_2 (\cos \theta_2 + i \sin \theta_2)$ are represented by the following formulas:

$$z_1 z_2 = r_1 r_2 [\cos (\theta_1 + \theta_2) + i \sin (\theta_1 + \theta_2)]$$
$$\frac{z_1}{z_2} = \frac{r_1}{r_2}[\cos (\theta_1 - \theta_2) + i \sin (\theta_1 - \theta_2)]$$

Find each product or quotient. Express answers first in polar form and then in
rectangular form. 3 cis $\dfrac{7\pi}{16}$; $0.5853 + 2.9$

16. $\left(6 \text{ cis } \dfrac{7\pi}{8}\right)\left(3 \text{ cis } \dfrac{3\pi}{8}\right)$ 18 cis $\dfrac{5\pi}{4}$; $-9\sqrt{2} - 9\sqrt{2}i$ **17.** $\left(12 \text{ cis } \dfrac{11\pi}{16}\right) \div \left(4 \text{ cis } \dfrac{\pi}{4}\right)$

21.

Powers of Complex Numbers   DeMoivre's theorem states that if   **10.5**
$z = r (\cos \theta + i \sin \theta)$ is a complex number in polar form, then for any integer n,
$z^n = r^n (\cos n\theta + i \sin n\theta)$.

Use DeMoivre's theorem to evaluate each power. Express answers in
rectangular form.

18. $\left(3 \text{ cis } \dfrac{11\pi}{12}\right)^3$ $-\dfrac{27}{2}\sqrt{2} + \dfrac{27}{2}\sqrt{2}i$ **19.** $(6 + 3i)^4$ $-567 + 1944i$ **20.** $(2 + i)^{-2}$ $0.12 - 0.16i$

22.

Roots of Complex Numbers   The complex roots theorem states that for any positive   **10.6**
integer n and any complex number $z = r$ cis θ, the complex numbers $\sqrt[n]{r}$ cis $\dfrac{\theta + 2k\pi}{n}$
for $k = 0, 1, 2, \ldots, n - 1$ are the n distinct nth roots of z.

Find the indicated roots of each complex number and locate them on the
complex plane. 5 cis $\dfrac{\pi}{2}$, 5 cis $\dfrac{7\pi}{6}$, 5 cis $\dfrac{11\pi}{6}$ 5 cis $\dfrac{3\pi}{16}$, 5 cis $\dfrac{11\pi}{16}$, 5 cis $\dfrac{19\pi}{16}$, 5 cis $\dfrac{27\pi}{16}$
21. three cube roots of $-125i$ **22.** four fourth roots of 625 cis $\dfrac{3\pi}{4}$

23. Factor the polynomial $p(x) = x^3 - 16$ into linear factors with complex
coefficients. $(x - 2\sqrt[3]{2})\left(x - 2\sqrt[3]{2} \text{ cis } \dfrac{2\pi}{3}\right)\left(x - 2\sqrt[3]{2} \text{ cis } \dfrac{4\pi}{3}\right)$

Chapter 10 Summary and Review   **529**

Additional Answers

7.

12. $2 \operatorname{cis} \dfrac{7\pi}{8}$; $-1.85 + 0.77i$

13. $2 \operatorname{cis} \dfrac{7\pi}{12}$; $-0.52 + 1.93i$

16.

17.

Challenge

The graph of $r = \sin b(\theta - c)$ is the
graph of $r = \sin b\theta$ rotated c degrees or
radians.

Chapter 10   Test

Find the rectangular coordinates of each point with the given polar coordinates.

1. $\left(\sqrt{3}, -\dfrac{\pi}{4}\right)$ $\left(\dfrac{\sqrt{6}}{2}, -\dfrac{\sqrt{6}}{2}\right)$ **2.** $\left(-4, \dfrac{7\pi}{6}\right)$ $(2\sqrt{3}, 2)$

Find the polar coordinates of each point with the given rectangular coordinates.

3. $(-5, 3)$ $(\sqrt{34}, 2.6012)$ **4.** $(\sqrt{3}, -\sqrt{3})$ $\left(\sqrt{6}, -\dfrac{\pi}{4}\right)$

Use the tests for symmetry to identify the kinds of symmetry the graph of each polar equation possesses.

5. $r^2 = 36 \sin 2\theta$ pole   **6.** $r = 3 - 3 \cos \theta$ polar axis

7. Graph the polar equation $r = 1 + \sin \theta$.

Express each complex number in rectangular form.

8. $3\left(\cos \dfrac{11\pi}{12} + i \sin \dfrac{11\pi}{12}\right)$ $-2.8978 + 0.7765i$ **9.** $4 \operatorname{cis}\left(-\dfrac{\pi}{3}\right)$ $2 - 2\sqrt{3}i$

Express each complex number in polar form.

10. $4 - 4i$ $4\sqrt{2}\left[\cos\left(-\dfrac{\pi}{4}\right) + i \sin\left(-\dfrac{\pi}{4}\right)\right]$ **11.** $i\sqrt{3}$ $\sqrt{3} \operatorname{cis} \dfrac{\pi}{2}$

Find each product or quotient. Express answers first in polar form and then in rectangular form.

12. $\left(\dfrac{1}{2} \operatorname{cis} \dfrac{5\pi}{8}\right) \cdot \left(4 \operatorname{cis} \dfrac{\pi}{4}\right)$ **13.** $\left(6 \operatorname{cis} \dfrac{11\pi}{12}\right) \div \left(3 \operatorname{cis} \dfrac{\pi}{3}\right)$

Use DeMoivre's theorem to evaluate each power. Express answers in rectangular form.

14. $\left(5 \operatorname{cis} \dfrac{3\pi}{8}\right)^4$ $-625i$ **15.** $(2 + i\sqrt{3})^5$ $-117.97 - 53.80i$

Find the indicated roots of each complex number and locate them on the complex plane.

16. the three cube roots of $-27i$ **17.** the four fourth roots of $\operatorname{cis}\left(-\dfrac{\pi}{4}\right)$

18. Factor the polynomial $p(x) = x^3 - 64i$ into linear factors with complex coefficients. $\left(x - 4 \operatorname{cis} \dfrac{\pi}{6}\right)\left(x - 4 \operatorname{cis} \dfrac{5\pi}{6}\right)\left(x - 4 \operatorname{cis} \dfrac{9\pi}{6}\right)$

Challenge

How is the graph of $r = \sin b(\theta - c)$ related to the graph of $r = \sin b\theta$?

Cumulative Review

1. Simplify: $\sqrt{8x} + 3\sqrt{50x} - \left(\sqrt{\frac{1}{18x}}\right)^{-1}$ $14\sqrt{2x}$ 9.1

2. Graph $r = 4\cos\theta$ using a graphing utility and state the symmetry of the graph.   symmetric with respect to the polar axis   10.2

3. Solve: $\begin{cases} y + 2 = 4x - x^2 \\ -6 = 2x - 6 \end{cases}$ $(0, -2)$ 8.1

4. Identify the property that is illustrated: $(a + b) + c = a + (b + c)$ assoc. add.   1.2

5. Find the product of $(4 - 3i)(6 + 5i)$. Express your answer in rectangular form. $39 + 2i$ 10.4

6. Determine the rational zeros of $f(x) = 8x^3 - 4x^2 - 7x + 5$. -1 7.3

7. A 30-ft ladder rests against a 40-ft building. Determine which two trigonometric functions could be used to find the angle of elevation.   sine; cosecant   5.1

8. Express in condensed form: $5\log 2x - 2\log y + 4\log 3z$ $\log\frac{2592x^5z^4}{y^2}$ 9.4

9. Graph $-\sqrt{5} + i$ on the complex plane.   10.3

10. Use a graphing utility to graph $y = \tan^2\theta + 1$ and $y = \sec^2\theta$ on the same set of axes. Do they suggest an identity?   yes   6.2

11. The function $F(x) = e^x$ is called the _?_.   natural exponential function   9.2

12. Solve the system of inequalities graphically: $\begin{cases} x^2 - 3x > y + 4 \\ x + 2y \geq 13 \end{cases}$ 8.5

13. Evaluate z^3 for $z = 2(\cos 30° - i\sin 30°)$ $0 - 8i$ 10.5

14. Without using a calculator, find the value of $\cos 40° \cos 50° - \sin 40° \sin 50°$.   0   6.1

15. Prove: $\frac{1}{\cos\theta} = \sec\theta$ $\frac{1}{\cos\theta} = \frac{1}{\frac{x}{r}} = \frac{r}{x} = \sec\theta$ 3.8

16. Graph the point $\left(4, \frac{\pi}{6}\right)$ on the $r\theta$-plane.   10.1

17. Since $\cot(-x) = -\cot x$, is the cotangent function an odd function or an even function? What is the symmetry of its graph?   odd; symmetric about the origin   4.3

18. Find the logarithm of 837 to four decimal places using a scientific calculator.   2.9227   9.3

19. Determine the vertex of the quadratic function $f(x) = x^2 - 6x + 3$. $(3, -6)$ 2.5

20. Find the four fourth roots of -16. $\pm\sqrt{2} + i\sqrt{2}$; $\pm\sqrt{2} - i\sqrt{2}$ 10.6

21. Solve for x to the nearest hundredth using a graphing utility: $\log_x 2 = 2.6354$ 1.30   9.5

Determine if each statement is always true, sometimes true, or never true.

22. A turning point is a point on a graph such that the value of the function is a relative maximum or a relative minimum.   always   7.2

23. A mathematical model consisting of a linear function to be optimized and a set of linear inequalities representing the restriction on resources is called a linear program.   always   8.6

24. When graphing $r = a\cos\theta$, if $a > 0$, the circle is to the left of the pole, and if $a < 0$, the circle is to the right of the pole.   never   10.2

Cumulative Review   **531**

2.

9.

12.

16.

Summary

Conic sections are presented both from an algebraic and a geometric point of view. Rotations and translations of graphs are developed to assist in the manipulation of complicated conic equations. Quadratic systems are analyzed as are tangent and normal lines to various conics. Polar equations of conics are also discussed.

Chapter Objectives

- To determine a relationship between the equation of a circle and its center and radius
- To determine a relationship between the equation of an ellipse and its foci and intercepts
- To graph an ellipse
- To determine a relationship between the equation of a hyperbola and its foci, intercepts, and asymptotes
- To graph a hyperbola
- To determine a relationship between the equation of a parabola and its focus, directrix, vertex, and axis of symmetry
- To graph a parabola
- To use the translation formulas to simplify the equations of conic sections
- To solve a quadratic system algebraically
- To determine the slopes of tangents to conic sections and of normals to conic sections
- To determine the equations of tangents to conic sections and of normals to conic sections
- To determine and identify polar equations of conic sections

11 Conic Sections

Mathematical Power

Modeling   Since they were first explored by the Greeks more than 2000 years ago, the curves called *conic sections* have played an important role. The geometer Apollonius, who lived in the third century B.C., first named the conics—the *hyperbola, parabola,* and *ellipse*—and showed that they could be produced by slicing a right circular cone.

Since then, science has found numerous applications for the conics. Some of the more familiar applications are in the field of astronomy. But did you know that the unique properties of the conic sections are also used widely in contemporary medicine?

The ellipse is an oval-shaped curve; inside the ellipse are two fixed points called *foci*. It has long been recognized that an ellipse has a special *reflective property*—any energy in the form of rays or waves emitted from one focus will be reflected by the ellipse to the other focus.

In the nonsurgical treatment of kidney stones, called *lithotripsy*, the reflective property of the ellipse is used to direct ultrasound waves. Ultrasounds (sounds whose frequency is beyond the range of human hearing) are commonly produced electronically. The ultrasonic emitter can be placed at one focus point within an elliptical reflector. When the ultrasound waves are produced, they strike the

walls of the reflector at different places, but they are all reflected back to a single point—the other focus. The patient is positioned so that the location of the kidney stone coincides with this other focal point. The concentrated energy of the ultrasound waves is dissipated in the kidney stone, causing it to shatter, and the microscopic fragments can then easily pass through the patient's system.

A major advantage of ultrasound therapy is that it may be used as a destructive force at a hard-to-reach point without damaging the surrounding tissue. Moreover, it involves no

532

Features

Modeling

Although most of what is known today about the conic sections was known to the Greeks over 2000 years ago, imaginative questions and insights have led to some very modern applications of these geometric ideas. The models of planetary orbits, based first on circles and then on ellipses, are of great historical importance and are discussed later in the chapter.

The reflective properties of the conics are the basis of many common applications such as automotive headlights and satellite dish antennas. A lesser-known application in medical technology is discussed in this lesson. The *lithotriptor* was developed by West German scientists and approved for use in the United States in 1984.

Emphasize that invention depends on the ingenuity of the human mind. Researchers must understand and then reinterpret the key properties of an abstract geometric model in a new setting.

Thinking Critically   The shape of the ceiling is ellipsoidal. Acoustical engineers use the focal property of an ellipse to design spaces, called "whispering galleries," in which the reflected sound waves of a whisper at one focus are brought together at the other focus. The Mormon Tabernacle in Salt Lake City and the Capitol Building in Washington, D.C., have whispering galleries.

radiation and avoids complications such as bleeding, infection, or reactions to drugs that may occur with other methods. As a result, the procedure is safer for the patient, recovery time is shorter, and hence, hospital costs are lower.

The use of lasers in medicine—especially for delicate procedures such as eye surgery—is rapidly expanding. The reflective property of the ellipse was also applied in the early development of laser technology. A laser is an intense, narrow beam of light produced by rod-shaped ruby crystals. If the ruby rod is placed

at one focus of an elliptical cylinder and a source of radiation is placed at the other focus, then all the energy from the source can be "pumped" into the ruby rod until it is sufficiently stimulated to emit its laser beam.

Thinking Critically   In certain rooms, even if the room is crowded and noisy, a person standing at one spot can clearly hear the whisper of another person at a point a considerable distance away. What do you think the shape of the ceiling is in these rooms? How does this explain the "whispering" phenomenon?

Project   Find other examples of how geometric concepts have helped to revolutionize medical technology. You may wish to discuss diagnostic methods such as CAT-scanning (computerized axial tomography) or MRI (magnetic resonance imaging).

533

Review and Assessment

Student Text
- Test Yourself   563, 589
- Summary and Review   590–591
- Chapter Test   592

Teacher's Resource Book
- Tests   49–52
- Practice   70–77

Vocabulary
center of a circle
circle
conic sections
degenerate circle
radius

Ⓜ **Materials/Manipulatives**
breakaway conic sections model
chalk
string

Technology
computer
geometric supposer (circles)
graphing utility
green globs software

FOCUS
Have students collect pictures and/or diagrams of examples of circles in use in everyday objects. This may help to make them aware of the geometry and mathematics around them.

INSTRUCTION
Ⓜ • To emphasize the locus definition of a circle, use a piece of string with a piece of chalk attached to draw a circle on the board. Then shorten the string and draw another circle.
• Use a breakaway model for conic sections to show how the intersection of a plane parallel to the base of a cone forms a circle.
• Use the green globs software so that students may see a direct correlation between the change in the graph and a change in the equation.

11.1 Introduction to Conic Sections and the Circle

Objective: To determine the relationship between the equation of a circle and its center and radius

Focus

Few topics in mathematics have so many and such varied applications as conic sections. The term *conic sections* is derived from the various figures or sections that are obtained when a double right circular cone is sliced from different angles by a plane. These figures were studied more than 2000 years ago by Greek mathematicians. Indeed, Apollonius wrote a book entitled, "On Conic Sections" in the third century B.C. In more recent times, Charlotte Angus Scott (1858–1931) contributed to the study of plane analytical geometry with her text, *An Introductory Account of Certain Modern Ideas and Methods in Plane Analytical Geometry.*

Circular wheels, gears, and pistons are found in almost every machine. The endpoint of the blade of a fan, the end of an automobile windshield wiper, the tip of a helicopter rotor, and the hands of a clock all trace out circles or portions of circles. Planets and satellites have moved on paths that are ellipses since the formation of the solar system. The parabola is used in designing reflective mirrors and lenses of telescopes. The hyperbola is used in certain kinds of radio communication.

Conic sections are curves formed by the intersection of a plane and a double right circular cone, as shown below. Each cone consists of all lines, or **elements,** through a point V that form a constant angle with line a. Point V is called the *vertex* of the cone, and line a is the *axis.* When the plane is perpendicular to the axis of the cone, a circle is formed. As the plane tilts from horizontal to vertical, it traces out, successively, a circle, an ellipse, a parabola, and a hyperbola.

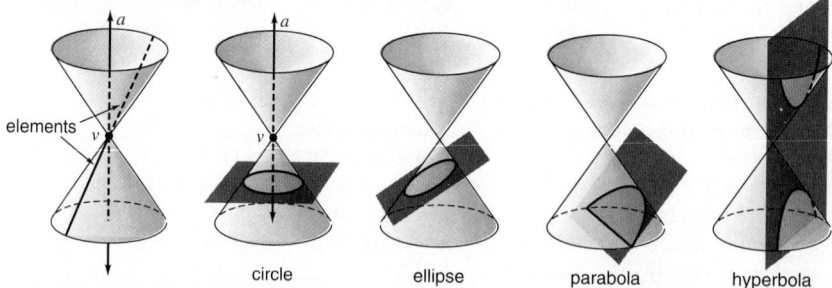

circle   ellipse   parabola   hyperbola

A **circle** is the set of all points in a plane that are a fixed distance from a fixed point. The fixed distance is the **radius** and the fixed point is the *center* of the circle. To derive the equation of a circle with center $C(h, k)$ and radius r, use the distance formula. Let $P(x, y)$ represent an arbitrary point on the circle. The distance from P to C is equal to the radius r.

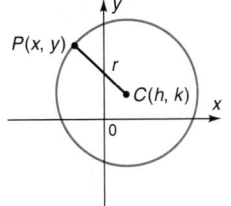

$$r = \sqrt{(x - h)^2 + (y - k)^2} \qquad \textit{Distance formula}$$
$$r^2 = (x - h)^2 + (y - k)^2 \qquad \textit{Square both sides.}$$

> The standard form of the equation of a circle with center $C(h, k)$ and radius r is
> $$(x - h)^2 + (y - k)^2 = r^2$$

The circle with equation $(x - 3)^2 + (y - 2)^2 = 25$ has center at $(3, 2)$ and radius 5. The circle with standard equation $(x + 5)^2 + (y - 3)^2 = 36$ represents the circle with center at $(-5, 3)$ and radius 6. The equation $x^2 + y^2 = r^2$ represents a circle with center at the origin and radius r. *Why?*

Every point in the plane whose coordinates (x, y) satisfy the equation of a circle lies on the circle. The converse is also true. All graphs of circles in the plane may be thought of as translations of circles with centers at the origin.

Example 1 Discuss the relationship between the graph of the circle with equation $(x - 4)^2 + (y + 5)^2 = 16$ and the graph of the circle with equation $x^2 + y^2 = 16$.

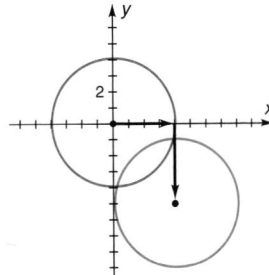

The graphs are congruent. The circle with center $(4, -5)$ is the result of shifting the circle with center $(0, 0)$ 4 units to the right and 5 units down.

In general, replacing x with $(x - h)$ will result in a horizontal translation of the graph of h units. When h is positive, the shift is to the right, and when h is negative, the shift is to the left. Replacing y with $(y - k)$ will result in a vertical translation of the graph of k units. When k is positive, the shift is upward, and when k is negative, the shift is downward.

Example 2 Determine the equation of the circle with center at $(3, -1)$ that passes through the point $(-2, 2)$.

$$r = \sqrt{(3 - (-2))^2 + (-1 - 2)^2} = \sqrt{34} \qquad \textit{Use the distance formula.}$$
$$(x - 3)^2 + (y - (-1))^2 = (\sqrt{34})^2 \qquad \textit{Standard form}$$
$$(x - 3)^2 + (y + 1)^2 = 34$$

11.1 Introduction to Conic Sections and the Circle **535**

Thinking Critically
At the origin, $h = 0$ and $k = 0$.

For Example 3

Determine the center and radius of the circle with the given equation, and then graph the equation.

1. $x^2 + y^2 + 4x - 12y + 40 = 0$

center: $(-2, 6)$; radius: 0

2. $x^2 + y^2 - 2x - 8y + 42 = 0$

No circle exists since the radius is negative.

For Example 4

Use a graphing utility to graph the circle with the given equation.

1. $x^2 + y^2 - 2x + 14y + 41 = 0$

2. $x^2 + y^2 + 4x + 10y - 35 = 0$

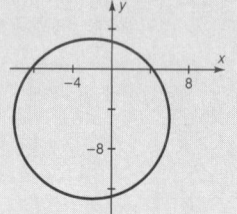

The standard form of the equation of a circle provides two important characteristics of the circle, the center and the radius. Equations of circles may be expressed in the *general form* of the equation of a circle, $x^2 + y^2 + Dx + Ey + F = 0$. Note that the coefficients of x^2 and y^2 are equal and the equation contains no xy-term. You can use the method of *completing the square* to transform an equation in general form to one in standard form.

Example 3 Determine the center and radius of the circle with equation $x^2 + y^2 + 4x + 6y - 3 = 0$, and then graph it.

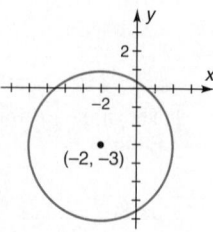

$$x^2 + y^2 + 4x + 6y - 3 = 0$$
$$(x^2 + 4x + \underline{?\,}) + (y^2 + 6y + \underline{?\,}) = 3 \qquad \text{Group the terms.}$$
$$(x^2 + 4x + 4) + (y^2 + 6y + 9) = 3 + 4 + 9 \qquad \text{Complete the}$$
$$(x + 2)^2 + (y + 3)^2 = 16 \qquad \text{square.}$$

The center is $(-2, -3)$, and the radius is 4.

Do all equations of the form $x^2 + y^2 + Dx + Ey + F = 0$ determine circles? The answer depends on the values of D, E, and F. For example, completing the square on the equation $x^2 + y^2 + 8x - 10y + 41 = 0$ yields $(x + 4)^2 + (y - 5)^2 = 0$. The center is $(-4, 5)$, and the radius is 0. The result is a point circle which is sometimes called a **degenerate circle.** Similarly, the equation $x^2 + y^2 + 8x - 10y + 45 = 0$ yields $(x + 4)^2 + (y - 5)^2 = -4$. Since a circle cannot have a negative radius, there are no points with real coordinates that satisfy the equation. The graph of such a circle is the empty set.

Completing the square is one method that can be used to help you obtain the graph of a circle. You can also use a graphing utility. However, many graphing utilities require that the equation be expressed in function form, and the graph of a circle does not pass the vertical line test. The equation for a circle is not a function, but it can be expressed as two functions using the quadratic formula. Then you can input both functions to obtain the graph. In order to see a more accurate circle, you can use the zoom square feature on your graphing utility. *Can you obtain the same result by setting the range values?*

Example 4 Use a graphing utility to graph the circle with equation $x^2 + y^2 - 6x - 2y = 26$.

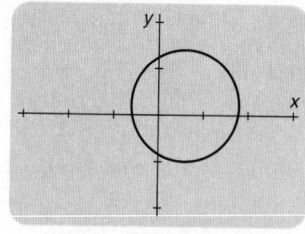

$$x^2 + y^2 - 6x - 2y = 26$$
$$y^2 - 2y + (x^2 - 6x - 26) = 0$$

Use the quadratic formula with $a = 1$, $b = -2$, and $c = x^2 - 6x - 26$.

$$y_1 = \frac{2 + \sqrt{4 - 4(x^2 - 6x - 26)}}{2}$$

$$y_2 = \frac{2 - \sqrt{4 - 4(x^2 - 6x - 26)}}{2}$$

[−15, 15] by [−10, 10]
x scl: 5 y scl: 5

The graph is a circle with center at $(3, 1)$ and radius 6.

Thinking Critically
Setting the range would give you the same result.

Both the general form and the standard form of the equation of a circle have three arbitrary constants. In the general form they are D, E, and F. In the standard form they are h, k, and r. If three conditions that determine a circle are given, then you can find the equation of that circle.

Example 5   Determine the equation of the circle that passes through the points $(1, 7)$, $(-2, -2)$, and $(-8, 10)$.

Substitute coordinates of each point into the general form of the equation of the circle.

$$x^2 + y^2 + Dx + Ey + F = 0$$
$$1 + 49 + D + 7E + F = 0 \qquad x = 1,\ y = 7$$
$$4 + 4 - 2D - 2E + F = 0 \qquad x = -2,\ y = -2$$
$$64 + 100 - 8D + 10E + F = 0 \qquad x = -8,\ y = 10$$

Solve the simplified system of equations.

$$\begin{cases} D + 7E + F = -50 \\ -2D - 2E + F = -8 \\ -8D + 10E + F = -164 \end{cases} \begin{aligned} &\rightarrow 3D + 9E = -42 \rightarrow -6D - 18E = 84 \\ &\rightarrow 6D - 12E = 164 \rightarrow \underline{6D - 12E = 164} \\ & -30E = 248 \\ & E = -8 \end{aligned}$$

Substitute to obtain $D = 10$, and $F = -4$.

Thus, the equation of the circle is $x^2 + y^2 + 10x - 8y - 4 = 0$.

Class Exercises

Determine the center and radius of the circle with the given equation.

1. $(x + 1)^2 + (y - 3)^2 = 25$ $(-1, 3); 5$ **2.** $x^2 + y^2 - 4x + 6y = 12$ $(2, -3); 5$

Determine an equation of a circle that satisfies the given conditions. Express your answers in standard form.

3. Center $(1, -7)$, radius 6 $(x - 1)^2 + (y + 7)^2 = 36$ **4.** Center $\left(\frac{1}{3}, -\frac{1}{2}\right)$, radius $\frac{3}{2}$ $\left(x - \frac{1}{3}\right)^2 + \left(y + \frac{1}{2}\right)^2 = \frac{9}{4}$

5. Congruent to the graph of $x^2 + y^2 = 64$ and translated 2 units to the left $(x + 2)^2 + y^2 = 64$

6. Congruent to the graph of $x^2 + y^2 = 17$ and translated 2 units upward and 4 units to the right $(x - 4)^2 + (y - 2)^2 = 17$

7. Passes through the points $(10, 2)$, $(3, 9)$, and $(-2, 10)$ $(x + 2)^2 + (y + 3)^2 = 169$

Determine whether the graph of each equation represents a circle, a point circle, or the empty set. Graph all circles without using a graphing utility.

8. $x^2 + y^2 = 4$ **9.** $(x - 3)^2 + (y + 2)^2 = 25$ **10.** $x^2 + y^2 - 2x + 10y + 1 = 0$

Identify each center and radius.

11. $x^2 + y^2 - 4x + 2y - 31 = 0$ $(2, -1); 6$ **12.** $x^2 + y^2 + 2x + 6y - 71 = 0$ $(-1, -3); 9$

13. Writing in Mathematics   Determine the point and angle at which a plane must intersect a double right circular cone to produce a point circle.

Writing in Mathematics
13. The plane must intersect the cone at a 0° angle and must also go through point v.

For Example 5
Determine the equation of the circle that passes through the given points.
1. $(8, 2)$, $(1, 9)$, $(1, 1)$
$(x - 4)^2 + (y - 5)^2 = 25$
2. $(0, 0)$, $(1, 1)$, $(1, -2)$
$\left(x - \frac{3}{2}\right)^2 + \left(y + \frac{1}{2}\right)^2 = \frac{5}{2}$

CLOSURE

Have students summarize this lesson in their math journals.

INDEPENDENT PRACTICE

Assignment Guide
Basic: 1–25, 29–31
Average: 9–11, 20–44
Enriched: 10, 24, 30–56

Teacher's Resource Book
  Practice, page 70

Additional Answers
Class Exercises
8.

9.

10.

Practice Exercises

 Use appropriate technology.

Determine the center and radius of the circle with the given equation.

A 1. $x^2 + y^2 = 81$ (0, 0); 9
2. $x^2 + y^2 = 100$ (0, 0); 10
3. $x^2 + (y - 1)^2 = 16$ (0, 1); 4
4. $x^2 + (y + 3)^2 = 25$ (0, −3); 5
5. $(x - 7)^2 + (y + 2)^2 = 25$ (7, −2); 5
6. $(x + 3)^2 + (y - 4)^2 = 36$ (−3, 4); 6
7. $x^2 + y^2 + 8x - 12y = -3$ (−4, 6); 7
8. $x^2 + y^2 + 8x - 10y = 23$ (−4, 5); 8

9. Determine the area of a triangle with base $5\sqrt{3}$ cm and height $10\sqrt{2}$ cm. $25\sqrt{6}$ cm²

10. **Writing in Mathematics** Describe how to determine the equation of a circle whose diameter has its endpoints at (3, −4) and (−5, 6).

11. Graph $y = \sin^2 x + 1.5$.

Determine an equation of a circle that satisfies the given conditions. Express your answers in standard form.

12. Center (0, 0), radius 3 $x^2 + y^2 = 9$
13. Center (0, 0), radius 5 $x^2 + y^2 = 25$
14. Center (5, 6), radius 1 $(x - 5)^2 + (y - 6)^2 = 1$
15. Center (−2, 4), radius 4
16. Center (1, 5), passes through (7, 2) $(x - 1)^2 + (y - 5)^2 = 45$ $(x + 2)^2 + (y - 4)^2 = 16$
17. Center (2, 6), passes through (8, 3) $(x - 2)^2 + (y - 6)^2 = 45$
18. Congruent to the graph of $x^2 + y^2 = 25$ and translated 3 units downward $x^2 + (y + 3)^2 = 25$
19. Congruent to the graph of $x^2 + y^2 = 49$ and translated 2 units to the left $(x + 2)^2 + y^2 = 49$
20. Congruent to the graph of $x^2 + y^2 = 16$ and translated 3 units to the right and 1 unit up $(x - 3)^2 + (y - 1)^2 = 16$
21. Congruent to the graph of $x^2 + y^2 = 36$ and translated 5 units down and 3 units to the left $(x + 3)^2 + (y + 5)^2 = 36$

22. *Landscaping* A landscape designer is planning to plant a circular garden on a square plot of land. She must decide between the two configurations displayed at the right. One layout is one large circle tangent to the sides of the square. The other is four smaller circles of equal size that are tangent to the sides of the square. Which configuration has a larger area? Do the equations of the circles influence your answer? Same area; no

23. Determine the perimeter of an isosceles triangle with base 9 in. and base angles of 30°. $(9 + 6\sqrt{3})$ in.

24. **Writing in Mathematics** Explain in your own words why the general equation of a circle, $x^2 + y^2 + Dx + Ey + F = 0$, is a special case of the general second degree equation $Ax^2 + Bxy + Cy^2 + Dx + Ey + F = 0$.

Determine the equation of the circle that passes through each set of three points. $(x - 3)^2 + (y - 1)^2 = 9$ $x^2 + (y + 2)^2 = 9$

B 25. (3, 4), (6, 1), and (3, −2)
26. (0, 1), (3, −2), and (−3, −2)
27. (1, 5), (4, 2), and (−1, −1)
28. (5, 3), (−1, 9), and (3, −3)

$\left(x - \dfrac{3}{4}\right)^2 + \left(y - \dfrac{7}{4}\right)^2 = \dfrac{170}{16}$ $(x + 2)^2 + (y - 2)^2 = 50$

538 Chapter 11 Conic Sections

Writing in Mathematics
10. Determine the center of the circle by finding the midpoint of the two given points, and the radius of the circle by taking half the distance between the two given points. Then use the technique in the lesson to find the equation of the circle.
24. The general equation of a circle has $A = C$. Also, it contains no xy-term. If it did, it could not be written in standard form.

29. Determine the central angle of a regular octagon inscribed in a circle. 45°

30. Thinking Critically How can you determine the area between the circles with equations $x^2 + y^2 + 8x - 12y - 14 = 0$ and $x^2 + y^2 + 8x - 12y - 12 = 0$?

31. Determine the distance between the point $(6, 2)$ and the line $3x + 4y - 8 = 0$. $\frac{18}{5}$

Determine whether the graph of each equation represents a circle, a point circle, or the empty set. Graph all circles without using a graphing utility.

32. $x^2 + y^2 - 3x + 5y + 7 = 0$

33. $x^2 + y^2 + 5x - 3y + 7 = 0$

34. $3x^2 + 3y^2 - 6x + 4y = 1$

35. $2x^2 + 2y^2 = 5y - 4x - 2$

36. $5x^2 + 5y^2 - 10x - 20y + 25 = 0$

37. $3x^2 + 3y^2 - 30x + 18y + 178 = 0$

38. $2x^2 + 2y^2 + 2x - 6y + 5 = 0$

39. $4x^2 + 4y^2 + 32x - 8y + 12 = 0$

Identify each center and radius. (3, 4); 1

40. $2x^2 + 2y^2 + 8x - 12y - 24 = 0$ (−2, 3); 5 **41.** $2x^2 + 2y^2 - 12x - 16y + 48 = 0$

42. $x^2 + y^2 - 10x - 12y = 60$ (5, 6); 11 **43.** $x^2 + y^2 + 14x - 2y = 94$ (−7, 1); 12

44. *Design* The flowerlike design at the right can be drawn by setting a compass opening to the length of the radius of the circle and inscribing an arc. Then the point of the compass is set at the intersection of the arc and the circumference of the circle, and the process is repeated. Exactly six such arcs can be constructed within a circle. If the equation of the circle is $x^2 + y^2 = 1$ and the point of the compass is first placed at $(1, 0)$, determine the coordinates of the tips of the other five petals.

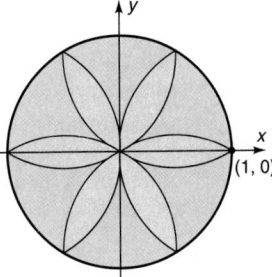

C 45. Writing in Mathematics Describe how to determine the equation of a circle with center on the line $y = 0.5x + 3$ that is tangent to both the x- and y-axes.

Determine an equation of a circle that satisfies the given conditions. Express your answers in standard form.

46. Center $(2, 3)$, tangent to the line $5x + 6y = 14$ $(x - 2)^2 + (y - 3)^2 = \frac{196}{61}$

47. Center $(5, 1)$, tangent to the line $7x + 2y = 17$ $(x - 5)^2 + (y - 1)^2 = \frac{400}{53}$

48. Passes through the points of intersection of the circles $x^2 + y^2 - 16x - 6y + 37 = 0$ and $x^2 + y^2 - 2x + 8y - 33 = 0$ and the point $(-8, 5)$

49. Passes through the points of intersection of the circles $x^2 + y^2 + 10x - 8y - 4 = 0$ and $x^2 + y^2 + 11x - 5y - 26 = 0$ and the point $(-1, -4)$

50. Prove that if the graph of the general form of the equation of a circle $x^2 + y^2 + Dx + Ey + F = 0$ is a point circle, then $D^2 + E^2 - 4F = 0$.

51. Prove that the equations of the two lines with slope 3 that are tangent to the circle $x^2 + y^2 = 40$ are $3x - y + 20 = 0$ and $3x - y - 20 = 0$.

52. Consider the circle with the equation $(x - a)^2 + y^2 = r^2$, $0 < a < r$. Determine the midpoint of all chords through the origin.

Writing in Mathematics
45. Determine the point on the line that is equidistant from both the x- and y-axes. This point is the center, and the distance from each axis will be the radius of the circle.

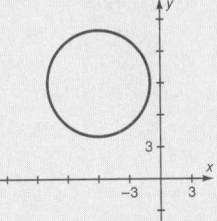

540

Alternative Assessment

Have students write an essay describing how to find the center and radius for a circle with equation $x^2 + y^2 + Ax + By + C = 0$.

Enrichment

Determine the standard equation of a sphere. Compare it to the equation of a circle. Describe how they are alike and how they are different.

Answers may vary. The equation of a sphere is similar to the equation of a circle, except there is a third term added. The denominators of all terms remain the same.

Additional Answers

53. $168x^2 - 1690x + 168y^2 - 4056y + 28,561 = 0$

55. Place the corner of the paper on the wheel so that it touches the circumference. Mark off the points on the circumference where the edges of the paper intersect it, then connect those points to give a diameter. Repeat this process placing the corner of the paper on another point on the circumference to give another diameter. The center of the circle is at the point where the diameters intersect.

56. Answers may vary. Make sure that no two sets of points have the same slope. Otherwise there is no circle containing the points.

---

53. Determine an equation for the locus of all points whose distance from (0, 0) is 13 times the distance from (5, 12).

54. *Archaeology* An archaeologist finds a piece of a circular pipe. He places the ends of a meterstick against the inside of the pipe and finds that the midpoint of the stick is 8 cm from the pipe wall. Determine the inside diameter of the pipe. 320.5 cm

55. *Construction* Marci purchases a kit to make a picnic table for the patio. The completed table will have two solid wood wheels on the supports at one end of the table. Unfortunately, the center holes are not drilled. How can she determine the center of the wheels using an ordinary piece of notebook paper?

56. *Programming* Write a program that will allow you to input the coordinates of three points that are not all on the same line and output the coordinates of the center and the length of the radius of the circle that passes through the three points.

Review

1. Prove that if C is the circumference of a circle with diameter of length d and a radius of length r, then $C = 2\pi r$. $\frac{C}{d} = \pi$, $C = \pi d$; $d = 2r$, $C = 2\pi r$

2. A coin bank contains nickels, dimes, and quarters. There are 12 coins in the bank that have a total value of $1.20. The number of quarters and dimes combined is the same as the number of nickels. Find the number of each coin. 6 N, 4 D, 2 Q

Find the area of each figure to the nearest tenth.

3.
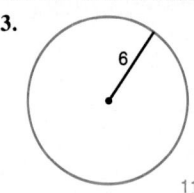

113.1

4.
14

30°

2

48.5

5.

12

374.1

6.

10

6.9

172.5

From the description of the following lines, determine if they would have at least one common solution.

7. Two lines with the same slope but different y-intercepts. no common solution

8. Two lines with the same slope and the same y-intercept. yes; lines coincide

For each equation, find the value of k that would make the left side a perfect square trinomial.

9. $x^2 + kx + 81 = 0$ 18

10. $\frac{1}{4}x^2 + kx + \frac{9}{16} = 0$ $\frac{3}{4}$

11. A 25-ft ladder is placed up against treehouse at an angle of 51° with the ground. Determine the height of the treehouse. 19.43 ft

12. An 80-ft pole casts a shadow 150 ft long. Determine the measure of the angle of elevation of the sun, to the nearest degree. 28°

11.2 The Ellipse

Objectives: *To determine the relationship between the equation of an ellipse and its foci and intercepts*
To graph an ellipse

Focus

Visitors who tour the U.S. Capitol Building in Washington, D.C., are often treated to an example of one of the properties of the conic section called an ellipse. When the tour reaches the great rotunda between the Senate and House Chambers, the tour guide usually leaves the tour group at a certain spot to cross to the other side of the rotunda. From a predetermined spot on the other side, the tour guide whispers to the group, and is easily heard across the rotunda. What characteristic of the ellipse makes it possible for the whisper to be heard despite the people, noise, and space between the tour guide and the tour group?

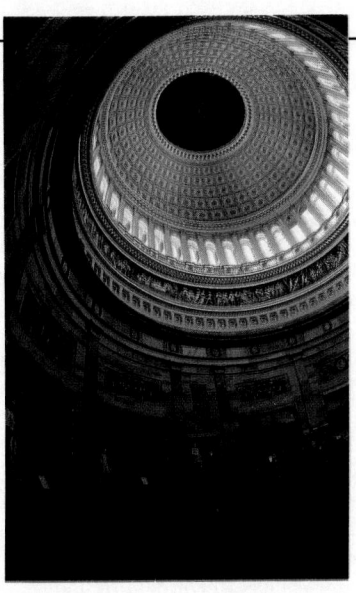

An **ellipse** is the set of all points P in a plane such that the sum of the distances from P to two fixed points is a constant. Each of the fixed points is a **focus** (plural: *foci*). An ellipse is formed by the intersection of a right circular cone and a plane that is neither perpendicular nor parallel to the axis of the cone and that is not parallel to an element of the cone.

To derive the standard equation for an ellipse in the coordinate plane, place the foci on the x-axis at equal distances from the origin. Label the foci $F_1(-c, 0)$ and $F_2(c, 0)$. If $P(x, y)$ is any point on the ellipse, then the sum $PF_1 + PF_2$ is constant by definition. Let $2a$ represent this distance. Notice that $2a > 2c$, so $a > c > 0$. The derivation follows at the top of the next page.

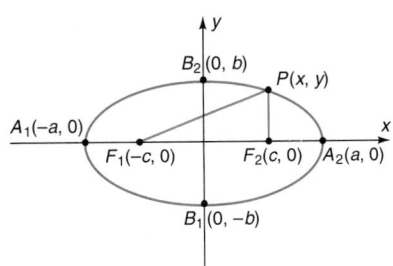

• Use a breakaway model for conic sections to show the ellipse as the intersection of a cone with a plane that is not perpendicular to the axis of cone.

• Use the corkboard, two pins, and loop of string to illustrate the locus definition of an ellipse. Lengthen or shorten the loop of string to change the shape of the ellipse with the same foci. Change the foci and keep the loop of string the same length to demonstrate eccentricity.

• The procedure above may be accomplished on an overhead projector with two small suction cups for foci.

• Make the connection between the symmetry exhibited by graphs and that in everyday experiences. For example, have students consider the symmetries of digital readouts like 101 and 689, or the symmetries of letters like H, A, O, T, and S.

Alternative Learning Styles

Ⓜ Covering the corkboard with paper and allowing students to experiment with placing the pins (foci) and lengthening or shortening the string, will help students who are "hands on" learners.

$$PF_1 + PF_2 = 2a$$

$$\sqrt{(x + c)^2 + (y - 0)^2} + \sqrt{(x - c)^2 + (y - 0)^2} = 2a \qquad \textit{Use the distance formula.}$$

$$\sqrt{(x + c)^2 + y^2} = 2a - \sqrt{(x - c)^2 + y^2} \qquad \textit{Isolate one radical.}$$

$$(x + c)^2 + y^2 = 4a^2 - 4a\sqrt{(x - c)^2 + y^2} + (x - c)^2 + y^2$$

$$x^2 + 2cx + c^2 + y^2 = 4a^2 - 4a\sqrt{(x - c)^2 + y^2} + x^2 - 2cx + c^2 + y^2$$

$$2cx = 4a^2 - 4a\sqrt{(x - c)^2 + y^2} - 2cx$$

$$4a\sqrt{(x - c)^2 + y^2} = 4a^2 - 4cx$$

$$a\sqrt{(x - c)^2 + y^2} = a^2 - cx \qquad \textit{Isolate the radical.}$$

$$a^2(x - c)^2 + a^2y^2 = a^4 - 2a^2cx + c^2x^2 \qquad \textit{Square both sides.}$$

$$a^2x^2 - 2a^2cx + a^2c^2 + a^2y^2 = a^4 - 2a^2cx + c^2x^2$$

$$a^2x^2 + a^2c^2 + a^2y^2 = a^4 + c^2x^2$$

$$a^2x^2 - c^2x^2 + a^2y^2 = a^4 - a^2c^2$$

$$(a^2 - c^2)x^2 + a^2y^2 = a^2(a^2 - c^2)$$

$$\frac{x^2}{a^2} + \frac{y^2}{a^2 - c^2} = 1 \qquad \textit{Since } a > c, a^2 - c^2 > 0.$$

$$\frac{x^2}{a^2} + \frac{y^2}{b^2} = 1 \qquad \textit{Let } b^2 = a^2 - c^2.$$

Thus, $\frac{x^2}{a^2} + \frac{y^2}{b^2} = 1$ is the standard equation of an ellipse centered at the origin with foci on the x-axis. An ellipse may also have its foci on the y-axis. Then, the equation of the ellipse is $\frac{x^2}{b^2} + \frac{y^2}{a^2} = 1$, $a > b$.

In each graph below, the center of the ellipse is at the origin. For the graph at the left the x-intercepts are $(a, 0)$ and $(-a, 0)$, and the y-intercepts are $(0, b)$ and $(0, -b)$. For the graph at the right, the x-intercepts are $(b, 0)$ and $(-b, 0)$, and the y-intercepts are $(0, a)$ and $(0, -a)$. Why?

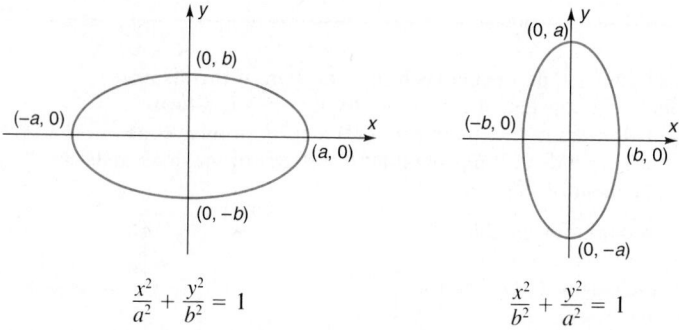

$$\frac{x^2}{a^2} + \frac{y^2}{b^2} = 1 \qquad\qquad \frac{x^2}{b^2} + \frac{y^2}{a^2} = 1$$

For the ellipse at the top of page 543, line segment $\overline{A_1A_2}$, which contains the foci, is the **major axis**. The endpoints of the major axis are often called the **vertices** of the ellipse. The shorter segment $\overline{B_1B_2}$ is the **minor axis**. The *center* is the point of intersection of the major and minor axes. The segment from the center to a vertex is the **semimajor** axis. Note the relationship between a, b,

542 Chapter 11 Conic Sections

Thinking Critically

In the graph at the left, the major axis is along the x-axis, and in the graph at the right, it is along the y-axis.

and c. The point $B_2(0, b)$ is on the ellipse, and it is also equidistant from $F_1(-c, 0)$ and $F_2(c, 0)$. By the definition, the sum of the distances is $2a$. Thus, the distance from $B_2(0, b)$ to $F_2(c, 0)$ should be a. Therefore, $a^2 = b^2 + c^2$.

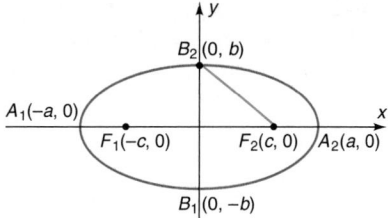

Example 1 Determine the endpoints of the major and minor axes and the foci of the ellipse with equation $\frac{x^2}{36} + \frac{y^2}{16} = 1$. Then graph it.

Endpoints of major axis:
$(-6, 0)$ and $(6, 0)$ $a^2 = 36, a = 6$

Endpoints of minor axis:
$(0, -4)$ and $(0, 4)$ $b^2 = 16, b = 4$

$c^2 = a^2 - b^2 = 36 - 16 = 20$
$c = \pm 2\sqrt{5}$

Foci: $(-2\sqrt{5}, 0)$ and $(2\sqrt{5}, 0)$

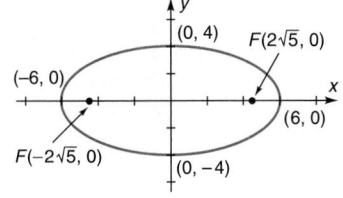

In the next example, the foci are on the y-axis.

Example 2 Determine the endpoints of the major and minor axes and the foci of the ellipse with equation $25x^2 + 9y^2 = 225$. Then graph.

$\frac{x^2}{9} + \frac{y^2}{25} = 1$ *Express in standard form*

Endpoints of major axis:
$(0, -5)$ and $(0, 5)$ $a^2 = 25, a = 5$

Endpoints of minor axis:
$(-3, 0)$ and $(3, 0)$ $b^2 = 9, b = 3$

$c^2 = a^2 - b^2 = 25 - 9 = 16$
$c = \pm 4$

Foci: $(0, -4)$ and $(0, 4)$

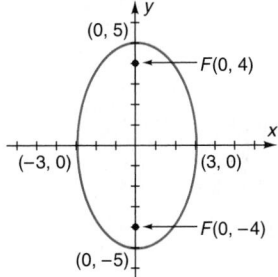

The shape of an ellipse is measured by a constant called the *eccentricity*. The **eccentricity** e of an ellipse or hyperbola is equal to the ratio of the distance between the center and a focus to the distance between the center and the corresponding vertex. Thus, $e = \frac{c}{a}$. A conic is an ellipse, if and only if $0 < e < 1$. The closer e is to zero, the more circular the ellipse. The closer e is to one, the more elongated the ellipse. A circle has an eccentricity of zero. *Why?*

GUIDED PRACTICE

For Example 1
Determine the endpoints of the major and minor axes and the foci of the ellipse with the equation $\frac{x^2}{64} + \frac{y^2}{16} = 1$. Then graph it.

major axis: $(-8, 0), (8, 0)$
minor axis: $(0, -4), (0, 4)$
foci: $(-4\sqrt{3}, 0), (4\sqrt{3}, 0)$

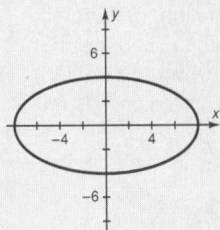

For Example 2
Determine the endpoints of the major and minor axes and the foci of the ellipse with the equation $169x^2 + 25y^2 = 4225$. Then graph it.

major axis: $(0, -13), (0, 13)$
minor axis: $(-5, 0), (5, 0)$
foci: $(0, -12), (0, 12)$

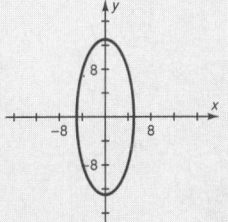

For Example 3

A communication satellite is to be put into an elliptical orbit around the earth so that the earth is at one focus. The maximum and minimum distances of the satellite from the earth are 20 mi and 15 mi, respectively. Find the eccentricity of the orbit. $e = 0.14$

For Example 4

Determine an equation in standard form for each ellipse. Then graph it.

1. The foci are (10, 5) and (−2, 5) and the length of major axis is 16. $\dfrac{(x-4)^2}{64} + \dfrac{(y-5)^2}{28} = 1$

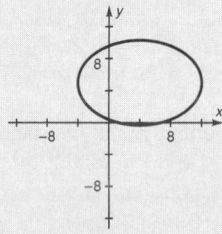

2. The foci are (1, 7) and (1, −3) and the length of minor axis is 8. $\dfrac{(x-1)^2}{16} + \dfrac{(y-2)^2}{41} = 1$

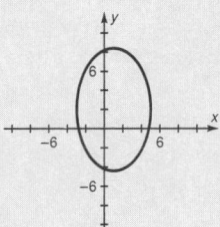

Example 3 *Astronomy* The planet Pluto has an elliptical orbit with the sun at one focus. The minimum and maximum distances of Pluto from the sun occur at the vertices of the ellipse. The minimum distance is 2.7 billion mi, and the maximum distance is 4.5 billion mi. Find the eccentricity of Pluto in orbit.

The length of the major axis is $2a$.

$$2a = 4.5 + 2.7 = 7.2$$
$$a = 3.6 \text{ billion mi}$$

The distance F_2 from the center is c.

$$c = 3.6 - 2.7 = 0.9 \text{ billion mi}$$
$$e = \frac{c}{a} = \frac{0.9}{3.6} = 0.25$$

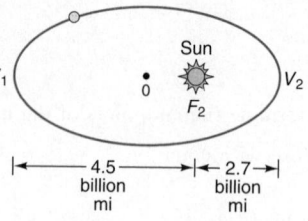

The eccentricity of Pluto is 0.2481, which is the greatest eccentricity of the nine planetary orbits. The least eccentric (most nearly circular) orbit is that of Venus, which has an eccentricity of 0.0068.

Not all ellipses have their centers at the origin. If x is replaced by $x - h$ and y by $y - k$ in the equation of an ellipse, its graph is shifted h units horizontally and k units vertically.

> The standard form of the equation of an ellipse with center at (h, k) and with axes parallel to the coordinate axes is
>
> $$\frac{(x-h)^2}{a^2} + \frac{(y-k)^2}{b^2} = 1 \quad \text{or} \quad \frac{(x-h)^2}{b^2} + \frac{(y-k)^2}{a^2} = 1 \qquad a > b$$

Example 4 Determine an equation of an ellipse in standard form with foci (8, 3) and (−4, 3) if the length of the major axis is 14. Then graph it.

The length of the major axis is $2a$.

$$2a = 14$$
$$a = 7 \text{ and } a^2 = 49$$

The center is halfway between the foci.

$$\frac{8 - (-4)}{2} = 6$$

Center: $(-4 + 6, 3) = (2, 3)$
Since $c = 6$, $c^2 = 36$.

$$b^2 = a^2 - c^2$$
$$b^2 = 49 - 36 = 13$$

$$\frac{(x-2)^2}{49} + \frac{(y-3)^2}{13} = 1 \qquad \textit{Standard form}$$

The general form of an equation of an ellipse with axes parallel to the coordinate axes is $Ax^2 + Cy^2 + Dx + Ey + F = 0$. The general form may be converted to the standard form by completing the squares.

Example 5   Determine the center, the endpoints of the major and minor axes, the foci, and the eccentricity of the ellipse with equation $x^2 + 4y^2 - 6x - 16y - 11 = 0$. Then graph it.

$(x^2 - 6x + \underline{\ ?\ }) + 4(y^2 - 4y + \underline{\ ?\ }) = 11$ *Complete the square in x and in y.*
$(x^2 - 6x + 9) + 4(y^2 - 4y + 4) = 11 + 9 + 16$
$(x - 3)^2 + 4(y - 2)^2 = 36$
$\dfrac{(x - 3)^2}{36} + \dfrac{(y - 2)^2}{9} = 1$ *Divide both sides by 36.*

Center: (3, 2)   *(h, k)*
Endpoints of major axis: (9, 2) and (−3, 2)   *(h + a, k), (h − a, k)*
Endpoints of minor axis: (3, 5) and (3, −1)   *(h, k + b), (h, k − b)*

$c^2 = a^2 - b^2$
$c^2 = 36 - 9$
$c = 3\sqrt{3}$

Since the major axis is horizontal, the foci are to the right and to the left of the center. The coordinates of the foci are $(3 + 3\sqrt{3}, 2)$ and $(3 - 3\sqrt{3}, 2)$.

Eccentricity: $e = \dfrac{c}{a} = \dfrac{3\sqrt{3}}{6} = \dfrac{\sqrt{3}}{2} \approx 0.87$

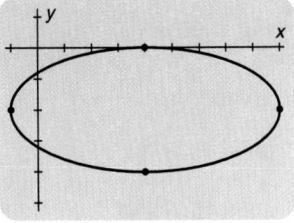 To graph an ellipse using a graphing utility, you must use the quadratic formula to express its equation as two functions. Some graphing utilities leave a small "hole" in the graph of an ellipse. In this instance, use the zoom and trace features and estimation to determine values to the desired degree of accuracy.

Example 6   Use a graphing utility to graph the ellipse with equation $4x^2 + 25y^2 - 32x + 100y + 64 = 0$. Determine the endpoints of the major and minor axes.

$4x^2 + 25y^2 - 32x + 100y + 64 = 0$
$25y^2 + 100y + (4x^2 - 32x + 64) = 0$

Use the quadratic formula.

$y_1 = \dfrac{-100 + \sqrt{10{,}000 - 100(4x^2 - 32x + 64)}}{50}$

$y_2 = \dfrac{-100 - \sqrt{10{,}000 - 100(4x^2 - 32x + 64)}}{50}$

[−1, 9] by [−5, 1]

11.2 The Ellipse   **545**

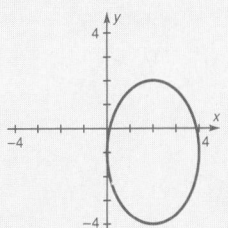

Have students write you a letter describing the relationship between the equation of an ellipse and its foci and intercepts.

INDEPENDENT PRACTICE

Assignment Guide
Basic: 1–21, 31
Average: 14–35
Enriched: 14, 21, 25–30, 32–45

Teacher's Resource Book
Practice, page 71

Ⓡ Review
Exercises 13, 15, 17, 31, and 41 review the concepts of solving absolute value inequalities, finding the inverse of a function, evaluating trigonometric functions of the sum of two angles, performing symbolic substitution, and proving trigonometric identities.

Technology
A graphing utility or a computer makes it possible for students to experiment with changes in the conditions that define a particular ellipse and to draw their own conclusions about it.

Additional Answers
Class Exercises
4. $\dfrac{(x-2)^2}{9} + \dfrac{(y-3)^2}{13} = 1$

5. $\dfrac{(x-1)^2}{4} + \dfrac{(y+1)^2}{9} = 1$

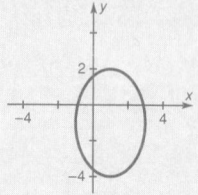

Use the zoom and trace features to obtain the x values of the endpoints of the major axis at -1 and 9. Average the y values on either side of the "hole" to estimate a y value of -2 on the major axis. Thus, the endpoints of the major axis are $(-1, -2)$ and $(9, -2)$. Use the zoom and trace features to locate the endpoints of the minor axis at $(4, -4)$ and $(4, 0)$.

Class Exercises

Determine the endpoints of the major and minor axes, the foci, and the eccentricity of each ellipse. Then graph.

1. $\dfrac{x^2}{16} + \dfrac{y^2}{81} = 1$ 2. $\dfrac{(x-1)^2}{9} + \dfrac{(y-2)^2}{16} = 1$ 3. $4x^2 + 9y^2 = 36$

Determine an equation in standard form for each ellipse. Graph it.

4. Center $(2, 3)$, foci $(2, 5)$ and $(2, 1)$, and minor axis of length 6.

5. $9x^2 + 4y^2 - 18x + 8y - 23 = 0$.

Use a graphing utility to graph each ellipse. Determine the endpoints of the major and minor axes.

6. $3x^2 + y^2 - 5x - 3y - 10 = 0$ 7. $x^2 + 5y^2 + 2x - 2y - 8 = 0$

8. **Thinking Critically** Describe the conic that has the standard equation $\dfrac{x^2}{a^2} + \dfrac{y^2}{b^2} = 1$ with $a = b$. circle; center $(0, 0)$; $r = a$

9. **Writing in Mathematics** Describe how the "whispering chamber" in the Capitol Building in Washington, D.C. works.

Practice Exercises

 Use appropriate technology.

Determine the endpoints of the major and minor axes, the foci, and the eccentricity of each ellipse. Then graph.

A 1. $\dfrac{x^2}{25} + \dfrac{y^2}{36} = 1$ 2. $\dfrac{x^2}{49} + \dfrac{y^2}{64} = 1$ 3. $\dfrac{x^2}{64} + \dfrac{y^2}{16} = 1$

4. $\dfrac{x^2}{81} + \dfrac{y^2}{49} = 1$ 5. $\dfrac{x^2}{6} + \dfrac{y^2}{2} = 1$ 6. $\dfrac{x^2}{8} + \dfrac{y^2}{10} = 1$

7. $25x^2 + 4y^2 = 100$ 8. $x^2 + 2y^2 = 2$ 9. $9x^2 + 25y^2 = 225$

10. $9x^2 + 16y^2 = 144$ 11. $15x^2 + 3y^2 = 5$ 12. $14x^2 + 2y^2 = 7$

Ⓡ 13. Solve: $|3x + 5| \geq 19$ $\left\{x : x \leq -8 \text{ or } x \geq \dfrac{14}{3}\right\}$

14. **Thinking Critically** If the latus rectum of an ellipse is the chord through either focus perpendicular to the major axis, what is its length for the ellipse with equation $\dfrac{x^2}{a^2} + \dfrac{y^2}{b^2} = 1$? $\dfrac{2b^2}{a}$

Ⓡ 15. Determine $f^{-1}(x)$ if $f(x) = x^3 + 7$. $f^{-1}(x) = \sqrt[3]{x - 7}$

16. *Astronomy* The mean distance from the sun to Mars is 141.7 million mi. If the eccentricity of the orbit of Mars is 0.093, determine the maximum distance that Mars orbits from the sun. 154.9 million mi

546   Chapter 11 Conic Sections

Writing in Mathematics
9. If one person stands at one focus of the elliptical chamber and another person stands at the other focus, a whisper can be easily heard.

17. Determine $\cos(\alpha + \beta)$ if $\cos \alpha = 0.2468$ and $\sin \beta = 0.9876$ and α and β are located in quadrant I. -0.9183

Determine the equation of an ellipse in standard form with the given foci and length of major axis.

18. Foci $(6, 2)$ and $(-2, 2)$ and major axis of length 10 $\quad \frac{(x-2)^2}{25} + \frac{(y-2)^2}{9} = 1$

19. Foci $(1, 7)$ and $(1, -3)$ and major axis of length 12 $\quad \frac{(x-1)^2}{11} + \frac{(y-2)^2}{36} = 1$

20. *Astronomy* The mean distance from the sun to Jupiter is 484 million mi. If the eccentricity of Jupiter's orbit is 0.05, determine the minimum distance that Jupiter orbits from the sun. 459.8 million mi

21. Writing in Mathematics Describe the meaning of eccentricity in your own words.

Determine the center, endpoints of the major and minor axes, foci, and eccentricity of each ellipse. Then graph.

B

22. $x^2 + 4y^2 - 32y + 48 = 0$ **23.** $4x^2 + y^2 - 16x = 0$

24. $2x^2 + y^2 + 8x - 8y - 48 = 0$ **25.** $4x^2 + 9y^2 - 48x + 72y + 144 = 0$

26. $x^2 + 5y^2 - 5 = 0$ **27.** $7x^2 + y^2 - 7 = 0$

28. $x^2 + 3y^2 + 4x + 6y + 4 = 0$ **29.** $x^2 + 4y^2 - 10x - 8y + 13 = 0$

30. *Space Science* A spacecraft in one of its orbits about the earth, had a minimum altitude of 200 mi and a maximum altitude of 1000 mi. The path of the spacecraft was elliptical, with the center of the earth at one focus. Find the equation of the path if the diameter of the earth is approximately 8000 mi.

31. Evaluate $P(2)$ for $P(x) = x^4 - 5x^3 + 2x^2 - 3x - 10$ using synthetic substitution. -32

Use a graphing utility to graph each ellipse. Determine the endpoints of the major and minor axes.

32. $4x^2 + y^2 - 8x - 4y + 7 = 0$ **33.** $3x^2 + y^2 - 5x - 5y + 1 = 0$

34. $x^2 + 2y^2 + 2x - 3y - 3 = 0$ **35.** $x^2 + 3y^2 - 3x + 2y + 2 = 0$

Graph each pair of relations on the same axes and compare them.

C

36. $\frac{|x|}{4} + \frac{|y|}{9} = 1$ and $\frac{x^2}{16} + \frac{y^2}{81} = 1$ **37.** $\frac{|x|}{16} + \frac{|y|}{25} = 1$ and $\frac{x^2}{256} + \frac{y^2}{625} = 1$

38. $\frac{(x+1)^2}{25} + \frac{(y-5)^2}{36} = 1$ and $\frac{|x+1|}{5} + \frac{|y-5|}{6} = 1$

39. $\frac{(x-2)^2}{16} + \frac{(y+3)^2}{81} = 1$ and $\frac{|x-2|}{4} + \frac{|y+3|}{9} = 1$

40. Writing in Mathematics In medicine, a lithotripter is used to crush kidney stones without surgery. Explain how a lithotripter is related to an ellipse and how it works.

41. Prove: $\tan^2\left(\frac{\alpha}{2}\right) = 1 - \frac{2\cos\alpha}{1 + \cos\alpha}$

Writing in Mathematics

21. Answers may vary. Check students' answers and make sure they understand how eccentricity affects the shape of a conic.

40. Light or sound emitted from one focus of an ellipse is reflected through the other focus. A patient is immersed into an ellipsoid-shaped tub. The stones are positioned at one focus and the shock waves originate at the other focus. The reflection of the waves by the tub destroys the stones.

Lesson Quiz

Determine the endpoints of the major and minor axes and the foci of each ellipse. Then graph it.

1. $\frac{x^2}{45} + \frac{y^2}{121} = 1$

major axis: $(0, -11), (0, 11)$

minor axis: $(-3\sqrt{5}, 0), (3\sqrt{5}, 0)$

foci: $(0, -2\sqrt{19}), (0, 2\sqrt{19})$

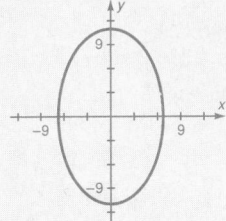

2. $36x^2 + 16y^2 - 288x + 64y + 64 = 0$

major axis: $(4, 4), (4, -8)$

minor axis: $(8, -2), (0, -2)$

foci: $(4, -2 + 2\sqrt{5}), (4, -2 - 2\sqrt{5})$

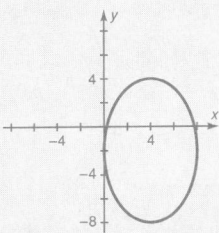

3. Determine the eccentricity of the ellipse with equation $4x^2 + 25y^2 - 40x - 100y + 100 = 0$. $e = 0.92$

4. Determine an equation in standard form for the ellipse with foci $(1, 6)$ and $(-5, 6)$ and a major axis of length 10. $\frac{(x+2)^2}{25} + \frac{(y-6)^2}{16} = 1$

Additional Answers

41. $\tan^2\left(\frac{\alpha}{2}\right) = \left(\pm\sqrt{\frac{1-\cos\alpha}{1+\cos\alpha}}\right)^2 =$

$\frac{1-\cos\alpha}{1+\cos\alpha}; \quad 1 - \frac{2\cos\alpha}{1+\cos\alpha} =$

$\frac{1+\cos\alpha}{1+\cos\alpha} - \frac{2\cos\alpha}{1+\cos\alpha} = \frac{1-\cos\alpha}{1+\cos\alpha}$

42. Writing in Mathematics   There is a certain type of map projection designed to preserve relative areas. Determine how ellipses are used in the projection process.

43. *Entertainment*   A "pool" table in the shape of an ellipse has only one hole in the surface as pictured. There are only two balls in the game, a cue ball and a target ball. The object of the game is to hit the target ball with the cue ball and deposit the target ball into the hole after one bounce off the elliptical cushion. The cue ball can be placed anywhere on the table. Describe a technique that will ensure that the target ball will go into the hole every time given proper placement of the cue ball.

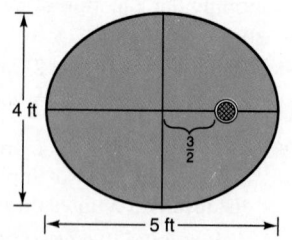

44. *Programming*   Write a program that will allow the user to input the coefficients of $Ax^2 + Cy^2 + Dx + Ey + F = 0$ (A and C positive) and output the coordinates of the center of the ellipse and the foci and the lengths of the major and minor axes.

45. *Engineering*   A tunnel through a mountain for a four-lane highway is to have a semi-elliptical opening. The total width of the highway (not the opening) is to be 48 ft, and the height at the edge of the road must be sufficient for a truck 11 ft high to clear. If the highest point of the opening is to be 15 ft, approximately how wide must the opening be? 70.6 ft

Challenge

1. Find the number of degrees between each minute mark of a standard 12-h clock. Find the number of degrees between each minute mark in a military 24-h clock. 6°, 3°

2. Find three consecutive positive even integers such that the difference between the sum of the squares of the smaller two numbers and the square of the largest number is 20. 8, 10, 12

3. A baseball batter takes a full swing at a thrown pitch by revolving a bat in a full circle. Find the angular velocity of the bat if it takes the batter 0.5 s to complete the swing. Find the linear velocity in miles per hour, to the nearest tenth, of the tip of the bat for a 34-in. bat given that the batter's arms are extended 27 in. away from the body. $\omega = 4\pi$ rad/s; $V = 43.6$ mi/h

Find values of θ in the interval $0° \le \theta < 360°$ for which the following equations hold: 45°, 135°, 225°, 315°

4. $\tan \theta = \cot \theta$ 5. $\sin \theta = \csc \theta$ 90°, 270°   6. $\cos \theta = \sec \theta$ 0°, 180°

7. The integer 24 can be factored into positive integer pairs in four different ways. For example, 24×1, 12×2, 8×3, and 6×4. Find all of the other integers less than 100 that also have four positive integer pair factors. 40, 54, 56, 88

8. On a trip by car, the distance read from the panel was 350 mi. On the return trip over the same route, the reading was 340 mi because snow tires were on. Determine, to the nearest hundredth of an inch, the increase in the radius of the wheels if the original radius was 14 in. 0.41 in.

11.3 The Hyperbola

Objectives: To determine the relationship between the equation of a hyperbola and its foci, intercepts, and asymptotes
To graph a hyperbola

Focus

For centuries, ships have been using the stars to aid in navigating the oceans. Airline pilots have also used celestial maps to determine their location during long flights. Since World War II, ships and planes have used another navigational aid, the LORAN (*LO*ng *RA*nge *N*avigation) system. The LORAN system makes use of radio pulses that are broadcast at the same time from widely separated transmitters. Thus, it is not dependent upon visibility conditions. The radio signals allow a ship to locate itself at the intersection of hyperbolic curves.

A **hyperbola** is the set of all points P in a plane such that the absolute value of the difference of the distances from two fixed points is a constant. The two fixed points are called foci. The line segments from P to the foci are called focal radii at P. A hyperbola is formed when a right circular cone is cut with a plane parallel to its axis.

Let $P(x, y)$ be an arbitrary point on a hyperbola with foci $F_1(-c, 0)$ and $F_2(c, 0)$ and with the difference between the distances PF_1 and PF_2 equal to a constant $2a$ with $0 < a < c$. The definition of a hyperbola and the distance formula can be used to derive the standard equation of the hyperbola, $\frac{x^2}{a^2} - \frac{y^2}{b^2} = 1$, where $a^2 + b^2 = c^2$. The derivation follows the same steps as those used for the ellipse in the previous lesson and is therefore left as an exercise.

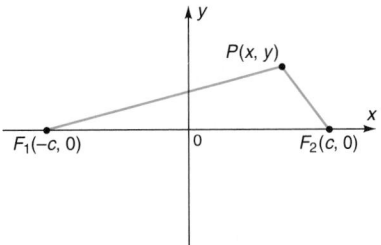

Thus, $\frac{x^2}{a^2} - \frac{y^2}{b^2} = 1$ is the standard form for the equation of a hyperbola with center at the origin and foci on the x-axis. The x-intercepts are $\pm a$. The vertices are $(a, 0)$ and $(-a, 0)$. There are no y-intercepts. *Why?*

Thinking Critically

If $x = 0$, then $\frac{y^2}{b^2}$ would have to be equal to -1, which is impossible.

LESSON PLAN

Vocabulary
asymptotes
center
conjugate axis
focal axis
foci
hyperbola
rectangular hyperbola
transverse axis

Ⓜ Materials/Manipulatives
breakaway conic sections
flashlight

Technology
computer
graphing utility
green globs software

FOCUS

If it is possible, invite an airline navigator to your class to explain how a location in flight may be determined if the onboard computers should fail.

INSTRUCTION

Ⓜ • Use a breakaway conic sections model to demonstrate that a hyperbola is the result of the intersection of a cone with a plane parallel to the axis of two nappes of the cone.

• Use a flashlight to demonstrate that the light emanating from it is in the shape of a cone. Ask them how they would hold the flashlight with reference to a wall (plane) so that the light on the wall is a circle, an ellipse, a parabola, and one branch of a hyperbola.

Some students need assistance to make the connections between what is done in mathematics classes and what exists outside of those classes. The flashlight activity described on page 549 may help them to be receptive to the mathematics around them.

GUIDED PRACTICE

For Example 1

Determine the vertices, endpoints of the conjugate axis, foci, and asymptotes of the hyperbola with equation $\frac{x^2}{16} - \frac{y^2}{25} = 1$ and sketch its graph.

vertices: $(\pm 4, 0)$; endpoints: $(0, \pm 5)$;

foci: $(\pm\sqrt{41}, 0)$; asymptotes: $y = \pm\frac{5}{4}x$

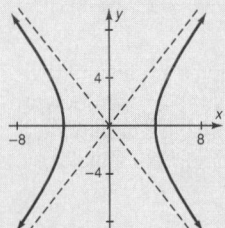

The hyperbola has two parts, or *branches*. $\overleftrightarrow{V_1 V_2}$ is the *principal axis* and contains the foci. $\overline{V_1 V_2}$ is the **transverse axis** and is of length $2a$. $\overline{B_1 B_2}$ is the **conjugate axis** and is of length $2b$. The *center* of the hyperbola is the midpoint of $\overline{F_1 F_2}$. The endpoints of the conjugate axis are $(0, b)$ and $(0, -b)$. The foci are $(c, 0)$ and $(-c, 0)$ with $c^2 = a^2 + b^2$.

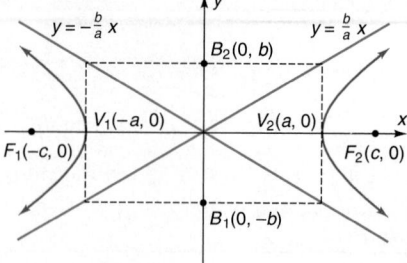

To graph a hyperbola, first draw the graph of a rectangle centered at the origin that is $2a$ units wide and $2b$ units high. The extended diagonals of the rectangle are the *asymptotes* of the hyperbola. The hyperbola never meets its asymptotes, but approaches them more and more closely as $|x|$ and $|y|$ increase. The equations of the asymptotes are $y = \pm\frac{b}{a}x$.

A hyperbola may also have its foci on the y-axis, in which case the transverse axis is vertical. The equations for hyperbolas centered at the origin with foci on a coordinate axis are provided in the following table.

Hyperbola Centered at the Origin		
Standard form of equation	$\dfrac{x^2}{a^2} - \dfrac{y^2}{b^2} = 1$	$\dfrac{y^2}{a^2} - \dfrac{x^2}{b^2} = 1$
x-intercepts	$\pm a$	None
y-intercepts	None	$\pm a$
Transverse axis	On x-axis; length $2a$	On y-axis; length $2a$
Conjugate axis	On y-axis; length $2b$	On x-axis; length $2b$
Foci	$(\pm c, 0)$, where $c^2 = a^2 + b^2$	$(0, \pm c)$, where $c^2 = a^2 + b^2$
Asymptotes	$y = \pm\dfrac{b}{a}x$	$y = \pm\dfrac{a}{b}x$

Example 1 Determine the vertices, the endpoints of the conjugate axis, the foci, and the asymptotes of the hyperbola with equation $\frac{x^2}{9} - \frac{y^2}{4} = 1$. Then graph it.

Since $a^2 = 9$, $a = 3$. Thus, the vertices are $(3, 0)$ and $(-3, 0)$.

Since $b^2 = 4$, $b = \pm 2$. The endpoints of the conjugate axis are $(0, 2)$ and $(0, -2)$.

$$c^2 = a^2 + b^2 = 9 + 4 = 13$$
$$c = \sqrt{13}$$

The foci are $(\sqrt{13}, 0)$ and $(-\sqrt{13}, 0)$.

The asymptotes are $y = \pm\frac{2}{3}x$.

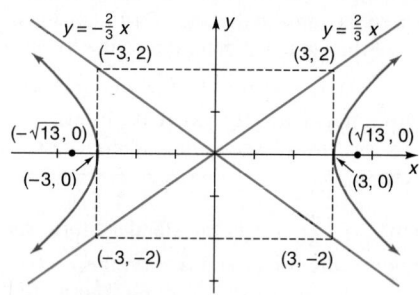

550   Chapter 11 Conic Sections

In the next example, the transverse axis is vertical.

Example 2 Determine the vertices, the endpoints of the conjugate axis, the foci, and the asymptotes of the hyperbola with equation $\dfrac{y^2}{9} - \dfrac{x^2}{16} = 1$. Then graph it.

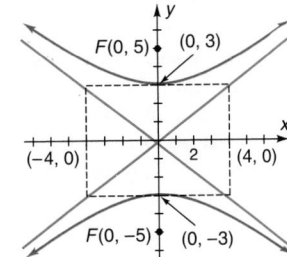

Since $a^2 = 9$, $a = 3$. The vertices are $(0, 3)$ and $(0, -3)$.

Since $b^2 = 16$, $b = 4$. The endpoints of the conjugate axis are $(4, 0)$ and $(-4, 0)$.

$$c^2 = a^2 + b^2 = 9 + 16 = 25$$
$$c = 5$$

The foci are $(0, 5)$ and $(0, -5)$.

The asymptotes are $y = \pm\dfrac{3}{4}x$, since $y = \pm\dfrac{a}{b}x$.

The graphs of hyperbolas may have different shapes. The shape of a hyperbola is measured by its *eccentricity*. As with an ellipse, the eccentricity e is equal to the ratio $\dfrac{\text{distance from center to a focus}}{\text{distance from center to a vertex}}$. Thus, $e = \dfrac{c}{a}$. For the hyperbola, $e > 1$. The eccentricity of the hyperbola in Example 1 is $e = \dfrac{\sqrt{13}}{3} \approx 1.2$. Note that the eccentricity of a conic indicates its type. *Which conic has eccentricity $0 < e < 1$?*

If a hyperbola centered at the origin is shifted h units horizontally and k units vertically, its new center is (h, k).

> The standard form of the equation of a hyperbola with center (h, k) and axes parallel to the coordinate axes is
>
> $$\dfrac{(x - h)^2}{a^2} - \dfrac{(y - k)^2}{b^2} = 1 \quad \text{or} \quad \dfrac{(y - k)^2}{a^2} - \dfrac{(x - h)^2}{b^2} = 1$$

Example 3 Graph the hyperbola $\dfrac{(x - 4)^2}{25} - \dfrac{(y + 3)^2}{16} = 1$.

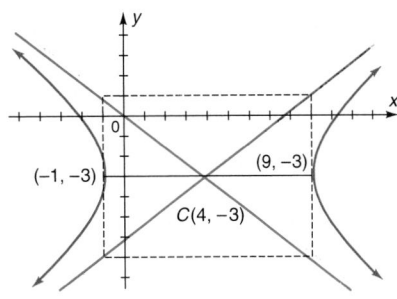

The graph is congruent to that of the hyperbola $\dfrac{x^2}{25} - \dfrac{y^2}{16}$, but the center is $(4, -3)$.

Graph the hyperbola with center at the origin and x-intercepts 5 and -5. Then shift this basic graph 4 units to the right and 3 units downward.

11.3 The Hyperbola   **551**

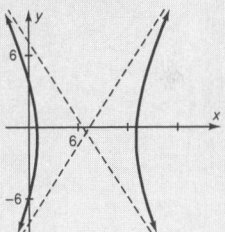
Thinking Critically
An ellipse has eccentricity $0 < e < 1$.

Modeling

The modeling provides an important application of hyperbolas in search and rescue missions. Students may be interested in reading more about the LORAN system.

For Example 4

Determine the standard equation for each hyperbola.

1. The vertices are at (4, 0) and (−4, 0), with points (5, 4.5) and (−8, 6√3) being two points on the hyperbola. $\frac{x^2}{16} - \frac{y^2}{36} = 1$

2. The vertices are at (0, 2) and (0, −8), with points (12, −16) and (−6, √61 − 3) being two points on the hyperbola. $\frac{(y+3)^2}{25} - \frac{x^2}{25} = 1$

Modeling

How can a navigator determine the location of a ship in the ocean?

In the LORAN system, a navigator uses radio pulses broadcast at the same time from widely separated radio transmitters to accurately compute the location of the ship. One pair of transmitters located at F_1 and F_2 sends the same signal, which is received by the ship at two different times. The navigator can then determine the distances d_1 and d_2 from the two transmitters. This locates the ship at point P on a hyperbola with foci at F_1 and F_2. Using signals from the pair of points F_2 and F_3, point P can be located on a hyperbola with foci at F_2 and F_3. The intersection of these two hyperbolas determines the location of the ship.

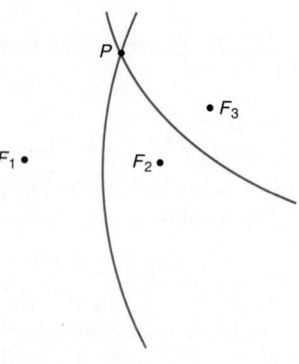

Modern ships have on-board computers that are programmed to receive the radio signals from the three stations. Using the locations of the three transmitting stations, the program determines the two hyperbolas and finds the intersection point, thereby locating the ship.

Example 4   *Navigation*   Two Coast Guard stations are located 600 mi apart at points $A(0, 0)$ and $B(0, 600)$. A distress signal from a ship is received at slightly different times by the two stations. It is determined that the ship is 200 mi farther from station A than it is from station B. Determine the equation of a hyperbola that passes through the location of the ship.

The equation of the hyperbola is of the form

$$\frac{(y-k)^2}{a^2} - \frac{(x-h)^2}{b^2} = 1$$

Since the center is located at (0, 300), midway between the two foci, which are the Coast Guard stations, the equation is

$$\frac{(y-300)^2}{a^2} - \frac{(x-0)^2}{b^2} = 1$$

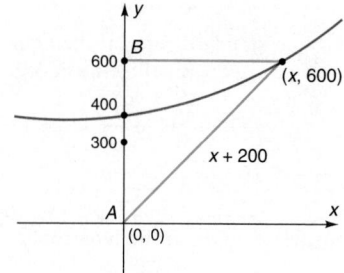

To determine the values of a and b, select two points known to be on the hyperbola and substitute each point in the above equation.

The point (0, 400) lies on the hyperbola, since it is 200 mi farther from station A than it is from station B.

$$\frac{(400-300)^2}{a^2} - \frac{0^2}{b^2} = 1 \qquad \text{\textit{Substitute.}}$$

$$\frac{100^2}{a^2} = 1$$

$$a^2 = 10{,}000$$

There is also a point $(x, 600)$ on the hyperbola such that

$$600^2 + x^2 = (x + 200)^2 \qquad \textit{Pythagorean theorem}$$
$$360{,}000 + x^2 = x^2 + 400x + 40{,}000$$
$$800 = x$$

$$\frac{(600 - 300)^2}{10{,}000} - \frac{(800 - 0)^2}{b^2} = 1 \qquad \textit{Substitute for x, y, and } a^2.$$
$$9 - \frac{640{,}000}{b^2} = 1$$
$$b^2 = 80{,}000$$

Thus, the equation of the hyperbola is $\dfrac{(y - 300)^2}{10{,}000} - \dfrac{x^2}{80{,}000} = 1$. The ship lies somewhere on this hyperbola. The exact location can be determined using data from a third station.

The general form of the equation of a hyperbola is $Ax^2 + Cy^2 + Dx + Ey + F = 0$ with A and C of opposite sign. The general form may be changed to the standard form by completing the square.

Example 5 Determine the center, vertices, foci, and asymptotes of the hyperbola with equation $3x^2 - y^2 - 12x - 6y = 0$. Then graph it.

$$3(x^2 - 4x + \underline{\ ?\ }) - (y^2 + 6y + \underline{\ ?\ }) = 0 \qquad \textit{Group like terms.}$$
$$3(x^2 - 4x + 4) - (y^2 + 6y + 9) = 12 - 9 \qquad \textit{Complete the squares.}$$
$$3(x - 2)^2 - (y + 3)^2 = 3$$
$$\frac{(x - 2)^2}{1} - \frac{(y + 3)^2}{3} = 1$$

The coordinates of the center are $(2, -3)$.
The principal axis is horizontal along the line $y = -3$.

Since $a = 1$, the vertices are 1 unit to the right and left of the center. Thus, $(3, -3)$ and $(1, -3)$ are the vertices.

Since $c^2 = a^2 + b^2 = 1 + 3 = 4$, $c = 2$. The foci are 2 units to the right and left of the center and are located at $(4, -3)$ and $(0, -3)$.

The equations of the asymptotes are $y = -3 \pm \sqrt{3}(x - 2)$.

The endpoints of the conjugate axis are $(2, -3 + \sqrt{3})$ and $(2, -3 - \sqrt{3})$.

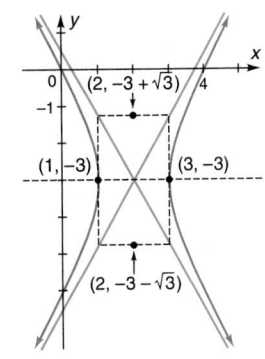

You can also use a graphing utility to determine the vertices of a hyperbola. It is particularly useful when the vertices are not integers. You must use the quadratic formula to express the equation of the hyperbola as two functions. Some graphing utilities leave a small "hole" in the graph. In this instance, use the zoom and trace features and estimation to determine values to the desired degree of accuracy.

For Example 5
Determine the center, vertices, foci, and asymptotes of the hyperbola with equation $9x^2 - 4y^2 - 36x - 48y - 144 = 0$ and sketch its graph. center: $(2, -6)$; vertices: $(4, -6)$ and $(0, -6)$; foci: $(2 \pm \sqrt{13}, -6)$; asymptotes: $y = \pm\frac{3}{2}(x - 2) - 6$

For Example 6

Use a graphing utility to graph $x^2 - y^2 + 2x - 6y + 1 = 0$. Then determine the principal axis, center, and vertices.

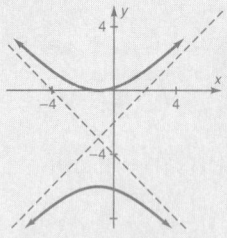

axis: $x = -1$; center: $(-1, -3)$; vertices: $(-1, 0)$ and $(-1, -6)$

CLOSURE

Have students write in their math journals an essay giving the reasons they found some parts of the lesson easy to understand and some parts difficult.

Example 6 Use a graphing utility to graph the hyperbola with equation $x^2 - 4y^2 - 2x + 16y - 19 = 0$. Determine the principal axis, the center, and the vertices.

$$x^2 - 4y^2 - 2x + 16y - 19 = 0$$
$$-4y^2 + 16y + (x^2 - 2x - 19) = 0$$

Use the quadratic formula:

$$y_1 = \frac{-16 + \sqrt{256 + 16(x^2 - 2x - 19)}}{-8}$$

$$y_2 = \frac{-16 - \sqrt{256 + 16(x^2 - 2x - 19)}}{-8}$$

The principal axis is the line $y = 2$. The center is $(1, 2)$, and the vertices are $(-1, 2)$ and $(3, 2)$.

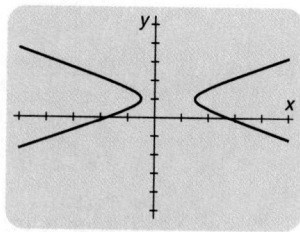

[−10, 10] by [−10, 10]
x scl: 2   y scl: 2

The graph of an equation of the form $xy = k$, where $k \neq 0$, is a hyperbola. It is called a **rectangular hyperbola**, and its asymptotes are the coordinate axes. The graph of the hyperbola $xy = 4$, shown on the left, is in the first and third quadrants since $k > 0$, and the graph of $xy = -4$, shown on the right, is in the second and fourth quadrants since $k < 0$.

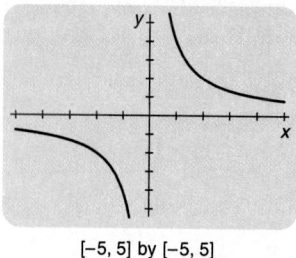

[−5, 5] by [−5, 5]
x scl: 1   y scl: 1

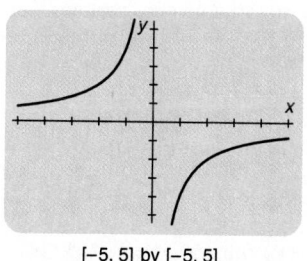

[−5, 5] by [−5, 5]
x scl: 1   y scl: 1

Class Exercises

Determine the vertices, the endpoints of the conjugate axis, the foci, the asymptotes, and the eccentricity of each hyperbola. Then graph.

1. $\frac{x^2}{49} - \frac{y^2}{9} = 1$

2. $\frac{y^2}{64} - \frac{x^2}{25} = 1$

3. $4x^2 - 9y^2 = 36$

4. $16x^2 - 9y^2 = 144$

5. $\frac{(x-3)^2}{25} - \frac{(y-4)^2}{36} = 1$

6. $\frac{(y+2)^2}{4} - \frac{(x+1)^2}{81} = 1$

7. $x^2 - 3y^2 - 4x + 18y - 50 = 0$

8. $9y^2 - 5x^2 + 30x - 36y - 54 = 0$

9. **Writing in Mathematics** The hyperbolas with equations $\frac{x^2}{a^2} - \frac{y^2}{b^2} = 1$ and $\frac{y^2}{b^2} - \frac{x^2}{a^2} = 1$ are called conjugate hyperbolas. Describe how the graphs are similar and how they differ.

Use a graphing utility to graph each hyperbola. Determine the vertices.

10. $-x^2 + 9y^2 + 72y + 135 = 0$

11. $xy = -36$

12. $xy = 100$

554 Chapter 11 Conic Sections

Determine an equation in standard form for each hyperbola.

13. The absolute value of the difference of the focal radii is 8 and the foci are (6, 0) and (−6, 0). $\frac{x^2}{16} - \frac{y^2}{20} = 1$

14. Center at (4, 2) with one focus at (4, 7) and $e = \frac{5}{3}$ $\frac{(y-2)^2}{9} - \frac{(x-4)^2}{16} = 1$

Practice Exercises   Use appropriate technology.

Determine the vertices, the endpoints of the conjugate axis, the foci, the asymptotes, and the eccentricity of each hyperbola. Then graph.

A 1. $\frac{y^2}{36} - \frac{x^2}{4} = 1$ 2. $\frac{y^2}{64} - \frac{x^2}{9} = 1$ 3. $\frac{x^2}{81} - \frac{y^2}{1} = 1$

4. $\frac{x^2}{100} - \frac{y^2}{16} = 1$ 5. $\frac{x^2}{121} - \frac{y^2}{49} = 1$ 6. $\frac{y^2}{169} - \frac{x^2}{144} = 1$

7. $25x^2 - 4y^2 = 100$ 8. $16x^2 - 36y^2 = 144$ 9. $9y^2 - 25x^2 = 225$

10. $2y^2 - x^2 = 2$ 11. $18x^2 - 9y^2 = 2$ 12. $21x^2 - 3y^2 = 7$

R 13. Evaluate: $\sqrt[4]{256^3}$ 64

14. **Thinking Critically** If the latus rectum of a hyperbola is the chord through either focus perpendicular to the principal axis, determine its length for the hyperbola with equation $\frac{x^2}{a^2} - \frac{y^2}{b^2} = 1$. $\frac{2b^2}{a}$

R 15. Solve ln $x = 2.3436$ to the nearest hundredth. 10.42

Graph each hyperbola.

16. $\frac{(x+2)^2}{16} - \frac{(y+1)^2}{4} = 1$ 17. $\frac{(y-1)^2}{49} - \frac{(x+4)^2}{36} = 1$ 18. $\frac{x^2}{25} - \frac{(y-3)^2}{9} = 1$

R 19. Solve: $\sqrt{y+6} - 15 = 0$ 219

20. **Writing in Mathematics** Describe the points on a hyperbola at which the focal radii are parallel.

Express the equation for each hyperbola in standard form. Determine the center, vertices, foci, and asymptotes for each.

B 21. $4x^2 - 9y^2 + 8x - 36y + 4 = 0$ 22. $9x^2 - 4y^2 - 18x + 16y - 11 = 0$

23. $3y^2 - 4x^2 - 8x - 24y - 40 = 0$ 24. $4y^2 - 9x^2 + 16y + 18x - 29 = 0$

25. $x^2 - 7y^2 + 7 = 0$ 26. $11x^2 - y^2 + 11 = 0$

R 27. *Sports* Laura rides a bicycle with tires of radius 14 in. at 18 mph. Determine the angular velocity of her tire in radians per minute. 1358 rad/min

Use a graphing utility to graph each hyperbola. Determine the vertices.

28. $9x^2 - 16y^2 - 18x + 64y - 199 = 0$ 29. $x^2 - 4y^2 + 6x + 8y + 1 = 0$

30. $xy = 16$ 31. $xy = -25$

Determine the standard equation for each hyperbola.

32. Foci (4, 1) and (−2, 1) with transverse axis of length 2 $\frac{(x-1)^2}{1} - \frac{(y-1)^2}{8} = 1$

33. Foci (0, 2) and (10, 2) with transverse axis of length 8 $\frac{(x-5)^2}{16} - \frac{(y-2)^2}{9} = 1$

11.3 The Hyperbola   **555**

Writing in Mathematics
20. The focal radii can never be parallel since they intersect at point *P*, a particular point on the hyperbola.

Assignment Guide
Basic: 1–20, 27
Average: 13–15, 19–36
Enriched: 14, 20, 28–45

Teacher's Resource Book
Practice, page 72

R **Review**
Exercises 13, 15, 19, 27, and 41 review concepts such as evaluating roots, solving logarithmic, radical, and exponential functions, and determining angular velocity.

Technology
Point out to students that on some graphing utilities, it is necessary to graph the upper and lower halves of the hyperbola separately.

Project
The situation described in the project uses principles similar to those used in the LORAN model.

LESSON FOLLOW-UP

Lesson Quiz
Determine the vertices, endpoints of the conjugate axis, foci, and asymptotes of each hyperbola.

1. $\frac{x^2}{1} - \frac{y^2}{49} = 1$
   vertices: ($\pm$1, 0); endpoints: (0, $\pm$7); foci: ($\pm5\sqrt{2}$, 0); asymptotes: $y = \pm7x$

2. $\frac{(y+3)^2}{64} - \frac{(x-6)^2}{9} = 1$
   vertices: (6, 5) and (6, −11); endpoints: (3, −3) and (9, −3); foci: (6, −3 $\pm \sqrt{73}$); asymptotes: $y = \pm\frac{8}{3}(x-6) - 3$

3. Determine the principal axis, center, and vertices of the hyperbola $25y^2 + 200y - 4x^2 - 40x + 200 = 0$.
   axis: $x = -5$; center: (−5, −4); vertices: (−5, −2) and (−5, −6)

34. Center $(-2, -1)$ with one vertex at $(-2, 9)$ and one focus at $(-2, 12)$ $\quad \frac{(y+1)^2}{100} - \frac{(x+2)^2}{69} = 1$

35. Center $(-3, -4)$ with one vertex at $(7, -4)$ and one focus at $(9, -4)$ $\quad \frac{(x+3)^2}{100} - \frac{(y+4)^2}{44} = 1$

36. *Physics* The vertical cross section of a cooling tower for a nuclear power plant is a truncated hyperbola. The diameter of the circular base of the tower is 100 ft. The diameter 100 ft above the ground (the narrowest point) is 44 ft. Find the equation of vertical cross section of the cooling tower. Determine the approximate diameter of the top of the tower if it is 140 ft high.

C 37. Determine the equation for the set of points P that are twice as far from $(4, 0)$ as from the line $x - 1 = 0$. $\quad 3x^2 - y^2 - 12 = 0$

38. Determine the equation for the set of points P that are twice as far from $(-4, 0)$ as from the line $x + 1 = 0$. $\quad 3x^2 - y^2 - 12 = 0$

39. Derive the standard equation for a hyperbola.

40. *Engineering* Two microphones that are placed 2000 ft apart record an explosion. The first microphone receives the sound 1 s before the second microphone. Where did the explosion come from?

Ⓡ 41. Solve: $\frac{e^{3x+2}}{10^x} = 1$ $\quad -2.87$

42. *Programming* Write a program that will allow the user to input the coefficients of $Ax^2 + Cy^2 + Dx + Ey + F = 0$ (A and C of different signs) and output the coordinates of the center, the coordinates of the foci, and the lengths of the transverse and conjugate axes of the hyperbola.

43. If e_1 and e_2 are the respective eccentricities of a hyperbola and its conjugate hyperbola, prove $\frac{1}{e_1^2} + \frac{1}{e_2^2} = 1$.

44. Prove that the conics with equations $16x^2 - 9y^2 = 144$ and $11x^2 + 36y^2 = 396$ have the same foci.

45. Find the equation of the hyperbola that passes through $(6, 2\sqrt{3})$ and $(-3, 0)$ and has center at the origin and principal axis on the coordinate axes. $\quad \frac{x^2}{9} - \frac{y^2}{4} = 1$

Project

A downed plane sends out an impulse that travels at the speed of sound (1100 ft/s). Three receiving stations A, B, and C with fixed positions record the times of reception of the impulse. Explain to a classmate how this information can be used to determine the position of the plane.

Review

1. Find a quadratic equation that has $5a + 4b$ and $5a - 4b$ as a solution. $\quad x^2 - 10ax + 25a^2 - 16b^2 = 0$

2. Evaluate: $6 \log_2 2 + \log_3 9$ $\quad 8$

3. Evaluate: Arc tan 0.3839 $\quad 0.3666$

4. Solve for x: $2^{x+1} = 128$ $\quad 6$

11.4 The Parabola

Objectives: *To determine the relationship between the equation of a parabola and its focus, directrix, vertex, and axis of symmetry*
To graph a parabola

Focus

The suspension bridge is one of the wonders of modern engineering. Combining art and science, a suspension bridge is both useful and beautiful. The success of the suspension structure followed the development of steel, which is stronger than any material that had previously been used in construction. However, the suspension bridge also depends on mathematics. The span of a suspension bridge is in the shape of a parabola because that is the shape that most evenly distributes the great weight of the bridge that must be supported.

A **parabola** is defined as the set of all points P in a plane that are equidistant from a fixed line and a fixed point not on the line. The fixed point is called the *focus* and the fixed line is called the **directrix** of the parabola. The line through the focus perpendicular to the directrix is the *axis of symmetry* of the parabola. Parabolas with an axis of symmetry parallel to one of the coordinate axes will be considered in this lesson. A parabola is formed by the intersection of a right circular cone and a plane parallel to an element of the cone.

In the figure at the right, PF is the distance from an arbitrary point $P(x, y)$ on a parabola to the focus $F(0, c)$. PF is equal to the distance PA from point P to the directrix, line ℓ, which has equation $y = -c$. The *vertex* is halfway between the focus and the directrix. Thus, the distance between the vertex and focus is $|c|$, and the distance between the vertex and directrix is $|c|$. To determine an equation of this parabola with vertex at the origin and focus $F(0, c)$ on the y-axis, use the definition and the distance formula.

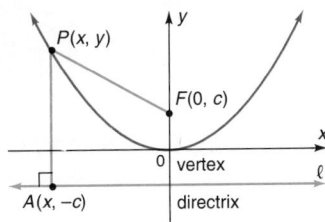

$$PF = PA$$
$$\sqrt{(x - 0)^2 + (y - c)^2} = \sqrt{(x - x)^2 + (y + c)^2}$$
$$x^2 + (y - c)^2 = (y + c)^2 \qquad \textit{Square both sides.}$$
$$x^2 + y^2 - 2cy + c^2 = y^2 + 2cy + c^2 \qquad \textit{Simplify.}$$
$$x^2 = 4cy$$
$$y = \frac{1}{4c}x^2$$

11.4 The Parabola **557**

GUIDED PRACTICE

For Example 1
Determine the vertex, the axis of symmetry, the focus, and the directrix of the parabola with the given equation. Then graph it.

1. $x^2 = -4y$
vertex: (0, 0); axis: $x = 0$; focus: (0, -1); directrix: $y = 1$

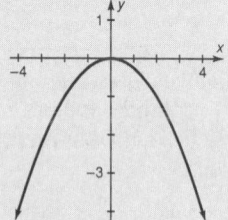

2. $y^2 = 6x$
vertex: (0, 0); axis: $y = 0$; focus: $\left(\frac{3}{2}, 0\right)$; directrix: $x = -\frac{3}{2}$

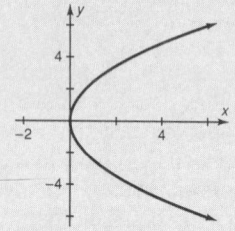

Note that if $c > 0$, the parabola opens upward. If $c < 0$, the parabola opens downward. Note also that this equation defines y as a function of x and implicitly defines the function $f(x) = \frac{1}{4c}x^2$.

> The equation of a parabola with vertex (0, 0), focus (0, c), directrix $y = -c$, and the y-axis as its axis of symmetry is
> $$x^2 = 4cy \qquad \text{or} \qquad y = \frac{1}{4c}x^2$$

Example 1 Determine the vertex, the axis of symmetry, the focus, and the directrix of the parabola with equation $x^2 = 12y$. Then graph it.

Compare $x^2 = 12y$ with $x^2 = 4cy$.

Vertex:	(0, 0)
Axis of symmetry:	$x = 0$
Focus:	(0, 3)
Directrix:	$y = -3$

$4c = 12$, so $c = 3$

Since $c > 0$, the parabola opens upward.

If the focus of a parabola is on the x-axis, then its equation is of the form $y^2 = 4cx$. You will be asked to show this derivation in the exercises. Here, the set of ordered pairs (x, y) that satisfies this equation is not a function of x because $y = \pm 2\sqrt{cx}$.

> The equation of a parabola with vertex (0, 0), focus (c, 0), directrix $x = -c$, and the x-axis as its axis of symmetry is
> $$y^2 = 4cx \qquad \text{or} \qquad x = \frac{1}{4c}y^2$$

 Since y is not a function of x, graph the functions $y_1 = 2\sqrt{cx}$ and $y_2 = -2\sqrt{cx}$ when using a graphing utility.

If the vertex of a parabola is not at the origin, its equation can also be derived using the definition and the distance formula. For example, for a parabola with focus $F(3, 4)$ and directrix $y = -2$, let $P(x, y)$ represent an arbitrary point on the parabola. Then

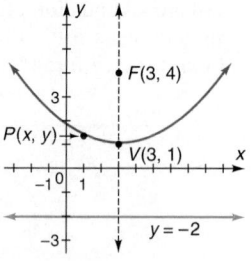

$$PF = PA$$
$$\sqrt{(x-3)^2 + (y-4)^2} = \sqrt{(x-x)^2 + (y+2)^2}$$
$$(x-3)^2 + (y-4)^2 = (x-x)^2 + (y+2)^2$$
$$x^2 - 6x + 9 + y^2 - 8y + 16 = y^2 + 4y + 4$$
$$x^2 - 6x + 9 = 12y - 12$$
$$(x-3)^2 = 12(y-1)$$

558   Chapter 11 Conic Sections

The equation of this parabola is of the form $(x - h)^2 = 4c(y - k)$. The vertex of the parabola (h, k) is $(3, 1)$, and the line of symmetry is the line $x = h$, or $x = 3$ in this case. Recall that the vertex of the basic parabola $y = x^2$ is $(0, 0)$. With the vertex at (h, k), the basic graph is shifted h units horizontally and k units vertically. The standard forms of the equation of a parabola with vertex (h, k) and axis parallel to a coordinate axis are

$$(x - h)^2 = 4c(y - k) \quad \text{and} \quad (y - k)^2 = 4c(x - h)$$

Parabola Centered at (h, k)

Standard form of equation	$(x - h)^2 = 4c(y - k)$	$(y - k)^2 = 4c(x - h)$
Vertex	(h, k)	(h, k)
Axis of symmetry	$x = h$	$y = k$
Focus	$(h, k + c)$	$(h + c, k)$
Directrix	$y = k - c$	$x = h - c$
Opening	Upward if $c > 0$ Downward if $c < 0$	Right if $c > 0$ Left if $c < 0$

Example 2 Determine the vertex, the axis of symmetry, the focus, and the directrix of the parabola with equation $(y - 3)^2 = 8(x - 2)$. Then graph it.

Vertex: $(2, 3)$	(h, k)
Axis of symmetry: $y = 3$	$y = k$
Focus: $(2 + 2, 3)$, or $(4, 3)$	$(h + c, k)$
Directrix: $x = 2 - 2$, or $x = 0$.	$x = h - c$

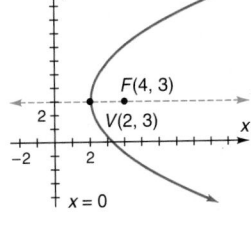

Since $c > 0$, the graph opens to the right.

A graphing utility can be helpful when graphing parabolas. For parabolas opening to the right or left, you will need to determine two functions.

Example 3 Graph the parabola $(y - 3)^2 = 8(x - 2)$ presented in the previous example using a graphing utility.

$$(y - 3)^2 = 8(x - 2)$$
$$y^2 - 6y + 9 = 8x - 16$$
$$y^2 - 6y - (8x - 25) = 0$$

Use the quadratic formula to determine two functions.

$$y_1 = \frac{6 + \sqrt{36 + 4(8x - 25)}}{2}$$

$$y_2 = \frac{6 - \sqrt{36 + 4(8x - 25)}}{2}$$

[−2, 10] by [−4, 10]

11.4 The Parabola   **559**

For Example 2
Determine the vertex, the axis of symmetry, the focus, and the directrix of the parabola with the given equation. Then graph it.
1. $(y - 1)^2 = 24(x - 3)$
   vertex: $(3, 1)$; axis: $y = 1$; focus: $(9, 1)$; directrix: $x = -3$

2. $(x + 4)^2 = -8(y + 3)$
   vertex: $(-4, -3)$; axis: $x = -4$; focus: $(-4, -5)$; directrix: $y = -1$

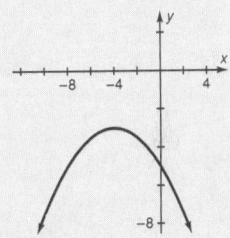

For Example 3
Graph the parabola $(y - 1)^2 = 24(x - 3)$ using a graphing utility.
Re-express in input form as $y = \sqrt{24(x - 3)} + 1$ and $y = -\sqrt{24(x - 3)} + 1$

Determine the vertex, the axis of symmetry, the focus, and the directrix of the parabola with the given equation.

1. $4x^2 - 12x + y + 6 = 0$

   vertex: $\left(\frac{3}{2}, 3\right)$; axis: $x = \frac{3}{2}$; focus:

   $\left(\frac{3}{2}, \frac{47}{16}\right)$; directrix: $y = \frac{49}{16}$

2. $12y^2 + 24y - 48x - 18 = 0$

   vertex: $\left(-\frac{5}{8}, -1\right)$; axis: $y = -1$;

   focus: $\left(\frac{3}{8}, -1\right)$; directrix: $x = -\frac{13}{8}$

For Example 5

Determine an equation in standard form for each parabola.

1. The focus is $(-1, 6)$ and the directrix is $y = 3$.

   $(x + 1)^2 = 6\left(y - \frac{9}{2}\right)$

2. The vertex is $(-3, 5)$ and the focus is $(2, 5)$. $(y - 5)^2 = 20(x + 3)$

The general forms for the equations of parabolas with axes of symmetry that are vertical or horizontal are $Ax^2 + Dx + Ey + F = 0$ and $Cy^2 + Dx + Ey + F = 0$, respectively. Each can be written in standard form by completing the square on the squared variable.

Example 4 Find the vertex, the axis of symmetry, the focus, and the directrix of the parabola with equation $2x^2 - 4x + y + 4 = 0$.

$$2x^2 - 4x + y + 4 = 0$$
$$2(x^2 - 2x + 1) + (y + 4) = 2$$
$$2(x - 1)^2 = -y - 2$$
$$(x - 1)^2 = -\frac{1}{2}(y + 2)$$

Vertex: $(1, -2)$

Axis of symmetry: $x = 1$

Focus: $\left(1, -2 - \frac{1}{8}\right) = \left(1, -\frac{17}{8}\right)$ $\quad c = -\frac{1}{8}$

Directrix: $y = -2 + \frac{1}{8} = -\frac{15}{8}$

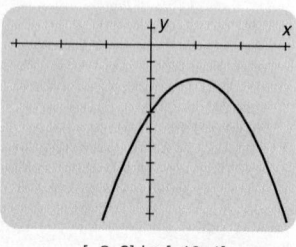

[-3, 3] by [-10, 1]

The next example illustrates how to find the equation of a parabola when certain geometric information is given.

Example 5 Determine an equation of the parabola with focus $(3, -4)$ and directrix $y = 2$.

$$PF = PQ \qquad \textit{Definition of a parabola}$$
$$\sqrt{(x - 3)^2 + (y + 4)^2} = \sqrt{(x - x)^2 + (y - 2)^2}$$
$$x^2 - 6x + 9 + y^2 + 8y + 16 = y^2 - 4y + 4$$
$$x^2 - 6x + 9 = -12y - 12$$
$$(x - 3)^2 = -12(y + 1)$$

You can also use translations to find the equation of the parabola in Example 5. The parabola opens downward because the focus is below the directrix. Recall that the vertex is half-way between the focus and the directrix. Therefore, the vertex is $V(3, -1)$. Thus, the parabola is shifted 3 units to the right and 1 unit down. The distance between the focus and the vertex is 3. Thus, $c = -3$, and an equation of the parabola is $(x - 3)^2 = -12(y + 1)$.

The reflective properties of a parabola are utilized by both automotive and audio engineers. If a light source is located at the focus of a parabola, the light rays will reflect off the parabola parallel to the axis of symmetry of the parabola. Automobile headlights are often designed with parabolic reflectors. Audio engineers use the reverse concept to collect sound waves at the focus. A parabolic microphone operates in this way.

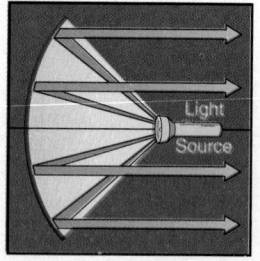

Conics other than the parabola can be defined in terms of the focus-directrix definition used in this lesson. A *conic section* is the set of all points P in a plane for which the distances of each point from a fixed point F, called the focus, and a fixed line called the directrix are in constant ratio. If Q is the foot of the perpendicular from P to the directrix, then $\dfrac{PF}{PQ} = e$, where e is the **eccentricity of a conic**. The value of e determines the particular conic section. Since PF is the distance from a point on the conic to the focus and PQ is the distance from P to the directrix, e must be 1 in the case of a parabola. For an ellipse, $0 < e < 1$, and for the hyperbola, $e > 1$.

Class Exercises

Determine the vertex, the axis of symmetry, the focus, the directrix, and the direction in which the parabola opens. Then graph.

1. $y = x^2 + 3$
2. $y = -x^2 - 1$
3. $(y + 2)^2 = 8(x - 3)$
4. $(x + 5)^2 = -4(y - 2)$
5. $y^2 - 2y - 8x + 25 = 0$
6. $2x^2 - 10x + 5y = 0$

Use a graphing utility to graph each parabola.

7. $y = x^2 - 2$
8. $y = -2x^2 + 3$
9. $(x + 3)^2 = 8(y - 1)$
10. $(y + 2)^2 = 12(x - 3)$

Determine an equation in standard form for each parabola described by the given geometry.

$10\left(x - \dfrac{3}{2}\right) = (y - 6)^2$

$(x + 2)^2 = -32(y + 3)$

11. Focus (4, 6), directrix $x = -1$
12. Vertex $(-2, -3)$, directrix $y = 5$

13. Vertex (1, 4), focus (1, -1) $20(y - 4) = -(x - 1)^2$

14. Determine a, b, and c so that the parabola $y = ax^2 + bx + c$ passes through (1, 0), (2, -3), and (-1, 12). $a = 1; b = -6; c = 5$

Practice Exercises

 Use appropriate technology.

Determine the vertex, the axis of symmetry, the focus, the directrix, and the direction in which each parabola opens. Then graph.

A 1. $y = x^2 - 5$
2. $y = x^2 + 2$
3. $y = -2x^2 - 3$
4. $x = y^2 - 3$
5. $x = -y^2 + 4$
6. $x = -y^2 - 1$
7. $y = -3x^2 - 2$
8. $(y + 1)^2 = -8(x + 5)$
9. $(y + 2)^2 = -4(x - 3)$
10. $(x - 7)^2 = 6(y + 2)$
11. $(x - 4)^2 = 2(y - 1)$
12. $(x - 2)^2 = 3(y + 1)$
13. $y^2 - 4y + 8x + 29 = 0$
14. $y^2 + 6y - 10x - 21 = 0$
15. $3x^2 + 12x - 5y + 7 = 0$
16. $5y^2 + 10y - 7x - 2 = 0$
17. $y = x^2 - 6x + 5$
18. $y = 4x^2 - 12x + 9$
19. $y = -2x^2 + 5x - 3$
20. $y = -3x^2 + 7x - 5$

R 21. If $\sin \alpha = -\dfrac{5}{6}$ and $\dfrac{3\pi}{2} < \alpha < 2\pi$, determine the values of the other five trigonometric functions of α.

11.4 The Parabola   **561**

Additional Answers, Class Exercises

7.
8.
9.
10.

Lesson Quiz

Determine the vertex, the axis of symmetry, the focus, and the directrix of the parabola with the given equation.

1. $x^2 = -36y$
vertex: $(0, 0)$; axis: $x = 0$; focus: $(0, -9)$; directrix: $y = 9$

2. $(y + 3)^2 = -12(x - 1)$
vertex: $(1, -3)$; axis: $y = -3$; focus: $(-2, -3)$; directrix: $x = 4$

3. $x^2 - 6x - y = 0$
vertex: $(3, -9)$; axis: $x = 3$; focus: $\left(3, -\frac{35}{4}\right)$; directrix: $y = -\frac{37}{4}$

Determine an equation in standard form for each parabola.

4. The focus is $(2, 1)$ and the vertex is $(2, -1)$. $(x - 2)^2 = 8(y + 1)$

5. The directrix is $x = -4$ and the vertex is $(2, 5)$.
$(y - 5)^2 = 24(x - 2)$

Additional Answers

22. The focus and directrix are getting farther from the vertex.
30. $(y + 10)^2 = 16(x - 2)$
31. $(y + 2)^2 = 24(x - 2)$
32. $(x - 4)^2 = 32(y - 2)$
33. $(x + 8)^2 = -12(y - 5)$
34. $(x + 3)^2 = -40(y + 5)$
35. $(x + 5)^2 = 8(y + 3)$
36. $(y - 1)^2 = 16(x - 11)$
37. $(y + 2)^2 = -24(x + 7)$
38. $(x + 7)^2 = -68(y + 8)$
39. $(x + 5)^2 = -24(y + 1)$
40. $(x - 7)^2 = -\frac{2}{3}\left(y - \frac{5}{6}\right)$
41. $(x - 8)^2 = \frac{9}{2}\left(y + \frac{7}{8}\right)$

22. Thinking Critically The latus rectum of a parabola is the line segment with endpoints on the parabola that passes through the focus and is perpendicular to the axis of symmetry. What is the relationship between the focus and directrix when the length of the latus rectum is increasing?

Ⓡ **23.** Determine the area of a triangle with sides of length 17 cm, 36 cm, and 39 cm. 305.6 cm²

Ⓡ **24.** Determine the period of $y = \sin 3\beta + \sin \beta$. 2π

Ⓑ **25. Writing in Mathematics** Explain why Apollonius described the ellipse, the parabola, the hyperbola on the basis of their eccentricities being "deficient" ($e < 1$), "perfect" ($e = 1$), or "in excess" ($e > 1$).

Use a graphing utility to graph each parabola.

26. $(x - 2)^2 = 4(y + 1)$ **27.** $(y - 1)^2 = 3(x - 5)$ **28.** $(y - 4)^2 = 3(x - 2)$

Ⓡ **29.** Solve $\sec^2 \alpha + 7 \sec \alpha + 10 = 0$ for all values of α, $0° \le \alpha < 360°$. 101.5°, 258.4°, 120°, 240°

Determine an equation in standard form for each parabola described by the given geometry.

30. Focus $(6, -10)$, directrix $x = -2$ **31.** Focus $(8, -2)$, directrix $x = -4$

32. Focus $(4, 10)$, directrix $y = -6$ **33.** Focus $(-8, 2)$, directrix $y = 8$

34. Vertex $(-3, -5)$, directrix $y = 5$ **35.** Vertex $(-5, -3)$, directrix $y = -5$

36. Vertex $(11, 1)$, directrix $x = 7$ **37.** Vertex $(-7, -2)$, directrix $x = -1$

38. Directrix $y = 9$, vertex $(-7, -8)$ **39.** Directrix $y = 5$, vertex $(-5, -1)$

40. Focus $\left(7, \frac{2}{3}\right)$, vertex $\left(7, \frac{5}{6}\right)$ **41.** Focus $\left(8, \frac{1}{4}\right)$, vertex $\left(8, -\frac{7}{8}\right)$

Ⓡ **42.** Solve $2x^2 + 5x + 9 = 0$. $\frac{-5 \pm i\sqrt{47}}{4}$

Determine a, b, and c so that the parabola $y = ax^2 + bx + c$ passes through the given points.

Ⓒ **43.** $(1, 1)$, $(-1, 5)$, and $\left(\frac{1}{2}, \frac{1}{2}\right)$ $a = 2$; $b = -2$; $c = 1$ **44.** $(0, 9)$, $(1, 1)$, and $(2, 1)$ $a = 4$; $b = -12$; $c = 9$

45. Writing in Mathematics Using the reflective properties of parabolas, how would you design a headlight for a car that has both low and high beams?

46. *Construction* The length of fencing available to enclose a rectangular lot is 200 ft. Express the enclosed area as a function of the width of the lot. When will the area be a maximum? $A = -w^2 + 100w$; $w = \ell = 50$ ft

47. *Engineering* The cable of a suspension bridge hangs in the form of a parabola when the load is uniformly distributed horizontally. If the distance between two towers is 500 ft with the points of support of the cable on the towers 60 ft above the roadway and the lowest point on the cable 25 ft above the roadway, determine the vertical distance to the cable from a point in the roadway 17 ft from the foot of the tower. 55.4 ft

Ⓡ **48.** *Physics* If a ball is thrown vertically upward from the ground with initial velocity 20 ft/s, its distance above the ground at the end of t seconds is given by the formula $y = 20t - 16t^2$. At what time(s) will the ball be 5 ft above the ground? 0.345 s and 0.905 s

562   Chapter 11 Conic Sections

Writing in Mathematics

25. Answers may vary. When e is equal to 1, then PF and PQ are in "perfect" proportion. When e is less than 1, PF is "deficient" with respect to PQ, and when e is greater than 1, PF is "in excess" of PQ.

45. Answers may vary. A "narrower" parabolic mirror in a headlight will result in a stronger beam being reflected.

49. *Engineering*   A bridge has a parabolic arch that is 50 ft high in the center and 150 ft wide at the bottom. Find the height of the arch 30 ft from the center.   42 ft

50. *Communications*   A parabolic communications antenna has a focus 6 ft from the vertex of the antenna. Find the width of the antenna 9 ft from the vertex. $12\sqrt{6}$ ft

51. Use the distance formula and the definition of a parabola to derive the equation of a parabola with focus $F(c, 0)$ and directrix $x = -c$.

52. Writing in Mathematics   Describe the connection between the definition of eccentricity presented in this lesson and the definition presented in the lessons on ellipses and hyperbolas.

Test Yourself

Determine the center and radius of each circle.   (3, −8); $\sqrt{17}$

1. $(x - 5)^2 + (y + 6)^2 = 121$ (5, −6); 11   **2.** $x^2 + y^2 - 6x + 16y + 56 = 0$ 11.1

Determine the equation of the circle that satisfies the given conditions.

3. Center at (6, 1) and radius 5 $(x - 6)^2 + (y - 1)^2 = 25$

4. Center at (4, −2) and passes through (6, 3) $(x - 4)^2 + (y + 2)^2 = 29$

Determine whether the graph of each equation represents a circle, a point circle, or the empty set. Graph any that are circles.

5. $x^2 + y^2 - 14x + 4y + 53 = 0$ **6.** $2x^2 + 2y^2 - 6x + 2y - 13 = 0$

Determine the endpoints of the major and minor axes, the foci, and the eccentricity of each ellipse. Then graph.

7. $\dfrac{x^2}{49} + \dfrac{y^2}{25} = 1$ **8.** $25x^2 + 16y^2 = 400$ 11.2

Determine an equation in standard form for each ellipse, and then graph.

9. $25x^2 + y^2 - 50x + 12y - 39 = 0$ $\dfrac{(x - 1)^2}{4} + \dfrac{(y + 6)^2}{100} = 1$

10. Foci at (2, 7) and (−6, 7) and major axis of length 10 $\dfrac{(x + 2)^2}{25} + \dfrac{(y - 7)^2}{9} = 1$

Determine the endpoints of the conjugate axis, the vertices, the foci, the asymptotes, and the eccentricity of each hyperbola. Then graph.

11. $\dfrac{y^2}{9} - \dfrac{x^2}{81} = 1$ **12.** $25x^2 - 16y^2 = 400$ 11.3

Determine an equation in standard form for each hyperbola, and then graph.

13. $4x^2 - y^2 + 16x + 6y + 23 = 0$

14. Center at (3, −1), vertex at (6, −1) and a focus at (8, −1)

Determine the vertex, the axis of symmetry, the focus, the directrix, and the direction in which each parabola opens. Then graph.

15. $y = x^2 - 5$ **16.** $(y + 1)^2 = 4(x - 3)$ 11.4

Determine an equation in standard form for each parabola.

17. Focus (2, 5), directrix $y = -1$ **18.** Vertex (−4, 3), directrix $x = 1$
   $(x - 2)^2 = 12(y - 2)$ $(y - 3)^2 = -20(x + 4)$

11.4 The Parabola   **563**

Writing in Mathematics
52. Answers may vary. Definitions of eccentricity in previous lessons focused more on the ratios of constants in the equations of the conics than on the geometry that was presented in this lesson.

Vocabulary
translation
translation equations

Ⓜ **Materials/Manipulatives**
transparencies
transparent bingo markers

Technology
computer
graphing utility

FOCUS

Invite discussion about other instances where it is easier to move the measuring instrument than the object being measured, and tie this to the concept of translation of axes.

INSTRUCTION

Ⓜ • Use a grid transparency and a bingo chip to demonstrate a translation of a point.
• Use an $x'y'$ transparency to name a point with reference to it and the xy coordinate system.
• For the function $y = x^2$, have students determine the equation representing it with reference to the $x'y'$ coordinate system.

11.5 Translation of Axes and the General Form of the Conic Equation

Objective: *To use the translation formulas to simplify the equations of conic sections*

Focus

When weighing or measuring something, you sometimes must bring the object to be measured to the measuring device and at other times you must bring the device to the object. For example, if a truck is to be weighed, it must go to a weighing station and be driven onto the scale. However, to measure the dimensions of a house, you must take the measuring tape to the house. Something like this happens with the graphs of equations in the coordinate system.

You have seen that a function can be transformed in such a way that its graph will be translated to another position on the coordinate system. In a similar way, the coordinate axes can be translated to show the graphs of functions and equations in different locations.

The graph of a function has a particular position on the coordinate system. If, however, the axes of a system are translated so that the origin of the new system is the point (h, k) of the old system, then every point P in the plane will have two representations. The ordered pair (x, y) represents a point P in the old coordinate system and the ordered pair (x', y') represents the point P in the new coordinate system.

The relationship between the old and new coordinate system results in the **translation equations:**

$$x = x' + h \quad \text{or} \quad x' = x - h$$
$$y = y' + k \quad \text{or} \quad y' = y - k$$

The ellipse with equation $\dfrac{(x-1)^2}{16} + \dfrac{(y-3)^2}{9} = 1$ has center $(1, 3)$ with respect to the xy-coordinate system. Since $(h, k) = (1, 3)$, then $x' = x - h = x - 1$ and $y' = y - k = y - 3$. Thus, the equation of the ellipse with respect to the $x'y'$-coordinate system and origin at $(x, y) = (1, 3)$ is $\dfrac{(x')^2}{16} + \dfrac{(y')^2}{9} = 1$.

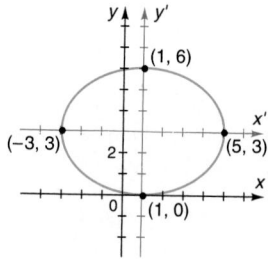

The point $(1, 6)$ on the ellipse with respect to the xy-coordinate system is $(0, 3)$ with respect to the $x'y'$-coordinate system since $x' = 1 - 1 = 0$ and $y' = 6 - 3 = 3$ when $x = 1$ and $y = 6$.

Example 1 Translate the axes so that the graph for the equation $(y - 2)^2 = 4(x + 5)$ has its vertex at the origin.

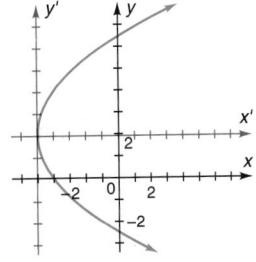

The graph of this equation is a parabola opening to the right; its vertex is at $(-5, 2)$.

Thus $(h, k) = (-5, 2)$ and $x' = x + 5$; $y' = y - 2$. The equation with respect to the $x'y'$-coordinate system is

$$(y')^2 = 4(x')$$

The translation equations may be used to find the equation of a curve with respect to a new pair of axes.

Example 2 Graph the parabola with equation $y = 6x - x^2$. Draw the x'- and y'-axes through the point $(3, 9)$ and parallel to the original axes. Find the equation of the parabola with respect to the x'- and y'-axes.

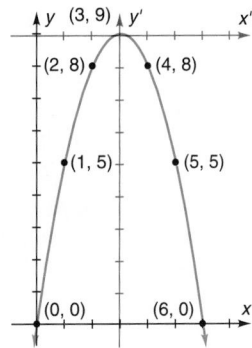

The graph is shown at the right. The point $(3, 9)$ is the vertex of the parabola. Draw the x'- and y'-axes through $(3, 9)$. Replace x with $x' + 3$ and y with $y' + 9$.

$$y' + 9 = 6(x' + 3) - (x' + 3)^2$$
$$y' + 9 = 6x' + 18 - (x')^2 - 6x' - 9$$
$$y' = -(x')^2$$

Note that the result of Example 2 could also have been achieved by completing the square on x and making the substitution of x' for $x - 3$ and y' for $y - 9$.

$$y = -x^2 + 6x$$
$$y = -(x^2 - 6x + 9) + 9$$
$$y - 9 = -(x - 3)^2$$
$$y' = -(x')^2$$

Example 3 Graph the equation $16x^2 - 9y^2 + 54y - 225 = 0$ by first translating the axes to put the center at the origin.

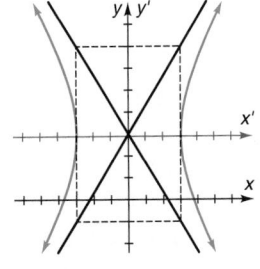

$$16x^2 - 9y^2 + 54y - 225 = 0$$
$$16x^2 - 9(y^2 - 6y + 9) = 225 - 81 \quad \text{\textit{Complete the square in y.}}$$
$$16x^2 - 9(y - 3)^2 = 144$$
$$\frac{x^2}{9} - \frac{(y - 3)^2}{16} = 1$$
$$\frac{(x')^2}{9} - \frac{(y')^2}{16} = 1 \quad \text{\textit{Let } x' = x \text{ and } y' = y - 3.}$$

GUIDED PRACTICE

For Example 1
Translate the axes so that the graph for the equation $(y + 4)^2 = 8(x - 7)$ has its vertex at the origin.
$(h, k) = (7, -4)$; $x' = x - 7$; $y' = y + 4$; $(y')^2 = 8(x)'$

For Example 2
Graph the parabola with the equation $y = 4x - x^2$. Draw the x'- and y'-axes through the point $(2, 4)$ parallel to the original axes and find the equation of the parabola with respect to the $x'y'$-axes. $y' = -(x')^2$

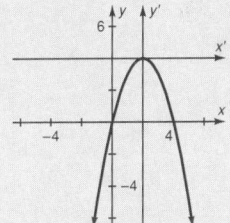

For Example 3
Graph the equation $4x^2 + y^2 + 8x - 12 = 0$ by first translating the axes.
$\frac{(x')^2}{4} + \frac{(y')^2}{16} = 1$

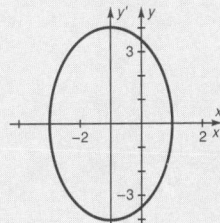

1. $x^2 + xy + 4y^2 = 1$ ellipse

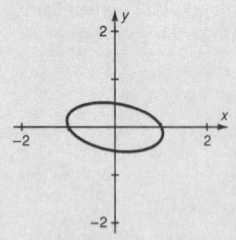

2. $9x^2 + 6xy + y^2 = 4$
parallel lines (degenerate parabola)

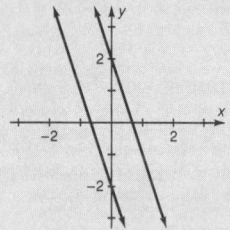

The new coordinate system has its origin at $(0, 3)$ of the old system. The vertices are $(3, 0)$ and $(-3, 0)$ in the $x'y'$-coordinate system. The endpoints of the conjugate axis are $(0, 4)$ and $(0, -4)$ in the $x'y'$-coordinate system. The equations of the asymptotes are $y' = \pm\frac{4}{3}x'$ and the foci are $(5, 0)$ and $(-5, 0)$ in the $x'y'$-coordinate system.

Note that the equations of the asymptotes in the xy-coordinate system are obtained by substituting $y - 3$ for y' and x for x'. The result is $y - 3 = \pm\frac{4}{3}x$.

The general form of the equation for a conic section is

$$Ax^2 + Bxy + Cy^2 + Dx + Ey + F = 0$$

The graph of an equation of this form is always a conic or a degenerate conic. The xy-term distinguishes this equation from the conics you have seen thus far. The presence of the xy-term means that the graph of the equation will have a major axis that is not parallel to the x- or y-axis. The following will help you determine the type of conic that a particular equation will give. You must, however, always be alert to the possibility of a degenerate form, that is, a point, a pair of lines, or no graph at all. The relationship between the discriminant, $B^2 - 4AC$, and conics is described below.

- If $B^2 - 4AC < 0$, then the conic is a circle or ellipse; a circle is obtained when $B = 0$ and $A = C$.
- If $B^2 - 4AC = 0$, then the conic is a parabola.
- If $B^2 - 4AC > 0$, then the conic is a hyperbola.

When you graph a conic using a graphing utility, it may happen that a viewing rectangle will show only one branch of a hyperbola, leading you to think that it is a parabola. Therefore, it is important to examine the discriminant.

Example 4   Identify each of the following conics and graph using a graphing utility.
   a. $x^2 + xy + y^2 = 1$ **b.** $x^2 + 2xy + y^2 - 2x + y - 3 = 0$
   c. $3x^2 - 3xy - y^2 + 2x + 2y - 10 = 0$

a. $B^2 - 4AC = 1 - 4 = -3$ $A = 1, B = 1, C = 1$

Since $B^2 - 4AC < 0$, the graph is an ellipse.
Express the equation in function-form.

$$y^2 + xy + x^2 - 1 = 0 \qquad \text{Solve the equation for } y.$$

$$y = \frac{-x \pm \sqrt{x^2 - 4(x^2 - 1)}}{2} \qquad \begin{array}{l}\text{Use the quadratic} \\ \text{formula with } a = 1, \\ b = x, \text{ and}\end{array}$$

$$y = \frac{-x \pm \sqrt{4 - 3x^2}}{2} \qquad c = x^2 - 1.$$

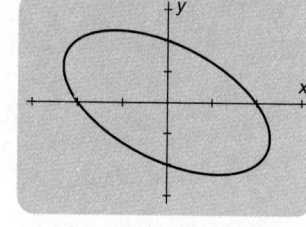

[−1.5, 1.5] by [−1.5, 1.5]
x scl: 0.5   y scl: 0.5

Enter the two functions $y = \dfrac{-x + \sqrt{4 - 3x^2}}{2}$ and $y = \dfrac{-x - \sqrt{4 - 3x^2}}{2}$.

The result is the entire graph. Good approximations for the vertices, center, and other appropriate points can be determined by using the trace function of the graphing utility.

b. $B^2 - 4AC = 0$

The graph is a parabola.

$$y^2 + (2x + 1)y + (x^2 - 2x - 3) = 0$$
$$y = \frac{-(2x + 1) \pm \sqrt{(2x + 1)^2 - 4(x^2 - 2x - 3)}}{4}$$

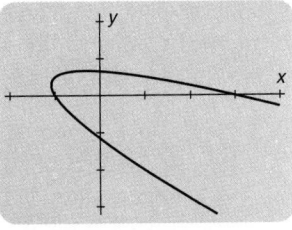

[-2, 4] by [-3, 2]

c. $B^2 - 4AC = 21$

The graph is a hyperbola.

$$-y^2 + (-3x + 2)y + (3x^2 + 2x - 10) = 0$$
$$y = \frac{-(-3x + 2) \pm \sqrt{[-(-3x + 2)]^2 + 4(3x^2 + 2x - 10)}}{-2}$$

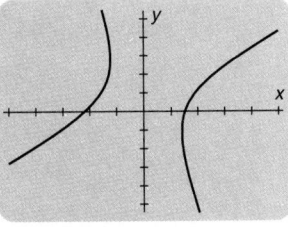

[-5, 5] by [-5, 5]

In Example 4, the quadratic formula was used to write the equations in function-form. The equations were then graphed. This method may be used with the general form of the conic equation.

$$Ax^2 + Bxy + Cy^2 + Dx + Ey + F = 0$$
$$Cy^2 + (Bx + E)y + (Ax^2 + Dx + F) = 0$$
$$y = \frac{-(Bx + E) \pm \sqrt{(Bx + E)^2 - 4C(Ax^2 + Dx + F)}}{2C}$$

Class Exercises

Find the translation equations given the equation and the new origin.

1. $x^2 + y^2 + 6x + 4y = 0$, $(1, 7)$
$(x')^2 + (y')^2 + 8x' + 18y' + 84 = 0$

2. $x^2 - 4x - 8y - 28 = 0$, $(-2, -5)$
$(x')^2 - 8x' - 8y' + 24 = 0$

Translate the axes so that the graph is symmetric about at least one coordinate axis (both axes, if possible). For a parabola, have the vertex positioned at the origin. Find the equation with respect to the new $x'y'$-coordinate system.

3. $3x^2 - y^2 + 18x - 2y + 14 = 0$

4. $8x^2 + 9y^2 + 48x - 18y + 9 = 0$

5. $x^2 - 6x - 8y + 33 = 0$

6. $x^2 + y^2 - 6x + 8y + 5 = 0$

Translate the axes to simplify and then graph the conic.

7. $3x^2 - y^2 + 18x + 6y = 9$

8. $x = 2y^2 + 10y + 3$

9. $9x^2 + 4y^2 - 18x + 24y + 9 = 0$

10. $x^2 + y^2 + 5x + 7y + 8 = 0$

Without graphing determine the conic corresponding to each equation.

11. $2x^2 + 3xy + y^2 + 6x - 2y + 1 = 0$
hyperbola

12. $3x^2 + xy + y^2 - 2y + 3 = 0$
ellipse

11.5 Translation of Axes and the General Form of the Conic Equation **567**

CLOSURE

Have students summarize the methods for translating axes in their math journals. Encourage them to write about the impact of technology on the study of translations.

INDEPENDENT PRACTICE

Assignment Guide
Basic: 1–20, 33–36
Average: 3–5, 10–12, 19–36
Enriched: 21–32, 34–45

Teacher's Resource Book
  Practice, page 74

R Review
Exercises 5, 33, 35, and 39 review the concepts of determining the equation of a line, finding the domain and range of functions, finding the equations of asymptotes, and using DeMoivre's theorem.

Additional Answers
Class Exercises

3. $\frac{(x')^2}{4} - \frac{(y')^2}{12} = 1$; $(-3, -1)$

4. $\frac{(x')^2}{9} + \frac{(y')^2}{8} = 1$; $(-3, 1)$

5. $(x')^2 = 8y'$; $(3, 3)$

6. $(x')^2 + (y')^2 = 20$; $(3, -4)$

7.

$\frac{(x + 3)^2}{9} - \frac{(y - 3)^2}{27} = 1$

8.

$\frac{1}{2}\left(x + \frac{19}{2}\right) = \left(y + \frac{5}{2}\right)^2$

9.

$\frac{(x - 1)^2}{4} + \frac{(y + 3)^2}{9} = 1$

10.

$\left(x + \frac{5}{2}\right)^2 + \left(y + \frac{7}{2}\right)^2 = \frac{21}{2}$

LESSON FOLLOW-UP

Lesson Quiz

1. Find the translation equations for the equation $x^2 - 6x + 10y + 29 = 0$, so that the new origin is at (5, 6).
$x = x' + 5$; $y = y' + 6$; $(x')^2 + 4x' + 10y' + 84 = 0$

Translate the axes to simplify. Then graph each conic.

2. $x^2 - 4y^2 - 10x - 8y + 5 = 0$
$\dfrac{(x')^2}{16} - \dfrac{(y')^2}{4} = 1$

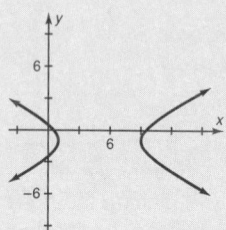

3. $25x^2 + 9y^2 + 50x - 36y - 164 = 0$
$\dfrac{(x')^2}{9} + \dfrac{(y')^2}{25} = 1$

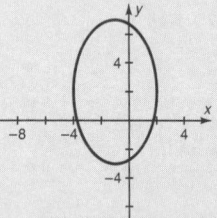

Without graphing, determine the conic corresponding to each equation.

4. $x^2 - xy - 4y^2 = 6$
hyperbola

5. $3x^2 - 10xy - 12 + 3y^2 = 0$
hyperbola

6. $5x^2 + 4xy + 2y^2 - 3x + 5y = 5$
ellipse

Additional Answers
Practice Exercises
1. $(x')^2 + (y')^2 + 10x' - 10y' + 34 = 0$
2. $(x')^2 + (y')^2 + 20x' + 10y' + 121 = 0$
3. $2(x')^2 - 3(y')^2 - 12x' - 30y' - 32 = 0$
4. $5(x')^2 - 4(y')^2 - 64y' - 216 = 0$

---

13. Use a graphing utility to graph the equation in Exercise 11.

14. **Thinking Critically** Did you have any difficulty recognizing the graph in Exercise 13? How did you resolve the difficulty?

Practice Exercises Use appropriate technology.

Find the translation equations given the equation and the new origin.

A 1. $x^2 + y^2 + 8x - 6y + 9 = 0$, (1, −2)
2. $x^2 + y^2 + 10x + 12y + 57 = 0$, (5, −1)
3. $2x^2 - 3y^2 + 4x - 12y + 15 = 0$, (−4, 3)
4. $5x^2 - 4y^2 + 10x - 16y + 29 = 0$, (−1, 6)

Ⓡ 5. Find the equation of the line with slope 7 that passes through (1, 8). $y = 7x + 1$

Identify the conic by using the discriminant and graph using a graphing utility.

6. $x^2 - xy + y^2 + x + y = 0$
7. $x^2 - xy - y^2 + x + y = 0$
8. $3x^2 + 4xy - 4y^2 - 12 = 0$
9. $x^2 - 4xy + 4y^2 - 4x + 8 = 0$
10. $9x^2 + 6xy + y^2 - 2y - 10 = 0$
11. $3x^2 - 10xy + y^2 + 22x - 26y + 43 = 0$
12. $11x^2 + 6xy + 3y^2 - 12x - 12y - 12 = 0$

Translate the axes so that the graph is symmetric about at least one coordinate axis (both axes, if possible). For a parabola, have the vertex positioned at the origin. Find the equation with respect to the new $x'y'$-coordinate system.

13. $4x^2 - 3y^2 - 8x + 12y - 8 = 0$
14. $4x^2 - 9y^2 - 32x + 54y - 17 = 0$
15. $4x^2 + y^2 - 24x + 4y + 36 = 0$
16. $25x^2 + 4y^2 + 50x - 12y - 66 = 0$
17. $y^2 - 8x - 8y + 32 = 0$
18. $x^2 + 2x - 4y - 3 = 0$
19. $2x^2 + 2y^2 - 4x - 8y - 1 = 0$
20. $3x^2 + 3y^2 - 12x + 4 = 0$

B 21. *Ballistics* A shell is fired so that its height above the ground as a function of time is given by the equation, $f(t) = -16t^2 + 96$. Draw the graph of the function. Translate the axes to eliminate the constant term. Write the function in terms of the new coordinate system. $f'(t) = -16(t')^2$; (0, 96)

22. *Ballistics* Interpret the meaning of negative time in the $x'y'$-coordinate system that you developed for Exercise 21.

Translate the axes so that the graph is symmetric about at least one coordinate axis (both axes, if possible). For a parabola, have the vertex positioned at the origin. Find the equation with respect to the new $x'y'$-coordinate system. Then graph the conic.

23. $x^2 + y^2 - 2x - 4y - 20 = 0$
24. $x^2 + y^2 - 4x - 2y - 20 = 0$
25. $x^2 - 4y^2 - 2x - 16y - 19 = 0$
26. $x^2 - 4y^2 - 16x - 4y - 19 = 0$
27. $3x^2 + 4y^2 + 12x + 8y + 8 = 0$
28. $9x^2 + y^2 + 36x - 8y + 43 = 0$
29. $y^2 - 4y - 8x + 20 = 0$
30. $2x^2 - 6x + 5y - 13 = 0$
31. $9x^2 + 16y^2 + 54x - 32y - 47 = 0$
32. $25y^2 - 9x^2 - 50y - 54x - 281 = 0$

Ⓡ 33. Determine the domain and range of the function: $f(x) = \begin{cases} \sqrt{x-1}, & \text{if } x \geq 1 \\ 1-x, & \text{if } x < 1 \end{cases}$

---

13. $4(x')^2 - 3(y')^2 = 0$; (1, 2)
14. $4(x')^2 - 9(y')^2 = 0$; (4, 3)
15. $\dfrac{(x')^2}{1} + \dfrac{(y')^2}{4} = 1$; (3, −2)
16. $\dfrac{(x')^2}{4} + \dfrac{(y')^2}{25} = 1$; $\left(-1, \dfrac{3}{2}\right)$
17. $(y')^2 = 8x'$; (2, 4)
18. $(x')^2 = 4y'$; (−1, −1)
19. $(x')^2 + (y')^2 = \dfrac{11}{2}$; (1, 2)
20. $(x')^2 + (y')^2 = \dfrac{8}{3}$; (2, 0)

34. Writing in Mathematics Describe the degenerate conic whose equation is $x^2 - 4y^2 - 4x + 8y = 0$.

Ⓡ **35.** Find the asymptote(s) for the graph of $y = \dfrac{x^2}{x^2 - 3}$. $x = \sqrt{3}, x = -\sqrt{3}, y = 1$

36. Writing in Mathematics Describe the degenerate conic whose equation is $4x^2 - y^2 - 16x + 2y + 15 = 0$.

C **37.** *Astronomy* Establish an appropriate coordinate system and find an equation for the path of the earth as it travels around the sun. The least distance of the earth to the sun is 91.1 million mi, and the greatest distance is 94.9 million mi.

38. *Business* The equation relating the price x of an article to its profit is $f(x) = -8x^2 + 50x + 120$. Graph the function. Translate the axes to show the function in a form that is appropriate for a manager who is not interested in any profit under $120.

Ⓡ **39.** Express $(1 - i)^{\frac{2}{3}}$ in rectangular form, where $i = \sqrt{-1}$. $\sqrt[3]{2}\left(\dfrac{\sqrt{3}}{2} - \dfrac{1}{2}i\right)$

40. A parabola has its vertex at the focus of a second parabola, and its focus at the vertex of the second parabola. Given that the equation of the second parabola is $y^2 = 8x$, find the equation of the first parabola. $y^2 = -8(x - 2)$

41. A parabola has its vertex at the focus of a second parabola, and its focus at the vertex of the second parabola. Given that the equation of the second parabola is $x^2 = 8y$, find the equation of the first parabola. $x^2 = -8(y - 2)$

42. The length of the legs and the hypotenuse of a right triangle are x, y, and $x + 4$, respectively. What type of curve is represented by the equation relating x and y? parabola

43. The length of the legs and the hypotenuse of a right triangle are x, y, and $x + 6$, respectively. What type of curve is represented by the equation relating x and y? parabola

44. Writing in Mathematics Describe a procedure by which the center of a hyperbola with equation of the form $Ax^2 + Bxy + Cy^2 + Dx + Ey + F = 0$, $B = 0$, may be determined.

45. Writing in Mathematics Describe a procedure by which the vertices of an ellipse with equation of the form $Ax^2 + Bxy + Cy^2 + Dx + Ey + F = 0$, $B = 0$, may be determined.

Challenge

1. A ray is swept around to complete one whole circle. Find
  a. The central angle of this circle in radians 2π
  b. The arc length if the radius is r $2\pi r$
  c. The circumference of the circle in terms of r and compare with the result in part (b) $2\pi r$; The arc length of one complete circle is the circumference.

2. Find the slope of the line connecting the two points of intersection of the following curves:
$$y = x^3 - 3x^2 + 3x - 1 \quad \text{and} \quad y = x^4 - 4x^3 + 6x^2 - 4x + 1 \quad \text{(1, 0) and (2, 1);}$$
$$m = 1$$

3. If $n = x - y^{x-y}$, find n when $x = 2$ and $y = -2$. -14

11.5 Translation of Axes and the General Form of the Conic Equation **569**

Writing in Mathematics

34. The graph is a degenerate hyperbola, which is the pair of intersecting lines $y' = \pm\dfrac{1}{2}x'$.

36. The graph is a degenerate hyperbola, which is the pair of intersecting lines $y' = \pm 2x'$.

44. The first step is to eliminate the xy-term by rotating the axes through an angle θ, and determining a new equation based on the new axes. Then find the new center.

45. Repeat the procedure in Exercise 44, and then find the vertices for the new equation.

Ⓜ **Materials/Manipulatives**
overhead projector
transparencies

Technology
computer
graphing utility
green globs software

FOCUS

Some students may be interested in finding out how NASA determines the orbit of satellites put into space.

INSTRUCTION

Ⓜ • Use the transparencies of conics to demonstrate the possible points of intersection of two conics by placing an ellipse and hyperbola on the overhead simultaneously for example.
• Draw graphs of systems whose intersection points are integers. Point out that algebraic methods are needed to determine points of intersection (solutions to the system) when the points of intersection are not integers.

Alternative Learning Styles
Some students are visual learners. The use of transparencies, like those described above, is encouraged.

11.6   Solving Quadratic Systems

Objective: To solve a quadratic system algebraically

Focus

In recent decades, dozens of scientific and communications satellites have been launched into elliptical orbits about the earth. Before a new satellite is launched, the equations of its orbit are checked in order to determine whether the orbit intersects that of an existing satellite. If not, then there is no danger that the two satellites will collide. Even if the paths do intersect, the probability of a collision is low. However, steps must then be taken to eliminate that remote possibility. This can be done by conducting a computer simulation of the movement of the satellites based upon the equations of their elliptical paths.

In this lesson you will study how to determine the points of intersection of the graphs of ellipses and other conic sections. This kind of analysis is closely related to the tracking of satellites.

You know that the graph associated with the equation of the form $Ax^2 + Bxy + Cy^2 + Dx + Ey + F = 0$ is always a conic or a degenerate conic. When two or more such equations are considered simultaneously, the resulting system is called a **quadratic system.** (Note that if A, B, and C are all zero, the graph is a straight line.) Recall that to solve a system over the real numbers means to find the coordinates of the points that the graphs have in common. If the particular kind of conics in a system are known, then it is possible to determine the maximum and minimum number of solutions that the system can have. For example, a system that consists of a hyperbola and a circle may have 0, 1, 2, 3, or 4 points of intersection.

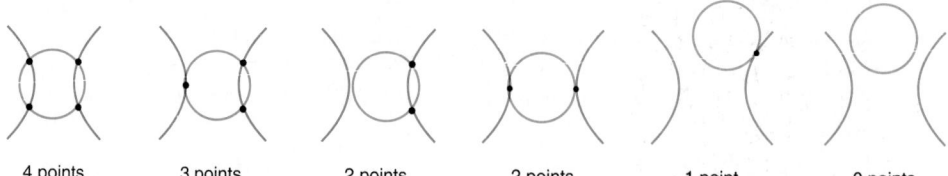

| 4 points | 3 points | 2 points | 2 points | 1 point | 0 points |

570   Chapter 11 Conic Sections

The maximum number of points of intersection is four, and the minimum number is zero. A graphing utility can be used to graph the systems and determine approximate answers. For many systems, however, algebraic solutions are faster.

Example 1 Identify and solve. Then graph the system of equations. $\begin{cases} x^2 + y^2 = 34 \\ x - y = 2 \end{cases}$

The system consists of the equation of a circle and the equation of a line. The maximum number of solutions is two.

$$x - y = 2$$
$$x = 2 + y \qquad \text{\textit{Solve for x.}}$$

$$x^2 + y^2 = 34$$
$$(2 + y)^2 + y^2 = 34 \qquad \text{\textit{Substitute x = 2 + y.}}$$
$$4 + 4y + y^2 + y^2 = 34$$
$$2y^2 + 4y - 30 = 0$$
$$2(y^2 + 2y - 15) = 0$$
$$2(y + 5)(y - 3) = 0$$
$$y + 5 = 0 \quad \text{or} \quad y - 3 = 0$$
$$y = -5 \quad \text{or} \qquad y = 3$$

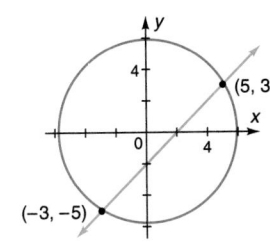

$$x = 2 + y \qquad x = 2 + y$$
$$x = 2 - 5 \qquad x = 2 + 3$$
$$x = -3 \qquad x = 5$$

The solutions are $(-3, -5)$ and $(5, 3)$.

When both equations of a system are quadratic, the addition method may be used.

Example 2 Identify each conic. Then solve and graph the system of equations.
$$\begin{cases} 2x^2 - 3y^2 = 6 \\ x^2 + 2y^2 = 17 \end{cases}$$

The system contains the equations of a hyperbola and an ellipse. The maximum number of solutions is four.

$$\begin{cases} 2x^2 - 3y^2 = 6 \\ x^2 + 2y^2 = 17 \end{cases}$$

$$\begin{array}{rcl} 2x^2 - 3y^2 &=& 6 \\ -2x^2 - 4y^2 &=& -34 \\ \hline -7y^2 &=& -28 \end{array} \qquad \text{\textit{Multiply the second equation by } -2 \text{ \textit{and}}}$$
$$\text{\textit{add the result to the first equation.}}$$
$$y^2 = 4$$
$$y^2 - 4 = 0$$
$$(y + 2)(y - 2) = 0$$
$$y + 2 = 0 \quad \text{or} \quad y - 2 = 0$$
$$y = -2 \quad \text{or} \qquad y = 2$$

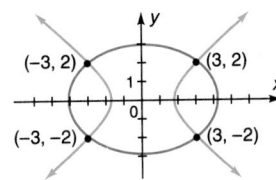

11.6 Solving Quadratic Systems   **571**

For Example 1

Identify and solve the system.

$$\begin{cases} x^2 - y^2 = 8 \\ x + y = 4 \end{cases}$$

Then graph the system.
hyperbola and line; (3, 1)

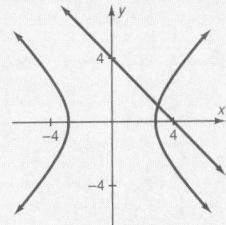

For Example 2

Identify each conic. Then solve and graph the system of equations.

$$\begin{cases} x^2 - 2y^2 = 8 \\ x^2 + 2y^2 = 10 \end{cases}$$

hyperbola and ellipse;

$$\left(3, \frac{\sqrt{2}}{2}\right), \left(3, -\frac{\sqrt{2}}{2}\right), \left(-3, \frac{\sqrt{2}}{2}\right), \left(-3, -\frac{\sqrt{2}}{2}\right)$$

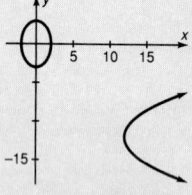
For $y = -2$:

$$x^2 + 2y^2 = 17$$
$$x^2 + 2(-2)^2 = 17$$
$$x^2 + 8 = 17$$
$$x^2 = 9$$
$$x^2 - 9 = 0$$
$$(x - 3)(x + 3) = 0$$
$$x - 3 = 0 \quad \text{or} \quad x + 3 = 0$$
$$x = 3 \quad \text{or} \quad x = -3$$

For $y = 2$:

$$x^2 + 2y^2 = 17$$
$$x^2 + 2(2)^2 = 17$$
$$x^2 + 8 = 17$$
$$x^2 = 9$$
$$x^2 - 9 = 0$$
$$(x - 3)(x + 3) = 0$$
$$x - 3 = 0 \quad \text{or} \quad x + 3 = 0$$
$$x = 3 \quad \text{or} \quad x = -3$$

The solutions are $(3, -2)$, $(-3, -2)$, $(3, 2)$, and $(-3, 2)$.

Sometimes the algebraic approach to solving a system yields imaginary solutions.

Example 3   Identify each conic. Then solve and graph the system: $\begin{cases} 2x^2 - 5y^2 + 8 = 0 \\ x^2 - 7y^2 + 4 = 0 \end{cases}$

The graph of each equation is a hyperbola. The maximum number of solutions is four.

$$\begin{cases} 2x^2 - 5y^2 + 8 = 0 \\ x^2 - 7y^2 + 4 = 0 \end{cases}$$

$$\begin{array}{r} 2x^2 - 5y^2 + 8 = 0 \\ -2x^2 + 14y^2 - 8 = 0 \\ \hline 9y^2 = 0 \\ y = 0 \end{array}$$

Multiply the second equation by -2 and add it to the first equation.

$$2x^2 - 5y^2 + 8 = 0$$
$$2x^2 - 5(0)^2 + 8 = 0$$
$$2x^2 - 0 + 8 = 0$$
$$2x^2 = -8$$
$$x^2 = -4$$
$$x = \pm 2i$$

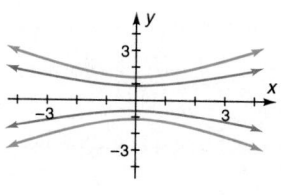

The solution is the empty set. Since there are no real solutions, the graphs do not intersect.

The solution of Example 3 is the kind of solution that is usually desired when the equations represent two satellite orbits. An imaginary solution simply means that the two satellites will not meet in space.

Example 4   Use a graphing utility to solve the system of equations: $\begin{cases} 5x^2 + 12y^2 = 128 \\ 3x^2 + 4xy - 4y^2 = 0 \end{cases}$

$$\begin{cases} 12y^2 + 5x^2 - 128 = 0 \\ -4y^2 + 4xy + 3x^2 = 0 \end{cases}$$

Rewrite the equations in a form suitable for using the quadratic formula.

$$y = \frac{\pm\sqrt{-48(5x^2 - 128)}}{24}$$

$a = 12, b = 0, c = 5x^2 - 128$.

$$y = \frac{-4x \pm \sqrt{16x^2 + 48x^2}}{-8}$$

$a = -4, b = 4x, c = 3x^2$

572   Chapter 11 Conic Sections

The graph of the first equation is an ellipse. The second is a pair of lines. Using the trace feature, find the points of intersection at (2, 3), (−2, −3), (−4, 2), and (4, −2). By direct substitution, it may be verified that these coordinates are solutions to each equation.

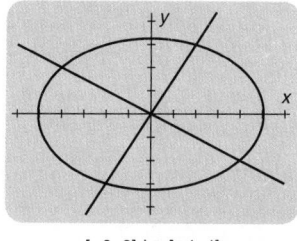

[−6, 6] by [−4, 4]

In Example 4, $3x^2 + 4xy − 4y^2 = 0$ was found to be an equation of two intersecting lines. *What degenerate curve does this represent?*

It is easy to make errors when entering a complicated function in a graphing utility. When in doubt about how expressions are grouped, use parentheses (for example, about the entire expression under a radical sign). Always check solutions in the original equations.

Example 5   Identify each conic and solve the system using a graphing utility. Give answers to the nearest hundredth. $\begin{cases} x^2 + y^2 = 16 \\ xy = 3 \end{cases}$

The system consists of the equation of a circle and a hyperbola. The maximum number of solutions is four. Express each equation of the system in function-form.

$$y^2 = 16 − x^2$$
$$y = \sqrt{16 − x^2} \quad \text{and} \quad y = −\sqrt{16 − x^2}$$

Enter these two functions to obtain the graph of the circle. Next, enter the function $y = \dfrac{3}{x}$ to obtain the graph of the hyperbola. Then use the trace feature to approximate the solutions. The solutions are (0.76, 3.9), (3.9, 0.76), (−0.76, −3.9), and (−3.9, −0.76).

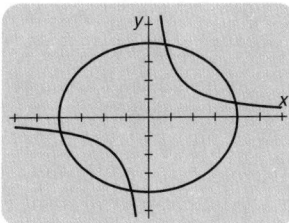

[−6, 6] by [−6, 6]

Class Exercises
Identify, solve, and graph the system of equations.

1. $\begin{cases} x^2 + y^2 = 25 \\ 2x + y = 10 \end{cases}$ 2. $\begin{cases} x^2 + 3y^2 = 12 \\ x + 3y = 6 \end{cases}$ 3. $\begin{cases} x^2 − y^2 = 7 \\ x^2 + y^2 = 25 \end{cases}$

4. $\begin{cases} x^2 − y^2 = 5 \\ 2x^2 + y^2 = 22 \end{cases}$ 5. $\begin{cases} 3x^2 − 2y^2 = 10 \\ x^2 + 3y^2 = 7 \end{cases}$ 6. $\begin{cases} x^2 − y^2 + 7 = 0 \\ 2x^2 + 3y^2 = 66 \end{cases}$

7. $\begin{cases} x^2 + y^2 = 25 \\ 12x^2 + 7xy − 12y^2 = 0 \end{cases}$ 8. $\begin{cases} x^2 + y^2 = 25 \\ 12x^2 − 25xy + 12y^2 = 0 \end{cases}$

9. Determine two positive numbers whose difference is 2 and whose product is 143.

10. The area of a right triangle is 60 ft² and its hypotenuse is 17 ft long. Find the length of the legs.

         8 ft, 15 ft

11.6 Solving Quadratic Systems   **573**

Thinking Critically
An equation of two intersecting lines represents a degenerate hyperbola.

Lesson Quiz

Identify and solve each system.

1. $\begin{cases} x^2 + y^2 = 36 \\ x + y = 10 \end{cases}$

circle and line; $\varnothing$

2. $\begin{cases} x^2 + y^2 = 29 \\ x^2 - y + 1 = 0 \end{cases}$

circle and parabola; $(2, 5), (-2, 5)$

3. $\begin{cases} 5x^2 - y^2 = 1 \\ x^2 + 6y^2 = 25 \end{cases}$

hyperbola and ellipse; $(1, 2), (1, -2),$ $(-1, 2), (-1, -2)$

Additional Answers

1. circle, line; $(3, 4), (4, 3)$
2. hyperbola, line; $\left(\frac{9}{2}, \frac{5}{2}\right)$
3. line, parabola; $(1 + \sqrt{2}, \sqrt{2}),$ $(1 - \sqrt{2}, -\sqrt{2})$
4. parabola, line; $\left(\frac{-1 + \sqrt{11}}{2}, -2 + \sqrt{11}\right),$ $\left(\frac{-1 - \sqrt{11}}{2}, -2 - \sqrt{11}\right)$
5. hyperbola, line; $\left(\frac{17}{5}, \frac{8}{5}\right)$
6. circle, line; $(6, 0), (-6, 0)$
7. circle, parabola; $(2\sqrt{2}, 0),$ $(-2\sqrt{2}, 0)$
8. hyperbola, parabola; $(2\sqrt{3}, 0),$ $(-2\sqrt{3}, 0), (\sqrt{61}, 7), (-\sqrt{61}, 7)$
9. circle, hyperbola; $(3, 1), (3, -1),$ $(-3, 1), (-3, -1)$
10. intersecting lines, point; $(0, 0)$
11. circle, circle; no solution
12. circle, hyperbola; $(\sqrt{11}, \sqrt{5}),$ $(\sqrt{11}, -\sqrt{5}), (-\sqrt{11}, \sqrt{5}),$ $(-\sqrt{11}, -\sqrt{5})$
13. parabola, parabola; $(0, 3), (3, 0)$
14. parabola, parabola; $(-\sqrt{2}, 5 + 4\sqrt{2}), (\sqrt{2}, 5 - 4\sqrt{2})$
24. Answers may vary. Example: $x^2 + y^2 = 1; x^2 + y^2 = 2; x^2 - y^2 = 1$
25. Answers may vary. Example: $xy = 1; xy = -1$

---

11. **Thinking Critically** Given that a system consists of two nondegenerate conics and that the number of real solutions is three, what are the possible conics in the system and how are they related graphically?

Practice Exercises

 Use appropriate technology.

Identify, solve, and graph the system of equations.

A 1. $\begin{cases} x^2 + y^2 = 25 \\ x + y = 7 \end{cases}$ 2. $\begin{cases} x^2 - y^2 = 14 \\ x + y = 7 \end{cases}$ 3. $\begin{cases} x - y = 1 \\ x^2 = 2y + 3 \end{cases}$ 4. $\begin{cases} 2x^2 + y = 4 \\ 2x - y = 1 \end{cases}$

5. $\begin{cases} x^2 - y^2 = 9 \\ x + y = 5 \end{cases}$ 6. $\begin{cases} x^2 + y^2 = 36 \\ x - y + 6 = 0 \end{cases}$ 7. $\begin{cases} x^2 + y^2 = 8 \\ x^2 + 5y = 8 \end{cases}$ 8. $\begin{cases} x^2 - y^2 = 12 \\ x^2 - 7y = 12 \end{cases}$

9. $\begin{cases} x^2 + y^2 = 10 \\ 2x^2 - y^2 = 17 \end{cases}$ 10. $\begin{cases} 5x^2 - y^2 = 0 \\ 3x^2 + 4y^2 = 0 \end{cases}$ 11. $\begin{cases} 5x^2 + 5y^2 = 20 \\ x^2 + y^2 = 9 \end{cases}$ 12. $\begin{cases} x^2 + y^2 = 16 \\ 4x^2 - 4y^2 = 24 \end{cases}$

13. $\begin{cases} x^2 - y - 4x + 3 = 0 \\ x^2 + y - 2x - 3 = 0 \end{cases}$ 14. $\begin{cases} 2x^2 - y - 4x + 1 = 0 \\ x^2 - y - 4x + 3 = 0 \end{cases}$

15. Determine two positive numbers whose sum is 18 and the sum of whose squares is 194. 5, 13

16. Determine two positive numbers whose sum is 17 and whose product is 72. 8, 9

Ⓡ 17. Solve $\sin 3x = 0.5$ over the interval $2\pi < x < 4\pi$. $\frac{37\pi}{18}, \frac{41\pi}{18}, \frac{49\pi}{18}, \frac{53\pi}{18}, \frac{61\pi}{18}, \frac{65\pi}{18}$

18. A rectangular lot has a perimeter of 60 ft and an area of 200 ft². What are its dimensions? 10 ft × 20 ft

Ⓡ 19. Solve $\cos 3x = 0.5$ over the interval $-2\pi < x < 0$. $-\frac{\pi}{9}, -\frac{5\pi}{9}, -\frac{11\pi}{9}, -\frac{17\pi}{9}, -\frac{7\pi}{9}, -\frac{13\pi}{9}$

20. A rectangular lot has a perimeter of 70 m and an area of 250 m². What are its dimensions? 25 m × 10 m

B 21. The hypotenuse of a right triangle is 19.5 ft long. If each leg were increased by 4.5 ft, the hypotenuse would be increased by 6 ft. Find the length of the legs of the original triangle. 7.5 ft, 18 ft

22. The diagonal of a rectangle is 37 in. long. If the length of the rectangle were decreased by 5 in. and its width increased by 4 in., the diagonal would be decreased by 3 in. Find the length and width of the original rectangle. $\ell = 35$ in.; $w = 12$ in.

Ⓡ 23. Determine a value for K so that -2 is a solution of the equation $3x^3 + 5x^2 + Kx - 10 = 0$. -7

24. **Thinking Critically** Write the equations for two concentric circles and a hyperbola such that one circle intersects the hyperbola in exactly two points and the other circle intersects the hyperbola in exactly four points.

25. **Thinking Critically** Find the equations of two nonintersecting hyperbolas with axes that are not parallel to the x- or y-axis.

26. **Writing in Mathematics** Describe how two distinct nondegenerate conics with the same center may intersect in exactly two points.

Ⓡ 27. Determine a value for K so that 3 is a solution of the equation $2x^3 + 3Kx^2 - 5x + 15 = 0$. -2

Writing in Mathematics
26. The two conics may be tangent at the vertices or at the endpoints of the conjugate axis.

28. *Landscaping* A rectangular flower plot has an area of 504 ft² and is surrounded by a path 3 ft wide. The area of the path is 312 ft². Find the length and width of the flower plot. 18 ft × 28 ft

29. *Landscaping* A rectangular garden has an area of 648 ft². A path 3 ft wide along one side and one end reduces the area of the garden by 153 ft². Find the length and width of the garden. 36 ft × 18 ft

30. *Packaging* A rectangular piece of cardboard has an area of 216 in.² An open box containing 224 in.³ can be made from the cardboard by cutting a 2-in. square from each corner and turning up the ends and sides. What are the dimensions of the piece of cardboard? 18 in. × 12 in.

Ⓡ 31. Determine the values of c and d in the equation $3x^3 - 5x^2 + cx + d = 0$ given that 3 and -1 are two solutions. $c = -11; d = -3$

32. *Packaging* A rectangular piece of cardboard has an area of 120 in.² An open box containing 96 in.³ can be made from the cardboard by cutting a 2-in. square from each corner and turning up the ends and sides. What are the dimensions of the piece of cardboard? 12 in. × 10 in.

Identify and solve the system of equations. You may use a graphing utility to find approximate solutions. Then check the original equations.

33. $\begin{cases} 3x^2 - 5y^2 - 7 = 0 \\ 2x^2 - 7xy + 6y^2 = 0 \end{cases}$

34. $\begin{cases} 2x^2 + xy + y^2 = 8 \\ y^2 + 3xy - 10 = 0 \end{cases}$

35. $\begin{cases} 2x^2 - 7xy + 2y^2 + 1 = 0 \\ x^2 - 3xy + y^2 - 1 = 0 \end{cases}$

36. $\begin{cases} 3x^2 + 4xy + 5y^2 - 36 = 0 \\ x^2 + xy + y^2 - 9 = 0 \end{cases}$

Graph each system of inequalities.

C 37. $\begin{cases} 2x^2 - 3y^2 > 6 \\ x^2 + 2y^2 < 17 \end{cases}$

38. $\begin{cases} 8x^2 - y^2 + 9 > 0 \\ 3x^2 + y^2 < 31 \end{cases}$

39. $\begin{cases} 16x^2 - 9y^2 > 144 \\ x^2 + y^2 < 36 \end{cases}$

40. $\begin{cases} x^2 + y^2 < 25 \\ 4x^2 + 25y^2 > 100 \end{cases}$

41. $\begin{cases} x^2 + 2xy + y^2 < 1 \\ xy + 2y^2 > 2 \end{cases}$

42. $\begin{cases} 2x^2 + xy + y^2 > 8 \\ 3xy + y^2 < 10 \end{cases}$

43. *Traffic Control* A large circular traffic sign of radius 6.5 ft is to have a rectangular region of area 60 ft² inscribed in the circle on which to letter a message. What are the dimensions of the rectangle? 12 ft × 5 ft

44. *Gardening* A gardener has a triangular region in the corner of a rectangular lot. The hypotenuse of the triangle 13 ft long. If each side is extended by 3 ft, the length of the hypotenuse increases by 4 ft. By how much will the garden area increase if the extensions are made? 30 ft²

45. *Surveying* A trapezoidal lot has bases of 100 ft and 160 ft and two equal sides of 50 ft. A line is to be drawn parallel to the bases that divides the area of the lot into two equal parts. Find the distance of this line from the shorter base, to the nearest foot. 26 ft

Review

1. In triangle *RST*, $\angle S = 58°$, $s = 20$, and $\angle R = 42°$. Find r. 16
2. In triangle *DEF*, $e = 18$, $f = 10$, and $d = 15$. Find $\angle F$. 34°

40.

PH/ANS 11.6.26

41.
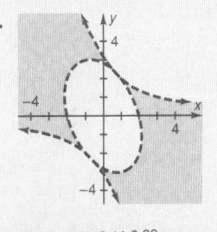
PH/ANS 11.6.27

42.
PH/ANS 11.6.28

Vocabulary
normal
tangent

Technology
computer
graphing utility

FOCUS

If you have access to a reflecting telescope, use it to give students a "hands on" introduction to the material in the Focus. Ask students to speculate as to why images are inverted or distorted by some telescopes.

INSTRUCTION

- Finding the slope of a tangent line is an essential skill for students intending to study calculus. You can use this information as a motivator for the lesson.
- Refer to the opener for this chapter on pages 532 to 533 for a discussion of other uses of the reflective properties of the conic sections.

11.7 | Tangents and Normals to Conic Sections

Objectives: To determine the slopes of tangents to conic sections and of normals to conic sections
To determine equations of tangents to conic sections and of normals to conic sections

Focus

The reflective properties of the parabola, ellipse, and hyperbola have been used in the design of telescopes since the seventeenth century. In 1672, astronomer Guillaume Cassegrain designed the first telescope to use a parabolic mirror and a hyperbolic mirror having a common focus. Today, some telescopes are built that use parabolic, elliptical, and hyperbolical mirrors, as illustrated in the diagram.

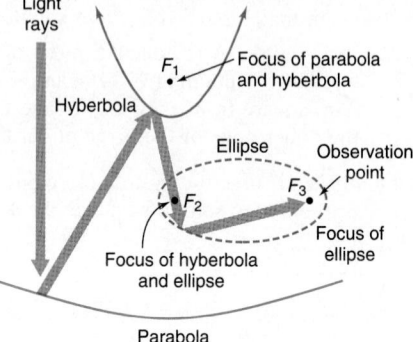

In these telescopes, incoming light is reflected off the parabolic mirror toward F_1, a common focus of the parabola and the hyperbola. The light is then reflected off the hyperbolic mirror toward the second focus of the hyperbola, F_2. After passing through F_2, which is also a focus of the ellipse, the light is reflected off the ellipse toward F_3, the second focus of the ellipse.

The tangent and normal lines to a conic section play an important role in the field of optics. This is evidenced especially in the construction of telescopes.

Modeling

What effect does a reflecting surface have on a light ray?

When a light source is positioned at a focus of an elliptical mirror or a focus of a hyperbolic mirror, the light rays from that source are all reflected in such a way that they pass through the second focus of the ellipse or hyperbola.

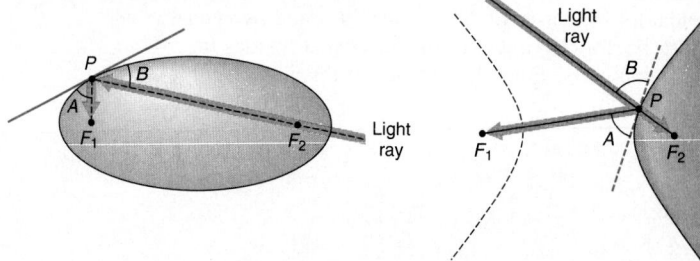

In each diagram above, the incident ray and the reflected ray make equal angles with the **tangent** drawn at the point of contact P. Equal angles are also formed with the line perpendicular to the tangent at P. This perpendicular line is called the **normal** to the conic at P.

Example 1 *Technology* A telescope is to be designed using the mirror configuration presented in the Focus. In order to build the telescope, equations are needed to represent the mirrors.

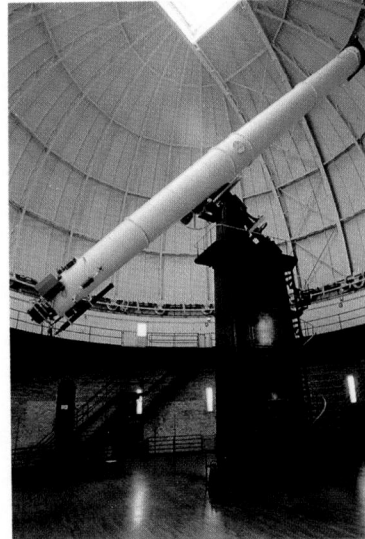

a. The hyperbolic mirror in the telescope can be modeled using a section of the hyperbola $\frac{(y-2)^2}{4} - \frac{x^2}{5} = 1$. Locate and plot the coordinates of the foci F_1 and F_2 for this hyperbola and graph a section of the hyperbolic mirror.

b. The parabolic mirror for the telescope has its vertex at $(0, -2)$ and focus at F_1. Determine the equation of the parabolic mirror and graph a section of the mirror.

a. The center of the hyperbola is at $(0, 2)$. Since $a^2 = 4$ and $b^2 = 5$, $c^2 = 4 + 5 = 9$ and $c = 3$. The coordinates of F_1 are $(0, 5)$, and F_2 is located at $(0, -1)$.

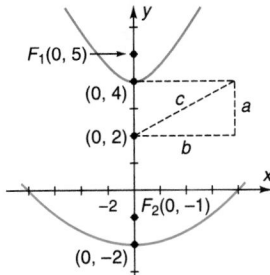

b. The equation of the parabolic mirror with vertex at $(0, -2)$ is

$$(x - 0)^2 = 4c(y + 2)$$

The distance from the focus $(0, 5)$ to the vertex is 7; thus $c = 7$. The equation of the parabolic mirror is $x^2 = 28y + 56$.

It is sometimes useful to know an equation of the tangent line to a curve and of the normal line to a curve. This is true of conics in particular.

The tangent to a circle intersects the circle in exactly one point and is perpendicular to the radius at the point of tangency. Recall that perpendicular lines have negative reciprocal slopes. The slope of $\overline{OP} = \frac{y_0}{x_0}$, and the slope of the tangent line is $-\frac{x_0}{y_0}$, where $x_0 \neq 0$ and $y_0 \neq 0$.

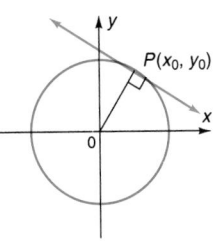

GUIDED PRACTICE

Modeling
For another example of how a series of mirrors is used to reflect an image, students can research the inner workings of a navigational device called a sextant.

For Example 1
1. A section of the hyperbola $\frac{(y-3)^2}{9} - \frac{x^2}{7} = 1$ models a hyperbolic mirror in a telescope. Plot the coordinates of the foci and graph the section.
foci: $(0, -1)$ and $(0, 7)$

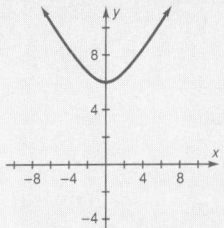

2. Determine the equation of a parabolic mirror that has vertex at $(0, -8)$ and focus at $(0, -7)$.
$x^2 = 4(y + 8)$

For Example 2
Determine an equation of the tangent line and of the normal line to each circle at the given point.

1. $x^2 + y^2 = 74;\ (7, -5)$
   tangent: $7x - 5y = 74$
   normal: $5x + 7y = 0$
2. $x^2 + y^2 = 5;\ (-\sqrt{3}, \sqrt{2})$
   tangent: $-\sqrt{3}x + \sqrt{2}y = 5$
   normal: $\sqrt{2}x + \sqrt{3}y = 0$

An equation of the line tangent to the circle at (x_0, y_0) is derived as follows.

$$y - y_0 = -\frac{x_0}{y_0}(x - x_0) \qquad \textit{Point-slope form of equation of a line}$$

$$yy_0 - y_0^2 = -xx_0 + x_0^2$$

$$xx_0 + yy_0 = x_0^2 + y_0^2$$

$$xx_0 + yy_0 = r^2 \qquad \textit{x}_0^2 + y_0^2 = r^2$$

Since the slope of the normal is the negative reciprocal of the slope of the tangent line, an equation of the normal line is:

$$y - y_0 = \frac{y_0}{x_0}(x - x_0)$$

$$yx_0 - x_0y_0 = xy_0 - x_0y_0$$

$$xy_0 - yx_0 = 0$$

> An equation of the tangent line to a circle with equation $x^2 + y^2 = r^2$ at $P(x_0, y_0)$ on the circle is
>
> $$xx_0 + yy_0 = r^2$$
>
> An equation of the normal line to a circle with equation $x^2 + y^2 = r^2$ at $P(x_0, y_0)$ on the circle is
>
> $$xy_0 - yx_0 = 0$$

It is clear from the second equation above that a normal to a circle with center at the origin passes through the origin.

Example 2 Find an equation of the tangent line and of the normal line to the circle with equation $x^2 + y^2 = 25$ at $P(-3, 4)$.

$$xx_0 + yy_0 = r^2 \qquad \textit{Equation of tangent line}$$
$$x(-3) + y(4) = 25$$
$$-3x + 4y = 25$$

$$xy_0 - yx_0 = 0 \qquad \textit{Equation of normal line}$$
$$x(4) - y(-3) = 0$$
$$4x + 3y = 0$$

In Example 2, note that the slope of the tangent line is $\frac{3}{4}$ and the slope of the normal line is $-\frac{4}{3}$.

Formulas for the slopes of tangent lines for conic sections centered at the origin are given on the next page. These formulas can be used to derive formulas for the slope of the normal line and for the equations of tangent and normal lines.

578   Chapter 11 Conic Sections

Conic Section	Equation	Slope of Tangent at $P(x_0, y_0)$, $y_0 \neq 0$
Circle	$x^2 + y^2 = r^2$	$-\dfrac{x_0}{y_0}$
Ellipse	$\dfrac{x^2}{a^2} + \dfrac{y^2}{b^2} = 1,\ a > b$	$-\dfrac{b^2 x_0}{a^2 y_0}$
	$\dfrac{y^2}{a^2} + \dfrac{x^2}{b^2} = 1,\ a > b$	$-\dfrac{a^2 x_0}{b^2 y_0}$
Hyperbola	$\dfrac{x^2}{a^2} - \dfrac{y^2}{b^2} = 1$	$\dfrac{b^2 x_0}{a^2 y_0}$
	$\dfrac{y^2}{a^2} - \dfrac{x^2}{b^2} = 1$	$-\dfrac{a^2 x_0}{b^2 y_0}$
Parabola	$y^2 = 4cx$	$\dfrac{2c}{y_0}$
	$x^2 = 4cy$	$\dfrac{x_0}{2c}$

For Example 3
Determine the equation of the tangent line and of the normal line to each conic at the given point.

1. $\dfrac{x^2}{4} + \dfrac{y^2}{3} = 1;\ \left(1, -\dfrac{3}{2}\right)$

tangent: $x - 2y = 4$
normal: $4x + 2y = 1$

2. $\dfrac{x^2}{7} - \dfrac{y^2}{7} = 1;\ (-4, -3)$

tangent: $4x - 3y = -7$
normal: $3x + 4y = -24$

You can use the slope of the tangent and the point-slope form of a linear equation to determine equations of the tangent line and the normal line at any point on a conic.

Example 3 Find the equation of the tangent line and normal line to the hyperbola with equation $\dfrac{x^2}{9} - \dfrac{y^2}{16} = 1$ at $P\left(\dfrac{15}{4}, 3\right)$.

The slope of the tangent is found using $\dfrac{b^2 x_0}{a^2 y_0} = \dfrac{16 \times \frac{15}{4}}{9 \times 3} = \dfrac{60}{27} = \dfrac{20}{9}$.

$y - 3 = \dfrac{20}{9}\left(x - \dfrac{15}{4}\right)$ *Point-slope form*

$9(y - 3) = 20\left(x - \dfrac{15}{4}\right)$

$9y - 27 = 20x - 75$
$20x - 9y = 48$

The slope of the normal is the negative reciprocal of the slope of the tangent: $-\dfrac{9}{20}$

$y - 3 = -\dfrac{9}{20}\left(x - \dfrac{15}{4}\right)$ *Point-slope form*

$20(y - 3) = -9x + \dfrac{135}{4}$

$80y - 240 = -36x + 135$
$80y + 36x = 375$

11.7 Tangents and Normals to Conic Sections   **579**

For Example 4

Determine the equation of the line tangent to each parabola at the given point. Then graph the parabola and the tangent line.

1. $y^2 = -16x;\ \left(-\frac{1}{4}, -2\right)$ $y = 4x - 1$

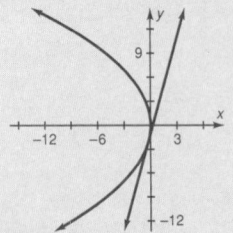

2. $x^2 = 12y;\ (6, 3)$ $y = x - 3$

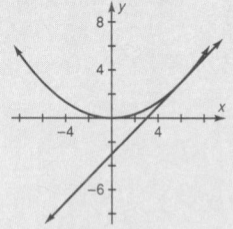

CLOSURE

Have students compose a letter to you explaining how to determine the equations of the lines tangent to and normal to a conic section at a given point.

Additional Answers
Class Exercises
1. circle; tangent: $2x + \sqrt{5}y = 18$; normal: $\sqrt{5}x - 2y = 0$
2. parabola; tangent: $y = x - 2$; normal: $y = -x - 6$
3. ellipse; tangent: $x = 5$; normal: $y = 0$
4. hyperbola; tangent: $4x + \sqrt{3}y = -8$ normal: $\sqrt{3}x - 4y = -40\sqrt{3}$
5. hyperbola; tangent: $3x + \sqrt{5}y = 10$; normal: $\sqrt{5}x - 3y = \frac{34\sqrt{5}}{5}$
6. parabola; tangent: $6x - 5y = 18$; normal: $25x + 30y = 258$

Example 4 Determine the equation of the line tangent to the parabola with equation $y^2 = 12x$ at the point $(3, 6)$. Graph the parabola and the tangent line.

Rewrite the equation $y^2 = 4(3x)$.

$c = 3$; slope $= \frac{2c}{y_0}$

$y - 6 = \frac{2 \times 3}{6}(x - 3)$

$y - 6 = x - 3$

$6 - y = x + 3$

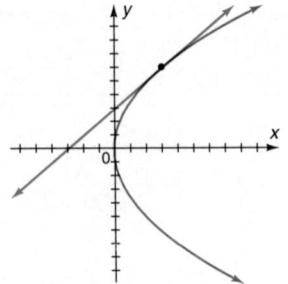

Class Exercises

Identify the conic. Then determine an equation of the tangent line and an equation of the normal line to the conic at the given point.

1. $x^2 + y^2 = 36,\ (4, 2\sqrt{5})$
2. $y^2 = -8x,\ (-2, -4)$
3. $\frac{x^2}{25} + \frac{y^2}{36} = 1,\ (5, 0)$
4. $\frac{x^2}{16} - \frac{y^2}{64} = 1,\ (-8, 8\sqrt{3})$
5. $4x^2 - 5y^2 = 80,\ \left(6, -\frac{8\sqrt{5}}{5}\right)$
6. $x^2 = 10y,\ (6, 3.6)$

7. Thinking Critically Find the equations of two lines with slope 3 which are tangent to the circle $x^2 + y^2 = 40$. ex: $y = 3x + 20, y = 3x - 20$
8. Writing in Mathematics Does the equation $xx_0 = 2c(y + y_0)$ represent an equation of the tangent line to the parabola with the equation $x^2 = 4cy$ at the point $P(x_0, y_0)$? Explain why it does or why it does not.

Practice Exercises   Use appropriate technology.

Identify the conic. Then determine the slope of the tangent and normal lines at the given point.

A **1.** $x^2 + y^2 = 4,\ (\sqrt{2}, -\sqrt{2})$
2. $\frac{y^2}{16} + \frac{x^2}{4} = 1,\ (\sqrt{2}, 2\sqrt{2})$
3. $y^2 = 8x,\ (2, 4)$
4. $\frac{x^2}{9} - \frac{y^2}{4} = 1,\ (3, 0)$
5. $\frac{x^2}{25} + \frac{y^2}{5} = 1,\ (\sqrt{5}, 2)$
6. $x^2 = -4y,\ (-6, -2\sqrt{6})$

Identify the conic and then find the equations of the tangent line and the normal line to the conic at the given point.

7. $x^2 + y^2 = 16,\ (3, \sqrt{7})$
8. $x^2 + y^2 = 16,\ (-\sqrt{7}, 3)$
9. $x^2 - y^2 = 25,\ (5, 0)$
10. $x^2 - y^2 = 36,\ (-6, 0)$
11. $y^2 - x^2 = 49,\ (0, -7)$
12. $y^2 - x^2 = 64,\ (0, 8)$
13. $y^2 = 12x,\ (3, -6)$
14. $y^2 = -16x,\ (-4, 8)$

580 Chapter 11 Conic Sections

Writing in Mathematics
8. no; The equation of the tangent line through the point (x_0, y_0) is $y - y_0 = \frac{x_0}{2c}(x - x_0)$ which can be expressed $2c(y - y_0) = x_0(x - x_0)$. Thus, it contains the term $(x_0)^2$ which is not in the given linear equation.

15. $\frac{x^2}{25} + \frac{y^2}{9} = 1$, $(0, -3)$

16. $\frac{x^2}{16} + \frac{y^2}{36} = 1$, $(0, 6)$

17. $5x^2 + y^2 = 80$, $(2, -2\sqrt{15})$

18. $x^2 + 4y^2 = 100$, $(-4, \sqrt{21})$

19. $y^2 - 3x^2 = 27$, $(1, -\sqrt{30})$

20. $4y^2 - x^2 = 36$, $(-2, -\sqrt{10})$

R **21.** Find an equation with lowest possible degree with integer coefficients that has $2 - \sqrt{5}$ and 3 as real solutions. $x^3 - 7x^2 + 11x + 3 = 0$

For each of the following conics, use the formula for the tangent at point (x_0, y_0) and the point-slope form of a linear equation to determine a general equation for the tangent line at point (x_0, y_0).

B **22.** Ellipse: $\frac{x^2}{a^2} + \frac{y^2}{b^2} = 1$

23. Ellipse: $\frac{y^2}{a^2} + \frac{x^2}{b^2} = 1$

24. Hyperbola: $\frac{x^2}{a^2} - \frac{y^2}{b^2} = 1$

25. Parabola: $y^2 = 4cx$

For each of the following conics, use the formula for the normal at point (x_0, y_0) and the point-slope form of a linear equation to determine a general equation for the normal line at point (x_0, y_0).

26. Ellipse: $\frac{x^2}{a^2} + \frac{y^2}{b^2} = 1$

27. Hyperbola: $\frac{x^2}{a^2} - \frac{y^2}{b^2} = 1$

28. Thinking Critically Find an equation of each of two lines that have a slope of -4 and that are tangent to the circle $x^2 + y^2 = 68$. ex: $y = -4x + 34$, $y = -4x - 34$

R **29.** Find the distance from the point $(3, 4)$ to the line $7x + y - 10 = 0$. 2.12

30. *Optics* An equation of the elliptical part of an optical lens system is $\frac{x^2}{9} + \frac{y^2}{4} = 1$. The parabolic part of the system has a focus in common with the right focus of the ellipse. The vertex of the parabola is at the origin and the parabola opens to the right. Determine the equation of the parabola. $y^2 = 4\sqrt{5}x$

31. Thinking Critically Find an equation of each of two lines that have a slope of 5 and that are tangent to the circle $x^2 + y^2 = 104$. ex: $y = 5x + 52$, $y = 5x - 52$

32. Writing in Mathematics Does the equation $\frac{yy_0}{b^2} - \frac{xx_0}{a^2} = 1$ represent an equation of the tangent line to the hyperbola with the equation $\frac{y^2}{b^2} - \frac{x^2}{a^2} = 1$ at the point $P(x_0, y_0)$? Explain why it does or why it does not.

R **33.** If a coin is tossed 5 times, what is the probability of 2 heads and 3 tails? $\frac{5}{16}$

34. *Construction* A highway bridge has the shape of the upper half of an ellipse with a major axis of 120 ft. The height in the center of the bridge is 30 ft. How high is the arch of the bridge at a point 20 ft from the center of the bridge? 28.3 ft

35. *Construction* The roadway over the bridge in Exercise 34 is 10 ft above the highest point on the arch of the bridge. Find the distance from the arch to the roadway at a point 20 ft on either side of the center of the bridge. 11.7 ft

11.7 Tangents and Normals to Conic Sections **581**

Writing in Mathematics

32. no; The equation of the tangent line through the point (x_0, y_0) is $y - y_0 = -\frac{a^2 x_0}{b^2 y_0}(x - x_0)$ which cannot be re-expressed in the form of the given linear equation.

INDEPENDENT PRACTICE

Basic: 1–21, 28–29, 31–33, 37, Project
Average: 3–6, 15–37, Project
Enriched: 17–20, 22–28, 30–32, 34–46, Project

Teacher's Resource Book
Practice, page 76

R **Review**
Exercises 21, 29, 33, and 37 review concepts such as using the factor theorem, finding the distance from a point to a line, using simple probability, and solving logarithmic equations.

Technology
Exercises 34 and 35 can be solved easily with a graphing calculator. Exercise 37 requires the use of a graphing utility.

Project
For a more hands-on approach to the project, you may want to have students design their own simple telescopes and describe, in terms of the conic sections, some of the principles by which they work.

LESSON FOLLOW-UP

Lesson Quiz
1. Determine the equation of the hyperbolic mirror with vertices at $(5, 0)$ and $(-5, 0)$ and one focus at $(7, 0)$. $\frac{x^2}{25} - \frac{y^2}{24} = 1$

Identify each conic and then find the equation of the tangent line and of the normal line to the conic at the given point.
2. $x^2 + y^2 = 100$; $(8, -6)$
   circle; tangent: $4x - 3y = 50$;
   normal: $3x + 4y = 0$
3. $\frac{x^2}{16} - \frac{y^2}{4} = 1$; $(4\sqrt{5}, 4)$
   hyperbola; tangent: $\sqrt{5}x - 4y = 4$;
   normal: $4x + \sqrt{5}y - 20\sqrt{5} = 0$
4. $\frac{x^2}{25} + \frac{y^2}{16} = 1$; $\left(-\frac{5\sqrt{3}}{2}, 2\right)$
   ellipse; tangent: $4\sqrt{3}x - 5y = -40$;
   normal: $10x + 8\sqrt{3}y + 9\sqrt{3} = 0$
5. $y^2 = 10x$; $(1, 3)$
   parabola; tangent: $5x - 3y = -4$;
   normal: $3x + 5y = 18$

581

582

Alternative Assessment

Instruct students to graph a circle on the coordinate plane. Then have them draw a square so that the circle is inscribed within it. Have students find the equations of the lines that contain the sides of the square. You can repeat the exercise using an ellipse and a rectangle or a circle and an equilateral triangle. Be sure that the equations of the conics, with which students start, are specific.

Enrichment

The circles $x^2 + y^2 = 25$ and $(x - 4)^2 + (y - 7)^2 = 10$ are tangent to each other. Find the point of tangency and the equation of the line that is tangent to both circles at that point. $3x + 4y = 25$

Additional Answers

36. $\dfrac{(x - 3)^2}{16} + \dfrac{(y + 1)^2}{7} = 1$

40. The equation of the tangent line is $xx_0 = 2c(y + y_0)$. Let $x = 0$. Then $0(x_0) = 2c(y + y_0)$, $0 = 2c(y + y_0)$, $0. = y + y_0$, $y = -y_0$. Thus, the tangent line intersects the y-axis at $(0, -y_0)$.

41. The equation of the tangent line is $xx_0 = -2c(y + y_0)$. Let $x = 0$. Then $0(x_0) = -2c(y + y_0)$, $0 = -2c(y + y_0)$, $0 = y + y_0$, $y = -y_0$. Thus, the tangent line intersects the y-axis at $(0, -y_0)$.

36. Suppose that the telescope in Example 1 has an elliptical mirror with one focus at F_2 and one focus at $(6, -1)$. The ellipse passes through the points $(-1, -1)$ and $(3, 2)$. Determine the equation of the ellipse.

Ⓡ 37. Solve for x: $\log_4 (x - 12) + \log_4 x = 3$. 16

Ⓒ 38. Find the equations of the tangents to the circle $x^2 + y^2 = 10$ that intersect at $(5, 5)$. $y = 3x - 10$, $y = \frac{1}{3}x + \frac{10}{3}$

39. Find the equations of the tangents to the circle $x^2 + y^2 = 12$ that intersect at $(6, 6)$. $(1 + \sqrt{5})x + (1 - \sqrt{5})y = 12$, $(1 - \sqrt{5})x + (1 + \sqrt{5})y = 12$

40. Show that the tangent line to the parabola $x^2 = 4cy$ at the point (x_0, y_0) intersects the y-axis at $(0, -y_0)$.

41. Show that the tangent line to the parabola $x^2 = -4cy$ at the point (x_0, y_0) intersects the y-axis at $(0, -y_0)$.

42. Show that the line $y = mx + k$ is tangent to the ellipse $\dfrac{x^2}{a^2} + \dfrac{y^2}{b^2} = 1$ if $k = \pm\sqrt{a^2m^2 + b^2}$.

43. Show that the line $y = mx + k$ is tangent to the hyperbola $\dfrac{x^2}{a^2} - \dfrac{y^2}{b^2} = 1$ if $k = \pm\sqrt{a^2m^2 - b^2}$.

The figure shows a circle with radius r and center at (h, k). $\overline{PT}$ is tangent to the circle at P.

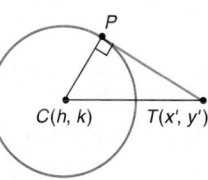

44. Find the equation of the circle. $(x - h)^2 + (y - k)^2 = r^2$

45. Determine an equation that gives the length TP in terms of x', y', h, k, and r. $TP = \sqrt{(x' - h)^2 + (y' - k)^2 - r^2}$

46. Use the equation derived in Exercise 45 to find the length of the tangent drawn from the point $(2, 5)$ to the circle $x^2 + y^2 - 2x - 3y - 1 = 0$. 3

Project

Report on the development of the telescope from the beginning of the seventeenth century to the end of the nineteenth century. Explain how technical improvements in the telescope depended on the properties of conic sections.

Challenge

1. Each side of triangle ABC is 18 cm. Point D is the foot of the perpendicular from A on $\overline{BC}$, and E is the midpoint of $\overline{AD}$. Find the length of $\overline{BE}$. 11.906 cm

2. Let θ be an angle in standard position. Let $f(\theta) = \dfrac{\sin \theta}{\cos \theta}$.

   a. What values of θ in degrees will make the function undefined? 90°, 270°, and coterminal angles

   b. In which quadrant(s) can θ lie under the condition $f(\theta) > 0$? I, III

   c. In which quadrant(s) can θ lie under the condition $f(\theta) < 0$? II, IV

3. An ice cream cone with height h and radius r is half filled by volume with frozen yogurt. In terms of h and r, find the height h' and radius r' of the frozen yogurt in the cone. $h' = \sqrt[3]{\dfrac{h^3}{2}}$; $r' = \sqrt[3]{\dfrac{r^3}{2}}$

582 Chapter 11 Conic Sections

11.8 Polar Equations of Conic Sections

Objective: *To determine and identify polar equations of conic sections*

Focus

Mathematical models of the physical universe often change. In particular, models of the solar system have been revised several times to encompass new observations and to accommodate new ideas. Ancient and medieval astronomers developed a mathematical model involving a combination of several circular motions. They believed that a planet *A* traveled around a circle, called an epicycle, centered at point *C*, which in turn traveled in a large circle around the earth *E*. This model was refined by Ptolemy in the second century and survived for well over 1000 years.

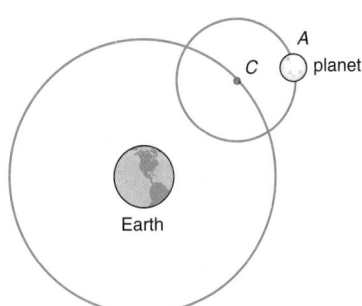

In the early sixteenth century, Copernicus modified the Ptolemaic point of view by considering the sun, not the earth, as the center of the solar system. In this model, the earth and the other planets revolve around the sun in perfectly circular orbits. Several decades later, Johannes Kepler (1571–1630) refined the Copernican model, showing that the planets revolve around the sun in elliptical, not circular, orbits.

In previous lessons of this chapter, conic sections were introduced using equations in the Cartesian coordinate system. These curves can also be described using the polar coordinate system studied in Chapter 10. For example, the circle whose equation in Cartesian coordinates is $x^2 + y^2 = 64$ has $r = 8$ as its polar equation. In order to develop polar equations for the parabola, ellipse, and hyperbola, it is useful to have a new definition of *conic section*.

General Definition of Conic Section

Let $e > 0$ be a fixed real number. Let ℓ be a line and F a point not on ℓ. Then a *conic section* is the set of all points P in a plane such that $e = \dfrac{d(P, F)}{d(P, \ell)}$, where $d(P, F)$ is the distance from P to F and $d(P, \ell)$ is the perpendicular distance from P to the line ℓ.

The constant e is the *eccentricity* of the conic section, F is a focus, and ℓ is the directrix.

11.8 Polar Equations of Conic Sections **583**

Although this definition of eccentricity is different from that given for the ellipse and hyperbola in Lessons 11.2 and 11.3, it can be shown that it is equivalent to those earlier definitions. This definition is sometimes called the **point locus definition for conics.** The focus-directrix definition given for parabolas in Lesson 11.4 also uses this approach. From the above definition, it can be shown that a conic is a parabola if $e = 1$, an ellipse if $0 < e < 1$, and a hyperbola if $e > 1$.

It is possible to derive polar equations for all conics (except circles) that have a focus at the pole and a directrix parallel or perpendicular to the polar axis.

In the diagram at the right, $y = d$ is the Cartesian equation of the directrix ℓ of a conic and $F(0, 0)$ is a focus. The distance from P to F is represented by $d(P, F)$ and $d(P, \ell)$ is the distance from P to ℓ. From the definition of eccentricity,

$$e = \frac{d(P, F)}{d(P, \ell)}$$

$$e = \frac{\sqrt{(x - 0)^2 + (y - 0)^2}}{\sqrt{(x - x)^2 + (y - d)^2}}$$

$$e = \frac{\sqrt{x^2 + y^2}}{|y - d|}$$

$$e = \frac{r}{|y - d|} \qquad r = \sqrt{x^2 + y^2}$$

$$r = e|y - d|$$

$$r = e(d - y) \qquad y - d < 0$$

$$r = e(d - r \sin \theta) \qquad y = r \sin \theta$$

$$r = ed - er \sin \theta$$

$$r + re \sin \theta = ed$$

$$r(1 + e \sin \theta) = ed$$

$$r = \frac{ed}{1 + e \sin \theta}$$

This is the polar equation for a conic with directrix $y = d$ and a focus at the pole.

In a similar manner, equations for conics with directrix $y = -d$, $x = d$, or $x = -d$ with a focus at the pole can be derived. The results are summarized on the next page.

584   Chapter 11 Conic Sections

Polar Equation	Directrix	Axis	To determine vertices, let:
$r = \dfrac{ed}{1 - e\cos\theta}$	$x = -d,\ d > 0$	Horizontal	$\theta = 0$ and $\theta = \pi$
$r = \dfrac{ed}{1 + e\cos\theta}$	$x = d,\ d > 0$	Horizontal	$\theta = 0$ and $\theta = \pi$
$r = \dfrac{ed}{1 - e\sin\theta}$	$y = -d,\ d > 0$	Vertical	$\theta = \dfrac{\pi}{2}$ and $\theta = \dfrac{3}{2}\pi$
$r = \dfrac{ed}{1 + e\sin\theta}$	$y = d,\ d > 0$	Vertical	$\theta = \dfrac{\pi}{2}$ and $\theta = \dfrac{3}{2}\pi$

Example 1 Identify the conic with equation $r = \dfrac{18}{3 - 6\cos\theta}$. Then find the vertices and graph the conic.

$$r = \frac{18}{3 - 6\cos\theta} = \frac{6}{1 - 2\cos\theta} \qquad \textit{Standard form}$$

Since $e = 2$, the conic is a hyperbola.

$$ed = 6$$
$$2d = 6$$
$$d = 3$$

The directrix is $x = -3$.

Let $\theta = 0$.

$$r = \frac{6}{1 - 2\cos\theta}$$
$$r = \frac{6}{1 - 2\cos 0}$$
$$r = \frac{6}{1 - 2(1)}$$
$$r = -6$$

Let $\theta = \pi$.

$$r = \frac{6}{1 - 2\cos\theta}$$
$$r = \frac{6}{1 - 2\cos\pi}$$
$$r = \frac{6}{1 - 2(-1)}$$
$$r = 2$$

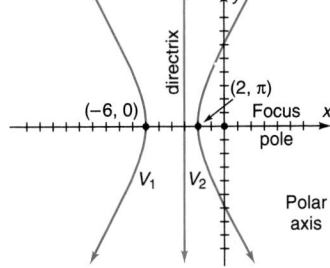

The vertices are $(-6, 0)$ and $(2, \pi)$.

You can use a graphing utility with polar-coordinate capabilities to verify that the graph of Example 1 is correct.

Example 2 Find a polar equation of the ellipse with a focus at the pole. An equation of the directrix is $y = -3$ and the eccentricity is $\frac{2}{3}$.

The polar equation is of the form $r = \dfrac{ed}{1 - e\sin\theta}$.

$$r = \frac{\frac{2}{3}(3)}{1 - \frac{2}{3}\sin\theta} = \frac{2}{1 - \frac{2}{3}\sin\theta} = \frac{6}{3 - 2\sin\theta} \qquad d = 3 \text{ and } e = \frac{2}{3}$$

11.8 Polar Equations of Conic Sections **585**

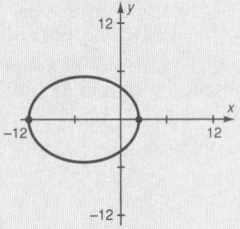

GUIDED PRACTICE

For Example 1
Identify the conic with the equation $r = \dfrac{12}{3 + 2\cos\theta}$. Then find the vertices and graph the conic.
ellipse; $\left(\dfrac{12}{5}, 0\right)$ and $(12, \pi)$

For Example 2
Determine a polar equation for the conic section with a focus at the pole, directrix at $x = -2$, and eccentricity $= 1$. $r = \dfrac{2}{1 - \cos\theta}$

Modeling

How can you determine the orbit of a satellite?

The model of the solar system that Kepler devised is still valid today. It is expressed in the form of his three laws of planetary motion:

- The orbit of each planet is an ellipse with the sun at one focus.
- The line segment from the sun to a planet sweeps out area at a constant rate as the planet moves in its orbit.
- The square of the time for a planet to complete one revolution around the sun is directly proportional to the cube of its mean distance from the sun, which is the semimajor axis of the planet's elliptical orbit.

In the late seventeenth century, Newton used Kepler's laws to help him formulate his own discoveries in celestial mechanics.

The elliptical model of planetary motion about the sun can be represented in a Cartesian coordinate system. It is, however, often more useful to represent the location of a planet in terms of its distance d from a fixed point F_1 (the sun at one focus) and the angle θ formed by the major axis and the line from the sun to the planet. When a planet's location is indicated in this way, it is easier to use the polar coordinate representation of the ellipse.

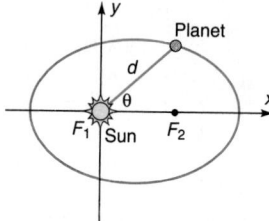

Kepler's third law applies not only to movements of planets about the sun but also to movements of satellites about the earth. The model can be used to find the radius of a satellite's synchronous orbit, that is, a (nearly circular) orbit in which the satellite appears to be stationary in the sky. Example 3 shows how this effect can be achieved.

Example 3   *Communications*   A satellite is placed in a synchronous orbit around the earth. Using Kepler's third law, $T^2 = kr^3$, where T is the period of time for one revolution and r is the mean distance of the satellite from the center of the earth, find how high above the surface of the earth the satellite should be placed in orbit. To find k, use $T = 27.32$ days and $r = 238,850$ mi, the time and mean distance of a known satellite—the moon.

To determine the value of k, substitute for T and r in the given equation.

$$(27.32)^2 = k(238,850)^3 \qquad T^2 = kr^3$$

$$k = \frac{(27.32)^2}{(238,850)^3}$$

Kepler's third law for earth orbit thus becomes

$$T^2 = \frac{(27.32)^2}{(238,850)^3} r^3$$

For a synchronous orbit the desired time is $T = 1$ day.

$$1^2 = \frac{(27.32)^2}{(238,850)^3}r^3 \quad \textit{Substitute } T = 1.$$

$$r = \frac{238,850}{\sqrt[3]{(27.32)^2}} \quad \textit{Calculation-ready from}$$

$$r = 26,331$$

Since the radius of the earth is 3960 mi, the satellite should be placed in orbit at a mean distance of 26,331 − 3960, or 22,371 mi above the surface of the earth.

Class Exercises

Identify the conic with the given polar equation.

1. $r = \dfrac{8}{2 - \sin\theta}$ ellipse

2. $r = \dfrac{12}{3 + 2\sin\theta}$ ellipse

3. $r = \dfrac{8}{3 + 3\cos\theta}$ parabola

4. $r = \dfrac{6}{2 - 3\cos\theta}$ hyperbola

Identify the conic with the given polar equation. Then determine the vertices and graph the conic.

5. $r = \dfrac{2}{1 - \sin\theta}$

6. $r = \dfrac{4}{2 + \cos\theta}$

7. $r = \dfrac{2}{1 + 4\cos\theta}$

8. $r = \dfrac{2}{4 + 4\sin\theta}$

Determine a polar equation for the conic section with the given characteristics.

9. Parabola, focus (0, 0), vertex $\left(1, -\dfrac{\pi}{2}\right)$ $r = \dfrac{2}{1 - \sin\theta}$

10. Focus at pole, directrix $x = -4$, $e = \dfrac{1}{2}$ $r = \dfrac{4}{2 - \cos\theta}$

Practice Exercises Use appropriate technology.

Identify the conic with the given polar equation.

A **1.** $r = \dfrac{12}{3 - 2\cos\theta}$ ellipse

2. $r = \dfrac{15}{5 + 2\sin\theta}$ ellipse

3. $r = \dfrac{-8}{3 - 2\sin\theta}$ ellipse

4. $r = \dfrac{-6}{4 - 2\cos\theta}$ ellipse

5. $r = \dfrac{10}{2 - 4\cos\theta}$ hyperbola

6. $r = \dfrac{14}{7 - 14\sin\theta}$ hyperbola

7. $r = 9$ circle

8. $r = 11$ circle

9. $r = \dfrac{16}{6 + 6\sin\theta}$ parabola

10. $r = \dfrac{18}{9 - 9\cos\theta}$ parabola

11. $r = \dfrac{4.8}{1.6 + 1.2\sin\theta}$ ellipse

12. $r = \dfrac{3.6}{1.8 + 0.9\cos\theta}$ ellipse

11.8 Polar Equations of Conic Sections **587**

587

LESSON FOLLOW-UP

Test Yourself

Teacher's Resource Book
Tests—Quiz, form A, page 50
Tests—Quiz, form B, page 50

Lesson Quiz

1. Identify the conic with equation $r = \dfrac{12}{3 - 2\cos\theta}$. Then find the vertices and graph the conic.

ellipse; (12, 0) and $\left(\dfrac{12}{5}, \pi\right)$

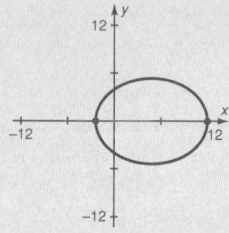

2. Determine a polar equation for the ellipse with a focus at the pole, directrix at $x = -4$, and eccentricity $= \dfrac{5}{6}$. $r = \dfrac{20}{6 - 5\cos\theta}$

Additional Answers

13. parabola; $(3, \pi)$

14. parabola; $\left(3, \dfrac{3\pi}{2}\right)$

15. ellipse; $\left(\dfrac{4}{3}, \dfrac{\pi}{2}\right), \left(4, \dfrac{3\pi}{2}\right)$

16. ellipse; $\left(\dfrac{4}{3}, 0\right), (4, \pi)$

17. hyperbola; $\left(\dfrac{1}{2}, 0\right), (-1, \pi)$

18. hyperbola; $\left(-1, \dfrac{\pi}{2}\right), \left(\dfrac{1}{2}, \dfrac{3\pi}{2}\right)$

22. $r = \dfrac{8}{3 + 2\cos\theta}$

23. $r = \dfrac{8}{3 + 2\sin\theta}$

24. $r = \dfrac{3}{1 - \sin\theta}$

25. $r = \dfrac{3}{1 - \cos\theta}$

26. $r = \dfrac{12}{1 + 2\sin\theta}$

27. $r = \dfrac{16}{1 + 2\cos\theta}$

28. $r = \dfrac{16}{5 + 3\cos\theta}$

29. $r = \dfrac{16}{5 + 3\sin\theta}$

30. $r = \dfrac{8}{1 + \sin\theta}$

Identify the conic with the given polar equation. Then find the vertices and graph the conic.

13. $r = \dfrac{6}{1 - \cos\theta}$

14. $r = \dfrac{6}{1 - \sin\theta}$

15. $r = \dfrac{4}{2 + \sin\theta}$

16. $r = \dfrac{4}{2 + \cos\theta}$

17. $r = \dfrac{8}{4 + 12\cos\theta}$

18. $r = \dfrac{8}{4 - 12\sin\theta}$

Use a graphing utility with polar coordinate capabilities to graph each conic.

19. $r = \dfrac{4}{3 + 2\cos\theta}$

20. $r = \dfrac{8}{4 + 4\cos\theta}$

Ⓡ 21. Determine whether $x + 1$ is a factor of $x^5 - x^3 - 2x^2 + 7x + 9$. yes

Find a polar equation for the conic section with the given geometric characteristics.

B 22. Focus at pole, directrix $x = 4$, $e = \dfrac{2}{3}$ 23. Focus at pole, directrix $y = 4$, $e = \dfrac{2}{3}$

24. Focus at pole, directrix $y = -3$, $e = 1$ 25. Focus at pole, directrix $x = -3$, $e = 1$

26. Focus at pole, directrix $y = 6$, $e = 2$ 27. Focus at pole, directrix $x = 8$, $e = 2$

28. Ellipse, focus (0, 0), vertices (2, 0), (8, π)

29. Ellipse, focus (0, 0), vertices $\left(2, \dfrac{\pi}{2}\right), \left(8, \dfrac{3\pi}{2}\right)$

30. Parabola, focus (0, 0), vertex $\left(4, \dfrac{\pi}{2}\right)$

Ⓡ 31. Determine the zeros of the function $f(x) = x^3 - 2x^2 - 5x + 6$. 1, −2, 3

32. *Astronomy* Use the data in Example 3 to determine the value of k in the equation $T^2 = kr^3$. 5.47754×10^{-14}

33. *Space Science* Use the data in Example 3 to determine the time per revolution of a satellite that orbits the earth at a mean distance of 180 mi above the surface of the earth. 1.5 h/rev

34. *Space Science* Use the data in Example 3 to determine the mean distance above the surface of the earth of a satellite that orbits the earth every 2 h. 1064 mi

Ⓡ 35. Solve for x: $\sqrt{2x + 5} - \sqrt{x - 6} = 3$ 10, 22

36. **Writing in Mathematics** Explain why the general polar equations cannot be used for circles.

C 37. **Writing in Mathematics** Describe the changes in shape of a conic as its eccentricity changes from a value near but greater than zero to a value near 1.

38. Graph the equation: $r^2 = \dfrac{144}{9\cos^2\theta + 16\sin^2\theta}$

39. Graph the equation: $r^2 = \dfrac{64}{16\cos^2\theta + 9\sin^2\theta}$

40. Graph the equation: $r^2 = \dfrac{36}{4 - 13\sin^2\theta}$

588   Chapter 11 Conic Sections

Writing in Mathematics

36. The general polar equations cannot be used for circles because circles have eccentricity equal to zero, and the equation would be $r = 0$.

37. The shape of the conic goes from an almost perfect circle to a parabola.

41. Graph the equation: $r^2 = \dfrac{72}{9 - 25 \sin^2 \theta}$

42. Show that $r = \dfrac{a}{\cos \theta + 1}$ and $r = \dfrac{a}{\cos \theta - 1}$ represent the same parabola.

43. Show that $r = \dfrac{a}{\sin \theta + 1}$ and $r = \dfrac{a}{\sin \theta - 1}$ represent the same parabola.

44. Determine the points of intersection of the two curves with equations $r = 2 \cos \theta$ and $2r(1 + \cos \theta) = 3$. $\left(1, \dfrac{\pi}{3}\right), \left(1, \dfrac{5\pi}{3}\right)$

45. Determine the points of intersection of the two curves with equations $r = 2(1 + \cos \theta)$ and $r(1 - \cos \theta) = 1$. $\left(2 + \sqrt{2}, \dfrac{\pi}{4}\right), \left(2 + \sqrt{2}, \dfrac{7\pi}{4}\right),$ $\left(2 - \sqrt{2}, \dfrac{3\pi}{4}\right), \left(2 - \sqrt{2}, \dfrac{5\pi}{4}\right)$

Project

Write a short report on one of the following men: Ptolemy, Copernicus, or Kepler. In your research try to find out what, or who, prompted the person to develop his model of the solar system. Look for other contributions that the person made to mathematics or astronomy.

Test Yourself

Translate the axes so that the graph is symmetric about at least one coordinate axis (both axes, if possible). For a parabola, have the vertex positioned at the origin. Find the equation with respect to the new $x'y'$-coordinate system.   11.5

1. $x^2 + y^2 + 6x - 10y - 2 = 0$ 2. $x^2 + 4y^2 + 10x - 16y + 37 = 0$

3. $2x^2 + 40x - y + 201 = 0$

4. Identify the following conic by using the discriminant. Then graph the conic using a graphing utility.

$$3x^2 + xy - 2y^2 + y + 4 = 0$$

Identify, solve, and graph the system of equations.   11.6

5. $\begin{cases} y^2 - x^2 = 24 \\ y = 4x + 1 \end{cases}$ 6. $\begin{cases} y = x^2 + 4x - 2 \\ 3x^2 - 7xy + 2y^2 = 0 \end{cases}$ 7. $\begin{cases} x^2 - 9y^2 = 81 \\ x^2 + 9y^2 = 81 \end{cases}$

Identify the conic. Then find an equation of the tangent line and an equation of the normal line to the conic at the given point.   11.7

8. $x^2 + y^2 = 50$, $(7, -1)$ 9. $x^2 - y^2 = 25$, $(13, 12)$

Identify the conic with the given polar equation. Then find the vertices and graph the conic.   11.8

10. $r = \dfrac{8}{1 - 4 \cos \theta}$ 11. $r = \dfrac{6}{4 + 2 \sin \theta}$

Find a polar equation of the conic section with the given geometric characteristics. $r = \dfrac{4}{1 - \cos \theta}$

12. Focus at pole, directrix $x = -4$, $e = 6$ 13. Parabola, focus $(0, 0)$, vertex $(2, \pi)$

$r = \dfrac{24}{1 - 6 \cos \theta}$

11.8 Polar Equations of Conic Sections   **589**

Additional Answers

41.

42. $r = \dfrac{a}{\cos \theta + 1}$, $r \cos \theta + r = a$, $x + \sqrt{x^2 + y^2} = a$, $x^2 + y^2 = a^2 - 2ax + x^2$, $y^2 = a(a - 2x)$; $r = \dfrac{a}{\cos \theta - 1}$, $r \cos \theta - r = a$, $x - \sqrt{x^2 + y^2} = a$, $x^2 + y^2 = a^2 - 2ax + x^2$, $y^2 = a(a - 2x)$

43. $r = \dfrac{a}{\sin \theta + 1}$, $r \sin \theta + r = a$, $y + \sqrt{x^2 + y^2} = a$, $x^2 + y^2 = a^2 - 2ay + y^2$, $x^2 = a(a - 2y)$; $r = \dfrac{a}{\sin \theta - 1}$, $r \sin \theta - r = a$, $y - \sqrt{x^2 + y^2} = a$, $x^2 + y^2 = a^2 - 2ay + y^2$, $x^2 = a(a - 2y)$

1.

2.

3. major axis: $(\pm3, 0)$;
minor axis: $(0, \pm\sqrt{5})$;
foci: $(\pm2, 0)$; $e = \dfrac{2}{3}$

4.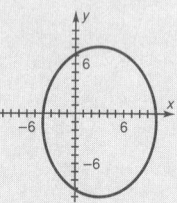

5. vertices: $(0, \pm2)$;
endpoints: $(\pm8, 0)$;
foci: $(0, \pm2\sqrt{17})$;
asymptotes: $y = \pm\dfrac{1}{4}x$; $e = \sqrt{17}$

6.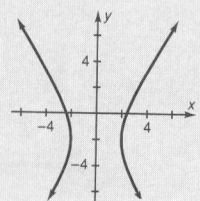

Chapter 11 Summary and Review

Vocabulary

circle (535)
conic sections (534)
conjugate axis (550)
degenerate circle (536)
directrix (557)
eccentricity (543)
eccentricity of a conic (561)
element of a cone (534)

ellipse (541)
focus (541)
hyperbola (549)
major axis (542)
minor axis (542)
normal (577)
parabola (557)
point locus definition for conics (584)

quadratic system (570)
radius (535)
rectangular hyperbola (554)
semimajor axis (542)
tangent (577)
translation equations (564)
transverse axis (550)
vertices (542)

Circle Standard forms of the equation: **11.1**

Center at $(0, 0)$: $x^2 + y^2 = r^2$, radius r.
Center at (h, k): $(x - h)^2 + (y - k)^2 = r^2$, radius r

Graph each circle when possible. Label the center and find the radius.

1. $x^2 + y^2 - 12x + 2y - 12 = 0$ $(6, -1); 7$ **2.** $x^2 + y^2 - 6x + 5y + 9 = 0$ $\left(3, -\dfrac{5}{2}\right); \dfrac{5}{2}$

Ellipse Standard forms of the equation ($a > b$, $c^2 = a^2 - b^2$): **11.2**

Center at $(0, 0)$: $\dfrac{x^2}{a^2} + \dfrac{y^2}{b^2} = 1$, foci $(\pm c, 0)$; $\dfrac{x^2}{b^2} + \dfrac{y^2}{a^2} = 1$, foci $(0, \pm c)$

Center at (h, k): $\dfrac{(x - h)^2}{a^2} + \dfrac{(y - k)^2}{b^2} = 1$; $\dfrac{(x - h)^2}{b^2} + \dfrac{(y - k)^2}{a^2} = 1$

3. Determine the endpoints of the major and minor axes, the foci, and the eccentricity. Then graph the ellipse.

$$5x^2 + 9y^2 = 45$$

4. Express in standard form and graph:

$$81x^2 + 49y^2 - 486x + 98y - 3191 = 0 \quad \dfrac{(x - 3)^2}{49} + \dfrac{(y + 1)^2}{81} = 1$$

Hyperbola Standard forms of the equation ($c^2 = a^2 + b^2$): **11.3**

Center at $(0, 0)$: $\dfrac{x^2}{a^2} - \dfrac{y^2}{b^2} = 1$, foci $(\pm c, 0)$; $\dfrac{y^2}{a^2} - \dfrac{x^2}{b^2} = 1$, foci $(0, \pm c)$

Center at (h, k): $\dfrac{(x - h)^2}{a^2} - \dfrac{(y - k)^2}{b^2} = 1$; $\dfrac{(y - k)^2}{a^2} - \dfrac{(x - h)^2}{b^2} = 1$

5. Find the endpoints of the conjugate axis, the vertices, the foci, the asymptotes, and the eccentricity. Then graph the hyperbola.

$$16y^2 - x^2 = 64$$

6. Express an equation in standard form for the hyperbola. Then graph.

$$9x^2 - 4y^2 - 16y - 52 = 0 \quad \dfrac{x^2}{4} - \dfrac{(y + 2)^2}{9} = 1$$

Parabola Equations (vertex $(0, 0)$): $x^2 = 4cy$, focus $(0, c)$; $y^2 = 4cx$, focus $(c, 0)$ 11.4

Standard forms of the equation (vertex (h, k)): $(x - h)^2 = 4c(y - k)$;
$$(y - k)^2 = 4c(x - h)$$

Determine the vertex, the focus, the axis of symmetry, and the directrix. Then graph.

7. $2y = x^2 + 10x + 29$

8. $x = -y^2 - 12y - 26$

Translation of Axes   Translation equations are: 11.5

$$\begin{array}{lll} x = x' + h & \text{or} & x' = x - h \\ y = y' + k & \text{or} & y' = y - k \end{array}$$

Translate the axes so that the graph is symmetric about both coordinate axes. Find the equation with respect to the new $x'y'$-coordinate system. Identify the conic.

9. $x^2 + y^2 - x + 7y + \frac{41}{4} = 0$

10. $16x^2 - y^2 + 32x - 8y - 64 = 0$

General Form   The general form of the equation of a conic section is $Ax^2 + Bxy + Cy^2 + Dx + Ey + F = 0$.

11. Identify the following conic by using the discriminant. Then graph the conic using a graphing utility.

$$3x^2 + 2xy - 3y^2 + x - 5y + 1 = 0 \quad \text{hyperbola}$$

Solving Quadratic Systems   Quadratic systems may be solved by using the   11.6
substitution and the addition methods.

Identify, solve, and graph the system of equations.

12. $\begin{cases} x^2 - 2y^2 = 68 \quad \text{hyperbola} \\ x = y^2 - 6 \quad \text{parabola} \end{cases}$ $(10, \pm 4)$

13. $\begin{cases} x^2 + y^2 = 25 \quad \text{circle} \\ (x - 1)^2 + (y + 2)^2 = 40 \quad \text{circle} \end{cases}$ $(-5, 0), (3, 4)$

Tangents and Normals to Conic Sections   Given a circle with equation $x^2 + y^2 = r^2$,   11.7
the tangent line at point (x_0, y_0) has slope $-\frac{x_0}{y_0}$. The normal line at (x_0, y_0) has slope $\frac{y_0}{x_0}$.

14. Identify the conic. Then find an equation of the tangent line and an equation of the normal line to the conic at the given point.

$$x^2 + 5y^2 = 9, \ (2, 1)$$

Polar Equations of Conic Sections   The polar equation of a conic section with   11.8
directrix $y = d$, a focus at the pole, and eccentricity e is $r = \dfrac{ed}{1 + e \sin \theta}$.

15. Identify the conic with the polar equation given below. Then find the vertices and graph the conic.

$$r = \frac{1}{3 - 3 \sin \theta} \quad \text{parabola;} \ \left(\frac{1}{6}, \frac{3\pi}{2}\right)$$

16. Find a polar equation for the conic section with a focus at $(0, 0)$, its directrix at $x = 4$, and with an eccentricity of 3. $r = \dfrac{12}{1 + 3 \cos \theta}$

15.

7. vertex: $(-5, 2)$; focus: $\left(-5, \frac{5}{2}\right)$;
axis: $(x = -5)$; directrix: $y = \frac{3}{2}$

8. vertex: $(10, -6)$; focus: $\left(\frac{39}{4}, -6\right)$;
axis: $(y = -6)$; directrix: $x = \frac{41}{4}$

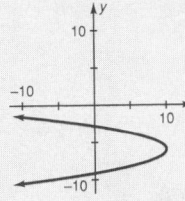

9. $(x')^2 + (y')^2 = \frac{9}{4}$, origin at $\left(\frac{1}{2}, -\frac{7}{2}\right)$;
circle

10. $\dfrac{(x')^2}{4} - \dfrac{(y')^2}{64} = 1$, origin at $(-1, -4)$;
hyperbola

11.

12.

13.

14. ellipse; tangent: $2x + 5y = 9$;
normal: $5x - 2y = 8$

591

Additional Answers

1.

2. major axis: $(0, \pm6)$;
minor axis: $(\pm2, 0)$;
foci: $(0, \pm4\sqrt{2})$; $e = \dfrac{2\sqrt{2}}{3}$

3.

4. endpoints: $(0, \pm1)$;
vertices: $(\pm7, 0)$; foci: $(\pm5\sqrt{2}, 0)$;
asymptotes: $y = \pm\dfrac{1}{7}x$; $e = \dfrac{5\sqrt{2}}{7}$

6. vertex: $(-2, 4)$; focus: $\left(-2, \dfrac{13}{4}\right)$;
latus rectum: 3; directrix: $y = \dfrac{19}{4}$

592

Chapter 11 Test

1. Graph the circle with equation $x^2 + y^2 - 10x + 24 = 0$. Label the center and radius. (5, 0); 1

2. Find the endpoints of the major and minor axes, the foci, and the eccentricity. Then graph the equation.
$$9x^2 + y^2 = 36$$

3. Express the equation in standard form. Then graph the equation.
$$4x^2 + 3y^2 - 16x + 6y + 7 = 0 \quad \dfrac{(x-2)^2}{3} + \dfrac{(y+1)^2}{4} = 1$$

4. Find the endpoints of the conjugate axes, the vertices, the foci, the asymptotes, and the eccentricity. Then graph the equation.
$$x^2 - 49y^2 = 49$$

5. Find the equation of a parabola with focus (4, 6) and directrix $x = 0$. $(y-6)^2 = 8(x-2)$

6. Find the vertex, the focus, the length of the latus rectum, and the directrix. Then graph the equation.
$$-(x+2)^2 = 3y - 12$$

7. Translate the axes so that the graph is symmetric about both coordinate axes. Find the equation with respect to the new $x'y'$-coordinate system. Identify the conic.
$$x^2 + 4y^2 + 2x - 12y - 6 = 0 \quad \dfrac{(x')^2}{16} + \dfrac{(y')^2}{4} = 1;\ \text{ellipse}$$

8. Identify the following conic by using the discriminant. Then graph the conic using a graphing utility.
$$3x^2 + 4xy + y^2 + y - 10 = 0 \quad \text{hyperbola}$$

9. Identify, solve, and graph the following system.
$$\begin{aligned} x^2 + 6y^2 &= 36 \quad \text{ellipse} \\ y &= x^2 - 1 \quad \text{parabola} \end{aligned} \qquad \left(\pm\dfrac{\sqrt{30}}{3}, \dfrac{7}{3}\right)$$

10. Identify the conic $3x^2 - 4y^2 = 11$. Then find an equation of the tangent line and an equation of the normal line to the conic at the point $(3, -2)$.

11. Identify the conic having the given equation. Then find the vertices and graph the conic.
$$r = \dfrac{12}{1 + 5\cos\theta} \quad \text{hyperbola; } (2, 0), (-3, \pi)$$

Challenge

Find in standard form the equation of a parabola with focus (1, 1) and directrix $y = -x$. $x^2 - 2xy + y^2 - 4x - 4y + 4 = 0$

8.

9.

10. hyperbola;
tangent:
$9x + 8y = 11$;
normal:
$8x - 9y = 42$

11.

Cumulative Review

Select the best choice for each question.

1. Find the multiplicative inverse of $\quad$ 10.4
E $\quad$ the complex number $5 + \pi i$.
   A. $-5 + \pi i$ $\quad$ **B.** $-5 + i$ $\quad$ **C.** $5 + i$
   D. $5 - \pi i$ $\quad$ **E.** none of these

2. The graph of $2x - y > 6$ is $\quad$ 8.2
C $\quad$ drawn as:
   A. dotted line shaded above
   B. solid line shaded above
   C. dotted line shaded below
   D. solid line shaded below
   E. none of these

3. Given $f(x) = 3x^2 - 2x + 1$, $\quad$ 1.4
A $\quad$ evaluate $f(-2)$.
   A. 17 $\quad$ **B.** 7 $\quad$ **C.** 41 $\quad$ **D.** -41
   E. none of these

4. The equations of the asymptotes $\quad$ 11.3
A $\quad$ of a hyperbola with transverse axis on
   the x-axis and center at the origin are
   A. $y = \pm\dfrac{b}{a}x$ $\qquad$ **B.** $x = \pm\dfrac{b}{a}y$
   C. $e = \dfrac{a}{b}y$ $\qquad$ **D.** $e = \dfrac{b}{a}y$
   E. none of these

5. Classify the polynomial function $\quad$ 7.2
E $\quad$ $P(x) = x^4 + 9x^2 - 1 - 2x^5$.
   A. linear $\quad$ **B.** quadratic $\quad$ **C.** cubic
   D. quartic $\quad$ **E.** quintic

6. Using $Ax^2 + Bxy + Cy^2 + Dx + Ey +$
C $\quad$ $F = 0$, if $B^2 - 4AC > 0$, $\quad$ 11.5
   then the conic is a
   A. parabola $\quad$ **B.** ellipse $\quad$ **C.** hyperbola
   D. circle $\quad$ **E.** none of these

7. Without drawing, identify the $\quad$ 10.2
D $\quad$ graph of $r = 8 \cos \theta$.
   A. line $\quad$ **B.** spiral $\quad$ **C.** cone
   D. circle $\quad$ **E.** none of these

8. Identify the conic with polar $\quad$ 11.8
A $\quad$ equation $r = \sin \theta$.
   A. circle $\quad$ **B.** ellipse $\quad$ **C.** parabola
   D. hyperbola $\quad$ **E.** none of these

9. Determine the arc length of a $\quad$ 3.2
A $\quad$ circle of radius 9 cm intercepted by a
   central angle of $\dfrac{2\pi}{3}$.
   A. 6π cm $\quad$ **B.** 10π cm $\quad$ **C.** 3π cm
   D. 8π cm $\quad$ **E.** none of these

10. Determine the center of the circle $\quad$ 11.1
C $\quad$ with equation $x^2 + y^2 = 81$.
   A. $(9, 9)$ $\quad$ **B.** $(9, -9)$ $\quad$ **C.** $(0, 0)$
   D. $(0, 9)$ $\quad$ **E.** none of these

11. Since the logarithmic function $\quad$ 9.3
A $\quad$ $f(x) = \log_b x$ and the exponential function
   $g(x) = b^x$ are inverses, their graphs are
   symmetric with respect to the line
   A. $y = x$ $\quad$ **B.** $y = -x$ $\quad$ **C.** $y = \dfrac{1}{x}$
   D. $y = -\dfrac{1}{x}$ $\quad$ **E.** none of these

12. Determine the length of the $\quad$ 5.3
B $\quad$ shadow, to the nearest foot, that is cast
   by a flagpole that is 15 ft high and has
   an angle of depression of $28°$.
   A. 18 $\quad$ **B.** 28 $\quad$ **C.** 6 $\quad$ **D.** 79
   E. none of these

13. Simplify: $\dfrac{2 \tan 25°}{1 - \tan^2 25°}$ $\quad$ 6.3
C
   A. $\tan 25°$ $\quad$ **B.** $\tan 100°$ $\quad$ **C.** $\tan 50°$
   D. $\tan 75°$ $\quad$ **E.** none of these

14. The shape of an ellipse is $\quad$ 11.2
B $\quad$ dependent upon a constant called
   A. discriminant $\qquad$ **B.** eccentricity
   C. logarithm $\qquad$ **D.** slope
   E. none of these

15. Determine the polar coordinates $\quad$ 10.1
A $\quad$ for $(\sqrt{3}, 1)$
   A. $\left(2, \dfrac{\pi}{6}\right)$ $\quad$ **B.** $\left(4, \dfrac{\pi}{6}\right)$ $\quad$ **C.** $\left(\sqrt{3}, \dfrac{\pi}{6}\right)$
   A. $\left(-2, \dfrac{5\pi}{6}\right)$ $\quad$ **E.** none

Cumulative Review $\quad$ **593**

Summary

Matrix operations are defined and used and systems of equations are solved using matrices. Matrix transformations are also discussed. Vector operations in both 2- and 3-dimensional space are developed. Both polar and component form of vectors are utilized. Parametric as well as vector equations are used to represent lines, curves, and planes.

Chapter Objectives

- To find the sum and difference of two matrices
- To find the product of a matrix and a scalar and of two matrices
- To construct a matrix corresponding to a directed graph and to draw a directed graph corresponding to a matrix
- To find the multiplicative inverse of a matrix and to use it to solve a system of equations
- To solve a system of linear equations in three variables using the augmented matrix method
- To use transformation matrices to find the image of a point under a reflection or rotation
- To find the sum and difference of two vectors
- To multiply a vector by a scalar
- To find the norm of a vector
- To express a vector in polar or component form given its endpoints,
- To perform vector operations in component form
- To find, given two points on a line, a direction vector, a vector equation, and a pair of parametric equations
- To determine whether two vectors are parallel or perpendicular
- To solve problems in three-dimensional space using three-dimensional analogues of two-dimensional forms
- To find an equation of a plane using vectors in three dimensions

12 Matrices and Vectors

Mathematical Power

Modeling   A *matrix* is an arrangement of numbers in rows and columns. You may think of a matrix as a way of storing data. Since their invention, matrices have become an important tool in almost every field of study—from physics and biology to business and social science. The model below illustrates how matrices can be used by public health officials.

It is important for the government to be able to predict the health of the country's population in the future so that required medical services can be planned. The U.S. General Accounting Office (GAO) classifies different age groups into health categories. Suppose individuals 65 to 69 years old are placed into health groups labeled Good, Fair, and Poor. The GAO then sets up a *transition matrix* like this:

		Two-Year Health Probabilities			
		Good	Fair	Poor	Deceased
Current	Good	0.75	0.10	0.08	0.07
Health	Fair	0.04	0.70	0.18	0.08
Status	Poor	0.00	0.06	0.80	0.14
	Deceased	0	0	0	1

The numbers in the matrix are called *transition probabilities* – so, for example, a person who is currently in fair health has a probability of 0.18 of being in poor health in 2 years and only a probability of 0.04 of having his or her health improve to good over that time span. The transition probabilities are derived from analyzing large amounts of data collected over time.

To predict how healthy the population will be 2 years from now, you must first know the general health of the population today. Suppose 50% the people in the 65–69 age group are in good health, 30% are in fair health, and 20% are in poor health. You can represent

594

Features

Modeling

this information in a shorthand way using a matrix with only one row:

$$[0.5 \quad 0.3 \quad 0.2 \quad 0]$$

This type of matrix is called a *row vector*.

In Lesson 12.2 you will learn that you can multiply the transition matrix by the row vector to obtain a new row vector:

$$[0.387 \quad 0.272 \quad 0.254 \quad 0.087]$$

This row vector is the predictor for 2 years from now; 38.7% of the people will be in good health, 27.2% will be in fair health, 25.4% will be in poor health, and 8.7% will be deceased. Of course, it is important to compare the actual percents observed after 2 years with those that were predicted. This is to judge the accuracy of the model. Remember that a variety of factors can affect the probabilities greatly over a period of 2 years. For instance, public awareness of proper nutrition and fitness could very well decrease the probability of worsening health. Hence, the model must be reviewed and modified regularly.

Thinking Critically Suppose you saw a transition matrix for the 40–44 age group and the first row looked like this:

$$\text{Good} \quad [0.84 \quad 0.09 \quad 0.06 \quad 0.03]$$

What would your reaction be? Explain.

Project Suppose the possible grades on mathematics exams are A, B, C, D, and F. Make up reasonable probabilities for the final exam grade based on the midterm grade. For example, you may decide that if someone gets a C on the midterm, the probability of an A on the final is 0.05 while the probability of another C is 0.70. Try to use as much real data as you can to determine your probabilities. Display all the information in a clearly labeled transition matrix. Present your findings to the class.

595

Mathematical Power

Matrices and vectors are basic concepts in the branch of mathematics known as *linear algebra*. The fact that matrices, and the different operations that are defined for matrices, can be handled efficiently by high-speed computers make them especially useful for many diverse modern applications.

Students do not need to know the mechanics of matrix multiplication to understand what is accomplished by this public-health model. The transition probabilities and current group percentages are the results of statisticians' analyses of vast amounts of data. These results are then stored efficiently in matrix form, and matrix operations are used to make predictions for the future. Emphasize that the purpose of this type of model is to show *how a situation will change* over time. Transition matrices can also be used to study how social classes or genetic characteristics of a population may change. Students who grasp the key parts of the lesson should be able to suggest other reasonable applications of transition matrices.

When you discuss mathematical details of the model, be sure students can explain why the final number in the row vector is 0. (No member of the current population is deceased.)

Thinking Critically Students should understand that the sum of the probabilities across a row in a transition matrix must add up to exactly 1 because a row gives information for a whole group.

Vocabulary

additive identity of a matrix
additive inverse of a matrix
column matrix
dimensions of a matrix
element of a matrix
equal matrices
matrix
matrix equation
row matrix
scalar
scalar multiplication
square matrix
zero matrix

Ⓜ **Materials/Manipulatives**

weekly delivery inventory sheets
monthly retail sales sheets

Technology

calculator with matrix capabilities
computer

FOCUS

Students working in retail stores or other businesses may have encountered data arranged in matrix form. Ask them to bring copies of such matrices to class. Compile a list of all the uses of matrices that they have found.

12.1 Addition of Matrices

Objectives: To find the sum and difference of two matrices
To find the product of a matrix and a scalar

Focus

Collecting, storing, and analyzing data are routine activities in the world of business. For example, a company running stores in different locations may want to compare sales generated by the stores from one month to another. The sales figures may be represented by data arranged in a rectangular array of rows and columns called a *matrix*. The two matrices within the brackets below represent the sales of cassette tapes and compact discs sold by three stores for the first 2 months of the year.

	\multicolumn{3}{c}{January}	\multicolumn{3}{c}{February}
Store	1	2	3	1	2	3

$$\begin{array}{c}\text{Tapes}\\\text{CDs}\end{array}\begin{bmatrix} 23 & 14 & 19 \\ 65 & 46 & 52 \end{bmatrix} \qquad \begin{bmatrix} 21 & 17 & 23 \\ 72 & 59 & 64 \end{bmatrix}$$

New information can be obtained from such data by performing mathematical operations on the matrices.

A **matrix** is any rectangular array of numbers written within brackets. A matrix is usually represented by a capital letter and classified by its dimensions. The ***dimensions of a matrix*** are the numbers of rows and columns. For example,

$$\text{matrix } A = \begin{bmatrix} 3 & -2 \\ 4 & 5 \\ -8 & 1 \end{bmatrix} \text{ is a } 3 \times 2 \text{ (read "three by two") matrix since it has}$$

three rows and two columns. A matrix with m rows and n columns is an $m \times n$ matrix and may be written $A_{m \times n}$.

Each number in a matrix is an **element** of the matrix. An element of a matrix is identified by its position, given by the row and column numbers. The notation a_{ij} is used to identify the position of an element with subscript i representing the row and subscript j representing the column of the matrix. A general representation of a 3×3 matrix is

$$A_{3 \times 3} = [a_{ij}] = \begin{bmatrix} a_{11} & a_{12} & a_{13} \\ a_{21} & a_{22} & a_{23} \\ a_{31} & a_{32} & a_{33} \end{bmatrix}$$

A **square matrix** is a matrix that has the same number of rows and columns. A matrix with just one row is a **row matrix,** and a matrix with just one column is a **column matrix.**

596 Chapter 12 Matrices and Vectors

Example 1   Classify each matrix as row, column, or square. State the dimensions.

a. $D = \begin{bmatrix} 5 & -2 & \pi \end{bmatrix}$ b. $E = \begin{bmatrix} 4 \\ 8 \\ -1 \\ 0 \\ 5 \end{bmatrix}$ c. $F = \begin{bmatrix} 5 & 7 \\ 8 & 10 \end{bmatrix}$

a. D is a row matrix since it has one row. Its dimensions are 1×3.

b. E is a column matrix since it has one column. Its dimensions are 5×1.

c. F is a square matrix with two rows and two columns. Its dimensions are 2×2.

Two matrices are **equal** if and only if they have the same dimensions and their *corresponding elements* are equal. In general, matrix A is equal to matrix B if and only if $a_{ij} = b_{ij}$ for each i and j.

Matrix addition is defined only for matrices with the same dimensions. Two matrices with the same dimensions are said to be *conformable for addition.*

Matrix Addition

If two matrices, A and B, have the same dimensions, then their sum, $A + B$, is a matrix of the same dimensions whose elements are the sums of the corresponding elements of A and B.

Example 2   Given $A = \begin{bmatrix} 1 & 5 & 9 \\ -2 & -4 & 7 \end{bmatrix}$ and $B = \begin{bmatrix} 0 & 4 & -7 \\ 5 & -6 & 8 \end{bmatrix}$, find: a. $A + B$ b. $B + A$

a. $A + B = \begin{bmatrix} 1 & 5 & 9 \\ -2 & -4 & 7 \end{bmatrix} + \begin{bmatrix} 0 & 4 & -7 \\ 5 & -6 & 8 \end{bmatrix} = \begin{bmatrix} 1+0 & 5+4 & 9-7 \\ -2+5 & -4-6 & 7+8 \end{bmatrix} = \begin{bmatrix} 1 & 9 & 2 \\ 3 & -10 & 15 \end{bmatrix}$

b. $B + A = \begin{bmatrix} 0 & 4 & -7 \\ 5 & -6 & 8 \end{bmatrix} + \begin{bmatrix} 1 & 5 & 9 \\ -2 & -4 & 7 \end{bmatrix} = \begin{bmatrix} 0+1 & 4+5 & -7+9 \\ 5-2 & -6-4 & 8+7 \end{bmatrix} = \begin{bmatrix} 1 & 9 & 2 \\ 3 & -10 & 15 \end{bmatrix}$

Example 2 illustrates that matrix addition is commutative. This is true in general for matrix addition, since the addition of real numbers is commutative.

A **zero matrix** is a matrix all of whose elements are zeros. For example,

$O_{1 \times 4} = \begin{bmatrix} 0 & 0 & 0 & 0 \end{bmatrix}$ and $O_{3 \times 2} = \begin{bmatrix} 0 & 0 \\ 0 & 0 \\ 0 & 0 \end{bmatrix}$. The *additive identity* matrix for

the set of all $m \times n$ matrices is the $m \times n$ zero matrix.

The *additive inverse* of an $m \times n$ matrix A is the $m \times n$ matrix $-A$, such that $A + (-A) = O_{m \times n}$. It follows that $-A$ is the matrix whose elements are the additive inverses of the corresponding elements of A. For example,

if $A = \begin{bmatrix} 8 & 5 & -2 \\ 4 & 0 & 3 \end{bmatrix}$, then $-A = \begin{bmatrix} -8 & -5 & 2 \\ -4 & 0 & -3 \end{bmatrix}$.

12.1 Addition of Matrices   **597**

INSTRUCTION

Ⓜ • Distribute copies of actual weekly inventory or monthly sales reports to demonstrate the use and importance of matrices in the business world.
• Emphasize that when giving the dimensions of a matrix, the number of rows (horizontal) must be given first.
• Before students see the definition of matrix addition, encourage them to develop their own rules for adding matrices and to apply them; adding two 2×2 matrices or a 1×3 matrix and a 3×1 matrix. Ask them to describe problems they encounter when adding the second pair of matrices. Then have them look in the text for the actual definition of addition of matrices and the restrictions on matrices being added.
• Stress that scalar multiplication may be the first operation that they have encountered that is defined on different types of objects: a scalar and a matrix.
• Using a frame, such as in the example below, when writing equations helps students to see that X is not a number.

$3X + \begin{bmatrix} 4 & 5 \\ 6 & 2 \end{bmatrix} = \begin{bmatrix} 7 & 8 \\ 1 & 9 \end{bmatrix}$

$3 \begin{bmatrix} \\ \end{bmatrix} + \begin{bmatrix} 4 & 5 \\ 6 & 2 \end{bmatrix} = \begin{bmatrix} 7 & 8 \\ 1 & 9 \end{bmatrix}$

Alternative Learning Styles

Some students benefit from structure and organization that facilitates their understanding of new concepts by extending their understanding of previously learned concepts. In their math journals, have students make a chart that compares and contrasts each of the following properties for real numbers and for matrices.
• closure property
• additive identity property
• additive inverse property
• associative property
• commutative property

Classify each of the matrices as row, column, or square.

1. [2 4 9 10] row

2. $\begin{bmatrix} 3 & 4 & 1 \\ 2 & 0 & 4 \\ 1 & 5 & 7 \end{bmatrix}$ square

3. $\begin{bmatrix} 1 \\ 1 \\ 1 \end{bmatrix}$ column

4. [5 7] row

For Example 2

Given: $A = \begin{bmatrix} 1 & -1 \\ 2 & 3 \end{bmatrix}, B = \begin{bmatrix} 5 & 0 \\ -6 & 3 \end{bmatrix}$,

find:

1. $A + B \begin{bmatrix} 6 & -1 \\ -4 & 6 \end{bmatrix}$

2. $B + A \begin{bmatrix} 6 & -1 \\ -4 & 6 \end{bmatrix}$

Technology To add matrices using a calculator or computer software with matrix capabilities, have students consult the manual. On some utilities, students must first designate the size of a matrix A, B, or C, and then assign values to the appropriate positions in each matrix.

For Example 3

Given: $A = \begin{bmatrix} 5 & 6 & 7 \\ 1 & 0 & 2 \end{bmatrix}$ and

$B = \begin{bmatrix} 4 & 2 & 1 \\ -5 & 1 & -4 \end{bmatrix}$, find:

1. $B - A \begin{bmatrix} -1 & -4 & -6 \\ -6 & 1 & -6 \end{bmatrix}$

2. $A - B \begin{bmatrix} 1 & 4 & 6 \\ 6 & -1 & 6 \end{bmatrix}$

Properties of matrices can be proved by using the properties of real numbers. The properties of matrix addition are summarized below. You are asked to write proofs for some of these properties in the exercises.

Properties of Matrix Addition	
If A, B, and C are $m \times n$ matrices, then	
$A + B$ is an $m \times n$ matrix.	*Closure*
$A + B = B + A$	*Commutative*
$(A + B) + C = A + (B + C)$	*Associative*
There exists a unique $m \times n$ matrix O such that $O + A = A + O = A$.	*Additive identity*
For each A, there exists a unique matrix, $-A$, such that $A + (-A) = O$.	*Additive inverse*

Since $a - b = a + (-b)$ for real numbers, subtraction of matrices is defined using the additive inverse of a matrix.

Matrix Subtraction
If two matrices, A and B, have the same dimensions, then $A - B = A + (-B)$.

Example 3 Given $A = \begin{bmatrix} 1 & 2 & 1 \\ 3 & 0 & 5 \\ 7 & 8 & 10 \end{bmatrix}$ and $B = \begin{bmatrix} -2 & 4 & 6 \\ -1 & 0 & 1 \\ -2 & -1 & 3 \end{bmatrix}$, find $A - B$.

$$A - B = A + (-B) = \begin{bmatrix} 1 & 2 & 1 \\ 3 & 0 & 5 \\ 7 & 8 & 10 \end{bmatrix} + \begin{bmatrix} 2 & -4 & -6 \\ 1 & 0 & -1 \\ 2 & 1 & -3 \end{bmatrix} = \begin{bmatrix} 3 & -2 & -5 \\ 4 & 0 & 4 \\ 9 & 9 & 7 \end{bmatrix}$$

A real number is called a **scalar** in matrix algebra; **scalar multiplication** is defined as follows. Suppose that c is a scalar and A is a matrix. Then cA is the matrix whose elements are the products of c and each element of A. For example,

$$-5 \begin{bmatrix} 2 & 1 & -3 \\ 7 & -9 & 5 \end{bmatrix} = \begin{bmatrix} (-5)2 & (-5)1 & (-5)(-3) \\ (-5)7 & (-5)(-9) & (-5)5 \end{bmatrix} = \begin{bmatrix} -10 & -5 & 15 \\ -35 & 45 & -25 \end{bmatrix}$$

Matrices may be used to solve many real world problems.

Example 4 *Manufacturing* A manufacturer of basketballs has two plants that produce both rubber and leather basketballs. The basketballs carry an NBA label or a high school regulation label. The production levels for one shift at each plant are given by the production matrices below. What would be the total of each type of ball produced if plant 1 went to two shifts and plant 2 to three shifts?

598 Chapter 12 Matrices and Vectors

Production Matrices

	Plant 1			Plant 2	
	Leather	Rubber		Leather	Rubber

$$A = \begin{matrix} \text{NBA} \\ \text{H.S.} \end{matrix} \begin{bmatrix} 500 & 700 \\ 1300 & 1900 \end{bmatrix} \qquad B = \begin{matrix} \text{NBA} \\ \text{H.S.} \end{matrix} \begin{bmatrix} 400 & 1200 \\ 600 & 1600 \end{bmatrix}$$

$$2A = \begin{bmatrix} 2(500) & 2(700) \\ 2(1300) & 2(1900) \end{bmatrix} = \begin{bmatrix} 1000 & 1400 \\ 2600 & 3800 \end{bmatrix} \quad \textit{Production at plant 1 for two shifts}$$

$$3B = \begin{bmatrix} 3(400) & 3(1200) \\ 3(600) & 3(1600) \end{bmatrix} = \begin{bmatrix} 1200 & 3600 \\ 1800 & 4800 \end{bmatrix} \quad \textit{Production at plant 2 for three shifts}$$

$$2A + 3B = \begin{bmatrix} 1000 & 1400 \\ 2600 & 3800 \end{bmatrix} + \begin{bmatrix} 1200 & 3600 \\ 1800 & 4800 \end{bmatrix} = \begin{bmatrix} 2200 & 5000 \\ 4400 & 8600 \end{bmatrix}$$

Thus, there would be 2200 NBA leather, 5000 NBA rubber, 4400 H.S. leather, and 8600 H.S. rubber balls produced.

You can now verify or prove the following properties.

Properties of Scalar Multiplication

If A, B, and O are $m \times n$ matrices and c and d are scalars, then

cA is an $m \times n$ matrix.	*Closure*
$(cd)A = c(dA)$	*Associative*
$1 \cdot A = A$	*Multiplicative identity*
$0A = O$ and $cO = O$	*Multiplicative property of the zero scalar and of the zero matrix*
$c(A + B) = cA + cB$	*Distributive properties*
$(c + d)A = cA + dA$	

An equation that involves matrices is called a *matrix equation*. Simple matrix equations can be solved using the definitions of matrix addition, subtraction, and scalar multiplication. In a matrix equation, the variable represents a matrix or an element of a matrix.

Example 5 Solve: $3X + 2\begin{bmatrix} 1 & 5 & 0 \\ 2 & -1 & -3 \end{bmatrix} = \begin{bmatrix} 5 & 13 & 9 \\ -2 & 1 & 15 \end{bmatrix}$

$$3X + \begin{bmatrix} 2 & 10 & 0 \\ 4 & -2 & -6 \end{bmatrix} = \begin{bmatrix} 5 & 13 & 9 \\ -2 & 1 & 15 \end{bmatrix} \quad \textit{Scalar multiplication}$$

$$3X = \begin{bmatrix} 5 & 13 & 9 \\ -2 & 1 & 15 \end{bmatrix} - \begin{bmatrix} 2 & 10 & 0 \\ 4 & -2 & -6 \end{bmatrix} = \begin{bmatrix} 3 & 3 & 9 \\ -6 & 3 & 21 \end{bmatrix} \quad \textit{Matrix subtraction}$$

$$X = \tfrac{1}{3}\begin{bmatrix} 3 & 3 & 9 \\ -6 & 3 & 21 \end{bmatrix} = \begin{bmatrix} 1 & 1 & 3 \\ -2 & 1 & 7 \end{bmatrix} \quad \textit{Scalar multiplication}$$

You can check by substituting for X in the original equation.

For Example 4

Carl and Flo are training for a triathlon by running, cycling, and swimming. The matrices below show the number of miles that each devotes to each activity, both on weekdays and weekend days. What is the total number of miles that each devotes to each activity in a 7-day week?

$$A = \begin{matrix} \text{Running} \\ \text{Cycling} \\ \text{Swimming} \end{matrix} \overset{\begin{matrix} \text{Weekday} \\ \text{Carl} \quad \text{Flo} \end{matrix}}{\begin{bmatrix} 8 & 10 \\ 50 & 40 \\ 4 & 2 \end{bmatrix}}$$

$$B = \begin{matrix} \text{Running} \\ \text{Cycling} \\ \text{Swimming} \end{matrix} \overset{\begin{matrix} \text{Weekend Day} \\ \text{Carl} \quad \text{Flo} \end{matrix}}{\begin{bmatrix} 6 & 8 \\ 40 & 45 \\ 2 & 3 \end{bmatrix}}$$

Carl: 52 mi running, 330 mi cycling, 24 mi swimming; Flo: 66 mi running, 290 mi cycling, 16 mi swimming

Technology Note that on some calculators, the exercise above cannot be done in one step. For example, to find $5A + 2B$ you must calculate $5A$ then press [Ans] $+ 2 * B$.

For Example 5

1. Solve: $2X + 3\begin{bmatrix} 1 & 2 \\ 4 & 1 \end{bmatrix} = \begin{bmatrix} 1 & -2 \\ 6 & 5 \end{bmatrix}$

$\begin{bmatrix} -1 & -4 \\ -3 & 1 \end{bmatrix}$

2. Solve: $5X - 4\begin{bmatrix} 1 & 2 \\ 4 & 0 \\ 6 & 4 \end{bmatrix} = \begin{bmatrix} 1 & 2 \\ -6 & 10 \\ 16 & 4 \end{bmatrix}$

$\begin{bmatrix} 1 & 2 \\ 2 & 2 \\ 8 & 4 \end{bmatrix}$

Have students explain how to simplify the following matrix expression.

$$\begin{bmatrix} -3 & 8 \\ 6 & 5 \\ -2 & 0 \end{bmatrix} - \begin{bmatrix} 4 & 6 \\ 8 & -1 \\ -2 & -3 \end{bmatrix} + 2\begin{bmatrix} 0 & -2 \\ -1 & 3 \\ 1 & -2 \end{bmatrix}$$

INDEPENDENT PRACTICE

Assignment Guide

Basic: 1–30
Average: 1–33 odd, 34–44
Enriched: 10–43 odd, 44–54

Teacher's Resource Book
  Practice, page 78

Ⓡ Review

Exercise 7 reviews the concept of slope. Exercises 21 and 30 involve solving systems of equations and Exercise 33, a logarithmic equation. Exercise 41 reviews identifying a conic equation.

Technology

All exercises of this lesson may be completed without the aid of a calculator with matrix capabilities. However, Exercises 8 to 29 may be done using such a device.

Additional Answers
Class Exercises

4. $\begin{bmatrix} -1 & -1 & 12 & 16 \\ 7 & 8 & 7 & -1 \end{bmatrix}$

5. $\begin{bmatrix} -1 & -1 & 12 & 16 \\ 7 & 8 & 7 & -1 \end{bmatrix}$

6. $\begin{bmatrix} 4 & 10 & 0 & -1 \\ -1 & 10 & 17 & 28 \end{bmatrix}$

7. $\begin{bmatrix} 3 & 6 \\ 9 & 12 \\ 21 & 15 \\ 12 & 9 \end{bmatrix}$

8. $\begin{bmatrix} -12 & -36 \\ -4 & 0 \end{bmatrix}$

9. not conformable

 If you use a calculator to solve the matrix equation of Example 5, assign each **2** × 3 matrix to one of the calculator's designated storage locations. Then use the calculator's keying steps to perform the matrix operations.

Class Exercises

State the dimensions of each matrix. Identify any row, column, or square matrices.

1. $\begin{bmatrix} 7 \\ 2 \\ 8 \end{bmatrix}$ 3 × 1; column

2. $\begin{bmatrix} 4 & 5 & 9 \\ 1 & 1 & 1 \end{bmatrix}$ 2 × 3

3. $\begin{bmatrix} 17 & 20 & 14 \\ 23 & -12 & -17 \\ 56 & 80 & -29 \end{bmatrix}$ 3 × 3; square

Use matrices *A, B, C, D, E,* and scalars $a = 3$ and $b = -4$ to perform the indicated operations. If an operation is not possible, explain why.

$$A = \begin{bmatrix} 1 & 3 & 4 & 5 \\ 2 & 6 & 8 & 9 \end{bmatrix} \quad B = \begin{bmatrix} -2 & -4 & 8 & 11 \\ 5 & 2 & -1 & -10 \end{bmatrix} \quad C = \begin{bmatrix} 1 & 2 \\ 3 & 4 \\ 7 & 5 \\ 4 & 3 \end{bmatrix} \quad D = \begin{bmatrix} 3 & 9 \\ 1 & 0 \end{bmatrix}$$

4. $A + B$ 5. $B + A$ 6. $2A - B$ 7. aC 8. bD 9. $A - C$

Solve each matrix equation.

10. $X + \begin{bmatrix} 2 & -1 \\ 4 & 6 \end{bmatrix} = \begin{bmatrix} 7 & 1 \\ 9 & 14 \end{bmatrix}\begin{bmatrix} 5 & 2 \\ 5 & 8 \end{bmatrix}$

11. $5X - \begin{bmatrix} 1 \\ 4 \end{bmatrix} = \begin{bmatrix} 4 \\ 6 \end{bmatrix}\begin{bmatrix} 1 \\ 2 \end{bmatrix}$

12. **Thinking Critically** Is it possible to add two 2 × 3 matrices to get a sum matrix of $\begin{bmatrix} 0 & 0 \\ 0 & 0 \end{bmatrix}$? Why or why not?

Practice Exercises   Use appropriate technology.

State the dimensions of each matrix. Identify any row, column, or square matrices.

A 1. $[4 \quad 7 \quad 9 \quad 1 \quad 5]$ 1 × 5; row

2. $[-2 \quad -5 \quad 8 \quad 15]$ 1 × 4; row

3. $\begin{bmatrix} 5 & 2 & 1 \\ 7 & 11 & 3 \end{bmatrix}$ 2 × 3

4. $\begin{bmatrix} 5 & 2 \\ 1 & 4 \end{bmatrix}$ 2 × 2; square

5. $\begin{bmatrix} 4 & 2 & 7 & 8 \\ 15 & 9 & 6 & 1 \\ 5 & -3 & -1 & -7 \end{bmatrix}$ 3 × 4

6. $\begin{bmatrix} 9 \\ 8 \\ -7 \end{bmatrix}$ 3 × 1; column

Ⓡ 7. Find the slope of the line with equation $\frac{2}{3}x - \frac{3}{4}y = \frac{1}{5}$. $\frac{8}{9}$

Use matrices *A, B, C, D, F,* and *G* to perform the indicated operations. If an operation is not possible, explain why.

$$A = \begin{bmatrix} 1 & 3 \\ 2 & 4 \\ 6 & 7 \end{bmatrix} \quad B = \begin{bmatrix} 6 & 7 \\ 11 & 10 \\ 15 & 1 \end{bmatrix} \quad C = [1 \quad 2 \quad 3] \quad D = [-2 \quad -1 \quad -4] \quad F = \begin{bmatrix} 7 & 2 \\ 1 & 4 \end{bmatrix} \quad G = \begin{bmatrix} 0 & 0 \\ 0 & 0 \end{bmatrix}$$

8. $A + B$ 9. $B + A$ 10. $B - A$ 11. $A - B$
12. $C + D$ 13. $F + G$ 14. $3A + 4B$ 15. $G - 3F$
16. $D + B$ 17. $\sqrt{2}D$ 18. $-\sqrt{3}G$ 19. $\frac{1}{2}A$

12. no; A 2 × 3 matrix added to a 2 × 3 matrix will produce a sum matrix which is also 2 × 3.

20. *Real Estate*   An apartment owner rents apartments in buildings A and B. Each building has efficiency, one bedroom, and two bedroom apartments. Using the matrices below, determine a matrix that shows the total number of rented and vacant apartments.

$$
\begin{array}{c}
A \\
\begin{array}{cc}
\text{Rented} & \text{Vacant}
\end{array}
\end{array}
\qquad\qquad
\begin{array}{c}
B \\
\begin{array}{cc}
\text{Rented} & \text{Vacant}
\end{array}
\end{array}
$$

$$
\begin{array}{l}
\text{Efficiency} \\
\text{One bedroom} \\
\text{Two bedroom}
\end{array}
\begin{bmatrix} 10 & 2 \\ 12 & 0 \\ 9 & 3 \end{bmatrix}
\qquad
\begin{array}{l}
\text{Efficiency} \\
\text{One bedroom} \\
\text{Two bedroom}
\end{array}
\begin{bmatrix} 8 & 0 \\ 14 & 1 \\ 6 & 3 \end{bmatrix}
$$

Ⓡ **21.** Solve the system: $\begin{cases} x + z = 8 \\ y - z = 3 \\ x + 4y = 26 \end{cases}$ $(6, 5, 2)$

Solve each matrix equation.

B **22.** $\begin{bmatrix} 1 & 2 & -3 \\ 2 & 1 & 3 \end{bmatrix} + X = \begin{bmatrix} 5 & 1 & 8 \\ -6 & 0 & 5 \end{bmatrix}$

23. $\begin{bmatrix} 1 & 2 \\ 2 & 1 \\ -3 & 4 \end{bmatrix} + X = \begin{bmatrix} 5 & -6 \\ 1 & 0 \\ 8 & 5 \end{bmatrix}$

24. $4\begin{bmatrix} 1 & 1 \\ 3 & 2 \end{bmatrix} + X = -2\begin{bmatrix} 0 & 1 \\ 8 & 9 \end{bmatrix}$

25. $5\begin{bmatrix} 8 & 4 \\ 6 & 9 \end{bmatrix} + X = -7\begin{bmatrix} 1 & 1 \\ 10 & 5 \end{bmatrix}$

26. $8X - [8 \quad 7 \quad 3] = 5X + [-2 \quad 11 \quad 13]$

27. $7X + [1 \quad 4 \quad 9 \quad 5] = 3X - [0 \quad -1 \quad -8 \quad 6]$

28. $7X - \begin{bmatrix} 4 & 12 \\ 75 & -1 \end{bmatrix} = 2\begin{bmatrix} 5 & 50 \\ 50 & -10 \end{bmatrix}$

29. $3\begin{bmatrix} 2 & 1 & -1 \\ 0 & 2 & 1 \end{bmatrix} + 5X = \begin{bmatrix} 11 & 3 & -13 \\ 15 & -9 & 8 \end{bmatrix}$

Ⓡ **30.** Solve the system: $\begin{cases} 2(3x + 2y) = 0 \\ 4x = 3(y - 1) \end{cases}$ $\left(-\frac{6}{17}, \frac{9}{17}\right)$

31. *Nutrition*   An independent nutritionist gathered data about the best and worst sandwiches of two fast food restaurants. For restaurant A, the best sandwich had 320 calories and 10 grams of fat while the worst sandwich had 440 calories and 26 grams of fat. For restaurant B, the best sandwich had 379 calories and 18 grams of fat and the worst had 935 calories and 61 grams of fat. Organize the data for each restaurant in matrix form. By how much does the fat content differ between the best A and the best B sandwiches? For which sandwich would the calorie content increase the most when eating in restaurant B rather than restaurant A? 8; worst

32. Thinking Critically   How do you use the properties of real numbers to prove the closure property for the addition of $m \times n$ matrices?

Ⓡ **33.** Solve: $\log_{0.1} x = -3$ 1000

Find the value of each variable.

34. $x[2 \quad 7] + y[3 \quad 8] = [5 \quad 10]$ $x = -2; y = 3$

35. $-3[x \quad y] = [x \quad 4] - [8 \quad -2y]$ $x = 2; y = -\frac{4}{5}$

36. $x\begin{bmatrix} 3 \\ 4 \end{bmatrix} + y\begin{bmatrix} 1 \\ 7 \end{bmatrix} = \begin{bmatrix} -4 \\ -11 \end{bmatrix}$ $x = -1; y = -1$

37. $x\begin{bmatrix} -2 \\ 1 \end{bmatrix} - y\begin{bmatrix} 0 \\ 3 \end{bmatrix} = \begin{bmatrix} 6 \\ 12 \end{bmatrix}$ $x = -3; y = -5$

38. Writing in Mathematics   Explain why the elements x and y in the matrix equation must be 2 and -5, respectively. $\begin{bmatrix} x & -7 & -5 \\ 4 & y & 2 \end{bmatrix} = \begin{bmatrix} 4 & 2 & 1 \\ 0 & x & 3 \end{bmatrix} - \begin{bmatrix} x & 9 & 6 \\ -4 & 7 & 1 \end{bmatrix}$

12.1 Addition of Matrices   **601**

Writing in Mathematics
38. To find x, solve the equation $x = 4 - x$. Therefore, $x = 2$. To find y, solve the equation $y = x - 7$. Since $x = 2$, $y = -5$.

Alternative Assessment

Instruct students to write a paragraph explaining how to add two 3×3 matrices for the benefit of a person who has never done this before. Be sure that they consider the knowledge of the person when choosing names and definitions, and making analogies, and have them include one or two real world applications to justify learning such a skill. Encourage the students to find a person to use their explanation for adding two matrices.

Enrichment

Find two matrices whose sum is
$$\begin{bmatrix} 7 & 7 & 3 \\ 3 & 0 & -2 \\ 11 & -1 & 1 \end{bmatrix}$$ and whose difference is
$$\begin{bmatrix} 3 & 5 & 3 \\ -1 & 2 & -2 \\ -3 & 5 & -3 \end{bmatrix}.$$
$$\begin{bmatrix} 5 & 6 & 3 \\ 1 & 1 & -2 \\ 4 & 2 & -1 \end{bmatrix}, \begin{bmatrix} 2 & 1 & 0 \\ 2 & -1 & 0 \\ 7 & -3 & 2 \end{bmatrix}$$

Additional Answers
39. Portland; 6; Chicago; The new matrix would give the increase in off-road miles, auto restricted zones, and number of parks in each city.

39. *Health/Fitness* A magazine rated the nation's 10 best walking cities in 1980 and 1990. Five of the cities were in the top 10 both times. They were San Francisco, California; Chicago, Illinois; Portland, Oregon; New Orleans, Louisiana; and Boston, Massachusetts. Some of the data collected is organized in the two matrices below. Which city had the largest increase in the number of off-road miles for walkers and joggers? At the end of the decade, how many more auto-restricted zones were there in all five cities combined? Which city had the largest increase in the number of parks? Suppose you subtract the matrix for 1980 from the matrix for 1990. What information would the new matrix give?

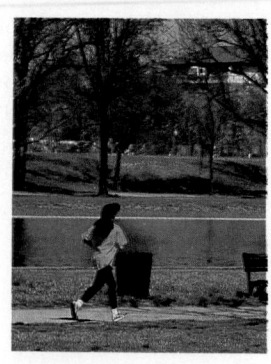

1980

	Off-road miles	Auto-restricted zones	Number of parks
San Francisco	127	3	245
Chicago	49	1	551
Portland	150	1	205
New Orleans	1	2	249
Boston	15	1	238

1990

	Off-road miles	Auto-restricted zones	Number of parks
San Francisco	134	6	250
Chicago	53	1	563
Portland	170	2	207
New Orleans	2	3	250
Boston	18	2	240

C 40. **Writing in Mathematics** Gather data from a current periodical that compares several categories of information for two different years (such as the data in Exercise 39). Write an exercise that will use the data in matrix form to answer at least two questions.

R 41. Identify the conic with equation $3x^2 - xy + 5y^2 + 3x - 2y + 4 = 0$. ellipse

Solve for x, y, and z.

42. $[2x \quad x - y \quad x - y + z] = [8 \quad 7 \quad 10]$ (4, −3, 3)

43. $[3x \quad x + y \quad x + y - z] = [-9 \quad 4 \quad 2]$ (−3, 7, 2)

44. $[x + y \quad y + z \quad x + y + z] = [-1 \quad -5 \quad -3]$ (2, −3, −2)

45. Prove that the addition of 2 by 2 matrices is associative.

46. Prove that the addition of 2 by 3 matrices is associative.

47. Prove that matrix addition is commutative for all $m \times n$ matrices. *Hint:* Let a_{ij} and b_{ij} represent corresponding elements of two $m \times n$ matrices A and B.

48. Prove that $0 \times A = O$, where O and A have the same dimensions, 0 is a scalar, and O is a zero matrix.

49. Prove that for any scalar c, $c(A + B) = cA + cB$.

Review

1. Solve the following system: $\begin{cases} 3x + 2y = 16 \\ 4x - 6y = 4 \end{cases}$ (4, 2)

2. In triangle ABC, $\angle A = 52°$, $c = 10$, and $a = 15$. Find $\angle C$, to the nearest degree. 32°

602 Chapter 12 Matrices and Vectors

Writing in Mathematics
40. Answers may vary.

Multiplication of Matrices

Objective: *To find the product of two matrices*

Focus

Matrix theory was developed by Arthur Cayley (1821–1895), an outstanding English mathematician of his time. Even though he practiced law for over 20 years, he managed during this time to publish over 200 papers in mathematics. Finally, in 1863, he gave up law entirely to accept a chair of mathematics at Cambridge. His work with matrices found no practical use until long after his death. Since then some matrix concepts have been used by physicists to develop the theory of quantum mechanics. The somewhat complicated definition of matrix multiplication given in this lesson was chosen by Cayley because he saw that it could be used to represent a change of coordinate systems.

Addition is not the only operation that can be defined for matrices; multiplication is another. For example, consider a retail store that sells three types of milk, skim, 1% fat, and 2% fat. The prices per one-half gallon are displayed below in a 1 × 3 row matrix and the number of one-half gallons sold on Monday per day is displayed in a 3 × 1 column matrix.

Price per Half-Gallon

Skim   1%   2%
[$1.29 $1.39 $1.49]

Number of Half-Gallons
Sold Monday

Skim $\begin{bmatrix} 18 \\ 25 \\ 30 \end{bmatrix}$
1%
2%

To determine the gross income for the day, multiply the elements of the row matrix by corresponding elements of the column matrix and add.

($1.29)(18) + ($1.39)(25) + ($1.49)(30) = $23.22 + $34.75 + $44.70 = $102.67

Suppose that the number of half-gallons of skim, 1%, and 2% milk sold on Tuesday are 20, 22, and 25, respectively. Then the gross income for Tuesday is calculated as shown below.

($1.29)(20) + ($1.39)(22) + ($1.49)(25) = $93.63

You can display the number of half-gallons sold for both days in a single two-column matrix. The product of the matrices is a 1 × 2 matrix.

$$[\$1.29 \quad \$1.39 \quad \$1.49] \begin{bmatrix} 18 & 20 \\ 25 & 22 \\ 30 & 25 \end{bmatrix} = \begin{matrix} \text{Mon.} & \text{Tue.} \\ [\$102.67 & \$93.63] \end{matrix} \text{Income}$$

12.2 Multiplication of Matrices   **603**

LESSON PLAN

Vocabulary
identity matrix
matrix multiplication
transpose of a matrix

Ⓜ Materials/Manipulatives
overhead projector
colored markers

Technology
calculator with matrix capabilities
computer

FOCUS

The idea that conceptual mathematical discoveries are often made centuries before any practical applications are found for them is interesting to many students. Citing examples of this trend can go a long way toward addressing students who frequently ask, "Why do I have to learn this?" Such students may be interested in learning about Nikolai Lobachevski, who demonstrated his own tendency for progressive thinking with his pioneering work with non-Euclidean geometry. He believed that every mathematical discovery, no matter how abstract, would eventually be used for some practical purpose.

This example illustrates the row-into-column pattern that is used in multiplying matrices $A_{2 \times 3}$ and $B_{3 \times 4}$ below.

$$\underset{A}{\begin{bmatrix} 2 & 3 & 5 \\ 1 & 2 & 3 \end{bmatrix}} \underset{B}{\begin{bmatrix} 8 & 4 & 0 & 6 \\ 8 & 10 & 5 & 3 \\ 10 & 15 & 7 & 10 \end{bmatrix}} = \underset{AB}{\begin{bmatrix} 90 & — & — & — \\ — & — & 31 & — \end{bmatrix}}$$

The number in the first row and first column of AB is 90, since

$$2(8) + 3(8) + 5(10) = 16 + 24 + 50 = 90$$

Similarly, the number in the second row and third column is 31, since

$$1(0) + 2(5) + 3(7) = 0 + 10 + 21 = 31$$

You can verify the remaining elements in the product $AB = \begin{bmatrix} 90 & 113 & 50 & 71 \\ 54 & 69 & 31 & 42 \end{bmatrix}$.

Notice that the multiplication of A and B is possible because the three columns in A match the three rows in B, as illustrated at the right.

The pattern shown suggests the following definition for matrix multiplication.

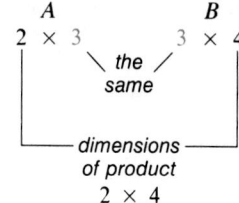

Matrix Multiplication

The product of two matrices, $A_{m \times p}$ and $B_{p \times n}$, is the matrix AB with dimensions $m \times n$. Any element in the ith row and jth column of this product matrix is the sum of the products of the corresponding elements of the ith row of A and the jth column of B.

The product of two matrices A and B is defined only if the number of columns in A is equal to the number of rows in B. Two matrices whose product is defined are said to be *conformable* for multiplication.

Example 1 Given $A = \begin{bmatrix} 4 & 5 \\ 7 & 2 \\ 1 & 3 \end{bmatrix}$ and $B = \begin{bmatrix} 2 & 3 \\ 5 & 6 \end{bmatrix}$, find AB.

Since A is a 3×2 matrix and B is a 2×2 matrix, the product is defined, and its dimensions are 3×2.

$$AB = \begin{bmatrix} 4 & 5 \\ 7 & 2 \\ 1 & 3 \end{bmatrix} \begin{bmatrix} 2 & 3 \\ 5 & 6 \end{bmatrix} = \begin{bmatrix} 4(2) + 5(5) & 4(3) + 5(6) \\ 7(2) + 2(5) & 7(3) + 2(6) \\ 1(2) + 3(5) & 1(3) + 3(6) \end{bmatrix} = \begin{bmatrix} 33 & 42 \\ 24 & 33 \\ 17 & 21 \end{bmatrix}$$

604 Chapter 12 Matrices and Vectors

In Example 1, note that BA is not defined since the number of columns in B is not equal to the number of rows in A. Thus, $AB \neq BA$, which means that, in general, matrix multiplication is *not* a commutative operation. Check the products AB and BA with a calculator or computer. *What happens when you try to find BA?* Raising a matrix to a power is defined only for square matrices. *Why?*

Example 2 Given $A = \begin{bmatrix} 1 & 2 & -4 \\ -5 & 0 & 3 \end{bmatrix}$ and $B = \begin{bmatrix} 1 & -1 & 2 \\ 3 & 0 & 4 \\ 5 & 2 & -3 \end{bmatrix}$, find the following matrix products:

    a. B^2 **b.** AB^2 **c.** B^2A

a. $B^2 = \begin{bmatrix} 1 & -1 & 2 \\ 3 & 0 & 4 \\ 5 & 2 & -3 \end{bmatrix} \begin{bmatrix} 1 & -1 & 2 \\ 3 & 0 & 4 \\ 5 & 2 & -3 \end{bmatrix}$

$= \begin{bmatrix} 1(1) + (-1)3 + 2(5) & 1(-1) + (-1)0 + 2(2) & 1(2) + (-1)4 + 2(-3) \\ 3(1) + 0(3) + 4(5) & 3(-1) + 0(0) + 4(2) & 3(2) + 0(4) + 4(-3) \\ 5(1) + 2(3) + (-3)5 & 5(-1) + 2(0) + (-3)2 & 5(2) + 2(4) + (-3)(-3) \end{bmatrix}$

$= \begin{bmatrix} 8 & 3 & -8 \\ 23 & 5 & -6 \\ -4 & -11 & 27 \end{bmatrix}$

b. $AB^2 = \begin{bmatrix} 1 & 2 & -4 \\ -5 & 0 & 3 \end{bmatrix} \begin{bmatrix} 8 & 3 & -8 \\ 23 & 5 & -6 \\ -4 & -11 & 27 \end{bmatrix} = \begin{bmatrix} 70 & 57 & -128 \\ -52 & -48 & 121 \end{bmatrix}$

c. Since the number of columns in B^2 is not equal to the number of rows in A, B^2A is not defined.

You may need to multiply matrices in order to solve for unknown elements of a matrix equation.

Example 3 Solve for x and y: $\begin{bmatrix} 3 & 1 \\ -2 & 0 \end{bmatrix} \begin{bmatrix} x & 4 \\ -4 & 5y \end{bmatrix} = \begin{bmatrix} 2 & -3 \\ -4 & -8 \end{bmatrix}$

Multiply matrices and then use the definition of equal matrices.

$\begin{bmatrix} 3 & 1 \\ -2 & 0 \end{bmatrix} \begin{bmatrix} x & 4 \\ -4 & 5y \end{bmatrix} = \begin{bmatrix} 2 & -3 \\ -4 & -8 \end{bmatrix}$

$\begin{bmatrix} 3x - 4 & 12 + 5y \\ -2x + 0 & -8 + 0 \end{bmatrix} = \begin{bmatrix} 2 & -3 \\ -4 & -8 \end{bmatrix}$ *Definition of matrix multiplication*

$3x - 4 = 2$ $12 + 5y = -3$ *Definition of equal matrices*
$3x = 6$ $5y = -15$
$x = 2$ $y = -3$

Note that the equation $-2x = -4$ could have been used to solve for x. Check that the values $x = 2$ and $y = -3$ satisfy the given matrix equation.

For Example 2

If $A = \begin{bmatrix} 1 & 3 \\ -1 & -2 \end{bmatrix}$ and $B = \begin{bmatrix} 5 & 0 & 9 \\ 1 & 3 & 6 \end{bmatrix}$, find:

1. A^2 $\begin{bmatrix} -2 & -3 \\ 1 & 1 \end{bmatrix}$

2. A^2B $\begin{bmatrix} -13 & -9 & -36 \\ 6 & 3 & 15 \end{bmatrix}$

3. $(BA)B$ not conformable

For Example 3

Solve for x and y.

$\begin{bmatrix} -3 & -4 \\ 2 & -2 \end{bmatrix} \begin{bmatrix} x & 5 \\ y & -2 \end{bmatrix} = \begin{bmatrix} -5 & -7 \\ 8 & 14 \end{bmatrix}$

$x = 3; y = -1$

Thinking Critically

The product is undefined, since the number of columns in B is not equal to the number of rows in A.

This is true because only square matrices have the same number of columns and rows, which is necessary to be able to square a matrix.

For a promotion, a music store has packaged LP records, cassette tapes, and CDs in three types of arrangements. The least expensive package contains 3 records, 2 tapes, and 1 CD. The medium-priced package contains 2 records, 3 tapes, and 2 CDs. The most expensive package contains no records, 4 tapes, and 6 CDs. The cost to the store for an LP record, a tape, and a CD is $4.00, $6.00, and $11.00, respectively. What is the cost to prepare each kind of package?

$35, $48, and $90, respectively

The **identity matrix** is the square matrix I of dimensions $n \times n$, whose main diagonal from upper left corner to lower right corner contains only 1's. All other elements are 0. A square matrix with dimensions $n \times n$ is said to be of "the nth order." For example, the identity matrix of the third order is

$$I_{3 \times 3} = \begin{bmatrix} 1 & 0 & 0 \\ 0 & 1 & 0 \\ 0 & 0 & 1 \end{bmatrix}.$$

The product of $I_{n \times n}$ and any matrix A of equal order is readily seen to be the matrix A. That is, $AI = A = IA$. You can verify these equalities with examples of your own, such as $I_{2 \times 2} = \begin{bmatrix} 1 & 0 \\ 0 & 1 \end{bmatrix}$ and $A_{2 \times 2} = \begin{bmatrix} 2 & 3 \\ -4 & 5 \end{bmatrix}$. When the product of two square matrices A and B is the identity matrix, then A and B are multiplicative inverses of each other. Thus, $B = A^{-1}$ and $A = B^{-1}$.

You can multiply any matrix $A_{n \times n}$ by the zero matrix $O_{n \times n}$ and note that the matrix AO is equal to $O_{n \times n}$. Thus, identity matrices for addition and multiplication are analogous to the numbers 0 and 1 in the set of real numbers. With the definition of matrix multiplication and multiplicative identity, it is now possible to state the following properties of square matrices. You are asked to prove some of them in the exercises.

**Properties of Matrix Multiplication
for Square Matrices**

If A, B, and C are $n \times n$ matrices, then

AB is an $n \times n$ matrix.	*Closure*
$(AB)C = A(BC)$	*Associative*
$I_{n \times n}A = AI_{n \times n} = A$	*Multiplicative identity*
$O_{n \times n}A = AO_{n \times n} = O_{n \times n}$	*Multiplicative property of the zero matrix*
A^{-1} is the multiplicative inverse of A if A^{-1} is defined and $AA^{-1} = A^{-1}A = I_{n \times n}$.	*Multiplicative inverse*
$A(B + C) = AB + AC$ $(B + C)A = BA + CA$	*Distributive properties*

The information given in Example 4 must be stored in matrices that are conformable for multiplication.

Example 4   *Business*   A fruit store operator packages fruit in three different ways for gift packages. The economy package E has 6 apples, 3 oranges, and 3 pears. The standard package S has 5 apples, 4 oranges, and 4 pears. The luxury package L has 6 of each type of fruit. The cost is $0.50, $1.10, and $0.80 for an apple, orange, and pear, respectively. What is the cost of preparing each package of fruit?

Arrange the given data in matrix form.

	Cost		
	Apple	Orange	Pear
$A =$	[$0.50	$1.10	$0.80]

Number of Items

$$\begin{array}{c} \\ \text{Apples} \\ \text{Oranges} \\ \text{Pears} \end{array} \begin{array}{ccc} E & S & L \\ \left[\begin{array}{ccc} 6 & 5 & 6 \\ 3 & 4 & 6 \\ 3 & 4 & 6 \end{array}\right] \end{array} = B$$

To find the cost of each package, multiply the number-of-items matrix B and the cost matrix A.

$$AB = [\$0.50 \quad \$1.10 \quad \$0.80] \left[\begin{array}{ccc} 6 & 5 & 6 \\ 3 & 4 & 6 \\ 3 & 4 & 6 \end{array}\right] = [\$8.70 \quad \$10.10 \quad \$14.40]$$

The costs of the economy, the standard, and the luxury packages are $8.70, $10.10, and $14.40, respectively.

In Example 4, the information in matrix B could have been shown with rows and columns interchanged as:

Number of Items

$$\begin{array}{c} \\ E \\ S \\ L \end{array} \begin{array}{ccc} \text{Apples} & \text{Oranges} & \text{Pears} \\ \left[\begin{array}{ccc} 6 & 3 & 3 \\ 5 & 4 & 4 \\ 6 & 6 & 6 \end{array}\right] \end{array}$$

This matrix is called the **transpose** of B, denoted by B'. The transpose of A is a 3×1 column matrix. In some problems it is necessary to use the transpose of a matrix in order to multiply. *If the transpose matrices A' and B' had been used in Example 4, in what order would the factors appear in the multiplication? Why?*

Class Exercises

Use the matrices given below. Determine which of the following products are defined, and state the dimensions of the products. If a product is not defined, state why.

$$A = \left[\begin{array}{cc} 3 & 0 \\ 1 & 7 \\ 4 & 2 \end{array}\right] \quad B = \left[\begin{array}{ccc} 7 & 8 & 15 \\ -3 & 5 & -6 \end{array}\right] \quad C = \left[\begin{array}{ccc} 3 & 5 & 9 \\ -1 & -2 & 4 \\ 0 & 6 & 0 \end{array}\right] \quad I = \left[\begin{array}{ccc} 1 & 0 & 0 \\ 0 & 1 & 0 \\ 0 & 0 & 1 \end{array}\right]$$

1. AB 3×3
2. BA 2×2
3. BC 2×3
4. CB not conformable
5. C^2 3×3
6. A^2 not conformable
7. $(C + I)B$ not conformable
8. $(C + B)I$ not conformable

Use the matrices given above to perform the indicated operations if they are defined. If an operation is not defined, label it "undefined."

9. BC
10. AB
11. C^2
12. CI

13. **Thinking Critically** Given matrices $A_{f \times g}$ and $B_{s \times t}$, under what condition is the product AB defined? The product BA? $g = s; t = f$

12.2 Multiplication of Matrices **607**

Thinking Critically
The factors would have appeared in the same order because you would still first be multiplying the cost of the Apples, Oranges, and Pears by the numbers of Apples, Oranges, and Pears.

607

Ask students what condition must be met before two matrices can be multiplied.

Additional Answers

9. $\left[\begin{array}{ccc} 13 & 109 & 95 \\ -14 & -61 & -7 \end{array}\right]$

10. $\left[\begin{array}{ccc} 21 & 24 & 45 \\ -14 & 43 & -27 \\ 22 & 42 & 48 \end{array}\right]$

11. $\left[\begin{array}{ccc} 4 & 59 & 47 \\ -1 & 23 & -17 \\ -6 & -12 & 24 \end{array}\right]$

12. $\left[\begin{array}{ccc} 3 & 5 & 9 \\ -1 & -2 & 4 \\ 0 & 6 & 0 \end{array}\right]$

INDEPENDENT PRACTICE

Assignment Guide
Basic: 1–25, 29, 30
Average: 1–25 odd, 26–37
Enriched: 1–31 odd, 32–45

Teacher's Resource Book
Practice, page 79

® Review
Exercises 11, 13, 27, and 35 review concepts of solving systems of equations, solving an equation in quadratic form, using the factor theorem, and solving triangles.

Technology
Although all exercises in this lesson may be completed without the use of a calculator with matrix capabilities, its use frees students of lengthy calculations, particularly in Exercises 1 to 10.

Additional Answers

1. [17]   2. [31]

3. $\begin{bmatrix} 36 & -2 \\ 33 & -84 \end{bmatrix}$ 4. $\begin{bmatrix} -103 & 41 \\ 11 & 74 \end{bmatrix}$

5. undefined   6. undefined

7. $\begin{bmatrix} -25 \\ 18 \\ 10 \end{bmatrix}$ 8. $\begin{bmatrix} 121 \\ -16 \\ 1 \end{bmatrix}$

9. $\begin{bmatrix} 1 & 0 \\ 0 & 1 \end{bmatrix}$ 10. $\begin{bmatrix} 1 & 0 \\ 0 & 1 \end{bmatrix}$

12. Example: $B = \begin{bmatrix} 4 \\ 6 \end{bmatrix}$; $AB = [32]$;

$BA = \begin{bmatrix} 20 & 8 \\ 30 & 12 \end{bmatrix}$

14. The product may or may not exist. If it does, it is not necessarily equal to AB.

18. $\begin{bmatrix} \$1.75 \\ \$2.50 \end{bmatrix}$

19. $\begin{bmatrix} \$2.80 \\ \$4.00 \end{bmatrix}$

20. $2.80; $4.00

Practice Exercises Use appropriate technology.

Find the product, if it is defined. If it is not defined, label it "undefined."

A 1. $\begin{bmatrix} 1 & 5 \end{bmatrix} \begin{bmatrix} 2 \\ 3 \end{bmatrix}$

2. $\begin{bmatrix} -7 & 4 \end{bmatrix} \begin{bmatrix} -1 \\ 6 \end{bmatrix}$

3. $\begin{bmatrix} 5 & 1 \\ 6 & -9 \end{bmatrix} \begin{bmatrix} 7 & -2 \\ 1 & 8 \end{bmatrix}$

4. $\begin{bmatrix} 17 & 3 \\ 5 & -6 \end{bmatrix} \begin{bmatrix} -5 & 4 \\ -6 & -9 \end{bmatrix}$

5. $\begin{bmatrix} 1 & 2 & 3 \\ 4 & 5 & 6 \end{bmatrix} \begin{bmatrix} -1 & -2 \\ -5 & 0 \end{bmatrix}$

6. $\begin{bmatrix} 7 & 8 \\ 0 & 3 \end{bmatrix} \begin{bmatrix} 9 \\ 1 \\ 4 \end{bmatrix}$

7. $\begin{bmatrix} -4 & 5 & -7 \\ 0 & 8 & 2 \\ 1 & 1 & 1 \end{bmatrix} \begin{bmatrix} 7 \\ 2 \\ 1 \end{bmatrix}$

8. $\begin{bmatrix} -1 & 5 & 9 \\ 8 & 0 & 0 \\ 5 & 0 & 1 \end{bmatrix} \begin{bmatrix} -2 \\ 4 \\ 11 \end{bmatrix}$

9. $\begin{bmatrix} 5 & 6 \\ 4 & 5 \end{bmatrix} \begin{bmatrix} 5 & -6 \\ -4 & 5 \end{bmatrix}$

10. $\begin{bmatrix} 7 & 6 \\ 8 & 7 \end{bmatrix} \begin{bmatrix} 7 & -6 \\ -8 & 7 \end{bmatrix}$

® 11. Solve the system: $\begin{cases} 2x + y = 6 \\ x - 2y = 8 \end{cases}$ $x = 4; y = -2$

12. **Thinking Critically** If matrix $A = \begin{bmatrix} 5 & 2 \end{bmatrix}$, give an example of a matrix B such that AB and BA are both defined. Find each product.

® 13. Solve: $z^{-4} - z^{-2} - 6 = 0$ $\pm\frac{\sqrt{3}}{3}, \pm\frac{\sqrt{2}}{2}i$

14. **Thinking Critically** If the product AB of matrices A and B is the matrix C, what can be said about the product BA?

A local theatre company put on performances Thursday, Friday, and Saturday. Matrix A shows prices for three types of tickets. Matrix B shows the numbers of tickets sold for each performance.

	Price per Ticket		
	Regular	Student	Sr. Citizen
$A =$	[$5	$2	$4]

	Number of Tickets Sold			
	Thu.	Fri.	Sat.	
	50	63	75	Regular
$B =$	25	70	80	Student
	60	52	50	Sr. Citizen

15. Find the matrix product AB, and label it. [$540 $663 $735]

16. What were the total ticket receipts on Thursday? $540

17. What were the total receipts for the three performances? $1938

Business Tara mixed nuts to sell at a bazaar. She packaged different mixtures of peanuts, cashews, and almonds in two types of boxes, plain and deluxe. Matrix A shows the percent of nuts in each type of box. Matrix B shows the cost per pound of each kind of nut.

	Peanuts	Cashews	Almonds	
Plain	70%	10%	20%	$= A$
Deluxe	20%	60%	20%	

	Cost per Pound	
Peanuts	$1.50	
Cashews	$3.00	$= B$
Almonds	$2.00	

18. Tara put 1 lb of nuts in each box. Multiply matrices to find the cost of the nuts in each plain box and each deluxe box.

19. Tara priced the nuts so that there would be a 60% profit. Multiply the product matrix AB by 1.6 to find the selling price for each box.

20. What was the price of a plain box? A deluxe box?

608 Chapter 12 Matrices and Vectors

Determine whether the expressions in each pair are equal.

$$A = \begin{bmatrix} 2 & -1 \\ 3 & 4 \end{bmatrix} \quad B = \begin{bmatrix} 5 & -2 \\ 6 & 3 \end{bmatrix} \quad C = \begin{bmatrix} 4 & -2 \\ 1 & 5 \end{bmatrix} \quad D = \begin{bmatrix} 1 & 5 \\ -3 & 0 \end{bmatrix}$$

B 21. $A(BC)$ and $(AB)C$ yes   **22.** $B(CD)$ and $(BC)D$ yes   **23.** $2(BD)$ and $(2B)D$ yes

24. $3(DA)$ and $(3D)A$ yes   **25.** $A(B + C)$ and $AB + AC$ **26.** $A(B - C)$ and $AB - AC$
yes   yes

R 27. Determine the value of K that will make $x - 3$ a factor of $x^3 - 5x^2 - 2x + K$. 24

28. Writing in Mathematics Some properties of real numbers are not valid for matrices. For example, for real numbers a, b, and c $(a \neq 0)$, if $ab = ac$, then $b = c$. Explain why this property is not valid for matrices. Use matrices $A = \begin{bmatrix} 3 & 9 \\ 2 & 6 \end{bmatrix}$, $B = \begin{bmatrix} 1 & 4 \\ 4 & -2 \end{bmatrix}$, and $C = \begin{bmatrix} 10 & 1 \\ 1 & -1 \end{bmatrix}$. Then describe another property of real numbers that is not valid for matrices by studying the product $\begin{bmatrix} 1 & 2 & 4 \end{bmatrix} \begin{bmatrix} -2 \\ -1 \\ 1 \end{bmatrix}$.

Solve for x and y.

29. $\begin{bmatrix} 0 & -1 \\ 2 & 0 \end{bmatrix} \begin{bmatrix} x & 3 \\ -3 & 2y \end{bmatrix} = \begin{bmatrix} 3 & -6 \\ -4 & 6 \end{bmatrix}$ $(-2, 3)$ **30.** $\begin{bmatrix} x & -2 \\ 1 & 0 \end{bmatrix} \begin{bmatrix} 3 & -2 \\ 1 & y \end{bmatrix} = \begin{bmatrix} 4 & -14 \\ 3 & -2 \end{bmatrix}$ $(2, 5)$

31. $\begin{bmatrix} x & 2y \\ 3 & 4 \end{bmatrix} \begin{bmatrix} 1 & -2 \\ -3 & 5 \end{bmatrix} = \begin{bmatrix} -3 & 6 \\ -9 & 14 \end{bmatrix}$ $(-3, 0)$ **32.** $\begin{bmatrix} x & 1 \\ 2 & -y \end{bmatrix} \begin{bmatrix} 3 & -2 \\ 1 & 0 \end{bmatrix} = \begin{bmatrix} 4 & -2 \\ 7 & -4 \end{bmatrix}$ $(1, -1)$

33. Thinking Critically If the product AB of square matrices A and B is not the identity matrix, what can be said about the product BA?

34. Education In a course on public speaking, three teams had a debating competition. Each team's score was based on the number of students who ranked first, second, or third place in a debate. The results of 10 debates are shown in the ranking matrix R.

Number of Students

Team	First	Second	Third	
A	3	3	3	
B	5	4	3	$= R$
C	2	1	5	

Teams were awarded 5 points for each first place, 4 points for each second, and 2 points for each third. Show this information in a matrix K and find the product RK. Which team won the competition? How many points did this team score?

R 35. Solve triangle ABC if $\angle A = 95°$, $b = 52$, and $c = 61$. $\angle B = 38°; \angle C = 47°; a = 84$

36. Given matrices $D_{3 \times 1}$, $E_{1 \times 2}$, $F_{2 \times 3}$, determine all arrangements for which the three matrices can be multiplied. Find the dimensions of each product.

C 37. Consider the set of matrices of the form $\begin{bmatrix} a & -b \\ b & a \end{bmatrix}$, where a and b are real numbers. Show that the set is closed under matrix multiplication.

12.2 Multiplication of Matrices   **609**

Writing in Mathematics

28. Answers may vary. The product $AB = AC = \begin{bmatrix} 39 & -6 \\ 26 & -4 \end{bmatrix}$, but $B \neq C$.

Another property that is not valid for matrices is: If $ab = 0$ then either $a = 0$ or $b = 0$. The product $ab = 0$, using the two matrices given in the question, but neither a nor b is a zero matrix.

Lesson Quiz
Given the following matrices, find the product if it is defined. If it is not defined, label it undefined.

$$A = \begin{bmatrix} 1 & 5 \\ 9 & 3 \end{bmatrix}, B = \begin{bmatrix} 0 & -2 \\ 3 & 1 \end{bmatrix},$$

$$C = \begin{bmatrix} 1 & 4 & 11 \\ 0 & 0 & 2 \end{bmatrix}, D = \begin{bmatrix} 4 \\ -5 \\ -2 \end{bmatrix},$$

$$E = \begin{bmatrix} 1 & 0 & 5 \\ 0 & 2 & 3 \\ 1 & 8 & 4 \end{bmatrix}$$

1. A^2 $\begin{bmatrix} 46 & 20 \\ 36 & 54 \end{bmatrix}$

2. CB undefined

3. E^2D $\begin{bmatrix} -226 \\ -164 \\ -310 \end{bmatrix}$

4. $(AC)D$ $\begin{bmatrix} -58 \\ -354 \end{bmatrix}$

5. CE $\begin{bmatrix} 12 & 96 & 61 \\ 2 & 16 & 8 \end{bmatrix}$

6. B^2D undefined

7. BA $\begin{bmatrix} -18 & -6 \\ 12 & 18 \end{bmatrix}$

Additional Answers
33. The product BA is also not the identity matrix.

34. $K = \begin{bmatrix} 5 \\ 4 \\ 2 \end{bmatrix}$; $RK = \begin{bmatrix} 33 \\ 47 \\ 24 \end{bmatrix}$; Team B won with 47 points.

36. DEF: 3×3; FDE: 2×2; EFD: 1×1

37. Let $\begin{bmatrix} c & -d \\ d & c \end{bmatrix}$ be another matrix of this form. Then the product is $\begin{bmatrix} ac - bd & -ad - bc \\ bc + ad & -bd + ac \end{bmatrix} = \begin{bmatrix} ac - bd & -(ad + bc) \\ ad + bc & ac - bd \end{bmatrix}$, and therefore the set is closed.

38. Show that the only matrices of the form $\begin{bmatrix} a & -b \\ b & a \end{bmatrix}$ that are equal to their squares are $\begin{bmatrix} 0 & 0 \\ 0 & 0 \end{bmatrix}$ and $\begin{bmatrix} 1 & 0 \\ 0 & 1 \end{bmatrix}$.

39. Prove that the multiplication of 2×2 matrices is associative.

40. Prove that $A(B + C) = AB + AC$ for any 3×3 matrices A, B, and C.

A company that produces posters has three plants: one on the West Coast, one on the East Coast, and one in the Midwest. Among their many posters, each plant produces a Michael Jordan, Magic Johnson, and Larry Bird poster. Personnel are needed to print, package, and ship the posters. Matrix T gives the times in hours of each type of labor required to make each type of poster; matrix P gives the daily production capacity at each plant; matrix W provides hourly wages of the different workers at each plant; and matrix O contains the total orders received by the company in May and June.

Hours Required per Poster

	Print	Package	Ship
Jordan	0.04	0.06	0.02
$T = $ Johnson	0.05	0.07	0.03
Bird	0.03	0.05	0.02

Daily Production Capacity

	Jordan	Johnson	Bird
West	500	1,000	200
$P = $ East	600	400	800
Midwest	1,200	300	300

Hourly Wages

	Print	Package	Ship
West	8.00	5.00	6.00
$W = $ East	7.40	6.30	7.20
Midwest	8.20	6.10	6.70

Total Orders

	May	June
Jordan	100,000	200,000
$O = $ Johnson	80,000	100,000
Bird	40,000	20,000

Use the matrices to compute the following. In some cases you will need to write the transpose of a matrix.

41. What are the hours of each type of labor needed in May and June to fill all orders?

42. What is the labor cost per poster at each plant?

43. What is the cost of filling all the June orders at the Midwest plant?

44. What are the daily hours of each type of labor needed at each plant if production levels are at capacity?

45. What is the daily amount that each plant will pay its personnel when producing at capacity?

Challenge

1. Point A is in the interior of a square of side length s such that it is equally distant from two consecutive vertices and from the side opposite these vertices. If d represents the common distance, find d. $\frac{5s}{8}$

2. If the parabola $y = ax^2 + bx + c$ passes through the points $(0, 2)$, $(1, -2)$, and $(-1, 3)$, find the value of $a + b + c$. -2

38. If $\begin{bmatrix} a & -b \\ b & a \end{bmatrix}$ equals its square, then $a = a^2 - b^2$ and $b = 2ab$. Then $2ab - b = 0$. So

$b = 0$ or $a = \frac{1}{2}$. If $b = 0$, then $a^2 = a$, and $a = 0$ or $a = 1$. If $a = \frac{1}{2}$, then $\frac{1}{2} = \frac{1}{4} -$

b^2, and $b^2 = -\frac{1}{4}$, which is not possible. Therefore, $a = 0$ or $a = 1$ and $b = 0$, giving

$\begin{bmatrix} 0 & 0 \\ 0 & 0 \end{bmatrix}$ or $\begin{bmatrix} 1 & 0 \\ 0 & 1 \end{bmatrix}$.

12.3 Directed Graphs

Objectives: To use directed graphs to represent problems
To construct a matrix corresponding to a directed graph
To draw a directed graph corresponding to a matrix

Focus

Modern libraries depend upon the computer to assist patrons with finding information. Each document in the information retrieval system is labeled with a number of descriptors or index terms. If each index term is drawn as a point and joined by a segment to another point when closely related, the result is a diagram called a *similarity graph*. Here is a similarity graph that might be used by a librarian in a medical library.

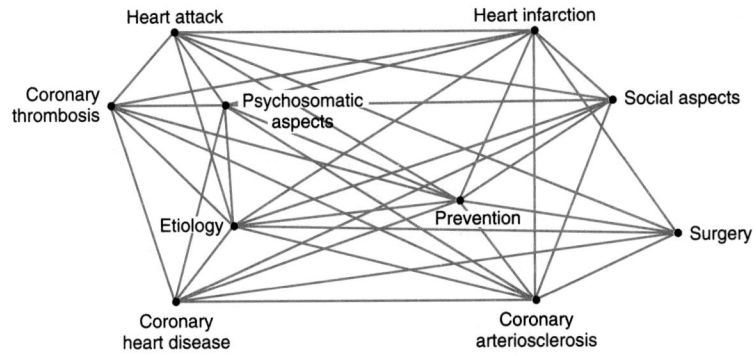

Part of a Similarity Graph

The librarian can use the graph to obtain a classification of documents and also as an aid in the retrieval of large amounts of medical information.

Similarity graphs illustrate one aspect of graph theory, which has many applications in fields such as electrical engineering, computer science, chemistry, political science, ecology, genetics, transportation, and information processing. The ability to use matrices with graph theory aids in understanding the study of communication networks, transportation networks, telephone and pipeline networks, ecosystems, tournaments, and information retrieval. Graph theory has therefore become increasingly important in mathematical modeling.

An important aspect of graph theory is the study of *finite graphs*. A **finite graph** is simply a set of points, called *nodes*, and a set of lines, called *edges*, which connect the nodes. The information in a finite graph may be represented by a special matrix called the **adjacency matrix** as shown on the next page.

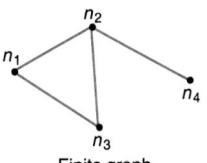

Finite graph

12.3 Directed Graphs   **611**

LESSON PLAN

Vocabulary
adjacency matrix
communications matrix
directed graph
edges
finite graph
nodes

Ⓜ **Materials/Manipulatives**
copies of airline or train schedules
business organization flowcharts

Technology
calculator with matrix capabilities
computer

FOCUS

Discuss with students examples of similarity graphs that they have encountered in biology, ecology, genetics, or other subject areas. Encourage interested students to research further examples of similarity graphs and their connections to matrices.

Ⓜ • Use data obtained from an airline schedule to construct a directed graph. Have students use arrows to show direct flights from one location to another. Then have students represent this data in an adjacency matrix similar to that in the text using a 1 to show that a direct flight exists and a 0 if one does not exist.

Ⓜ • Students may find it interesting to use business organization charts to construct directed graphs and communications matrices.

• For Examples 2 and 3, students may find it helpful to use a directed graph to verify that the elements of matrix M^2 do indeed represent the number of two-step ways to relay a message from one person to another. Students also may wish to use directed graphs to verify the accuracy of matrices raised to higher powers.

Alternative Learning Styles

Students often benefit by taking a step back to evaluate what they are learning and to relate it to their own experience.

Have students work in small groups to discuss and record the advantages and disadvantages of representing data such as that found in Example 1 in each of three forms: paragraph, directed graphs, and matrices. Encourage students not only to give general explanations but also to provide examples from either their direct experience or their readings in other subject areas.

Points n_1, n_2, n_3, and n_4 are the nodes of the graph. Two nodes connected by an edge are said to be *adjacent*. A 1 in the first row, second column indicates that node n_1 is adjacent to node n_2. Since node n_2 is also adjacent to node n_1, there is a 1 in the second row, first column as well. Notice the symmetry of numbers about the main diagonal of the adjacency matrix. A zero indicates that the respective nodes are not adjacent. The zeros on the main diagonal of the adjacency matrix show that no node is adjacent to itself.

$$\begin{array}{c} \quad \begin{array}{cccc} n_1 & n_2 & n_3 & n_4 \end{array} \\ \begin{array}{c} n_1 \\ n_2 \\ n_3 \\ n_4 \end{array} \begin{bmatrix} 0 & 1 & 1 & 0 \\ 1 & 0 & 1 & 1 \\ 1 & 1 & 0 & 0 \\ 0 & 1 & 0 & 0 \end{bmatrix} \end{array}$$

Adjacency Matrix

Finite graphs may need to include information about direction. A **directed graph** is a finite graph that has a direction associated with its edges. For example, the airline service graph indicates that there is service between Chicago and New York in both directions. A person traveling from St. Louis to New York has a direct flight. However, the flight from New York to St. Louis must include Chicago.

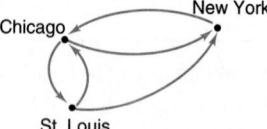

Directed Graph

The matrix that represents the airline service is shown at the right. The flight from St. Louis to New York is shown by the 1 in the S row and N column. Notice how the matrix reflects the two-way service, with 1's in the first row matching 1's in the first column. This symmetry of entries about the main diagonal does not exist for the one-way service. Other information can be seen from the matrix, such as the number of different flights that leave and arrive at each airport, and the total number of different flights, which is 5.

$$\begin{array}{c} \qquad\qquad \text{To} \\ \qquad \begin{array}{ccc} C & N & S \end{array} \\ \text{From} \begin{array}{c} C \\ N \\ S \end{array} \begin{bmatrix} 0 & 1 & 1 \\ 1 & 0 & 0 \\ 1 & 1 & 0 \end{bmatrix} \end{array}$$

Suppose you leave Chicago and want to return to Chicago on a second flight. In how many ways can this be done? From the graph, you can see there are two ways:

$$C \rightarrow N \rightarrow C \quad \text{and} \quad C \rightarrow S \rightarrow C$$

Trace the other routes that are possible in two successive flights.

From Chicago:	From New York:	From St. Louis:
$C \rightarrow S \rightarrow N$	$N \rightarrow C \rightarrow N$	$S \rightarrow C \rightarrow S$
	$N \rightarrow C \rightarrow S$	$S \rightarrow C \rightarrow N$
		$S \rightarrow N \rightarrow C$

You can now put these two-flight results in another matrix as shown at the right. A simpler way to obtain the matrix for two successive flights is to square the original matrix. Notice how you can trace the steps in finding the first entry of 2.

$$\begin{array}{c} \qquad \begin{array}{ccc} C & N & S \end{array} \\ \begin{array}{c} C \\ N \\ S \end{array} \begin{bmatrix} 2 & 1 & 0 \\ 0 & 1 & 1 \\ 1 & 1 & 1 \end{bmatrix} \end{array}$$

$$\begin{array}{c} C \\ N \\ S \end{array} \begin{bmatrix} 0 & 1 & 1 \\ 1 & 0 & 0 \\ 1 & 1 & 0 \end{bmatrix} \begin{bmatrix} 0 & 1 & 1 \\ 1 & 0 & 0 \\ 1 & 1 & 0 \end{bmatrix} = \begin{bmatrix} 2 & 1 & 0 \\ 0 & 1 & 1 \\ 1 & 1 & 1 \end{bmatrix} \begin{array}{c} C \\ N \\ S \end{array}$$

To find the numbers of ways to reach a destination in one or two flights, just add the original and the squared matrices.

612   Chapter 12 Matrices and Vectors

Modeling communication systems by graphs and matrices makes it easier to analyze and improve the systems. Adjacency matrices that are used to represent communications systems are called *communications matrices*.

Example 1 The president P of a company communicates directly with vice presidents v_1 and v_2, secretaries s_1 and s_2, and the building engineer E. The engineer E communicates with s_1 and s_2, while s_1 and s_2 communicate with each other and vice president v_2. Vice presidents v_1 and v_2 communicate with each other and president P. Draw a directed graph to show the communication system and write the communications matrix, using 1 to mean direct communication and zero to mean no direct communication. Use the matrix to find the number of ways two people can communicate with one another in two steps.

Let the nodes be represented by the letters, P, v_1, v_2, s_1, s_2, and E.

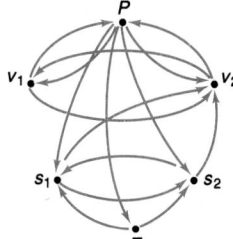

$$\begin{array}{c}\text{To}\\ \text{From}\quad\begin{array}{c}P\\v_1\\v_2\\s_1\\s_2\\E\end{array}\begin{bmatrix}0&1&1&1&1&1\\1&0&1&0&0&0\\1&1&0&0&0&0\\0&0&1&0&1&0\\0&0&1&1&0&0\\0&0&0&1&1&0\end{bmatrix}\end{array}$$

Suppose that M represents the communications matrix of Example 1. Then the second-stage matrix M^2 yields the number of ways the people can communicate in two steps indirectly through another member of the company.

$$M^2 = \begin{bmatrix}0&1&1&1&1&1\\1&0&1&0&0&0\\1&1&0&0&0&0\\0&0&1&0&1&0\\0&0&1&1&0&0\\0&0&0&1&1&0\end{bmatrix}\begin{bmatrix}0&1&1&1&1&1\\1&0&1&0&0&0\\1&1&0&0&0&0\\0&0&1&0&1&0\\0&0&1&1&0&0\\0&0&0&1&1&0\end{bmatrix} = \begin{array}{c}P\\v_1\\v_2\\s_1\\s_2\\E\end{array}\begin{bmatrix}2&1&3&2&2&0\\1&2&1&1&1&1\\1&1&2&1&1&1\\1&1&1&1&0&0\\1&1&1&0&1&0\\0&0&2&1&1&0\end{bmatrix}$$

The number 2 in the first row, fourth column indicates that the president may communicate with secretary s_1 in two different ways in two steps. The president may communicate with s_2 who then communicates with s_1 or with E who then communicates with s_1.

The successive powers of M in Example 1, that is, M^3, M^4, M^5, . . . , M^n, represent the number of ways each person in the system of that example may communicate with each other in 3, 4, 5, . . . , and n steps, respectively. A calculator makes it possible to find powers of a matrix quickly and accurately.

A directed graph along with a description of the nodes and edges may give valuable information in a relatively compact form.

12.3 Directed Graphs   **613**

GUIDED PRACTICE

For Example 1
The manager M of the secretarial pool in a large company communicates directly with two assistant managers m_1 and m_2 and the production room supervisor p. Assistant managers m_1 and m_2 communicate with each other and the manager M. Assistant manager m_1 communicates with the production room supervisor p and secretary s_1, while m_2 communicates with secretary s_2. Secretary s_1 communicates with m_1, while s_2 communicates with m_2. Draw a directed graph to show the communication system and write the communication matrix using 1 to mean direct communication and 0 to mean no direct communication. Let the nodes be represented by M, m_1, m_2, p, s_1, and s_2.

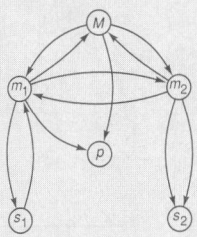

$$\begin{array}{c}\text{To}\\ \text{From}\quad\begin{array}{c}M\\m_1\\m_2\\p\\s_1\\s_2\end{array}\begin{bmatrix}0&1&1&1&0&0\\1&0&1&1&1&0\\1&1&0&0&0&1\\0&0&0&0&0&0\\0&1&0&0&0&0\\0&0&1&0&0&0\end{bmatrix}\end{array}$$

613

For Example 2

Suppose that the nodes in the diagram represent power companies and that a directed edge means that the first company buys power from the second company when there is heavy demand. Interpret the data in the graph both descriptively and in matrix form.

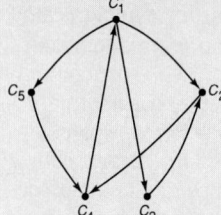

C_1 buys power from C_2, C_3, and C_5 when there is heavy demand; C_2, from C_4; C_3, from C_2; C_4, from C_1; C_5, from C_4.

$$\begin{array}{c} \\ C_1 \\ C_2 \\ C_3 \\ C_4 \\ C_5 \end{array} \begin{array}{ccccc} C_1 & C_2 & C_3 & C_4 & C_5 \\ \left[\begin{array}{ccccc} 0 & 1 & 1 & 0 & 1 \\ 0 & 0 & 0 & 1 & 0 \\ 0 & 1 & 0 & 0 & 0 \\ 1 & 0 & 0 & 0 & 0 \\ 0 & 0 & 0 & 1 & 0 \end{array}\right] \end{array}$$

For Example 3

Use the directed graph from Example 2 to determine the following.

1. In how many ways may C_1 buy power from C_4 by way of one intermediary company? **2**

2. Is it possible for C_1 to buy power from C_4 by way of two intermediary companies? **yes**

Example 2 *Networking*   Suppose that the nodes in the diagram represent people and that a directed edge means that the first person knows the phone number of the second person. Interpret the data in the graph both descriptively and in matrix form.

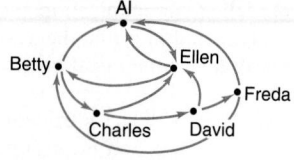

Al knows the phone number of Ellen. Betty knows the phone numbers of Charles and Al. Charles knows the phone numbers of Ellen and David. David knows the phone numbers of Freda and Ellen. Ellen knows the phone numbers of Al and Betty. Freda knows the phone numbers of Al and Betty.

$$\begin{array}{c} \\ A \\ B \\ C \\ D \\ E \\ F \end{array} \begin{array}{cccccc} A & B & C & D & E & F \\ \left[\begin{array}{cccccc} 0 & 0 & 0 & 0 & 1 & 0 \\ 1 & 0 & 1 & 0 & 0 & 0 \\ 0 & 0 & 0 & 1 & 1 & 0 \\ 0 & 0 & 0 & 0 & 1 & 1 \\ 1 & 1 & 0 & 0 & 0 & 0 \\ 1 & 1 & 0 & 0 & 0 & 0 \end{array}\right] \end{array}$$

The zeros on the diagonal indicate that no person will call himself or herself.

Many different questions may be answered from a directed graph.

Example 3 *Communication*   Refer to the directed graph of Example 2.

   a. In how many ways may a message get from Betty to Ellen in three or fewer calls?

   b. Is it possible to get a message from Freda to Charles? If so, what is the minimum number of calls to accomplish this?

Use the adjacency matrix of Example 2 and raise to powers. A calculator that handles matrices can be used to perform the multiplication.

$$M = \begin{array}{c} A \\ B \\ C \\ D \\ E \\ F \end{array}\begin{array}{c} \begin{array}{cccccc} A & B & C & D & E & F \end{array} \\ \left[\begin{array}{cccccc} 0 & 0 & 0 & 0 & 1 & 0 \\ 1 & 0 & 1 & 0 & 0 & 0 \\ 0 & 0 & 0 & 1 & 1 & 0 \\ 0 & 0 & 0 & 0 & 1 & 1 \\ 1 & 1 & 0 & 0 & 0 & 0 \\ 1 & 1 & 0 & 0 & 0 & 0 \end{array}\right] \end{array}$$

$$M^2 = \begin{array}{c} A \\ B \\ C \\ D \\ E \\ F \end{array}\begin{array}{c} \begin{array}{cccccc} A & B & C & D & E & F \end{array} \\ \left[\begin{array}{cccccc} 1 & 1 & 0 & 0 & 0 & 0 \\ 0 & 0 & 0 & 1 & 2 & 0 \\ 1 & 1 & 0 & 0 & 1 & 1 \\ 2 & 2 & 0 & 0 & 0 & 0 \\ 1 & 0 & 1 & 0 & 1 & 0 \\ 1 & 0 & 1 & 0 & 1 & 0 \end{array}\right] \end{array}$$

$$M^3 = \begin{array}{c} A \\ B \\ C \\ D \\ E \\ F \end{array}\begin{array}{c} \begin{array}{cccccc} A & B & C & D & E & F \end{array} \\ \left[\begin{array}{cccccc} 1 & 0 & 1 & 0 & 1 & 0 \\ 2 & 2 & 0 & 0 & 1 & 1 \\ 3 & 2 & 1 & 0 & 1 & 0 \\ 2 & 0 & 2 & 0 & 2 & 0 \\ 1 & 1 & 0 & 1 & 2 & 0 \\ 1 & 1 & 0 & 1 & 2 & 0 \end{array}\right] \end{array}$$

   a. To find the number of ways to get a message from Betty to Ellen in three calls or fewer, add the entries in the second row (Betty), fifth column (Ellen) in the matrices M, M^2, and M^3. Thus, there are $0 + 2 + 1 = 3$ ways. There are no direct ways, 2 two-call ways, and 1 three-call way.

   b. To determine whether it is possible to get a message from Freda to Charles, look at the entries in the sixth row (Freda) and third column (Charles) to find a nonzero element. The first time a nonzero element appears is in M^2. Thus, the minimum number of calls is 2.

The approach of Example 3 can also be used to model transportation patterns among several plants in a manufacturing company.

Example 4 A manufacturing plant has three buildings: an administration building, a factory, and a garage. A network of roads for the plant is shown. The finite graph corresponds to a time when all roads had two-way traffic, so no arrows are needed. Later some roads became one-way. This is reflected in the directed graph, where two-way traffic is indicated by arrows pointing in both directions.

a. Determine a matrix for the finite graph of the network of two-way roads.

b. Determine a matrix for the directed graph of roads, some of which are one-way.

c. Compare the two matrices with respect to symmetry about the main diagonal. Explain the difference in entries for traffic on the loop.

Finite graph   Directed graph

a.

$$\text{From} \quad \begin{array}{c} \\ A \\ F \\ G \end{array} \begin{array}{c} \quad\quad \text{To} \\ \begin{array}{ccc} A & F & G \end{array} \\ \left[\begin{array}{ccc} 0 & 1 & 1 \\ 1 & 0 & 1 \\ 1 & 1 & 2 \end{array} \right] \end{array}$$

b.

$$\text{From} \quad \begin{array}{c} \\ A \\ F \\ G \end{array} \begin{array}{c} \quad\quad \text{To} \\ \begin{array}{ccc} A & F & G \end{array} \\ \left[\begin{array}{ccc} 0 & 1 & 1 \\ 1 & 0 & 0 \\ 0 & 1 & 1 \end{array} \right] \end{array}$$

c. The first adjacency matrix is symmetric about the main diagonal but the second is not. The first matrix indicates the two ways of traveling on the loop; the second indicates one way.

Class Exercises

For each of the graphs, construct the adjacency matrix.

1.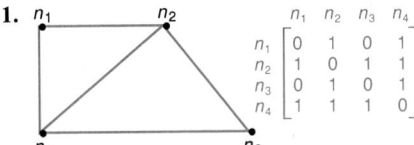

$$\begin{array}{c} \\ n_1 \\ n_2 \\ n_3 \\ n_4 \end{array} \begin{array}{c} \begin{array}{cccc} n_1 & n_2 & n_3 & n_4 \end{array} \\ \left[\begin{array}{cccc} 0 & 1 & 0 & 1 \\ 1 & 0 & 1 & 1 \\ 0 & 1 & 0 & 1 \\ 1 & 1 & 1 & 0 \end{array} \right] \end{array}$$

2.

$$\begin{array}{c} \\ n_1 \\ n_2 \\ n_3 \\ n_4 \end{array} \begin{array}{c} \begin{array}{cccc} n_1 & n_2 & n_3 & n_4 \end{array} \\ \left[\begin{array}{cccc} 0 & 0 & 0 & 1 \\ 0 & 0 & 0 & 1 \\ 0 & 0 & 0 & 1 \\ 1 & 1 & 1 & 0 \end{array} \right] \end{array}$$

3. *Travel* Draw the directed graph that represents the data in the airline route matrix.

$$\text{From} \quad \begin{array}{c} \\ \text{London} \\ \text{Moscow} \\ \text{Paris} \\ \text{Chicago} \end{array} \begin{array}{c} \quad\quad\quad\quad\quad \text{To} \\ \begin{array}{cccc} \text{London} & \text{Moscow} & \text{Paris} & \text{Chicago} \end{array} \\ \left[\begin{array}{cccc} 0 & 1 & 1 & 1 \\ 0 & 0 & 1 & 1 \\ 1 & 0 & 0 & 1 \\ 1 & 1 & 1 & 0 \end{array} \right] \end{array}$$

4. Thinking Critically Given that the nodes of a finite graph represent the intersections of streets and every intersection is connected to every other intersection, describe the nature of the adjacency matrix. Draw a finite graph and construct its matrix for four intersections.

5. Writing in Mathematics Describe a communication system involving at least three people. Draw a directed graph and construct the adjacency matrix for the system. Then determine the number of ways in which each person can communicate with each of the others in three steps.

12.3 Directed Graphs **615**

Writing in Mathematics
5. Answers may vary. Check students' answers. Make sure students correctly set up the graphs and matrices to their problems, and then correctly calculate the squares and cubes of their respective matrices.

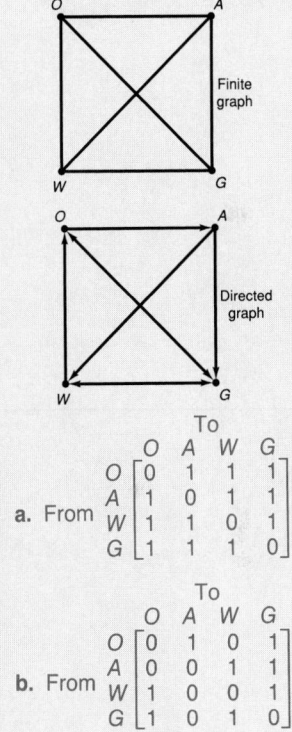

INDEPENDENT PRACTICE

Basic: 1–23
Average: 1–11 odd, 13–37, 45
Enriched: 9, 15, 24–45

Teacher's Resource Book
Practice, page 80

® Review

Exercises 21, 33, 37, and 43 review concepts of solving matrix equations, evaluating a composite function, and approximating radicals.

Technology

A calculator or computer with matrix capabilities would be useful for most exercises.

Additional Answers

5.
$$\begin{array}{c c c c c c} & n_1 & n_2 & n_3 & n_4 & n_5 \\ n_1 & 0 & 1 & 0 & 0 & 0 \\ n_2 & 1 & 0 & 1 & 0 & 0 \\ n_3 & 0 & 1 & 0 & 1 & 1 \\ n_4 & 0 & 0 & 1 & 0 & 1 \\ n_5 & 0 & 0 & 1 & 1 & 0 \end{array}$$

6.
$$\begin{array}{c c c c c} & n_1 & n_2 & n_3 & n_4 \\ n_1 & 0 & 1 & 0 & 0 \\ n_2 & 1 & 0 & 1 & 1 \\ n_3 & 0 & 1 & 0 & 0 \\ n_4 & 0 & 1 & 0 & 0 \end{array}$$

7.
$$\begin{array}{c c c c c} & n_1 & n_2 & n_3 & n_4 \\ n_1 & 0 & 1 & 1 & 1 \\ n_2 & 1 & 0 & 1 & 1 \\ n_3 & 1 & 1 & 0 & 1 \\ n_4 & 1 & 1 & 1 & 0 \end{array}$$

8.
$$\begin{array}{c c c c c} & n_1 & n_2 & n_3 & n_4 \\ n_1 & 0 & 1 & 1 & 1 \\ n_2 & 1 & 0 & 1 & 0 \\ n_3 & 1 & 1 & 0 & 1 \\ n_4 & 1 & 0 & 1 & 0 \end{array}$$

11.

12.

Practice Exercises Use appropriate technology.

Match each finite graph with its corresponding matrix, *P*, *Q*, *R*, or *S*.

$$\begin{array}{c c c c} & A & B & C \\ A & \begin{bmatrix} 0 & 0 & 1 \\ B & 1 & 0 & 0 \\ C & 0 & 1 & 0 \end{bmatrix} = P \end{array} \quad \begin{array}{c c c c} & A & B & C \\ A & \begin{bmatrix} 2 & 1 & 1 \\ B & 1 & 2 & 1 \\ C & 1 & 1 & 0 \end{bmatrix} = Q \end{array} \quad \begin{array}{c c c c} & A & B & C \\ A & \begin{bmatrix} 2 & 1 & 1 \\ B & 1 & 0 & 1 \\ C & 1 & 1 & 0 \end{bmatrix} = R \end{array} \quad \begin{array}{c c c c} & A & B & C \\ A & \begin{bmatrix} 1 & 1 & 1 \\ B & 1 & 1 & 0 \\ C & 0 & 0 & 0 \end{bmatrix} = S \end{array}$$

A **1.** **2.** **3.** **4.**

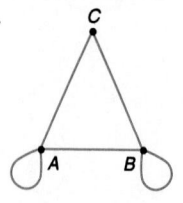

For each of the finite graphs, construct the adjacency matrix.

5. **6.** **7.** **8.**

   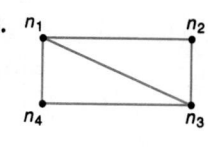

Construct the matrix for each directed graph.

9. **10.**

 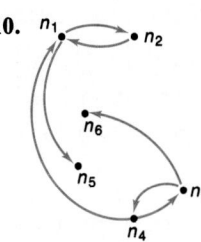

Draw the directed graph that represents the data in the communications matrix.

$$\begin{array}{c c c c} & A & B & C \\ A & \begin{bmatrix} 1 & 0 & 0 \\ B & 0 & 0 & 1 \\ C & 1 & 1 & 1 \end{bmatrix} \end{array}$$ 11.

$$\begin{array}{c c c c} & D & E & F \\ D & \begin{bmatrix} 0 & 1 & 0 \\ E & 0 & 0 & 1 \\ F & 1 & 1 & 0 \end{bmatrix} \end{array}$$ 12.

$$\begin{array}{c c c c c} & P & Q & R & S \\ P & \begin{bmatrix} 1 & 1 & 1 & 1 \\ Q & 0 & 0 & 1 & 0 \\ R & 1 & 1 & 0 & 1 \\ S & 0 & 1 & 1 & 1 \end{bmatrix} \end{array}$$ 13.

14.
$$\begin{array}{c c c c c} & A & B & C & D \\ A & \begin{bmatrix} 0 & 0 & 1 & 0 \\ B & 1 & 1 & 1 & 1 \\ C & 1 & 0 & 0 & 1 \\ D & 0 & 0 & 0 & 1 \end{bmatrix} \end{array}$$

15.
$$\begin{array}{c c c c c c} & A & B & C & D & E \\ A & \begin{bmatrix} 0 & 0 & 1 & 0 & 0 \\ B & 1 & 0 & 0 & 1 & 0 \\ C & 1 & 1 & 1 & 0 & 0 \\ D & 0 & 1 & 0 & 1 & 1 \\ E & 1 & 1 & 1 & 1 & 1 \end{bmatrix} \end{array}$$

16.
$$\begin{array}{c c c c c c} & P & Q & R & S & T \\ P & \begin{bmatrix} 1 & 1 & 0 & 0 & 1 \\ Q & 1 & 0 & 0 & 1 & 0 \\ R & 0 & 1 & 1 & 0 & 1 \\ S & 1 & 1 & 1 & 0 & 0 \\ T & 0 & 0 & 1 & 1 & 1 \end{bmatrix} \end{array}$$

616 Chapter 12 Matrices and Vectors

13. **14.** **15.** **16.**

   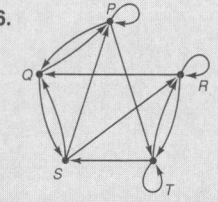

Six diplomats are seated around a table. Each one gives a message to the diplomat on the left. This is shown on the graph where arrows indicate that the second person on the left of the first person. The same information is given in matrix R.

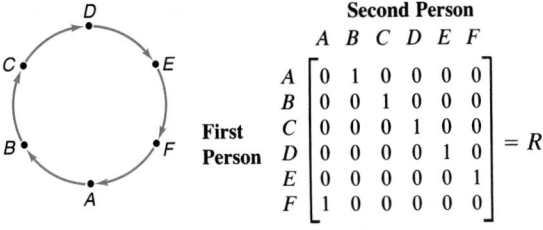

$$R = \begin{array}{c c} & \begin{array}{c} \text{Second Person} \\ A\ B\ C\ D\ E\ F \end{array} \\ \begin{array}{c} A \\ B \\ C \\ D \\ E \\ F \end{array} & \left[\begin{array}{cccccc} 0 & 1 & 0 & 0 & 0 & 0 \\ 0 & 0 & 1 & 0 & 0 & 0 \\ 0 & 0 & 0 & 1 & 0 & 0 \\ 0 & 0 & 0 & 0 & 1 & 0 \\ 0 & 0 & 0 & 0 & 0 & 1 \\ 1 & 0 & 0 & 0 & 0 & 0 \end{array} \right] \end{array}$$

First Person

17. Find R^2 to show how second-stage messages are received. In R^2, what is the relation between the second person and the first person?

18. Construct R^3. What relation is shown between the second and the first person in this matrix?

19. Use the pattern in R, R^2, and R^3 to construct matrices for R^4 and R^5.

20. Which diplomat can receive the message from A in five stages? In matrix R^5, what is the relation between the second person and the first?

Ⓡ 21. Solve for x: $\begin{bmatrix} 2 & 3 \\ 10 & 1 \end{bmatrix} \begin{bmatrix} 1 \\ x \end{bmatrix} = \begin{bmatrix} 8 \\ 12 \end{bmatrix}$ 2

B 22. Cathy is one of eight students in a class. Alicia and Fran are always talking, as are David and Hallie, and Elvin, Gino, and Bill. Draw the finite graph.

23. Draw the finite graph to represent the situation in Exercise 22 if it is discovered that Cathy talks with Alicia, Gino, Fran, and Elvin.

Recreation   Let $A = \begin{array}{c} \\ v_1 \\ v_2 \\ v_3 \end{array} \begin{array}{c} v_1\ v_2\ v_3 \\ \begin{bmatrix} 1 & 1 & 2 \\ 1 & 0 & 1 \\ 2 & 1 & 0 \end{bmatrix} \end{array}$ be the matrix for a finite graph of the hiking

trails in a large park with starting points v_1, v_2, and v_3. The starting points v_1, v_2, and v_3 are each on 1-mi trails from the other two.

24. Determine the number of different hikes of length 2 mi from v_1 to v_3.   3

25. Determine the number of different hikes of length 3 mi from v_1 to v_3.   15

26. **Thinking Critically**   Is it possible for five different people to hike 3 mi from v_3 to v_3 in the park of Exercises 24 and 25 without any of them following the exact same path?   no

27. **Thinking Critically**   What is the maximum number of different people that could walk different paths of length 3 mi from v_2 to v_2 in the park of Exercises 24 and 25?   5

At the Barton airport, a helicopter takes passengers for short rides on a loop from the airport or on flights to Anneville and back. Refer to the graph.

28. Construct matrix R for the direct routes. Then construct R^2, R^3, and R^4.

29. In how many ways can a passenger start from and return to Barton on a two-stage flight? *Hint:* The pilot can fly the loop twice in succession.   2

30. A passenger who boards at Anneville stays on the helicopter for three flights. How many different routes are possible if the passenger gets off at Anneville? if the passenger gets off at Barton?   1; 2

12.3 Directed Graphs   **617**

Lesson Quiz

1. Construct the adjacency matrix for the following graph.

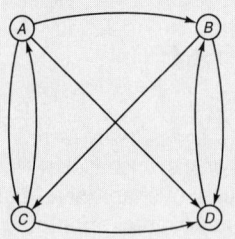

$$\begin{array}{c c} & \begin{array}{c} A\ B\ C\ D \end{array} \\ \begin{array}{c} A \\ B \\ C \\ D \end{array} & \begin{bmatrix} 0 & 1 & 1 & 1 \\ 0 & 0 & 1 & 1 \\ 1 & 0 & 0 & 1 \\ 0 & 1 & 0 & 0 \end{bmatrix} \end{array}$$

2. Sketch the directed graph that represents the data in the communication matrix given.

$$\begin{array}{c c} & \begin{array}{c} R\ S\ T \end{array} \\ \begin{array}{c} R \\ S \\ T \end{array} & \begin{bmatrix} 0 & 1 & 1 \\ 1 & 0 & 1 \\ 1 & 1 & 0 \end{bmatrix} \end{array}$$

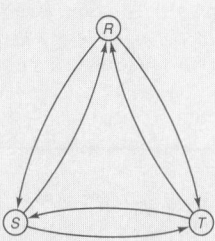

Let $A = \begin{bmatrix} 2 & 1 & 2 \\ 1 & 1 & 1 \\ 1 & 2 & 2 \end{bmatrix}$ be the adjacency

matrix for a graph of airline connections between three cities c_1, c_2, and c_3. Each city is 500 mi from each other city.

3. Determine the number of trips of length 1000 mi from c_1 to c_3.   9

4. Determine the number of trips of length 1500 mi from c_2 to c_1.   17

617

Alternative Assessment

Have students describe in words a "friend" network. For example, Mary has John and Jeff for friends, John has Mary and Alice for friends, etc. Have them write the adjacency matrix and draw the graph.

Enrichment

Have students find subway or bus routes for 10 or more locations. Note that when routes overlap, there may be more than one direct route between two locations. Have students represent the data using both a directed graph and an adjacency matrix. Then have them write and solve their own problems such as: How many direct routes are there from location *A* to location *B*? With one stop between them? With two stops between them? Answers may vary.

Additional Answers

34. direct-route: all zeros, because you cannot go back on a one-way street; two-stage: all zeros, since you cannot return to any point in two steps; three-stage: 2 twos and 2 ones, since you can get back to 2 points by one path and the other 2 points using two different paths.

35. Answers may vary. See Exercise 36 for description.

44.

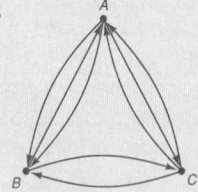

31. The pilot runs flights in succession. How many different four-stage flights are possible? In how many different ways can the pilot start at Anneville and return to Anneville? 13; 2

32. Predict how many different five-stage flights are possible. If necessary, construct R^5. 21

R 33. Solve for x: $\begin{bmatrix} 1 & 5 \\ 7 & 2 \end{bmatrix} \begin{bmatrix} x \\ 4 \end{bmatrix} = \begin{bmatrix} 6 \\ -90 \end{bmatrix}$ -14

34. Thinking Critically Refer to the one-way street map at the right. Without constructing a matrix, discuss the numbers that would appear on the main diagonal of a direct-route matrix, a two-stage matrix, and a three-stage matrix.

35. *Traffic Engineering* Create and describe a one-way street problem graphically.

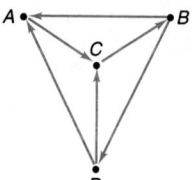

36. Writing in Mathematics Write and describe the problem from Exercise 35 in matrix form.

R 37. Given $f(x) = 2x^3$ and $g(x) = x - 1$, evaluate $(f \circ g)(x)$. $2x^3 - 6x^2 + 6x - 2$

Sports Armond, Brenda, Carl, and Daphne played in a ping pong tournament. The edges on the directed graph show that the first person won in a game with the second person. For example, Armond won in a game with Carl.

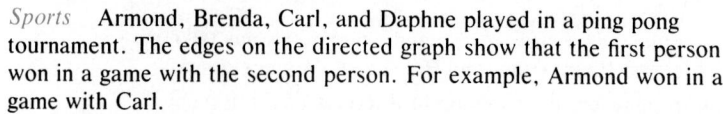

C 38. Organize the outcomes of the games in a matrix T, where 1's in the rows indicate games won and 1's in the columns indicate games lost.

39. Find each person's score by subtracting the number of games lost from the number won. Why do the scores not determine a winner?

40. Find T^2, which records second-stage wins. For example, Armond beat Carl who won over Brenda, so Armond had a second-stage win over Brenda.

41. By adding matrices $T + T^2$, recompute the scores of the players. Why is the winner still not determined?

42. Find T^3, and add $T + T^2 + T^3$. Use this matrix sum to recompute the scores. Who won, and who was in second and third place?

R 43. Evaluate to the nearest tenth: $\sqrt[3]{\sqrt{121}}$ 1.5

44. Thinking Critically Draw a finite graph of the street system described by matrix P at the right.

45. Writing in Mathematics Create and describe a real-world communications problem. Then write and describe the problem in matrix form.

$$\text{From } \begin{matrix} A \\ B \\ C \end{matrix} \begin{bmatrix} 0 & 2 & 1 \\ 1 & 0 & 1 \\ 2 & 1 & 0 \end{bmatrix} = P$$

To
A B C

Review

Identify the conic section represented by each equation.

1. $7y^2 + 8 = 5y^2 - 3x$ parabola

2. $4x^2 - 14x = y^2 - 32$ hyperbola

3. In triangle XYZ, $\angle Z = 32°$, $x = 10$, and $y = 17$. Find z. 10

Writing in Mathematics

$$\text{36. From } \begin{matrix} n_1 \\ n_2 \\ n_3 \\ n_4 \end{matrix} \begin{bmatrix} 0 & 1 & 0 & 0 \\ 0 & 0 & 1 & 0 \\ 0 & 0 & 0 & 1 \\ 1 & 0 & 0 & 0 \end{bmatrix}$$

To
n_1 n_2 n_3 n_4

; Once you go from one point to another, you have to go through at least three "moves" to return to the point from which you started.

45. Answers may vary. Check students' answers.

12.4 Inverses of Matrices

Objectives: To find the multiplicative inverse of a matrix
To use the multiplicative inverse of a matrix to solve a system
of equations

Focus

Cryptographers use a variety of schemes for
encoding messages. A simple substitution cipher was
presented in Lesson 1.4. To ensure security of
sensitive information, a cryptographer may also use
matrix operations to encode messages.

A matrix-based cryptography system will usually
replace a group of two or three letters in a row by
an equal number of letters in the encoded message.
By using matrix multiplication in the encoding
process, an individual letter can be encoded as a
different letter in different parts of the coded
message. Such ciphers are designed to be difficult to
decode since they require the use of the *inverse* of
the encoding matrix. During World War II, Allied
analysts such as Alan Turing (1921–1954) were able
to break German codes produced by the Enigma
machine using sophisticated decoding techniques.

Recall that the product of an identity matrix with any matrix A of equal order
is the matrix A, that is, $AI = A = IA$. When the product of two square
matrices A and B is the identity matrix, $AB = BA = I$, then A and B are
multiplicative inverses of one another. The notation A^{-1} is used to denote the
multiplicative inverse of matrix A. Thus, $B = A^{-1}$ and $A = B^{-1}$. Note that
only square matrices can have multiplicative inverses. *Why?*

Example 1 Show that matrix B is the multiplicative inverse of matrix A.

$$A = \begin{bmatrix} 4 & 3 \\ 3 & 2 \end{bmatrix} \text{ and } B = \begin{bmatrix} -2 & 3 \\ 3 & -4 \end{bmatrix}$$

$$AB = \begin{bmatrix} 4 & 3 \\ 3 & 2 \end{bmatrix}\begin{bmatrix} -2 & 3 \\ 3 & -4 \end{bmatrix} = \begin{bmatrix} -8+9 & 12-12 \\ -6+6 & 9-8 \end{bmatrix} = \begin{bmatrix} 1 & 0 \\ 0 & 1 \end{bmatrix}$$

$$BA = \begin{bmatrix} -2 & 3 \\ 3 & -4 \end{bmatrix}\begin{bmatrix} 4 & 3 \\ 3 & 2 \end{bmatrix} = \begin{bmatrix} -8+9 & -6+6 \\ 12-12 & 9-8 \end{bmatrix} = \begin{bmatrix} 1 & 0 \\ 0 & 1 \end{bmatrix}$$

Since $AB = BA = I$, then A and B are inverses of one another. Thus,

$$A^{-1} = \begin{bmatrix} -2 & 3 \\ 3 & -4 \end{bmatrix} \text{ and } B^{-1} = \begin{bmatrix} 4 & 3 \\ 3 & 2 \end{bmatrix}.$$

12.4 Inverses of Matrices   **619**

LESSON PLAN

Vocabulary
determinant
multiplicative inverse of a matrix
row operations

Technology
calculator with matrix capabilities
computer

FOCUS

Have students research the job opportunities for a cryptographer. They
might begin by referring to banks,
credit card agencies, and security
systems operations. Have them find
the applications of matrices in these
fields.

Thinking Critically
In order to be able to square a matrix, the matrix must have the same number of rows and
columns.

INSTRUCTION

- Review the following properties of multiplication for real numbers: identity, inverse, and commutative. Ask students to explain when and how these properties apply to matrices. Students should recall that the identity property of multiplication applies to square matrices of the same dimensions. Square matrices of the same dimensions do not possess the inverse property of multiplication since not every matrix in this set necessarily has a multiplicative inverse. A matrix and the identity matrix of the same dimensions commute as do a matrix and its inverse; however, matrices do not have the commutative property of multiplication.

- Work through the two methods for finding the multiplicative inverse of a matrix. One way to explain why method II works is to start with the equation: $AA^{-1} = I$. By performing the same operations on A and I, the equation still holds. When A becomes I, the original identity matrix becomes some matrix, B, and the equation reads: $IA^{-1} = B$. But B is A^{-1} by the identity property.

- In Example 4, solving systems of equations with matrix methods, the terms *coefficient matrix* and *constant matrix* may be useful in writing the elements of matrices A and C.

 You can use a calculator with matrix operations to show that matrix A and matrix B of Example 1 are multiplicative inverses of one another. Name and input matrix A and matrix B. Then calculate AB and BA. The result is the identity matrix in each case.

To find the inverse of a 2×2 matrix, use one of the two methods shown here.

Method I   Use a formula. First note how to derive the formula. Let $A = \begin{bmatrix} a & b \\ c & d \end{bmatrix}$. Assume that A^{-1} is $\begin{bmatrix} e & f \\ g & h \end{bmatrix}$ and solve the following matrix equation for e, f, g, and h.

$$\begin{bmatrix} a & b \\ c & d \end{bmatrix}\begin{bmatrix} e & f \\ g & h \end{bmatrix} = \begin{bmatrix} 1 & 0 \\ 0 & 1 \end{bmatrix} \quad \text{or} \quad \begin{bmatrix} ae + bg & af + bh \\ ce + dg & cf + dh \end{bmatrix} = \begin{bmatrix} 1 & 0 \\ 0 & 1 \end{bmatrix}$$

You can now solve two linear systems to find e, g, f, and h. The solution steps are left for you.

$$ae + bg = 1 \qquad \textit{Eliminate g and solve for e.} \qquad e = \frac{d}{ad - bc}$$

$$ce + dg = 0 \qquad \textit{Eliminate e and solve for g.} \qquad g = \frac{-c}{ad - bc}$$

$$af + bh = 0 \qquad \textit{Eliminate h and solve for f.} \qquad f = \frac{-b}{ad - bc}$$

$$cf + dh = 1 \qquad \textit{Eliminate f and solve for h.} \qquad h = \frac{a}{ad - bc}$$

Thus, $A^{-1} = \begin{bmatrix} \dfrac{d}{ad - bc} & \dfrac{-b}{ad - bc} \\ \dfrac{-c}{ad - bc} & \dfrac{a}{ad - bc} \end{bmatrix}$ or $A^{-1} = \dfrac{1}{ad - bc}\begin{bmatrix} d & -b \\ -c & a \end{bmatrix}$

For the above matrices A and A^{-1}, $AA^{-1} = I_{2\times 2}$. It is also true that $A^{-1}A = I_{2\times 2}$. *Why?*

Now use the formula to find the inverse of $A = \begin{bmatrix} 4 & 3 \\ 3 & 2 \end{bmatrix}$ in Example 1. Here, $a = 4$, $b = 3$, $c = 3$, and $d = 2$, so $ad - bc = (4)(2) - (3)(3) = -1$. Then

$$A^{-1} = \frac{1}{ad - bc}\begin{bmatrix} d & -b \\ -c & a \end{bmatrix} = \frac{1}{-1}\begin{bmatrix} 2 & -3 \\ -3 & 4 \end{bmatrix} = \begin{bmatrix} -2 & 3 \\ 3 & -4 \end{bmatrix}$$

The number $ad - bc$ is called the **determinant** of the 2×2 matrix $A = \begin{bmatrix} a & b \\ c & d \end{bmatrix}$. The determinant is sometimes denoted with vertical bars as $\begin{vmatrix} a & b \\ c & d \end{vmatrix}$, or $|A|$. If $ad - bc = 0$, matrix A has no inverse. *Why?*

A second method for finding the inverse of a matrix can be used for a square matrix of any dimensions.

Method II   Begin by constructing a matrix that consists of the elements of matrix A on the left and the elements of the corresponding identity matrix I on the right.

$$[A|I] = \begin{bmatrix} a & b & \vline & 1 & 0 \\ c & d & \vline & 0 & 1 \end{bmatrix}$$

620   Chapter 12 Matrices and Vectors

Thinking Critically

This is true because matrix multiplication of square matrices is commutative.

If $ad - bc = 0$, then the formula for finding the inverse of a matrix would result in division by zero.

The vertical line is used to separate the two matrices. Use the following **row operations** to transform this matrix into an equivalent matrix of the form [*I*|*B*] where

$$[I|B] = \begin{bmatrix} 1 & 0 & e & f \\ 0 & 1 & g & h \end{bmatrix}$$

- Interchange any two rows of a matrix.
- Multiply each element of a row by the same nonzero constant.
- Multiply each element of a row by a nonzero number and add the result to another row.

If the matrix [*I*|*B*] exists, then *B* is the multiplicative inverse of *A*. No attempt is made here to justify these operations, but proofs exist that they are valid.

Example 2 Find the multiplicative inverse of matrix $A = \begin{bmatrix} 2 & 1 \\ 1 & 1 \end{bmatrix}$, if it exists.

$\begin{bmatrix} 2 & 1 & 1 & 0 \\ 1 & 1 & 0 & 1 \end{bmatrix}$ *Form the matrix [A|I].*

$\begin{bmatrix} 1 & 1 & 0 & 1 \\ 2 & 1 & 1 & 0 \end{bmatrix}$ *Interchange rows 1 and 2 so that a 1 is in the upper-left-hand position.*

$\begin{bmatrix} 1 & 1 & 0 & 1 \\ 0 & -1 & 1 & -2 \end{bmatrix}$ *Multiply row 1 by −2 and add to row 2. This becomes the new row 2.*

$\begin{bmatrix} 1 & 0 & 1 & -1 \\ 0 & -1 & 1 & -2 \end{bmatrix}$ *Add row 2 to row 1. This becomes the new row 1.*

$\begin{bmatrix} 1 & 0 & 1 & -1 \\ 0 & 1 & -1 & 2 \end{bmatrix}$ *Multiply row 2 by −1.*
$\quad I \qquad\quad A^{-1}$

The identity matrix is on the left and A^{-1} is on the right. Check by showing that $AA^{-1} = A^{-1}A = I$.

This procedure for finding an inverse, if it exists, may be extended to a square matrix of any size and to its identity matrix. If it is not possible to obtain the identity matrix on the left, then A^{-1} does not exist. For example, any attempt to obtain an identity matrix for $\begin{bmatrix} 9 & 8 & 7 \\ 6 & 5 & 4 \\ 3 & 2 & 1 \end{bmatrix}$ will fail. Row operations on the

matrix $\begin{bmatrix} 9 & 8 & 7 & 1 & 0 & 0 \\ 6 & 5 & 4 & 0 & 1 & 0 \\ 3 & 2 & 1 & 0 & 0 & 1 \end{bmatrix}$ will produce a result such as

$$\begin{bmatrix} 3 & 2 & 1 & 0 & 0 & 1 \\ 0 & 1 & 2 & 0 & 1 & -2 \\ 0 & 0 & 0 & 1 & -2 & 1 \end{bmatrix}$$

It can be seen that it is not possible to obtain a 1 in the position in the third row and third column without introducing new nonzero elements in the bottom row. You can try to use a different sequence of steps to obtain the identity matrix on the left. In any case, you will find the same difficulty with a row of zeros. The matrix *A* has no multiplicative inverse.

Alternative Learning Styles
Encoding messages in a group setting is an interesting way for students to obtain practice multiplying matrices and finding inverse matrices. Each student secretly writes a message and uses the encoding matrix (the multiplier) and the method of Example 4 to encode the message. Students exchange encoded messages and use the inverse of the encoding matrix to decode them. To vary this exercise, have groups develop their own encoding matrix, perhaps with different dimensions.

GUIDED PRACTICE

For Example 1
Show that matrix *B* is the multiplicative inverse of matrix *A*.

1. $A = \begin{bmatrix} 1 & 2 \\ 1 & 1 \end{bmatrix}, B = \begin{bmatrix} -1 & 2 \\ 1 & -1 \end{bmatrix}$

$\begin{bmatrix} -1 + 2 & 2 + (-2) \\ -1 + 1 & 2 + (-1) \end{bmatrix} = \begin{bmatrix} 1 & 0 \\ 0 & 1 \end{bmatrix}$

2. $A = \begin{bmatrix} 5 & 6 \\ 3 & 4 \end{bmatrix}, B = \begin{bmatrix} 2 & -3 \\ -\frac{3}{2} & \frac{5}{2} \end{bmatrix}$

$\begin{bmatrix} 10 + (-9) & -15 + 15 \\ 6 + (-6) & -9 + 10 \end{bmatrix} = \begin{bmatrix} 1 & 0 \\ 0 & 1 \end{bmatrix}$

For Example 2
Find the multiplicative inverse of matrix *A*, if it exists.

1. $A = \begin{bmatrix} 9 & 4 \\ 7 & 3 \end{bmatrix}$ $\begin{bmatrix} -3 & 4 \\ 7 & -9 \end{bmatrix}$

2. $A = \begin{bmatrix} -2 & -5 \\ 6 & 15 \end{bmatrix}$ does not exist

Common Error Some students may perform calculations only on matrix *A* in the augmented matrix [*A*|*I*], and not on *I*. Encourage these students to write out the row operations to be performed before calculating to find the new elements in both matrices.

Solve the system of equations using the multiplicative inverse of a matrix.

1. $\begin{cases} 5x - 2y = 22 \\ 7x + 3y = -4 \end{cases}$ $x = 2; y = -6$

2. $\begin{cases} x + y + z = 6 \\ 2x - y + 3z = 9 \\ -x + 2y + 2z = 9 \end{cases}$ $x = 1; y = 2; z = 3$

Modeling

Encoding and decoding messages is an interesting but perhaps somewhat unfamiliar field for many students. You may want to have students research other occupations that involve encoding and decoding techniques.

Systems of equations such as $\begin{cases} 2x - 5y = -16 \\ 5x + 3y = -9 \end{cases}$ can be solved using matrices.

First write the system in the matrix form $AX = C$, where A is the matrix of the coefficients, X is the matrix of variables, and C is the matrix of the constants. The system has a solution if the coefficient matrix has an inverse.

$$AX = C$$
$$A^{-1}(AX) = A^{-1}C \qquad \textit{Multiply both sides by } A^{-1}$$
$$(A^{-1}A)X = A^{-1}C \qquad \textit{Associative property}$$
$$IX = A^{-1}C \qquad \textit{Definition of multiplicative inverse}$$
$$X = A^{-1}C \qquad \textit{Definition of multiplicative identity}$$

Example 3 Solve the system of equations $\begin{cases} 2x - 5y = -16 \\ 5x + 3y = -9 \end{cases}$ using the multiplicative inverse of a matrix.

$$\overset{A}{\begin{bmatrix} 2 & -5 \\ 5 & 3 \end{bmatrix}} \overset{X}{\begin{bmatrix} x \\ y \end{bmatrix}} = \overset{C}{\begin{bmatrix} -16 \\ -9 \end{bmatrix}} \qquad \textit{Write the matrix equation } AX = C.$$

$$A^{-1} = \begin{bmatrix} \frac{3}{31} & \frac{5}{31} \\ -\frac{5}{31} & \frac{2}{31} \end{bmatrix} \qquad \textit{Find } A^{-1} \textit{ (use method I or II).}$$

$$X = A^{-1}C = \begin{bmatrix} \frac{3}{31} & \frac{5}{31} \\ -\frac{5}{31} & \frac{2}{31} \end{bmatrix} \begin{bmatrix} -16 \\ -9 \end{bmatrix} = \begin{bmatrix} -3 \\ 2 \end{bmatrix} \qquad X = \begin{bmatrix} x \\ y \end{bmatrix} = \begin{bmatrix} -3 \\ 2 \end{bmatrix}$$

Therefore, $x = -3$ and $y = 2$.

Some calculators identify their matrix storage locations with capital letters, such as A, B, C. If you solve Example 3 using a calculator, you can, for simplicity, use the A and C locations to define the similarly named matrices of the example. Follow these steps.

Step	Display
1. Use the inverse key to find and display A^{-1}.	$\begin{bmatrix} 0.0967741935 & .1612903226 \\ -.1612903226 & .064516129 \end{bmatrix}$

2. [Ans] [(C)] $\begin{bmatrix} -3 \\ 2 \end{bmatrix}$

The inverse matrix A^{-1} of step 1 is stored in a location called Answers and then used in the matrix multiplication of step 2.

Modeling

Matrix multiplication may be used to encode messages transmitted electronically. If this is done, how can the message be decoded?

When a message is encoded by multiplying by a matrix A, then the decoding of the message requires multiplication by the inverse of matrix A. Matrix A must be carefully selected to ensure that it has an inverse.

622   Chapter 12 Matrices and Vectors

Example 4 *Cryptography* A cryptographer wishes to encode the message "PUT OUT THE TRASH" using a matrix cipher. Develop a scheme for encoding the message and find an inverse scheme for deciphering the code.

First group the letters into three-letter strings:

PUT   OUT   THE   TRA   SHW   (Add W to complete a string.)

Assign a numerical value to each letter; $A = 1, B = 2, C = 3$, and so on.

Now use the matrix $\begin{bmatrix} 6 & 5 & 2 \\ 5 & 5 & 2 \\ 2 & 2 & 1 \end{bmatrix}$ as a multiplier of each string of three letters as indicated below. Since $P = 16$, $U = 21$, and $T = 20$, PUT will be encoded as [241 225 094] by the matrix multiplication

$$\begin{bmatrix} 6 & 5 & 2 \\ 5 & 5 & 2 \\ 2 & 2 & 1 \end{bmatrix}\begin{bmatrix} 16 \\ 21 \\ 20 \end{bmatrix} = \begin{bmatrix} 241 \\ 225 \\ 094 \end{bmatrix}$$

The word OUT will be encoded as [235 220 092] since

$$\begin{bmatrix} 6 & 5 & 2 \\ 5 & 5 & 2 \\ 2 & 2 & 1 \end{bmatrix}\begin{bmatrix} 15 \\ 21 \\ 20 \end{bmatrix} = \begin{bmatrix} 235 \\ 220 \\ 092 \end{bmatrix}$$

Although PUT and OUT have two letters in common, the encoded strings are different. The encoded string is transmitted in sequence and the receiver of the message needs to use the inverse of the encoding matrix to decode the message.

Since $\begin{bmatrix} 6 & 5 & 2 \\ 5 & 5 & 2 \\ 2 & 2 & 1 \end{bmatrix}^{-1} = \begin{bmatrix} 1 & -1 & -0 \\ -1 & 2 & -2 \\ 0 & -2 & 5 \end{bmatrix}$

the message is decoded by multiplying the coded message by the inverse of the encoding matrix, as shown below.

$$\begin{bmatrix} 1 & -1 & 0 \\ -1 & 2 & -2 \\ 0 & -2 & 5 \end{bmatrix}\begin{bmatrix} 241 \\ 225 \\ 094 \end{bmatrix} = \begin{bmatrix} 16 \\ 21 \\ 20 \end{bmatrix} = \begin{bmatrix} P \\ U \\ T \end{bmatrix} \quad \text{and} \quad \begin{bmatrix} 1 & -1 & 0 \\ -1 & 2 & -2 \\ 0 & -2 & 5 \end{bmatrix}\begin{bmatrix} 235 \\ 220 \\ 092 \end{bmatrix} = \begin{bmatrix} 15 \\ 21 \\ 20 \end{bmatrix} = \begin{bmatrix} O \\ U \\ T \end{bmatrix}$$

In a similar manner the rest of the message can be coded and decoded.

Class Exercises

1. Show that $\begin{bmatrix} 7 & 5 \\ -2 & -1 \end{bmatrix}$ and $\begin{bmatrix} -\frac{1}{3} & -\frac{5}{3} \\ \frac{2}{3} & \frac{7}{3} \end{bmatrix}$ are multiplicative inverses of each other.

Find the multiplicative inverse, if it exists. If it does not exist, write "no inverse."

2. $\begin{bmatrix} 5 & 4 \\ 4 & 3 \end{bmatrix}$ $\begin{bmatrix} -3 & 4 \\ 4 & -5 \end{bmatrix}$ **3.** $\begin{bmatrix} 6 & -8 \\ -3 & 4 \end{bmatrix}$ no inverse **4.** $\begin{bmatrix} 1 & -1 & 1 \\ 1 & 0 & 1 \\ 2 & 1 & 0 \end{bmatrix}$ **5.** $\begin{bmatrix} 1 & 2 & 3 & 4 \\ 2 & 0 & 3 & 1 \\ 7 & -1 & 0 & 0 \end{bmatrix}$

12.4 Inverses of Matrices **623**

Additional Answers

4. $\begin{bmatrix} \frac{1}{2} & -\frac{1}{2} & \frac{1}{2} \\ -1 & 1 & 0 \\ -\frac{1}{2} & \frac{3}{2} & -\frac{1}{2} \end{bmatrix}$ **5.** no inverse

For Example 4
Encode the given message by assigning numerical values to each letter. For example, $A = 1$, $B = 2$, $C = 3$, and so on. Use the encoding matrix from Example 4 given in the lesson as a multiplier for each string of three letters. For a blank in the last string, use 0.

1. DO NOT PASS GO
$\begin{bmatrix} 127 \\ 123 \\ 52 \end{bmatrix} \begin{bmatrix} 222 \\ 207 \\ 86 \end{bmatrix} \begin{bmatrix} 139 \\ 138 \\ 59 \end{bmatrix} \begin{bmatrix} 117 \\ 110 \\ 44 \end{bmatrix}$

2. THE BRITISH ARE COMING
$\begin{bmatrix} 170 \\ 150 \\ 61 \end{bmatrix} \begin{bmatrix} 120 \\ 118 \\ 49 \end{bmatrix} \begin{bmatrix} 203 \\ 183 \\ 77 \end{bmatrix} \begin{bmatrix} 89 \\ 81 \\ 36 \end{bmatrix}$
$\begin{bmatrix} 75 \\ 70 \\ 31 \end{bmatrix} \begin{bmatrix} 151 \\ 138 \\ 58 \end{bmatrix} \begin{bmatrix} 42 \\ 35 \\ 14 \end{bmatrix}$

CLOSURE

Have students explain in their own words the two methods for finding the multiplicative inverse matrix of a square matrix, as outlined in this lesson.

INDEPENDENT PRACTICE

Assignment Guide
Basic: 1–15, 19–28
Average: 1–13 odd, 18–40, Project
Enriched: 1–35 odd, 38–45, Project

Teacher's Resource Book
   Practice, page 81

Ⓡ **Review**
Exercises 15, 17, 19, 35, and 37 review concepts of solving inequalities, evaluating functions, and converting equations from rectangular to polar form.

Technology
Exercises 1 to 12, 21 to 34, 38 to 44, and 45 can be readily solved using a calculator with matrix capabilities.

LESSON FOLLOW-UP

Lesson Quiz

Find the multiplicative inverse of matrix A, if it exists.

1. $A = \begin{bmatrix} 4 & 11 \\ 1 & 3 \end{bmatrix}$ $\begin{bmatrix} 3 & -11 \\ -1 & 4 \end{bmatrix}$

2. $A = \begin{bmatrix} -0.4 & 0.6 & 0.2 \\ 0.6 & 0.6 & 0.2 \\ -0.4 & 1.6 & 0.2 \end{bmatrix}$ $\begin{bmatrix} -1 & 1 & 0 \\ -1 & 0 & 1 \\ 6 & 2 & -3 \end{bmatrix}$

3. $A = \begin{bmatrix} 6 & -3 \\ 8 & -4 \end{bmatrix}$ does not exist

Solve the system of equations using the multiplicative inverse of a matrix.

4. $\begin{cases} 2x - 3y = -8 \\ 9x + 3y = -3 \end{cases}$ $x = -1; y = 2$

5. $\begin{cases} 2x - 3y + z = 5 \\ x + 3y + 8z = 22 \\ 3x - y + 2z = 12 \end{cases}$ $x = 3; y = 1;$ $z = 2$

Encode the message by assigning numerical values to each letter. For example, $A = 1$, $B = 2$, $C = 3$, and so on. Use the encoding matrix from Example 5 given in the lesson as a multiplier of each string of three letters. For a blank in the last string, use 0.

6. MATH IS FUN

$\begin{bmatrix} 123 \\ 110 \\ 48 \end{bmatrix}$ $\begin{bmatrix} 131 \\ 123 \\ 53 \end{bmatrix}$ $\begin{bmatrix} 169 \\ 163 \\ 68 \end{bmatrix}$

Additional Answers

Practice Exercises

3. $\begin{bmatrix} 1 & -2 \\ -5 & 11 \end{bmatrix}$ **4.** $\begin{bmatrix} 1 & -7 \\ -2 & 15 \end{bmatrix}$

5. no inverse **6.** no inverse

7. no inverse **8.** no inverse

9. $\begin{bmatrix} -\frac{5}{6} & \frac{7}{6} & \frac{1}{2} \\ \frac{3}{2} & -\frac{3}{2} & -\frac{1}{2} \\ -\frac{7}{6} & \frac{5}{6} & \frac{1}{2} \end{bmatrix}$ **10.** $\begin{bmatrix} \frac{1}{6} & \frac{1}{3} & -\frac{1}{6} \\ 0 & -\frac{1}{5} & \frac{2}{5} \\ \frac{1}{6} & -\frac{7}{15} & \frac{13}{30} \end{bmatrix}$

Solve each matrix equation for the matrix X.

6. $\begin{bmatrix} 3 & 2 \\ 1 & 4 \end{bmatrix} X = \begin{bmatrix} 5 \\ -1 \end{bmatrix} \begin{bmatrix} 2.2 \\ -0.8 \end{bmatrix}$

7. $\begin{bmatrix} 5 & 4 \\ 3 & -5 \end{bmatrix} X = \begin{bmatrix} 11 \\ -23 \end{bmatrix} \begin{bmatrix} -1 \\ 4 \end{bmatrix}$

8. Solve by using the multiplicative inverse of a matrix: $\begin{cases} 3x - 2y = 12 \\ 7x + 2y = 8 \end{cases}$ $(2, -3)$

9. Thinking Critically Given that $A = \begin{bmatrix} 10 & 7 \\ 5 & 4 \end{bmatrix}$ and $B = \begin{bmatrix} 4 & -7 \\ -5 & 10 \end{bmatrix}$, find AB and BA. Explain how you can use the result to find A^{-1} and B^{-1}.

Practice Exercises Use appropriate technology.

Show by multiplication that B and A are multiplicative inverses of each other.

A **1.** $A = \begin{bmatrix} 7 & 3 \\ 5 & 2 \end{bmatrix}$, $B = \begin{bmatrix} -2 & 3 \\ 5 & -7 \end{bmatrix}$

2. $A = \begin{bmatrix} 8 & 6 \\ 5 & 4 \end{bmatrix}$, $B = \begin{bmatrix} 2 & -3 \\ -\frac{5}{2} & 4 \end{bmatrix}$

Find the multiplicative inverse, if it exists. If it does not exist, write "no inverse."

3. $\begin{bmatrix} 11 & 2 \\ 5 & 1 \end{bmatrix}$

4. $\begin{bmatrix} 15 & 7 \\ 2 & 1 \end{bmatrix}$

5. $\begin{bmatrix} 8 & 2 \\ 16 & 4 \end{bmatrix}$

6. $\begin{bmatrix} 16 & 8 \\ -6 & -3 \end{bmatrix}$

7. $\begin{bmatrix} 5 & 2 & 1 \\ 4 & 3 & 9 \end{bmatrix}$

8. $\begin{bmatrix} -2 & 6 & 3 \\ 7 & 1 & 8 \end{bmatrix}$

9. $\begin{bmatrix} 2 & 1 & -1 \\ 1 & -1 & -2 \\ 3 & 4 & 3 \end{bmatrix}$

10. $\begin{bmatrix} 3 & -2 & 3 \\ 2 & 3 & -2 \\ 1 & 4 & -1 \end{bmatrix}$

11. $\begin{bmatrix} 5 & -3 & 2 \\ 2 & 4 & -3 \\ 4 & -2 & 5 \end{bmatrix}$

12. $\begin{bmatrix} 4 & -2 & 3 \\ 3 & -5 & -2 \\ 2 & 4 & -3 \end{bmatrix}$

13. $\begin{bmatrix} 7 & 2 \\ 4 & 1 \\ 8 & 6 \end{bmatrix}$

14. $\begin{bmatrix} 15 & 1 \\ -3 & 7 \\ 6 & 4 \end{bmatrix}$

Ⓡ **15.** Solve: $2(2x + 3) - 10 < 6(x - 2)$ $x > 4$

16. Solve for the matrix X: $\begin{bmatrix} 5 & -3 \\ 4 & -2 \end{bmatrix} X = \begin{bmatrix} 5 \\ 10 \end{bmatrix} \begin{bmatrix} 10 \\ 15 \end{bmatrix}$

Ⓡ **17.** Solve: $\frac{x + 2}{x - 3} \le 1$ $x < 3$

18. Thinking Critically Given square matrices P and Q with all zeros in the second row of matrix P, which row in the product PQ must have zeros only? How does this prove that matrix P has no inverse?

Ⓡ **19.** Solve: $15 \le 5x + 10 \le 45$ $1 \le x \le 7$

20. *Economics* Twenty shares of stock P and 40 shares of stock Q cost \$700. Ten shares of stock P and 30 shares of stock Q cost \$450. Find the price per share of each stock. stock P: \$15/share; stock Q: \$10/share

21. *Construction* A builder bought two types of doors to complete two housing projects. For one site, the cost for 5 doors of type A and 10 doors of type B was \$1700. For the other site, the cost for 10 doors of type A and 5 doors of type B was \$1600. Find the cost per door of each type. type A: \$100 type B: \$120

B **22.** Show that the matrices $\begin{bmatrix} 16 & -8 \\ -3 & 4 \end{bmatrix}$ and $\begin{bmatrix} \frac{1}{10} & \frac{1}{5} \\ \frac{3}{40} & \frac{2}{5} \end{bmatrix}$ are inverses of each other.

624 Chapter 12 Matrices and Vectors

---

11. $\begin{bmatrix} \frac{7}{48} & \frac{11}{96} & \frac{1}{96} \\ -\frac{11}{48} & \frac{17}{96} & \frac{19}{96} \\ \frac{5}{24} & -\frac{1}{48} & \frac{13}{48} \end{bmatrix}$ **12.** $\begin{bmatrix} \frac{23}{148} & \frac{3}{74} & \frac{19}{148} \\ \frac{5}{148} & \frac{9}{74} & \frac{17}{148} \\ \frac{11}{74} & \frac{5}{37} & -\frac{7}{74} \end{bmatrix}$ **13.** no inverse **14.** no inverse

Solve each matrix equation for the matrix X. If there is no solution, explain why.

23. $\begin{bmatrix} 3 & -5 \\ 2 & -4 \end{bmatrix} X = \begin{bmatrix} 4 \\ 7 \end{bmatrix}$ **24.** $\begin{bmatrix} 2 & -3 \\ 4 & -5 \end{bmatrix} X = \begin{bmatrix} 6 \\ 11 \end{bmatrix}$ **25.** $\begin{bmatrix} 2 & -4 \\ 5 & -10 \end{bmatrix} X = \begin{bmatrix} 9 \\ 6 \end{bmatrix}$

26. $\begin{bmatrix} 2 & -1 \\ 8 & -4 \end{bmatrix} X = \begin{bmatrix} -1 \\ -4 \end{bmatrix}$ **27.** $\begin{bmatrix} 7 & 3 \\ 1 & 3 \end{bmatrix} X = \begin{bmatrix} 40 \\ 4 \end{bmatrix}$ **28.** $\begin{bmatrix} 7 & -5 \\ 6 & 5 \end{bmatrix} X = \begin{bmatrix} 61 \\ -22 \end{bmatrix}$

29. $\begin{bmatrix} \frac{1}{2} & -1 \\ -\frac{1}{4} & -1 \end{bmatrix} X = \begin{bmatrix} -\frac{1}{3} \\ -7 \end{bmatrix}$ **30.** $\begin{bmatrix} \frac{1}{2} & \frac{1}{3} \\ \frac{1}{4} & \frac{1}{3} \end{bmatrix} X = \begin{bmatrix} 20 \\ 18 \end{bmatrix}$ **31.** $\begin{bmatrix} 5 & 1 & -4 \\ 2 & -3 & -5 \\ 7 & 2 & -6 \end{bmatrix} X = \begin{bmatrix} 5 \\ 2 \\ 5 \end{bmatrix}$

32. $\begin{bmatrix} 1 & 1 & 1 \\ 1 & -4 & 3 \\ 1 & 6 & 2 \end{bmatrix} X = \begin{bmatrix} 16 \\ 42 \\ 14 \end{bmatrix}$ **33.** $\begin{bmatrix} 6 & 10 & -13 \\ 4 & -2 & 7 \\ 0 & 9 & -8 \end{bmatrix} X = \begin{bmatrix} 84 \\ 18 \\ 56 \end{bmatrix}$ **34.** $\begin{bmatrix} 3 & 1 & -4 \\ 5 & 2 & -4 \\ 0 & 6 & -7 \end{bmatrix} X = \begin{bmatrix} -1 \\ 8 \\ -23 \end{bmatrix}$

35. Find $f(x + h) - f(x)$ when $f(x) = x^2 - 5x + 6$. $h^2 + 2xh - 5h$

36. *Cryptography*   Use the encoding matrix and the method of Example 4 to encode the word THE. Use the inverse matrix to decode your answer.   [170   150   61]

37. Convert $x^2 + y^2 = 10x$ to polar-coordinate form. $r = 10 \cos \theta$

Use matrices to solve the systems.

38. $\begin{cases} 6x - y = 22 \\ 2x + y = 2 \end{cases}$ **39.** $\begin{cases} 5x + y = -24 \\ 10x + y = -39 \end{cases}$ **40.** $\begin{cases} 15x + 17y = 30 \\ 8x - 19y = 16 \end{cases}$

41. $\begin{cases} 12x + 5y + 2z = -1 \\ 7x + 8y - 3z = 23 \\ 4x + 3y + 2z = 1 \end{cases}$ **42.** $\begin{cases} 3x + 4y - 6z = -6 \\ 8x - 2y + 7z = 68 \\ 5x + 3y + 4z = 29 \end{cases}$ **43.** $\begin{cases} 2x + 3y + 12z = 4 \\ 4x - 6y + 6z = 1 \\ x + y + z = 1 \end{cases}$

44. *Business*   A manufacturer sells a package of pencils and erasers for $2.25. A pencil costs $0.35 and an eraser costs $0.25. Another manufacturer sells a similar package with the same number of pencils and erasers for $2.40. In this package, a pencil costs $0.40 and an eraser costs $0.20. Find the number of pencils and erasers in each package.

45. For matrix $A = \begin{bmatrix} 1 & 3 \\ 1 & 4 \end{bmatrix}$, verify that $(A^{-1})^2 = (A^2)^{-1}$.

Project

Write a computer program that will encode and decode a message using the method presented in Example 4. Your program should ask the user whether the task is encoding or decoding and then should apply the appropriate matrix operations. Output both the encoded message and the decoded message. Discuss the rounding errors in finding the inverse matrix.

Challenge

1. Determine the value of $[\log_{10} (2 \log_{10} 100{,}000)]^2$.   1

2. If m represents the number of real values of q for which the solutions of $x^2 - qx + q = 0$ are equal, find m.   2

12.4 Inverses of Matrices   **625**

Alternative Assessment
Have students describe in writing how to find the solution of a system of three equations with three unknowns, using matrix methods. Then have the students provide an example of such a system and solve it using the procedures they just described.

Enrichment
A symmetric matrix is a matrix whose elements are symmetric about its diagonal. Show that the sum of two symmetric 3×3 matrices is symmetric. Determine whether multiplying two symmetric matrices is a closed operation.

$A = \begin{bmatrix} a_{11} & a_{12} & a_{13} \\ a_{12} & a_{11} & a_{23} \\ a_{13} & a_{23} & a_{11} \end{bmatrix}; B = \begin{bmatrix} b_{11} & b_{12} & b_{13} \\ b_{12} & b_{11} & b_{23} \\ b_{13} & b_{23} & b_{11} \end{bmatrix}$

$A + B = \begin{bmatrix} a_{11} + b_{11} & a_{12} + b_{12} & a_{13} + b_{13} \\ a_{12} + b_{12} & a_{11} + b_{11} & a_{23} + b_{23} \\ a_{13} + b_{13} & a_{23} + b_{23} & a_{11} + b_{11} \end{bmatrix}$

which is symmetric; Multiplication of two matrices is not a closed operation.

Additional Answers
32. $\begin{bmatrix} 10 \\ -2 \\ 8 \end{bmatrix}$ **33.** $\begin{bmatrix} 5 \\ 8 \\ 2 \end{bmatrix}$ **34.** $\begin{bmatrix} 238 \\ \frac{55}{19} \\ \frac{55}{197} \\ 55 \end{bmatrix}$

38. $\begin{bmatrix} 3 \\ -4 \end{bmatrix}$ **39.** $\begin{bmatrix} -3 \\ -9 \end{bmatrix}$ **40.** $\begin{bmatrix} 2 \\ 0 \end{bmatrix}$

41. $\begin{bmatrix} -1 \\ 3 \\ -2 \end{bmatrix}$ **42.** $\begin{bmatrix} 6 \\ -3 \\ 2 \end{bmatrix}$ **43.** $\begin{bmatrix} 1 \\ 2 \\ \frac{1}{3} \\ \frac{1}{6} \end{bmatrix}$

44. 5 pencils; 2 erasers
45. $A^{-1} = \begin{bmatrix} 4 & -3 \\ -1 & 1 \end{bmatrix}; A^2 = \begin{bmatrix} 4 & 15 \\ 5 & 19 \end{bmatrix};$

$(A^{-1})^2 = \begin{bmatrix} 19 & -15 \\ -5 & 4 \end{bmatrix}; (A^2)^{-1} = \begin{bmatrix} 19 & -15 \\ -5 & 4 \end{bmatrix}; (A^{-1})^2 = (A^2)^{-1}$

23. $\begin{bmatrix} -\frac{19}{2} \\ -\frac{13}{2} \end{bmatrix}$ **24.** $\begin{bmatrix} \frac{3}{2} \\ -1 \end{bmatrix}$ **25.** no solution; inverse does not exist   **26.** no solution; inverse does not exist

27. $\begin{bmatrix} 6 \\ -\frac{2}{3} \end{bmatrix}$ **28.** $\begin{bmatrix} 3 \\ -8 \end{bmatrix}$ **29.** $\begin{bmatrix} \frac{80}{9} \\ \frac{43}{9} \end{bmatrix}$ **30.** $\begin{bmatrix} 8 \\ 48 \end{bmatrix}$ **31.** $\begin{bmatrix} 3 \\ -2 \\ 2 \end{bmatrix}$

Technology
calculator with matrix capabilities
computer

FOCUS

Discuss with students other examples of inventory control, such as parts for automobile assembly lines, grocery store foods for the shelves, and gasoline supplies for filling stations.

INSTRUCTION

- Students have had some experience using augmented matrices in the last lesson when finding the multiplicative inverse of a matrix. In this lesson students use augmented matrices to solve systems of equations. Working through Example 1, students should see how the Gauss-Jordan procedure involving augmented matrices is a shorthand method for operating on equations within a system.

- Before students read the solutions to Examples 3 and 4, have them discuss methods they would use to solve each problem. Then compare these methods to the matrix solution in the text.

12.5 Augmented Matrix Solutions

Objective: *To solve a system of linear equations in three variables using the augmented matrix method*

Focus

To save on warehouse space and inventory storage costs, manufacturers often try to avoid maintaining large inventories of parts and supplies. Instead, they schedule deliveries to coincide with production needs. This requires very accurate projections of needed supplies. Matrix algebra is frequently used to aid in maintaining the smooth flow of parts and supplies through the assembly process. This is especially true when the same materials and components are involved in several different products.

For example, the required information may be organized as follows: The columns of one matrix may represent three different models of a product and the rows may represent different parts. The matrix elements represent the materials components for all models. Then a production supervisor can use the matrix to answer questions such as how many of each model can be produced using the parts on hand.

$$\begin{array}{c}\text{Model}\\ \begin{array}{ccc} A & B & C \end{array} \end{array}$$

$$\begin{array}{l}\text{Part I}\\ \text{Part II}\\ \text{Part III}\end{array} \begin{bmatrix} 4 & 6 & 8 \\ 3 & 0 & 9 \\ 8 & 9 & 7 \end{bmatrix}$$

One procedure for solving a system of equations employs an **augmented matrix** formed by writing the constants on the right hand sides of the equations as a column and attaching this column to the matrix of coefficients, as shown below.

System of Equations	Augmented Matrix

$$\begin{array}{rl} 3x - 2y + z &= 2 \\ x + 4y &= 9 \\ 2x + z &= 5 \end{array} \qquad \begin{bmatrix} 3 & -2 & 1 & \bigg| & 2 \\ 1 & 4 & 0 & \bigg| & 9 \\ 2 & 0 & 1 & \bigg| & 5 \end{bmatrix}$$

Note that when a variable is missing in an equation, its coefficient in the matrix is 0. The row-equivalent operations of Lesson 12.4 can be used to solve the system of equations. The objective is to transform the coefficient matrix

$$\begin{bmatrix} a_{11} & a_{12} & a_{13} & \bigg| & d \\ a_{21} & a_{22} & a_{23} & \bigg| & e \\ a_{31} & a_{32} & a_{33} & \bigg| & f \end{bmatrix} \quad \text{to the form} \quad \begin{bmatrix} 1 & 0 & 0 & \bigg| & r \\ 0 & 1 & 0 & \bigg| & s \\ 0 & 0 & 1 & \bigg| & t \end{bmatrix}$$

where the solution of the system of equations is

$$x = r \qquad y = s \qquad z = t$$

This procedure, called the *augmented matrix method*, or the *Gaussian elimination method*, is illustrated in Example 1. You begin by making the element in the first row, first column 1. Then make the other elements in the first column 0's. Continue by making the element in the second row, second column 1. Using the row-equivalent operations continue until the desired form is obtained.

Example 1   Solve the system of equations using the augmented matrix method.

$$\begin{cases} x + 3y + 8z = 22 \\ 2x - 3y + z = 5 \\ 3x - y + 2z = 12 \end{cases}$$

$$\begin{bmatrix} 1 & 3 & 8 & | & 22 \\ 2 & -3 & 1 & | & 5 \\ 3 & -1 & 2 & | & 12 \end{bmatrix}$$

Determine the augmented matrix consisting of the coefficient matrix and the constant matrix. There is a 1 in the first row, first column.

$$\begin{bmatrix} 1 & 3 & 8 & | & 22 \\ 0 & -9 & -15 & | & -39 \\ 3 & -1 & 2 & | & 12 \end{bmatrix}$$

To obtain a 0 in the second row, first column, multiply the elements in row 1 by −2 and add the results to the corresponding elements in row 2.

$$\begin{bmatrix} 1 & 3 & 8 & | & 22 \\ 0 & -9 & -15 & | & -39 \\ 0 & -10 & -22 & | & -54 \end{bmatrix}$$

To obtain a 0 in the third row, first column, multiply the elements in row 1 by −3 and add the results to the corresponding elements in row 3.

$$\begin{bmatrix} 1 & 3 & 8 & | & 22 \\ 0 & 1 & \frac{5}{3} & | & \frac{13}{3} \\ 0 & -10 & -22 & | & -54 \end{bmatrix}$$

To obtain a 1 in the second row, second column, multiply the elements in row 2 by $-\frac{1}{9}$.

$$\begin{bmatrix} 1 & 3 & 8 & | & 22 \\ 0 & 1 & \frac{5}{3} & | & \frac{13}{3} \\ 0 & 0 & -\frac{16}{3} & | & -\frac{32}{3} \end{bmatrix}$$

To obtain a 0 in the third row, second column, multiply the elements in row 2 by 10 and add the results to the corresponding elements in row 3.

$$\begin{bmatrix} 1 & 0 & 3 & | & 9 \\ 0 & 1 & \frac{5}{3} & | & \frac{13}{3} \\ 0 & 0 & -\frac{16}{3} & | & -\frac{32}{3} \end{bmatrix}$$

To obtain a 0 in the first row, second column, multiply the elements in row 2 by −3 and add the results to the corresponding elements in row 1.

$$\begin{bmatrix} 1 & 0 & 3 & | & 9 \\ 0 & 1 & \frac{5}{3} & | & \frac{13}{3} \\ 0 & 0 & 1 & | & 2 \end{bmatrix}$$

To obtain a 1 in the third row, third column, multiply the elements in row 3 by $-\frac{3}{16}$.

$$\begin{bmatrix} 1 & 0 & 3 & | & 9 \\ 0 & 1 & 0 & | & 1 \\ 0 & 0 & 1 & | & 2 \end{bmatrix}$$

To obtain a 0 in the second row, third column, multiply the elements in row 3 by $-\frac{5}{3}$ and add the results to the corresponding elements in row 2.

$$\begin{bmatrix} 1 & 0 & 0 & | & 3 \\ 0 & 1 & 0 & | & 1 \\ 0 & 0 & 1 & | & 2 \end{bmatrix}$$

To obtain a 0 in the first row, third column, multiply the elements in row 3 by −3 and add the results to the corresponding elements in row 1.

The last augmented matrix corresponds to the system of equations $x = 3$, $y = 1$, and $z = 2$. Therefore, the solution is the ordered triple (3, 1, 2). Check by substituting for x, y, and z in the three original equations.

GUIDED PRACTICE

For Example 1
Solve the system of equations using the augmented matrix method.

1. $\begin{cases} 3x - 2y + 7z = 13 \\ x + 8y - 6z = -47 \\ 7x - 9y - 9z = -3 \end{cases}$ $(-3, -4, 2)$

2. $\begin{cases} 2A + 3B + 12C = 4 \\ 4A - 6B + 6C = 1 \\ A + B + C = 1 \end{cases}$ $\left(\frac{1}{2}, \frac{1}{3}, \frac{1}{6}\right)$

For Example 2

Solve the system of equations using the augmented matrix method.

1. $\begin{cases} A + 2B - C = -8 \\ 2A - B + C = 4 \\ 8A + B + C = 2 \end{cases}$ no solution

2. $\begin{cases} x + y + 2z = 1 \\ 2x + 3z = 2 \\ x - y + 2z = 1 \end{cases}$ $(1, 0, 0)$

Modeling

This model provides an excellent opportunity to engage students in a discussion about the use of mathematics in the workplace. More and more industries require their employees to have some proficiency in math and have even implemented programs for employees to continue their mathematical education.

If a row of the matrix reduces to all zeros except for a nonzero constant in the last column, then the system has *no* solution since the equation $0x + 0y + 0z = b$, where $b \neq 0$, has no solution. Such a result is illustrated in Example 2. If, however, a row reduces to all zeros including the constant and no other row reduces to all zeros except for a nonzero constant, the system has an *infinite* number of solutions since the equation $0x + 0y + 0z = 0$ has an infinite number of solutions. The augmented matrix method of solving a system of linear equations can be applied to a system with any number of variables.

If the number of variables is not too great, the method can be used conveniently with calculators that perform row operations. If you are not using a calculator or computer, obtaining 1's on the diagonal of the coefficient matrix may involve awkward fractions. In order to avoid these, you can first obtain *any* integers on the diagonal (not necessarily 1's) with zeros in the other positions. Then divide each row by an integer to obtain the desired 1.

Example 2 Use an augmented matrix to solve the system of equations at the right.

$$\begin{cases} 2x - 3y + z = 2 \\ x - y + 4z = 1 \\ -3x + 5y + 2z = 3 \end{cases}$$

$\begin{bmatrix} 2 & -3 & 1 & | & 2 \\ 1 & -1 & 4 & | & 1 \\ -3 & 5 & 2 & | & 3 \end{bmatrix}$ *Write the augmented matrix.*

$\begin{bmatrix} 1 & -1 & 4 & | & 1 \\ 2 & -3 & 1 & | & 2 \\ -3 & 5 & 2 & | & 3 \end{bmatrix}$ *Interchange row 1 and row 2.*

$\begin{bmatrix} 1 & -1 & 4 & | & 1 \\ 0 & -1 & -7 & | & 0 \\ 0 & 2 & 14 & | & 6 \end{bmatrix}$ *Multiply row 1 by -2 and add to row 2. Multiply row 1 by 3 and add to row 3.*

$\begin{bmatrix} 1 & -1 & 4 & | & 1 \\ 0 & 1 & 7 & | & 0 \\ 0 & 2 & 14 & | & 6 \end{bmatrix}$ *Multiply row 2 by -1 to get a 1 in the second row, second column.*

$\begin{bmatrix} 1 & 0 & 11 & | & 1 \\ 0 & 1 & 7 & | & 0 \\ 0 & 0 & 0 & | & 6 \end{bmatrix}$ *Multiply row 2 by -2 and add to row 3. Add row 2 to row 1.*

The bottom row corresponds to the equation $0x + 0y + 0z = 6$, or $0 = 6$. Therefore, this system of equations has no solution.

Modeling

Industrial engineers often find it necessary to solve a system of linear equations. How might a system of equations arise in a manufacturing environment?

The Focus described several requirements for a manufacturing plant to run efficiently. One way to avoid unnecessary expense is to keep inventories low. Before manufacturing a product, it is necessary to analyze the materials needed and the supplies available. This kind of problem is illustrated in Example 3.

628   Chapter 12 Matrices and Vectors

Example 3 *Manufacturing* A fertilizer processing plant produces three grades of fertilizer. A bag of grade A contains 30 lb of component I, 20 lb of component II, and 50 lb of component III. A bag of grade B contains 20 lb of component I, 20 lb of component II, and 60 lb of component III. A bag of grade C contains 50 lb of component II and 50 lb of component III. Given that the plant has 980 lb of component I, 1800 lb of component II, and 3220 lb of component III, how many bags of each grade should be packaged to use all the available supplies?

Let x represent the number of bags of grade A, y the number of bags of grade B and z the number of bags of grade C. Then represent the problem in matrix form.

$$\text{Components } \begin{matrix} \text{I} \\ \text{II} \\ \text{III} \end{matrix} \begin{array}{c} \text{Grade} \\ \begin{matrix} A & B & C \end{matrix} \\ \begin{bmatrix} 30 & 20 & 0 \\ 20 & 20 & 50 \\ 50 & 60 & 50 \end{bmatrix} \end{array} \begin{bmatrix} x \\ y \\ z \end{bmatrix} \qquad \begin{array}{c} \text{Total Supplies} \\ \text{Available} \\ \begin{bmatrix} 980 \\ 1800 \\ 3200 \end{bmatrix} \begin{matrix} \text{I} \\ \text{II} \\ \text{III} \end{matrix} \end{array} \text{Components}$$

$$\begin{cases} 30x + 20y + 0z = 980 \\ 20x + 20y + 50z = 1800 \\ 50x + 60y + 50z = 3220 \end{cases}$$

The system of equations represents the distribution of components I, II, and III among the three grades.

$$\begin{bmatrix} 30 & 20 & 0 & | & 980 \\ 20 & 20 & 50 & | & 1800 \\ 50 & 60 & 50 & | & 3220 \end{bmatrix}$$

Construct the augmented matrix for the system of equations.

$$\begin{bmatrix} 1 & 0 & 0 & | & 18 \\ 0 & 1 & 0 & | & 22 \\ 0 & 0 & 1 & | & 20 \end{bmatrix}$$

Use row operations to transform the matrix.

Therefore, $x = 18$, $y = 22$, and $z = 20$. The processing plant should make 18 bags of grade A, 22 bags of grade B, and 20 bags of grade C.

In Example 3, note that the components-grade matrix can be used many times while the supplies and output will vary.

Example 4 Determine an equation of the circle that passes through the points $(2, 9)$, $(8, 7)$, and $(-8, -1)$.

Recall that the equation of a circle may be written in the form $x^2 + y^2 + Dx + Ey + F = 0$. Substitute the coordinates of the points in the equation and simplify.

$$\begin{cases} 2D + 9E + F = -85 \\ 8D + 7E + F = -113 \\ 8D + E - F = 65 \end{cases}$$

$$\begin{bmatrix} 2 & 9 & 1 & | & -85 \\ 8 & 7 & 1 & | & -113 \\ 8 & 1 & -1 & | & 65 \end{bmatrix}$$

Corresponding augmented matrix

$$\begin{bmatrix} 1 & 0 & 0 & | & -4 \\ 0 & 1 & 0 & | & 2 \\ 0 & 0 & 1 & | & -95 \end{bmatrix}$$

Use row operations to transform the matrix.
$D = -4, E = 2, F = -95$

An equation of the circle is $x^2 + y^2 - 4x + 2y - 95 = 0$.

For Example 3
A newspaper has 40 pages available for ads in 1 issue. It can process at most 120 ads which consist of full-page, half-page, and quarter-page ads. The paper would like to earn $10,800 from the sale of the ads, which cost $200 for a full page, $125 for a half page, and $75 for a quarter page. What combination of ads should the newspaper sell?
8 full-page, 16 half-page, 96 quarter-page

For Example 4
1. Determine the equation of the circle that passes through the points $(10, -4)$, $(3, 3)$, and $(-4, -4)$.
$x^2 + y^2 - 6x + 8y - 24 = 0$
2. Determine the equation of the parabola with equation $y = ax^2 + bx + c$ that passes through the points $(1, 4)$, $(-1, 28)$, and $(3, -4)$.
$- 12x + 14$

Common Error Some students may not set up the augmented matrix correctly when solving an application problem. Have these students first determine what the unknown values are and use them to write a system of equations.

CLOSURE

Have students describe the conditions in an augmented matrix that determine when a system of equations has exactly one solution, no solution, and infinitely many solutions.

Class Exercises

Solve each system of equations using the augmented matrix method.

1. $\begin{cases} 3x + y - 4z = -1 \\ 5x + 2y - 4z = 8 \\ 6x - 7y = -23 \end{cases}$ (2, 5, 3)

2. $\begin{cases} 7x + 11y + 5z = 11 \\ 5x + 2y + 8z = -70 \\ 5x + 3y + 3z = -27 \end{cases}$ (-6, 8, -7)

3. $\begin{cases} x + y = 2 \\ y + z = 17 \\ z + x = 5 \end{cases}$ (-5, 7, 10)

4. *Manufacturing*   Assembly lines A, B, and C can produce 8400 TV dinners per day. Lines A and B together can produce 4900 TV dinners, while B and C can produce 5600 TV dinners. By using the augmented matrix method of solving a system of linear equations, find the number of TV dinners each assembly line can produce. A: 2800; B: 2100; C: 3500

Practice Exercises   Use appropriate technology.

Solve each system of equations using the augmented matrix method.

A 1. $\begin{cases} x + 2y + z = 1 \\ 7x + 3y - z = -2 \\ x + 5y + 3z = 2 \end{cases}$

2. $\begin{cases} 4a - b - c = 4 \\ 2a + b + c = -1 \\ 6a - 3b - 2c = 3 \end{cases}$

3. $\begin{cases} 2r - 3s + 3t = -15 \\ 3r + 2s - 5t = 19 \\ 4r - 4s - 2t = -2 \end{cases}$

4. $\begin{cases} 4d - 2e + 3f = 0 \\ 3d - 5e - 2f = -12 \\ 2d + 4e - 3f = -4 \end{cases}$

5. $\begin{cases} 2a + 4b - 10c = -2 \\ 3a + 9b - 21c = 0 \\ a + 5b - 12c = 1 \end{cases}$

6. $\begin{cases} 3r + 8s - t = -18 \\ 2r + s + 5t = 8 \\ 2r + 4s + 2t = -4 \end{cases}$

7. $\begin{cases} x + 2y + 3z = 8 \\ 3x - y + 2z = 5 \\ -2x - 4y - 6z = 5 \end{cases}$

8. $\begin{cases} 4x - y + 3z = -2 \\ 3x + 5y - z = 15 \\ -2x + y + 4z = 14 \end{cases}$

9. $\begin{cases} x + 2y + z = 0 \\ 3x + 3y - z = 10 \\ x + 3y + 2z = 5 \end{cases}$

10. $\begin{cases} x - y + 5z = -6 \\ 4x - y + z = 0 \\ -x - 2y - z = 0 \end{cases}$

11. $\begin{cases} x + 2y - z = 29 \\ 3x - 1.5y + 12z = -18 \\ 2x + 0.5y - 5z = 39 \end{cases}$

12. $\begin{cases} 2x - y + 6.4z = 44 \\ 5x + 1.5y = 6 \\ -4x + 0.2z = -11 \end{cases}$

R 13. Evaluate: $y = \arcsin \frac{\pi}{3}$ does not exist

Determine the equation of the circle that passes through the three given points.

14. $(-2, -2)$, $(10, -8)$, $(7, 1)$
$x^2 + y^2 - 8x + 10y - 4 = 0$

15. $(1, 1)$, $(5, 3)$, $(4, 2)$
$x^2 + y^2 - 2x - 12y + 12 = 0$

16. $(1, 1)$, $(4, 0)$ $(2, -1)$
$x^2 + y^2 - 5x - y + 4 = 0$

Determine the equation of the parabola with equation $y = ax^2 + bx + c$ that passes through the three given points.

17. $(-2, 7)$, $(1, -8)$, $(4, -5)$ $y = x^2 - 4x - 5$

18. $(1, -1)$, $(2, 8)$, $(-2, -4)$
$y = 2x^2 + 3x - 6$

Determine the equation of the circle circumscribing the triangle whose vertices are given. $x^2 + y^2 - 5x - y - 6 = 0$

19. $(0, 3)$, $(6, 1)$, $(3, -3)$

20. $(-2, -2)$, $(-1, 6)$, $(0, 1)$ $x^2 + y^2 + 11x - 5y + 4 = 0$

R 21. Evaluate: $y = \arctan \frac{\pi}{6}$ 0.4823

B 22. Find three numbers whose sum is 50, if the first is 2 more than the second, and the third is two-thirds of the second. Solve this problem by using an augmented matrix for a system of three linear equations. 20, 18, 12

630   Chapter 12 Matrices and Vectors

23. *Manufacturing*   The processing plant in Example 3 needs to produce 10 bags of grade *A*, 16 bags of grade *B*, and 26 bags of grade *C* fertilizer. How much of each of the three components I, II, and III will be needed to fill this order?

24. *Manufacturing*   The processing plant in Example 3 changed the composition of grade *C* fertilizer to include 10 lb of component I, 40 lb of component II, and 50 lb of component III. How many bags of each grade should be made to use all the available supplies?

Ⓡ 25. Evaluate: $y = \log_5 9$ 1.3652

26. **Thinking Critically**   How could you show that the points $(-1, 3)$, $(1, 0)$, $(4, -2)$, and $(14, 13)$ all lie on the same circle?

27. *Manufacturing*   A cookie manufacturer mixes vanilla, chocolate, and vanilla/chocolate cookies to create an assortment for sale. The cookies are packaged in three different sizes according to the following proportions.

Package size I	7 lb chocolate, 5 lb vanilla, 1 lb mixed
Package size II	3 lb chocolate, 2 lb vanilla, 2 lb mixed
Package size III	4 lb chocolate, 3 lb vanilla, 3 lb mixed

If 67 lb of chocolate, 48 lb of vanilla, and 32 lb of mixed are available, how much of each size package may be produced?

28. *Education*   Meredith has a total of 264 on three tests. The sum of the scores on her first and third tests exceeds her second score by 30. Her first score exceeds her third by 7. Find the three scores. 77, 117, 70

Ⓡ 29. Find the length of the common chord of the parabolas $y^2 = 2x + 12$ and $y^2 + 2y = 4x$. $10\sqrt{2}$

30. **Thinking Critically**   How would you determine the coefficients of the system if $(1, 2, 3)$ is a solution of the system?

$$\begin{cases} ax + by + cz = 6 \\ 2bx - cy + 3az = 9 \\ -cx + 2by + 2az = 9 \end{cases}$$

Ⓡ 31. Simplify $-2x^3y^4z^2 - 3x^2y^3z$ if $x = -1$, $y = -2$, and $z = 3$. 360

32. *Investment*   James invests $20,000 in three ways. With one part, he buys mutual funds which offer a return of 8% per year. The second part, which amounts to twice the first, is used to buy government bonds at 9% per year. He puts the rest in the bank at 5% annual interest. The first year his investments bring a return of $1,660. How much did he invest each way?

33. *Investment*   Jane invests $5,000 in three ways. With one part, she buys mutual funds which offer a return of 10% per year. The second part, which amounts to three times the first, is used to buy government bonds at 8% per year. She puts the rest in the bank at 6% annual interest. The first year her investments bring a return of $420. How much did she invest each way?

mutual funds: $1200; government bonds: $3600; savings: $200

34. Alan, Brian, and Charles together invested $3,000. If Alan receives 6%, Brian 7%, and Charles 8% on their respective investments, they earn together $219. If instead Alan receives 7%, Brian 8%, and Charles 6%, the sum of their incomes is $204. How much has each invested?

Alan: $600; Brian: $900; Charles: $1500

12.5 Augmented Matrix Solutions   **631**

Assignment Guide
Basic: 1–21, 23–29 odd
Average: 1–19 odd, 20–37, Project
Enriched: 1–29 odd, 30–46, Project

Teacher's Resource Book
  Practice, page 82

Ⓡ **Review**
Exercises 13, 21, 25, 29, and 31 review concepts of evaluating inverse trigonometric functions, evaluating logarithmic functions, using coordinate geometry, and simplifying expressions.

Technology
A computer or a calculator with matrix capabilities would facilitate finding the solutions of systems of equations throughout the exercise set.

Project
You may want students to work in groups on this particular project. This way students can pay closer attention to detail and can also be more creative, thereby making the assignment more meaningful.

Additional Answers
23. component I: 620 lb
    component II: 1820 lb
    component III: 2760 lb
24. Grade *A*: 8 bags
    Grade *B*: 22 bags
    Grade *C*: 30 bags
26. Substitute each of the points for *x* and *y* in the equation $(x - h)^2 + (y - k)^2 = r^2$. This will give a system of four equations in three unknowns. If it yields a unique solution, the points all lie on the same circle.
27. size I: 4 packages
    size II: 5 packages
    size III: 6 packages
30. Substitute 1, 2, and 3 for *x*, *y*, and *z*, respectively, in each equation. Solve the resulting system for *a*, *b*, and *c*.
32. mutual funds: $6000
    bonds: $12,000
    savings: $2000

Test Yourself

Teacher's Resource Book
   Tests—Quiz, form A, page 53
   Tests—Quiz, form B, page 53

Lesson Quiz

Solve the system of equations using the augmented matrix method.

1. $\begin{cases} x + 3y + 6z = 17 \\ 3x + 9y + 18z = 37 \\ 2x + 6y + 12z = 12 \end{cases}$ no solution

2. $\begin{cases} 3x - 5y + 4z = 7 \\ 2x + y + z = -2 \\ 2x - y + 3z = 6 \end{cases}$ $(-3, 0, 4)$

3. In a factory there are three punch presses P, Q, and R. When all three of them are operating, 5700 parts are punched in one week. When only P and Q are operating, 3400 parts are punched in one week. When only Q and R are operating 4200 parts are punched in one week. How many parts can be punched in a week by each machine?
   P: 1500; Q: 1900; R: 2300

4. Determine an equation of the circle that passes through the points $(1, 2)$, $(3, 7)$, and $(-2, -5)$.
   $x^2 + y^2 + 491x - 207y - 82 = 0$

For each of the following equations, determine the values of constants A, B, and C, that make the equation an identity. *Hint:* If $ax^2 + bx + c$ equals 0 for all values of x, then $a = 0$, $b = 0$, and $c = 0$. Use an augmented matrix to solve a linear system in three variables.

35. $\dfrac{2x^2 - 3x + 3}{x(x-1)^2} = \dfrac{A}{x} + \dfrac{B}{x-1} + \dfrac{C}{(x-1)^2}$
   $A = 3; B = -1; C = 2$

36. $\dfrac{5x^2 + 20x + 6}{x(x+1)^2} = \dfrac{A}{x} + \dfrac{B}{x+1} + \dfrac{C}{(x+1)^2}$
   $A = 6; B = -1; C = 9$

Solve each system of equations using the augmented matrix method.

C 37. $\begin{cases} \dfrac{1}{x} + \dfrac{1}{y} + \dfrac{2}{z} = 1 \\ \dfrac{2}{x} + \dfrac{1}{y} - \dfrac{2}{z} = 1 \\ \dfrac{3}{x} + \dfrac{4}{y} - \dfrac{4}{z} = 2 \end{cases}$ $(2, 4, 8)$

38. $\begin{cases} \dfrac{1}{x} - \dfrac{1}{y} - \dfrac{1}{z} = 0 \\ \dfrac{3}{x} + \dfrac{1}{y} + \dfrac{3}{z} = 1 \\ \dfrac{2}{x} + \dfrac{1}{y} + \dfrac{1}{z} = 1 \end{cases}$ $(3, 2, -6)$

39. $\begin{cases} \dfrac{3}{x} - \dfrac{4}{y} + \dfrac{6}{z} = 1 \\ \dfrac{9}{x} + \dfrac{8}{y} - \dfrac{12}{z} = 3 \\ \dfrac{9}{x} - \dfrac{4}{y} + \dfrac{12}{z} = 4 \end{cases}$ $(3, 4, 6)$

40. $\begin{cases} \dfrac{2}{x} + \dfrac{3}{y} - \dfrac{2}{z} = -1 \\ \dfrac{8}{x} - \dfrac{12}{y} + \dfrac{5}{z} = 5 \\ \dfrac{6}{x} + \dfrac{3}{y} - \dfrac{1}{z} = 1 \end{cases}$ $(4, 6, 1)$

Solve for x, y, and z in terms of a, b, and c.

41. $\begin{cases} 2x + y + 2z = a \\ x - y + 2z = b \\ x + y + z = c \end{cases}$

42. $\begin{cases} x - y + z = a \\ 2x - y - z = b \\ x - 3y + 2z = c \end{cases}$
   $x = a + 0.2b - 0.4c$
   $y = a - 0.2b - 0.6c$
   $z = a - 0.4b - 0.2c$

43. $\begin{cases} 2x + y + z = 7a \\ x + 2y + z = 3a \\ x + y + 2z = 6a \end{cases}$
   $x = 3a$
   $y = -a$
   $z = 2a$

44. $\begin{cases} x + y - z = 6a - 5b \\ x - y + z = 2a - b \\ x + y + z = 8a - 3b \end{cases}$
   $x = 4a - 3b$
   $y = 3a - b$
   $z = a + b$

45. *Civil Engineering*   Three pumps X, Y, Z are used to pump water from a flooded underpass. When all three pumps are used, 4200 gal/h may be pumped. When only X and Y are running, 3000 gal/h may be pumped. When X and Z are running, 2800 gal/h can be pumped. What is the pumping capacity of each pump? X: 1600 gal/h; Y: 1400 gal/h; Z: 1200 gal/h

46. *Civil Engineering*   Three pipes supply an oil storage tank. The tank can be filled by pipes A and B running for 10 h, by pipes B and C running for 15 h, or by pipes A and C running for 20 h. How long does it take to fill the tank if all three pipes run? $\dfrac{120}{13}$ h

Project

Describe a manufacturing problem that can be represented by a system of linear equations, where coefficients of the variables represent fixed conditions for producing the items, while the variables and constants represent the conditions that may vary, such as available labor or supplies, or changing demand for the product. Express the system in augmented matrix form. Then list the row operations that are needed to transform the matrix and solve the problem.

632   Chapter 12 Matrices and Vectors

Test Yourself

Given $A = \begin{bmatrix} 3 & -5 \\ -4 & 2 \\ -1 & 1 \end{bmatrix}$ and $B = \begin{bmatrix} -2 & -4 \\ 0 & 1 \\ 5 & 2 \end{bmatrix}$, find:

12.1

1. $A + 2B$

2. $2A - B$

3. Solve the matrix equation: $\quad 2\begin{bmatrix} 4 & \frac{1}{2} \\ 1 & \frac{1}{4} \end{bmatrix} + X = \frac{1}{3}\begin{bmatrix} 6 & -15 \\ -9 & 3 \end{bmatrix}$ $\begin{bmatrix} -6 & -6 \\ -5 & \frac{1}{2} \end{bmatrix}$

4. Given that $3[x \quad 2y] = [6 \quad y] + [x \quad -9]$, find the values of x and y. $\left(3, -\frac{9}{5}\right)$

5. Given $A = \begin{bmatrix} 2 & 5 \\ -1 & 0 \\ 3 & 1 \end{bmatrix}$ and $B = \begin{bmatrix} 3 & 1 \\ -2 & -3 \end{bmatrix}$, find AB. $\begin{bmatrix} -4 & -13 \\ -3 & -1 \\ 7 & 0 \end{bmatrix}$

12.2

Given $A = \begin{bmatrix} 2 & 4 \\ -3 & -5 \end{bmatrix}$ and $B = \begin{bmatrix} -1 & 2 \\ 0 & -3 \end{bmatrix}$, find:

6. B^2 $\begin{bmatrix} 1 & -8 \\ 0 & 9 \end{bmatrix}$

7. B^2A $\begin{bmatrix} 26 & 44 \\ -27 & -45 \end{bmatrix}$

8. Construct the adjacency matrix for the graph at the right.

12.3

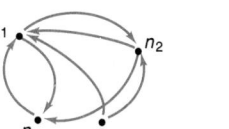

9. Sketch the directed graph that represents the data in the transportation matrix.

$$\begin{array}{c} \\ A \\ B \\ C \\ D \end{array} \begin{array}{cccc} A & B & C & D \\ \begin{bmatrix} 1 & 1 & 1 & 1 \\ 0 & 1 & 0 & 0 \\ 1 & 1 & 0 & 1 \\ 0 & 0 & 1 & 0 \end{bmatrix} \end{array}$$

10. Find the multiplicative inverse of the matrix $A = \begin{bmatrix} 1 & -4 \\ 2 & 3 \end{bmatrix}$, if it exists.

12.4

11. Solve the matrix equation for the matrix X: $\begin{bmatrix} 3 & -2 \\ 5 & 6 \end{bmatrix} X = \begin{bmatrix} 1 \\ -3 \end{bmatrix}$

12. Solve the system $\begin{cases} 3x + 2y = 3 \\ -4x + 3y = 10 \end{cases}$ using matrices. $\left(-\frac{11}{17}, \frac{42}{17}\right)$

13. Solve the system of equations using the augmented matrix method.

12.5

$$\begin{cases} 3x + 2y - z = -3 \\ -x + 3y + 2z = 8 \\ 2x - y + z = -1 \end{cases} \quad (-1, 1, 2)$$

14. *Manufacturing* Assembly lines A, B, and C can produce 7700 gadgets per day. A and B together can produce 5500 gadgets, while A and C together can produce 5200 gadgets. Find the number of gadgets each assembly line can produce. $A: 3000, B = 2500, C: 2200$

12.5 Augmented Matrix Solutions **633**

Alternative Assessment

Have students write a word problem where the solution involves solving a system of three equations with three unknowns. Have them include a strategy for solving the problem and give a complete solution.

Enrichment

Ask students to solve the system

$$\begin{cases} 2x + 3y - 2z = 8 \\ 3x + 2y - 2z = 14 \\ 4x + 5y + 3z = 38 \end{cases}$$

by the following:
1. elimination
2. matrix equation
3. augmented matrix
Have the students explain the advantages and disadvantages of each method. $x = \frac{214}{33}; y = \frac{16}{33}; z = \frac{106}{33}$

Additional Answers

Test Yourself

1. $\begin{bmatrix} -1 & -13 \\ -4 & 4 \\ 9 & 5 \end{bmatrix}$

2. $\begin{bmatrix} 8 & -6 \\ -8 & 3 \\ -7 & 0 \end{bmatrix}$

8.
$$\begin{array}{c} \\ n_1 \\ n_2 \\ n_3 \\ n_4 \end{array} \begin{array}{cccc} n_1 & n_2 & n_3 & n_4 \\ \begin{bmatrix} 0 & 1 & 1 & 0 \\ 1 & 0 & 1 & 0 \\ 1 & 0 & 0 & 0 \\ 1 & 1 & 0 & 0 \end{bmatrix} \end{array}$$

9.

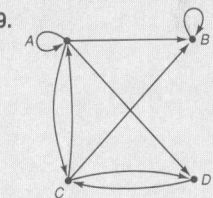

10. $\begin{bmatrix} \frac{3}{11} & \frac{4}{11} \\ \frac{2}{11} & \frac{1}{11} \end{bmatrix}$

11. $\begin{bmatrix} 0 \\ -\frac{1}{2} \end{bmatrix}$

633

Vocabulary
reflection matrix
rotation matrix
transformation matrix

Ⓜ **Materials/Manipulatives**
compass
graph paper
protractor

Technology
scientific calculator
calculator with matrix capabilities

FOCUS

In Lesson 2.2 students worked with reflections and translations of points and functions, and found them to preserve both distance and angle measures. Students will see in this lesson that rotations have this same property. Discuss the possible advantages of representing transformations of points and functions using matrices.

12.6 Matrices and Transformations

Objective: To use transformation matrices to find the image of a point under a reflection or rotation

Focus

Whenever you reflect ("flip") a straight line about x- or y-axis or rotate the line about the origin, the figure that you obtain is also a straight line. Partly for this reason, reflections and rotations are called *linear transformations*. By using matrices to represent transformations, you may better appreciate their structure. For example, with matrices it is possible to show that two successive rotations are equivalent to a single rotation but that two successive reflections are not equivalent to a single reflection. Thus, the set of rotation matrices is closed under matrix multiplication but the set of reflection matrices is not.

As mentioned in the Focus, transformations may be interpreted as matrices. In order to see how this is done, consider the case of a reflection of a point about the x-axis. (Reflections were introduced without the aid of matrices in Lesson 2.2.) Here it is helpful to interpret an ordered pair of numbers not in the usual way, that is, (x, y), but as a 2-by-1 *column matrix* $\begin{bmatrix} x \\ y \end{bmatrix}$, as shown in the figure at the right. Also shown are the reflection of $\begin{bmatrix} x \\ y \end{bmatrix}$ in the x-axis and in the y-axis. Examine the results of the following two matrix multiplications.

$$\begin{bmatrix} 1 & 0 \\ 0 & -1 \end{bmatrix} \begin{bmatrix} x \\ y \end{bmatrix} = \begin{bmatrix} x \\ -y \end{bmatrix} \qquad \begin{bmatrix} -1 & 0 \\ 0 & 1 \end{bmatrix} \begin{bmatrix} x \\ y \end{bmatrix} = \begin{bmatrix} -x \\ y \end{bmatrix}$$

The first matrix multiplication reflects the point $\begin{bmatrix} x \\ y \end{bmatrix}$ in the x-axis. The second matrix multiplication reflects the point $\begin{bmatrix} x \\ y \end{bmatrix}$ in the y-axis. For this reason, the two matrices $\begin{bmatrix} 1 & 0 \\ 0 & -1 \end{bmatrix}$ and $\begin{bmatrix} -1 & 0 \\ 0 & 1 \end{bmatrix}$ are called, respectively, the **reflection matrix with respect to the x-axis** and the **reflection matrix with respect to the y-axis**. These matrices, abbreviated as $T_{x\text{-axis}}$ and $T_{y\text{-axis}}$, respectively, are examples of *transformation matrices*.

> A 2-by-2 **transformation matrix** is a matrix of the form $\begin{bmatrix} a & c \\ b & d \end{bmatrix}$; it maps each point $P(x, y)$ of the plane to its image point $P'(x', y')$.

634 Chapter 12 Matrices and Vectors

Example 1 Find and graph the image of each point. Use the indicated transformation matrix.

a. $\begin{bmatrix} -5 \\ 3 \end{bmatrix}$; $T_{x\text{-axis}}$ b. $\begin{bmatrix} 7 \\ 0 \end{bmatrix}$; $T_{y\text{-axis}}$ c. $\begin{bmatrix} 3 \\ 0 \end{bmatrix}$; $T_{x\text{-axis}}$

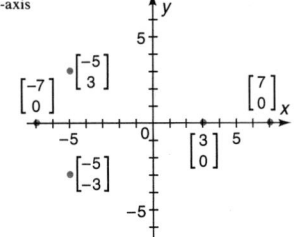

a. $\begin{bmatrix} 1 & 0 \\ 0 & -1 \end{bmatrix}\begin{bmatrix} -5 \\ 3 \end{bmatrix} = \begin{bmatrix} 1(-)5 + 0(3) \\ 0(-5) + (-1)(3) \end{bmatrix} = \begin{bmatrix} -5 \\ -3 \end{bmatrix}$

b. $\begin{bmatrix} -1 & 0 \\ 0 & 1 \end{bmatrix}\begin{bmatrix} 7 \\ 0 \end{bmatrix} = \begin{bmatrix} -7 \\ 0 \end{bmatrix}$

c. $\begin{bmatrix} 1 & 0 \\ 0 & -1 \end{bmatrix}\begin{bmatrix} 3 \\ 0 \end{bmatrix} = \begin{bmatrix} 3 \\ 0 \end{bmatrix}$

A transformation matrix can be used to find the image of the graph of a function.

Example 2 Find and graph the image of $f(x) = x^2 - x + 2$ under the given transformation.

a. $T_{x\text{-axis}}$ b. $T_{y\text{-axis}}$

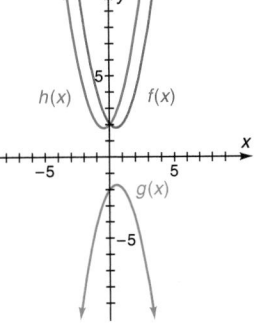

a. $\begin{bmatrix} 1 & 0 \\ 0 & -1 \end{bmatrix}\begin{bmatrix} x \\ x^2 - x + 2 \end{bmatrix} = \begin{bmatrix} 1 \cdot x + 0 \cdot (x^2 - x + 2) \\ 0 \cdot x + (-1) \cdot (x^2 - x + 2) \end{bmatrix}$

$= \begin{bmatrix} x \\ -x^2 + x - 2 \end{bmatrix}$

The reflection of $f(x)$ in the x-axis is
$g(x) = -f(x)$
$g(x) = -x^2 + x - 2$

b. $\begin{bmatrix} -1 & 0 \\ 0 & 1 \end{bmatrix}\begin{bmatrix} x \\ x^2 - x + 2 \end{bmatrix} = \begin{bmatrix} -1 \cdot x + 0 \cdot (x^2 - x + 2) \\ 0 \cdot x + 1 \cdot (x^2 - x + 2) \end{bmatrix}$

$= \begin{bmatrix} -x \\ x^2 - x + 2 \end{bmatrix}$

The reflection of $f(x)$ in the y-axis is
$h(x) = f(-x)$
$h(x) = (-x^2) - (-x) + 2 = x^2 + x + 2$

There are matrices for transformations other than reflections. One such transformation is the *rotation* of points of the coordinate plane about the origin through an angle α. To find the elements of this matrix, it will be helpful to use the following theorem. You are asked to prove this theorem in the exercises.

If $\begin{bmatrix} a & c \\ b & d \end{bmatrix}$ is a transformation matrix, then $\begin{bmatrix} a \\ b \end{bmatrix}$ is the image of the point $(1, 0)$ and $\begin{bmatrix} c \\ d \end{bmatrix}$ is the image of the point $(0, 1)$.

• Point out to students that if a point is represented by a 2×1 column matrix, then the lefthand transformation matrix being multiplied with the point matrix must be a 2×2 matrix to obtain another 2×1 matrix, the image point.

• To motivate this lesson, have students find transformation matrices such as the reflection matrix with respect to the x-axis. Since this transformation maps x to x and y to $-y$, you can write: $\begin{bmatrix} a & c \\ b & d \end{bmatrix} \cdot \begin{bmatrix} x \\ y \end{bmatrix} = \begin{bmatrix} x \\ -y \end{bmatrix}$ where $\begin{bmatrix} a & c \\ b & d \end{bmatrix}$ is the reflection matrix. To find the values of a, b, c, and d, solve the equations $ax + cy = x$ and $bx + dy = -y$. Clearly, $a = 1$, $c = 0$, $b = 0$, and $d = -1$. Repeat this procedure to find the reflection matrices with respect to the y-axis and the line $y = x$, as well as the rotation matrix through the angle $180°$.

• Students should be able to check mentally the image points under $T_{x\text{-axis}}$ and $T_{y\text{-axis}}$.

• Have students read carefully to understand the derivation of the rotation matrix through any angle α. Some students may need a review of sine and cosine functions and the cofunction identities of Lesson 4.1.

• To graph points whose coordinates contain radicals, encourage students first to round these values to the nearest tenth.

GUIDED PRACTICE

For Example 1

Find the image of the point $\begin{bmatrix} 4 \\ -1 \end{bmatrix}$ using the transformation $T_{y\text{-axis}}$. $\begin{bmatrix} -4 \\ -1 \end{bmatrix}$

Technology Students may use a calculator with matrix capabilities to find matrix products, or image points.

For Example 2

Find and graph the image of $f(x) = x^2 + 2x - 3$ using the transformation $T_{x\text{-axis}}$. $g(x) = -x^2 - 2x + 3$

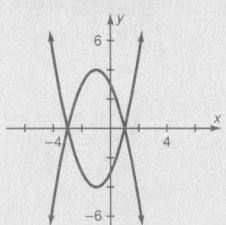

For Example 3

Find the image of the point $(-2, 6)$ using the rotation matrix $R_{120°}$.
$(1 - 3\sqrt{3}, -3 - \sqrt{3})$

In the figure, the points $(1, 0)$ and $(0, 1)$ have been rotated about the origin through an angle α to produce the images $\begin{bmatrix} a \\ b \end{bmatrix}$ and $\begin{bmatrix} c \\ d \end{bmatrix}$, respectively. From the definitions of the sine and cosine functions and the cofunction identities of Lesson 4.1, it is easy to verify the following relationships:

$$a = \cos \alpha$$
$$b = \sin \alpha$$
$$c = \cos \left(\frac{\pi}{2} + \alpha\right) = -\sin \alpha$$
$$d = \sin \left(\frac{\pi}{2} + \alpha\right) = \cos \alpha$$

It follows that the transformation matrix for a rotation of the points of a plane about the origin through an angle α is given by

$$\begin{bmatrix} a & c \\ b & d \end{bmatrix} = \begin{bmatrix} \cos \alpha & -\sin \alpha \\ \sin \alpha & \cos \alpha \end{bmatrix}$$

The above **rotation matrix** is abbreviated as R_α.

Example 3 Find and graph the image of each point. Use the indicated rotation matrix.
  a. $(\sqrt{2}, -\sqrt{2}); R_{45°}$ **b.** $(-3, 4); R_{90°}$

a. $\begin{bmatrix} \dfrac{\sqrt{2}}{2} & -\dfrac{\sqrt{2}}{2} \\ \dfrac{\sqrt{2}}{2} & \dfrac{\sqrt{2}}{2} \end{bmatrix} \begin{bmatrix} \sqrt{2} \\ -\sqrt{2} \end{bmatrix} = \begin{bmatrix} 1 - (-1) \\ 1 - 1 \end{bmatrix} = \begin{bmatrix} 2 \\ 0 \end{bmatrix}$

b. $\begin{bmatrix} 0 & -1 \\ 1 & 0 \end{bmatrix} \begin{bmatrix} -3 \\ 4 \end{bmatrix} = \begin{bmatrix} 0 - 4 \\ -3 + 0 \end{bmatrix} = \begin{bmatrix} -4 \\ -3 \end{bmatrix}$

Class Exercises

Find and graph the image of the given point. Use the indicated transformation matrix.

1. $\begin{bmatrix} 5 \\ 0 \end{bmatrix}; \begin{bmatrix} 2 & -1 \\ 0 & 3 \end{bmatrix}$ $\begin{bmatrix} 10 \\ 0 \end{bmatrix}$

2. $\begin{bmatrix} -7 \\ -2 \end{bmatrix}; \begin{bmatrix} 4 & 2 \\ 1 & 3 \end{bmatrix}$ $\begin{bmatrix} -32 \\ -13 \end{bmatrix}$

3. $\begin{bmatrix} 2 \\ \sqrt{2} \end{bmatrix}; \begin{bmatrix} 0 & 1 \\ 1 & 0 \end{bmatrix}$ $\begin{bmatrix} \sqrt{2} \\ 2 \end{bmatrix}$

Use the formula for the rotation matrix R_α to find an explicit expression for the given rotation matrix.

4. $R_{0°}$ 5. $R_{45°}$ 6. $R_{60°}$ 7. $R_{90°}$ 8. $R_{180°}$

9. $R_{30°}$ 10. $R_{120°}$ 11. $R_{270°}$ 12. $R_{-60°}$ 13. $R_{34°}$

Find and graph the image of the given point or curve. Use the indicated transformation matrix.

14. $\begin{bmatrix} 3 \\ 4 \end{bmatrix}; T_{x\text{-axis}}$ $\begin{bmatrix} 3 \\ -4 \end{bmatrix}$

15. $\begin{bmatrix} -3 \\ -4 \end{bmatrix}; T_{y\text{-axis}}$ $\begin{bmatrix} 3 \\ -4 \end{bmatrix}$

16. $\begin{bmatrix} \sqrt{3} \\ 1 \end{bmatrix}; R_{45°}$ $\begin{bmatrix} 0.5176 \\ 1.9319 \end{bmatrix}$

17. $(2, 1); R_{60°}$ $\begin{bmatrix} 0.1340 \\ 2.2321 \end{bmatrix}$

18. $f(x) = -2x + 1;$ $T_{y\text{-axis}}$ $\begin{bmatrix} -x \\ -2x + 1 \end{bmatrix}$

19. $f(x) = -2x^2 + 4x - 3;$ $T_{x\text{-axis}}$ $\begin{bmatrix} x \\ 2x^2 - 4x + 3 \end{bmatrix}$

Practice Exercises   ⌁ Use appropriate technology.

Find and graph the image of the given point. Use the indicated transformation matrix. Where appropriate, use the rotation matrices of Class Exercises 4 to 13.

A 1. $\begin{bmatrix} 2 \\ 4 \end{bmatrix}$; $T_{x\text{-axis}}$

2. $\begin{bmatrix} -3 \\ 1 \end{bmatrix}$; $T_{y\text{-axis}}$

3. $\begin{bmatrix} 0 \\ 3 \end{bmatrix}$; $T_{x\text{-axis}}$

4. $(-6, 2)$; $T_{y\text{-axis}}$

5. $(-2, 0)$; $T_{y\text{-axis}}$

6. $\left(\frac{1}{2}\sqrt{2}, -\frac{1}{2}\sqrt{2}\right)$; $T_{x\text{-axis}}$

7. $(\sqrt{2}, \sqrt{2})$; $R_{45°}$

8. $(4, -3)$; $R_{90°}$

9. $(5, -12)$; $R_{180°}$

10. $(3, 0)$; $R_{270°}$

11. $(0, -4)$; $R_{60°}$

12. $(1, 1)$; $R_{34°}$

13. Graph the function: $f(x) = 2x^2 - 3x + 4$

Find and graph the image of the graph of the given equation. Use the indicated transformation matrix.

14. $f(x) = 2x - 1$; $T_{x\text{-axis}}$

15. $f(x) = x^3 + 1$; $T_{y\text{-axis}}$

16. $f(x) = \sqrt{16 - x^2}$; $T_{x\text{-axis}}$

17. Determine whether the function $f(x) = x^7 - x^5 + 3x^3 - x + 1$ is odd, even, or neither. neither

18. **Thinking Critically** The transformations of Exercises 14 to 16 do not change the shape of the transformed curves. Does a transformation always preserve shape? If a figure encloses a region, will the area of the transformed figure necessarily be preserved? Answer these questions by considering the triangle with vertices $A(3, 1)$, $B(-2, -3)$, and $C(4, -4)$ and applying the transformation matrix $\begin{bmatrix} 2 & 1 \\ -1 & -2 \end{bmatrix}$ to the triangle's three vertices.

19. Show that $\begin{bmatrix} 0 & 1 \\ 1 & 0 \end{bmatrix}$ is the transformation $R_{y=x}$ that reflects the point (a, b) about the line $y = x$.

20. Show that $\begin{bmatrix} 0 & -1 \\ -1 & 0 \end{bmatrix}$ is the transformation $T_{y=-x}$ that reflects the point (a, b) about line $y = -x$.

$T_1 = \begin{bmatrix} 1 & 2 \\ 0 & -1 \end{bmatrix}$ and $T_2 = \begin{bmatrix} 3 & -1 \\ 2 & 1 \end{bmatrix}$ are transformation matrices and $\begin{bmatrix} a \\ b \end{bmatrix}$ is a point in the coordinate plane. The two matrix products of T_1 and T_2, T_1T_2 and T_2T_1, are also transformations.

21. Find T_1T_2 and T_2T_1. $\begin{bmatrix} 7 & 1 \\ -2 & -1 \end{bmatrix}$; $\begin{bmatrix} 3 & 7 \\ 2 & 3 \end{bmatrix}$; $\begin{bmatrix} 7a + b \\ -2a - b \end{bmatrix}$; $\begin{bmatrix} 3a + 7b \\ 2a + 3b \end{bmatrix}$

22. Find the image of $\begin{bmatrix} a \\ b \end{bmatrix}$ under the transformations T_1T_2 and T_2T_1.

Use the rotation matrices that you found in Class Exercises 4 to 13 to find the transformation formed by the indicated product.

23. $R_{45°} R_{45°} R_{90°}$

24. $R_{30°} R_{90°} R_{120°}$

25. $R_{90°} R_{30°} R_{120°}$

B 26. $R_{60°} R_{120°} R_{180°}$

27. $R_{270°} R_{-60°} R_{210°}$

28. $R_{90°} R_{34°}$

12.6 Matrices and Transformations   **637**

14.

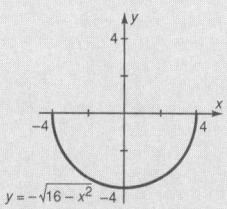

15. $y = -x^3 + 1$

16. $y = -\sqrt{16 - x^2}$

29. **Thinking Critically** Based upon your answers to Practice Exercises 23 to 28, what conclusions can you draw about the transformation matrix that is obtained as a result of applying two successive rotation matrices to a point in the coordinate plane? What can you say about the order in which the two rotations are performed? $R_\alpha R_\beta = R_{\alpha+\beta}$; $R_\alpha R_\beta = R_\beta R_\alpha$

Use the reflection matrices of the lesson and of Exercises 19 and 20 to find the transformation formed by the indicated product.

30. $T_{y=x} T_{x\text{-axis}} R_{90°}$

31. $T_{y\text{-axis}} T_{x\text{-axis}} R_{180°}$

32. $T_{x\text{-axis}} T_{y=-x} R_{90°}$

33. $T_{x\text{-axis}} T_{y=x} R_{270°}$

34. **Thinking Critically** Based upon your answers to Practice Exercises 30 to 33, what conclusions can you draw about the transformation matrix that is obtained as the result of applying two successive reflections about lines through the origin to a point in the plane?

Ⓡ 35. Find the real solutions of $2x^4 - 5x^3 - 17x^2 + 14x + 24 = 0$. $-1, -2, \frac{3}{2}, 4$

36. Prove the theorem that is stated on page 635 of the lesson.

C 37. Draw the graph of the rectangular hyperbola $xy = 1$ and rotate it about the origin through an angle of 45°. Notice that, by symmetry, the equation of the hyperbola in its new position is of the form $(y')^2 - (x')^2 = a^2$. Use the rotation matrix $R_{45°}$ to show that $a^2 = 2$.

In Lesson 11.5, the equations for *translation of axes* were presented as shown at the left below. Here, the point P is fixed and the coordinate axes are translated. The opposite viewpoint is assumed in the diagram at the right below; the axes are fixed and point P is translated. Here, the equations for the *translation of a point* are shown together with the corresponding matrix equation.

$x = x' + h$
$y = y' + k$

Translation of axes

$x' = x + h$ or $\begin{bmatrix} x' \\ y' \end{bmatrix} = \begin{bmatrix} x \\ y \end{bmatrix} + \begin{bmatrix} h \\ k \end{bmatrix}$
$y' = y + k$

Translation of a point

For each matrix equation, describe the motion that is required (up or down, left or right) to reach the image point $P(x', y')$ starting from point $P(x, y)$.

38. $\begin{bmatrix} x \\ y \end{bmatrix} + \begin{bmatrix} 3 \\ 1 \end{bmatrix} = \begin{bmatrix} x' \\ y' \end{bmatrix}$

39. $\begin{bmatrix} x \\ y \end{bmatrix} + \begin{bmatrix} -2 \\ -4 \end{bmatrix} = \begin{bmatrix} x' \\ y' \end{bmatrix}$

40. $\begin{bmatrix} x \\ y \end{bmatrix} + \begin{bmatrix} -5 \\ 0 \end{bmatrix} = \begin{bmatrix} x' \\ y' \end{bmatrix}$

Express as a matrix equation the translation of point $P(x, y)$ to point $P'(x', y')$.

41. $P(1, 4)$; $P'(6, 6)$

42. $P(2, -5)$; $P'(0, -4)$

43. $P(-3, -1)$; $P'(-4, 7)$

44. **Thinking Critically** Explain why the primed variables in the equations of the translation of axes occupy different positions from those in the equations for the translation of a point.

Review

Evaluate: $\csc^{-1} 2$ 30°

Objectives: To find the sum and difference of two vectors
To multiply a vector by scalar
To find the norm of a vector

Focus

A pilot constructing a flight plan has to be concerned about the plane's course, heading, air speed, and ground speed. In order for the plane to proceed directly toward its destination, it must head into the wind at an angle such that the wind is exactly counteracted. If available, a navigation computer will do the calculations quickly and accurately. If, however, a navigation computer is not accessible, the pilot may have to depend on pencil-and-paper work supplemented by a calculator. An understanding of vectors and their operations is therefore vitally important.

A *vector quantity,* or **vector,** is any quantity that has both magnitude and direction. As with matrices, a *scalar quantity,* or simply a *scalar,* is a quantity that is measured by a real number. A vector can be represented geometrically as a directed line segment. For example, the directed line segment AB, denoted by $\overrightarrow{AB}$, is the line segment from the initial point A (tail) to the terminal point B (head).

Since $\overrightarrow{BA}$ has initial point B and terminal point A, the two vectors $\overrightarrow{AB}$ and $\overrightarrow{BA}$ have the same length but opposite directions. The vector $\overrightarrow{BA}$ is called the opposite of $\overrightarrow{AB}$ and denoted also as $-\overrightarrow{AB}$. In this textbook, a vector is designated by a single letter in boldface print, **v**. In doing your work, denote the vector by $\vec{v}$. The **norm of v,** denoted by $\|\mathbf{v}\|$, is the magnitude, or length, of vector **v**. Vector **w** at the right has magnitude 5, as can be seen by applying the Pythagorean theorem.

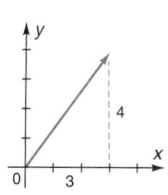

Any directed line segment of the same length as **w** making the same angle with the horizontal is also vector **w**. Such vectors are *equivalent.*

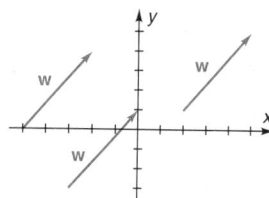

12.7 Geometric Vectors **639**

LESSON PLAN

Vocabulary
component vectors
directed line segment
equivalent vectors
magnitude of a vector
norm of a vector
resultant
resultant triangle
scalar
scalar quantity
sum of two vectors
vector
x-component of a vector
y-component of a vector
zero vector

Ⓜ **Materials/Manipulatives**
board compass and straightedge
protractor
graph paper
toothpicks

Technology
scientific calculator

FOCUS

Have students investigate what dead reckoning navigation means and write a paper describing it. You may wish to refer students back to the opening pages of Chapter 6, which gives a discussion on navigation.

Draw accurate representations of vectors on the overhead projector or the chalkboard. Copy the vector length and angle, and the direction of the vector with respect to the x-axis, using a straightedge and a protractor. Ask students to do the same.

• A compass is helpful when demonstrating scalar multiplication. To draw 3**v**, extend vector **v** and mark off three lengths of **v**.

• Emphasize that a vector may be resolved into many component pairs. However, the x- and y-components are the standard ones used. Have students draw sketches of several component pairs for one vector to demonstrate this concept. One way to do this is to place the corner of a piece of paper so that the tail and head of the vector fall on the edges of the paper.

Ⓜ **Alternative Learning Styles**
Kinesthetic learners would benefit from the use of manipulatives for finding resultant vectors and component vectors. Have students model vectors using toothpicks on graph paper. Mark the head of each toothpick in blue; the tail, in red. Students can find resultant vectors by using the toothpicks to connect the tail of one vector to the head of the other. The x- and y-component vectors can be found by counting the units along the horizontal and the vertical. Students can use a protractor and scientific calculator to verify that $x = r \cos \theta$ and $y = r \sin \theta$.

To add two vectors that share the same initial point, use equivalent vectors to form a parallelogram. The diagonal is the desired sum, or **resultant**.

To add two vectors that do not share the same initial point, draw representations of the two vectors such that the tail of one coincides with the head of the other. Complete the triangle, called the *resultant triangle*, by connecting the tail of one vector to the head of the other. The vector **u**′ is the representation of **u** with its head coinciding with the tail of **v**. The resultant is **u** + **v**.

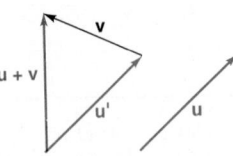

To subtract vector **u** from **v**, add the opposite of **u** to **v**. This subtraction is represented as **v** − **u** = **v** + (−**u**) in the resultant triangle at the left below. At the right below the shorter diagonal of the parallelogram also represents the vector difference **v** − **u**.

Example 1 Given vectors **v** and **u** shown at the right, find each of the following.
  a. v + u   **b. v − u**

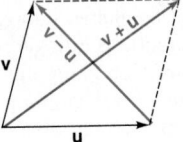

  a. Copy **v** and **u** so that the tail of **u** corresponds to the head of **v**.

  Draw the resultant from the tail of **v** to the head of **u**. This is the sum **u** + **v**.

  b. Copy **v** and **u** so that the heads of both coincide.

  Reverse the direction of **u**.

  Draw the resultant from the tail of **v** to the head of −**u**. This is the difference **v** − **u**.

If **v** = **u**, then **v** − **u** = **0**, the **zero vector**. The zero vector has a magnitude of 0 and any direction you please.

The product of a scalar and a vector may result in the lengthening or shortening of a vector, a reversal of its direction, or both these results. If a is a scalar and **v** is a vector, then a**v** is longer than **v** when $|a| > 1$ and shorter than **v** when $|a| < 1$. If $a < 0$, then the direction of a**v** is opposite that of **v**. In general, $\|a\mathbf{v}\| = |a| \|\mathbf{v}\|$.

640   Chapter 12 Matrices and Vectors

Example 2 Use vector **v** shown at the right to draw and find the norm of each vector.
  a. 2**v**   **b.** 0.5**v**   **c.** −3**v**

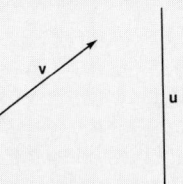

First, find the value of ‖**v**‖.

$$\|\mathbf{v}\| = \sqrt{x^2 + y^2} = \sqrt{4^2 + 3^2} = 5$$

a. $\|2\mathbf{v}\| = |2|\,\|\mathbf{v}\|$ **b.** $\|0.5\mathbf{v}\| = |0.5|\,\|\mathbf{v}\|$ **c.** $\|-3\mathbf{v}\| = |-3|\,\|\mathbf{v}\|$
  $= 2 \cdot 5 = 10$ $= 0.5 \cdot 5 = 2.5$ $= 3 \cdot 5 = 15$

0.5**v**

−3**v**

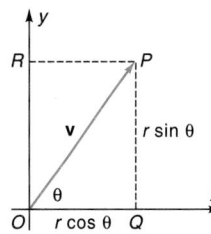

It is possible to resolve a vector **v** into two vectors whose sum is **v**. Vectors **u** and **w** are *component vectors* of vector **v**, since **u** + **w** = **v**. There is an unlimited number of such vector pairs that have **v** as their sum. Often it is desired that the two component vectors be perpendicular to one another.

To find perpendicular component vectors of vector **v** with magnitude *r*, place **v** on a coordinate axis so that the tail of **v** is at the origin. Let θ be the direction of **v** with respect to the *x*-axis. The head of **v** is located at point $P(x, y)$ in the coordinate plane with $x = r \cos \theta$ and $y = r \sin \theta$, where $\|\mathbf{v}\| = r$.

Let *Q* be the point on the *x* axis at the base of a perpendicular segment drawn from *P*. Let *R* be the point on the *y*-axis at the base of a perpendicular segment drawn from *P*. Vectors $\overrightarrow{OQ}$ and $\overrightarrow{OR}$ are perpendicular vector components of **v**.

Since $x = r \cos \theta$, it follows that $|x| = \|\overrightarrow{OQ}\|$, the length of $\overrightarrow{OQ}$. For this reason, the scalar *x* is called the *x-component* of vector **v**. In a similar way, $|y| = |r \sin \theta| = \|\overrightarrow{OR}\|$ and the scalar *y* is called the *y-component* of **v**.

Example 3 Given that vector **w** has a magnitude of 10 and a direction of 135°, find the *x*- and *y*-components of **w**.

$x = 10 \cos 135° = -5\sqrt{2}$ *x-component* $= r \cos \theta$
$y = 10 \sin 135° = 5\sqrt{2}$ *y-component* $= r \sin \theta$

The *x*-component is $-5\sqrt{2}$ and the *y*-component is $5\sqrt{2}$.

12.7 Geometric Vectors   **641**

GUIDED PRACTICE

For Example 1
Given vectors **v** and **u** shown below, find each of the following vectors.

1. **u** + **v**

2. **v** − **u**

For Example 2
Given that ‖**v**‖ = 2, use vector **v** shown in the previous example to draw and find the norm for each vector.
1. 3**v** 6

3v

2. −2**v** 4

−2v

Vectors can be used together with the law of cosines or the law of sines to solve problems involving physical quantities such as force, velocity, and acceleration.

The figure shown represents an airplane in flight. The engines provide *air velocity*, a vector quantity. The norm of the air velocity is the *air speed*. The direction of the air velocity is the plane's *heading*, measured in degrees clockwise from the north. The vector sum of the air velocity and wind velocity is the *ground velocity*. The *course* is the direction of ground velocity, in degrees.

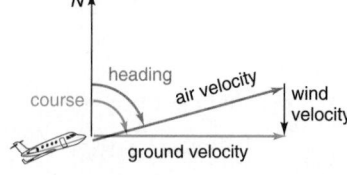

Example 4   *Aviation*   An airplane has an air speed of 520 mi/h and a heading of 115°. Wind blows from the east at 37 mi/h. Find the plane's ground speed (the norm of its ground velocity) to the nearest mile per hour and course to the nearest degree.

Let $\|\mathbf{v}\|$ represent the ground speed. Then use the law of cosines. First note that $\angle A$ and $\angle ACD$ are congruent angles. *Why?* Thus, $\angle A = \angle ACD = 115° - 90°$, or 25°.

$$a^2 = b^2 + c^2 - 2bc \cos A$$
$$\|\mathbf{v}\|^2 = (520)^2 + (37)^2 - 2(520)(37) \cos 25°$$
$$\|\mathbf{v}\|^2 = 236{,}894$$
$$\|\mathbf{v}\| = 487 \text{ mi/h} \qquad \text{The ground speed is about 487 mi/h.}$$

To determine α, the difference between the course and the heading, apply the law of sines to the resultant triangle.

$$\frac{\sin C}{37} = \frac{\sin 25°}{487}$$
$$\sin C = \frac{37 \sin 25°}{487}$$
$$C \approx 1.84, \text{ or about } 2°$$

Therefore, the course is about $115° + 2°$, or 117°.

Class Exercises

Draw each pair of given vectors on a separate sheet of paper. Then use your drawing to show geometrically the indicated sum or difference of the vectors.

1. **a** + **b**   **2.** **c** + **d**   **3.** **u** + **v**   **4.** **v** + **w**

5. For the given vector **v** at the right, find 4**v**, −2**v**, and 0.25**v** and give the norm of each.

6. *Physics*   Forces of 12 lb and 20 lb make an angle of 44° with each other and are applied to an object at the same point. Find the magnitude of the resultant force. 29.8 lb

Thinking Critically
Since $\overline{AB}$ and $\overline{CD}$ are parallel, $\angle A$ and $\angle ACD$ are alternate interior angles and are therefore congruent.

Copy the given vector on a separate sheet of paper. Then use your drawing to resolve the vector into horizontal and vertical component vectors.

7.

8.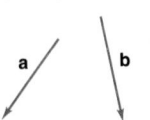

Practice Exercises

Draw each pair of given vectors on a separate sheet of paper. Then use your drawing to show geometrically the indicated sum or difference of the vectors.

A **1.** a + b   **2.** c + d   **3.** m + n   **4.** v + w

5. p + q   **6.** g + h   **7.** a − b   **8.** c − d

    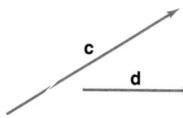

Ⓡ **9.** Is the function $f(x) = x^3 - 2x + 3$ even, odd, or neither? neither

10. *Sports* In a football game, a football comes at a receiver at 30 ft/s at an angle of 45°. Determine the x- and y-components of the velocity. $15\sqrt{2}$ ft/s; $15\sqrt{2}$ ft/s

Ⓡ **11.** Solve: $|3x + 8| > -6$ all real numbers

Copy the vectors in the diagram on a separate sheet of paper. Then draw and give the norm for each.

12. 4b 8   **13.** −w $2\sqrt{5}$ **14.** $\frac{1}{3}$a 1

15. $-\frac{1}{4}$b $\frac{1}{2}$ **16.** 5v $10\sqrt{2}$ **17.** a + b $\sqrt{13}$

18. −3b + v $2\sqrt{17}$ **19.** 2v − w $2\sqrt{17}$ **20.** w − b $2\sqrt{2}$

B **21.** a + b + v 5   **22.** w − a + b $\sqrt{37}$ **23.** $\frac{1}{3}$a − $\frac{1}{2}$b $\sqrt{2}$

24. Thinking Critically Describe the x- and y-components of a vector that is vertical.

Ⓡ **25.** Determine the coordinates of the vertex of the parabola with equation
$y = 5x^2 + 7x - 3$. $\left(-\frac{7}{10}, -\frac{109}{20}\right)$

Vector **v** has magnitude *M*. Its tail is at the origin. Find the vertical and horizontal component vectors of the vector. Angle θ is the counterclockwise angle that the vector makes with the x-axis.

26. $M = 310$, θ = 63° 140.74; 276.21   **27.** $M = 175$, θ = 37° 139.76; 105.32

28. $M = 42.58$, θ = 83.6° 4.75; 42.31   **29.** $M = 53.42$, θ = 88.4° 1.49; 53.40

30. *Physics* Forces of 18 lb and 26 lb make an angle of 56° with each other. Find the magnitude of the resultant force. 39 lb

Lesson Quiz
Given vectors **v** and **w** shown below, find the following vectors.

1. v + w.

2. w − v.

3. 3v + 2w.

Given that $|\mathbf{w}| = 4$, find the norm for each vector.

4. 0.5w 2

5. −2w 8

6. If vector **u** has magnitude of 22 and a direction of 80°, find the x- and y-components of **u**.
(3.82, 21.67)

7. Forces of 34 lb and 46 lb make an angle of 42° with each other and are applied to an object at the same point. Find the magnitude of the resultant force. 74.8 lb

Alternative Assessment

Discuss how the sum of three vectors may be determined geometrically. Give an example.

Enrichment

A baseball is thrown straight ahead (parallel to the ground) at 90 mi/h. It is released from a height of 6.5 ft. If all forces except gravity are ignored, how far will it travel before it hits the ground? about 84 ft

Additional Answers

34. Vectors **w** and −**w** have equal magnitudes but opposite directions.

41. Let **u** = (x_1, y_1) and **v** = (x_2, y_2).
$\|u − v\| = \sqrt{(x_1 − x_2)^2 + (y_1 − y_2)^2} = \sqrt{(x_2 − x_1)^2 + (y_2 − y_1)^2} = \|v − u\|$

42. Let **u** = (x_1, y_1) and **v** = (x_2, y_2).
$\|u + v\| = \sqrt{(x_1 + x_2)^2 + (y_1 + y_2)^2} = \sqrt{x_1^2 + 2x_1 x_2 + x_2^2 + y_1^2 + 2y_1 y_2 + y_2^2}$;
$\|u\| + \|v\| = \sqrt{x_1^2 + y_1^2} + \sqrt{x_2^2 + y_2^2}$

43. Example: **u** = (2, 3) and **v** = (4, 6).

44. If **u**, **v**, and **u** + **v** are graphed, the result is either a triangle, where their norms represent their lengths, a line, or a point. If a triangle is obtained, then by the triangular inequality, $\|u\| + \|v\| \geq \|u + v\|$.

45. Since $\|u − v\| + \|v\| \geq \|(u − v) + v\|$ from Exercise 44, then $\|u − v\| + \|v\| \geq \|u\|$, and $\|u − v\| \geq \|u\| − \|v\|$.

R 31. In $\triangle ABC$, $a = 24$, $b = 16$, and $\angle A = 32°$. Find $\angle B$. 21°

32. *Aviation*   An airplane has an air speed of 530 mi/h on a heading of 153°. There is a 45 mi/h wind from the south. Find the course and ground speed. 150.61°; 490.33 mi/h

R 33. Determine the equations of the asymptotes of the hyperbola with equation $x^2 − y^2 + 4x − 6y = 6$. $y = x − 1$, $y = −x − 5$

34. **Thinking Critically**   A nonzero vector **w** has the property **w** + (−**w**) = **0**. What is the relationship of the two vectors **w** and −**w**?

35. *Navigation*   A ferry boat leaves the east bank of the Mississippi River with a compass heading of 300°. It is traveling at 10 mi/h relative to the water. Given that the velocity of the downstream current is 4 mi/h toward the south, find the speed of the boat relative to land and its course. 8.718 mi/h; 277°

C 36. *Aviation*   An airplane has a ground speed of 400 mi/h on a course of 208°. The wind is blowing at 25 mi/h from 20° east of south. Find the air speed of the plane and its heading. 417 mi/h; 205°

Vectors **v** and **u** form two sides of parallelogram *PQRS*, as shown. Express each vector in terms of **v** and **u**.

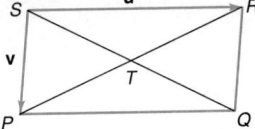

37. $\overrightarrow{PR}$ u − v   38. $\overrightarrow{PT}$ $\frac{1}{2}$(u − v)   39. $\overrightarrow{TS}$ $\frac{1}{2}$(v + u)

40. **Writing in Mathematics**   Does the set of vectors appear to be closed under the operation of vector addition? Explain.
Hint: Examine Exercise 34.

41. Show that for any two vectors **u** and **v**, $\|u − v\| = \|v − u\|$.

42. Prove that, in general, it is not the case that for two vectors **u** and **v**, $\|u + v\| = \|u\| + \|v\|$.

43. Find two vectors **u** and **v** for which the relationship of Exercise 42 *is* true.

A basic inequality of geometry, called the *triangular inequality*, states that the sum of the lengths of two sides of a triangle is greater than the third side. In $\triangle ABC$, all of the following inequalities are true.

$$a + b > c \qquad a + c > b \qquad b + c > a$$

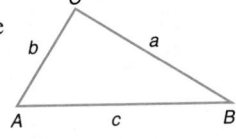

Use this inequality to show that the following inequalities are true for any two vectors **u** and **v**.

44. $\|u + v\| \leq \|u\| + \|v\|$ 45. $\|u − v\| \geq \|u\| − \|v\|$

Challenge

1. One side of a triangle is 16 cm. A line segment is drawn parallel to this side forming a trapezoid whose area is one-fourth that of the triangle. Find the length of the line segment. $8\sqrt{3}$

2. Find the sum of the numerical coefficients of all the terms in the expansion of $(x − 2y)^{12}$. 1

644   Chapter 12 Matrices and Vectors

Writing in Mathematics
40. The set of vectors is closed under vector addition. No assumptions are necessary since the zero vector is still a vector.

12.8 Algebraic Vectors and Parametric Equations

Objectives: *To express a vector in polar or component form given its endpoints*
To perform vector operations in component form
To find, given two points on a line, a direction vector, a vector equation, and a pair of parametric equations

Focus

Early in your study of plane geometry you may have learned that "the shortest distance between two points is a straight line." However, the shortest *time* to travel between two points may not occur along a straight line. Suppose a ball at point *O* is allowed to drop and then to slide down a curve to a bell at point *B* not directly under *O*. Along what path should the ball travel to reach the bell in the least amount of time? A line? A circle? A parabola? The word *brachistochrone* comes from two Greek words that mean "shortest time." For that reason this problem is known as the *brachistochrone problem.* It was studied in the 1690s by the Bernoulli brothers and also by Sir Isaac Newton. The path of "quickest descent" is the one taken by the ball and is conveniently expressed in terms of time *t* by the two equations $x = a(t - \sin t)$ and $y = -a(1 - \cos t)$, where *a* is a positive constant. The curve represented by these equations is called a *cycloid.* An amazing fact about this curve is that no matter where the ball is released on the cycloid, it will take the same amount of time to reach the bell.

Some curves, such as the cycloid mentioned in the Focus, are more conveniently described using two equations rather than one. To work with such equations, called *parametric equations*, it is also convenient to use vectors. In the previous lesson, the geometric nature of vectors was emphasized. In this lesson, their algebraic properties will be stressed. Since every vector in the plane can be translated so that its tail is at the origin, a vector can be represented algebraically by an ordered pair of real numbers. The notation $\mathbf{v} = (x, y)$ is used to denote vector **v** with its tail at the origin and its head at (x, y). The coordinates *x* and *y* represent the *x*- and *y*-components of the vector. The magnitude or norm of **v** is $\|\mathbf{v}\| = \sqrt{x^2 + y^2}$.

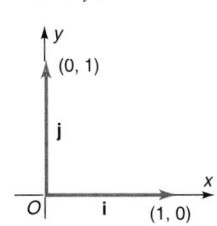

A **unit vector** is a vector with a magnitude of 1. The unit vector in the horizontal direction is denoted by $\mathbf{i} = (1, 0)$, and the unit vector in the vertical direction is denoted by $\mathbf{j} = (0, 1)$. The vector $(3, 4)$ can be expressed as $3(1, 0) + 4(0, 1)$. That is, $(3, 4)$ can be expressed as the sum of scalar multiples of the perpendicular unit vectors $(1, 0)$ and $(0, 1)$.

$$(3, 4) = 3(1, 0) + 4(0, 1) = 3\mathbf{i} + 4\mathbf{j}$$

12.8 Algebraic Vectors and Parametric Equations   **645**

LESSON PLAN

Vocabulary
direction vector
parametric equations
unit vector
vector equation

Technology
graphing utility
scientific calculator

M Materials/Manipulatives
compass
graph paper
protractor
straightedge

FOCUS

The Bernoulli family, producing five generations of mathematicians, is probably the most renowned family in the history of mathematics. Family members made contributions to such fields as integral calculus, probability, and hydrodynamics. The first generation brothers Jacques and Jean worked with Leibniz to solve the brachistochrone problem. Encourage interested students to research the Bernoullis and to make a list of the contributions of each mathematical family member.

Ⓜ • Make the connection between the
    algebraic representation of a vec-
    tor and the geometric one from the
    previous lesson. For example, the
    vector (4, 3) is

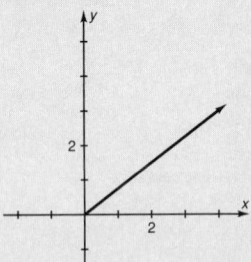

• For Examples 1 and 2, have students verify that both the component and polar forms of a vector
  are equal. Some students may enjoy doing this on a graphing utility.
• You may wish to point out that a
  direction vector is related to the
  slope of the line. For example, the
  line with direction vector (3, 4) has
  slope $\frac{4}{3}$. In general, the slope of a
  nonvertical line with direction vector (a, b) has slope $\frac{b}{a}$.
• For Example 3, note that there are
  infinitely many equations using vectors that students may write to
  describe the line $\overleftrightarrow{PQ}$, two of which
  may include $(x, y) = P + t(Q - P)$
  and $(x, y) = Q + t(P - Q)$.

In general, a vector (x, y) may be expressed in the component form
$x(1, 0) + y(0, 1) = x\mathbf{i} + y\mathbf{j}$. If the vector is represented in polar form, then
$(x, y) = r \cos \theta (1, 0) + r \sin \theta (1, 0) = r \cos \theta \mathbf{i} + r \sin \theta \mathbf{j}$, where θ is the
direction angle of the vector (x, y) in standard position. If $\mathbf{v}$ is any nonzero
vector, then $\frac{\mathbf{v}}{\|\mathbf{v}\|}$ is the unit vector in the same direction as $\mathbf{v}$.

It is possible to determine a vector in component or polar form when
the vector is described by its initial and terminal points. A vector $\mathbf{w}$
with initial point (x_1, y_1) and terminal point (x_2, y_2) can be described
by its horizontal and vertical components as follows. The x
displacement is $x_2 - x_1$ and the y displacement is $y_2 - y_1$. Thus, a
representation of the vector $\mathbf{w}$ with its tail at the point $P(x_1, y_1)$ and
head at $Q(x_2, y_2)$ is $(x_2 - x_1)\mathbf{i} + (y_2 - y_1)\mathbf{j}$.

Example 1 Given $\mathbf{v}$ with an initial point of $(2, 3)$ and a terminal point of $(7, 9)$, determine the
  a. component form **b.** polar form **c.** unit vector in the same direction as $\mathbf{v}$

a. $\mathbf{v} = (7 - 2)\mathbf{i} + (9 - 3)\mathbf{j} = 5\mathbf{i} + 6\mathbf{j}$
b. $r = \sqrt{(5)^2 + (6)^2} = \sqrt{61}$

  $\tan \theta = \frac{6}{5}$

  $\theta = 50.2°$

  $(5, 6) = \sqrt{61} \cos 50.2°\mathbf{i} + \sqrt{61} \sin 50.2°\mathbf{j}$

c. $\frac{(5, 6)}{\|(5, 6)\|} = \frac{(5, 6)}{\sqrt{61}} = \frac{\sqrt{61}}{61}(5, 6) = \left(\frac{5\sqrt{61}}{61}, \frac{6\sqrt{61}}{61}\right)$

The vector operations performed geometrically in Lesson 12.7 may be
duplicated algebraically.

Given the vectors $\mathbf{v} = (x, y)$ and $\mathbf{w} = (r, s)$, then

$\mathbf{v} + \mathbf{w} = (x, y) + (r, s)$ *Vector sum*
$\qquad = (x + r, y + s)$

$\mathbf{v} - \mathbf{w} = (x, y) - (r, s)$ *Vector difference*
$\qquad = (x - r, y - s)$

$r(x, y) = (rx, ry)$ *Scalar multiplication*

Example 2 Given $\mathbf{s} = (3, 5)$, $\mathbf{w} = (-6, 1)$, and $\mathbf{u} = (7, -3)$, determine a vector $\mathbf{v}$ that
  satisfies the given equation.
  a. $\mathbf{v} = \mathbf{s} + \mathbf{w}$ **b.** $\mathbf{v} = \mathbf{u} - \mathbf{w}$ **c.** $\mathbf{v} = 2\mathbf{s} + \mathbf{u}$

a. $\mathbf{v} = \mathbf{s} + \mathbf{w} = (3, 5) + (-6, 1) = (-3, 6)$
b. $\mathbf{v} = \mathbf{u} - \mathbf{w} = (7, -3) - (-6, 1) = (13, -4)$
c. $\mathbf{v} = 2\mathbf{s} + \mathbf{u} = 2(3, 5) + (7, -3) = (6, 10) + (7, -3) = (13, 7)$

646   Chapter 12 Matrices and Vectors

Algebraic operations between vectors can be represented geometrically. A geometric representation of Example 2c is shown at the right.

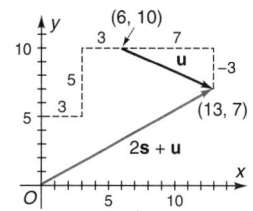

In the middle figure, $Q(x, y)$ represents any point on line $\overleftrightarrow{PQ}$, and $P(a, b)$ is a fixed point of that line. If **v** is any nonzero vector that is parallel to $\overleftrightarrow{PQ}$, then the relationship among the vectors $\overrightarrow{OQ}$, $\overrightarrow{OP}$, and **v** can be expressed in the form

$$(x, y) = (a, b) + t\mathbf{v}$$

for some real value of t. This is a *vector equation* of $\overleftrightarrow{PQ}$ with *direction vector v*. In the diagram, you can see that if the value of t is chosen properly, then that value will stretch the vector **v** so that $t\mathbf{v}$ terminates at point Q. You also know that the scalar t may assume any real value. Each of these values corresponds to one of the possible locations of Q on $\overleftrightarrow{PQ}$. In particular, if Q coincides with P, then $t = 0$. *Why?*

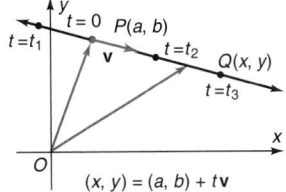

A vector equation of the line $\overleftrightarrow{RS}$ through $R(1, 5)$ with direction vector $\mathbf{v} = (2, 3)$ is

$$(x, y) = (1, 5) + t(2, 3)$$

To find points on $\overleftrightarrow{RS}$ other than $R(1, 5)$, let the scalar t take on various values. For example, when $t = 1$, a particular point is

$$(1, 5) + 1(2, 3) = (3, 8)$$

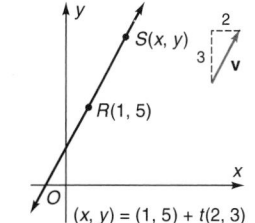

When two points on a line are given, a direction vector for the line can be determined. In particular, if $P(x_1, y_1)$ and $Q(x_2, y_2)$ are two points on a line, a direction vector of the line is $Q - P$ or $(x_2 - x_1, y_2 - y_1)$. Suppose that (c, d) is a direction vector of $\overrightarrow{PQ}$. Then when the vector equation $(x, y) = (a, b) + t(c, d)$ is simplified by scalar multiplication and vector addition, the equation can be written in another form:

$$(x, y) = (a, b) + t(c, d)$$
$$(x, y) = (a, b) + (tc, td)$$
$$(x, y) = (a + tc, b + td)$$

By the property of equality of vectors, $x = a + tc$, and $y = b + td$. These two equations are called **parametric equations** with parameter t of the line with vector equation $(x, y) = (a, b) + t(c, d)$.

Example 3 Determine a direction vector of the line containing the two points $P(5, 8)$ and $Q(11, 2)$. Then find a vector equation of the line and a pair of parametric equations of the line.

A direction vector for the line is $Q - P = (11 - 5, 2 - 8) = (6, -6)$. A vector equation of the line is $(x, y) = (5, 8) + t(6, -6)$. A set of parametric equations for the line is

$$x = 5 + 6t \qquad \text{and} \qquad y = 8 - 6t$$

GUIDED PRACTICE

For Example 1
Determine the vector **w** with given initial and terminal points in component and polar forms.

1. **w** with initial point $(1, 8)$ and terminal point $(5, 4)$
   $4\mathbf{i} - 4\mathbf{j}$; $4\sqrt{2} \cos(-45°)\mathbf{i} + 4\sqrt{2} \sin(-45°)\mathbf{j}$

2. **w** with initial point $(-5, -6)$ and terminal point $(-7, 2)$
   $-2\mathbf{i} + 8\mathbf{j}$; $2\sqrt{17} \cos(-76°)\mathbf{i} + 2\sqrt{17} \sin(-76°)\mathbf{j}$

Technology For Example 1, students may use a scientific calculator to determine the direction angle of a vector from a trigonometric equation. Remind students to set their calculators to the degree mode.

For Example 2
If $\mathbf{s} = (4, 9)$, $\mathbf{t} = (-2, 6)$, and $\mathbf{u} = (8, -4)$, determine **v** such that:
1. $\mathbf{v} = \mathbf{t} + \mathbf{u}$ $(6, 2)$
2. $\mathbf{v} = \mathbf{u} - \mathbf{s}$ $(4, -13)$
3. $\mathbf{v} = 2\mathbf{s} + 4\mathbf{t} - 3\mathbf{u}$ $(-24, 54)$

Thinking Critically
Since the distance from P to Q is given by $t\mathbf{v}$ where **v** is a nonzero vector, points P and Q will coincide only when $t = 0$.

For Example 3

Determine a direction vector of the line containing the given points. Then find the equation of the line in both vector and parametric form.

1. $P(7, 3)$, $Q(15, 6)$
   $(x, y) = (7, 3) + t(8, 3)$; $x = 7 + 8t$; $y = 3 + 3t$
2. $P(-4, 8)$, $Q(1, -5)$
   $(x, y) = (-4, 8) + t(5, -13)$; $x = -4 + 5t$; $y = 8 - 13t$

For Example 4

Graph the curve with parametric equations $x = 3 + t$ and $y = 2 - t$. Then find an equation for the curve that contains no variables other than x and y.

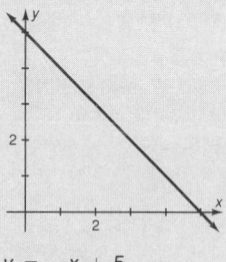

$y = -x + 5$

Note in Example 3 that the direction vector $(6, -6)$ is not unique. Any nonzero vector in the same or opposite direction can be used as a direction vector for the line. For example, point Q as the fixed point and direction vector $P - Q$ can also be used to formulate a vector equation of the line:

$$(x, y) = (11, 2) + t(-6, 6)$$

Thus, another set of parametric equations for the line is

$$x = 11 - 6t \quad \text{and} \quad y = 2 + 6t$$

From the above discussion, it is clear that a point (x, y) is on a line through $P(a, b)$ with direction vector (c, d) if and only if there exists a parameter t such that $(x, y) = (a, b) + t(c, d)$. For example, to determine whether $(14, 13)$ is on the line with vector equation $(x, y) = (-1, 4) + t(5, 3)$, let $x = 14$ and $y = 13$ in the parametric equations $x = -1 + 5t$, $y = 4 + 3t$.

$$14 = -1 + 5t \quad \text{and} \quad 13 = 4 + 3t$$
$$15 = 5t \quad \text{and} \quad 9 = 3t$$
$$3 = t \quad \text{and} \quad 3 = t$$

The two equations yield the same value for t. Thus, when $t = 3$, $(14, 13) = (-1, 4) + 3(5, 3)$ and the point is on the line.

Parametric equations can be used to represent graphs that are not straight lines.

Example 4 Graph the curve with parametric equations $x = 3 \cos t$ and $y = 5 \sin t$. Then find an equation of the curve that contains no variable other than x and y.

If you use a graphing utility, be sure to set the utility in parametric mode. Choose the dimensions of the viewing rectangle carefully so that the scales on both axes are the same. The graph is shown at the right.

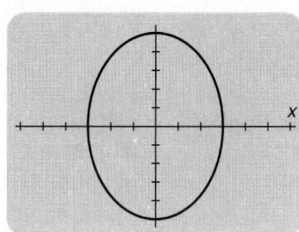

[-7.5, 7.5] by [-5.5, 5.5]
T min: 0 T max: 2π T step: 0.1

To find a single equation for the curve, square each side of the parametric equations, and solve for $\cos^2 t$ and $\sin^2 t$. Then combine the results using the fact that $\cos^2 t + \sin^2 t = 1$.

$$x = 3 \cos t \qquad y = 5 \sin t$$
$$x^2 = 9 \cos^2 t \qquad y^2 = 25 \sin^2 t$$
$$\frac{x^2}{9} = \cos^2 t \qquad \frac{y^2}{25} = \sin^2 t$$

Add the last pair of equations.

$$\frac{x^2}{9} + \frac{y^2}{25} = \cos^2 t + \sin^2 t$$
$$\frac{x^2}{9} + \frac{y^2}{25} = 1$$

The curve is an ellipse with its center at the origin.

Modeling

Because of a technical malfunction, a space vehicle veers into a suborbital trajectory several seconds after it is launched. How can the safety officer monitor the vehicle's position during each second of its flight?

Parametric equations are used to model many real world phenomena, especially those in which more than one variable is dependent upon time. For example, if an object is launched into the air at an angle of $\theta°$ with the ground and with an initial velocity of magnitude v_0 ft/s, then the position of the object may be described by the parametric equations

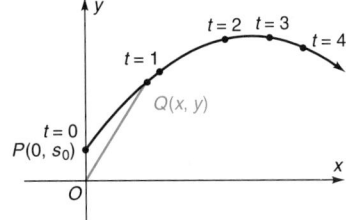

$$x = (v_0 \cos \theta)t$$
$$y = -16t^2 + (v_0 \sin \theta)t + s_0$$

In this model $v_0 \cos \theta$ is the horizontal component of the initial velocity and $v_0 \sin \theta$ is the vertical component of the initial velocity. The constant s_0 is the vertical distance in feet between the ground and the point from which the object is thrown. The term $-16t^2$ represents the portion of the vertical displacement caused by the force of gravity on the object. This model neglects air resistance.

Example 5 *Space Exploration* A space vehicle rises from its launch pad and reaches a height of 5 mi. Because of a computer malfunction, the booster rockets are turned off prematurely, at a moment when the vehicle is moving at a velocity of 6 mi/s at an angle of 40° with an imaginary reference plane tangent to the earth directly below. The rocket's velocity is thus below the velocity needed to attain earth orbit. Determine each of the following for the space vehicle.

a. parametric equations that model its flight
b. number of seconds for it to hit the ocean
c. horizontal distance traveled by the space vehicle

Assume that the curvature of the earth is a straight line. What action, if any, should the safety officer take concerning the space vehicle?

First change all dimensions to feet or feet per second.

$$5 \text{ mi} \times \frac{5280 \text{ ft}}{1 \text{ mi}} = 26{,}400 \text{ ft} \qquad \frac{6 \text{ mi}}{1 \text{ s}} \times \frac{5280 \text{ ft}}{1 \text{ mi}} = 31{,}680 \text{ ft/s}$$

a. The horizontal component of the initial velocity is $31{,}680 \cos 40°$, thus $x = (31{,}680 \cos 40°)t$ represents the horizontal position of the space vehicle. The vertical component of the initial velocity is $31{,}680 \sin 40°$ and thus the vertical position is given by $y = -16t^2 + (31{,}680 \sin 40°)t + 26{,}400$.

12.8 Algebraic Vectors and Parametric Equations **649**

Modeling

The model provides a good opportunity to see the connection between different disciplines. You may want to have students read more about physics and space to see how closely related math is with the physical world.

For Example 5

A football is thrown into the air from a height 7 ft at an angle of 35° from the ground and with an initial velocity of 55 ft/s. Determine the parametric equations which model the flight of the ball. $x = (55 \cos 35°)t$
$y = -16t^2 + (55 \sin 35°)t + 7$

b. When the space vehicle hits the ocean, $y = 0$, that is,

$$0 = -16t^2 + (31,680 \sin 40°)t + 26,400$$
$$0 = -16t^2 + 20,364t + 26,400$$
$$t = \frac{-20,364 \pm \sqrt{(-20,364)^2 - 4(-16)(26,400)}}{2(-16)} \quad \text{\textit{Quadratic formula}}$$
$$t = -1.30 \quad \text{or} \quad t = 1274 \quad \text{\textit{Reject the negative root.}}$$

The vehicle takes 1274 s, or about 21 min, to hit the ocean. (The effect of air resistance is neglected.)

c. The horizontal position of the vehicle is given approximately by $x = (31,680 \cos 40°)t$, or $x = 24,268t$. When $t = 1274$ s,

$$x = 24,268(1274) = 30,917,799 \text{ ft}$$

The horizontal distance is 30,917,799 ft, or about 5860 mi.

The safety officer will have to know whether the probable crash point is in an ocean area that is far from all boats and ships. If not, he may choose to destroy the space vehicle in flight.

A graphing utility can be used to visualize the motion of Example 5. However, some utilities cannot graph equations with very large numbers. In that case, use the following form of the equations that uses miles and seconds rather than feet and seconds. Note that it is necessary to change -16 ft/s² to $-\frac{16}{5280}$ mi/s².

$$x(t) = (6 \cos 40°)t$$
$$y(t) = -\frac{16}{5280}t^2 + (6 \sin 40°)t + 5$$

Be sure to use degree, not radian mode. Use the zoom and trace features to verify the answers to parts (b) and (c).

[5600, 6000] by [−5, 15]
x scl: 50   y scl: 5
T min: 1218 T max: 1305 T step: 1

Class Exercises

Determine each vector **v** in component form and in polar form. Then find the unit vector in the same direction as **v**.

1. $\mathbf{v} = (3, 4)$ **2.** $\mathbf{v} = (7, 24)$ **3.** $\mathbf{v} = (-5, 8)$ **4.** $\mathbf{v} = (-6, 11)$

Determine the vector **w** with given initial point P and terminal point Q in component form and polar form.

5. $P = (4, 9)$, $Q = (13, 2)$ **6.** $P = (-7, -1)$, $Q = (-3, 5)$

Given $\mathbf{s} = (9, 4)$, $\mathbf{t} = (-5, 2)$, and $\mathbf{u} = (10, -7)$, find a vector **v** satisfying each equation.

7. $\mathbf{v} = \mathbf{s} + \mathbf{t}$ (4, 6)   **8.** $\mathbf{v} = \mathbf{u} - \mathbf{t}$ (15, −9)   **9.** $\mathbf{v} = 4\mathbf{t} + 5\mathbf{s}$ (25, 28)

10. Determine whether the point $(-5, 10)$ is on the line with the vector equation $(x, y) = (-7, 2) + t(-1, 6)$. no

Practice Exercises Use appropriate technology.

Determine each vector **v** in component form and in polar form. Then find the unit vector in the same direction as **v**.

A 1. $\mathbf{v} = (8, 15)$ **2.** $\mathbf{v} = (-3, 4)$ **3.** $\mathbf{v} = (\sqrt{3}, \sqrt{5})$ **4.** $\mathbf{v} = (\sqrt{7}, \sqrt{2})$

Ⓡ **5.** Find an equation of the line that passes through the point $(-1, 2)$ and is parallel to the line with equation $3x - 4y = 8$. $3x - 4y = -11$

6. Thinking Critically How could you write the equations of all lines through the point $(20, 17)$ in vector form? $(x, y) = (20, 17) + (a, b)t$

Ⓡ **7.** Find a quadratic equation with solutions -8 and $\frac{1}{2}$. $2x^2 + 15x - 8 = 0$

Determine the vector **v** with the given initial point P and terminal point Q. Give both the component form and polar form.

8. $P = (13, 1), Q = (17, 5)$ **9.** $P = (15, 3), Q = (20, 9)$

10. $P = (-6, 5), Q = (-3, -2)$ **11.** $P = (\sqrt{11}, -\sqrt{2}), Q = (\sqrt{13}, \sqrt{3})$

12. Thinking Critically What is the relationship between the lines that have $(3, 8)$ and $(-6, -16)$ for direction vectors? They are the same.

Ⓡ **13.** Solve: $|2x - 3| \leq 15$ $-6 \leq x \leq 9$

14. *Space Exploration* Use a graphing utility to graph the parametric equations for the model in Example 5. Use the zoom and trace features to approximate, to the nearest hundredth, the maximum height that the space vehicle reaches.

Graph the curve with the given parametric equations. Then find an equation for the curve that contains no variables other than x and y.

15. $x = 2 + t$ **16.** $x = 5 \cos t$ **17.** $x = \tan t$ **18.** $x = 2 \sin^2 t$
$y = 1 - t$ $y = 5 \sin t$ $y = \sec t$ $y = \sin 2t$
$y = -x + 3$ $\frac{x^2}{25} + \frac{y^2}{25} = 1$ $y^2 - x^2 = 1$ $(x - 1)^2 + y^2 = 1$

19. Thinking Critically Consider the parametric equations $x = |t|$ and $y = |t|$, where t is any real number. Is the function defined by these equations identical to the function with $y = x$ as its rule? Why or why not?

Find a direction vector of the line described. Then find a vector equation of the line and a pair of of parametric equations of the line.

20. Contains the points $(23, 7)$ and $(17, 3)$ **21.** Contains the point $(31, 13)$ and $(19, 8)$

B 22. Has the equation $2x - y = 10$ **23.** Has the equation $\frac{1}{2}x - \frac{1}{3}y = 1$

24. *Physics* Force is a vector quantity. In the figure, a rope is used to pull a heavy box across a room. The force along the rope is 70 lb. Find the component of the force that is responsible for moving the box.

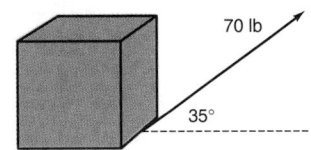
70 lb
35°

Ⓡ **25.** Find the equation(s) of the lines that are vertical, horizontal, or slant asymptotes of $f(x) = \dfrac{x^2}{1 - x^2}$. $x = \pm 1; y = -1$

26. Given that $x = a + tc, c \neq 0$ and $y = b + td, d \neq 0$ are parametric equations of a function, show that the function is linear.

12.8 Algebraic Vectors and Parametric Equations **651**

Technology
Students will need to use a graphing utility for Exercises 14, 15 to 18, 27, 38, 39, 46, and 47 which involve parametric equations.

Project
Interested students can contact NASA to find out more about the use of satellites in the space program.

Additional Answers

1. $8i + 15j$; $17 \cos 61.9°i + 17 \sin 61.9°j$; $\left(\frac{8}{17}, \frac{15}{17}\right)$

2. $-3i + 4j$; $5 \cos 126.9°i + 5 \sin 126.9°j$; $\left(-\frac{3}{5}, \frac{4}{5}\right)$

3. $\sqrt{3}i + \sqrt{5}j$; $2\sqrt{2} \cos 52.2°i + 2\sqrt{2} \sin 52.2°j$; $\left(\frac{\sqrt{6}}{4}, \frac{\sqrt{10}}{4}\right)$

4. $\sqrt{7}i + \sqrt{2}j$; $3 \cos 28.1°i + 3 \sin 28.1°j$; $\left(\frac{\sqrt{7}}{3}, \frac{\sqrt{2}}{3}\right)$

8. $4i + 4j$; $4\sqrt{2} \cos 45°i + 4\sqrt{2} \sin 45°j$

9. $5i + 6j$; $\sqrt{61} \cos 50.2°i + \sqrt{61} \sin 50.2°j$

10. $3i - 7j$; $\sqrt{58} \cos 293.2°i + \sqrt{58} \sin 293.2°j$

11. $(\sqrt{13} - \sqrt{11})i + (\sqrt{3} + \sqrt{2})j$; $3.16 \cos 84.8°i + 3.16 \sin 84.8°j$

15.

16.

17.

18.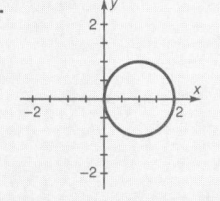

Lesson Quiz

1. Write vector **v** = (10, −24) in component and polar forms, and write a unit vector in the same direction as **v**. 10**i** − 24**j**; 26 cos 292.6°**i** + 26 sin 292.6°**j**; $\left(\frac{10}{26}, -\frac{24}{26}\right)$

2. Determine the vector **w** with initial point (−5, −8) and terminal point (2, 3) in component and polar form. 7**i** + 11**j**; $\sqrt{170}$ cos 57.5°**i** + $\sqrt{170}$ sin 57.5°**j**

If **r** = (5, 4), **s** = (−1, 8) and **t** = (11, 2), determine **v** such that:

3. **v** = **r** + **t** (16, 6)
4. **v** = **s** − **t** (−12, 6)
5. **v** = 3**s** + 4**r** (17, 40)

6. Determine a direction vector of the line containing P(13, −4) and Q(−5, 6) and write the equation of the line in both vector and parametric form. (−18, 10); (x, y) = (13, −4) + t(−18, 10); x = 13 − 18t; y = −4 + 10t

7. Determine whether the point P(6, −17) is on the line (x, y) = (−2, −3) + t(4, −7). yes

8. A football is kicked from the ground into the air at an angle of 45° with an initial velocity of 65 ft/s. Determine the parametric equations which model the flight of the ball. x = (65 cos 45°)t; y = −16t² + (65 sin 45°)t

Additional Answers

42. The horizontal equations are the same, but the vertical asymptotes are opposites because the brachistochrone is an inverted cycloid.

27. *Sports* The parametric equations x = 2(t − sin t) and y = −2(1 − cos t) describe the shape of a skateboard ramp. Draw the graph represented by these equations for 0 < t < 2π. Compare the graph with the cycloid presented in the Focus. How would this skateboard ramp compare with all other ramps of the same height?

Given **s** = (14, 5), **t** = (−6, 11), **u** = (−1, −7), find a vector **v** that satisfies the given equation.

28. **v** = **s** + **u** (13, −2)
29. **v** = **u** − **t** (5, −18)
30. **v** = **s** + 3**t** (−4, 38)
31. **v** = 4**u** + 3**t** (−22, 5)
32. **v** = ½(**s** − **u**) $\left(\frac{15}{2}, 6\right)$
33. **v** = −3**t** + 8**u** (10, −89)

Determine whether the given points are on the line with the vector equation (x, y) = (−8, −5) + t(9, 4).

34. (1, −1) yes
35. (−17, 9) no
36. $\left(-\frac{7}{2}, -3\right)$ yes

37. *Sports* A batter hits a baseball 4 ft above the ground at an angle of 25° and with an initial velocity of 130 ft/s. Will the ball be a home run if the outfield fence is 380 ft from home plate and 8 ft high? (Trace the graph using the trace function on a graphing utility to determine how high the ball is when it is 380 ft from home plate.) no

38. **Writing in Mathematics** Use a graphing utility to generate each of the following four sets of parametric equations. Set the step value of t at a sufficiently low value (such as 3° in degree mode) so that the curve will be generated slowly enough for you to observe how it grows.

| x = 4 sin t | x = −4 sin t | x = 4 sin t | x = −4 sin t |
| y = 3 cos t | y = 3 cos t | y = −3 cos t | y = −3 cos t |

Tell what you observe and explain why it happens.

C 39. Use a graphing utility to graph the parametric equations x = cos t, y = sin 2t. Then find an equation for the curve that has no variables except x and y. y² = 4x²(1 − x²)

40. A circle with equation (x + 2)² + y² = 100 is intersected by a straight line with parametric equations x = 3 − t and y = 5 + t. Find the intersection points of the circle and the line. Suppose that t represents the time that an object traveling along the line crosses the circle. Where will the object cross the circle first? (−2, 10), (8, 0); (8, 0)

41. A *cycloid* is the curve generated by a fixed point on the circumference of a circle as the circle rolls, without slipping, along a straight line. Use the figure at the right below to show that the parametric equations of a cycloid are x = a(t − sin t) and y = a(1 − cos t), where a is the radius of the rolling circle R and t is the measure of angle PRQ.

42. How are the parametric equations of Exercise 41 related to those of the brachistochrone discussed in the Focus?

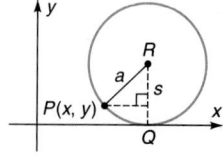

Writing in Mathematics

38. Answers may vary. The x- and y-values in each set are computed by finding values for t from 0° to 360°. The single sign change within the first pair of sets and the second pair of sets accounts for the change in direction between each pair of graphs.

43. In the diagram, M is the midpoint of $\overline{BC}$ and N is the midpoint of $\overline{AB}$. Given that $\overrightarrow{AG} = k \, \overrightarrow{AM}$ and $\overrightarrow{CG} = k \, \overrightarrow{CN}$, find the value of k. *Hint:* $\overrightarrow{AC} + \overrightarrow{CG} = \overrightarrow{AG}$. $\frac{\overline{AC}}{\overline{AM} - \overline{CN}}$

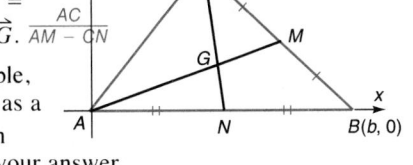

44. Thinking Critically   Earlier in the text, for example, in Lesson 10.3, a complex number was described as a number of the form $a + bi$, where $i = \sqrt{-1}$. Can complex numbers be considered vectors? Justify your answer.

45. Thinking Critically   In Lesson 12.1, a column matrix was defined as a matrix with just one column. Consider the 2×1 column matrix $\begin{bmatrix} a \\ b \end{bmatrix}$. Can it be considered a vector? Justify your answer.

46. An *astroid* is a curve with the pair of parametric equations $x = a \cos^3 t$ and $y = a \sin^3 t$, where $0 \le t < 2\pi$ and a is a positive constant. Use a graphing utility to graph the curve. Then find an equation for the curve that contains no variables other than x and y.

47. Writing in Mathematics   If a circle of radius r rolls on the outside of a fixed circle of radius R, then the path created by a fixed point on the rolling circle is called an *epicycloid*. Its parametric equations are:

$$x = (R + r) \cos t - r \cos \left(\frac{R + r}{r} t \right)$$

$$y = (R + r) \sin t - r \sin \left(\frac{R + r}{r} t \right), \text{ where } 0 \le t < 2\pi$$

If $r = 1$, the equations simplify to $x = a \cos t - \cos at$ and $y = a \sin t - \sin at$, where $a = R + 1$. Use a graphing utility to investigate the above curve for various values of a, such as $a = 2, 3, 4, 5, 6, 7,$ and 8. Write a paragraph generalizing the result of your investigations.

Project

When a space vehicle is launched into a planetary orbit, its path is an ellipse. Find parametric equations for such an orbit. Then use a graphing utility to trace the orbit. Find the number of minutes required for a satellite to complete one elliptical orbit about the earth.

Review

Determine the number of intercepts for each graph.

1. $y = 3x + \frac{1}{2}$ 2

2. $xy = 8$ 0

3. $x^2 + y^2 = 16$ 4

4. Determine a quadratic equation in x that has the solutions $\frac{5 + 7\sqrt{3}}{2}$ and $\frac{5 - 7\sqrt{3}}{2}$. $2x^2 - 10x - 61 = 0$

5. If y varies directly as r and s and inversely as the cube of t, determine a variation equation using k as a constant. $y = \frac{krs}{t^3}$

6. Show that $i(-i) = 1$. $i(-i) = -i^2 = -(-1) = 1$

12.8 Algebraic Vectors and Parametric Equations   **653**

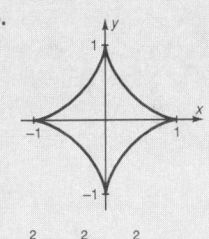

Vocabulary
dot product
inner product
orthogonal vectors
scalar product

Ⓜ **Materials/Manipulatives**
chalkboard protractor and grid
graph paper
protractor

Technology
scientific calculator

FOCUS

The critical angle is the angle of incidence of light that produces an angle of refraction equal to 90°. Point out that the critical angles given in the text are only valid when light passes from these substances into air. Because light travels at different speeds in different mediums, scientists define an *index of refraction, n*, of a medium equal to the ratio *c/v*, where *c* is the speed of light in a vacuum and *v* is the speed of light in the medium. The relationship between the angle of incidence and the angle of refraction can be described using Snell's law. Students interested in physics may wish to research this law and its applications.

12.9 Parallel and Perpendicular Vectors in Two Dimensions

Objective: To determine whether two vectors are parallel or perpendicular

Focus

Recall from the Focus of Lesson 3.6 that you can use trigonometry to describe the manner in which a ray of light passes from a medium of given optical density into one of higher or lower optical density. It is possible also to use vectors to illustrate this phenomenon. Let vector $\overrightarrow{PO}$ represent the ray of light from point P in the water, and vector $\overrightarrow{ON}$ the refracted ray in air. As i, the angle of incidence, increases, the angle of refraction r also increases. When approaching its limiting value of 90°, the refracted ray emerges from the water along a path approaching closer and closer to the water surface. When the angle of refraction equals 90°, the refracted ray travels on a path on the surface of the water. The value of the angle of incidence corresponding to this refractive angle is known as the critical angle. Different substances have different critical angles. For example, the critical angle for water is 48.5°, whereas for a diamond it is 24°.

Recall that the product of a scalar c and a vector **v** results in vector $c\mathbf{v}$. It is possible also to define a product of two vectors **v** and **w** that results in a scalar rather than another vector. It is called the **dot product** and denoted by $\mathbf{v} \cdot \mathbf{w}$.

Dot Product
If $\mathbf{v} = (v_1, v_2)$ and $\mathbf{w} = (w_1, w_2)$, then
$$\mathbf{v} \cdot \mathbf{w} = v_1w_1 + v_2w_2$$

The dot product is the name most often used for the operation defined on ordered pairs and ordered triples, that is, for vectors in two or three dimensions. It is possible also to define the operation for space of four dimensions and higher, but when this is done, the operation is usually called the *scalar product*, or *inner product*.

Example 1 Find the dot product for each pair of vectors:
   a. (3, 4), (7, 2)   **b.** (−2, −1), (−5, −3)   **c.** (8, 6), (−3, 4)

a. $(3, 4) \cdot (7, 2) = 3(7) + 4(2) = 29$
b. $(−2, −1) \cdot (−5, −3) = −2(−5) + (−1)(−3) = 13$
c. $(8, 6) \cdot (−3, 4) = 8(−3) + 6(4) = 0$

You can see that the right triangle represented by vectors **v** and **w** will satisfy the Pythagorean theorem if and only if the length of **w** − **v** is equal to the sum of the squares of the lengths of **w** and **v**. In symbols,

$$\|\mathbf{w} - \mathbf{v}\|^2 = \|\mathbf{w}\|^2 + \|\mathbf{v}\|^2$$

If **w** = (w_1, w_2) and **v** = (v_1, v_2), then

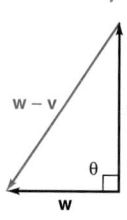

$$\begin{aligned}\|\mathbf{w} - \mathbf{v}\|^2 &= \|(w_1 - v_1, w_2 - v_2)\|^2 \\ &= (w_1 - v_1)^2 + (w_2 - v_2)^2 \\ &= w_1^2 - 2w_1v_1 + v_1^2 + w_2^2 - 2w_2v_2 + v_2^2 \\ &= (w_1^2 + w_2^2) + (v_1^2 + v_2^2) - 2(w_1v_1 + w_2v_2) \\ &= \|\mathbf{w}\|^2 + \|\mathbf{v}\|^2 - 2\mathbf{w} \cdot \mathbf{v}\end{aligned}$$

Note that $\|\mathbf{w} - \mathbf{v}\|^2 = \|\mathbf{w}\|^2 + \|\mathbf{v}\|^2$ if and only if $\mathbf{w} \cdot \mathbf{v} = 0$. Therefore, **w** and **v** are perpendicular if and only if $\mathbf{w} \cdot \mathbf{v} = 0$.

Perpendicular vectors are often called **orthogonal** vectors. The vectors in Example 1 part (c) are orthogonal since their dot product is 0. If the triangle is not a right triangle, then

$$\|\mathbf{w} - \mathbf{v}\|^2 = \|\mathbf{w}\|^2 + \|\mathbf{v}\|^2 - 2\mathbf{w} \cdot \mathbf{v}$$

Now it is also the case that

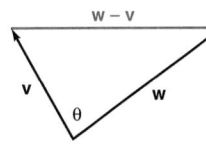

$$\|\mathbf{w} - \mathbf{v}\|^2 = \|\mathbf{w}\|^2 + \|\mathbf{v}\|^2 - 2\|\mathbf{w}\| \cdot \|\mathbf{v}\| \cos \theta$$

by the law of cosines, where θ is the angle between **w** and **v**. Thus,

$$\|\mathbf{w}\|^2 + \|\mathbf{v}\|^2 - 2\mathbf{w} \cdot \mathbf{v} = \|\mathbf{w}\|^2 + \|\mathbf{v}\|^2 - 2\|\mathbf{w}\| \cdot \|\mathbf{v}\| \cos \theta$$

$$-2\mathbf{w} \cdot \mathbf{v} = -2\|\mathbf{w}\| \cdot \|\mathbf{v}\| \cos \theta$$

$$\frac{\mathbf{w} \cdot \mathbf{v}}{\|\mathbf{w}\| \cdot \|\mathbf{v}\|} = \cos \theta$$

Therefore, the cosine of the angle between two vectors can be found by dividing the dot product of the vectors by the product of their respective norms.

Example 2 Find the measure of the angle between the vectors **w** = (9, 5) and **v** = (−7, 1).

$$\cos \theta = \frac{(9, 5) \cdot (-7, 1)}{\sqrt{81 + 25} \cdot \sqrt{49 + 1}} \qquad \cos \theta = \frac{\mathbf{w} \cdot \mathbf{v}}{\|\mathbf{w}\|\|\mathbf{v}\|}$$

$$= \frac{-63 + 5}{\sqrt{106} \cdot \sqrt{50}} = \frac{-58}{\sqrt{106} \cdot \sqrt{50}}$$

$$\theta = 37.2°$$

Recall that two vectors **w** = (w_1, w_2) and **v** = (v_1, v_2) are parallel if and only if one of the vectors is a scalar multiple of the other. In symbols, this means that there is a number a, $a \neq 0$, such that **w** = a**v**. From this, it follows that

$$(w_1, w_2) \cdot (-v_2, v_1) = [a(v_1, v_2)] \cdot (-v_2, v_1) = a(-v_1v_2 + v_2v_1) = a(0) = 0$$

Thus, if **w** and **v** are parallel, $(w_1, w_2) \cdot (-v_2, v_1) = 0$. Conversely, if $(w_1, w_2) \cdot (-v_2, v_1) = 0$, then **w** and **v** are parallel. *Why?*

12.9 Parallel and Perpendicular Vectors in Two Dimensions **655**

Thinking Critically
The equation $(w_1, w_2) \cdot (v_1, v_2) = 0$ is only true when **w** is a scalar multiple of **v** and since one vector is a scalar multiple of the other, **w** and **v** are parallel.

For Example 3
Determine if the given pairs of vectors are parallel, perpendicular, or neither.
1. (5, 1), (1, −5) perpendicular
2. (9, 8), (−2, 3) neither
3. (5, 13), (10, 26) parallel

For Example 4
A box is dragged 40 m along a horizontal surface by a force of 20 newtons. Determine the amount of work done in each of the following cases.
1. The force makes an angle of 60° with the horizontal.
   400 Newton-meters or joules
2. The force is applied in the direction of the displacement of the box. 800 Newton-meters or joules

For Example 5
Students are asked to prove the other four properties of dot products in Exercises 39 to 42.

Example 3 Determine whether the given pairs of vectors are parallel, perpendicular, or neither.

  a. $(\sqrt{3}, \sqrt{2}), (2, -\sqrt{6})$ **b.** $(8, 6), (4, -3)$

  a. $(\sqrt{3}, \sqrt{2}) \cdot (2, -\sqrt{6}) = \sqrt{3}(2) + \sqrt{2}(-\sqrt{6}) = 2\sqrt{3} - 2\sqrt{3} = 0$
  Thus, the two vectors are perpendicular.

  b. $(8, 6) \cdot (4, -3) = 8(4) + 6(-3) = 32 - 18 = 14$
  Thus, the two vectors are not perpendicular.

  $(8, 6) \cdot (3, 4) = 8(3) + 6(4) = 24 + 24 = 48$
  Thus, the two vectors are not parallel.

  Therefore, the two vectors are neither perpendicular nor parallel.

An important application of the dot product in physics is the calculation of work done on a body through a distance. This is given by the formula $W = \mathbf{F} \cdot \mathbf{d}$ where W is work, $\mathbf{F}$ is the force (a vector) acting on the body, and $\mathbf{d}$ (also a vector) is the displacement (change of position) that the body undergoes under the influence of the force. To find the value of W, find the product of $\|\mathbf{d}\|$ and $\|\mathbf{F}\| \cos \theta$, the component of the force in the direction of the displacement. Thus,

$$W = \mathbf{F} \cdot \mathbf{d} = \|\mathbf{F}\| \|\mathbf{d}\| \cos \theta, \text{ where } \theta \text{ is the angle between } \mathbf{F} \text{ and } \mathbf{d}$$

Example 4 Determine the work done by a force of magnitude $\|\mathbf{F}\| = 8$ N (newtons) in moving a box 20 m along a floor that makes an angle of 30° with $\mathbf{F}$. Give the answers in newton-meters (N-m).

$W = (8)(20) \cos 30°$
$\quad = 160(0.8660)$
$\quad = 138.4$, or about 138 N-m

The basic unit of work is the joule (J). One joule is the work done by a force of one newton in moving an object one meter. Thus, 1 J = 1 N-m.

An interesting observation is that a satellite in nearly circular orbit does no work to overcome the gravitational force exerted by the earth since that force is orthogonal to the direction of motion. That is, the angle between the force and the displacement is 90°. Thus,

$$W = \|\mathbf{F}\| \|\mathbf{d}\| \cos 90° = F \cdot d \cdot 0 = 0$$

The following dot product properties are useful in calculations involving vectors.

656   Chapter 12 Matrices and Vectors

Properties of the Dot Product

If **u**, **v**, and **w** are vectors in two dimensionals, and r is a scalar, then

$\mathbf{v} \cdot \mathbf{v} = \|\mathbf{v}\|^2$	Norm
$\mathbf{v} \cdot \mathbf{w} = \mathbf{w} \cdot \mathbf{v}$	Commutative property
$\mathbf{u} \cdot (\mathbf{v} + \mathbf{w}) = \mathbf{u} \cdot \mathbf{v} + \mathbf{u} \cdot \mathbf{w}$	Distributive property
$(r\mathbf{u}) \cdot \mathbf{v} = r(\mathbf{u} \cdot \mathbf{v})$	Associative property
$\|r\mathbf{w}\| = (|r|)(\|\mathbf{w}\|)$	Scalar

Example 5 Prove that the dot product is a commutative operation.

Let $\mathbf{u} = (u_1, u_2)$ and $\mathbf{v} = (v_1, v_2)$, then

$$\begin{aligned}
\mathbf{u} \cdot \mathbf{v} &= u_1v_1 + u_2v_2 \\
&= v_1u_1 + v_2u_2 \qquad \text{\textit{Commutative property of multiplication of real numbers}} \\
&= \mathbf{v} \cdot \mathbf{u}
\end{aligned}$$

Class Exercises

Find the dot product of each pair of vectors.

1. $(11, 2) \cdot (-6, 7)$ -52

2. $(\sqrt{5}, \sqrt{3}) \cdot (2\sqrt{5}, \sqrt{6})$ $10 + 3\sqrt{2}$

3. $(5, 12) \cdot (-24, 10)$ 0

4. $\left(\frac{1}{2}, \frac{1}{4}\right) \cdot (2, -1)$ $\frac{3}{4}$

Find the measure of the angle between the given vectors.

5. $\mathbf{v} = (5, 14)$
$\mathbf{w} = (-1, 8)$ $26.8°$

6. $\mathbf{v} = (2, 1)$
$\mathbf{w} = (-2, -1)$ $180°$

7. $\mathbf{v} = \left(\frac{3}{5}, \frac{1}{7}\right)$
$\mathbf{w} = \left(\frac{3}{7}, -\frac{2}{5}\right)$ $56.4°$

8. $\mathbf{v} = \left(\frac{3}{4}, \frac{1}{3}\right)$
$\mathbf{w} = \left(\frac{2}{3}, -\frac{1}{4}\right)$ $44.5°$

Determine whether the given pairs of vectors are parallel, perpendicular, or neither.

9. $(1, 5), (5, -1)$
perpendicular

10. $(-6, 5), \left(\frac{1}{6}, -\frac{1}{5}\right)$
neither

11. $(13, 8), \left(\frac{13}{4}, 2\right)$
parallel

12. $(17, 9), (-5, 11)$
neither

Practice Exercises
Use appropriate technology.

Find the dot product of each pair of vectors.

A **1.** $(4, 3) \cdot (2, 5)$ 23

2. $(3, 4) \cdot (5, 2)$ 23

3. $(12, 7) \cdot (-2, 3)$ -3

4. $(14, 9) \cdot (-3, 4)$ -6

5. $\left(\frac{1}{2}, \frac{1}{4}\right) \cdot (2, -1)$ $\frac{3}{4}$

6. $\left(\frac{1}{6}, \frac{1}{3}\right) \cdot (3, -1)$ $\frac{1}{6}$

7. $(-\sqrt{5}, \sqrt{2}) \cdot (\sqrt{3}, \sqrt{2})$ $2 - \sqrt{15}$

8. $(\sqrt{2}, -\sqrt{3}) \cdot (\sqrt{2}, \sqrt{5})$ $2 - \sqrt{15}$

Ⓡ 9. Is $x - 3$ a factor of $x^6 - 8x^5 + 12x^4 + 11x^3 - 3x^2 - 16x + 21$? yes

Find the measure of the angle between the given vectors.

10. $(3, 4), (-4, 3)$ $90°$

11. $(5, 5), (-2, -2)$ $180°$

12. $(2\sqrt{3}, \sqrt{3}), (\sqrt{2}, 4\sqrt{3})$ $51.9°$

13. $(5\sqrt{2}, \sqrt{2}), (\sqrt{3}, 2\sqrt{3})$ $52.1°$

14. $\left(-\frac{1}{4}, \frac{2}{3}\right), \left(8, -\frac{9}{2}\right)$ $139.9°$

15. $\left(-\frac{1}{5}, \frac{3}{4}\right), \left(10, -\frac{8}{3}\right)$ $119.9°$

16. Thinking Critically What may be said about the dot product of two vectors that are neither perpendicular nor parallel?

12.9 Parallel and Perpendicular Vectors in Two Dimensions **657**

Have students explain in their math journals why if the dot product of two vectors is zero, then the vectors are perpendicular, or orthogonal.

INDEPENDENT PRACTICE

Assignment Guide

Basic: 1–24, 25–35 odd
Average: 1–15 odd, 16–38
Enriched: 1–37 odd, 38–47

Teacher's Resource Book
  Practice, page 86

Ⓡ Review

Exercises 9, 17, 19, and 21 review the factor theorem and graphing functions. Exercise 37 involves finding the equation of a line from given conditions.

Additional Answers

16. The dot product is between zero and the product of the magnitudes of the two vectors.

Lesson Quiz

1. Determine the dot product for the vectors (12, 5) and (−6, −7). −107
2. Determine the measure of the angle between the vectors **w** = (−4, 10) and **v** = (7, −6). 152.4°

Determine whether the vectors are parallel, perpendicular, or neither.

3. ($\sqrt{7}$, $\sqrt{3}$) and (7, $\sqrt{21}$) parallel
4. (15, 7) and (−5, 2) neither
5. Determine the work done by a force of 25 newtons applied at an angle of 45° with the horizontal that moves an object 10 m along the horizontal floor.
176.78 Newton-meters or joules

Alternative Assessment

Explain what is meant by the angle between two vectors when the vectors do not share an endpoint.

Enrichment

Vectors **u** and **v** represent the legs of a right triangle. Show that **u** · **v** = 0.
Recall that $\cos \theta = \dfrac{\mathbf{u} \cdot \mathbf{v}}{\|\mathbf{u}\| \cdot \|\mathbf{v}\|}$. If **u** and **v** are the legs of a right triangle, then the angle between them, θ, measures 90°. Then cos θ = cos 90° = 0. Therefore, **u** · **v** must equal 0.

Additional Answers

28. 18; $-\dfrac{8}{9}$ 29. $\dfrac{50}{3}$; $-\dfrac{3}{2}$

30. 3; −3   31. $\dfrac{5\sqrt{3}}{3}$; $-5\sqrt{3}$

32. 0; $\pm\sqrt{2}$ 33. 0, ±2

34. $\dfrac{\sqrt{15}}{2}$; $-\dfrac{2\sqrt{15}}{5}$ 35. $\dfrac{\sqrt{10}}{3}$; $-\dfrac{3\sqrt{10}}{5}$

36. sometimes; Vectors **v** and **u** are equal if the following conditions exist. Generally, if the sum of the ordered pairs(triples) of **v** is equal to the sum of the ordered pairs(triples) of **u**, then **v** = **u**. Specifically, if the corresponding ordered pairs(triples) are equal, then **v** = **u**.

Ⓡ 17. Graph: $g(x) = \dfrac{3}{(x-1)^2}$

18. *Physics*   Determine the work done by a force of 10 N (newtons) exerted by a rope attached to a box at an angle of 40° with the floor and that pulls the box 25 m along the floor. 192 joules

Ⓡ 19. Graph: $h(x) = 2^{x-1}$

20. *Physics*   Determine the work done by a force of 12 N in pushing a box a distance of 17 m along the floor given that the force is exerted at an angle of 45° with the floor. 144 joules

Ⓡ 21. Graph: $t(x) = \log x$

Determine whether the given pairs of vectors are parallel, perpendicular, or neither.

B 22. (2, 4), (−2, 10) neither
23. (5, 8), (−16, 10) perpendicular
24. (−5, 15), (1, −3) parallel
25. (−7, 21), (2, −6) parallel
26. (4, 17), (−2, 5) neither
27. (7, 19), (−3, 8) neither

Determine the value of *K* for which each pair of vectors is parallel and the value of *K* for which the vectors are perpendicular.

28. (2, 9), (4, *K*)
29. (3, 10), (5, *K*)
30. (*K*, 3), (2, 2)
31. (*K*, 5), ($\sqrt{3}$, 3)
32. (*K*, 1), (*K*, −2)
33. (*K*, 2), (*K*, −2)
34. ($\sqrt{3}$, *K*), (2, $\sqrt{5}$)
35. ($\sqrt{2}$, *K*), (3, $\sqrt{5}$)

36. **Thinking Critically**   If **w** is a nonzero vector and **w** · **v** = **w** · **u** is true, is **v** = **u** also true? Explain.

Ⓡ 37. Determine the equation of the line through (−2, 3) and perpendicular to the line 3x − 4y + 6 = 0. 4x + 3y = 1

38. **Writing in Mathematics**   Explain why the expression ‖**v** · **w**‖ is meaningless.

Let **t**, **u**, **v**, and **w** be vectors in two dimensions, and let *r* denote a scalar.

C 39. Prove: **v** · **v** = ‖**v**‖²
40. Prove: **u** · (**v** + **w**) = **u** · **v** + **u** · **w**
41. Prove: (*r***u**) · **v** = *r*(**u** · **v**)
42. Prove: ‖*r***w**‖ = (|*r*|)(‖**w**‖)
43. Prove: ‖**v** + **w**‖ = ‖**v** − **w**‖ if and only if **v** is perpendicular to **w**.
44. Prove: ‖**t** + **u**‖ ≤ ‖**t**‖ + ‖**u**‖   *Hint:* Show first that **t** · **u** ≤ (‖**t**‖)(‖**u**‖).
45. Prove: (**u** − **w**) · (**u** + **w**) = ‖**u**‖² − ‖**w**‖²

46. Determine whether the lines with equations (x, y) = (1, 5) + t(7, 8) and (x, y) = (−10, 2) + r(−16, 4) are parallel, perpendicular, or neither. neither

47. Determine whether the lines with equations (x, y) = (6, 4) + t(8, −4) and (x, y) = (−2, 3) + r(1, 6) are parallel, perpendicular, or neither. neither

Challenge

1. Find the value of $(27)^{-(3^{-1})}$. $\dfrac{1}{3}$

2. If $\dfrac{25x - 34}{x^2 - 5x + 6} = \dfrac{A}{(x-2)} + \dfrac{B}{(x-3)}$ is an identity in *x*, find the value of *AB*. −656

658   Chapter 12 Matrices and Vectors

Writing in Mathematics
38. The dot product is a scalar and does not have a length.

12.10 Vectors in Space

Objectives: *To solve problems involving three-dimensional space using three-dimensional analogues of two-dimensional formulas*
To find an equation of a plane using vectors in three dimensions

Focus

Until modern times, the polarization of light was a laboratory curiosity. Now it is studied for both its theoretical and technological interest. Polaroid sunglasses are probably the most familiar example of the practical value of this phenomenon.

To understand polarized light, it helps to visualize light vibrations as vectors acting in three dimensions. If the vibrations are confined mainly to a single direction, then the light is polarized. In the figure below, light vibrations, represented as vectors, initially radiate in all directions within a plane perpendicular to the ray of the light's propagation.

After the light strikes a pile of glass plates, all the vectors parallel to the plane of incidence are refracted, whereas most of the vectors perpendicular to the plane of incidence are reflected. In this way both the refracted light and the reflected light have been polarized by the process.

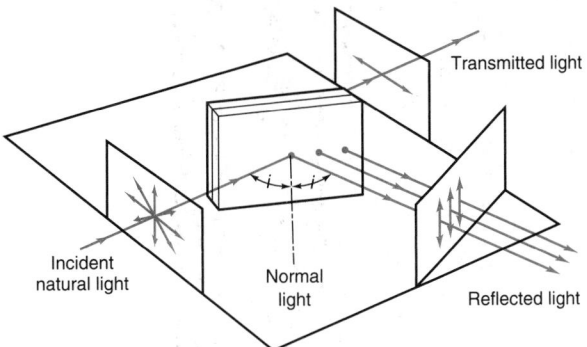

Transmitted light

Incident natural light

Normal light

Reflected light

There are applications of polarized light other than sunglasses. For example, manufacturers of airplanes and space capsules use polarized light with models made of photoelastic materials to study the effects of stresses on various structures. The strains induced in the structures show clearly when analyzed by polarized light.

LESSON PLAN

Vocabulary
cross product of two three-dimensional vectors
direction angles
normal vector
perpendicular to a plane
vector relationships in three dimensions
vector equation of a line

M Materials/Manipulatives
rulers or string
sheets of paper or oaktag
three dowel rods

Technology
scientific calculator

FOCUS

Have students investigate some of the uses of polarized light and prepare a short report on them. This can be a motivational introduction to the mathematics of 3-space.

Ⓜ • Bind together three dowel rods to
indicate the *x*-, *y*-, and *z*-axes in
three-dimensional space. Use this
model to demonstrate vectors, using pens or pencils, with tails at
the origin in each of the octants.
Point out the *i*-, *j*-, and *k*-compo-
nents of a vector, and the angle
between two vectors.

• Stress that the vector relationships
in three dimensions are logical extensions of those in two dimensions. Have students make a chart
listing these relationships with examples in both dimensions. Be
sure students include finding
angles between vectors, and writing vector and parametric equations of lines in space.

• Before proceeding to Example 4,
students may need to review the
following geometric concepts: A
plane is determined by a line and
a point not on the line, by three
noncollinear points, or by two lines
that intersect in exactly one point.

Ⓜ **Alternative Learning Styles**

Many students will have difficulty visualizing in three dimensions. Have
students develop a system of locating the position of objects in your
classroom. Suggestions may include
establishing a reference point such
as the northeast floor corner and locating a point by saying that it is 6 ft
due west, 10 ft due south, and 3 ft
high. Note that three reference lines
are sufficient to locate points in
space. Vectors can be shown using
rulers or string, and planes, by
sheets of paper or oaktag.

The study of vectors in three dimensions can be considered from both an
algebraic and a geometric approach. In this lesson, both viewpoints are
presented. In two dimensions, a vector is represented by an ordered pair of
real numbers and denoted by the notation $\mathbf{v} = (x, y)$. In a similar way, a three-
dimensional vector can be represented by an ordered triple of real numbers and
denoted by $\mathbf{v} = (x, y, z)$. The numbers x, y, and z are the components of
vector $\mathbf{v}$. When visualized as a position vector, $\mathbf{v}$ is drawn with its tail at the
origin.

Many of the characteristics of three-dimensional
vectors are just extensions of the same
characteristics for two-dimensional vectors. For
example, the magnitude, or norm, of vector
$\mathbf{v} = (v_1, v_2, v_3)$ is given by

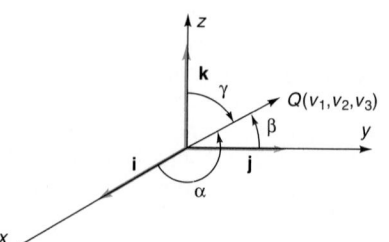

$$\|\mathbf{v}\| = \sqrt{v_1^2 + v_2^2 + v_3^2}$$

The **direction angles** of a nonzero vector are the
three smallest positive angles α, β, and τ measured
from the x, y, and z axes, respectively, to the
position representation of the vector.

The three basic unit vectors in 3-space are $\mathbf{i} = (1, 0, 0)$, $\mathbf{j} = (0, 1, 0)$, and
$\mathbf{k} = (0, 0, 1)$. The vector $(3, 4, 5)$, for example, can be written as the sum of
scalar multiples of the three basic unit vectors.

$$(3, 4, 5) = 3(1, 0, 0) + 4(0, 1, 0) + 5(0, 0, 1) = 3\mathbf{i} + 4\mathbf{j} + 5\mathbf{k}$$

Vector Relationships in Three Dimensions

If $\mathbf{v} = (v_1, v_2, v_3)$, $\mathbf{w} = (w_1, w_2, w_3)$, and a is a scalar, then

$$\mathbf{v} + \mathbf{w} = (v_1 + w_1, v_2 + w_2, v_3 + w_3)$$
$$\mathbf{v} - \mathbf{w} = (v_1 - w_1, v_2 - w_2, v_3 - w_3)$$
$$a\mathbf{v} = a(v_1, v_2, v_3) = (av_1, av_2, av_3)$$
$$\mathbf{v} \cdot \mathbf{w} = (v_1, v_2, v_3) \cdot (w_1, w_2, w_3) = v_1 w_1 + v_2 w_2 + v_3 w_3$$

The unit vector in the same direction as vector $\mathbf{v}$ is

$$\mathbf{u} = \frac{v_1}{\|\mathbf{v}\|}\mathbf{i} + \frac{v_2}{\|\mathbf{v}\|}\mathbf{j} + \frac{v_3}{\|\mathbf{v}\|}\mathbf{k}$$

Example 1 Given $\mathbf{v} = (1, -2, 5)$, $\mathbf{w} = (-2, 7, 11)$, $a = -2$, and $b = 4$, find:

    a. $\mathbf{v} + \mathbf{w}$ **b.** $\mathbf{w} - \mathbf{v}$ **c.** $\mathbf{v} \cdot \mathbf{w}$ **d.** $a\mathbf{v}$ **e.** $b\mathbf{w}$ **f.** $a\mathbf{w} + b\mathbf{v}$

a. $\mathbf{v} + \mathbf{w} = (1, -2, 5) + (-2, 7, 11) = (-1, 5, 16)$

b. $\mathbf{w} - \mathbf{v} = (-2, 7, 11) - (1, -2, 5) = (-3, 9, 6)$

c. $\mathbf{v} \cdot \mathbf{w} = (1, -2, 5) \cdot (-2, 7, 11) = 1(-2) + (-2)(7) + 5(11) =$
    $-2 - 14 + 55 = 39$

d. $a\mathbf{v} = -2\mathbf{v} = -2(1, -2, 5) = (-2, 4, -10)$

660   Chapter 12 Matrices and Vectors

e. $b\mathbf{w} = 4\mathbf{w} = 4(-2, 7, 11) = (-8, 28, 44)$

f. $a\mathbf{w} + b\mathbf{v} = -2\mathbf{w} + 4\mathbf{v} = -2(-2, 7, 11) + 4(1, -2, 5) =$
$(4, -14, -22) + (4, -8, 20) = (8, -22, -2)$

Many of the relationships between three-dimensional vectors are similar to the relationships between two-dimensional vectors. Some of these will be stated, although not proved. One of these relationships is the *dot product of two vectors*. If θ is the angle between the two three-dimensional vectors $\mathbf{v}$ and $\mathbf{w}$, then $\mathbf{v} \cdot \mathbf{w} = \|\mathbf{v}\| \cdot \|\mathbf{w}\| \cos \theta$. Solving for $\cos \theta$, you obtain

$$\cos \theta = \frac{\mathbf{v} \cdot \mathbf{w}}{\|\mathbf{v}\|\|\mathbf{w}\|}$$

When $\mathbf{v} \cdot \mathbf{w} = 0$, $\cos \theta = 0$ and the angle θ between $\mathbf{v}$ and $\mathbf{w}$ is 90°. Thus, as in the two-dimensional case, $\mathbf{v}$ and $\mathbf{w}$ are perpendicular. The converse is also the case; if the vectors are perpendicular, then $\mathbf{v} \cdot \mathbf{w} = 0$.

Example 2 Determine the angle between the vectors $\mathbf{v} = \mathbf{i} - \sqrt{5}\mathbf{j} + 2\mathbf{k}$ and $\mathbf{w} = 3\mathbf{i} + \mathbf{k}$.

$$\cos \theta = \frac{(1, -\sqrt{5}, 2) \cdot (3, 0, 1)}{\sqrt{(1)^2 + (-\sqrt{5})^2 + (2)^2} \cdot \sqrt{(3)^2 + (1)^2}} \qquad \cos \theta = \frac{\mathbf{v} \cdot \mathbf{w}}{\|\mathbf{v}\|\|\mathbf{w}\|}$$

$$= \frac{1(3) + (-\sqrt{5})(0) + 2(1)}{\sqrt{1 + 5 + 4} \cdot \sqrt{9 + 1}} = \frac{5}{\sqrt{10} \cdot \sqrt{10}} = \frac{1}{2}$$

$$\theta = 60°$$

Here is another example of a three-dimensional vector relationship that is similar to the two-dimensional case. A **vector equation** of a line in space has the form

$$Q = P + t\mathbf{v}$$

where Q is the set of points (x, y, z) in space that are on the line determined by a point $P(a, b, c)$ and the nonzero direction vector

$$\mathbf{v} = (v_1, v_2, v_3)$$

The parametric equations representing the same line are

$$x = a + v_1 t \qquad y = b + v_2 t \qquad z = c + v_3 t$$

What is a first degree equation for this line that has x, y, and z as its three variables and that contains the three constants a, b, and c?

Example 3 Determine both vector and parametric equations of the line in space determined by $P(1, 4, 7)$ and $R(-6, -4, -8)$.

$R - P = (-6 - 1, -4 - 4, -8 - 7) = (-7, -8, -15)$ *Direction vector of the line*

$(x, y, z) = (1, 4, 7) + t(-7, -8, -15)$ *Vector equation of the line*

$x = 1 - 7t \qquad y = 4 - 8t \qquad z = 7 - 15t$ *Parametric equations of the line*

12.10 Vectors in Space   **661**

For Example 1
Given: $\mathbf{v} = (4, -2, 1)$, $\mathbf{w} = (-3, -1, 5)$, $a = -6$, $b = 8$, find:
1. $\mathbf{v} + \mathbf{w}$ $(1, -3, 6)$
2. $\mathbf{w} - \mathbf{v}$ $(-7, 1, 4)$
3. $\mathbf{w} \cdot \mathbf{v}$ -5
4. $a\mathbf{w}$ $(18, 6, -30)$
5. $b\mathbf{v}$ $(32, -16, 8)$
6. $a\mathbf{v} - b\mathbf{w}$ $(0, 20, -46)$

For Example 2
Determine the angle between the vectors.
1. $\mathbf{v} = \mathbf{i} + 8\mathbf{j} - 3\mathbf{k}$, $\mathbf{w} = 2\mathbf{i} + 3\mathbf{j} + 4\mathbf{k}$. 72.4°
2. $\mathbf{v} = -4\mathbf{i} + 6\mathbf{k}$, $\mathbf{w} = 5\mathbf{i} - 3\mathbf{j}$ 154.7°

For Example 3
Determine both the vector and parametric equations of the line in space determined by the given points.
1. $P(8, -3, 7)$, $Q(-1, 5, 17)$
$(x, y, z) = (8, -3, 7) + t(-9, 8, 10)$
$x = 8 - 9t$; $y = -3 + 8t$; $z = 7 + 10t$
2. $P(0, 1, 1)$, $Q(15, 21, -34)$
$(x, y, z) = (0, 1, 1) + t(15, 20, -35)$
$x = 15t$; $y = 1 + 20t$; $z = 1 - 35t$

For Example 4

Determine the equation of the plane containing the given point P with the given normal vector **n**.

1. $P(4, 13, -7)$, **n** $= (5, 6, 7)$
   $5x + 6y + 7z = 49$
2. $P(-8, 0, 20)$, **n** $= (-1, 5, -13)$
   $x - 5y + 13z = 252$

Suppose that a nonzero vector **n** contains a point P that is in plane H. Then **n** is said to be *perpendicular* to plane H if it is perpendicular to every vector in H that contains P. In particular, if $Q(x, y, z)$ is any position vector that terminates in H, then **n** is perpendicular to $Q - P$, a vector that contains P and is in plane H. It immediately follows that

$$\mathbf{n} \cdot (Q - P) = 0$$

The position vector Q corresponds to any point (x, y, z) of the plane, so the above equation may be considered an equation of the plane. Because **n** is perpendicular to the plane, it is called a **normal vector.**

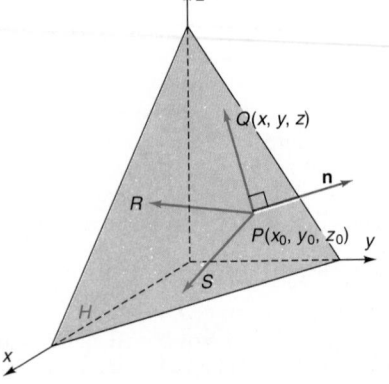

Example 4 Determine an equation of the plane containing the point $P(1, 2, 3)$ with normal vector $(-2, 4, 7)$.

Let (x, y, z) represent all points in the plane. Then,

$$(-2, 4, 7) \cdot (x - 1, y - 2, z - 3) = 0 \qquad \mathbf{n} \cdot (Q - P) = 0$$
$$-2(x - 1) + 4(y - 2) + 7(z - 3) = 0$$
$$-2x + 4y + 7z = 27$$

Notice in Example 4 that the coefficients of the variables in the equation of the plane are the same as the three components of the normal vector. In the exercises you are asked to show that if a plane has (a, b, c) as a normal vector, then an equation of the plane is $ax + by + cz = d$, where d is a constant. *Given that $P(x_0, y_0, z_0)$ is a point of the plane in the above generalization, what is a possible expression for the constant d?*

The vector operations considered so far have applied to both two-dimensional vectors and three-dimensional vectors. An operation known as the cross product is defined for three dimensions but not two.

Cross Product of Two Three-dimensional Vectors

If **v** $= (v_1, v_2, v_3)$ and **u** $= (u_1, u_2, u_3)$, then

$$\mathbf{v} \times \mathbf{u} = (v_2 u_3 - v_3 u_2, \ v_3 u_1 - v_1 u_3, \ v_1 u_2 - v_2 u_1)$$

The formula in this form is not easy to remember. It is the result of expanding a 3×3 determinant. Recall that the value of a 2×2 determinant is

$$\begin{vmatrix} a & b \\ c & d \end{vmatrix} = ad - bc$$

The value of a 3×3 determinant may be defined in terms of 2×2 determinants according to the following expansion.

662   Chapter 12 Matrices and Vectors

Thinking Critically
A possible equation for d is $d = ax_0 + by_0 + cz_0$.

$$\begin{vmatrix} a_1 & a_2 & a_3 \\ b_1 & b_2 & b_3 \\ c_1 & c_2 & c_3 \end{vmatrix} = a_1 \begin{vmatrix} b_2 & b_3 \\ c_2 & c_3 \end{vmatrix} - a_2 \begin{vmatrix} b_1 & b_3 \\ c_1 & c_3 \end{vmatrix} + a_3 \begin{vmatrix} b_1 & b_2 \\ c_1 & c_2 \end{vmatrix}$$

Using determinants, you can express the cross product in the form

$$\mathbf{v} \times \mathbf{u} = \begin{vmatrix} \mathbf{i} & \mathbf{j} & \mathbf{k} \\ v_1 & v_2 & v_3 \\ u_1 & u_2 & u_3 \end{vmatrix} = \begin{vmatrix} v_2 & v_3 \\ u_2 & u_3 \end{vmatrix} \mathbf{i} - \begin{vmatrix} v_1 & v_3 \\ u_1 & u_3 \end{vmatrix} \mathbf{j} + \begin{vmatrix} v_1 & v_2 \\ u_1 & u_2 \end{vmatrix} \mathbf{k}$$

Note that the cross product $\mathbf{v} \times \mathbf{u}$ is a vector, not a scalar, and is perpendicular to both $\mathbf{v}$ and $\mathbf{u}$. (You are asked to show that this is the case in the exercises.) It can be shown that if a vector is perpendicular to two nonparallel vectors in a plane, then it is perpendicular to the plane also. The perpendicular relationship between a vector and a plane is used by physicists as an aid in understanding the interplay of mechanical or electromagnetic forces in three dimensions. An example of the latter is the polarization of light mentioned in the Focus.

To find the equation of a plane determined by three noncollinear points, you may begin by finding the cross product of two vectors that contain those points. For example, the equation of the plane containing three noncollinear points $P(p_1, p_2, p_3)$, $Q(q_1, q_2, q_3)$, and $R(r_1, r_2, r_3)$ can be found by first forming the vectors $\overrightarrow{PQ}$ and $\overrightarrow{PR}$. Find a normal to the plane determined by $\overrightarrow{PQ}$ and $\overrightarrow{PR}$ by finding the cross product $\overrightarrow{PQ} \times \overrightarrow{PR}$. Then follow the procedure of Example 3 using any one of the three points P, Q, or R.

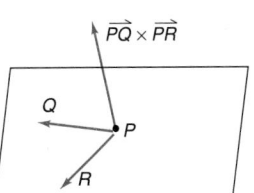

Example 5 Find an equation of the plane containing the points $P(2, -1, 6)$, $Q(0, 1, 5)$, and $R(4, -1, 2)$.

First, determine vectors $\overrightarrow{PQ}$ and $\overrightarrow{PR}$.

$$\overrightarrow{PQ} = (0 - 2, 1 - (-1), 5 - 6) = (-2, 2, -1)$$

$$\overrightarrow{PR} = (4 - 2, -1 - (-1), 2 - 6) = (2, 0, -4)$$

$$\overrightarrow{PQ} \times \overrightarrow{PR} = \begin{vmatrix} \mathbf{i} & \mathbf{j} & \mathbf{k} \\ -2 & 2 & -1 \\ 2 & 0 & -4 \end{vmatrix} = \begin{vmatrix} 2 & -1 \\ 0 & -4 \end{vmatrix} \mathbf{i} - \begin{vmatrix} -2 & -1 \\ 2 & -4 \end{vmatrix} \mathbf{j} + \begin{vmatrix} -2 & 2 \\ 2 & 0 \end{vmatrix} \mathbf{k} = -8\mathbf{i} - 10\mathbf{j} - 4\mathbf{k}$$

This is a normal to the plane. An equation of the plane using point P is:

$$(-8, -10, -4) \cdot (x - 2, y + 1, z - 6) = 0$$
$$-8(x - 2) - 10(y + 1) - 4(z - 6) = 0$$
$$8x + 10y + 4z = 30$$

Class Exercises

Given $\mathbf{v} = (2, 0, 3)$, $\mathbf{w} = (-1, 7, -5)$, $a = -3$, and $b = 6$, find:

1. $\mathbf{v} + \mathbf{w}$ (1, 7, -2) **2.** $\mathbf{w} - \mathbf{v}$ (-3, 7, -8) **3.** $\mathbf{v} \cdot \mathbf{w}$ -17 **4.** $a\mathbf{w}$ (3, -21, 15)

5. $b\mathbf{v}$ (12, 0, 18) **6.** $a\mathbf{v} + b\mathbf{w}$ (-12, 42, -39) **7.** $\mathbf{v} \times \mathbf{w}$ (-21, 7, 14) **8.** $a\mathbf{v} \times b\mathbf{w}$ (378, 126, -252)

9. a unit vector in the same direction as $\mathbf{v}$ $\left(\frac{2\sqrt{13}}{13}, 0, \frac{3\sqrt{13}}{13}\right)$ **10.** a vector perpendicular to $\mathbf{w}$ ex: (2, 1, 1)

12.10 Vectors in Space **663**

Find an equation of the plane containing the three given points.
1. $P(1, 1, 1)$, $Q(0, -2, 6)$, $R(5, -3, 3)$
$7x + 11y + 8z = 26$
2. $P(4, -5, 8)$, $Q(1, 3, -1)$,
$R(13, 4, -9)$ $5x + 12y + 9z = 32$

CLOSURE

Ask students how they can find the normal to a plane, given three points in the plane. Then have them explain how the normal is used to write an equation of the plane.

INDEPENDENT PRACTICE

Assignment Guide
Basic: 1–29
Average: 1–29 odd, 30–41
Enriched: 1–35 odd, 37–46

Teacher's Resource Book
  Practice, page 87

® Review
Exercises 17, 21, 23, and 29 involve using laws of exponents to evaluate expressions and solve equations. Exercise 33 reviews solving radical equations.

Technology
Exercises 18 to 20 require the use of a calculator or trigonometric tables.

LESSON FOLLOW-UP

Test Yourself

Teacher's Resource Book
Tests—Quiz, form A, page 54
Tests—Quiz, form B, page 54

Lesson Quiz

Given: $\mathbf{v} = (6, 2, 1)$, $\mathbf{w} = (-5, -2, 0)$,
$a = -7$, $b = 5$, find:

1. $\mathbf{w} + \mathbf{v}$ $(1, 0, 1)$
2. $\mathbf{v} - \mathbf{w}$ $(11, 4, 1)$
3. $\mathbf{v} \cdot \mathbf{w}$ -34
4. $a\mathbf{v}$ $(-42, -14, -7)$
5. $b\mathbf{w}$ $(-25, -10, 0)$
6. $a\mathbf{w} + b\mathbf{v}$ $(65, 24, 5)$
7. The angle between $\mathbf{v}$ and $\mathbf{w}$ $170.4°$
8. Determine both the vector and parametric equations of the line in space determined by $P(5, 8, 9)$ and $Q(-6, 3, 1)$.
   $(x, y, z) = (5, 8, 9) + t(-11, -5, -8)$
   $x = 5 - 11t; y = 8 - 5t; z = 9 - 8t$
9. Determine the equation of the plane containing the point $P(7, 16, -4)$ with normal $\mathbf{n} = (3, -2, 5)$. $3x - 2y + 5z = -33$
10. Find an equation of the plane containing the three points $P(2, 3, 4)$, $Q(5, 7, -1)$, and $R(10, 5, -6)$.
    $15x + 5y + 13z = 97$

Additional Answers

Class Exercises
12. $(x, y, z) = (1, 0, 4) + t(-4, 4, -5)$
13. $x = 1 - 3t, y = -5t, z = 4 + 4t$
14. $9x - 31y - 32z = -119$

---

11. Determine the angle between the vectors $\mathbf{v} = 7\mathbf{i} - 2\mathbf{j} + \mathbf{k}$ and $\mathbf{w} = -\mathbf{i} + 3\mathbf{j} + 5\mathbf{k}$. $100.6°$

Given points $P(1, 0, 4)$, $Q(-2, -5, 8)$, and $R(-3, 4, -1)$, find:
12. a vector equation of $\overleftrightarrow{PR}$
13. a parametric equation of $\overleftrightarrow{PQ}$
14. an equation of the plane containing points P, Q, and R

Practice Exercises   Use appropriate technology.

Given $\mathbf{u} = (11, 1, 5)$, $\mathbf{v} = (-8, 3, -1)$, $\mathbf{w} = (-1, 2, -4)$, $a = -5$, $b = 3$, and $c = 12$, find each of the following.

A 1. $\mathbf{u} + \mathbf{w}$ 2. $\mathbf{v} + \mathbf{w}$ 3. $\mathbf{v} - \mathbf{u}$ 4. $\mathbf{w} - \mathbf{v}$
5. $\mathbf{u} \cdot \mathbf{v}$ 6. $\mathbf{v} \cdot \mathbf{w}$ 7. $a\mathbf{v}$ 8. $b\mathbf{w}$
9. $b\mathbf{u} - a\mathbf{w}$ 10. $c\mathbf{w} - a\mathbf{v}$ 11. $\mathbf{u} \times \mathbf{w}$ 12. $\mathbf{w} \times \mathbf{v}$
13. $-\mathbf{u} \times \mathbf{v}$ 14. $-\mathbf{w} \times \mathbf{u}$ 15. $b\mathbf{v} \times \mathbf{u}$ 16. $a\mathbf{u} \times c\mathbf{w}$

Ⓡ 17. Simplify: $5^{m+n} \cdot 25^{m-n}$ 5^{3m-n}

Determine the angle between the vectors.
18. $\mathbf{v} = 5\mathbf{i} - 3\mathbf{j} + 2\mathbf{k}$ 19. $\mathbf{v} = -\mathbf{i} + \sqrt{2}\mathbf{j} - 5\mathbf{k}$ $99.9°$ 20. $\mathbf{v} = (10, 5, 2)$
   $\mathbf{w} = -2\mathbf{i} + 4\mathbf{j} + 7\mathbf{k}$ $99°$ $\mathbf{w} = 9\mathbf{i} + 11\mathbf{j} + 4\mathbf{k}$ $\mathbf{w} = (-6, 0, -4)$ $146.1°$

Ⓡ 21. Simplify: $64^{a+b} \div 8^{a-b}$. 8^{a+3b}

B 22. **Thinking Critically** Consider the four-dimensional vector $\mathbf{v} = (v_1, v_2, v_3, v_4)$. How would you go about finding a unit vector in the same direction as $\mathbf{v}$?

Ⓡ 23. Solve: $x^{0.25} + x^{0.5} = 2$ 1

Given points $P(5, 4, 1)$, $Q(-7, -3, 2)$, $R(0, 5, -6)$, and $S(7, 1, -3)$:
24. Find a vector equation of $\overleftrightarrow{PR}$.   25. Find a vector equation of $\overleftrightarrow{QR}$.
26. Find a vector equation of $\overleftrightarrow{RS}$.   27. Find parametric equations of $\overleftrightarrow{SP}$.
28. Find parametric equations of $\overleftrightarrow{RP}$.

Ⓡ 29. Solve: $x^{\frac{1}{9}} - x^{\frac{1}{3}} = 6$ -512

Determine an equation of the plane that contains the given point and that has the given normal vector.
30. $P(3, 0, -1)$; $(8, 2, -3)$ 31. $P(7, -4, 5)$; $(-12, 7, 4)$ 32. $P(-7, 8, 2)$; $(6, -6, -1)$

Ⓡ 33. Solve: $\sqrt[4]{x - 4} = -2 + \sqrt{x - 4}$ 20

Given points $P(2, 5, 1)$, $Q(-4, 7, 3)$, $R(2, 0, 6)$, and $S(-4, 0, -2)$, find an equation of the plane containing points:
34. P, Q, and R 35. P, Q, and S 36. Q, R, and S 37. P, R, and S

Use the definition of cross product to verify the following relations involving arbitrary vectors $\mathbf{u}$, $\mathbf{v}$, and $\mathbf{w}$.
C 38. $\mathbf{u} \times \mathbf{v} = -(\mathbf{v} \times \mathbf{u})$ 39. $\mathbf{w} \times \mathbf{w} = 0$, where 0 is the zero vector $(0, 0, 0)$
40. $c\mathbf{u} \times \mathbf{w} = c(\mathbf{u} \times \mathbf{w})$ 41. $\mathbf{u} \cdot (\mathbf{v} \times \mathbf{w}) = \mathbf{v} \cdot (\mathbf{w} \times \mathbf{u})$

664   Chapter 12 Matrices and Vectors

Practice Exercises
1. $(10, 3, 1)$ 2. $(-9, 5, -5)$ 3. $(-19, 2, -6)$ 4. $(7, -1, -3)$
5. -90 6. 18 7. $(40, -15, 5)$ 8. $(-3, 6, -12)$
9. $(28, 13, -5)$ 10. $(-52, 39, -53)$ 11. $(-14, 39, 23)$ 12. $(10, 31, 13)$
13. $(16, 29, -41)$ 14. $(-14, 39, 23)$ 15. $(48, 87, -123)$ 16. $(840, -2340, -1380)$

42. **Writing in Mathematics** Review the relations of Exercises 38 to 41. Then write a paragraph describing whatever geometric significance you discern in any of the exercises.

43. **Thinking Critically** Using vectors, how can you determine that two planes are orthogonal? Parallel?

44. Prove that if a plane has (a, b, c) as a normal vector and $P(x_0, y_0, z_0)$ is a point of the plane, then an equation of the plane is $ax + by + cz = d$, where d is a constant.

45. Use the dot product to prove that if **u** and **v** are nonzero vectors, then **u** × **v** and **v** are perpendicular.

46. Prove that if $\mathbf{u} = u_1\mathbf{i} + u_2\mathbf{j} + u_3\mathbf{k}$ and $\mathbf{v} = v_1\mathbf{i} + v_2\mathbf{j} + v_3\mathbf{k}$ form adjacent sides of a parallelogram, then the area of the parallelogram is $\|\mathbf{u} \times \mathbf{v}\|$. *Hint:* If θ is the angle between the vectors, then $\|\mathbf{u}\|$ is the length of the base and $\|\mathbf{v}\| \sin \theta$ is the length of an altitude to the base.

Test Yourself

Find and graph the image of the given point. Use the indicated transformation matrix.

1. $\begin{bmatrix} 1 \\ 5 \end{bmatrix}$; $T_{x\text{-axis}}$ 2. $\begin{bmatrix} 3 \\ -2 \end{bmatrix}$; $T_{y\text{-axis}}$ 3. $\begin{bmatrix} -1 \\ 0 \end{bmatrix}$; $R_{-45°}$ **12.6**

For each vector, find the *x*- and *y*-components to the nearest whole number.

4. Magnitude: 8; angle with the *x*-axis: 25° (7, 3)   **12.7**

5. Magnitude: 15; angle with the *x*-axis: 70° (5, 14)

6. *Physics* Forces of 28 lb and 36 lb make an angle of 48° with each other and are applied to an object at the same point. Find the magnitude of the resultant force. 58.6 lb

7. Determine vector **v** with the initial point (4, 5) and terminal point (8, 12). Give both the component form and polar form.   **12.8**

8. Find a direction vector of the line containing the two points $P(4, 7)$ and $Q(12, 3)$. Then find a vector equation of the line and a pair of parametric equations of the line.

9. Find the dot product for $\mathbf{v} = (5, 2)$ and $\mathbf{u} = (4, 9)$. 38   **12.9**

10. Find the measure of the angle between the vectors $\mathbf{w} = (7, 3)$ and $\mathbf{v} = (-5, 2)$. 135°

Determine whether the given pairs of vectors are parallel, perpendicular, or neither.

11. $(-12, 9), (4, -3)$ parallel   12. $(\sqrt{7}, \sqrt{4}), (\sqrt{2}, -\sqrt{5})$ neither   13. $(5, 10), (4, -2)$ perpendicular

Given that $\mathbf{v} = (2, -1, 4)$ and $\mathbf{u} = (3, 8, -12)$, find each of the following.   **12.10**

14. $\mathbf{v} + \mathbf{u}$ (5, 7, −8)   15. $\mathbf{v} \cdot \mathbf{u}$ −50

16. Determine the angle, to the nearest degree, between the vectors $\mathbf{v} = \mathbf{i} - 3\mathbf{j} + 4\mathbf{k}$ and $\mathbf{w} = 2\mathbf{i} + 3\mathbf{k}$. 40°

12.10 Vectors in Space   **665**

Writing in Mathematics
42. Answers may vary. Students' answers should reflect that they are comfortable discussing concepts in three-dimensional mathematics.

Alternative Assessment
Have students construct a three-dimensional model with two vectors in space and indicate each of the following:
• The *x*-, *y*-, and *z*-components of each vector
• The angle between the two vectors
• A normal to the plane containing the two vectors
• An equation of the plane containing the two vectors

Enrichment
Determine the area of the parallelogram that has the given vectors $\mathbf{u} = (1, 4, 1)$ and $\mathbf{v} = (12, 5, -3)$ as adjacent sides. 48.6 square units

Additional Answers
43. Given two planes, if the dot product of two vectors, one in each plane, is 0, then the planes containing the vectors are orthogonal; if the cross product of two vectors is 0, then the planes containing the vectors are parallel.

44. Let $P(x_1, y_1, z_1)$ be a point in the plane with normal vector (a, b, c). Then the equation in the plane is $(a, b, c) \cdot (x - x_1, y - y_1, z - z_1) = 0$, $ax - ax_1 + by - by_1 + cz - cz_1 = 0$, $ax + by + cz = ax_1 + by_1 + cz_1$, where $ax_1 + by_1 + cz_1$ is a constant, say, d. So $ax + by + cz = d$ is an equation of the plane.

Test Yourself
7. $4\mathbf{i} + 7\mathbf{j}$; $\sqrt{65} \cos 60.3° \mathbf{i} + \sqrt{65} \sin 60.3° \mathbf{j}$
8. $(8, -4)$; $(x, y) = (4, 7) + t(8, -4)$; $x = 4 + 8t$, $y = 7 - 4t$

665

1. $\begin{bmatrix} 1 & -\frac{11}{2} & 8 \\ 5 & -2 & 8 \\ -1 & 2 & 3 \end{bmatrix}$

2. $\begin{bmatrix} 4 & -12 & 4 \\ 6 & -1 & -38 \\ -11 & 8 & -2 \end{bmatrix}$

3. $\begin{bmatrix} 2\sqrt{2} & -5\sqrt{2} & 8\sqrt{2} \\ 6\sqrt{2} & -2\sqrt{2} & -4\sqrt{2} \\ -4\sqrt{2} & 4\sqrt{2} & 2\sqrt{2} \end{bmatrix}$

5. $\begin{bmatrix} -8 & -2 & -5 \\ -7 & 1 & -11 \\ -10 & -13 & 19 \end{bmatrix}$

6. $\begin{bmatrix} -1 & 4 & -5 \\ -7 & 9 & -9 \\ 21 & -16 & 12 \end{bmatrix}$

7. $\begin{bmatrix} -6 & 9 & -29 \\ 5 & 25 & -54 \\ -42 & -53 & 76 \end{bmatrix}$

8.

	n_1	n_2	n_3	n_4
n_1	0	1	0	0
n_2	0	0	1	1
n_3	1	1	0	1
n_4	0	0	1	0

9. $\begin{bmatrix} -\frac{1}{3} & -\frac{2}{3} \\ \frac{5}{3} & \frac{7}{3} \end{bmatrix}$

Chapter 12 Summary and Review

Vocabulary

adjacency matrix (612)
augmented matrix (626)
column matrix (596)
cross product of vectors (662)
determinant (620)
directed graph (612)
dimensions of a matrix (596)
direction angle (660)
dot product (654)
element of a matrix (596)
equal matrices (597)

finite graph (612)
identity matrix (606)
matrix (596)
matrix multiplication (604)
norm of a vector (639)
normal vector (662)
orthogonal vectors (655)
parametric equations (647)
reflection matrix (634)
resultant (640)
rotation matrix (636)

row matrix (596)
row operation (621)
scalar (598)
scalar multiplication (598)
square matrix (596)
transformation matrix (634)
unit vector (645)
vector (639)
zero matrix (597)
zero vector (600)

Addition of Matrices   If two matrices, A and B, have the same dimensions, then their sum, $A + B$, is a matrix whose elements are the sums of the corresponding elements of A and B.   **12.1**

Given that $A = \begin{bmatrix} 2 & -5 & 8 \\ 6 & -2 & -4 \\ -4 & 4 & 2 \end{bmatrix}$ and $B = \begin{bmatrix} 0 & -3 & 4 \\ 2 & -1 & 10 \\ 1 & 0 & 2 \end{bmatrix}$, find:

1. $\frac{1}{2}A + B$ **2.** $2A - 3B$ **3.** $\sqrt{2}A$

4. Given that $\frac{2}{3}[6x - 3y \quad 12] + [x \quad -2y] = [4 \quad y]$, find the values of x and y. $\left(\frac{28}{15}, \frac{8}{3}\right)$

Multiplication of Matrices   The product of two matrices, $A_{m \times p}$ and $B_{p \times n}$, is a matrix AB with dimensions $m \times n$. The element in the ith row and jth column of this product matrix is the sum of the products of the corresponding elements of the ith row of A and the jth column of B.   **12.2**

Given $A = \begin{bmatrix} 2 & 0 & -1 \\ 1 & 1 & -2 \\ 5 & -4 & 3 \end{bmatrix}$ and $B = \begin{bmatrix} -2 & -1 & 0 \\ 3 & 2 & -1 \\ 4 & 0 & 5 \end{bmatrix}$, find:

5. AB **6.** A^2 **7.** A^2B

Directed Graphs   A finite graph is a set of points, called nodes, and a set of lines, called edges, which connect the nodes. A directed graph is a finite graph that has a direction associated with its edges.   **12.3**

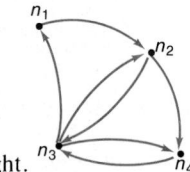

8. Construct the adjacency matrix for the directed graph at the right.

Inverses of Matrices   When the product of two square matrices A and B is such that $AB = BA = I$, then A and B are multiplicative inverses of one another.   **12.4**

9. Find the multiplicative inverse of matrix $A = \begin{bmatrix} 7 & 2 \\ -5 & -1 \end{bmatrix}$, if it exists.

10. Solve the matrix equation for the matrix X: $\begin{bmatrix} 1 & 4 & -1 \\ -3 & 5 & 2 \\ -2 & 1 & 1 \end{bmatrix} X = \begin{bmatrix} 6 \\ 3 \\ -4 \end{bmatrix}$

Augmented Matrix Solutions   When solving an augmented matrix, find a matrix equivalent to the coefficient matrix with 1's on the main diagonal and 0's elsewhere.

12.5

11. Solve using the augmented matrix method: $\begin{cases} x - 4y + 2z = 3 \\ 3x - y - z = 12 \\ -2x + 5y + z = -13 \end{cases}$ $\begin{bmatrix} 3 \\ -1 \\ -2 \end{bmatrix}$

Transformation Matrices   Matrices can be used to reflect and rotate points in the coordinate plane.

Find and graph the image of the given point. Use the indicated transformation matrix.

12. $\begin{bmatrix} -4 \\ 0 \end{bmatrix}$; $T_{y\text{-axis}}$ $\begin{bmatrix} 4 \\ 0 \end{bmatrix}$ 13. $\begin{bmatrix} 7 \\ 1 \end{bmatrix}$; $T_{x\text{-axis}}$ $\begin{bmatrix} 7 \\ -1 \end{bmatrix}$ 14. $\begin{bmatrix} -\sqrt{3} \\ 1 \end{bmatrix}$; R_{60} $\begin{bmatrix} -\sqrt{3} \\ -1 \end{bmatrix}$ 12.6

Geometric Vectors   A vector is a quantity having both magnitude and direction.

12.7

15. Find the x- and y-components, to the nearest whole number, of vector $\mathbf{u}$ that has a magnitude of 12 and makes a counterclockwise angle of 62° with the x-axis. (6, 11)

16. An airplane has an air speed of 450 mi/h and a heading of 110°. The wind is blowing from the east at 23 mi/h. Find the ground speed of the plane to the nearest mile per hour and its course to the nearest degree. 428 mi/h; 111°

Algebraic Vectors and Parametric Equations   The norm of vector $\mathbf{v} = (x, y)$ is $\|\mathbf{v}\| = \sqrt{x^2 + y^2}$. The vector equation of a line is $(x, y) = (a, b) + t(c, d)$.

12.8

17. Given $\mathbf{v} = (6, 8)$, determine the component form and the polar form of vector $\mathbf{v}$.

18. Determine a direction vector of the line containing the two points $P(6, 9)$ and $Q(10, 4)$. Then find a vector equation of the line and a pair of parametric equations of the line.

Parallel and Perpendicular Vectors in Two Dimensions   Two vectors $\mathbf{v}$ and $\mathbf{w}$ are perpendicular if and only if $\mathbf{v} \cdot \mathbf{w} = 0$. Two vectors $\mathbf{w} = (w_1, w_2)$ and $\mathbf{v} = (v_1, v_2)$ are parallel if and only if $(w_1, w_2) \cdot (-v_2, v_1) = 0$.

12.9

19. Determine the measure of the angle between $\mathbf{v} = (5, -2)$ and $\mathbf{w} = (6, 3)$. 48°

20. Determine whether the vectors $\mathbf{u} = (3, 2)$ and $\mathbf{w} = (-6, 9)$ are parallel, perpendicular, or neither. perpendicular

Vectors in Space   Vector operations in three dimensions are analogous to vector operations in two dimensions.

12.10

21. Find both a vector equation and parametric equations of the line in space determined by $P(3, 4, 7)$ and $Q(-1, -2, -5)$.

22. Find an equation of the plane containing $P(-3, 1, 4)$, $Q(2, 0, 5)$, and $R(6, -2, 7)$. $y + z - 5 = 0$

Summary and Review   **667**

Additional Answers

1. $\begin{bmatrix} 9 & 2 \\ 5 & -4 \\ 6 & -\frac{17}{2} \end{bmatrix}$

2. $\begin{bmatrix} -4 & 3 \\ 11 & 1 \\ 2 & -11 \end{bmatrix}$

3. $\begin{bmatrix} -\frac{14}{3} & 1 \\ 0 & -\frac{2}{3} \end{bmatrix}$

5. $\begin{bmatrix} 7 & -5 \\ 10 & 2 \end{bmatrix}$

6. $\begin{bmatrix} -45 & -22 \\ -46 & -4 \end{bmatrix}$

7. $\begin{array}{c c} & \begin{array}{ccccc} n_1 & n_2 & n_3 & n_4 & n_5 \end{array} \\ \begin{array}{c} n_1 \\ n_2 \\ n_3 \\ n_4 \\ n_5 \end{array} & \begin{bmatrix} 0 & 0 & 1 & 1 & 0 \\ 1 & 0 & 1 & 0 & 0 \\ 1 & 1 & 0 & 1 & 0 \\ 0 & 0 & 0 & 0 & 0 \\ 1 & 0 & 0 & 0 & 0 \end{bmatrix} \end{array}$

8. $\begin{bmatrix} -\frac{1}{13} & \frac{2}{13} \\ \frac{5}{13} & \frac{3}{13} \end{bmatrix}$

14. $(14, -12)$; $(x, y) = (-6, 9) + (14, -12)t$; $x = -6 + 14t$, $y = 9 - 12t$

Given that $A = \begin{bmatrix} -10 & 0 \\ 2 & 4 \\ -4 & 1 \end{bmatrix}$ and $B = \begin{bmatrix} 2 & 1 \\ 3 & -1 \\ 2 & -4 \end{bmatrix}$, find:

1. $2B - \frac{1}{2}A$

2. $A + 3B$

3. Solve the matrix equation: $2\begin{bmatrix} 3 & 0 \\ -1 & 1 \end{bmatrix} + 3X = \frac{1}{2}\begin{bmatrix} -16 & 6 \\ -4 & 0 \end{bmatrix}$

4. If $A = \begin{bmatrix} -2 & 0 & -1 \\ 1 & -5 & 3 \end{bmatrix}$ and $B = \begin{bmatrix} 5 & -2 \\ 0 & 3 \\ -4 & 0 \end{bmatrix}$, find AB. $\begin{bmatrix} -6 & 4 \\ -7 & -17 \end{bmatrix}$

If $A = \begin{bmatrix} 3 & -1 \\ 2 & 2 \end{bmatrix}$ and $B = \begin{bmatrix} -5 & -1 \\ 2 & 3 \end{bmatrix}$, find:

5. A^2

6. A^2B

7. Construct the adjacency matrix for the directed graph.

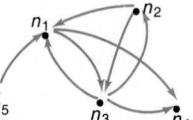

8. Find the multiplicative inverse of matrix $A = \begin{bmatrix} -3 & 2 \\ 5 & 1 \end{bmatrix}$, if it exists.

9. Solve the matrix equation for X: $\begin{bmatrix} 2 & 3 \\ -1 & -2 \end{bmatrix} X = \begin{bmatrix} -5 \\ 2 \end{bmatrix} \begin{bmatrix} -4 \\ 1 \end{bmatrix}$

10. Use matrices to solve the system of equations: $\begin{cases} -4x + 3y = 2 \\ 3x - y = 1 \end{cases}$ $(1, 2)$

11. Solve using the augmented matrix method: $\begin{cases} x + 2y + z = 7 \\ 2x - 3y + 2z = -14 \\ -4x + 3y - z = 22 \end{cases}$ $(-3, 4, 2)$

12. Find the image of $P(-\sqrt{2}, -\sqrt{2})$ under $R_{45°}$. $\begin{bmatrix} 0 \\ -2 \end{bmatrix}$

13. Find, to the nearest whole number, the horizontal and vertical components of vector $\mathbf{v}$ that has a magnitude of 14 and that makes an angle of 37° with the x-axis. $(11, 8)$

14. Determine a direction vector of the line containing the two points $P(-6, 9)$ and $Q(8, -3)$. Then find a vector equation of the line and a pair of parametric equations of the line.

15. In $\triangle ABC$, $A = (3, 2)$, $B = (1, -1)$, and $C = (4, -2)$. Find the measure of angle B to the nearest degree. $75°$

16. First the value of k given that the vectors $(\sqrt{2}, 5)$ and $(k, -\sqrt{8})$ are perpendicular. 10

17. Given that $\mathbf{v} = (4, 5, -6)$ and $\mathbf{w} = (3, -1, 2)$, find $\mathbf{v} \times \mathbf{w}$. $4\mathbf{i} - 26\mathbf{j} - 19\mathbf{k}$

Challenge

Describe the line segment represented by the vector equation
$(x, y) = (2, 0) + t(-3, 4)$, $0 \le t \le 2$. It is the segment with endpoints $(2, 0)$ and $(-4, 8)$.

668   Chapter 12 Matrices and Vectors

Cumulative Review

In each item you are to compare a quantity in Column 1 with a quantity in Column 2. Write the letter of the correct answer from these choices:

A. The quantity in Column 1 is greater than the quantity in Column 2.
B. The quantity in Column 2 is greater than the quantity in Column 1.
C. The quantity in Column 1 is equal to the quantity in Column 2.
D. The relationship cannot be determined from the given information.

Notes: Information centered over both columns refers to one or both of the quantities being compared. A symbol that appears in both columns has the same meaning in each column. All variables represent real numbers. Most figures are not drawn to scale.

Column 1	Column 2	
I: $(x - 6)^2 + (y + 3)^2 = 25$		
II: $x^2 + y^2 = 9$		
1. radius of I A	radius of II	11.1
$\sqrt{x + 4} = 2$		
2. x B	1	7.7
3. i^{36} C	i^{52}	10.4
4. $\sin 195°$ B	$\sin 30°$	6.1
amplitude		
5. $y = 3 \cos x$ A	$y = \frac{1}{2} \sin x$	4.2
vector $\mathbf{v} = (4, 5)$		
vector $\mathbf{w} = (6, 3)$		
6. $\mathbf{v} \cdot \mathbf{w}$ C	39	12.9
7. $(625)^{-\frac{1}{4}}$ B	$(-64)^{\frac{2}{3}}$	9.1
$A(5, -7)$, $B(-3, 2)$,		
$C(4, 8)$		
8. distance AB A	distance BC	2.7
$|3x - 2| \le 8$		
9. x A	-3	8.2

Column 1	Column 2	
$\tan \theta = \frac{3}{5}$		
10. $\cos \theta$ B	$\cot \theta$	3.5
11. modulus of B	modulus of	10.3
$3 - 4i$	$6 + 3i$	
$\sqrt[3]{2x + 5} - 3 = 0$		
12. x C	11	7.7
13. $\log_5 24$ A	$\log_{24} 5$	9.3
$\begin{cases} 3x - 2y = -1 \\ 2x + 3y = 8 \end{cases}$		
14. x B	y	8.1
15. $\sin(-135°)$ C	$\cos(-135°)$	3.6
$f(x) = -x^2 - 3x + 4$		
$g(x) = 2x^2 + 6x - 5$		
16. maximum value A	minimum value	2.5
of $f(x)$	of $g(x)$	
17. $\dfrac{7x + 9}{x^2 + x - 30}$ C	$\dfrac{4}{x - 5} + \dfrac{3}{x + 6}$	7.8
Solve for x.		
18. $\ln x = 3.0855$ B	$\log x = 2.3174$	9.5

30.

41.

49.

50.

19. Determine the exact value of $\tan^{-1}\sqrt{3}$. 60° 4.6

20. Determine the vertex of the parabola with equation $(x + 2)^2 + 12(y + 5) = 0$. $(-2, -5)$ 11.4

21. Solve for x. $27^x = \sqrt[3]{3}$ $\frac{1}{9}$ 9.2

22. Determine the area of triangle ABC. $60\sqrt{3}$ 5.5

23. Determine the axis of symmetry of the parabola $y = 4x^2 - 3x + 1$. $x = \frac{3}{8}$ 2.5

24. What is the eccentricity of a circle? zero 11.2

25. What is the range of the tangent function? the set of all real numbers 4.3

26. Given $A = \begin{bmatrix} 3 & 6 \\ 8 & 1 \\ 2 & 4 \end{bmatrix}$ and $B = \begin{bmatrix} 3 & 4 \\ 6 & 8 \end{bmatrix}$, find AB. $\begin{bmatrix} 45 & 60 \\ 30 & 40 \\ 30 & 40 \end{bmatrix}$ 12.2

27. Evaluate: $16^{-\frac{1}{2}}$ $\frac{1}{4}$ 9.1

28. What is another name given to the x-coordinate? abscissa 1.3

29. A vector can be represented geometrically as a __?__. directed line segment 12.6

30. Graph the polar equation $r = 5$. 10.1

31. Solve the system of equations $\begin{cases} 3x - 4y = 12 \\ 2x - 6y = 18 \end{cases}$ using the multiplicative inverse of a matrix. $(0, -3)$ 12.4

32. The inverse of an exponential function is called a __?__. logarithmic function 9.3

33. Find the value of $\sin\theta$ for angle θ in standard position that passes through the point $(2, 6)$. $\frac{3\sqrt{10}}{10}$ 3.4

34. Determine the equation of the circle with center at $(5, -3)$ that passes through the point $(8, 6)$. $(x - 5)^2 + (y + 3)^2 = 90$ 11.1

35. If the measure of two angles and the included side of a triangle are given, then which law can be used to solve the triangle __?__. law of sines 5.2

36. Classify the matrix as a row, column, or square. State the dimensions. $R = \begin{bmatrix} 3 \\ 6 \\ -1 \\ 2 \\ 4 \end{bmatrix}$ column, 5×1 12.1

37. The graph of the function $r = \theta$ for $\theta \geq 0$ is called a __?__. Spiral of Archimedes 10.2

38. Solve the inequality $|2x + 1| > 3$. Express the solution in interval notation. $(-\infty, -2) \cup (1, \infty)$ 8.2

39. Determine the vertex, axis of symmetry, and the directrix of the parabola with the equation $(y - 6)^2 = 4(x - 3)$. $V(3, 6)$; axis of symmetry: $y = 6$; directrix: $x = 2$ 11.4

40. A unit vector is a vector with a magnitude of __?__. one 12.7

41. Solve the linear system of inequalities graphically: $\begin{cases} y < 0 \\ x - y > -1 \end{cases}$ 8.3

42. Solve $3\cos^2 x + 2\cos x - 2 = 0$, where $0 \leq x < 2\pi$, to the nearest hundredth of a radian. 0.99, 5.29

43. The transverse axis of a hyperbola has a length of _?_. 2a   11.3

44. Find the dot product for the pair of vectors $(4, 7)$ and $(8, -3)$. 11   12.9

45. Determine if $x - 3$ is a factor of $x^3 - 5x^2 + 3x + 9$. yes   7.1

46. Determine the number of solutions in triangle ABC if $a = b \sin A$. one   5.3

47. Simplify: $\left(3x^{\frac{2}{3}}y^{\frac{1}{6}}\right)\left(4x^{\frac{1}{5}}y^{\frac{5}{18}}\right)$ $12x^{\frac{13}{15}}y^{\frac{4}{9}}$ 9.1

48. Determine whether the equation $y = 50e^{-0.4t}$ represents exponential growth or decay. Use a graphing utility to justify your answer. exponential decay   9.6

49. Solve $y < 2 \log 5x$ using a graphing utility.   9.5

50. Graph the function $f(x) = e^x - 3$ and state whether it is increasing or decreasing. increasing   9.2

51. Express in rectangular form: $(1 - 6i)^0$ $1 + 0i$ 10.5

52. Find the modulus of the complex number $5 - i$. $\sqrt{26}$ 10.3

53. Simplify: $\dfrac{\sin 2A}{1 - \cos 2A}$ $\cot A$ 6.3

54. Evaluate: $\sqrt{\sqrt[3]{64x^6}}$ $2|x|$ 9.1

55. Determine the midpoint of the segment joining the points $(-6, 2)$ and $(-4, -6)$. $(-5, -2)$ 2.7

56. Determine the vertex of the parabola with equation $x = y^2 - 16y + 68$. $(4, 8)$ 11.4

57. Solve the system of equations: $\begin{cases} 0.2y = 1.2x \\ 0.6x + 0.3y = 1.8 \end{cases}$ $\left(\dfrac{3}{4}, \dfrac{9}{2}\right)$ 8.1

58. Find an equation of the tangent line to the circle with equation $x^2 + y^2 = 100$ at $P(-6, 8)$. $-6x + 8y = 100$ 11.7

59. A rotation of $\frac{7}{9}$ in a clockwise direction would terminate in which quadrant? I   3.1

60. Determine the zeros of the function $g(x) = (x^2 - 16)(x^2 + 36)$. $\pm 4, \pm 6i$ 7.3

61. What is the length of the conjugate axis of a hyperbola? 2b   11.3

62. A graph that is a set of points called nodes and a set of lines called edges which connect the nodes is called _?_. finite   12.3

63. Determine the vertex of the parabola with the equation $x^2 = 4y$. $(0, 0)$ 11.4

64. Express the function $\cos 50°$ in terms of its cofunction. $\sin 40°$ 4.1

65. Solve the inequality $\dfrac{x^2 - 5x - 6}{(x - 3)^2} \le 0$. $[-1, 3) \cup (3, 6]$ 8.4

Determine if each statement is always true, sometimes true, or never true.

66. To divide one complex number in polar form by another, you should find the quotient of their moduli and the difference of their arguments. always   10.4

67. The graph of the sequence $a_n = n^2$ is a continuous line or curve. never   13.2

68. The orbit of each planet is an ellipse with the sun at one focus. always   11.8

69. The value of e is defined as the number that the expression $\left(1 + \dfrac{1}{n}\right)^n$ approaches as n approaches infinity. always   9.2

Summary

Sequences are introduced and examples are given of both explicit rules and recursive formulas. Arithmetic and geometric sequences and series are explored in detail. Mathematical induction is introduced and is used to prove the binomial theorem. Limits of sequences are discussed; convergence and divergence of sequences are defined. The limit of a sequence of partial sums is used to define the convergence and divergence of such series. Power series are presented as a way of approximating functions.

Chapter Objectives

- To find a rule of a sequence and to use a rule to find a specified term of a sequence
- To find specified terms and the common difference in an arithmetic sequence
- To find specified terms and the common ratio in a geometric sequence
- To find arithmetic and geometric means
- To use sigma notation to represent the sum of a series
- To find the partial sum of an arithmetic or a geometric series
- To prove statements using the principles of mathematical induction
- To use the binomial theorem to expand a binomial and to find a specified term of a binomial expansion
- To find the limit of an infinite sequence
- To determine when the limit of an infinite sequence does not exist
- To find the sum of a convergent infinite geometric series
- To express a repeating decimal as a ratio of two integers
- To identify certain power series
- To estimate values of functions using power series

13 Sequences and Series

Mathematical Power

Modeling   Where does the money go? That is a question people often ask, but it has a special meaning to economists. Economists, people who study patterns of production and consumption, want to know the total effect that an initial expenditure, either by the government or the corporate sector, might have on the economy. Mathematical modeling is a fundamental tool for solving all types of economic problems.

Some economists believe that if the government spends a certain amount of money, for example, by funding public works projects, the value of this expenditure is multiplied many times and helps to stimulate the economy. Expansion will take place—there will be more people with jobs which leads to increased demand for goods and services which leads to more private investment in business. Theoretically, everyone will benefit, including the government which ends up with increased tax revenues.

Assume that the government spends $1 million for road construction. Suppose also that economists have determined that, on average, people spend three-fourths of the income they receive. So the suppliers, contractors, workers, and others who receive the government money will spend $\frac{3}{4} \times \$1,000,000 = \$750,000$ on other goods and services.

The people who receive this money will spend

$$\frac{3}{4} \times \$750,000$$

or $$\frac{3}{4} \times \left(\frac{3}{4} \times \$1,000,000\right)$$

or $$\left(\frac{3}{4}\right)^2 \times \$1,000,000 = \$562,500$$

The next time, the amount spent will be

$$\frac{3}{4} \times \$562,500$$

672

or $$\left(\frac{3}{4}\right)^3 \times \$1,000,000 = \$421,880$$

Each new round of spending is three-fourths of the previous round. The effect of the initial expenditure of $1 million is an endless chain of secondary spending. However, although the chain is endless, it is a decreasing chain, and all the expenditures add up to a finite amount. Can you tell what the total amount is for this example?

The terms on the left form an *infinite geometric series* of the form $1 + r + r^2 + r^3 + \cdots + r^n$, where $r < 1$. In this chapter you will learn that the sum of such a series is $\frac{1}{1 - r}$. So, in this case, $\frac{1}{1 - \frac{3}{4}} = \frac{1}{\frac{1}{4}} = 4$. Therefore, the sum of the expenditures is

$$4 \times \$1,000,000 = \$4,000,000$$

Features

Modeling

$$1 \times \$1,000,000 = \$1,000,000$$
$$+$$
$$\left(\tfrac{3}{4}\right) \times \$1,000,000 = \$750,000$$
$$+$$
$$\left(\tfrac{3}{4}\right)^2 \times \$1,000,000 = \$562,500$$
$$+$$
$$\left(\tfrac{3}{4}\right)^3 \times \$1,000,000 = \$421,880$$
$$+$$
$$\vdots$$
$$+$$
$$\left(\tfrac{3}{4}\right)^n \times \$1,000,000 = ?$$

Notice that this sum is 4 times the initial expenditure of $1 million. Economists call this chain of expenditures the *multiplier effect*—in this case, the value of the multiplier is 4.

Thinking Critically The more people spend, the less they save, and the reverse. In an economy with a large multiplier, what do you think is true about the amount of income people save? In an economy where people save a substantial part of their income, what do you think is true about the multiplier? What other factors might affect the outcome of the economic model discussed above?

Project Research two or more countries with very different spending habits. Approximate the multiplier for each country and compute the total effect of an initial expenditure of $1 million for each country. What factors do you think influence the spending habits of people in different economies at different times?

673

Mathematical Power

A brief discussion about the theories of English economist John Maynard Keynes (1883–1946) can provide background for this model. Instead of the classical concepts of a free economy, Keynes endorsed government public-works programs to promote employment and, especially during periods of recession, government spending to stimulate business activity. Students can offer reasons for agreeing or disagreeing with Keynes' ideas.

The lesson uses an informal notion of limits to explain that the sum of an infinite number of terms can be a finite number. Emphasize that with geometric series, the sum is finite if and only if the constant ratio of the terms r is such that $|r| < 1$. In this example $r = \tfrac{3}{4} < 1$, and the series is $1 + \tfrac{3}{4} + \tfrac{9}{16} + \tfrac{27}{64} + \tfrac{81}{256} + \cdots$. Elicit from students that as n gets larger and larger, the nth terms gets smaller and smaller and *approaches* 0. Contrast the case of nonzero arithmetic series where the sum is always infinite.

Thinking Critically Students should see that the multiplier is large when the denominator of $\tfrac{1}{1-r}$ is small. This implies r is close to 1 which means people are spending most of the income they receive and saving very little. In an economy with a high rate of savings, the multiplier is small.

Review and Assessment

Student Text
- Test Yourself   705, 735
- Summary and Review   736–737
- Chapter Test   738

Teacher's Resource Book
- Tests   57–60
- Practice   88–95

Vocabulary

explicit formula
finite sequence
infinite sequence
initial terms
*n*th (general) term of a sequence
recursive formula
sequence
terms of a sequence

Ⓜ **Materials/Manipulatives**

pineapples
pine cones
sunflowers

Technology

graphing utility
scientific calculator
spreadsheet program

FOCUS

Fibonacci numbers were discovered by the Italian mathematician Leonardo of Pisa, also known as Leonardo Fibonacci (ca. 1175–1250). In his work *Liber abaci,* Fibonacci states a famous problem, sometimes called the "rabbit problem," which supposes that rabbits obey the following law of breeding: Every pair of rabbits at least two months old will produce exactly one pair of rabbits (male and female) as offspring every month. Therefore, starting with one pair of newly born rabbits, the number of rabbits alive at month *n* is precisely the Fibonacci number F_n.

The Fibonacci sequence has many interesting patterns. For example, the sum of the first *n* Fibonacci numbers is always one less than the $(n + 2)$nd Fibonacci number. Students may enjoy verifying this pattern and looking for and verifying other patterns.

Objectives: To use a rule to find specified terms of a sequence
To find a rule for a sequence

Focus

Botanists have examined plants from all over the world and studied the arrangement of their flowers, leaves, stems, and seeds. They have been surprised to note that the arrangements fall into a limited number of patterns. The study of leaf patterns is called *phyllotaxis.*

The numbers that occur most often in the description of plant-element arrangements form part of a sequence of numbers called the *Fibonacci sequence.* This sequence is 1, 1, 2, 3, 5, 8, 13, 21, 34, 55, 89, 144, 233, ... For example, the seeds in a sunflower head are distributed in two distinct sets of spirals that radiate in opposite directions about the center. An average sunflower head has 34 spirals winding in one direction and 55 in the other.

Smaller heads have 21 and 34, or 13 and 21, spirals. The scales on pineapples form three distinct families of spirals and usually have either 5, 8, and 13, or 8, 13, and 21, spirals in these sets. Botanists are fascinated by the consistent appearance of the Fibonacci numbers in phyllotaxis, and researchers are still seeking an explanation of the phenomenon.

The *Fibonacci* numbers are easy to obtain. After the first two numbers, 1 and 1, each successive number is the sum of the two preceding numbers. The sequence has not only intriguing mathematical properties but also a wide variety of applications in fields such as physics, ecology, and genealogy.

Many applications of mathematics involve ordered lists of numbers called *sequences.* Here are some examples of sequences that cover many areas of experience.

Counting 10, 20, 30, 40, 50, 60, . . .

Graphing (1, 1), (2, 4), (3, 9), (4, 16), (5, 25), . . .

Charting growth

Month	1	2	3	4	5	6
Height (cm)	0.8	1.0	1.1	1.3	1.3	1.4

Computing interest

Year	1	2	3	4
Interest	$121.38	$134.56	$119.05	$144.00

674   Chapter 13 Sequences and Series

Note that in each case there is a correspondence between a positive integer, which indicates order or position, and another number. This correspondence is a function, and so the following definition is reasonable.

> A **sequence** is a function whose domain is the set of positive integers or a subset of the positive integers that consists of the n integers 1, 2, 3, . . . , n.

Sometimes only the range of a sequence is given. Thus, the counting sequence (1, 10), (2, 20), (3, 30), (4, 40), (5, 50), (6, 60), . . . is more simply listed as 10, 20, 30, 40, 50, 60, ... The counting example is also an example of an **infinite sequence,** since its domain is the set of *all* positive integers. The computing interest example illustrates a **finite sequence,** whose domain is {1, 2, 3, 4}.

Example 1 Find the first five terms of the infinite sequence defined by $f(n) = 3n$.

The first five elements of this sequence are

$$f(1) = 3 \qquad f(2) = 6 \qquad f(3) = 9 \qquad f(4) = 12 \qquad f(5) = 15$$

The sequence defined by f is therefore 3, 6, 9, 12, 15, ...

The numbers in the range of the sequence function, that is, the numbers that make up the ordered list, are called the **terms** of the sequence. The notation a_1, a_2, a_3, . . . is often used for the terms. The ***n*th** or **general term** of a sequence is denoted a_n, where n denotes the number of the term of the sequence.

Example 2 Find the first five terms of the infinite sequence with general term $a_n = 2^n$.

The first five terms of this sequence are

$$a_1 = 2^1 = 2 \qquad a_2 = 2^2 = 4 \qquad a_3 = 2^3 = 8 \qquad a_4 = 2^4 = 16 \qquad a_5 = 2^5 = 32$$

The sequence with general term $a_n = 2^n$ is therefore 2, 4, 8, 16, 32, ...

A formula that describes the nth term of a sequence (or its function) is referred to as the *rule of a sequence*. The rule of a sequence may be given explicitly, as in Examples 1 and 2. In each of these examples, any term of the sequence may be found directly from the rule.

Example 3 Find the 23rd term of the sequence given by each rule.
  a. $f(n) = 3n$ **b.** $a_n = 2^n$

  a. To find the 23rd term of this sequence, compute $f(23)$.

$$f(23) = 3 \cdot 23 = 69$$

  b. The 23rd term of the sequence is a_{23}.

$$a_{23} = 2^{23} = 8{,}388{,}608$$

13.1 Sequences   **675**

INSTRUCTION

Ⓜ• Use pine cones, sunflowers, pineapples, and so on to illustrate the frequent natural occurrence of the Fibonacci numbers in nature. •
• Present Fibonacci's rabbit problem to students after they have read the Focus of this lesson. Ask them to identify the next term(s) of the sequence, and then see if anyone recognizes it as the sequence of the Focus. Point out that the same mathematical concepts often occur in a wide variety of situations.
• Be sure that students understand that not all sequences have formulas, either recursive or explicit.

Alternative Learning Styles
Students who are global learners respond well to seeing examples before trying to learn a formal definition. These students will benefit from a discussion of the rabbit problem as suggested above before a discussion of recursive formulas.

GUIDED PRACTICE

For Example 1
Find the first five terms of the infinite sequence defined by $f(n) = 2n + 3$.
5, 7, 9, 11, 13

For Example 2
Find the first five terms of the infinite sequence with general term $b_n = 3^{n-1}$. 1, 3, 9, 27, 81

For Example 3
1. Find the sixteenth term of the sequence given by the rule $f(n) = 10n - 8$. 152
2. Find the nineteenth term of the sequence given by the rule $b_n = 3^n - 1$. 1,162,261,466

For Example 4

Find an explicit formula for each sequence.

1. 10, 20, 30, 40, 50, . . . $a_n = 10n$

2. $\frac{2}{3}, \frac{2}{9}, \frac{2}{27}, \frac{2}{81}, \ldots$ $a_n = \frac{2}{3^n}$

Common Error Some students assume that the explicit formula suggested by the first few terms of a sequence proves that the formula generates all terms of the sequence. Discuss Class Exercise 16 to help reinforce the fact that an observed pattern may change even after a large number of terms of the sequence has been examined.

For Example 5

Find the next four terms of the sequence given by each recursive formula.

1. $a_1 = 3$ and $a_n = 2a_{n-1} - 1$
5, 9, 17, 33

2. $a_1 = -1$, $a_2 = 2$ and $a_n = 2a_{n-1} + a_{n-2}$ 3, 8, 19, 46

For Example 6

Find an explicit formula for the sequence defined by each recursive formula.

1. $a_1 = 7$ and $a_n = a_{n-1} + 3$
$a_n = 4 + 3n$

2. $a_1 = 6$ and $a_n = a_{n-1} - 3$
$a_n = 9 - 3n$

In Example 3, the rules $f(n) = 3n$ and $a_n = 2^n$ are called **explicit formulas;** each gives the nth term as a function of n. It is often possible to find an explicit formula for a sequence if enough terms of the sequence are known. Note that no finite number of terms completely determines an infinite sequence, since an observed pattern may change even after a large number of terms has been examined. However, in this book you may assume that an observed pattern does continue.

Example 4 Find an explicit formula for each sequence.

$$\textbf{a. } 1, \frac{1}{2}, \frac{1}{3}, \frac{1}{4}, \frac{1}{5}, \frac{1}{6}, \ldots \qquad \textbf{b. } 1, 3, 5, 7, 9, 11, 13, \ldots$$

a. It is apparent by inspection that a rule of the sequence is $a_n = \frac{1}{n}$.

b. This is the sequence of odd numbers, which can be generated from the rule $a_n = 2n - 1$.

Another way to give the rule of a sequence is by using a **recursive formula.** A recursive formula gives one or more *initial terms* of a sequence and then defines a_n using preceding terms. The Fibonacci sequence 1, 1, 2, 3, 5, 8, 13, 21, 34, 55, 89, 144, 233, . . . is an example of a sequence defined by a recursive formula, since each number after the first two numbers is the sum of the two preceding numbers. For the Fibonacci sequence, $a_1 = 1$, $a_2 = 1$, and the recursive formula for the remaining terms is $a_n = a_{n-1} + a_{n-2}$.

Example 5 Find the next four terms of the sequence given by each recursive formula.
$$\textbf{a. } a_1 = 3 \text{ and } a_n = a_{n-1} + 5, n > 1 \qquad \textbf{b. } a_1 = 2 \text{ and } a_n = 2a_{n-1}, n > 1$$

a. The first term is 3 and each number is obtained by adding 5 to the number before it. The sequence is then 3, 8, 13, 18, 23.

b. The first term is 2 and each number is obtained by multiplying the number before it by 2. The sequence is therefore 2, 4, 8, 16, 32.

Note that the sequence defined recursively in Example 5b is the same as the one defined explicitly in Example 2. It is sometimes desirable to find an explicit formula for a sequence defined recursively. Unfortunately, it isn't always easy to do so.

Example 6 Find an explicit formula for the sequence defined recursively by $a_1 = 10$ and $a_n = a_{n-1} + 5$.

The sequence defined by $a_1 = 10$ and $a_n = a_{n-1} + 5$ is 10, 15, 20, 25, 30, 35, . . . , which may be thought of as $5 \cdot 2, 5 \cdot 3, 5 \cdot 4, 5 \cdot 5, 5 \cdot 6, 5 \cdot 7, \ldots$

An explicit formula is then $a_n = 5(n + 1)$, or $a_n = 5n + 5$.

If enough terms of a sequence are known, a recursive formula may sometimes be discovered.

Example 7   In order gradually to acquire the habit of thrift, George saved money from his summer job by setting aside $1 in savings after the first week of work, $2 after the second week, $4 after the third week, $7 after the fourth week, and so on in a manner that generated the sequence 1, 2, 4, 7, 11, 16, 22, ... Find a recursive formula for the sequence.

Examining the sequence for a pattern reveals that the second number may be obtained by adding 1 to the first number, the third by adding 2 to the second, the fourth by adding 3 to the third, and so on. In general, $a_n = a_{n-1} + n - 1$ with $a_1 = 1$.

For Example 7, note that without the specification of a_1 the recursive formula is incomplete. Different values of a_1 would yield very different sequences. Try the same formula with $a_1 = 3$, for example. Note also that if only a finite number of terms of a sequence are known, it is possible to find different formulas that yield those same terms. For example, if the sequence of Example 7 had been presented as 1, 2, 4, . . . , the formula $a_n = 2a_{n-1}$ with $a_1 = 1$ would have given the same first three terms, but the rest of the sequence would be different.

Class Exercises

Find the first five terms of the infinite sequence defined explicitly by each rule.

1. $f(n) = 3n + 2$ **2.** $f(n) = n^2 - 1$
 5, 8, 11, 14, 17   0, 3, 8, 15, 24
3. $a_n = (-1)^n(2n - 1)$ **4.** $a_n = 1 - 5n$
 −1, 3, −5, 7, −9   −4, −9, −14, −19, −24

Find an explicit formula for each sequence.

5. 2, 4, 6, 8, 10, . . . $a_n = 2n$
6. 1, 4, 9, 16, 25, . . . $a_n = n^2$
7. $1, \frac{1}{2}, \frac{1}{4}, \frac{1}{8}, \frac{1}{16}, \ldots$ $a_n = \frac{1}{2^{n-1}}$
8. 3, 3, 3, 3, 3, . . . $a_n = 3$

Find the next four terms of the sequence given by each recursive formula.

9. $a_1 = 6$ and $a_n = a_{n-1} + 4$ 10, 14, 18, 22
10. $a_1 = 4$ and $a_n = a_{n-1} + n$ 6, 9, 13, 18
11. $a_1 = 2$ and $a_n = a_{n-1} - 2$ 0, −2, −4, −6
12. $a_1 = \frac{1}{2}$ and $a_n = a_{n-1} + \frac{1}{4}$ $\frac{3}{4}, 1, \frac{5}{4}, \frac{3}{2}$

Find a recursive formula for each sequence.

13. 2, 4, 6, 8, 10, . . . $a_1 = 2$ and $a_n = a_{n-1} + 2$ **14.** 1, 3, 5, 7, 9, . . . $a_1 = 1$ and $a_n = a_{n-1} + 2$

15. Find an explicit formula for the sequence defined recursively by $a_1 = 3$ and $a_n = 3a_{n-1}$. $a_n = 3^n$

16. Thinking Critically   Find an example of two formulas that define sequences that agree on their first four terms, but differ on the fifth term and all succeeding terms.

Practice Exercises   Use appropriate technology.

Find the first five terms of the infinite sequence defined explicitly by each rule.

A **1.** $f(n) = n^2 - 3$ **2.** $f(n) = \cos n\pi$ **3.** $a_n = \dfrac{1}{n^2 + 1}$ **4.** $c_n = \left(-\dfrac{1}{2}\right)^n$
  −2, 1, 6, 13, 22   −1, 1, −1, 1, −1 $\frac{1}{2}, \frac{1}{5}, \frac{1}{10}, \frac{1}{17}, \frac{1}{26}$ $-\frac{1}{2}, \frac{1}{4}, -\frac{1}{8}, \frac{1}{16}, -\frac{1}{32}$

13.1 Sequences   **677**

For Example 7
Find a recursive formula for each sequence.
1. 21, 17, 13, 9, 5, 1, −3, . . .
  $a_1 = 21$ and $a_n = a_{n-1} - 4$
2. 10, 12, 16, 22, 30, 40, . . .
  $a_1 = 10$ and $a_n = a_{n-1} + 2(n - 1)$

Common Error   Students may neglect to specify the first term when giving a recursive formula. Have those students apply their formulas to two different initial terms and compare the results.

CLOSURE

Ask students to write you a letter explaining the difference(s) between an explicit formula and a recursive formula. Have them illustrate their explanation by finding both an explicit and recursive formula for the sequence 0, 3, 6, 9, 12, ...

INDEPENDENT PRACTICE

Assignment Guide
Basic: 1–21, 31–33, 35
Average: 13–37
Enriched: 18, 20, 22–47

Teacher's Resource Book
  Practice, page 88

Ⓡ Review
Exercises 17, 19, 21, 31, 35, and 45 review concepts of finding equations of conic sections, graphing functions, and solving compound interest problems.

Additional Answers
Class Exercises
16. Answers may vary.
  Example: $f(n) = \frac{1}{n}$; $g(n) = \frac{1}{n} + (n-1)(n-2)(n-3)(n-4)$

677

Find the 32nd term of the sequence given by each rule.

5. $f(n) = \frac{1}{2}n$ 16

6. $a_n = \left(\frac{1}{2}\right)^n$ $\frac{1}{4{,}294{,}967{,}296}$

Find an explicit formula for each sequence.

7. 1, 11, 21, 31, 41, 51, . . . $a_n = 10(n-1) + 1$

8. $-3, -5, -7, -9, -11, \ldots$ $a_n = -2n - 1$

9. $\frac{1}{3}, \frac{1}{9}, \frac{1}{27}, \frac{1}{81}, \frac{1}{243}, \ldots$ $a_n = \frac{1}{3^n}$

10. 0.1, 0.01, 0.001, 0.0001, 0.00001, . . . $a_n = (0.1)^n$

Find the next four terms of the sequence given by each recursive formula.

11. $a_1 = 24$ and $a_n = \frac{1}{2}a_{n-1}$ $12, 6, 3, \frac{3}{2}$

12. $a_1 = 2$, $a_2 = 1$, and $a_n = a_{n-1} + a_{n-2}$ 3, 4, 7, 11

Find a recursive formula for each sequence.

13. $-12, -7, -2, 3, 8, 13, \ldots$

14. 0.1, 0.01, 0.001, 0.0001, 0.00001, . . .

15. 10, 11, 13, 16, 20, 25, . . .

16. $3, -3, 3, -3, 3, -3, \ldots$

Ⓡ 17. Find the equation of the parabola with vertex $V(2, 1)$ and focus $F(2, 4)$. $y = \frac{1}{12}(x-2)^2 + 1$

18. **Writing in Mathematics**   Keep a journal recording all the sequences, numerical and nonnumerical, you encounter in a week. For example, the alphabet is a sequence of letters, and a phone book contains several different kinds of sequences (ordered lists).

Ⓡ 19. Find the equation of the ellipse with vertices $(0, \pm 8)$ and foci $(0, \pm 4)$. $\frac{x^2}{48} + \frac{y^2}{64} = 1$

20. **Thinking Critically**   Criticize this recursive formula for the sequence $a_1 = 2$ and $a_n = a_{n-1} - a_{n-2}$. Must give two initial terms.

Ⓡ 21. Find the equation of the circle with center $(4, -5)$ and point $P(7, 11)$.
$(x-4)^2 + (y+5)^2 = 265$

Find an explicit formula for the sequence defined by each recursive formula.

B   22. $a_1 = 6$ and $a_n = a_{n-1} + 6$ $a_n = 6n$

23. $a_1 = 1$ and $a_n = a_{n-1} + 8$ $a_n = 8n - 7$

24. $a_1 = 9$ and $a_n = -a_{n-1}$ $a_n = (-1)^{n+1}(9)$

25. $a_1 = 1$ and $a_n = 2a_{n-1} - 1$ $a_n = 1$

Use a calculator to find the first five terms of each sequence. Use the calculator's entire output for computing each term. Then round the term to four places.

26. $a_1 = 10$ and $a_n = \sqrt{a_{n-1}}$

27. $a_1 = 1.1$ and $a_n = (a_{n-1})^2$

28. $a_n = \ln n$

29. $a_n = e^n$

30. *Travel*   To save for a vacation trip, Bernice made an initial deposit of \$40 into her savings account. She then deposited \$15 into the account the first week, \$20 the second week, \$25 the third week, \$30 the fourth week, and so on until she had enough money for the trip. Write a recursive formula for the rule of the sequence. $a_1 = 55$ and $a_n = a_{n-1} + 5(n+2)$

Ⓡ 31. Graph: $f(x) = \frac{1}{x^2 + 1}$

32. Plot the points (n, a_n) for $a_n = \frac{1}{n^2 + 1}$ and $n = 1, 2, 3, \ldots, 10$.

33. **Thinking Critically**   What is the relationship between the *sequence* $a_n = \frac{1}{n^2 + 1}$ and the *real function* $f(x) = \frac{1}{x^2 + 1}$?

678   Chapter 13 Sequences and Series

34. *Number Theory*   The sequence of *prime numbers* is an example of a sequence for which no rule, either explicit or recursive, is known. Write the first ten terms of this sequence. 2, 3, 5, 7, 11, 13, 17, 19, 23, 29

35. *Finance*   Recall that if a sum of money P is invested at an annual rate of interest r compounded k times a year for t years, then at the end of the t years the value of the investment is given by $A = P\left(1 + \dfrac{r}{k}\right)^{kt}$. A baby is given a gift of \$200 that is invested at an annual interest rate of 8% compounded quarterly. Let a_n represent the value of the investment at the end of n years and find the sequence $a_1, a_2, \ldots, a_{10}$.

36. *Philately*   A stamp dealer plans to sell three sheets of his 90-sheet collection each week until the collection is completely sold. Write a recursive formula for the rule of the sequence of the cumulative number of sheets sold each week. For what values of n is the rule valid? $a_1 = 3$ and $a_n = a_{n-1} + 3$; $1 \le n \le 30$

37. *Programming*   Because of the repetitive nature of the formula for most sequences, the computer is a good tool for generating terms of a sequence. Write a program that generates the first 20 terms of the Fibonacci sequence. If you can, modify the program so that the user can choose the number of terms to generate.

38. *Entomology*   The male bee (drone) has only one parent, a mother, while the female bee has two parents, a mother and a father. Let a_n be the number of ancestors in the nth generation of the male bee's "family tree," with the bee himself the first generation ($n = 1$). For example, the male bee has one parent ($n = 2$), two grandparents ($n = 3$), and three great grandparents ($n = 4$). Why? Find the first eight terms of the sequence a_n and find a pattern. Then identify the sequence. 1, 1, 2, 3, 5, 8, 13, 21; Fibonacci

39. *Aquaculture*   One model for predicting the number of lobsters caught yearly is based on the assumption that the number of lobsters caught in one year is the average of the number caught in the two previous years. Let L_n be the number of lobsters caught in year n, and suppose that 120,000 were caught in year 1 and 360,000 were caught in year 2. Find a recursive formula for L_n and compute the first six terms of the sequence.

40. *Biology*   Suppose that a bacteria colony doubles in size every day, and that on the first day of observation there are 200 bacteria. Find a recursive formula for the number of bacteria b_n on the nth day of observation. How many bacteria are there on the fifth day? $b_1 = 200$ and $b_n = 2b_{n-1}$; $b_5 = 3200$

41. *Botany*   The height of a plant is measured once a month and its growth is charted. The first month the height is recorded as 6.0 cm, and the height increases by 12% per month for a year. Find a recursive formula for the height h_n of the plant in the nth month, and use the formula to generate the first ten terms of the sequence h_n.

13.1 Sequences   **679**

Have students write a paragraph describing how to obtain the terms of the Fibonacci sequence without using symbols like a_n or F_n.

Enrichment
Consider strings of length n composed of 0's and 1's. Identify as code words those strings that do not contain two consecutive 0's. For example, 010, 110, and 111 are code words of length 3, but 001 and 100 are not. Let a_n be the number of code words of length n. Write the first four terms of the sequence, and then find a recursive formula for a_n.
$a_1 = 2$, $a_2 = 3$, $a_3 = 5$, $a_4 = 8$; $a_1 = 2$, $a_2 = 3$, $a_n = a_{n-1} + a_{n-2}$

Additional Answers

46. $F_1 = \dfrac{1}{\sqrt{5}}\left(\dfrac{1+\sqrt{5}}{2}\right) - \dfrac{1}{\sqrt{5}}\left(\dfrac{1-\sqrt{5}}{2}\right)$

$ = \dfrac{1+\sqrt{5}-1+\sqrt{5}}{2\sqrt{5}} = \dfrac{2\sqrt{5}}{2\sqrt{5}} = 1$

$F_2 = \dfrac{1}{\sqrt{5}}\left(\dfrac{1+\sqrt{5}}{2}\right)^2 - \dfrac{1}{\sqrt{5}}\left(\dfrac{1-\sqrt{5}}{2}\right)^2$

$ = \dfrac{6+2\sqrt{5}-6+2\sqrt{5}}{4\sqrt{5}} = \dfrac{4\sqrt{5}}{4\sqrt{5}} = 1$

$F_3 = \dfrac{1}{\sqrt{5}}\left(\dfrac{1+\sqrt{5}}{2}\right)^3 - \dfrac{1}{\sqrt{5}}\left(\dfrac{1-\sqrt{5}}{2}\right)^3$

$ = \dfrac{16+8\sqrt{5}-16+8\sqrt{5}}{8\sqrt{5}} = \dfrac{16\sqrt{5}}{8\sqrt{5}}$

$ = 2$

$F_4 = \dfrac{1}{\sqrt{5}}\left(\dfrac{1+\sqrt{5}}{2}\right)^4 - \dfrac{1}{\sqrt{5}}\left(\dfrac{1-\sqrt{5}}{2}\right)^4$

$ = \dfrac{14+6\sqrt{5}-14+6\sqrt{5}}{4\sqrt{5}}$

$ = \dfrac{12\sqrt{5}}{4\sqrt{5}} = 3$

An electronic spreadsheet is an excellent tool for studying sequences that are defined recursively. In particular, it allows the user to see almost instantly the effect of changes in the initial term(s).

42. *Technology*   Set up a spreadsheet to generate terms of the Fibonacci sequence by entering "1" in cells $A1$ and $A2$ and the expression $+A1 + A2$ in cell $A3$. Then *replicate*, or *copy*, the expression in $A3$ down column A. For example, in LOTUS 1-2-3, use the command COPY FROM A3 TO A4.A25 to generate the first 25 terms of the Fibonacci sequence. Then change the numbers in cells $A1$ and $A2$ and recalculate. What are the effects of the initial values on the Fibonacci sequence?

43. **Thinking Critically**   If you use initial values $a_1 = 1$ and $a_2 = 3$ in Exercise 42, the resulting numbers are called the Lucas Numbers named for François Eduard Lucas (1842–1891), who discovered many of the properties of the Fibonacci numbers. How are the Lucas numbers related to the Fibonacci numbers? $a_n = F_{n-1} + F_{n+1}$

44. *Technology*   Repeat Exercise 42 for the sequence defined recursively by $a_1 = 1$, $a_2 = 2$, and $a_n = a_{n-1}a_{n-2}$. Examine the effects of changing the relative sizes of a_1 and a_2.

45. Sequences of complex numbers defined recursively are central to the study of *fractals*. An important sequence in this field is defined by the formula $a_1 = 1 + i$ and $a_n = (a_{n-1})^2$. Use this definition to generate the first five terms of the sequence. $1 + i,\ 2i,\ -4,\ 16,\ 256$

46. An explicit formula for the Fibonacci numbers is difficult to obtain. If F_n is the nth Fibonacci number, verify that

$$F_n = \frac{1}{\sqrt{5}}\left(\frac{1+\sqrt{5}}{2}\right)^n - \frac{1}{\sqrt{5}}\left(\frac{1-\sqrt{5}}{2}\right)^n \qquad \text{for } n = 1, 2, 3, \text{ and } 4$$

47. Find the fraction that is in the 900th position of the sequence

$$\frac{1}{1}, \frac{1}{2}, \frac{2}{2}, \frac{1}{2}, \frac{1}{3}, \frac{2}{3}, \frac{3}{3}, \frac{2}{3}, \frac{1}{3}, \frac{1}{4}, \frac{2}{4}, \frac{3}{4}, \frac{4}{4}, \frac{3}{4}, \frac{2}{4}, \frac{1}{4}, \cdots \frac{1}{30}$$

Review

1. Show that the product of a complex number $a + bi$ and its conjugate is a real number. $(a + bi)(a - bi) = a^2 - b^2i^2 = a^2 + b^2$

2. Evaluate the determinant using the elements in the third row and their minors.
$\begin{vmatrix} 1 & 1 & -2 \\ -3 & 1 & 0 \\ 4 & -5 & 9 \end{vmatrix}$ 14

3. The first three terms of an arithmetic progression are $x - 1$, $x + 4$, and $2x + 2$. Find the value of x. 7

Identify the conic represented by each curve.

4. $x^2 - 6y + y^2 = 0$ circle

5. $x^2 + 9y^2 - 4 = 0$ ellipse

6. The sum of a number and its reciprocal is $2\frac{1}{12}$. Find the number. $\frac{3}{4}$ or $\frac{4}{3}$

680   Chapter 13 Sequences and Series

Arithmetic and Geometric Sequences

Objectives: *To find specified terms and the common difference in an arithmetic sequence*
To find specified terms and the common ratio in a geometric sequence
To find arithmetic and geometric means

Focus

Numerical sequences play an important role in the work of health professionals. When a medication is being administered intravenously to a patient at a constant rate, a medical attendant needs to be able to determine how much medication the patient has absorbed at any time. For example, the sequence 2.1, 4.2, 6.3, 8.4, 10.5 might represent the number of cubic centimeters of medicine the patient absorbed at the end of each hour for 5 hours.

In another case, a patient may have been injected with a single dose of medication that decays at the rate of 30% per hour. The number of milligrams of the substance remaining in the patient's body at the end of each hour for 5 hours might be represented by the sequence 100, 70, 49, 34, 24.

The above cases represent useful applications of two very different types of sequences. Knowing which type of sequence to use and how to apply it is critical in the work of health professionals.

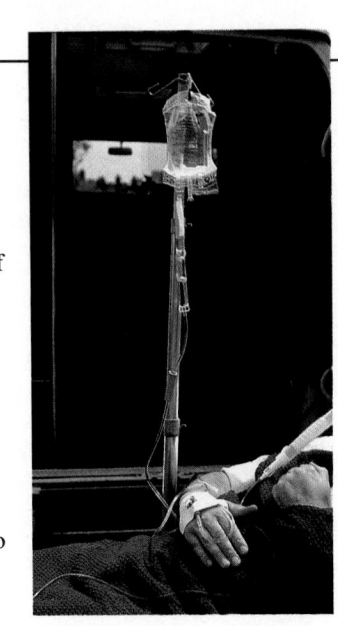

Classifying mathematical objects and ideas is a typical and useful aspect of doing mathematics. In this lesson, two important classes of sequences are identified. Some conclusions are then drawn about each class. First, examine the following sequences and the most likely recursive formula for each sequence.

Sequence	*Recursive Formula*
8, 16, 24, 32, 40, 48, . . .	$a_1 = 8$ and $a_n = a_{n-1} + 8$
1, 7, 13, 19, 25, 31, . . .	$a_1 = 1$ and $a_n = a_{n-1} + 6$
10, 7, 4, 1, −2, −5, . . .	$a_1 = 10$ and $a_n = a_{n-1} + (−3)$

Note that in each sequence, each term is formed by adding a constant to the preceding term. This is also the case with the first sequence in the Focus. Sequences that are formed in this way are *arithmetic sequences*.

13.2 Arithmetic and Geometric Sequences **681**

LESSON PLAN

Vocabulary
arithmetic means
arithmetic sequence
common difference
common ratio
geometric means
geometric sequence
graph of a sequence

FOCUS

Sequences can be found in a wide variety of situations, from the sequence of house numbers on a street to a listing of telephone numbers in a phone book to the sequence of scores a student has earned in weekly math quizzes. Sequences are of special interest when known values can be used to predict later values as described in modeling. Dosages of medicine, daily blood sugar, blood pressure, and heart rate readings can be viewed as sequences, as can hourly temperature readings, weekly stress test results and other information. Often students are particularly interested in applications of math in medicine, and they may enjoy looking for other examples.

- An arithmetic sequence with a small common difference can be illustrated effectively on a number line. The distances between pairs of adjacent points will be equal. Compare this with the graph of the sequence on the Cartesian plane.
- Have students make up their own sets of arithmetic and geometric sequences, identifying the common difference or ratio in each case.
- Point out that the explicit formulas for the general term of an arithmetic and geometric sequence are not proven in this lesson. They are only illustrated for a few cases. The formulas can be proven after Lesson 13.4, when the tool of mathematical induction is available.

Alternative Learning Styles

Students who are subjective learners respond better when they can relate new ideas to themselves and their experiences. The use of examples, like the sequence of their ages each time they are eligible to vote in a presidential election or the sequence of their ages in the various census years, is therefore encouraged.

GUIDED PRACTICE

For Example 1

Determine which of the following sequences are arithmetic. For each arithmetic sequence, identify the common difference.

1. 5, 10, 15, 20, 25, 30, . . .
arithmetic; $d = 5$

2. 1, -2, 4, -8, 16, -32, . . .
not arithmetic

3. 16, 9, 2, -5, -12, . . .
arithmetic; $d = -7$

4. 1, 10, 11, 21, 32, 53, . . .
not arithmetic

A sequence $a_1, a_2, a_3, \ldots$ is an **arithmetic sequence** or *arithmetic progression* if there is a constant d for which

$$a_n = a_{n-1} + d$$

for all integers $n > 1$. The constant d represents the **common difference** of the sequence, and $d = a_n - a_{n-1}$ for all integers $n > 1$.

What is the common difference in the first sequence of the Focus?

Example 1 Determine which of the following sequences are arithmetic. For each arithmetic sequence, name the common difference.
 a. 1, 3, 5, 7, 9, . . .   **b.** 1, 2, 4, 7, 11, . . .
 c. 20, 12, 4, -4, -12, . . .   **d.** 9.3, 9.9, 10.5, 11.1, 11.7, . . .

Sequences (a), (c), and (d) are arithmetic, since in each of these sequences the difference between each term and the term before it is constant. To show that sequence (b) is *not* arithmetic, note that $a_2 - a_1 = 2 - 1 = 1$ while $a_3 - a_2 = 4 - 2 = 2$.

a. For the sequence 1, 3, 5, 7, 9, . . . , the common difference is 2.

c. For the sequence 20, 12, 4, -4, -12, . . . , the common difference is -8.

d. For the sequence 9.3, 9.9, 10.5, 11.1, 11.7, . . . , the common difference is 0.6.

By definition, an arithmetic sequence is given by a recursive formula. It is always possible to give an explicit formula for an arithmetic sequence as well. For example, consider the arithmetic sequence 1, 7, 13, 19, 25, . . . discussed earlier. For this sequence, the common difference is 6, and each term of the sequence can be obtained by adding a certain number of sixes to the initial term, 1.

$$
\begin{aligned}
a_1 &= 1 \\
a_2 &= 7 = 1 + 6 \\
a_3 &= 13 = 1 + 2 \cdot 6 \\
a_4 &= 19 = 1 + 3 \cdot 6 \\
a_5 &= 25 = 1 + 4 \cdot 6 \\
&\;\;\vdots
\end{aligned}
$$

Notice that any term a_n of an arithmetic sequence is the sum of the initial term a_1 and a multiple of the common difference d.

$$
\begin{aligned}
a_1 &= a_1 \\
a_2 &= a_1 + d \\
a_3 &= a_2 + d = (a_1 + d) + d = a_1 + 2d \\
a_4 &= a_3 + d = (a_1 + 2d) + d = a_1 + 3d \\
a_5 &= a_4 + d = (a_1 + 3d) + d = a_1 + 4d \\
&\;\;\vdots
\end{aligned}
$$

Thinking Critically
The common difference in the Focus is 2.1.

This pattern continues, and is generalized as follows.

> The *general term* a_n of an arithmetic sequence with common difference d may be expressed explicitly as
>
> $$a_n = a_1 + (n - 1)d$$

This result is useful for finding specific terms of an arithmetic sequence.

Example 2   Find the 102nd term of the sequence 5, 13, 21, 29, 37, 45, ...

This is an arithmetic sequence with $a_1 = 5$ and $d = 8$. Therefore,

$$a_{102} = a_1 + 101d = 5 + (101)(8) = 813$$

The **graph** of a sequence $a_1, a_2, a_3, . . .$ consists of the points (n, a_n) where n is a positive integer. Notice that the graph will be a discrete set of points rather than a continuous line or curve.

Graph of a sequence

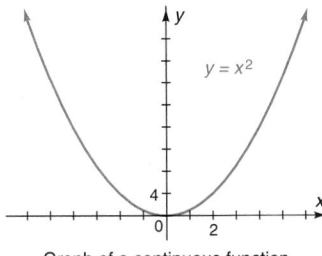

Graph of a continuous function

In the exercises, you are asked to show that the points that make up the graph of an arithmetic sequence fall on a straight line. For example, the graph of the sequence $-6, -1, 4, 9, 14, . . .$ is on a rising straight line, as shown at the right.

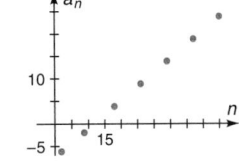

If any two terms of an arithmetic sequence are known, the sequence is completely determined.

Example 3   In an arithmetic sequence, $a_5 = 24$ and $a_9 = 40$. Find an explicit formula for the general term of the sequence.

To find an explicit formula for the sequence, the values of a_1 and d are needed. Each of the known terms can be expressed in terms of a_1 and d: $a_5 = a_1 + 4d$ and $a_9 = a_1 + 8d$. This gives a linear system in the two variables a_1 and d.

$$40 = a_1 + 8d \quad \text{and} \quad 24 = a_1 + 4d$$

Solving the linear system yields $d = 4$ and $a_1 = 8$. Thus, the general term of the sequence is $a_n = 8 + (n - 1) \cdot 4$ or $a_n = 4 + 4n$.

13.2 Arithmetic and Geometric Sequences   **683**

For Example 2
1. Find the 53rd term of the sequence 3, 11, 19, 27, 35, ... $a_{53} = 419$
2. Find the 19th term of the sequence 65, 54, 43, 32, 21, ... $a_{19} = -133$

For Example 3
1. In an arithmetic sequence, $a_3 = 15$ and $a_8 = 50$. Find an explicit formula for the general term. $a_n = 7n - 6$
2. In an arithmetic sequence, $a_4 = 59$ and $a_9 = -11$. Find an explicit formula for the general term. $a_n = 115 - 14n$

For Example 4
1. Find two arithmetic means between 8 and 56. 24, 40
2. Find four arithmetic means between 1 and −89. −17, −35, −53, −71

Observe that if a, b, and c are three consecutive terms in an arithmetic sequence, then the middle term is the "average" of the other two, that is, $\frac{a + c}{2}$. (You will be asked to prove this in the exercises.) The number b is then referred to as *the arithmetic mean* of a and c. The following definition allows this idea to be generalized to more than one arithmetic mean.

> If the numbers $a_1, a_2, \ldots, a_{k-1}, a_k$ form an arithmetic sequence, then $a_2, a_3, \ldots, a_{k-1}$ are **arithmetic means** between a_1 and a_k.

It is possible to locate any number of arithmetic means between two numbers.

Example 4 Find three arithmetic means between 9 and 29.

For the sequence 9, a_2, a_3, a_4, 29, $a_1 = 9$ and $a_5 = 29$. By the formula $a_n = a_1 + (n − 1)d$, $a_5 = a_1 + 4d$ so that $29 = 9 + 4d$. Thus, $d = 5$, and so

$$a_2 = a_1 + d = 9 + 5 = 14$$
$$a_3 = a_1 + 2d = 9 + 10 = 19$$
$$a_4 = a_1 + 3d = 9 + 15 = 24$$

The three arithmetic means are then 14, 19, and 24.

A second important class of sequences is illustrated by the second sequence in the Focus. It is the class of *geometric sequences*, in which each term after the first is formed by *multiplying* the preceding term by a constant.

> A sequence $a_1, a_2, a_3, \ldots$ is a **geometric sequence,** or a *geometric progression*, if there is a constant r for which
>
> $$a_n = a_{n-1} \cdot r$$
>
> for all integers $n > 1$. The constant r is called the **common ratio** of the sequence, and $r = \frac{a_n}{a_{n-1}}$, for all integers $n > 1$.

The sequence 4, 8, 16, 32, 64, . . . is geometric with common ratio $r = 2$. The sequence 1, $-\frac{2}{3}$, $\frac{4}{9}$, $-\frac{8}{27}$, $\frac{16}{81}$, . . . is geometric with common ratio $r = -\frac{2}{3}$. *What is the common ratio for the second sequence in the Focus?*

Like the arithmetic sequence, a geometric sequence is given by a recursive formula. To find an explicit formula for the geometric sequence 7, 14, 28, 56, 112, . . . , note first that the common ratio of this sequence is 2. Each term in the sequence can be expressed as the initial term multiplied by some power of 2.

$a_1 = 7$	$a_2 = 14 = 7 \cdot 2$	$a_3 = 28 = 7 \cdot 4 = 7 \cdot 2^2$
$a_4 = 56 = 7 \cdot 8 = 7 \cdot 2^3$	$a_5 = 112 = 7 \cdot 16 = 7 \cdot 2^4$	and so on

684   Chapter 13 Sequences and Series

Thinking Critically
The common ratio in the Focus is 0.7.

In general, if a_n is the general term of a geometric sequence with common ratio r, a_n may be expressed in terms of r and the initial term a_1. Observe that

$$a_1 = a_1$$
$$a_2 = a_1 \cdot r$$
$$a_3 = a_2 \cdot r = (a_1 \cdot r) \cdot r = a_1 \cdot r^2$$
$$a_4 = a_3 \cdot r = (a_1 \cdot r^2) \cdot r = a_1 \cdot r^3$$
$$a_5 = a_4 \cdot r = (a_1 \cdot r^3) \cdot r = a_1 \cdot r^4$$
$$\vdots$$

The *general term a_n* of a geometric sequence with common ratio r may be expressed explicitly as

$$a_n = a_1 r^{n-1}$$

Example 5   Find an explicit formula for the geometric sequence 4, 20, 100, 500, . . . , and use it to obtain the ninth term.

The common ratio of this sequence is $\frac{20}{4} = 5$, and the initial term is 4. By the formula $a_n = a_1 r^{n-1} = 4 \cdot 5^{n-1}$, so

$$a_9 = 4 \cdot 5^8 = 4 \cdot 390{,}625 = 1{,}562{,}500$$

Modeling

A nurse is charting the amount of medication remaining in a patient's body. How can she determine the concentration of the medication at any given time?

The amount of medication in a patient's body measured in intervals over a period of time will form a sequence of numbers. After observing several terms of the sequence, the nurse can determine whether the sequence is arithmetic, geometric, or neither. The amount of medication can then be modeled using the appropriate rule for the sequence, if the rule is known. For an arithmetic sequence, use $a_n = a_1 + (n-1)d$. For a geometric sequence, use $a_n = a_1 \cdot r^{n-1}$.

Example 6   *Medicine*   At noon, 1000 mg of medicine is administered to a patient. At the end of each hour, the concentration of the medication is 60% of the amount present at the beginning of the hour.
  a. What portion of the medication remains in the patient's body at 4:00 p.m. if no additional medication has been administered?
  b. If a second dosage of 1000 mg is administered at 2:00 p.m., what is the total concentration of the medication in the patient's body immediately following this dosage?

  a. The model is $a_n = a_1 r^{n-1}$. Since you need to determine the concentration at 4:00 p.m., $n = 5$ and $a_5 = 1000(0.6)^4$. The amount of medication in the patient's body at 4:00 p.m. will be 129.6 mg.

For Example 5
1. Find an explicit formula for the geometric sequence 33, 99, 297, 891, . . . and use it to obtain the eleventh term.
   $a_n = 11(3^n)$; $a_{11} = 1{,}948{,}617$
2. Find an explicit formula for the geometric sequence 120, 60, 30, 15, 7.5, . . . and use it to obtain the eighth term.
   $a_n = 240\left(\frac{1}{2}\right)^n$; $a_8 = 0.9375$

Modeling
The modeling in this lesson provides a real world application of mathematics in medicine, and should only be used for the purposes of teaching mathematics.

For Example 6
At 8:00 a.m., 750 mg of medicine is given to a patient. At the end of each hour the concentration of the medication is three-fourths the amount present at the beginning of the hour.
1. What portion of the medicine remains in the patient's body at noon if no additional medication has been given? 237.30 mg
2. If a second dosage of 750 mg is given at noon, what is the total concentration of the medication in the patient's body immediately following this dose? 987.30 mg

For Example 7

1. Locate two geometric means between 7 and 15.379. 9.1, 11.83
2. Locate three geometric means
   between 8 and 40.5.
   $-12, 18, -27; 12, 18, 27$

Common Error Students may neglect to find the second possible triple of geometric means between 8
and 40.5. Have these students examine a geometric sequence with
negative common ratio to see why
they should look for two sets of geometric means when an odd number
of geometric means is desired.

For Example 8

Find the mean proportional, if it exists, between each pair of numbers.

1. 9 and 28 15.87
2. -6 and 15 none
3. -6 and -15 -9.49

b. At 2:00 p.m. the medication from the first dosage is $a_3 = 1000(0.6)^2$, which is 360 mg. The total amount of medication in the patient's body just after the second dosage is administered is 1360 mg.

The terms between any two terms of a geometric sequence are called *geometric means*. This definition is analogous to that of arithmetic means.

If the numbers $a_1, a_2, \ldots, a_{k-1}, a_k$ form a geometric sequence, then $a_2, a_3, \ldots, a_{k-1}$ are called **geometric means** between a_1 and a_k.

Any number of geometric means may be located between two positive numbers.

Example 7 Locate three geometric means between 4 and 324.

The three means form a geometric sequence with 4 and 324: 4, a_2, a_3, a_4, 324.

$$324 = a_5$$
$$324 = 4 \cdot r^4 \qquad a_n = a_1 \cdot r^{n-1}$$
$$81 = r^4$$

Note that two values of r satisfy this equation, $r = 3$ and $r = -3$. Each determines a geometric sequence with $a_1 = 4$ and $a_5 = 324$. For $r = 3$, the sequence is 4, 12, 36, 108, 324. For $r = -3$, the sequence is 4, -12, 36, -108, 324. Thus, there are two sets of three geometric means between 4 and 324: 12, 36, 108 and -12, 36, -108.

A single geometric mean between two numbers is called *the geometric mean*, or *mean proportional*, between the two numbers. Notice that if m is the mean proportional between a and b, then a, m, and b form a geometric sequence. This implies that for some real number r, $ar = m$ and $mr = b$, so that $\frac{m}{a} = \frac{b}{m}$ or $m^2 = ab$.

For a and b both positive or both negative, $m = \pm\sqrt{ab}$. It is customary to let $m = \sqrt{ab}$ when a and b are both positive, and $m = -\sqrt{ab}$ when a and b are both negative. When a and b have opposite signs, there is no *real* mean proportional. In fact, it is not possible to find any *odd* number of *real* geometric means between two numbers having opposite signs.

Example 8 Find the mean proportional m (if one exists) between each pair of numbers.
     a. 10 and 56   **b.** -42 and -378 **c.** 1 and -16

a. Since 10 and 56 are both positive, $m = \sqrt{10 \cdot 56} = \sqrt{560} \approx 23.66$.

b. Since -42 and -378 are both negative, $m = -\sqrt{(-42)(-378)} = -\sqrt{15{,}876} = -126$.

c. No real mean proportional exists between two numbers having opposite signs. Thus, there is no mean proportional between 1 and -16.

686   Chapter 13 Sequences and Series

Class Exercises

Determine whether each sequence is arithmetic, geometric, or neither. For arithmetic sequences, find the common difference d; for geometric sequences, find the common ratio r.

1. 2, 4, 6, 8, 10, . . . arithmetic; 2

2. 2, 4, 5, 5, 4, 2, -1, . . . neither

3. 5, 18, 31, 44, 57, . . . arithmetic; 13

4. 5, 15, 45, 135, 405, . . . geometric; 3

5. 2, -12, 72, -432, 2592, . . . geometric; -6

6. 6.5, 6.2, 5.9, 5.6, 5.3, . . . arithmetic; -0.3

7. 1, 3, 5, 7, 11, . . . neither

8. 9, 7.2, 5.76, 4.608, 3.6864, . . . geometric; 0.8

Find an explicit formula for the sequence in each indicated exercise and use it to find the 12th term.

9. Exercise 3   **10.** Exercise 4   **11.** Exercise 5   **12.** Exercise 8

13. Find four arithmetic means between 2 and 37. 9, 16, 23, 30

14. In an arithmetic sequence, $a_4 = 11$ and $a_{11} = 39$. Find an explicit formula for the general term a_n. $a_n = 4n - 5$

15. Find four geometric means between 3 and 3072. 12, 48, 192, 768

Find the mean proportional (if one exists) between each pair of numbers.

16. 6 and 17 $\sqrt{102}$ **17.** -5 and 43 none   **18.** -7 and -196 $-14\sqrt{7}$

19. Thinking Critically   What does the sign of the common difference tell about an arithmetic sequence?

Practice Exercises   Use appropriate technology.

Determine whether each sequence is arithmetic, geometric, or neither. For arithmetic sequences, find the common difference d; for geometric sequences, find the common ratio r.

A **1.** 62, 64, 66, 68, 70, . . . arithmetic; 2

2. 1, 3, 9, 27, 81, . . . geometric; 3

3. 15, 9, 3, -3, -9, -15, . . . arithmetic; -6

4. 8, 16, 24, 30, 36, 42, . . . neither

5. 100, -50, 25, $-12\frac{1}{2}$, $6\frac{1}{4}$, . . . geometric; $-\frac{1}{2}$

6. 2, 3, 6, 18, 108, . . . neither

7. 9.27, 9.29, 9.31, 9.33, 9.35, . . . arithmetic; 0.02

8. 1, 0.1, 0.01, 0.001, 0.0001, . . . geometric; 0.1

9. Writing in Mathematics   Write a paragraph comparing and contrasting arithmetic sequences with geometric sequences.

Find an explicit formula for the sequence in each indicated exercise and use it to find the 16th term.

10. Exercise 1   **11.** Exercise 3   **12.** Exercise 5   **13.** Exercise 8

14. Find three arithmetic means between 50 and 66. 54, 58, 62

Find an explicit formula for the general term of the arithmetic sequence with the given terms.

15. $a_3 = 14$ and $a_6 = 29$ $a_n = 5n - 1$

16. $a_7 = -10$ and $a_{13} = -48$

$a_n = 28 + (n - 1)\left(-\frac{19}{3}\right)$

13.2 Arithmetic and Geometric Sequences   **687**

CLOSURE

Have students summarize the lesson in their math journals.

INDEPENDENT PRACTICE

Assignment Guide
Basic: 1–23, 28–29, 39, Project
Average: 9, 15–39, Project
Enriched: 9, 25–46, Project

Teacher's Resource Book
  Practice, page 89

® Review
Exercises 19, 21, 27, and 37 review the concepts of graphing sequences and their corresponding functions, determining the multiplicative inverse of a matrix, and determining the maximum height of a projectile.

Project
Students who are particularly adept at programming may want to experiment with different criteria by which the program can compare the two sequences that are input.

Additional Answers
Class Exercises
9. $a_n = 13n - 8$; 148
10. $a_n = 5(3^{n-1})$; 885,735
11. $a_n = 2(-6)^{n-1}$; $-725,594,112$
12. $a_n = 9(0.8)^{n-1}$; 0.7731
19. If $d > 0$ the sequence is increasing, and if $d < 0$ the sequence is decreasing.

Practice Exercises
10. $a_n = 2n + 60$; 92
11. $a_n = 21 - 6n$; -75
12. $a_n = 100\left(-\frac{1}{2}\right)^{n-1}$; -0.0030518
13. $a_n = (0.1)^{n-1}$; 1×10^{-15}

Writing in Mathematics
9. Answers may vary. Both have explicit formulas associated with them. For a geometric sequence with common ratio $x > 1$, and a corresponding arithmetic sequence with common difference x, the geometric sequence increases more quickly than the arithmetic sequence. An arithmetic sequence can change signs at most once; a geometric sequence either keeps the same sign throughout or alternates signs.

Lesson Quiz

Determine whether each sequence is arithmetic, geometric, or neither. For arithmetic sequences, find the common difference d; for geometric sequences find the common ratio r.

1. 6, 15, 24, 33, 42, ...
   arithmetic; $d = 9$

2. 6, 15, 23, 30, 36, 41, ...
   neither

3. 6, 9, 13.5, 20.25, 30.375, ...
   geometric; $r = 1.5$

4. 7, -7, 7, -7, 7, -7, 7, ...
   geometric; $r = -1$

5. 100, 81, 62, 43, 24, ...
   arithmetic; $d = -19$

6. In an arithmetic sequence, $a_3 = 48$ and $a_7 = -12$. Find an explicit formula for the general term and use it to find a_{10}.
   $a_n = 93 - 15n; a_{10} = -57$

7. Find an explicit formula for the geometric sequence 5, 5.5, 6.05, 6.655, ... and use it to find a_9.
   $a_n = (5)(1.1)^{n-1}; a_9 = 10.7179$

8. Find two arithmetic means between 18 and 57. 31, 44

9. Find two geometric means between 18 and 60.75. 27, 40.5

10. Find the mean proportional between -10 and -36. -18.9737

Additional Answers

22. $b = a + (n - 1)d; c = b + (n - 1)d; \dfrac{a + c}{2} = \dfrac{a + b + (n-1)d}{2} = \dfrac{a + (n-1)d + b}{2} = \dfrac{2b}{2} = b$

26. Since they have opposite signs, there must be an odd number of sign changes when the geometric means are added. Thus, there must be an even number of geometric means to make this possible.

27. $\begin{bmatrix} 7 & 6 & -3 \\ 2 & 2 & -1 \\ -6 & -5 & 3 \end{bmatrix}$

17. Find the mean proportional between -11 and -27. $-3\sqrt{33}$

18. *Medicine* A patient is given 1000 mg of medicine at noon. At the end of an hour, the amount of medication present in the patient's body is 75% of the amount present at the beginning of the hour. How much of this medication will be present in the patient's body at 8:00 p.m.? 100.11 mg

Ⓡ 19. Graph the function $y = x^2 - 1$ and the sequence $a_n = n^2 - 1$ on the same set of axes.

20. Find the first five terms of the sequence defined by $a_1 = 4$, $a_2 = 3$ and $a_n = 2a_{n-2} - a_{n-1}$. 4, 3, 5, 1, 9

Ⓡ 21. Compare and contrast the graphs of the function $f(x) = e^x$ and the sequence $a_n = e^n$.

B 22. Prove that if a, b, and c are three consecutive terms of an arithmetic sequence, then $b = \dfrac{a + c}{2}$.

23. Find three geometric means between 6 and 486. 18, 54, 162 or -18, 54, -162

24. Find four geometric means between -3 and -3072. -12, -48, -192, -768

25. Find the mean proportional between -10 and 56. none

26. **Thinking Critically** Explain why it isn't possible to find an odd number of geometric means between two numbers of opposite signs.

Ⓡ 27. Find the multiplicative inverse of the matrix $\begin{bmatrix} 1 & -3 & 0 \\ 0 & 3 & 1 \\ 2 & -1 & 2 \end{bmatrix}$.

28. The arithmetic mean between two terms of a sequence is 14 and one of the terms is -4. What is the other? 32

29. The mean proportional between two terms is 70 and one of the terms is 98. What is the other? 50

30. *Real Estate* A house purchased for $56,000 appreciates at a rate of 5% a year. Find a sequence representing the value of the house for 8 years.

31. *Economics* Two fast food restaurants start their part-time employees with $5.00/h. Restaurant A promises a $0.30/h raise every 3 months for the first year. Restaurant B promises a 4% raise every 3 months for the first year. At which restaurant will a new employee's salary be higher after 1 year? restaurant A

32. *Economics* A firm offers a job candidate a starting salary of $26,000 with a guaranteed minimum annual raise of $900. What would be the minimum salary this offer represents for the candidate's ninth year with the firm? $33,200

33. *Economics* Compare the offer of Exercise 32 with an offer of a starting salary of $27,500 with a guaranteed minimum annual raise of $700. How do they compare for the fifth year? The tenth year?

34. *Physics* A ball is dropped from a height of 10 m, and on each bounce it rises to about seven-eighths of its previous height. How high does the ball rise on its fifth bounce? 5.1291 m

35. *Biology* A colony of 300 bacteria doubles every day beginning on September 1. If b_n represents the number of bacteria on the nth day, write an explicit formula for b_n. How many bacteria are there on September 6? $b_n = 300(2^{n-1})$; 9600

688   Chapter 13 Sequences and Series

19.

21.

36. *Sports* A runner begins training on May 1 by running a mile, and increases the length of the run by 0.1 mi/day. Find the length of the run on May 21. 3 mi

37. *Physics* A projectile is given an initial upward velocity of 32 ft/s, and its height after t seconds is given by $h = 32t - 16t^2$. Find the maximum height the projectile will reach. 16 ft

38. *Genealogy* Assume there are 30 years in a generation. How many direct ancestors (parents, grandparents, and so on) did you have 300 years ago? 1024

Let a_n be the general term of an arithmetic sequence with common difference d.

39. Two representative points of the graph of this sequence are $P(n, a_1 + (n - 1)d)$ and $Q(k, a_1 + (k - 1)d)$ where n and k are positive integers. Show that all points of the sequence are on a straight line with slope d.

40. Use the results of Exercise 39 to find the equation of the line on which the points of the arithmetic sequence lie. $y = dx + (a_1 - d)$

Prove each of the following:

41. If $a_1, a_2, a_3, \ldots$ is an arithmetic sequence and c is a constant, then $a_1 + c$, $a_2 + c, a_3 + c, \ldots$ is also an arithmetic sequence.

42. If $a_1, a_2, a_3, \ldots$ and $b_1, b_2, b_3, \ldots$ are both arithmetic sequences, then $a_1 + b_1, a_2 + b_2, a_3 + b_3, \ldots$ is also an arithmetic sequence.

43. If $a_1, a_2, a_3, \ldots$ is a geometric sequence and c is a constant $(c \neq 0)$, then $ca_1, ca_2, ca_3, \ldots$ is also a geometric sequence.

44. If $a_1, a_2, a_3, \ldots$ is a geometric sequence, then $(a_1)^2, (a_2)^2, (a_3)^2, \ldots$ is also a geometric sequence.

45. Three numbers in arithmetic progression have a sum of 27. If 2 is subtracted from the first number and 14 is added to the third number, the resulting numbers are in geometric progression. Find the three original numbers. 5, 9, 13 and 29, 9, −11

46. When the square of the geometric mean of two numbers is subtracted from the square of their arithmetic mean, the result is 25. Find the result when the square of the arithmetic mean is subtracted from the arithmetic mean of their squares. 25

Project

Write a computer program to generate the terms of a geometric sequence $a, ar,$ $ar^2, ar^3, \ldots, ar^{n-1}$ and the terms of the arithmetic sequence $b, b + d, b + 2d,$ $b + 3d, \ldots, b + (n - 1)d$. Try different procedures for stopping the sequences. Input the values for $a, r, b, d,$ and n. Test the program using data in the Focus.

Challenge

A circle passes through the vertices of a triangle with side lengths $10\frac{1}{2}$, 14, and $17\frac{1}{2}$. $\frac{35}{4}$

Find the radius of the circle.

13.2 Arithmetic and Geometric Sequences **689**

44. Let $a_n = a_1 r^{n-1}$. Then $(a_n)^2 = (a_1 r^{n-1})^2 = a_1^2 r^{2n-2} = a_1^2 (r^2)^{n-1}$, which is a geometric sequence with a ratio of r^2.

Vocabulary
arithmetic series
geometric series
index of summation
nth partial sum
series
sigma notation
summation notation

FOCUS

Another famous mathematical legend, called the Tower of Brahma, involves the number $2^{64} - 1$. This is the legend:

> In the temple which marks the center of the world is a brass plate on which there are three diamond needles. At the beginning of time the Creator placed 64 discs of pure gold on one of these needles, with the largest disc at the bottom and the others resting in order of size. All day and all night the priests of the temple move the discs from one needle to another. Only one disc at a time may be moved, and a larger disc may never be placed on a smaller one. When the 64 discs have been transferred from the original needle to another, the world will end.

The number of moves needed to complete the task is $2^{64} - 1$. Assuming that the priests can move one disc each second, work unceasingly, and never make a mistake, it would take more than 58,454,204,609 centuries for the prophecy to be fulfilled.

A popular game called the "Tower of Hanoi" presents the same task for a small number of discs. Students may enjoy determining the number of moves required to solve the puzzle for 1, 2, 3, . . . discs. The sequence of these numbers has a straightforward recursive formula.

13.3 Arithmetic and Geometric Series

Objectives: To use sigma notation to represent the sum of a series
To find the partial sum of an arithmetic series
To find the partial sum of a geometric series

Focus

Legend holds that the game of chess was invented by the Grand Vizier Sissa Ben Dahir for the Indian King Shirham. Pleased with the game, the King asked the Vizier what he would like as a reward. The Vizier asked for one grain of wheat to be placed on the first square of the chessboard, two grains on the second, four on the third, and so on, each time doubling the number of grains. The King was surprised at the request, and even told the Vizier that he was a fool to ask for so little!

The inventor of chess was no fool. He told the King, "What I have asked for is more wheat than you have in the entire kingdom, in fact it's more than there is in the whole world." He was right. There are 64 squares on a chess board, and on the nth square he was asking for 2^{n-1} grains. If you add the numbers $1 + 2 + 2^2 + 2^3 + \cdots + 2^{63}$, the result is a number that represents more wheat than has been produced on the earth in all of recorded history:
$$2^{64} - 1 = 18{,}446{,}744{,}073{,}709{,}551{,}615 \text{ grains.}$$

Finding the sum of a sequence of numbers is a task that occurs often in mathematics. Special terminology, notation, and techniques have been developed to handle it.

A **series** is the indicated sum of the terms of a sequence. Like a sequence, a series may be finite or infinite. For example, $1 + 2 + 2^2 + \cdots + 2^{63}$ is the series corresponding to the sequence $1, 2, 2^2, \ldots, 2^{63}$. The infinite series $\frac{1}{2} + \left(\frac{1}{2}\right)^2 + \left(\frac{1}{2}\right)^3 + \cdots$ corresponds to the infinite sequence $\frac{1}{2}, \left(\frac{1}{2}\right)^2, \left(\frac{1}{2}\right)^3, \ldots$.
A series may be written using **sigma notation**, also called *summation notation*, because it involves the Greek capital letter *sigma*. Sigma (Σ) corresponds to the letter S, for sum. For any sequence $a_1, a_2, a_3, \ldots$, the sum of the first n terms may be written $\displaystyle\sum_{k=1}^{n} a_k$, which is read "the sum of a_k from $k = 1$ to $k = n$." Thus, $\displaystyle\sum_{k=1}^{n} a_k = a_1 + a_2 + a_3 + \cdots + a_n$. The letter k is called the **index** of the summation, but other letters may be used instead. It is also not necessary that the sum start with the index equal to 1.

690 Chapter 13 Sequences and Series

Example 1 Express $3 - 6 + 9 - 12 + 15$ using sigma notation.

The general term is $3k(-1)^{k+1}$ and there are five terms. So, the series may be written as $\sum_{k=1}^{5} 3k(-1)^{k+1}$.

Example 2 Find the following sums.

  a. $\sum_{k=1}^{5} (2k + 1)$ **b.** $\sum_{j=1}^{4} \left(\frac{1}{2}\right)^j$ **c.** $\sum_{t=3}^{6} t^2$

  a. This summation notation represents the sum of the first five terms of the sequence with general term $a_k = 2k + 1$.

  $3 + 5 + 7 + 9 + 11 = 35$

  b. This summation notation represents the sum

  $\left(\frac{1}{2}\right)^1 + \left(\frac{1}{2}\right)^2 + \left(\frac{1}{2}\right)^3 + \left(\frac{1}{2}\right)^4 = \frac{1}{2} + \frac{1}{4} + \frac{1}{8} + \frac{1}{16} = \frac{15}{16}$

  c. This notation represents the sum $a_3 + a_4 + a_5 + a_6$, where $a_t = t^2$.

  $3^2 + 4^2 + 5^2 + 6^2 = 9 + 16 + 25 + 36 = 86$

An infinite series $a_1 + a_2 + a_3 + \cdots$ is denoted by $\sum_{k=1}^{\infty} a_k$. The symbol "∞" indicates that the summation process never ends. Since you cannot add up infinitely many terms, it is reasonable to ask whether infinite sums make sense. In a later lesson, it will be shown how to define *infinite sum* using the concept of *partial sums*. The sum of the first n terms of a series is called the nth **partial sum** of the series and is denoted S_n.

Example 3 **a.** Find the partial sum S_6 for the series $\sum_{k=1}^{\infty} 5k$.

  b. Use sigma notation to write S_{10} for the arithmetic series $1 + 3 + 5 + 7 + \cdots$ and evaluate this partial sum.

  a. The indicated series is $5 + 10 + 15 + 20 + \cdots$ and so

  $S_6 = a_1 + a_2 + a_3 + a_4 + a_5 + a_6 = 5 + 10 + 15 + 20 + 25 + 30 = 105$

  b. An explicit formula for a general term of the sequence $1, 3, 5, 7, \ldots$ is $a_n = 2n - 1$. Therefore, sigma notation for S_{10} is $S_{10} = \sum_{n=1}^{10} (2n - 1)$.

  $S_{10} = 1 + 3 + \cdots + 19 = 100$

The partial sum of a series related to an arithmetic or a geometric sequence can be found without adding all of its terms directly. An **arithmetic series** is the indicated sum of an arithmetic sequence. Similarly, a **geometric series** is the indicated sum of a geometric sequence.

13.3 Arithmetic and Geometric Series   **691**

For Example 4

Find each indicated partial sum.
1. S_8 for 15, 9, 3, −3, ...   −48

2. S_{24} for $\displaystyle\sum_{t=1}^{\infty} (1.5t - 6)$ 306

It is possible to find the partial sum of an arithmetic series without actually adding all the terms. For example, consider the task of finding S_{50} for the series

$$2 + 5 + 8 + 11 + \cdots$$

This is an arithmetic series with $a_1 = 2$ and $d = 3$. Its 50th term is therefore $2 + 49 \cdot 3 = 149$. Express S_{50} in two ways and add the two expressions:

$$
\begin{aligned}
S_{50} &= 2 + 5 + 8 + 11 + \cdots + 140 + 143 + 146 + 149 \\
S_{50} &= 149 + 146 + 143 + 140 + \cdots + 11 + 8 + 5 + 2 \\
\hline
2S_{50} &= 151 + 151 + 151 + 151 + \cdots + 151 + 151 + 151 + 151
\end{aligned}
$$

There are 50 terms in this sum, and so

$$
\begin{aligned}
2S_{50} &= (50)(151) = 7550 \\
S_{50} &= 3775
\end{aligned}
$$

The reasoning just used can be generalized to any arithmetic series to develop a formula for the partial sum S_n.

Let a_k be the general term of an arithmetic sequence with common difference d. As in Example 3, write the nth partial sum S_n in two ways and add.

$$
\begin{aligned}
S_n &= a_1 + (a_1 + d) + (a_1 + 2d) + \cdots + (a_n - d) + a_n \\
S_n &= a_n + (a_n - d) + (a_n - 2d) + \cdots + (a_1 + d) + a_1 \\
\hline
2S_n &= (a_1 + a_n) + (a_1 + a_n) + (a_1 + a_n) + \cdots + (a_1 + a_n) + (a_1 + a_n)
\end{aligned}
$$

Because there are n identical terms in the sum, the right-hand side may be expressed as a product, giving $2S_n = n(a_1 + a_n)$ and thus

$$S_n = \frac{n(a_1 + a_n)}{2}$$

Since the nth term of an arithmetic sequence may also be expressed as $a_1 + (n - 1)d$, an equivalent formula for S_n is $\dfrac{n[2a_1 + (n - 1)d]}{2}$. *Why?* These results are summarized below.

> If $a_1, a_2, a_3, \ldots$ is an arithmetic sequence with common difference d, and if $S_n = a_1 + a_2 + a_3 + \cdots + a_n$, then $S_n = \dfrac{n(a_1 + a_n)}{2}$ and, equivalently, $S_n = \dfrac{n[2a_1 + (n - 1)d]}{2}$.

Example 4   Find each indicated partial sum.

  a. S_{10} for $\displaystyle\sum_{k=1}^{\infty} (3n + 1)$ **b.** S_{34} for $12 + 7 + 2 + (-3) + \cdots$

  a. $a_1 = 4$ and $a_{10} = 31$, so by the first sum formula given above,

$$S_{10} = \frac{10(4 + 31)}{2} = 175$$

Thinking Critically

Substituting for a_n gives $S_n = \dfrac{n[a_1 + a_1 + (n - 1)d]}{2}$, which simplifies to $S_n = \dfrac{n[2a_1 + (n - 1)d]}{2}$.

b. This is an arithmetic series with $a_1 = 12$ and $d = -5$. By the second sum formula, $S_{34} = \dfrac{34[2 \cdot 12 + 33 \cdot (-5)]}{2} = -2397$.

A formula for the partial sum S_n of a geometric series may be derived using similar reasoning.

Let a_k be the general term of a geometric series with common ratio r. Then $a_k = a_1 r^{k-1}$, and so the partial sum may be expressed in terms of a_1 and r.

$$S_n = a_1 + a_1 r + a_1 r^2 + \cdots + a_1 r^{n-1}$$

Multiply both sides of this equation by r, and subtract the second equation from the first.

$$
\begin{array}{rl}
S_n = & a_1 + a_1 r + a_1 r^2 + a_1 r^3 + \cdots + a_1 r^{n-1} \cdot \\
rS_n = & \quad\quad a_1 r + a_1 r^2 + a_1 r^3 + \cdots + a_1 r^{n-1} + a_1 r^n \\
\hline
S_n - rS_n = & a_1 \quad\quad\quad\quad\quad\quad\quad\quad\quad\quad\quad\quad\quad - a_1 r^n
\end{array}
$$

$$S_n(1 - r) = a_1(1 - r^n) \qquad \text{Factor.}$$

$$S_n = \frac{a_1(1 - r^n)}{1 - r} \qquad r \neq 1 \qquad \text{Divide each side by } (1 - r).$$

This reasoning leads to the following generalization.

If $a_1, a_2, a_3, \ldots$ is a geometric sequence with common ratio r, and if $S_n = a_1 + a_2 + a_3 + \cdots + a_n$, then $S_n = \dfrac{a_1(1 - r^n)}{1 - r}$ for $r \neq 1$.

Example 5 Find each indicated partial sum.
  a. S_7 for the series $1 - 0.8 + 0.64 - 0.512 \cdots$
  b. S_6 for $\displaystyle\sum_{k=1}^{\infty} \frac{3}{4^k}$

a. This is a geometric series with $a_1 = 1$ and $r = -0.8$. By the sum formula presented earlier,

$$S_7 = \frac{1[1 - (-0.8)^7]}{1 - (-0.8)} = \frac{1.2097152}{1.8} \approx 0.672064$$

b. Observe that this series is $\frac{3}{4} + \frac{3}{16} + \frac{3}{64} + \cdots$, a geometric series with $a_1 = \frac{3}{4}$ and $r = \frac{1}{4}$. By the sum formula, then,

$$S_6 = \frac{\frac{3}{4}\left[1 - \left(\frac{1}{4}\right)^6\right]}{1 - \frac{1}{4}} = \frac{0.7498169}{0.75} \approx 0.99976$$

The partial sums of both arithmetic and geometric series have applications in many fields.

Marc's grandmother gives him $100 on his birthday every year beginning with his third birthday. It is deposited in an account that earns 7.5% interest compounded annually.

1. How much is the account worth the day after Marc's tenth birthday? $1044.64
2. What is the value of the account immediately after Marc's twentieth birthday? $S_{18} = \$3567.74$

CLOSURE

Have students write you a letter indicating which parts of the lesson were easy and which parts were difficult to understand, and explaining why.

INDEPENDENT PRACTICE

Assignment Guide

Basic: 1–18, 21–24, 31, 33, 35, 39–40, Project
Average: 16–42, Project
Enriched: 24–30, 32, 34, 36–53, Project

Teacher's Resource Book
Practice, page 90

Additional Answers

Class Exercises

12. $S_{64} = \dfrac{1(1 - 2^{64})}{1 - 2} = \dfrac{1 - 2^{64}}{-1} = 2^{64} - 1$

14. Determine three consecutive terms a_n, a_{n+1}, and a_{n+2}. If $a_{n+2} - a_{n+1} = a_{n+1} - a_n$, then use the partial sum for an arithmetic series. If $\dfrac{a_{n+2}}{a_{n+1}} = \dfrac{a_{n+1}}{a_n}$, then use the partial sum for a geometric series.

Example 6   *Finance*   On the day she was born and on each of her birthdays thereafter, Jesse's grandparents have deposited $200 in a special account for her. The account earns 7% interest compounded annually. How much money is in the account the day after Jesse's eighteenth birthday? Assume that income taxes on the account are paid from another source.

The amount deposited on her eighteenth birthday hasn't earned any interest, so it is worth $200. The values of the amounts deposited on the other birthdays are shown in the chart below. (Each amount is computed using the formula for compound interest.)

Day of deposit	Value
18th birthday	$200
17th birthday	$200(1.07)^1$
16th birthday	$200(1.07)^2$
15th birthday	$200(1.07)^3$
⋮	⋮
2nd birthday	$200(1.07)^{16}$
1st birthday	$200(1.07)^{17}$
Day Jesse was born	$200(1.07)^{18}$

The total of these amounts is the value of the account. This total is the partial sum of a geometric series with $a_1 = 200$ and $r = 1.07$.

$$S_{19} = 200 + 200(1.07) + 200(1.07)^2 + \cdots + 200(1.07)^{18} = \frac{200[1 - (1.07)^{19}]}{1 - 1.07}$$

$$= \$7475.79$$

Class Exercises

Express each series using sigma notation.

1. $2 + 4 + 6 + 8 + 10 + 12$ $\sum_{k=1}^{6} 2k$
2. $2 + 4 + 6 + 8 + 10 + 12 + \cdots$ $\sum_{k=1}^{\infty} 2k$
3. $1 + 4 + 9 + 16 + \cdots$ $\sum_{k=1}^{\infty} k^2$
4. $6 + 11 + 16 + 21 + 26 + 31 + 36$ $\sum_{k=1}^{7} 5k + 1$

Find the indicated partial sum.

5. S_5 for $\sum_{t=1}^{\infty} t^2$ 55
6. S_{21} for $\sum_{k=1}^{100} (3k + 2)$ 735
7. S_6 for $6 + 15 + 24 + 33 + 42 + \cdots$ 171
8. S_9 for $1 + 1 + 2 + 3 + 5 + 8 + 13 + 21 + \cdots$ 88
9. S_7 for $\sum_{j=1}^{\infty} 5^j$ 97,655
10. S_8 for $\sum_{n=1}^{\infty} 5(-0.3)^n$ −1.1538

11. Find the value of $\sum_{k=7}^{12} (6k - 9)$.   288

12. Verify that $1 + 2 + 4 + 8 + \cdots + 2^{63} = 2^{64} - 1$ as claimed in the Focus of this lesson.

13. Find the value of $1 + 2 + 4 + 8 + \cdots + 2^N$ for N any positive integer. $2^{N+1} - 1$

14. **Thinking Critically**   Discuss ways of recognizing when to use the formulas for the partial sum S_n of an arithmetic series or geometric series. Use Class Exercises 5 to 10 of this lesson as examples.

694   Chapter 13 Sequences and Series

15. *Finance* A payment of $500 is made into a fund every 6 months. The fund earns 8% interest compounded semiannually. What is the value of the fund when the 25th payment is made? $20,822.95

Practice Exercises Use appropriate technology.

Express each series using sigma notation.

A **1.** $4 + 8 + 12 + 16 + 20 + \cdots$ $\displaystyle\sum_{k=1}^{\infty} 4k$ **2.** $4 + 8 + 12 + 16 + 20 + 24$ $\displaystyle\sum_{k=1}^{6} 4k$

3. $1 + 4 + 16 + 64 + \cdots$ $\displaystyle\sum_{k=1}^{\infty} 4^{k-1}$ **4.** $21 + 30 + 39 + 48 + 57 + \cdots$ $\displaystyle\sum_{k=1}^{\infty} (9k + 12)$

5. $1 + 8 + 27 + 64 + \cdots$ $\displaystyle\sum_{k=1}^{\infty} k^3$ **6.** $1 - 0.2 + 0.04 - 0.008 + 0.0016$ $\displaystyle\sum_{k=1}^{5} (-0.2)^{k-1}$

Find the indicated partial sum.

7. $3 + 9 + 15 + 21 + 27 + 33 + 39$ 147 **8.** $16 + 12 + 8 + 4 + \cdots + (-56)$ −380

9. $\displaystyle\sum_{k=1}^{6} k^3$ 441 **10.** $\displaystyle\sum_{k=1}^{7} 2k$ 56 **11.** $\displaystyle\sum_{m=1}^{23} (10 - 4m)$ −874 **12.** $\displaystyle\sum_{i=1}^{4} 4 \cdot 3^{k-1}$ 160

13. S_{12} for $28 + 34 + 40 + 46 + \cdots$ 732 **14.** S_{14} for $-1 + 0.3 - 0.09 + \cdots$ −0.769

15. S_9 for $2 - 6 + 18 - 54 + 162 - \cdots$ 9842 **16.** S_{10} for $-1 + 0.3 + 1.6 + \cdots$ 48.5

17. Sum of the first six terms of an arithmetic series with $a_1 = 7$ and $d = 11$ 207 **18.** Sum of the first eight terms of a geometric series with $a_1 = -2$ and $r = 1.5$ −98.516

19. S_7 for $\displaystyle\sum_{t=1}^{\infty} (1.1t + 8)$ 86.8 **20.** S_{14} for $\displaystyle\sum_{b=1}^{\infty} \frac{9}{5^b}$ 2.25

21. Solve: $|3x - 9| = 17.8$ −2.9$\overline{3}$, 8.9$\overline{3}$

22. *Finance* A payment of $125 is made into a fund every 6 months. The fund earns 7.4% interest compounded semiannually. What is the value of the fund when the 15th payment is made? $2447.88

23. Graph: $y = |12 - 7x|$

24. *Finance* For the ten days before his birthday, Aaron gets a gift every day. This year his parents told him that he will get a penny the first day, 2 cents the second day, 4 cents the third day, 8 cents the fourth day, and so on. What is the total value of his gift? $10.23

Find the indicated partial sum.

B **25.** S_{56} for $\displaystyle\sum_{k=1}^{\infty} (1.1k + 5)$ 2035.6 **26.** S_{100} for $\displaystyle\sum_{t=1}^{\infty} (1.2)^t$ 496,907,841.1 **27.** $\displaystyle\sum_{m=3}^{10} (2m + 8)$ 168 **28.** $\displaystyle\sum_{h=15}^{24} (1 - 4h)$ −770

29. Find the sum of the first 25 terms of an arithmetic series whose third term is 24 and whose common difference is 3.5. 1475

30. Find the sum of the first 14 terms of a geometric series whose fifth term is 17.1366 and whose common ratio is 1.3. 767.4753

31. Let $a_1, a_2, \ldots, a_n$ be positive real numbers. Express $\log_{10} (a_1 a_2 \cdots a_n)$ as a finite series. $\displaystyle\sum_{k=1}^{n} \log (a_k)$

32. Compute the sum of the positive integers less than 100 by expressing it as a series and finding the appropriate partial sum. 4950

13.3 Arithmetic and Geometric Series **695**

R Review

Exercises 21, 23, 31, 33, and 35 review the concepts of solving and graphing absolute value equations, using logarithms, finding roots of polynomial equations, and finding a geometric mean.

Project

Students should be aware that changing the first two terms of a Fibonacci sequence will affect all subsequent terms in the sequence.

LESSON FOLLOW-UP

Lesson Quiz

1. Find the value of $\displaystyle\sum_{t=3}^{8} (t^3 - 10)$
1227

2. Find the partial sum S_8 for the arithmetic series $22 + 15 + 8 + 1 - 6, \ldots$ −20

3. Find the partial sum S_6 for $\displaystyle\sum_{k=1}^{\infty} (1.3k + 2)$ 39.3

4. Find the partial sum S_5 for the geometric series with $a_1 = 30$ and $r = 0.9$. 122.853

5. Find the partial sum S_{15} of the series $\displaystyle\sum_{t=1}^{\infty} \frac{15}{4^t}$ 4.999999995

6. A scofflaw has collected parking tickets totaling $240. A judge declares that he must pay the value of the tickets plus $10 the first day, $15 the second day, $20 the third day, and so on for every day the bill is not paid. What is the total bill if the scofflaw waits 18 days to pay? $1185

Additional Answers
23.

® 33. Find the six sixth roots of 2. $\pm\sqrt[6]{2}, \sqrt[6]{2}\left(\pm\frac{1}{2} \pm \frac{\sqrt{3}}{2}i\right)$

34. *Business*   A company that fails to meet EPA pollution standards by a preassigned date is fined $1000 the first day, and each day thereafter the fine is increased by $200. What is the fine for a company that fails to meet the standards for 12 days after the deadline? $25,200

® 35. Find the geometric mean between $-\frac{3}{10}$ and $-\frac{5}{6}$. $-\frac{1}{2}$

36. *Physics*   A ball is dropped from a height of 12 ft. Each time it bounces, it rises to a height of 60% of the distance it fell. How far does it travel by the end of its fifth bounce? 45.2 ft

37. *Physics*   The tip of a pendulum travels 15 cm on its first swing. On each subsequent swing it travels 86% of the previous distance. How far has it traveled after nine swings? 79.57 cm

38. *Finance*   An investor deposits $550 every March 1 and September 1 for 8 years in an account that earns 8.4% a year compounded semiannually. What is the value of the account at the time of the last payment? $12,197.56

39. **Thinking Critically**   Use the method that was used to prove the sum formula $S_n = \frac{a_1(1 - r^n)}{1 - r}$ to compute the sum of the geometric series $\sum_{k=1}^{20} 5(3^k)$. 26,150,883,000

40. **Writing in Mathematics**   Follow the example of the Focus to write a "legend" that involves the sum of an arithmetic series.

41. *Programming*   Write a program that will print the sequence of partial sums $S_1, S_2, \ldots, S_n$ for an arithmetic series $\sum_{k=1}^{\infty} a_k$. Define a_k within the program and allow the user to input the value of n. Test the program with the series in Practice Exercise 25.

42. *Programming*   Write a program that will print the sequence of partial sums $S_1, S_2, \ldots, S_n$ for a geometric series $\sum_{k=1}^{\infty} a_k$. Define a_k within the program and allow the user to input the value of n. Test the program with the series in Example 6.

C 43. What is the sum of the geometric series $\sum_{k=1}^{N} ar^k$ if $r = 1$? Na

44. How many terms of the sequence 2, 4, 6, 8, 10, . . . yield a sum of 132? 11

45. How many terms of the sequence 1, 6, 11, 16, 21, 26, . . . yield a sum of 616? 16

46. What is the value of $\sum_{k=1}^{21} 2^{-k}$? 0.9999995232

47. Find the sum of the sequence $a_1, a_2, a_3, \ldots, a_{20}$ where: $a_k = \begin{cases} 1 - 3k, & \text{if } k \text{ is odd} \\ 4(3^k), & \text{if } k \text{ is even} \end{cases}$ 15,690,529,510

48. The sum of a geometric series is $\frac{9}{7}$ and its first term is 1. Identify the series. $\sum_{k=0}^{\infty}\left(\frac{2}{9}\right)^k$

49. Find the sum of the first 50 terms of the series $a + \pi, a^2 + 2\pi, a^3 + 3\pi, a^4 + 4\pi, \ldots$, where a is a fixed real number. $1275\pi + \frac{a(1 - a^{50})}{1 - a}$

Writing in Mathematics
40. Answers may vary. Some examples are penalties that increase daily and sponsors who pay you for each mile you walk in a marathon.

50. *Business*   A company spends $10,000 in 1990 for pollution control. Assume that these costs increase by 7% per year. What would the company spend for pollution control in 1995? What would be its total expenditure in this category from 1990 through 1995? $14,025.52; $71,532.91

51. Find the sum of all integers between 20 and 200 that are multiples of 3. 6570

52. *Computer Science*   The largest integer that can be stored in an IBM/360-370 computer is expressed in binary form by a zero followed by 31 ones. In decimal notation this number is $(0 \times 2^{31}) + (1 \times 2^{30}) + (1 \times 2^{29}) + \cdots + (1 \times 2^1) + (1 \times 2^0)$. What is the decimal value of this number? 2,147,483,647

53. *Figurate numbers* are natural numbers that can be represented as an array of dots arranged to form a regular polygon. Two such arrays are shown below to illustrate *triangular numbers* and *square numbers*. The column Additional Dots refers to the number of dots required to proceed from a given figurate number to the next larger such number.

	Additional dots	Cumulative dots		Additional dots	Cumulative dots
	1	1		1	1
	2	3		3	4
	3	6		5	9
	4	10		7	16

The triangular numbers 1, 3, 6, 10, . . . , t_n and the square numbers 1, 4, 9, 16, . . . , s_n each form a pattern. Use the patterns that you observe to find the *n*th triangular number and the *n*th square number. *Hint*: Each triangular number and each square number can be expressed as the sum of a finite arithmetic series. $t_n = \sum_{k=1}^{n} k$; $S_n = \sum_{k=1}^{n} 2k - 1$

Project

Many interesting sequences are neither arithmetic nor geometric. A spreadsheet is one way that technology can sometimes be used to compute sums of the terms of a sequence. Use a spreadsheet to find partial sums of the Fibonacci sequence. Determine what happens when the first two terms of the sequence are changed.

Review

Determine a quadratic equation that has the given solutions.

1. $\frac{4}{5}$ and $\frac{7}{3}$ $15x^2 - 47x + 28 = 0$

2. $3 + 4i$ and $3 - 4i$ $x^2 - 6x + 25 = 0$

3. The endpoints of a diameter of a circle are (11, 7) and (5, 11). Determine the coordinates of the center of the circle. (8, 9)

Solve for *x*.

4. $\log_x 216 = 3.$ 6

5. $\log_5 x = 4$ 625

6. $\log_3 243 = x$ 5

Vocabulary

mathematical induction

Ⓜ **Materials/Manipulatives**

dominoes

FOCUS

Klaus Friedrich holds the record for the number of dominoes toppled single-handedly, but not for the greatest number of dominoes toppled. In 1988 students from three Dutch universities set up 1,500,000 dominoes, and 1,382,101 of these toppled with one push on January 3, 1988. Many students enjoy the *Guiness Book of World Records,* where information like the greatest number of dominoes toppled may be found. The important connection between dominoes and this lesson is that dominoes help in visualizing an abstract concept. This is especially important for students who are concrete learners.

INSTRUCTION

Ⓜ • Have students set up dominoes in patterns to be toppled with one push. They may need to research or experiment in order to find an effective set-up.

• Students may need additional practice in representing statements for P_n as equations or inequalities.

• Recognizing P_{k+1} can be a stumbling block for students. Providing additional practice in determining P_{k+1} is therefore encouraged.

Objective: *To prove statements using the principle of mathematical induction*

Focus

On January 27, 1984, Klaus Friedrich of West Germany set a world record for single-handedly setting up and toppling dominoes. Friedrich set up 320,236 dominoes in 31 days working 10 hours per day. When he gave the lead domino a single push, 281,581 of those dominoes toppled in 12 min 57.3 s. The domino effect Friedrich achieved is used as imagery in fields as varied as sports, music, geology, economics, and political science. In mathematics, the domino effect is often used to visualize an important method of proof called *mathematical induction*.

Many interesting and important results in mathematics have been discovered by first observing patterns in some specific cases and then making generalizations from the observations, that is, by applying *inductive reasoning*. For example, it is easy to form a conjecture about the sum of the first k odd positive integers.

$$
\begin{aligned}
1 &= 1 \\
1 + 3 &= 4 \\
1 + 3 + 5 &= 9 \\
1 + 3 + 5 + 7 &= 16 \\
1 + 3 + 5 + 7 + 9 &= 25 \\
&\vdots
\end{aligned}
$$

The numbers 1, 4, 9, 16, and 25 are the squares of the first five odd positive integers, and so it appears that the sum of the first k odd positive integers is exactly k^2. Since the kth odd positive integer may be written as $2k - 1$, the conjecture may also be expressed as an equation.

$$ 1 + 3 + 5 + \cdots + (2k - 1) = k^2 $$

Recall that no number of examples that satisfy a conjectured rule constitutes a proof that the conjecture is true. On the other hand, *one* unsuccessful example, called a *counterexample,* is sufficient to show that a conjecture is not true.

698   Chapter 13 Sequences and Series

Example 1 It was once guessed that the equation $n^2 - n + 41$ gives a prime number for every positive integer value of n. Verify that this conjecture is true for $n = 1$, 2, 3, 4, 5. Then find a counterexample to show that it is *not* true for all n.

The table shows that $n^2 - n + 41$ is prime for $n = 1, 2, 3, 4, 5$.

n	1	2	3	4	5
$n^2 - n + 41$	41	43	47	53	61

A *counterexample* to the guess is given by $n = 41$; $41^2 - 41 + 41 = 41^2$ and 41^2 is certainly not a prime number.

Since no number of examples is sufficient to prove that a conjecture is always true, other approaches are required. One approach is **mathematical induction.** Note that "inductive reasoning" and "mathematical induction" are not the same. The first is a way of arriving at conjectures, the second is a way of proving them. Mathematical induction is useful particularly for proving conjectures involving the positive integers. To formulate the principle of mathematical induction, it is convenient to let P_n be a statement involving the positive integer n. In the first example of this lesson, P_n is the conjecture "The sum of the first n odd positive integers is n^2." The statement P_5 is "The sum of the first five odd positive integers is 25," and P_{k+1} is "The sum of the first $k + 1$ positive integers is $(k + 1)^2$."

The Principle of Mathematical Induction

Let P_n be a statement involving the positive integer n. The statement is true for every $n \geq 1$ if the following two conditions hold.
1. The statement is true for $n = 1$, that is, P_1 is true.
2. For any positive integer k, whenever P_k is true, then P_{k+1} is true.

The domino effect is a good visual image for mathematical induction. Proving that P_1 is true is like knocking over the first domino. Proving that whenever P_k is true then P_{k+1} is also true is like having the dominoes arranged so that each one knocks over the next.

Since P_1 is true, then P_2 must be true. Since P_2 is true, P_3 must also be true. Since P_3 is true, then P_4 must also be true, and so on.

In order to prove a statement using mathematical induction, you may need to rephrase the statement in a form P_n that is more suitable for the proof.

Example 2 Represent the following statement using an equation or inequality. Then find P_{k+1} for the statement

P_n: The sum of the first n odd positive integers is n^2.

An odd integer may be represented as $2n - 1$, where n is a positive integer. Therefore, the statement may be represented as

P_n: $1 + 3 + 5 + \cdots + (2n - 1) = n^2$

M **Alternative Learning Styles**
The domino effect is the best imagery of mathematical induction for most students, but especially for those who are concrete learners. They are helped by seeing that there has to be a first domino toppled in order to get things started, and that each domino must knock over the next one in order for the action to continue.

GUIDED PRACTICE

For Example 1
1. Verify that the conjecture $n^2 - n + 2 = 2^n$ is true for $n = 1, 2$, 3. Then find a counterexample to show that it is *not* true for all positive integers n.
$n = 1$: $1^2 - 1 + 2 = 2 = 2^1$
$n = 2$: $2^2 - 2 + 2 = 2^2$
$n = 3$: $3^2 - 3 + 2 = 8 = 2^3$
For $n = 4$: $4^2 - 4 + 2 = 14 \neq 2^4$
Other counterexamples are possible.

2. Find a counterexample to show that the conjecture $n^3 > 2^n$ is not true for all positive integers n.
Answers may vary.
$10^3 \overset{?}{>} 2^{10}$
$1000 < 1024$

For Example 2
Represent each statement using an equation or inequality. Then find P_{k+1} for the statement.
1. The sum of the first n even positive integers is $n(n + 1)$.
P_n: $2 + 4 + 6 + \cdots + 2n = n(n + 1)$
P_{k+1}: $2 + 4 + 6 + \cdots + [2(k + 1)]$
$= (k + 1)[(k + 1) + 1]$
$= (k + 1)(k + 2)$

2. The sum of the first n positive cubes is $\dfrac{n^2(n + 1)^2}{4}$.
P_n: $1^3 + 2^3 + 3^3 + \cdots + n^3$
$= \dfrac{n^2(n + 1)^2}{4}$
P_{k+1}: $1^3 + 2^3 + 3^3 + \cdots + (k + 1)^3$
$= \dfrac{(k + 1)^2[(k + 1) + 1]^2}{4}$
$= \dfrac{(k + 1)^2(k + 2)^2}{4}$

$$P_{k+1}: 1 + 3 + 5 + \cdots + [2(k + 1) - 1] = (k + 1)^2$$

When a statement concerning the set of positive integers has been precisely formulated, it may then be possible to prove it using mathematical induction.

Example 3 Use the principle of mathematical induction to prove that the sum of the first n odd positive integers is n^2.

1. Since the sum of the first odd positive integer, 1, is $1\ (= 1^2)$, P_1 is true.
2. The statement P_k may be expressed as the equation

$$1 + 3 + 5 + \cdots + (2k - 1) = k^2$$

Assume that this statement is true, and use it to *prove* that P_{k+1} is then also true. First restate the target statement P_{k+1} as

$$1 + 3 + 5 + \cdots + (2k - 1) + [2(k + 1) - 1] = (k + 1)^2$$

which simplifies to

$$1 + 3 + 5 + \cdots + (2k - 1) + (2k + 1) = (k + 1)^2$$

How could this statement be obtained from P_k? If you add $(2k + 1)$ to the left-hand side of P_k, you will obtain the left-hand side of P_{k+1}. Algebra is then an appropriate tool.

$1 + 3 + 5 + \cdots + (2k - 1) = k^2$	*Assume that P_k is true.*
$1 + 3 + 5 + \cdots + (2k - 1) + (2k + 1) = k^2 + (2k + 1)$	*Add $2k + 1$ to each side.*
$1 + 3 + 5 + \cdots + (2k - 1) + (2k + 1) = (k + 1)^2$	$k^2 + 2k + 1 = (k + 1)^2$

Since this last equation is precisely P_{k+1}, the second condition of the principle of mathematical induction holds. Therefore, P_n is true for all positive integers n.

Many formulas that have been presented intuitively using expressions such as "the pattern continues" or "and so on" may be proved formally using mathematical induction.

Example 4 Use mathematical induction to prove DeMoivre's theorem:

If n is any positive integer then $(r \operatorname{cis} \theta)^n = r^n \operatorname{cis} n\theta$.

1. P_1 is the statement $(r \operatorname{cis} \theta)^1 = r^1 \operatorname{cis} 1\theta$, which is obviously true.
2. Suppose that P_k: $(r \operatorname{cis} \theta)^k = r^k \operatorname{cis} k\theta$ is true.

From this, show that P_{k+1}: $(r \operatorname{cis} \theta)^{k+1} = r^{k+1}[\operatorname{cis} (k + 1)\theta]$ is also true. Notice that to obtain the left-hand side of P_{k+1} from P_k, you must multiply by $r \operatorname{cis} \theta$.

$(r \operatorname{cis} \theta)^k \cdot (r \operatorname{cis} \theta) = (r^k \operatorname{cis} k\theta)(r \operatorname{cis} \theta)$	*P_k is assumed to be true.*
$(r \operatorname{cis} \theta)^{k+1} \qquad = r^{k+1}[\operatorname{cis} (k\theta + \theta)]$	*$(a \operatorname{cis} \theta_1)(b \operatorname{cis} \theta_2) = ab \operatorname{cis} (\theta_1 + \theta_2)$*
$(r \operatorname{cis} \theta)^{k+1} \qquad = r^{k+1}[\operatorname{cis} (k + 1)\theta]$	

700 Chapter 13 Sequences and Series

For Example 3

Use the principle of mathematical induction to prove:

$3 + 5 + 7 + \cdots + (2n + 1) = n(n + 2)$.

$P_k: 3 + 5 + 7 + \cdots + (2k + 1)$
$\quad = k(k + 2)$

$P_{k+1}: 3 + 5 + 7 + \cdots + [2(k + 1) + 1]$
$\quad = (k + 1)[(k + 1) + 2]$

or $3 + 5 + 7 + \cdots + (2k + 3)$
$\quad = (k + 1)(k + 3)$

Proof: Since $3 = 1(1 + 2)$, P_1 is true. Assume $P_k: 3 + 5 + 7 + \cdots + (2k + 1) = k(k + 2)$ is true.
Add $2k + 3$ to both sides of P_k, giving
$3 + 5 + 7 + \cdots + (2k + 1) + (2k + 3) = k(k + 2) + (2k + 3)$.
$3 + 5 + 7 + \cdots + (2k + 1) + (2k + 3) = k^2 + 4k + 3 = (k + 1)(k + 3)$, which is precisely P_{k+1}.
Therefore, P_n is true for all positive integers n.

For Example 4

Use the principle of mathematical induction and the fact that $\ln (ab) = \ln a + \ln b$ to prove that for all positive integers n and all real numbers $x > 0$, $\ln (x^n) = n \cdot \ln (x)$.
Since $\ln (x^1) = 1 \cdot \ln (x)$, P_1 is true.
Assume that $P_k: \ln (x^k) = k \cdot \ln (x)$ is true.
Then $\ln (x^{k+1}) = \ln (x^k \cdot x)$
$\qquad = \ln x^k + \ln (x)$
$\qquad = k \cdot \ln (x) + \ln (x)$
$\qquad = (k + 1) \ln (x)$

Common Error Students become easily dependent on the technique "Add the next term to both sides to obtain P_{k+1}." It is important to provide examples like this one to keep the focus on the induction process.

Since the last line is precisely the statement P_{k+1}, it follows that P_{k+1} is true whenever P_k is true. Therefore, by the principle of mathematical induction, DeMoivre's theorem is true for all positive integers n.

It is necessary to show that *both* conditions of the principle of mathematical induction hold in order to prove a conjecture using this method. Some famous and bizarre results have been "proved" using mathematical induction incorrectly.

Example 5   *Logic*   Find the flaw in the following argument. Let P_k be the statement "In any set of k cows, all k cows are blue." Prove that if P_k is true, then the statement P_{k+1}:   "In any set of $k + 1$ cows, all $k + 1$ cows are blue," is also true. Then if there exists at least one blue cow, then all cows are blue.

> *Proof*:   Let $\{c_1, c_2, \ldots, c_{k+1}\}$ be a set of $k + 1$ cows. Then $\{c_1, c_2, \ldots, c_k\}$ is a set of k cows, and so by assumption, all those cows are blue. Also, $\{c_2, c_3, \ldots, c_{k+1}\}$ is a set of k cows, so all those cows, in particular c_{k+1}, are blue. Thus, every cow in the set $\{c_1, c_2, \ldots, c_k, c_{k+1}\}$ is blue. Since P_{k+1} is true whenever P_k is true, you may conclude that the statement is true for any k. This means that, if there is at least one blue cow, then all cows are blue.

The flaw in this "proof" is the fact that P_1 is not the same as the statement "There exists at least 1 blue cow." Rather, it is the statement "In any set of 1 cow, that 1 cow is blue," which is false. Thus, the statement "In any set of k cows, all k cows are blue," is not true for $k = 1$.

As has been emphasized, the importance of having P_1 true is that it provides a starting point. In some cases, a statement P_n is true for all values of n greater than or equal to a given number N. In this kind of situation, mathematical induction may be used with the first step, "P_1 is true," replaced by "P_N is true." The conclusion is that P_n is true for all $n \geq N$.

Example 6   Show that $2^n > 2n + 1$ for all $n \geq 3$.

Observe that the statement is not true for $n = 1$ or $n = 2$.

1. Use $n = 3$ as the starting point. The statement P_3: $2^3 > 2 \cdot 3 + 1$ is true, since $8 > 7$.
2. Suppose that P_k: $2^k > 2k + 1$ is true. From this, show that P_{k+1}: $2^{k+1} > 2(k + 1) + 1$ is also true.

$$
\begin{array}{ll}
2^k > 2k + 1 & \text{\textit{Assume that} } P_k \text{ \textit{is true.}} \\
2 \cdot 2^k > 2(2k + 1) & \text{\textit{Multiply both sides by the positive number 2.}} \\
2^{k+1} > 4k + 2 & \\
2^{k+1} > 2k + 2 + 2k & \text{\textit{Express 4k as 2k} } + 2k. \\
2^{k+1} > 2(k + 1) + 2k & \\
2^{k+1} > 2(k + 1) + 1 & \text{\textit{Since 2k} > 1, 2(k + 1) + 2k > 2(k + 1) + 1}
\end{array}
$$

Thus, P_{k+1} is true whenever P_k is, and so the statement is true for all $n \geq 3$.

13.4 Mathematical Induction   **701**

For Example 5
Let T_n be the following statement:
$$1 + 2 + \cdots + n = \frac{n(n + 1)}{2} + 3$$
Show that if T_k is true, then T_{k+1} is also true. Then explain why it is not true that T_n holds for all n.
If T_k is true, then $1 + 2 + \cdots + k = \frac{k(k + 1)}{2} + 3$ is true. Then $1 + 2 + \cdots + k + (k + 1) = \frac{k(k + 1)}{2} + 3 + (k + 1) = \frac{k^2 + k}{2} + \frac{2k + 2}{2} + 3 = \frac{k^2 + 3k + 2}{2} + 3 = \frac{(k + 1)(k + 2)}{2} + 3 = T_{k+1}$.
However, the counterexample T_1:
$\frac{1(1 + 1)}{2} + 3 = 4 \neq 1$ shows that T_n is not true for all n.

For Example 6
Prove that $5^n - 1$ is divisible by 4 for all positive integers n.
$5^1 - 1 = 4$, which is divisible by 4; Suppose $5^k - 1$ is divisible by 4. Then $5^k - 1 = 4m$ for some integer m.
$$(5^k - 1) \cdot 5 = (4m) \cdot 5$$
$$5^{k+1} - 5 = 20m$$
$$5^{k+1} - 1 = 20m + 4$$
$$5^{k+1} - 1 = 4(5m + 1)$$
Thus, $5^{k+1} - 1$ is divisible by 4.

Have students summarize in their math journals the procedure for proving a statement using the principle of mathematical induction.

INDEPENDENT PRACTICE

Assignment Guide
Basic: 1–20, 31–35
Average: 3, 6–7, 10–11, 17–36
Enriched: 16, 18, 20–30, 32, 34, 36–45

Teacher's Resource Book
   Practice, page 91

Ⓡ **Review**
Exercises 11, 17, 19, 31, 33, and 35 review finding a quadratic equation for a specified root in the set of complex numbers, using DeMoivre's theorem to evaluate expressions and to find the roots of a complex number, and graphing polar equations.

LESSON FOLLOW-UP

Test Yourself

Teacher's Resource Book
   Tests—Quiz, form A, page 57
   Tests—Quiz, form B, page 57

Additional Answers
Class Exercises

8. Since $1 = \frac{1(1 + 1)}{2}$, P_1 is true.

Assume P_k: $1 + 2 + 3 + \cdots + k = \frac{k(k + 1)}{2}$ is true. Add $k + 1$ to both sides. $1 + 2 + 3 + \cdots + k + k + 1 = \frac{k(k + 1)}{2} + k + 1 = \frac{k(k + 1) + 2(k + 1)}{2} = \frac{(k + 1)(k + 2)}{2} = \frac{(k + 1)[(k + 1) + 1]}{2} = P_{k+1}$

9. Since $2^5 > 5^2$ or $32 > 25$, P_5 is true. Assume P_k: $2^k > k^2$ is true. Multiply both sides by 2, giving $2^{k+1} > 2k^2$ or $2^{k+1} > k^2 + k^2$ for $k \geq 5$, $k^2 > 2k + 1$. Then $2^{k+1} > k^2 + (2k + 1)$. $2^{k+1} > (k + 1)^2$

702

Class Exercises

In Exercises 1 to 3, let n be a positive integer. Find a counterexample to disprove each statement.

1. For all n, $n^2 - n + 17$ is a prime number. $n = 17$
2. If n is an odd number, then n is prime. $n = 9$
3. If n is prime, then n is an odd number. $n = 2$

Find P_{k+1} for each of the following statements. $1^2 + 2^2 + 3^2 + \cdots + n^2 + (n + 1)^2 =$

4. P_n: $1^2 + 2^2 + 3^2 + \cdots + n^2 = \frac{n(n + 1)(2n + 1)}{6}$ $\frac{(n + 1)(n + 2)(2n + 3)}{6}$

5. P_n: $\sum_{t=1}^{n} t(t + 1) = \frac{n(n + 1)(n + 2)}{3}$ $\sum_{t=1}^{n+1} t(t + 1) = \frac{(n + 1)(n + 2)(n + 3)}{3}$

6. P_n: 6 is a factor of $n^3 + 3n^2 + 2n$ 6 is a factor of $(n + 1)^3 + 3(n + 1)^2 + 2(n + 1)$

7. Express as an equation. P_n: The sum of the first n even integers is $n(n + 1)$. $\sum_{k=1}^{n} 2k = n(n + 1)$

Use the principle of mathematical induction to prove that each statement is true for all positive integers n.

8. $\sum_{i=1}^{n} i = 1 + 2 + 3 + \cdots + n = \frac{n(n + 1)}{2}$
9. If $n \geq 5$, then $2^n > n^2$.

Practice Exercises

In Exercises 1 to 3, let n be a positive integer. Find a counterexample to disprove each statement.

A 1. Any positive integer greater than 5 is the sum of either two or three consecutive positive integers. For example, $9 = 4 + 5$, $15 = 4 + 5 + 6$. 8

2. The sum of the digits of 11^n is 2^n. For example, $11^3 = 1331$ and $1 + 3 + 3 + 1 = 8 = 2^3$. $n = 5$

3. The number 2^n equals n^2. For example, $2^4 = 4^2$. $n = 3$

Find P_{k+1} for each statement.

4. P_n: $\sum_{t=1}^{n} \frac{1}{(3t - 2)(3t + 1)} = \frac{n}{3n + 1}$

5. P_n: $(ab)^n = a^n b^n$

6. P_n: $\frac{1}{1 \cdot 2} + \frac{1}{2 \cdot 3} + \frac{1}{3 \cdot 4} + \cdots + \frac{1}{n(n + 1)} = \frac{n}{n + 1}$

7. P_n: $1^4 + 2^4 + 3^4 + \cdots + n^4 = \frac{n(n + 1)(2n + 1)(3n^2 + 3n - 1)}{30}$

Represent each statement using an equation or inequality.

8. The sum of the cubes of the first n positive integers is one-fourth the product of the square of n and the square of $(n + 1)$. $1^3 + 2^3 + 3^3 + \cdots + n^3 = \frac{n^2(n + 1)^2}{4}$

9. The product of the first n integers is greater than the square of n provided n is greater than 3. $n! > n^2$ for $n > 3$

10. The sum of the first n powers of $\frac{1}{2}$ is the difference between 1 and the nth power of $\frac{1}{2}$. $\frac{1}{2} + \left(\frac{1}{2}\right)^2 + \left(\frac{1}{2}\right)^3 + \cdots + \left(\frac{1}{2}\right)^n = 1 - \left(\frac{1}{2}\right)^n$

702   Chapter 13 Sequences and Series

Practice Exercises

4. $\sum_{t=1}^{k+1} \frac{1}{(3t - 2)(3t + 1)} = \frac{k + 1}{3k + 4}$

5. P_{k+1}: $(ab)^{k+1} = a^{k+1} b^{k+1}$

6. P_{k+1}: $\frac{1}{1 \cdot 2} + \frac{1}{2 \cdot 3} + \frac{1}{3 \cdot 4} + \cdots + \frac{1}{k(k + 1)} + \frac{1}{(k + 1)(k + 2)} = \frac{k + 1}{k + 2}$

7. P_{k+1}: $1^4 + 2^4 + 3^4 + \cdots + k^4 + (k + 1)^4 = \frac{(k + 1)(k + 2)(2k + 3)(3k^2 + 9k + 5)}{30}$

® **11.** Find a quadratic equation with real coefficients that has $2 + i$ as a solution. $x^2 - 4x + 5 = 0$

Use the principle of mathematical induction to prove that each statement is true for all positive integers n.

12. $1^2 + 2^2 + 3^2 + \cdots + n^2 = \dfrac{n(n + 1)(2n + 1)}{6}$

13. $3 + 5 + 7 + \cdots + (2n + 1) = n(n + 2)$

14. $2^2 + 4^2 + 6^2 + \cdots + (2n)^2 = \dfrac{2n(n + 1)(2n + 1)}{3}$

15. $1 + 4 + 7 + \cdots + (3n - 2) = \dfrac{n(3n - 1)}{2}$

16. $5 + 5^2 + 5^3 + \cdots + 5^n = \dfrac{5^{n+1} - 5}{4}$

® **17.** Use DeMoivre's theorem to find $\left(4 \operatorname{cis} \dfrac{\pi}{4}\right)^6$. $4096 \operatorname{cis} \dfrac{3\pi}{2} = -4096i$

18. Prove that if a and b are real numbers, then $(ab)^n = a^n b^n$.

® **19.** Graph the rational function $y = \dfrac{x}{x - 1}$.

20. Thinking Critically Examine the two concepts of "inductive reasoning" and "proof by mathematical induction" and explain why the two concepts are quite different. Answers may vary.

Use the principle of mathematical induction to prove that each statement is true for all positive integers n.

B **21.** $1 \cdot 2 + 2 \cdot 3 + 3 \cdot 4 + \cdots + n(n + 1) = \dfrac{n(n + 1)(n + 2)}{3}$

22. $\dfrac{1}{1 \cdot 2} + \dfrac{1}{2 \cdot 3} + \dfrac{1}{3 \cdot 4} + \cdots + \dfrac{1}{n(n + 1)} = \dfrac{n}{n + 1}$

23. $\dfrac{1}{2} + \left(\dfrac{1}{2}\right)^2 + \left(\dfrac{1}{2}\right)^3 + \left(\dfrac{1}{2}\right)^4 + \cdots + \left(\dfrac{1}{2}\right)^n = 1 - \left(\dfrac{1}{2}\right)^n$

24. If a is a real number greater than 1, then $a^{n+1} > a^n$.

25. For $n \geq 7$, $3^n < n!$ **26.** $n < 2^n$ **27.** $4^n - 1$ is a multiple of 3

28. $n^2 + n$ is divisible by 2   **29.** $a^n < 1, 0 < a < 1$ **30.** $e^n > 2^n$

® **31.** Use DeMoivre's theorem to find the 6 sixth roots of $-\sqrt{3} + i$.

32. Thinking Critically Criticize the following proof that concludes that all positive integers are equal. All positive integers are equal if each number equals the one that follows it, that is, if for each n, $n = n + 1$. The proof is by mathematical induction. Let P_k be the statement $k = k + 1$. Assume that P_k is true, and use this to show that P_{k+1} is also true. Note that P_{k+1} is the statement

$$k + 1 = (k + 1) + 1 = k + 2$$

$k = k + 1$	Assume that P_k is true.
$k + 1 = (k + 1) + 1$	Add 1 to each side of the equation
$k + 1 = k + 2$	Associative property for addition

Thus, whenever P_k is true, P_{k+1} is true, and so the statement is proved. All positive integers are equal.

13.4 Mathematical Induction **703**

Lesson Quiz

1. Find a counterexample to show that the conjecture $1 + 3 + 5 + \cdots + (2n - 1) = 3n - 2$ does not hold for all positive integers n.
For $n = 3$, $1 + 3 + 5 = 9 \neq 3(3) - 2$

2. Find S_{k+1} for the statement S_k: $7 + 13 + 19 + \cdots + (6k + 1) = k(3k + 4)$. S_{k+1}: $7 + 13 + 19 + \cdots + (6k + 7) = (k + 1)(3k + 7)$

3. Use the principle of mathematical induction to prove that for all positive integers n, $1 + 4 + 7 + \cdots + (3n - 2) = \frac{1}{2}n(3n - 1)$

Since $1 = \frac{1}{2}(1)(3 \cdot 1 - 1)$, P_1 is true.

Assume that P_k: $1 + 4 + 7 + \cdots + (3k - 2) = \frac{1}{2}(k)(3k - 1)$ is true. Then

$1 + 4 + 7 + \cdots + (3k - 2) + (3k + 1) = \frac{1}{2}(k)(3k - 1) + (3k + 1) =$

$\dfrac{3k^2 - k}{2} + \dfrac{6k + 2}{2} = \dfrac{3k^2 + 5k + 2}{2} =$

$\frac{1}{2}(k + 1)(3k + 2) = P_{k+1}$

4. Use the principle of mathematical induction to show that $4^{2n} - 1$ is divisible by 3 for all positive integers n.
P_1: $4^2 - 1 = 15$ is divisible by 3, so P_1 is true.
Suppose that P_k: $4^{2k} - 1 = 3t$ is true for some integer t. Then
$(4^{2k} - 1)4^2 = (3t)4^2$
$4^{2k+2} - 16 = 48t$
$4^{2(k+1)} - 1 = 48t + 15$
$4^{2(k+1)} - 1 = 3(16t + 5)$
Thus P_{k+1} is divisible by 3.

Additional Answers

19.

703

Additional Answers

33.

35.

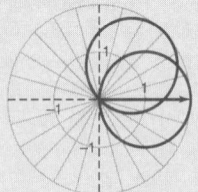

The second graph is the first graph shifted counterclockwise $\frac{\pi}{4}$.

36. Since $x - 1$ is a factor of $x^1 - 1$, P_1 is true. Assume P_k: $x - 1$ is a factor of $x^k - 1$. Then $x - 1$ is a factor of $x^k(x - 1) + (x^k - 1)$ because it is a factor of both terms. Multiplying yields $x^{k+1} - x^k + x^k - 1 = x^{k+1} - 1 = P_{k+1}$.

37. Since $(a^m)^1 = a^{m \cdot 1} = a^m$, P_1 is true. Assume P_k: $(a^m)^k = a^{mk}$. Then $(a^m)^{k+1} = (a^m)^k \cdot (a^m)^1 = a^{mk} \cdot a^m = a^{mk+m} = a^{m(k+1)} = P_{k+1}$.

33. Graph the lemniscate $r^2 = 16 \sin 2\theta$.

34. **Writing in Mathematics** Write a paragraph explaining why a correct application of the principle of mathematical induction can *prove* a statement involving positive integers while even a million examples don't constitute a proof.

35. Graph the polar equations $r = 2 \cos \theta$ and $r = 2 \cos \left(\theta - \frac{\pi}{4} \right)$. How are the graphs related?

36. Use the principle of mathematical induction to prove that $x - 1$ is a factor of $x^n - 1$.

C 37. Let a be a real number and let m and n be positive integers. Use the principle of mathematical induction to prove that $(a^m)^n = a^{mn}$.

38. Use the principle of mathematical induction to prove that the general term of an arithmetic sequence with initial term a_1 and common difference d is $a_1 + (n - 1)d$.

39. Use the principle of mathematical induction to prove that the general term of a geometric sequence with initial term a_1 and common ratio r is $a_1 r^{n-1}$.

40. Use the principle of mathematical induction to prove that $a + ar + ar^2 + \cdots + ar^{n-1} = \frac{a(1 - r^n)}{1 - r}$, $r \neq 1$.

41. Make a conjecture of an explicit formula for the sequence defined by the recursive formula $a_1 = \sqrt{5}$ and $a_{n+1} = \sqrt{5a_n}$. Use the mathematical induction to prove your conjecture.

42. Suppose that n straight lines are drawn in the plane in such a way that no two are parallel and no three meet in a single point. Use the principle of mathematical induction to show that the number of points of intersection of the lines is $\frac{1}{2}(n^2 - n)$.

43. Use mathematical induction to prove that the number of diagonals in a polygon with n sides is $\frac{1}{2}n(n - 3)$ for $n \geq 3$.

44. Use the principle of mathematical induction to prove that for the Fibonacci numbers F_k,

$$F_1 + F_2 + F_3 + \cdots + F_n = F_{n+2} - 1$$

45. Criticize the following proof that concludes that in any set of n people, if one is left-handed, then all n are left-handed. Let P_n be the given statement.

  1. P_1 is the statement: In any set of one person, if one is left-handed, then all are left-handed. This is obviously true.
  2. Assume that P_k is true, and use this assumption to show that P_{k+1} is also true for all k.

  Let $\{p_1, p_2, p_3, \ldots, p_k, p_{k+1}\}$ be a set of $k + 1$ people, and suppose that one of them is left-handed. Rearranging numbers if necessary, let p_1 be left-handed. Then $\{p_1, p_2, p_3, \ldots, p_k\}$ is a set of k people, at least one of whom is left-handed. Therefore, since P_k is assumed true, all the people in

Writing in Mathematics

34. No matter how many examples of a conjecture are examined, there is always the possibility that for some example not yet studied, the conjecture fails. A correct application of the principle of mathematical induction guarantees that the conjecture is true for all n by providing a starting point and a proof that once the statement is true for a number, it is true for the next number, and so for all n.

the set are left-handed. The set $\{p_2, p_3, p_4, \ldots, p_k, p_{k+1}\}$ is also a set of k people at least one of whom is left-handed. Everyone in this set must also be left-handed. Thus, all $k + 1$ of those people are left-handed, and P_{k+1} is true. It follows by the principle of mathematical induction that if anyone of a group of people is left-handed, everyone in the group is left-handed.

Test Yourself

Find the first five terms of the infinite sequence defined explicitly by each rule.

1. $f(n) = n^2 - 4$ $-3, 0, 5, 12, 21$

2. $a_n = \dfrac{1}{(-2)^n(3n - 2)}$ 13.1

$-\dfrac{1}{2}, \dfrac{1}{16}, -\dfrac{1}{56}, \dfrac{1}{160}, -\dfrac{1}{416}$

Find an explicit formula for each sequence.

3. $\dfrac{1}{2}, \dfrac{1}{3}, \dfrac{1}{4}, \dfrac{1}{5}, \dfrac{1}{6}, \ldots$ $a_n = \dfrac{1}{n+1}$

4. $0, 1, 8, 27, 64, \ldots$ $a_n = (n-1)^3$

Find the next four terms of the sequence given by each recursive formula.

5. $a_1 = 5$ and $a_n = \frac{1}{4}a_{n-1}$ $\frac{5}{4}, \frac{5}{16}, \frac{5}{64}, \frac{5}{256}$

6. $a_1 = -3, a_2 = 2,$ and $a_n = a_{n-1} - a_{n-2}$ $5, 3, -2, -5$

Find a recursive formula for each sequence.

7. $-13, -6, 1, 8, 15, 22, \ldots$ $a_1 = -13$ and $a_{n+1} = a_n + 7$

8. $0.1, -0.01, 0.001, -0.0001, 0.00001, \ldots$ $a_1 = 0.1$ and $a_{n+1} = (-0.1)a_n$ 13.2

Name each sequence as arithmetic, geometric, or neither. For an arithmetic sequence, find the common difference d; for a geometric sequence, find the common ratio r.

9. $15, 8, 1, -6, -13, -20, \ldots$ A; -7

10. $48, 24, 8, 2, \frac{2}{5}, \ldots$ N

11. $27, 9, 3, 1, \frac{1}{3}, \ldots$ G; $\frac{1}{3}$

Find an explicit formula for the sequence in each indicated exercise and use it to find the fifteenth term.

12. Exercise 9 $a_n = -7n + 22; -83$

13. Exercise 11 $a_n = 27\left(\frac{1}{3}\right)^{n-1}; 0.0000056$

14. Find three arithmetic means between 74 and 90. 78, 82, 86

15. Find two geometric means between 8 and 64. 16, 32

16. Find the mean proportional between -3 and -27. -9

Write each series using sigma notation. $\sum\limits_{k=1}^{\infty} 2(-0.3)^{k-1}$ $\sum\limits_{k=1}^{\infty}(6k-2)$

17. $2 - 0.6 + 0.18 - 0.054 + 0.0162 - \cdots$

18. $4 + 10 + 16 + 22 + 28 + \cdots$ 13.3

19. Find the value of $\sum\limits_{k=1}^{15}(12 - 3k)$. -180

20. Find S_8 for $\sum\limits_{m=1}^{\infty}(2.3m + 6)$. 130.8

21. Use the principle of mathematical induction to prove that the following statement is true for all positive integers n.

$$1^3 + 2^3 + 3^3 + \cdots + n^3 = \frac{n^2(n+1)^2}{4}$$ 13.4

13.4 Mathematical Induction   **705**

Vocabulary
binomial
binomial coefficient
binomial theorem
factorial notation

Technology
calculator
symbolic manipulator

FOCUS

The array we now call Pascal's triangle appeared in a number of works before Pascal's *Traité du triangle arithmétique,* which was written in 1653 and published in 1665. Thirteenth century Arab and Chinese mathematicians were familiar with it. The triangle was named after Pascal because of his development of many of its properties and applications of those properties.

The numbers in Pascal's triangle have many interesting properties, which students may enjoy exploring. For example, the sum of the numbers in the nth row of the triangle is 2^n. Also, the product of the six entries surrounding any given entry is a perfect square. The "hockey stick" formula states that if successive elements in any diagonal are added downward to the left, the sum at any point is the element just below and to the right of the last addend.

13.5 The Binomial Theorem

Objectives: To use the binomial theorem to expand a binomial
To find a specified term of a binomial expansion

Focus

As every historian knows, seemingly minor events can profoundly affect the course of history. One illustration of this from the history of mathematics can be found in the life of Blaise Pascal (1623–1662), the French mathematician and physicist for whom a popular computer language has been named.

Pascal worked in geometry, probability theory, algebra, number theory, and physics. After a mystical experience, however, he decided to devote himself to philosophy and religion and only occasionally to think about mathematical or scientific ideas. On one such occasion he was working on a problem in geometry while suffering from a severe toothache. To his delight and surprise, the pain disappeared at the very moment he was discovering the solution to his problem. Pascal took the simultaneous occurrence of these two events as a sign that he should continue to work in geometry. He went on to develop the theory he had begun and came very close to discovering some of the basic concepts of calculus.

Many students remember Pascal for a "triangle" of numbers that are useful in both algebra and probability. It is now recognized that "Pascal's triangle," as it is now called, was known to Chinese mathematicians as early as the thirteenth century.

Recall that a **binomial** is an algebraic expression with two terms, for example, $a + b$, $x^2 - 3y$, or $1 + 0.0001$. Formulas for expanding powers of binomials are found throughout the early history of mathematics; as early as the third century B.C. Chinese scholars knew the expansion of $(a + b)^3$.

Examining several expansions of binomials may offer clues to a general formula for $(a + b)^n$. By using the distributive, commutative, and associative properties, you can easily obtain the following results.

$$(a + b)^0 = 1$$
$$(a + b)^1 = a + b$$
$$(a + b)^2 = a^2 + 2ab + b^2$$
$$(a + b)^3 = a^3 + 3a^2b + 3ab^2 + b^3$$
$$(a + b)^4 = a^4 + 4a^3b + 6a^2b^2 + 4ab^3 + b^4$$
$$(a + b)^5 = a^5 + 5a^4b + 10a^3b^2 + 10a^2b^3 + 5ab^4 + b^5$$

706   Chapter 13 Sequences and Series

These formulas can be used to expand binomial expressions.

Example 1   Expand and simplify the expression $(2x^3 - \sqrt{5}x^{-1})^4$.

Use the formula for $(a + b)^4$ with $a = 2x^3$ and $b = -\sqrt{5}x^{-1}$.

$(2x^3 - \sqrt{5}x^{-1})^4$

$= [2x^3 + (-\sqrt{5}x^{-1})]^4$

$= (2x^3)^4 + 4(2x^3)^3(-\sqrt{5}x^{-1}) + 6(2x^3)^2(-\sqrt{5}x^{-1})^2 + 4(2x^3)(-\sqrt{5}x^{-1})^3 + (-\sqrt{5}x^{-1})^4$

$= 16x^{12} + 4 \cdot 8x^9(-\sqrt{5}x^{-1}) + 6 \cdot 4x^6 \cdot 5x^{-2} + 8x^3(-5\sqrt{5}x^{-3}) + 25x^{-4}$

$= 16x^{12} - 32\sqrt{5}x^8 + 120x^4 - 40\sqrt{5} + 25x^{-4}$

Now return to the six formulas, and look for patterns that may be generalized to a formula for $(a + b)^n$.

- In the expansion of $(a + b)^n$ there are $n + 1$ terms.
- The first term is a^n and the last is b^n.
- The second term is $na^{n-1}b$ and the next-to-last term is nab^{n-1}.
- The powers of a decrease by 1 from left to right, and the powers of b increase by 1 from left to right. (Think of the first and last terms as a^nb^0 and a^0b^n.)
- The sum of the exponents in each term is n.

At this point, there is enough information to deduce everything but the coefficients of $(a + b)^n$ for $n = 6, 7, 8, \ldots$. For example, it appears that $(a + b)^6 = a^6 + 6a^5b + \underline{?} \ a^4b^2 + \underline{?} \ a^3b^3 + \underline{?} \ a^2b^4 + 6ab^5 + b^6$ where $\underline{?}$ denotes an unknown coefficient.

One way to find the missing coefficients is by using **Pascal's triangle.** This triangle is an array of numbers with many applications and interesting properties. To see the development of Pascal's triangle, first write the coefficients from the six formulas shown earlier in a triangular array like this.

$$
\begin{array}{ccccccccccc}
 & & & & & 1 & & & & & \\
 & & & & 1 & & 1 & & & & \\
 & & & 1 & & 2 & & 1 & & & \\
 & & 1 & & 3 & & 3 & & 1 & & \\
 & 1 & & 4 & & 6 & & 4 & & 1 & \\
1 & & 5 & & 10 & & 10 & & 5 & & 1 \\
\end{array}
$$

Notice that each row begins and ends with 1, and every other number is the sum of the two nearest numbers in the row above it. You can use this observation to extend Pascal's triangle by two more rows.

$$
\begin{array}{ccccccccccccc}
 & & & & & & 1 & & & & & & \\
 & & & & & 1 & & 1 & & & & & \\
 & & & & 1 & & 2 & & 1 & & & & \\
 & & & 1 & & 3 & & 3 & & 1 & & & \\
 & & 1 & & 4 & & 6 & & 4 & & 1 & & \\
 & 1 & & 5 & & 10 & & 10 & & 5 & & 1 & \\
1 & & 6 & & 15 & & 20 & & 15 & & 6 & & 1 \\
 & 1 & 7 & & 21 & & 35 & & 35 & & 21 & 7 & 1 \\
\end{array}
$$

13.5 The Binomial Theorem   **707**

- Have students identify as many patterns as they can in the expansions of $(a + b)^n$ for $n = 0, 1, 2, 3, 4, 5$ before pointing out the ones suggested in the text.
- The ability to apply a formula to a particular example is important in many fields that use mathematics. Some students will need extensive practice with problems like Example 1.
- Students may enjoy looking for patterns in Pascal's triangle, and then researching patterns that have been identified by others and verifying those patterns. For example, the number of odd entries in the nth row of Pascal's triangle is 2^t, where t is the number of 1's in the binary representation of n.

Alternative Learning Styles

Focusing on patterns in both Pascal's triangle and the binomial theorem is helpful to students who are global learners.

GUIDED PRACTICE

For Example 1

Expand and simplify the expression.

1. $\left(\sqrt{2}x + \frac{1}{2}x^2\right)^3$

$2\sqrt{2}x^3 + 3x^4 + \frac{3\sqrt{2}}{4}x^5 + \frac{1}{8}x^6$

Common Error   Sometimes students may find the number of terms to be simplified distracting. Encourage these students to write out the application of the formula using the terms from the exercise before doing any simplification. Then it is easier to find any error in computation. For example, for $\left(2x + \frac{1}{2}x^2\right)^3$, write $(2x)^3 + 3(2x)^2\left(\frac{1}{2}x^2\right) + 3(2x)\left(\frac{1}{2}x^2\right)^2 + \left(\frac{1}{2}x^2\right)^3$ as a first line.

For Example 2

Compute the value of each binomial coefficient.

1. $\begin{pmatrix} 10 \\ 6 \end{pmatrix}$ 210

2. $\begin{pmatrix} 16 \\ 11 \end{pmatrix}$ 4368

For Example 3

Find the value of each expression.

1. 9! 362,880

2. $\dfrac{10!}{10}$ 362,880

You can probably guess that the numbers in the last two rows should be the coefficients for the expansions of $(a + b)^6$ and $(a + b)^7$ so that

$$(a + b)^6 = a^6 + 6a^5b + 15a^4b^2 + 20a^3b^3 + 15a^2b^4 + 6ab^5 + b^6$$
$$(a + b)^7 = a^7 + 7a^6b + 21a^5b^2 + 35a^4b^3 + 35a^3b^4 + 21a^2b^5 + 7ab^6 + b^7$$

The values in Pascal's triangle are obtained recursively; to find the 1001st row you would need to compute all the rows that precede it. As with many sequences that are defined recursively, it is possible to find an explicit formula for the coefficients that Pascal's triangle provides.

The symbol $\begin{pmatrix} n \\ r \end{pmatrix}$, read "$n$ over r," is defined by the formula

$$\begin{pmatrix} n \\ r \end{pmatrix} = \frac{n(n - 1)(n - 2) \cdots (n - r + 2)(n - r + 1)}{r(r - 1)(r - 2) \cdots 3 \cdot 2 \cdot 1}$$

where n and r are positive integers with $1 \le r \le n$. For example,

$$\begin{pmatrix} 6 \\ 3 \end{pmatrix} = \frac{6 \cdot 5 \cdot 4}{3 \cdot 2 \cdot 1} = 20 \quad \text{and} \quad \begin{pmatrix} 7 \\ 4 \end{pmatrix} = \frac{7 \cdot 6 \cdot 5 \cdot 4}{4 \cdot 3 \cdot 2 \cdot 1} = 35$$

The numbers $\begin{pmatrix} n \\ r \end{pmatrix}$ are the coefficients in the expanded form of $(a + b)^n$. They are therefore called **binomial coefficients.** Notice that both the numerator and the denominator of $\begin{pmatrix} n \\ r \end{pmatrix}$ are products of r factors, the numerator beginning at n and the denominator beginning at r, with each factor decreasing by 1.

Example 2   Compute the value of the binomial coefficients $\begin{pmatrix} 15 \\ 6 \end{pmatrix}$ and $\begin{pmatrix} 35 \\ 2 \end{pmatrix}$.

By the formula above, $\begin{pmatrix} 15 \\ 6 \end{pmatrix} = \dfrac{15 \cdot 14 \cdot 13 \cdot 12 \cdot 11 \cdot 10}{6 \cdot 5 \cdot 4 \cdot 3 \cdot 2 \cdot 1} = 5005$ and

$\begin{pmatrix} 35 \\ 2 \end{pmatrix} = \dfrac{35 \cdot 34}{2 \cdot 1} = 595$.

The use of **factorial notation** makes writing the formula for the binomial coefficient more efficient. For any integer $n \ge 1$, $n!$ (read "n-factorial") is defined by the formula

$$n! = n(n - 1)(n - 2) \cdots 3 \cdot 2 \cdot 1$$

For example, $3! = 3 \cdot 2 \cdot 1 = 6$ and $6! = 6 \cdot 5 \cdot 4 \cdot 3 \cdot 2 \cdot 1 = 720$. The expression $0!$ is *defined* to be 1.

Example 3   Find the value of each expression.   **a.** $8!$ **b.** $8 \cdot 7!$ **c.** $\dfrac{12!}{6!}$

a. $8! = 8 \cdot 7 \cdot 6 \cdot 5 \cdot 4 \cdot 3 \cdot 2 \cdot 1 = 40{,}320$ *Use a calculator.*

b. $8 \cdot 7! = 8 \cdot (7 \cdot 6 \cdot 5 \cdot 4 \cdot 3 \cdot 2 \cdot 1) = 8! = 40{,}320$

c. $\dfrac{12!}{6!} = \dfrac{12 \cdot 11 \cdot 10 \cdot 9 \cdot 8 \cdot 7 \cdot 6!}{6!} = 12 \cdot 11 \cdot 10 \cdot 9 \cdot 8 \cdot 7 = 665{,}280$

708   Chapter 13 Sequences and Series

The denominator in the definition of the binomial coefficient $\binom{n}{r}$ is exactly $r!$.
If you multiply the numerator and denominator in this definition by $(n - r)!$,

$$\binom{n}{r} = \frac{n(n - 1)(n - 2) \cdots (n - r + 2)(n - r + 1) \cdot (n - r)!}{r(r - 1)(r - 2) \cdots 3 \cdot 2 \cdot 1 \cdot (n - r)!}$$

$$= \frac{n(n - 1)(n - 2) \cdots (n - r + 2)(n - r + 1) \cdot (n - r)(n - r - 1) \cdots 3 \cdot 2 \cdot 1}{r(r - 1)(r - 2) \cdots 3 \cdot 2 \cdot 1 \cdot (n - r)!}$$

$$= \frac{n!}{r!(n - r)!}$$

From this version of the definition $\binom{n}{0}$ which was previously undefined, has the

value $\frac{n!}{0!(n - 0)!} = \frac{n!}{n!} = 1$. It is in order to obtain this result that $0!$ is defined to

be 1. It is also immediately clear that $\binom{n}{r} = \binom{n}{n - r}$. Some calculators

have keys that enable you to compute $n!$ and $\binom{n}{r}$ directly.

The binomial coefficients $\binom{n}{r}$ are precisely the numbers given by Pascal's

triangle and can be used to compute the coefficients in the expansion of
$(a + b)^n$ directly. The $n + 1$ coefficients in the expansion are

$$\binom{n}{0}, \quad \binom{n}{1}, \quad \binom{n}{2}, \quad \binom{n}{3}, \quad \cdots, \quad \binom{n}{n - 1}, \quad \binom{n}{n}$$

The r in the symbol $\binom{n}{r}$ corresponds to the power of b in the expansion. The

first and last coefficients are 1, and the second and next-to-last coefficients are

$$\binom{n}{1} = \frac{n!}{1!(n - 1)!} = \frac{n \cdot (n - 1)(n - 2) \cdots 3 \cdot 2 \cdot 1}{1 \cdot (n - 1)(n - 2) \cdots 3 \cdot 2 \cdot 1} = n$$

This corresponds to the observations made earlier about the coefficients of a^n,
b^n, a^{n-1} and b^{n-1}.

Example 4   What is the coefficient of $x^8 y^7$ in the expansion of $(x + y)^{15}$?

$$\binom{15}{7} = \frac{15!}{8!7!} = 6435 \qquad \textit{The exponent on x is 8. The exponent on y is 7.}$$

The relationships observed so far are summarized in the *binomial theorem*.

Binomial Theorem

If a and b are real numbers and n is a positive integer, then

$$(a + b)^n = \binom{n}{0}a^n + \binom{n}{1}a^{n-1}b + \binom{n}{2}a^{n-2}b^2 + \cdots + \binom{n}{n - 1}ab^{n-1} + \binom{n}{n}b^n$$

where $\binom{n}{k}$ is the binomial coefficient $\binom{n}{k} = \frac{n!}{k!(n - k)!}$.

13.5 The Binomial Theorem   **709**

For Example 4
What is the coefficient of $a^6 b^9$ in the
expansion of $(a + b)^{15}$? 5005

Common Error   Some students
may not realize that the *r*th term in
the expansion of $(a + b)^n$ involves

the coefficient $\binom{n}{r - 1}$ and the pow-

ers $a^{n-(r-1)}$ and b^r. Point this out to
these students after they have
worked a few exercises.

In order to prove the theorem, it is useful to prove a relationship between two binomial coefficients first.

If r and k are positive integers with $r \leq k$, then

$$\binom{k}{r-1} + \binom{k}{r} = \binom{k+1}{r}$$

Notice that this corresponds to the fact that in Pascal's triangle any number is obtained by adding its two neighbors at the upper left and upper right. To prove the relationship, use the definition of the binomial coefficient to add the two quantities on the left-hand side. In the steps below, note that $r(r-1)! = r!$, $(k-r+1)(k-r)! = (k-r+1)!$, and so on.

$$\binom{k}{r-1} + \binom{k}{r} = \frac{k!}{(r-1)!(k-r+1)!} + \frac{k!}{r! \cdot (k-r)!} \qquad \text{\textit{Definition of the binomial coefficient}}$$

$$= \frac{k!}{(r-1)!(k-r)!} \cdot \left(\frac{1}{k-r+1} + \frac{1}{r} \right) \qquad \text{\textit{Distributive property}}$$

$$= \frac{k!}{(r-1)!(k-r)!} \cdot \frac{k+1}{r(k-r+1)} \qquad \text{\textit{Addition of fractions}}$$

$$= \frac{(k+1)!}{r!(k-r+1)!}$$

$$= \binom{k+1}{r}$$

With this fact established, the binomial theorem can now be proved by mathematical induction. First verify that the formula holds for the case $n = 1$.

For this case, $(a+b)^1 = \binom{1}{0}a^1 + \binom{1}{1}b^1$. Since both coefficients equal 1, the equation reduces to $(a+b)^1 = a + b$.

Next, suppose that the formula holds for $n = k$:

$$P_k: (a+b)^k = \binom{k}{0}a^k + \binom{k}{1}a^{k-1}b + \binom{k}{2}a^{k-2}b^2 + \cdots + \binom{k}{k-1}ab^{k-1} + \binom{k}{k}b^k$$

Now use this fact to show that the following is true.

$$P_{k+1}: (a+b)^{k+1} = \binom{k+1}{0}a^{k+1} + \binom{k+1}{1}a^k b + \cdots + \binom{k+1}{k}ab^k + \binom{k+1}{k+1}b^{k+1}$$

To do this, multiply both sides of the formula for $n = k$ by $a + b$ to obtain

$$(a+b)^{k+1} = \binom{k}{0}a^{k+1} + \binom{k}{1}a^k b + \binom{k}{2}a^{k-1}b^2 + \binom{k}{3}a^{k-2}b^3 + \cdots + \binom{k}{k}ab^k$$

$$+ \binom{k}{0}a^k b + \binom{k}{1}a^{k-1}b^2 + \binom{k}{2}a^{k-2}b^3 + \cdots + \binom{k}{k-1}ab^k + \binom{k}{k}b^{k+1}$$

Add like terms, such as $\binom{k}{1}a^k b$ and $\binom{k}{0}a^k b$, as indicated, using the established fact that

$$\binom{k}{r-1} + \binom{k}{r} = \binom{k+1}{r}$$

For example, $\binom{k}{0} + \binom{k}{1} = \binom{k+1}{1}$ and $\binom{k}{1} + \binom{k}{2} = \binom{k+1}{2}$. This gives

$$(a + b)^{k+1} = \binom{k+1}{0}a^{k+1} + \binom{k+1}{1}a^k b + \cdots + \binom{k+1}{k}ab^k + \binom{k+1}{k+1}b^{k+1}$$

In the last line above, $\binom{k}{0}$ and $\binom{k}{k}$ have been replaced by $\binom{k+1}{0}$ and $\binom{k+1}{k+1}$, respectively. *Why is this replacement allowed?*

Thus, by the principle of mathematical induction, the binomial theorem holds for every positive integer n.

Example 5   Use the binomial theorem to expand and simplify $(a + b)^5$.

$$(a + b)^5 = \binom{5}{0}a^5 b^0 + \binom{5}{1}a^4 b^1 + \binom{5}{2}a^3 b^2 + \binom{5}{3}a^2 b^3 + \binom{5}{4}a^1 b^4 + \binom{5}{5}a^0 b^5$$
$$= a^5 + 5a^4 b + 10a^3 b^2 + 10a^2 b^3 + 5ab^4 + b^5$$

You can check the expansion of a binomial for errors by verifying such things as the number of terms and the degree of each term. In Example 5, the number of terms should be (and is) equal to 1 more than the degree of the polynomial $(5 + 1 = 6)$. The degree of the polynomial, 5, is also the sum of the two exponents of the factors a and b in each term. The first and last terms have equal coefficients (1 and 1) as do the second and fifth terms (5 and 5) and the third and fourth terms (10 and 10).

Example 6   Find the fourth term of $(2a - 6b)^{11}$.

First note that $-6b$, the second term of the binomial, is raised to the *third* power (1 less than 4) in the fourth term. Then $2a$, the first term of the binomial, must be raised to the *eighth* power $(8 + 3 = 11)$. Thus, the fourth term, without its binomial coefficient, is $(2a)^8(-6b)^3$. With the binomial coefficient, the term is

$$\binom{11}{3}(2a)^8(-6b)^3 = 165 \cdot 256a^8 \cdot (-216b^3) = -9{,}123{,}840a^8 b^3$$

 In Example 6, many calculators can compute the binomial coefficient $\binom{11}{3}$ automatically. Often, the symbol $_{11}C_3$ is used rather than $\binom{11}{3}$.

Class Exercises

Find the value of each expression.

1. $7!$ 5040   **2.** $9!$ 362,880   **3.** $\dfrac{12!}{8!}$ 11,880   **4.** $\binom{8}{5}$ 56   **5.** $\binom{20}{7}$ 77,520   **6.** $\binom{100}{2}$ 4950

Tell whether each statement is true or false. If false, give a reason or counterexample. Let n and r be positive integers with $r \le n$.

7. $r! \le n!$ T   **8.** $(2n)! = 2(n!)$ F   **9.** $0! = 0$ F

10. $\binom{8}{0} = \binom{22}{0}$ T   **11.** $\binom{98}{r} = \binom{98}{98-r}$ T   **12.** $n! + r! = (n + r)!$ F

13.5 The Binomial Theorem   **711**

---

1. Expand and simplify the expression $(2q + t^3)^7$. $128q^7 + 448q^6t^3 + 672q^5t^6 + 560q^4t^9 + 280q^3t^{12} + 84q^2t^{15} + 14qt^{18} + t^{21}$

2. Find the value of $\binom{21}{8}$. $203{,}490$

3. Find the value of $\dfrac{13!}{10!}$. 1716

4. What is the coefficient of a^7b^2 in the expansion of $(a + b)^9$? 36

5. Use the binomial theorem to expand and simplify $(f + g)^4$.
$f^4 + 4f^3g + 6f^2g^2 + 4fg^3 + g^4$

6. Find the third term of $(2x - 3y)^7$.
$6048x^5y^2$

Additional Answers

Class Exercises

13. 1 8 28 56 70 56 28 8 1
1 9 36 84 126 126 84 36 9 1

14. $x^9 + 9x^8y + 36x^7y^2 + 84x^6y^3 + 126x^5y^4 + 126x^4y^5 + 84x^3y^6 + 36x^2y^7 + 9xy^8 + y^9$

15. $a^4 + 20a^3 + 150a^2 + 500a + 625$

16. $1024x^5 - 640x^4y^3 + 160x^3y^6 - 20x^2y^9 + \dfrac{5}{4}xy^{12} - \dfrac{1}{32}y^{15}$

Practice Exercises

7. $x^8 + 8x^7y + 28x^6y^2 + 56x^5y^3 + 70x^4y^4 + 56x^3y^5 + 28x^2y^6 + 8xy^7 + y^8$

8. $x^6 - 30x^5y + 375x^4y^2 - 2500x^3y^3 + 9375x^2y^4 - 18{,}750xy^5 + 15{,}625y^6$

9. $1 - 10x^3 + 40x^6 - 80x^9 + 80x^{12} - 32x^{15}$

10. $z^{12} + 16z^7 + 96z^2 + \dfrac{256}{z^3} + \dfrac{256}{z^8}$

12. $n! = n \cdot (n - 1) \cdot (n - 2) \cdots 2 \cdot 1 = n[(n - 1) \cdot (n - 2) \cdots 2 \cdot 1] = n(n - 1)!$

13. $n = 2;\ (2^2)! = 24;\ (2!)^2 = 4$

14. $\binom{n}{r} = \dfrac{n!}{r!(n - r)!};\ \binom{n}{n - r} = \dfrac{n!}{(n - r)![n - (n - r)]!} = \dfrac{n!}{(n - r)!r!}$

30. Even-numbered terms get a negative sign and odd-numbered terms get a positive sign.

---

13. Write the rows of Pascal's triangle corresponding to $(a + b)^8$ and $(a + b)^9$.

14. Use the result of Class Exercise 13 to write the expansion of $(x + y)^9$.

15. Use the binomial theorem to expand and simplify $(a + 5)^4$.

16. Use the binomial theorem to expand and simplify $\left(4x - \frac{1}{2}y^3\right)^5$.

17. What is the coefficient of the term a^5b^{16} in the expansion of $(a + b)^{21}$? $20{,}349$

18. What is the coefficient of the term involving x^9 in the expansion of $(x + 2)^{14}$? $64{,}064$

Practice Exercises   ⊖⊘ Use appropriate technology.

Find the value of each expression.

A 1. $6!$ 720 2. $\dfrac{56!}{52!}$ $8{,}814{,}960$ 3. $\dfrac{29!}{25!4!}$ $23{,}751$ 4. $\binom{7}{3}$ 35 5. $\binom{16}{9}$ $11{,}440$ 6. $\binom{75}{72}$
$67{,}525$

7. Use Pascal's triangle to write the expansion of $(x + y)^8$.

Use the binomial theorem to expand and simplify each expression.

8. $(x - 5y)^6$ 9. $(1 - 2x^3)^5$ 10. $(z^3 + 4z^{-2})^4$

Ⓡ 11. In an arithmetic sequence, $a_1 = 4$ and $a_7 = 22$. Find the common difference and use it to find a_5 and a_{55}. $3;\ 16,\ 166$

12. Show that for any positive integer n, $n! = n \cdot (n - 1)!$.

13. Find a counterexample to the claim that $(n^2)! = (n!)^2$.

14. Show that for any positive integers n and r with $r \le n$, $\binom{n}{r} = \binom{n}{n - r}$.

Ⓡ 15. Find the partial sum S_7 for the arithmetic sequence in Exercise 11. 91

Find the coefficient of the indicated term in the expansion of the given power of a binomial. Identify the missing exponents in each term.

16. $x^?y^9;\ (x + y)^{11}$ $55;\ 2$ 17. $x^4y^5;\ (x + y)^?$ $126;\ 9$ 18. $x^3y^?;\ (x + y)^8$ $56;\ 5$

Find the terms involving the specified variable in each expansion.

19. b^4 in $(a + b)^{10}$ $210a^6b^4$ 20. a^5 in $(a + b)^{12}$ $792a^5b^7$ 21. b^6 in $(a - b)^{14}$ $3003a^8b^6$

Find the indicated term of each expansion.

B 22. third term of $(a + 5b)^4$ $150a^2b^2$ 23. fifth term of $(2m - k)^9$ $4032m^5k^4$

24. seventh term of $(x + x^2)^{12}$ $924x^{18}$ 25. sixth term of $(3x - 2y)^8$ $-48{,}384x^3y^5$

26. fourth term of $\left(2 + \frac{1}{2}x^4\right)^7$ $70x^{12}$ 27. eighth term of $(k - \sqrt{2})^{10}$ $-960\sqrt{2}k^3$

28. Simplify: $\dfrac{n!(n + 2)!}{(n + 1)!(n + 3)!}$ $\dfrac{1}{(n + 1)(n + 3)}$

Ⓡ 29. In a geometric sequence $a_4 = \frac{1}{4}$ and $a_7 = 1$. What is the common ratio r? $4^{\frac{1}{3}}$

30. **Thinking Critically**   Write the expansion of $(a - b)^n$ for $n = 1, 2, 3, 4,$ and 5. How can the *sign* of a term be determined without writing out the entire expansion?

Ⓡ 31. Find the partial sum S_{10} for the sequence in Exercise 29. 10.70326

32. Use the binomial theorem to find the value of $(2 + i)^7$ where $i = \sqrt{-1}$. $-278 - 29i$

33. Use the binomial theorem to approximate the value of 1.02^4 by expanding $(1 + 0.02)^4$. 1.08243216

34. Use the binomial theorem to approximate the value of 0.97^3 by expanding $(1 - 0.03)^3$. 0.912673

Ⓡ 35. *Finance*   In planning for a winter vacation, Lynn decides to save $1.50 in March, $3.00 in April, $6.00 in May, and so on, doubling the amount saved through the following January. How much has Lynn saved when she begins her vacation on January 31? $3070.50

36. **Writing in Mathematics**   Discuss the places in the binomial theorem in which symmetry is involved. Tell how symmetry can help cut down the amount of information you need to memorize or compute.

37. **Thinking Critically**   Describe how to use the binomial theorem to expand $(x + y + z)^{10}$.

C 38. Find the term involving x^4 in $\left(x^2 + \dfrac{3}{x}\right)^8$. $5670x^4$

39. Find the term that does not contain t in $\left(5t + \dfrac{1}{2}t^{-1}\right)^8$. 2734.375

40. The expression $\dfrac{f(x + h) - f(x)}{h}$, $h \neq 0$, appears often in calculus. Let $f(x) = x^{16}$ and find the term in the expanded and simplified form of this expression that does not contain h. $16x^{15}$

41. Repeat Exercise 40 for $f(x) = x^n$, where n is an arbitrary positive integer. nx^{n-1}

42. Find the sum of the numbers in each row of Pascal's triangle through $n = 8$. Use the convention that the row corresponding to the coefficients in $(a + b)^n$ is row n; the top row, which contains just the number 1, is row 0. Formulate a hypothesis about the sum of the numbers in row n of Pascal's triangle. sum $= 2^n$

43. Write 2^n as $(1 + 1)^n$ and expand this expression using the binomial theorem. Compare the results with those of Exercise 42.

44. Find the sum of the numbers on each "rising diagonal" in Pascal's triangle shown at the right. What do you notice?

45. Write 0 as $1 + (-1)$ and show that
$$\binom{n}{0} - \binom{n}{1} + \binom{n}{2} - \binom{n}{3} + \cdots \pm \binom{n}{n} = 0$$
(The symbol $\pm$ denotes $+$ if n is odd, $-$ if n is even.)

46. Determine the value of $\displaystyle\sum_{k=0}^{n}\binom{n}{k}2^k$. To what binomial expansion does this sum correspond? $3^n = (2 + 1)^n$

Challenge

1. In a certain sequence of numbers, the first number is 1, and, for all $n \geq 2$, the product of the first n numbers in the sequence is n^2. Find the sum of the second and fourth numbers in the sequence. $\dfrac{52}{9}$

2. Find the degree of $(x^3 + 1)^2(x^4 + 2)^3$ as a polynomial in x. 18

13.5 The Binomial Theorem   **713**

713

Vocabulary
converge
convergent sequence
diverge
divergent sequence
harmonic sequence
limit

Ⓜ **Materials/Manipulatives**
thousands cubes

FOCUS

Some students enjoy working with very large numbers, but it is sometimes difficult for them to get a real sense of the relative sizes of those numbers. Because our number system enables us to write very large numbers so compactly, readers tend to underestimate their actual sizes greatly. Real world examples are a good way to help develop a sense of number size. For example, to count one trillion dollars at the rate of one dollar bill a second would take over 31,000 years. Students may also enjoy the challenge of finding out the names of numbers like 10^{21} (sextillion), 10^{42} (tredecillion), and 10^{63} (vigintillion).

INSTRUCTION

Ⓜ • Use thousands cubes and other physical representations of large numbers to help students visualize their sizes.
• You may also wish to have students look for examples of numbers larger than a million in newspapers and magazines.
• Use examples of sets of things (like "all the drops of water in all the oceans on earth") and have students judge whether the sets are finite or infinite.

13.6   Limits of Sequences

Objectives: To find the limit of an infinite sequence, if it exists
To determine when the limit of an infinite sequence does not exist

Focus

It can be very difficult to visualize the relative sizes of large numbers. You may know that a million is 1,000,000 or 10^6, a billion is 1,000,000,000 or 10^9, and a trillion is 1,000,000,000,000 or 10^{12}. But how big are 10^6, 10^9, 10^{12}?

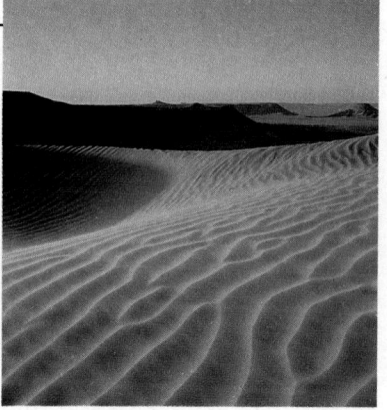

A physical comparison may help. A million seconds take about 11.6 days to pass; a billion seconds take 31.7 years. A trillion seconds take about 31,700 years, much longer than all of recorded human history. Interest in large numbers is not a recent phenomenon. Archimedes estimated that the number of grains of sand needed to fill up the earth and heavens is no more than 10^{63}.

No matter how large a number you can express, there is always another number that is greater. Given enough time, you could count all the grains of sand in the world. But no matter how much time is available, and how quickly you can count, you would never run out of counting numbers. The set of counting numbers is infinite.

Mathematicians have devised many ways of describing infinite sets of numbers. One of these ways is the notion of limits. Consider the infinite sequence 1, $\frac{1}{2}, \frac{1}{3}, \frac{1}{4}, \ldots$ whose general term is $a_n = \frac{1}{n}$.

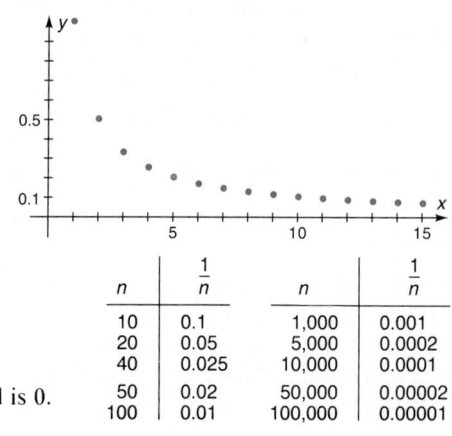

There are several ways you could explore how the terms of this sequence behave as n gets larger and larger without bound. For example, you could graph some terms of the sequence and use the graph to help predict the behavior of $\frac{1}{n}$ as n moves to the right along the x-axis. You would eventually conclude that as n increases without bound, the numbers $a_n = \frac{1}{n}$ get closer and closer to zero. The mathematical formulation of this fact is the statement:

The **limit** of $a_n = \frac{1}{n}$ as n increases without bound is 0.

n	$\frac{1}{n}$	n	$\frac{1}{n}$
10	0.1	1,000	0.001
20	0.05	5,000	0.0002
40	0.025	10,000	0.0001
50	0.02	50,000	0.00002
100	0.01	100,000	0.00001

714   Chapter 13 Sequences and Series

Mathematical shorthand for this statement is $\lim\limits_{n \to \infty} \frac{1}{n} = 0$. It is important to observe that there is no value of n for which $\frac{1}{n}$ actually equals zero. Saying that the limit of a sequence is zero simply says that as n gets larger and larger, the terms of the sequence get closer and closer to zero.

The sequence $1, \frac{1}{2}, \frac{1}{3}, \frac{1}{4}, \frac{1}{5}, \ldots, \frac{1}{n}, \ldots$ is known as the **harmonic sequence.** There is a musical basis for this name. The fundamental tone of a string (for example, a violin string) is obtained by vibrating the string. The first harmonic is obtained by lightly touching the vibrating string at its midpoint, the second harmonic by touching it one third the way down, and so on. The $(n-1)$st harmonic is obtained by touching the vibrating string at a point $\frac{1}{n}$ the way down.

Example 1   Find the limit of each sequence as n increases without bound.

$\quad$ **a.** $a_n = \dfrac{n+1}{n}$ $\qquad$ **b.** $b_n = \dfrac{3n+2}{n+1}$

$\quad$ **a.** Terms of the sequence are 2, 1.5, 1.3333, 1.25, 1.2, 1.1667, 1.1429, ... Division shows that $\frac{n+1}{n} = 1 + \frac{1}{n}$, and since $\frac{1}{n}$ approaches 0 as n increases without bound, it follows that $1 + \frac{1}{n}$ approaches 1, that is, $\lim\limits_{n \to \infty} \frac{n+1}{n} = 1$.

$\quad$ **b.** Another useful algebraic technique is to divide the numerator and denominator by the highest power of n common to both, in this case, by n. This gives the equivalent expression $b_n = \dfrac{3 + \frac{2}{n}}{1 + \frac{1}{n}}$. As n increases without bound, both $\frac{2}{n}$ and $\frac{1}{n}$ approach zero. Thus, b_n gets closer and closer to $\frac{3+0}{1+0} = 3$, that is, $\lim\limits_{n \to \infty} b_n = 3$.

If a sequence gets closer and closer to a number L as n increases without bound, the sequence is said to **converge** to that number, and to be a *convergent sequence*. Not all sequences converge; those that do not are said to **diverge.**

Example 2   Find the first seven terms of the sequence $a_n = 2^n$. Then describe the behavior of the sequence as n increases without bound.

Terms of this sequence are 2, 4, 8, 16, 32, 64, 128, ... It is evident that the larger n gets, the larger 2^n gets. As n increases without bound ($n \to \infty$), 2^n increases without bound as well. The sequence diverges.

A graph of the sequence is shown at the right. If the sequence were convergent, then there would be a horizontal line $y = L$ that the sequence approached but never crossed. This is clearly not the case.

13.6 Limits of Sequences $\quad$ **715**

715

GUIDED PRACTICE

For Example 1
Find the limit of each sequence as n increases without bound.

1. $a_n = \dfrac{2n+8}{n}$

$\lim\limits_{n \to \infty} \dfrac{2n+8}{n} = 2$

2. $b_n = \dfrac{n^2 + 5}{3n^2}$

$\lim\limits_{n \to \infty} \dfrac{n^2 + 5}{3n^2} = \dfrac{1}{3}$

For Example 2
Find the first five terms of each sequence. Then describe the behavior of the sequence as n increases without bound.

1. $a_n = \sqrt{n}$ $\quad$ 1, $\sqrt{2}$, $\sqrt{3}$, 2, $\sqrt{5}$; As n increases without bound, a_n increases without bound.

2. $b_n = \dfrac{n^3 + 1}{2n^2 - n}$ $\quad$ 2, $\frac{9}{6}$, $\frac{28}{15}$, $\frac{65}{28}$, $\frac{126}{45}$; After the second term of the sequence, b_n increases without bound as n increases without bound.

Common Error   Some students may say that $\lim\limits_{n \to \infty} b_n = \frac{1}{2}$. Encourage these students to carefully think through several examples involving the ratio of polynomial expressions including these three possibilities: The degree of the numerator is less than the degree of the denominator, greater than the degree of the denominator, and equal to the degree of the denominator.

Ⓜ Alternative Learning Styles
Students who are concrete learners will benefit from seeing and handling physical representations of large numbers and will also appreciate real life comparisons and examples. These students need to see examples of larger and larger numbers in order to think about "infinity."

For Example 3

For Example 3

Determine whether each sequence converges or diverges. If it converges, give the limit.

1. $a_n = (-10)^n$ diverges

2. $b_n = 5^n$ diverges

For Example 4

Determine whether each sequence converges or diverges. If it converges, give the limit.

1. $a_n = \left(\dfrac{1}{4}\right)^n$

converges; The limit is 0.

2. $b_n = \left(-\dfrac{1}{4}\right)^n$

converges; The limit is 0.

For Example 5

Characterize each sequence as either convergent or divergent. If it converges, give the limit.

1. $a_n = 6 + \dfrac{4n - 2}{n + 8}$

convergent; The limit is 10.

2. $b_n = \dfrac{5 + \sqrt{2}}{n + 1}$

convergent; The limit is 0.

3. $c_n = \dfrac{3n^6 + n}{5n^2 + 8}$ divergent

Some sequences diverge even though they are bounded.

Example 3 Determine whether the sequence $b_n = (-1)^n$ converges or diverges. If it converges, give the limit.

Terms of this sequence are $-1, 1, -1, 1, -1, 1, -1, 1, \dots$ and the terms continue to oscillate between -1 and 1 as n increases without bound. As soon as the sequence gets to the number 1, it moves away; as soon as it gets to -1, it moves away. Although bounded, this sequence has no limit and therefore diverges. Its graph is shown at the right.

If you use a graphing utility to graph the sequence $b_n = (-1)^n$ some points may be missing from the display. This happens because the utility attempts to graph $(-1)^n$ as if it were a function with the real numbers as its domain. A large *sample* of real numbers is selected for possible plotting. As a result of this sampling procedure, many integral values are not selected. Most of the real numbers selected cannot be graphed in the real plane. Can $(-1)^{3.1}$ be graphed? *Why?* To rectify the situation, choose screen dimensions for x (try $[-9, 10]$) that make it likely that the calculator will not skip any integral values of n.

Do not conclude that oscillating sequences always diverge. For questions of convergence, always test to determine whether the sequence has a limit.

Example 4 Determine whether the sequence $a_n = \left(-\dfrac{1}{2}\right)^n$ converges or diverges. If it converges, give the limit.

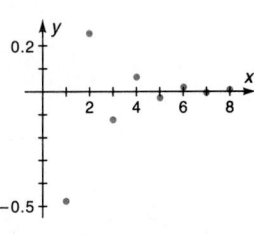

Terms of the sequence are $-\dfrac{1}{2}, \dfrac{1}{4}, -\dfrac{1}{8}, \dfrac{1}{16}, -\dfrac{1}{32}, \dfrac{1}{64}, \dots$ Although the terms are alternately positive and negative, they are getting closer and closer to zero. Therefore, $\lim\limits_{n \to \infty} \left(-\dfrac{1}{2}\right)^n = 0$, and the sequence converges.

Example 5 Characterize each sequence as either convergent or divergent. If it converges, give the limit.

a. $a_n = \sqrt{9 - \dfrac{1}{n}}$ **b.** $b_n = 7$ **c.** $c_n = \dfrac{n^3 + n + 4}{n^2 + 1}$

a. As n increases without bound, $\dfrac{1}{n}$ gets closer and closer to 0. Thus, a_n gets closer and closer to $\sqrt{9 - 0}$ or 3. Therefore, $\lim\limits_{n \to \infty} a_n = 3$, so the sequence is convergent.

b. The sequence is constant with terms $7, 7, 7, 7, 7, \dots$. No matter how large n gets, b_n is as close as it can get to 7, so $\lim\limits_{n \to \infty} b_n = 7$. This sequence is convergent.

c. Division shows that $c_n = n + \dfrac{4}{n^2 + 1}$. As n gets larger and larger, the fractional part gets closer and closer to 0, but the sum $n + \dfrac{4}{n^2 + 1}$ gets larger and larger without bound. *Why?* There is no limit. The sequence is divergent.

716 Chapter 13 Sequences and Series

Thinking Critically

The number $(-1)^{3.1}$ can be written $\sqrt[10]{(-1)^{31}}$. This is clearly an imaginary number and therefore cannot be graphed in the real plane.

Since n gets larger and larger, $n + 0$ gets larger and larger without bound.

How are the notions of "getting larger and larger" and "getting closer and closer" measured? The notion of *arbitrarily close* provides a more precise definition of limit.

The limit of a sequence a_n is L if as n increases without bound, the terms of a_n get arbitrarily close to L. By "arbitrarily close" is meant simply "as close as you please." In other words, no matter how small a positive number ϵ (Greek epsilon) is chosen, for large enough N, all the terms after a_N are within ϵ of L. Stated even more precisely, a sequence a_n has a **limit** L if for any choice of $\epsilon > 0$, there exists a number N such that for all $n > N$, $|a_n - L| < \epsilon$.

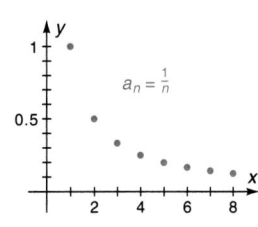

For example, the limit of the harmonic sequence $\frac{1}{n}$ is 0. To illustrate this, let ϵ be a very small number, say $\epsilon = 0.000001$. For n large enough, in this case, if $n > N = 1{,}000{,}000$, then $|a_n - 0| = \left|\frac{1}{n} - 0\right| = \frac{1}{n} < 0.000001$. No matter how small a number ϵ is chosen, n can always be chosen large enough to guarantee that $\left|\frac{1}{n} - 0\right| < \epsilon$. As a further illustration of these ideas, the three sequences of Example 5 are graphed below.

  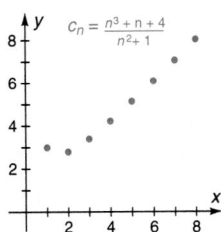

Class Exercises

Find the limit of the indicated sequence as n increases without bound.

1. $a_n = \dfrac{1}{n^2}$ 0   **2.** $b_n = \dfrac{3n+1}{n^2}$ 0   **3.** $c_n = \sqrt{2} + \left(\dfrac{1}{2}\right)^n$ $\sqrt{2}$

Determine whether each sequence converges. If it converges, give the limit.

4. $d_n = \left(\dfrac{1}{4}\right)^n$ converges; 0   **5.** $t_n = 4^n$ diverges   **6.** $m_k = (-3)^k$ diverges

7. $c_n = \dfrac{2n^2+4}{n^2+2}$ converges; 2   **8.** $\dfrac{2n^3+2n+4}{n^2+1}$ diverges   **9.** $\dfrac{2}{n^2+1}$ converges; 0

10. $a_n = \cos n\pi$ diverges   **11.** $b_n = (-0.1)^n$ converges; 0   **12.** $c_n = 10^n$ diverges

13. Thinking Critically A certain infinite sequence has the property that terms with odd subscripts are positive and those with even subscripts are negative. The sequence converges. What must its limit be? Why?

14. Does the sequence of prime numbers seem to be convergent? Why?

15. Find the first ten terms of the sequence of the reciprocals of the prime numbers. Does this sequence seem to be convergent or divergent? Why?

13.6 Limits of Sequences   **717**

Lesson Quiz

Determine whether each sequence converges or diverges. If it converges, give the limit.

1. $a_n = \dfrac{n-3}{5n+2}$

   converges; The limit is $\frac{1}{5}$.

2. $b_n = \dfrac{n-3}{5n^2+2}$

   converges; The limit is 0.

3. $c_n = \sqrt{(25+n)}$

   diverges

4. $c_n = \sqrt{\left(25+\dfrac{1}{n}\right)}$

   converges; The limit is 5.

5. $f_n = (-3)^n$

   diverges

6. $g_n = \left(-\dfrac{1}{3}\right)^n$

   converges; The limit is 0.

Additional Answers

1. $3, \dfrac{3}{8}, \dfrac{1}{9}, \dfrac{3}{64}, \dfrac{3}{125}, \dfrac{1}{72}$; convergent

2. $1, \sqrt{2}, \sqrt{3}, 2, \sqrt{5}, \sqrt{6}$; divergent

3. $-1, -1, -1, -1, -1, -1$; convergent

16. divergent; The limit of the negative terms is -1 and the limit of the positive terms is 0.

Practice Exercises   Use appropriate technology.

Find the first six terms of each sequence. Tell whether the sequence is convergent or divergent. Justify your response using a graph.

A 1. $a_n = \dfrac{3}{n^3}$ 2. $b_n = \sqrt{n}$ 3. $c_n = -1$

Determine whether each sequence converges. If it converges, give the limit.

4. $d_n = 5^n$ diverges

5. $t_n = \dfrac{n-3}{n+3}$ converges; 1

6. $r_n = \dfrac{n^2+n-2}{n+1}$ diverges

7. $a_n = (-1)^{n+1}\pi$ diverges

8. $b_n = \dfrac{2n+1}{3n+1}$ converges; $\frac{2}{3}$

9. $c_n = \dfrac{2n^2}{n^2+1}$ converges; 2

10. $r_n = \sin\frac{1}{2}n\pi$ diverges

11. $d_n = \cos\frac{1}{2}n\pi$ diverges

12. $m_k = \left(-\dfrac{1}{4}\right)^k$ converges; 0

13. $a_n = \dfrac{3n^5+n}{4n^5+8}$ converges; $\frac{3}{4}$

14. $b_n = \dfrac{3n^5+n}{4n^8+5}$ converges; 0

15. $c_n = \dfrac{3n^5+n}{4n^3+8}$ diverges

16. Is the sequence $-1, 1, -1, \frac{1}{2}, -1, \frac{1}{4}, -1, \frac{1}{8}, -1, \frac{1}{16}, \ldots$ convergent or divergent? Why?

Ⓡ 17. Graph $f(x) = \sin 2x$, when $0 \le x < 2\pi$.

18. Is the Fibonacci sequence convergent or divergent? Why?

Ⓡ 19. Find the sum of the first 15 terms of the sequence $c_n = 3n + 2$. 390

20. Let a_n be a constant sequence. Is this sequence convergent or divergent? Why?

Ⓡ 21. Find the 56th term of the sequence $-31, -27, -23, -19, -15, \ldots$. 189

Determine whether each geometric sequence is convergent or divergent. If it is convergent, give the limit.

B 22. $a_n = 4(3^n)$ diverges

23. $b_n = 4(0.2)^n$ converges; 0

24. $c_n = 10\left(\dfrac{1}{2}\right)^n$ converges; 0

25. $r_k = \dfrac{1}{2}(10)^k$ diverges

26. $t_n = 6(-1)^n$ diverges

27. $d_n = 6\left(-\dfrac{1}{2}\right)^n$ converges; 0

28. **Thinking Critically** Let ar^n be a geometric sequence. What conditions on the common ratio r will make the sequence convergent? Divergent? Why?

Ⓡ 29. Given triangle ABC with $c = 6$ ft, $b = 9$ ft, and $\angle C = 35°$, solve the triangle.
$a = 10.4$; $\angle A = 85.6°$; $\angle B = 59.4°$ or $a = 4.3$; $\angle A = 24.4°$; $\angle B = 120.6°$

Determine whether each arithmetic sequence is convergent or divergent.

30. $a_n = 2n + 1$ diverges

31. $b_n = 4 - 2n$ diverges

32. $c_n = -2.8$ converges

Ⓡ 33. *Landscaping* Describe the rectangular plot of maximum area that can be enclosed using 180 ft of fencing given that one side of the plot is along a building and needs no fencing.

34. **Thinking Critically** Let $a_n = a + (n-1)d$ be an arithmetic sequence. What conditions on the common difference d will make the sequence convergent? Divergent? Why?

35. Find the first six terms of the sequence $a_n = e^n$. Is it convergent? Why?

36. Find the first six terms of the sequence $a_n = e^{-n}$. Is it convergent? Why?

---

18. divergent; The Fibonacci sequence increases without bound.
20. convergent; Its limit is the constant term.
28. The sequence will be convergent for $|r| < 1$, because the limit will be 0. It will be divergent for $|r| \ge 1$, because the terms will increase without bound.
33. The side parallel to the building would be 90 ft and the other two sides would be 45 ft.
34. If $d = 0$, the sequence will be convergent since the limit will be $a_1 = a_n$. If $d \ne 0$, the sequence will be divergent since $|a_n|$ will increase without bound.

37. **Writing in Mathematics**   Write about a physical comparison that will help someone understand the relative sizes of a million, a billion, and a trillion. For example, how tall is a stack of one million (billion/trillion) dollar bills?

C 38. Suppose that a_n is a sequence that is divergent because as n increases without bound, a_n also increases without bound. What conclusion can you draw about the reciprocal sequence $b_n = \dfrac{1}{a_n}$? Why?

Given the two infinite sequences $a_n = 5 + \dfrac{1}{n}$ and $b_n = 3 - \left(\dfrac{1}{2}\right)^n$, verify that:

39. $\lim\limits_{n \to \infty} [a_n + b_n] = \lim\limits_{n \to \infty} a_n + \lim\limits_{n \to \infty} b_n$

40. $\lim\limits_{n \to \infty} [a_n \cdot b_n] = [\lim\limits_{n \to \infty} a_n][\lim\limits_{n \to \infty} b_n]$

41. $\lim\limits_{n \to \infty} \dfrac{a_n}{b_n} = \dfrac{\lim\limits_{n \to \infty} a_n}{\lim\limits_{n \to \infty} b_n}$

42. **Thinking Critically**   In Exercises 39 to 41, did you *prove* that each of the three relationships holds for all sequences a_n and b_n? Why or why not?

43. Suppose that a_n is a ratio of two polynomials in n, as shown below.

$$a_n = \frac{p(n)}{q(n)} = \frac{c_k n^k + c_{k-1}n^{k-1} + \cdots + c_1 n + c_0}{b_t n^t + b_{t-1}n^{t-1} + \cdots + b_1 n + b_0}$$

What conditions on the polynomials will cause the sequence a_n to converge? To diverge? If the sequence converges, what is the limit?

The statement $\lim\limits_{n \to \infty} \dfrac{1}{n} = 0$ means that for any number $\epsilon > 0$ you can find a number N with the property that all terms of the sequence $\dfrac{1}{n}$ are within ϵ of 0, that is, for all $n > N$, $\left|\dfrac{1}{n} - 0\right| < \epsilon$. Find a number N that "works" for each ϵ.

44. $\epsilon = 0.1000$ *N > 10*

45. $\epsilon = 0.00005$ *N > 20,000*

46. When the sequence $b_n = (-1)^n$ is displayed on one model of calculator, using $[-9, 10]$ as the horizontal dimension, two extra points, $(-0.2, -1)$ and $(0.2, -1)$, appear that are not in the sequence. (See Example 3.) Find a plausible explanation for the appearance of these two extraneous points. Could there be any other such points? Answers may vary.

Project

Explore the relationship between $\lim\limits_{n \to \infty} a_n$ of the sequence $a_n = f(n)$ and the horizontal asymptote of the graph of the related function $y = f(x)$. Graph the function, identify the horizontal asymptote and compare it to the limit. As examples, use Class Exercises 1 and 9 and Practice Exercises 1, 5, 8, 9.

Review

What is the value of

$(\tan 60°)(\tan 45°)(\sin 30°)(\sin 90°)(\cos 90°)(\cos 145°)$ 0

13.6 Limits of Sequences   **719**

Writing in Mathematics
37. Answers may vary. A stack of one million dollar bills is 10 m high. A billion bills form a stack 10 km high and a trillion, a stack 10,000 km high.

FOCUS

Students are familiar with the exponential model for population growth from Lesson 6 of Chapter 9. The modified growth curve was also introduced there. This is a good place to discuss the built-in limitations of a mathematical model and the need to continually test and adapt models. The model suggested in Example 5 provides another example. Physical limitations prevent the ball from bouncing forever, but the model gives a good approximation for the total distance it travels.

Students may look for data in various almanacs and statistical abstracts to test the assumptions of the Malthusian model of population growth. For example, by examining data giving the population of the United States at 10 year intervals (census years), students can see whether the population growth rate seems to be almost constant.

INSTRUCTION

• Have students make an art connection by having them create various designs to represent the infinite sum $\frac{1}{2} + \frac{1}{4} + \frac{1}{8} + \frac{1}{16} + \cdots$. They can use the rectangular model as suggested in the text, a circle, or some other figure.
• The area inside the Koch snowflake, a fractal, can be found using an infinite geometric series. Students may enjoy researching this application.

13.7 Sums of Infinite Series

Objectives: *To find the sum of a convergent infinite geometric series*
To express a repeating decimal as a ratio of two integers

Focus

Modeling the growth of populations has long been a challenge for biologists. As described in Lesson 9.2, one of the simplest models of population growth, the Malthusian model, assumes that the growth rate is constant. This model is represented by a sequence of numbers that increases without bound and predicts that a population will grow exponentially. Such a model may appropriately represent the growth of a population for a limited time, but no population can grow indefinitely at a constant rate.

More realistic models attempt to account for declining growth rates that accompany increased competition for the resources (food, space, and so on) contributing to growth. One such model was presented in Lesson 9.6. The graph of another limited-growth model is shown at the right. In such models, the growth rate may increase for a period of time and then decrease nearly to zero. The model shown yields a sequence of population numbers that continue to increase, but with a declining rate of growth. The result is a slowing of the increase in population, and thus an upper limit on the population.

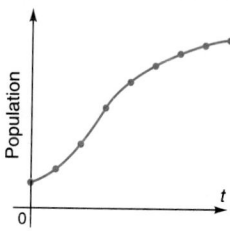

In Lesson 13.6, the notion of a limit was introduced as a way to describe the behavior of terms of an infinite *sequence*. To say that a sequence has a limit means that as n gets greater and greater, the terms a_n of the sequence get arbitrarily close to a fixed number L. In this lesson, the idea of a limit is adapted to describe an infinite *series* or sum. Is it even meaningful to talk about an infinite sum? Can the sum of infinitely many numbers be determined if no matter how many numbers are added there are always more to add?

To pose the issue concretely, suppose that you have a wall to paint, which you decide to tackle by painting half the wall on the first day, then painting half of what's left on the second day, then half of what's left on the third day, and so on. You may visualize your project like this:

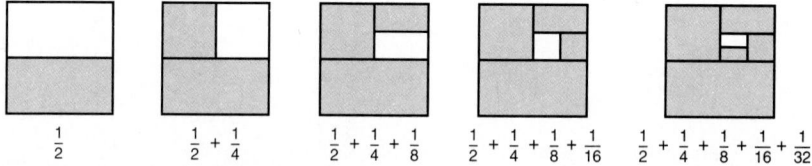

720   Chapter 13 Sequences and Series

If you stick to your plan, you will never finish since there always will be some part of the wall left unpainted! On the other hand, the area of the wall may be thought of as the sum of the infinitely many "pieces." This suggests the equality

$$1 = \frac{1}{2} + \frac{1}{4} + \frac{1}{8} + \frac{1}{16} + \cdots + \frac{1}{2^n} + \cdots$$

The right side of this equality is the sum of an infinite geometric series with first term $a = \frac{1}{2}$ and common ratio $r = \frac{1}{2}$. The amount of wall painted at the end of the nth day is $\frac{1}{2} + \frac{1}{4} + \frac{1}{8} + \cdots + \frac{1}{2^n}$, which is the nth partial sum S_n of the infinite geometric series. As the number of days increases, the partial sum gets closer and closer to the total area of the wall. In terms of limits, this means that the limit of the *sequence* $S_1, S_2, S_3, \ldots$ should equal 1.

Recall that for the infinite geometric series $\sum_{k=1}^{\infty} ar^{k-1}$, the value of the nth partial sum is $S_n = \frac{a(1 - r^n)}{1 - r}$. For this example, the formula becomes

$$S_n = \frac{\frac{1}{2}\left[1 - \left(\frac{1}{2}\right)^n\right]}{1 - \frac{1}{2}} = 1 - \left(\frac{1}{2}\right)^n. \text{ Therefore, } \lim_{n \to \infty} S_n = \lim_{n \to \infty}\left[1 - \left(\frac{1}{2}\right)^n\right] = 1 - 0 = 1,$$

as expected. This suggests a way of resolving the issue of infinite sums.

The **sum of an infinite series** of numbers (or "infinite sum") *is defined to be* the limit of its associated sequence of partial sums as the number of the sequence's terms increases without bound. Thus, an infinite sum exists if and only if the limit of its associated sequence of partial sums exists.

Example 1   Find the sum, if one exists, of the infinite series $\sum_{k=1}^{\infty} \frac{1}{k(k + 1)}$.

To find the infinite sum

$$\frac{1}{1 \cdot 2} + \frac{1}{2 \cdot 3} + \frac{1}{3 \cdot 4} + \cdots$$

look at the associated sequence of partial sums.

$$S_1 = \frac{1}{2}$$

$$S_2 = \frac{1}{2} + \frac{1}{6} = \frac{2}{3}$$

$$S_3 = \frac{1}{2} + \frac{1}{6} + \frac{1}{12} = \frac{3}{4}$$

$$S_4 = \frac{1}{2} + \frac{1}{6} + \frac{1}{12} + \frac{1}{20} = \frac{4}{5}$$

$$\vdots$$

It seems from the first four terms, and was proved in the practice exercises of Lesson 13.4, that a general term for S_n is $\frac{n}{n + 1}$. As n increases without bound, the partial sums get closer and closer to 1.

$$\lim_{n \to \infty} S_n = \lim_{n \to \infty} \frac{n}{n + 1} = 1 \qquad \textit{Why?}$$

Therefore, by the definition of *infinite sum*, $\sum_{k=1}^{\infty} \frac{1}{k(k + 1)}$ is 1.

Alternative Learning Styles
Students who are concrete and visual learners will benefit from the art experience suggested in Instruction.

GUIDED PRACTICE

For Example 1
Find the sum, if one exists, of the infinite series $\sum_{k=1}^{\infty} \frac{1}{k(k + 1)(k + 2)}$.

$$S_1 = \frac{1}{1 \cdot 2 \cdot 3} = \frac{1}{6}$$

$$S_2 = \frac{1}{6} + \frac{1}{2 \cdot 3 \cdot 4} = \frac{5}{24}$$

$$S_3 = \frac{1}{6} + \frac{1}{24} + \frac{1}{3 \cdot 4 \cdot 5} = \frac{9}{40}$$

$$S_4 = \frac{1}{6} + \frac{1}{24} + \frac{1}{60} + \frac{1}{4 \cdot 5 \cdot 6} = \frac{7}{30}$$

$$\vdots$$

$$S_n = \frac{n(n + 3)}{4(n + 1)(n + 2)}$$

$$\lim_{n \to \infty} S_n = \lim_{n \to \infty} \frac{n(n + 3)}{4(n + 1)(n + 2)} = \frac{1}{4}$$

Common Error   Students may believe that it should always be possible to express the partial sum of a series in a closed form. Be sure that they understand that these examples are chosen so that they can examine the behavior of a few partial sums of series in detail. In general, infinite series are more difficult to analyze.

Thinking Critically
Dividing the numerator and denominator of the fraction by n yields $\dfrac{1}{1 + \frac{1}{n}}$, which clearly approaches 1 as n increases without bound.

Determine whether each series converges or diverges. If it diverges, tell
why it diverges.

1. $\displaystyle\sum_{k=1}^{\infty} \frac{1}{2}k$

   diverges; The sequence of partial
   sums gets larger without bound.

2. $\displaystyle\sum_{k=1}^{\infty} (-1)^k (10)$

   diverges; The sequence of partial
   sums oscillates between -10 and 0.

It is not always the case that the limit of the sequence of partial sums
associated with an infinite series exists. When the limit does exist, the series is
said to *converge* and to have that limit as its sum. When the limit does not
exist, the series is said to *diverge*.

Example 2   Determine whether each series converges or diverges. If it diverges, tell why
it diverges.

$$\textbf{a.}\ \sum_{k=1}^{\infty} (2k-1) \qquad \textbf{b.}\ \sum_{k=1}^{\infty} (-1)^k$$

a. This is the sum of all odd numbers; intuition suggests that it cannot be finite.
Look at its associated sequence of partial sums. (See Lesson 13.4.)

$$S_n = 1 + 3 + 5 \cdots + (2n-1) = n^2$$

Thus, $\displaystyle\lim_{n\to\infty} S_n = \lim_{n\to\infty} n^2$.

As n increases without bound, n^2 increases without bound as well. Thus, the
sequence of partial sums diverges, and the series diverges.

b. This is the sum $1 + (-1) + 1 + (-1) + \cdots$. The sequence of partial sums
oscillates between 1 and 0:

$$S_1 = 1$$
$$S_2 = 1 + (-1) = 0$$
$$S_3 = 1 + (-1) + 1 = 1$$
$$S_4 = 1 + (-1) + 1 + (-1) = 0$$

This sequence of partial sums diverges, so the series $\displaystyle\sum_{k=1}^{\infty} (-1)^k$ diverges also.

In order to determine whether an infinite series converges or diverges, it is
useful to find an expression for the associated nth partial sum S_n. In general,
this is not a simple task. However, one series that *is* easy to analyze is the
infinite *geometric* series.

Let $a + ar + ar^2 + ar^3 + \cdots$ be an infinite series. The nth partial sum of
this series is $\dfrac{a(1-r^n)}{1-r}$. Before looking at the limit of this expression as $n \to \infty$,
observe that if $|r| < 1$, then as n increases without bound, r^n gets closer and
closer to 0. If, however, $|r| > 1$, as n increases without bound, r^n also increases
without bound. Thus,

$$\text{if } |r| < 1,\ \lim_{n\to\infty} S_n = \lim_{n\to\infty} \frac{a(1-r^n)}{1-r} = \frac{a}{1-r}$$

and the series converges to this value;

$$\text{if } |r| > 1,\ \lim_{n\to\infty} S_n \text{ does not exist, so the series diverges.}$$

For $r = 1$ and $r = -1$, the geometric series $a + ar + ar^2 + ar^3 + \cdots$,
$a \neq 0$ diverges. *Why?*

722   Chapter 13 Sequences and Series

Thinking Critically
For $r = 1$, the sequence of partial sums increases without bound.
For $r = -1$, the sequence of partial sums oscillates between a and 0.

Example 3 Determine whether each series converges or diverges. If it converges, find the sum. If it diverges, tell why it diverges.

a. $6 + 2 + \frac{2}{3} + \frac{2}{9} + \cdots$

b. $0.1 + 0.2 + 0.4 + 0.8 + \cdots$

c. $5 + 0.2 + 0.04 + 0.008 + 0.0016 + \cdots$

a. This is a geometric series with $a = 6$ and $r = \frac{1}{3}$. Since $|r| < 1$, the sum is

$$\frac{6}{1 - \frac{1}{3}} = \frac{6}{\frac{2}{3}} = 9.$$

b. This is a geometric series with $a = 0.1$ and $r = 2$. Since $|r| > 1$, the series diverges, and so has no sum.

c. Including the first term, this is not a geometric series. However, terms from the second term on form a geometric series with $a = 0.2$ and $r = 0.2$. The sum of the entire series is therefore $5 + \dfrac{0.2}{1 - 0.2} = 5 + 0.25 = 5.25$.

The sum of a geometric series may be used to express a repeating decimal as a rational number in fractional form.

Express the repeating decimal $1.6413413413413 \cdots$ as a ratio of two integers.

This number can be written as $1.6 + 0.0413 + 0.0000413 + 0.0000000413 + \cdots$, which is 1.6 plus an infinite geometric series. The series has $a = 0.0413$ as its first term and $r = 0.001$ as its constant rate, so its sum is $\dfrac{0.0413}{1 - 0.001} = \dfrac{0.0413}{0.999} = \dfrac{413}{9990}$.

The given repeating decimal then has the fractional form

$$1.6 + \frac{413}{9990} = \frac{16}{10} + \frac{413}{9990} = \frac{15{,}984 + 413}{9990} = \frac{16{,}397}{9990}$$

Sums of geometric series may be used to analyze some physical situations.

Example 5 *Physics* A ball is dropped from a height of 24 m. Each time it strikes the ground it rebounds to a height of 75% of the distance it fell. Find the total distance the ball travels.

An infinite geometric series is a mathematical model for the travels of this ball. Note that except for the first vertical drop, it travels each height twice, once up and once down. The total distance is therefore

$$d = 24 + 2(0.75)(24) + 2(0.75)^2(24) + 2(0.75)^3(24) + \cdots$$
$$= 24 + 2[(0.75)(24) + (0.75)^2(24) + (0.75)^3(24) + \cdots]$$

The sum in brackets is an infinite geometric series with $a = (0.75)(24) = 18$ and $r = 0.75$. Then the sum is $\dfrac{18}{1 - 0.75} = 72$. Therefore, $d = 24 + 2[72] = 168$ m.

Modeling

This modeling problem provides a good opportunity for cross-curricular learning. You may want to relate the material to developments in the students' science classes.

For Example 6

A scientist measures a bacteria population over a period of 10 days, and finds the following. The number of bacteria is given in thousands.

Day	1	2	3	4	5
Number	4	8	16	32	40

Day	6	7	8	9	10
Number	44	46	48	49	50

Think of each number as a partial sum of the series of growth amounts and estimate the limit of S_n if it exists. The limit is a little more than 50.

CLOSURE

Ask students to summarize the lesson in their math journals and to include any new math corrections they made.

INDEPENDENT PRACTICE

Assignment Guide

Basic: 1–20, 25–28, 33, Project
Average: 11–15, 20–38, 44, Project
Enriched: 14, 20, 23–45, Project

Teacher's Resource Book
   Practice, page 94

® **Review**
Exercises 15, 25, and 27 review using an augmented matrix to solve a system of linear equations and using the principle of mathematical induction to prove statements.

Modeling

How can a biologist determine the sum of a nongeometric series?

In modeling population growth, or laboratory growth experiments, the population at time t_n may represent the partial sum S_n of a series, where S_n is the sum of S_{n-1} and the increase generated by S_{n-1}. However, the series may not be a geometric series, or even have a simple rule for generating the series.

Example 6   *Biology*   While performing a laboratory experiment in which yeast is grown in a culture, a biologist charted the estimated units of yeast for various times shown in the table below. Given that each number in the table is a partial sum of the series of growth amounts, find the limit of S_n if it exists.

Time (hours)	0	2	4	6	8	10	12	14	16	18	20	22
Yeast (units)	10	29	71	175	350	515	595	640	655	662	665	666

A plot of the first six data points suggests that the sequence of sums of growth amounts 10, 29, 71, 175, 350, 515, is going to increase without bound. However, when all of the data is considered, the sequence of sums appears to be approaching a limit just above 666. The series for this experiment is a convergent series with a limit of about 666.

Class Exercises

Find the first five terms of the sequence of partial sums for each series. $\frac{1}{4}, \frac{5}{16}, \frac{21}{64}, \frac{85}{256}, \frac{341}{1024}$

1. $2 + 4 + 6 + 8 + \cdots$ 2, 6, 12, 20, 30

2. $\frac{1}{4} + \left(\frac{1}{4}\right)^2 + \left(\frac{1}{4}\right)^3 + \left(\frac{1}{4}\right)^4 + \cdots$

3. $\sum_{k=1}^{\infty} 10(0.6)^k$ 6, 9.6, 11.76, 13.056, 13.8336

4. $\sum_{k=1}^{\infty} (0.6)10^k$ 6, 66, 666, 6666, 66,666

724   Chapter 13 Sequences and Series

Determine whether each series converges or diverges. If it converges, find the sum. If it diverges, tell why it diverges.

5. $\frac{1}{4} + \left(\frac{1}{4}\right)^2 + \left(\frac{1}{4}\right)^3 + \left(\frac{1}{4}\right)^4 + \cdots$ $\frac{1}{3}$

6. $1 + 5 + 5^2 + 5^3 + \cdots$ diverges

7. $\sum_{k=1}^{\infty} (0.15)^k$ 0.1765

8. $\sum_{t=1}^{\infty} 3\left(\frac{8}{9}\right)^t$ 24

9. $\sum_{k=1}^{\infty} \left(-\frac{1}{4}\right)^k$ $-\frac{1}{5}$

10. $\sum_{j=1}^{\infty} 3 \cdot \pi^j$ diverges

Express each repeating decimal as a ratio of two integers.

11. 0.2323232323 . . . $\frac{23}{99}$

12. 2.040404040 . . . $\frac{202}{99}$

13. 12.899999999 . . . $\frac{129}{10}$

14. -36.7777777 . . . $-\frac{331}{9}$

Practice Exercises   ⬡ Use appropriate technology.

Find the first five terms of the sequence of partial sums for each series.

A 1. $3 + 6 + 9 + 12 + \cdots$ 3, 9, 18, 30, 45

2. $0.6 + (0.6)^2 + (0.6)^3 + \cdots$ 0.6, 0.96, 1.176, 1.3056, 1.38336

3. $\sum_{k=1}^{\infty} \frac{1}{k^2}$ 1, 1.25, 1.3611, 1.423611, 1.4636111

4. $\sum_{t=1}^{\infty} 5(0.9)^t$ 4.5, 8.55, 12.195, 15.4755, 18.42795

5. Determine whether each series of Exercises 1 and 2 converges or diverges. If the series converges, find the sum. If it diverges, tell why it diverges.

Determine whether each series converges or diverges. If the series converges, find the sum. If it diverges, tell why it diverges.

6. $18 + 18(0.2) + 18(0.2)^2 + \cdots$ 22.5

7. $1 + 0.1 + 0.01 + 0.001 + \cdots$ $\frac{110}{99}$

8. $\sum_{k=1}^{\infty} 8\left(\frac{2}{5}\right)^k$ $\frac{16}{3}$

9. $\sum_{j=1}^{\infty} \left(\frac{-3}{11}\right)^j$ $-\frac{3}{14}$

10. $\sum_{k=1}^{\infty} -9(0.7)^k$ -21

11. $\sum_{t=1}^{\infty} (1.1)^t$ diverges

12. $\sum_{k=1}^{\infty} -3^k$ diverges

13. $\sum_{n=1}^{\infty} (-3)^n$ diverges

14. Thinking Critically Suppose that the terms of a sequence $a_1, a_2, a_3, \ldots$ increase without bound. What conclusion can you draw about the related series $\sum_{n=1}^{\infty} a_n$?

Ⓡ 15. Solve the system of linear equations using an augmented matrix.
$$\begin{cases} x + 3y - z = 4 \\ 2x + 4y - 5z = 6 \\ 2y + 3z = 7 \end{cases}$$ inconsistent system; no solutions

Express each decimal as a ratio of two integers.

16. 0.45454545 . . . $\frac{5}{11}$

17. 12.999999 . . . $\frac{117}{9}$

18. 0.6758585858 . . . $\frac{6691}{9900}$

19. -8.9312424 $-\frac{89,312,424}{10,000,000}$

20. Thinking Critically In the lesson, it is pointed out that $\lim_{n\to\infty} \frac{a(1 - r^n)}{1 - r} = \frac{a}{1 - r}$ because r^n gets closer and closer to 0 as n increases without bound, providing $|r| < 1$. Discuss why the restriction $|r| < 1$ is necessary.

B 21. In the class exercises of Lesson 13.4 it was proved that $1 + 2 + 3 + \cdots + n = \frac{1}{2}n(n + 1)$. Use this fact to show that the series $\sum_{k=1}^{\infty} k$ is divergent.

13.7 Sums of Infinite Series   **725**

11. diverges; It is a geometric series with $r = 1.1$, which is greater than 1.
12. diverges; It is a geometric series with $r = 3$, which is greater than 1.
13. diverges; S_n oscillates between positive and negative values.
14. It diverges because the partial sums increase without bound.
20. If $|r| \geq 1$, the limit would not exist, so the series would be divergent.

Have students write a paragraph defining the sequence of partial sums of a series and describing how this sequence can be used to find the sum of a convergent infinite series.

Enrichment

Suppose you start at point A and walk 4 mi east, then 2 mi south, 1 mi west, $\frac{1}{2}$ mi north, $\frac{1}{4}$ mi east, and so on. If you continued in this pattern indefinitely, on what distance from point A would you be converging? $\frac{8\sqrt{5}}{5}$

Additional Answers

22. $\frac{1}{3}, \frac{1}{2}, \frac{3}{5}, \frac{2}{3}, \frac{5}{7}$; $S_n = \frac{n}{n+2}$, Sum is 1.

23. $\frac{3}{4}, \frac{8}{9}, \frac{15}{16}, \frac{24}{25}, \frac{35}{36}$; $\frac{(n+1)^2 - 1}{(n+1)^2}$

25. Since $\frac{1}{2 \cdot 5} = \frac{1}{2[3(1) + 2]}$, P_1 is true.

Assume P_k: $\frac{1}{2 \cdot 5} + \frac{1}{5 \cdot 8} + \cdots +$

$\frac{1}{(3k-1)(3k+2)} = \frac{k}{2(3k+2)}$. Then

$\frac{1}{2 \cdot 5} + \frac{1}{5 \cdot 8} + \cdots + \frac{1}{(3k-1)(3k+2)} +$

$\frac{1}{[3(k+1) - 1][3(k+1) + 2]} = \frac{k}{2(3k+2)} +$

$\frac{1}{[3(k+1) - 1][3(k+1) + 2]} =$

$\frac{3k^2 + 5k + 2}{2(3k+2)(3k+5)} = \frac{(3k+2)(k+1)}{2(3k+2)(3k+5)} =$

$\frac{k+1}{2[3(k+1) + 2]} = P_{k+1}$

27. Since $\frac{1}{1 \cdot 3} = \frac{1}{2(1) + 1}$, P_1 is true. Assume P_k: $\frac{1}{1 \cdot 3} + \frac{1}{3 \cdot 5} + \cdots +$

$\frac{1}{(2k-1)(2k+1)} = \frac{k}{2k+1}$. Then $\frac{1}{1 \cdot 3} +$

$\frac{1}{3 \cdot 5} + \cdots + \frac{1}{(2k-1)(2k+1)} +$

$\frac{1}{(2k+1)(2k+3)} = \frac{k}{2k+1} +$

$\frac{1}{(2k+1)(2k+3)} = \frac{2k^2 + 3k + 1}{(2k+1)(2k+3)} =$

$\frac{(k+1)(2k+1)}{(2k+1)(2k+3)} = \frac{k+1}{2k+3} =$

$\frac{k+1}{[2(k+1) + 1]} = P_{k+1}$

---

22. Find the first five partial sums S_1, S_2, S_3, S_4, and S_5 of the infinite series $\frac{1}{3} + \frac{1}{6} + \frac{1}{10} + \frac{1}{15} + \frac{1}{21} + \frac{1}{28} + \cdots$. From the pattern, find a possible formula for S_n. Then use the definition of "infinite sum" to evaluate the sum of the infinite series. *Hint*: Express S_2 and S_4 as unreduced fractions.

23. Find the first five partial sums S_1, S_2, S_3, S_4, and S_5 of the following series.

$$\frac{3}{1 \cdot 4} + \frac{5}{4 \cdot 9} + \frac{7}{9 \cdot 16} + \frac{9}{16 \cdot 25} + \cdots + \frac{2n+1}{n^2(n+1)^2} + \cdots$$

From the pattern that you observe, what seems to be a formula for S_n?

24. Use your formula for S_n and the definition of "infinite sum" to find the sum of the infinite series. 1

25. Use the principle of mathematical induction to prove that

$$\frac{1}{2 \cdot 5} + \frac{1}{5 \cdot 8} + \frac{1}{8 \cdot 11} + \cdots + \frac{1}{(3n-1)(3n+2)} = \frac{n}{2(3n+2)}$$

26. Use the result of Exercise 25 to find the sum of the series $\sum_{k=1}^{\infty} \frac{1}{(3k-1)(3k+2)}$. $\frac{1}{6}$

27. Use the principle of mathematical induction to prove that

$$\frac{1}{1 \cdot 3} + \frac{1}{3 \cdot 5} + \frac{1}{5 \cdot 7} + \cdots + \frac{1}{(2n-1)(2n+1)} = \frac{n}{2n+1}$$

28. Use the result of Exercise 27 to find the sum of the series $\sum_{k=1}^{\infty} \frac{1}{(2k-1)(2k+1)}$. $\frac{1}{2}$

29. *Physics* A ball is dropped from a height of 36 m. Each time it strikes the ground it rebounds to a height of 70% of the distance it fell. Find the total distance the ball travels after four bounces. 163.66 m

30. *Physics* A ball is dropped from a height of 40 m. Each time it strikes the ground it rebounds to a height of 45% of the distance it fell. Find the total distance the ball travels. 105.4545 m

31. *Economics* A federal tax cut adds $10 billion to the income of taxpayers. Assume that each taxpayer as a result of this tax cut spends 90% of the money and the recipients of this money in turn spend 90% of the money. Find the total amount of spending that results from the initial tax cut. $90 billion

32. *Ecology* A radioactive substance is leaking from an underground storage tank. It spread 1000 m from the source during the first year, 800 m the second year, and 640 m the third year. If this pattern continues, how far will it spread in 6 years? Will the radioactive substance ever reach a river 6000 m from the source? Why or why not? 3689.28 m; no; sum of the series is 5000 m

33. **Writing in Mathematics** Devise several situations that, like the wall-painting problem, can be described mathematically by the infinite series $\frac{1}{2} + \left(\frac{1}{2}\right)^2 + \left(\frac{1}{2}\right)^3 + \cdots$. Show how one of them is described by the series.

34. Identify an infinite geometric series that has a sum of 6 and a first term of 2.

35. Identify an infinite geometric series that has a sum of $\frac{8}{3}$ and a common ratio of $\frac{1}{4}$.

36. **Thinking Critically** Find an example of a geometric series with a negative sum that has a positive common ratio. Can an infinite geometric series with a negative sum have a positive first term? Why or why not?

726 Chapter 13 Sequences and Series

Writing in Mathematics

33. Answers may vary. Some examples are: paper folding; cutting a string in half, then cutting the remaining piece in half, and so on; eating half a pie, then half of what is left, and so on.

C **37.** *Nature*   The snowflake patterns below are generated by starting with an equilateral triangle and replacing the middle third of each side with another equilateral triangle. If a side of the triangle has length a, then the length of one side of the 12-sided snowflake is $\frac{a}{3}$. As the procedure is repeated indefinitely, will the perimeter approach a finite limit? Why or why not?

 a $\frac{a}{3}$ $\frac{a}{9}$ $\frac{a}{27}$

38. Thinking Critically   Discuss the possible convergence of an *arithmetic* series with common difference d.

39. Evaluate the sum $e + e^0 + e^{-1} + e^{-2} + e^{-3} + \cdots .$ $\frac{e^2}{e-1}$

40. Use properties of logarithms to simplify the nth partial sum of the series $\sum_{k=1}^{\infty} \log\left(\frac{k}{k+1}\right)$. Then decide whether the series is convergent.

41. Find the sum of the series $\sum_{k=1}^{\infty} \left(\frac{1}{\sqrt{k}} - \frac{1}{\sqrt{k+1}}\right)$ 1

Design   The midpoints of a unit square are joined to form a new square. This procedure is repeated to form another, then another, and so on.

42. Find the sum of the areas of all the squares formed this way. 2

43. Find the sum of the lengths of the line segments used to form all the squares. $8 + 4\sqrt{2}$

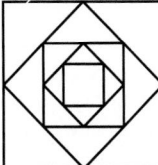

44. Writing in Mathematics   The Greek philosopher Zeno of Elea (c. 490–c. 430 B.C.) argued that a moving body can never cover the distance between two points A and B, since it must first travel half the distance AB, then half the remaining distance, and so on indefinitely. Since the number of line segments to be covered is infinite, the trip can never be completed. Discuss how you would respond to this argument.

45. The nth partial sum of a certain infinite series is $S_n = \frac{1}{2^n}$. Identify the series and discuss its convergence.

Project

There are models of population growth other than the Malthusian one. An example of such a model is the *logistic* model. Research this model. Answers may vary.

Challenge

Determine the sum of all the integers between 50 and 450 which end in 1. 9840

Writing in Mathematics
44. Answers may vary. Students answers should address the fact that Zeno's paradox does not take into account the concept of a limit.

Additional Answers

34. $\sum_{k=0}^{\infty} 2\left(\frac{2}{3}\right)^k$

35. $\sum_{k=0}^{\infty} 2\left(\frac{1}{4}\right)^k$

36. Answers may vary. Example:
$\sum_{k=0}^{\infty} (-2)\left(\frac{1}{2}\right)^k$; no; since $|r| < 1$,
$1 - r > 0$, so $\frac{a}{1-r} > 0$ if $a > 0$.

37. No. The perimeter of the nth figure is $S_n = \left(\frac{4}{3}\right)^{n-1} (3a)$. The limit of S_n is not finite.

38. An arithmetic series does not converge unless it has a limited number of terms.

40. $\sum_{k=1}^{\infty} \log\left(\frac{k}{k+1}\right) = \sum_{k=1}^{\infty} [\log k - \log (k+1)] = \log 1 - \log 2 + \log 2 - \log 3 + \log 3 - \log 4 + \cdots + \log (k-1) - \log k + \log k - \log (k+1) = \log 1 - \log (k+1) = -\log (k+1)$. As k increases without bound, the sum decreases without bound.

45. The series is $\frac{1}{2} - \frac{1}{4} - \frac{1}{8} - \frac{1}{16} - \frac{1}{32} - \cdots$. It converges to 0.

Vocabulary
Euler's formula
power series

Technology
computer
graphing utility
scientific calculator

FOCUS

The question "What's in a name?" applies to mathematics as well as to other fields. Although the best known power series are named for Brook Taylor, they were actually known earlier to James Gregory (1638–1675), a young Scotsman. Gregory was introduced to mathematics by his mathematician mother, Janet Anderson. Other members of the Gregory family were also well known as mathematicians.

A special class of Taylor series are named for the British mathematician Colin Maclaurin (1698–1746). Like Taylor, however, Maclaurin was not the first to study the series that bear his name. Another British mathematician, James Stirling (1692–1770), wrote about the "Maclaurin series" more than ten years before Maclaurin's writings were published.

Students may appreciate anecdotes that illustrate the "human side" of mathematics. Encourage them to read about the people whose names are attached to theorems and formulas as they learn them.

13.8   Power Series

Objectives: To identify certain power series
To estimate values of functions using power series

Focus

In Chapter 8 you saw how polynomials could be used to approximate the sine and cosine functions. Each of these polynomials represents the first few terms of a special group of series known as *Taylor series*. A British mathematician, Brook Taylor, published much of the work on these series in 1715. Now more than two centuries later, Taylor series provide a practical way of approximating trigonometric functions and other functions in computers and calculators. When you use a calculator function key such as sin, cos, tan, log, e^x, or $\tan^{-1}$, the calculator probably evaluates the function using the first few terms of a series.

Polynomials are the simplest functions to evaluate, requiring only the basic operations of addition and multiplication. Fortunately, polynomials can be used to estimate other, more complicated functions with great accuracy. Calculators and computers use this kind of estimation to give you values of expressions such as $\sqrt{2}$ and $e^{1.5}$. Polynomials used in this way are often the partial sums of *power series*.

> *Polynomial:* $a_0 + a_1x + a_2x^2 + \cdots + a_nx^n$
> *Power series:* $a_0 + a_1x + a_2x^2 + \cdots$

Polynomials and power series can both be expressed in sigma notation. A polynomial is a finite series of the form $\sum_{k=0}^{n} a_k x^k$, while a **power series** is an infinite series of the form $\sum_{k=0}^{\infty} a_k x^k$. Notice that in both cases, the index k begins with 0, not 1, to allow the inclusion of a constant term, $a_0 = a_0 x^0$. Notice also that an infinite geometric series, which was discussed in Lesson 13.7, is a power series in which all of the coefficients a_k are equal.

> *General power series:* $\sum_{k=0}^{\infty} a_k x^k = a_0 + a_1x + a_2x^2 + \cdots$
>
> *Infinite geometric series:* $\sum_{k=0}^{\infty} ax^k = a + ax + ax^2 + ax^3 + \cdots$

The first information needed about a power series is its domain. For what values of x is such a series defined? This is the same as asking "For what values of x does the series $\sum_{k=0}^{\infty} a_k x^k$ converge?"

728   Chapter 13 Sequences and Series

Example 1 For what values of x does the series $\sum_{k=0}^{\infty} 2x^n$ converge?

Terms of this geometric series are $2 + 2x + 2x^2 + 2x^3 + \cdots$ with common ratio $r = x$, and first term $a = 2$. As observed in the preceding lesson, this series will converge to $\dfrac{2}{1-x}$ for all x with $|x| < 1$. If $|x| \geq 1$, the series will diverge.

In Example 1, as n increases without bound, the partial sums S_n of the series get arbitrarily close to a limit, in this case to $\dfrac{2}{1-x}$. The partial sums of power series are polynomials; $S_n = 2 + 2x + 2x^2 + 2x^3 + \cdots + 2x^{n-1}$. Here is a situation in which a nonpolynomial function, $f(x) = \dfrac{2}{1-x}$, can be approximated as closely as desired by polynomials (the S_n's).

You should note that the result of Example 1 was generalized once before, in Lesson 13.7. That generalization is repeated below in a slightly different form.

> For any constant a, the infinite geometric series $\sum_{k=0}^{\infty} ax^k$ converges to $\dfrac{a}{1-x}$ for all x with $|x| < 1$. The series diverges if $|x| \geq 1$.

Example 2 Find a power series that converges to the function $g(x) = \dfrac{5}{1 - \frac{1}{2}x}$. For what values of x does the series converge to the function?

The function g has the desired form for the sum of an infinite geometric series with $a = 5$ and $r = \frac{1}{2}x$. The series is

$$5 + 5\left(\tfrac{1}{2}x\right) + 5\left(\tfrac{1}{2}x\right)^2 + 5\left(\tfrac{1}{2}x\right)^3 + \cdots = \sum_{k=0}^{\infty} 5\left(\tfrac{1}{2}x\right)^k$$

It will converge for all x with $\left|\frac{1}{2}x\right| < 1$, that is, for $-1 < \frac{1}{2}x < 1$, or $-2 < x < 2$. Therefore, the series converges for $x \in (-2, 2)$.

In Example 2, the interval of convergence was $(-2, 2)$, not $(-1, 1)$, because of the substitution of $\frac{1}{2}x$ for x in $\sum_{k=0}^{\infty} ax^k$. Other substitutions will similarly affect the values of the variable for which the series converges.

Example 3 Find the values of x for which each power series converges.
a. $1 + (x + 2) + (x + 2)^2 + (x + 2)^3 + (x + 2)^4 + \cdots$
b. $6 + 6(2x - 3) + 6(2x - 3)^2 + 6(2x - 3)^3 + \cdots$

a. This is an infinite geometric series with $a = 1$ and $r = x + 2$. It will converge to $\dfrac{1}{1 - (x + 2)} = \dfrac{1}{-1 - x} = \dfrac{-1}{1 + x}$ for all x with $|x + 2| < 1$, that is, for $-1 < x + 2 < 1$, or $-3 < x < -1$. The series converges for $x \in (-3, -1)$.

13.8 Power Series **729**

- Have students make up examples of power series to see if they understand the definition. It may help to point out that a polynomial may be viewed as a power series for which all but a finite number of the coefficients a_k are zero.
- Have students perform the division indicated by a function like $f(x) = \dfrac{2}{1-x}$ to obtain the power series that converges to $f(x)$. It helps many students to see the relationship between new material (power series) and old (long division of polynomials).
- Use a graphing utility to illustrate how the partial sums of a power series approximate the function to which the series converges on the domain of convergence. The graphs of successive partial sums look more and more like the graph of the function on that domain.
- Point out that the power series given for the sine and cosine functions may be more easily remembered from the fact that sine is an odd function and cosine an even function. The coefficients and exponents for the power series for sine are all odd; those for cosine are all even.

Alternative Learning Styles

It may be difficult for students who have been using calculators for years to appreciate the importance of polynomial approximations to more complicated functions. Point out that it is this method that provided the values used in tables for the trigonometric functions and logarithms from the time of James Gregory, and this is a method calculators and computers use to give us the values we use today.

For Example 1

For what values of x does each power series converge?

1. $\displaystyle\sum_{k=0}^{\infty} \frac{5}{3}x^k \quad |x| < 1$

2. $3 + 3\left(\frac{1}{4}x\right) + 3\left(\frac{1}{4}x\right)^2 + 3\left(\frac{1}{4}x\right)^3 + 3\left(\frac{1}{4}x\right)^4 + \cdots \quad |x| < 4$

Common Error   Some students may not realize the importance of having all a_k's constant before results about geometric series apply. They may think that any example they create ought to converge to some function in the form $\frac{a}{1-r}$.

Emphasize to these students that the generalization holds for any constant a.

For Example 2

Find a power series that converges to each function. For what values of x does the series converge to the function?

1. $h(x) = \dfrac{10}{1 - 10x}$

$\displaystyle\sum_{k=0}^{\infty} 10(10x)^k ; x \in \left(-\frac{1}{10}, \frac{1}{10}\right)$

2. $f(x) = \dfrac{1}{1 - \sqrt{2}x}$

$\displaystyle\sum_{k=0}^{\infty} (\sqrt{2}x)^k ; x \in \left(-\frac{\sqrt{2}}{2}, \frac{\sqrt{2}}{2}\right)$

For Example 3

Find the values of x for which each power series converges.

1. $2 + 2(x - 5) + 2(x - 5)^2 + 2(x - 5)^3 + 2(x - 5)^4 + \cdots$
$x \in (4, 6)$

2. $1 + (3x - 8) + (3x - 8)^2 + (3x - 8)^3 + (3x - 8)^4 + \cdots$
$x \in \left(\frac{7}{3}, 3\right)$

b. This is an infinite geometric series with first term $a = 6$ and common ratio $r = 2x - 3$. It will converge to $\dfrac{6}{1 - (2x - 3)} = \dfrac{6}{4 - 2x}$ for all x with

$$|2x - 3| < 1$$
$$-1 < 2x - 3 < 1$$
$$2 < 2x < 4$$
$$1 < x < 2 \qquad \text{Therefore, the series converges for } x \in (1, 2).$$

The functions to which the power series of Examples 1, 2, and 3 converge are *rational functions*, that is, functions that are ratios of polynomials. Of even greater interest are cases where functions that are not rational can be approximated with great accuracy by polynomials.

Three familiar functions, e^x, $\sin x$, and $\cos x$, have power series that converge to the functions for all values of x. Partial sums of the series can then be used to approximate functional values. The power series in question are referred to as the *series expansions* of the functions and are shown in calculus to be:

$$e^x = 1 + x + \frac{x^2}{2!} + \frac{x^3}{3!} + \frac{x^4}{4!} + \cdots + \frac{x^k}{k!} + \cdots = \sum_{k=0}^{\infty} \frac{x^k}{k!}$$

$$\sin x = x - \frac{x^3}{3!} + \frac{x^5}{5!} - \frac{x^7}{7!} + \frac{x^9}{9!} + \cdots + \frac{(-1)^k x^{2k+1}}{(2k+1)!} + \cdots = \sum_{k=0}^{\infty} \frac{(-1)^k x^{2k+1}}{(2k+1)!}$$

$$\cos x = 1 - \frac{x^2}{2!} + \frac{x^4}{4!} - \frac{x^6}{6!} + \frac{x^8}{8!} + \cdots + \frac{(-1)^k x^{2k}}{(2k)!} + \cdots = \sum_{k=0}^{\infty} \frac{(-1)^k x^{2k}}{(2k)!}$$

The partial sums of each of these series are polynomials that can be used to approximate values of the function for any x.

Example 4   Use seven terms of the appropriate power series to approximate e^2.

Since for all x, $e^x = 1 + x + \dfrac{x^2}{2!} + \dfrac{x^3}{3!} + \cdots$,

$$e^2 \approx 1 + 2 + \frac{2^2}{2} + \frac{2^3}{6} + \frac{2^4}{24} + \frac{2^5}{120} + \frac{2^6}{720} \approx 7.3556$$

Compare the result of Example 4 with a calculator value of e^2 to four places: $e^2 \approx 7.3891$. If you are not impressed, remember that you used just seven of infinitely many terms to approximate the functional value and did so with an error of less than 0.04.

A graphing utility can be used effectively to show how the various partial sums of a series expansion approximate a function, and how that approximation improves as more terms of the series are included. First of all, the graph at the right makes it clear that the constant polynomial $y = 1$ and the first degree polynomial $y = 1 + x$ are reasonable approximations for $y = e^x$ only very near $x = 0$.

[−7, 7] by [−2, 5]

Next, use a graphing utility to graph $y = e^x$, and on the same axes graph successively

$$S_3: \quad y = 1 + x + \frac{x^2}{2}$$

$$S_4: \quad y = 1 + x + \frac{x^2}{2} + \frac{x^3}{6}$$

$$S_5: \quad y = 1 + x + \frac{x^2}{2} + \frac{x^3}{6} + \frac{x^4}{24}$$

and so on. As the graphs show, the larger n is, the more the graph of the partial sum S_n resembles the graph of $y = e^x$.

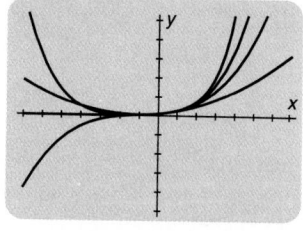

$[-7, 7]$ by $[-50, 50]$
x scl: 1 y scl: 10

Modeling

An engineer is studying the inclinations of the exit ramps on a state turnpike. How can the angle of inclination be determined in radians?

The radian measure of an angle of inclination x can be modeled using the power series $x - \frac{x^3}{3} + \frac{x^5}{5} - \frac{x^7}{7} + \cdots$, which converges to $\text{Tan}^{-1} x$ for all $x \in [-1, 1]$. The accuracy of the approximation depends on how many terms in the polynomial are computed.

Example 5   *Civil Engineering*   While surveying a steep mountain road, an engineer used a calculator to calculate $\text{Tan}^{-1} 0.8$. The calculator found the answer using a finite number of terms of the infinite series

$$\text{Tan}^{-1} x = x - \frac{x^3}{3} + \frac{x^5}{5} - \frac{x^7}{7} + \cdots$$

Find $\text{Tan}^{-1} 0.8$ using the above series.

$S_1 = 0.8.$ *Use one term.*

$S_2 = 0.8 - \dfrac{0.8^3}{3} = 0.6293$ *Use two terms.*

$S_3 = 0.8 - \dfrac{0.8^3}{3} + \dfrac{0.8^5}{5} = 0.6949$

$S_4 = 0.8 - \dfrac{0.8^3}{3} + \dfrac{0.8^5}{5} - \dfrac{0.8^7}{7} = 0.6649$

Continuing in this manner, you can obtain the partial sums $S_9 = 0.6752$, $S_{11} = 0.6749$, and $S_{13} = 0.6748$. The partial sums are approaching $\text{Tan}^{-1} 0.8 = 0.6747$, or about $38.7°$. This power series can be shown in calculus to converge to $\text{Tan}^{-1} 0.8$ since $0.8 \in [-1, 1]$.

Power series provide a way of defining the exponential and trigonometric functions for complex numbers. (Note that e^z, $\sin z$, and $\cos z$ have as yet no meaning if z is a complex number that is not a real number.) Since the four basic arithmetic operations are defined for complex numbers, it is reasonable to *define* e^z, $\sin z$, and $\cos z$ as follows for all complex numbers z.

13.8 Power Series   **731**

CLOSURE

Have students write you a note describing any connections they made
in this lesson.

$$e^z = 1 + z + \frac{z^2}{2!} + \frac{z^3}{3!} + \frac{z^4}{4!} + \cdots + \frac{z^k}{k!}$$

$$\sin z = z - \frac{z^3}{3!} + \frac{z^5}{5!} - \frac{z^7}{7!} + \frac{z^9}{9!} + \cdots + \frac{(-1)^k z^{2k+1}}{(2k+1)!} + \cdots$$

$$\cos z = 1 - \frac{z^2}{2!} + \frac{z^4}{4!} - \frac{z^6}{6!} + \frac{z^8}{8!} + \cdots + \frac{(-1)^k z^{2k}}{(2k)!} + \cdots$$

In particular, if z is a "pure imaginary" number, that is, $z = ix$ for some real
number x, a very interesting relationship becomes apparent from these power
series definitions. Keeping in mind that $i^2 = -1$, $i^3 = -i$, $i^4 = 1$, and so on,
you can evaluate e^z for $z = ix$, which leads to

$$e^{ix} = 1 + ix + \frac{(ix)^2}{2!} + \frac{(ix)^3}{3!} + \frac{(ix)^4}{4!} + \frac{(ix)^5}{5!} + \frac{(ix)^6}{6!} + \frac{(ix)^7}{7!} + \cdots$$

$$= 1 + ix - \frac{x^2}{2!} - \frac{ix^3}{3!} + \frac{x^4}{4!} + \frac{ix^5}{5!} - \frac{x^6}{6!} - \frac{ix^7}{7!} + \frac{x^8}{8!} + \frac{ix^9}{9!} - \frac{x^{10}}{10!} + \cdots$$

$$= \left(1 - \frac{x^2}{2!} + \frac{x^4}{4!} - \frac{x^6}{6!} + \frac{x^8}{8!} + \cdots\right) + i\left(x - \frac{x^3}{3!} + \frac{x^5}{5!} - \frac{x^7}{7!} + \frac{x^9}{9!} + \cdots\right)$$

$$= \cos x + i \sin x$$

The relationship $e^{ix} = \cos x + i \sin x$ is called **Euler's formula** after the
eighteenth century Swiss mathematician Leonhard Euler. It was Euler who first
observed that for $x = \pi$, the formula becomes $e^{i\pi} = \cos \pi + i \sin \pi$ or $e^{i\pi} = -1$.
When expressed in the form $e^{i\pi} + 1 = 0$, the equation relates five of the most
important numbers in mathematics, 0, 1, π, e, and i.

Since any complex number can be expressed in polar form as $r(\cos x + i \sin x)$,
where x is a real number, it follows that any complex number can be expressed
in the form re^{ix}, where r and x are real numbers.

Example 6 Express the complex number $\sqrt{3} + i$ in the form re^{ix}.

The modulus r of $\sqrt{3} + i$ is $\sqrt{(\sqrt{3})^2 + 1^2} = 2$ and its argument x is $\frac{\pi}{6}$. In polar

form $\sqrt{3} + i = 2\left(\cos\frac{\pi}{6} + i \sin\frac{\pi}{6}\right) = 2e^{\frac{i\pi}{6}}$.

Class Exercises

Find the values of x for which the given power series converges.

1. $1 + (x - 5) + (x - 5)^2 + (x - 5)^3 + (x - 5)^4 + \cdots$ $4 < x < 6$

2. $7 + 7(2x - 9) + 7(2x - 9)^2 + 7(2x - 9)^3 + \cdots$ $4 < x < 5$

3. $1 + \left(\frac{1}{4}x\right) + \left(\frac{1}{4}x\right)^2 + \left(\frac{1}{4}x\right)^3 + \left(\frac{1}{4}x\right)^4 + \cdots$ $-4 < x < 4$

4. $1 + 0.1x + 0.01x^2 + 0.001x^3 + 0.0001x^4 + \cdots$ $-10 < x < 10$

Find a power series that converges to the given function.

5. $f(x) = \dfrac{7}{1 - x}$ $\displaystyle\sum_{k=0}^{\infty} 7x^k$

6. $g(x) = \dfrac{\sqrt{3}}{2 - 3x}$ $\displaystyle\sum_{k=0}^{\infty} \frac{\sqrt{3}}{2}\left(\frac{3}{2}x\right)^k$

Use N terms of the power series expansion of the function to estimate each value.

7. $e^{0.1}$, $N = 5$ **8.** $\sin 0.2$, $N = 4$ **9.** $\cos 1.1$, $N = 6$ **10.** $\sqrt{e}$, $N = 5$
   1.10517   0.198669   0.453596   1.64844

Write each complex number in the form re^{ix}, where x and r are real numbers.

11. $2 - 2i$ $\quad 2\sqrt{2}e^{-\frac{i\pi}{4}}$

12. i $\quad e^{\frac{i\pi}{2}}$

13. $1 + i$ $\quad \sqrt{2}e^{\frac{i\pi}{4}}$

14. Use six terms of the power series definition to estimate $e^{0.5i}$. $\quad 0.87760 + 0.47943i$

Practice Exercises

 Use appropriate technology.

Find the values of x for which each power series converges.

A 1. $1 + \left(x + \frac{1}{4}\right) + \left(x + \frac{1}{4}\right)^2 + \left(x + \frac{1}{4}\right)^3 + \left(x + \frac{1}{4}\right)^4 + \cdots$ $\quad -\frac{5}{4} < x < \frac{3}{4}$

2. $3 + 3(5 - 4x) + 3(5 - 4x)^2 + 3(5 - 4x)^3 + \cdots$ $\quad 1 < x < \frac{3}{2}$

3. $1 - x + x^2 - x^3 + x^4 - x^5 + \cdots$ $\quad -1 < x < 1$

4. $1 + (8x) + (8x)^2 + (8x)^3 + (8x)^4 + \cdots$ $\quad -\frac{1}{8} < x < \frac{1}{8}$

5. $1 - 0.2x + 0.04x^2 - 0.008x^3 + 0.0016x^4 + \cdots$ $\quad -5 < x < 5$

6. $1.1 + 1.1(3 - \sqrt{6}x) + 1.1(3 - \sqrt{6}x)^2 + 1.1(3 - \sqrt{6}x)^3 + \cdots$ $\quad \frac{\sqrt{6}}{3} < x < \frac{2\sqrt{6}}{3}$

Find a power series that converges to each function.

7. $f(x) = \frac{\sqrt{11}}{1 - x} \quad \sum_{k=0}^{\infty} \sqrt{11}x^k$

8. $g(x) = \frac{1.6}{1 - 10x} \quad \sum_{k=0}^{\infty} 1.6(10x)^k$

9. $h(x) = \frac{2\pi}{3 - 6x} \quad \sum_{k=0}^{\infty} \frac{2\pi}{3}(2x)^k$

10. $m(x) = \frac{4}{2x - 1} \quad \sum_{k=0}^{\infty} -4(2x)^k$

11. $n(x) = \frac{3}{3 - 5x} \quad \sum_{k=0}^{\infty} \left(\frac{5}{3}x\right)^k$

12. $p(x) = \frac{7}{3x - 4} \quad \sum_{k=0}^{\infty} -\frac{7}{4}\left(\frac{3}{4}x\right)^k$

Use N terms of the power series expansion of the appropriate function to estimate each value.

13. $e^{-0.3}$, $N = 3$ $\quad 0.745$

14. e, $N = 6$ $\quad 2.71667$

15. $\sin 0.11$, $N = 4$ $\quad 0.109778$

16. $\cos\left(-\frac{1}{2}\right)$, $N = 4$ $\quad 0.877582$

17. $\cos 0.4$, $N = 5$ $\quad 0.921061$

18. $\sin\left(-\frac{1}{4}\right)$, $N = 4$ $\quad -0.247407$

Ⓡ 19. Express the complex number $-3 + 4i$ in polar form. $\quad 5(\cos 126.8699° + i \sin 126.8699°)$

20. **Writing in Mathematics** Write a paragraph explaining how to identify values of x for which an infinite geometric series of the form $\sum_{k=0}^{\infty} a|f(x)|^k$ converges.

Ⓡ 21. Use DeMoivre's theorem to evaluate $(-3\sqrt{3} + 2i)^5$. $\quad 1408.1573 + 5162.0000i$

B 22. The power series for $\text{Tan}^{-1} x$ given in Example 5 can be used to approximate $\frac{\pi}{4}$ by using an appropriate value for x. What value should be used? Use S_5 to find an approximation for π. $\quad x = 1; \pi = 3.339683$

23. Use a graphing utility to graph $\text{Tan}^{-1} x$ and the approximating polynomials formed by taking one, two, or three terms from the series $x - \frac{x^3}{3} + \frac{x^5}{5} - \frac{x^7}{7} + \cdots$. For what values of x do the polynomials give good approximations for $\text{Tan}^{-1} x$?

Express each complex number in the form re^{ix}, with x and r real numbers.

24. $5 + 5i$ $\quad 5\sqrt{2}e^{\frac{i\pi}{4}}$

25. $4i$ $\quad 4e^{\frac{i\pi}{2}}$

26. $-3 + 4i$ $\quad 5e^{2.21i}$

27. $1 + \sqrt{3}i$ $\quad 2e^{\frac{i\pi}{3}}$

Use N terms of the power series definition to estimate each complex value.

28. e^{-2i}, $N = 6$

29. $\sin \frac{1}{2}i$, $N = 4$

30. $\cos -0.1i$, $N = 4$

31. e^{1+i}, $N = 3$

13.8 Power Series   **733**

INDEPENDENT PRACTICE

Assignment Guide

Basic: 1–21, 33–37, Project

Average: 5–6, 11–12, 17–38, Project

Enriched: 18, 20, 22–32, 34, 36, 38–47, Project

Teacher's Resource Book
Practice, page 95

Ⓡ **Review**

Exercises 19, 21, 33, 35, and 37 review expressing complex numbers in polar form, using DeMoivre's theorem to evaluate powers or to find roots of complex numbers, and finding the complex solutions of an equation.

Project

Students' calculations should show that the series gives fairly accurate approximations for the binomial expansions subject to the given conditions.

Additional Answers

23.

If $|x| \leq 1$, then using three terms of the expansion gives a good approximation.

28. $-0.333 - 0.933i$

29. $0.5211i$

30. 1.0050

31. $2 + 2i$

32. $e^{i(x + 2n\pi)} = e^{ix}e^{i(2n\pi)} = e^{ix}(\cos 2n\pi + i \sin 2n\pi) = e^{ix}$

Writing in Mathematics

20. The values for which an infinite geometric series of the form $\sum_{k=0}^{\infty} a|f(x)|$ converges can be identified by solving the equation $|f(x)| < 1$.

Test Yourself

Teacher's Resource Book
  Tests—Quiz, form A, page 58
  Tests—Quiz, form B, page 58

Lesson Quiz

1. For what values of x does the power series $\sum_{k=0}^{\infty} \frac{6}{7} x^k$ converge? $|x| < 1$

2. Find a power series that converges to the function $h(x) = \frac{7}{1 - 5x}$.
$7 + 7(5x) + 7(5x)^2 + 7(5x)^3 + \cdots$
$\sum_{k=0}^{\infty} 7(5x)^k$

3. Find the values of x for which the power series $4 + 4(x - 9) + 4(x - 9)^2 + 4(x - 9)^3 + 4(x - 9)^4 + \cdots$ converges. $x \in (8, 10)$

4. Use five terms of the appropriate power series to approximate $e^{\frac{1}{2}}$.
$1 + \frac{1}{2} + \frac{\left(\frac{1}{2}\right)^2}{2} + \frac{\left(\frac{1}{2}\right)^3}{6} + \frac{\left(\frac{1}{2}\right)^4}{24} \approx 1.648$

5. Express the complex number $-5 + 5i$ in the form re^{ix}. $5\sqrt{2}e^{\frac{3\pi}{4}}$

Additional Answers

36.

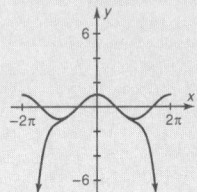

If $|x| \le 3$, then using four terms of the expansion gives a good approximation.

37. $\sqrt[10]{2}$ cis $9°$, $\sqrt[10]{2}$ cis $81°$, $\sqrt[10]{2}$ cis $153°$, $\sqrt[10]{2}$ cis $225°$, $\sqrt[10]{2}$ cis $297°$

39. using four terms: 0.5235258553; using calculator: 0.5235987756; Using more terms would increase accuracy.

40. using six terms: -0.6911458333; using calculator: -0.6931472

42. $\cos \sqrt{x} = 1 - \frac{x}{2!} + \frac{x^2}{4!} - \cdots;$
$\cos \sqrt{\frac{1}{2}} \approx 0.7602446$

32. Show that $e^{ix} = e^{i(x + 2n\pi)}$ for all real numbers x and all integers n.

Ⓡ 33. Use DeMoivre's theorem to find the four fourth roots of 2. $2^{\frac{1}{4}}, \ 2^{\frac{1}{4}}i, \ -2^{\frac{1}{4}}, \ -2^{\frac{1}{4}}i$

34. *Programming*   Write a program that will approximate the function $\sin x$ using the first four terms of the power series for $\sin x$. Use a loop to output x, the polynomial evaluated at x, and the value of $\sin x$. Output a table of values for x ranging from $x = -3$ to 3 in steps of 0.5. Where is the polynomial approximation most accurate? How could you modify your program to get a more accurate approximation?

Ⓡ 35. Find the three cube roots of $125i$. $\frac{5\sqrt{3}}{2} + \frac{5}{2}i, \ -\frac{5\sqrt{3}}{2} + \frac{5}{2}i, \ -5i$

36. **Thinking Critically**   Use a graphing utility to examine how the series expansion of $y = \cos x$ approximates the function. Describe the values of x for which the fewest terms of the expansion are required for a reasonable approximation.

Ⓡ 37. Find all complex solutions to the equation $x^5 - i = 1$.

38. *Programming*   Write a program similar to the program of Exercise 34 that will use four terms of the power series for $\cos x$ to approximate the function $\cos x$.

C 39. The following series expansion of $\operatorname{Sin}^{-1} x$ holds for all $x \in [-1, 1]$.
$$\operatorname{Sin}^{-1} x = x + \frac{x^3}{2 \cdot 3} + \frac{1 \cdot 3 \cdot x^5}{2 \cdot 4 \cdot 5} + \frac{1 \cdot 3 \cdot 5 \cdot x^7}{2 \cdot 4 \cdot 6 \cdot 7} + \cdots$$

Use four terms of this series to approximate $\operatorname{Sin}^{-1} \frac{1}{2}$ and compare this estimate to a calculator value. How could you increase the accuracy of the estimate?

40. The following series expansion of $\ln (1 + x)$ holds for all $x \in (-1, 1]$.
$$\ln (1 + x) = x - \frac{x^2}{2} + \frac{x^3}{3} - \frac{x^4}{4} + \cdots$$

Use six terms of this series to approximate $\ln 0.5$ and compare this estimate to a calculator value. How could you increase the accuracy of the estimate?

41. Use more terms of the series $\ln (1 + x)$ of Exercise 40 to improve the estimate. Use a graphing utility to graph the series and the polynomials formed by taking one, two, or three terms from the series $x - \frac{x^2}{2} + \frac{x^3}{3} - \frac{x^4}{4} + \frac{x^5}{5} - \cdots$. Use the trace and zoom features to compare the three polynomials with $\ln (1 + x)$ at $x = 0.5$. From the graphs, estimate the values of x for which the series will give good approximations to $\ln (1 + x)$.

42. Use the power series for $\cos x$ to obtain a series expansion for $\cos \sqrt{x}$. Use five terms of this expansion to estimate $\cos \sqrt{\frac{1}{2}}$.

43. Show that for all real numbers x, $\sin x = \frac{e^{ix} - e^{-ix}}{2i}$ and $\cos x = \frac{e^{ix} + e^{-ix}}{2}$.

Each of the following infinite sums may be evaluated by recognizing the function it represents. Find the indicated values.

44. $2 + \frac{1}{2!} + \frac{1}{3!} + \frac{1}{4!} + \frac{1}{5!} + \frac{1}{6!} + \cdots$ e

45. $1 - \frac{\pi^2}{2!} + \frac{\pi^4}{4!} - \frac{\pi^6}{6!} + \frac{\pi^8}{8!} - \frac{\pi^{10}}{10!} + \cdots$ $\cos \pi = -1$

46. $\frac{\pi}{2} - \frac{\pi^3}{2^3 \cdot 3!} + \frac{\pi^5}{2^5 \cdot 5!} - \frac{\pi^7}{2^7 \cdot 7!} + \frac{\pi^9}{2^9 \cdot 9!} - \cdots$ $\sin \frac{\pi}{2} = 1$

734   Chapter 13 Sequences and Series

43. $\dfrac{e^{ix} - e^{-ix}}{2i} = \dfrac{\cos x + i \sin x - (\cos x - i \sin x)}{2i} = \dfrac{2i \sin x}{2i} = \sin x; \ \dfrac{e^{ix} + e^{-ix}}{2} =$
$\dfrac{\cos x + i \sin x + \cos x - i \sin x}{2} = \dfrac{2 \cos x}{2} = \cos x$

47. *Construction*   A tunnel connects two points A and B on the earth's surface as shown at the right. The surface distance from A to B is 200 mi. Use two terms of the power series for cos x to approximate the maximum depth of the tunnel. Use the approximation 4000 mi for the radius of the earth.   1.25 mi

Project

You have used the binomial theorem to expand $(a + b)^n$ where n is a positive integer. What if the exponent is not an integer? Can any meaning be attached to $(a + b)^r$ if r is a fraction?

Generalizing the binomial theorem to noninteger exponents leads to the binomial series, one of Sir Isaac Newton's great achievements. Let $a = 1$ and $b = x$. Then $(1 + x)^r = 1 + rx + \dfrac{r(r-1)x^2}{2!} + \dfrac{r(r-1)(r-2)x^3}{3!} + \cdots$.

This series converges for values of x in the interval $(-1, 1)$. (Convergence also depends on the value of r.) Find binomial series that may be used to approximate the square root function and the cube root function. Test the accuracy of each series by computing the first three terms, using $x = 0.5$ and $x = -0.5$.

Test Yourself

Use the binomial theorem to expand and simplify each expression.

1. $(x - 3y)^5$

2. $(x - 2x^{-3})^7$ 13.5

Find the indicated term of each expansion.

3. fourth term of $(2x + 3y)^8$ $48{,}384x^5y^3$

4. sixth term of $(a - 5c^2)^9$ $-393{,}750a^4c^{10}$

Tell whether each sequence converges or diverges. If it converges, give the limit.

5. $c_n = 3(-1)^n$ diverges

6. $t_n = n - \dfrac{5}{n} + 5$ diverges

7. $m_k = \dfrac{1}{2}\sin n\pi$ converges; 0

8. $d_k = \left(-\dfrac{1}{3}\right)^k$ converges; 0   13.6

Determine whether each series converges or diverges. If the series converges, find the sum. If it diverges, tell why it diverges.

9. $2 + 0.2 + 0.02 + 0.002 + 0.0002 + \cdots$ $\dfrac{20}{9}$ 13.7

10. $\displaystyle\sum_{j=1}^{\infty} 3\left(\dfrac{3}{4}\right)^j$ 9

11. $\displaystyle\sum_{k=1}^{\infty} (-1.2)^k$ diverges

12. $\displaystyle\sum_{t=1}^{\infty} -5(0.2)^t$ $-\dfrac{5}{4}$

Express each repeating decimal as the ratio of two integers.

13. $0.3462626262\cdots$ $\dfrac{857}{2475}$

14. $-5.333333\cdots$ $-\dfrac{16}{3}$

Find the values of x for which each power series converges.

15. $1 + \left(x + \dfrac{1}{2}\right) + \left(x + \dfrac{1}{2}\right)^2 + \left(x + \dfrac{1}{2}\right)^3 + \left(x + \dfrac{1}{2}\right)^4 \cdots$ $-\dfrac{3}{2} < x < \dfrac{1}{2}$ 13.8

16. $1 - 0.3x + 0.09x^2 - 0.027x^3 + 0.0081x^4 - \cdots$ $-\dfrac{10}{3} < x < \dfrac{10}{3}$

17. Find a power series that converges to $f(x) = \dfrac{3}{1 - 2x}$. $\displaystyle\sum_{k=0}^{\infty} 3(2x)^k$

13.8 Power Series   **735**

Chapter 13   Summary and Review

Vocabulary

arithmetic means (684)	factorial notation (708)	nth (general) term (675)
arithmetic sequence (682)	finite sequence (675)	partial sum (691)
arithmetic series (691)	geometric means (686)	Pascal's triangle (707)
binomial coefficient (708)	geometric sequence (684)	power series (728)
binomial theorem (709)	geometric series (691)	recursive formula (676)
common difference (682)	graph of a sequence (683)	sequence (675)
common ratio (684)	index of summation (690)	series (690)
converge (715)	infinite sequence (675)	sigma notation (690)
diverge (715)	limit of a sequence (714)	sum of an infinite series
Euler's formula (732)	mathematical induction	(721)
explicit formula (676)	(699)	terms of a sequence (675)

Sequences   The rule of a sequence is a formula that describes the nth term of the   **13.1**
sequence. An explicit formula gives the nth term of a sequence as a function of n. A
recursive formula gives one or more initial terms of the sequence and then defines
the nth term using preceding terms.

1. Find the first five terms of the infinite sequence defined explicitly
   by $a_n = \dfrac{2}{n^3} + 1$. $3, 1\frac{1}{4}, 1\frac{2}{27}, 1\frac{1}{32}, 1\frac{2}{125}$

2. Find a recursive formula for the sequence $-15, -8, -1, 6, 13, 20, \ldots$.

3. *Biology*   A certain population of bacteria increases at the rate of 15%
   every hour. Find a recursive formula for the number of bacteria in the
   colony after n hours. Given that there are 100 bacteria at the beginning of
   the first hour, find the size of the colony after 4 h.

Arithmetic and Geometric Sequences   In an arithmetic sequence, the difference   **13.2**
between any two consecutive terms is constant. In a geometric sequence, the ratio
of any two consecutive terms is constant. To find any specified term of an arithmetic
sequence with common difference d, use the explicit formula $a_n = a_1 + (n - 1)d$.
To find any specified term of a geometric sequence with common ratio r, use the
explicit formula $a_n = a_1 \cdot r^{n-1}$. In an arithmetic sequence $a_1, a_2, a_3, \ldots, a_{k-1}, a_k$,
the *arithmetic means* between a_1 and a_k are the terms $a_2, a_3, \ldots, a_{k-1}$. Similarly,
the terms between any two terms in a geometric sequence are *geometric means*.

Determine whether each sequence is arithmetic or geometric. If arithmetic, find
the common difference d; if geometric, find the common ratio r.

4. $8.31, 8.36, 8.41, 8.46, 8.51, 8.56, \ldots$ 5. $64, -16, 4, -1, \frac{1}{4}, -\frac{1}{16}, \ldots$ geometric; $-\frac{1}{4}$
   arithmetic; 0.05

6. Find an explicit formula for the geometric sequence with $a_1 = -3$ and
   $a_4 = 81$ and then use it to find the twelfth term of the sequence. $a_n = (-3)^n$; 531,441

7. Find four arithmetic means between 27 and 47. 31, 35, 39, 43

8. Find three geometric means between -2 and -2592. $-12, -72, -432$ or $12, -72, 432$

9. Find the mean proportional between -6 and -18. $-6\sqrt{3}$

Arithmetic and Geometric Series   Summation or sigma (Σ) notation may be used   13.3

to indicate a series. The sum $S_n = \sum\limits_{k=1}^{n} a_k$ is called the nth partial sum of the infinite

series $\sum\limits_{k=1}^{\infty} a_k$. For an arithmetic series, use $S_n = \frac{1}{2}n(a_1 + a_n)$ or $S_n = \frac{1}{2}n(2a_1 + (n-1)d)$.

For a geometric series with $r \neq 1$, use $S_n = \dfrac{a_1(1 - r^n)}{1 - r}$.

10. Use sigma notation to express the series $1 + 6 + 36 + 216 + \cdots$. $\sum\limits_{k=1}^{\infty} 6^{k-1}$

Find the indicated partial sum.

11. S_7 for $14 + 9 + 4 + -1 + \cdots$ -7 **12.** $\sum\limits_{k=1}^{4} k^4$ 354

Mathematical Induction   The principle of mathematical induction allows you to   13.4
assert that a statement P_n involving the positive integer n is true for every $n \geq 1$
providing both of the following two conditions hold.

1. The statement is true for $n = 1$, that is, P_1 is true.
2. Whenever P_k is true, then P_{k+1} is also true.

13. Use the principle of mathematical induction to prove that for all positive

integers n, $2^2 + 4^2 + 6^2 + \cdots + (2n)^2 = \dfrac{2n(n+1)(2n+1)}{3}$.

The Binomial Theorem   If a and b are real numbers and n is a positive integer, then   13.5

$(a + b)^n = \binom{n}{0}a^n + \binom{n}{1}a^{n-1}b + \binom{n}{2}a^{n-2}b^2 + \cdots + \binom{n}{n-1}ab^{n-1} + \binom{n}{n}b^n$,

where $\binom{n}{k}$ is the binomial coefficient $\binom{n}{k} = \dfrac{n!}{k!(n-k)!}$.

14. Use the binomial theorem to expand and simplify $(m^4 + 3m^{-3})^5$.

15. Find the eighth term of the expansion of $(x - 3)^{12}$. $-1{,}732{,}104x^5$

Limits of Sequences   A convergent sequence is a sequence that gets arbitrarily close   13.6
to a number L for sufficiently large values of n. A sequence that does not converge
is said to diverge.

Determine whether each sequence converges. If it converges, give the limit.

16. $a_n = 3^n$ diverges   **17.** $r_k = \dfrac{3k - 2}{2k + 1}$ converges; $\frac{3}{2}$ **18.** $c_t = \sin\frac{1}{4}t\pi$ diverges

Sums of Infinite Series   If the partial sums of an infinite sequence have a limit as the   13.7
number of terms increases without bound, then the *sum of the infinite series* is
defined to be the limit of the partial sums.

Determine whether each series converges. If it converges, find the sum.

19. $3 + 0.3 + 0.03 + 0.003 + 0.0003 + \cdots$ converges; $\frac{10}{3}$ **20.** $\sum\limits_{t=1}^{\infty} 6\left(\frac{1}{7}\right)^t$ converges; 1   **21.** $\sum\limits_{k=1}^{\infty} (2.3)^k$ diverges

Power Series   A power series is an infinite series of the form $\sum\limits_{k=0}^{\infty} a_k x^k$. If the   13.8
coefficients a_k are all equal to a constant a, then the power series is also an *infinite
geometric series* and converges to $\dfrac{a}{1 - x}$ for all x for which $|x| < 1$.

22. Find the values of x for which the power series $2 + 2(3 - x) + 2(3 - x)^2 +$
$2(3 - x)^3 + \cdots$ converges. $2 < x < 4$

23. Find a power series that converges to the function $f(x) = \dfrac{3.4}{1 - 8x}$. $\sum\limits_{k=0}^{\infty} 3.4(8x)^k$

Additional Answers

13. Since $1 = \frac{1}{3}(1)(3)$, P_1 is true. Assume P_k: $1 + 9 + 25 + \cdots +$

$(2k - 1)^2 = \frac{k}{3}(2k - 1)(2k + 1)$.

Then, $P_{k+1} = 1 + 9 + 25 + \cdots + (2k - 1)^2 + (2k + 1)^2 =$

$\frac{k(2k - 1)(2k + 1)}{3} + (2k + 1)^2 =$

$\frac{(2k + 1)(k + 1)(2k + 3)}{3} =$

$\frac{k + 1}{3}[2(k + 1) - 1][2(k + 1) + 1] = P_{k+1}$.

14. $64x^6 - \frac{576x^5}{y^2} + \frac{2160x^4}{y^4} - \frac{4320x^3}{y^6} + \frac{4860x^2}{y^8} - \frac{2916x}{y^{10}} + \frac{729}{y^{12}}$

Chapter 13 Test

1. Find the first five terms of the infinite sequence defined explicitly by
   $f(n) = (-1)^n 3n$. $\quad$ -3, 6, -9, 12, -15

2. Find an explicit formula for the sequence $-5, 1, 7, 13, \ldots$ $\quad a_n = 6n - 11$

3. Find the next four terms of the sequence given by the recursive formula
   $a_1 = 2$ and $a_n = a_{n-1} - 3$. $\quad$ -1, -4, -7, -10

4. Find a recursive formula for the sequence $\frac{3}{2}, \frac{9}{4}, \frac{27}{8}, \frac{81}{16}, \ldots$ $\quad a_1 = \frac{3}{2}$ and $a_n = \frac{3a_{n-1}}{2}$

5. Find an explicit formula for the arithmetic sequence $a_4 = -8$ and $a_6 = 2$
   and then use it to find the thirteenth term of the sequence. $\quad a_n = -28 + 5n$; 37

Determine whether each sequence is arithmetic, geometric, or neither. If
arithmetic, find the common difference d; if geometric, find the common ratio r.

6. $36, -12, 4, -\frac{4}{3}, \frac{4}{9}, \ldots$ geometric; $-\frac{1}{3}$ $\qquad$ 7. $72, 24, 12, 3, 1, \frac{1}{4}, \ldots$ neither

8. $-19, -14, -9, -4, 1, \ldots$ arithmetic; 5

9. Find three arithmetic means between 27 and 47. $\quad$ 32, 37, 42

10. Find the mean proportional between -9 and -17. $\quad -3\sqrt{17}$

11. Use sigma notation to express the series $0.3 - 0.6 + 1.2 - 2.4 + 4.8 - \cdots$. $\quad \sum_{k=1}^{\infty} 3(-0.2)^{k-1}$

12. Find the partial sum S_7 for $\displaystyle\sum_{k=1}^{\infty} (3.2k - 4)$. $\quad$ 61.6

13. Use the principle of mathematical induction to prove that for all positive
    integers n, $1 + 9 + 25 + 49 + 81 + \cdots + (2n - 1)^2 = \frac{n}{3}(2n - 1)(2n + 1)$.

14. Use the binomial theorem to expand and simplify $(2x - 3y^{-2})^6$.

15. Find the seventh term of the expansion of $(m - 4n)^{15}$. $\quad$ 20,500,480m^9n^6

Determine whether each sequence converges. If it converges, give the limit.

16. $a_n = \dfrac{2n}{n + 1}$ converges; 2 $\qquad\qquad$ 17. $d_k = (0.05)^k$ converges; 0

18. Determine whether the series $\displaystyle\sum_{n=1}^{\infty} \left(\frac{1}{2}\right)^{n+2}$ converges or diverges. If it
    converges, find the sum. If it diverges, tell why it diverges. converges; $\frac{1}{4}$

19. A ball is dropped from a height of 60 ft. Each time it strikes the ground it
    rebounds to a height of 60% of the distance it fell. Find the total distance
    the ball travels. $\quad$ 240 ft

20. Find the values of x for which the power series $1 - 0.4x + 0.16x^2 - 0.064x^3 + 0.0256x^4 - \cdots$ converges. $\quad -\frac{5}{2} < x < \frac{5}{2}$

21. Find a power series that converges to the function $f(x) = \dfrac{2}{4 - 3x}$. $\quad \displaystyle\sum_{k=0}^{\infty} \frac{1}{2}\left(\frac{3}{4}x\right)^k$

Challenge

Determine whether the series $\displaystyle\sum_{n=1}^{\infty} \frac{3^n}{n!}$ converges or diverges. $\quad$ converges

738 Chapter 13 Sequences and Series

Cumulative Review

Select the best choice for each question.

1. Use matrices to solve the system of equations. *12.5*
B

$$\begin{cases} 6x - 9y - 8z = 3 \\ 3x + 5y - 9z = 26 \\ 4x + 7y + 2z = -7 \end{cases}$$

A. $(1, -2, 3)$ **B.** $(-2, 1, -3)$
C. $(2, -1, 3)$ **D.** $(3, -1, 2)$
E. none of these

2. Solve $\dfrac{e^x}{e^x - 2} = 3$ for x to the *9.5*
E
nearest hundredth. Check answer using a graphing utility.

A. $\frac{2}{3}$ **B.** $\frac{3}{2}$ **C.** $\log 2e$ **D.** $\log e$
E. none of these

3. Identify the property that is *1.2*
E illustrated: $a + (-a) = 0$
A. identity element of addition
B. reflexive   **C.** symmetric
D. associative of addition
E. none of these

4. In triangle ABC, if $\angle A$ is an *5.3*
C obtuse or right angle, then:

  I. If $a > b$, there is one solution.
  II. If $a \le b$, there is no solution.
  III. If $a = b$, there are two solutions.

A. I only   **B.** II only   **C.** I and II
D. I and III   **E.** none of these

5. The graph of $r = 2 + 2\cos\theta$ *10.2*
D can be identified as a
A. leaf   **B.** rose   **C.** lemniscate
D. cardioid   **E.** none of these

6. Determine the equation of the *11.1*
B circle with center $(-3, 5)$ and tangent to the y-axis.
A. $(x - 3)^2 + (y + 5)^2 = 9$
B. $(x + 3)^2 + (y - 5)^2 = 9$
C. $(x - 5)^2 + (y + 3)^2 = 9$
D. $(x + 5)^2 + (y - 3)^2 = 9$
E. none of these

7. Find $-4\begin{bmatrix} 3 & 2 & -4 \\ -8 & 10 & 6 \end{bmatrix}$. *12.1*
A

A. $\begin{bmatrix} -12 & -8 & 16 \\ 32 & -40 & -24 \end{bmatrix}$
B. $\begin{bmatrix} 12 & 8 & -16 \\ -32 & 40 & 24 \end{bmatrix}$ **C.** $\begin{bmatrix} -12 & 8 & 16 \end{bmatrix}$
D. $\begin{bmatrix} 24 & -8 & 12 \end{bmatrix}$ **E.** none of these

8. Determine whether the series *13.7*
C
$12 + 8 + \frac{16}{3} + \frac{32}{9} + \cdots$ converges or diverges. If it converges, find the sum.
A. converges, sum $= 16$
B. diverges
C. converges, sum $= 36$
D. converges, sum $= 63$

9. Find the matrix product *12.2*
E $\begin{bmatrix} -6 \\ 2 \end{bmatrix}\begin{bmatrix} -1 & 12 \\ 0 & -4 \end{bmatrix}$.

A. $\begin{bmatrix} 12 \\ 2 \end{bmatrix}$ **B.** $\begin{bmatrix} -6 & -72 \\ 0 & -24 \end{bmatrix}$ **C.** $\begin{bmatrix} 0 \\ 12 \end{bmatrix}$
D. $\begin{bmatrix} -24 & -6 \\ 0 & 72 \end{bmatrix}$ **E.** not defined

10. Determine the value of k needed *2.5*
B to solve when completing the square for $x^2 - 18x + k$.
A. 36   **B.** 81   **C.** 9   **D.** 72
E. none of these

11. Determine the number of *6.6*
C solutions when $0 \le x \le 2\pi$ for the equation $10\sin^2 x + 17\sin x + 3 = 0$.
A. 0   **B.** 1   **C.** 2   **D.** 4
E. none of these

12. Determine the endpoints of the *11.2*
B major and minor axes of the ellipse with equation $9x^2 + 4y^2 = 36$.
A. $(0, \pm2)$ and $(\pm3, 0)$
B. $(0, \pm3)$ and $(\pm2, 0)$
C. $(\pm4, 0)$ and $(0, \pm9)$
D. $(\pm9, 0)$ and $(0, \pm4)$
E. none of these

CHAPTER OVERVIEW

Summary

Basic counting principles are introduced, with emphasis on the addition and multiplication principles. Methods of counting permutations and combinations are developed. The concept of probability is introduced, and the classical and empirical interpretations are explored. Several topics in probability are presented, including conditional probability, binomial distribution, mathematical expectation, and Bayes' formula.

Chapter Objectives

- To use the addition and multiplication principles for counting
- To determine the number of permutations or combinations of a set of n elements taken r at a time
- To specify the sample space for a random experiment
- To calculate the probability that a given event will occur
- To solve problems involving mutually exclusive events and independent events
- To solve problems involving conditional probability
- To define and give examples of binomial experiments and Bernoulli trials
- To solve problems involving binomial distributions
- To define random variables and mathematical expectation and to solve problems involving them
- To use Bayes' formula to solve probability problems
- To use the theorem of total probability to solve probability problems

14 Probability

Mathematical Power

Modeling   Because people have such strong intuitive feelings about probability, problems in this area of mathematics can easily confuse even the experts. The essential question and analysis discussed below was actually debated in national newspapers for months.

Imagine you are a contestant on a game show and you are asked to choose from among three boxes—A, B, and C. One of the boxes contains a diamond ring, but two of them contain jack-in-the-boxes. After you have made a choice, the master of ceremonies (who knows where the ring is located) will always open one of the other two boxes to reveal a jack-in-the-box. You will then be offered a choice to either stay with the box you originally chose or to switch to the other unopened box. Are your chances of winning better if you stay with your original choice or if you switch? Or does it matter? What is the probability of getting the ring in each case? Before you continue reading, think about the problem and formulate your own solution.

You are faced with a decision—to stay or to switch. In a complex situation such as this, constructing some type of model can help you gain insight into what is really happening. The diagrams shown are *pictorial* models of each strategy. Study each case carefully to convince yourself which strategy is better.

Did the results agree with your thinking before you saw the model? Intuitively, many people feel that when there are only two boxes left, the probability for each one must be $\frac{1}{2}$.

To see what is wrong with that reasoning, suppose you start by choosing box A. When one of the other boxes is opened to reveal a jack-in-the-box, that does not change the probability for box A. The probability that the ring was in box A was $\frac{1}{3}$ at the start, and the probability is still $\frac{1}{3}$ after another box is opened. You knew that the emcee was going to open another box no matter what was in box A, so you *did*

STAY STRATEGY

Stay strategy wins 1 out of 3 times

740

not gain any new information when another box was opened. Therefore, since the probability for box A is $\frac{1}{3}$, and the only other place the ring could be is in the remaining box, the probability for that remaining box must now be $\frac{2}{3}$. That is why you should switch.

Thinking Critically   Suppose the rules of the game are changed: The emcee may or may not open another box and offer a switch after you choose. Discuss what this might mean, and how it might affect your strategy.

Project   You can turn the pictorial model into a *simulation*. Work in pairs and alternate roles. Use index cards marked to represent the boxes and follow the original rules. The emcee should rearrange the cards and place them face down after each trial. Play 20 times using the stay strategy and another 20 times using the switch strategy. Record the wins and losses. How do the results compare with the analysis using the model? If the simulation results are very different, does this mean the analysis was incorrect? Explain.

If you have access to a computer with a random function, try writing a program to simulate the game show. Run a large number of trials and report on your results.

SWITCH STRATEGY

A   B   C

LOSE

Pick   Switch   Emcee shows

WIN

Switch   Pick   Emcee shows

WIN

Switch   Emcee shows   Pick

Switch strategy wins 2 out of 3 times

Mathematical Power
Students may recognize that the situation in this problem is analogous to the format of a popular television game show. Although the mathematical explanation hinges on a careful application of conditional probability theory, the pictorial model is the means by which most people convince themselves that the switch strategy is better.

Emphasize the statement in the problem which tells that the emcee will *always* open one of the other two boxes to reveal a jack-in-the-box; clearly, the emcee will never open the box with the ring. Remind students that conditional probability allows for a revision of the chances of an event occurring *when additional information is obtained*. The key idea in the analysis is that there really is *not* any new information when the second box is opened.

It is worth pointing out to students that, when a theory or formula seems to lead to an erroneous conclusion, careful examination often reveals that it is not the theory itself, but the improper use of that theory, that causes the error.

Thinking Critically   Answers may vary. One answer addresses the possibility that the emcee will open another box and offer a switch only when you have picked the box with the ring. If you suspect this is the case, then a stay strategy is better.

Review and Assessment

Vocabulary

addition principle
fundamental counting principle
multiplication principle
tree diagram

ⓜ Materials/Manipulatives

cards
coins
dice
tree diagram with removable labels

FOCUS

Counting techniques are central to probability. You need to know the number of all possible outcomes of an event before discussing the probability of any outcome. It is important for students to be able to decide whether an exact count is required or an estimate is satisfactory.

The topic of Fermi problems provides a good basis for a discussion of exact count vs estimates. Students may enjoy researching Fermi problems, or writing their own Fermi-type problems and posing the problems to one another. Variations on this task include collecting data and seeking conclusions from the data. One example is "How fast in miles per hour does human hair grow?" (10^{-8} mi/h)

14.1 | Basic Counting Principles

Objective: To use the addition and multiplication principles for counting

Focus

A *Fermi problem* is a counting problem for which a solution is found using a series of estimates. Fermi problems are named for the physicist Enrico Fermi (1901–1954) who enjoyed challenging people with problems like "How many piano tuners are there in Chicago?" and "How many railroad freight cars are there in the United States?"

Most people are surprised to learn that Fermi problems can be solved by a series of steps that involve information that is either generally known or can be estimated without recourse to reference books. The solution is, of course, an estimate, but in the real world an estimate is often all that is needed.

With the national debt now measured in trillions, an interesting Fermi problem is "How many trees would be needed to make a trillion dollar bills?" Counting problems have been important in the history and development of mathematics. This lesson focuses on two elementary counting principles.

Many problems in probability require knowing the number of ways in which an event can occur. A **tree diagram** can be useful in organizing the information.

Example 1 Suppose that you toss a penny, a nickel, and a dime and record whether each comes up heads or tails. What are the different possible outcomes?

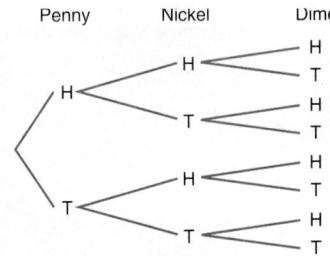

Arrange all the possible outcomes in a tree diagram. Each *branch* of the tree, read from left to right, represents one outcome of the coin tossing. The top branch, HHH, is the event "all coins come up heads;" the next, HHT, is the event "the penny and the nickel come up heads and the dime tails," and so on. This diagram shows that there are eight different possible outcomes for the coin toss problem.

The same diagram could be used to represent three tosses of the same coin. By changing the symbols H and T, it could be used to study other events with exactly two outcomes. A tree diagram shows every possible outcome. Sometimes, only the *number* of outcomes is needed. One method for finding this number uses the *multiplication principle of counting*, also called the *fundamental counting principle*.

742 Chapter 14 Probability

Multiplication Principle of Counting

If one event can occur in n different ways, and for each of these another event can occur in k different ways, then together the two events can occur in $n \cdot k$ different ways.

Example 2 A jeweler sells class rings, for which each purchaser has the choice of a stone and a setting. If the jeweler has 6 different settings and 9 different stones, how many options does the purchaser have?

Think of the two events as: First choose a stone, and then choose a setting. There are 9 choices for a stone, and for each of these, the purchaser may choose 6 settings.

$9 \times 6 = 54$ different options   *Multiplication principle*

Often the two events are thought of as stages of a decision.

Example 3 A club with 25 members must choose a president and secretary. In how many ways can this happen if each member is eligible for each position?

There are 25 ways a president can be chosen. Then, since the same person cannot be both president and secretary, for each of the 25 possible presidents there are 24 ways a secretary can be chosen.

$25 \times 24 = 600$ There are 600 ways to choose a president and a secretary.

The multiplication principle can be extended to more than two events.

Extended Multiplication Principle of Counting

Suppose that t events occur. If the first may occur in n_1 ways, and for each of these the second may occur in n_2 ways, and for each of these the third may occur in n_3 ways, and so on, then the t events together may occur in $n_1 \times n_2 \times n_3 \times \cdots \times n_t$ ways.

Example 4 *Restaurant Management* A restaurant offers a special in which you choose one each from 3 appetizers, 8 entrees, and 6 desserts. How many different menus are available for the special?

$3 \times 8 \times 6 = 144$ choices   *Extended multiplication principle*

There are 144 different ways to choose the special.

The key to recognizing when to apply the multiplication principle is the notion that for each of the n ways a first step can be taken, there are k ways a second step can be taken. If this condition is absent, the multiplication principle does not apply.

14.1 Basic Counting Principles **743**

For Example 2

Luisa is packing for a business trip and chooses 3 suits and 5 blouses that can be worn with any of the suits. How many different outfits can she make from these? 15

For Example 3

A company has 38 applicants for two sales positions, one in Los Angeles and one in Detroit. In how many ways can the positions be filled? 1406

For Example 4

There are 27 entries in the middle school division of a science fair. In how many ways can first prize, second prize, and honorable mention be awarded? 17,550

For Example 5

A family is choosing a vacation site and has narrowed their choices to 4 ski resorts and 6 dude ranches.
1. How many choices do they have if they can vacation at a ski resort or a dude ranch? 10
2. How many choices do they have if their budget permits them to have a winter vacation at a ski resort and a summer vacation at a dude ranch? 24

Common Error Some students may apply the multiplication principle incorrectly in question 1 above. Some students try to use one strategy to solve all problems without thinking through each situation. Compare and contrast problems such as the ones above to help these students see the need to read carefully.

Example 5 On a given day, to travel from Atlanta, Georgia, to Gary, Indiana, you may take 1 of 5 flights to Chicago and then 1 of 3 buses to Gary. To travel from Atlanta to Washington, D.C., you may take 1 of 6 flights or 1 of 4 buses. Determine the number of routes for traveling
a. from Atlanta to Chicago *and then* to Gary
b. from Atlanta to Washington, D.C., by plane *or* by train

a. Each of the 5 planes can connect with 3 different buses. There are 5×3 or 15 routes from Atlanta to Gary.

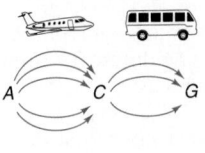

b. A route may be 1 of 6 flights or 4 buses. There are 10 routes from Atlanta to Washington, D.C.

Addition Principle of Counting

If an event can occur in n ways, and a second event can occur in k different ways, then there are $n + k$ ways in which the first *or* the second event can occur. More generally, suppose that t events can occur. If the first can occur in n_1 ways, the second in n_2 different ways, the third in n_3 different ways, and so on, then the number of ways in which any one of the t events can occur is $n_1 + n_2 + n_3 + \cdots + n_t$.

Example 5b illustrates the addition principle of counting. For the addition principle to apply, the events must occur in *different* ways. In how many ways can you select a king or a queen from a deck of cards? There are 4 kings and 4 queens, giving a total of $4 + 4 = 8$ ways to select one or the other.

In how many ways can you draw a heart or a king from a deck of cards? There are 4 kings and 13 hearts. But one of those 4 kings is also a heart, so there are only 16 ways to draw either a king or a heart.

Some examples require both the multiplication and the addition principles.

Example 6 An international committee consists of 5 representatives from New Zealand, 6 from Canada, and 4 from Mexico. In how many ways can a subcommittee be chosen consisting of two members from different countries?

Members of the subcommittee can come from New Zealand/Canada *or* New Zealand/Mexico *or* Canada/Mexico. Subcommittees can be formed as follows:

One from New Zealand and one from Canada in $5 \times 6 = 30$ ways
One from New Zealand and one from Mexico in $5 \times 4 = 20$ ways
One from Canada and one from Mexico in $6 \times 4 = 24$ ways

Thus, the subcommittee can be formed in $30 + 20 + 24 = 74$ ways.

As a rule of thumb, remember that a situation described using "or" *usually* calls for the addition principle; one described using "and" *usually* calls for the multiplication principle.

Class Exercises

1. What are the different outcomes if four coins, a penny, a nickel, a dime, and a quarter, are tossed? Use a tree diagram to represent your answer.

2. *Sales* A car dealer offers you a choice of automatic or manual transmission, 3 colors (silver, blue, and red), and either a radio or tape deck. Use a tree diagram to represent these option packages.

3. In how many ways can a quiz with five true-false questions be answered? 32

4. How many outfits can be made from 3 pairs of slacks and 5 coordinating tops? 15

5. *Sports* How many different batteries consisting of a pitcher and a catcher can a baseball manager form from 8 pitchers and 6 catchers? 48

6. How many different slates consisting of a president, vice-president, and secretary-treasurer can be formed from a club with 32 members? 29,760

Manufacturing How many different license plates can be made under the given conditions?

7. The plate has 2 letters followed by 3 digits with repetition allowed. 676,000

8. The plate has 2 letters followed by 3 digits with no repetition. 468,000

9. The plate has 3 letters followed by 3 digits with repetition permitted or 2 letters followed by 5 digits with no repetition. 37,232,000

10. **Thinking Critically** Give some advantages and disadvantages of using a rule of thumb like the one presented at the end of this lesson.

Practice Exercises

A 1. A coin is tossed and a single die is rolled. Make a tree diagram to represent the outcomes of this experiment.

2. *Biology* A geneticist is doing a study on the sexes and birth order of the children in families having 4 children. Make a tree diagram to represent all possibilities.

3. *Politics* In a local election there are 3 candidates for member of council: A, B, and C. There are also 5 candidates, V, W, X, Y, and Z, for ward leader. Make a tree diagram to represent the possible choices a voter has.

4. A tetrahedron is a four-sided pyramid with each side a triangle. Suppose two tetrahedrons have all four sides congruent triangles, labeled 1, 2, 3, 4 and Q, R, S, T. Make a tree diagram to represent the possible outcomes when the tetrahedrons are rolled and the labels on the bottom are recorded.

14.1 Basic Counting Principles **745**

10. Answers may vary. Some advantages might be they are easy to remember, or they may help in getting started on a problem. Some disadvantages might be they can be applied incorrectly, or they may block a creative thought on how to solve the problem.

For Example 6
A scientific society has among its members 12 chemists, 8 physicists, 10 microbiologists, and 4 geologists.
1. In how many ways can a delegation be chosen from this group consisting of 2 scientists from different fields? 416
2. How many ways can the same delegation be formed if 1 of the chemists resigns and 2 more geologists join? 452

CLOSURE

Have students explain how the multiplication principle and the addition principle can be used to solve the following problem:

A restaurant offers 6 choices of soups, 3 choices of salads, and 4 choices of bread. Two people enter the restaurant. One orders a soup, a salad, and a slice of bread. If the second person wishes to order only 2 items different than those ordered by the first, how many choices does he have?

Additional Answers
Class Exercises
1.

2.

Assignment Guide

Basic: 1–20, 21–31 odd, 32
Average: 1–15 odd, 16–37
Enriched: 5–25 odd, 26–44

Teacher's Resource Book
Practice, page 96

Ⓡ **Review**

Exercises 6, 7, and 30 through 34 review graphing functions and their inverses, writing equations of circles, factorial notation, and the binomial theorem.

LESSON FOLLOW-UP

Lesson Quiz

1. List all ways to choose two letters from the set {a, e, i, o, u} if the same letter may not be used twice. {a, e}, {a, i}, {a, o}, {a, u}, {e, i}, {e, o}, {e, u}, {i, o}, {i, u}, {o, u}

2. A local bakery offers a special on a half dozen each of donuts and muffins. If the bakery stocks 9 kinds of donuts and 6 kinds of muffins, how many choices do they offer in the special? 54

3. In designing a formal invitation, the printer offers you a choice of 8 lettering styles, 10 paper colors, 5 ink colors, and 3 paper weights. How many different kinds of invitations could you design? 1200

4. In how many ways could first prize and second prize be offered in the pumpkin category at the State Fair if there are 26 entries? 650

There are 6 languages and 5 math courses for which a college freshman is qualified.

5. How many choices does the freshman have if she wishes to take both math and a language? 30

6. How many choices does the freshman have if she can take either math or a language? 11

---

5. *Management*   A college needs to hire a computer scientist and an English professor. In how many ways can these positions be filled if there are 9 applicants for the computer science position and 12 for the English faculty position? 108

Ⓡ 6. Graph the function $h(x) = (x + 2)^3$ and its inverse h^{-1} on the same axes.

Ⓡ 7. Find the equation of the circle with center at $C(17, 9)$ that is tangent to the positive y-axis. $(x - 17)^2 + (y - 9)^2 = 289$

Two dice, one red and one green, are rolled.

8. How many different outcomes are there? 36

9. Make a table of ordered pairs to organize the possible outcomes with the first representing the red die and the second number the green die. For example, (4, 3) would mean a 4 on the red die and a 3 on the green.

10. How many outcomes have an even number on the red die? 18

11. How many outcomes are there with a 6 on the red die? 6

12. How many outcomes have a prime number on the green die? 18

13. How many outcomes have a 6 on the red die and a prime number on the green die? 3

14. *Sports*   In how many ways can a basketball team of 23 players elect a captain and an assistant captain? 506

15. *Sports*   There are nine athletes competing in the gymnastics finals. In how many ways can the gold, silver, and bronze medals be awarded? 504

16. *Gardening*   An amateur gardener may enter only one item in each category of the horticultural show. If a gardener has 3 excellent specimens in the vegetable category, 5 in the annuals, 2 in the perennials, and 4 in the fruit category, how many possible choices does he have? 120

17. *Computer Science*   Suppose that your computer password must contain four characters, must begin with a letter, and may contain digits and letters only. How many different passwords can you create? 1,213,056

18. A combination lock has a dial with 30 numbers from 1 through 30. How many three-number combinations are possible if the numbers must be different?

19. Repeat Exercise 18 so that the second number is different from the first and the third number is different from the second. 25,230   24,360

20. *Consumerism*   To order a miniature gift basket, you must choose one each from 5 kinds of fruits, 4 kinds of nuts, 4 kinds of candies, and 2 novelties. How many different gift baskets are possible? 160

Programming   A *bit* or *binary digit* is a 0 or a 1. A *bit string* is a sequence of bits, such as 0011 or 101.

B 21. How many different 5-bit strings are there? 32

22. How many different 6-bit strings are there? 64

23. How many different 6-bit strings are there that end with 0? 32

24. How many different 12-bit strings are there? 4096

Additional Answers

6.

9. (1, 1), (2, 1), (3, 1), (4, 1), (5, 1), (6, 1)
(1, 2), (2, 2), (3, 2), (4, 2), (5, 2), (6, 2)
(1, 3), (2, 3), (3, 3), (4, 3), (5, 3), (6, 3)
(1, 4), (2, 4), (3, 4), (4, 4), (5, 4), (6, 4)
(1, 5), (2, 5), (3, 5), (4, 5), (5, 5), (6, 5)
(1, 6), (2, 6), (3, 6), (4, 6), (5, 6), (6, 6)

On a shelf there are 11 different books: 3 novels, 4 math books, 4 art books.

25. In how many ways can one book of each type be chosen? 48

26. In how many ways can 2 books of different types be chosen? 40

27. If 5 reference books are added to the shelf, in how many ways can one book of each type be chosen? 240

28. If 5 reference books are added to the shelf, in how many ways can 2 books of different types be chosen? 95

29. Writing in Mathematics Write two problems that use the multiplication principle, two that use the addition principle, and one that uses both.

Evaluate.

Ⓡ **30.** 5! 120   Ⓡ **31.** 7! 5040   Ⓡ **32.** $\frac{7!}{5!}$ 42   Ⓡ **33.** $\frac{12!}{8!4!}$ 495

Ⓡ **34.** Use the binomial theorem to expand $(2x - x^3)^5$.

In the octal, or base eight, system, numbers are formed using only the digits $\{0, 1, 2, 3, 4, 5, 6, 7\}$.

35. How many four-digit numbers are there in the octal system? 3584

36. How many numbers in the octal system have three or fewer digits? 512

37. In the base twelve system, numbers are formed from the symbols $\{0, 1, 2, 3, 4, 5, 6, 7, 8, 9, T, E\}$. How many three-digit base twelve numbers are there? 1584

C **38.** In how many ways can five finalists be seated in a row of eight chairs? 6720

39. A six-person committee including Alice and Bob must choose a chairperson and a secretary. In how many ways can this be done if either Alice or Bob must be chairperson? 10

40. *Programming*   How many 8-bit strings are there (see Exercise 21) which begin with either 11 or 00? 128

41. Bit strings (see Exercise 21) of a fixed length are needed to form a code. What is the minimum length of the string if one string is needed to represent each letter of the alphabet and each decimal digit? 6

42. In how many ways can a face card (jack, queen, or king) or a diamond be selected from a standard deck of cards? 22

43. Thinking Critically   Use the multiplication principle to show that a set of n elements has exactly 2^n subsets.

44. How many distinct positive divisors does the number $3^2 \times 5^3 \times 13$ have? 24

Review

1. Express the ratio $-16n^4$ to $2n^2$ in simplest form. $-8n^2$

Find the value of n.

2. $\begin{vmatrix} n & 3 & 0 \\ 1 & n & 5 \\ 7 & 0 & n \end{vmatrix} = 107$ 2, -1

3. $\begin{vmatrix} n & 2 & 1 \\ 1 & 5 & n \\ 6 & 0 & n \end{vmatrix} = 90$ 4, -6

14.1 Basic Counting Principles   **747**

Alternative Assessment
Have students write a counting problem that involves both the multiplication principle and the addition principle, and write a solution to the problem. Then have the students exchange problems with a classmate, and discuss their solutions.

Enrichment
Let A be a set of n elements, and B a set of k elements. How many functions from A to B are there? Explain. k^n; For each of the n elements in A, there is a choice of k elements in B as functional values. This gives a total of $k \times k \times k \times \cdots k = k^n$.

Additional Answers
34. $32x^5 - 80x^7 + 80x^9 - 40x^{11} + 10x^{13} - x^{15}$

43. Let A be the set. Choose a subset of A with n elements. For each element, it is either "in" or "not in" the subset. So there are a total of $2 \times 2 \times \cdots \times 2$ (n times) $= 2^n$ subsets.

Writing in Mathematics
29. Answers may vary. Some problems that use the product principle may involve ways to award prizes or ways to choose officers for a club. Some problems that use the addition principle may involve ways to travel from one city to another. Some problems that use both the product principle and sum principle may involve ways to choose one item from each of several categories.

LESSON PLAN

Vocabulary

combination

combination of n elements taken r at a time ${}_nC_r$

permutation

permutation of n elements taken r at a time ${}_nP_r$

Ⓜ Materials/Manipulatives

concordance

Technology

calculator or computer program with:
- factorial key
- menu item to compute ${}_nP_r$ and ${}_nC_r$

FOCUS

Students may be familiar with concordances from literature classes or other contexts. They may also be familiar with a word processor's capacity to search a text, and so recognize that putting together a concordance is a much simpler task today than it used to be.

Uses of a concordance in literary detective work may be both unfamiliar and intriguing to them. Have interested students research and report on the dispute over the authorship of the *Federalist Papers*. Here is a truly interdisciplinary project where mathematics, literature, and history meet.

14.2 Permutations and Combinations

Objectives: *To determine the number of permutations of a set of n elements taken r at a time*

To determine the number of combinations of a set of n elements taken r at a time

Focus

A *concordance* is an alphabetical list of the key words that appear in a written work, giving the passages in which they occur. Concordances are tools for scholars who study the way language is used. Knowing how often a word occurs is vital information for literary analysis. In recent years computerized concordances have been used for literary detective work, providing evidence of authorship, timeline, and influence. For example, one scholar studied Hemingway's *The Old Man and the Sea* and concluded that this work was actually written 16 years before it was published. Other analysts used a concordance to help determine that James Madison was the actual author of 15 of the famous *Federalist Papers* whose origin was in dispute.

This use of concordances illustrates that counting is a simple mathematical concept with far-reaching applications. The computer is a tool that has made counting easier and faster in many contexts. Mathematical tools are also available to simplify counting. Among these are *permutations* and *combinations*.

An important application of the fundamental counting principle is to find the number of ways a set of elements can be ordered. Such an ordered arrangement is called a **permutation.**

Example 1 List the permutations of the three letters q, r, and s.

The six ordered arrangements are qrs, qsr, rsq, rqs, sqr, and srq.

Permutations can be applied to many situations involving the ordering of objects. The possible arrangements of books on a shelf, the possible line-ups of shows on a television station's prime-time schedule, and the possible batting orders for a baseball team are all examples of permutations.

Factorial notation is useful for counting permutations.

For any positive integer n, $n! = n \cdot (n - 1) \cdot (n - 2) \cdots 3 \cdot 2 \cdot 1$. By definition, $0! = 1$.

Example 2 In how many ways can 9 members of a chess club be lined up for a picture?

Think of having 9 places in line to be filled with members of the club. There are 9 choices for the first spot, then for each of these choices, there are 8 choices for the second spot, 7 for the third, 6 for the fourth, and so on.

$$9 \times 8 \times 7 \times 6 \times 5 \times 4 \times 3 \times 2 \times 1 = 9! = 362{,}880 \quad \textit{Multiplication principle}$$

There are 9!, or 362,880, possible arrangements of the club members.

In general, the following rule applies for permutations:

There are $n!$ permutations of n distinct elements.

In a permutation of n elements, if r of the elements are alike, then $r!$ of the permutations will be the same. In this case the number of distinct permutations is $\frac{n!}{r!}$. If r elements are alike and q other elements are alike, then the number of distinct permutations will be $\frac{n!}{r!q!}$.

Example 3 Find the number of distinguishable permutations of the letters in each word.
  a. ESTEEM   **b.** INDEFINITE

a. The number of permutations of 6 elements is 6!. For the word ESTEEM one such permutation is MESETE. If the E's were distinguishable, there would be 3!, or 6, permutations of the E's in MESETE. But the E's are not distinguishable so the total number of permutations must be divided by 3!: $\frac{6!}{3!} = 120$ permutations.

b. There are 10 letters in the word INDEFINITE. There are 3 I's, 2 N's, and 2 E's. The total number of permutations is $\frac{10!}{3!2!2!} = 151{,}200$.

For n elements with r_1 alike, r_2 alike, and so on up to r_t elements alike, the number of distinguishable permutations is

$$\frac{n!}{r_1! \times r_2! \times r_3! \times \cdots \times r_t!}$$

Example 4 *Sports* If there are 15 gymnasts in a competition, in how many ways can the gold, silver, and bronze medals be awarded?

There are 15 choices for the gold medal winner. *For each of these* there are 14 choices for the silver medalist, then 13 choices for the bronze medalist.

$$15 \times 14 \times 13 = 2730 \text{ ways} \quad \textit{Multiplication principle}$$

There are 2730 ways to award the medals.

14.2 Permutations and Combinations   **749**

List the permutations of the 4 letters
q, r, s, t. *qrst, rstq, sqrt, tqrs, qrts, rsqt,*
sqtr, tqsr, qstr, rtsq, srqt, trsq, qstr, rtqs,
srtq, trqs, qtrs, rqts, strq, tsrq, qtsr, rqst,
stqr, tsqr

For Example 2

In how many ways can 6 trophies be
placed on a mantlepiece? 720

For Example 3

Determine the number of distinct
permutations for the letters or numbers in each of the following.
1. INDEPENDENT 554,400
2. 410012232 15,120

For Example 4

1. In how many ways can the 24
   entrants in a spelling bee come in
   first and second? 552

For Example 5

Determine each of the following.
1. $_{17}P_6$ 8,910,720
2. In how many ways can computer
   passwords be chosen if each
   password is a string of 4 letters
   without any repeated letters?
   358,800

For Example 6

The school chess team is allowed to
send 3 representatives to the re-
gional chess tournament. In how
many ways could the choice be
made from among the 6 best competitors Frank, Julie, Reiko, Carlos,
Vanessa, and Tim? 20

The solution in Example 3 may be thought of as the number of ordered subsets
of 3 elements from a set of 15 elements, or the number of permutations of 15
elements taken 3 at a time, denoted $_{15}P_3$. This is another useful idea to
generalize. Notice that $_{15}P_3 = 15 \times 14 \times 13 = \dfrac{15!}{12!} = \dfrac{15!}{(15 - 3)!}$.

> The number of **permutations of n elements taken r at a time,** that is,
> the number of ordered subsets of r elements taken from a set of n
> elements is
>
> $$_nP_r = \frac{n!}{(n - r)!} \qquad \text{where } 0 \le r \le n$$

Example 5 Determine each of the following.
  a. $_{22}P_7$
  b. The number of "words" of 5 letters with no repeated letters formed from
     letters of the English alphabet

a. $_{22}P_7 = \dfrac{22!}{(22 - 7)!} = \dfrac{22 \times 21 \times 20 \times \cdots \times 3 \times 2 \times 1}{15 \times 14 \times 13 \times \cdots \times 3 \times 2 \times 1}$ $_nP_r = \dfrac{n!}{(n - r)!}$

$= 22 \times 21 \times 20 \times 19 \times 18 \times 17 \times 16 = 859,541,760$

b. Since there are 26 letters in the English alphabet, use the formula for $_{26}P_5$.

$_{26}P_5 = \dfrac{26!}{(26 - 5)!} = \dfrac{26!}{21!} = 26 \times 25 \times 24 \times 23 \times 22 = 7,893,600$

The formula for $_nP_r$ in terms of factorials is convenient to use with a
calculator that has a factorial key or with a computer program. Some
calculators also permit you to calculate $_nP_r$ directly.

A key idea connected with permutations is that of *order*. A permutation is an
ordered arrangement. If the order of the objects does not matter, you are not
dealing with permutations. Suppose you must write a term paper on any 3 of the
13 original United States. In how many ways could you choose the 3 states? In
this example, the order in which you choose does not matter. Choosing Georgia,
Virginia, and Delaware is equivalent to choosing Delaware, Georgia, and Virginia.

A selection of a fixed number of elements of a set without regard to order is
called a **combination**. The number of combinations of r elements chosen from a
set of n elements is denoted $_nC_r$. You will see that the formula for $_nC_r$ is related
to the formula for $_nP_r$.

Example 6 *Sports* A swim club is entitled to send 2 swimmers to local pre-Olympic
     trials. In how many ways could the choice be made from among their 4 best
     competitors, Toni, Sara, Juan, and Bob?

There are 12 possible *permutations* of the 4 swimmers, abbreviated

TS	TJ	TB	SJ	SB	JB
ST	JT	BT	JS	BS	BJ

However, each pair is counted twice, and since in this case the order does *not* matter, the number of ways the choice could be made is $12 \div 2 = 6$. The club could send {Toni, Sara}, {Toni, Juan}, {Toni, Bob}, {Sara, Juan}, {Sara, Bob}, or {Juan, Bob}.

Extend the reasoning of Example 6 to the problem of choosing 3 of the original 13 states on which to write a term paper. There are $_{13}P_3 = 13 \times 12 \times 11 = 1716$ *ordered* subsets of 3 states. However, each *unordered* subset is counted $3! = 6$ times among these permutations. For example, the subset {Georgia, Virginia, Delaware} corresponds to the permutations abbreviated GVD, GDV, DGV, DVG, VGD, and VDG. Since the order of choice is unimportant, the number of combinations may be found by dividing $_{13}P_3$ by $3!$.

$$_{13}C_3 = \frac{_{13}P_3}{3!} = \frac{1716}{6} = 286$$

In general, the formula for $_nC_r$ may be expressed in terms of the formula for $_nP_r$.

The number of **combinations of n objects taken r at a time** is

$$_nC_r = \frac{_nP_r}{r!} = \frac{n!}{r!(n-r)!} \qquad \text{where } 0 \le r \le n$$

Example 7 Determine the value of each of the following.
  a. $_{17}C_5$
  b. The number of unordered subsets with 4 elements taken from the set {a, b, c, d, e, f, g}

a. $_{17}C_5 = \frac{17!}{5!12!} = 6188$

b. The number of unordered subsets of a set of 7 elements is $_7C_4 = \frac{7!}{4!3!} = 35$.

Note that you can use a calculator with a factorial key to compute $_nC_r$. Some calculators also permit you to compute $_nC_r$ directly.

In many applications, the concept of combination is used along with other counting principles.

Example 8 How many subsets of a set of 10 elements have either 3 or 4 elements?

Since the collections of 3-element subsets and 4-element subsets have no subsets in common, the sum principle applies. The desired number will be the number of 3-element subsets plus the number of 4-element subsets.

$$_{10}C_3 + _{10}C_4 = \frac{10!}{3!7!} + \frac{10!}{4!6!} = 120 + 210 = 330$$

You may have noticed that the formula for $_nC_r$ coincides with the formula for the binomial coefficient $\binom{n}{r}$. The reason for this becomes clear when you recall how these numbers are related to the expansion of a binomial such as $(x + y)^n$.

14.2 Permutations and Combinations **751**

For Example 7
Determine each of the following.
1. $_{12}C_8$ 495
2. The number of unordered subsets of 4 elements chosen from the set of the Seven Wonders of the World. 35

For Example 8
How many subsets of a set of 8 elements have fewer than 4 members?
93

Consider $(x + y)^7 = \binom{7}{0}x^7 + \binom{7}{1}x^6y + \binom{7}{2}x^5y^2 + \binom{7}{3}x^4y^3 + \binom{7}{4}x^3y^4 + \binom{7}{5}x^2y^5 + \binom{7}{6}xy^6 + \binom{7}{7}y^7$. Each term in the unsimplified expansion of $(x + y)^7$ contains a certain number, say, *k* *x*'s and $(7 - k)$ *y*'s. Those terms which contain 4 *x*'s and 3 *y*'s simplify to x^4y^3. How many of these are there? There are $\binom{7}{3}$ of them, corresponding to the number of ways to choose exactly 3 *y*'s from the 7 $(x + y)$'s. The observation that $_nC_r = \binom{n}{r}$ means that you may use Pascal's triangle to find values for $_nC_r$.

Class Exercises

1. Determine the number of permutations of a set of 8 objects. 40,320

2. List the 6 permutations of the numerals 0, 1, 2. 012, 021, 102, 120, 201, 210

3. Determine the number of permutations of 20 objects taken 6 at a time. 27,907,200

4. List the 20 permutations of the letters *a*, *b*, *c*, *d*, and *e* taken two at a time.

Determine the value of each expression.

5. $_{16}P_4$ 43,680

6. $_{30}P_5$ 17,100,720

7. **Thinking Critically** Give two reasons why $_nP_1 = n$ for all integers *n*. One of your reasons should be in terms of the formula, the other in terms of what the formula counts.

8. Find the number of combinations of 10 objects taken 5 at a time. 252

9. *Entertainment* In how many ways can a 5-card hand be dealt from a standard deck of 52 cards? 2,598,960

10. *Consumer Behavior* In how many ways can a gift of 6 kinds of fruit be chosen from a selection of 11 kinds of fruit offered? 462

11. *International Relations* A special UN committee consists of 7 U.S. representatives and 8 Canadian representatives. In how many ways can a delegation be formed with 2 representatives of each country? 588

12. *International Relations* Repeat the preceding exercise for a delegation of 3 members with at least 1 member from each country. 364

Determine the number of distinguishable permutations for the letters of each word.

13. APPLE 60   14. BANANA 60   15. STRAWBERRY 604, 800

Practice Exercises   ⟨∿⟩ Use appropriate technology.

A 1. Find the number of permutations of a set of 10 objects. 3,628,800

2. List the 24 three-letter permutations of the letters *w, x, y, z*.

3. From the permutations of Exercise 2, identify the combinations of the letters *w, x, y, z* taken 3 at a time. *wxy, wyz, wxz, xyz*

4. Find the number of permutations of 24 objects taken 4 at a time. 255,024

5. List the 24 permutations of the numerals 0, 1, 2, 3 taken 3 at a time.

6. Find the number of ordered subsets of 5 objects taken from a set of 30 objects. 17,100,720

7. Find the value of $\dfrac{n!}{r!(n-r)!}$, where $n = 100$, $r = 1$. 100

Find the value of each expression.

8. $_{100}P_4$ 94,109,400   9. $_{25}P_5$ 6,375,600   10. $_{14}C_6$ 3003   11. $_{21}C_{20}$ 21

Determine the number of distinguishable permutations for the letters of each.

12. SEATTLE 1260   13. CINCINNATI   14. MANHATTAN 15,120

15. How many ways are there to choose 4 books from a collection of 11 books? 330

16. *Marketing*   Use factorial notation to represent the number of ways to arrange 100 new cars in 100 fixed locations on a dealer's lot. 100!

17. *Education*   In a science fair, first, second, third, and one honorable mention will be awarded. In how many ways can this be done if there are 36 entries? 1,413,720

18. *Marketing*   A pizza shop offers a special of any 3 toppings for a fixed Price. If there are 8 toppings on the menu, how many choices does the special offer? 56

Ⓡ 19. What is the domain of the function $f(x) = \ln(3x - 4)$? $\left\{x : x > \dfrac{4}{3}\right\}$

Ⓡ 20. Graph the inverse functions $f(x) = 3^x$ and $g(x) = \log_3 x$ on the same axes. Include the graph of $y = x$ and explain the graphical relationship among the three. The graph of g is the graph of f reflected over $y = x$.

B 21. *Entertainment*   To participate in a state lottery, a person must choose 4 numbers from 1 to 40. If the order of the choice matters, in how many ways can this be done? 2,193,360

22. *Entertainment*   If you play the state lottery described in the preceding exercise, you may also "box" your entry and settle for a smaller prize if you win. When you box your entry, you win if your numbers come up in any order. In how many ways can this happen? 91,390

23. How many subsets of a set of 12 elements have at least 10 elements? 79

24. How many distinct linear arrangements can be made by using the following shapes? □ □ △ △ △ ○ ○ ○ 560

25. *Education*   To earn a B in a science course, a student must complete and report on at least 8 of 10 experiments. In how many ways can this be done? 56

26. In how many ways can an honor society with 16 senior and 10 junior members choose a committee of 3 seniors and 2 juniors? 25,200

Business   A company sends out a shipment of 48 microcomputers, 3 of which are defective.

27. In how many ways could an inspector choose 8 microcomputers to inspect? 377,348,994

28. In how many ways could an inspector choose 8 microcomputers and have all of them be nondefective? 215,553,195

29. In how many ways could 8 microcomputers be chosen of which exactly 1 is defective? 136,138,860

30. In how many ways could 8 microcomputers be chosen of which at least 1 is defective? 161,795,799

14.2 Permutations and Combinations   **753**

Alternative Assessment

Have students write a list of situations where a permutation is involved, and a list where a combination is involved. Choose one from each list and write and solve a problem about it.

Enrichment

In how many seven letter arrangements of *a, b, c, d, e, f, g* does the letter *a* come first? In how many of the arrangements does the letter *a* immediately precede the letter *b*?
720; 720

Additional Answers

34. Input *n* and *r*. Use a loop to compute $n(n-1)(n-2) \cdots (n-r+1)$. Use a loop to compute *r*! Output the results.

35. They both equal 1. The number of ways to choose all elements from a set is $_nC_n$, and the number of ways to choose no elements from a set is $_nC_0$.

39. $\binom{n+1}{2} = \dfrac{(n+1)!}{2!(n-1)!} = \dfrac{(n+1)n}{2}$

40. $_nC_r = \dfrac{n!}{r!(n-r)!}$; $_nC_{n-r} =$

$\dfrac{n!}{(n-r)![n-(n-r)]!} = \dfrac{n!}{(n-r)!r!}$;

Each subset of *r* elements leaves a corresponding set of $n-r$ elements.

Ⓡ 31. Find the zeros of the function $f(x) = 2 \ln (2x - 1) - \ln 25$. 3

Ⓡ 32. Solve the logarithmic equation $\log_{10} x^2 = 20$. $\pm 10^{10}$

Ⓡ 33. Solve the exponential equation $3e^{0.5x} = 40$. 5.1805

34. *Programming*   Write a program to evaluate $_nC_r$, where *n* and *r* are input by the user. Output *n*, *r*, and the value of $_nC_r$.

35. **Thinking Critically**   Find the values of $_nC_n$ and $_nC_0$ for an arbitrary positive integer *n*. Interpret these values in terms of what $_nC_r$ counts.

C 36. *Computer Science*   How many 8-bit strings contain exactly three 1's? (Recall that a bit string is a sequence of 0's and 1's.) 56

37. *Education*   In how many ways can a student answer a 24-question true and false test marking exactly half the questions true? 2,704,156

38. At a luncheon in honor of a winner of a heroism award, each of the 25 guests shakes the hand of every other guest exactly once. How many handshakes are there at that luncheon? 300

39. In Lesson 13.4 it was proved that the sum of the first *n* positive integers is $\dfrac{n(n+1)}{2}$. Show that the sum of the first *n* positive integers is also $_{n+1}C_2$.

40. **Thinking Critically**   Use the formula for $_nC_r$ to show that $_nC_r = {}_nC_{n-r}$ for all *n* and *r* with $0 \leq r \leq n$. Explain why this is reasonable in terms of what $_nC_r$ and $_nC_{n-r}$ represent.

41. In how many ways can 8 people be seated around a circular table if only the person's neighbors, not his or her specific seat, matter? 5040

42. In how many ways can the members of two families be lined up for a portrait if one family has 3 members, the other family has 4 members, and members of the same family want to stand together? 288

43. A person has 5 math books, 4 science books, and 8 literature books to be arranged on a shelf. In how many ways can this be done if the books are to be grouped by topic? 696,729,600

An *anagram* is a rearrangement of the letters of a word or phrase.

44. How many *distinguishable* anagrams are there of the word SCHOOL? 360

45. How many *distinguishable* anagrams are there of the word MATHEMATICS?
4,989,600

Challenge

1. *AB* is a diameter of a circle centered at *O*. Point *C* is on the circle such that angle *BOC* is 60°. If the diameter of the circle is 10 in., find the length of *AC*. $5\sqrt{3}$

2. In an arithmetic sequence the first term is 2, the last term is 29, and the sum of all the terms is 155. Determine the common difference. 3

3. If $\dfrac{2^x}{2^{x+y}} = 8$ and $\dfrac{9^{x+y}}{3^{5y}} = 27$, where *x* and *y* are real numbers, find the value of *xy*. 9

4. If *p* and *q* are the solutions of $x^2 + px + q = 0$, $p \neq 0$, $q \neq 0$, determine the sum of the solutions. -1

14.3 Probability

Objectives: *To specify the sample space for a random experiment*
To calculate the probability that a given event will occur

Focus

Triskaidekaphobia, fear of the number 13, is shared by many cultures, and has ancient roots. For example, the belief that having 13 people dine together is likely to bring disaster is found in Nordic mythology. In modern France a *quatorzième*, a professional fourteenth dinner guest, can be hired at the last minute to join a dinner party of 13. Many architects bypass the number 13 when labeling rooms and floors of a building.

Friday the thirteenth is considered a particularly unlucky day by those who suffer from triskaidekaphobia. How likely is it that the thirteenth will fall on a Friday? Mathematicians have analyzed a 400-year cycle, and have concluded that the thirteenth of a month occurs on Sunday and on Wednesday 687 times each, on Monday and on Tuesday 685 times each, on Thursday and on Saturday 684 times each, and on Friday 688 times. This means that the likelihood, or *probability*, of having the thirteenth fall on a Friday is slightly greater than having it fall on any one of the other days of the week.

Probability is a way of assigning measures of uncertainty. A weather report giving a 30% chance of rain, and the small print on a lottery ticket that says "odds against winning are 5,000,000 to 1" are examples of probability.

There are several ways of assigning probabilities, including asking the opinion of an expert. In this lesson, the focus is on the classical probability concept, the oldest and best known way of measuring uncertainty.

In classical probability, an occurrence whose result is uncertain is called a **random experiment.** The possible results of the experiment are called **outcomes,** and the collection of all outcomes is the **sample space** of the experiment. For example, if the experiment is rolling a die, the sample space S is the set of the six possible outcomes, that is, $S = \{1, 2, 3, 4, 5, 6\}$.

Any subset of the sample space is called an **event.** For example, in rolling a die, an event E might be "rolling a number less than 5," that is, $E = \{1, 2, 3, 4\}$.

14.3 Probability **755**

Vocabulary
complement
empirical probability
event
odds
outcome
probability
random experiment
sample space

Ⓜ **Materials/Manipulatives**
bingo or lotto game
coins
dice
marbles
Scrabble tiles
spinner/roulette wheel
standard deck of cards
thumbtacks

Technology
calculator
random number generator

FOCUS

Both Herbert Hoover and Franklin Delano Roosevelt were said to have suffered from triskaidekaphobia. Roosevelt's secretary was accustomed to being invited at the last minute to a lunch or dinner that was found to have 13 guests.

On the other hand, in the late 1800s "Thirteen Clubs" were founded in both London and New York. The numbers of members, the numbers who ate together at table, the dues, and the dates of meetings all involved the number 13 or its multiples. The members of the "Thirteen Clubs" probably rejoiced to learn that the 13th has a greater probability of falling on a Friday than on any other day.

- In addition to the classical and frequency probability interpretations, most students have had experience with the "subjective" probability interpretation. In this scenario probabilities express the strength of a person's belief in the face of uncertainty. The expert opinion in medicine, financial decisions, and even weather forecasting may be viewed as examples of subjective probability.
- Although odds are generally defined in terms of probabilities, many students find it helpful to think of the odds in favor of an event as the ratio of the number of successes to the number of failures. The odds against an event are then the ratio of failures to successes. You can use the classical definition of probability to show that the two concepts are equivalent.

Alternative Learning Styles

Ⓜ Students with a concrete learning style benefit greatly from small group experiments involving empirical probability.

Pose a probability problem such as, "What is the probability that a thumbtack lands point up when tossed?" Each member of the group performs the experiment 10 times, and then the members pool their results. The ratio of the number of "successes" to the number of trials is the empirical probability. Have someone in the group report the results to the class. Other examples of empirical problems include finding the probability of:
- Obtaining a 7 in a roll of two dice
- Choosing a blue marble from a jar of different colored marbles
- Landing on an even number in one spin of a roulette wheel
- Choosing a K from a bag of Scrabble tiles

Example 1 An experiment consists of rolling two dice. Determine the sample space. Then determine the event:
  a. a total of 6   **b.** a total greater than 8

Each die can show from 1 to 6. There are 6 × 6, or 36, outcomes in the sample space, as shown in the diagram.
a. The event "a total of 6" includes all the outcomes circled in red.
b. The event "a total greater than 8" includes all the outcomes circled in blue.

If the sample space of an experiment is finite, and if the outcomes in it are equally likely, then the **probability** of an event E, denoted $P(E)$, is the ratio of the number of outcomes m in the event to the number of outcomes n in the sample space.

$$P(E) = \frac{m}{n}$$

For example, the probability of a total of 6 in Example 1 is $\frac{5}{36}$ because there are 5 outcomes in the event and 36 outcomes in the sample space. The probability of a total greater than 8 is $\frac{10}{36} = \frac{5}{18}$. *Why?*

Example 2 A committee of 5 members (Mark, Anna, Nori, David, and Lynn) wants to appoint a subcommittee of 2 members by putting names of all possible subcommittees in a hat and drawing one at random. List the sample space S for this experiment and find the probability of each of the following events.
  a. X: The subcommittee consists of Nori and David.
  b. Y: Anna is on the subcommittee.
  c. Z: Anna is not on the subcommittee.

The number of possible subcommittees is $_5C_2 = 10$. Using abbreviations, $S = \{MA, MN, MD, ML, AN, AD, AL, ND, NL, DL\}$.
a. Event X is $\{ND\}$. $P(X) = \frac{1}{10}$
b. Event Y is $\{MA, AN, AD, AL\}$. $P(Y) = \frac{4}{10} = \frac{2}{5}$
c. Event Z is $\{MN, MD, ML, ND, NL, DL\}$. $P(Z) = \frac{6}{10} = \frac{3}{5}$

Counting techniques can be used to determine the number of outcomes in a sample space or event.

Example 3 *Manufacturing*   A carton of 144 light bulbs includes 3 that are defective. If 2 lightbulbs are chosen at random, what is the probability that neither of them is defective?

The number of outcomes in the sample space is $_{144}C_2 = 10{,}296$.

The number of outcomes in the event that both lightbulbs are among the 141 nondefective lightbulbs is $_{141}C_2 = 9870$.

Therefore, the probability that neither of the 2 is defective is $\frac{9{,}870}{10{,}296} \approx 0.96$.

756   Chapter 14 Probability

Thinking Critically

The probability is $\frac{10}{36}$ because there are 10 ways to get a total greater than 8, and there are 36 different possible outcomes for the total.

Four useful properties follow from the definition of probability.

P_1: A probability is a number between 0 and 1, inclusive.
P_2: The probability of an event that cannot happen is 0.
P_3: The probability of an event that must happen is 1.
P_4: If the probability of an event E is p, then the probability of the **complement** of E (E does not happen) is $1 - p$.

The proofs of P_1, P_2, and P_3 are straightforward. To see that P_4 is true, observe that if there are n outcomes in the sample space and k outcomes in an event E, then there are $n - k$ outcomes in the complement of E. Therefore, the probability that E does not occur is $\frac{n - k}{n} = \frac{n}{n} - \frac{k}{n} = 1 - P(E)$. For instance, since the probability of getting a number less than 5 on the roll of one die is $\frac{2}{3}$, the probability of getting a number that is not less than 5 is $\frac{1}{3}$.

The *frequency* or **empirical** interpretation of probability is based on data. For example, when a weather forecaster announces that there is a 60% chance of rain, the forecaster means that under similar conditions in the past it has rained 60% of the time. According to the frequency interpretation, the probability of an event is the ratio that expresses how often events of the same kind will occur in the long run.

Example 4 *Marketing* A market researcher found that 341 of the 522 customers who entered a store on a Friday made a purchase. Based on this survey, what is the probability that a randomly selected customer on a similar day will make a purchase?

Since 341 of 522 customers in a similar situation made a purchase, use that ratio to estimate the probability.

$$p = \tfrac{341}{522} \approx 0.65$$

Another way of expressing measures of uncertainty is by giving *odds* for or against an event's occurring. If you hear that the odds that a business venture will succeed are 2 to 1, you conclude that the venture is twice as likely to succeed as to fail.

The **odds** that an event will occur are given by the ratio of the probability p that the event will occur to the probability $1 - p$ that the event will not occur, $\frac{p}{1 - p}$. It is customary to express odds as the ratio of two positive integers. If the weather forecaster says that the probability of rain is 30%, then the probability that it will not rain is $1 - 0.3 = 0.7$, and the odds that it will rain are $\frac{0.3}{0.7} = \frac{3}{7}$, or 3 to 7. Odds can also be determined directly from the sample space by taking the ratio of number of elements in the event to the number of elements in its complement.

14.3 Probability **757**

GUIDED PRACTICE

For Example 1
An experiment consists of choosing a single letter of the English alphabet. Determine the sample space. Then determine the event "choosing a vowel."
$\{a, b, c, \cdots, z\}$; $\{a, e, i, o, u\}$

For Example 2
Using the sample space for Example 2 given in the lesson, find the probability of these events.
1. The subcommittee members do not include either David or Nori.
$\frac{3}{10}$
2. Members of the subcommittee have names that begin with consonants. $\frac{3}{5}$

For Example 3
A shipment of 120 microwaves includes 5 that are defective. If 2 are inspected at random, what is the probability that neither is defective? That both are defective?
$\frac{_{115}C_2}{_{120}C_2} \approx 0.92$; $\frac{_{5}C_2}{_{120}C_2} \approx 0.0014$

Common Error Some students may assume incorrectly that the two events above are complementary and that the probability that both microwaves are defective is 1 minus the probability that neither is defective. Point out the other possibility that exactly one is defective.

For Example 4
If 11 of the 53 people who come to a family reunion are lefthanded, what is the probability that a member of this group picked at random is lefthanded? Is righthanded? 0.21; 0.79

For Example 5

1. What are the odds that when a fair die is rolled that the number on top is a 4 or a 5? What are the odds against this event?
   2 to 4; 4 to 2

2. What are the odds that when a card is picked at random from an ordinary shuffled deck, it is a spade? What are the odds against this event? 1 to 3; 3 to 1

CLOSURE

Have students differentiate between a theoretical or classical probability and an empirical or frequency probability.

INDEPENDENT PRACTICE

Assignment Guide

Basic: 1–30
Average: 1–15 odd, 16–40, Project
Enriched: 9–19 odd, 20–46, Project

Teacher's Resource Book
Practice, page 98

Ⓡ Review
Exercise 17, 21, and 24 review $_nC_r$.
Exercise 30 reviews $_nP_r$ and the multiplication principle.

Additional Answers
Class Exercises

2. {H2, H4, H6}, $P = \frac{1}{4}$

3. {H1, H3, H5, T1, T3, T5}; $P = \frac{1}{2}$

4. {T1, T2, T3, T4, T5, T6}; $P = \frac{1}{2}$

5. {H1, H2, H3, H4, H5, H6}; $P = \frac{1}{2}$

6. { }; $P = 0$

7. {H1, H2, H3, H4, H5, H6, T1, T2, T3, T4, T5, T6}; $P = 1$

Practice Exercises

1. {HHHH, HHHT, HHTH, HTHH, HHTT, HTHT, HTTH, HTTT, THHH, THHT, THTH, THTT, TTHH, TTHT, TTTH, TTTT}

2. {HHHH}; $P = \frac{1}{16}$

3. {HHTT, HTHT, HTTH, THHT, THTH, TTHH}; $P = \frac{3}{8}$

758

Example 5   What are the odds that the last digit of a randomly chosen telephone number is 9 or 0?

The probability that the last digit is 9 or 0 is $\frac{2}{10} = 0.2$ and so the probability that it is not 9 or 0 is 0.8. The odds are therefore $\frac{0.2}{0.8} = \frac{1}{4}$, or 1 to 4.

The odds against an event's happening are the reciprocal of the odds in favor of the event. Since the odds that the last digit of a randomly chosen telephone number is either 9 or 0 are 1 to 4, then the odds against that event are 4 to 1.

Class Exercises

An experiment consists of tossing a coin and rolling a die.

1. Determine the sample for this experiment. H1, H2, H3, H4, H5, H6, T1, T2, T3, T4, T5, T6

For the experiment of tossing a coin and rolling a die, list the event corresponding to each description and find its probability.

2. heads and an even number
3. an odd number
4. tails
5. no tails
6. a number greater than 10
7. a number less than 10

A spinner is made of a circle divided into five equal parts as shown. Find the probability of each event.

8. The spinner lands on red. $\frac{1}{5}$
9. The spinner does not land on green. $\frac{4}{5}$

10. A box of candy has 5 caramels, 4 nut clusters, 4 mints, 3 jellies, and 6 creams. What is the probability of picking 2 jellies? $\frac{1}{77}$

A scientist has tagged 60 of the 550 fish in a pond.

11. What is the probability that the first fish caught from that pond is tagged? $\frac{6}{55}$
12. What are the odds that the first fish caught is tagged? 6 to 49

13. **Thinking Critically**   Do the classical and frequency interpretations of probability always agree? For example, if you flip a coin 24 times and do not get exactly 12 heads, may you conclude that there is something wrong with the coin? Why or why not?

Practice Exercises

An experiment consists of tossing four coins.

A 1. Determine a sample space for this experiment.

For the experiment of tossing four coins, list the event corresponding to each description and find its probability.

2. 4 heads
3. exactly 2 tails
4. not exactly 2 tails
5. at least 2 tails
6. an odd number of heads
7. 6 heads

758   Chapter 14 Probability

---

4. {HHHH, HHHT, HHTH, HTHH, HTTT, THHH, THTT, TTHT, TTTH, TTTT}; $P = \frac{5}{8}$

5. {HHTT, HTHT, HTTH, HTTT, THHT, THTH, THTT, TTHH, TTHT, TTTH, TTTT}; $P = \frac{11}{16}$

6. {HHHT, HHTH, HTHH, THHH, HTTT, THTT, TTHT, TTTH}; $P = \frac{1}{2}$

7. { }; $P = 0$

A card is drawn at random from a well-shuffled 52-card deck. Find the probability of each event.

8. a heart $\frac{1}{4}$ **9.** a jack $\frac{1}{13}$ **10.** not a heart $\frac{3}{4}$ **11.** the jack of hearts $\frac{1}{52}$

12. a red card $\frac{1}{2}$ **13.** a face card (jack, queen, or king) $\frac{3}{13}$

14. What are the odds that a flipped coin comes up heads? 1 to 1

Recreation   The probability that Fernando will hit a home run in his next at bat is 0.25.

15. What are the odds in favor of Fernando's hitting a home run? 1 to 3

16. What are the odds against Fernando's hitting a home run? 3 to 1

Education   A reading list contains 14 titles.

Ⓡ **17.** In how many ways can you choose 3 books to read from a list of 14 if the order of reading does not matter? 364

18. Suppose that exactly 3 of the 14 books are plays. What is the probability that all of the books chosen are plays? $\frac{1}{364}$

19. Suppose that 8 of the 14 books are written by twentieth century authors. What is the probability that all of the books chosen are by twentieth century authors? $\frac{56}{364}$

B **20.** **Writing in Mathematics**   List ways probability affects your life and ask two others for ways probability affects them. Then write one or more paragraphs showing why a basic understanding of probability is valuable for everyone.

Business   Two members of a company's top 50 salespeople are chosen at random to represent the company at a convention.

Ⓡ **21.** In how many ways can the 2 representatives be chosen? 1225

22. What is the probability that Eliza and José, who are among the top 50, are the 2 selected? $\frac{1}{1225}$

23. If there are 26 women and 24 men among the top 50 salespeople, what is the probability that both winners are women? $\frac{13}{49}$

Recreation   The Lucky Numbers is a computer game in which a player chooses 3 different numbers between 1 and 36. The order of the numbers does not matter. You win if your choices match the computer's random choices.

Ⓡ **24.** How many choices does a player have? 7140

25. What is the probability that the winning triplet is {1, 2, 3}? $\frac{1}{7140}$

26. What is the probability that the winning triplet consists of only even numbers? $\frac{4}{35}$

27. What is the probability of winning this game on your first try? $\frac{1}{7140}$

28. What are the odds of winning this game on your first try? 1 to 7139

29. What are the odds against winning this game on your first try? 7139 to 1

Ⓡ **30.** A book store manager has a collection of 6 books written in French, 8 books written in German, and 5 books written in Spanish. In how many ways can these books be arranged on a shelf if the books written in a particular language are to be kept together? 20,901,888,000

14.3 Probability   **759**

LESSON FOLLOW-UP

Lesson Quiz

1. Determine the sample space for the experiment that consists of flipping 2 coins. List the event corresponding to matching coins. {HH, HT, TH, TT}; {HH, TT}

2. For the experiment of question 1 above, what is the probability that there is exactly 1 head? $\frac{1}{2}$

A jar of 65 jellybeans contains 14 licorice beans.

3. What is the probability that if 2 beans are chosen at random, both are licorice? $\frac{_{14}C_2}{_{65}C_2} \approx 0.04$

4. What is the probability that if 2 are chosen at random, neither is licorice? $\frac{_{51}C_2}{_{65}C_2} \approx 0.61$

In a carton of 288 shirts, 7 are defective.

5. What is the probability that a shirt chosen at random from the carton is defective? $\frac{7}{288} \approx 0.02$

6. What are the odds that a shirt chosen at random is not defective? 281 to 7

Writing in Mathematics
20. Answers may vary. Some examples may include insurance, health decisions, investment and other business decisions, weather forecasting, sports, and games of chance. It is important because probability may affect your actions, such as buying a car or deciding where to buy a house.

Industry   A supervisor observed that assembly line workers made 46 errors in 2052 jobs one week.

31. What is the probability that an item produced by that assembly line that week is defective? $\frac{23}{1026}$

32. When the supervisor increased the number of 10-min breaks, the number of errors decreased to 31 in 2048 jobs. What is the probability that an item produced under the new system is defective? $\frac{31}{2048}$

33. Of 134 people surveyed, 11 like caviar. What is the probability that one of the people in the survey likes caviar? $\frac{11}{134}$

34. What is the probability that one of the persons described in Exercise 33 doesn't like caviar? $\frac{123}{134}$

35. **Thinking Critically**   Recall that the frequency or empirical probability of an event is the ratio of the number of times an event has actually occurred to the number of trials observed. Explain why properties P_1 and P_4 of probability hold for the frequency interpretation of probability. Interpret P_2 and P_3 for empirical probability.

C 36. A car salesperson offers 10 to 1 odds that a new car will be "trouble-free" for the first 25,000 mi. Based on these odds, what is the probability of "trouble"? $\frac{1}{11}$

37. If you want to offer fair odds that a 7 or 11 comes up when two dice are rolled, what should those odds be? 2 to 7

What is the probability that a 5-card hand dealt from a standard deck contains

38. 4 aces and a king
    1.539×10^{-6}
39. 4 aces and 2 hearts
    4.617×10^{-6}
40. 4 aces
    1.84689×10^{-5}

41. What is the probability that a randomly selected number between 1 and 100, inclusive, is divisible by 3? By 3 and by 5? $\frac{33}{100}, \frac{3}{50}$

42. The letters in the word RANDOM are arranged randomly. What is the probability that an arrangement chosen at random ends with a vowel? $\frac{1}{3}$

43. If the odds are 3 to 2 that a package will arrive on time, what is the probability that the package will arrive late? $\frac{2}{5}$

44. *Programming*   Write the steps that would be included in a program that will simulate the Lucky Numbers game described for Exercises 24 to 29.

Project

Empirical probability is found by repeating the same experiment many times. Design an experiment to find the probability of something of interest to you.

Review

1. Find the length of the radius of a circle that has its center at the origin and passes through (7, 4). $\sqrt{65}$

2. From an airplane at an altitude of 1500 m, the angle of depression of the end of a runway is 38°. Find the distance from the plane to the end of the runway. 2436 m

Objectives: *To solve problems involving mutually exclusive events and*
independent events
To solve problems involving conditional probability

Focus

Collecting data that accurately represents human
behavior is a challenge to many social science
researchers. Therefore, probability has become a very
useful tool in the mathematical modeling of real world
phenomena. Using probability in data collection can
often improve the reliability of the information collected.

A goal of any researcher is to obtain accurate, honest
responses on a survey. This is not always possible when
questions are asked directly. For example, a company
surveying its employees on their feelings about
supervisors may not get accurate responses. Some
employees may be reluctant to give negative comments
about their supervisors. By using conditional probability,
it is possible to design surveys that obtain information on a sensitive topic,
while making it impossible to link a response to an individual respondent.

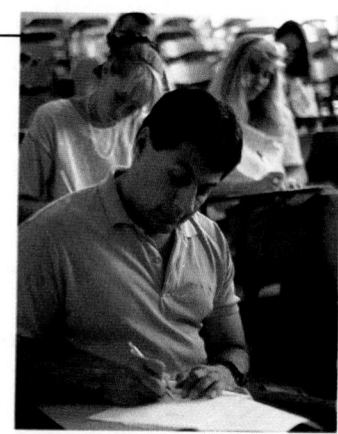

In many applications of probability, more than one event is acceptable or even
desirable. For instance, you may be happy with either an A *or* a B in math. A
runner will make the pre-Olympic trials by placing first, second, or third in the
qualifying meet. In examples like these, you may need to find the probability
that event A or event B occurs, $P(A \cup B)$. This task is simplest when A and B
have no outcomes in common. If A and B are events that have no outcomes in
common, they are said to be **mutually exclusive.** This means that $A \cap B = \varnothing$.
Mutually exclusive events cannot occur together.

Example 1   Consider the experiment of drawing a card from an ordinary deck, and tell
whether each pair of events is mutually exclusive.
  a. *A:* The card is a king.   **b.** *C:* The card is red.
     B: The card is a 10.   *D:* The card is a 3.

a. There is no card that is both a king and a 10, so the events are
mutually exclusive. Notice that $A = \{K\spadesuit, K\clubsuit, K\heartsuit, K\diamondsuit\}$,
$B = \{10\spadesuit, 10\clubsuit, 10\heartsuit, 10\diamondsuit\}$, and $A \cap B = \varnothing$.

b. The 3 of hearts and the 3 of diamonds are both red, so the events
are *not* mutually exclusive: $C \cap D = \{3\heartsuit, 3\diamondsuit\}$.

14.4 Conditional Probability   **761**

- Have students give examples of events that are mutually exclusive and of events that are not mutually exclusive.
- Students may need to see several examples like that of Example 6, which can be verified using counting principles, before moving to a more general situation like that of Example 7. (See Class Exercises 11 to 14.)
- Ⓜ Discuss with students the distinction between selections *with replacement* and *without replacement*. Demonstrate the following using a deck of cards. If several selections are made without replacement, they are not independent events; if selections are made with replacement, they are independent.

Alternative Learning Styles

Some students benefit from concrete examples that connect new material to familiar information. Before presenting the general addition rule for probabilities, have students look at several examples of pairs of sets and formulate a rule for the number of elements in the union of two sets. This should reinforce the connection between set theory and probability as well as help to make the general addition rule both concrete and reasonable.

GUIDED PRACTICE

For Example 1

Consider the experiment of rolling two dice. Tell whether each pair of events is mutually exclusive.

1. *A*: The sum is even.
   B: The sum is prime. no
2. *C*: The dice show the same number.
   D: The sum is odd. yes

If *A* and *B* are mutually exclusive events, then the probability that either *A* or *B* occurs is $P(A \cup B)$. For example, for the roll of a single die let *A* be the event "a number less than 3" and let *B* be the event "a number greater than 5." Then, $A = \{1, 2\}$ and $B = \{6\}$. Then the event "a number less than 3 or greater than 5" is $\{1, 2, 6\} = A \cup B$. For this example, $P(A) = \frac{2}{6}$ and $P(B) = \frac{1}{6}$. The probability that either *A* or *B* occurs is $P(A \cup B) = \frac{3}{6} = \frac{2}{6} + \frac{1}{6}$.

> If *A* and *B* are *mutually exclusive* events, then the probability that either *A* or *B* occurs is given by $P(A \cup B) = P(A) + P(B)$.

Example 2 Determine the probabilities of event *A* and event *B* of Example 1, and use them to compute the probability of *A* or *B*.

$$P(A) = \frac{4}{52} \qquad P(B) = \frac{4}{52} \qquad \textit{There are exactly 4 kings and 4 tens in a deck of 52 cards.}$$

$$P(A \cup B) = P(A) + P(B) = \frac{4}{52} + \frac{4}{52} = \frac{8}{52} = \frac{2}{13} \qquad \textit{A and B are mutually exclusive.}$$

Two events are said to be **complementary** if their union is the entire sample space and their intersection is the empty set. For example, for the experiment of rolling one die, the events "an even number" and "an odd number" are complementary. Complementary events are mutually exclusive. Thus, if *E* and *F* are complementary events, $P(E) + P(F) = P(E \cup F) = 1$.

Example 3 For the roll of a single die, let *D* be the event "an even number," and let *E* be the event "a number less than 3." What is the probability of the event "an even number or a number less than 3"?

$$D = \{2, 4, 6\} \qquad E = \{1, 2\} \qquad P(D) = \frac{1}{2} \qquad P(E) = \frac{1}{3}$$

The event an even number or a number less than 3 is

$$D \cup E = \{1, 2, 4, 6\} \qquad P(D \cup E) = \frac{4}{6} = \frac{2}{3}$$

Notice that in this case, $P(D \cup E) \neq P(D) + P(E)$.

Example 3 illustrates the problem that occurs when trying to compute the probability of the union of two events *D* and *E* that are *not* mutually exclusive by simply adding $P(D) + P(E)$. Outcomes that are common to *D* and *E* are counted twice. To correct this, recall that outcomes common to *D* and *E* form the intersection $D \cap E$. Therefore, if $P(D \cap E)$ is known, it can be used to compute $P(D \cup E)$ by the following.

> **General Addition Rule**
>
> For any events *D* and *E*, $P(D \cup E) = P(D) + P(E) - P(D \cap E)$.

Example 4 For the spinner shown, probabilities for some events are:

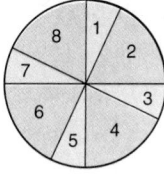

R: an even number $\qquad P(R) = 0.72$
Q: a number less than 4 $\qquad P(Q) = 0.32$
T: the number 2 $\qquad P(T) = 0.18$

Determine the probability of R or Q.

$P(R \cup Q) = P(R) + P(Q) - P(R \cap Q) = 0.72 + 0.32 - 0.18 = 0.86$
Why is $P(R \cap Q) = 0.18$?

When computing the probabilities of two events that occur in succession, it is important to know whether the outcome of the first affects the outcome of the second. For example, if a coin is tossed twice, the result of the first toss does not affect the second toss. However, if two cards are drawn in succession from a standard deck, what happens on the first draw *does* affect the second. If the first card is the queen of hearts, the second one cannot be the queen of hearts.

Two events are said to be **independent** if the outcome of one has no effect on the outcome of the other; otherwise the events are **dependent**. The next example illustrates how independence and dependence affect probabilities.

Example 5 What is the probability of drawing 2 aces in succession from a standard deck of cards:
  a. If the first card is replaced before the second is chosen?
  b. If the first card is not replaced before the second is chosen?

  a. By the multiplication principle, there are 52×52 ways to choose 2 cards under these circumstances. There are 4×4 ways to choose an ace, and then choose a second ace. Therefore, the probability of drawing 2 aces is $\dfrac{4 \times 4}{52 \times 52} = \dfrac{1}{169}$.

  b. There are 52×51 ways to choose 2 cards if the first is *not* replaced before the second is drawn. If the first is an ace, then on the second draw there are 3 remaining aces, so there are 4×3 ways of choosing 2 aces. The probability of 2 aces is therefore $\dfrac{4 \times 3}{52 \times 51} = \dfrac{1}{221}$.

For the situation in Example 5, let X be the event "drawing the first ace" and let Y be the event "drawing the second ace." The probability of 2 aces is $P(X \cap Y)$. When the first card is replaced before the second is drawn, the events X and Y are independent, and $P(X \cap Y) = \dfrac{4 \times 4}{52 \times 52} = \dfrac{4}{52} \cdot \dfrac{4}{52} = P(A) \cdot P(B)$. This is true in general. If A and B are independent events, then the probability that A *and* B occur is simply the probability that A occurs times the probability that B occurs.

If A and B are *independent* events, then
$$P(A \cap B) = P(A) \cdot P(B).$$

14.4 Conditional Probability **763**

For Example 2
1. Find the probabilities of events C and D above, and use them to compute the probability of C or D.
$P(C) = \dfrac{6}{36}, P(D) = \dfrac{18}{36}; P(C \cup D) = \dfrac{2}{3}$

2. Consider an experiment of drawing a card from an ordinary deck. Let X be the event "the card is a queen" and let Y be the event "the card is an even number." Find the probabilities of events X and Y and use them to compute the probability of $X \cup Y$.
$P(X) = \dfrac{4}{52}, P(Y) = \dfrac{20}{52}; P(X \cup Y) = \dfrac{6}{13}$

Common Error Students may not realize that this method of computing the probability of the union of two mutually exclusive events may be extended to more than two events. If A, B, and C are mutually exclusive, then $P(A \cup B \cup C) = P(A) + P(B) + P(C)$. This follows from the associative law for the union of sets and can be shown using simple examples.

For Example 3
Consider the experiment of rolling a single die. Find each probability.

1. The number is prime or even. $\dfrac{5}{6}$

2. The number is odd or greater than 4. $\dfrac{2}{3}$

For Example 4
For the experiment of Example 4, $P(1) = P(3) = P(5) = P(7) = 0.07$. Find each probability.
1. a number that is odd or less than 4 0.46
2. a prime number or an even number 0.93

763

For Example 5

What is the probability of drawing 2 hearts in succession from a standard deck of cards:

1. if the first is replaced before the second is chosen?
$\frac{13}{52} \times \frac{13}{52} = 0.0625$

2. if the first is not replaced before the second is chosen?
$\frac{13}{52} \times \frac{12}{51} = 0.0588$

For Example 6

1. A math teacher estimates that the probability is 85% that a student has mastered the necessary algebra skills before taking a precalculus course. Experience shows that the probability is 90% that a student with good algebra skills earns a grade of 80 or better in precalculus. What is the probability that a precalculus student chosen at random has good algebra skills and earns a grade of 80 or better? 0.765

2. A card is chosen at random from a standard deck. What is the probability that it is a diamond? Given that it is a diamond, what is the probability that it is a jack? Compare the product of those two probabilities with the probability that a card chosen at random is the jack of diamonds.
$\frac{1}{4}; \frac{1}{13}; P(J\blacklozenge) = \frac{1}{52} = \frac{1}{4} \times \frac{1}{13}$

In Example 5b, when the first card is not replaced before the second is drawn, the events X and Y are *not* independent. In this case $P(X \cap Y) = \frac{4 \times 3}{52 \times 51} = \frac{4}{52} \times \frac{3}{51}$. The first factor is the probability of X, and second is the probability of Y *given that X has occurred*. Note that if the first card had not been an ace, the probability of an ace on the second draw would have been $\frac{4}{51}$; *given that X has occurred* is crucial. This relationship may also be generalized. If A and B are dependent events, the probability that A *and* B occur is the probability that A occurs times the probability that B occurs given that A has occurred.

> If A and B are *dependent* events, then
> $$P(A \cap B) = P(A) \cdot P(B \text{ given } A).$$

The rule for finding the probabilities of dependent events is often useful in problems involving empirical probability.

Example 6 *Health*   Based on records, a dentist estimates that the probability is 0.68 that a patient will come in for regular check-ups and cleaning. The dentist further claims that the probability is 0.91 that a patient who comes for regular check-ups and cleaning has no cavities. What is the probability that one of this dentist's patients chosen at random comes in regularly and has no cavities on the next visit?

Let R be the event "regular check-ups" and let N be "no cavities."

$P(R) = 0.68 \qquad P(N \text{ given } R) = 0.91$

$P(R \cap N) = P(R) \times P(N \text{ given } R) = (0.68)(0.91) \approx 0.62$

If two events A and B are independent, then the probability of B given A is the same as the probability of B. In fact, the independence of two events is often defined by the statement:

Events A and B are independent if and only if $P(A \cap B) = P(A) \cdot P(B)$

The probability that one event occurs given that another has occurred is called **conditional probability.** From the rule for finding the probabilities of dependent events, it is clear that the probability of B given A is given by the following equation. The notation $P(B|A)$ is often used for $P(B \text{ given } A)$.

> $$P(B \text{ given } A) = \frac{P(A \cap B)}{P(A)}, \ P(A) \neq 0$$
>
> or
>
> $$P(B|A) = \frac{P(A \cap B)}{P(A)}, \ P(A) \neq 0$$

Modeling

How can reliable data be collected on sensitive issues?

It is sometimes necessary to ensure that responses cannot be linked to the individuals responding to the questions. One method to protect the anonymity of the person completing the survey uses conditional probability.

When a sensitive question such as "Have you ever been arrested?" appears on the survey, the respondent is instructed to flip a coin. If the coin shows heads, the respondent is to answer the given question honestly. If the coin shows tails, the respondent is to flip the coin again and answer the question, "Did the coin turn up heads on this toss?" Each respondent is then able to return the survey form with just one response of yes or no, with no indication of which question was answered. To interpret the responses to the survey, conditional probability is used to find the likelihood that a person responding yes is actually responding to the original question.

Example 7   *Survey Research*   The administration at a high school conducted a survey in which students were asked, "Do you feel that you are getting an inadequate education at this school?" To ensure honest responses, the students were asked to use the coin-toss method described above. The percentage of yes responses received was 28.4%. From this information, estimate the percentage of the students who likely indicated yes to the original question.

First draw a diagram of the possible survey responses.

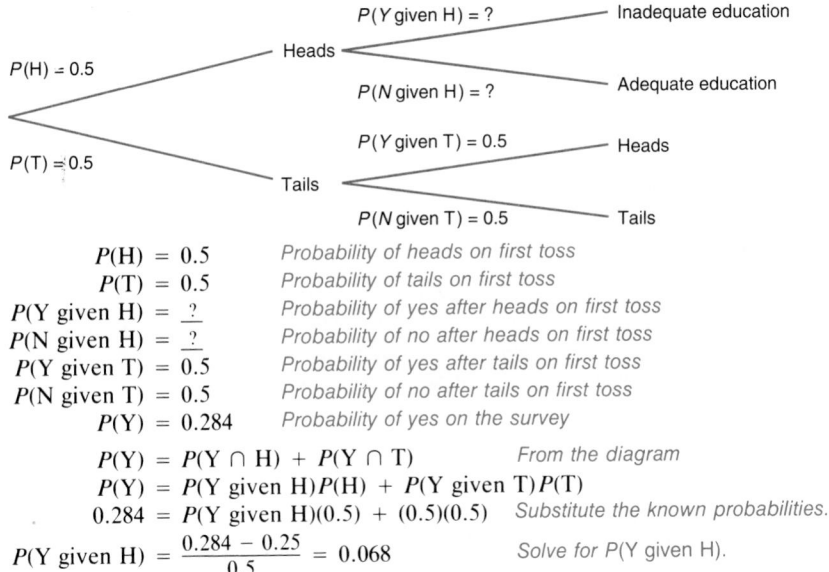

$$P(H) = 0.5 \qquad \text{Probability of heads on first toss}$$
$$P(T) = 0.5 \qquad \text{Probability of tails on first toss}$$
$$P(Y \text{ given } H) = \underline{\ ?\ } \qquad \text{Probability of yes after heads on first toss}$$
$$P(N \text{ given } H) = \underline{\ ?\ } \qquad \text{Probability of no after heads on first toss}$$
$$P(Y \text{ given } T) = 0.5 \qquad \text{Probability of yes after tails on first toss}$$
$$P(N \text{ given } T) = 0.5 \qquad \text{Probability of no after tails on first toss}$$
$$P(Y) = 0.284 \qquad \text{Probability of yes on the survey}$$

$$P(Y) = P(Y \cap H) + P(Y \cap T) \qquad \text{From the diagram}$$
$$P(Y) = P(Y \text{ given } H)P(H) + P(Y \text{ given } T)P(T)$$
$$0.284 = P(Y \text{ given } H)(0.5) + (0.5)(0.5) \qquad \text{Substitute the known probabilities.}$$
$$P(Y \text{ given } H) = \frac{0.284 - 0.25}{0.5} = 0.068 \qquad \text{Solve for P(Y given H).}$$

The estimated percentage of students reporting that they feel they are receiving an inadequate education is 6.8%. *What factors could make this estimate inaccurate?*

14.4 Conditional Probability   **765**

The modeling techniques presented here can be applied to many topics that are currently discussed and debated. This will help give students an appreciation for the validity of the subject matter.

For Example 7

1. A small firm has 2 copying machines, a large one and a small one. The probability that both are malfunctioning on a given day is 0.06, and the probability that the larger one is out of order is 0.22. On Friday the 13th the large machine breaks down at 8:00 a.m. What is the probability that the smaller one breaks down? 0.2727

2. A survey shows that 13% of students on a local college campus are women who belong to sororities. At this particular college, 54% of all students are women. What is the probability that a female student is a member of a sorority? 0.2407

Common Error   Some students may have difficulty distinguishing between the probability of *A and B* and the probability of *A given B*. Have these students work through a set of exercises, interpreting the questions before doing any computations.

Have students work in pairs to provide an example and write a rule or equation for finding the probability for each situation.
- A or B if A and B are mutually exclusive
- A or B if A and B are not mutually exclusive
- A and B if A and B are independent
- A and B if A and B are dependent

Additional Answers

Class Exercises

8. independent; One roll does not affect another roll.

9. dependent; One child might catch a cold from the other.

10. independent; The outcome of one does not affect the outcome of the other.

Class Exercises

For the experiment of rolling two dice, one red and one green, tell if each pair of events is mutually exclusive. For pairs that are not mutually exclusive, give an example of an event they have in common.

1. A: Both dice show the same number. B: The sum of the numbers is 7. yes

2. C: Both dice show the same number. D: The sum of the numbers is 8. no; (4, 4)

3. E: The red die shows a 2. F: The sum of the numbers is less than 5. no; (2, 1)

For the experiment of tossing three fair coins, find each probability.

4. H: All coins show heads. $\frac{1}{8}$
   T: All coins show tails. $\frac{1}{8}$
   $H \cup T$ $\frac{1}{4}$

5. A: The coins show no heads. $\frac{1}{8}$
   B: The coins show 1 head. $\frac{3}{8}$
   $A \cup B$ $\frac{1}{2}$

6. *Recreation*   A local fisherman tells a visitor that the probability of catching trout is 0.4, the probability of catching bass is 0.25, and the probability of catching both is 0.1. What is the probability that the visitor will catch trout or bass? 0.55

7. A waiter estimates that for the average customer, the probability of ordering pie for dessert is 0.27, the probability of ordering ice cream is 0.35, and the probability of ordering both is 0.11. According to this waiter, what is the probability that a customer will order pie or ice cream? 0.51

Can each pair of events be assumed to be independent? Give reasons.

8. A sum of 7 and a sum of 13 on two rolls of a pair of dice

9. A second grader's getting a cold and his sister's getting a cold

10. Your winning the lottery and a friend's winning the lottery

A jar contains 12 blue, 6 yellow, and 10 red marbles. Two marbles are drawn in succession without replacement. Find the probability of each event.

11. Both marbles are red. $\frac{5}{42}$

12. The first is red and the second is not red. $\frac{5}{21}$

13. Repeat Exercise 12 with the assumption that the first marble is replaced before the second is drawn. $\frac{45}{196}$

14. *Marketing*   A door-to-door salesperson estimates that the probability is 0.35 that a resident is at home when he calls. He further estimates that the probability that a person makes a purchase is 0.68. What is the probability that a person whose home he visits is at home and makes a purchase? 0.238

Practice Exercises

For the experiment of rolling two dice, one red and one green, tell if each pair of events is mutually exclusive. For pairs that are not mutually exclusive, give an example of an event they have in common.

A 1. A: Both dice show the same number. B: The sum of the numbers is odd. yes

2. C: One of the dice shows a 6. D: The sum of the numbers is 8. no; (6, 2), (2, 6)

3. E: The green die shows a 4. F: The sum of the numbers is less than 5. yes

A spinner is marked with the numbers 1 to 15 and is constructed so that the numbers are equally likely to result. Compute each probability.

4. *A*: a number less than 5 $\frac{4}{15}$ 5. *R*: an even number $\frac{7}{15}$ 6. *X*: a prime number $\frac{2}{5}$
   B: a number greater than 8 $\frac{7}{15}$ *S*: 5 $\frac{1}{15}$ *Y*: an even number
   $A \cup B$ $\frac{11}{15}$ $R \cup S$ $\frac{8}{15}$ $X \cup Y$ $\frac{4}{5}$ $\frac{7}{15}$

An air traffic controller at a large airport estimates that the probabilities of there being 0, 1, 2, 3 or more airplanes waiting to land at this airport are:

$$P(0) = 0.10 \quad P(1) = 0.20 \quad P(2) = 0.40 \quad P(3) = 0.20 \quad P(\text{more than } 3) = 0.10$$

Determine the probability of each event.

7. 3 or more planes are waiting. 0.30   8. 1 or 2 planes are waiting. 0.60

9. Fewer than 2 planes are waiting. 0.30   10. At least one plane is waiting. 0.90

11. Not more than 3 planes are waiting. 0.90   12. More than 2 planes are waiting. 0.30

13. **Thinking Critically** Luke claims that the probability of his earning an *A* or a *B* on the next precalculus test is 75%, and the probability of a *C* or less is only 35%. What is the flaw in Luke's thinking? The sum does not equal 1.

Tell whether each pair of events may be assumed to be independent. Give reasons for your answers.

14. Two heads in two tosses of a fair coin   15. Earning an A in math and an A in music

16. Picking two caramels in a row from a box of assorted chocolates (The first is eaten before the second is picked.)

17. Suppose that when you drop an ordinary thumbtack, the probability that it lands point up is 0.38. What is the probability that when you toss 2 thumbtacks, both land point up? 0.144

Ⓡ 18. A dancing teacher has eight 6-year-olds who will perform in a recital. In how many ways can their eight solo dances be arranged? 40,320

Ⓡ 19. From the menu at a Chinese restaurant a group may choose 2 items from the 14 on the first page, 3 from the 18 on the second page, and 1 from the 8 on the third page. How many choices do they have? 594,048

20. Records show that the probability that an applicant is admitted to a certain college is 65%. The probability that an applicant will be both admitted and offered financial aid is 30%. What is the probability that an applicant is offered financial aid given that she is admitted to the college? 0.46

21. **Thinking Critically** A person rolling dice throws four 7's in a row and then quits, claiming, "I've used up today's luck; another 7 is very unlikely." What is the flaw in this reasoning?

Two dice, a red and a green, are tossed. Find the probability of each event.

B 22. The red shows a 1 and the green shows an even number. $\frac{1}{12}$

23. The red shows a prime number and the green shows an odd number. $\frac{1}{4}$

24. Both show prime numbers. $\frac{1}{4}$

25. Both show 3's. $\frac{1}{36}$

14.4 Conditional Probability   **767**

Assignment Guide
Basic: 1–20, 1–29 odd
Average: 1–19 odd, 20–35, Project
Enriched: 19–45, Project

Teacher's Resource Book
   Practice, page 99

Ⓡ **Review**
Exercises 18, 19, and 36 review counting techniques. Exercises 31 and 34 recall the definition of probability from the empirical and the classical viewpoints.

Project
Having the students conduct their own surveys will help to tie the mathematics to their own realm of experience. Be sure that students employ both survey methods suggested and that they comment on any discrepancies between the two.

LESSON FOLLOW-UP
Test Yourself

Teacher's Resource Book
   Tests—Quiz, form A, page 61
   Tests—Quiz, form B, page 61

Additional Answers
14. independent; The first toss doesn't affect the outcome of the second toss.
15. dependent; General intelligence may be reflected in each grade.
16. dependent; The first event affects the probability of the second event.
21. Another roll of 7 is independent of what has already been rolled.

Lesson Quiz

1. A principal determines that 18% of the children in his school are the oldest in a family of 2 or more children, and 13% are only children. What is the probability that a child chosen at random from this school is either an only child or the oldest child? 0.31

2. What is the probability that a number chosen at random from the numbers 1 through 25 will be either odd or a multiple of 5? 0.6

3. A survey shows that 42% of registered voters in a city voted in the mayoral election, and that 59% of those people voted for the incumbent. What is the probability that a person chosen at random from the voter registration lists voted for the incumbent? 0.2478

Two cards are drawn in succession from a standard deck. What is the probability that both have even numbers:

4. if the first is replaced before the second is drawn? 0.1479

5. if the first is not replaced before the second is drawn? 0.1433

6. The personnel director of a large firm estimates that the probability that a person applying for a technical position has the appropriate qualifications is 0.85. The probability that a qualified person is hired is 0.20. What is the probability that a randomly chosen applicant is both qualified and hired? 0.17

Alternative Assessment

Have students write a paragraph comparing and contrasting *mutually exclusive* and *independent* events.

Two cards are drawn in succession from an ordinary deck. The first is not replaced before the second is drawn. Find the probability of each event.

26. The first is an ace, and the second a queen. $\frac{4}{663}$

27. Both are hearts. $\frac{1}{17}$

28. The first is a heart, and the second a club. $\frac{13}{204}$

29. Both are red. $\frac{25}{102}$

30. *Meteorology* According to one meteorologist, on a randomly chosen day in January the probability of snow in Buffalo is 65%. Given that it snows in Buffalo, the probability of snow in Toronto is 75%. What is the probability that on a randomly chosen day in January, it snows in both Buffalo and Toronto? 0.4875

Sales A store has 15 microwaves in stock, but 3 of these are defective.

Ⓡ 31. What is the probability that the first person to buy a microwave from this store buys a defective one? $\frac{1}{5}$

32. What is the probability that the second person to buy a microwave gets a defective one given that the first customer's was defective? $\frac{1}{7}$

33. What is the probability that the second person to buy a microwave gets a defective one given that the first customer's was not defective? $\frac{3}{14}$

Ⓡ 34. Two members of a math department are to be chosen at random to attend a convention. If the department has 9 men and 6 women members, what is the probability that 2 men attend the conference? $\frac{12}{35}$

35. *Income Tax* A government researcher wants to estimate the percent of taxpayers who cheat on their income taxes. The researcher designs a survey similar to the survey in Example 7. If the first coin toss is heads, the question "Have you ever cheated on your income taxes?" is to be answered honestly. If the coin toss is tails, the question "Were you born on an odd-numbered day of the month?" is to be answered. If there were 30.2% yes answers in the survey, estimate the percent of taxpayers who say that they cheat on their taxes. 10.4%

Ⓡ 36. In how many ways can you answer a 6-question true-false quiz randomly? 64

Ⓒ 37. *Driving* The probability of passing a test for a driver's license on the first try is 0.80. The probability of passing on the second try, after failing the first test, is 0.86. What is the probability that a person has to take the test more than two times? 0.028

38. *Medicine* According to the Red Cross, the probabilities of an individual's having the 4 blood types are:

   type A: 40%   type O: 30%   type B: 20%   type AB: 10%

   If two persons are picked at random, what is the probability that they have the same blood type? 0.30

39. *Marketing* A popular "game" that some companies offer with their product provides a ticket with each purchase. You rub off a spot to uncover a letter, and when the letters on your tickets spell a given word, you win. Suppose that the lucky word is WIN, and for any ticket there is a probability of 0.65 of uncovering a *W*, 0.33 of uncovering an *N*, and 0.02 of uncovering an *I*. What is the probability that you win if you have exactly 3 tickets? 0.0043

768 Chapter 14 Probability

40. Sal is surprised by a 6-question true-false quiz and answers randomly. What is the probability of earning a passing grade of 4 or more out of 6? $\frac{11}{32}$

Two cards are drawn in succession from an ordinary deck; the first is not replaced before the second is drawn.

41. What is the probability that the first is a diamond and the second a king? 0.0192

42. What is the probability that the first is red and the second is a jack? 0.0385

43. Repeat Exercises 41 and 42 under the assumption that the first card is replaced before the second card is drawn. Describe the differences.

44. Show that if 3 events A, B, and C are independent, then the probability that all 3 occur is $P(A) \cdot P(B) \cdot P(C)$.

45. Thinking Critically   Suppose that 2 events are independent. Can they also be mutually exclusive? Why or why not?

Project

Work with one or more other students to design two surveys on a current events issue. One survey should be conducted as in Example 7. The second survey should ask the question directly. Compare the results of the two surveys.

Test Yourself

How many different license plates can be made under the given conditions?

1. The plate has 3 digits followed by 3 letters, with repetition allowed. 17,576,000   14.1

2. The plate has 4 digits or 4 letters with no repetition. 363,840

Find the value of each expression.

3. $_{17}P_5$ 742,560   **4.** $_{28}C_3$ 3276   14.2

5. Determine the number of distinct permutations of the letters of *CALCULUS*. 5040

6. A caterer allows you to choose 5 items on the menu for a fixed price. If there are 22 items on the menu, how many ways can you choose the 5 items? 26,334

7. List the sample space for the experiment of flipping 3 coins.   14.3

Given the experiment for Exercise 7, list the event corresponding to each description and compute its probability.

8. Exactly 1 coin shows tails.   **9.** Fewer than 2 coins show heads.

10. *Sports*   The odds that Argentina will beat Italy in a World Cup soccer game are 12 to 7. What is the probability that Italy will beat Argentina in this game? $\frac{7}{19}$

Determine if each set of events is independent and compute the probability.

11. A pair of dice is rolled twice. What is the probability of getting a 7 on the   14.4 first roll and something other than a 7 on the second? independent; $\frac{5}{36}$

12. Three cards are drawn at random from an ordinary deck of cards, without replacement. What is the probability that all 3 are red? not independent; $\frac{2}{17}$

14.4 Conditional Probability   **769**

Additional Answers
43. 0.0192; 0.0385; In Exercises 41 and 42, it matters if the first card is a king or red jack, respectively, since this will affect the second choice. In this exercise, the first choice does not affect the second.

44. $P(A \cap B \cap C) = P([A \cap B] \cap C) = P(A \cap B) \times P(C) = P(A) \times P(B) \times P(C)$

45. no, unless one event is impossible; If they are independent, $P(A \cap B) = P(A) \times P(B)$. If they are mutually exclusive, $P(A \cap B) = 0$; This implies $P(A)$ or $P(B)$ is zero.

FOCUS

Another formulation of the famous birthday problem is, "What is the smallest number of people for which the probability that at least two of them have the same birthday is 50% or better?" The surprising answer is 23. The birthday problem is solved using complementary probabilities and the assumption that birthdates in an arbitrary group of people are in-dependent events.

First consider the problem for just two people. Whatever the date of the first person's birthday, the probability that the second person has a *different* birthday is $\frac{364}{365}$. If a third person is added to the group, the probability that his or her birthday is different from the first two is $\frac{363}{365}$, and so the probability that three have different birthdays is $\frac{364}{365} \times \frac{363}{365}$. Similarly, the probability that four people have dif-ferent birthdays is $\frac{364}{365} \times \frac{363}{365} \times \frac{362}{365}$, and so for 23 people, the probability that all 23 have *different* birth-days is $\frac{364}{365} \times \frac{363}{365} \times \cdots \times \frac{344}{365} \times \frac{343}{365} \approx 0.49$. This means that the probability of the *complement* of this event, or at least two having the same birthday, is $1 - 0.49 = 0.51$.

14.5 Bernoulli Trials and the Binomial Distribution

Objectives: To define and give examples of binomial experiments and Bernoulli trials
To solve problems involving binomial distributions

Focus

Coincidences are often a topic of conversation and a source of amazement. How likely is it that two strangers have an acquaintance in common? . . . That in a group of 30 people, at least two have the same birthday? . . . That on your next breath you inhale a molecule exhaled by Julius Caesar as he breathed his dying words, "Et tu, Brute . . ."? The answer to each of these questions is "More likely than you think." Mathematicians estimate that the probability is about $\frac{1}{100}$ that two strangers have an acquaintance in common, and better than $\frac{99}{100}$ that you and Julius Caesar will share a molecule in your next breath! The birthday problem is a famous one that can be solved using just the concepts of independent events and complementary events. The probability is well over 0.5.

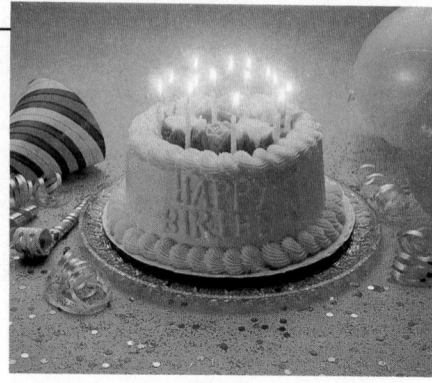

In decision making, it is often important to know how likely it is that an experiment repeated a number of times will result in a certain number of successes. For example, a coach may want to know the likelihood that a basketball player with a free throw average of 0.7 will make at least 3 of her next 5 shots. This is an example of a **binomial experiment.** In binomial experiments, four criteria must be met.

- The experiment consists of a fixed number n of identical trials.
- Each trial results in one of two outcomes, called *success* and *failure*.
- The probability p of success for any trial is the same.
- The trials are independent; that is, the result of one does not affect the outcome of the others.

The individual trials of a binomial experiment are often called **Bernoulli trials** in honor of Jacob Bernoulli (1654–1705), a Swiss mathematician who is credited with a key result in probability theory. In some applications independence of the trials cannot be proved, but independence is assumed if it seems reasonable.

770 Chapter 14 Probability

Example 1 Tell whether each of the following is a binomial experiment. Give reasons for your answers.

   a. A quarter is tossed 4 times. You are interested in the probability that it shows heads exactly 3 times.

   b. Given that 40% of the people who come to a certain store on a Saturday make a purchase, the manager is interested in the probability that of the first 50 people, more than 20 make a purchase.

   c. A penny is tossed until it shows tails. You are interested in the number of tosses required.

   a. This is a binomial experiment with $n = 4$ trials. The probability of success (heads) on any trial is $p = \frac{1}{2}$, and the trials are independent.

   b. If success is "makes a purchase," then $p = 0.4$ for each trial (person). The number of trials is $n = 50$ and the trials may be assumed to be independent. This is a binomial experiment.

   c. This is not a binomial experiment, since the number of trials (tosses) is not fixed.

The task in a binomial experiment is to find the probability of a certain number of successes among the n trials. If there are 5 trials, there can be 0, 1, 2, 3, 4, or 5 successes. In general, there can be 0, 1, 2, . . . , or n successes in n trials. A listing of these $n + 1$ possibilities and their associated probabilities is called a **probability distribution.**

Example 2 *Research* A geneticist wishes to study the numbers of boys in three-child families. Assume that a child is equally likely to be a girl or a boy, and find the probabilities of having 0, 1, 2, or 3 boys.

$S = \{$BBB, BBG, BGB, BGG, GBB, GBG, GGB, GGG$\}$ *Sample space*

By counting it is easy to obtain the probabilities at the right. This is an example of a probability distribution. The sum of the probabilities is equal to 1.

Number of boys	0	1	2	3
Probability	$\frac{1}{8}$	$\frac{3}{8}$	$\frac{3}{8}$	$\frac{1}{8}$

For a binomial experiment, a formula can be derived to give the probability of r successes in n trials, where $0 \le r \le n$. For the basketball player with a free throw average of 0.7, the probability of success on any free throw is 0.7, and the probability of failure is 0.3. Assuming that each shot is independent of the others, the probability that she makes 5 out of 5 is $(0.7)(0.7)(0.7)(0.7)(0.7) = (0.7)^5 \approx 0.168$.

What is the probability that she makes exactly 4 of 5 shots? Abbreviating success as S and failure as F, there are 5 ways that this can happen.

   FSSSS   SFSSS   SSFSS   SSSFS   SSSSF

To find the probability of FSSSS or SFSSS or SSFSS or SSSFS or SSSSF, add the 5 corresponding probabilities. *Why?* The probability of FSSSS is

$$(0.3)(0.7)(0.7)(0.7)(0.7) = (0.7)^4(0.3) \approx 0.072$$

14.5 Bernoulli Trials and the Binomial Distribution **771**

Thinking Critically
They are all mutually exclusive events.

772

Alternative Learning Styles

Students who are subjective learners may enjoy trying out the birthday problem in groups of various sizes. Have each person in the room give his or her birthday until a "match" is heard. Be sure that students understand first that this problem gives probability, not certitude. In a group of 366 people there may not be 2 identical birthdays, and in a group of 2 there could be a match, but neither is likely.

GUIDED PRACTICE

For Example 1

Tell whether each of the following is a binomial experiment. Give a reason for your answer.

1. A dog breeder is interested in the probability that in a litter of 8 pups, exactly 4 are female. yes; This experiment satisfies the four criteria for a binomial experiment.

2. A town council is interested in the probability that putting in new lights in a remote parking area will cut down on crime in that spot. no; There is no fixed number of trials.

For Example 2

Using the information from Example 2 given in the lesson, find the probabilities of a set of nonidentical twins having 0, 1, or 2 boys.
{BB, BG, GB, GG}; $P(0) = \frac{1}{4}$; $P(1) = \frac{1}{2}$; $P(2) = \frac{1}{4}$

For Example 3

If 25% of the population is over 6 ft tall, what is the probability that in a group of 12 people, exactly 4 are over 6 ft tall? 0.1936

In fact, the probability of each of the outcomes that represent 4 successes and 1 failure is exactly $(0.7)^4(0.3)$, so that the probability of exactly 4 successes is $5(0.7)^4(0.3) \approx 0.36$.

What is the probability that she makes exactly 3 of 5 shots? First determine the number of ways to make 3 of 5 shots. This is simply the binomial coefficient $\binom{5}{3} = 10$. Each of these 10 ways represents 3 successes and 2 failures, so the probability of each will be $(0.7)^3(0.3)^2 \approx 0.031$. Thus, the probability of making exactly 3 of the 5 shots is $10(0.7)^3(0.3)^2 \approx 0.31$.

The same method may be used to find the probability of making 0, 1, or 2 shots. The probability distribution is shown below. Since this is a binomial experiment, the distribution is called a **binomial distribution.**

Number of successes	0	1	2	3	4	5
Probability	0.002	0.028	0.132	0.310	0.360	0.168

> If an experiment consists of n independent trials, and if the probability of success for each trial is p, then the probability of exactly r successes is $\binom{n}{r} p^r (1 - p)^{n-r}$.

Example 3 If 20% of the population is left-handed, what is the probability that in a group of 16 people, exactly 3 are left-handed?

This is a binomial experiment, success defined as left-handed; $p = 0.2$, $n = 16$, $r = 3$. The number of ways to have 3 left-handed people in a group of 16 is $\binom{16}{3}$. Therefore, the probability of exactly 3 left-handed people in the group is $\binom{16}{3}(0.2)^3 (1 - 0.2)^{13} \approx 0.246$.

 Calculators and simple computer programs enable you to solve problems involving binomial distributions even when n is very large.

Example 4 A botanist has developed a new strain of beans whose seeds have a probability of 0.8 of germinating. If the botanist plants 18 seeds, what is the probability that the following germinate:
  a. exactly 15   **b.** at least 15   **c.** fewer than 15

a. $P(15 \text{ successes}) = \binom{18}{15}(0.8)^{15}(0.2)^3 \approx 0.230$ $n = 18, p = 0.8, r = 15, 1 - p = 0.2$

b. At least 15 seeds germinate when 15 *or* 16 *or* 17 *or* 18 seeds germinate.

$P(\text{at least 15 successes}) = P(15) + P(16) + P(17) + P(18)$ *Mutually exclusive events*

$= \binom{18}{15}(0.8)^{15}(0.2)^3 + \binom{18}{16}(0.8)^{16}(0.2)^2 + \binom{18}{17}(0.8)^{17}(0.2) + \binom{18}{18}(0.8)^{18} \approx 0.501$

c. Since "at least 15" and "fewer than 15" are complementary events,
$P(\text{fewer than 15}) = 1 - P(\text{at least 15}) = 1 - 0.501 = 0.499$.

Class Exercises

Tell whether each experiment is binomial. If it is, identify the Bernoulli trial, the probability p of success per trial, the number n of trials, and the number r of successes sought. If it is not binomial, state why not.

1. A single die is rolled 10 times. You are interested in the probability that 3 of the rolls result in a 6.

2. Cards are drawn from a deck without replacement. You are interested in the probability that of the first 9 cards, 2 are spades.

3. Data shows that 40% of all football injuries are knee injuries. You are interested in the probability that of 6 injuries in a game, none are knee injuries.

4. A die is rolled until a 1 shows. You are interested in the probability that it takes more than 3 rolls for this to happen.

A coin is tossed 8 times. Use the formula for binomial probabilities to find each probability.

5. exactly 3 heads 0.219

6. at least 3 heads 0.855

7. no more than 3 heads 0.363

8. more than 3 heads 0.637

Marketing   A door-to-door salesperson believes that the probability of making a sale when a person is at home is 0.4. He visits 10 homes where someone is at home. Find each probability.

9. exactly 7 sales 0.042

10. more than 7 sales 0.0123

11. at most 7 sales 0.9877

Practice Exercises

Tell whether each experiment is binomial. If it is, identify the Bernoulli trial, the probability p of success per trial, the number n of trials, and the number r of successes sought. If it is not binomial, tell why not.

A 1. *Medicine*   A new medicine causes a side effect of weight gain 5% of the time. You are interested in the probability that in a study of 50 patients taking this medicine, exactly 4 experience the weight gain.

2. *Sales*   A street vendor knows that there is an 85% chance of making a profit of $90 when the weather is good, but only a 45% chance of making that profit when the weather is bad. You are interested in the probability that of the 25 days he worked in October, he made a $90 profit on 20 days.

3. A weighted coin is tossed 24 times. You know that the probability of heads on any toss is 0.65, and you are interested in the probability that exactly 12 heads come up.

4. Cards are drawn from a deck without replacement. You are interested in the probability that of 8 cards, exactly 6 are red.

5. A student is unprepared for a 20 question true-or-false quiz and answers each question by tossing a coin. The student is interested in the probability of obtaining a passing grade of 14 out of 20.

14.5 Bernoulli Trials and the Binomial Distribution   **773**

For Example 4

A nursery guarantees that its rose-bushes will bloom within a year of being planted. A new strain has a probability of 0.85 of blooming within a year. If 20 of these bushes are sold by the nursery, find the probability that:

1. Exactly 16 bloom within a year. 0.1821

2. At least 16 bloom within a year. 0.8298

3. Fewer than 16 bloom within a year. 0.1702

Common Error   Some students may have difficulty precisely interpreting "at least," "at most," and similar expressions. Have these students work through a set of exercises and explain to you how to go about solving the problems.

CLOSURE

Have students write in their math journals how to identify whether an experiment is a binomial one and how to compute the probability of an event in a binomial experiment.

Additional Answers
Class Exercises

1. yes; roll of the die; $p = \frac{1}{6}$; $n = 10$; $r = 3$

2. no; The trials are not independent and the probabilities are not constant.

3. yes; examine injuries; $p = 0.4$; $n = 6$; $r = 0$

4. no; The number of trials is not fixed.

Practice Exercises

1. yes; whether or not a patient experiences weight gain; $p = 0.05$; $n = 50$; $r = 4$

2. no; p is not constant

3. yes; getting a "heads" on a toss; $p = 0.65$; $n = 24$; $r = 12$

4. no; p is not constant

5. yes; whether or not the student answers correctly; $p = 0.5$; $n = 20$; $r = 14$

Assignment Guide

Basic: 1–23, 27, 30–32

Average: 1–19 odd, 20–35, 37, Project

Enriched: 1–19 odd, 20, 21–39 odd, 40–45, Project

Teacher's Resource Book
  Practice, page 100

ⓡ Review

Exercise 16 reviews the multiplication principle. Exercises 17, 22, 23, 34, and 35 review concepts of probability. Exercises like these that do not call on the binomial distribution help students distinguish when to use this distribution.

Project

Encourage students who are adept at programming to be creative when finding an algorithm for the simulation. For the situation described in the project, one such approach might be this: Have the program generate random numbers between 1 and 100. Interpret numbers between 1 and 68 as "sinking a basket" and interpret numbers between 69 and 100 as "missing." Generate 24 such numbers.

Additional Answers

15. $P(0) = \frac{9}{16}; P(1) = \frac{3}{8}; P(2) = \frac{1}{16}$

19. The sum of the probabilities in a probability distribution should equal 1 since they represent the probability of every possible outcome, and the outcomes are all mutually exclusive.

---

6. A fair coin is flipped 4 times. Use the sample space to write the probability distribution for the number of tails that show. Check that the sum of the probabilities is 1. $P(0) = \frac{1}{16}; P(1) = \frac{4}{16}; P(2) = \frac{6}{16}; P(3) = \frac{4}{16}; P(4) = \frac{1}{16}$

7. *Genetics* Assume that the probabilities of having a boy and of having a girl are each 0.5. Use the sample space to write the probability distribution for the number of girls in a three-child family. Check that the sum of the probabilities is 1. $P(0) = \frac{1}{8}; P(1) = \frac{3}{8}; P(2) = \frac{3}{8}; P(3) = \frac{1}{8}$

A coin is flipped twice. The coin is *biased* and the probability that it will show heads after any flip is 0.6.

8. Use the formula for binomial probabilities to find the probability that neither flip of the coin shows heads. 0.16

9. Find the probability that exactly 1 flip of the coin shows heads. 0.48

10. Find the probability that both flips of the coin show heads. 0.36

11. Write the probability distribution for the number of heads when the biased coin is flipped twice. Check to see that the sum of the probabilities is 1.
  $P(0) = 0.16; P(1) = 0.48; P(2) = 0.36$

A card is drawn from a standard deck, its suit is noted, and it is replaced. Then the deck is shuffled and a second card is drawn.

12. Use the formula for binomial probabilities to find the probability that exactly 1 of the 2 cards is a heart. $\frac{3}{8}$

13. Find the probability that none of the cards is a heart. $\frac{9}{16}$

14. Find the probability that both of the cards are hearts. $\frac{1}{16}$

15. Write the probability distribution for the number of hearts when two cards are drawn with replacement. Check to see that the sum of the probabilities is 1.

ⓡ 16. Find the number of ways to answer a multiple choice test if there are 8 questions, each of which has 4 choices. 65,536

ⓡ 17. Assuming that telephone numbers are randomly assigned, find the probability that the last digit of a person's telephone number is 5. $\frac{1}{10}$

18. **Thinking Critically** Determine whether the following values could be a probability distribution for the number of hits in 5 times at bat. $P(0) = 0.1$, $P(1) = 0.2$, $P(3) = 0.4$, $P(4) = 0.3$, and $P(5) = 0.15$. Justify your answer. *no; The sum of the probabilities is not 1.*

19. **Thinking Critically** Explain why the sum of the probabilities in a probability distribution should equal 1.

20. **Writing in Mathematics** Write a problem whose solution uses the binomial probability distribution. Write out the solution of your problem, identifying the Bernoulli trial, probability of success per trial, number of trials, and number of successes per trial.

B 21. Two dice are rolled. Use the sample space to write the probability distribution for the sum of the numbers rolled.

ⓡ 22. What is the probability that when two dice are rolled, the sum will be greater than 8? $\frac{5}{18}$

ⓡ 23. What is the probability that when two dice are rolled, the sum of the numbers will be at most 8? $\frac{13}{18}$

Sociology   Data shows that 65% of the families in a suburban area have a pet. In a study, 6 families are chosen at random and asked if they have a pet. Find each probability.

24. exactly 3 have a pet
0.2355

25. none has a pet
0.0018

26. all have pets
0.0754

27. *Health*   A survey showed that 15% of incoming freshmen residents at a university are smokers. Frank, a nonsmoker, is assigned to a suite with 5 other freshmen by a lottery. What is the probability that none of the 5 is a smoker?
0.4437

28. *Marketing*   A television rating service claims that on any evening at 8:00, 35% of viewers in a metropolitan area are watching cable TV. What is the probability that of 8 families surveyed at random at 8:00 p.m., exactly 3 of them are watching cable TV? 0.2786

29. *Manufacturing*   Two managers believe that only 3% of the automobile parts assembled at their plant are defective. What is the probability that of 40 items from that plant inspected at random, exactly 2 of them are defective?
0.2206

Zoology   A zoologist has found that 30% of the deer in a state carry a certain parasite. Twelve deer are chosen at random and examined for this parasite. Use binomial probabilities to answer the following.

30. What is the probability that exactly 4 of the 12 deer have the parasite? 0.2311

31. What is the probability that fewer than 4 have the parasites? 0.4925

32. What is the probability that 4 or more have the parasite? 0.5075

33. *Medicine*   When a person is given a certain vaccine, the probability is 95% that he or she will develop immunity to the virus strain as desired. Find the probability that of 15 people inoculated, fewer than 14 will develop immunity to the virus. 0.171

Ⓡ **34.** *Education*   A survey shows that 24% of the women at Community College major in accounting. If 55% of the students at Community College are women, what is the probability that a student chosen at random at Community College is a female accounting major? 0.132

Ⓡ **35.** What is the probability that the student of Exercise 34 is a male accounting major if 22% of the men at Community College major in accounting? 0.099

A recent poll showed that 26% of the people living in a rural area surveyed supported the construction of a new nuclear facility in their state, 68% opposed the facility, and 6% had no opinion.

C **36.** What is the probability that of 30 randomly chosen people from that area, exactly 8 support the construction of the new facility? 0.1623

37. What is the probability that of 50 randomly chosen people from that area, exactly 32 oppose the construction of the new facility? 0.0976

38. What is the probability that of 5 randomly chosen people from that area, at least 3 have no opinion? 0.0020

39. What is the probability that of 5 randomly chosen people from that area, at least 4 do not oppose the construction? 0.0390

14.5 Bernoulli Trials and the Binomial Distribution   **775**

Writing in Mathematics
20. Answers may vary. Check students' problems and make sure all four criteria of a binomial experiment are satisfied.

Have students write a paragraph explaining why the binomial coefficient $\binom{n}{r}$ is part of the formula for the probability in a binomial experiment.

Enrichment

Adapt the thinking used to determine the probability of r successes in n trials of a binomial experiment to the following situation:

Find the probability that for repeated rolls of a fair die, the first "1" will occur on the fourth roll. Since there is only one way to obtain three failures and one success in that order, the coefficient is 1 and the probability is $\left(\frac{5}{6}\right)^3 \times \frac{1}{6} \approx$ 0.0965.

40. *Manufacturing* A manufacturer agrees to accept a large shipment of parts if an inspection of 18 randomly chosen parts shows no more than 1 defective part. Find the probability that the shipment is accepted if 5% of the total shipment is defective. 0.7735

41. *Marketing* A telephone marketer estimates that 15% of the people called respond to a certain sales technique. How many people must be called to be 99% sure that at least one person responds? 29

42. *Health* The probability is 45% that a person living in the United States has type O blood. How large a group of people is needed to be 99% certain of having at least one person of blood type O? at least 8

43. Solve the *birthday problem* cited in the Focus of this lesson. Find the probability that in a group of 30 people, at least two have the same birthday. For simplicity, assume 365 days in any year. This is a reasonable assumption since you are working with *probabilities* rather than *exact values*. *Hint:* What is the probability that no two have the same birthday? 0.706

44. *Programming* Write the steps that would be used in a computer program to solve the birthday problem for groups of n people, with n ranging from 2 to 100. For what value of n is the probability 50% that at least two people in a group of n have the same birthday? 23

45. What *odds* would be fair to give that among the next 30 people you meet, at least two have the same birthday? 706 to 294

Project

Computers and some calculators have built-in *random number generators*. These can be used to *simulate* the results of a random experiment. For example, to simulate the roll of a die, the computer or calculator can use the generator to randomly output 1, 2, 3, 4, 5, or 6. A formula to do this would be INT(6*RND + 1). Simulation techniques like this can be used to study things like traffic flow, the spread of epidemics, or the effects of advertising campaigns. Such applications of simulations are referred to as *Monte Carlo methods*.

Suppose that a basketball player's foul shot percentage is 68%. Use a random number generator to simulate the player's performance for the next 24 times at the foul line. Describe the results of the simulation in writing.

Research an area of interest to you to find at least one probability that affects your topic. Then use a random number generator and construct and carry out a simulation exercise.

Challenge

1. A square and an equilateral triangle have equal perimeters. The area of the triangle is $8\sqrt{3}$ in.² Determine the diagonal of the square. 6

2. Points P and Q are both in the line segment $\overline{AB}$ and on the same side of its midpoint. Point P divides $\overline{AB}$ in the ratio 2:3, and point Q divides $\overline{AB}$ in the ratio 3:4. Find the length of $\overline{AB}$ if $PQ = 2$. 70

776 Chapter 14 Probability

14.6 Random Variables and Mathematical Expectation

Objectives: To define random variables and mathematical expectation
To solve problems involving random variables and mathematical expectation

Focus

Two 18-year-old students get their driver's licenses at the same time. The insurance on the family car of one student, a female, increases $160 per year, while the insurance for the other student, a male, increases $290. Why? How are insurance premiums determined?

Mathematical modeling in the insurance industry uses probability extensively. Mathematicians developing these models are known as actuaries. They use recent data and trends to update models which predict accident rates and death rates for groups of individuals. These models are used in determining insurance rates. The success or failure of a company can depend upon the accuracy of the models developed by the actuaries. The actuarial science field offers challenging and interesting career opportunities.

In most decision-making situations, only one aspect of an experiment is of interest. For example, for the roll of two dice, you might be interested in the sum of the outcomes rather than the individual numbers that show on the dice. This sum is an example of a **random variable,** a variable which can take on different values depending on chance. Other examples of random variables include the number of defective items in a 10-item inspection lot and the number of rainy days in July. A *probability distribution* may be thought of as a function that assigns probabilities to the values of a random variable.

Example 1 Find the probability distribution for the random variable that represents the sum of the outcomes when two fair dice are rolled.

Let X be the random variable. Then X may take on the values 2 through 12, and the corresponding probabilities are readily found from the sample space.

X	2	3	4	5	6	7	8	9	10	11	12
$P(X)$	$\frac{1}{36}$	$\frac{2}{36}$	$\frac{3}{36}$	$\frac{4}{36}$	$\frac{5}{36}$	$\frac{6}{36}$	$\frac{5}{36}$	$\frac{4}{36}$	$\frac{3}{36}$	$\frac{2}{36}$	$\frac{1}{36}$

An important tool for decision making in the face of uncertainty is the concept of *mathematical expectation.* Mathematical expectation tells a decision maker what to expect as the average outcome if an experiment were to be repeated many times.

14.6 Random Variables and Mathematical Expectation **777**

INSTRUCTION

- You may wish to refer to the results of Practice Exercise 9 of Lesson 14.1 before examining Example 1 of this lesson.
- Emphasize that mathematical expectation does not tell what will happen. Rather, it gives a value to an experiment and provides information that may be useful for making a decision.
- Ask students to discuss the difference in the value of a lottery ticket before the drawing and after the drawing. Note that the difference comes from the fact that after the drawing there is no need to use probability to give a value to the ticket; either it is a winning ticket or it isn't.

Alternative Learning Styles

Students whose learning style benefits from structure may be helped by constructing a "payoff table" to find an expected value. This is an organizational tool that shows each event, its payoff, and associated probability. For example, for Example 2, the payoff table is:

Event	1	2	3	4	5	6
Payoff	$1	−$2	$3	$4	$5	$6
Probability	$\frac{1}{6}$	$\frac{1}{6}$	$\frac{1}{6}$	$\frac{1}{6}$	$\frac{1}{6}$	$\frac{1}{6}$

GUIDED PRACTICE

For Example 1

Find the probability distribution for the random variable that represents the number of girls in a 3-child family.

$P(0) = \frac{1}{8}$; $P(1) = \frac{3}{8}$; $P(2) = \frac{3}{8}$; $P(3) = \frac{1}{8}$

For Example 2

What is the mathematical expectation for a game of chance in which you flip a coin and win $3.00 if the coin shows heads, but pay $3.00 if the coin shows tails? $0

Consider a simple game of chance in which you win $2 every time a fair coin shows heads and you win $1 when it comes up tails. Since the probability of heads is $\frac{1}{2}$, you can expect that in the long run you will win $2 half the time and $1 half the time, for an average gain of $\frac{1}{2}(\$2) + \frac{1}{2}(\$1) = \$1.50$ a game. For the game to be perfectly fair, you should pay $1.50 to play each time.

If you hold 1 of 100 tickets for a prize worth $700, what is the value of the ticket? The probability of winning $700 is 0.01 and the probability of winning $0 is 0.99. If the lottery were repeated *many* times, 1% of the time you would win $700 and 99% of the time you would win nothing. In the long run your average gain would be $0.01(\$700) + 0.99(0) = \$7.00$.

This is the *mathematical expectation* or *expected value* of the experiment. Notice that in no case do you ever win $7.00; you win either $700 or nothing. The expected value is simply a way of assigning a value to the ticket that takes into account the uncertainty involved. It is the sum of the possible values to be won multiplied by their respective probabilities.

> If a random variable X can take on the values $a_1, a_2, \ldots, a_n$ with probabilities $p_1, p_2, \ldots, p_n$ respectively, then the **mathematical expectation,** or **expected value,** of the random variable is
>
> $$E(X) = a_1 p_1 + a_2 p_2 + \cdots + a_n p_n$$

Example 2 What is the mathematical expectation of a game of chance in which a die is rolled and you win in dollars the number shown unless the number is a 2, in which case you pay $2?

Let the random variable X represent the number of dollars won. Then X can take on the values 1, 3, 4, 5, 6 or -2, each with probability $\frac{1}{6}$.

$$E(X) = 1\left(\frac{1}{6}\right) + 3\left(\frac{1}{6}\right) + 4\left(\frac{1}{6}\right) + 5\left(\frac{1}{6}\right) + 6\left(\frac{1}{6}\right) - 2\left(\frac{1}{6}\right) = \$2.83$$

Modeling

How are insurance premiums determined?

When a person applies for automobile insurance, the insurance company may use a model based on mathematical expectation to determine the premium. Factors such as age of the applicant, make of car, location of residence, and distance to workplace are used to determine the average amount that the company can expect to pay on the policy. Then a premium charge is determined.

To determine the expected cost of a policy, the company first must determine the probability that the driver will have an accident during the year. This empirical probability is based on numerous statistics such as the age and gender of the driver, the average distance the driver drives in a year, and even the scholastic achievements of the driver. The company then determines the average cost of an accident. The expected cost of the policy is determined by

Expected cost = P(the driver has an accident) × the cost of an accident

Example 3 *Insurance*   A single male driver aged 23 living in a suburb of a midwestern city pays a car insurance premium of $496 per year. The insurance company's actuarial model for this driver predicts the following probabilities for 1 year: 0.065 for an accident averaging $4600 in damages; 0.03 for $2400 in damages; and 0.015 for $1000 in damages. What is the expected damage cost that the insurance company should be prepared to pay for such a driver? What amount is this policy expected to contribute to the operation and profit of the company?

Expected damage cost = (0.065)(4600) + (0.03)(2400) + (0.015)(1000) + (0.89)(0) = $386

The difference between the premium cost and the expected damage cost represents the premium contributions to the company's operation and profit.

$$496 - 386 = \$110$$

The expected value of a random variable is not limited to financial values.

Example 4 *Nursing*   A night nurse has found that there is a probability of 0.30, 0.20, 0.25, 0.15, and 0.10 that she will receive 8, 9, 10, 11, or 12 calls between midnight and 1:00 a.m., respectively. What is the expected number of calls during this hour?

Let the random variable X represent the number of calls. The expected value of X is

$E = 8(0.30) + 9(0.20) + 10(0.25) + 11(0.15) + 12(0.10)$
$\quad = 9.55$ calls between midnight and 1:00 a.m.

Notice that in Example 4 the probability that the nurse will receive no calls is 0. *How is this possible?*

Often people base their decisions on mathematical expectation, at least intuitively. If this is the case, their choices can give information about the probabilities that they assign to various events.

Class Exercises

For a roll of two dice, let the random variable X represent the larger of the two outcomes or their common value if they are equal.

1. What are the possible values of the random variable? 1, 2, 3, 4, 5, 6
2. Find the probability distribution for the random variable X.
3. What is the expected value of the random variable? 4.47

At a county fair there is a raffle with a prize of a compact disc player worth $450. What is the expected payoff to a participant in the raffle

4. If 200 tickets are sold? $2.25
5. If 1000 tickets are sold? $0.45

6. A marketing specialist has found that the probabilities that a person who comes into a certain store will make 0, 1, 2, 3, 4, and 5 or more purchases on a Saturday are 0.12, 0.24, 0.18, 0.16, 0.15, and 0.15. What is the expected number of purchases? 2.43

Modeling

Be sure that students understand that the scenarios presented in models such as this one may be simplified. Their purpose is to give an appreciation for how the mathematics is applied. Interested students can research some of the more complex models that are used in actuarial science.

For Example 3

A single female driver of age 23 has an insurance premium of $500 annually. If the actuarial model predicts a probability of 0.085 that this driver will have an accident averaging $4000 in damages, what is the estimated damage cost the insurance company should expect to pay? What amount is this policy expected to contribute to the operation and profit of the company?
$340; profit: $160

For Example 4

1. A fire chief estimates that there is a probability of 0.5, 0.3, 0.1, 0.08, and 0.02 of there being 0, 1, 2, 3, or 4 cases of arson in a month in his town, respectively. What is the expected number of cases of arson monthly? 0.82

2. A toll collector estimates that the numbers of passengers in cars during the morning rush hours vary from 1 to 5 with the probabilities:

1	2	3	4	5
0.21	0.33	0.26	0.12	0.08

What is the expected number of passengers? 2.53

Thinking Critically

Normally, it would be unlikely that there would be zero probability of receiving no calls. However, the probabilities are based on empirical data and perhaps the probability of no calls was very small and rounded to zero. This might be the case if the nurse had several workers *assigned* to phone in at different times.

Have students work in pairs to discuss the definition of random variable, and the procedures for finding
the probability distribution for a random variable and the expected value
of a random variable. Then have
students write and solve their own
problem involving these three items.

Additional Answers

Class Exercises

2. $P(1) = \frac{1}{36}, P(2) = \frac{3}{36}, P(3) = \frac{5}{36},$

   $P(4) = \frac{7}{36}, P(5) = \frac{9}{36}, P(6) = \frac{11}{36}$

7. $P(4) = 0.025, P(5) = 0.05, P(6) = 0.06, P(7) = 0.085, P(8) = 0.11, P(9) = 0.12, P(10) = 0.14, P(11) = 0.13, P(12) = 0.095, P(13) = 0.075, P(14) = 0.06, P(15) = 0.05$

8. 9.8

9. Answers may vary. It is a tool because it provides information on which
   a decision can be based, but other information may be considered.

A quality control expert studied the output of an assembly line for 200 days looking for avoidable errors and found the following data:

No. errors	4	5	6	7	8	9	10	11	12	13	14	15
No. days	5	10	12	17	22	24	28	26	19	15	12	10

That is, on 10 of the days there were 5 errors, and so on.

7. Use the *frequency interpretation of probability* and find the probability distribution for the number of errors.

8. Find the mathematical expectation for the number of errors.

9. **Thinking Critically**   Why is mathematical expectation referred to as a *tool* for decision making rather than a *rule* for decision making?

10. *Job Placement*   A college graduate turn down a firm offer for a position paying $15,500 a year because she believes she has a good chance of being offered one worth $18,000 a year. Her decision is based on salary alone. What probability is she assigning to getting the higher-paying job? 0.86

Practice Exercises

A club sells lottery tickets for a prize worth $250.

1. What is the expected value of the lottery if 100 tickets are sold? $2.50

2. What is the expected value of the lottery if 500 tickets are sold? $0.50

3. A class has a lottery with a first prize worth $200 and a consolation prize worth $50. What is the expected value of the lottery if 140 tickets are sold? $1.79

For a game of chance a die is tossed and a coin is flipped. Let X be the random variable that represents the outcome of the die plus 1 if the coin shows heads and minus 1 if the coin shows tails.

4. What are the possible values of the random variable? 0, 1, 2, 3, 4, 5, 6, 7

5. Find the probability distribution for the random variable X.

6. What is the expected value of the random variable? 3.5

For a game of chance a die is tossed and a coin is flipped. Let X be the random variable that represents the outcome of the die plus 2 if the coin shows heads and minus 1 if the coin shows tails.

7. What are the possible values of the random variable? 0, 1, 2, 3, 4, 5, 6, 7, 8

8. Find the probability distribution for the random variable X.

Ⓡ 9. What are the odds in favor of X taking on the value 5? 1 to 5

10. What is the expected value of the random variable? 4

11. In a game of chance you are paid $6 each time you roll a 5 or a 6 with a fair die and nothing for any other outcome. How much should you pay to play the game in order for it to be fair game? $2

12. A game of chance offers you $4 each time you draw a heart from a shuffled deck of cards (with the card replaced each time) and nothing for any other suit. How much should you pay to play the game in order for it to be fair? $1

780   Chapter 14 Probability

13. *Investment* A broker has the opportunity to buy stock at $28 a share. He estimates that there is a probability of 0.35 that he will be able to sell it within the month for $36 a share, and a probability of 0.65 that it will have to be sold for $23 a share. What is the expected value of this deal? $27.55

Two batteries are chosen at random from a carton of 48 batteries, 4 of which are defective. What is the probability that

Ⓡ **14.** Both are defective? 0.0053

Ⓡ **15.** Neither is defective? 0.8387

16. Thinking Critically During the second half of 1990 gasoline prices increased an average of $0.50 per gallon. During that same period the insurance company of Example 3 experienced a 16% increase in its profits. Explain how these two facts may be related.

Travel A highway patrol officer estimates that the number of passengers in a car during the afternoon rush hour has the following probability distribution.

No. passengers X	1	2	3	4	5	6
Probability	0.38	0.27	0.14	0.12	0.06	0.03

17. What is the expected value of X? 2.3

B **18. Writing in Mathematics** Write a short paragraph interpreting the information presented in the chart and the expected value of X. Describe a situation in which this information might be useful for decision making.

The head of security of a large company tabulated the number of emergency calls received each week. Over the course of 42 weeks, the following data was collected. Let Y be the random variable representing the number of emergency calls received in a week.

No. emergency calls	10	11	12	13	14	15	16
No. weeks	5	7	10	9	6	3	2

Ⓡ **19.** Use the *frequency interpretation of probability* to find the probability distribution for the random variable Y.

20. What is the expected value of the random variable? 12.5

Ⓡ **21.** What are the odds against getting 16 emergency calls? 40 to 2

For the experiment tossing a coin 5 times (or tossing 5 coins), let X be the random variable representing the number of tails.

Ⓡ **22.** Find the probability distribution for X.   **23.** What is the expected value of X? 2.5

Recreation In the finals of a bowling tournament, the winner will receive $10,000 and the runner-up $6,000.

24. What are the players' mathematical expectations if they are equally likely to win? $8000

25. If the probability that Robbie will win is 0.70, what is his mathematical expectation? $8800

26. If the probability that Robbie will win is 0.70, what is his opponent's mathematical expectation? $7200

14.6 Random Variables and Mathematical Expectation   **781**

Lesson Quiz

1. Determine the probability distribution for the random variable that represents the number of right turns a rat makes in running a maze if there are 4 places for it to turn left or right. $P(0) = \frac{1}{16}$; $P(1) = \frac{4}{16}$; $P(2) = \frac{6}{16}$; $P(3) = \frac{4}{16}$; $P(4) = \frac{1}{16}$

2. What is the expectation for a game of chance in which you flip a coin twice and win $3.00 if the coins match, and pay $3.00 if they do not match? $0

3. A survey shows a probability of 0.1, 0.1, 0.2, 0.15, 0.15, 0.08, 0.07, 0.09, and 0.06 that the numbers of riders on a certain bus are 0, 1, 2, ···, 8, respectively, during the midnight to 2:00 a.m. period. Find the expected number of riders during this shift. 3.48

4. A fund raising group sells 1000 tickets for a lottery for a prize valued at $675. What is the expected value of each ticket? $0.68

5. A recent graduate turns down a firm offer for a job paying $22,000 for a chance at a job that will pay $26,000. What probability does she assign to getting the second job? $p > 0.8462$

Additional Answers

19. $P(10) = \frac{5}{42}$, $P(11) = \frac{7}{42}$, $P(12) = \frac{10}{42}$, $P(13) = \frac{9}{42}$, $P(14) = \frac{6}{42}$, $P(15) = \frac{3}{42}$, $P(16) = \frac{2}{42}$

22. $P(0) = \frac{1}{32}$, $P(1) = \frac{5}{32}$, $P(2) = \frac{10}{32}$, $P(3) = \frac{10}{32}$, $P(4) = \frac{5}{32}$, $P(5) = \frac{1}{32}$

27. *Travel* A customer relations specialist for an airline has collected extensive data about customer complaints. Based on this data he assigns these probabilities to the number of complaints about lost luggage he receives in a week.

No. complaints	5	6	7	8	9	10	11
Probability	0.36	0.22	0.14	0.10	0.07	0.06	0.05

What is the expected number of complaints about lost luggage per week? 6.68

28. **Writing in Mathematics** Describe how mathematical expectation can be a useful part of the decision-making process.

29. *Job Placement* A statistician working for a large corporation turns down another company's job offer which would mean a $3000 pay increase because he expects a promotion within his own firm. The promotion would include a $4400 raise, and the raise is the basis for the decision. What minimum probability does the statistician assign to getting the promotion? 0.68

30. *Marketing* A magazine sweepstakes offers a grand prize of $1,000,000, 2 second prizes of $100,000 each, 4 third prizes of $10,000 each, and 20 fourth prizes of $500 each. If the magazine distributed 6 million numbers (one per letter) in a mass mailing, determine the expected payoff to a person who enters the sweepstakes. Is the expected value sufficient to cover the cost of the postage to return the entry? $E = 0.21; no

A florist orders 5 dozen of a very fragile flower priced at $10 a dozen. The probability of selling all X dozen flowers is given in the following table:

No. dozens sold	0	1	2	3	4	5
Probability	0.05	0.10	0.35	0.25	0.15	0.10

31. Make a probability distribution for the florist's profit if the flowers are sold at $20 a dozen.

32. What is the florist's expected profit if the flowers are sold at $20 a dozen? $3

33. Repeat Exercises 31 and 32 if the flowers are sold at $25 a dozen.

C 34. *Job Placement* A salesperson is offered a choice between a salary of $28,000 and a salary of $25,000 with a bonus of $5500 provided sales meet a given quota. If the salesperson chooses the lower salary with bonus, what is the probability of meeting the quota that this choice implies? 0.55

35. A lottery has a prize valued at $2400, and k tickets are sold at $2.00 each. Express the expected value of a ticket as a function of k. $f(k) = \frac{2400 - 2k}{k}$

36. *Finance* You have a portfolio of 4 different stocks and are interested in how many of them will increase in value by December 31. Your broker informs you that the probability that none of them will increase is 0.05, and the probabilities that exactly 1, 2, or 3 of them will increase are 0.15, 0.20, and 0.35, respectively. What is the expected value of the number of stocks that will increase? 2.6

37. *Insurance* An insurance company offers a health and accident policy for $100 per year. If the insured person has a work loss illness the company

782 Chapter 14 Probability

pays $450, if the person misses work due to an accident the payment is $1500, and if both illness and an accident occur then the payment is $5000. If the probability of the person getting ill is 0.045 and the probability of having an accident is 0.025, determine the expected cost of this policy to the company. $63.38

Two teams play a "best of five" tournament; that is, the first team to win three games wins the tournament. These teams are evenly matched, so that each is equally likely to win a game.

38. Let Y be a random variable representing the number of games played in the tournament. What are the possible values of Y? Find a probability distribution for the random variable Y.

39. What is the expected number of games for this tournament? 4.5

40. Find the expected number of games for a "best of seven" tournament between two evenly matched teams. 6.4

41. *Programming* Write a program to simulate the rolling of a pair of six-sided dice 360 times. Have the program count and output the number of times that a sum of 7 is computed. How does the simulated result compare with the expected value for this sum?

42. *Programming* Write a program that will simulate the rolling of a pair of four-sided dice (see Practice Exercise 4 in Lesson 14.1) 128 times. Count the number of times each possible sum is computed. Are the simulated results close to the expected results for 128 rolls of the dice?

Project

Suppose that an insurance company has the following data about drivers in city A and in county X, which is contiguous to city A. Show how the company might obtain 4 different empirical probabilities for a 20-year-old male living in city A. Research other factors that might account for different costs of insurance premiums.

Age cohort	City A		County X	
	No. drivers	No. accidents	No. drivers	No. accidents
18–24	10,000	800	20,000	400
25–30	8,000	300	22,000	150

Review

1. The third term of an arithmetic sequence is 11 and the ninth term is 35. Find the fifth term. 19

Simplify.

2. $\dfrac{2 + \frac{5}{2}}{3 - \frac{6}{4}}$ 3

3. $\dfrac{3 - \frac{1}{xy}}{\frac{1}{xy} - 3} - 1$

14.6 Random Variables and Mathematical Expectation   **783**

31.	Profit $	−50	−30	−10	10	30	50
	Probability	0.05	0.10	0.35	0.25	0.15	0.10

33.	Profit $	−50	−25	0	25	50	75
	Probability	0.05	0.10	0.35	0.25	0.15	0.10

; $16.25

Vocabulary
Bayes' formula
theorem of total probability

Ⓜ **Materials/Manipulatives**
grid paper

Technology
calculator

FOCUS

One of the things that was learned in the study done at the Grand Canyon was that it is easier to find a lost hiker on a cloudy day than on a sunny day. There is a "victim" in the photograph that accompanies this Focus, but he is obscured by shadows caused by bright sun. Have students see if they can find the victim in the photo.

Another photograph accompanies the model on page 787. However, that picture was taken on a cloudy day. Have students try to locate the victim in that photo as well. See the Modeling commentary in the side-column of page 787 for a comparison.

14.7   More Topics in Probability

Objective: To use Bayes' formula to solve probability problems
To use the theorem of total probability to solve probability problems

Focus

Rangers at Grand Canyon National Park are sometimes called upon to organize a massive search operation when a park visitor is reported missing. Canyon searches are especially complicated due to the size of the park, the terrain involved, and weather conditions. Often the missing person is days overdue from a lengthy hiking trip in the canyon.

A University of Arizona mathematics professor, David Lovelock, has developed a computer program that models the search area and uses conditional probabilities to assist park rangers in organizing searches. The search area is divided into regions, and several search experts assign probabilities to the regions that reflect where they think the person is likely to be found. The program, which makes use of *Bayes' formula,* determines a composite probability of the missing person's being in each region. Search leaders then use this information to help determine how the search resources will be deployed.

Reverend Thomas Bayes (1702–1761), a Presbyterian minister and mathematician, developed a useful formula that extends the concept of conditional probability. Now that you are familiar with conditional probability the notation $P(B|A)$ will be used for $P(B$ given $A)$.

> **Recall**
>
> If A and B are two events, then the probability that B occurs given that A occurs can be found using the formula $P(B|A) = \dfrac{P(A \cap B)}{P(A)}$, $P(A) \neq 0$, which is equivalent to $P(A \cap B) = P(A) \cdot P(B|A)$.

For example, if the probability that a student in a certain class studies for a test is 75%, and the probability that a student who studies passes the test is 90%, then the probability that a student both studies and passes the test is $(0.75)(0.90) = 0.675$. In this example, A is the event "studies" and B is the event "passes," and so the probability that a student who studies passes the test is $P(B|A)$. *How would $P(A|B)$ be interpreted?*

784   Chapter 14 Probability

Thinking Critically
The expression $P(A|B)$ can be interpreted as the probability that a student who passes the test actually studied.

Example 1 If C is the event "has a coupon for the product" and B is the event "buys the product," write symbolically the probability that a person
   a. With a coupon buys the product
   b. Who buys the product has a coupon

a. $P(B|C)$ **b.** $P(C|B)$

The two conditional probabilities $P(A|B)$ and $P(B|A)$ are related. You have already seen that $P(A \cap B) = P(A) \cdot P(B|A)$. The same reasoning that was used above to derive this equation can be used to show that the formula for $P(A|B)$ can be expressed as $P(A \cap B) = P(B) \cdot P(A|B)$. Substituting for the expression $P(A \cap B)$ yields $P(A) \cdot P(B|A) = P(B) \cdot P(A|B)$. Therefore,

$$P(B|A) = \frac{P(B) \cdot P(A|B)}{P(A)}.$$

Example 2 *Employment* The probability that an applicant for a job at an advertising agency has a college degree is 80%, and the probability that the applicant has experience in the field is 35%. If 22% of those with college degrees have experience, what is the probability that an applicant with experience has a college degree?

Let E be the event "has experience" and let D be "has a degree." $P(E) = 0.35$, $P(D) = 0.80$, and $P(E|D) = 0.22$.

$$P(D|E) = \frac{P(D)\,P(E|D)}{P(E)} = \frac{(0.80)(0.22)}{0.35} \approx 0.50$$

The probability is about 0.50 that an experienced applicant will have a degree.

More interesting applications of the relationship between conditional probabilities can be analyzed with the help of a theorem sometimes called the **theorem of total probability.**

Suppose that three plants produce parts that are purchased by a manufacturer, who is interested in the probability that a part is defective. Let D be the event "is defective," and let A, B, and C be the events "produced at plant A," "produced at plant B," "produced at plant C." A part is defective if it is produced at plant A and is defective, or is produced at plant B and is defective, or is produced at plant C and is defective. These conditions are represented symbolically by $A \cap D$, $B \cap D$, and $C \cap D$, respectively.

Since these three possibilities are mutually exclusive and one of them must happen, it follows that $P(D) = P(A \cap D) + P(B \cap D) + P(C \cap D)$. Use the formula for the probability of the intersection of events three times to obtain the equation

$$P(D) = P(A) \cdot P(D|A) + P(B) \cdot P(D|B) + P(C) \cdot P(D|C)$$

This is the *theorem of total probability for three conditions*. The theorem may be restated for any number of conditions provided that the conditions are mutually exclusive and one of them must occur.

INSTRUCTION

- Have students practice translating sentences into mathematical symbols and conversely. Class Exercises 1 to 6 and Practice Exercises 1 to 8 provide examples.
- Encourage students to discuss what they have heard of "false positives" in medical tests such as those described in Example 4.
- For Example 5, encourage students to find the percents of the gifts under $20 made by Mr. Lee, Mrs. Sanches, and by Ms. Molloy. Have them verify that the sum of these percents is 1.

Alternative Learning Styles

Ⓜ Students whose learning style is strongly visual may be helped by making a diagram of a situation such as the following for Example 5.

- Divide appropriately a 10 by 10 grid, representing all items in the boutique in 3 sections, labeled S, M, and L.
- Shade the percent of each section that is under $20.
- Find the percent for the shaded area in section L.

GUIDED PRACTICE

For Example 1

If X is the event "has a library card" and Y is the event "reads one book a week," write each expression symbolically.

1. Probability that a person who has a library card reads one book a week $P(Y|X)$
2. Probability that a person who reads one book a week has a library card $P(X|Y)$

For Example 2

Using the information from Example 2 given in the lesson, determine the probability that an applicant has both a college degree and experience in the field. 0.176

For Example 3

A high school draws its students from 4 area middle schools, 10% from school *W*, 30% from school *X*, 35% from school *Y*, and 25% from school *Z*. The percentage of bilingual students at the 4 schools are 17% at *W*, 9% at *X*, 35% at *Y*, and 6% at *Z*. What is the probability that a randomly chosen student at the high school is bilingual? 0.1815

For Example 4

Using the information from Example 4 given in the lesson, what is the probability that someone who tests positive has the disease if only 3% of people without the disease also test positive? 0.5026

Example 3 *Manufacturing* Suppose that a manufacturer buys 45% of its parts from plant *A*, 35% from plant *B*, and 20% from plant *C*. What is the probability that a part chosen at random is defective if plant *A* has a defect record of 2%, plant *B* a defect record of 3%, and plant *C* a defect record of 5%?

Use the theorem of total probability.

$$P(D) = P(A) \cdot P(D|A) + P(B) \cdot P(D|B) + P(C) \cdot P(D|C)$$
$$= (0.45)(0.02) + (0.35)(0.03) + (0.20)(0.05) = 0.0295$$

The theorem of total probability enables you to apply formulas for conditional probability in new ways.

Example 4 *Medicine* Doctors are trying to determine the viability of a new test for a certain disease. It is known that 3% of the population have this disease and that 98% of people with the disease test positive. However, 6% of people without the disease also test positive. What is the probability that someone who tests positive has the disease?

Let *A* be the event "tests positive," and let *B* be "has the disease."

$$P(B) = 0.03 \qquad P(A|B) = 0.98$$

You know that $P(B|A) = \dfrac{P(B) \cdot P(A|B)}{P(A)}$, but to use this fact you need the value of $P(A)$. Use the theorem of total probability. Let B' be the event "does not have the disease." The events *B* and B' are mutually exclusive. Therefore,

$$P(A) = P(B) \cdot P(A|B) + P(B') \cdot P(A|B')$$
$$= (0.03)(0.98) + (0.97)(0.06) \qquad P(B') = 1 - P(B)$$
$$= 0.0876$$
$$P(B|A) = \frac{P(B) \cdot P(A|B)}{P(A)} = \frac{(0.03)(0.98)}{0.0876} = 0.3356164384$$

This implies that fewer than 34% of those who test positive for the disease actually have it, important information for evaluating the test.

Combining the theorem of total probability with the equation for $P(B|A)$ as in the preceding example gives the simplest case of **Bayes' formula.**

If B' is the event "*B* does not occur," then

$$P(B|A) = \frac{P(B) \cdot P(A|B)}{P(B) \cdot P(A|B) + P(B') \cdot P(A|B')}$$

Bayes' formula may also be stated for any number of mutually exclusive conditions, one of which must occur.

If $B_1, B_2, \ldots, B_n$ are mutually exclusive events of which one must occur, then

$$P(B_1|A) = \frac{P(B_1) \cdot P(A|B_1)}{P(B_1) \cdot P(A|B_1) + P(B_2) \cdot P(A|B_2) + \cdots + P(B_n) \cdot P(A|B_n)}$$

Notice that any of the events B_2 through B_n can be renumbered B_1, so this formula holds for any of them.

786 Chapter 14 Probability

Example 5 *Marketing* A handmade goods boutique gets 40% of its inventory from Mrs. Sanchez, 35% from Ms. Molloy, and 25% from Mr. Lee. A customer is interested in buying a large quantity of gifts priced under $20. Half of Mrs. Sanchez' items, 60% of Ms. Molloy's, and 30% of Mr. Lee's fall in this category. What is the probability that an item chosen is one of Mr. Lee's?

Let S be the event "made by Mrs. Sanchez," let M be "made by Ms. Molloy," and let L be "made by Mr. Lee." Let U be the event "under $20."

$$P(S) = 0.40 \qquad P(M) = 0.35 \qquad P(L) = 0.25$$

$P(U|S) = 0.50$, $P(U|M) = 0.60$ and $P(U|L) = 0.30$. You wish to find $P(L|U)$.

$$P(L|U) = \frac{P(L) \cdot P(U|L)}{P(L) \cdot P(U|L) + P(M) \cdot P(U|M) + P(S) \cdot P(U|S)} \qquad \textit{Use Bayes' formula.}$$

$$= \frac{(0.25)(0.30)}{(0.25)(0.30) + (0.35)(0.60) + (0.40)(0.50)} \approx 0.155$$

Modeling

How can Bayes' formula be used to improve the efficiency of search and rescue missions?

Bayes' formula is frequently used in so-called "expert systems." Expert computer systems are models of real world situations which often incorporate known facts about the situation, probabilities determined by experts, and mathematical relationships. Physicians studying medical problems, such as the one presented in Example 3, sometimes use expert systems as aids in diagnostic work. The search and rescue computer model described in the Focus of this lesson is an example of a system which uses Bayes' formula.

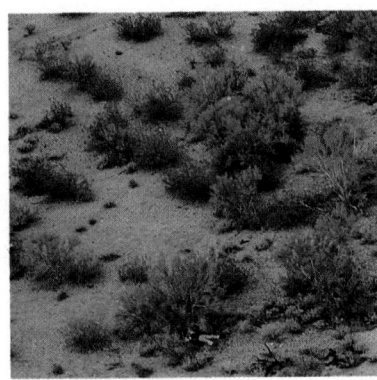

Example 6 *Search and Rescue* In organizing a search for a lost hiker, a group of experts agree that there are two general regions, A and B, that need to be searched. Within each region there is a river valley and hilly area. The probabilities assigned by the experts are:

$P(A) = 0.35$ — *Probability hiker is in region A*
$P(B) = 0.65$ — *Probability hiker is in region B*
$P(R|A) = 0.40$ — *Probability hiker in A is in river valley*
$P(H|A) = 0.60$ — *Probability hiker in A is in hilly area*
$P(R|B) = 0.70$ — *Probability hiker in B is in river valley*
$P(H|B) = 0.30$ — *Probability hiker in B is in hilly area*

After a 2-hour air search of the hilly area the experts agree that the hiker is most likely in a river valley. Under this assumption what is the probability that the hiker is in region B?

$$P(B|R) = \frac{P(B)P(R|B)}{P(B)P(R|B) + P(A)P(R|A)} = \frac{(0.65)(0.70)}{(0.65)(0.70) + (0.35)(0.40)} \approx 0.76 \qquad \text{Use Bayes' formula.}$$

14.7 More Topics in Probability   **787**

For Example 5
A study relates income level (low, average, high) to voting patterns (Republican, Democrat). In a certain area 35% of the people fall in the low income bracket, 45% in the middle income bracket, and 20% in the high income bracket. Half of the people in the low income bracket, 25% of the middle income bracket, and 40% of the high income bracket voted Democrat in the last election.
1. What is the probability that someone who voted Democrat in the last election fell in the low income bracket? 0.4762
2. What is the probability that someone who voted Democrat in the last election fell in the high income? 0.2177

Common Error   In question 1 above, some students may incorrectly find the probability that someone who voted Democrat fell in the low income bracket to be (0.5)(0.35). Point out to these students that this would be the probability based on all the people who voted, not just those who voted Democrat.

Modeling
The lost hiker should be more visible in the photograph that accompanies this model than in the "sunny day" in the Focus on page 784. In both cases, the hiker is basically located in the center of the photo, lying prone under a bush.

For Example 6
Using the information from Example 6 given in the lesson, what is the probability that the hiker is in region A if the experts agree that he is more likely in a hilly area? 0.5185

Have students pair up with a class-mate and write an explanation of Bayes' formula for four mutually ex-clusive events of which one must oc-cur. Then have them describe the conditions of a situation for which Bayes' formula may be applied and give an example problem that can be solved using the formula.

INDEPENDENT PRACTICE

Assignment Guide
Basic: 1–25
Average: 9–35, Project
Enriched: 9, 10, 14–39, Project

Teacher's Resource Book
  Practice, page 102

Ⓡ **Review**
Exercises 11, 13, 22, and 23 review the probability of complementary events and conditional probability. Exercises 16 and 19 review probabil-ity and Exercise 37 reviews odds.

Project
Students may wish to use the terrain around their own school to set up their search and rescue scenarios.

LESSON FOLLOW-UP

Test Yourself

Teacher's Resource Book
  Tests—Quiz, form A, page 62
  Tests—Quiz, form B, page 62

Additional Answers
Class Exercises
8. $P(N) = P(A)P(N|A) + P(B)P(N|B) + P(C)P(N|C) + P(D)P(N|D)$

Using this information, the search leaders might deploy about 75% of their search resources to region B and 25% to region A.

Class Exercises

For a group of students let S be the event "belongs to a service organization," and let B be the event "has an average of B or better." Write symbolically the probability that:

1. A member of a service organization has an average of B or better. $P(B|S)$

2. A student with an average of B or better is a member of a service organization. $P(S|B)$

3. A student has an average of B or better and is a member of a service organization. $P(S \cap B)$

Let C be the event "is colorblind," let M be "is male," and let F be "is female." Write symbolically the probability that:

4. A male is colorblind. $P(C|M)$
5. A colorblind person is female. $P(F|C)$
6. A female is colorblind. $P(C|F)$

7. *Employment*   A manager reports that 30% of the applicants for a position are bilingual, and 60% are female. If 45% of the female applicants are bilingual, what is the probability that a bilingual applicant is female? 0.9

8. **Thinking Critically**   State the theorem of total probability for four conditions.

9. It is estimated that 20% of the industries in an urban area actually violate pollution control laws. The probability is 0.85 that an inspector at one of these plants finds the violations and levies fines. There is also a probability of 0.06 that a plant in compliance with the laws is mistakenly fined. What is the probability that a plant that is fined is actually in violation of the laws? 0.7798

Practice Exercises

Let A be the event "is a U.S. citizen," let B be "is 18 or older," and let V be "voted in the last election." Write symbolically the probability that:

A 1. A U.S. citizen voted in the last election. $P(V|A)$ 2. A U.S. citizen is 18 or older. $P(B|A)$

3. A person 18 or older voted in the last election. $P(V|B)$
4. A person 18 or older is a U.S. citizen. $P(A|B)$

Let C be the event "bought a computer," let M be "bought a color monitor," and let P be "bought a printer." Write symbolically the probability that:

5. A person who bought a computer also bought a color monitor. $P(M|C)$

6. A person who bought a printer also bought a computer. $P(C|P)$

7. A person bought both a printer and a computer. $P(P \cap C)$

8. A person who bought a printer also bought a color monitor. $P(M|P)$

9. *Sociology*   Records show that 67% of the employees of a large insurance company have children, and that 71% of the employees own their own homes. If 80% of those with children own their own homes, what is the probability that a homeowner chosen at random from among the employees has children? 0.7549

788   Chapter 14 Probability

10. *Development* The alumni office of a small college reports that 38% of the college's alumni give regularly to the college's expansion fund, and that 21% attend the annual reunion. If 90% of those who attend the annual reunion are regular donors, what is the probability that a regular donor will attend the annual reunion? 0.4974

Health Suppose that 7% of the men living in a city are colorblind and that 3.5% of the women are colorblind.

Ⓡ 11. What is the probability that a man living in that city is not colorblind? 0.93

12. If the population is known to be 56% male and 44% female, what is the probability that a resident of that city is colorblind? 0.0546

Ⓡ 13. If two cards are drawn at random from an ordinary, well-shuffled deck without replacement, what is the probability that both are threes? $\frac{1}{221}$

14. **Thinking Critically** State Bayes' formula for the case of three mutually exclusive events, B_1, B_2, and B_3, one of which must occur.

15. **Writing in Mathematics** Use an example to illustrate the differences among $P(A|B)$, $P(B|A)$, and $P(A \cap B)$.

Three jars contain red, white, and blue chips in the numbers given in the table. A jar is picked at random, and a chip is drawn from that jar at random.

	No. chips		
Jar	Red	White	Blue
1	10	10	15
2	5	20	10
3	12	8	5

Ⓡ 16. What is the probability that the jar chosen is jar 2? $\frac{1}{3}$

17. What is the probability that the chip chosen is red? 0.3029

18. Given that the chip chosen is red, what is the probability that it came from jar 2? 0.1572

Manufacturing A plant has one full-time inspector, Jim, and two part-time inspectors, Joann and Ed. Jim inspects 48% of the plant's products, Joann inspects 30%, and Ed inspects 22% of the products. Records show that Jim finds 96% of the defects among the parts he inspects, Joann 97%, and Ed 95%.

Ⓡ 19. What is the probability that a part is checked by Joann or Ed? 0.52

20. What is the probability that a defective part manufactured at this plant is found by an inspector? 0.9608

21. *Marketing* For the situation described in Example 5 of this lesson, find the probability that an item the customer chooses was made by Ms. Molloy. 0.4330

A seasoned traveler has her own version of Murphy's law. She estimates that the probability that her plane will be late is 35%, and the probability that when her plane is late her luggage will be lost is 45%.

Ⓡ 22. According to her estimates, what is the probability that on her next flight the plane will be late and her luggage will be lost? 0.1575

Ⓡ 23. According to her estimates, what is the probability that her plane will be late and her luggage will not be lost? 0.1925

Writing in Mathematics
15. Answers may vary. Example: A certain study by a local pet society reveals that 60% of the families in that city have at least one child, and 65% have a pet. If 25% of those families with at least one child have a pet, what is the probability that a family with a pet has at least one child?

$P(P|C) = 0.25$; $P(C|P) = \frac{(0.60)(0.25)}{0.65} = 0.23$; $P(C \cap P) = 0.15$

Let D be the event "has a valid driver's license" and let C be the event "has access to a car." Write each of the following symbolically.

1. Probability that a person has a license and a car $P(C \cap D)$

2. Probability that a person who has a license also has access to a car $P(C|D)$

3. Probability that a person with access to a car has a driver's license $P(D|C)$

4. It is known that 70% of the members of a chess club have played in a tournament, and 40% are in the math club. If 50% of those who have played in a tournament are in the math club, what is the probability that a person in the math club has played in a tournament? 0.875

5. A furniture store gets 60% of its stock from manufacturer A, 12% from manufacturer B, and 28% from manufacturer C. What is the probability that a piece of furniture chosen at random from its stock is defective if the defect records from A, B, and C are 2%, 4%, and 6%, respectively? 0.0336

6. A test for a certain disease is positive 98.5% of the time the disease is present and negative 96% of the time the disease is not present. It is known that 1.5% of the population has the disease. What is the probability that someone who tests positive has the disease? 0.2727

7. A company has 3 supervisors, Stu, Cindy, and Ann. Stu supervises 30% of the staff, Cindy 42%, and Ann 28%. Records show that 7% of Stu's workers, 4% of Cindy's, and 12% of Ann's put in overtime hours in a week. What is the probability that a worker at this company puts in overtime hours in a given week? 0.0714

34.

Test results   Disease?

P — ≈ 0.10662 — Y
  — ≈ 0.89338 — N
0.04455

0.95545
N — ≈ 0.00026 — Y
  — ≈ 0.99974 — N

35.

houses   air cond.

            0.46 — Y
0.5 — 1 fam.
            0.54 — N

            0.15 — Y
0.35 — 2 fam.
            0.85 — N

            1 — Y
0.15 — town.
            0 — N

38. P(A|H) = 0.5185; About 52% of the resources should go to region A and about 48% should go to region B.

39. Answers may vary. Example: From Exercises 36, P("fail" given "meets standards") = 0.04 and P("fail" given "does not meet standards") = 0.94; 0.04 + 0.94 ≠ 1; Choose one card from a standard deck. P(red given king) = 0.5 and P(red given not a king) = 0.5; 0.5 + 0.5 = 1.

Education   In order to apply for a grant, a school board needs to know the likelihood that elementary and middle school students have computers at home. The superintendent reports that 24% of the children in her district's elementary schools and 30% of the students in the district's middle schools have computers in their homes. In this district, 64% of the children are in elementary schools and 36% are in middle schools.

24. What is the probability that a child in this district has a computer at home? 0.2616

25. Given that a child has a computer at home, what is the probability that he or she is in middle school? 0.4128

26. Given that a child has a computer at home, what is the probability that the child is in elementary school? 0.5872

Marketing   Of the homes listed with a real estate agency, half are single-family dwellings, and 46% of these are centrally air-conditioned; 35% are two-family homes, and 15% of these are centrally air-conditioned; and 15% are townhouses, all of which are centrally air-conditioned.

27. What is the probability that a house listed with this agency is centrally air-conditioned? 0.4325

28. Given that a house is centrally air-conditioned, find the probability that it is a single-family home. 0.5318

29. Find the probability that a house that is centrally air-conditioned is a townhouse. 0.3468

Three special fair dice are placed in a box. One is an ordinary die, one has on each of two faces a 1, on two faces a 2, and on two faces a 3. The third has a 1 on each of three faces and a 6 on the remaining faces. A die is chosen at random from the box and tossed. What is the probability that the die

30. Shows a 1? $\frac{1}{3}$ **31.** Shows a 2? $\frac{1}{6}$ **32.** Does not show a 6? $\frac{7}{9}$

C **33.** *Medicine*   A blood test for a recently identified disease has been developed. It is known that 0.5% of the population of an area has this disease and that 95% of people with the disease test positive. However, 4% of people without the disease also test positive. What is the probability that someone who tests positive has the disease? 0.1066

34. Make a tree diagram to represent the situation described in Exercise 33. Let the first level of branches represent test results, and the second level those having the disease or not. Label each branch with the corresponding probability.

35. Make a tree diagram to represent the situation described in Exercises 27 to 29. Let the first level of branches represent the kinds of houses, and the second level those having air-conditioning or not. Label each branch with the corresponding probability.

36. *Driving Safety*   State inspectors estimate that 18% of cars on the road do not meet inspection standards. When inspected, 94% of those that do not meet the standards fail the inspection, but 4% of those that do meet the standards are incorrectly labeled as failing as well. What is the probability that a car that fails inspection actually does not meet the state standards? 0.8376

37. *Sports* A State College alumnus follows the basketball team closely and assigns odds for all its games. In a poor basketball year the odds are 3 to 1 that the team will not win at homecoming, and 5 to 1 that it will not win its first away game. What are the odds that the team will not win either game? 5 to 3

38. *Search and Rescue* Suppose the searchers in Example 6 first searched the river valleys and concluded that the lost hiker was most likely in one of the hilly regions. Using the probabilities in Example 6, determine the probability that the hiker is in region A, given that he is in a hilly region. How should the search resources be divided between regions A and B?

39. Show by means of examples that $P(A|B) + P(A|B')$ may equal 1 or may be different from 1, where B' is the event "B does not happen."

Project

Create a search and rescue scenario in which Bayes' formula can be used to determine how the rescue resources should be divided. Remember to detail the factors that go into determining the "expert" probabilities involved. Present your scenario to a group of other students and discuss it.

Test Yourself

1. An experiment consists of rolling a die 6 times and recording whether each roll results in an odd number or an even number. Give the probability distribution for this experiment.   *14.5*

2. If 28% of the students in a college are nearsighted, what is the probability that in a group of 20 students from this college exactly 4 of them are nearsighted? 0.1553

3. For the situation described in Exercise 2 what is the probability that of the 20 students, fewer than 2 of them are nearsighted? 0.0123

4. You play a game in which you draw 1 card from an ordinary deck and you win $3.00 if it is a spade, $2.00 if it is a heart, and $1.00 if it is a diamond. You must pay $2.00 if the card is a club. How much should you pay to play this game if it is to be fair? $1   *14.6*

5. *Banking* A bank teller determines through experimentation that between 1:00 p.m. and 1:20 p.m. the probability is 0.05 that no customers will arrive at the bank, 0.10 that 1 will arrive, 0.10 that 2 will arrive, 0.25 that 3 will arrive, 0.20 that 4 will arrive, and 0.30 that 5 will arrive. What is the expected number of customers for this time period? 3.35

6. *Demographics* In a certain office building, 55% of the employees drive to work and 45% of the employees live out of state. If 62% of those who live out of state drive to work, what is the probability that an employee who drives to work lives out of state? 0.5073   *14.7*

7. A committee for an international sports event is testing competitors for steroid use. The committee estimates that 5% of the entries use steroids and that 99% of all steroid users test positive. However, 2% of all people who do not use steroids also test positive. What is the probability that an athlete who tests positive uses steroids? 0.7226

14.7 More Topics in Probability   **791**

Additional Answers, Test Yourself
1. $P(0) = 0.015625$; $P(1) = 0.09375$; $P(2) = 0.234375$; $P(3) = 0.3125$; $P(4) = 0.234375$; $P(5) = 0.09375$; $P(6) = 0.015625$

Alternative Assessment
Have students write an essay discussing the issue of false positives, that is, a reading on a medical test indicating the presence of a disease where none exists. Have them explain in their essay why a positive test result can have a relatively low probability of indicating a disease even when a high percentage of those with the disease test positive and a high percentage of those without the disease test negative.

Enrichment
A child's eye color is determined by a pair of genes, one from each parent. Suppose that B indicates a gene for brown eyes and b a gene for blue eyes, and that the parents in question have only these genes. Suppose also that each of the mother's two genes and each of the father's two genes are equally likely to be transmitted. If a child has genotype BB, bB, or Bb, he or she will have brown eyes. Only a bb genotype results in blue eyes.

1. Determine the probability distribution for each of the genotypes and the probability distribution for eye color for a child whose parents each have the Bb genotype.

$P(BB) = \frac{1}{4}$, $P(Bb) = \frac{1}{4}$,

$P(bB) = \frac{1}{4}$, $P(bb) = \frac{1}{4}$;

$P(\text{blue}) = \frac{1}{4}$, $P(\text{Brown}) = \frac{3}{4}$

2. Given that the child has brown eyes, what is the probability that he or she has the BB genotype?

$\frac{1}{3}$

3. Suppose that the mother has brown eyes and the father blue eyes. What is the conditional probability that the mother has BB genotype given that the couple has a child with brown eyes?

$\frac{1}{2}$

Chapter 14   Summary and Review

Vocabulary

Addition principle of counting (744)

Bayes' formula (786)

Bernoulli trial (770)

binomial distribution (772)

binomial experiment (770)

combination (750)

complement (757)

complementary events (762)

conditional probability (764)

dependent events (763)

empirical probability (757)

event (755)

expected value (778)

general addition rule (762)

independent events (763)

mathematical expectation (778)

multiplication principle of counting (743)

mutually exclusive (761)

odds (757)

outcome (755)

permutation (748)

probability (756)

probability distribution (771)

random experiment (755)

random variable (777)

sample space (755)

theorem of total probability (785)

tree diagram (742)

Basic Counting Principles   The multiplication principle of counting states that if one   14.1
event can occur in n different ways, and for each of these another event can occur
in k different ways, then together the two events can occur in $n \cdot k$ different ways.
The addition principle of counting states that if an event can occur in n ways, and a
second event can occur in k different ways, then there are $n + k$ ways in which the
first *or* the second event can occur.

1. If you can choose one of 6 kinds of sandwiches and one of 5 cold drinks,
   in how many ways can you choose a sandwich and a cold drink? 30

2. A question on a test asks you to name 1 of the 11 provinces of Canada or 1
   of the 7 Central American countries. How many ways can this be done? 18

Permutations and Combinations   The number of permutations of n elements taken r 14.2
at a time is $_nP_r = \dfrac{n!}{(n-r)!}$, where $0 \le r \le n$. The number of combinations of n
objects taken r at a time is $_nC_r = \dfrac{n!}{r!(n-r)!}$, where $0 \le r \le n$.

3. How many ways are there to choose 5 student representatives from a class
   of 150? 591,600,030

4. When registering for fall classes you must list 3 choices for an elective in
   order of preference. How many ways can you do this if there are 18
   electives to choose from? 4896

Probability   The probability of an event is defined to be the ratio of the number of   14.3
outcomes in the event to the number of outcomes in the sample space.

5. A computer is programmed to randomly print two of the capital vowels A,
   E, I, O, or U. List the sample space for this experiment.

For the experiment in exercise 5, list the event that corresponds to each
description and compute its probability.

6. Both vowels are the same. {AA, EE, II, OO, UU}; $\frac{1}{5}$

7. Both vowels are made up entirely of straight line segments. (Use the
   figures printed above for the vowels.)

Conditional Probability   If A and B are mutually exclusive events, then the probability that either A or B occurs is given by $P(A \cup B) = P(A) + P(B)$. The general addition rule states that for any events D and E, $P(D \cup E) = P(D) + P(E) - P(D \cap E)$. If A and B are independent events, then $P(A \cap B) = P(A) \cdot P(B)$. If A and B are dependent events, then $P(A \cap B) = P(A) \cdot P(B$ given $A)$.

14.4

Determine if each set of events is dependent or independent and compute the probability.

8. You have 5 pennies, 3 nickels, 2 dimes, and a quarter in your pocket. However, there is a hole in your pocket and three of the coins fall out. What is the probability that they are all pennies? dependent; 0.061

9. It is determined that 7 out of every 12 cars on the road have 4 doors. What is the probability that of 3 cars chosen at random, none will have 4 doors?
independent; 0.0723

Bernoulli Trials and Binomial Distribution   A binomial experiment consists of a fixed number of identical independent trials, each of which can result in one of two possible outcomes called "success" and "failure," where the probability of success is the same for each trial. The probability of exactly r successes in n trials of a binomial experiment is then given by the formula $\binom{n}{r} p^r (1-p)^{n-r}$.

14.5

10. You determine through experimentation that 15% of all the mail you receive is "junk mail." If you receive 8 letters, what is the probability that more than 6 of them are not junk mail? 0.6572

Random Variables and Mathematical Expectation   A random variable is a variable which can take on different values depending on chance. A probability distribution may be thought of as a function that assigns probabilities to the values of a random variable. If a random variable X can take on the values $a_1, a_2, \ldots, a_n$ with probabilities $p_1, p_2, \ldots, p_n$, respectively, then the expected value of the random variable is $E(X) = a_1 p_1 + a_2 p_2 + \cdots + a_n p_n$.

14.6

11. Find the probability distribution for the random variable that represents the number of letters in the word when each number 1 through 10 is spelled out. $P(3) = 0.4;$ $P(4) = 0.3;$ $P(5) = 0.3$

12. You play a game in which a die is rolled. If the die shows an odd number you win the dollar amount of the number showing, and if the die shows an even number you pay $3.00. What is the mathematical expectation for this game? $0

More Topics in Probability   Bayes' formula states that if $B_1, B_2, \ldots, B_n$ are mutually exclusive events of which one must occur, then

14.7

$$P(B_1|A) = \frac{P(B_1) \cdot P(A|B_1)}{P(B_1) \cdot P(A|B_1) + P(B_2) \cdot P(A|B_2) + \cdots + P(B_n) \cdot P(A|B_n)}$$

13. *Research*   A researcher is testing a new drug that is said to relieve arthritis pain. The drug is administered to 65% of the test subjects and placebos are given to the other 35%. Of the subjects who received the drug, 82% claimed that their arthritis pain subsided. However, 21% of those who received placebos also claimed that their pain subsided. What is the probability that a person reporting pain relief actually received the drug? 0.8788

Chapter 14 Test

A cafeteria menu lists 4 appetizers, 3 soups, 3 salads, 5 entrees, and 2 desserts.

1. If you can choose one item from each of the categories, how many 5-course meals are possible? 360

2. If you can choose an appetizer, a soup, *or* a salad, plus an entree and a dessert, how many different 3-course meals are possible? 100

Find the value of each expression.

3. $_{15}P_7$ 32,432,400

4. $_{32}C_8$ 10,518,300

5. *Education*   A student may choose any 3 electives from the list of 27 electives on the fall schedule. In how many ways can this be done? 2925

6. List the sample space for the experiment of spinning the wheel shown at the right twice.

List the event corresponding to each description and compute its probability.

7. The same number shows for both spins. $\frac{1}{5}$

8. Both spins show a number greater than 3. $\frac{4}{25}$

Determine whether each set of events is independent or dependent and compute the probability.

9. You have two $10 bills, three $5 bills, and seven $1 bills in your pocket. You randomly draw two bills out of your pocket in succession. What is the probability that they are both $1's? dependent; 0.3182

10. *Sports*   It is determined that the odds that a certain ball player will get a hit are 7 to 20 for any time at bat. If the player comes to bat 3 times in a game, what is the probability that he will get a hit all three times? independent; 0.0174

11. The probability that Nigel will hit the bull's-eye when throwing darts is 0.18. If Nigel throws 6 darts, what is the probability that he will throw exactly 1 bull's-eye? 0.4004

12. For the situation described in Exercise 11, what is the probability that more than 3 of Nigel's 6 throws will be bull's-eyes? 0.0116

13. You are playing a game in which a wheel like the one given for Exercise 6 is spun. If an even number comes up you win $5.00. How much would you have to pay to play for the game to be fair? $2

14. In a certain high school, 85% of the students participate in extracurricular activities and 35% of the students have an average of B or better. If 30% of the students who participate in extracurricular activities have an average of B or better, what is the probability that a student with an average of B or better participates in extracurricular activities? 0.7286

Challenge

A hand of 5 cards is dealt from a standard deck. What is the probability that all 5 will be of the same suit given that the first 3 are of the same suit?

Cumulative Review

1. If a hyperbola has its foci on the y-axis, the transverse axis is __?__. vertical   11.3
2. Evaluate to four decimal places: $\cot^{-1} 0.48$ 1.1233   4.6
3. Find the rectangular coordinates of the point with the polar coordinates   10.1
   $\left(4\sqrt{2}, \dfrac{5\pi}{4}\right)$. $(-4, -4)$
4. Find the value of the expression $6 \cdot 5!$ 720   13.5
5. Determine $_{18}P_6$.   13,366,080   14.2
6. Given $f(x) = 6x^2 - x + 2$, evaluate $f(-3)$.   59   1.4
7. Given $A = \begin{bmatrix} 6 & 4 & -3 \\ 2 & -5 & 0 \end{bmatrix}$, find $-A$. $\begin{bmatrix} -6 & -4 & 3 \\ -2 & 5 & 0 \end{bmatrix}$ 12.1
8. If $2i$ is a zero of $f(x) = x^4 + x^2 + a$, find the value of a. -12 7.3
9. A bag contains marbles labeled 1 to 20. What is the probability of pulling a prime number from that bag on the first try? $\dfrac{2}{5}$ 14.4
10. Determine the center and the endpoints of the major and minor axes of the ellipse with equation $\dfrac{(x-7)^2}{16} + \dfrac{(y+4)^2}{49} = 1$. Then graph it. center: $(7, -4)$; $(7, 3)$ and $(7, -11)$; $(3, -4)$ and $(11, -4)$ 11.2
11. Determine the symmetry of $x = y^2$. x-axis   2.1
12. Identify the graph of $r = \cos 4\theta$.   an eight-leaved rose   10.2
13. Determine the common difference for the sequence 18, 12, 6, 0, ... $d = -6$ 13.2
14. In triangle ABC, if $b = 12$, $\angle A = 32°$, and $\angle B = 28°$, determine a to the nearest tenth.   13.5   5.2
15. If $A = \begin{bmatrix} 5 & 11 \\ -3 & -7 \end{bmatrix}$, find $A^{-1}A$. $\begin{bmatrix} 1 & 0 \\ 0 & 1 \end{bmatrix}$ 12.4
16. Graph the inequality $2x + 5y < 12$ in the coordinate plane.   8.2
17. In how many ways can 4 girls who are in a math competition be seated in a row of 9 chairs set up for that day?   3024   14.1
18. Find the first five terms of the sequence $a_n = 3^n$ and state if it converges or diverges.   3, 9, 27, 81, 243; diverges   13.6
19. Find the first five terms of the infinite sequence defined by $f(n) = 3n^2 + 1$.   4, 13, 28, 49, 76   13.1
20. Express 315° in radians. $\dfrac{7\pi}{4}$ 3.2
21. What is the probability of drawing a face card from an ordinary deck of cards on the first draw? $\dfrac{3}{13}$ 14.3
22. Graph $g(x) = e^x + 4$ using transformations. Determine the equation of the asymptote of the graph. $y = 4$ 9.2
23. If 30% of the students are known to be voting yes on an issue, what is the probability that in a group of 20 students exactly 5 will vote yes for the issue?   0.1789   14.5
24. Find the sum: $\displaystyle\sum_{k=1}^{51} (3k + 3)$ 4131   13.3

10.

16.

22.

15 Statistics and Data Analysis

CHAPTER OVERVIEW

Summary

The organization of data using frequency distributions and histograms is presented. Percentiles and quartiles are described as ways of locating data in a ranked set, and are then used to create box-and-whisker plots. The mean, median, and mode are defined and used as measures of central tendency, and the range and standard deviation are shown to be the principal measures of variability. The normal distribution and its applications in probability are discussed. Hypothesis testing and curve fitting are described as ways of using statistics in decision making and prediction.

Chapter Objectives

- To record and read data using histograms and frequency distributions
- To use data from histograms and frequency distributions to solve problems
- To determine percentiles and quartiles for sets of data
- To define measures of central tendency and to use them to describe sets of data
- To define measures of variability and to use them to describe sets of data
- To use the normal distribution to find probabilities
- To test a hypothesis over a given confidence interval
- To define and give examples of curve fitting
- To interpret the linear correlation coefficient

Mathematical Power

Modeling   American mathematician Morris Kline once said, "Let the world be our laboratory and let us gather statistics on what occurs therein." Today, in just about any field you name, the analysis of numerical data is a fundamental tool. At times, such analysis may reveal startling trends that would otherwise be overlooked.

Consider, for example, the data listed in the table below, which shows observed changes in the sea level for New York City in this century. The data shows an obvious pattern, namely, a steady rise in sea level over the years. Because the rise occurred over a long period of time, it would have gone unnoticed had statistical records not been kept.

Year	Change in sea level (cm)
1900	0
1905	0.3
1910	7
1915	7
1920	9.1
1925	5.8
1930	4.6
1935	11.6
1940	14.6
1945	18.6
1950	13.4
1955	19.2
1960	22.6
1965	21
1970	24
1975	24
1980	20.4
1985	24

As you have seen in previous models, further information can be gained by plotting the data on the coordinate plane. Such a graph is known as a *scattergram*. Although all the points in a scattergram do not usually lie exactly on a straight line, statisticians have various methods for finding a line that goes "between" the points and seems to fit the data fairly well. This *line of best fit* for the sea level model is shown on the scattergram.

Features

Modeling

15.5 Sherman Anti-Trust Act	Projects	810, 831, 837, 845
15.6 Quality control	Challenge	810, 831
15.7 Rates of stride in running	Review	804, 816, 837

The line of best fit for this model was found using a technique called the *least squares method*. The object of the least squares method is to find a line such that the sum of the vertical distances from the data points to the line is a minimum. The equation of the *least squares line* that relates the change in sea level s to the time elapsed t is

$$s = 1.237 + 0.294t$$

The equation can be tested against values of t to see how well it fits the data. For example, for $t = 50$, the equation yields $s = 15.397$ while the table shows 13.4. You will learn in this chapter that the relative "goodness of fit" can then be measured using a gauge called a *correlation coefficient*. This and other methods in the study of statistics will allow you to make powerful use of the data analysis skills that you have been applying since the very first lesson of this course.

Thinking Critically   What conclusions do you draw from examining the model for cumulative changes in sea level? Are the changes occurring rapidly? Do they indicate a cause for immediate concern? What are some possible effects of the rise in sea level, and what precautions may be needed?

Project   Do research to obtain data on changes in weather patterns over an extended period. For example, find the average temperature for the summer months in your region over the last century. Graph the data and sketch a line that appears to fit the data closely. Draw conclusions based on your analysis of the data and present them to the class.

Review and Assessment

Vocabulary
classes
frequency
frequency distribution
frequency polygon
histogram
order
ranking
stem-and-leaf plot

Ⓜ **Materials/Manipulatives**
almanacs
magazines
newspapers
science texts
social studies texts

Technology
computer
graphing utility

FOCUS

Students should be familiar with the concept of a census from experience and/or from social studies classes. Remind them that the reapportionment of Congressional districts is a direct result of a census. Newspaper reports from a year immediately following a census can provide information about local reapportionments and the resulting concerns.

Other experiences of data collection and interpretation can help students realize the importance of studying statistics. They are probably aware of marketing research, such as the Nielsen ratings for television shows, and sports statistics. A discussion of the implications of this information will encourage them to become critical thinkers.

15.1 Histograms and Frequency Distributions

Objectives: To record and read data using histograms and frequency distributions
To use data from histograms and frequency distributions to solve problems

Focus

In 1787 the framers of the United States Constitution proposed that a census be taken every 10 years to measure the population. The resulting information would be used to determine the number of representatives each state would have in Congress. Article 1, Section 2 of the Constitution provides for such a census.

Each of the 21 censuses taken since 1787 contains an enormous amount of information. Collectively they reflect the social, economic, and political history of this country. How can conclusions be drawn and history written from thousands of responses to dozens of questions? The task of organizing and summarizing large collections of data is part of a branch of mathematics called *descriptive statistics*.

One of the simplest ways to organize a collection of numerical data is by **ranking.** In a set of ranked data, the numbers are listed in order from lowest to highest or from highest to lowest. It is often convenient to list repeated values once, indicating how often each value occurs. The number of times a value occurs is called its **frequency.**

Example 1 A supermarket manager studies the amount of time customers stand in line before being checked out by tracking one customer each half hour. The times in minutes the first 20 customers wait are 3, 2, 5, 2, 0, 1, 2, 4, 6, 4, 4, 8, 3, 0, 2, 1, 6, 3, 3, 1. Organize this information into a set of ranked data.

List the times in order from least to greatest, and indicate the frequency for each.

Note that the sum of the frequencies is 20, the number of customers in the study. Even though no one waited 7 min, the value is included and given a frequency of 0.

Minutes waiting	Frequency
0	2
1	3
2	4
3	4
4	3
5	1
6	2
7	0
8	1

798   Chapter 15 Statistics and Data Analysis

Many computer programs and even calculators can *order* a set of data, so that you can obtain a set of ranked data quite easily. When small sets of data are ranked, a good overview is achieved without loss of detail. Large sets of data can be grouped into **classes.** Grouping sacrifices some specific information but makes a large data set more manageable. The resulting table is called a **frequency distribution.**

Example 2 *Employment* A careers publication surveyed 23 companies and asked the average starting salaries of jobs offered in 1989. The information obtained is summarized in the frequency distribution at the right. How many of the starting salaries were

Starting salaries	Frequency
$19,000–22,999	3
23,000–26,999	1
27,000–30,999	5
31,000–34,999	5
35,000–38,999	5
39,000–42,999	4

   a. less than $23,000?   **b.** less than $31,000?   **c.** equal to $31,000?

  a. The 3 salaries in the class $19,000–22,999 are less than $23,000.

  b. The salaries in the first 3 classes are less than $31,000, so the total is 3 + 1 + 5 = 9 in this category.

  c. It is impossible to tell from the table how many, if any, of the salaries are equal to $31,000.

In Example 2, it is impossible to tell the largest or the smallest starting salary. A frequency distribution presents an overall picture of the results of a survey but does not include every detail. Choosing the classes for a frequency distribution is a matter of judgment. The only requirements are:

   Classes may not overlap.
   Every piece of data must fall into one of the classes.

Whenever possible, classes should cover equal ranges of values. The number of classes depends on the number of values to be organized; ordinarily use between 6 and 15 classes.

Example 3 *Health* A health professional studying the effect of smoking on blood pressure collected the following readings of systolic blood pressure from a control group of 26 people: 150, 121, 134, 129, 165, 148, 125, 130, 182, 164, 142, 110, 177, 139, 188, 151, 190, 205, 128, 160, 125, 178, 162, 149, 156, 137. Construct a frequency distribution to summarize this information.

Systolic blood pressure	Tallies	Frequency
105–119	|	1
120–134	⊬⊬ ||	7
135–149	⊬⊬	5
150–164	⊬⊬ |	6
165–179	|||	3
180–194	|||	3
195–209	|	1

The data ranges from 110 to 205. One way to organize the information is into 7 classes, each covering 15 possible readings. Tally the data and count the number of tallies in each class.

It is often advantageous to
display the information in a
frequency distribution
graphically. To do this you
use the **histogram,** a vertical
bar graph with no spaces
between the bars. In a
histogram, the classes are
represented on the horizontal
axis and the frequencies are
shown on the vertical axis. A
histogram for Example 3 illustrates this.

The endpoints of the intervals representing the classes actually fall halfway
between the class limits. For example, the second class permits values between
120 and 134. Its endpoints on the horizontal axis are 119.5 and 134.5. For
simplicity, classes are often labeled with actual lower and upper values *or* with
midpoint values.

A **frequency polygon** is another form of graphical presentation of data that is
related to the histogram. For a frequency polygon, a line graph is formed by
plotting each point whose x-value is the midpoint of a class and whose y-value
is the frequency of that class, and then joining those points with line segments.
The line graph forms a polygon with the x-axis when it is "tied" to the axis by
plotting the midpoints for classes immediately above and below those of the
distribution.

Example 4   Draw a frequency polygon
for the data of Example 3.

Graphing calculators and both graphing and statistical
programs for the computer can be used to obtain
histograms. At the right is a graphing utility display of the
histogram obtained in Example 3.

[105, 210] by [0, 8]
x scl: 15 y scl: 1

800   Chapter 15 Statistics and Data Analysis

In instances when it is important to organize data without loss of detail, a **stem-and-leaf plot** may be useful. A stem-and-leaf plot is a way of displaying numerical data in a compact form. The digits of each data value are broken into two parts, the *stem* and the *leaf*. Each stem is recorded once, followed by the associated leaves. In Example 5, where the data consists of two-digit numbers, each stem represents a tens digit and each leaf represents a units digit.

Example 5 *Marketing* An independent marketing firm gathered data on the ages of people who watched the pilot of a new TV show. The following data represent the ages of 30 viewers:

$$22 \quad 26 \quad 37 \quad 64 \quad 18 \quad 10 \quad 12 \quad 55 \quad 32 \quad 45$$
$$49 \quad 50 \quad 27 \quad 68 \quad 59 \quad 71 \quad 43 \quad 17 \quad 15 \quad 70$$
$$50 \quad 29 \quad 61 \quad 73 \quad 67 \quad 65 \quad 20 \quad 62 \quad 70 \quad 48$$

Use a stem-and-leaf plot to display the data.

Let a stem and a leaf each contain 1 digit. For age 32, for example, the stem is 3 and the leaf 2. Observe that the display groups the data without losing detail. A key helps the reader interpret the display. In this example, a key would be "1|8 represents 18 years."

Stem	Leaf
1	0 2 5 7 8
2	0 2 6 7 9
3	2 7
4	3 5 8 9
5	0 0 5 9
6	1 2 4 5 7 8
7	0 0 1 3

Class Exercises

Conservation Owners of new compact cars were asked to keep track of their mileage (miles per gallon) for 6 months. The results of the survey are listed in the frequency distribution at the right.

Miles per gallon	Frequency
15.0–19.9	14
20.0–24.9	23
25.0–29.9	31
30.0–34.9	34
35.0–39.0	26
40.0–44.9	8

1. How many cars averaged less than 20 mi/gal? 14
2. How many cars averaged more than 29.9 mi/gal? 68
3. How many cars averaged less than 30 mi/gal? 68
4. How many cars averaged 35 or more mi/gal? 34
5. What was the best miles per gallon of any of the cars? cannot tell
6. How many car owners responded to the survey? 136

Education The final exam in a computer course was worth 150 points. The 28 student scores were: 120, 140, 98, 134, 136, 115, 109, 87, 102, 144, 136, 120, 142, 98, 136, 148, 102, 140, 133, 95, 109, 139, 126, 122, 130, 99, 142, 90.

7. Organize this information into a set of ranked data.
8. Make a stem-and-leaf plot for this data.
9. Make a frequency distribution for the data using classes of length 8.
10. Draw a histogram for the frequency distribution of Exercise 9.
11. Label the *midpoint* of each class in the histogram of Exercise 10.
12. Draw the frequency polygon for the final exam data.

15.1 Histograms and Frequency Distributions **801**

For Example 5
The following data represent the weights in grams of 30 rats used in an experiment to determine the effects of calcium in the diet.

93	99	101	108	119	111
114	125	136	128	106	103
124	126	104	110	132	119
92	128	115	103	126	125
143	125	126	95	113	148

Use a stem-and-leaf plot to display the data.

10|4 represents 104 grams

Stem	Leaf
9	2 3 5 9
10	1 3 3 4 6 8
11	0 1 3 4 5 9 9
12	4 5 5 6 6 6 8 8
13	2 6
14	3 8

CLOSURE

Have students write a summary in their math journals of how each of the following may be used to display a set of data: ranked data, frequency distribution, frequency polygon, histogram, and stem-and-leaf plot.

INDEPENDENT PRACTICE

Assignment Guide
Basic: 1–24
Average: 6, 13, 18–39
Enriched: 21–22, 26–43

Teacher's Resource Book
  Practice, page 103

Ⓡ **Review**
Exercises 6, 13, and 37 to 39 review concepts of probability, sum and convergence of geometric series, and combinations.

Technology

Practice Exercise 31 provides an opportunity for a discussion of choosing the viewing rectangle for a histogram.

LESSON FOLLOW-UP

Lesson Quiz

The number of deer observed in 36 areas of a wildlife preserve were

15	10	16	14	29	17
4	18	18	8	9	22
20	33	15	16	14	8
10	10	16	9	10	7
16	6	13	18	12	19
16	17	11	28	17	17

1. Make a frequency distribution for the data using classes of length 5.

Number of deer	Frequency
1–5	1
6–10	10
11–15	7
16–20	14
21–25	1
26–30	2
31–35	1

2. Draw a histogram and frequency polygon for the frequency distribution.

PH/TE 15.1.2a

---

13. Thinking Critically   The numbers of years of experience of applicants for a manager's position are grouped into these classes:

$$0–4, \ 5–9, \ 10–14, \ 14–18, \ 19–20$$

Comment on problems that might arise from this grouping.

Practice Exercises   Use appropriate technology.

Health   A researcher recorded the cholesterol levels of 80 patients and summarized the findings in a frequency distribution.

Cholesterol level	Frequency
155–169	8
170–184	13
185–199	21
200–214	14
215–229	8
230–244	7
245–259	4
260–274	3
275–289	2

A **1.** How many patients had a cholesterol reading above 259? 5

2. How many patients had a cholesterol reading below 215? 56

3. How many patients had a cholesterol reading between 200 and 259? 33

4. How many patients had a cholesterol reading above 200? cannot tell

5. What is the lowest cholesterol reading among these patients? cannot tell

Ⓡ **6.** What is the probability that a patient chosen at random from this group has a cholesterol reading below 200? $\frac{21}{40}$

7. Draw a histogram representing this information.

8. Draw a frequency polygon representing the information.

Nutrition   The numbers of grams of protein in servings of 20 protein-rich foods are:

$$14.0, 8.5, 7.1, 6.1, 2.4, 32.0, 31.2, 30.7, 26.7, 8.0,$$
$$6.0, 6.0, 5.5, 5.0, 4.0, \ 2.0, \ 2.5, 12.0, \ 7.1, 4.8$$

9. Organize this information into a set of ranked data.

10. Make a frequency distribution for the data using classes of length 5.

11. Draw a histogram for the frequency distribution.

12. Draw a frequency polygon for the frequency distribution.

Ⓡ **13.** Find the sum of the geometric series $1 + 0.6 + (0.6)^2 + (0.6)^3 + \cdots$. 2.5

History   The Montgomery Ward Catalogue of 1895 lists 81 varieties of saddles with weights ranging from 3.5 lb to 40 lb. The weights are summarized in a histogram.

14. How many saddles weigh more than 20 lb? 21

15. How many saddles weigh between 6 and 15 lb? 41

16. How many saddles weigh 40 lb? cannot tell

17. How many saddles weigh more than 31 lb? cannot tell

18. Explain why it is correct to say that more than half the saddles weigh less than 16 lb.

19. Thinking Critically   Explain why you cannot be certain that more than half the saddles weigh less than 15 lb.

802   Chapter 15 Statistics and Data Analysis

Additional Answers, Class Exercises

13. Answers may vary. The intervals 10–14 and 14–18 overlap. The intervals are not all the same length. The distribution gives the same weight to someone with no experience as to someone with 4 years experience.

B **20.** Frequency distributions and histograms may also be created for qualitative as well as for numerical data. Make a histogram to represent the information presented in this frequency distribution for complaints registered with a department store about its catalog service.

Type of complaint	Frequency
Incorrect item sent	23
Shipping damage	35
Slow service	18
Incorrect bill	16
Catalog description misleading	17
Other complaints	9

21. Thinking Critically What does the vertical axis represent in a histogram for qualitative data? Is it meaningful to talk about class length?

22. Thinking Critically Explain why it is possible to have different frequency distributions for the same set of data with classes of the same length. Illustrate using an example from this section, or one of your own.

23. Make a stem-and-leaf plot for the data of Example 3 of this lesson.

24. How does a stem-and-leaf plot resemble a histogram?

Business A business publication asked a number of large companies about the number of employees on their staff. The responses ranged from 1342 to 216,000 and are summarized in a histogram.

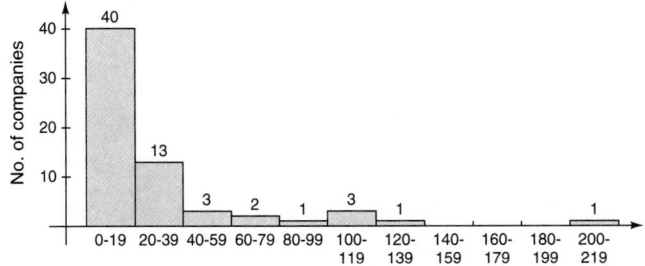

25. How many companies responded to the survey? 64

26. What is the length of each class in this histogram? 20,000

27. What percent of the companies surveyed had fewer than 20,000 employees? 62.5%

28. What is the significance of the "gap" in the rectangles between 139,000 and 200,000?

This histogram uses the information from the survey above but focuses on companies with fewer than 140,000 employees.

29. What is the length of each class in this histogram? 10,000

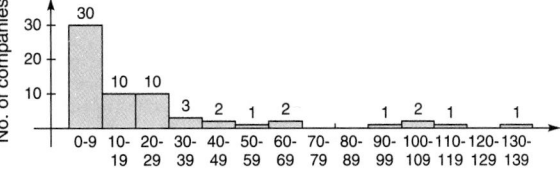

30. Thinking Critically How can there be a gap between 69,000 and 90,000 in this histogram when there is no gap in the previous graph until 139,000? What does this gap reveal?

31. What is an advantage of ignoring the company with more than 200,000 employees when obtaining this histogram with a graphing utility?

15.1 Histograms and Frequency Distributions **803**

---

3. Use a stem-and-leaf plot to display the data.

0|4 represents 4

Stem	Leaf
0	4 6 7 8 8 9 9
1	0 0 0 0 1 2 3 4
	4 5 5 6 6 6 6 6
	7 7 7 7 8 8 8 9
2	0 2 8 9
3	3

The number of meals that 40 executives of a firm charged to their expense accounts in December is summarized below.

Number of meals	Frequency
0–5	5
6–11	9
12–17	15
18–23	7
24–29	3
30–35	1

4. How many executives charged at least 12 meals? 26

5. How many executives charged more than 18 meals? cannot tell

Additional Answers

21. The vertical axis represents frequency. It is not meaningful to talk about class length because classes represent nonnumerical data.

22. This can happen when the lower limit of the first class and/or the upper limit of the last class are not values from the data set.

24. The stems divide the data into classes if regularly spaced. The length of the line of leaves shows the frequency associated with the stem (class).

---

28. No company surveyed had between 140,000 and 199,000 employees.

30. Smaller classes give more detail. The gap shows no company surveyed had between 69,000 and 88,999 employees.

Alternative Assessment

Have students collect information about the number of hours of television viewed per week by young adults, or another project of interest to them. Then have them summarize the data in a frequency distribution, draw a histogram for the frequency distribution, and prepare a stem-and-leaf plot for the data. Finally, have students present the various representations to the class and discuss their findings.

Enrichment

An *ogive* is a variation on a frequency polygon. Research the characteristics of an ogive, and prepare one for the data of Example 3 in the text.

Additional Answers

37. $P(0) = \frac{1}{32}$; $P(1) = \frac{5}{32}$;

$P(2) = \frac{10}{32}$; $P(3) = \frac{10}{32}$;

$P(4) = \frac{5}{32}$; $P(5) = \frac{1}{32}$

38. If r is the common ratio, $|r| < 1$.

42.

Starting salaries	Percent
$19,000–22,999	13.0
$23,000–26,999	4.3
$27,000–30,999	21.7
$31,000–34,999	21.7
$35,000–38,999	21.7
$39,000–42,999	17.4

Since more than 80% of the companies surveyed have fewer than 40,000 employees, the last histogram in this series focuses on companies with fewer than 40,000 employees.

32. What is the probability that a company chosen from those surveyed has between 5,000 and 14,999 employees? 0.453

33. What is the probability that a company chosen from those surveyed has fewer than 19,000 employees? cannot tell

34. What is the largest number of employees of companies represented in this histogram? cannot tell

35. Writing in Mathematics Write a paragraph summarizing the conclusions you can draw about the information in the survey studied in Exercises 25 to 34.

36. Draw a histogram for the data of Example 5.

Ⓡ **37.** Find the probability distribution for the number of tails obtained when 5 fair coins are tossed.

Ⓡ **38.** Describe the criterion for the convergence of a geometric series.

Ⓡ **39.** In how many ways can a committee of 4 be chosen from a club with 15 members? In how many ways can a slate consisting of president, vice president, secretary, and treasurer be formed from the same club? 1365; 32,760

Ⓒ **40.** A **cumulative frequency distribution** represents accumulated frequencies. Use the data of Exercises 1 to 7 to complete this cumulative frequency distribution.

Cholesterol level	Frequency
less than 170	8
less than 185	21
less than 200	42
less than 215	56
less than 230	64
less than 245	71
less than 260	75
less than 275	78
less than 290	80

41. The distribution in Exercise 40 is sometimes called a "cumulative less than distribution." Create an analogous "cumulative more than distribution" for the same data.

42. A frequency distribution can be converted to a *percentage distribution* by rewriting each frequency as a percentage of the total number of items grouped. Convert the frequency distribution of Example 2 to a percentage distribution.

43. Extend the ideas of Exercises 40 and 42 to design a *cumulative percentage distribution* ("less than") for the frequency distribution of Example 3.

Review

1. Show that the reciprocal of a nonzero complex number $a + bi$ is $\frac{a - bi}{a^2 + b^2}$. $\frac{1}{a + bi} \cdot \frac{a - bi}{a - bi} = \frac{a - bi}{a^2 - b^2 i^2} = \frac{a - bi}{a^2 + b^2}$

How many intercepts does the graph have?

2. $y = 6x$ 1

3. $x^2 = y + 2$ 3

4. In triangle ABC, $\angle C = 43°$, $a = 16$, and $b = 24$. Find c, to the nearest whole number. 16

804 Chapter 15 Statistics and Data Analysis

Writing in Mathematics

35. Answers may vary. The first histogram shows that 40 of the 64 companies are "small" in the sense that they have fewer than 20,000 employees. Only one company is very large; that is, it has 200,000 or more employees. The second histogram shows that nearly half of the companies have fewer than 10,000 employees. Fifty-eight, or 90% of the companies, have fewer than 70,000 employees.

15.2 Percentiles, Quartiles, and Box-and-Whisker Plots

Objective: To determine percentiles and quartiles for sets of data

Focus

The science of *cliometrics* is named for Clio, the muse of history. A cliometrician uses statistics in the study of history, looking for patterns and information in sources such as shipping records, census information, and voting records.

A computer is an invaluable tool for the cliometrician, and computerized data banks have enabled historians to answer questions once thought unanswerable, to validate some theories and to overturn others. For example, in the late 1960s cliometric scholars overturned the popular thesis that the economy based on slavery had been on the verge of collapse just before the Civil War. Statistics shed new light on an important period of history.

Locating numerical data in a distribution is useful in many applications of statistics. One way to do this uses *percentiles*. You may have heard descriptions such as "She graduated in the top 10% of her class" or "He ranks among the top 2% of amateur skiers in the country." Sometimes knowing where an item of data is in a set of ranked data is actually more useful than knowing its value. Percentiles provide one way to locate an item of data in a distribution. Percentiles are values that divide a distribution of values into 100 groups of equal frequency.

If you score at the 87th percentile on a standardized test, you may conclude that you scored as high as or higher than 87% of those who took the test. There are 99 percentiles, ranging from a low of 1 to a high of 99. Each indicates the percentage of the distribution ranking at or below it.

> The **kth percentile** of a distribution is a value such that $k\%$ of the distribution falls at or below it. The kth percentile is often denoted P_k, where k is an integer between 1 and 99.

Example 1 *Education* In a class of 600 students, Mei Li ranks 120th and Stan ranks 275th. Find their respective percentiles.

Since Mei Li ranks 120th, 480 students rank below her.

$$\frac{480}{600} = 0.8$$

Therefore, Mei Li is at the 80th percentile, P_{80}.

LESSON PLAN

Vocabulary
box-and-whisker plot
*k*th percentile
median
percentile

Technology
calculator
computer

FOCUS

It is important for students whose interests lie in the arts to recognize that mathematics can be a valuable tool in fields like history, art, and music. Have students research recent findings of cliometricians and applications of statistics to archeology, art history, and music history.

INSTRUCTION

- Most students are familiar with percentiles from standardized tests they have taken. Discuss the difference between scoring at the *k*th percentile and earning a score of *k*.
- Have students discuss the pros and cons of using ranking as a way of evaluating performance. Help them to recognize that ranking small sets of data can lead to inaccurate conclusions.
- Have students use sorting programs on a calculator or computer to find the median, quartiles, and percentiles.

Similarly, 325 students are ranked below Stan.

$$\frac{325}{600} = 0.542$$

Since 54.2% of the students rank equal to or below Stan, he is at the 54th percentile, P_{54}.

If you know the total number in a population, you can use percentile to determine the number of scores above or below the given percentile. But several scores may have the same percentile. You might, therefore, only be able to state an approximate number of scores above or below a given percentile. Percentiles are rounded as decimals. The 80th percentile includes those values greater than or equal to 0.795 but less than 0.805.

Example 2 Jerry scored in the 74th percentile on a test. If 685 students took the test, about how many scored above Jerry?

74% of those taking the test scored below or even with Jerry.

$$0.74 \times 685 = 506.9 \qquad 685 - 507 = 178$$

About 178 students scored higher than Jerry on the test.

Can you determine 3 other numbers that are in the 74th percentile for the data?

A percentile of particular interest is P_{50}, the **median,** which locates the middle of a set of ordered data. For an ordered set of 11 test scores, the 50th percentile is the 6th score. What if there were 12 test scores? In this case, P_{50} would be the average of the two middle scores.

Just as the median divides a set of data into two equal parts, a **quartile** divides each part in half. The lower quartile Q_1 is the median of the data below the overall median. The upper quartile, Q_3 is the median of the data above the overall median. A quartile, like a median, may be an item of data in the set or it may be the average of two items.

Example 3 Determine for the data set

$$\{56, 78, 90, 85, 67, 66, 82, 94, 81, 80, 77, 69, 64, 90, 80\}$$

    a. the median   **b.** Q_1 **c.** Q_3

First order the data:

    56, 64, 66, 67, 69, 77, 78, 80, 80, 81, 82, 85, 90, 90, 94

a. There are 15 pieces of data. The median m is in the 8th position; therefore, $m = 80$.
b. Q_1 is the median of the data below the median: $Q_1 = 67$.
c. Q_3 is the median of the data above the median: $Q_3 = 85$.

Thinking Critically
Answers may vary. Make sure students' answers are between 505 and 510.

The sorting capability of computers and some calculators makes finding the mean and the quartiles easier.

The quartiles for a set of data are also called **hinges.** The two hinges and the median are used in a graphical presentation of data called a **box-and-whisker plot.** This graph is a tool in an area of statistics called *exploratory data analysis* (EDA). Analysts use it to develop intuition about data they are studying.

A box-and-whisker plot shows the middle half of the data, that is, the data between the hinges, Q_1 and Q_3, as a *box*. Lines called *whiskers* indicate the remaining portion of the data. The median, two hinges, and the smallest and largest values are used in its construction. The length of the interval from Q_1 to Q_3 is called the *interquartile range*. The smallest value is called the *lower extreme*. The largest value is called the *upper extreme*.

Example 4   Identify the median, the hinges, and the upper and lower extremes for the box-and-whisker plot shown. Determine the interquartile range.

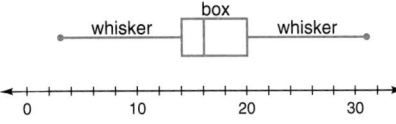

The median is 16. $Q_1 = 14$. $Q_3 = 20$.
The lower extreme is 3. The upper extreme is 31.
The interquartile range is 6.

A box-and-whisker plot may also be in a vertical format. The following example shows how a box-and-whisker plot is constructed from data.

Example 5   *Meteorology*   The high temperatures in degrees Fahrenheit on the days of November in a midwestern city were:

36, 32, 40, 33, 28, 27, 30, 28, 25, 24, 30, 24, 24, 22, 22,
25, 19, 20, 26, 21, 24, 27, 24, 26, 28, 30, 26, 25, 22, 19

First, order the data:

19, 19, 20, 21, 22, 22, 22, 24, 24, 24, 24, 24, 25, 25, 25,
26, 26, 26, 27, 27, 28, 28, 28, 30, 30, 30, 32, 33, 36, 40

The median is 25.5. $Q_1 = 24$. $Q_3 = 28$.
The upper extreme is 40.
The lower extreme is 19.

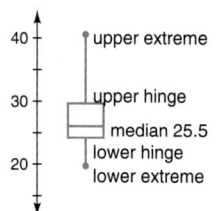

Class Exercises

Find the percentile for students with these rankings in a class of 800.

1. 10th 99   2. 64th 92   3. 160th 80   4. 524th 35   5. 700th 13   6. 425th 47

7. In a class of 200 students, Andrea ranks 25th, Elliot ranks at P_{20}, and Cindy at Q_1. Which of these students ranks highest? Lowest? Explain.

15.2 Percentiles, Quartiles, and Box-and-Whisker Plots   **807**

For Example 4

Identify the median, the hinges, and the upper and lower extremes for the box-and-whisker plot shown. Determine the interquartile range.

$m = 36$; $Q_1 = 29$; $Q_3 = 52$; lower extreme = 9; upper extreme = 61; interquartile range = 23

For Example 5

Make a box-and-whisker plot for the final exam scores in Example 3.

CLOSURE

Have students write you a letter identifying the parts of the lesson that were easy to understand and those that were difficult to understand, along with reasons for their selections.

Additional Answers

7. Andrea ranks highest at the 88th percentile, P_{88}. Elliot ranks lowest at P_{20}.

The numbers of white blood cells in 28 blood samples were recorded. The numbers of thousands of cells per cubic millimeter of blood were:

6.7, 5.1, 9.0, 5.1, 7.2, 3.9, 4.8, 5.0, 5.2, 9.9, 3.5, 6.6, 8.2, 4.4,
8.1, 10.0, 9.6, 5.4, 5.9, 7.7, 9.8, 6.8, 6.5, 6.5, 5.0, 8.2, 3.7, 4.8

Find each indicated value for this set of data.

8. P_{50} 6.5   **9.** Q_1 5.0   **10.** Q_3 8.15

11. Find the median, hinges, and upper and lower extremes for the blood count data.

12. Make a box-and-whisker plot for the blood count data.

Practice Exercises   Use appropriate technology.

A **1.** Sally took an aptitude test for a computer training program and scored at the 73rd percentile. What percent of those who took the test scored the same as or lower than Sally? What percent scored higher? 73%; 27%

2. If you rank at Q_1 for scores on a geography survey test, what percent of those tested have higher scores? 75%

3. **Writing in Mathematics**   Your neighbors' child comes home with information about a standardized test he took. He scored at the 65th percentile, and your neighbors are quite concerned about this. In their experience 65 is not even a passing mark. Explain the meaning of that score to them.

Thinking Critically   Describe a situation in which scoring in each of these kinds of percentiles would be desirable.

4. a low percentile   **5.** a percentile near P_{50} **6.** a high percentile

Find the percentile for students with these rankings in a class of 350.

7. 35th 90   **8.** 245th 30   **9.** 280th 20   **10.** 74th 79   **11.** 159th 55   **12.** 220th 38

13. Repeat Exercises 7 and 12 for a class of 250. 86; 12

14. *Job Placement*   The 140 applicants for a civil service job took an aptitude exam. Those who scored above the 65th percentile in that group went on to the next phase of the hiring process. How many applicants did this represent? 49

15. *Education*   Of the 560 people who took a language exam, 339 scored below Andy. Find the percentile for Andy's score. 61

16. *Education*   Julie took a scholarship exam and scored in the 90th percentile. If there were 160 competitors for the scholarship, about how many scored higher than Julie? 16

Ⓡ **17.** In how many ways could a committee of 3 or 4 people be formed from a staff of 15? 1820

Ⓡ **18.** For the situation of Exercise 17, what is the probability that the committee consists of exactly Henri, Marcy, and Jorge? $\frac{1}{1820}$

Ⓡ **19.** For the situation of Exercise 17, what is the probability that Henri, Marcy, and Jorge are all on the committee? $\frac{13}{1820}$

808   Chapter 15 Statistics and Data Analysis

20. Identify the median, hinges, and upper and lower extremes of the data represented by this box-and-whisker plot.

Miles traveled to work

21. Identify the median, hinges, and upper and lower extremes of the data represented by this box-and-whisker plot.

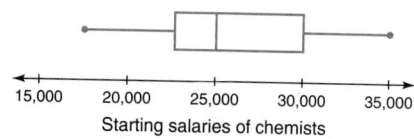

Starting salaries of chemists

An airline did a study of the number of empty seats in its early bird weekday commuter flight from New York to Toronto for 6 weeks. The results were:

7, 8, 3, 11, 10, 2, 3, 11, 9, 14, 11, 5, 3, 6, 10,
9, 9, 3, 12, 15, 5, 6, 3, 9, 11, 12, 4, 9, 9

Find each of the three quartiles for this data.

B **22.** Q_1 4.5   **23.** Q_2 9   **24.** Q_3 11

25. Make a box-and-whisker plot for the airline data.

26. How much of the data in a distribution is located between Q_1 and Q_3? Explain.

Politics Based on the census of 1980, the numbers of representatives each state sends to the House of Representatives are:

2, 2, 1, 11, 2, 6, 34, 14, 23, 21, 10, 22, 18, 9, 8, 6, 9, 1, 1, 3, 5, 1, 8, 10,
4, 11, 6, 10, 19, 7, 9, 7, 5, 4, 8, 6, 27, 2, 2, 1, 6, 3, 5, 3, 2, 8, 5, 45, 1, 2

Ⓡ **27.** Construct a histogram to represent this information using classes of length 5.

Ⓡ **28.** Construct a frequency polygon for the number of representatives.

Find each percentile for the number of representatives.

29. P_{80} 11   **30.** P_{60} 8   **31.** P_{24} 2

32. Make a box-and-whisker plot for the number of representatives data.

33. Thinking Critically Show by example that although the upper and lower hinges are close to P_{25} and P_{75}, they need not always equal those values. Answers may vary.

34. *Travel* Make a box-and-whisker plot for the following luggage weights (in pounds) on an overseas flight: 10, 11, 14, 14, 16, 21, 23, 27, 27, 29, 32, 33, 36, 36, 38, 40.

For a ranked set of data, nine *deciles* $D_1, D_2, \ldots, D_9$ are defined as follows:

D_k is the value for which k tenths of the data falls at or below it.

35. Define the 9 deciles in terms of percentile.

36. Find D_6 for the data set listed in Exercise 34. 29

15.2 Percentiles, Quartiles, and Box-and-Whisker Plots   **809**

Alternative Assessment

Have students collect data on the heights of at least 20 persons of the same age group. Then have them find the median and the first and third quartiles for this data, and finally have them make a box-and-whisker plot to represent the data.

Enrichment

A study of the weights of boxes delivered by a trucking company resulted in the histogram below. Note that the vertical scale represents relative frequency. Estimate Q_1, the median, and Q_3.

$Q_1 = 40$ lb; median $= 46$ lb; $Q_3 = 54$ lb

Additional Answers

41. $Q_1 = 14$; $Q_3 = 20$; $IQR = 6$; potential outliers: 36, 40; no serious outliers

42. The IQR is the length of the box. Compare this length to the two whiskers.

44. For P_k, let $R = \frac{k}{100}(n + 1)$.
    Then $P_x = x_{INT(R)} + [R - INT(R)](x_{INT(R)+1} - x_{INT(R)})$.

45. Answers may vary. This is often the most representative part of the data since it omits extreme values which may be exceptional.

46. It is symmetric if the mark representing the median is in the middle of the box and the tails have equal length.

Television Programming   Fifty people are surveyed about the number of hours of television they watched the previous Saturday night between 6:00 p.m. and midnight. The responses are given in a frequency distribution. Find the following for this data.

No. hours	Frequency
0	12
1	9
2	6
3	10
4	5
5	5
6	3

C 37. P_{50} 2   38. Q_1 1   39. Q_3 4
40. The interquartile range 3

Outliers are items of data "far" from the middle 50% of the data. According to one definition, a *potential outlier* is an item of data more than 1.5 times the interquartile range away from the nearer quartile. A *serious outlier* is any item of data more than three times the interquartile range from the nearest quartile.

41. Use the data of Example 5 of this section to determine the interquartile range. Identify any potential and serious outliers for this set of data.

42. Examine the box-and-whisker plot for this data. How could you use the box-and-whisker plot to tell whether or not a data set has outliers?

43. Examine the box-and-whisker plots for Exercises 20, 21, 25, and 32. Which of these indicate the presence of outliers in their data sets? 20 and 32

44. *Programming*   Write a formula that could be used in a program for a computer or programmable calculator to find a given percentile for a set of n pieces of data. Assume that the data has been ordered and labeled $x_1, x_2, \ldots, x_n$ and that the computer or calculator has a function INT that outputs the integer part of any real number.

45. **Thinking Critically**   Why might a statistician be interested in looking at the data that represents the middle 50% of a distribution?

46. **Thinking Critically**   How can an analyst tell by looking at a box-and-whisker plot whether or not the data is symmetric about the median?

Project

Research *stanines,* another way of locating data in a ranked set. Describe how to interpret information about a stanine.

Challenge

1. Determine the sum of the real values of x that satisfy the equation $|x + 3| = 3|x - 3|$. $7\frac{1}{2}$

2. If an arc of 45° on circle I has the same length as an arc of 30° on circle II, determine the ratio of the area of circle I to that of circle II. $\frac{4}{9}$

3. Determine the value of x and y if $\frac{4^{x+y}}{2^x} = 16$ and $\frac{3^y}{9^x} = 27$. $x = -\frac{2}{5}$, $y = 2\frac{1}{5}$

4. Simplify: $\log 6 \div \log \frac{1}{6}$ -1

15.3 Measures of Central Tendency

Objectives: To define measures of central tendency
To use measures of central tendency to describe sets of data

Focus

American sports fans are fascinated by statistics. Win-loss statistics, batting averages, and records of every kind sprinkle the sports pages of newspapers and the dialogue of commentators. Young baseball fans cite batting, fielding, and earned run averages before they have mastered the multiplication tables.

Allen Guttmann, a specialist in sports studies, claims that baseball calls not for literacy, but for *numeracy,* the ability to work with numbers. There is even an organization devoted solely to baseball statistics, the Society of American Baseball Research, or SABR for short. Statisticians who are specialists in analyzing data from the game of baseball are thus called *sabermetricians.*

In a frequency distribution, large sets of data are condensed into a small number of classes giving an overview of the information. A **statistic** is a single number that characterizes a set of data. A statistic that describes the center of a set of data is called an **average** or **measure of central tendency.** The most common kinds of averages are the *mean,* the *median,* and the *mode.*

The *mean* of a set of numerical data is the *arithmetic average* of all the values in the set. It is found by adding all the values and then dividing by the number of values in the set.

For a set $\{x_1, x_2, \ldots, x_n\}$ of n pieces of numerical data, the **mean,** denoted $\bar{x}$, is given by

$$\bar{x} = \frac{1}{n} \sum_{i=1}^{n} x_i$$

Example 1 *Meteorology* The low temperatures in degrees Fahrenheit for 15 days in March in Omaha, Nebraska, were 5, 9, 11, 2, 7, 1, 4, 9, 10, 4, 2, 2, 8, 5, 3. Find the mean temperature for those days.

To find the mean, add the 15 values and divide by 15:

$$\bar{x} = \frac{5 + 9 + 11 + 2 + 7 + 1 + 4 + 9 + 10 + 4 + 2 + 2 + 8 + 5 + 3}{15} = \frac{82}{15} \approx 5.5°$$

15.3 Measures of Central Tendency **811**

Vocabulary
average
mean
measure of central tendency
median
mode

Ⓜ **Materials/Manipulatives**
magazines
newspapers

FOCUS

Baseball fans have been interested in statistics since 1845 when the *New York Herald* printed the first box scores. That summary included only the runs scored and outs totaled by each player. Today fans can analyze batting averages, earned run averages, on-base percentages, hitting percentages, errors per game, and so on.

Teams rely on computer analysis of statistics to plan new strategies and correct errors, and *sabermetricians* make their livings providing facts and their interpretations.

Almost every sport has statistics of special interest. Encourage interested students to investigate the statistics of importance in their favorite sports and how those statistics are used by players, coaches, managers, and fans in their favorite sports.

- Discuss contexts in which the mean is a more desirable representative of the data than the median, and vice versa. For example, the mean salary of all members of a firm can be inflated by a CEO's or president's salary, while the median would not be affected by one or two large salaries.
- Have students investigate the use of the *midrange* as a measure of central tendency.
- (M) Have students find examples of the use of the word "average" in advertising. Discuss possible interpretations of average in each context and ways in which the use of the term could be misleading.

Alternative Learning Styles

Students whose learning style is primarily subjective often benefit from working with examples drawn from familiar material. Have these students work in small groups to design a way of identifying the "average" precalculus student using the concepts of mean, median, and mode.

GUIDED PRACTICE

For Example 1

After a severe storm, the director of an arboretum measured the diameters of the 12 trees that were toppled. The diameters (in feet) were: 4.4, 4.1, 3.8, 2.5, 2.7, 3.4, 1.9, 2.6, 3.1, 3.5, 2.6, 2.4. Find the mean diameter. 3.08 ft

One characteristic of the mean is that it is sensitive to every item of data in the set, and in particular to extreme values. For example, had the high temperature in the list been 35 instead of 11, the mean would have been $\bar{x} = \frac{106}{15} = 7.1$. This new mean of 7.1° represents an increase of 29% caused by a change in just one data value.

To find the mean using a calculator, enter the data as x-values. Select the menu that gives the calculations for the data. Usually "$\bar{x}$" indicates the mean.

Recall that the *median* is the middle value of a set of ranked data, that is, the 50th percentile. If the data set has an even number of values, the median is the mean of the two middle values. You can use a calculator to sort the data and find the median.

Example 2   Find the median temperature for the data set of Example 1.

First rank the data.

1, 2, 2, 2, 3, 4, 4, 5, 5, 7, 8, 9, 9, 10, 11

$n = 15;$ $\quad \frac{15 + 1}{2} = 8$ $\quad$ *Median is at the $\frac{n+1}{2}$ position.*

The median is the 8th item of data, which is 5.

Notice in Example 2 that if the high temperature 11 were replaced by 35, the median would not change. Unlike the mean, the median is not generally sensitive to extreme values.

Both the mean and the median are descriptors of sets of numerical data. To find the representative eye color or birth month of a group of people, or a single representative of any set of nonnumerical data, a different way of measuring central tendency is needed. The **mode** of a set of data is the most frequently occurring value. For example, the mode of the data set of Example 1 is 2°.

Example 3   *Sports*   Below is a list of the home run total for each of the American League home run leaders from 1920 to 1949. Find the mode for the set of data.

54, 59, 39, 41, 46, 33, 47, 60, 54, 46, 49, 46, 58, 48, 49,
36, 49, 46, 58, 35, 41, 37, 36, 34, 22, 24, 44, 32, 39, 43

The mode, the value occurring the greatest number of times, is 46. It occurs four times. *How could you tell the mode of a set of data by examining a histogram?*

A set of data may have one mode, no mode, or more than one mode. For example, if 3 baseball players with the best statistics played for the Blue Jays, 3 for the Twins, and none played more often for other teams, the data would have two modes. If each player played for a different team, there would be no mode.

812   Chapter 15 Statistics and Data Analysis

Thinking Critically
On a histogram, the bar of the longest length represents the mode.

If data is presented in a frequency distribution without classes, the median and mode can be determined directly.

Example 4 The secretary of a professional society keeps a record of the attendance of board members at meetings. During the last 5 years there have been 20 meetings, with the attendance summarized in the following frequency distribution.

Number present	11	12	13	14	15	16
Frequency	1	2	1	6	7	3

For this distribution find:
a. the mode **b.** the median **c.** the mean

a. The mode, 15, can be read directly from the frequency distribution.

b. $n = 20$ $\frac{1}{2}(20 + 1) = 10.5$

The median is the arithmetic average of the 10th and 11th values in the distribution.

$x_{10} = 14$ and $x_{11} = 15; \frac{1}{2}(14 + 15) = 14.5$

c. The sum of the data must take into account the number of times each value appears. Therefore

$$\bar{x} = \frac{11 + 2(12) + 13 + 6(14) + 7(15) + 3(16)}{20} = \frac{285}{20} = 14.25$$

Class Exercises

Sports The numbers of college football teams in the United States for the years 1980–1988 were 642, 648, 649, 651, 654, 661, 666, 667, and 673.

1. Find the mean. 656.78 **2.** Find the median. 654 **3.** Find the mode. no mode

Health A study measured the cholesterol content, in milligrams, in 3 oz of meat, poultry, fish, and shellfish. The resulting data are 77, 78, 79, 128, 270, 400, 329, 1746, 164, 72, 79, 59, 72, 74, 55, 90, 57, 45, 85, 61, 93, 35, 166.

4. Find the mode. 72 and 79 **5.** Find the median. 79 **6.** Find the mean. 187.56

7. Compute the mean of this data set with the high value 1746 omitted. 116.73

8. Compute the median of this data set with the high value 1746 omitted. 78.5

9. Thinking Critically Compare the mean and the median of the original data set. Which of them better reflects the data? Explain.

A psychologist surveyed 50 people and asked for the number of their brothers and sisters. The results are summarized in a frequency distribution.

No. siblings	0	1	2	3	4	5	6	7
Frequency	14	16	11	4	3	0	1	1

10. Find the mode. 1 **11.** Find the median. 1 **12.** Find the mean. 1.5

15.3 Measures of Central Tendency **813**

For Example 2
1. Find the median diameter of the toppled trees of Example 1 above. 2.9 ft

For Example 3
1. A group of 50 people were asked to give their place of birth. The total responses were: 2 New Jersey, 5 Florida, 2 Uganda, 11 Illinois, 5 South Carolina, 1 Brazil, 9 Texas, 1 New Mexico, 8 New York, 3 Ohio, 1 Italy, 2 Tennessee. What is the mode of the responses? Illinois
2. Suppose the group above was increased to 80 and 15 were born in Hawaii and 15 in Pennsylvania, what would be the mode? Hawaii and Pennsylvania

For Example 4
The heights of 50 students are given in the distribution below. For this distribution find:
a. mode **b.** median **c.** mean

Height (in.)	60	61	62	63	64
Frequency	5	7	4	8	10
Height (in.)	65	66	67	68	69
Frequency	8	4	1	2	1

a. The mode is 64 in.
b. The median is 64 in.
c. The mean is 63.5 in.

Technology On some calculators data and their weights may be entered directly and the mean computed from a menu item. On others, the mean should be computed using a single equation, for example

(60*5 + 61*7 + · · · + 69*1)/50

CLOSURE

Group students in pairs and have them summarize the lesson to each other.

Additional Answers

6. The total crowd size will be smaller for years when fewer games are played.
13. mode; The data is not quantitative.
14. median; The two "outliers" will affect the mean but not the median.
15. mode; The manufacturer needs to know how many shoes to make in each size.
16. mean; Since each skill is essential, all scores should affect the average.
18. Answers may vary. Example: {Blue, Green, Blue, Brown, Hazel}
19. Answers may vary. Example: {Blue, Green, Blue, Brown, Hazel, Brown}
20. Answers may vary. Example: {Blue, Green, Brown, Hazel, Grey}
22. Answers may vary. Example: You were feeling ill one day and received a particularly low grade that would lower the mean but not the median.

Practice Exercises Use appropriate technology.

Health For a 150-lb adult, the numbers of calories burned per hour in 10 popular activities are 564, 492, 330, 360, 222, 486, 678, 864, 636, and 324.

A 1. Find the mean. 495.6

2. Find the median. 489

Sports The numbers of baseball fans at the World Series for the years 1980–1988 were 325,000, 338,000, 385,000, 304,000, 272,000, 327,000, 322,000, 387,000, and 260,000.

3. Find the median. 325,000

4. Find the mean. 324,444

5. Find the mode. no mode

6. **Thinking Critically** What is a logical reason for the fluctuation in the number of people who attended the World Series in these years?

Fund Raising Volunteers at a fund raiser worked the following numbers of hours: 3, 5, 2, 5, 6, 1, 4, 4, 5, 6, 3, 7, 10, 3, 5, 8, 8, 4, 5, 9.

7. Find the mean. 5.15

8. Find the median. 5

9. Find the mode. 5

10. What is the probability that a volunteer chosen randomly worked more than 5 h? $\frac{7}{20}$

The chairperson of the above fund raiser worked 10 h at the event. If the number of preparation hours were included, the chairperson worked 31 h.

11. Recompute the mean of the set of data when 10 is replaced by 31. 6.2

12. What is the median of the data set with 10 replaced by 31? 5

Tell which measure of central tendency would probably best represent the data described. Give a reason for each answer.

13. A decorator surveys 36 people to ask their favorite colors.

14. A professor wants to describe class performance on a test for which the scores range from 13 to 99, with all but two students scoring above 65.

15. A manufacturer wants to know what shoe size the "average" woman wears.

16. A job applicant takes an aptitude test with six parts, each of which tests a skill essential to the job.

17. *Education* A student earns a grade of 94 on an essay test. Her other scores are all below 82. What kind of average would give her the best possible grade? mean

Give an example of a set of nonnumerical data:

18. with a unique mode

19. that has two distinct modes

20. that has no mode

21. *Fund Raising* A large school has three service clubs that jointly sponsor a walk-a-thon to raise funds for a local soup kitchen. The first club collects 124 pledges with a mean of $1.10 per mile. The second club collects 90 pledges with a mean of $0.90 per mile. The third club collects 56 pledges with a mean of $1.35 per mile. What is the mean pledge for this walk-a-thon? $1.09

22. **Thinking Critically** Give an example of a situation in which it would be to your advantage that your average score in a course be the median of your test scores rather than the mean.

23. Use a tree diagram to determine the number of ways Anna can win or lose in a series of three tennis matches.

B 24. *Transportation*   A truck has a cargo capacity of 5600 lb. Is it overloaded if it contains 59 crates whose mean weight is 91 lb? Explain.

25. Writing in Mathematics   A travel agency has a list of the mean daily maximum temperatures for each month of the year in Albuquerque, New Mexico. The temperatures in degrees Fahrenheit from January through December are 47.2, 52.9, 60.7, 70.6, 79.9, 90.6, 92.8, 89.4, 83.0, 71.7, 57.2, and 48.0. Comment on the travel agent who advertises that the average temperature in Albuquerque is a comfortable 70.3°.

26. *Economics*   In reporting some data, the Census Bureau divides the United States into four regions: Northeast with 50.8 million people, Midwest with 60.1 million, South with 85.5 million, and West with 51.8 million. If in 1988 residents of the Northeast have a mean income of $19,214, residents of the Midwest $15,989, residents of the South $14,793, and residents of the West $17,190, what is the mean income of U.S. residents in 1988? $16,487.73

27. *Education*   An instructor graded papers for 12 students and then computed a class mean of 76. One of the papers was lost. From the other scores of 82, 80, 76, 66, 82, 87, 61, 90, 77, 79, 76 and the mean, find the score of the lost paper. 56

28. *Education*   In a psychology course, the two-hour final exam counts twice as much as each of the three one-hour exams during the semester. A student's hour-exam scores are 77, 81, and 90, and his final exam score is 63. What is his average? 74.8

29. Repeat Exercise 28 for a student with the same hour-exam scores, but with a final exam score of 88. 84.8

30. Thinking Critically   A statistics student is given the task of finding the birth month of the average member of his class. He decides to use the usual convention January = 1, February = 2, March = 3, and so on, and take the mean of the numbers representing the class members' birth months. Why will the number he obtains not represent the average person's birth month? Give an example to clarify your answer.

31. Thinking Critically   Suppose the student described in Exercise 30 decides to use the median instead of the mean. Will the number obtained represent the average person's birth month? Why or why not?

In a quality control study in a knitting mill, a manager examines 10 randomly chosen sweaters a day for 6 weeks. The numbers of defects he finds in each group of 10 are summarized in this frequency distribution:

No. defects	0	1	2	3	4	5	6	7	8	9	10
Frequency	12	7	4	1	2	1	2	0	1	0	0

32. Find the median. 1   **33.** Find the mean. 1.7   **34.** Find the mode. 0

R 35. Find the third quartile Q_3 for the distribution of Exercise 32. 2

36. Find the mean, median, and mode for the data of Exercise 37 of Lesson 15.2.
2.28; 2; 0

15.3 Measures of Central Tendency   **815**

Writing in Mathematics
25. Answers may vary. In this example the comfortable "average" of 70.3° comes from uncomfortable extremes. The travel agent is probably guilty of false advertising.

Ⓡ 37. Write the repeating decimal $6.789789789\cdots$ as a rational number. $\dfrac{2261}{333}$

Ⓡ 38. Use the binomial theorem to evaluate $(3x - y^2)^5$. $243x^5 - 405x^4y^2 + 270x^3y^4 - 90x^2y^6 + 15xy^8 - y^{10}$

Ⓒ 39. **Thinking Critically** The means of two sets of data are $\bar{x}$ and $\bar{y}$. Under what circumstances will the mean of the combined data sets be the average $\frac{1}{2}(\bar{x} + \bar{y})$?

40. The average age of members of a club is 28. In 5 years, what will the average age be? Prove your answer.

41. The mean of a set of numerical data is x. Prove that if each value in the set is multiplied by a constant c, then the mean of the resulting set is $c \cdot x$.

42. If data is available only in a frequency distribution with classes, the mean cannot be found exactly. It can be approximated by using the midpoint of a class to represent all values in that class and the method of Example 4. Approximate the mean of the distribution at the right of 100 scores on an SAT test. 527.5

Score	Midpoint	Frequency
200–299	249.5	5
300–399	349.5	9
400–499	449.5	26
500–599	549.5	32
600–699	649.5	19
700–799	749.5	9

43. **Thinking Critically** How would you represent the mode of the distribution in Exercise 42?

44. Repeat Exercise 42 for the data of Example 2 of Lesson 15.1. 32,477.76

The *mean of a probability distribution* is the expected value of the distribution. Recall that if a random variable X can take on the values $a_1, a_2, \ldots, a_n$ with probabilities $p_1, p_2, \ldots, p_n$, respectively, then the *mathematical expectation*, or *expected value*, of the random variable is $E(X) = a_1p_1 + a_2p_2 + \cdots + a_np_n$.

Suppose that a doctor is interested in studying the number of times her beeper goes off during a week. Records over 6 months give the following data:

No. beeper calls in a week	5	6	7	8	9	10	11	12
Frequency	4	6	8	3	1	2	1	1

45. Find the mean of this set of data. 7.23

46. Find the probability for each data value and use these to find the expected value of the number of beeper calls.

47. **Thinking Critically** Explain the relationship between the mean and the expected value found in Exercises 45 and 46.

Review

1. In a 30°-60°-90° triangle, if $\angle B = 60°$, $\angle C = 90°$, and $c = 26$, find the lengths of the remaining two sides. $a = 13, b = 13\sqrt{3}$

Solve by completing the square.

2. $x^2 + 8x + 19 = 0$ $x = -4 \pm i\sqrt{3}$

3. $7x^2 + 70x + 42 = 0$ $x = -5 \pm \sqrt{19}$

Is the given transformation a translation?

4. $T(x, y) = (x + 2, y - 7)$ yes

5. $T(x, y) = (3x, y + 6)$ no

43. Find the midpoint of the class with the greatest frequency; in this case, 549.5.
46. $P(5) = 0.15; P(6) = 0.23; P(7) = 0.31; P(8) = 0.12; P(9) = 0.04; P(10) = 0.08;$
$P(11) = 0.04; P(12) = 0.04; E(x) = 7.23$
47. Ignoring rounding errors, they are the same.

15.4 Measures of Variability

Objectives: To define the measures of variability
To use measures of variability to describe sets of data

Focus

The broad applicability of statistics is evident in the work of *Gertrude Mary Cox* (1900–1978). Cox studied psychological statistics at the University of California in Berkeley, and worked as a statistician at Iowa State University. In 1940, she accepted a position as head of the new department of experimental statistics at North Carolina State College. There she trained staff for the U.S. Department of Agriculture and organized statistical conferences on topics such as plant science, agricultural economics, animal sciences, and plant genetics. In 1960 Cox became director of the Statistics Section of the Research Triangle Institute in Durham, North Carolina. Gertrude Cox applied the tools of statistics, such as *measures of variability*, to areas as diverse as botany, psychology, and government.

You have seen that the mean, median, and mode can be useful ways of summarizing data. However, if you want to know about the climate of a particular place, the fact that the yearly mean temperature is 45° is not enough information. You may also want to know how hot it gets in summer and how cold in winter. Statistics are needed to describe how the values in a data set vary. The two most important **measures of variability,** or *dispersion*, are the *range* and the *standard deviation*. The **range** of a set of data is the difference between the largest and the smallest values. The range is easy to compute, and in some circumstances it gives very useful information about the spread of the data.

Example 1   The numbers of professional rodeos in the United States for each year from 1980 to 1988 are 631, 641, 643, 650, 643, 617, 616, 637, and 707. What is the range of this set of data?

The largest piece of data is 707, and the smallest is 616. Therefore the range is 707 − 616 = 91.

If you know the mean and the range of a distribution, what can you conclude? For the data in Example 1, the mean is 642.8, and the range is 91. Since the range is small *relative to the mean*, you can conclude that most of the data is relatively close to the mean, which is valuable information. If, on the other hand, the range is large, it is not possible to draw strong conclusions.

15.4 Measures of Variability   **817**

LESSON PLAN

Vocabulary
dispersion
range
standard deviation
variability
variance

Technology
calculators
computers

FOCUS

Many students enjoy biographical material and find it a way to make mathematics personal and interesting. Students interested in history may enjoy knowing that Florence Nightingale greatly encouraged the use of statistics by administrators, legislators, and politicians.

INSTRUCTION

- Use anecdotes like the one at the beginning of this lesson to illustrate the need for knowing more than just an average in order to make decisions. For example, a "comfortable" average temperature in a city could come from extremely cold winters and hot summers.
- You may want to have students find the range, variance, and standard deviation for the data they collected as suggested in Alternative Assessment for Lesson 15.1. Ask them to explain what those statistics tell about the data set.
- Comparing the range or standard deviation to the mean is a way of helping to judge the information they convey. For example, a range of $100 is small for a study of adults' weekly salaries but quite large for a study of children's weekly allowances. The "size" of the data studied is indicated by the mean.

Students with a global learning style are helped by seeing why a concept is important before tackling the mechanics of how it is defined. These students will benefit from the biographical sketch of Gertrude Mary Cox in the Focus.

GUIDED PRACTICE

For Example 1

1. A hotel manager collected information about the number of rooms occupied on Wednesdays for several weeks. The numbers were: 54, 36, 40, 21, 18, 41, 39, and 28. What is the range of this set of data? 36

2. The diameters (in feet) of 12 trees that toppled during a storm were: 4.4, 4.1, 3.8, 2.5, 2.7, 3.4, 1.9, 2.6, 3.1, 3.5, 2.6, and 2.4. Find the range of this set of data. 2.5 ft

For Example 2

Each of the following sets of data has 10 pieces of data, mean 50, and range 30. For each set, describe the distribution of data.

1. {35, 50, 50, 50, 50, 50, 50, 50, 50, 65}
   Most of the data is at the mean, with just two pieces located away from 50.

2. {35, 35, 35, 35, 35, 65, 65, 65, 65, 65}
   The data clusters at the two extremes of 35 and 65, with no values near the mean.

3. {35, 40, 45, 50, 50, 50, 50, 55, 60, 65}
   The values are spread evenly above and below the mean.

Example 2 Each of the following data sets has eight items of data, mean 75, and range 100. For each set, describe the distribution of the data.
   a. {0, 0, 100, 100, 100, 100, 100, 100}   **b.** {25, 75, 75, 75, 75, 75, 75, 125}
   c. {25, 40, 55, 70, 80, 95, 110, 125}

   a. The data clusters at the two extremes of 0 and 100, with no values near the mean.
   b. Most of the data is at the mean, with just two values located away from 75.
   c. The values are spread evenly from 25 to 125.

Example 2 illustrates the great variation possible among sets of data with the same mean and range. A better way of measuring the variability of a data set is needed. The most widely used measure of variability is the *standard deviation*.

A dentist routinely asks new patients how many times they have seen a dentist in the past 5 years. Responses from 10 patients are 2, 0, 3, 4, 7, 3, 9, 4, 7, and 1. The mean of this data set is 4. To measure how the data varies from the mean, look at the differences between the data values x and the mean $\bar{x}$. Find the mean of the numbers in the $x - \bar{x}$ column. The sum of these variations is zero, giving no information about the spread of the data.

x	$x - \bar{x}$	$(x - \bar{x})^2$
0	−4	16
1	−3	9
2	−2	4
3	−1	1
3	−1	1
4	0	0
4	0	0
7	3	9
7	3	9
9	5	25
	0	74

$$74 \div 10 = 7.4$$
$$\sqrt{7.4} \approx 2.7$$

To avoid a sum of zero, square each of the $x - \bar{x}$ values, take the average, and then take the square root. For this example, the mean is 74, and the average of these squares is $74 \div 10 = 7.4$. This number is referred to as the *variance*. Its square root, $\sqrt{7.4} \approx 2.7$, is the *standard deviation*. Notice that the variance and standard deviation are affected by each piece of data, and so are a better measure of the spread of the data than the range.

> For any set of numerical data $\{x_1, x_2, \ldots, x_n\}$ with mean $\bar{x}$, the **standard deviation** σ (sigma) is
> $$\sigma = \sqrt{\frac{1}{n} \sum_{i=1}^{n} (x_i - \bar{x})^2}$$

The square of the standard deviation is called the **variance** σ^2 of the data.

Example 3 *Science* A botanist is studying the chlorophyll content of leaves. In one part of the study, the following eight measurements were made: 2.7, 3.1, 3.0, 2.9, 2.7, 3.1, 3.3, 2.5. Find the standard deviation and variance of this set of data.

$$\bar{x} = \frac{2.7 + 3.1 + 3.0 + 2.9 + 2.7 + 3.1 + 3.3 + 2.5}{8} = \frac{23.3}{8} \approx 2.9$$

The sum of the squares of the variations is 0.49.

$$\sigma^2 = 0.49 \div 8 = 0.06125$$
$$\sigma = \sqrt{0.06125} \approx 0.247 \qquad \sigma = \sqrt{\frac{1}{n} \sum_{i=1}^{n} (x_i - \bar{x})^2}$$

Thus the standard deviation is $\sigma \approx 0.247$. The variance is $\sigma^2 = 0.06125$.

818 Chapter 15 Statistics and Data Analysis

The statistical mode of calculators makes finding the standard deviation of a set of data quite simple.

Example 4 Appendix A contains tables of data. Enter the data indicated; use a computer or calculator to find the mean and standard deviation, and a histogram. Describe the relationship between the statistics and the graph.
    a. The highest annual temperatures of record for 71 selected cities in the United States, listed on page 901.
    b. The lowest annual temperatures of record for 71 selected cities in the United States, listed on page 901.

a. $\bar{x} = 104.77°F$ $\sigma = 4.82°F$

The standard deviation is small. This reflects the fact that the data is clustered close to the mean. The range is only 28°, and 51 of the 71 values are between 100° and 110°.

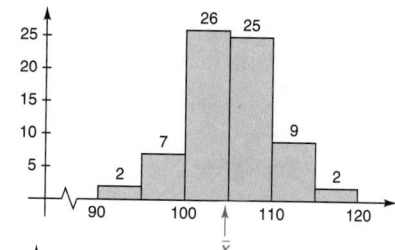

b. $\bar{x} = -11.72°F$
    $\sigma = 20.4°F$

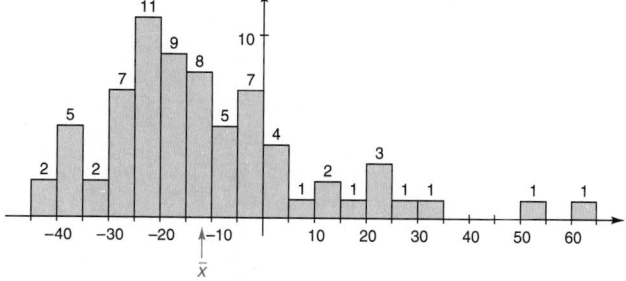

The standard deviation is relatively large. This reflects the fact that the data is not clustered about the mean. The range is 104° and even when extreme values are ignored, the range is large.

When a set of data is collected as representative of a larger collection, it is referred to as a *sample*. The mean and standard deviation of the sample are used as estimates for the mean and standard deviation of the larger set, which is called the *population*. The standard deviation of a sample usually underestimates the standard deviation of the population. Because of this, when data is viewed as a sample, its standard deviation is computed using $n - 1$ instead of n to find the mean of the squares of the variations. If you are using technology, you may have an option to choose between σ and s, or σ_n and σ_{n-1}. In this case, σ and σ_n refer to the standard deviation of a population. The variables s and σ_{n-1} refer to the standard deviation of a sample, and are defined by the equation

$$s = \sigma_{n-1} = \sqrt{\frac{1}{n-1} \sum_{i=1}^{n} (x_i - \bar{x})^2}$$

15.4 Measures of Variability   **819**

For Example 3
Find the standard deviation and variance of the following numbers of accidents reported in a year by drivers with suspended licenses.

$$2, 5, 3, 7, 2, 6, 1, 2$$

$\sigma \approx 2.06$ to the nearest hundredth
$\sigma^2 \approx 4.25$ to the nearest hundredth

For Example 4
Refer to Appendix A, page 900, to find a list of the highest points in each of the 50 states. Using a calculator or computer, enter the data in feet. Find the mean and standard deviation and then draw a histogram. Describe the relationship between the statistics and the graph.
mean: 6048.84 ft
standard deviation: 5047.64 ft

Have students write you a letter describing the terms variability, standard deviation, and variance for a data set.

INDEPENDENT PRACTICE

Assignment Guide

Basic: 1–24
Average: 13–36
Enriched: 16, 23–47

Teacher's Resource Book
Practice, page 106

Additional Answers

Class Exercises

2. The data does not vary greatly from the mean.

7. $\bar{x} = 113.14$ days; range = 184 days; $\sigma = 33.02$ days; $\sigma^2 = 1090.32$ days.^{2}

8. Answers may vary.

9. The standard deviation and the variance would change. $s = 33.25$; $s^2 = 1105.896$

For large values of n, the difference between σ and s is small. The importance of the standard deviation in describing a set of data is seen in a theoretical result called *Chebyshev's theorem*. You are asked to apply the theorem, stated on page 823, in Exercises 44 to 47.

Class Exercises

1. *Publishing* The numbers of daily newspapers published in the United States in the years 1978–1988 were 1756, 1763, 1745, 1730, 1711, 1701, 1688, 1676, 1657, 1645, and 1642. What is the range of this set of data? 121

2. **Thinking Critically** The numbers of Sunday newspapers published in the United States in the years 1978–1988 have a mean of 771.8 and a range of 144. What conclusion can you draw about the variability of the data?

Political Science The estimated populations of 11 regions of the world are, in millions of people, shown in the table.

China	1253
Africa	646
former USSR	289
Europe	499
Japan	123
Middle East	182
North America	275
South America	290
Central America	148
Southeast Asia	404
India	1097

3. What is the mean? 473.27

4. What is the range? 1130

5. Find the standard deviation. 363.38

6. What is the variance? 132,045.11

Meteorology Refer to Appendix A, page 901, to find data about the average number of days with precipitation of 0.01 in. or more for selected cities in the United States. Using a calculator or computer, enter the data for the *annual* number of days with precipitation.

7. Find the mean, range, standard deviation, and variance for this data.

8. Obtain a histogram representing this data. You may need to experiment with maximum and minimum x- and y-values and scales to obtain a good representation of the data.

9. **Thinking Critically** If you were using the selected cities as representative of all cities in the United States, which of the statistics obtained in Exercise 7 would change? If possible, find its new value and compare it to the former value.

Practice Exercises

 Use appropriate technology.

A 1. Using the given histogram as a reference, make a histogram representing a set of data with a larger range. Answers may vary.

2. Using the given histogram as a reference, make a histogram representing a set of data with a smaller range. Answers may vary.

3. *Consumer Behavior* The numbers of pounds of apples eaten per capita in the United States for 10 years are 16.2, 18.2, 18.3, 16.1, 17.1, 17.6, 17.6, 16.6, 17.3, and 20.3. What is the range of this set of data? 4.2 lb

4. **Thinking Critically** The numbers of professional basketball teams in the United States between 1980 and 1988 have a mean of 22.9 and a standard deviation of 1. What conclusion can you draw about the variability of the data?

If the values in a set of data are measured in grams, what unit should be used to describe each statistic?

5. mean grams   6. range grams   7. standard deviation grams   8. variance grams²

9. **Thinking Critically** The numbers of employees in nine large chemical companies have a mean of 26,088 and a range of 128,000. What conclusion can you draw about the variability of the data?

Sociology Data was collected about the cost of day care per week in 10 suburban areas where it is most expensive. The costs, in dollars, were 109, 95, 91, 90, 87, 87, 86, 86, 83, and 79.

Ⓡ 10. Find the mean. $89.30   11. Find the range. $30   12. Find the standard deviation. $7.76

Astronomy The 21 brightest stars and their distances from the earth in light years are given in the table.

Achernar	85	Minosa	420
Aldebaran	68	Spica	260
Rigel	900	Hadar	460
Capella	42	Arcturus	36
Betelgeuse	300	Rigil	
Canopus	1200	Kentaurus	4.2
Sirius	8.8	Antares	330
Procyon	11.4	Vega	26
Pollux	36	Altair	16.6
Regulus	85	Deneb	1800
Acrux	360	Fomalhaut	22

Ⓡ 13. What is the mean? 308.14

14. What is the range? 1795.8

15. Find the standard deviation. 452.78

16. **Thinking Critically** What can you conclude about a set of data whose standard deviation is zero? Explain.

Ⓡ 17. Determine the equation of the parabola with vertex $(-1, 2)$ and focus $(-1, 0)$. $(x + 1)^2 = -8(y - 2)$

18. **Writing in Mathematics** Explain what the standard deviation measures and why it is generally a better measure of variability than the range.

Ⓡ 19. Determine the equation of the ellipse with foci $(0, 0)$ and $(0, 8)$ and major axis of length 16. $\frac{x^2}{48} + \frac{(y - 4)^2}{64} = 1$

20. Find the range of the data of Example 3 of this lesson. 0.8

Ⓡ 21. Determine the equation of the circle with center $(8, -2)$ that passes through the point $(-9, 4)$. $(x - 8)^2 + (y + 2)^2 = 325$

22. Find the standard deviation for the data of Example 1 of this lesson. 25.24

B 23. **Thinking Critically** Recompute the standard deviation for Example 1 by first subtracting 600 from each data piece. Compare the answer with that of Exercise 22. What conclusion can you draw?

24. *Scheduling* An airline's flights have a mean arrival time of 5.8 min late with standard deviation of 2.1 min. What would be an appropriate x-scale for a histogram?

15.4 Measures of Variability   **821**

Ⓡ **Review**
Exercises 10, 13, 17, 19, 21, 35 and and 36 review concepts such as mean, equations of conics, probability, and combinations.

LESSON FOLLOW-UP
Test Yourself

Teacher's Resource Book
    Tests—Quiz, form A, page 65
    Tests—Quiz, form B, page 65

Additional Answers
Practice Exercises
  4. Answers may vary. The data does not vary much from the mean since $\sigma = 1$, which is small relative to a mean of 22.9.
  9. Answers may vary. At least some of the data varies greatly from the mean.
 16. All the data points are equal. There is no variation from the mean.
 23. 25.24; Subtracting did not change the result but simplified the calculations.
 24. Answers may vary. The x-scale might go from -10 to 10 in increments of 2 min.

Writing in Mathematics
18. The standard deviation measures how the data spreads from the mean. If σ is large, the spread of the data is large; if σ is small, the spread of the data (on the average) is small. The standard deviation is generally a better measure of dispersion than the range because it reflects all the data. The range actually only measures the spread of the two extreme pieces of data.

Lesson Quiz

On eight weekly quizzes, a student scored 6, 8, 9, 10, 10, 8, 3, and 9 points out of a possible 10 points.

1. What is the range of this data? 7
2. Find the variance of this data. 4.859
3. What is the standard deviation of this data? 2.204
4. If a student's 12 quiz scores had a mean of 8 and range of 2, what conclusion could you draw about the scores? All 12 scores were close to 8.
5. If a student's 12 quiz scores had a mean of 6 and range of 8, what conclusion could you draw about At least some of the scores were not close to 6.

Additional Answers

25. No. A large standard deviation indicates that the data varies greatly from the mean and any great variation will be reflected in a large range.
26. $\bar{x} = 1841.49$ m; $\sigma = 1541.22$ m; $\sigma^2 = 2,375,362.29$ m^2
29. Answers may vary. Example: σ is large relative to $\bar{x}$
33. Answers may vary. Example: σ is small relative to $\bar{x}$; More than 60% of the data lie within ± 15 years of the mean.
34. Sorting can be used to identify the largest and smallest values.

---

25. **Thinking Critically** Is it possible for a set of data to have a large standard deviation and a small range? Explain.

Geography   Refer to Appendix A, page 900, to find data about the highest points in each of the 50 states and the District of Columbia. Using a calculator or computer, enter the data for the elevation in meters.

26. Find the mean, standard deviation, and variance for this data.
27. What is the range of this data? 6073 m
28. Obtain a histogram representing this data. You may need to experiment with maximum and minimum x- and y-values and scales to obtain a good representation of the data.
29. **Thinking Critically** Describe the relationship between the information obtained in Exercises 26 and 27 and that of Exercise 28.

Health   Refer to Appendix A, page 900, to find data about the expectation of life at birth in 61 countries throughout the world. Using a calculator or computer, enter the data for the expectations for children born in 1989.

30. Find the mean, standard deviation, and variance for this data. $\bar{x} = 62.29y$; $\sigma = 11.08y$: $\sigma^2 = 122.78y$
31. What is the range of this data? 37.9 y
32. Obtain a histogram representing this data. You may need to experiment with maximum and minimum x- and y-values and scales to obtain a good representation of the data.
33. **Thinking Critically** Describe the relationship between the information obtained in Exercises 30 and 31 and that of Exercise 32.
34. How can a calculator or computer with data-sorting capabilities simplify finding the range for a large set of data?
Ⓡ 35. What is the probability that a 5-card poker hand will contain 4 aces? 1.8469×10^{-5}
Ⓡ 36. How many subsets of 6 elements can be formed from a set of 37 elements? 2,324,784

For Exercises 37 and 38, consider the data to be a sample. Recall that s is the estimated standard deviation of the population based on the sample.

37. Determine s for the data about the patients of a dentist used to explain standard deviation early in the lesson. 2.87
38. Determine s for the data given in Example 3. 0.265
Ⓒ 39. *Business*   The mean salary in a small company is $25,600 with a standard deviation of $2200. At New Year's, everyone in the company gets a one-time raise of $500. Find the new mean and standard deviation of the salaries. $26,100; $2200

The *mean deviation* is found by taking the mean of the absolute values of variations from the mean. That is, if $x_1, x_2, \ldots, x_n$ are numerical data, then

$$\text{Mean deviation} = \frac{|x_1 - x| + |x_2 - x| + \cdots + |x_n - x|}{n}$$

40. Find the mean deviation for the data of Exercise 10. $5.56
41. Find the mean deviation for the data of Exercise 13. 315.52

822   Chapter 15 Statistics and Data Analysis

42. *Education*   On a pretest, 23 students in a probability class made between 6 and 13 errors with the following distribution.

No. errors	6	7	8	9	10	11	12	13
Frequency	1	4	4	5	2	3	2	2

Find the mean and standard deviation of this set of data. 9.3; 1.99

43. On a questionnaire, 15 people were asked to respond to questions with ratings from 1 = strongly disagree to 5 = strongly agree. Their responses are summarized below. Find the mean and standard deviation of this distribution. 2.47; 1.31

Response	1	2	3	4	5
Frequency	4	5	3	1	2

Chebyshev's Theorem   For any set of data, the proportion of data within k standard deviations of the mean is at least $1 - \frac{1}{k^2}$, where $k > 1$.

44. Employees of a large company have a mean age of 41 years with standard deviation 6 years. At least what percentage of the people must be between 29 and 53 years old? 75%

45. *Education*   Applicants to a university have an average ACT math score of 21.3 with standard deviation of 3.2. Between what values must the scores be of at least $\frac{8}{9}$ of the applicants? 11.7 and 30.9

46. *Medicine*   In a blood pressure study, subjects had a mean pressure of 163 with standard deviation 9.4. Between what values must the readings be for at least $\frac{24}{25}$ of the subjects? 116 and 210

47. *Programming*   Write a program to compute and output the mean, standard deviation, and variance for a set of n numbers. Use the formula for the standard deviation of a population and test your program with the data in Example 3.

Test Yourself

The heights, in feet, of 20 selected buildings in the United States are listed below.

330, 723, 625, 390, 529, 1454, 708, 405, 720, 334,
1002, 535, 400, 858, 1350, 483, 388, 410, 667, 535

1. Make a frequency distribution using classes of length 200.   15.1

2. Construct a histogram for the frequency distribution.

3. Find P_{30}. 405   **4.** Find Q_3. 721.5   15.2

5. Make a box-and-whisker plot.   **6.** Find the mean. 642.3   15.3

7. Find the mode. 535   **8.** Find the range. 1124   15.4

9. Find the standard deviation. 308.59   **10.** Find the variance. 95,227.79

15.4 Measures of Variability   **823**

Test Yourself

1.

Height	Frequency
301–500	8
501–700	5
701–900	4
901–1100	1
1101–1300	0
1301–1500	2

2.
PH/ANS 15.4.3

5.

Vocabulary
bell curve
empirical rule
normal curve
normal distribution
standard normal distribution
standard score

FOCUS

Numerous court cases have been argued using statistics, and many laws have been passed and decisions made on the basis of statistical information. For example, the Food and Drug Administration regularly uses statistics in making decisions about new medicines. Students who have an interest in medicine may want to research one or more of these decisions. Other students may be interested in researching how laws regulating smoking were enacted.

15.5 The Normal Distribution

Objective: To use the normal distribution to find probabilities

Focus

Professional golfer Jane Blalock used statistics to win a court case against the Ladies Professional Golf Association (LPGA). In the May, 1972, Bluegrass Invitational Tournament she was disqualified for a supposed infraction of the rules of golf. A committee of LPGA golfers also suspended her from playing in the Lady Carling Open 2 weeks later.

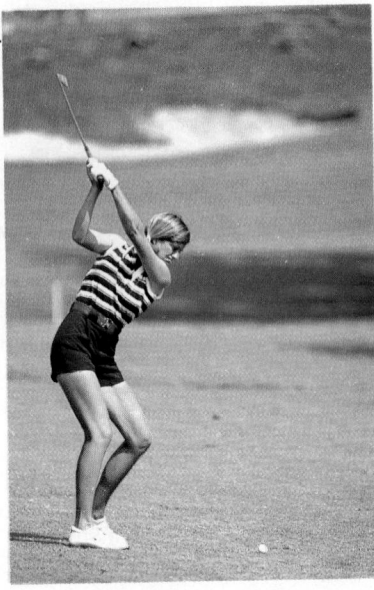

Blalock was the leading money winner on the 1972 LPGA tour, having won two of the eight tournaments completed. She sought a court injunction against the LPGA ban, arguing that she should not be suspended by her competitors who would likely benefit from her being out of the competition. Blalock won the injunction but arrived at the tournament too late to play. Ms. Blalock filed suit against the LPGA under the Sherman Anti-Trust Act, seeking damages for lost earnings in the Lady Carling Open. Her case relied upon the statistical estimation of her score, and her likely winnings, if she had played.

When a large set of data is represented graphically, its frequency polygon is often replaced by a smooth curve.

Curves representing data sets that are *normally distributed* have similar characteristics and are called **normal curves.**

- The normal curve has the general shape of a bell, and so is called a *bell curve.*
- The normal curve is symmetric about the vertical line through the mean of the distribution.
- The normal curve approaches the horizontal axis at both extremes.

The middle graph above represents a normally distributed set of data, also called a **normal distribution.** *What characteristics of the first and third graphs suggest that they do not represent normal distributions?*

824   Chapter 15 Statistics and Data Analysis

Thinking Critically
In the first graph the curve does not approach the horizontal axis at the upper extreme. In the third graph the curve is not symmetric about the vertical line through the mean of the distribution.

Data that is normally distributed clusters about its mean. The farther away from the mean a value is, the fewer data pieces there are with that value. Large values are always "balanced" by corresponding small values, and vice versa. Examples of large data sets that can be expected to be nearly normally distributed are heights of 6-year-olds, IQs of twelfth-graders, and lifespans of lightbulbs. Note, however, that small collections of data should not be expected to be normally distributed.

In a normally distributed set of data, the mean, median, and mode are equal, and are located at a vertical line of symmetry for the curve. The standard deviation measures how the data varies from this point. Therefore, for normal distributions with the same mean, the smaller the standard deviation is, the taller and narrower the bell curve will be.

In a histogram, the frequency associated with a class is represented graphically by the height of a rectangle. If the lengths of the classes are equal, you may think of each length as one unit, and so the *area* of the rectangle represents frequency as well, as shown in the histogram at the left below.

A histogram may also be used to represent *relative frequency*. In this case, shown in the middle below, the height and the area of each rectangle represent the proportion of the data that falls within the class.

Similarly, the area under a normal curve between two values a and b represents the proportion of the data that falls between a and b. This idea is key to applications of the normal curve. Note that the Greek letter μ is used to represent the mean of a population.

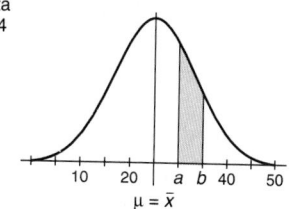

It follows immediately that the total area under a normal curve is 1. *Why?* Other information about the area is always given in terms of standard deviations. For any normal distribution, the following, sometimes called the *empirical rule*, holds:

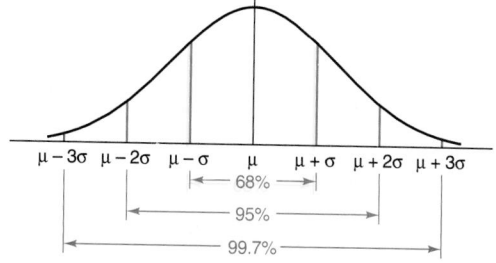

- About 68% of the data is within one standard deviation of the mean.
- About 95% of the data is within two standard deviations of the mean.
- About 99.7% of the data is within three standard deviations of the mean.

15.5 The Normal Distribution **825**

Thinking Critically
The total area under a curve is equal to 1 because it represents the total probability distribution, which must also equal 1.

For Example 1

Approximately what percent of the population has IQ scores:

1. between 70 and 130? 95%
2. above 70? 97.5%

For Example 2

1. Compare the performance of a student in Sandy's math class with an average of 78 to that of a student in her psychology class with an average of 75. The first student performs better, with a z-score of 1.5 compared to a z-score of 1.125 for the second student.

2. Do you need to compute z-scores to compare students in the same class? Why or why not? No. The mean and the standard deviation will be the same for both students.

Example 1   For the general population, IQ scores are normally distributed with a mean of 100 and standard deviation of 15. Approximately what percent of the population have IQ scores:
  a. Between 85 and 115?   **b.** Above 115?   **c.** Below 130?

  a. Since $\sigma = 15$, one standard deviation from the mean is from $100 - 15$ to $100 + 15$, that is, from 85 to 115. Therefore, by the empirical rule, 68% of the scores fall in this interval.

  b. By symmetry of the normal curve about the mean, 50% of the scores fall to the right of $x = 100$. Half of 68%, or 34%, are between 100 and 115, so $(50 - 34)\% = 16\%$ are above 115.

  c. About 95% of the scores lie between $100 - 2\sigma$ and $100 + 2\sigma$, that is, between 70 and 130. The remaining 5% are above and below these values, so by symmetry, $2\frac{1}{2}\%$ of the scores are above 130 and $97\frac{1}{2}\%$ are below 130.

The fact that 68% of the data in a normal distribution lies within one standard deviation of the mean may be restated in terms of probability. If an item of data is chosen at random from a normally distributed data set, the *probability* is 0.68 that it will be within one standard deviation of the mean.

Statisticians have formulated a table that can be used to find areas under the curve that represents the normal distribution with mean $\mu = 0$ and standard deviation $\sigma = 1$, $y = \frac{1}{\sqrt{2\pi}}e^{-\frac{1}{2}x^2}$, called the **standard normal distribution.**

Questions about any normal distribution can be translated into questions about the standard normal distribution, and so this one table can be used for normal distributions with any mean and standard deviation.

Example 2   *Education*   In her first year at college, Sandy received a grade of 80 in math and 74 in psychology. The 80 in math was in a class with a mean of 72 and a standard deviation of 4. The 74 in psychology was in a class with a mean of 66 and a standard deviation of 8. Which grade is relatively better?

Each score is 8 points above the mean. Determine how many *standard deviations* above the mean the scores are. The math score is $\frac{80 - 72}{4} = 2$ standard deviations above the mean.

The psychology score is $\dfrac{74 - 66}{8} = 1$ standard deviation above the mean.

The math grade is relatively better as the figures illustrate.

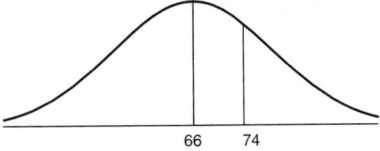

66   74

To answer the question "How many standard deviations above or below the mean is this piece of data?" is to find the associated *standard score* or *z*-**score.** If μ is the mean and σ the standard deviation, then the standard score for a value x is given by the formula

$$z = \dfrac{x - \mu}{\sigma}$$

z-score	Area from mean to z-score	Area of larger portion	Area of smaller portion
0.90	0.3159	0.8159	0.1841
0.91	0.3186	0.8186	0.1814

The *z*-score is the tool for translating questions about any normal distribution into questions about the standard normal distribution. The table that gives values for the area under the standard normal curve is in Appendix B, beginning on page 902. An excerpt from the table is shown above. Note that the first column gives the *z*-score, and the second column gives the area under the standard normal curve for the interval from 0 (the mean) to the *z*-score. The third column gives the area of the larger portion under the curve from the *z*-score, and the fourth column gives the area of the smaller portion. Only positive values of *z* are given but symmetry allows you to find areas for negative *z*-scores as well.

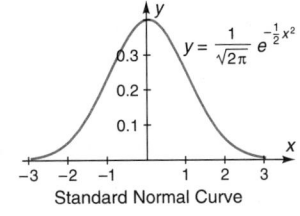

$$y = \dfrac{1}{\sqrt{2\pi}}\, e^{-\frac{1}{2}x^2}$$

Standard Normal Curve

Example 3   Find the indicated areas under the standard normal curve.
    a. between $z = 0$ and $z = 1.03$ **b.** between $z = -0.9$ and $z = 0.9$
    c. to the right of $z = 0.81$ **d.** to the right of $z = -0.81$

a. This value is in the second column of the table:
$A = 0.3485$.

b. By symmetry, the area from $z = -0.9$ to $z = 0$ equals the area from $z = 0$ to $z = 0.9$, which can be read from the table. Therefore, $A = 2(0.3159) = 0.6318$.

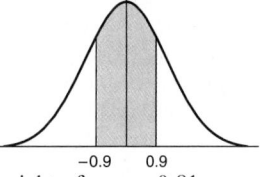

−0.9   0.9

c. The area to the right of $z = 0.81$ is the smaller portion. Reading from the fourth column, $A = 0.2090$.

d. The area to the right of $z = -0.81$ is the larger portion. Reading from the third column, $A = 0.7910$.

0 0.81

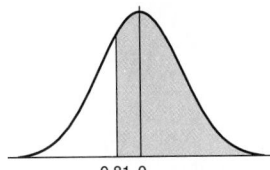

−0.81 0

For Example 3
Find the indicated areas under the standard normal curve.
1. between $z = 0$ and $z = -1.2$
   0.3849
2. to the left of $z = 0.45$ 0.6736
3. to the left of $z = -0.45$ 0.3264

828

For Example 4

A researcher studies the lengths of times it takes subjects to complete a standardized test. The times are normally distributed with a mean of 85 min and standard deviation of 8 min.

1. What is the probability that a randomly selected subject will take more than 90 min to complete the exam? 0.2643
2. What proportion of the population takes between 75 and 95 min to complete the exam? 0.7888

Modeling

Students may be interested in finding other examples of how statistics were used to resolve controversial issues.

For Example 5

Use the normal distribution to determine the probability that Jane Blalock would have scored less than 209 and won the tournament. 0.03

Since the mean of the standard normal distribution is 0 and the standard deviation is 1, the area found in Example 3b represents the proportion of data within 0.9 standard deviations of the mean. The area of Example 3c represents the proportion of data more than 0.81 standard deviations above the mean. *What do the areas in 3a and 3d represent?* You can answer questions about any normal distribution by using z-scores and the standard normal distribution.

Example 4 *Automotive Engineering*   An automobile manufacturer claims that a new car gets an average 42 mpg, and that mileage is normally distributed with a standard deviation of 4.5 mpg. If this claim is true, what percent of these new cars will get less than 40 mpg?

$$z = \frac{40 - 42}{4.5} = -0.44 \qquad \textit{z-score associated with 40 mpg}$$

The question is, "What percent of the data is more than 0.44 standard deviations to the left of the mean?" Use the standard normal distribution. Reading from the fourth column of the normal distribution table, $A = 0.3300$. Thus 33% of the cars will have a mileage less than 40 mpg.

Note that the question of Example 4 could also have been phrased, "What is the *probability* that one of these cars will have mileage less than 40 mpg?"

Modeling

How can the normal distribution be used to estimate the probability that a golfer might win a certain tournament?

The normal distribution played an important role in resolving the Jane Blalock case described in the Focus. To predict her score in the Lady Carling Open, researchers analyzed the data from her previous nine tournaments. For each tournament they compared her score with every player who finished with the lowest 25 scores. (In golf the lowest score wins.) They then used this information to determine how she might have fared against the top 25 finishers in the Lady Carling Open. Her estimated score for this tournament was 217.98, with a standard deviation of 4.90. A score of 218 strokes would have given her a tie for fifth place and prize money of $1427.50.

Example 5 *Sports*   The winner of the Lady Carling Open scored 210. Use the normal distribution to determine the probability that Jane Blalock would have scored less than 210 and won the tournament.

$$x = 210 \qquad \mu = 217.98 \qquad \sigma = 4.90$$
$$z = \frac{210 - 217.98}{4.90} = -1.63 \qquad\qquad \text{To the nearest hundredth}$$

The area under the normal curve to the *left* of $z = -1.63$ is found in the fourth column, $A = 0.0516$. Thus, the probability is about 0.05 that Ms. Blalock would have won the tournament.

828   Chapter 15 Statistics and Data Analysis

Thinking Critically

The area in 3a represents the area under the standard normal curve for the interval from the mean to the z-score. The area in 3d represents the proportion of data at least -0.81 standard deviations from the mean.

Class Exercises

Tell whether the data set represented by each histogram is approximately normal in its distribution. If your answer is "no," give a reason.

1.
yes

2.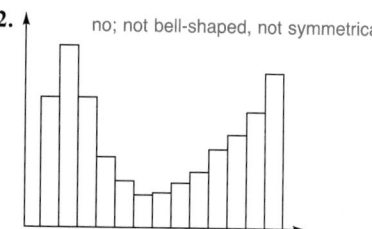
no; not bell-shaped, not symmetrical

Testing SAT (Scholastic Aptitude Test) scores are nearly normally distributed with mean of 500 and standard deviation of 100. Use the empirical rule to find approximately what percent of SAT scores fall within the following intervals.

3. between 300 and 700 95   **4.** greater than 400 84   **5.** greater than 600 16

6. What is the probability that a student's SAT score is between 500 and 700? 0.475

Find the area under the standard normal curve corresponding to each description.

7. between $z = 0$ and $z = 2.31$ 0.4896   **8.** to the right of $z = 1.45$ 0.0735

9. to the left of $z = 2.26$ 0.9881   **10.** between $z = -1.1$ and $z = 1$ 0.7056

The amount of annual rainfall in an area is assumed to be normally distributed with mean 122 cm and standard deviation 9 cm.

11. Find the z-score corresponding to 118 cm. −0.444

12. Find the z-score corresponding to 136 cm. 1.5556

13. What is the probability that in a given year the annual rainfall is less than 136 cm? Less than 118 cm? Between 118 and 136 cm? 0.9406; 0.3300; 0.6106

Practice Exercises   Use appropriate technology.

Testing SAT scores are nearly normally distributed with mean of 500 and standard deviation of 100. Use the *empirical rule* to determine approximately what percent of SAT scores fall within the following intervals.

A **1.** between 400 and 600 68   **2.** greater than 700 $2\frac{1}{2}$ **3.** greater than 300 $97\frac{1}{2}$

4. What is the probability that a student's SAT scores are between 400 and 500? 0.34

5. What is the probability that a student's SAT scores are between 400 and 700? 0.815

Eight students took the SAT and their *standardized* or *z-scores* were as follows:

    a. −1   **b.** 0   **c.** 0.5   **d.** 0   **e.** −0.1   **f.** 2   **g.** 1.9   **h.** 0.8

                    c, f, g, h   a, e
6. Which of the students scored above the mean? Below the mean?

7. Which of the students scored at the mean? b, d

8. Thinking Critically What information do the standardized scores give?

15.5 The Normal Distribution   **829**

Lesson Quiz

1. Sketch a curve that does *not* represent a normal distribution.
   Answers may vary.

2. Assume that SAT scores are normally distributed with a mean of 500 and that approximately 68% of the population scores between 400 and 600. What percent of the population scores above 600?
   16%

Find the indicated areas under the standard normal curve.

3. between $z = 0$ and $z = 2.3$
   0.4893
4. to the left of $z = -1.43$ 0.0764
5. to the left of $z = 2.05$ 0.9798
6. The lifetime of a piece of machinery is normally distributed with a mean of 11.4 years and standard deviation 0.76 years. What is the probability that one of these machines will last more than 13 years? 0.0174

Additional Answers
13. $P(5) = 0.1000$; $P(6) = 0.1000$;
    $P(7) = 0.1143$; $P(8) = 0.1429$;
    $P(9) = 0.1571$; $P(10) = 0.1286$;
    $P(11) = 0.1143$; $P(12) = 0.0857$;
    $P(13) = 0.0429$; $P(14) = 0.0143$;

9. The lowest z-score of the 8 students was -1. What was the actual score? 400
10. The highest z-score of the 8 students was 2. What was the actual score? 700
11. IQ tests have a mean of 100 and a standard deviation of 15. What is the standard score (z-score) corresponding to a score of 140? What does this z-score tell? 2.67; a score of 140 is 2.67 standard deviations above the mean.
12. *Sports* Use the information in Example 5 to determine the probability that Ms. Blalock would score above 232, which would have put her out of the money. 0.21%

A nursing supervisor studies the number of calls received on his floor between 10:00 p.m. and 6:00 a.m. Over 10 weeks, he tallies the following data:

No. calls	5	6	7	8	9	10	11	12	13	14
Frequency	7	7	8	10	11	9	8	6	3	1

Let Y be the random variable representing the number of calls received during the specified time period.

Ⓡ 13. Find the probability distribution for the random variable Y.
Ⓡ 14. What is the expected value of Y? 8.79
Ⓡ 15. What is the probability of getting 10 or more calls? 0.3857
Ⓡ 16. What are the odds against getting fewer than 10 calls? 27 to 43

Ⓑ 17. *Education* The final examination in a Spanish course had two parts, written and oral. Scores in both parts were normally distributed. In the written part, the mean was 71 with standard deviation 6; in the oral part, the mean was 62 with standard deviation 9. In which part did Ellie perform better if her written score was 78 and her oral score 73? Explain. oral; $z_{written} = 1.1667$ $z_{oral} = 1.2222$

Find the area under the standard normal curve corresponding to each description. Refer to the Appendix.

18. between $z = 0$ and $z = 1.06$ 0.3554
19. to the left of $z = 1.29$ 0.9015
20. between $z = 0$ and $z = -2.03$ 0.4788
21. between $z = -2.1$ and $z = 1.43$ 0.9057
22. to the left of $z = -0.67$ 0.2514
23. between $z = 1.3$ and $z = 2.45$ 0.0897

24. **Writing in Mathematics** Write a description of how the standard normal curve is used to solve problems involving any normal distribution.

25. *Quality Control* The lifetime of a certain kind of light bulb is normally distributed with mean 1200 h and standard deviation 60 h. What is the probability that a light bulb will last more than 1100 h? 0.9525

26. *Biology* The mean weight of a large fish is 30 kg with a standard deviation of 5 kg. Assuming that the weights are normally distributed, what percent of the fish weigh less than 36 kg? 88.49%

27. *Manufacturing* A plant manager has determined that the time it takes to assemble a component is normally distributed with mean 16.2 min and standard deviation 3 min. What is the probability that a worker assembles the component in less than 15 min? 0.3446

830 Chapter 15 Statistics and Data Analysis

Writing in Mathematics
24. Answers may vary. The standard normal curve has mean 0 and standard deviation 1. Thus a z value in the standard normal distribution is precisely $|z|$ units above or below the mean. For equations involving any normal curve, data is translated into z-scores, which tell how many standard deviations above or below the mean the data lies. Then questions about that data can be answered using the standard normal curve.

28. *Quality Control*   The amount of soda dispensed by a machine is normally distributed with mean 7.5 oz and standard deviation 0.2 oz. What is the probability that an 8-oz cup will overflow? 0.0062

29. *Sports*   In the Lady Carling Open described in the Focus, the second-, third-, and fourth-place finishers scored 212, 213, and 215, respectively. Using the information in Example 5, determine the probability that Jane Blalock would have finished in fourth place or better. 0.2709

In statistics, the symbol z_β denotes the value of z for which the area under the standard normal curve to the right of z_β is β. Find the following values.

C 30. $z_{0.05}$ 1.65   31. $z_{0.02}$ 2.05   32. $z_{0.85}$ -1.04

33. **Thinking Critically**   Why would the symbol $z_{1.2}$ be meaningless in the context of Exercises 30, 31, and 32?

34. Find z if the area under the standard normal curve between z and $-z$ is 0.6578. 0.95

35. *Education*   The average time to complete an exam is 74 min with standard deviation 12 min. Assuming that the times are normally distributed, how much time should be allowed so that 95% of those taking the exam complete it within the given time? 93.8 min

36. A data set has a normal distribution with mean $\mu = 64$. If 72% of the area under the curve is to the right of $x = 50$, what is the standard deviation of the distribution? 24.14

37. *Manufacturing*   Let x represent the life of a VCR in years. Assume that x is normally distributed with mean 4.5 years and standard deviation 0.6 year. The manufacturer wishes to offer a guarantee under which any machine that breaks down within a certain number of years will be replaced free. However, the manufacturer does not want to replace more than 2% of all VCRs. How long should the guarantee specify for replacement? 3 years 3 months

Ⓡ 38. What is the 95th percentile for IQ scores? (See Example 1.) 124.75

39. *Quality Control*   The amount of sugar that a machine puts into a 5-lb bag is normally distributed with a standard deviation of 0.05 lb. The quality control manager wants to be sure that no more than 5% of the bags contain less than 5 lb of sugar. What must the mean be in order to guarantee this? 5.0825

Project

Research other cases of the Sherman Anti-Trust Act involving athletes. Two such cases are the Rozelle rule in football or the Curt Flood case in baseball. Report on any use of mathematics in the case you choose to read about. Answers may vary.

Challenge

1. Find the value of x, if $x = \dfrac{1}{1 + \sqrt[4]{2}} \cdot -(1 - \sqrt[4]{2})(1 + \sqrt{2})$

2. How many pairs (x, y) of integers satisfy the equation $x + y = xy$. 2

Objective: *To test a hypothesis over a given confidence interval*

FOCUS

Quality control addresses two distinct issues: the acceptance of items supplied by others and the creation of goods. *Acceptance sampling* is used to determine whether a batch of items supplied by others should be accepted or rejected. *Statistical process controls* are applied during production to monitor the process and its outcomes. These controls help managers detect and correct problems early and prevent the production of defective goods.

Quality control is another example of statistics serving as a *tool* for decision making. Based on available statistics, a worker or manager decides when and how to make an adjustment.

Focus

Quality control in manufacturing is increasingly the responsibility of every employee. This process control chart, designed by a plant engineer, may be monitored and updated by the production workers on an assembly line. Each dot represents the average measurements for four parts. The desired measurement for each part is 2.5 cm, with a tolerance of 0.20 cm. Workers may stop the machining process if an average is not between the control limits of 2.3 and 2.7 cm, or adjust the machine when a sequence of averages is above or below the target measurement. This is an example of *statistical process control.*

Modeling manufacturing processes through the use of statistical process control is an important tool in enabling companies to remain competitive. Quality control reduces waste and improves product reliability.

Recall that in a statistical problem a *population* is the set of all data of interest, and a *sample* is a subset of the population. Information about the sample is used to draw conclusions about the population. The problem of determining how likely it is that these conclusions are accurate is central to the branch of statistics called *inferential statistics.*

A T-shirt manufacturer needs to know how many of each size shirt to make. A sample of the population is chosen and measured. The proportions that result are 15% small, 25% medium, 35% large, and 30% extra-large. In choosing a sample, it is important that each member of the population have an equal chance of being part of the sample. A sample chosen in this way is called a **random sample.** The larger the sample, the better the information from the sample represents information about the population from which it has been chosen.

Example 1 Tell whether each sample is a random sample of voters in a district.
   a. The names of all voters are put into a box and mixed well. Ten names are chosen from the box.
   b. The first 10 people who arrive for a meeting of the Young Republican Club are chosen as the sample.

   a. The sample is random. All voters are equally likely to be chosen.
   b. The sample is not random and will not represent all voters. For example, Democracts and other non-Republicans will not be chosen.

In the context of inferential statistics, a *hypothesis* is an assumption about a population. **Hypothesis testing** is a procedure by which a decision is made to *accept* or to *reject* the hypothesis.

A hypothesis is often a statement about a population mean. The *alternative hypothesis* states the conditions for which the original hypothesis is not true.

Example 2 The producer of a TV program claims that the program has an average viewing audience of 10 million people. State this as a hypothesis and also state the alternative hypothesis.

Hypothesis: $\mu = 10$ million   Alternative hypothesis: $\mu \neq 10$ million

An important theorem in statistics states that if all random samples of a fixed size $n \geq 30$ are taken from a large population, then the means $\bar{x}$ of those samples will be normally distributed. Furthermore, the mean $\mu_{\bar{x}}$ of the sample means will equal the mean μ of the original population. If the population is normally distributed to start with, the result holds even for small samples

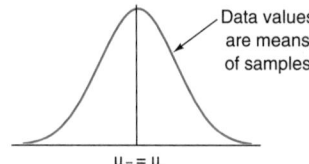
Data values are means of samples

$\mu_{\bar{x}} = \mu$

It is also known that if σ is the standard deviation of the population, then the standard deviation of the sample means is $\sigma_{\bar{x}} = \dfrac{\sigma}{\sqrt{n}}$ where n is the sample size.

The standard deviation of the sample means is often called the **standard error of the mean.** Notice that the larger the sample size, the smaller the value of $\sigma_{\bar{x}}$; that is, the less the sample means will vary from the mean of the population.

Since sample means are normally distributed with mean μ and standard deviation $\sigma_{\bar{x}}$, 95% of them lie between $\mu - 1.96\sigma_{\bar{x}}$ and $\mu + 1.96\sigma_{\bar{x}}$. *Why?* Similarly, 99% of them lie between $\mu - 2.58\sigma_{\bar{x}}$ and $\mu + 2.58\sigma_{\bar{x}}$. These are referred to as the 95% and 99% **confidence intervals.** If the mean of the population is what the hypothesis says it is, then 95% of the sample means are within $\pm 1.96\sigma_{\bar{x}}$ of that number, and 99% of the sample means are within $\pm 2.58\sigma_{\bar{x}}$ of it.

Example 3 A random sample of size 36 is chosen from a large population of weights of trucks whose standard deviation is known to be 440 lb. What is the 95% confidence interval?

The standard deviation of the sample means is $\sigma_{\bar{x}} = \dfrac{\sigma}{\sqrt{36}} = \dfrac{440}{6} = 73.33$. The 95% confidence interval is then from $\mu - (1.96)(73.33)$ to $\mu + (1.96)(73.33)$ or from $\mu - 143.73$ to $\mu + 143.73$.

In hypothesis testing, decide in advance the confidence level you can accept. Also decide on a sample size n. Then choose a random sample of size n and compute its mean. If the mean lies outside your confidence interval, reject the hypothesis.

A 95% confidence interval is referred to as the *0.05 level of significance.* Similarly, the 99% confidence level corresponds to the *0.01 level of significance.*

15.6 Confidence Intervals and Hypothesis Testing   **833**

Thinking Critically
From the table, the area under the normal curve from the mean to a z-score of 1.96 is 0.4750. Therefore, the area under the normal curve between z-scores of −1.96 and 1.96 is 0.950, which represents a probability of 95%.

For Example 2

State each of the following as a hypothesis and also state the alternative hypothesis.

1. The mean number of fish caught by passengers in an all-day fishing boat trip is greater than 3.
   Hypothesis: $\mu > 3$
   Alternative hypothesis: $\mu \leq 3$
2. The mean number of passengers in a taxi crossing Broadway at Main Street on a weekday afternoon is 1.3.
   Hypothesis: $\mu = 1.3$
   Alternative hypothesis: $\mu \neq 1.3$

For Example 3

A random sample of size 100 is chosen from a large population of diameters of flower pots whose standard deviation is 0.3 in.

1. What is the 95% confidence interval? $[\mu - 0.0588, \mu + 0.0588]$
2. What is the 99% confidence interval? $[\mu - 0.0774, \mu + 0.0774]$

Modeling

To enhance the model have students measure the contents of packages of various products and then use hypothesis testing to check their findings against the claims on the labels of those products.

For Example 4

1. Find the control limits corresponding to a 99% confidence interval on the means of a sample of size 10 for the machine in Example 4. 3.42 to 3.58
2. Suppose for a sample of size 4 the mean diameter is 3.365 in. Would you accept the manufacturer's claim at the 99% confidence level? No. For a sample of size 4, the 99% confidence interval is 3.371 to 3.629.

CLOSURE

Have students explain testing a hypothesis over a given confidence interval in a letter to a student who was absent.

Modeling

How can confidence intervals be used to ensure quality control in manufacturing?

A process control engineer is responsible for setting up a system for checking that certain parts that are manufactured meet measurement standards. A machine is designed to produce parts with a specific measurement, which is interpreted as the mean μ. The measurement of any given part that the machine produces may vary slightly from that mean, and therefore the machine has a standard deviation σ associated with it. The task of the engineer is to use this data to determine a confidence interval. Random samples of parts produced by the machine can then be tested to ensure that the machine is functioning correctly.

Example 4 *Manufacturing* A milling machine is designed to make parts that are 3.50 cm in diameter with a standard deviation of 0.10 cm. Find the control limits corresponding to a 95% confidence interval on the means of a sample of size four.

$\sigma_{\bar{x}} = \dfrac{0.10}{\sqrt{4}} = 0.05$ $\mu = 3.50; \sigma = 0.10; n = 4$ *Standard error*

$3.50 - 1.96(0.05)$ to $3.50 + 1.96(0.05)$ *95% confidence interval*

3.40 to 3.60

Assuming that the sizes of the parts that the machine produces are normally distributed, the process control engineer can periodically choose four parts from the assembly line. If the mean of their diameters is between 3.40 and 3.60, the engineer can be reasonably sure that the machine is functioning correctly.

Class Exercises

Identify the population for each experiment and suggest a way to choose a sample of size $n = 50$. Answers may vary.

1. *Medicine* A doctor wishes to study the time it takes for 6-year-olds to recover from strep throat.
2. *Sports* A sports commentator is interested in the length of time it takes to play a professional hockey game.
3. *Sports* For the situation of Exercise 2, explain why the lengths of all games played by the Philadelphia Flyers in the 1990–1991 season would *not* form a random sample.
4. The distribution of scores in a national French exam has standard deviation $\sigma = 11.5$. What is the standard error of the mean for random samples of size 40? 1.8183
5. It is known that the distribution of the number of pieces of candy per bag has standard deviation $\sigma = 3$ pieces. What is the standard error of the mean for random samples of size $n = 36$? $\frac{1}{2}$
6. A random sample of 36 bags has mean $\bar{x} = 41.7$ pieces of candy. Should the null hypothesis be rejected at the 0.01 level of significance (99% confidence interval)? no; $\bar{x} \in [40.72, 42.68]$

Additional Answers, Class Exercises

1. Answers may vary. The population is all 6-year-olds with strep throat. To choose a sample, interview 10 doctors randomly and ask for information on 5 patients that fit the criteria.
2. Answers may vary. The population is all professional hockey games. To choose a sample, call sports editors from 25 cities and ask each for data from 2 games.
3. The sample is not random because each professional hockey game does not have an equal chance of being part of the sample.

Practice Exercises Use appropriate technology.

Identify the population for each experiment and suggest a way to choose a sample of size $n = 100$. Answers may vary.

A **1.** *Education*   A researcher wishes to study IQ scores of bilingual 8-year-olds.

   2. *Botany*   A botanist is interested in the number of oranges produced by a new strain of trees.

   3. *Linguistics*   A linguist wants to verify a theory about the use of the word "like" in speech patterns of 15-year-olds.

   4. **Thinking Critically**   Give three reasons why a sample might be used to represent a population rather than dealing with the entire population.

   5. **Thinking Critically**   Give an example of a sample of potential T-shirt wearers for which large and extra-large sizes would be underrepresented.

   6. *Manufacturing*   A manager chooses every 50th item that comes off an assembly line for testing purposes. Why would this sample not be random?

   7. Suppose that all students in a school district have an ID number between 0001 and 9999. Use a calculator or computer program with a *random number generator* to give 30 four-digit random numbers. Students with these numbers form a sample in the district. Is this sample random? Why or why not?

   8. Statisticians interested in analyzing people's opinions often use questionnaires that must be filled out and returned by mail. Responses to those questionnaires form samples of the opinions of much larger groups. Name some groups of people that are likely to be underrepresented in those samples.

   9. Sometimes people's opinions are asked directly by interviewers who approach individuals at malls, outside places of business, and at other locations. Name some groups of people whose opinions might be underrepresented by this method of sampling.

Formulate an alternative hypothesis for each hypothesis.

   10. $\mu \neq 25.6$ $H_1: \mu = 25.6$ **11.** $\mu \leq 89$ $H_1: \mu > 89$ **12.** $\mu \geq 0$ $H_1: \mu < 0$ **13.** $\mu = 2$ $H_1: \mu \neq 2$

Ⓡ **14.** Solve triangle *DEF*, if $\angle F = 43°$, $d = 16$, and $f = 24$. $\angle D = 27.04°$; $\angle E = 109.96°$; $e = 33.08$

Ⓡ **15.** Solve triangle *RST*, if $\angle S = 54°$, $r = 14$, and $t = 20$. $\angle R = 43.90°$; $\angle T = 82.10°$; $s = 16.34$

   16. **Writing in Mathematics**   Write a definition of a hypothesis and explain why a hypothesis needs to be tested.

B **17.** *Zoology*   Random samples of size $n = 100$ are chosen from a very large population of the lengths of fish with mean $\mu = 2.4$ cm and standard deviation $\sigma = 0.08$ cm. Describe the distribution of the means of the samples. What are the mean and standard deviation of this distribution of sample means?

   18. *Sociology*   Random samples of size $n = 42$ are chosen from a very large population of the number of hours of television watched weekly by middle school students. The population has mean $\mu = 8.9$ h and standard deviation 1.1 h. Describe the distribution of the means of the samples. What are the mean and standard deviation of this distribution of sample means?

15.6 Confidence Intervals and Hypothesis Testing   **835**

INDEPENDENT PRACTICE

Assignment Guide
Basic: 1–16, 24–26, Project
Average: 4–6, 14–29, Project
Enriched: 4–5, 16, 20–23, 27–37, Project

Teacher's Resource Book
   Practice, page 108

Ⓡ **Review**
Exercises 14, 15, 24, and 25, review concepts of solving triangles, multiplying matrices, and probability.

Additional Answers
   1. The population is the set of IQ scores of all bilingual 8-year olds. Example: Ask for 5 bilingual 8-year olds from each of 20 schools.
   2. The population is the number of oranges produced by each of the trees. Example: Ask 10 orchard owners for information on 10 trees each.
   3. The population is the number of times 15-year olds use the word "like" in a given context. Example: Do a test with 100 15-year olds chosen at random.
   6. Answers may vary. The 50th item might be handled by the same assembler.
   7. The sample is random because each student is equally likely to be chosen.
   17. The means are normally distributed with $\mu_{\bar{x}} = 2.4$ cm and $\sigma_{\bar{x}} = 0.008$ cm.
   18. The means are normally distributed with $\mu_{\bar{x}} = 8.9$ h and $\sigma_{\bar{x}} = 0.1697$ h.

Lesson Quiz

Tell whether each sample is a random sample of songs played on a radio station. Explain.

1. The radio is turned on every day at noon during the month of December, and the first song heard is noted. No, only songs played in December would be the sample. Christmas songs, for example, could be overrepresented.

2. The sample consists of every song played on the first Friday of each month for a year. No, the sample is not completely random. If the station ran a jazz show only on Saturdays, for example, jazz would not be chosen.

3. Formulate an alternative hypothesis for this null hypothesis: The mean number of white rats in a litter is less than 5. $\mu \geq 5$

4. A random sample of size 64 is chosen from a large population of the number of minutes it takes first graders to put together a puzzle. The standard deviation of the population is known to be 3.1 min. What is the 95% confidence interval? $\mu - 0.7595$ to $\mu + 0.7595$

5. A psychologist claims that the mean time it takes children to put the puzzle together is 12.4 min. The mean of the random sample of size 64 is 10.8 min. State this as a hypothesis and also state the alternative hypothesis.
Hypothesis: $\mu = 12.4$
Alternative hypothesis: $\mu \neq 12.4$

6. Test the hypothesis of Exercise 5 at the 95% confidence level.
A mean of 10.8 is outside the interval 11.6405 to 13.1595, so reject the hypothesis.

Marketing A fast food restaurant claims that the average weight of the beef in its special sandwich is 0.25 lb.

19. Write a hypothesis and an alternative hypothesis that could be used to test this claim. $H_0: \mu = 0.25$ lb; $H_1: \mu \neq 0.25$ lb

20. It is known that the distribution of the weight of the beef in the sandwiches has standard deviation $\sigma = 0.05$ lb. A random sample of the amount of beef in 64 sandwiches has mean $\bar{x} = 0.22$ oz. Is the sample mean within the confidence interval at the 0.05 level of significance (95% confidence interval)? no; 0.22 is not in the interval [0.23775, 0.26225]

Education A school superintendent believes that the mean IQ of students in his district is 115.

21. Write a hypothesis and an alternative hypothesis that could be used to test this belief. $H_0: \mu = 115$; $H_1: \mu \neq 115$

22. It is known that the distribution of the IQ scores has standard deviation $\sigma = 15$. A random sample of IQ scores for 90 students in the district has mean $\bar{x} = 111.5$. Should the hypothesis be rejected at the 0.01 level of significance? no; 111.5 is in the interval [110.92, 119.

23. *Quality Control* A box is supposed to contain an average of 16 oz of macaroni with standard deviation of 0.41 oz. A random sample of 50 boxes is found to have mean weight 15.24 oz. Does the population of boxes of macaroni differ significantly at the 0.05 level from the standard?

Ⓡ 24. Given $A = \begin{vmatrix} 3 & 2 \\ -1 & -5 \end{vmatrix}$ and $B = \begin{vmatrix} -2 & 9 \\ 6 & -7 \end{vmatrix}$, find AB. 520

Ⓡ 25. The life span of batteries is normally distributed with mean 50 months and standard deviation 5.5 months. What is the probability that a battery will last less than 42 months? 0.0735

26. *Packaging* A box of sugar substitute packets should contain 150 packets with a standard deviation of 3 packets. A random sample of 36 boxes from one quality control lot has a mean of 153.1 packets. Does this lot differ significantly from the standard at the 0.05 level of significance? Why or why not?

27. *Manufacturing* A factory produces bottle caps which should have a mean diameter 1.90 cm and standard deviation 0.04 cm. A random sample of 50 caps from one shipment has a mean diameter of 1.92 cm. Does this shipment vary significantly from the standard at the 0.01 level of significance? Why or why not?

28. **Thinking Critically** Why should confidence intervals and the size of the sample be decided *before* a sample is chosen?

Ⓒ 29. **Thinking Critically** Explain why you expect the standard error of the mean to be smaller than the standard deviation.

30. *Manufacturing* It is common practice in American industry to set control limits at $\mu \pm \dfrac{3\sigma}{\sqrt{n}}$. Redo Example 4 using these limits. Approximately what confidence level corresponds to these limits? control limits: 3.35 to 3.65; 99.7%

836 Chapter 15 Statistics and Data Analysis

Additional Answers
23. yes; 15.24 is not in the interval 15.89 to 16.11.
26. yes; 153.1 is not in the interval 149.02 to 150.98.
27. yes; 1.92 is not in the interval 1.885 to 1.915.
28. Answers may vary. To maintain objectivity, the intervals and sample sizes should be chosen before a sample is taken, because otherwise the results might influence the choice.
29. By definition, the standard error $\dfrac{\sigma}{\sqrt{n}}$ will be less than σ for sample sizes greater than 1.

31. *Zoology*   The 95% confidence interval for the incubation time of Rhode Island Red chicks is between 20.72 and 21.28 days. The standard deviation for the incubation time is 1 day. What size random sample was used to determine the confidence interval? 49

32. *Manufacturing*   The 99% confidence interval for the average life of a car battery is from 45.57 to 50.43 months using a random sample of 72 batteries. What are the mean and standard deviation of the lifetimes of the car batteries? mean = 48; σ = 7.99

The hypothesis testing discussed in this lesson is referred to as a *two-tailed* test since the hypothesis is rejected if the mean of the sample varies significantly from the assumed mean in either direction. *One-tailed* tests are also useful.

33. Suppose in the situation of Exercise 23 you wished to test the hypothesis $\mu \geq 16$ at the 0.05 level of significance; that is, you would reject the hypothesis only if the sample mean fell in the leftmost 5% of the area under the normal curve. For what values of the sample mean would you reject the hypothesis? $\bar{x} < 15.89$

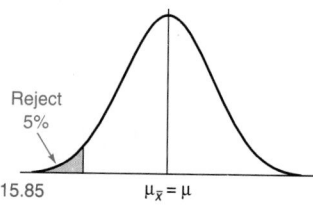

34. Repeat Exercise 33 for the 0.01 level of significance. $\bar{x} < 15.85$

35. Suppose in the situation in Exercise 18 you wished to test the hypothesis $\mu \leq 8.9$ at the 0.01 level of significance, that is, you would reject the hypothesis only if the sample mean fell in the rightmost 1% of the area under the normal curve. For what values of the sample mean would you reject the hypothesis? $\bar{x} > 9.3379$

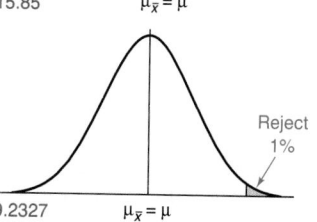

36. Repeat Exercise 35 for the 0.05 level of significance. $\bar{x} > 9.2327$

37. It is intuitively clear that the larger the size of a sample, the more likely it is that the mean of the sample is a good approximation for the mean of the population from which the sample was drawn. How is this reflected in the equation for $\sigma_{\bar{x}}$?

Project

Create a statistical process control experiment using data from your school. For example, find the mean number of students who are absent in a week and the standard deviation. Then use the number of absentees for a specific week to test this information for various levels of significance. Answers may vary.

Review

Evaluate for $x = -2.5$.

1. $-x^3$ 15.625   **2.** $\sqrt{x^2}$ 2.5   **3.** $-\sqrt{x^2}$ −2.5   **4.** x^{-1} −0.4

Evaluate.

5. $_7P_5$ 2520   **6.** $_8P_4$ 1680   **7.** $_{10}C_4$ 210   **8.** $_9C_3$ 84

37. $\sigma_{\bar{x}} = \dfrac{\sigma}{\sqrt{n}}$, so the larger the sample size *n*, the smaller the standard error $\sigma_{\bar{x}}$. Since $\sigma_{\bar{x}}$ measures the variation of the sample means from the mean of the population, a small $\sigma_{\bar{x}}$ suggests that the sample means are close to the population mean.

Vocabulary
correlation analysis
correlation coefficient
curvilinear
curvilinear regression
dependent variable
independent variable
linear regression equation
regression analysis
scatter diagram
scatter plot

Technology
computer
graphing utility

FOCUS

Students may be familiar with various theories about the relationship between diet and athletic performance.

One theory, for example, advises football players to eat quantities of pasta before an important game. Discuss how ideas for these theories arise. For example, someone notices a possible relationship between food and performance, seeks other examples of the relationship, and looks for an explanation. The strength of the relationship or correlation is measured using statistical techniques.

15.7 Curve Fitting

Objectives: To define and give examples of curve fitting
To interpret the linear correlation coefficient

Focus

Athletes are always looking for an edge over their competitors. Sometimes this involves finding measurable traits about themselves that can be worked on to achieve maximum performance. For example, a football lineman or a weight lifter will often "bulk up" to increase strength. A runner may try to find the best stride rate or pace that provides the stamina for a strong finish. Many athletes keep records of their performances. If an athlete can find a *correlation* between some controllable variable and the strength of his or her performance, it might provide the edge needed to be a winner.

In statistical applications, exact relationships between variables may not exist. However, *average* relationships may be observed and used for predictions.

Regression analysis is a collection of methods by which estimates are made of the values of one variable based on the values of another variable. **Correlation analysis** tells the degree to which the variables are related.

A valuable tool for recognizing and analyzing relationships is the **scatter plot,** or *scatter diagram.* The variable representing the prediction to be made is called the *dependent variable* and is plotted on the vertical or *y*-axis. The variable representing the basis for the prediction is called the *independent variable* and is plotted on the horizontal or *x*-axis.

Example 1   A college admissions committee wishes to predict students' first-year math averages from their math SAT scores. The following data is available.

Student No.	SAT score	Grade	Student No.	SAT score	Grade
1	550	90	11	590	88
2	470	84	12	530	80
3	600	87	13	480	79
4	450	77	14	700	92
5	500	80	15	660	90
6	600	93	16	680	95
7	650	94	17	570	82
8	490	80	18	630	86
9	450	65	19	500	68
10	520	85	20	590	81

Graph the points representing the performance of these 20 students. Take the grades as the dependent variable, since they are the values to be predicted.

The graph of Example 1 shows 20 points which clearly do not lie on a straight line or a simple curve. However, they do indicate a trend or average relationship. In general, higher SAT scores correspond to higher grades. This is referred to as a direct or positive linear relationship. Other kinds of relationships can also be visualized using scatter diagrams.

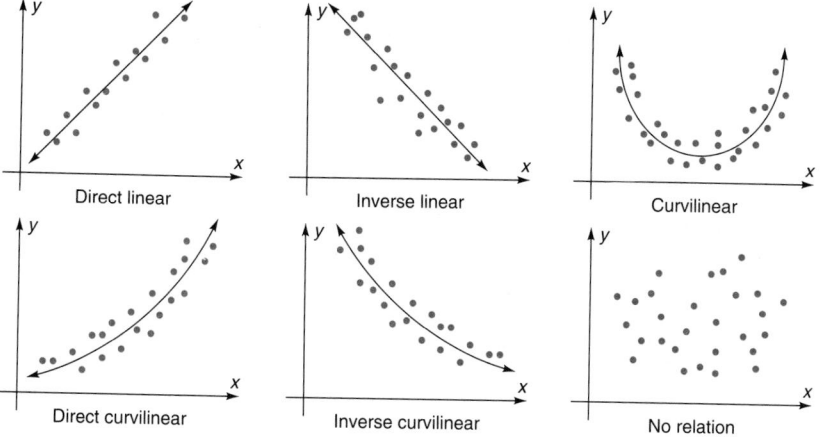

Direct linear   Inverse linear   Curvilinear

Direct curvilinear   Inverse curvilinear   No relation

Graphing calculators and computer programs may be used to graph scatter plots. Be sure to identify first which is the independent and which is the dependent variable. Enter the independent variable as x, the dependent as y.

Given a scatter diagram, one of the statistician's tasks is to identify the line or curve that "best fits" the points. Another task is to measure how good the fit is. Once the equation of the line or curve has been found, it can be used for prediction.

Statisticians use the *method of least squares* to obtain what is called the **linear regression** equation. This is the equation $y = a + bx$ of a line that has two properties. If Δy is the vertical distance from a point on the scatter diagram to the line, then:

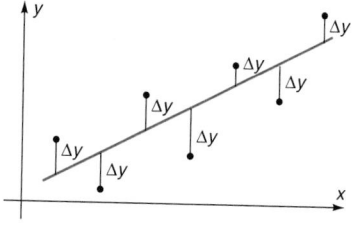

- The sum of all the values Δy is zero.
- The sum of the squares of the values Δy is as small as possible.

15.7 Curve Fitting   **839**

- Have students talk in small groups about examples of variables that are related, and whether the relationship is direct or inverse. Ask each group to present one example to the class.
- Have students collect data about paired variables like height and weight, parent's height and child's height, amount of water provided to a plant and the plant's height, and so on. Then have them make a scatter plot and judge whether or not there is a linear relationship, and if so whether it is direct or inverse. Finally, have them find the correlation coefficient and linear regression equation and make one or more predictions.
- Students should be encouraged to speculate about the causes of observed correlation. They should recognize that even though the value of one variable can be predicted from another, the change in the independent variable does not necessarily cause change in the dependent variable.
- Talented students may be interested in learning more about using the method of least squares to obtain the linear regression equation. Refer those students to any standard text on statistics for an explanation.
- Point out that rising costs due to inflation, depreciation of a car, amounts of memorized information retained, and temperatures of a cooling liquid may all be modeled with an exponential regression curve.

Alternative Learning Styles

Students who are subjective learners benefit from recognizing connections among content areas. These students should be encouraged to collect data from another subject area like science, as suggested above, and analyze correlation and regression.

For Example 1

Graph the data given in the following table. The heights are in inches.

Height	Shoe size	Height	Shoe size
61	6	66	9
60	$5\frac{1}{2}$	65	7
65	8	69	$9\frac{1}{2}$
64	$8\frac{1}{2}$	68	$8\frac{1}{2}$
64	$7\frac{1}{2}$	64	7
61	7	63	7

Modeling

Have students try to predict how rate of stride is related to speed. Then have them check their predictions by observing marathon runners and sprinters. Have the students explain why the rate of stride of a marathon runner is different from that of a sprinter.

For Example 2

Use linear regression to compute the linear model $y = a + bx$ for data of Class Exercise 1 on page 841. Let $x =$ the number of grams of fat and $y =$ the number of calories. Round coefficients to the nearest thousandth. $72.791 + 6.781x$

Common Error Some students may confuse the linear model, customarily given by statisticians in the form $y = a + bx$, with the slope-intercept form $y = mx + b$. Point out the difference. Encouraging these students to use a graphing utility or a computer can help them to avoid this type of error.

Modeling

How can you use data analysis to find an equation that will relate a runner's speed with his or her rate of stride?

Long distance runners are often concerned with their running form. One measure of form is a runner's stride rate, defined as the number of steps taken per second. A stride rate that is too low or too high will decrease a runner's efficiency. The stride rate should increase smoothly as the runner's speed increases. Researchers have collected data on the stride rates of many of the best American female runners for various running speeds, given in the table below.

Speed (ft/s)	15.86	16.88	17.50	18.62	19.97	21.06	22.11
Stride rate (steps/s)	3.05	3.12	3.17	3.25	3.36	3.46	3.55

Example 2 Use linear regression to compute the linear model $y = a + bx$ that relates a runner's stride rate y to her speed x. Round coefficients to the nearest thousandth.

Using an appropriate calculator or computer software, input the data as ordered pairs (x, y). Use the linear regression function.

$a = 1.766077145$ The linear model relating stride rate
$b = 0.0802837878$ to speed is $y = 1.766 + 0.080x$

When using a calculator or computer to obtain the coefficients for the model in Example 2, you may have noticed another value, r, in the output. In the case of linear regression, a number r between -1 and 1, called a **correlation coefficient,** is used to measure the strength of the linear relationship between x and y. When r is either 1 or -1, points on the scatter plot all lie on a straight line, a rising line if $r = 1$, and a falling line if $r = -1$. This is referred to as perfect linear correlation. In applications, perfect correlation is very rare. At the other extreme, a correlation coefficient of 0 indicates no linear relationship between the variables.

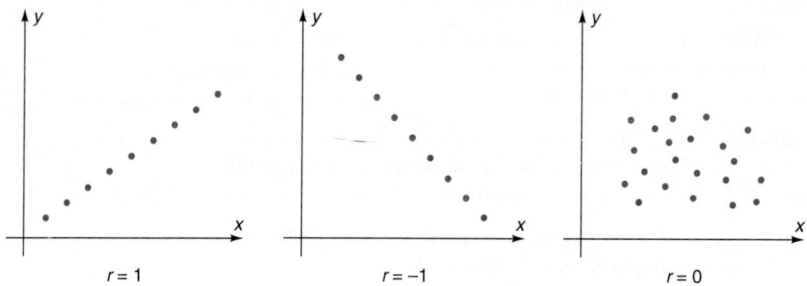

In most cases, the correlation coefficient falls between the extremes of perfect linear correlation and no linear correlation. The sign of r tells whether the relationship is direct or inverse. For $r > 0$, y increases as x increases and for $r < 0$, y decreases as x increases. The closer r is to 1 or -1, the better the points on the scatter plot "fit" a straight line. In Example 2 the correlation coefficient was $r = 0.998977247$, which suggests that the correlation is very strong.

Example 3 Match the scatter diagrams below with the correlation coefficients $r = 0.3$, $r = 0.9$, $r = -0.4$, and $r = -0.75$.

a. $r = 0.9$, a rising line that fits the points well
b. $r = -0.4$, a falling line that fits the points, but not closely
c. $r = 0.3$, a rising line that fits the points, but not closely

A straight line is not always the best way to describe the relationship between two variables. Various nonlinear functions may fit the data better. In these cases the relationship between x and y is described as *curvilinear*.

Curvilinear regression includes exponential, logarithmic, and power models.

Exponential: $y = ab^x$
Logarithmic: $y = a + b \ln (x)$
Power: $y = ax^b$

Example 4 *Business* An accountant presents this data about a company's profits in thousands of dollars for the 7 years after a management reorganization. Use technology to fit an exponential curve to this data. Then use the curve to predict the profit for year 8.

Year	Profits
1	150
2	210
3	348
4	490
5	660
6	872
7	1400

The equation will be of the form $y = ab^x$, where x is the number of years. A calculator gives the values $a = 107.2085139$ and $b = 1.438877784$. Graphing the equation

$$y = (107)(1.44)^x$$

on the same axes as the scatter plot for the data shows how good the fit is. For $x = 8$, $y = 1978.26$, and so a profit of $\$1,978,000$ is predicted for year 8.

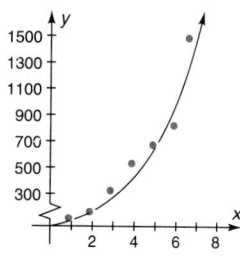

Class Exercises

An analysis of new products in the lowfat food market gives the following data for 10 new products.

1. Make a scatter plot for this data using grams of fat as the independent variable.

2. Give a reason why this relationship could not be described exactly using a function.

Product	Fat (g)	Calories
yogurt 1	3	190
yogurt 2	0	90
salad dressing 1	5	50
salad dressing 2	0	6
cheese 1	7	90
cheese 2	0	45
cake 1	5	120
cake 2	0	80
ice cream 1	7	140
ice cream 2	0	100

15.7 Curve Fitting **841**

Additional Answers

1.

2. Several values of the independent variables have more than one value associated with them.

The graph shows a scatter diagram and regression
line representing the distances in miles traveled to
work each day and the commuting times in
minutes for employees of a large company.

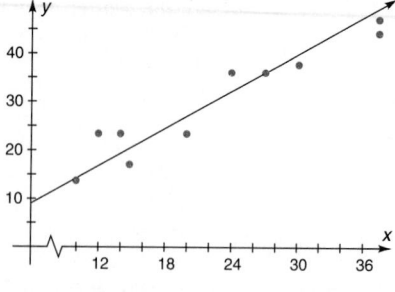

3. Use the graph to estimate the y-intercept and
   slope of the regression line. 8; 1.4

4. Use the estimates of Exercise 3 to write the
   equation of the regression line. $y = 1.4x + 8$

5. Use the equation of the regression line to
   predict the traveling time of an employee of
   the company who travels 21 mi. 37.4 min

Tell whether you would expect the correlation of each pair of variables to be
low, moderate, or high.

6. heights and shoe sizes of 14-year-old males high   7. heights of husbands and wives
8. ages and prices of cars on a used car lot   moderate to low
                                              high to moderate   9. weekly incomes and annual incomes
                                                                                                              high
10. Which, if any, of the variables described in Exercises 6 to 9 would you
    expect to be negatively correlated? age, price of cars

Practice Exercises   Use appropriate technology.

Health   A "Healthy Heart" program publishes the cholesterol and fat content
in milligrams for 3-oz portions of selected animal products. This data is found
in Appendix A, page 901.

A 1. Let the cholesterol content be the independent variable and the fat content
      the dependent variable, and plot the points.
                                                                        for $x = 79$, $y = 11.1$ and $y = 8.2$
   2. Give a reason why this relationship could not be described using a function.

   3. Do you expect that there is a straight line that estimates the relationship of
      fat content to cholesterol which could be used for predictions? Why or why not?
                                                                        No, scatter plot does not approximate a line.

Education   A professor collected data on midterm and final grades of students
in a statistics course. Let x = midterm grade, based on 100 points, and y =
final grade, based on 200 points.

x	68	91	75	90	52	78	40	88	95	83	75	74	70
y	140	183	164	178	114	150	100	180	191	155	148	156	131

4. Make a scatter diagram for these values.

5. Draw a straight line that you think best fits the data points.

6. Is the relationship shown on the scatter diagram direct or inverse? Explain.

7. The method of least squares gives $y = 27.44 + 1.67x$ as the line that best
   fits the data points. Use this model to predict the final grade for a student
   whose midterm grade is 80. 161.04

R 8. What is the slope of the line identified in Exercise 7? the y-intercept? 1.67; 27.44

9. Does a good grade in the midterm *cause* a good grade in the final? If not,
   how can the relationship between the variables be explained?

Demographics   A research institute collected data about the literacy rates and life expectancy in 11 parts of the world. Let *x* represent the literacy rate in percent and let *y* represent the life expectancy in years.

x	72	80	99	99	75	34	57	72	99	97	37
y	63	66	74	76	65	50	59	61	69	73	49

10. Make a scatter plot. Is the relationship direct or inverse? Explain.

11. The method of least squares gives $y = 36.57 + 0.3688x$ as the line that best fits the data points. Use this model to predict the life expectancy for people in an area with a 90% literacy rate. 69.76

12. Does the ability to read increase a person's life expectancy? If not, how can the relationship between the variables be explained?

Ⓡ 13. Find the equation of the line that passes through $P(-4, 0.9)$ and $Q(1, 5.7)$. $y = 0.96x + 4.74$

14. Make scatter diagrams of 12 points that show a perfect direct linear relationship, a perfect inverse linear relationship, no linear relationship.

15. **Writing in Mathematics**   Crickets are known to chirp more quickly as the temperature increases, and people have learned to use the crickets' chirping as a thermometer. Describe how you would come up with a formula to predict the temperature from the chirp rate.

16. Draw a scatter diagram representing variables whose relationship would best be modeled by a curvilinear model.

17. **Thinking Critically**   The set of data represented in this scatter plot has a correlation coefficient $r = 0$, yet the variables are clearly related. Explain this seeming contradiction. *r describes the degree of a linear relationship.*

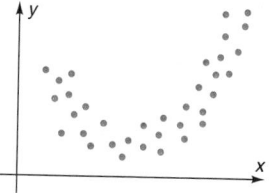

Suppose that the following pairs of variables are related linearly. Will the correlation coefficient describing the strength of the relationship be positive or negative?

B 18. heights and weights of 21-year-old males   19. temperature and heating oil usage negative
positive

20. hours of television watched per week by 16-year-olds and their math grades negative

21. number of years of formal education and annual income positive

22. number of cigarettes smoked a week and lung capacity in males negative

Sports   The table below provides the stride rate for the best American male runners for various speeds.

Speed (ft/s)	15.86	16.88	17.50	18.62	19.97	21.06	22.11
Stride rate	2.92	2.98	3.03	3.11	3.22	3.31	3.41

23. Make a scatter plot for the data.

24. Use linear regression to find an equation that relates stride rate *y* to speed *x*. Round coefficients to the nearest thousandth. Use the model to predict the stride rate for a speed of 14.95 ft/s. $y = 1.657 + 0.079x$

25. Find the correlation coefficient *r* for the data and tell whether it suggests that the correlation of the data is weak or strong. $r = 0.998$; strong

15.7 Curve Fitting   **843**

Writing in Mathematics
15. Use the chirp rate as the independent variable and the temperature as the dependent variable. Find the regression equation and use it as a predictor.

INDEPENDENT PRACTICE

Assignment Guide
Basic: 1–20, 29–32, Project
Average: 4–8, 14, 18–35, Project
Enriched: 18–29, 32–40, Project

Teacher's Resource Book
Practice, page 109

Ⓡ **Review**
Exercises 8, 13, 27–29, and 37 review the concepts of slope and y-intercept of a linear equation, equation of a line, statistics, and exponential growth.

Technology
Students should consult their owner's manual to be sure that they are familiar with the steps needed to solve problems involving correlations. In most cases several independent steps are involved: entering data, obtaining a scatter plot, obtaining values of *a*, *b*, and *r*, writing the regression equation, and graphing the regression equation.

LESSON FOLLOW-UP
Test Yourself

Teacher's Resource Book
Tests—Quiz, form A, page 66
Tests—Quiz, form B, page 66

Additional Answers
10. direct; the *y*-values tend to increase as *x*-values increase.

12. no; Answers may vary. Both variables tend to reflect societal development.

23.

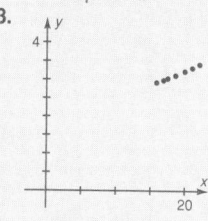

Lesson Quiz

Suppose that the following pairs of variables are related linearly. Tell whether the correlation coefficient describing the strength of the relationship would be positive or negative.

1. severity of disease and length of hospital stay *positive*
2. a person's age and his or her life expectancy *negative*
3. age of a machine and frequency of repairs *positive*
4. Determine which of the folowing correlation coefficients best represents the scatter diagram given below.

$r = 0.96$ $r = -0.93$
$r = 0.70$ $r = 0.1$

$r = -0.93$

Below is a list of data giving the record high temperatures for each month in Atlantic City, NJ. The temperatures are listed in order from January to December.

78, 75, 87, 94, 99, 106, 104, 102, 99, 90, 84, 75

5. Make a scatter diagram for this set of data.

26. **Thinking Critically** Compare the data in the table above with that used in Example 2. What reasons can you give for the differences in the two sets of data?

Ⓡ 27. Use the data of Exercise 10 to find the mean literacy rate for the areas studied. $\bar{x} = 74.6364$

Ⓡ 28. Use the data of Exercise 1 to find the median cholesterol content of the animal products studied. *78.5 mg*

Ⓡ 29. What is the range of the cholesterol content of the data of Exercise 1? *365 mg*

30. **Writing in Mathematics** A speaker made the claim that there is a correlation near zero between the amount of sugar consumed by young children and their hyperactivity as measured on a new scale. The newspaper reported that the more sugar children eat, the less hyperactive they are. Write a letter to the editor commenting on the newspaper's report. *Answers may vary.*

31. The equation $y = 99 - 0.85x$ is given as a regression equation relating the level of math anxiety a person exhibits and his or her scores on a math test. What does the slope of this line tell about the relationship? Is this reasonable? Why or why not?

32. **Thinking Critically** In the United States, what is the correlation between the age at which a person completes the eighth grade and the age at which he or she graduates from high school? Explain.

C Use a calculator or computer program to enter the annual highest temperature of record and the annual lowest temperature of record of selected cities found in Appendix A, page 901.

33. Would you predict a linear relationship between the lowest and highest temperatures in a city? What value of the correlation coefficent r would you predict?

34. Enter the data using the highest temperature in a city as x, the lowest temperature in the same city as the corresponding y. Use the calculator or software to obtain the scatter plot for this data. Does the scatter diagram seem to confirm or contradict your predictions in Exercise 33?

35. Use the calculator or software to find the correlation coefficient and the equation of the regression line. Compare this information to your answers to Exercises 33 and 34. $r = 0.1475$; $y = -78.1576 + 0.6468x$

36. **Thinking Critically** Statisticians caution those who use statistics not to use regression equations to make predictions for variables that lie considerably outside the range of the known data. Why is this advice given? Why is it important?

Ⓡ 37. **Thinking Critically** What kind of regression model would be most likely to fit the data describing the growth of a bacteria colony? Why?

38. Data is gathered to describe the growth of a colony of bacteria in an experimental medium. Draw a scatter plot for the data. Then use technology to fit an exponential curve to the data. Use the curve to predict the size of the colony on days 6 and 7.

Day(s) since culture introduced	Size of bacteria colony (thousands)
1	80
2	120
3	175
4	275
5	400

Writing in Mathematics

30. Answers may vary. Students should bring out the following in their letters. A correlation coefficient near zero indicates that there is little or no relationship between sugar consumption and hyperactivity. What was described was a (large) negative correlation, which the speaker did not claim.

39. Thinking Critically   Suppose the points on a scatter plot appear to lie on a horizontal line. What information would this give about the relationship between the variables? What correlation coefficient if any would you assign to this relationship?

40. Write a program that will compute the least squares regression line $y = ax + b$ for n observations (x, y). Input n and the n pairs of (x, y) points. Compute a and b using these relationships:

$$b = \frac{\sum (x - \bar{x})(y - \bar{y})}{\sum (x - \bar{x})^2} \quad \text{and} \quad a = y - bx$$

Test your program with the data in Example 1.

Project

Through experimentation, develop a linear model for the relationship between a person's height and his or her maximum distance in the broad jump. Organize your findings and state your conclusions.

Test Yourself

1. Scores on an IQ test are normally distributed with a mean of 100 and a standard deviation of 15. According to the empirical rule, what percent of IQ scores are greater than 130? $2\frac{1}{2}\%$ **15.5**

Quality Control   The average percentage of almonds in a bag of mixed nuts is 33.5% with a standard deviation of 1.4%.

2. Find the z-score that corresponds to each percentage.
   a. 30%   **b.** 35%   a. −2.5   b. 1.07

3. Find the probability that a bag of mixed nuts will contain less than 31% almonds.   0.0375

Quality Control   Suppose a quality control expert is testing the reliability that each bag contains 33.5% almonds, with standard deviation 1.4%.   **15.6**

4. Give the hypothesis and the alternate hypothesis. $H_0: \mu = 33.5\%$; $H_1: \mu \ne 33.5\%$

5. Give the standard error for a sample of size $n = 64$.   0.175

6. Suppose a test on a sample of 64 bags of mixed nuts shows it to contain 32.1% almonds. Should the quality control expert reject or accept the original claim at the 0.05 level of significance (95% confidence interval)? Explain.
Reject; 32.1% is not in the interval [33.157%, 33.843%].

Consult the table below to answer the questions that follow.   **15.7**

Height (in.)	62	64	66	68	70	72	74	76
Weight (lb)	123	130	136	145	154	162	171	181

7. Make a scatter diagram of the data.

8. Use linear regression to find the line of best fit. $y = -136.43 + 4.15x$

9. What is the correlation coefficient for the data, and what does it suggest about the strength of the correlation? $r = 0.998$; strong

15.7 Curve Fitting   **845**

39. As x changes, y tends to remain the same. It would not be meaningful to assign a correlation coefficient, since changes in y are not related to changes in x.

845

Additional Answers

1.

Classes	Frequency
220–234	5
235–249	6
250–264	3
265–279	3
280–294	1
295–309	1
310–324	0
325–339	1

2.

5.

Chapter 15   Summary and Review

Vocabulary

average (811)
box-and-whisker plot (807)
class (799)
confidence interval (833)
correlation analysis (838)
correlation coefficient (840)
cumulative frequency
   distribution (804)
curvilinear regression (841)
frequency (798)
frequency distribution (799)
frequency polygon (800)
hinge (807)

histogram (800)
hypothesis testing (833)
linear regression (839)
mean (811)
measures of central
   tendency (811)
measures of variability (817)
median (806)
mode (812)
normal curve (824)
normal distribution (824)
percentile (805)
quartile (806)

random sample (832)
range (817)
ranking (798)
regression analysis (838)
scatter plot (838)
standard deviation (818)
standard error (833)
standard normal
   distribution (826)
statistic (811)
stem-and-leaf plot (801)
variance (818)
z-score (827)

Histograms and Frequency Distribution   A frequency distribution is a table that lists   15.1
ordered data in classes of a specific length. A histogram is a way of representing a
frequency distribution as a graph.

Below is a list of the height, in meters, of 20 of the world's highest dams.

> 242, 233, 221, 300, 265, 265, 253, 325, 242, 220,
> 237, 250, 226, 235, 272, 242, 226, 237, 285, 261

1. Make a frequency distribution with classes of length 15 for the set of data.

2. Make a histogram for the frequency distribution.

Percentiles and Quartiles   Percentiles are values that divide a distribution into 100   15.2
groups of equal frequency. Quartiles divide a distribution into four groups of equal
frequency.

3. Determine the percentile for the score 237 in the data above. P_{35}

4. Find Q_3 for the set of data. 265   **5.** Make a box-and-whisker plot for the data.

Measures of Central Tendency   For a set of data, the mean is the arithmetic average   15.3
of all the values. The median is the middle value when the set is ranked, and the
mode is the value that has the greatest frequency.

6. Find the median and mode for the data given above. 242; 242

7. Find the mean of the data. 251.85

Measures of Variability   The range of a set of data is the difference between the   15.4
largest piece of data and the smallest piece. The formula for the standard deviation

is $\sigma = \sqrt{\dfrac{\sum_{i=1}^{n} (x_i - \bar{x})^2}{n}}$. The variance is the square of the standard deviation.

8. Find the range, standard deviation, and variance for the data given above.
   range = 105; σ = 26.7232; σ^2 = 714.13

The Normal Distribution   A set of data that is normally distributed can be
represented by a bell-shaped curve that is symmetric about the mean. The area
under a normal curve between two values a and b represents the proportion of the
data that falls between a and b. An element of data in a normal distribution can be
associated with the standard normal distribution, which has a mean of 0 and a
standard deviation of 1. This association is made by computing a z-score, using the
formula $z = \frac{x - \mu}{\sigma}$.

15.5

Wildlife Conservation   The mean weight for a certain type of freshwater fish is
28.2 oz with a standard deviation of 2.8 oz.

9. Give the z-score that corresponds to a weight of 25 oz. -1.14

10. The law requires that you throw back any fish of this type that weighs less
    than 24 oz. What is the probability that you will have to throw back a fish
    of this type that you have caught? 0.0668%

Hypothesis Testing and Confidence Intervals   A hypothesis is a statement about a
mean μ. If a hypothesis is rejected, then its alternate hypothesis is accepted. The
standard deviation of a set of n sample means is given by $\sigma_{\bar{x}} = \frac{\sigma}{\sqrt{n}}$. The 95%
confidence interval is between $\mu - 1.96\sigma_{\bar{x}}$ and $\mu + 1.96\sigma_{\bar{x}}$, and the 99% confidence
interval is between $\mu - 2.58\sigma_{\bar{x}}$ and $\mu + 2.58\sigma_{\bar{x}}$.

15.6

Wildlife Conservation   A game warden catches and weighs 25 fish from a
certain pond to see if they are significantly larger than the mean stated above.

11. Give the hypothesis and the alternate hypothesis for this situation and
    compute the standard error. $H_0: \mu > 28.2$; $H_1: \mu \le 28.2$; $\sigma_{\bar{x}} = 0.56$

12. If the mean of the sample is 30.9 oz, is it significantly larger than the
    population mean at the 0.05 level of significance? Explain.
    Yes; it is not in the interval [27.10, 29.30].

Curve Fitting   A scatter diagram is used to analyze two related sets of data. Linear
regression is used to give the line of best fit for a set of data. The correlation
coefficient r tells how well the data fits a straight line.

15.7

Politics   Below is a list giving the percentage of the popular vote and the
corresponding percentage of the electoral vote received by 10 "minority"
presidents.

Popular	47.9	48.3	48.8	47.8	46.0	41.8	49.3	49.5	49.7	43.4
Electoral	50.1	57.9	54.6	58.1	62.4	81.9	52.1	57.1	56.4	56.1

13. Make a scatter diagram for this set of data.

14. Use linear regression to find an equation that relates the percentage of the
    popular vote x to the percentage of the electoral vote y. $y = 171.73 - 2.393x$

15. Find the correlation coefficient r for the set of data. -0.7315

Additional Answers

1.

Classes	Frequency
600–699	6
700–799	4
800–899	1
900–999	1
1000–1099	4
1100–1199	1
1200–1299	2
1300–1399	0
1400–1499	1

2.

3.

7.

14.

Chapter 15   Test

Following are the lengths, in meters, of the world's twenty longest suspension bridges: 655, 988, 1158, 610, 853, 1410, 655, 1006, 1013, 712, 704, 1280, 608, 701, 1298, 610, 1067, 712, 668, 1074.

1. Make a frequency distribution of this data with classes of length 100.

2. Make a histogram for the frequency distribution.

3. Construct a frequency polygon for the distribution.

4. Determine the percentile for the bridge that is 988 m long. P_{60}

5. Determine Q_1 for the set of data. 661.5

6. Find the mean and the mode for the set of data. 889.1; 3 modes: 610, 655, 712

7. Make a box-and-whisker plot for the set of data.

8. Find the range, the standard deviation, and the variance for the set of data.
   802; 254.49; 64,765.16

Business   The mean number of hours that employees of a large corporation work in a week is 41.03 with a standard deviation of 1.78.

9. What z-score corresponds to a workweek of 40 h? -0.5787

10. What percentage of employees work more than 43 h in a week? 13.35%

Business   Suppose a manager in the company wants to check that the mean number of work hours given above is valid.

11. Give the hypothesis and the alternative hypothesis. H_0: $\mu = 41.03$; H_1: $\mu \neq 41.03$

12. Give the standard error for a sample of size $n = 36$. 0.2967

13. Suppose the manager reviews the time sheets for 36 employees and finds that the mean number of hours that they worked in a week was 39.7. Should the manager reject or accept the original mean at the 0.01 level of significance (99% confidence interval)? Reject, 39.7 is not in [40.26, 41.80].

Below is a list of the air mileage and the corresponding road mileage from Kansas City to 10 large U.S. cities.

Road	703	997	503	815	508	616	760	936	750	487
Air	579	861	414	700	451	558	645	839	644	453

14. Make a scatter diagram relating road mileage x to air mileage y.

15. Use linear regression to find an equation that relates air mileage to road mileage. Round coefficients to the nearest thousandth. Use the equation to predict the air mileage from Kansas City to Pittsburgh, Pennsylvania, which has a road distance of 847 mi. $y = 7.894 + 0.857x$; 733.8

16. Find the correlation coefficient for the data. 0.991

Challenge

Show how the distribution of probabilities for different outcomes when a coin tossed seven times can be presented in a histogram that looks like a normal distribution.

848   Chapter 15 Statistics and Data Analysis

Challenge
The probabilities of getting 0, 1, 2, 3, 4, 5, 6, or 7 heads in 7 tosses are 0.0078125, 0.0546875, 0.1640625, 0.2734375, 0.2734375, 0.1640625, 0.0546875, and 0.0078125, respectively.

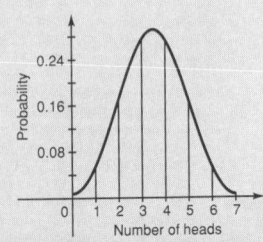

Cumulative Review

Select the best choice for each question.

1. A box was found with 15 blue   14.4
C   hats, 6 green hats, and 5 red hats. If one of the hats was given as a reward for the find, what is the probability that a red hat was selected?

  A. $\frac{1}{3}$ **B.** $\frac{5}{21}$ **C.** $\frac{5}{26}$ **D.** $\frac{26}{5}$
  E. none of these

2. The ages of children attending the   15.3
A   Junior Olympics were 8, 7, 9, 6, 7, 8, 7, 6, 7, 8, 9, and 6. Find the mean age of the children in attendance.
  A. 7.3   **B.** 8.2   **C.** 6.5   **D.** 9.3
  E. none of these

3. A $\frac{12}{5}$ clockwise rotation would   3.1
C   have its terminal side in which quadrant?
  A. I   **B.** II   **C.** III   **D.** IV
  E. none of these

4. Determine which are arithmetic   13.2
C   sequences.
       I. 3, 8, 13, 18, . . .
       II. −6, −2, 2, 6, . . .
       III. 2, 9, 15, 19, . . .
  A. I only   **B.** II only
  C. I and II only   **D.** I, II, and III
  E. none of these

5. Express $\sin 50° + \sin 40°$ as a   6.4
A   product.
  A. $2 \sin 45° \cos 5°$ **B.** $2 \sin 5° \cos 45°$
  C. $\sin 45° \cos 5°$ **D.** $\sin 5° \cos 45°$
  E. none of these

6. Find the norm of the   12.7
A   vector $-5\mathbf{v}$.
  A. 25   **B.** 5
  C. −5   **D.** −25
  E. none of these

7. Determine the value of $_{20}C_6$.   14.2
D   **A.** 83760   **B.** 76038   **C.** 87360
  D. 38760   **E.** none of these

8. The number of times a value   15.1
B   occurs when working with ranked data is called its
  A. mean   **B.** frequency   **C.** mode
  D. median   **E.** none of these

9. Find the limit of the sequence   13.6
E $d_n = \dfrac{2n^2 + 5}{n^2 + 3}$ as n increases without bound.
  A. 5   **B.** 3   **C.** $\frac{5}{3}$ **D.** $\frac{3}{5}$
  E. none of these

10. Determine the axis of symmetry   2.5
C   of the quadratic function $f(x) = 3x^2 - 5x - 1$.
  A. $y = \frac{5}{6}$ **B.** $x = \frac{6}{5}$ **C.** $x = \frac{5}{6}$
  D. $y = \frac{6}{5}$ **E.** none of these

11. Determine the foci of the ellipse   11.2
D   with the equation $\dfrac{x^2}{49} + \dfrac{y^2}{4} = 1$.
  A. $(0, \pm3\sqrt{5})$ **B.** $(\pm2, 0)$ **C.** $(0, \pm2)$
  D. $(\pm3\sqrt{5}, 0)$ **E.** none of these

12. A New York deli advertises "best   14.1
B   heros in town." They offer one each from 10 types of meat, 4 types of cheese, and 6 types of bread. How many heros can be made from these selections?
  A. 24   **B.** 240   **C.** 120   **D.** 12
  E. none of these

13. What is the coefficient of x^8y^5 in   13.5
A   the expansion of $(x + y)^{13}$?
  A. 1287   **B.** 2187   **C.** 8712   **D.** 7812
  E. none of these

14. The scores for the math selection   15.4
C   of the college board testing for a class are 550, 600, 725, 800, 625, 750, 450, 500, 700, 775. What is the range of this set of data?
  A. 200   **B.** 300   **C.** 350   **D.** 250
  E. none of these

CHAPTER OVERVIEW

Summary

The concept of a limit of a function is developed, and theorems for limits are introduced and applied. The derivative is defined and used to facilitate graphing higher-order functions. The derivative is also used to solve maxima and minima problems, and problems involving rates of change. The area under a curve is analyzed and evaluated using limits.

Chapter Objectives

- To find the limit of a function
- To apply theorems for the limit of a function
- To determine whether a function is continuous at a given point
- To find the slope of a line tangent to a curve at a given point
- To use the definition of a derivative to differentiate functions
- To use theorems in finding the derivative of a function
- To graph a function using the first derivative
- To use derivatives to solve problems involving rates of change
- To use the derivative to solve maxima and minima problems
- To represent the area under a curve as a sum of rectangles
- To find the area under a curve using limits

Mathematical Power

Modeling   You no doubt have noticed that wind blowing toward your body often makes you feel much colder than the actual temperature. The feeling of cold increases as the speed of the wind increases because the wind makes the body lose heat more quickly. Wind chill is the term given to the combined effects of wind and low temperatures. Wind chill measurements were developed from experiments performed during the 1939 Byrd expedition to Antarctica. A scientist in the group, Paul A. Siple, measured the rate of freezing water at various temperatures and wind speeds. By fitting a curve to the observed data, he obtained the following model for heat loss:

$$H = (10.45 + 10\sqrt{v} - v)(33 - T)$$

where v = velocity of the wind (m/s)

T = air temperature (°C)

H = heat lost (kilocalories per square meter of skin per hour)

The heat loss equation is one of several relationships used to compute equivalent wind chill temperatures.

In the above equation, the factor $(10.45 + 10\sqrt{v} - v)$ represents the heat loss due to wind velocity. This can be expressed as the function

$$L(v) = 10.45 + 10\sqrt{v} - v$$

The graph of this function is shown at the right. Notice that the maximum value of L occurs when v = 25 m/s. Thus, the model leads to the conclusion that wind speeds greater than 25 m/s have little *additional* chilling effect. This is true because a wind

850

Most students are familiar with the term *wind chill* since it is mentioned often in radio and television weather reports, and wind chill tables appear in print media. However, students may not realize that the notion of body-heat loss is the underlying scientific principle.

Emphasize that in the heat loss equation, the relationship among the variables is clearly *not* linear. This implies that a specific wind velocity occurring at 30°F will affect the body's heat loss differently from the same wind velocity occurring at 10°F. In fact, increased wind has a greater chilling effect at colder temperatures.

When discussing the graph of $L(v)$, you may want to point out that the tangent line can be thought of as a limit of secants. Elicit from students other examples in which they have encountered the notion of limit, such as values of functions with asymptotes, limits of sequences, or limits of repeating decimals. Help students understand intuitively that at a maximum or minimum, the graph of the function is changing direction.

Thinking Critically   Students should discover that 91.4°F = 33°C, so the factor $(33 - T)$ is the difference between skin temperature and air temperature.

of 25 m/s carries heat away from the body as quickly as it becomes available, so little more can be accomplished by a faster wind.

At the maximum value, the line tangent to the curve is horizontal, which means the slope of the tangent line at this point is zero. In calculus, the limit concept is used in a special function, called the *derivative*. The geometric interpretation of the derivative is that it gives the slope of the line tangent to a curve at any specific point. Hence, the derivative becomes a powerful tool in locating maximum and minimum values of functions.

Thinking Critically   Even when it is protected from the cold by adequate clothing, skin maintains a temperature of about 91.4°F. How is this fact used in the heat loss equation?

Project   The Greek philosopher *Zeno of Elea* (490–430 B.C.) proposed four paradoxes to suggest that common notions of time and space were incorrect. Research one or more of Zeno's paradoxes and explain how the concept of limit (developed about 2000 years later) resolved the problems.

851

Review and Assessment

Student Text		Teacher's Resource Book	
• Test Yourself	875, 893	• Tests	69–72
• Summary and Review	894–895	• Practice	110–116
• Chapter Test	896		

Vocabulary
limit of a function

Ⓜ **Materials/Manipulatives**
overhead projector

Technology
computer
graphing utility

FOCUS

Have students discuss the use of the word "limit" in everyday situations. This discussion may include speed limit, load limit on bridges, height limit on underpasses, and capacity limit on buildings.

INSTRUCTION

- Point out the difference between the graph of a sequence $f(n)$ and that of a function $f(x)$: The domain of $f(n)$ is the set of natural numbers, whereas the domain of $f(x)$ is the set of real numbers. Demonstrate this difference by drawing graphs of the sequence $f(n) = n^2$ and the function $f(x) = x^2$.
- Have students evaluate functions $f(x)$ for values of x closer and closer to c to help them get an understanding of a limit.
- Students may find it helpful to use the terminology *right limit* and *left limit* to describe the limits of a function $f(x)$ as x approaches a value c from the right and left. The limit of $f(x)$ as x approaches c exists if the right and left limits are equal.
- Provide several graphs of functions on the overhead projector to give students opportunities to find limiting values of functions, including right and left limits.
- Be sure that calculators are in radian mode when evaluating limits that involve trigonometric functions.

16.1 Limit of a Function of a Real Variable

Objective: To find the limit of a function

Focus

The velocity v of a falling object can be modeled using the function $v(t) = 32t$, where t is the time in seconds during which the object has been falling and the velocity v is in feet per second. Since it neglects air resistance, this model is not realistic for objects that fall a great distance. For example, the velocity of a skydiver will increase rapidly during the first part of a dive but will approach a limiting free-fall velocity as air resistance offsets the acceleration due to gravity. The limiting free-fall velocity of a skydiver might be as fast as 320 ft/s. When a diver's parachute opens, the velocity of the fall decreases until it approaches a limiting value of about 16 ft/s to ensure a safe landing.

Parachute manufacturers have to estimate limiting velocities of parachutes as accurately as possible. Mathematical models that do not neglect air resistance are used to aid in estimating these limiting velocities. This may involve finding the limit of one or more functions.

In Chapter 13, you were introduced to the idea of the limit of an infinite sequence such as

$$3, \frac{5}{2}, \frac{7}{3}, \frac{9}{4}, \ldots, a_n, \ldots$$

where $a_n = \dfrac{2n + 1}{n}$ and n is a positive integer. As n takes on sufficiently large values, the terms become arbitrarily close to 2. For example,

If $n = 10{,}000$, then $a_n = \dfrac{2(10{,}000) + 1}{10{,}000} = 2.0001$

If $n = 10{,}000{,}000$, then $a_n = \dfrac{2(10{,}000{,}000) + 1}{10{,}000{,}000} = 2.0000001$

For n large enough, a_n will be as close to 2 as you like. In symbols, this is

$$\lim_{n \to \infty} \frac{2n + 1}{n} = 2$$

Using functional notation, you may express the sequence as $f(n) = \dfrac{2n + 1}{n}$, where the domain of $f(n)$ is the set of natural numbers.

852 Chapter 16 Limits and an Introduction to Calculus

Now consider the function $f(x) = \dfrac{2x + 1}{x}$ when the domain of x is the set of all real numbers except 0. The graph shows that as x increases without bound in either the positive direction (∞) or the negative direction ($-\infty$), $f(x)$ becomes as close to 2 as you please, that is, the limit is 2. You can use the zoom and trace features of a graphing utility to see that this is so. In symbols,

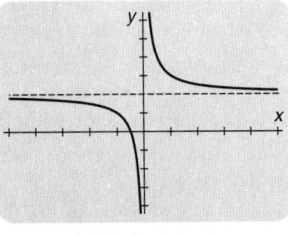

[−5, 5] by [−4, 6]

$$\lim_{x \to \infty} f(x) = 2 \qquad \text{and} \qquad \lim_{x \to -\infty} f(x) = 2$$

In this example, $f(x) \neq 2$ for all x. The graph shows that $y = 2$ is an equation of the horizontal asymptote, as was discussed in Lesson 7.6.

This asymptote can also be determined by expressing $f(x) = \dfrac{2x + 1}{x}$ as $f(x) = 2 + \dfrac{1}{x}$. As x grows large in either the positive or the negative direction, $\dfrac{1}{x}$ approaches 0 so that $f(x) = 2$ is a horizontal asymptote, as described above. The graph of $f(x) = \dfrac{2x + 1}{x}$, or $2 + \dfrac{1}{x}$, also has a vertical asymptote at $x = 0$. This is because $\dfrac{1}{x}$ increases without bound in the positive direction as positive values of x get closer to 0, and $\dfrac{1}{x}$ increases without bound in the negative direction as negative values of x get closer to 0. Recall that the two limits for $f(x)$ as x approaches zero from the right and from the left can be expressed as

$$\lim_{x \to 0^+} f(x) = \infty \qquad \text{and} \qquad \lim_{x \to 0^-} f(x) = -\infty$$

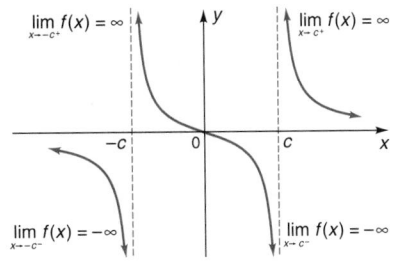

Note that ∞ and $-\infty$ do not represent numbers. To say that x approaches ∞ or $-\infty$ simply means that x gets large without bound in the positive or negative direction. Similarly, $\lim_{x \to c} f(x) = \infty$ means that for any value of M, however large, $f(x) > M$ provided x is sufficiently close to c when c is approached from the right. Analogous statements can be made for $\lim_{x \to c} f(x) = -\infty$, $\lim_{x \to c} f(x) = \infty$, and so on.

Example 1   Find each limit.

a. $\lim_{x \to \infty} x^3$ **b.** $\lim_{x \to -\infty} x^3$ **c.** $\lim_{x \to \infty} \operatorname{Tan}^{-1} x$ **d.** $\lim_{x \to -\infty} \operatorname{Tan}^{-1} x$

a. Since x^3 gets large without bound in the positive direction as x approaches ∞,

$$\lim_{x \to \infty} x^3 = \infty$$

b. Since x^3 gets large without bound in the negative direction as x approaches $-\infty$,

$$\lim_{x \to -\infty} x^3 = -\infty$$

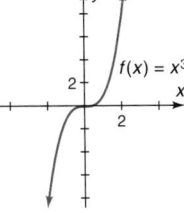

16.1 Limit of a Function of a Real Variable   **853**

GUIDED PRACTICE

For Example 1
Find each limit.
1. $\lim_{x \to +\infty} -2x^3$ $-\infty$
2. $\lim_{x \to -\infty} -2x^3$ $+\infty$
3. $\lim_{x \to \infty} \dfrac{1}{x}$ 0

c. As x increases without bound in the positive direction, the value of the function approaches $\frac{\pi}{2}$. Therefore, $\lim\limits_{x \to \infty} \text{Tan}^{-1} x = \frac{\pi}{2}$.

d. As x increases without bound in the negative direction, the value of the function approaches $-\frac{\pi}{2}$. Therefore, $\lim\limits_{x \to -\infty} f(x) = -\frac{\pi}{2}$.

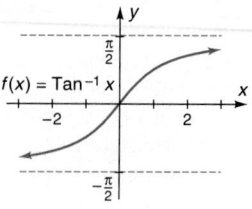

Many real world problems require information about the behavior of a function of a real variable $f(x)$ as x approaches a specific value. Recall from Chapter 7 that a function may approach a limit L at $x = c$ from either side of c. The symbol

$$\lim\limits_{x \to c^+} f(x) = L$$

means that the value of $f(x)$ approaches L as x approaches c from the right, and

$$\lim\limits_{x \to c^-} f(x) = L$$

means that the value of $f(x)$ approaches L as x approaches c from the left. If the limit from the left equals the limit from the right,

$$\lim\limits_{x \to c^+} f(x) = \lim\limits_{x \to c^-} f(x) = L$$

then $f(x)$ is said to have the limit L as x approaches c, that is,

$$\lim\limits_{x \to c} f(x) = L$$

Example 2 For the function graphed, find $\lim\limits_{x \to 1^-} f(x)$ and $\lim\limits_{x \to 1^+} f(x)$. Then state whether $\lim\limits_{x \to 1} f(x)$ exists. If it does, compare it to the function value $f(1)$.

As x approaches 1 from the left, the value of $f(x)$ approaches 1. Thus, $\lim\limits_{x \to 1^-} f(x) = 1$. As x approaches 1 from the right, the value of $f(x)$ approaches 2. Thus, $\lim\limits_{x \to 1^+} f(x) = 2$.

Since $\lim\limits_{x \to 1^-} f(x) \neq \lim\limits_{x \to 1^+} f(x)$, $\lim\limits_{x \to 1} f(x)$ does not exist.

Note in Example 2 that $f(1) = 3$ is a fact that does not affect $\lim\limits_{x \to 1} f(x)$.

If a function $f(x)$ happens to be a polynomial function, then the limit at c can be easily determined for any value of c. Consider, for example, the function $f(x) = x^2 - 4x - 12$. Is there a limit as x approaches 5? If so, is it the case that $\lim\limits_{x \to 5} (x^2 - 4x - 12) = f(5) = -7$? To answer this question, use a calculator to prepare a table of values of the function as close to 7 as desired.

x	4.9	4.99	4.999	$\cdots$	5.001	5.01	5.1
$x^2 - 4x - 12$	-7.59	-7.0599	-7.00599	$\cdots$	-6.993999	-6.9399	-6.39

854 Chapter 16 Limits and an Introduction to Calculus

Note that when x is close to 5 on the left and the right, $x^2 - 4x - 12$ is close to -7. It thus appears that $x^2 - 4x - 12$ is as close to $5^2 - 4(5) - 12 = -7$ as you please when x is close enough to 5 from both sides. If this is the case, then

$$\lim_{x \to 5^+} (x^2 - 4x - 12) = \lim_{x \to 5^-} (x^2 - 4x - 12) = -7$$

Thus, $\quad \lim_{x \to 5} (x^2 - 4x - 12) = -7$

In this example, it is obvious that $f(5) = \lim_{x \to 5} f(x)$. This illustrates an important property of polynomial functions that is stated below without proof.

If a function $f(x)$ is a polynomial function on an interval (a, b) and c is a real number in that interval, then

$$\lim_{x \to c} f(x) = f(c)$$

Example 3 Find $\lim_{x \to 2} f(x)$ given: $f(x) = \begin{cases} \dfrac{x^2 + x - 6}{x - 2}, & \text{if } x \neq 2 \\ -1, & \text{if } x = 2 \end{cases}$

Compare the limit to $f(2)$ and graph the function.

For $x \neq 2$, $f(x) = \dfrac{x^2 + x - 6}{x - 2} = \dfrac{(x - 2)(x + 3)}{x - 2} = x + 3$.

So, for $x \neq 2$, $\lim_{x \to 2} f(x) = \lim_{x \to 2} (x + 3) = 5$.

For $x = 2$, $f(x) = -1$, and so $f(2) = -1$. Therefore, $\lim_{x \to 2} f(x) \neq f(2)$. The graph consists of the point $(2, -1)$ and points on the line $y = x + 3$, with a hole at $(2, 5)$.

 A calculator can be helpful in finding limits involving trigonometric functions.

Example 4 Find $\lim_{x \to 0} \dfrac{\sin x}{x}$. Complete a table of values for $-1 \leq x \leq 1$.

x (rad)	1.0	0.6	0.2	0.01	-0.01	-0.2	-0.6	-1.0
$\dfrac{\sin x}{x}$	0.84147	0.94107	0.99335	0.99998	0.99998	0.99335	0.94107	0.84147

Note from the table of values that the value of the function seems to approach 1 as x approaches 0 from the right and the left. It thus appears that

$$\lim_{x \to 0} \frac{\sin x}{x} = 1$$

You can use the zoom and trace features of a graphing utility to verify this result. Note that the hole at $(0, 1)$ may not appear on the display, although $f(0)$ is undefined.

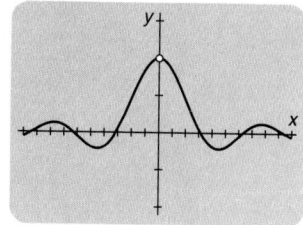

[−10, 10] by [−1, 1.5]
x scl: 1 y scl: 0.5

16.1 Limit of a Function of a Real Variable   **855**

Find the limit for each function as $x \to 1$ and compare the limit to $f(1)$.

1. $f(x) = \begin{cases} \dfrac{x^2 + 4x - 5}{x - 1}, & \text{if } x \neq 1 \\ 6, & \text{if } x = 1 \end{cases}$

$\lim_{x \to 1} f(x) = \lim_{x \to 1} (x + 5) = 6 = f(1)$

2. $f(x) = \begin{cases} \dfrac{x^2 - 3x + 2}{x - 1}, & \text{if } x \neq 1 \\ 0, & \text{if } x = 1 \end{cases}$

$\lim_{x \to 1} f(x) = \lim_{x \to 1} (x - 2) = -1 \neq f(1)$

For Example 4

Find $\lim_{x \to 0} \dfrac{x(\cos x)}{\sin x}$. Use a calculator in radian mode to complete a table of values for $-1 \leq x \leq 1$.

x	1.0	0.6	0.2	0.01
	-1.0	-0.6	-0.2	-0.01
$\dfrac{x(\cos x)}{\sin x}$	0.6421	0.8770	0.9866	0.9999

It appears that $\lim_{x \to 0} \dfrac{x(\cos x)}{\sin x} = 1$.

INDEPENDENT PRACTICE

Assignment Guide

Basic: 1–25
Average: 1–19 odd, 20–38
Enriched: 1–25 odd, 27–45

Teacher's Resource Book
  Practice, page 110

Ⓡ **Review**

Exercise 15 and 31 review summations of infinite series. Exercises 37 and 39 involve finding solutions to systems of equations.

Technology

Exercises 33 to 36 require the use of a calculator in radian mode.

Additional Answers

5. 0; $f(-2) = 0$; equal
6. -11; $f(-2) = 10$; not equal
7. 5; $f(-2)$ is undefined
10. 4; $f(2) = 4$; equal
11. does not exist; $f(2) = 5$
12. 4; $f(2) = 1$; not equal
13. 3; $f(2) = 3$; equal

In the discussion of the limit of a function, the meaning of the expression $\lim_{x \to c} f(x) = L$ has been interpreted through the use of phrases such as "$f(x)$ approaches L" and "x gets close to c." A more formal mathematical definition for the limit of a function follows.

> **Limit of a Function**
>
> The limit of the function $f(x)$ is L as x approaches c, denoted by $\lim_{x \to c} f(x) = L$, if for any positive number ϵ, however small, there is a positive number δ, such that $|f(x) - L| < \epsilon$ whenever $0 < |x - c| < \delta$.

In the graph of $y = f(x)$ at the right, this definitions means that $\lim_{x \to c} f(x) = L$ if $f(x)$ is in the interval $(L - \epsilon, L + \epsilon)$ whenever x is in the interval $(c - \delta, c + \delta)$. Note that the inequality $0 < |x - c| < \delta$ excludes c as a value of x since the limit of $f(x)$ as x approaches c does not depend on the value of $f(x)$ at c.

Class Exercises

Find each limit.

1. $\lim_{x \to \infty} x^4$ ∞

2. $\lim_{x \to -\infty} x^4$ ∞

3. $\lim_{x \to \infty} x^{\frac{1}{3}}$ ∞

4. $\lim_{x \to -\infty} x^{\frac{1}{3}}$ $-\infty$

Find the limit for each function as $x \to -2$ and compare the limit to $f(-2)$.

5. $f(x) = x^2 - 7x - 18$

6. $f(x) = \begin{cases} \dfrac{x^2 - 7x - 18}{x + 2}, & \text{if } x \neq -2 \\ 10, & \text{if } x = -2 \end{cases}$

7. $f(x) = \begin{cases} x^2 + 1, & \text{if } x > -2 \\ x + 7, & \text{if } x < -2 \end{cases}$

Verify the limit of each function by using a table of values.

8. $\lim_{x \to -3} (3x + 4) = -5$

9. $\lim_{x \to \frac{1}{2}} (5x - 2) = \frac{1}{2}$

Determine from the graph whether or not it appears that $\lim_{x \to 2} f(x)$ exists. If the limit exists, compare it to the function value $f(2)$.

10.

11.

12.

13.

856   Chapter 16 Limits and an Introduction to Calculus

8.

x	-3.1	-3.01	-3.001	-3	-2.999	-2.99	-2.9
$3x + 4$	-5.3	-5.03	-5.003	-5	-4.997	-4.97	-4.7

9.

x	0.4	0.49	0.499	0.5	0.501	0.51	0.6
$5x - 2$	0	0.45	0.495	0.5	0.505	0.55	1

For the function graphed, find each limit.

14. $\lim\limits_{x \to 1^-} f(x)$ ∞   **15.** $\lim\limits_{x \to 1^+} f(x)$ 1

For the function graphed, find each limit.

16. $\lim\limits_{x \to 3^+} g(x)$ 2   **17.** $\lim\limits_{x \to 3} g(x)$ 2

$y = f(x)$

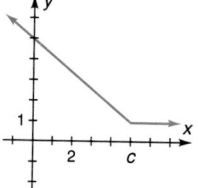

$y = g(x)$

18. Writing in Mathematics Describe the behavior of the graph of a function at a point where the limit of the function does not equal the function value.

Practice Exercises

Use appropriate technology.

Use the graphs to find $\lim\limits_{x \to c^-} f(x)$ and $\lim\limits_{x \to c^+} f(x)$. Then state whether $\lim\limits_{x \to c} f(x)$ exists. If it does, compare it to the function value $f(c)$, if it exists.

A 1.

2.

3.

4.

$c = 0$

5.

c

6.
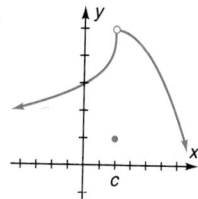

c

Use the graph to find each limit.

7. $\lim\limits_{x \to 0^+} t(x)$ 3   **8.** $\lim\limits_{x \to 0^-} t(x)$ 3

9. $\lim\limits_{x \to \infty} t(x)$ 2   **10.** $\lim\limits_{x \to -4^+} t(x)$ $-\infty$

Find each limit.

11. $\lim\limits_{x \to \infty} x^5$ ∞   **12.** $\lim\limits_{x \to -\infty} x^5$ $-\infty$

13. $\lim\limits_{x \to \infty} x^{\frac{1}{5}}$ ∞   **14.** $\lim\limits_{x \to -\infty} x^{\frac{1}{5}}$ $-\infty$

$y = t(x)$

Ⓡ 15. Find the twelfth term of the series $\sum\limits_{k=1}^{\infty} (5 + 3k)$. 41

16. Use a table of values to verify that $\lim\limits_{x \to -1} (5x + 7) = 2$.

16.1 Limit of a Function of a Real Variable   **857**

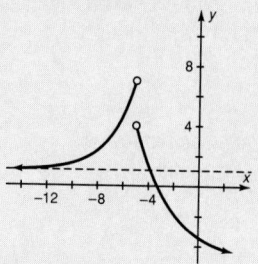
Writing in Mathematics
18. If the limit of $f(x)$ as x approaches c exists but does not equal $f(c)$, then there is a hole in the graph of $f(x)$ at the point $(c$, limit of $f(x)$ as x approaches $c)$ and a point drawn at $(c, f(c))$.

Find the limit of each function.

17. $\lim\limits_{x\to\frac{1}{4}} (4x + 2)$ 3   **18.** $\lim\limits_{x\to\frac{1}{5}} (5x + 3)$ 2   **19.** $\lim\limits_{x\to -1} |x + 4|$ 3   **20.** $\lim\limits_{x\to -2} |x - 7|$ 9

B 21. $\lim\limits_{x\to -1} (x^6 - 2)$ −1   **22.** $\lim\limits_{x\to -2} (6 - x^3)$ 14   **23.** $\lim\limits_{x\to 1} (x^4 - 6x^3 + 5x^2 - 4)$ −4

24. $\lim\limits_{x\to 2} (x^6 - 3x^3 + 2)$ 42   **25.** $\lim\limits_{x\to 4} \sqrt{x^2 - 2x + 1}$ 3   **26.** $\lim\limits_{x\to 1} \left(\frac{4}{x - 9}\right)$ 0

27. $f(x) = x^2 - 4x - 12$, as $x \to 6$ 0   **28.** $f(x) = x^2 - 5x + 6$, as $x \to 3$ 0

29. $f(x) = \begin{cases} \dfrac{x^2 + 3x - 10}{x + 5}, & \text{if } x \neq -5 \\ -7, & \text{if } x = -5 \end{cases}$ −7

as $x \to -5$

30. $f(x) = \begin{cases} -x^2 + 6x - 8, & \text{if } x > 2 \\ -\sqrt{4 - x^2}, & \text{if } x < 2 \end{cases}$ 0

as $x \to 2$

R 31. Find the fourth partial sum for the series $\sum\limits_{n=1}^{\infty} \left(\dfrac{1}{n} - \dfrac{1}{n + 1}\right)$. $\frac{4}{5}$

32. Writing in Mathematics   Describe the behavior of the graph at a point where the limit from the left does not equal the limit from the right.

Use a calculator in radian mode to make a table of values of the given function near the limit point. Use the results to find the limit or state that it does not exist. Use a graphing utility to check your answers.

33. $\lim\limits_{x\to 0} (x \sin x)$ 0   **34.** $\lim\limits_{x\to 0} (x \cos x)$ 0   **35.** $\lim\limits_{x\to 0} \left(\dfrac{\cos x}{x}\right)$ does not exist   **36.** $\lim\limits_{x\to 0} \left(\dfrac{\tan x}{x}\right)$ 1

R 37. Solve the system: $\begin{cases} y = x^2 + 3 \\ y = x + 5 \end{cases}$ (−1, 4), (2, 7)

C 38. Draw the graph of a function such that at each integer in its domain, the limit from the left does not equal the limit from the right.

R 39. Solve the system: $\begin{cases} 5x^2 + 8y^2 = 50 \\ 3x^2 - 10y^2 = 30 \end{cases}$ (±$\sqrt{10}$, 0)

40. Thinking Critically   Suppose that $f(x)$ represents a rational function. When is it true that $\lim\limits_{x\to c} f(x) = f(c)$?

Find the limit of each function.

41. $\lim\limits_{x\to\infty} 2^x$ ∞   **42.** $\lim\limits_{x\to\infty} 2^{\frac{1}{x}}$ 1   **43.** $\lim\limits_{x\to\infty} \left(\dfrac{1}{3}\right)^x$ 0   **44.** $\lim\limits_{x\to -\infty} \left(\dfrac{1}{3}\right)^x$ ∞

45. Thinking Critically   Discuss the intercepts and sketch the graph of a function such that $\lim\limits_{x\to 2} f(x) = \infty$, $\lim\limits_{x\to 2} f(x) = \infty$, $\lim\limits_{x\to\infty} f(x) = 4$, and $\lim\limits_{x\to -\infty} f(x) = 4$.

Review

1. In triangle RST, if $\angle R = 118°$, $\angle S = 16°$ and $s = 8.74$, determine t to the nearest hundredth. 22.81

2. Prove: $\dfrac{1 - \sin x}{\cos x} = \dfrac{\cos x}{1 + \sin x}$ $\dfrac{\cos x}{1 + \sin x}\left(\dfrac{1 - \sin x}{1 - \sin x}\right) = \dfrac{\cos x (1 - \sin x)}{1 - \sin^2 x} = \dfrac{\cos x (1 - \sin x)}{\cos^2 x} = \dfrac{1 - \sin x}{\cos x}$

3. The area of a circle is 60 cm². Determine the area of the sector intercepted by a central angle of 240°. 40 cm²

858   Chapter 16 Limits and an Introduction to Calculus

Writing in Mathematics

32. If the right and left limits are not equal, then there is a vertical segment gap in the graph of $f(x)$ at the limiting value c for x. Also, only one of the right or left graphs may be closed at $x = c$; the other must be open.

16.2 Limit Theorems

Objectives: To apply theorems for the limit of a function
To determine whether a function is continuous at a given point

Focus

It is human nature to simplify a task by finding an alternative method that saves time or effort. For example, industrial designers design robots that work tirelessly and accurately on tasks such as arc welding and paint spraying that may be dangerous or unhealthy for humans. An effective robotic system should also be able to perform repetitive motions at least as efficiently as a human operator. Computer scientists also look for labor-saving techniques. A common strategy is to create an algorithm (standardized procedure) that uses the power of a computer to perform a repetitive task that involves a large amount of data. A simple and familiar example is the SORT algorithm that quickly rearranges data into a preferred sequence such as alphabetical order.

The labor-saving strategies described in the Focus have their counterparts in the field of mathematics. For example, you may apply a useful general rule such as the quadratic formula, which allows you to solve any quadratic equation without special techniques such as factoring. In this lesson, some theorems will be presented that will help you to organize and simplify procedures for evaluating limits. Proofs of the limit theorems are left for a full course in calculus.

Limit Theorems

- If $f(x)$ is equal to a constant K, then $\lim_{x \to c} f(x) = K$.

- If $f(x) = x^m$, where m is a positive real number, then $\lim_{x \to c} x^m = c^m$.

Example 1 Evaluate: **a.** $\lim_{x \to 5} 7$ **b.** $\lim_{x \to 2} x^5$

a. Since 7 is a constant, $\lim_{x \to 5} 7 = 7$. **b.** $\lim_{x \to 2} x^5 = 2^5 = 32$

Functions may be considered as the sum, difference, product, or quotient of simpler functions. For example, $F(x) = x^2 + x$ may be considered the sum of the functions $f(x) = x^2$ and $g(x) = x$. Similarly, $f(x) = 3x$ may be considered as the product of the functions $f(x) = 3$ and $g(x) = x$. You will find the following theorems helpful when evaluating the limits of many functions.

Drawings aid visual learners in their understanding of the limit theorems. For example, to verify the first limit theorem, have students draw vertical segments of the function values at $x = 2$ for the functions $f(x) = x^2 - 3$, $g(x) = 2x$, and $(f + g)(x) = x^2 + 2x - 3$. Have them use a compass to copy the first two vertical segments of functional values end to end on a line and compare the sum of their lengths to the third segment. The second limit theorem can be verified in a similar manner, except that segments are subtracted instead of added.

GUIDED PRACTICE

For Example 1

Evaluate each limit.

1. $\lim_{x \to 3} 10$ 10

2. $\lim_{x \to -3} x^3$ -27

For Example 2

Find each limit.

1. $\lim_{x \to 3} x^2 + 5x$ 24

2. $\lim_{x \to -1} \dfrac{x^3 - 4x}{x^2 + x}$ does not exist

For Example 3

Find each limit, if it exists.

1. $\lim_{x \to -6} \dfrac{x^2 - 36}{x + 6}$ -12

2. $\lim_{x \to 3} \dfrac{x - 3}{x^2 - 9}$ $\dfrac{1}{6}$

More Limit Theorems

If $\lim_{x \to c} f(x) = L$ and $\lim_{x \to c} g(x) = M$ both exist, then

  i. $\lim_{x \to c} [f(x) + g(x)] = \lim_{x \to c} f(x) + \lim_{x \to c} g(x) = L + M$

  ii. $\lim_{x \to c} [f(x) - g(x)] = \lim_{x \to c} f(x) - \lim_{x \to c} g(x) = L - M$

  iii. $\lim_{x \to c} [f(x) \cdot g(x)] = \lim_{x \to c} f(x) \cdot \lim_{x \to c} g(x) = L \cdot M$

  iv. $\lim_{x \to c} \dfrac{f(x)}{g(x)} = \dfrac{\lim\limits_{x \to c} f(x)}{\lim\limits_{x \to c} g(x)} = \dfrac{L}{M}$, provided $M \neq 0$

Note that the first three theorems can be used to justify substitution in evaluating limits of polynomial functions.

$$\lim_{x \to 2} (x^2 + 3x - 5) = \lim_{x \to 2} x^2 + \lim_{x \to 2} 3 \cdot \lim_{x \to 2} x - \lim_{x \to 2} 5 = 2^2 + 3 \cdot 2 - 5 = 4 + 6 - 5 = 5$$

By substitution, $\lim_{x \to 2} (x^2 + 3x - 5) = 2^2 + 6 - 5 = 5$.

Example 2 Find $\lim_{x \to 4} \dfrac{x^2 + 5}{x^2 - 2x}$. Verify with a graphing utility.

$$\lim_{x \to 4} \frac{x^2 + 5}{x^2 - 2x} = \frac{\lim\limits_{x \to 4} (x^2 + 5)}{\lim\limits_{x \to 4} (x^2 - 2x)} = \frac{4^2 + 5}{4^2 - 2 \cdot 4} = \frac{21}{8}$$

The trace feature of a graphing utility will show $x = 4$, $y = 2.625$, or coordinates just above and below these values.

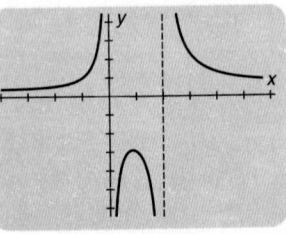

[−4, 6] by [−12, 8]
x scl: 1   y scl: 2

The fourth limit theorem does not apply in Example 3 because the limit of the denominator is 0.

Example 3 Find $\lim_{x \to -2} \dfrac{x + 3}{x + 2}$, if it exists. If it does not exist, determine whether the limit can be represented by either ∞ or $-\infty$.

Since the denominator $x + 2 \to 0$ when $x \to -2$, consider the limits from the left and the right.

$$\lim_{x \to -2^-} \frac{x + 3}{x + 2} = -\infty \qquad \text{and} \qquad \lim_{x \to -2^+} \frac{x + 3}{x + 2} = \infty$$

Therefore, $\lim_{x \to -2} \dfrac{x + 3}{x + 2}$ does not exist. Since the left-hand limit is $-\infty$ and the right-hand limit is ∞, the limit cannot be represented by either ∞ or $-\infty$.

860   Chapter 16 Limits and an Introduction to Calculus

In evaluating limits where the numerator and denominator both approach zero, try to express the function in a different form.

Example 4 Find $\lim\limits_{x \to 2} \dfrac{x^2 - 4}{x - 2}$.

$$\lim_{x \to 2} \frac{x^2 - 4}{x - 2} = \lim_{x \to 2} \frac{(x - 2)(x + 2)}{(x - 2)} = \lim_{x \to 2} (x + 2) = 4 \qquad \textit{Factor the numerator and simplify.}$$

Recall that as x increases without bound in the positive or negative direction, $\dfrac{1}{x}$ approaches 0. That is, $\lim\limits_{x \to \infty} \dfrac{1}{x} = 0$ and $\lim\limits_{x \to -\infty} \dfrac{1}{x} = 0$. This can be helpful in evaluating the limit of rational functions when x approaches ∞ or $-\infty$.

Example 5 Find each limit: **a.** $\lim\limits_{x \to \infty} \dfrac{x^2 + 7x}{3x^2 - 2}$ **b.** $\lim\limits_{x \to -\infty} \dfrac{x^2 - 5}{4x^3 + 2}$

Divide numerator and denominator by the highest power of x in the denominator.

a. $\lim\limits_{x \to \infty} \dfrac{x^2 + 7x}{3x^2 - 2} = \lim\limits_{x \to \infty} \dfrac{1 + \dfrac{7}{x}}{3 - \dfrac{2}{x^2}} = \dfrac{1 + 0}{3 - 0} = \dfrac{1}{3}$ **b.** $\lim\limits_{x \to -\infty} \dfrac{x^2 - 5}{4x^3 + 2} = \lim\limits_{x \to -\infty} \dfrac{\dfrac{1}{x} - \dfrac{5}{x^3}}{4 + \dfrac{2}{x^3}} = \dfrac{0 - 0}{4 + 0} = 0$

Note that the conditions for horizontal asymptotes given in Lesson 7.6 are also helpful in determining the limits of a rational function $\dfrac{f(x)}{g(x)}$ as x gets large without bound through positive or negative values. In Example 5a, $f(x)$ and $g(x)$ have the same degree, so the horizontal asymptote is $y = \frac{1}{3}$, the quotient of the leading coefficients. In Example 5b, the degree of $f(x)$ is less than the degree of $g(x)$, so $y = 0$ is a horizontal asymptote. If the degree of $f(x)$ is greater than the degree of $g(x)$, there is no horizontal asymptote, and the limit of $\dfrac{f(x)}{g(x)}$ is ∞ or $-\infty$ as x gets large without bound in either direction. Now that many ways to evaluate limits have been presented, the discussion of continuity in Chapter 7 may be revisited and continuity may be defined in a formal way.

Continuity of a Function

A function $f(x)$ is continuous at $x = c$ if and only if

    i. $f(x)$ is defined at $x = c$

    ii. $\lim\limits_{x \to c} f(x)$ exists

    iii. $\lim\limits_{x \to c} f(x) = f(c)$

16.2 Limit Theorems **861**

For Example 4
Find each limit.

1. $\lim\limits_{x \to 0} \dfrac{\sqrt{x + 4} - 2}{x}$ $\frac{1}{4}$

2. $\lim\limits_{x \to 3} \dfrac{5 - \sqrt{x + 22}}{x - 3}$ $-\frac{1}{10}$

For Example 5
Find each limit.

1. $\lim\limits_{x \to +\infty} \dfrac{x^2 + 13x}{2x^2 - 5}$ $\frac{1}{2}$

2. $\lim\limits_{x \to +\infty} \dfrac{7x^2 - 19}{x^4 + 8}$ 0

For Example 6
Determine whether the following function is continuous for all real values of *x*. If not, indicate which condition in the definition is not satisfied. Draw the graph.

$$f(x) = \begin{cases} \dfrac{x^2 - 5x + 6}{x - 3}, & \text{if } x \neq 3 \\ 1, & \text{if } x = 3 \end{cases}$$

continuous

CLOSURE

Have each student pair up with a classmate to discuss how their understanding of continuous and discontinuous functions has developed. Have students list the important components of continuous functions, providing two examples of functions that are continuous and two that are not.

INDEPENDENT PRACTICE

Assignment Guide

Basic: 1–25, 29–34
Average: 1–25 odd, 26–42
Enriched: 1–37 odd, 39–44

Teacher's Resource Book
  Practice, page 111

Additional Answers
Class Exercises
10. continuous

For a function to be continuous at a point, all three conditions in the definition must be met. If any one of the conditions is not satisfied, the function is said to be *discontinuous* at *x* = *c*. Consider the following graphs:

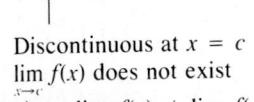

Discontinuous at $x = c$
$\lim\limits_{x \to c} f(x)$ does not exist
since $\lim\limits_{x \to c^-} f(x) \neq \lim\limits_{x \to c^+} f(x)$

Discontinuous at $x = c$
$\lim\limits_{x \to c} f(x)$ exists, but
$\lim\limits_{x \to c} f(x) \neq f(c)$

Continuous at $x = c$
$f(x)$ is defined at $x = c$.
$\lim\limits_{x \to c} f(x) = f(c)$

If a function is continuous at all points in an interval $a < x < b$, then it is said to be continuous in that interval. In particular, a polynomial function $f(x)$ is continuous for all x, $-\infty < x < \infty$, since $\lim\limits_{x \to c} f(x) = f(c)$ for all real numbers c.

> Polynomial functions are continuous at every real number c.

Example 6 Determine whether the given function is continuous for all real values of x. If not, indicate which condition in the definition is not satisfied. Draw the graph.

$$f(x) = \begin{cases} x^2 + 2, & \text{if } x < -1 \\ 1, & \text{if } x = -1 \\ 2x, & \text{if } x > -1 \end{cases}$$

$f(x)$ is defined at $x = -1$ since $f(-1) = 1$.

$\lim\limits_{x \to -1^-} f(x) = \lim\limits_{x \to -1^-} (x^2 + 2) = (-1)^2 + 2 = 3$

$\lim\limits_{x \to -1^+} f(x) = \lim\limits_{x \to -1^+} 2x = 2(-1) = -2$

Since the limit from the left does not equal the limit from the right, $\lim\limits_{x \to -1} f(x)$ does not exist. Thus, the function is discontinuous at $x = -1$. For all other values, the function is a polynomial, and thus continuous.

Class Exercises

Find each limit, if it exists.

1. $\lim\limits_{x \to 11} 17$ 17

2. $\lim\limits_{x \to -2} (5 - 4x)$ 13

3. $\lim\limits_{x \to -6} (3 + 4x - x^2)$ -57

4. $\lim\limits_{x \to 7} (x^2 - 7x)$ 0

5. $\lim\limits_{x \to 2} \dfrac{x^2 - 3}{x^2 + 4x}$ $\dfrac{1}{12}$

6. $\lim\limits_{x \to -2} \dfrac{x^3 + 7x}{x - 6}$ $\dfrac{11}{4}$

7. $\lim\limits_{x \to 3} \dfrac{x^2 - 9}{x - 3}$ 6

8. $\lim\limits_{x \to \infty} \dfrac{5x^2 + 12}{2x^2 - 9}$ $\dfrac{5}{2}$

9. $\lim\limits_{x \to \infty} \dfrac{x^3 - 2}{x^2 + 1}$ ∞

11. continuous

12. Answers may vary.

Determine whether the given function is continuous for all real values of x. If not, indicate which part of the definition is not satisfied. Draw the graph.

10. $f(x) = \begin{cases} \dfrac{x^2 - 5x - 6}{x + 1}, & \text{if } x \neq -1 \\ -7, & \text{if } x = -1 \end{cases}$

11. $g(x) = \begin{cases} x + 5, & \text{if } x \geq 2 \\ 9 - x, & \text{if } x < 2 \end{cases}$

12. Thinking Critically   Draw the graph of a function that satisfies the first two conditions of the definition of continuity at a point but fails the third one.

Practice Exercises   Use appropriate technology.

Find each limit, if it exists.

A **1.** $\lim\limits_{x \to -2} 2$ 2
   2. $\lim\limits_{x \to -9} 9$ 9
   3. $\lim\limits_{x \to 3} (2x + 13)$ 19
   4. $\lim\limits_{x \to 2} (x^2 + 4x + 9)$ 21

5. $\lim\limits_{x \to 1} x^7$ 1
6. $\lim\limits_{x \to -3} x^5$ −243
7. $\lim\limits_{x \to 1} \dfrac{4}{x - 9}$ $-\dfrac{1}{2}$
8. $\lim\limits_{x \to -3} \dfrac{6}{x + 9}$ 1

9. $\lim\limits_{x \to -3} \dfrac{5x^2 - 7x}{x^2 + 5}$ $\dfrac{33}{7}$
10. $\lim\limits_{x \to -4} \dfrac{x^2 - 16}{x + 4}$ −8
11. $\lim\limits_{x \to -9} \dfrac{x^2 - 81}{x + 9}$ −18
12. $\lim\limits_{x \to -2} \dfrac{x^2 - 2x - 8}{x + 2}$ −6

13. $\lim\limits_{x \to 5} \dfrac{x^2 - 8x + 15}{x - 5}$ 2
14. $\lim\limits_{x \to \infty} \dfrac{3x + 8}{2x^2 - 5}$ 0
15. $\lim\limits_{x \to \infty} \dfrac{4x - 7}{9x + 6}$ $\dfrac{4}{9}$
16. $\lim\limits_{x \to \infty} \dfrac{x^3}{x - 1}$ ∞

Ⓡ **17.** Draw the graph of $f(x) = [\![2x + 3]\!] + 2$.

18. Writing in Mathematics   If $f(x)$ and $g(x)$ are polynomial functions, explain how the following limit is possible, and give an example: $\lim\limits_{x \to \infty} \dfrac{f(x)}{g(x)} = \infty$.

19. Thinking Critically   Draw the graph of a function that is defined for all real numbers but is discontinuous at $x = b$.

20. Thinking Critically   Draw the graph of a function such that $\lim\limits_{x \to 1^+} f(x) = 6$ and $\lim\limits_{x \to 1^-} f(x) = 2$, where $f(1) = 4$.

Find each limit, if it exists.

B **21.** $\lim\limits_{x \to -10} \dfrac{100 - x^2}{10 + x}$ 20
   22. $\lim\limits_{x \to 11} \dfrac{121 - x^2}{11 - x}$ 22
   23. $\lim\limits_{x \to 3} \dfrac{x - 3}{x^2 - 7x + 12}$ −1

24. $\lim\limits_{x \to -6} \dfrac{x + 6}{x^2 + 3x - 18}$ $-\dfrac{1}{9}$
25. $\lim\limits_{x \to 2} \dfrac{x^3 - 8}{x - 2}$ 12
26. $\lim\limits_{x \to -3} \dfrac{x^3 + 27}{x + 3}$ 27

27. $\lim\limits_{x \to 0} \dfrac{(x - 5)^2 - 25}{x}$ −10
28. $\lim\limits_{x \to \infty} \dfrac{3x - 5x^2}{4x^2 + 1}$ $-\dfrac{5}{4}$
29. $\lim\limits_{x \to -\infty} \dfrac{2 - 3x^3}{x^2 + 4}$ ∞

30. *Chemistry*   A manufacturing firm is trying to determine how much weight a new adhesive will hold for 2 min. From the data in the table, what is an approximate limit of the weight that this adhesive can support for 2 min? 80 lb

	Held			Failed		
Weight (lb)	77	79	79.8	80.2	84	88
Time (min)	2	2	2	1.9	1.8	1.6

Ⓡ **31.** Express $p(x) = 20x^3 - 53x^2 - 27x + 18$ as a product of linear factors with integral coefficients. $p(x) = (5x - 2)(4x + 3)(x - 3)$

Writing in Mathematics
18. Answers may vary. The rational function may simplify to a polynomial.

Ⓡ **Review**
Exercises 17, 31, 35, and 39 review graphing functions, linear factors, and finding zeros of polynomial functions.

LESSON FOLLOW-UP

Lesson Quiz
Evaluate the limit, if it exists.

1. $\lim\limits_{x \to 0} 11$ 11

2. $\lim\limits_{x \to -2} 7$ 7

3. $\lim\limits_{x \to -2} -3x^4$ −48

4. $\lim\limits_{x \to 5} x^2 - 3x$ 10

5. $\lim\limits_{x \to -4} \dfrac{x^3 + 3}{x^2 + 4x}$ does not exist

6. $\lim\limits_{x \to 2} \dfrac{x^3 - 8x}{x + 2}$ −2

7. $\lim\limits_{x \to -8} \dfrac{64 - x^2}{x + 8}$ −16

8. $\lim\limits_{x \to +\infty} \dfrac{5x^2 - 7x}{x^2}$ 5

9. $\lim\limits_{x \to +\infty} \dfrac{6 - 8x^2}{4x^2}$ −2

10. $\lim\limits_{x \to 3} \dfrac{\sqrt{x + 6} - 3}{x - 3}$ $\dfrac{1}{6}$

11. Determine whether the function is continuous for all real values of x. If not, indicate which part of the definition is not satisfied. Draw the graph.

$f(x) = \begin{cases} \dfrac{x^2 - 7x + 12}{x - 4}, & \text{if } x \neq 4 \\ 1, & \text{if } x = 4 \end{cases}$

continuous

Alternative Assessment

Have students write three functions that include rational expressions and radicals, and graph the functions on well-marked grid paper. For each function, have them write several limit expressions where x approaches 0, 1, 2, $-\infty$, $+\infty$, and other values. Then instruct them to use the grid to evaluate each limit.

Enrichment

Evaluate the following limit:

$$\lim_{(x, y) \to (1, 1)} \frac{x^2 + xy - 6y^2}{x^2 + 6xy + 9y^2} \quad -\frac{1}{4}$$

Additional Answers

36.

37. $f(21) = 664.565$; $f(42) = 665$

38.

very good approximation

Determine whether the given function is continuous for all real values of x. If not, indicate which condition in the definition is not satisfied. Draw the graph.

32. $f(x) = \begin{cases} x^2 - 4x + 9, & \text{if } x \neq 3 \\ 6, & \text{if } x = 3 \end{cases}$

33. $h(x) = \begin{cases} \dfrac{x^2 + 4x - 21}{x + 7}, & \text{if } x \neq -7 \\ -10, & \text{if } x = -7 \end{cases}$

34. $h(x) = \begin{cases} \dfrac{x^2 + 11x + 24}{x + 8} & \text{if } x \neq -8 \\ 5, & \text{if } x = -8 \end{cases}$

Ⓡ 35. Find the rational zeros for $p(x) = 6x^3 + 25x^2 - 29x - 20$. $\ -5, -\frac{1}{2}, \frac{4}{3}$

Biology The growth of a yeast population is given in this table.

Time t (h)	0	3	6	9	12	15	18
Number $f(t)$	10	48	176	442	596	651	662

C 36. Graph $f(t)$ and estimate a limit for the number of yeast as t gets very large.

37. The function $f(t)$ may be approximated by $\dfrac{665}{1 + 68e^{-0.55t}}$. Use this function to approximate $f(21)$ and $f(42)$.

38. Graph the function in Exercise 37, where $e \approx 2.718$. How good an approximation is the formula for $f(t)$ for the points given in the table?

Ⓡ 39. Find all real zeros for $p(x) = x^4 + x^3 - 5x^2 - 3x + 6$. $\ 1, -2, \pm\sqrt{3}$

Find the values for a and b so that $f(x)$ is continuous for all real values of x.

40. $f(x) = \begin{cases} -x^2 + 2x + 4, & \text{if } x \geq 1 \\ ax + b, & \text{if } -1 < x < 1 \\ -x, & \text{if } x \leq -1 \end{cases}$ $\ a = 2;$ $b = 3$

41. $f(x) = \begin{cases} x + a, & \text{if } x > 4 \\ 3 - |x - 1|, & \text{if } -1 \leq x \leq 4 \\ b, & \text{if } x < -1 \end{cases}$ $\ a = -4;$ $b = 1$

42. $f(x) = \begin{cases} x - 3, & \text{if } x \geq 3 \\ \sqrt{a - x^2}, & \text{if } -3 < x < 3 \\ b - x, & \text{if } x \leq -3 \end{cases}$ $\ a = 9;$ $b = -3$

43. Prove that if f and g are both continuous at c, then their sum is continuous at c.

44. Prove that if f and g are both continuous at c, then their product is continuous at c.

Challenge

1. The square of an integer is a perfect square. If y is a perfect square, determine the next larger perfect square. $\ y + 2\sqrt{y} + 1$

2. Determine the area of the smallest region bounded by the graphs of $y = |x|$ and $x^2 + y^2 = 16$. $\ 4\pi$

3. Opposite sides of a regular hexagon are 18 in. apart. Determine the length of each side. $\ 6\sqrt{3}$ in.

864   Chapter 16 Limits and an Introduction to Calculus

32. continuous

33. continuous

34. discontinuous; Condition iii
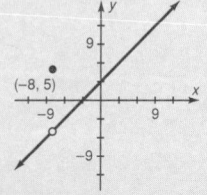

16.3 Tangent to a Curve

Objective: To find the slope of a line tangent to a curve at a given point

Focus

Radar guns are now the most popular tools for estimating the speed of an automobile. However, in the past, another system, called VASCAR (Visual Average Speed Computer and Recorder), was used to estimate the average speed of a vehicle over a measured distance. A measured distance along the highway was entered into the VASCAR system. Using a stopwatchlike device connected to the system, the officer could then record the time for a moving vehicle to cover the distance. For example, suppose that a car takes 5 s to cross a 300-ft bridge. Then the average velocity of the car while crossing the bridge is 300 ÷ 5, or 60 ft/s.

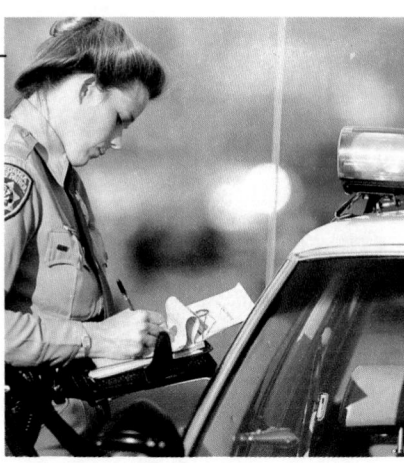

But how can you find the velocity at a particular moment of time, say, at 3 s past 10:32 a.m., when a car speeds up to pass another car? The velocity at a particular instant when there is no time difference to measure is called *instantaneous velocity*. A measurement such as this may seem impossible to calculate. What *can* be measured are average velocities for time intervals close to 3 s, such as from 3 s to 3.1 s, or 3 s to 3.01 s, which become closer and closer to the velocity at time 3 s. In this way, the instantaneous velocity can be determined as a limit of average velocities as the time difference approaches 0.

As mentioned in the Focus, limits are used in finding a rate of change called instantaneous velocity. The limit concept is also used to find instantaneous rates of change of other quantities, such as the rate of growth of bacteria over time, the rate at which a car engine heats up when there is too little antifreeze, and the rate at which water flows out of a leaking tank. To understand these special examples of instantaneous rate of change, it is helpful to ask a more general question, which was posed by mathematicians of antiquity: What is meant by a "tangent to a curve?" A satisfactory answer to this question will lead to the answer to a related question: How do you calculate the slope of a tangent line?

A student of algebra might phrase the question just posed in the following way: "I know that for a straight line the change of *y* with respect to *x* is measured by the slope of the line. But what does it mean to find the rate of change of *y* with respect to *x* when the graph is not a straight line?"

16.3 Tangent to a Curve   **865**

LESSON PLAN

Vocabulary
secant line
tangent line

Ⓜ **Materials/Manipulatives**
board straightedge
coin

Technology
computer
graphing utility

FOCUS

Invite discussion among students about the instantaneous velocity of a vehicle. A good starting point for this discussion is to have students calculate the average speeds for their trips to and from school each day. Then have them describe the actual changes in their speeds during the trip. Extend the discussion by drawing a comparison between instantaneous velocity and a tangent to a curve.

INSTRUCTION

Ⓜ • Using an overhead projector, sketch a function in the first quadrant of the coordinate plane, and a point *P* on the curve. Show another point *Q* on the curve using a coin. Place a straight edge on *P* and *Q*. Move *Q* along the curve toward *P*, and move the straightedge so that it represents the line *PQ*. The limiting position of the line is the tangent line at *P*.

• Some students may benefit from a review of slope and writing equations of lines before proceeding to the example problems.

GUIDED PRACTICE

For Example 1

Find the slope of the line tangent to the graph of the function at the given point.

1. $f(x) = x^2 - 5x + 8$; $(1, 4)$ -3
2. $g(x) = x^2 + 14x - 12$; $(2, 20)$
   18

Consider the graph of a function f. Let P and Q be two different points on the curve. The line drawn between points P and Q is a **secant line.** If P is fixed and Q moves along the curve toward P, the secant line approaches a limiting position, namely, a line **tangent** to the curve at P.

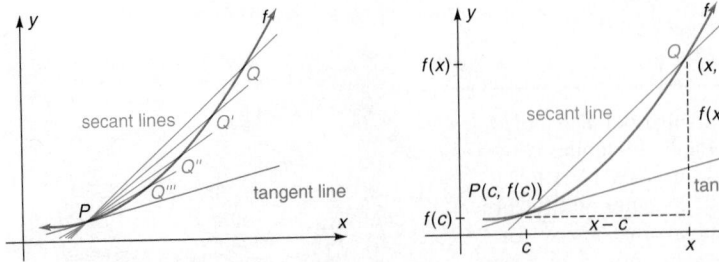

Let $P(c, f(c))$ and $Q(x, f(x))$ be the coordinates of the two points on the curve. Then as Q approaches P, x approaches c. Consequently, the slope of the secant line approaches the slope of the tangent line at P.

$$\text{Slope of the secant } \overleftrightarrow{PQ}: \quad m_s = \frac{f(x) - f(c)}{x - c}$$

The slope of the tangent line is the limit (if it exists) of the slope of the secant line as x approaches c.

$$\text{Slope of the tangent at } P: \quad m_t = \lim_{x \to c} \frac{f(x) - f(c)}{x - c}$$

The expression $\frac{f(x) - f(c)}{x - c}$ is called a *difference quotient.*

Example 1   Find the slope of the line tangent to the curve $f(x) = \sqrt{x + 4}$ at $P(5, 3)$.

First find the slope of the secant $\overleftrightarrow{PQ}$, where Q is any point on the curve other than P.

$$m_s = \frac{f(x) - f(5)}{x - 5} = \frac{\sqrt{x + 4} - 3}{x - 5}$$

$$= \frac{\sqrt{x + 4} - 3}{x - 5} \cdot \frac{\sqrt{x + 4} + 3}{\sqrt{x + 4} + 3} \qquad \textit{Rationalize the numerator.}$$

$$= \frac{x + 4 - 9}{(x - 5)(\sqrt{x + 4} + 3)} = \frac{1}{\sqrt{x + 4} + 3}$$

$$m_t = \lim_{x \to 5} \frac{1}{\sqrt{x + 4} + 3} = \frac{1}{\sqrt{5 + 4} + 3} = \frac{1}{6}$$

The slope of the tangent line to the curve is $\frac{1}{6}$.

You can find an equation of the tangent line at a given point on a curve by first finding the slope of the tangent line.

Example 2 Find an equation of the tangent line to the curve $f(x) = x^3 - 2x^2 + 3$ at $P(1, 2)$.

$$\frac{f(x) - f(c)}{x - c} = \frac{(x^3 - 2x^2 + 3) - (2)}{x - 1} = \frac{(x^3 - 2x^2 + 1)}{x - 1}$$

$$= \frac{(x^2 - x - 1)(x - 1)}{x - 1} = x^2 - x - 1$$

$$m_t = \lim_{x \to 1} (x^2 - x - 1) = 1^2 - 1 - 1 = -1$$

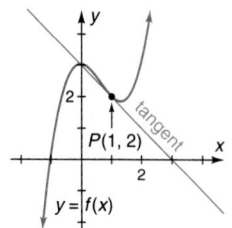

Thus, the slope of the tangent line is -1, and the equation of the line is

$$y - 2 = -1(x - 1) \qquad y - y_1 = m(x - x_1)$$
$$y - 2 = -x + 1$$
$$y = -x + 3 \qquad \textit{Equation of tangent line}$$

For Example 2
Find an equation of the line tangent to the graph of the given function at the given point.
1. $f(x) = x^3 - 4x^2 + 9$; $(2, 1)$
   $y = -4x + 9$
2. $g(x) = x^3 + 3x - 7$; $(1, -4)$
   $6x - y = 10$

For Example 3
Find the equation of the line with the given slope that is tangent to the graph of $f(x) = x^2 + 3x - 1$.
1. $m = 5$ $y = 5x - 2$
2. $m = 1$ $y = x - 2$
3. $m = -5$ $y = -5x - 17$

The ancient question concerning tangents has now been answered; the tangent to a curve at a point of the curve is the line with a slope that is the limiting value (if it exists) of the slopes of the related secant lines. It thus becomes possible to define the **slope of a curve** at a point P as the slope of the tangent line to the curve at point P.

The slope of a curve may vary from point to point. Therefore, it may be convenient to express the slope in terms of an arbitrary point and to use the result to find the slope at various points on the curve.

Example 3 A function is defined by $g(x) = x^2 + 5x - 3$. Find an equation of a line with slope 3 that is tangent to the curve.

First, find the slope of a secant line through $(x, g(x))$ and an arbitrary point $(c, g(c))$.

$$\frac{g(x) - g(c)}{x - c} = \frac{(x^2 + 5x - 3) - (c^2 + 5c - 3)}{x - c} = \frac{x^2 - c^2 + 5x - 5c}{x - c}$$

$$= \frac{(x - c)(x + c) + 5(x - c)}{(x - c)} = x + c + 5$$

The slope of the curve at the point $(c, g(c))$ is $\lim\limits_{x \to c} (x + c + 5) = 2c + 5$.

The slope of the tangent line is 3. Use $2c + 5$, the slope of the curve at any point $(c, g(c))$, to find the point on the curve where the tangent line has slope 3.

$$2c + 5 = 3 \qquad \text{so } c = -1$$

Then $g(-1) = (-1)^2 + 5(-1) - 3 = -7$.

Now find an equation of the line through $(-1, -7)$ with slope 3.

$$y + 7 = 3(x + 1)$$
$$y + 7 = 3x + 3$$
$$y = 3x - 4 \qquad \textit{Tangent line with slope 3}$$

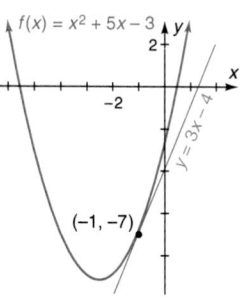

16.3 Tangent to a Curve   **867**

Modeling
A discussion of real world examples of instantaneous rates of change is very effective for validating the mathematics and motivating students to study calculus.

For Example 4
The motion of an object is given by the function $f(t) = t^2 - 3t + 5$, where $f(t)$ is the height of the object in feet at time t seconds.
1. What is the average velocity of the object between $t = 2$ s and $t = 4$ s? 3 ft/s
2. What is the instantaneous velocity of the object at time $t = 2.5$ s? 2 ft/s

Modeling

The average speed of an automobile, or any other moving object, is found by dividing the distance traveled by the time spent traveling. How can one determine the instantaneous speed of an object?

Consider the speed of the car described in the Focus. Suppose that the average velocity for time intervals close to 3 s had been determined as follows.

Time interval	Average velocity
3 s to 3.1 s	70.14 ft/s
3 s to 3.01 s	69.115 ft/s
3 s to 3.001 s	69.0114 ft/s
3 s to 3.0001 s	69.00105 ft/s

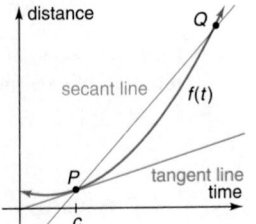

It appears that the average velocities approach 69 ft/s as time differences from 3 s grow shorter. Therefore, the instantaneous velocity of the car at $t = 3$ is taken to be 69 ft/s.

The relationship between average velocity and instantaneous velocity is modeled by the relationship between the slope of a secant line and the slope of a tangent line. The average velocity corresponds to the slope of the secant line and the instantaneous velocity corresponds to the slope of the tangent line.

$$\text{Average velocity} = \text{slope of } \overleftrightarrow{PQ} = \frac{f(t) - f(c)}{t - c}$$

$$\text{Instantaneous velocity} = \text{slope of the tangent line at } P = \lim_{t \to c} \frac{f(t) - f(c)}{t - c}$$

Suppose that $f(t)$ represents the position of a particle on a path as a function of time, as illustrated at the right. Then the function is called a *position function*. Note that the particle may move either forward or backward along the path.

Example 4 *Physics* The position of an object moving along a straight path is given by the position function $f(t) = t^2 + t + 2$, where $f(t)$ is the distance of the object in feet from a reference point at time t seconds. What is the average velocity of the object between $t = 1$ s and $t = 3$ s? What is the instantaneous velocity of the object at time $t = 1$?

The average velocity is $\dfrac{f(3) - f(1)}{3 - 1} = \dfrac{(3^2 + 3 + 2) - (1^2 + 1 + 2)}{3 - 1} = \dfrac{14 - 4}{3 - 1} = 5$ ft/s.

The instantaneous velocity at time $t = 1$ is found by simplifying the quotient in the formula for average velocity and then taking the limit.

$$\frac{f(t) - f(1)}{t - 1} = \frac{(t^2 + t + 2) - (1^2 + 1 + 2)}{t - 1} = \frac{t^2 + t - 2}{t - 1} = \frac{(t - 1)(t + 2)}{t - 1} = t + 2$$

$$\lim_{t \to 1} (t + 2) = 3$$

The instantaneous velocity of the object at time $t = 1$ is 3 ft/s.

868   Chapter 16 Limits and an Introduction to Calculus

Class Exercises

Find an equation of the line tangent to the curve at point P.

1. $f(x) = x^2 - 3$, $P(1, -2)$ **2.** $h(x) = \sqrt{x - 1}$, $P(5, 2)$ **3.** $f(x) = 3x^3$, $P(6, 648)$

Find the slope of the tangent line to the graph of $g(x)$ at $P(c, g(c))$.

4. $g(x) = 3x^2 - 2x$ $6c - 2$ **5.** $g(x) = 7 - 5x^2$ $-10c$

6. Writing in Mathematics   Describe how you might find the points on a graph at which the tangent line is horizontal.

7. Find the equation of a line that is tangent to the curve $f(x) = x^2 + 5$ and is parallel to the line $3x - y - 5 = 0$. $12x - 4y + 11 = 0$

Practice Exercises

Find the slope of the line tangent to the curve at point P.

A **1.** $f(x) = x^2 + 4$, $P(0, 4)$ 0   **2.** $h(x) = 3x^2$, $P(2, 12)$ 12

3. $f(x) = 4x^2 - 3$, $P(1, 1)$ 8   **4.** $g(x) = 5x^2 - 1$, $P(-1, 4)$ -10

5. $f(x) = x^2 + 5$, $P(-1, 6)$ -2 **6.** $g(x) = x^2 + 10$, $P(-2, 14)$ -4

7. $g(x) = -x^2 + 1$, $P(-3, -8)$ 6   **8.** $h(x) = -x^2 + 3$, $P(5, -22)$ -10

9. $h(x) = x^2 - 3x + 2$, $P(4, 6)$ 5   **10.** $f(x) = x^2 - 5x + 4$, $P(2, -2)$ -1

Ⓡ **11.** Determine the domain of $f(x) = \sqrt{x^2 - 16}$.   {$x: x \geq 4$ or $x \leq -4$}

Find the slope of the curve $g(x) = x^3 + 2x^2 + 1$ at each point.

12. $(c, g(c))$ $3c^2 + 4c$ **13.** $(-2, 1)$ 4   **14.** $(1, 4)$ 7

Find the slope of the curve $f(x) = 2x^2 - 7x + 3$ at each point.

15. $(c, f(c))$ $4c - 7$ **16.** $(3, 0)$ 5   **17.** $(1, -2)$ -3

18. Find an equation of a line with slope 1 that is tangent to the curve $f(x) = 2x^2 + 7x + 3$. $y = x - \frac{3}{2}$

Ⓡ **19.** Determine the domain of $g(x) = \sqrt{25 - x^2}$.   {$x: -5 \leq x \leq 5$}

20. Thinking Critically   Suppose that the position function $f(t) = 2t$ represents the distance in feet that an object moves in t seconds. What is the average velocity from $t = 1$ s to $t = 2$ s? From $t = 0$ s to $t = 3$ s? What geometric figure represents this motion on a graph of the position function?

Find an equation of the line tangent to the curve at point P.

B **21.** $g(x) = 2x^3 + x^2 + 1$, $P(-1, 0)$ $y = 4x + 4$ **22.** $h(x) = -x^2 + 4x$, $P(1, 3)$ $y = 2x + 1$

23. $h(x) = \sqrt{x + 6}$, $P(3, 3)$ $6y = x + 15$ **24.** $f(x) = \sqrt{x + 7}$, $P(9, 4)$ $8y = x + 23$

25. $f(x) = \sqrt{2 - x}$, $P(-7, 3)$ $6y = -x + 11$ **26.** $g(x) = \sqrt{3 - x}$, $P(-1, 2)$ $4y = -x + 7$

Find the slope of the curve at point $P(c, f(c))$.

27. $f(x) = 2x^2 + 3x$ $4c + 3$ **28.** $g(x) = 4x^2 + 5x$ $8c + 5$ **29.** $g(x) = x^3 + 5x$ $3c^2 + 5$

30. $h(x) = x^3 - 3x$ $3c^2 - 3$ **31.** $h(x) = \sqrt{5 - x}$ $-\dfrac{1}{2\sqrt{5 - c}}$ **32.** $f(x) = \sqrt{x + 8}$ $\dfrac{1}{2\sqrt{c + 8}}$

16.3 Tangent to a Curve   **869**

CLOSURE

Ask students to describe in their own words how they would find the equation of the tangent line and of the normal line to the function $f(x) = x^2 - 7x + 9$ at $P(1, 3)$.

INDEPENDENT PRACTICE

Assignment Guide

Basic: 1–28
Average: 1–27 odd, 28–37, Project
Enriched: 1–35 odd, 36–42, Project

Teacher's Resource Book
   Practice, page 112

Ⓡ **Review**

Exercises 11, 19, and 33 review finding domains of functions.

Technology

Exercise 42 requires the use of a graphing utility.

Project

Let D represent distance in feet and T the time in seconds. The speed S in miles per hour can be given by $S = 3600*D/(5280*T)$.

Additional Answers

Class Exercises
1. $y = 2x - 4$
2. $4y = x + 3$
3. $y = 324x - 1296$

Practice Exercises
20. 2 ft/s; 2 ft/s; line

Writing in Mathematics
6. At a point at which the tangent line is horizontal, the slope of the curve is 0. Find the slope of a line tangent to the curve at an arbitrary point $(c, f(c))$ by using the expression $\lim\limits_{x \to c} \dfrac{f(x) - f(c)}{x - c} = 0$. Solve for all possible values of c. At each point $(c, f(c))$, the tangent line is horizontal.

LESSON FOLLOW-UP

Lesson Quiz

1. Find the slope of the line tangent to $f(x) = x^2 - 9x + 11$ at $(1, 3)$. -7

2. Find the equation of the tangent line to $f(x) = x^2 - 7x - 5$ at $(-1, 3)$. $y - 3 = -9(x + 1)$

The motion of an object is given by the function $f(t) = t^2 + 12t - 27$, where $f(t)$ is the height of the object in feet at time t seconds.

3. What is the average velocity of the object between $t = 2$ s and $t = 5$ s? 19 ft/s

4. What is the instantaneous velocity of the object at time $t = 4.5$ s? 21 ft/s

5. Find the slope of the curve $f(x) = 2x^2 - 4x$ at the point $(2, 0)$. 4

Alternative Assessment

Instruct students to choose a function and graph it on graph paper. Then have them choose any point on the graph and find the slope of the curve at that point. Students should exchange problems with a classmate and compare results.

Enrichment

What is the slope of the curve $f(x) = \dfrac{2}{x - 1}$ at the point $\left(-3, -\dfrac{1}{2}\right)$?

What slope does the curve have at $x = 1$? $-\dfrac{1}{8}$; undefined slope

Additional Answers

42.

ℝ 33. Determine the domain of $f(x) = \dfrac{|x + 3|}{\sqrt{x + 3}}$. $\{x: x > -3\}$

34. *Physics* The motion of an object is given by the position function $f(t) = 3t^2 + t$, where $f(t)$ is the distance in meters from the origin at time t seconds. Find the average velocity of the object between $t = 2$ s and $t = 3$ s. Find the instantaneous velocity of the object at $t = 2$. 16 m/s; 13 m/s

35. *Biology* The growth of certain bacteria has been observed to be represented by $f(t) = t^2 + 1$, where $f(t)$ is the mass in grams after t hours. Find the average growth rate between $t = 2$ and $t = 2.03$. Find the instantaneous rate of growth at $t = 2$. 4.03 g/h; 4 g/h

C 36. Find an equation of a line that is tangent to the curve $f(x) = x^3$ and is parallel to the line $12x - y + 10 = 0$. $y = 12x \pm 16$

37. Find an equation of a line that is tangent to the curve $g(x) = 24 - x^2$ and is perpendicular to the line $x - 8y + 6 = 0$. $y = -8x + 40$

38. Find the slope of the curve $f(x) = ax + b$ at the point $(c, f(c))$ given that a and b are nonzero constants. a

39. Find the slopes of the curves $f(x) = x^2 + 1$ and $g(x) = 3 - x^2$ at the points where they intersect. $m_{f(x)} = \pm 2$ and $m_{g(x)} = \mp 2$ at $(\pm 1, 2)$

40. Find equations of the lines tangent to the curve $f(x) = x - x^3$ at the points where it crosses the x-axis. $y = x$; $y = -2x + 2$; $y = -2x - 2$

41. Find the slope of the curve $g(x) = ax^2 + bx + c$ at the point $(d, g(d))$ given that a, b, and c are nonzero constants. $2ad + b$

42. *Physics* The motion of an object is given by the position function $f(t) = t^2 + 4t + 3$, where $f(t)$ is the distance from the origin in miles at time t hours. Use a graphing utility to draw the graph of the function. Determine from the graph the position of the object when $t = 2$ and $t = 2.5$. Find the average velocity of the object during the time from $t = 2$ until $t = 2.5$. What is the instantaneous velocity when $t = 2$? 8.5 mi/h; 8 mi/h

Project

The heart of a VASCAR speed detector is a program that computes the speed of the vehicle, given the distance traveled and the time required to travel that distance. Write a program that allows the user to input a distance in feet and a time in seconds and outputs the speed in miles per hour.

Review

1. Two dice, a red and a green, are tossed. Find the probability that both show an even number. $\dfrac{1}{4}$

2. Find the rectangular coordinates of the point with the polar coordinates $P\left(4, \dfrac{2\pi}{3}\right)$. $(-2, 2\sqrt{3})$

3. Determine the equation of an ellipse in standard form with foci $(4, 3)$ and $(-2, 3)$ if the length of the major axis is 12. $\dfrac{(x - 1)^2}{36} + \dfrac{(y - 3)^2}{27} = 1$

4. Find $\log_3 5$ to four decimal places. 1.4650

16.4 Finding Derivatives

Objective: To use the definition of a derivative to differentiate functions

Focus

The two people who are given credit for inventing calculus are Isaac Newton (1642–1727) and Gottfried Leibniz (1646–1716). Working independently, they used different notations to represent the ideas of the calculus of tangents and instantaneous rates, now known as *differential calculus*. To represent the limit of the rate of change of a quantity y with respect to a change in x, Leibniz used $\frac{dy}{dx}$, a notation still

Sir Isaac Newton   Gottfried Leibniz

popular today. Newton's notation, although simple, was not practical for most everyday mathematical work. For this reason, it did not gain acceptance except in the United Kingdom, which finally abandoned it in the nineteenth century.

In finding the slope m_t of the line tangent to a curve, it is often convenient to let h represent the difference $x - c$, so that $x - c = h$ and $x = c + h$. Then $h \to 0$ as $x \to c$. When this notation is used, the limit of the difference quotient

$$\lim_{x \to c} \frac{f(x) - f(c)}{x - c} \quad \text{is expressed as} \quad \lim_{h \to 0} \frac{f(c + h) - f(c)}{h}$$

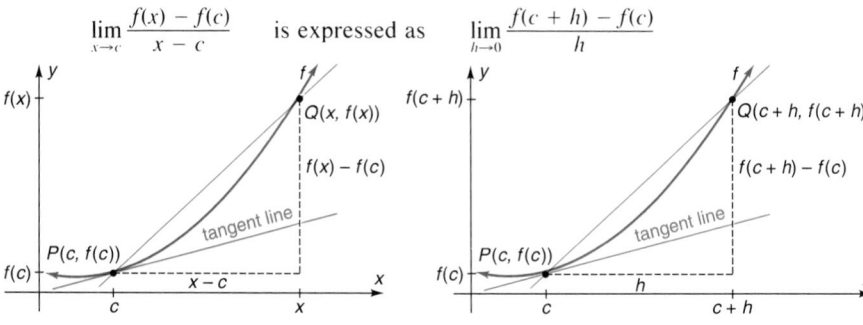

When $P(x, f(x))$ rather than $P(c, f(c))$ is used as an arbitrary point, the second expression becomes

$$m_t = \lim_{h \to 0} \frac{f(x + h) - f(x)}{h}$$

This expression is of fundamental importance in the study of calculus. It is called the *derivative* of f and is denoted by $f'(x)$, where $f'(x)$ is read, "f prime of x."

16.4 Finding Derivatives   **871**

The **derivative** of a function f is another function f' defined by

$$f'(x) = \lim_{h \to 0} \frac{f(x + h) - f(x)}{h}$$

The domain of f' consists of all those values of x in the domain of f for which the limit exists.

At each point $(x, f(x))$ for which the limit exists, f is said to be *differentiable* at x. The process of finding the derivative is called *differentiation*.

Example 1   Find the derivative of $f(x) = x^2 - 8x$.

$$
\begin{aligned}
f'(x) &= \lim_{h \to 0} \frac{[(x+h)^2 - 8(x+h)] - [x^2 - 8x]}{h} \\
&= \lim_{h \to 0} \frac{x^2 + 2xh + h^2 - 8x - 8h - x^2 + 8x}{h} \\
&= \lim_{h \to 0} \frac{2xh + h^2 - 8h}{h} \\
&= \lim_{h \to 0} \frac{h(2x + h - 8)}{h} \\
&= \lim_{h \to 0} 2x + h - 8 \\
&= 2x - 8
\end{aligned}
$$

$f'(x) = 2x - 8$

The derivative f' of the function f is also a function, with a domain that is a subset of the domain of f. The second derivative, denoted by f'', is the derivative of the derivative of f. Similarly, f''', the third derivative of f, is the derivative of f''.

The graphs below provide an idea of how a function and its first two derivatives are related to one another. The first graph is a position function for an object that has been thrust straight up in the air. The other two graphs illustrate the first and second derivatives of the position function.

The graph of f shows the height of the object at time t. The graph of f' shows the velocity at time t (rate at which the height changes with time), and the graph of f'' shows the acceleration at time t (rate at which the velocity changes with time). Note that $f''(t) = -32 \text{ ft/s}^2$. This constant represents the acceleration that a falling body experiences under the force of gravity acting in a direction opposite to the upward thrust.

872   Chapter 16 Limits and an Introduction to Calculus

To find the second derivative f'' of a function f, apply the definition of the derivative to the first derivative f'.

Example 2   Find the second derivative of the function in Example 1.

Apply the definition of the derivative to $f'(x) = 2x - 8$.

$$f''(x) = \lim_{h \to 0} \frac{[2(x+h)-8]-[2x-8]}{h}$$
$$= \lim_{h \to 0} \frac{2x+2h-8-2x+8}{h}$$
$$= \lim_{h \to 0} \frac{2h}{h} = \lim_{h \to 0} 2 = 2$$

When you use the definition of a derivative to find f'', you need to eliminate h as a factor in the denominator. Only then can the limit be taken.

Example 3   Find the derivative of the function $f(x) = \dfrac{3}{x-4}$. Find all points at which f has no derivative.

$$f'(x) = \lim_{h \to 0} \frac{f(x+h)-f(x)}{h} = \lim_{h \to 0} \frac{\dfrac{3}{x+h-4} - \dfrac{3}{x-4}}{h}$$

$$= \lim_{h \to 0} \frac{1}{h}\left[\frac{3(x-4)-3(x+h-4)}{(x+h-4)(x-4)}\right] = \lim_{h \to 0} \frac{1}{h}\left[\frac{3x-12-3x-3h+12}{(x+h-4)(x-4)}\right]$$

$$= \lim_{h \to 0} \frac{-3h}{h(x+h-4)(x-4)} = \lim_{h \to 0} \frac{-3}{(x+h-4)(x-4)} = -\frac{3}{(x-4)^2}$$

This expression is defined for all values of x except 4. Therefore, the derivative does not exist at $x = 4$.

An important relationship to explore is the relationship between differentiability and continuity. If a function has a derivative at a point, then it is continuous at that point. However, the converse is not true. A function may be continuous at a point but have no derivative there.

To prove the first statement, assume that $f'(x)$ exists at c. Then show that $\lim_{x \to c} f(x) = f(c)$. Given that $f'(x) = \lim_{x \to c} \dfrac{f(x)-f(c)}{x-c}$ exists, the difference $f(x) - f(c)$ can be expressed as follows:

$$f(x) - f(c) = \frac{f(x)-f(c)}{x-c} \cdot (x-c)$$

so that

$$f(x) = f(c) + \frac{f(x)-f(c)}{x-c} \cdot (x-c)$$

Then,

$$\lim_{x \to c} f(x) = \lim_{x \to c}\left[f(c) + \frac{f(x)-f(c)}{x-c} \cdot (x-c)\right]$$
$$= f(c) + f'(x) \cdot 0$$
$$= f(c)$$

Therefore, if $f'(x)$ exists at c, the function $f(x)$ is continuous at c.

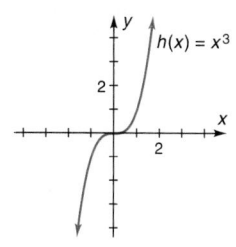

Differentiable and continuous at $x = 0$

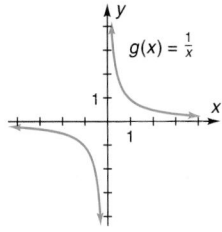

Not differentiable and not continuous at $x = 0$

16.4 Finding Derivatives   **873**

For Example 2
Find the second derivative of each function.
1. $f(x) = x^2 + 18x - 36$ $f''(x) = 2$
2. $g(x) = -x^2 - 6x + 10$
   $g''(x) = -2$

For Example 3
Find the derivative for each function.
1. $f(x) = \sqrt{x-3}$ $f'(x) = \dfrac{1}{2\sqrt{x-3}}$

2. $g(x) = 2\sqrt{x}$ $g'(x) = \dfrac{1}{\sqrt{x}}$

3. $h(x) = -\dfrac{5}{x-2}$ $h'(x) = \dfrac{5}{(x-2)^2}$

CLOSURE

Have students describe in their own words when a function is continuous at a point P, and when it is differentiable at P. Then have them describe the relationship between differentiable and continuous.

INDEPENDENT PRACTICE

Assignment Guide

Basic: 1–25, 29, 33
Average: 1–17 odd, 18–37
Enriched: 1–35 odd, 36–45

Teacher's Resource Book
  Practice, page 113

Ⓡ **Review**
Exercises 25 and 27 involve finding the square roots of complex numbers. Exercises 37 and 39 review finding zeros of functions.

Additional Answers

Practice Exercises

17. $-\dfrac{11}{(x+3)^2}$

18. $-\dfrac{13}{(x+2)^2}$

19. $\dfrac{1}{2\sqrt{x+9}}$

20. $\dfrac{1}{2\sqrt{x+15}}$

26. Linear functions have constant derivatives. Examples of linear functions will vary, but each derivative should equal the slope of the line.

To see that the converse is not true, consider $f(x) = |x|$ at $x = 0$. The function $f(x)$ is continuous at $x = 0$ since $\lim\limits_{x \to 0} f(x) = f(0) = 0$. However $f'(x)$ at $x = 0$ does not exist since

$$\lim_{h \to 0} \frac{f(x+h) - f(h)}{h} = \lim_{h \to 0} \frac{|0+h| - |0|}{h} = \lim_{h \to 0} \frac{|h|}{h} = -1$$

$$\lim_{h \to 0^-} \frac{f(x+h) - f(h)}{h} = \lim_{h \to 0^-} \frac{|h|}{h} = 1$$

So $f(x) = |x|$ is not differentiable at $x = 0$.

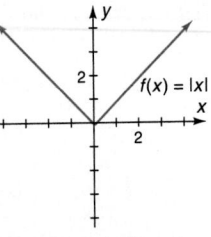

Not differentiable and continuous at $x = 0$

Class Exercises

Find the first and second derivatives.

1. $f(x) = x^2 + 3$ 2x; 2

2. $g(x) = x^2 - 5x + 7$ 2x − 5; 2

3. $h(x) = x^3 + 5x^2 - 7x + 3$
  3x² + 10x − 7; 6x + 10

4. $f(x) = x^3 - x^2 - 4x + 4$
  3x² − 2x − 4; 6x − 2

Find the first derivative.

5. $g(x) = \sqrt{x+2}$ $\frac{1}{2\sqrt{x+2}}$

6. $h(x) = \sqrt{x+5}$ $\frac{1}{2\sqrt{x+5}}$

7. $f(x) = \frac{1}{x}$ $-\frac{1}{x^2}$

8. $g(x) = \frac{3}{x+2}$ $-\frac{3}{(x+2)^2}$

Find all points in the domain of the function at which the function has no derivative.

9. $f(x) = \sqrt{x-7}$ 7

10. $g(x) = \sqrt{x-3}$ 3

11. $h(x) = -x^2 + 11x - 10$
  everywhere differentiable

12. $f(x) = |x+2|$ −2

Practice Exercises

Find the first and second derivatives.

A **1.** $f(x) = x^2 + 13$ 2x; 2

2. $g(x) = x^2 + 19$ 2x; 2

3. $g(x) = x^2 - 6x + 10$ 2x − 6; 2

4. $h(x) = x^2 - 7x + 12$ 2x − 7; 2

5. $h(x) = x^2 + 15x$ 2x + 15; 2

6. $f(x) = x^2 + 17x$ 2x + 17; 2

7. $g(x) = 3x^2 + 4x$ 6x + 4; 6

8. $h(x) = 5x^2 - 8x$ 10x − 8; 10

9. $f(x) = 3x^2 + 8x$ 6x + 8; 6

10. $g(x) = 10x^2 - 5x$ 20x − 5; 20

11. $h(x) = -6x^2 - 12x$ −12x − 12; −12

12. $f(x) = -8x^2 - 16x$ −16x − 16; −16

Find the first derivative.

13. $f(x) = \frac{4}{x}$ $-\frac{4}{x^2}$

14. $g(x) = \frac{5}{x}$ $-\frac{5}{x^2}$

15. $g(x) = -\frac{3}{x}$ $\frac{3}{x^2}$

16. $h(x) = -\frac{7}{x}$ $\frac{7}{x^2}$

17. $h(x) = \frac{11}{x+3}$

18. $f(x) = \frac{13}{x+2}$

19. $f(x) = \sqrt{x+9}$

20. $g(x) = \sqrt{x+15}$

B **21.** $f(x) = x^3 + 9x$ 3x² + 9

22. $g(x) = x^3 + 7x$ 3x² + 7

23. $h(x) = 5x^3 - 2x^2 + 4$ 15x² − 4x

24. $f(x) = 7x^3 - 3x^2 + 9$ 21x² − 6x

Ⓡ **25.** Find the square roots of $12 + 5i$. $\frac{5\sqrt{2}}{2} + \frac{\sqrt{2}}{2}i, \ -\frac{5\sqrt{2}}{2} - \frac{\sqrt{2}}{2}i$

26. Thinking Critically Describe the polynomial functions that have constant derivatives. Give an example of such a function and its derivative.

Ⓡ **27.** Find the square roots of $7 - 24i$. 4 − 3i, −4 + 3i

874 Chapter 16 Limits and an Introduction to Calculus

Find all points in the domain of the function at which the function has no derivative.

28. $f(x) = \sqrt{x - 20}$ **29.** $g(x) = \sqrt{x - 24}$ **30.** $f(x) = \dfrac{1}{\sqrt{x + 12}}$ **31.** $g(x) = \dfrac{1}{\sqrt{x + 16}}$
    20   24   none   none

32. $h(x) = 3|x + 1|$ -1 **33.** $f(x) = 2 + |x - 4|$ 4   **34.** $h(x) = x^3 - 7x^2 + 9x + 17$
                                                                   differentiable everywhere

Find the points on the graph that have tangent lines with the given slope.

35. $f(x) = \dfrac{16}{x - 6}$, $m = -4$ (8, 8), (4, −8)   **36.** $g(x) = \dfrac{36}{x - 10}$, $m = -9$ (12, 18), (8, −18)

Ⓡ **37.** Find the rational zeros of the function $g(x) = 15x^3 + 82x^2 + 33x - 10$. $-5, -\frac{2}{3}, \frac{1}{5}$

Ⓒ **38. Writing in Mathematics**   Describe how the graph of a third degree polynomial function may have one or two horizontal tangents. Write an equation for each type.

Ⓡ **39.** Find the real zeros of the function $h(x) = x^4 - 5x^3 - 8x^2 + 10x + 12$. $-1, -\sqrt{2}, \sqrt{2}, 6$

40. Given that $f(x) = ax^2 + bx + c$, use the definition of derivative to find $f'(x)$. $2ax + b$

Use your answer to Exercise 40 to find the derivative.

41. $f(x) = 6x^2 + 3x + 1$ $12x + 3$ **42.** $f(x) = x^2 - 5x$ $2x - 5$

43. For the function $f(x) = ax^2 + bx + c$, express in terms of a and b the value of x for which $f'(x) = 0$. $-\frac{b}{2a}$

44. Thinking Critically   Is it possible for the graph of a quadratic function to have two distinct tangent lines that are parallel? Why or why not?

45. The tangent to the curve $f(x) = x^2 + 6x + 8$ at $x = 2$ meets the x-axis at A and the y-axis at B. Find the coordinates of A and B. Find the length of $\overline{AB}$.
                                                   $A\left(-\frac{2}{5}, 0\right)$; $B(0, 4)$; $AB = \frac{2}{5}\sqrt{101}$

Test Yourself

For the function graphed, find: 16.1

1. $\lim\limits_{x \to 2^+} f(x)$ 2   **2.** $\lim\limits_{x \to 2^-} f(x)$ 2

Find the limit of the function.

3. $\lim\limits_{x \to 3} (x^2 - 2x + 5)$ 8   **4.** $\lim\limits_{x \to 5} \dfrac{x^2 - 2x - 15}{x - 5}$ 8

Find each limit, if it exists.   16.2

5. $\lim\limits_{x \to 7} \dfrac{x^2 - 49}{x^2 - 5x - 14}$ $\frac{14}{9}$ **6.** $\lim\limits_{x \to \infty} \dfrac{x^2 + 3x}{5x^3 - 1}$ 0

7. Determine whether the given function is continuous at $x = 0$. If not, indicate which part of the definition is not satisfied. Draw the graph. $f(x) = \begin{cases} \dfrac{x^2 - 3x}{x}, & \text{if } x \neq 0 \\ 3, & \text{if } x = 0 \end{cases}$

8. Find the equation of the line tangent to the curve of $f(x) = x^2 - 4x + 9$ at $P(2, 3)$.   16.3
                                                     $y = 3$

Find the first and second derivatives.

9. $f(x) = x^3 - 5x^2 + 4$ **10.** $f(x) = \dfrac{2}{x} - \dfrac{2}{x^2}$ $\frac{4}{x^3}$
   $3x^2 - 10x$; $6x - 10$

11. Find the point on the graph of $f(x) = 5x^2 - 4x$ that has a tangent line with slope $m = 1$. $\left(\frac{1}{2}, -\frac{3}{4}\right)$ 16.4

16.4 Finding Derivatives   **875**

Writing in Mathematics

38. A third-degree polynomial function such as $f(x) = ax^3$ is either increasing or decreasing over its entire domain, so that there is only one point where the slope of the tangent line is 0, and that is the point of inflection. For cubic polynomials of the form $f(x) = ax^3 + bx^2 + cx + d$, the curve has two "turns" or two points where the tangent line has a slope of 0.

LESSON FOLLOW-UP

Test Yourself

Teacher's Resource Book
   Tests—Quiz, form A, page 69
   Tests—Quiz, form B, page 69

Lesson Quiz

Find the derivative for each function.
1. $f(x) = x^2 + 15x$ $f'(x) = 2x + 15$
2. $g(x) = -3\sqrt{x}$ $g'(x) = -\dfrac{3}{2\sqrt{x}}$
Find the second derivative for each function.
3. $h(x) = x^3 - 4x + 2$ $h''(x) = 6x$
4. $p(x) = 3x^2 - 9$ $p''(x) = 6$
5. Find the point at which the function $f(x) = -\dfrac{4}{x + 7}$ does not have a derivative. $x = -7$

Alternative Assessment

On a grid, have students sketch accurately the graph of the function $f(x) = -2x^2 + 8x + 3$. Then have them graph the tangent to f at $x = 1$.

Enrichment

Can you discover any patterns for finding the derivatives of polynomial functions? Hint: Look at the coefficients and powers of corresponding terms in a function and its derivative. Use these patterns to find the derivative of each function.
1. $f(x) = x^2$ $2x$
2. $f(x) = x^5$ $5x^4$
3. $f(x) = 3x^2$ $6x$
4. $f(x) = -2x^2 - 3x - 1$ $-4x - 3 + 0$
5. $f(x) = 4x^3 - 5x^2$ $12x^2 - 10x$
Pattern: If $f(x) = ax^n$, $f'(x) = nax^{n-1}$.

Additional Answers

44. no; The derivative of a quadratic function is a linear equation in the form $f'(x) = ax + b$. Setting it equal to some value m will yield only one value for x, and for any x in the original quadratic function there is only one y. Therefore, for any tangent line with slope m there is only one point of tangency, (x, y).

875

Vocabulary

absolute maximum
absolute minimum
concave down
concave up
constant multiple theorem
constant theorem
critical number
decreasing function
increasing function
maximum value
minimum value
points of inflection
power theorem
relative minimum
relative maximum
stationary values
sum theorem

Technology

graphing utility
computer

FOCUS

The derivative of a function has applications in many subject areas, particularly where a quantity needs to be maximized or minimized. For example: In manufacturing, it is desirable to minimize costs and to maximize profits; in hospital management, it may be desirable to maximize the number of patients that can be treated; companies such as credit-card agencies may wish to minimize the waiting time for speaking to a service representative. Professionals in these fields develop mathematical models or functions to address their needs. In this lesson students will see that the first derivative of the function identifies potential relative extrema. For these points, the second derivative identifies the relative maxima and relative minima.

Objectives: *To use theorems in finding the derivative of a function*
To graph a function using the first derivative

Focus

The derivative of a function has many applications in economics. If x units of a commodity are produced, then the cost of the commodity is a function of x. The total cost function represents the total cost of producing x units of the commodity. Suppose that the cost function is $C(x) = -0.03x^2 + 18x + 1000$. Then the fixed costs are $1000 since $C(0) = 1000$ represents the production of zero commodities. A manufacturer may be interested in knowing how many more items to produce in order to minimize the additional cost per unit. The derivative can be used to find this information.

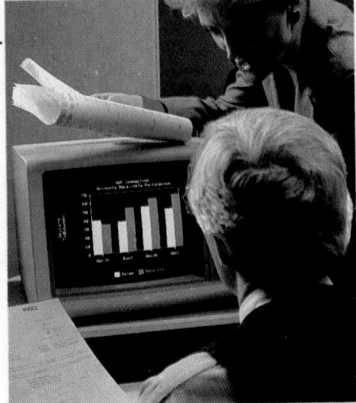

In Lesson 16.4, the first and second derivatives of functions were obtained directly from the definition of the derivative. Fortunately, there are several formulas for finding derivatives. The following four theorems are useful primarily for differentiating polynomial functions.

Recall that the graph of a constant function of the form $f(x) = c$ is a horizontal line, which has a slope of zero. This fact is the basis for the following theorem.

Derivative of a Constant

If $f(x) = c$, where c is a constant, then $f'(x) = 0$ for all x.

Proof: $f'(x) = \lim\limits_{h \to 0} \dfrac{f(x + h) - f(x)}{h}$

$\qquad\qquad = \lim\limits_{h \to 0} \dfrac{c - c}{h} = \lim\limits_{h \to 0} 0 = 0$

For example, if $f(x) = 8$, then $f'(x) = 0$.

Derivative of a Power

If $f(x) = x^n$, where n is any nonzero real number, then $f'(x) = nx^{n-1}$.

For example,

If $f(x) = x^3$, then $n = 3$ and $f'(x) = 3x^2$.

If $f(x) = \dfrac{1}{\sqrt{x}} = x^{-\frac{1}{2}}$, then $n = -\dfrac{1}{2}$ and $f'(x) = -\dfrac{1}{2}x^{-\frac{3}{2}}$, or $-\dfrac{\sqrt{x}}{2x^2}$.

If $f(x) = x$, then $n = 1$ and $f'(x) = 1x^0 = 1 \cdot 1 = 1$.

You can verify the above theorem for positive integral values of n by using the binomial theorem to expand $(x + h)^n$ as follows:

Proof: Given $f(x) = x^n$, then

$$
\begin{aligned}
f'(x) &= \lim_{h \to 0} \frac{f(x + h) - f(x)}{h} \\
&= \lim_{h \to 0} \frac{(x + h)^n - (x)^n}{h} \\
&= \lim_{h \to 0} \frac{(x^n + nx^{n-1}h + n(n-1)x^{n-2}h^2 + \cdots + h^n) - (x)^n}{h} \\
&= \lim_{h \to 0} \frac{nx^{n-1}h + n(n-1)x^{n-2}h^2 + \cdots + h^n}{h} \\
&= \lim_{h \to 0} (nx^{n-1} + n(n-1)x^{n-2}h + \cdots + h^{n-1}) \\
&= nx^{n-1} \qquad \text{\textit{The limit of all terms with h as a factor equals zero.}}
\end{aligned}
$$

Since the derivative of a power theorem is valid for any real number exponent n, you can apply the theorem for values of n that are rational.

Proofs of the next two theorems are asked for in the exercises.

Derivative of a Constant Multiple of a Power

If $f(x) = ax^n$, where a and n are any nonzero real numbers, then $f'(x) = anx^{n-1}$.

For example, if $f(x) = 3x^2$, then $f'(x) = 3 \cdot 2x = 6x$.

Derivative of a Sum

If $f(x) = g(x) + h(x)$, then $f'(x) = g'(x) + h'(x)$.

The above theorems can be used to differentiate polynomial functions. In fact, it immediately follows from these theorems that a polynomial function is differentiable at every point of its domain. To apply these theorems to rational functions, such as $f(x) = \sqrt{x}$, express the function with a rational exponent as $f(x) = x^{\frac{1}{2}}$.

GUIDED PRACTICE

For Example 1

Find $f'(x)$ and $f''(x)$ for each function.

1. $f(x) = x^7$

$f'(x) = 7x^6; f''(x) = 42x^5$

2. $f(x) = 6x^5$

$f'(x) = 30x^4; f''(x) = 120x^3$

3. $f(x) = 4x^2 - 12x + 7$

$f'(x) = 8x - 12; f''(x) = 8$

4. $f(x) = \sqrt{x} + \dfrac{3}{x}$

$f'(x) = \dfrac{1}{2x^{\frac{1}{2}}} - \dfrac{3}{x^2}; f''(x) = -\dfrac{1}{4x^{\frac{3}{2}}} + \dfrac{6}{x^3}$

For Example 2

For the given function, find: (a) the critical numbers, (b) the intervals where the function is increasing and decreasing, and (c) the relative minima and maxima.

1. $f(x) = \dfrac{x^3}{3} + \dfrac{x^2}{2} - 30x + 5$

a. $x = -6, x = 5$

b. inc: $x < -6, x > 5$

  dec: $-6 < x < 5$

c. relative maximum: $(-6, 131)$

  relative minimum: $\left(5, -\dfrac{545}{6}\right)$

2. $g(x) = -4x^3 + 15x^2 + 18x - 7$

a. $x = -\dfrac{1}{2}, x = 3$

b. inc: $-\dfrac{1}{2} < x < 3$

  dec: $x < -\dfrac{1}{2}, x > 3$

c. relative maximum: $(3, 74)$

  relative minimum: $\left(-\dfrac{1}{2}, -\dfrac{47}{4}\right)$

Example 1 Find $f'(x)$ and $f''(x)$ for each function.

a. $f(x) = x^6$ b. $f(x) = 5x^4$ c. $f(x) = 3x^2 - 5x + 8$ d. $f(x) = \sqrt{x} + \dfrac{1}{x}$

a. $f(x) = x^6$

$f'(x) = 6x^5$ *Power theorem*

$f''(x) = 6 \cdot 5x^4 = 30x^4$ *Constant multiple theorem*

b. $f(x) = 5x^4$

$f'(x) = 5 \cdot 4x^3 = 20x^3$ *Constant multiple theorem*

$f''(x) = 20 \cdot 3x^2 = 60x^2$

c. $f(x) = 3x^2 - 5x + 8$

$f'(x) = 3 \cdot 2x - 5 \cdot 1x^0 + 0 = 6x - 5$ *Sum theorem*

$f''(x) = 6 \cdot 1x^0 - 0 = 6$

d. $f(x) = \sqrt{x} + \dfrac{1}{x} = x^{\frac{1}{2}} + x^{-1}$ *Use rational exponents.*

$f'(x) = \dfrac{1}{2}x^{-\frac{1}{2}} + (-1)x^{-1-1} = \dfrac{1}{2}x^{-\frac{1}{2}} - x^{-2}$,   or $\dfrac{\sqrt{x}}{2x} - \dfrac{1}{x^2}$

$f''(x) = \dfrac{1}{2}\left(-\dfrac{1}{2}\right)x^{-\frac{3}{2}} - (-2)x^{-3} = -\dfrac{1}{4}x^{-\frac{3}{2}} + 2x^{-3}$,   or $-\dfrac{\sqrt{x}}{4x^2} + \dfrac{2}{x^3}$

In Chapter 7, you learned how to graph polynomial and rational functions using information about the degree of a polynomial, the zeros of the function, upper and lower bounds, the asymptotes of a graph, and a graphing utility. You can now use the derivative of a function as a tool in graphing a function.

Clearly, a function is *increasing* when the slope of the curve is positive, or $f'(x) > 0$. A function is *decreasing* when the slope of the curve is negative, or $f'(x) < 0$.

A value of x for which $f'(x) = 0$ is called a **critical number**. A point $(a, f(a))$ on a graph is a **relative maximum** if and only if $f'(x) = 0$, and f changes from an increasing function for $x < a$ to a decreasing function for $x > a$. A point $(b, f(b))$ on a graph is a **relative minimum** if and only if $f'(b) = 0$ and f changes from a decreasing function for $x < b$ to an increasing function for $x > b$. There may be more than one relative maximum or minimum.

At any point on a graph where the first derivative equals zero, the graph has a horizontal tangent. However, the point may *not* be a relative maximum or relative minimum as shown at the right.

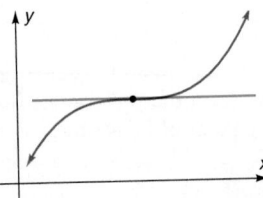

878   Chapter 16 Limits and an Introduction to Calculus

Example 2 Given $f(x) = \frac{1}{3}x^3 - x^2 - 3x + 4$, determine the critical numbers, the intervals where the function is increasing or decreasing, and the relative maximums and minimums.

$f(x) = \frac{1}{3}x^3 - x^2 - 3x + 4$ *Find the values of x where the first derivative equals zero.*

$f'(x) = x^2 - 2x - 3$ *Take the derivative.*

$0 = x^2 - 2x - 3$ *Set $f'(x) = 0$.*

$0 = (x + 1)(x - 3)$ *Factor.*

$x = -1$ or $x = 3$ *Critical numbers*

Determine whether $f'(x)$ is positive or negative in the intervals $(-\infty, -1)$, $(-1, 3)$, and $(3, \infty)$.

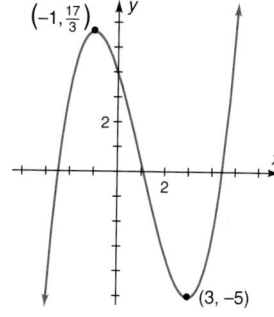

	$f'(x)$	Conclusion
$x < -1$	+	$f(x)$ is increasing
$x = -1$	0	relative maximum
$-1 < x < 3$	−	$f(x)$ is decreasing
$x = 3$	0	relative minimum
$x > 3$	+	$f(x)$ is increasing

A graph is **concave up** when it opens upward and **concave down** when it opens downward. The second derivative of a function gives information about its concavity, that is, the rate at which the function increases or decreases as x increases.

When $f''(x) > 0$, the graph is concave up. When $f''(x) < 0$, the graph is concave down.

The zeros of the second derivative help to locate **points of inflection,** that is, points on the graph at which the concavity changes. The second derivative is usually *positive* at a relative minimum and *negative* at a relative maximum. *Why?*

Example 3 *Economics* Given that $C(x) = -0.03x^2 + 18x + 1000$ is the total cost function for producing x units of a particular commodity, find the number of units that must be produced before the marginal cost begins to decrease. The *marginal cost* is the rate at which the total cost changes with an increase in x.

$C(x) = -0.03x^2 + 18x + 1000$

$C'(x) = -0.06x + 18$ *Take the derivative.*

$0 = -0.06x + 18$ *Set $f'(x) = 0$.*

$-18 = -0.06x$

$300 = x$

For $x < 300$, $C'(x) > 0$, and for $x > 300$, $C'(x) < 0$. Thus, $x = 300$ is the production level at which the marginal cost begins to decrease.

16.5 Using Derivatives in Graphing   **879**

For Example 3
If $c(x) = -0.04x^2 + 32x + 1500$ is the total cost function for producing a particular commodity, how many must be produced before costs decrease? 401

Thinking Critically
It is possible for the second derivative to be zero at a relative extremum. For example, for the function $f(x) = x^4$, $f''(x) = 12x^2$. This second derivative equals zero at the point $(0, 0)$, which is a relative minimum.

CLOSURE

Ask students to give the critical points or intervals for $f(x) = \frac{1}{3}x^3 + x^2 - 8x + 4$ and graph.

INDEPENDENT PRACTICE

Assignment Guide
Basic: 1–26, 29
Average: 1–19 odd, 20–36
Enriched: 1–31 odd, 32–40

Teacher's Resource Book
Practice, page 114

ⓡ Review
Exercises 17, 23, 31, and 38 review evaluating limits of functions, graphing trigonometric functions, and finding the equations of lines tangent to a curve.

Technology
Although a graphing calculator is not required, its use would help to verify graphs of functions.

LESSON FOLLOW-UP

Lesson Quiz
Find $f'(x)$ and $f''(x)$ for each function.
1. $f(x) = x^8$
$f'(x) = 8x^7; f''(x) = 56x^6$
2. $f(x) = -2x^3$
$f'(x) = -6x^2; f''(x) = -12x$
3. $f(x) = 5x^4 + 3x^2 - 2$
$f'(x) = 20x^3 + 6x; f''(x) = 60x^2 + 6$
4. $f(x) = \sqrt{x + 2} + \dfrac{6}{x}$
$f'(x) = \dfrac{1}{2(x + 2)^{\frac{1}{2}}} - \dfrac{6}{x^2}$
$f''(x) = -\dfrac{1}{4(x + 2)^{\frac{3}{2}}} + \dfrac{12}{x^3}$
5. For the function $f(x) = 2x^3 + 3x^2 - 12x + 1$, find (a) the critical numbers, (b) the intervals on which f is increasing and decreasing, and (c) the relative maximum and minimum values. (a) $1, -2$; (b) inc: $x < -2$, $x > 1$; dec: $-2 < x < 1$; (c) relative maximum: $(-2, 21)$; relative minimum: $(1, -6)$

The conditions of a problem may restrict the domain of a function to an interval $[a, b]$. In this case, maximum and minimum values of a function may also occur at the endpoints, where $f'(x)$ may be zero, nonzero, or may not exist. When more than one maximum or minimum occurs, the greatest function value determines the **absolute maximum** and the least function value determines the **absolute minimum**. In the graph at the right, T is an absolute maximum and P is an absolute minimum.

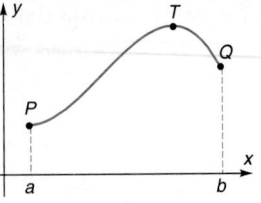

Class Exercises

Find the first and second derivatives of each function.

1. $f(x) = 7x^2 + 5$
2. $g(x) = -3x^4 + 5x^2$
3. $h(x) = x^5 + 3x^2 + 4x$
4. $f(x) = 6x^{-3} + 2x^3$
5. $f(x) = 2\sqrt{x}$
6. $f(x) = \sqrt[3]{x}$

Determine the critical numbers, the intervals where the function is increasing and decreasing, and the relative maximums and minimums. Graph the function.

7. $g(x) = -x^2 + 4x$
8. $f(x) = 3x^4$
9. $g(x) = x^4 - 2x^3 + 7$

Graph the function showing concavity, relative maximums and minimums, and intervals where the function is increasing or decreasing.

10. $f(x) = 2x^3 - 3x^2 - 36x + 17$
11. $g(x) = 2x^4 - 8x^3$

12. **Writing in Mathematics** Describe how the graph of a function may have an inflection point but no relative maximum or minimum.

Practice Exercises

Find the first and second derivatives of each function.

A
1. $f(x) = x^2 + 35$
2. $g(x) = x^2 - 27$
3. $g(x) = x^2 + 8x + 12$
4. $h(x) = x^2 - 9x + 15$
5. $h(x) = x^3 + 5x^2 + 3$
6. $f(x) = x^3 - 7x^2 + 9$
7. $f(x) = x^5 + 7x^3 - 6x$
8. $g(x) = x^5 + 5x^3 - 11x$
9. $g(x) = 5x^3 - 6x^2$

Express the derivative of each function without using negative or fractional exponents.

10. $h(x) = \dfrac{3}{x} - \dfrac{3}{x^2}$
11. $f(x) = \dfrac{13}{x} - \dfrac{13}{x^2}$
12. $f(x) = -10x^{\frac{1}{2}} - \dfrac{5\sqrt{x}}{x}$
13. $g(x) = -15x^{\frac{3}{2}} - \dfrac{45\sqrt{x}}{2}$
14. $f(x) = \dfrac{1}{2}x^6 + \dfrac{x^{-2}}{2} \cdot 3x^5 - \dfrac{1}{x^3}$
15. $f(x) = \dfrac{1}{2}x^4 - \dfrac{x^{-3}}{3} \cdot 2x^3 + \dfrac{1}{x^4}$

16. The graph of $f(x) = \frac{1}{3}x^3 + 3x^2 + 5x$ is shown at right. Find the coordinates of the relative maximum point A and the relative minimum point B. $A\left(-5, \frac{25}{3}\right)$; $B\left(-1, -\frac{7}{3}\right)$

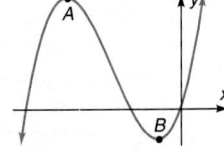

ⓡ 17. Evaluate: $\displaystyle\lim_{x \to 3} \dfrac{x^3 - 27}{x - 3}$ 27

18. *Business* Suppose that $f(x) = -300x^2 + 3600x - 6000$ represents the profit from selling video games, where x is the selling price for a game. Find the selling price that yields the maximum profit. $6.00

880 Chapter 16 Limits and an Introduction to Calculus

Writing in Mathematics
12. If the first derivative of the function is always positive (or negative), then its graph is always increasing (or decreasing), and there is no minimum or maximum point. Then, if the second derivative has a zero, the function may have an inflection point. An example of such a function is $f(x) = x^3$.

B Determine the critical numbers, the intervals where the function is increasing or decreasing, and the relative minimums or maximums. Then graph the function.

19. $h(x) = x^2 - 16x + 3$

20. $f(x) = x^2 - 18x + 10$

21. $g(x) = 4x^3$

22. $h(x) = -\frac{1}{3}x^3 + x^2 + 8x + 2$

Ⓡ 23. Evaluate: $\lim\limits_{x \to \infty} \dfrac{x^3 + x^2 + 1}{3x^2}$ ∞

24. **Thinking Critically** Is it possible for three different functions to have identical first and second derivatives? If not, why not? If so, give equations of three such functions.

25. *Business* A manufacturer can produce radios at a cost of $15 each. If the radios are sold for x dollars each, consumers will buy $140 - x$ of the radios a month. Find the price at which the profit will be the greatest. $77.50

Find the relative maximum and relative minimum points for each function.

26. $h(x) = x^3 - 2x$

27. $f(x) = 3x^2 - x^3$

28. $f(x) = x^3 + 2x^2 + x - 7$

29. $g(x) = x^3 - 6x^2 + 9x + 5$

30. **Thinking Critically** At which labeled points on the graph of f is $f'(x)$ equal to 0, positive, and negative? At which points is $f''(x)$ equal to 0, positive, and negative?

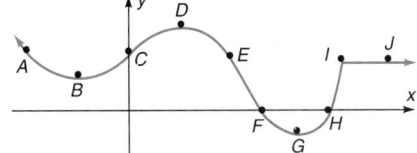

31. Graph two periods of the graph of
$$f(x) = \tan\left(x - \frac{\pi}{4}\right).$$

Graph the function showing concavity, relative maximums, relative minimums, inflection points, and intervals where the function is increasing or decreasing.

C 32. $f(x) = x^3 - 6x^2 + 9x + 1$ 33. $f(x) = x^3 - x^2 - x$ 34. $g(x) = x^3 + 2x^2 + 15$

35. $g(x) = x^3 - 12x^2 + 3$ 36. $h(x) = x^4 + 3$ 37. $f(x) = \dfrac{1}{3x^2}$

Ⓡ 38. Find the equations of two lines tangent to the curve $g(x) = x^3 + 3x^2 - 1$ that have a slope of 9. $y = 9x + 26, y = 9x - 6$

39. Prove: If $f(x) = ax^n$, where a is any nonzero real number and n is a positive integer, then $f'(x) = anx^{n-1}$.

40. Prove: If $f(x) = g(x) + j(x)$, then $f'(x) = g'(x) + j'(x)$.

Challenge

1. If $x \neq y$ and the sequence, x, p_1, p_2, y and x, q_1, q_2, q_3, y each are in arithmetic progression, determine the ratio of $\dfrac{p_2 - p_1}{q_2 - q_1}$. $\frac{4}{3}$

2. A particle projected vertically upward reaches a height of s feet where $s = 160t - 16t^2$ at the end of t seconds. Determine the maximum height the particle attains. 400 ft

3. If the points $(2, y_1)$ and $(-2, y_2)$ lie on the graph of $y = ax^2 + bx + c$, and $y_1 - y_2 = -8$, find the value of b. −2

16.5 Using Derivatives in Graphing   **881**

Enrichment
In the early 1600s, Pierre de Fermat used similar triangles to develop a procedure for finding the tangent at a point on a curve whose Cartesian equation is given. In the diagram below, coordinates of the point P are $(a, f(a))$; those of P' are $(a + E, f(a + E))$; and those of O are $(0, 0)$. If the distance from T to Q is c, and the distance between points P and P' approaches zero so that they share the same tangent line, what proportion could you write? How could you use this proportion to find the slope of the tangent line?

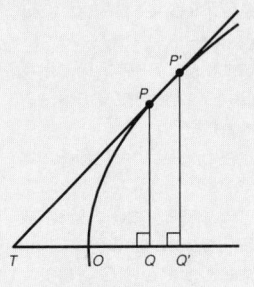

$$\frac{c}{E} = \frac{TP}{PP'}; \lim_{E \to 0} \frac{f(a + E) - f(a)}{E}$$

Additional Answers

24. yes; Example: $y = x^2, y = x^2 + 1,$
$y = x^2 + 2$

26. max: $\left(-\dfrac{\sqrt{6}}{3}, \dfrac{4\sqrt{6}}{9}\right)$; min: $\left(\dfrac{\sqrt{6}}{3}, -\dfrac{4\sqrt{6}}{9}\right)$

27. max: (2, 4); min: (0, 0)

28. max: $(-1, -7)$; min: $\left(-\dfrac{1}{3}, -\dfrac{193}{27}\right)$

29. max: (1, 9); min: (3, 5)

30. $f'(x) = 0$ at B, D, G;
$f'(x) > 0$ at C, H;
$f'(x) < 0$ at A, E, F;
$f''(x) = 0$ at C, E;
$f''(x) > 0$ at A, B, F, G, H;
$f''(x) < 0$ at D

39. $f'(x) = \lim\limits_{h \to 0} \dfrac{a(x + h)^n - ax^n}{h} = \lim\limits_{h \to 0} a\left[\dfrac{(x + h)^n - x^n}{h}\right] = a \lim\limits_{h \to 0} \left[\dfrac{(x + h)^n - x^n}{h}\right] = anx^{n-1}$

40. $f'(x) = \lim\limits_{h \to 0} \dfrac{g(x + h) + j(x + h) - g(x) - j(x)}{h} = \lim\limits_{h \to 0} \dfrac{g(x + h) - g(x) + j(x + h) - j(x)}{h} =$

$\lim\limits_{h \to 0} \dfrac{g(x + h) - g(x)}{h} + \lim\limits_{h \to 0} \dfrac{j(x + h) - j(x)}{h} = g'(x) + j'(x)$

Vocabulary
instantaneous rate of change

Ⓜ **Materials/Manipulatives**
board straightedge

Technology
computer
graphing utility

FOCUS

Discuss what students think is meant
by instantaneous velocity and instantaneous rate of growth of an animal
population. Have students describe
how the derivative facilitates understanding instantaneous rates of
change.

INSTRUCTION

• Some students incorrectly assume
that the derivative is always velocity. Use Examples 2 and 3 to show
other examples of instantaneous
rates of change.

• This lesson assumes that students
know basic geometric functions for
finding volume, area, and distance,
and can write basic functions for
finding income and profit. These
functions are used to solve problems such as the one in Example 2. Some students may benefit
from a review of these formulas
and functions.

16.6   Applying the Derivative

Objectives: To use the derivative to solve problems involving rates of change
To use the derivative to solve maxima and minima problems

Focus

In the early seventeenth century, investigators
such as Galileo, Cavalieri, and Torricelli sought to
understand the mathematical basis that underlay the
moving-body experiments of Stevin, Galileo and
others. Their efforts were only partly successful; it
was not until later in the century with the discovery
of the derivative that mathematicians were able
to devise satisfactory equations of motion. In
particular, the derivative made it possible for the
first time fully to understand what is meant by
"instantaneous velocity." In the intervening
centuries, the derivative has been applied to a large
number of diverse disciplines, such as physics, astronomy, chemistry, biology,
medicine, and economics. Indeed, the derivative is bound to be used as a
mathematical model in any field of study that involves rates of change.

A contemporary example of the role of the derivative is found in the field of
ecological systems. In a limited-growth model of an animal population, the rate of
change in the size of the population may be small at first, then increase rapidly,
and finally decrease to near zero when the resources to support growth have
diminished. The derivative helps determine these rates of change.

An important interpretation of the derivative is that of slope of a tangent line to
a curve. The Focus referred to another interpretation, one that is of great
importance in the physical sciences—*instantaneous rate of change*.

Instantaneous Rate of Change

The instantaneous rate of change of $y = f(x)$ per unit change in x
at x_0 is

$$f'(x_0) = \lim_{h \to 0} \frac{f(x_0 + h) - f(x_0)}{h}$$

You have seen examples of this concept in earlier lessons. *Instantaneous
velocity* is the instantaneous rate of change in the position of a particle with
respect to time. *Instantaneous acceleration* is the instantaneous rate of change
in the velocity of a particle with respect to time.

882   Chapter 16 Limits and an Introduction to Calculus

Example 1 *Physics*   Find the instantaneous velocity and acceleration of a moving particle with position function $f(t) = t^3 - 2t^2 + 5t + 1$ when $t = 3$. Assume that time is measured in seconds and distance in meters.

$$f'(t) = 3t^2 - 4t + 5 \quad \textit{The velocity at time t is } f'(t).$$

At $t = 3$: $f'(3) = 3(3)^2 - 4(3) + 5 = 27 - 12 + 5 = 20$ m/s

$$f''(t) = 6t - 4 \quad \textit{The acceleration at any time t is } f''(t).$$

At $t = 3$: $f''(3) = 6(3) - 4 = 18 - 4 = 14$ m/s^2

An instantaneous rate of change may be found with respect to a variable other than time.

Example 2   Let x represent the radius of a balloon that is being inflated. Find the instantaneous rate of change in the volume of the spherical balloon with respect to the radius x when $x = 2$ ft and when $x = 3$ ft.

The volume of a sphere is $V(x) = \frac{4}{3}\pi x^3$. $V'(x)$ represents the rate of change of the volume for each foot of change in the length of the radius.

$$V'(x) = \frac{4}{3}\pi \cdot 3x^2 = 4\pi x^2$$

When $x = 2$: $V'(2) = 4\pi(2)^2 = 16\pi$ When $x = 3$: $V'(3) = 4\pi(3)^2 = 36\pi$

When $x = 2$, the volume increases 16π ft^3 for each foot of increase in the radius.
When $x = 3$, the volume increases 36π ft^3 for each foot of increase in the radius.

A wide variety of problems involving maximums or minimums may be solved using derivatives. For example, a manufacturer may be able to use the derivative to maximize profits.

Example 3   *Business*   An oil refiner has 100,000 gal of gasoline that could be sold now with a profit of 25 cents/gal. For each week of delays, an additional 10,000 gal can be produced. However, for each such week, the profit decreases by 1 cent/gal. It is possible to sell all the gasoline that is on hand at any time. When should the gasoline be sold so that profit is maximized?

Let w represent the number of weeks the sale is delayed. The number of gallons sold after w weeks delay is $100,000 + 10,000w$. The number of dollars profit per gallon after w weeks delay is $0.25 - 0.01w$.

The profit function is number of gallons sold times number of dollars profit per gallon.

$$P(w) = (100,000 + 10,000w)(0.25 - 0.01w) = 25,000 + 1500w - 100w^2$$
$$P'(w) = 1500 - 200w$$
$$0 = 1500 - 200w \quad \textit{Set } f'(x) = 0.$$
$$7.5 = w$$

For $w < 7.5$, $P(w) > 0$ and for $w > 7.5$, $P(w) < 0$, so there is a maximum at $w = 7.5$. The refiner should sell in $7\frac{1}{2}$ weeks to maximize his profit.

16.6 Applying the Derivative   **883**

GUIDED PRACTICE

For Example 1
Find the velocity and the acceleration of a moving particle with the given position function at the given time.

1. $f(t) = t^3 - 5t^2 + t + 2$; $t = 4$
   $v(t) = 3t^2 - 10t + 1$; $v(4) = 9$
   $a(t) = 6t - 10$; $a(4) = 14$
2. $f(t) = 2t^3 - 4t + 1$; $t = 2$
   $v(t) = 6t^2 - 4$; $v(2) = 20$
   $a(t) = 12t$; $a(2) = 24$

For Example 2
Let x represent the length of a side of a square in feet. Find the instantaneous rate of change in the area of the square per unit change in x when $x = 5$.
10 ft^2 for each 1 ft change in x

For Example 3
A toy manufacturer has 800,000 electronic games that can be sold now with a profit of $2.00 per game. For each week that the shipment is delayed an additional 1600 games can be produced. However, for each week the shipment is delayed, the profit decreases by $0.20 per game. If it is possible to sell all of the games that are on hand at anytime, when should the games be sold so that profit is maximized. 2.5 weeks

CLOSURE

Have students explain in their own words how the derivative is used to find the relative maximum or minimum value of a function.

INDEPENDENT PRACTICE

Assignment Guide

Basic: 1–28
Average: 1–19 odd, 20–37
Enriched: 1–27 odd, 28–38, Project

Teacher's Resource Book
  Practice, page 115

®Review

Exercises 11, 15, 17, and 19 review areas of geometric figures. Exercises 21 and 23 involve working with matrices.

Technology

The use of a graphing utility is recommended to check Exercises 28 to 31; its use is required for Exercises 36 to 38. The project requires the use of a programmable calculator or a computer.

Project

One benefit of the program described in the project is that it allows students to evaluate derivatives of functions that are not polynomials.

Additional Answers
Practice Exercises
14. 13.73 in. × 5.46 in. × 2.27 in.

Class Exercises

Find the velocity and the acceleration of the moving particle with the given position function measured in feet at the given time measured in seconds.

1. $f(t) = t^2 + 7t + 3, t = 2$ 11 ft/s; 2 ft/s²
2. $f(t) = 3t^2 + 5t - 2, t = 3$ 23 ft/s; 6 ft/s²
3. $f(t) = t^3 + 6t^2 - 8t + 2, t = 4$ 88 ft/s; 36 ft/s²

4. *Construction*   A nursery school has received a gift of 500 ft of fencing for the purpose of constructing a rectangular fence around its play yard. No fence is needed along the school building. What is the maximum area that can be enclosed by the fence?   31,250 ft²

5. Find two numbers x and y whose sum is 96 and whose product is a maximum.   48, 48

6. *Sports*   An archer shoots an arrow toward a target 40 yd away. The arrow follows a path described by $f(x) = x - 0.05x^2$. Determine the maximum height of the arrow and the instantaneous rate of change of the height of the arrow with respect to x when $x = 15$.   5 yd; −0.5 yd

Practice Exercises   ⏣ Use appropriate technology.

Find the velocity and the acceleration of the moving particle with the given position function measured in meters at the given time measured in seconds.

A1. $f(t) = t^2 + 15t + 9, t = 1$ 17 m/s; 2 m/s²
2. $f(t) = 2t^2 - 8t + 3, t = 5$ 12 m/s; 4 m/s²
3. $f(t) = 5 - 3t - t^2, t = 2$ −7 m/s; −2 m/s²
4. $f(t) = 11 - 2t - t^2, t = 3$ −8 m/s; −2 m/s²
5. $f(t) = 49t - 7t^2, t = 0.5$ 42 m/s; −14 m/s²
6. $f(t) = 56t - 8t^2, t = 0.25$ 52 m/s; −16 m/s²
7. $f(t) = t^3 + 72t^2 - 1, t = \frac{1}{8}$ 18.05 m/s; 144.75 m/s²
8. $f(t) = t^3 + 23t^2 - 5, t = \frac{1}{2}$ $\frac{95}{4}$ m/s; 49 m/s²

9. The difference of two numbers is 40. Find the two numbers given that their product is to be as small as possible.   20, −20

10. Find two numbers x and y whose sum is 120 and whose product is a maximum.   60, 60

®11. Find the area of a circle with a diameter of 7 cm. $\frac{49\pi}{4}$ cm²

12. *Construction*   A rectangular flower bed is to be enclosed on three sides by a small decorative fence. The fourth side is a side of a house. What are the dimensions of the largest flower bed that can be enclosed by 24 ft of fencing?   6 ft × 12 ft

13. *Manufacturing*   An open box is to be made from a rectangular piece of material by cutting equal squares from each corner and turning up the sides. Find the dimensions of the box of maximum volume, given that the material has dimensions of 4 ft by 6 ft.   4.44 ft × 2.44 ft × 0.78 ft

14. *Manufacturing*   A commercial display box is to be made that is open both at the top and at one of the short ends. This is to be accomplished by cutting equal squares from two adjacent corners of a rectangular piece of material and turning up the sides. Find the dimensions of the box of maximum volume, given that the material has dimensions of 10 in. by 16 in.

®15. Find the area of a trapezoid with bases of 38 cm and 56 cm and a height of 26 cm.   1222 cm²

884   Chapter 16 Limits and an Introduction to Calculus

16. Let x be the radius of a spherical balloon that is being inflated. Find the instantaneous rate of change in the surface area of the balloon with respect to x when $x = 3$ ft. 24π ft²

Ⓡ 17. Find the area of a regular hexagon inscribed in a circle of radius 8 in. 96√3 in.²

B 18. Let x be the length of an edge of a cube. Find the instantaneous rate of change in the volume of the cube with respect to x when $x = 5$ in. 75 in.³

Ⓡ 19. Find the area of the rectangle with vertices at $(-3, -6)$, $(-6, -1)$, $(4, 5)$, and $(7, 0)$. 68

20. *Automotive Technology*   An automobile manufacturer found that the efficiency E of a new engine as a function of the speed S of the car was given by $E = 0.864S - 0.00008S^3$. Here E is given in percent and S is given in kilometers per hour. What is the maximum efficiency of the engine? 34.56%

Ⓡ 21. Find the inverse of the matrix $\begin{bmatrix} 1 & 7 \\ 5 & 20 \end{bmatrix}$. $\begin{bmatrix} -\frac{4}{3} & \frac{7}{15} \\ \frac{1}{3} & -\frac{1}{15} \end{bmatrix}$

22. *Business*   A local video store determines that it can rent 10,000 films per month if the rental price is $3 for each film. It also estimates that for each 25-cent reduction in price, 100 more films will be rented. Under these conditions, what is the maximum possible income and what rental price per film gives this income? max: $78,400 at $14 per rental

Ⓡ 23. Find the product: $\begin{bmatrix} 7 & 2 & 1 \\ 3 & 4 & 5 \end{bmatrix} \cdot \begin{bmatrix} 8 \\ 9 \\ 4 \end{bmatrix}$ $\begin{bmatrix} 78 \\ 80 \end{bmatrix}$

24. *Business*   A local theater manager determines that 700 tickets for a movie may be sold if the ticket price is $5 per ticket. He also estimates that for each 25 cent increase in price, 10 customers will not purchase tickets. Under these conditions, what is the maximum possible income and what ticket price should be set? max: $5062.50 at $11.25 per ticket

25. *Physics*   The height s (in feet) of an object thrown vertically upward from the ground is given by $s = 96t - 16t^2$, where t is measured in seconds. What is the maximum height that the object will attain? 144 ft

26. *Ecology*   A zoologist is using the function $P(t) = t^3 + 3t^2 - 3t + 200$, where t is time in years, to model the population of a species of turtles that has recently been assigned a protected status. Find the rate of growth of the turtle population when $t = 3$ and $t = 5$. 42 turtles/y; 102 turtles/y

27. *Construction*   A rancher wishes to fence in a rectangular plot of land and divide it into two corrals with a fence parallel to two of the sides. Given that 3000 ft of fencing is available, how large an area can the plot have? 375,000 ft²

Find the maximum slope of the given curve. Verify your answer using a graphing utility.

28. $f(x) = 8x^2 - x^4$ none

29. $f(x) = 10x^2 - x^5$ 15

30. $g(x) = 6x^5 - 20x^3$ none

31. $g(x) = 6x^5 - 80x^3$ none

C 32. Determine the constants a and b so that $f(x) = x^3 + ax^2 + bx + c$ will have a relative maximum at $x = -3$ and a relative minimum at $x = 5$. $a = -3$; $b = -45$

16.6 Applying the Derivative   **885**

33. Determine the constants a and b so that $f(x) = x^3 + ax^2 + bx + c$ will have a relative maximum at $x = -6$ and a relative minimum at $x = 2$. $a = 6; b = -36$

34. *Navigation* At 2:00 p.m. a lighthouse keeper sees two fishing vessels approaching. One of them is 9 mi due west and traveling east at 5 mi/h. The other is 6 mi due south traveling north at 4 mi/h. At what time will the two vessels be closest together, and how far apart will they be at that time? 0.937 mi apart at 3:40:59 p.m.

35. *Navigation* At 8:00 a.m. a lighthouse keeper sees two oil transports approaching. One of them is 20 mi due east and traveling west at 4 mi/h. The other is 30 mi due north traveling south at 3 mi/h. At what time will the transports be closest together, and how far apart will they be at that time? 12 mi apart at 2:48 p.m.

Biology The biomass of a culture of yeast is modeled by the function

$$f(x) = \frac{670}{1 + 74e^{-0.55x}}$$

where x is time in hours and $f(x)$ is the mass in grams. Use a graphing utility to draw this function and answer the following questions. (Use a viewing rectangle $[-10, 20]$ by $[0, 700]$ with an x-scale of 5 and a y-scale of 50.)

36. Approximate the mass when $x = 6$ h. 180 g

37. Approximate the maximum mass predicted by this model. 670 g

38. Approximate the value of x where the rate of increase of the function is greatest. 8.5

Project

Write a program that will approximate the value of the derivative of a function $f(x)$ at $x = a$. Use the definition of the derivative

$$f'(x) = \lim_{h \to 0} \frac{f(x + h) - f(x)}{h}$$

Output the values of this expression for $h = 1, 0.1, 0.01, 0.001, 0.0001, 0.00001, 0.000001$. Also output the value of a. Test your program with the function $f(x) = x^2 - 4x + 10$ and $x = 2, x = 6$.

Review

1. A lottery has a prize valued at $6000, and x tickets are sold at $2.00 each. Express the expected value of a ticket as a function of x. $f(x) = \dfrac{6000}{x}$

2. Determine an equation, in standard form, of a hyperbola with center $(3, -2)$, transverse axis of length 12, and conjugate axis of length 4. $\dfrac{(x-3)^2}{36} - \dfrac{(y+2)^2}{4} = 1$

3. Express the complex number $4\left(\cos \dfrac{\pi}{3} + i \sin \dfrac{\pi}{3}\right)$ in rectangular form. $2 + 2i\sqrt{3}$

4. Decompose into partial fractions $\dfrac{x+7}{x^2 - x - 6}$. $\dfrac{2}{x-3} - \dfrac{1}{x+2}$

5. Prove the identity: $\dfrac{1}{\sin x \cos x} - \dfrac{\cos x}{\sin x} = \tan x$

6. Solve and check the equation $\sqrt[3]{2x + 3} - \sqrt[3]{x} = 0$. -3

886 Chapter 16 Limits and an Introduction to Calculus

16.7 Area Under a Curve

Objectives: To represent the area under a curve as a sum of rectangles
To find the area under a curve using limits

Focus

Here is a mathematical problem that intrigued Greek scholars of the ancient world. Suppose that you have a plane region that is partly or entirely enclosed by a curve or a solid region partly or entirely bounded by a curved surface. How can you calculate the area or volume of such a region? The problem is illustrated in modern terms by the two graphs at the right. In both graphs, $v(t)$ represents the instantaneous velocity of a particle as a function of time. In the top graph, the instantaneous velocity is constant, 30 mi/h. Since $b - a$ represents an interval of time, the area under the graph between $a = 2$ and $b = 7$ clearly represents the distance traveled in a 5-hour time interval, namely, 5 h $\times$ 30 mi/h, or 150 mi. In the bottom graph, where $v(t)$ is not a constant, it seems plausible to interpret the area bounded by the curve and the three straight line segments in a similar fashion. However, as the ancients might have asked, how do you go about calculating the area?

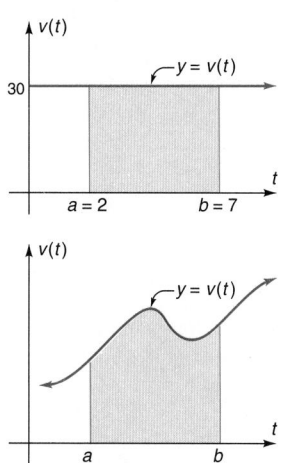

There are many ways of illustrating the ancient "area problem" other than the one involving time and instantaneous velocity. One of these interpretations is simply as area itself, as in the first illustration below. Two other interpretations are also shown.

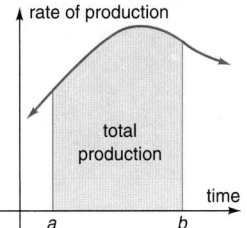

In earlier lessons, you have seen how the concept of *limit* was used to solve one of the major problems of modern post-Renaissance mathematics, namely, how to define what is meant by a tangent to a curve.

It is also necessary to use the limit concept in order to deal with a second old mathematical problem, the one discussed in the Focus: How can you calculate the area of a region partly or entirely enclosed by a curve? Over 2200 years ago. Archimedes was able to find partial answers to this question.

16.7 Area Under a Curve **887**

LESSON PLAN

Vocabulary
circumscribed rectangles
definite integral
inscribed rectangles

Technology
computer
graphing utility

FOCUS

In the previous lesson the derivative was used to find functions describing rates of change, such as the velocity and the rate of growth of a population of wolves. In this lesson students can work in reverse. They can find the position of an object from its velocity or the population of a group knowing its rate of growth. These problems are introduced through the technique of finding the area under a curve. For example, to find the position of an object in a given interval of time, students find the area under the graph of the velocity function (and above the x-axis) in that interval.

INSTRUCTION

- List the summation formulas, also seen in Chapter 13, on a side board for easy use when simplifying expressions and computing areas.
- For Example 1, emphasize that for an increasing function, circumscribed rectangles have a height determined by right-hand function values while decreasing functions have a height determined by left-hand function values. For inscribed rectangles, the height is determined by the opposite function values.

The concept of limit is used to calculate the area bounded by a function f and the x-axis between $x = a$ and $x = b$. However, before the calculations can be performed, it is necessary to review sigma notation and to list a few series formulas that appeared in the lessons or exercises of Chapter 13.

For n a positive integer,

$$\sum_{i=1}^{n} 1 = \underbrace{1 + 1 + 1 + \cdots + 1}_{n \text{ addends}} = n$$

$$\sum_{i=1}^{n} i = 1 + 2 + 3 + 4 + \cdots + n = \frac{n(n+1)}{2}$$

$$\sum_{i=1}^{n} i^2 = 1^2 + 2^2 + 3^2 + 4^2 + \cdots + n^2 = \frac{n(n+1)(2n+1)}{6}$$

$$\sum_{i=1}^{n} i^3 = \frac{n^2(n+1)^2}{4}$$

$$\sum_{i=1}^{n} i^4 = \frac{n(n+1)(6n^3 + 9n^2 + n - 1)}{30}$$

Some other statements involving sigma notation are also useful. If f and g are functions, c is a real number, and m and n are natural numbers, then

$$\sum_{i=1}^{n} cf(i) = c \sum_{i=1}^{n} f(i) \qquad\qquad \sum_{i=1}^{n} f(i) = \sum_{j=1}^{n} f(j) = \sum_{k=1}^{n} f(k)$$

$$\sum_{i=1}^{n} [f(i) + g(i)] = \sum_{i=1}^{n} f(i) + \sum_{i=1}^{n} g(i) \qquad\qquad \sum_{i=1}^{m-1} f(i) + \sum_{i=m}^{n} f(i) = \sum_{i=1}^{n} f(i) \qquad m < n$$

$$\sum_{i=1}^{n} [f(i) - g(i)] = \sum_{i=1}^{n} f(i) - \sum_{i=1}^{n} g(i)$$

Consider the area bounded by the function f, the x-axis, and the lines $x = a$ and $x = b$. The area may be approximated by drawing inscribed or circumscribed rectangles that partition the area and then finding the sum of the areas of the rectangles. The larger the number of rectangles, the better is the approximation. For a sufficiently large number, the difference between the area of the rectangles and the area bound by the curve and the three line segments becomes as small as you please.

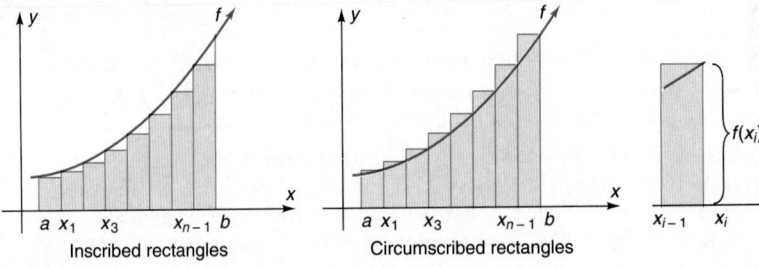

Inscribed rectangles   Circumscribed rectangles

888   Chapter 16 Limits and an Introduction to Calculus

Divide the interval $[a, b]$ into n subintervals, each of width $\frac{b-a}{n}$.

Let $x_1, x_2, \ldots, x_{n-1}$ be the points equally spaced between a and b. Then, draw vertical lines through $x_1, x_2, \ldots, x_{n-1}$ to form rectangles. The area under the curve can be approximated by adding the areas of the rectangles. When circumscribed rectangles are used, the value of $f(x)$ may be taken as the right-hand endpoint of each subinterval. Any other point in the interval can also be chosen. In symbols,

$$A \approx f(x_1)(x_1 - a) + f(x_2)(x_2 - x_1) + \cdots + f(b)(b - x_{n-1})$$

$$A \approx \sum_{i=1}^{n} f(x_i)(x_i - x_{i-1})$$

Example 1 Find an approximation of the area of the region bounded by $f(x) = x^2$, $y = 0$, $x = 1$, and $x = 4$ by using
   a. circumscribed rectangles with a width of 0.5 unit
   b. inscribed rectangles with a width of 0.5 unit

a. Draw a diagram of the described region with rectangles of width 0.5. The height of each rectangle can be determined by finding the value of the function at the right-hand side of each rectangle. The area of the first rectangle is

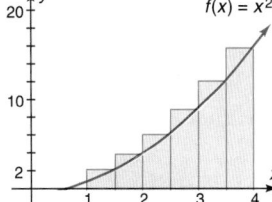

$$(0.5)(f(1.5)) = (0.5)(2.25) = 1.125$$

The area of the sixth rectangle is

$$(0.5)(f(4)) = (0.5)(16) = 8$$

The total approximated area is

$$\begin{aligned} A &= (0.5)[f(1.5) + f(2) + f(2.5) + f(3) + f(3.5) + f(4)] \\ &= (0.5)[2.25 + 4 + 6.25 + 9 + 12.25 + 16] \\ &= (0.5)[49.75] = 24.875 \text{ square units} \end{aligned}$$

This approximation of the area is larger than the actual area.

b. Draw a diagram of the described region with rectangles of width 0.5. The height of each rectangle is the function value at the left-hand side of the rectangle. The total approximated area is:

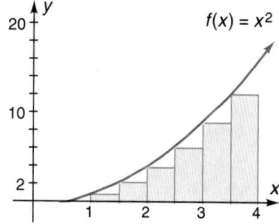

$$\begin{aligned} A &= (0.5)[f(1) + f(1.5) + f(2) + f(2.5) + f(3) + f(3.5)] \\ &= (0.5)[1 + 2.25 + 4 + 6.25 + 9 + 12.25] \\ &= (0.5)(34.75) = 17.375 \text{ square units} \end{aligned}$$

This approximation is smaller than the actual area.

There are ways to improve the approximation of the area. One way is to use the function values at the midpoint of each interval as the height. Another is to use trapezoids instead of rectangles. To compute the actual area under a curve, it is necessary to generalize the procedure of Example 1. Consider the length of

16.7 Area Under a Curve **889**

For Example 1
Find an approximation for the area of the region bounded by $f(x) = 2x^2$, $y = 0$, $x = 0$, and $x = 2$ by using:
1. circumscribed rectangles of width 0.5 units 7.5 square units
2. inscribed rectangles of width 0.5 units 3.5 square units

For Example 2
Find the area of the region bounded by $f(x) = 2x^2$, $y = 0$, $x = 0$, $x = 2$.
$\frac{16}{3}$ square units

Modeling
The modeling provides just one example of how calculus is used in physics. You may want to have students research the velocities of other projectiles, like space shuttles, to find out how far they actually travel in the course of an hour or a day.

the interval in that example, $4 - 1$ or 3 units. Divide that interval into n equal parts. Each rectangle will then have a width of $\frac{3}{n}$. As n increases, the number of rectangles will increase and the approximation for the area will improve. When n is allowed to increase without bound (limit as $n \to \infty$), the result is the *actual area*.

Example 2 Find the area of the region bounded by $f(x) = x^2$, $y = 0$, $x = 1$, and $x = 4$.

Draw a diagram of the described region with rectangles of width $\frac{3}{n}$. Use right-hand function values for heights.

$$A = \lim_{n \to \infty} \frac{3}{n}\left[f\left(1 + \frac{3}{n}\right) + f\left(1 + 2\left(\frac{3}{n}\right)\right) + f\left(1 + 3\left(\frac{3}{n}\right)\right) + \right.$$
$$\left. \cdots + f\left(1 + n\left(\frac{3}{n}\right)\right)\right]$$

$$= \lim_{n \to \infty} \sum_{i=1}^{n} f\left(1 + \frac{3i}{n}\right)\frac{3}{n} = \lim_{n \to \infty} \sum_{i=1}^{n}\left(1 + \frac{3i}{n}\right)^2\frac{3}{n}$$

$$= \lim_{n \to \infty} \sum_{i=1}^{n}\left(1 + \frac{6i}{n} + \frac{9i^2}{n^2}\right)\frac{3}{n} = \lim_{n \to \infty} \sum_{i=1}^{n}\left(\frac{3}{n} + \frac{18}{n^2}i + \frac{27}{n^3}i^2\right)$$

$$= \lim_{n \to \infty}\left(\frac{3}{n}\sum_{i=1}^{n}1 + \frac{18}{n^2}\sum_{i=1}^{n}i + \frac{27}{n^3}\sum_{i=1}^{n}i^2\right) \quad \textit{Use formulas for } \Sigma i \textit{ and } \Sigma i^2.$$

$$= \lim_{n \to \infty}\left[\frac{3}{n}\cdot n + \frac{18}{n^2}\cdot\frac{n(n+1)}{2} + \frac{27}{n^3}\cdot\frac{n(n+1)(2n+1)}{6}\right]$$

$$= \lim_{n \to \infty}\left[3 + \frac{9n+9}{n} + \frac{9(2n^2 + 3n + 1)}{2n^2}\right]$$

$$= \lim_{n \to \infty}\left[3 + 9 + \frac{9}{n} + 9 + \frac{27}{2n} + \frac{9}{2n^2}\right]$$

$$= 3 + 9 + 0 + 9 + 0 + 0 = 21 \qquad \lim_{n \to \infty}\frac{1}{n} = 0$$

The area is 21 square units.

Modeling

A physicist is modeling the motion of a projectile. How can he determine the distance the projectile travels over a given time interval?

This is one of the classical problems that was addressed while calculus was being developed in the seventeenth century. Galileo and others exerted much effort in modeling the relationship between the velocity of a falling object and its position.

In an earlier lesson it was pointed out that the rate of change of the position function of a point is its velocity, which is given by the derivative of the position function. If the velocity is represented by a function v, then the change in the position of a point over a time interval $[a, b]$ corresponds to the area under the graph of the velocity function v between $t = a$ and $t = b$.

890   Chapter 16 Limits and an Introduction to Calculus

Example 3 *Physics* The velocity of an object at time t seconds is given by the function $v(t) = 32t + 5$. What is the change in the position of the object between the time $t = 1$ s and the time $t = 3$ s?

The change in position is given by the area under the graph of $v(t) = 32t + 5$ between $t = 1$ and $t = 3$. The width of each rectangle is $\dfrac{3-1}{n} = \dfrac{2}{n}$. If right-hand function values are used, the area is calculated as follows.

$$A = \lim_{n \to \infty} \frac{2}{n}\left[v\left(1 + \frac{2}{n}\right) + v\left(1 + \frac{4}{n}\right) + \cdots + v\left(1 + \frac{2n}{n}\right) \right]$$

$$= \lim_{n \to \infty} \frac{2}{n} \sum_{i=1}^{n} v\left(1 + 2\frac{i}{n}\right) = \lim_{n \to \infty} \frac{2}{n} \sum_{i=1}^{n} \left[32\left(1 + 2\frac{i}{n}\right) + 5 \right]$$

$$= \lim_{n \to \infty} \frac{2}{n} \sum_{i=1}^{n} \left(37 + 64\frac{i}{n}\right) = \lim_{n \to \infty} \frac{2}{n}\left(\sum_{i=1}^{n} 37 + \sum_{i=1}^{n} 64\frac{i}{n}\right)$$

$$= \lim_{n \to \infty} \frac{2}{n}\left(37 \sum_{i=1}^{n} 1 + \frac{64}{n} \sum_{i=1}^{n} i\right) = \lim_{n \to \infty} \frac{2}{n}\left[37n + \frac{64}{n}\left(\frac{n(n+1)}{2}\right)\right]$$

$$= \lim_{n \to \infty}\left[74 + \frac{64(n+1)}{n}\right] = \lim_{n \to \infty}\left[74 + 64 + \frac{64}{n}\right] = 138 \text{ ft}$$

The change in position of the object from time $t = 1$ s to $t = 3$ s is 138 ft, the distance traveled by the object during this 2 s period. Since the area happens to be a trapezoid, you can check the answer using the formula $A = \frac{1}{2}h(a + b)$.

The limit-process method of this lesson is one way of finding the **area under a curve**. The expression $\lim_{n \to \infty} \sum_{i=1}^{n} f(x_i)(x_i - x_{i-1})$, called the **definite integral** of f from a to b, is symbolized as $\int_a^b f$, or as $\int_a^b f(x)\, dx$.

Class Exercises

Simplify the given expression so that it has no sigma or variables other than n.

1. $\displaystyle\sum_{i=1}^{n}\left(3\frac{i}{n} - 2\right) \cdot \frac{1}{n}$ **2.** $\displaystyle\sum_{i=1}^{n}(i^2 + 1)\cdot\frac{1}{n}$ **3.** $\displaystyle\sum_{i=1}^{n}(i-1)^3 \cdot \frac{2}{n}$ **4.** $\displaystyle\sum_{i=1}^{n} i\left(5i^2 - \frac{i}{n}\right)\cdot\frac{3}{n}$

Find an approximation for the area of the region bounded by the graphs of the given equations by using circumscribed rectangles of width 0.5.

5. $f(x) = x^2,\ y = 0,\ x = 0,\ x = 3$ 11.375 units²   **6.** $g(x) = x^3,\ y = 0,\ x = 1,\ x = 3$ 27 units²

Find an approximation for the area of the region bounded by the graphs of the given equations by using inscribed rectangles of width 0.5.

7. $f(x) = x^2,\ y = 0,\ x = 0,\ x = 3$ 6.875 units²   **8.** $g(x) = x^3,\ y = 0,\ x = 1,\ x = 3$ 14 units²

Find the area of the region bounded by the graphs of the given equations.

9. $f(x) = 2x^2,\ y = 0,\ x = 1,\ x = 3$ $\frac{52}{3}$ units²   **10.** $g(x) = x^3,\ y = 0,\ x = 2,\ x = 4$ 60 units²

16.7 Area Under a Curve   **891**

Additional Answers

1. $\dfrac{3-n}{2n}$ **2.** $\dfrac{2n^2 + 3n + 7}{6}$

3. $\dfrac{n(n-1)^2}{2}$ **4.** $\dfrac{15n^4 + 30n^3 + 11n^2 - 6n - 2}{4n}$

Teacher's Resource Book
  Tests—Quiz, form A, page 70
  Tests—Quiz, form B, page 70

Lesson Quiz

1. Simplify the expression

$$\sum_{i=1}^{n} i^2(6 - i)$$ so that it has no

sigma or variables other than n.
$$\frac{-n^4 + 6n^3 + 11n^2 + 4n}{4}$$

2. Find an approximation for the area of the region bounded by $f(x) = 4x^2$, $y = 0$, $x = 1$, $x = 3$ by using circumscribed rectangles of width 0.5 units. 43 square units

3. Find the area of the region bounded by $f(x) = 3x^2$, $y = 0$, $x = 1$, $x = 3$. 26 square units

4. Find the area of the region bounded by $g(x) = 5x^2$, $y = 0$, $x = -3$, $x = -1$. $\frac{130}{3}$ square units

5. The velocity of an object at time t seconds is given by the function $f(t) = 32t - 7$. What is the change in the position of the object between the time $t = 1$ and $t = 7$ seconds? 726 ft

Additional Answers

1. $\frac{5n - 1}{2}$

2. $\frac{21n + 45}{2}$

3. $\frac{50 - 3n - 2n^2}{3}$

4. $\frac{110 - 12n - 8n^2}{3}$

12. yes; Since $f(x)$ is symmetric about the origin, the area bounded by the curve between $x = 0$ and $x = 2$ has the same value as the area between $x = -2$ and $x = 0$.

13. $\begin{bmatrix} -\frac{17}{5} & -\frac{1}{5} & \frac{11}{5} \\ \frac{8}{5} & -\frac{1}{5} & -\frac{4}{5} \\ \frac{2}{5} & \frac{1}{5} & -\frac{1}{5} \end{bmatrix}$

Practice Exercises   Use appropriate technology.

Simplify the given statement so that it has no sigma or variables other than n.

A 1. $\sum_{i=1}^{n} (5i - 3) \cdot \frac{1}{n}$ 2. $\sum_{i=1}^{n} (7i + 4) \cdot \frac{3}{n}$ 3. $\sum_{i=1}^{n} (17 - 2i^2) \cdot \frac{1}{n}$ 4. $\sum_{i=1}^{n} (19 - 4i^2) \cdot \frac{2}{n}$

® 5. Find the multiplicative inverse of the matrix $\begin{bmatrix} 7 & 5 \\ 2 & 4 \end{bmatrix}$. $\begin{bmatrix} \frac{2}{9} & -\frac{5}{18} \\ -\frac{1}{9} & \frac{7}{18} \end{bmatrix}$

Find an approximation of the area of the region bounded by the graphs of the given equations by using circumscribed rectangles of the given width.

6. $f(x) = x^2$, $y = 0$, $x = 4$, $x = 6$; 0.5   7. $g(x) = x^2$, $y = 0$, $x = 5$, $x = 7$; 0.5
   55.75 units²   78.75 units²
8. $h(x) = x^3$, $y = 0$, $x = 1$, $x = 2$; 0.25 4.67 units²

Find an approximation of the area of the region bounded by the graphs of the given equations by using inscribed rectangles of the given width.

9. $f(x) = 2x^2$, $y = 0$, $x = 2$, $x = 4$; 0.5   10. $g(x) = 3x^2$, $y = 0$, $x = 1$, $x = 3$; 0.5
   31.5 units²   20.25 units²
11. $h(x) = -5x^2 + 12$, $y = 0$, $x = 0$, $x = 1$; 0.25 9.66 units²

12. **Thinking Critically**   Symmetry may be used to find the area bounded by $f(x) = -x^2 + 9$, $y = 0$, $x = -2$, and $x = 2$ by doubling the area under the curve between $x = 0$ and $x = 2$. Could symmetry be used to find the area bounded by $f(x) = x^3$, $y = 0$, $x = -2$, and $x = 2$? If so, how; if not, why not?

® 13. Find the multiplicative inverse of the matrix $\begin{bmatrix} 1 & 2 & 3 \\ 0 & -1 & 4 \\ 2 & 3 & 5 \end{bmatrix}$.

B 14. **Writing in Mathematics**   Write a paragraph to describe two ways to determine the area of the circle with $x^2 + y^2 = 16$ as its equation.

15. *Physics*   A particle is moving with velocity $f(t) = 12t + 4$ ft/s. Find the change in position of the particle between the times $t = 1$ s and $t = 2$ s. 22 ft

16. *Economics*   The rate of oil consumption in the United States during the 1960s is given by $f(t) = 0.05t^2 + 0.1t + 3$, where t is the number of years from 1960 and $f(t)$ is the number of billions of barrels of oil ($t = 0$ corresponds to 1960 and $f(0) = 3$ billion barrels). Find the number of barrels of oil consumed from 1960 until 1970. $\frac{155}{3}$ billion

® 17. Graph: $f(x) = \dfrac{(x - 3)(x - 2)}{x - 2}$

Use the limit process to find the area of the region bounded by the graphs of the given equations.

18. $g(x) = 6x^2$, $y = 0$, $x = 1$, $x = 4$ 126 units²   19. $h(x) = x^2 + 8$, $y = 0$, $x = 1$, $x = 3$ $\frac{74}{3}$ units²
20. $t(x) = x^2 + 10$, $y = 0$, $x = 1$, $x = 3$ $\frac{86}{3}$ units²   21. $f(x) = -x^2 + 15$, $y = 0$, $x = 2$, $x = 3$ $\frac{26}{3}$ units²
22. $f(x) = 4x^2$, $y = 0$, $x = -3$, $x = 1$ $\frac{112}{3}$ units²   23. $h(x) = -3x^2 + x + 5$, $y = 0$, $x = -1$, $x = 0$ $\frac{7}{2}$ units²
24. $h(x) = x^3 + 2$, $y = 0$, $x = -2$, $x = 1$ $\frac{9}{4}$ units²

Writing in Mathematics

14. Rewrite the equation in function form by solving for y to obtain $f(x) = (16 - x^2)^{\frac{1}{2}}$. Find the positive area bounded by the curve and the x-axis between $x = -2$ and $x = 2$ by integrating the function from -2 to 2, and multiply by 2 to find the area of the circle. Another way to find the area of the circle is to use the formula $A = \pi r^2$.

Meteorology The solar radiation readings
on a sunny summer afternoon are given in
this table. The total radiation received
between 1 p.m. and 5 p.m. is represented
by the area under the curve between 1 and 5.

Time	1	2	3	4	5
Radiation (cal/cm²/min)	1.2	1.0	0.7	0.5	0.25

C **25.** Plot the data and sketch a continuous curve $f(t)$ passing through the
five points.

26. Use four inscribed rectangles to approximate the area under the curve, and
thus to approximate the total radiation received between 1 p.m. and 5 p.m. 2.45 cal/cm²

27. Use four circumscribed rectangles to approximate the area under the curve,
and thus to approximate the total radiation received between 1 p.m. and 5 p.m.
3.4 cal/cm²

28. Thinking Critically What could be done to get a better approximation to
the solar radiation received between 1 p.m. and 5 p.m. in the above exercises?

29. *Ecology* The rate of growth of a certain animal population can be
modeled by the function $R(t) = 0.24t^2 + 2t + 12$, where t is given in
years. By how much does the population change between $t = 0$ and $t = 5$?
95 animals/y

30. *Demographics* The growth rate of a city t years after 1980 can be
modeled by the function $R(t) = 8050 + 600t$. What is the population
change given by this model for the period 1990 to 2000? *Hint:* Let 1980 be
represented by $t = 0$. 170,500 people/y

Project

Write a program that will approximate the change in position of an object
moving with an instantaneous velocity $v(t) = t^2 - 3t$ between the times $t = a$
and $t = b$. Use right-hand endpoints of intervals to approximate function
values (heights and rectangles). Your program should output the number of
rectangles n and the area approximation (which represents the change in the
object's position) of $\int_a^b v(t)\,dt$ for values of $n = 4, 8, 16, 32, 64, 128,$ and 256.
Run your program using a variety of values of a and b.

Test Yourself

Find the first and second derivatives of each function.

1. $f(x) = 3x^2 + 5x - 4$ 6x + 5; 6

2. $f(x) = x^3 - 4x^2 + 7x$ $3x^2 - 8x + 7; 6x - 8$ 16.5

3. For the function $f(x) = \frac{1}{3}x^3 - x^2 - 2x + 1$, find the critical numbers, the
intervals where the function is increasing and decreasing, and the relative
maximum and minimum values. Draw the graph.

4. Find the velocity and the acceleration of a moving object with position
function $f(t) = t^3 - 3t^2 + 4t + 2$ when $t = 2$. 4; 6 16.6

5. The increase in circulation of a local magazine over a period of t years is
found to be the function $C(t) = 200t + 1000$. What is the circulation and
the rate of increase when $t = 4$ years? 1800 magazines; 200 magazines/y

6. Find the area of the region bounded by the curves and lines given by
$f(x) = x^3$, $y = 0$, $x = 1$, and $x = 3$. 20 units² 16.7

16.7 Area Under a Curve **893**

Alternative Assessment
Have students work in pairs where
one creates an integration problem
and the other evaluates it. Then
have them alternate tasks.

Enrichment
Find an approximation of the area of
the region bounded by $f(x) = x^2$,
$y = 0$, $x = 1$ and $x = 4$ using trapezoids, each with a width of 0.5
units. Compare your results to the
answers obtained in Example 1.
21.125 square units; This result is the average of the areas using inscribed rectangles and circumscribed rectangles.

Additional Answers
25.

28. Answers may vary. Some examples
are finding the average of the areas
found by using inscribed and circumscribed rectangles, or shortening the
time intervals.

Test Yourself
3. Critical numbers: $x = 1 \pm \sqrt{3}$;
interval increasing: $x < 1 - \sqrt{3}$ or
$x > 1 + \sqrt{3}$; interval decreasing:
$1 - \sqrt{3} < x < 1 + \sqrt{3}$; relative
max: $(1 - \sqrt{3}, 1.80)$; relative min:
$(1 + \sqrt{3}, -5.13)$

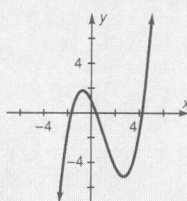

Chapter 16   Summary and Review

Vocabulary

absolute maximum (880)
absolute minimum (880)
area under a curve (891)
concave down (879)
concave up (879)
continuity of a function (861)

critical number (878)
definite integral (891)
derivative (872)
instantaneous rate of change (882)
limit of a function (856)
points of inflection (879)

position function (868)
relative maximum (878)
relative minimum (878)
secant line (866)
slope of a curve (867)
tangent line (866)

Limit of a Function of a Real Variable   The symbol $\lim\limits_{x \to c} f(x) = L$ means that $f(x)$ can   16.1
be made arbitrarily close to L by taking x sufficiently close but not equal to c.

For the function graphed, determine whether or not the
given limit exists. If the limit exists, compare it to the
corresponding function value.

1. $\lim\limits_{x \to 1} f(x)$
does not exist

2. $\lim\limits_{x \to -3^+} f(x)$
yes; -1; not equal

3. $\lim\limits_{x \to -3} f(x)$
yes; -1; not equal

4. Find the limit for the function below as $x \to 3$ and
compare it to $f(3)$.

$$f(x) = \begin{cases} 2x - 1, & \text{if } x < 3 \\ x^2 - 4, & \text{if } x > 3 \\ 7, & \text{if } x = 3 \end{cases}$$

$\lim\limits_{x \to 3} f(x) = 5$
$f(3) = 7$
$\lim\limits_{x \to 3} f(x) \neq f(3)$

Limit Theorems   If $f(x)$ is equal to a constant K, then $\lim\limits_{x \to c} f(x) = K$. If $f(x) = x^m$,   16.2
where m is a positive real number, then $\lim\limits_{x \to c} x^m = c^m$. A function $f(x)$ is continuous
at $x = c$ if and only if $f(x)$ is defined at $x = c$, $\lim\limits_{x \to c} f(x)$ exists, and $\lim\limits_{x \to c} f(x) = f(c)$.

Find each limit, if it exists.

5. $\lim\limits_{x \to -1} (2x^2 - 3x + 1)$ 6

6. $\lim\limits_{x \to 2} \dfrac{x^2 - 5x}{x + 1}$ -2

7. $\lim\limits_{x \to -2} \dfrac{x^2 - 4}{x + 2}$ -4

8. $\lim\limits_{x \to \infty} \dfrac{3x^2 + 2}{4x^2 - 1}$ $\frac{3}{4}$

Tangent to a Curve   Let P and Q be two different points on a curve. The line   16.3
drawn between points P and Q is a secant line. If P is fixed and Q moves along the
curve toward P, the secant line approaches a limiting position, a line **tangent** to the
curve at P.

Find an equation of the tangent line to the graph of the given function at point P.

9. $f(x) = 2x - 5$, $P(3, 1)$ $y = 2x - 5$

10. $g(x) = x^2 - 1$, $P(0, -1)$ $y = -1$

11. Find the slope of the tangent line to the graph of the function $f(x) = 2x^2 - x$
at point $P(c, f(c))$. $4c - 1$

894   Chapter 16 Limits and an Introduction to Calculus

Finding Derivatives   The derivative of a function f is another function f' defined by the expression

16.4

$$f'(x) = \lim_{h \to 0} \frac{f(x + h) - f(x)}{h}$$

Find the first and second derivatives, if they exist.

15x^2 + 6x − 1; 30x + 6

12. $f(x) = 5x^3 + 3x^2 - x$ **13.** $g(x) = \frac{2}{x} - \frac{2}{x^2}; \frac{4}{x^3}$ $\frac{1}{2\sqrt{x - 3}}; -\frac{1}{4(x - 3)^{\frac{3}{2}}}$ **14.** $h(x) = \sqrt{x - 3}$

15. Find the points on the graph of $f(x) = x^2 - 4x + 3$ that have tangent lines with a slope of -2. (1, 0)

16. Find all points at which the function $f(x) = \sqrt{x + 5}$ has no derivative. $x = -5$

Using Derivatives in Graphing   The zeros of the first derivative determine the critical numbers. The graph of a function is increasing if $f'(x) > 0$ and decreasing if $f'(x) < 0$.

16.5

Find the first and second derivatives of each function.

17. $f(x) = x^4 - 5x^3 + 8x^2 + 2$ **18.** $f(x) = (x + 1)(x - 1)$ 2x; 2
4x^3 − 15x^2 + 16x; 12x^2 − 30x + 16

19. Draw the graph of $f(x) = \dfrac{x^3}{3} + \dfrac{x^2}{2} - 2x + 6$ showing the relative maximum and relative minimum, and where the function is increasing or decreasing.

Applying the Derivative   The instantaneous rate of change of $y = f(x)$ per unit change in x at x_0 is

16.6

$$f'(x_0) = \lim_{h \to 0} \frac{f(x_0 + h) - f(x_0)}{h}$$

20. Find the velocity and the acceleration of a moving particle with position $f(t) = t^3 - 3t^2 + 3t$ when $t = 5$ seconds. 48 units/s; 24 units/s²

21. A box is to be made from a 10-ft-square cardboard by cutting equal squares out of the corners and folding up the sides. Determine the size of the square to be cut if the volume of the box is to be maximized. $\frac{5}{3}$ ft × $\frac{5}{3}$ ft

Area under a Curve   The area bounded by the function $y = f(x)$, the x-axis and the lines $x = a$ and $x = b$ is given by

16.7

$$A = \lim_{n \to \infty} \sum_{i=1}^{n} f(x_i)(x_i - x_{i-1})$$

22. Find an approximation to the area of the region bounded by the given curve and interval by using inscribed rectangles of width 0.5.

$$f(x) = x^2, y = 0, x = 0, x = 4 \quad \text{17.5 units}^2$$

23. Use the limit process to find the area of the region bounded by the given curve and interval.

$$f(x) = x^2 + 3x + 1, y = 0, x = 0, x = 5 \quad \frac{505}{6} \text{ units}^2$$

Summary and Review   **895**

Chapter 16   Test

6.

For the function graphed, find.

1. $\lim\limits_{x \to -1^-} f(x)$ -3 **2.** $\lim\limits_{x \to -1^+} f(x)$ 2

Find the limit of each function, if it exists.

3. $\lim\limits_{x \to -3} (x^2 + 3x - 7)$ -7 **4.** $\lim\limits_{x \to -4} \dfrac{2x^2 + 5x - 12}{x + 4}$ -11

5. $\lim\limits_{x \to \infty} \dfrac{x^2 - 5}{2 + 3x^2}$ $\frac{1}{3}$

8. $2x^3 + x^2 + \dfrac{x}{2} - \dfrac{1}{5};$

$6x^2 + 2x + \dfrac{1}{2}$

9. $\dfrac{6}{x^2}, -\dfrac{12}{x^3}$

10. $\dfrac{1}{2\sqrt{x + 9}}; -\dfrac{1}{4(x + 9)^{\frac{3}{2}}}$

12.

critical number: $x = 4$;
interval increasing: $x < 4$;
interval decreasing: $x > 4$;
relative max: (4, 16);
relative min: none

13.

critical numbers: $x = 0, -2$;
interval increasing: $x < -2$ or
$x > 0$; interval decreasing:
$-2 < x < 0$; relative max: $(-2, 3)$;
relative min: $(0, -1)$

6. Determine whether the given function is continuous at $x = 1$. If not, indicate which part of the definition is not satisfied. Draw the graph.

$$f(x) = \begin{cases} \dfrac{x^2 + 3x - 4}{x - 1}, & \text{if } x \neq 1 \\ 2, & \text{if } x = 1 \end{cases}$$

discontinuous; $f(1) \neq \lim\limits_{x \to 1} f(x)$

7. Find the equation of the tangent line to the graph of $f(x) = x^2 + 5x - 4$ at $P(1, 2)$. $y = 7x - 5$

Find the first and second derivatives, if they exist.

8. $\frac{1}{2}x^4 + \frac{1}{3}x^3 + \frac{1}{4}x^2 - \frac{1}{5}x + 10$ **9.** $-\dfrac{6}{x}$ **10.** $\sqrt{x + 9}$

11. Find the points on the graph of $f(x) = 3x^2 - 2x$ that have tangent lines with a slope of -1. $\left(\frac{1}{6}, -\frac{1}{4}\right)$

Find the critical numbers, the intervals where the function is increasing and decreasing, and the relative maximum and minimum values. Draw the graph.

12. $f(x) = 8x - x^2$ **13.** $f(x) = x^3 + 3x^2 - 1$

14. If $C(x) = -0.4x^2 + 12x + 500$ is the total cost function for producing a certain commodity, how many must be produced before costs decrease? 15

15. A body follows a path that is given by $f(t) = t^3 - 4t^2 + 5t + 3$. Find the velocity and acceleration when $t = 4$ seconds. 21 units/s; 16 units/s²

16. It is projected that the population of a certain town t years from now will be $f(t) = 50t^2 - 500t + 8000$. What are the population and growth rate when $t = 10$ years? 8000 people; 500 people/year

17. Find an approximation of the area of the region bounded by $f(x) = x^3$, $y = 0$, $x = 1$, and $x = 3$, by using inscribed rectangles of width 0.25. 16.88 units²

18. Use the limit process to find the area of the region bounded by $f(x) = x^3 + x^2 + 9$, $y = 0$, $x = 0$, and $x = 2$. $\frac{74}{3}$ units²

Challenge

Find the area of the region bounded by $f(x) = 2x - x^2$ and $g(x) = x^2 - 2x - 4$. Draw the graph. $8\sqrt{3}$ units²

Challenge

Cumulative Review

In each item you are to compare a quantity in Column 1 with a quantity in Column 2. Write the letter of the correct answer from these choices:

A. The quantity in Column 1 is greater than the quantity in Column 2.
B. The quantity in Column 2 is greater than the quantity in Column 1.
C. The quantity in Column 1 is equal to the quantity in Column 2.
D. The relationship cannot be determined from the given information.

Notes: Information centered over both columns refers to one or both of the quantities being compared. A symbol that appears in both columns has the same meaning in each column. All variables represent real numbers. Most figures are not drawn to scale.

	Column 1	Column 2	
1.	∞	$-\infty$	16.1
A			
2.	angle of depression	angle of elevation	5.1
C			
3.	$\cos 90°$	$\sin 90°$	3.6
B			
4.	$720°$	4π	3.2
C			
5.	$\lim_{x\to 3}(x^2 - 2x + 3)$	$\lim_{x\to 3}(x^2 + 5x - 1)$	16.2
B			
6.	$\sqrt{\sqrt[3]{x^{12}y^6}}$	$\sqrt[3]{\sqrt{x^{12}y^6}}$	9.1
C			

	Column 1	Column 2	
7.	a	c	5.2
B			
8.	$_8C_3$	$_8P_3$	14.2
B			

$$f(x) = 2x^4 - 5x^3 + 4x^2 - 9$$

	Column 1	Column 2	
9.	$f(-1)$	$f\left(-\frac{1}{2}\right)$	7.1
A			
10.	$\sum_{k=1}^{6}(3k - 2)$	S_8 for $\sum_{t=1}^{\infty}\frac{1}{3t}$	13.3
A			

$$\begin{cases} 3x - 2y = -1 \\ 2x + 3y = 8 \end{cases}$$

	Column 1	Column 2	
11.	x	y	8.1
B			
12.	$\sin 2\pi$	$\cos 360°$	3.4
B			

$$\begin{vmatrix} 3 & -2 \\ 6 & 5 \end{vmatrix} = d$$

	Column 1	Column 2	
13.	d	27	12.10
C			

$$f(x) = 3x^2 - 4x + 1$$

	Column 1	Column 2	
14.	$f'(x)$	$f''(x)$	16.4
D			
15.	$\log 420$	$\ln 60.5$	9.3
B			

$$3x - 2y = 12$$

	Column 1	Column 2	
16.	y-intercept	6	1.1
B			
17.	$\frac{8!}{6!}$	$\frac{9!}{7!3!}$	14.1
A			
18.	modulus of $5 + 2i$	modulus of $4 - i$	10.3
A			

$$f(x) = 3x^2 + 6x + 2$$
$$g(x) = 4x^2 - 8x - 3$$

	Column 1	Column 2	
19.	minimum value of $f(x)$	minimum value of $g(x)$	2.5
B			
20.	$\sin(-30°)$	$\cos(-30°)$	3.6
B			

21. Given $f(x) = \frac{1}{3}x^3 + \frac{1}{2}x^2 - 6x$, determine the critical numbers. $-3, 2$ 16.5

22. A chorus consists of 6 students from one high school, 8 from a second, and 3 from a third. In how many ways can they be chosen to form a duet consisting of 2 students from different high schools? 90   14.1

23. Using transformations, determine the equation of the asymptote of $g(x) = e^x + 9$. $y = 9$ 9.2

24. Find the fifth term of $(3a - 4b)^{12}$. $831409920a^8b^4$ 13.5

25. Determine if $y = \sin^{-1} x$ passes the vertical line test for functions. no   4.5

26. When a variable is missing in an equation, what is its coefficient in the matrix of coefficients? zero   12.5

27. Find an equation of the tangent line to the curve $f(x) = x^2 - 10x + 19$ at $P(4, -5)$. $y = -2x + 3$ 16.3

28. Find $\lim\limits_{x \to \infty} x^4$. ∞ 16.1

29. A vertical bar graph with no spaces between the bars, and on which the classes are represented on the horizontal axis and the frequencies on the vertical axis, is called a __?__. histogram   15.1

30. In how many ways can 6 members of an ice hockey team be lined up for entrance onto the ice? 720   14.2

31. Find the polar coordinates of point $(-6, -6)$. $(6\sqrt{2}, 225°)$ 10.1

32. The scores of 8 students on an oceanography test taken for the award ceremony were 98, 85, 78, 92, 88, 97, 80, 94. Find the median. 90   15.3

33. Find the exact value of $\sin \theta$ for angle θ in standard position with the point $P(-5, -8)$ on its terminal side. $\frac{-8\sqrt{89}}{89}$ 3.4

34. Find the slope of the line tangent to the curve $f(x) = x^2 + 2x - 6$ at $P(2, 2)$. 6   16.3

35. If the measures of two sides and the included angle of a triangle are given, then which law can be used to solve the triangle? law of cosines   5.2

36. Find the instantaneous velocity and acceleration of a moving particle with position function $f(t) = 2t^3 - t^2 + 6t + 2$ when $t = 4$. Assume that time is measured in seconds and distance in meters. 94 m/s; 46 m/s²   16.6

37. Decompose $\dfrac{8x - 14}{x^2 - 2x - 8}$ into partial fractions. $\dfrac{3}{x - 4} + \dfrac{5}{x + 2}$ 7.8

38. Find the derivative of $f(x) = 3x^4 - 2x^3 + 5x^2$. $12x^3 - 6x^2 + 10x$ 16.4

39. In working with probability, if A and B are events that have no outcomes in common, they are said to be __?__. mutually exclusive   14.4

40. Determine the slope of the line perpendicular to the line whose equation is $3y - 2x = 5$. $m = -\frac{3}{2}$ 2.3

41. Determine the common ratio of the geometric sequence 27, -18, 12, -8, ... $-\frac{2}{3}$ 13.2

42. Is matrix multiplication a commutative operation? no   12.2

43. Use a graphing utility to verify whether $\csc \theta \cos \theta = \cot \theta$ is an identity. yes   6.2

44. Determine an equation of a circle that is congruent to the graph of $x^2 + y^2 = 81$ and is translated 3 units to the left. $(x + 3)^2 + y^2 = 81$ 11.1

898   Chapter 16 Limits and an Introduction to Calculus

45. Name the two most important measures of variability when working with a data set. range and standard deviation 15.4

46. Determine the figures represented by each equation and then graph the system using a graphing utility: $\begin{cases} y = (x - 3)^2 + 5 \\ x^2 + y^2 = 36 \end{cases}$ parabola; circle 8.1

47. Evaluate: $\lim_{x \to 3} x^4$ 81 16.2

48. When a horizontal line passes through no more than one point on the graph, then the function will have an ? . inverse function 1.6

49. Given $f(x) = \frac{1}{2}x^2 - 5x + 2$, determine its critical numbers. $x = 5$ 16.5

50. Find the multiplicative inverse of the matrix $A = \begin{bmatrix} 9 & 3 \\ 10 & 6 \end{bmatrix}$, if it exists. 12.4

51. In a class of 800 students, Phuong ranks 150th. Find his percentile. 81st 15.2

52. How many license plates can be made using 4 letters and 2 digits with repetition allowed? 45,697,600 14.1

53. A robot can produce 4 bikes in 45 min. How many can it produce in 5 h 15 min? 28 1.3

54. A medical company claims that its bags of cough drops contain 30 drops per bag. It is known that the distribution of drops per bag has a standard deviation of 4 drops. To verify the company's claim, a random sample of 25 bags was made. What is the 95% confidence interval? $\mu - 1.568$ to $\mu + 1.568$ 15.6

55. Solve and express in interval notation $|4x + 3| < 5$. $\left(-2, \frac{1}{2}\right)$ 8.2

56. Determine the center and radius of the circle with equation $4x^2 + 4y^2 + 8x - 16y = 80$. $C(-1, 2); r = 5$ 11.1

57. For any normal distribution, the empirical rule holds. About what percent of the data is within two standard deviations of the mean? 95% 15.5

58. Simplify: $\left(\frac{8}{27}\right)^{-\frac{2}{3}}$ $\frac{9}{4}$ 9.1

59. Determine an equation of the circle that passes through the points (3, 10), (9, 6) and (−7, 0). $5x^2 + 5y^2 - 16x - 14y - 357 = 0$ 12.5

60. Determine the largest angle, to the nearest degree, in triangle DEF if $d = 15.4$, $e = 18.6$, and $f = 21.7$. 79° 5.4

61. What type of nonlinear functions are included in curvilinear regression? exponential, logarithmic, power 15.7

62. Find the values of x for which the power series $3 + 3(4x + 1) + 3(4x + 1)^2 + 3(4x + 1)^3 + \cdots$ converges. $x \in \left(-\frac{1}{2}, 0\right)$ 13.8

63. Find the explicit formula for the sequence 1, 4, 7, 10, ... $a_n = 3n - 2$ 13.1

Determine if each statement is always true, sometimes true, or never true.

64. If n is even and $a \geq 0$, then $\sqrt[n]{a}$ is the nonnegative nth root of a. always 9.1

65. Any polynomial function will change signs only when its graph passes through a zero of the function. always 8.4

66. The value of e is defined as the number that the expression $\left(1 + \frac{1}{n}\right)^n$ approaches as n approaches -1. never 9.2

Appendix A Data Tables

Life Expectancy: Selected Countries*

Country	Years	Country	Years	Country	Years
United States	75.4	Cuba	75.7	Iraq	66.1
Afghanistan	42.6	Czechoslovakia	71.7	Italy	76.8
Algeria	64.7	Denmark	75.5	Ivory Coast	53.4
Angola	41.1	Dominican Republic	62.4	Japan	79.0
Argentina	70.6	East Germany	72.8	Kenya	61.1
Australia	76.2	Ecuador	65.5	Madagascar	51.8
Austria	75.6	Egypt	59.8	Malawi	48.1
Bangladesh	53.2	El Salvador	62.3	Malaysia	67.3
Belgium	75.5	Ethiopia	51.4	Mali	45.6
Bolivia	54.3	France	75.9	Mexico	70.1
Brazil	66.9	Ghana	53.9	Morocco	63.6
Bulgaria	70.8	Greece	77.2	Mozambique	46.3
Burkina Faso	47.1	Guatemala	60.7	Myanmar (Burma)	54.1
Burundi	51.5	Guinea	42.0	Namibia	59.5
Cambodia	48.3	Haiti	55.7	Nepal	49.7
Cameroon	50.0	Hong Kong	78.3	Netherlands	77.2
Canada	77.2	Hungary	69.1	Niger	48.9
Chile	71.5	India	57.3	Nigeria	48.1
China Mainland	69.3	Indonesia	59.1	North Korea	69.8
China Taiwan	73.3	Iran	62.1	Pakistan	54.2
Colombia	65.6				

Highest Point of Elevation by State*

State	Feet	Meters	State	Feet	Meters
Alabama	2,405	733	Montana	12,799	3,904
Alaska	20,320	6,198	Nebraska	5,426	1,655
Arizona	12,633	3,853	Nevada	13,140	4,007
Arkansas	2,753	840	New Hampshire	6,288	1,918
California	14,494	4,421	New Jersey	1,803	550
Colorado	14,433	4,402	New Mexico	13,161	4,014
Connecticut	2,380	726	New York	5,344	1,630
Delaware	442	135	North Carolina	6,684	2.039
District of Columbia	410	125	North Dakota	3,506	1,069
Florida	345	125	Ohio	1,549	472
Georgia	4,784	1,459	Oklahoma	4,973	1,517
Hawaii	13,796	4,208	Oregon	11,239	3,428
Idaho	12,662	3,862	Pennsylvania	3,213	980
Illinois	1,235	377	Rhode Island	812	248
Indiana	1,257	383	South Carolina	3,560	1,086
Iowa	1,670	509	South Dakota	7,242	2,209
Kansas	4,039	1,032	Tennessee	6,643	2,026
Kentucky	4,139	1,262	Texas	8,749	2,668
Louisiana	535	163	Utah	13,528	4,126
Maine	5,267	1,606	Vermont	4,393	1,340
Maryland	3,360	1,025	Virginia	5,729	1,747
Massachusetts	3,487	1,064	Washington	14,410	4,395
Michigan	1,979	604	West Virginia	4,861	1,483
Minnesota	2,301	702	Wisconsin	1,951	595
Mississippi	806	246	Wyoming	13,804	4,210
Missouri	1,772	540			

* From *Statistical Abstract of the United States,* U.S. Government Printing Office, Washington, D.C., 1990.

Temperature and Precipitation Data: Selected Cities*

City	High[1]	Low[1]	Rainfall[2]	City	High[1]	Low[1]	Rainfall[2]
Mobile, AL	104	3	123	Reno, NV	105	−16	51
Juneau, AK	90	−22	220	Concord, NH	102	−37	125
Phoenix, AZ	118	17	36	Atlantic City, NJ	106	−11	112
Little Rock, AR	112	−5	103	Albuquerque, NM	105	−17	61
Los Angeles, CA	110	23	36	Albany, NY	100	−28	134
Sacramento, CA	115	20	58	Buffalo, NY	99	−20	169
San Diego, CA	111	29	43	New York, NY	106	−15	121
San Francisco, CA	106	20	62	Charlotte, NC	104	−5	111
Denver, CO	104	−30	89	Raleigh, NC	105	−9	111
Hartford, CT	102	−26	127	Bismarck, ND	109	−44	97
Wilmington, DE	102	−14	117	Cincinnati, OH	102	−25	129
Washington, DC	103	−5	111	Cleveland, OH	103	−19	156
Jacksonville, FL	105	7	116	Columbus, OH	102	−19	137
Miami, FL	98	30	129	Oklahoma City, OK	110	−4	82
Atlanta, GA	105	−8	115	Portland, OR	107	−3	152
Honolulu, HI	94	53	100	Philadelphia, PA	104	−7	117
Boise, ID	111	−23	91	Pittsburgh, PA	99	−18	154
Chicago, IL	102	−27	127	Providence, RI	104	−13	124
Peoria, IL	103	−25	114	Columbia, SC	107	−1	109
Indianapolis, IN	104	−22	125	Sioux Falls, SD	108	−36	97
Des Moines, IA	108	24	107	Memphis, TN	108	−13	106
Wichita, KS	113	−21	86	Nashville, TN	107	−17	119
Louisville, KY	105	−20	125	Dallas–Fort Worth, TX	113	4	78
New Orleans, LA	102	14	114	El Paso, TX	112	−8	48
Portland, ME	103	−39	128	Houston, TX	107	11	106
Baltimore, MD	105	−7	113	Salt Lake City, UT	107	−30	91
Boston, MA	102	−12	126	Burlington, VT	101	−30	154
Detroit, MI	102	−21	135	Norfolk, VA	104	−3	114
Sault Ste. Marie, MI	98	−36	165	Richmond, VA	105	−12	113
Duluth, MN	97	−39	134	Seattle, WA	99	0	156
Minneapolis–St. Paul, MN	104	−34	115	Spokane, WA	108	−25	113
Jackson, MS	106	2	109	Charleston, WV	102	−15	151
Kansas City, MO	109	−21	107	Milwaukee, WI	101	−26	125
St. Louis, MO	107	−18	111	Cheyenne, WY	100	−34	99
Great Falls, MT	106	−43	101	San Juan, PR	98	60	195
Omaha, NE	114	23	98				

* From *Statistical Abstract of the United States,* U.S. Government Printing Office, Washington, D.C., 1990.
[1] High and low are temperatures of record in °F.
[2] Rainfall is average number of days per year with at least 0.01 in. precipitation.

Cholesterol and Fat Content (mg): Selected Products

Source (3 oz)	Fat	Cholesterol	Source (3 oz)	Fat	Cholesterol
abalone	0.8	90	lobster	0.5	61
beef	8.7	77	oysters	4.5	93
blue crab	1.5	85	pancreas	2.8	400
chicken, dark	8.2	79	pork	11.1	79
chicken, light	3.8	72	salmon	9.3	74
clams	1.7	57	scallops	0.8	35
crab	1.3	45	shrimp	0.9	166
heart	4.8	164	tuna	0.7	55
kidney	2.9	329	turkey, dark	6.1	72
lamb	8.8	78	turkey, light	1.3	59
liver	4.0	270	veal	4.7	128

Appendix B Normal Distribution Table

z-score	Area from mean to z-score	Area of larger portion	Area of smaller portion	z-score	Area from mean to z-score	Area of larger portion	Area of smaller portion
0.00	0.0000	0.5000	0.5000	0.50	0.1915	0.6915	0.3085
0.01	0.0040	0.5040	0.4960	0.51	0.1950	0.6950	0.3050
0.02	0.0080	0.5080	0.4920	0.52	0.1985	0.6985	0.3015
0.03	0.0120	0.5120	0.4880	0.53	0.2019	0.7019	0.2961
0.04	0.0160	0.5160	0.4840	0.54	0.2054	0.7054	0.2946
0.05	0.0199	0.5199	0.4801	0.55	0.2088	0.7088	0.2912
0.06	0.0239	0.5239	0.4761	0.56	0.2123	0.7123	0.2877
0.07	0.0279	0.5279	0.4721	0.57	0.2157	0.7157	0.2843
0.08	0.0319	0.5319	0.4681	0.58	0.2190	0.7190	0.2810
0.09	0.0359	0.5359	0.4641	0.59	0.2224	0.7224	0.2776
0.10	0.0398	0.5398	0.4602	0.60	0.2257	0.7257	0.2743
0.11	0.0438	0.5438	0.4562	0.61	0.2291	0.7291	0.2709
0.12	0.0478	0.5478	0.4522	0.62	0.2324	0.7324	0.2676
0.13	0.0517	0.5517	0.4483	0.63	0.2357	0.7357	0.2643
0.14	0.0557	0.5557	0.4443	0.64	0.2389	0.7389	0.2611
0.15	0.0596	0.5596	0.4404	0.65	0.2422	0.7422	0.2578
0.16	0.0636	0.5636	0.4364	0.66	0.2454	0.7454	0.2546
0.17	0.0675	0.5675	0.4325	0.67	0.2486	0.7486	0.2514
0.18	0.0714	0.5714	0.4286	0.68	0.2517	0.7517	0.2483
0.19	0.0753	0.5753	0.4247	0.69	0.2549	0.7549	0.2451
0.20	0.0793	0.5793	0.4207	0.70	0.2580	0.7580	0.2420
0.21	0.0832	0.5832	0.4168	0.71	0.2611	0.7611	0.2389
0.22	0.0871	0.5871	0.4129	0.72	0.2642	0.7642	0.2358
0.23	0.0910	0.5910	0.4090	0.73	0.2673	0.7673	0.2327
0.24	0.0948	0.5948	0.4052	0.74	0.2704	0.7704	0.2296
0.25	0.0987	0.5987	0.4013	0.75	0.2734	0.7734	0.2266
0.26	0.1026	0.6026	0.3974	0.76	0.2764	0.7764	0.2236
0.27	0.1064	0.6064	0.3936	0.77	0.2794	0.7794	0.2206
0.28	0.1103	0.6103	0.3897	0.78	0.2823	0.7823	0.2177
0.29	0.1141	0.6141	0.3859	0.79	0.2852	0.7852	0.2148
0.30	0.1179	0.6179	0.3821	0.80	0.2881	0.7881	0.2119
0.31	0.1217	0.6217	0.3783	0.81	0.2910	0.7910	0.2090
0.32	0.1255	0.6255	0.3745	0.82	0.2939	0.7939	0.2061
0.33	0.1293	0.6293	0.3707	0.83	0.2967	0.7967	0.2033
0.34	0.1331	0.6331	0.3669	0.84	0.2995	0.7995	0.2005
0.35	0.1368	0.6368	0.3632	0.85	0.3023	0.8023	0.1977
0.36	0.1406	0.6406	0.3594	0.86	0.3051	0.8051	0.1949
0.37	0.1443	0.6443	0.3557	0.87	0.3078	0.8078	0.1922
0.38	0.1480	0.6480	0.3520	0.88	0.3106	0.8106	0.1894
0.39	0.1517	0.6517	0.3483	0.89	0.3133	0.8133	0.1867
0.40	0.1554	0.6554	0.3446	0.90	0.3159	0.8159	0.1841
0.41	0.1591	0.6591	0.3409	0.91	0.3186	0.8186	0.1814
0.42	0.1628	0.6628	0.3372	0.92	0.3212	0.8212	0.1788
0.43	0.1664	0.6664	0.3336	0.93	0.3238	0.8238	0.1762
0.44	0.1700	0.6700	0.3300	0.94	0.3264	0.8264	0.1736
0.45	0.1736	0.6736	0.3264	0.95	0.3289	0.8289	0.1711
0.46	0.1772	0.6772	0.3228	0.96	0.3315	0.8315	0.1685
0.47	0.1808	0.6808	0.3192	0.97	0.3340	0.8340	0.1660
0.48	0.1844	0.6844	0.3156	0.98	0.3365	0.8365	0.1635
0.49	0.1879	0.6879	0.3121	0.99	0.3389	0.8389	0.1611

z-score	Area from mean to z-score	Area of larger portion	Area of smaller portion	z-score	Area from mean to z-score	Area of larger portion	Area of smaller portion
1.00	0.3413	0.8413	0.1587	1.50	0.4332	0.9332	0.0668
1.01	0.3438	0.8438	0.1562	1.51	0.4345	0.9345	0.0655
1.02	0.3461	0.8461	0.1539	1.52	0.4357	0.9357	0.0643
1.03	0.3485	0.8485	0.1515	1.53	0.4370	0.9370	0.0630
1.04	0.3508	0.8508	0.1492	1.54	0.4382	0.9382	0.0618
1.05	0.3531	0.8531	0.1469	1.55	0.4394	0.9394	0.0606
1.06	0.3554	0.8554	0.1446	1.56	0.4406	0.9406	0.0594
1.07	0.3577	0.8577	0.1423	1.57	0.4418	0.9418	0.0582
1.08	0.3599	0.8599	0.1401	1.58	0.4429	0.9429	0.0571
1.09	0.3621	0.8621	0.1379	1.59	0.4441	0.9441	0.0559
1.10	0.3643	0.8643	0.1357	1.60	0.4452	0.9452	0.0548
1.11	0.3665	0.8665	0.1335	1.61	0.4463	0.9463	0.0537
1.12	0.3686	0.8686	0.1314	1.62	0.4474	0.9474	0.0526
1.13	0.3708	0.8708	0.1292	1.63	0.4484	0.9484	0.0516
1.14	0.3729	0.8729	0.1271	1.64	0.4495	0.9495	0.0505
1.15	0.3749	0.8749	0.1251	1.65	0.4505	0.9505	0.0495
1.16	0.3770	0.8770	0.1230	1.66	0.4515	0.9515	0.0485
1.17	0.3790	0.8790	0.1210	1.67	0.4525	0.9525	0.0475
1.18	0.3810	0.8810	0.1190	1.68	0.4535	0.9535	0.0465
1.19	0.3830	0.8830	0.1170	1.69	0.4545	0.9545	0.0455
1.20	0.3849	0.8849	0.1151	1.70	0.4554	0.9554	0.0446
1.21	0.3869	0.8869	0.1131	1.71	0.4564	0.9564	0.0436
1.22	0.3888	0.8888	0.1112	1.72	0.4573	0.9573	0.0427
1.23	0.3907	0.8907	0.1093	1.73	0.4582	0.9582	0.0418
1.24	0.3925	0.8925	0.1075	1.74	0.4591	0.9591	0.0409
1.25	0.3944	0.8944	0.1056	1.75	0.4599	0.9599	0.0401
1.26	0.3962	0.8962	0.1038	1.76	0.4608	0.9608	0.0392
1.27	0.3980	0.8980	0.1020	1.77	0.4616	0.9616	0.0384
1.28	0.3997	0.8997	0.1003	1.78	0.4625	0.9625	0.0375
1.29	0.4015	0.9015	0.0985	1.79	0.4633	0.9633	0.0367
1.30	0.4032	0.9032	0.0968	1.80	0.4641	0.9641	0.0359
1.31	0.4049	0.9049	0.0951	1.81	0.4649	0.9649	0.0351
1.32	0.4066	0.9066	0.0934	1.82	0.4656	0.9656	0.0344
1.33	0.4082	0.9082	0.0918	1.83	0.4664	0.9664	0.0336
1.34	0.4099	0.9099	0.0901	1.84	0.4671	0.9671	0.0329
1.35	0.4115	0.9115	0.0885	1.85	0.4678	0.9678	0.0322
1.36	0.4131	0.9131	0.0869	1.86	0.4686	0.9686	0.0314
1.37	0.4147	0.9147	0.0853	1.87	0.4693	0.9693	0.0307
1.38	0.4162	0.9162	0.0838	1.88	0.4699	0.9699	0.0301
1.39	0.4177	0.9177	0.0823	1.89	0.4706	0.9706	0.0294
1.40	0.4192	0.9192	0.0808	1.90	0.4713	0.9713	0.0287
1.41	0.4207	0.9207	0.0793	1.91	0.4719	0.9719	0.0281
1.42	0.4222	0.9222	0.0778	1.92	0.4726	0.9726	0.0274
1.43	0.4236	0.9236	0.0764	1.93	0.4732	0.9732	0.0268
1.44	0.4251	0.9251	0.0749	1.94	0.4738	0.9738	0.0262
1.45	0.4265	0.9265	0.0735	1.95	0.4744	0.9744	0.0256
1.46	0.4279	0.9279	0.0721	1.96	0.4750	0.9750	0.0250
1.47	0.4292	0.9292	0.0708	1.97	0.4756	0.9756	0.0244
1.48	0.4306	0.9306	0.0694	1.98	0.4761	0.9761	0.0239
1.49	0.4319	0.9319	0.0681	1.99	0.4767	0.9767	0.0233

z-score	Area from mean to z-score	Area of larger portion	Area of smaller portion	z-score	Area from mean to z-score	Area of larger portion	Area of smaller portion
2.00	0.4772	0.9772	0.0228	2.50	0.4938	0.9938	0.0062
2.01	0.4778	0.9778	0.0222	2.51	0.4940	0.9940	0.0060
2.02	0.4783	0.9783	0.0217	2.52	0.4941	0.9941	0.0059
2.03	0.4788	0.9788	0.0212	2.53	0.4943	0.9943	0.0057
2.04	0.4793	0.9793	0.0207	2.54	0.4945	0.9945	0.0055
2.05	0.4798	0.9798	0.0202	2.55	0.4946	0.9946	0.0054
2.06	0.4803	0.9803	0.0197	2.56	0.4948	0.9948	0.0052
2.07	0.4808	0.9808	0.0192	2.57	0.4949	0.9949	0.0051
2.08	0.4812	0.9812	0.0188	2.58	0.4951	0.9951	0.0049
2.09	0.4817	0.9817	0.0183	2.59	0.4952	0.9952	0.0048
2.10	0.4821	0.9821	0.0179	2.60	0.4953	0.9953	0.0047
2.11	0.4826	0.9826	0.0174	2.61	0.4955	0.9955	0.0045
2.12	0.4830	0.9830	0.0170	2.62	0.4956	0.9956	0.0044
2.13	0.4834	0.9834	0.0166	2.63	0.4957	0.9957	0.0043
2.14	0.4838	0.9838	0.0162	2.64	0.4959	0.9959	0.0041
2.15	0.4842	0.9842	0.0158	2.65	0.4960	0.9960	0.0040
2.16	0.4846	0.9846	0.0154	2.66	0.4961	0.9961	0.0039
2.17	0.4850	0.9850	0.0150	2.67	0.4962	0.9962	0.0038
2.18	0.4854	0.9854	0.0146	2.68	0.4963	0.9963	0.0037
2.19	0.4857	0.9857	0.0143	2.69	0.4964	0.9964	0.0036
2.20	0.4861	0.9861	0.0139	2.70	0.4965	0.9965	0.0035
2.21	0.4864	0.9864	0.0136	2.71	0.4966	0.9966	0.0034
2.22	0.4868	0.9868	0.0132	2.72	0.4967	0.9967	0.0033
2.23	0.4871	0.9871	0.0129	2.73	0.4968	0.9968	0.0032
2.24	0.4875	0.9875	0.0125	2.74	0.4969	0.9969	0.0031
2.25	0.4878	0.9878	0.0122	2.75	0.4970	0.9970	0.0030
2.26	0.4881	0.9881	0.0119	2.76	0.4971	0.9971	0.0029
2.27	0.4884	0.9884	0.0116	2.77	0.4972	0.9972	0.0028
2.28	0.4887	0.9887	0.0113	2.78	0.4973	0.9973	0.0027
2.29	0.4890	0.9890	0.0110	2.79	0.4974	0.9974	0.0026
2.30	0.4893	0.9893	0.0107	2.80	0.4974	0.9974	0.0026
2.31	0.4896	0.9896	0.0104	2.81	0.4975	0.9975	0.0025
2.32	0.4898	0.9898	0.0102	2.82	0.4976	0.9976	0.0024
2.33	0.4901	0.9901	0.0099	2.83	0.4977	0.9977	0.0023
2.34	0.4904	0.9904	0.0096	2.84	0.4977	0.9977	0.0023
2.35	0.4906	0.9906	0.0094	2.85	0.4978	0.9978	0.0022
2.36	0.4909	0.9909	0.0091	2.86	0.4979	0.9979	0.0021
2.37	0.4911	0.9911	0.0089	2.87	0.4979	0.9979	0.0021
2.38	0.4913	0.9913	0.0087	2.88	0.4980	0.9980	0.0020
2.39	0.4916	0.9916	0.0084	2.89	0.4981	0.9981	0.0019
2.40	0.4918	0.9918	0.0082	2.90	0.4981	0.9981	0.0019
2.41	0.4920	0.9920	0.0080	2.91	0.4982	0.9982	0.0018
2.42	0.4922	0.9922	0.0078	2.92	0.4982	0.9982	0.0018
2.43	0.4925	0.9925	0.0075	2.93	0.4983	0.9983	0.0017
2.44	0.4927	0.9927	0.0073	2.94	0.4984	0.9984	0.0016
2.45	0.4929	0.9929	0.0071	2.95	0.4984	0.9984	0.0016
2.46	0.4931	0.9931	0.0069	2.96	0.4985	0.9985	0.0015
2.47	0.4932	0.9932	0.0068	2.97	0.4985	0.9985	0.0015
2.48	0.4934	0.9934	0.0066	2.98	0.4986	0.9986	0.0014
2.49	0.4936	0.9936	0.0064	2.99	0.4986	0.9986	0.0014
				3.00	0.4987	0.9987	0.0013

Glossary

absolute value function (p. 45) The function $f(x) = |x|$ such that $f(a) = a$ for $a \geq 0$ and $f(a) = -a$ for $a < 0$.

amplitude of a periodic function (p. 190) If f is periodic with maximum value M and minimum value m, then the *amplitude* of f is $\frac{1}{2}(M - m)$.

angle of depression (p. 246) The acute angle measured from a horizontal line down to the line of sight.

angle of elevation (p. 246) The acute angle measured from a horizontal line up to the line of sight.

angular velocity (p. 134) The *angular velocity* ω of a point moving in a circular path with angular displacement θ per unit time t is $\omega = \frac{\theta}{t}$.

arccos x (p. 216) $y = \arccos x$ if and only if $\cos y = x$ and $0 \leq y \leq \pi$.

arccot x (p. 223) $y = \text{arccot } x$ if and only if $\cot y = x$ and $0 < y < \pi$.

arccsc x (p. 223) $y = \text{arccsc } x$ if and only if $\csc y = x$ and $-\frac{\pi}{2} \leq y \leq \frac{\pi}{2}$, $y \neq 0$.

arcsec x (p. 223) $y = \text{arcsec } x$ if and only if $\sec y = x$ and $0 \leq y \leq \pi$, $y \neq \frac{\pi}{2}$.

arcsin x (p. 215) $y = \arcsin x$ if and only if $\sin y = x$ and $-\frac{\pi}{2} \leq y \leq \frac{\pi}{2}$.

arctan x (p. 222) $y = \arctan x$ if and only if $\tan y = x$ and $-\frac{\pi}{2} < y < \frac{\pi}{2}$.

area of a sector of a circle (p. 129) The area A_S of a sector of a circle of radius r with central angle measure θ is $A_S = \frac{1}{2}r^2\theta$.

area of a triangle (p. 273) The area K of triangle ABC is given by $K = \frac{1}{2}bc \sin A$.

arithmetic means (p. 684) If the numbers $a_1, a_2, \ldots, a_{k-1}, a_k$ form an arithmetic sequence, then $a_2, a_3, \ldots, a_{k-1}$ are *arithmetic means* between a_1 and a_k.

arithmetic sequence (p. 682) A sequence of the form $a_n = a_{n-1} + d$ for all integers $n > 1$, where d is a constant.

box-and-whisker plot (p. 807) A graphical representation of a set of ordered data, showing the upper and lower extremes, the quartiles, and the median.

cardioid (p. 497) The graph of an equation of the form $r = a + a \cos \theta$ or $r = a + a \sin \theta$.

change-of-base formula (p. 456) $\log_b x = \frac{\log_a x}{\log_a b}$.

combination (p. 750) A selection of a fixed number of elements of a set without regard to order.

common logarithmic function (p. 455) A logarithmic function with base 10.

complex number (p. 82) A number that can be written in the form $a + bi$, where a and b are real numbers, and $i = \sqrt{-1}$.

composite function (p. 33) Given two functions f and g, the function $f \circ g$ defined by $(f \circ g)(x) = f(g(x))$.

concavity (p. 879) A graph is *concave down* when it opens downward, and *concave up* when it opens upward.

conditional probability (p. 764) The probability that one event, B, occurs given that another one, A, has occurred; denoted $P(B|A)$.

conic sections (p. 534) Curves formed by the intersection of a plane and a double right circular cone.

conjugate radical theorem (p. 352) If $a + \sqrt{b}$ is a zero of a polynomial function with rational coefficients, where a and b are rational, but $\sqrt{b}$ is irrational, then the conjugate number $a - \sqrt{b}$ is also a zero of the polynomial.

consistent system (p. 386) A system of equations that has at least one solution.

continuity of a function (p. 861) $f(x)$ is continuous at $x = c$ if and only if $f(x)$ is defined at $x = c$, $\lim_{x \to c} f(x)$ exists, and $\lim_{x \to c} f(x) = f(c)$.

convergent sequence (p. 715) A sequence whose terms approach a constant L as n increases without bound.

correlation coefficient (p. 840)   A number that measures the strength of the linear relationship between the points in a data set.

cosecant (p. 147)   If θ is an angle in standard position and (x, y) is a point distinct from the origin on the terminal side of θ, then cosecant $\theta = \dfrac{r}{y}$, $y \neq 0$, where $r = \sqrt{x^2 + y^2}$.

cotangent (p. 147)   If θ is an angle in standard position and (x, y) is a point distinct from the origin on the terminal side of θ, then cotangent $\theta = \dfrac{x}{y}$, $y \neq 0$, where $r = \sqrt{x^2 + y^2}$.

cosine (p. 143)   If θ is an angle in standard position and (x, y) is a point distinct from the origin on the terminal side of θ, then cosine $\theta = \dfrac{x}{r}$, where $r = \sqrt{x^2 + y^2}$.

coterminal angles (p. 122)   Angles of different measures in standard position that have the same terminal side.

cross product of vectors (p. 662)   If $\mathbf{v} = (v_1, v_2, v_3)$ and $\mathbf{u} = (u_1, u_2, u_3)$, then $\mathbf{v} \times \mathbf{u} = (v_2 u_3 - v_3 u_2, v_3 u_1 - v_1 u_3, v_1 u_2 - v_2 u_1)$.

decreasing (p. 46)   A function f is *decreasing on an interval* if, for any two real numbers x_1 and x_2 in the interval, $f(x_2) < f(x_1)$ when $x_2 > x_1$; f is a *decreasing function* if it is decreasing for all real numbers in its domain.

definite integral (p. 891)   If f is defined on the interval $[a, b]$, then the *definite integral* of f from a to b is given by
$$\int_a^b f = \lim_{n \to \infty} \sum_{i=1}^{n} f(x_i)(x_i - x_{i-1}).$$

degree of a polynomial $P(x)$ (p. 94)   The highest power of x that occurs when $P(x)$ is written in standard polynomial form.

DeMoivre's theorem (p. 517)   If $z = r(\cos \theta + i \sin \theta)$, then for any integer n, $z^n = r^n(\cos n\theta + i \sin n\theta)$.

dependent events (p. 763)   Two events are *dependent* if the outcome of one affects the outcome of the other.

dependent system (p. 386)   A consistent system of linear equations having infinitely many solutions.

derivative (p. 872)   The *derivative* of f with respect to x is a function f' defined by
$$f'(x) = \lim_{h \to 0} \frac{f(x + h) - f(x)}{h}.$$

differentiable (p. 872) f is *differentiable* at x if $f'(x)$ exists.

dilation (p. 67)   The graph of $y = af(x)$ is a vertical *dilation* of the graph of $f(x)$; if $a > 1$, the graph moves away from the x-axis, and if $0 < a < 1$, the graph moves toward the x-axis.

distance formula (p. 102)   The distance d between any two points $P(x_1, y_1)$ and $Q(x_2, y_2)$ in the coordinate plane is
$$d = \sqrt{(x_2 - x_1)^2 + (y_2 - y_1)^2}.$$

distance from a point to a line (p. 107)   The distance d from the point $P(x_1, y_1)$ to a nonvertical line $Ax + By + C = 0$ is
$$d = \frac{|Ax_1 + By_1 + C|}{\sqrt{A^2 + B^2}}.$$

domain (p. 24)   The set of all first coordinates of ordered pairs in a relation.

dot product of three-dimensional vectors (p. 661)   If θ is the angle between $\mathbf{v}$ and $\mathbf{w}$, then $\mathbf{v} \cdot \mathbf{w} = \|\mathbf{v}\| \cdot \|\mathbf{w}\| \cos \theta$.

dot product of two-dimensional vectors (p. 654)   If $\mathbf{v} = (v_1, v_2)$ and $\mathbf{w} = (w_1, w_2)$, then $\mathbf{v} \cdot \mathbf{w} = v_1 w_1 + v_2 w_2$.

ellipse (p. 541)   The set of all points P in a plane such that the sum of the distances from P to two fixed points, called *foci*, is constant.

Euler's formula (p. 732) $e^{ix} = \cos x + i \sin x$.

even function (p. 60)   A function f such that $f(-x) = f(x)$ for all x in its domain.

expected value (p. 778)   If a random variable X can take on the values $a_1, a_2, \ldots, a_n$ with probabilities $p_1, p_2, \ldots, p_n$ respectively, then the *expected value* of X is $E(X) = a_1 p_1 + a_2 p_2 + \cdots + a_n p_n$.

exponential function (p. 446)   A function of the form $f(x) = b^x$, $b > 0$ and $b \neq 1$.

exponential growth curve (p. 475)   The graph of a function of the form $P = P_0 e^{rt}$, where P_0 is the original population, P is the population after t years, and r is the annual growth rate of the population.

factorial (p. 708)   *n-factorial*, or $n!$, is given by $n! = n(n - 1)(n - 2) \cdots 3 \cdot 2 \cdot 1$; $0! = 1$.

feasible region (p. 412)   The solution to a system of inequalities, represented by a graph.

finite graph (p. 611)   A set of points, called *nodes*, and a set of lines, called *edges*, which connect the nodes.

frequency distribution (p. 799)   A table in which sets of data are grouped by classes and a frequency is given for each class.

frequency of a data value (p. 798)   The number of times a value occurs in a set of data.

frequency of a periodic function (p. 195)   The reciprocal of the period.

function (p. 24)   A relation in which each element in the domain is mapped to *exactly one* element in the range.

fundamental theorem of algebra (p. 349)   Every polynomial function of positive degree with complex coefficients has at least one complex zero.

geometric means (p. 686)   If the numbers $a_1, a_2, \ldots, a_{k-1}, a_k$ form a geometric sequence, then $a_2, a_3, \ldots, a_{k-1}$ are *geometric means* between a_1 and a_k.

geometric sequence (p. 684)   A sequence of the form $a_n = a_{n-1} \cdot r$ for all $n > 1$, where r is a constant.

greatest integer function (p. 45)   A function which assigns to each real number the greatest integer less than or equal to that number.

Heron's Formula (p. 274)   If a, b, and c are the measures of the sides of a triangle, then the area K of the triangle is given by $K = \sqrt{s(s-a)(s-b)(s-c)}$, for $s = \frac{a+b+c}{2}$.

histogram (p. 800)   A bar graph representation of the information in a frequency distribution.

horizontal asymptote (p. 365)   If $f(x)$ approaches b as $|x|$ increases without bound, then $y = b$ is a *horizontal asymptote* of f.

horizontal line test (p. 28)   If no horizontal line intersects the graph of a function at more than one point, then the graph represents a one-to-one function.

hyperbola (p. 549)   The set of all points P in the plane such that the absolute value of the difference of the distances from P to two fixed points is a constant.

identity matrix (p. 606)   A square matrix, called I, with entries of 1 along the main diagonal and 0 elsewhere.

inconsistent system (p. 386)   A system of equations with no solution.

increasing (p. 46)   A function f is *increasing on an interval* if, for any two real numbers x_1 and x_2 in the interval, $f(x_2) > f(x_1)$ when $x_2 > x_1$; f is an *increasing function* if it is increasing for all real numbers in its domain.

independent events (p. 763)   Two events are *independent* if the outcome of one has no effect on the outcome of the other.

independent system (p. 386)   A consistent system of linear equations having exactly one solution.

integers (p. 11) $Z = \{\ldots, -3, -2, -1, 0, 1, 2, 3, \ldots\}$.

inverse of a function (p. 39)   Function f has an *inverse function* f^{-1} if and only if $f(f^{-1}(x)) = x$ for all x in the domain of f^{-1} and $f^{-1}(f(x)) = x$ for all x in the domain of f.

inverse of a matrix (p. 619)   Given a square matrix A, its *inverse*, if it exists, is a square matrix A^{-1} such that $AA^{-1} = A^{-1}A = I$, the identity matrix.

irrational number (p. 12)   A real number that is not a rational number.

law of cosines (p. 265)   For any triangle ABC, where a, b, and c are the lengths of the sides opposite the angles with measures A, B, and C, respectively, $a^2 = b^2 + c^2 - 2bc \cos A$, $b^2 = a^2 + c^2 - 2ac \cos B$, $c^2 = a^2 + b^2 - 2ab \cos C$.

law of sines (p. 251)   For any triangle ABC, where a, b, and c are the lengths of the sides opposite the angles with measures A, B, C, respectively, $\frac{\sin A}{a} = \frac{\sin B}{b} = \frac{\sin C}{c}$.

length of an arc (p. 128)   The length s of an arc of a circle of radius r determined by central angle θ expressed in radians is given by $s = r\theta$.

limaçon (p. 497)   The graph of an equation of the form $r = a + b \cos \theta$ or $r = a + b \sin \theta$.

limit (p. 854) $f(x)$ has the *limit* L as x approaches c if the value of $f(x)$ gets closer to L as x gets closer to c from the left *and* as x gets closer to c from the right.

linear function (p. 73)   A function of the form $f(x) = mx + b$.

linear program (p. 418)   A mathematical model consisting of a linear function to be optimized, called the *objective function*, and a set of linear inequalities or *constraints* representing the restrictions on resources.

linear velocity (p. 134)   The *linear velocity* V of an object moving along a circle of radius r at a constant rate with an angular displacement θ in radians per unit time t is $V = \frac{r\theta}{t}$.

logarithmic function (p. 453)   The function $f(x)$ such that for all positive real numbers x and b, $b > 0$ and $b \neq 1$, $y = f(x) = \log_b x$ if and only if $x = b^y$.

matrix (p. 596)   A rectangular array of numbers written within brackets.

mean (p. 811)   The mean of a set of n pieces of numerical data is the sum of the pieces divided by n.

median (p. 806)   The middle of a set of ordered data.

midpoint formula (p. 102)   The coordinates of the midpoint M of the line segment with endpoints $P(x_1, y_1)$ and $Q(x_2, y_2)$ are $M\left(\dfrac{x_1 + x_2}{2}, \dfrac{y_1 + y_2}{2}\right)$.

mode (p. 812)   The most frequently occurring value in a set of data.

modulus (p. 504)   The distance from $a + bi$ to the origin is the *modulus* of $a + bi$, which is given by $\sqrt{a^2 + b^2}$.

mutually exclusive events (p. 761)   Events that have no outcomes in common.

natural exponential function (p. 448)   The function $f(x) = e^x$.

natural logarithmic function (p. 455) $f(x) = \ln x = \log_e x$.

natural numbers (p. 11) $N = \{1, 2, 3, 4, \ldots\}$.

norm (p. 639)   The magnitude, or length, of a vector.

normal curve (p. 824)   A curve, representing a data set, which has the shape of a bell, is symmetric about the vertical line through the mean of the distribution, and approaches the horizontal axis at both extremes.

normal vector (p. 662)   A vector perpendicular to a plane.

nth partial sum (p. 691)   The sum of the first n terms of a series.

odd function (p. 60)   A function f such that $f(-x) = -f(x)$ for all x in its domain.

one-to-one function (p. 28)   A function f such that, for any two elements x_1 and x_2 in the domain, $f(x_1) = f(x_2)$ if and only if $x_1 = x_2$.

parabola (p. 557)   The graph of a quadratic function; equivalently, the set of all points P in a plane that are equidistant from a fixed line and a fixed point not on the line.

periodic function (p. 182)   A function f is *periodic* if there is a positive real number h, called the *period* of f, such that $f(x + h) = f(x)$ for every x in the domain of f.

permutation (p. 748)   An ordered arrangement of a set of elements.

point of inflection (p. 879)   A point on a graph where the concavity changes.

point-slope form of a linear equation (p. 3) $y - y_1 = m(x - x_1)$, where m is the slope and (x_1, y_1) are the coordinates of a point on the line.

polynomial function (p. 94) $f(x) = a_n x^n + a_{n-1} x^{n-1} + \cdots + a_1 x + a_0$, where $a_n \neq 0$.

power series (p. 728)   A series of the form $\sum_{k=0}^{\infty} a_k x^k$.

probability of an event (p. 756)   The ratio of the number of outcomes in an event to the number of outcomes in the sample space.

quadratic formula (p. 5)   The solutions of a quadratic equation $ax^2 + bx + c = 0$, $a \neq 0$, are given by the formula $x = \dfrac{-b \pm \sqrt{b^2 - 4ac}}{2a}$.

quartile (p. 806)   The *lower quartile* is the median of the data below the overall median; the *upper quartile* is the median of the data above the overall median.

range (p. 24)   The set of all second coordinates of ordered pairs in a relation.

rational function (p. 365)   A quotient of two polynomials.

rational number (p. 11)   A number that can be written in the form $\dfrac{a}{b}$, where a and b are integers and $b \neq 0$.

real numbers (p. 11)   The union of the set of rational numbers and the set of irrational numbers.

relation (p. 24)   A set of ordered pairs.

rose curve (p. 499)   The graph of an equation of the form $r = a \cos n\theta$ or $r = a \sin n\theta$, where $a \neq 0$ and n is a nonzero integer.

sample space (p. 755)   The collection of all outcomes, or possible results, of an experiment.

secant (p. 147)   If θ is an angle in standard position and (x, y) is a point distinct from the origin on the terminal side of θ, then secant $\theta = \dfrac{r}{x}$, $x \neq 0$, where $r = \sqrt{x^2 + y^2}$.

secant line (p. 866)   A straight line drawn between two points on a curve.

sequence (p. 675)   A function whose domain is the set of positive integers or a subset of the positive integers that consists of the n integers $1, 2, 3, \ldots , n$.

series (p. 690) The sum of a finite or infinite sequence.

sine (p. 143) If θ is an angle in standard position and (x, y) is a point distinct from the origin on the terminal side of θ, then sine $\theta = \frac{y}{r}$, where $r = \sqrt{x^2 + y^2}$.

sinusoid (p. 193) A function f of the form $f(x) = a \sin b(x - c) + d$, where a, b, c, d are real numbers.

slope of a curve (p. 867) The *slope of a curve* at point P is the slope of the tangent line to the curve at point P.

slope of a line (p. 2) The ratio of the change in vertical distance to the change in horizontal distance.

slope-intercept form of a linear equation (p. 3) $y = mx + b$, where m is the slope and b is the y-intercept.

standard deviation (p. 818) For any set of numerical data $\{x_1, x_2, \ldots , x_n\}$ with mean $\bar{x}$, the *standard deviation* σ is

$$\sigma = \sqrt{\frac{1}{n} \sum_{i=1}^{n} (x_i - \bar{x})^2}.$$

symmetric with respect to a line (p. 56) Two points P and Q are *symmetric with respect to a line ℓ* if ℓ is the perpendicular bisector of $\overline{PQ}$.

symmetric with respect to a point (p. 56) Two points P and Q are *symmetric with respect to a point M* if M is the midpoint of $\overline{PQ}$.

tangent line (p. 866) Suppose a secant line is drawn between two points P and Q on a curve. If P is fixed and Q is allowed to move along the curve toward P, the resulting secant lines may approach a limiting position, called the *tangent line* to the curve at P.

translation (p. 66) A vertical or horizontal shift of a graph.

vector (p. 639) Any quantity that has both magnitude and direction.

vertical asymptote (p. 365) If $|f(x)|$ increases or decreases without bound as x approaches a, then the vertical line $x = a$ is a *vertical asymptote* for f.

vertical line test (p. 27) If no vertical line intersects a graph at more than one point, then the graph represents a function.

whole numbers (p. 11) $W = \{0, 1, 2, 3, 4, \ldots\}$.

x-intercept (p. 20) A point at which a graph intersects the x-axis.

y-intercept (p. 20) A point at which a graph intersects the y-axis.

zero of a function (p. 88) The x-intercepts of the function.

zero-product property (p. 80) For all real numbers a and b, $ab = 0$ if and only if $a = 0$ or $b = 0$.

Photo Credits

Continued on page 937.

909

Chapter 1 Functions

Practice Exercises, pages 8–10

1. $y = 0.11x + 0.26$ **3.** $x = -\frac{3}{2}$ **5.** $d = -16t^2$ **7.** 841 ft **9.** $y = -0.0000071x + 0.2957143$ **11.** 33,199 mi **12.** $x = \frac{2a^2}{3a - 6b}$
15. 85 **16.** $(-0.5, 1, -0.5)$ **17.** $A = 250\ell - \ell^2$ **19.** 125 ft **20.** No solution. $m \neq 7$
25. $y = -0.06x^2 + 7.83x$

Practice Exercises, pages 15–17

1.

7. add. inv.
9. comm. add.
11. closure, mult.
13. comm. mult.
15. $z = 0, \sqrt{5}, -\sqrt{5}$

17. add., subt., mult., div. **19.** 49.5 mi/h
23. $3x(x + 7)(x - 9)$ **25.** add. inv.: $3 + a = a + 3 = 0, a \notin \{0, 3, 6, 9, \ldots\}$; mult. ident.: $1 \notin \{0, 3, 6, 9, \ldots\}$; mult. inv.: $3 \cdot a = a \cdot 3 = 1, a \notin \{0, 3, 6, 9, \ldots\}$ **27.** clos. add.: $-3 + (-5) = -8, -8 \notin$ negative odd integers; clos. mult.: $(-3)(-5) = 15, 15 \notin$ negative odd integers; add. ident.: $0 \notin$ negative odd integers; add. inv.: $-1 + a = a + -1 = 0, a \notin$ negative odd integers; mult. ident.: $1 \notin$ negative odd integers; mult. inv.: $-3 \cdot a = a \cdot -3 = 1$, $a \notin$ negative odd integers **29.** closure add.: $1 + 1 = 2 \notin \{-1, 0, 1\}$ **31.** yes **33.** yes
34. $y = 4, -2$ **36.** $y = 1.2x + 0.1$ **41.** *a; b; c; d*, respectively **43.** no identity element

Practice Exercises, pages 21–23

1.

5.

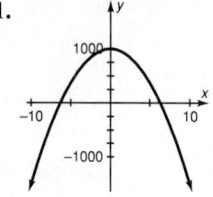

16. Closure, comm., assoc., mult. ident.
19. $19V$ **21.**

23.

27.

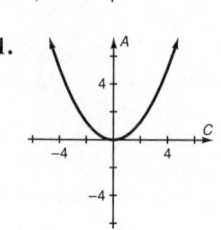

25. $x^2(5x - 2)(3x + 1)$
29.

31.

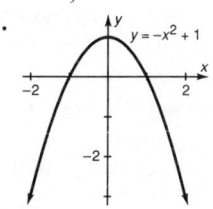

33. $\pm i\sqrt{2}$. No solution in $\mathcal{R}$.

Test Yourself, page 23

1. $y = 1.20 + 0.40x, x \geq 12$ **3.** $A = -w^2 + 150w$ **5.** Add. identity **7.** Closure, mult: $\frac{1}{3} \cdot \frac{2}{3} = \frac{2}{9} \notin \left\{ \ldots, -1, -\frac{2}{3}, -\frac{1}{3}, 0, \frac{1}{3}, \frac{2}{3}, 1, \ldots \right\}$; Mult. inv.: $\frac{2}{3} \cdot a = a \cdot \frac{2}{3} = 1, a \notin \left\{ \ldots, -1, -\frac{2}{3}, -\frac{1}{3}, 0, \frac{1}{3}, \frac{2}{3}, 1, \ldots \right\}$
9.

(8, 1.0)
(7, 0.9)
(6, 0.6)
(5, 0.3)

11.

$y = -x^2 + 1$

Practice Exercises, pages 29–31

1. $D = \{a, b, c, d\}; R = \{0, 2, 4, 6\}$; function
3. $D = \{-1, -2, 1, 2\}; R = \{1, 16\}$; function
5. $\frac{3y^2}{x^3}$ **7.** function **9.** $D_g = \{x: x \neq -6, x \neq 3\}; R_g = \{y: y \in \mathcal{R}\}$ **13.** Not a function
15. $2x\sqrt[5]{2xy^3}$ **17.** $16a^2$ **19.** $3\sqrt{b} + 4$
21. $x^2 - 8x + 16$ **23.** $D_g = \{x: x \neq -1\}$; $R_g = \{y: y \neq 1\}$ **25.** $D_H = \{x: x \geq 4\}$; $D_T = \{x: x \geq 4\}$; equal **27.** $D_m = \{x: x \neq 5\}$; $D_n = \{x: x \in \mathcal{R}\}$; not equal **29.** 0.8; 2.05; 3.05
31. $\pi^2 - 1$ **33.** $-3x + 14$ **35.** $x^4 - 1$
37. $2m + h$ **38.** $a^2b^3c(b - c)(b + c)$
39. $D_f = \{x: x \neq -2\}; D_g = \{x: x \in \mathcal{R}\}$; not equal **41.** $D_f = \{x: x \in \mathcal{R}; D_g = \{x: x \in \mathcal{R}\}$; equal **43.** $M = \frac{3k}{R - 2\pi}; R \neq 2\pi$

45. One-to-one function   **47.** function; not one-to-one   **49.** $\frac{2}{3}$ **51.** $D_w = \{x: x > 0\}$
53. $D_g = \{x: \neq 0\}$; $R_g = \{y: y \neq 0\}$
55. $D_1 = \{x: x > 2 \text{ or } x < -2\}$; $R_1 = \{y: y > 0\}$ **57.** not equal

Practice Exercises, page 36–37
1. $7x$; $D_{f+g} = \{x: x \in \mathcal{R}\}$; $-x$; $D_{f-g} = \{x: x \in \mathcal{R}\}$; $12x^2$; $D_{f \cdot g} = \{x: x \in \mathcal{R}\}$; $\frac{3}{4}$; $D_{f/g} = \{x: x \neq 0\}$;   **3.** $\frac{2x^2 - x}{x - 2}$, $D_{f+g} = \{x: x \neq 2\}$; $\frac{-2x^2 + 7x}{x - 2}$, $D_{f-g} = \{x: x \neq 2\}$; $\frac{6x^2}{x - 2}$, $D_{f \cdot g} = \{x: x \neq 2\}$; $\frac{3}{2x - 4}$, $D_{f/g} = \{x: x \neq 0, 2\}$
5. $\sqrt{x} + 4x^2$, $D_{f+g} = \{x: x \geq 0\}$; $\sqrt{x} - 4x^2$, $D_{f-g} = \{x: x \geq 0\}$; $2x^{\frac{5}{2}}$, $D_{f \cdot g} = \{x: x \geq 0\}$; $\frac{1}{4x^{\frac{3}{2}}}$, $D_{f/g} = \{x: x > 0\}$ **7.** $(x - 5)(x^2 + 5x + 25)$
9. 5π **11.** -3; 11 **13.** $-9x - 1$; $9x - 11$
15. $\sqrt{-2x + 3}$; $2\sqrt{x + 3}$ **17.** $x = 1, -2.5$
19. $f(x) = x^3$; $g(x) = x - 3$ **21.** $f(x) = \frac{x}{3}$; $g(x) = -x$ **23.** $\sqrt{a + 1}$; $a \geq -1$ **25.** $x - 1 - \sqrt{x}$; $D_{m-f} = \{x: x \geq 0\}$ **27.** x; $D_{h \cdot m} = \{x: x \in \mathcal{R}\}$ **29.** $c^2 + 2c + d^2 + d + 1$; $c \in \mathcal{R}, d \in \mathcal{R}\}$ **31.** $f(x) = \sqrt[4]{x}$; $g(x) = x + 4$
33. $D_f = \{x: x \neq 8, x \neq -3\}$ **35.** $y = -2x$; $D = \{-2, 0, 2, 4\}$; $R = \{4, 0, -4, -8\}$
37. $17.5x + 45$; \$97.50   **39.** $x = 0, -1$

Practice Exercises, pages 41–43
1. $\{(2, 5), (4, 7), (6, 9)\}$ **3.** $f^{-1}(x) = \frac{x}{3}$
5. $g^{-1}(x) = -\frac{x}{3} + \frac{1}{3}$ **7.** $h^{-1}(x) = \frac{1}{2x}$
9. $7; 25$
11.   **13.**
15.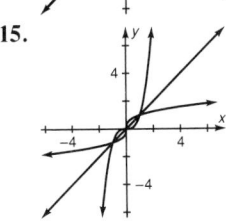
17. Inverse functions
19. Inverse functions
21. $f^{-1}(x) = \frac{1}{4}x - \frac{3}{4}$; Inverse is a function.

26. $-\frac{2}{3}$; $-\frac{7}{3}$ **27.** x^2; x^2 **29.** Inverse functions; $D_f = \{x: x \geq -2\}$; $R_f = \{y: y \geq 0\}$; $D_g = \{x: x \geq 0\}$; $R_g = \{y: y \geq -2\}$ **31.** Not inverse functions; $D_f = \{x: x \in \mathcal{R}\}$; $R_f = \{y: y \in \mathcal{R}\}$; $D_g = \{x: x \in \mathcal{R}\}$; $R_g = \{y: y \in \mathcal{R}\}$ **33.** Inverse functions; $D_f = \{x: x \neq 0\}$; $R_f = \{y: y \neq 1\}$; $D_g = \{x: x \neq 1\}$; $R_g = \{y: y \neq 0\}$ **36.** (1, 1, 2)
37. $f^{-1}(x) = -x^2 + 2$ **39.** $f^{-1}(x) = \sqrt{x + 5} + 3$; $D_f = \{x: x \geq 3\}$ **41.** $f^{-1}(x) = \sqrt{4 - x}$; $D_f = \{x: x \leq 0\}$

Practice Exercises, pages 47–49
1.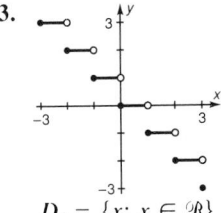
$D_f = \{x: x \in \mathcal{R}\}$
$R_f = \{y: y \geq 0\}$

3.
$D_f = \{x: x \in \mathcal{R}\}$
$R_f = \{y: y \in Z\}$

5.
$D_f = \{x: x \in \mathcal{R}\}$
$R_f = \{y: y \geq 0\}$

7.
$D_n = \{x: x \in \mathcal{R}\}$
$R_n = \{y: y \in \mathcal{R}\}$

9. $D_m = \{x: x \in \mathcal{R}\}$; $R_m = \{y: y \leq 3\}$
11. $x = 0, 3, 4$ **13.** $N, W, Z, \mathcal{R}$, Rational
15. Const.: $(-\infty, \infty)$ **17.** Inc.: $(0, 4)$;   Dec.: $(-\infty, 0)$;   Const.: $(4, \infty)$ **19.** $f^{-1}(x) = \sqrt[3]{\frac{x + 1}{2}}$
21. $D_g = \{x: x \in \mathcal{R}\}$; $R_g = \{y: y \geq -2\}$
23. $D_g = \{x: x \in \mathcal{R}\}$; $R_g = \{y: y \geq 0\}$
25. $D_g = \{x: x \in \mathcal{R}\}$; $R_g = \{y: y \in Z\}$
27. $D_g = \{x: x \in \mathcal{R}\}$; $R_g = \{y: y < 0\}$
29. $D_g = \{x: x \in \mathcal{R}\}$; $R_g = \{y: y \geq 0\}$
30. yes   **32.** $(-1.2, 1.5), (3.2, 10.4)$
33. Increasing: $(2.5, +\infty)$; Decreasing: $(-\infty, 2.5)$ **37.** $D_g = \{x: x \in \mathcal{R}\}$; $R_g = \{y: y \geq 0\}$ **39.** $D_f = \{x: x \in \mathcal{R}\}$; $R_f = \{y: 0 \leq y \leq 1, 2n - 1 < y \leq 2n, \text{ where } n \text{ is a positive integer}\}$
41. $f(x) = \begin{cases} -x^3, & x \leq 0 \\ -x, & x > 0 \end{cases}$
43. $f(x) = \begin{cases} -x^3, & x < -1, x > 1 \\ -x, & -1 \leq x \leq 1 \end{cases}$

Test Yourself, page 49

1. 32 3. $2a^2 + 4ab + 2b^2$ 5. $\dfrac{x^2 + 4x + 5}{x + 3}$;

$d_{f+g} = \{x: x \neq -3\}$ 7. $\dfrac{2x + 2}{x + 3}$; $D_{f \cdot g} =$

$\{x: x \neq -3\}$ 9. $1; \dfrac{1}{2}$ 11. $f^{-1}(x) = -\dfrac{1}{2}x + \dfrac{3}{2}$

13. yes 15. $D_f = \{x: x \in \mathcal{R}\}$; $R_f = \{y: y \in \mathcal{R}\}$

Summary and Review, pages 50–52

1. $y = 1.25x + 8$ 3. $y = 0.124x^2 - 1.34x$
5. add. inv. $(4 + (-4) = 0)$; mult. ident.

$(1 \notin \{0, 4, 8, \ldots\})$; mult. inv. $\left(4 \cdot \dfrac{1}{4} = 1\right)$

9. $9b^2 + 2$ 11. $a^2 - 2ab + b^2 + 2$
13. $D_f = \{x: x \neq -1, 2\}$; $R_f = \{y: y \in \mathcal{R}\}$

15. $\dfrac{3x^2 - 3x + 1}{x - 1}$; $D_{f+g} = \{x: x \neq 1\}$ 17. $\dfrac{3x}{x - 1}$;

$d_{f \cdot g} = \{x: x \neq 1\}$ 19. $-3; 8$ 21. $f^{-1}(x) = -x + 4$ 23. yes 25. $D_f = \{x: x \in \mathcal{R}\}$; $R_f = \{y: y \geq 0\}$

Chapter 2 Graphing Functions

Practice Exercises, pages 61–63

1. $(5, -3)$ 3. $(-6.5, -3.5)$ 5. $(a - 50b)$
$(a + 65b)$ 7. x-axis 9. y−axis 11. origin
13. none 15. no 21. x-axis, y-axis, origin
23. origin 25. odd 27. even 29. none
31. x-axis 33. 63 35. 3.4 h 37. 84°
41. true 43. false 45. true

Practice Exercises, pages 69–71

1.

3.

5.

7. $f^{-1}(x) = \dfrac{x}{5} + \dfrac{2}{5}$

9.

11. $11,700 19. The graph of y_2 is the graph of y_1 with a two-unit shift left and a three-unit shift down.

21.

31.

33. 19 yd 35. closure, assoc., comm., add.
ident. 37. $y = x^2 + 2$ 39. $y = \sqrt{x} - 2$
41. $y = x^3 + 2$ 43. $y = -[\![x + 2]\!]$
45. $y = -|x| - 1$ 47. $y = [\![-x]\!] + 1$
49. Vertical distance between the steps decreases as a increases.

Practice Exercises, pages 77–79

1. $C = 0.07d + 50$ 3. $74.92 7. $5x - 9y = -90$ 9. origin 11. -99 13. 0.03
15. parallel 17. Answers may vary. Ex: real, rational, and natural numbers 19. 27
21. closure, comm., assoc.

23.

25. $d = \dfrac{2}{3}t$

27. no

29.

31.

33. A wall with no insulation has an R-factor of zero.
35. $p = 22w + 100$
39. $2x + y = -0.7$

Practice Exercises, pages 84–86

1. $-8, -4$ 3. $\dfrac{1}{2}, -1$ 5. $1.8, -0.8$

7.

15.

9. $-0.4, 1.7$
11. 1
13. $-1.4, 1$

17. $x^2 + 9 = 0$
19. $x^2 + 2x + 5 = 0$
21. 6 s

23. $-\frac{7}{4}, \frac{8}{3}$ **25.** $f^{-1}(x) = \sqrt[3]{\dfrac{x+1}{9}}$ **27.** $\dfrac{2+11i}{5}$
29. $32.5, -0.5$ **31.** $4x^2 - 16x + 21 = 0$
33. MaryBeth: 6 h; Ron: 12 h **35.** add. inv.,
comm., assoc. **37.** 49 **39.** $A = s^2 - 2.6\,s$

Test Yourself, page 86
1. none **3.** even
5.

7.

9.

11.

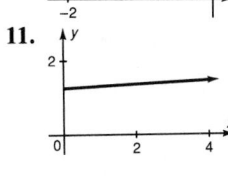

$5x - y + 125 = 0$

13. $\pm\dfrac{2\sqrt{3}}{3}, \pm\dfrac{\sqrt{2}}{2}$

Practice Exercises, pages 91–93
1. x-int: $(\pm 1, 0)$; y-int: $(0, -4)$; axis: $x = 0$;
vertex: $(0, -4)$ **3.** x-int: $(-1, 0)$, $(3, 0)$; y-int:
$(0, -3)$; axis: $x = 1$; vertex: $(1, -4)$ **5.** x-int:
$\left(\frac{3}{2}, 0\right)$, $(-1, 0)$; y-int: $(0, -1)$; axis: $x = \frac{1}{4}$;
vertex: $\left(\frac{1}{4}, -\frac{25}{24}\right)$ **7.** -2(mult. 2) **9.** $-2, 0.3$
11. origin

13.

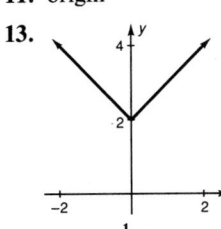

15. $f(x) =$
$-2\left(x - \frac{1}{2}\right)^2 - \frac{1}{2}$
17. $f(x) =$
$6(x - 3)^2 - 47$
19. $f(x) = -2(x - 3)^2$
21. yes

23. $f(x) = \frac{1}{2}(x - 1)^2 + \frac{3}{2}$ **25.** $f^{-1}(x) = \sqrt{x} - 2$;
$D = \{x: x \geq 0\}$ **27.** $-2x^2$
29.

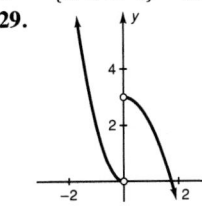

31. $y = 4(x - 3)^2 - 4$
33. $y = -\frac{1}{4}(x + 2)^2$
35. $y = 10x^2$
37. $(450, 127)$

39.

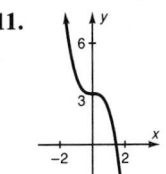

43. $y = -\frac{3}{2}x^2 + 6$
45. $y = -\frac{2}{3}(x + 3)^2 + 9$
49. 280 ft

Practice Exercises, pages 97–99
1. $0, \frac{15}{2}, -1$ **3.** 0 (mult. 2), $-3, 4$
5. $-\frac{1}{2}$ (mult. 2), $\frac{1}{2}$ **7.** 3 **9.** ± 2.8
11.

13. y-axis
15. $2x - 3y = -18$
19. 7 ft $\times$ 14 ft $\times$ 21 ft
21. no **23.** ± 0.3
25. 0 (mult. 4), 8
27. $2, \pm 1.6$ **29.** 0
31. $5, -\frac{1}{2}, \dfrac{1 \pm i\sqrt{3}}{4}$
33. $5(x + 1)^2 - 84$ **39.** $\dfrac{a\sqrt[3]{9}}{3}, -\dfrac{a\sqrt[3]{6}}{2}$
41. $\pm\dfrac{2a^2\sqrt{3}}{3}, \pm\dfrac{a^2\sqrt{2}}{2}$ **43.** $\pm 0.8, \pm 1.6$
45. 1 m $\times$ 2 m $\times$ 6 m

Practice Exercises, pages 104–106
1. 34 **3.** $0, \frac{1}{2}, \frac{2}{3}$ **7.** $2x - y - 3 = 0$
11.

15. yes
19. no
21. no
25. none
31. $f(\ell) = \ell + \dfrac{50,000}{\ell}$

Practice Exercises, pages 111–113
1. $y = 0$; 3 **3.** $3x + 4y - 2 = 0$; 1.8
5. $2x + y - 5 = 0$; 0.45 **7.** $y + 2 = 0$; 2
9. 2.06 **11.** $\frac{1}{2}, -\frac{5}{3}$
13.

15. 9.4375
21. $y - 4 = 0$; 1
23. $(1, -2)$
25. $5x - 2y \pm 4\sqrt{29}$
     $= 0$

31. 3.07 **33.** no **35.** 4 ft **37.** 7.34, 0.30
39. $|y| = 4\,|x|$ **41.** 1.15

Test Yourself, page 113

1.

3.

5. 1.10, 0.79

7.

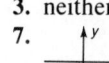 $m_{\overline{PQ}} = -\frac{2}{3}; \ m_{\overline{PR}} = \frac{3}{2};$

$\overline{PQ}$ and $\overline{PR}$ are perpendicular.

Summary and Review, pages 114–115

1. y-axis   **3.** neither

5.

7.

9.

11.

13. $\pm 1, \ \pm\frac{\sqrt{3}}{2}$

15.

17.

$f(x) = 3(x + 1)^2 - 5$

19. $\frac{3}{2}, \ \frac{-3 \pm 3i\sqrt{3}}{4}$ **21.** $\pm 2.8, \ \pm 2.2$

23.

No. $d_{PQ} = 7$;
$d_{QR} = \sqrt{17}$;
$d_{RP} = \sqrt{52}$
25. 2.60

Chapter 3 Trigonometric Functions

Practice Exercises, pages 123–125

1. $-225°$ **3.** $280°$ **5.** $-108°$ **7.** III

9. III   **11.** origin   **13.** $y = \frac{5}{3}x + \frac{31}{6}$

15. $-5.17°$ **17.** $-48.00°$ **19.** $20°6'36''$

21. $-10°19'48''$ **23.** $5400°$

25.   **27.** III
29. $135°; 315°$
31. $\dfrac{1 \pm \sqrt{97}}{6}$

33. $-\dfrac{1}{3}, \ \pm i\sqrt{5}$

35. $\sqrt{89}$ **37.** $570°$ **39.** $60°, 180°, 300°$
41. $80.79°$ **43.** $51,600°$ **45.** $99,450°$ **47.** $7.5°$

Practice Exercises, pages 130–132

1. $\dfrac{2\pi}{3}$ **3.** $-\dfrac{83\pi}{36}$ **5.** $\dfrac{17\pi}{120}$ **7.** $202.5°$

9. $-280°$ **11.** $432°$ **13.** $-401.1°$ **15.** 8 cm

17. 1.5 m   **19.** I   **21.** $f(t) = \dfrac{180t}{\pi}$ **23.** 1.3

25. 2.6   **27.** 24.7 cm   **29.** 0.7 cm   **31.** $4 \leq$
$x \leq 29$ **33.** $0.6 \ cm^2$ **35.** $15.7 \ cm^2$ **37.** 2
39. $\{z \in \mathcal{R} : |z| > \sqrt{5}\}$ **41.** 5555.6 rad

43. 3.2 m   **45.** 679.3 mi   **47.** $\dfrac{3\pi}{2}$

Practice Exercises, pages 137–140

1. 2.46π **3.** 12.99 rad/s   **5.** 0.16 rad/s

7. $\dfrac{19\pi}{45}$ **9.** 1441.9 rpm   **11.** $143.2°$

13. 4.55π m/s   **15.** 211.6 cm/s   **17.** 32.2 m/s
18. $-0.35; 0.60; 4.74$ **19.** 1.68π cm/s

21. $\dfrac{25\pi}{9}$ cm/s   **23.** $\dfrac{65\pi}{12}$ cm/s   **25.** 104.7 rad/s

27. 1.28 cm/s   **29.** $(-4, 0), (0, 0)$;
$(-4, -8), (0, -8); (-2, -2), (-2, -6)$
31. $\omega = 9.42$ rad/s; $V = 131.9$ in./s
33. Answers may vary. Examples:
$x^2 + 2x + 1 = 0; x^2 + 4x + 2 = 0$;
$x^2 + 5 = 0$ **39.** 35.1 mi/h to 62.3 mi/h
41. $V = 1920\pi$ cm/min; $\omega = 48\pi$ rad/min
43. 17,223 mi/h   **45.** 1102 mi/h   **47.** 1.9 m/s
49. 88.42 rpm

Practice Exercises, pages 145–146

1. $\cos \dfrac{3\pi}{2} = 0; \sin \dfrac{3\pi}{2} = -1; \cos 6\pi = 1$;

$\sin 6\pi = 0$ **3.** $\dfrac{7\pi}{4}$ **5.** +   **7.** +   **9.** +

11. $\frac{2\sqrt{5}}{5}$; $-\frac{\sqrt{5}}{5}$ **13.** $\frac{25\sqrt{641}}{641}$; $-\frac{4\sqrt{641}}{641}$

15. $\frac{\sqrt{101}}{101}$; $-\frac{10\sqrt{101}}{101}$ **17.** $-\frac{60}{61}$; $-\frac{11}{61}$

19. $-\frac{\sqrt{7}}{4}$ **21.** 10.625 ft **23.** $y = \frac{5}{3}x$

25. I, II **27.** II, III **29.** I, III **31.** I

35. 0.19 **37.** $y = -\frac{2}{\pi}x + 2$ **39.** 54 mi/h

41. $\left(-\frac{\sqrt{2}}{2}, \frac{\sqrt{2}}{2}\right)$; $\left(-\frac{\sqrt{2}}{2}, -\frac{\sqrt{2}}{2}\right)$; $\left(\frac{\sqrt{2}}{2}, -\frac{\sqrt{2}}{2}\right)$

43. $-1, 0, 1$; $-1 \le \sin\theta \le 1$ **45.** decreases from 0 to -1 **47.** decreases from 1 to 0

49. $\frac{3\pi}{4}, \frac{7\pi}{4}$

Practice Exercises, pages 150–151

1. $\sin\theta = -\frac{\sqrt{2}}{2}$; $\csc\theta = -\sqrt{2}$; $\cos\theta = \frac{\sqrt{2}}{2}$; $\sec\theta = \sqrt{2}$; $\tan\theta = -1$; $\cot\theta = -1$

3. $\sin\theta = \frac{5\sqrt{41}}{41}$; $\csc\theta = \frac{\sqrt{41}}{5}$; $\cos\theta = -\frac{4\sqrt{41}}{41}$; $\sec\theta = -\frac{\sqrt{41}}{4}$; $\tan\theta = -\frac{5}{4}$; $\cot\theta = -\frac{4}{5}$

5. $\sin\theta = -\frac{5\sqrt{29}}{29}$; $\csc\theta = -\frac{\sqrt{29}}{5}$; $\cos\theta = \frac{2\sqrt{29}}{29}$; $\sec\theta = \frac{\sqrt{29}}{2}$; $\tan\theta = -\frac{5}{2}$; $\cot\theta = -\frac{2}{5}$

7. $\frac{4.84\pi}{9}$ m² **9.** $-\frac{20}{59}$ **11.** $\frac{2}{11}$ **13.** $\frac{4}{3\pi}$ **15.** II, IV **17.** 70.05 ft **19.** $\cos\theta = \frac{3}{5}$; $\tan\theta = -\frac{4}{3}$; $\csc\theta = -\frac{5}{4}$; $\sec\theta = \frac{5}{3}$; $\cot\theta = -\frac{3}{4}$

21. $\sin\phi = -\frac{5}{8}$; $\cos\phi = -\frac{\sqrt{39}}{8}$; $\tan\phi = \frac{5\sqrt{39}}{39}$; $\sec\phi = -\frac{8\sqrt{39}}{39}$; $\cot\phi = \frac{\sqrt{39}}{5}$

23. $\tan\theta = -\frac{3}{2}$; $\csc\theta = -\frac{\sqrt{13}}{3}$; $\sec\theta = \frac{\sqrt{13}}{2}$; $\cot\theta = -\frac{2}{3}$ **25.** $\tan\theta$ is undefined; $\csc\theta = -1$; $\sec\theta$ is undefined; $\cot\theta = 0$

27. $\sin\theta = -\frac{4\sqrt{17}}{17}$; $\cos\theta = -\frac{\sqrt{17}}{17}$; $\tan\theta = 4$; $\csc\theta = -\frac{\sqrt{17}}{4}$; $\sec\theta = -\sqrt{17}$

29. $\sin\theta = \frac{8}{17}$; $\cos\theta = -\frac{15}{17}$; $\csc\theta = \frac{17}{8}$; $\sec\theta = -\frac{17}{15}$; $\cot\theta = -\frac{15}{8}$ **31.** $\{\theta \in \mathcal{R} : \theta \ne$

$k\pi, k \in Z\}$ **33.** $\sec 0 = \sec 2\pi = 1$; $\csc\frac{\pi}{2} = $

$\csc\frac{5\pi}{2} = 1$ **35.** $f(g(x)) = \frac{\sqrt{1-x^2}}{|x|}$;

$g(f(x)) = \frac{\sqrt{x^2-1}}{x^2-1}$ **37.** 31.4 ft/min

39. $\{y \in \mathcal{R} : |y| \ge 1\}$ **43.** $\frac{1}{2}$ **45.** $-\frac{1}{2}$

47. $\cos\theta = \frac{\sqrt{3}}{2}$; $\cos(\theta + 2\pi) = \frac{\sqrt{3}}{2}$; $\cos(-\theta) = \frac{\sqrt{3}}{2}$; $\cos(\theta + \pi) = -\frac{\sqrt{3}}{2}$;

$\cos(\theta - \pi) = -\frac{\sqrt{3}}{2}$

Test Yourself, page 151
1. 200° **3.** $(612 + 360k)°$, $k \in Z$; 252°
5. 330° **7.** 502.7 rad/s
9. $\cos\theta = -\frac{2\sqrt{13}}{13}$; $\sin\theta = \frac{3\sqrt{13}}{13}$

11. $\sin\theta = \frac{5}{13}$; $\cos\theta = -\frac{12}{13}$; $\tan\theta = \frac{-5}{12}$; $\cot\theta = -\frac{12}{5}$; $\sec\theta = -\frac{13}{12}$

Practice Exercises, pages 157–158
1. $\sin 2\pi = 0$; $\cos 2\pi = 1$; $\tan 2\pi = 0$; $\cot 2\pi$ is undefined; $\sec 2\pi = 1$; $\csc 2\pi$ is undefined.

3. 20° **5.** $\frac{3\pi}{8}$ **7.** 1.3 **9.** $-\frac{2\sqrt{6}}{7}$

11. $\sin 390° = \frac{1}{2}$; $\csc 390° = 2$; $\cos 390° = \frac{\sqrt{3}}{2}$; $\sec 390° = \frac{2\sqrt{3}}{3}$; $\tan 390° = \frac{\sqrt{3}}{3}$; $\cot 390° = \sqrt{3}$; **13.** $\sin(-135°) = -\frac{\sqrt{2}}{2}$; $\csc(-135°) = -\sqrt{2}$; $\cos(-135°) = -\frac{\sqrt{2}}{2}$; $\sec(-135°) = -\sqrt{2}$; $\tan(-135°) = 1$; $\cot(-135°) = 1$ **15.** $\sin\left(-\frac{7\pi}{4}\right) = \frac{\sqrt{2}}{2}$; $\csc\left(-\frac{7\pi}{4}\right) = \sqrt{2}$; $\cos\left(-\frac{7\pi}{4}\right) = \frac{\sqrt{2}}{2}$; $\sec\left(-\frac{7\pi}{4}\right) = \sqrt{2}$; $\tan\left(-\frac{7\pi}{4}\right) = 1$; $\cot\left(-\frac{7\pi}{4}\right) = 1$ **17.** $\sin\frac{5\pi}{6} = \frac{1}{2}$; $\csc\frac{5\pi}{6} = 2$; $\cos\frac{5\pi}{6} = -\frac{\sqrt{3}}{2}$; $\sec\frac{5\pi}{6} = -\frac{2\sqrt{3}}{3}$; $\tan\frac{5\pi}{6} = -\frac{\sqrt{3}}{3}$; $\cot\frac{5\pi}{6} = -\sqrt{3}$

19. 1.22; -0.98 **21.** 2 ft^2 **23.** $\left\{t \in \mathcal{R} \mid t \neq \right.$

$\left. \frac{3\pi}{2} + 2k\pi, k \in \mathbb{Z}\right\}$ **25.** $\frac{\pi}{4}; \frac{5\pi}{4}$ **27.** $\frac{\pi}{4}; \frac{3\pi}{4}$

29. $\frac{\pi}{6}; \frac{7\pi}{6}$ **31.** $0; \pi$ **33.** $0; \pi$

35. $\{y \in \mathcal{R} : 0 \leq y \leq 2\}$ **37.** $5x - 8y +$

$\left(8 - \frac{5\pi}{4}\right) = 0$ **39.** 14.3 mi/h   **41.** $\frac{1}{3}$

43. $\frac{7\pi}{4}; \frac{15\pi}{4}$ **45.** 330°   **49.** $\sqrt{2}$ or 1.414

Practice Exercises, pages 163–165
1. -0.9563 **3.** 0.7977   **5.** 1.0515

7. -0.7265 **9.** 0.5354   **11.** -0.9898 **13.** $\frac{1}{2}$;

undefined   **15.** 120.2°; 239.8°   **17.** 0.95; 2.19

19. 2.88; 6.02   **21.** $\frac{\pi}{4}; \frac{5\pi}{4}$ **23.** 25.8°; 334.2°

25. 23.6°; 156.4°   **27.** 1.04; 4.18
29. $(241.8 + 360k)°, k \in \mathbb{Z}$ **31.** $-1 < x < 5$

33. -1 **35.** -1 **37.** 6; 9   **39.** $\theta = \frac{\pi}{2}$

41. 9.80675 m/s^2 **43.** 9.80975 m/s^2

Practice Exercises, pages 169–170

1. $\cot \theta = \frac{y}{x}$; $\tan \theta = \frac{x}{y}$; $\cot \theta \cdot \tan \theta =$

$\frac{y}{x} \cdot \frac{x}{y} = 1$ **3.** $1 + (-1)^2 = (\sqrt{2})^2$ **5.** $\frac{1}{2} = \frac{1}{2}$

7. $1^2 + 0^2 = 1$ **9.** $2 = \frac{1}{\frac{1}{2}} = 1 \cdot \frac{2}{1} = 2$

11. 2.5 m   **13.** $(-1.9416)^2 = 1 + (1.6643)^2 =$
3.7698   **15.** $-0.3869 = -\frac{0.3609}{0.9326}$ **17.** $0.2675 =$
0.2675   **19.** $1.0485 = 1.0485$ **21.** 132 lb;
kg = 2.2 lb; lb = 0.45 kg   **23.** 5.84 cm
25. $g(-x) = (-x)^3 - (-x) = -x^3 + x =$
$-(x^3 - x) = -g(x)$ **27.** $h(-x) = (-x)^2 +$
$(-x) + 1 = x^2 - x + 1$. Therefore, $h(-x) \neq$
$h(x)$. $-h(x) = -(x^2 + x + 1) = -x^2 - x - 1$.
Therefore, $h(-x) \neq -h(x)$ **31.** $\sin \beta$

33. $\frac{1}{\cos \phi}$ **35.** $\frac{1}{\cos^4 \theta}$ **37.** $\frac{1}{\cos \theta}$ **39.** -1.3812

40. 6 s   **41.** 1.0164   **43.** $\frac{2}{\sin \theta}$ **45.** $0, \pi$

Practice Exercises, pages 174–175

1. $\sin \theta \cdot \frac{1}{\sin \theta} = 1$ **3.** $\frac{1}{1 - \sin \theta} + \frac{1}{1 + \sin \theta} =$

$\frac{1 + \sin \theta + 1 - \sin \theta}{(1 - \sin \theta)(1 + \sin \theta)} = \frac{2}{1 - \sin^2 \theta} = \frac{2}{\cos^2 \theta} = 2 \sec^2 \theta$
5. $(\csc \theta + 1)(\csc \theta - 1) = \csc^2 \theta - 1 =$

$\cot^2 \theta$ **7.** $\cot^2 \theta + \sec^2 \theta - \tan^2 \theta = \cot^2 \theta +$
$1 = \csc^2 \theta$ **9.** $\cos \phi (\sec \phi - \cos \phi) = \cos \phi$
$\sec \phi - \cos^2 \phi = 1 - \cos^2 \phi = \sin^2 \phi$
11. 0.6479   **13.** 0.50 rad/min   **14.** 0.20
mi/min = 12.06 mi/h   **15.** $8|\sin \alpha|$
17. $10|\cot \theta|$ **19.** $\sec^2 \theta$ **21.** $2 \tan \theta$

23. 12° or $\frac{\pi}{15}$ **25.** $\theta = \pi$ and $\beta = \frac{\pi}{6}$;

$\cos \left(\pi - \frac{\pi}{6}\right) = -\frac{\sqrt{3}}{2}$; $\cos \pi - \cos \frac{\pi}{6} =$

$-1 - \frac{\sqrt{3}}{2}$ **27.** $\phi = \frac{\pi}{3}$; $\frac{1}{2} \sec \frac{\pi}{3} = 1$; $\sec \frac{\pi}{6} =$

$\frac{2\sqrt{3}}{3}$ **29.** $\theta = \frac{\pi}{4}$; $\sqrt{1 - \sin^2 \frac{\pi}{4}} = \frac{\sqrt{2}}{2}$;

$-\cos \frac{\pi}{4} = -\frac{\sqrt{2}}{2}$ **31.** $F^{-1}(t) = \frac{t^3 + 1}{5}$

Test Yourself, page 175

1. 70°   **3.** $\frac{\pi}{5}$ **5.** $\sin 420° = \frac{\sqrt{3}}{2}$; $\cos 420° = \frac{1}{2}$;

$\tan 420° = \sqrt{3}$; $\cot 420° = \frac{\sqrt{3}}{3}$; $\sec 420° = 2$;

$\csc 420° = \frac{2\sqrt{3}}{3}$ **7.** -1.1357 **9.** -2.7475

11. 46.4°; 226.4°   **13.** $\sin^2 \left(-\frac{\pi}{4}\right) + \cos^2 \left(-\frac{\pi}{4}\right) =$

$\left(-\frac{\sqrt{2}}{2}\right)^2 + \left(\frac{\sqrt{2}}{2}\right)^2 = \frac{1}{2} + \frac{1}{2} = 1$ **15.** $1 - \frac{1}{\csc^2 \phi} =$
$1 - \sin^2 \phi = \cos^2 \phi$

Summary and Review, pages 176–177
1. $-60°$ **3.** 72.26°   **5.** $-585°$ **7.** 0.13 rad/s;
12.57 ft/s   **9.** $\sin \theta = -\frac{15}{17}$; $\tan \theta = \frac{15}{8}$;

$\cot \theta = \frac{8}{15}$; $\sec \theta = -\frac{17}{8}$; $\csc \theta = -\frac{17}{15}$

11. $\sin \left(\frac{5\pi}{3}\right) = -\frac{\sqrt{3}}{2}$; $\cos \left(\frac{5\pi}{3}\right) = \frac{1}{2}$;

$\tan \left(\frac{5\pi}{3}\right) = -\sqrt{3}$; $\cot \left(\frac{5\pi}{3}\right) = -\frac{\sqrt{3}}{3}$;

$\sec \left(\frac{5\pi}{3}\right) = 2$; $\csc \left(\frac{5\pi}{3}\right) = -\frac{2\sqrt{3}}{3}$ **13.** 164.9°;

344.9°   **15.** $\cot \frac{\pi}{4} = \frac{\cos \frac{\pi}{4}}{\sin \frac{\pi}{4}}$; $1 = \frac{\frac{\sqrt{2}}{2}}{\frac{\sqrt{2}}{2}}$; $1 = 1$

17. $\cos^2 \theta \tan \theta \cdot \cot \theta =$
$\cos^2 \theta \tan \theta \cdot \frac{1}{\tan \theta} = \cos^2 \theta = 1 - \sin^2 \theta$

Chapter 4   Graphs and Inverses of Trigonometric Functions

Practice Exercises, pages 187–189

1. yes; 20   **3.** no

5.

shifted 0.5 units down

7.

9.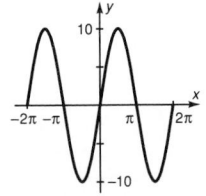

dilated 10 units
vertically

11.

17. 6, 8, 13   **19.** 7068.58 ft²   **21.** $\cos \frac{\pi}{26}$

23. sin 7.7°   **25.** Since sin x is an odd function,

$\sin \left(\frac{\pi}{2} - x\right) = -\sin \left(x - \frac{\pi}{2}\right)$. When graphed, this

will give a sine graph shifted $\frac{\pi}{2}$ units left, which

is the graph of cos x.   **27.** $\left[-\frac{1}{2}, \frac{1}{2}\right]$ **29.** 2

39. $\left[-\frac{3}{2}, -\frac{1}{2}\right]$ **41.** 1036.73 mi/h

Practice Exercises, pages 196–199

1. 7.5   **3.** 2000   **5.** $-\frac{\sqrt{13}}{7}$ **7.** 8π   **9.** $\frac{5\pi}{2}$

11. 200π; 75   **13.** 0.299π; $3\sqrt{3}$ **15.** 15

19. $f(x) = 2 \sin \frac{1}{2}\left(x - \frac{\pi}{2}\right)$ **21.** $f(x) = 5 \sin 2x$

23. $h(x) = \sin \frac{x}{2} + 1$ **24.** $y = \frac{6}{11}x + 3$

25. even

35.

37. $\left\{\theta: \theta \neq \left(\frac{2k+1}{2}\right)\pi,\right.$
$\left. k \in Z\right\}$

39. $f(x) = -|x|$
41. $h(x) = -\sin 3x$
43. 0.001; $\frac{1}{440}$; 440

Practice Exercises, pages 205–207

1. 4π   **3.** $\frac{\pi}{5}$ **5.** $\frac{2\pi}{3}$ **7.** $\frac{5}{3}(2k + 1)\pi, k \in Z$

9. $\left[\frac{1}{4139} \text{ s}, \frac{1}{27} \text{ s}\right]$ **17.** $\frac{\pi}{3}; \frac{\pi}{4}$ left; 0; example:

$x = -\frac{\pi}{12}, x = \frac{\pi}{4}$ **21.** $f(x) = \tan \frac{1}{2}x + 2$

25. yes; They are all the same distance from the
center.   **27.** $y = \csc x - 1$ **29.** $(-2\pi, -\pi)$,
$(0, \pi); (-\pi, 0), (\pi, 2\pi)$ **33.** $D = \{x: x \geq 0\}$;
$R = \{f(x): f(x) \geq -1\}$ **41.** neither   **43.** even
45. π

Practice Exercises, pages 211–213

1. $\left\{x: x \neq 0, x \neq \left(\frac{2k+1}{2}\right)\pi, k \in Z\right\}$ **3.** all real

numbers   **13.** 2π   **15.** 2π   **17.** $0 + \cos 0 \neq$
$2\pi + \cos 2\pi, 1 \neq 2\pi + 1$

19. $3 \cos \left[\frac{1}{2}(0) - \frac{1}{4}\pi\right] \neq 3 \cos \left[\frac{1}{2}(2\pi) - \frac{1}{4}\pi\right]$,

$3 \cos \left(-\frac{1}{4}\pi\right) \neq 3 \cos \left(\frac{3}{4}\pi\right)$ **21.** purse: $120;

scarf: $40; book: $20   **23.** Heidi: 10 km;
Gretchen: 6 km   **25.** 2π   **27.** 4π

29. 4π   **31.** 12π   **33.** $\frac{1}{120}; \frac{1}{150}; \frac{1}{30}$

35. Let $P(x, y)$ be on the terminal side of angle t
in standard position, and let $r = \sqrt{x^2 + y^2}$. Then
$Q(-x, -y)$ is on the terminal side of $t - \pi$ and
$\sin (t - \pi) = \frac{y}{r} = -\sin t$.   **37.** 50

Test Yourself, page 213

1.

3.

amp: 3, per: π;
phase shift: π right
vertical shift:
1 down

5.

9. 2π

Practice Exercises, pages 220–221

1. $\frac{\pi}{3}$ **3.** $\frac{\pi}{3}$ **5.** 0.9991 **7.** 282.6799

9. -0.0505 **11.** 61.8° **15.** 0.67π **17.** $\frac{\sqrt{2}}{2}$

19. $y = -4.64x + 4.64$ **25.** 10.71 mi/h **27.** 40°

29. 0 **31.** $\frac{2\sqrt{2}}{3}$ **35.** 0.8660 **37.** $\frac{\sqrt[3]{25x + 300}}{5}$

39. $t = \frac{35}{\pi} \cos^{-1}\left(\frac{y - 1050}{100}\right)$ **41.** $-\frac{\sqrt{2}}{2}$ **43.** $\frac{\pi}{2}$

45. $\frac{\sqrt{2}}{2}$ **47.** Arccos (1) = 0; Arccos (−1) = π

Practice Exercises, pages 226–228

1. $\frac{\pi}{4}$ **3.** $\frac{\pi}{4}$ **5.** 1.4675 **7.** 0.0667 **9.** 61.5°

11. 102.8° **13.** 0.8 **15.** $\frac{\sqrt{2}}{2}$

17. $-\frac{3\sqrt{13}}{13}$ **19.** $4118.36 **21.** $\frac{t\sqrt{1 + t^2}}{1 + t^2}$

27.   **29.** $\left(\frac{\pi}{2}, \frac{3\pi}{2}\right)$

33. 77.3°

37. $\frac{\pi}{12}$

39. $y = \frac{\sqrt{1 + u^2}}{1 + u^2}$

45. 31° **47.** $Z = \frac{7\sqrt{x^2 + 49}}{x^2 + 49}$ **49.** $g^{-1}(t) =$ $\cos^{-1}(1 - t)$; $0 \le g^{-1}(t) \le \pi$; $0 \le t \le 2$; If $t = \frac{\pi}{3}$, then $g(t) = 1 - \cos\frac{\pi}{3} = 0.5$. If $g(t) = 0.5$, then $g^{-1}(t) = \cos^{-1}(1 - 0.5) = \frac{\pi}{3}$.

51. $\frac{5\sqrt{25 - v^2}}{25 - v^2}$

Practice Exercises, pages 233–236

1. 30; $\frac{1}{60}$; 60 **3.** 24; 2π; $\frac{1}{2\pi}$ **5.** 5; $\frac{1}{60}$; 60

7. 3.8; $\frac{1}{20}$; 20 **9.** $y = 1.5 \sin 528\pi t$ **11.** 284

13. 2.5; $\frac{4\pi}{3}$; $\frac{3}{4\pi}$; $y = 2.5 \cos\frac{3}{2}t$

15.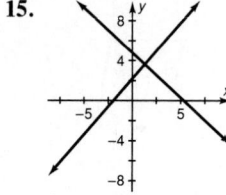
$9x + 10y = 48$

17.
$y = -10.4 \cos\frac{\pi}{2}t$

21. $y = \frac{6}{\pi} \cos^{-1}\left(\frac{t}{4}\right)$ **25.** $y = 12 \sin \pi t$

27. $y = 6 \sin\frac{\pi}{2}t$ **29.** 3.1 **31.** Since $f(x)$ is never decreasing, then it must be one-to-one. The inverse of $f(x)$ is $f^{-1}(x) = \sqrt[3]{\frac{x}{5}} + 7.1$.

33. $y = 0.35 \sin 0.37\pi t + 4$ **35.** $y = 10 \sin\frac{20\pi}{9}\left(t - \frac{3}{40}\right)$ **37.** $y = 2 \sin 3t$ **39.** $y = 2.1 \cos\frac{\pi}{6}t$

Test Yourself, page 236

1. $\frac{\pi}{6}$ **3.** $\frac{3\pi}{4}$

5.

7. $-\frac{\pi}{4}$

9. $\frac{\pi}{6}$

11. $y = \frac{\sqrt{1 + t^2}}{1 + t^2}$

Summary and Review, pages 237–238

1.

3.

5.

7.

9.

11. $-\frac{\pi}{6}$

13. $\frac{\pi}{6}$

15. 2.4189

19. 1.3467

21. 1.4289

23.

25. $\frac{5\sqrt{119}}{119}$

Chapter 5 Applications of Trigonometry

Practice Exercises, pages 248–250

1. $\angle B = 71°$; $a = 4$; $c = 13$ **3.** $\angle A = 52°$;
$a = 33$ **5.** $\angle A = 38°$; $\angle C = 104°$; $c = 28$
7. $\angle A = 20°$; $b = 98.9$; $c = 105.3$ **9.** $\angle A = 58°$; $a = 288.3$; $b = 180.2$ **11.** $\angle A = 73.7°$;
$\angle B = 16.3°$; $a = 24$ **13.** 4.5 **15.** 16.7°
17. 1 ft **19.** −8.9 **21.** 3 ft **23.** 60th
parallel **25.** 18°; 72°; 162° **27.** $\angle BAR = 30°$;
$\angle RAD = 32°$; $\angle ABR = 92°$; $\angle RBC = 38°$;
$\angle BCR = 20°$; $\angle RCD = 95°$; $\angle CDR = 27°$;
$\angle RDA = 26°$; $\angle ARB = \angle DRC = 58°$; $\angle BRS = \angle DRA = 122°$

29.

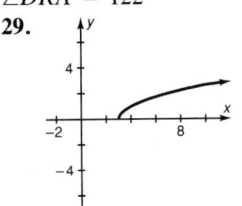

31. 28.2 cm
33. 16,604 ft
35.

37. 56 ft **39.** 166 in. **41.** 14 in. **43.** yes

Practice Exercises, pages 254–256

1. $b = 157$ **3.** $b = 138$ **5.** $a = 32$
7. $c = 289$ **9.** $c = 102$ **11.** $\angle C = 52°$; $a = 60$; $c = 58$ **13.** $\angle C = 84°$; $b = 33$; $c = 55$
15. $\angle B = 30°$; $a = 31$; $c = 8$ **17.** $\angle C = 32°$;
$a = 165$; $b = 121$ **19.** odd **23.** not a
triangle. The sum of the measures of the angles
is > 180°.

25.

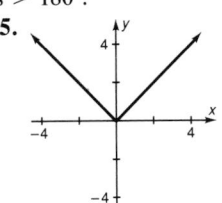

27. 57 ft
29. 1206 ft
31. 2989 ft

33. $\sin \alpha = \frac{5\sqrt{61}}{61}$; $\cos \alpha = \frac{6\sqrt{61}}{61}$; $\tan \alpha = \frac{5}{6}$;

$\csc \alpha = \frac{\sqrt{61}}{5}$; $\sec \alpha = \frac{\sqrt{61}}{6}$; $\cot \alpha = \frac{6}{5}$

41. 126° **43.** 10.6 ft **45.** 1148 ft **47.** 396 m

Practice Exercises, pages 261–263

1. one **3.** none **5.** two **7.** none **9.** one
11. two **13.** π **15.** two solutions: $\angle E = 69°$;
$\angle F = 58°$; $f = 37$ or $\angle E = 111°$; $\angle F = 16°$;
$f = 12$ **17.** $\angle Q = 41°$; $\angle R = 64°$; $q = 28$

19. two solutions: $\angle K = 77.3°$; $\angle M = 58.5°$;
$k = 27.0$ or $\angle K = 14.3°$; $\angle M = 121.5°$; $k = 6.8$ **21.** 3 **23.** yes **25.** 48 cm

27.

29. $\angle A = 21°$; $\angle C = 111°$; $a = 8.6$
31. $\angle B = 77°$; $\angle C = 60°$; $b = 19.1$
33. 38 ft **35.** 409 ft

37. 2483 ft **39.** 100°

Test Yourself, page 263

1. $\angle A = 22°$; $b = 91.6$; $c = 98.8$ **3.** $\angle B = 59°$; $a = 160.7$; $b = 267.4$ **5.** 17.0 cm
7. 107 ft **9.** $\angle C = 37°$; $a = 54$; $b = 26$
11. two **13.** $\angle B = 46.8°$; $\angle C = 93.2°$; $c = 116.5$ or $\angle B = 133.2°$; $\angle C = 6.8°$; $c = 13.8$

Practice Exercises, pages 269–271

1. $\angle A = 45°$; $\angle B = 56°$; $c = 34$ **3.** $\angle B = 38°$; $\angle C = 100°$; $a = 13$ **5.** $\angle Q = 57°$; $\angle R = 89°$; $p = 48$ **7.** $\angle A = 23°$; $\angle B = 27°$; $\angle C = 130°$ **9.** $\angle L = 52°$; $\angle M = 72°$; $k = 3.6$

11. $-\frac{11}{15}$ **13.** -67 **17.** 366.1 ft

19. $-\frac{\pi}{2} \le x \le \frac{\pi}{2}$ **21.** 512 ft **23.** $x = \pi$

25. 2331 mi **27.** 28° **29.** 1394 mi **31.** 28 ft
33. 837 yd **35.** 369 lb **37.** 112 mi
39. $\angle A = 72°$; $\angle B = 62°$

Practice Exercises, pages 276–279

1. 111 **3.** 621 **5.** 313 **7.** 2524 **9.** 22.5
11. 235 **13.** not an identity **15.** 8.3
17. 8.0 **19.** 0.8 rad **21.** $\sqrt{2}$ **23.** csc A
27. 58.2 in. **29.** 1115 **31.** 182.45 ft^2
33. 324.98 cm^2 **35.** 69 ft^2 **37.** 737 cm^2
39. 4 **41.** 15 **45.** 3937.60 in.^{2} **47.** 385.7 yd^2
49. 26 **51.** 37 **53.** 88

Test Yourself, page 279

1. $\angle A = 45°$; $\angle B = 57°$; $\angle C = 78°$ **3.** $\angle A = 96°$; $\angle B = 36°$; $c = 40$ **5.** 133 cm^2 **7.** 71 cm^2

Summary and Review, pages 280–281

1. $\angle A = 36°$; $b = 231$; $c = 286$ **3.** 25.3 cm
5. $b = 31$; $c = 34$; $\angle C = 61°$ **7.** one
9. none **11.** two **13.** $\angle A = 57.5°$; $\angle B = 88.3°$; $\angle C = 34.2°$ **15.** 538 mi **17.** 140
19. 185
21. 393 in.^{2}

Chapter 6   Sum and Difference Identities

Practice Exercises, pages 290–292

1. $\sin \dfrac{7\pi}{6}$ **3.** $\cos \dfrac{31\pi}{24}$ **5.** $\tan 57°$ **7.** 220 ft^2

9. false   **11.** true   **13.** false   **15.** 6.3 mi

17. $\dfrac{\sqrt{2} - \sqrt{6}}{4}$ **19.** $\dfrac{-\sqrt{2} + \sqrt{6}}{4}$ **21.** 1   **23.** $-\dfrac{56}{65}$

25. $-\dfrac{63}{65}$ **27.** $-\dfrac{16}{63}$ **29.** $2x - 7y = 0$ **31.** $\dfrac{87}{425}$

33. $-\dfrac{416}{87}$ **35.** $-\dfrac{304}{425}$ **39.** $\dfrac{\sqrt{2} + \sqrt{6}}{4}$ **41.** $2 +$

$\sqrt{3}$ **43.** $\dfrac{-\sqrt{6} + \sqrt{2}}{4}$ **45.** decreases by 3°

46. $d = 1 \text{ m}, w = 3 \text{ m}, \ell = 5 \text{ m}$ **47.** 24°

48. $f^{-1}(x) = \dfrac{x - 5}{3}$; function   **49.** $\dfrac{99}{\sqrt{10,642}}$

Practice Exercises, pages 295–296

1. yes   **3.** yes   **5.** no   **7.** no   **9.** no   **11.** yes
13. no   **15.** no   **17.** yes   **19.** 176   **21.** $940
22. 19.7 ft   **25.** yes   **27.** no   **29.** yes
31. yes   **33.** no   **35.** no   **37.** 127.3 ft

38. $8; \dfrac{1}{40}; 40$ **39.** no   **41.** yes   **43.** yes

45. yes   **47.** yes

Practice Exercises, pages 302–305

1. $\dfrac{\sqrt{2 + \sqrt{3}}}{2}$ **3.** $-\dfrac{\sqrt{2 + \sqrt{2}}}{2}$ **5.** $\sqrt{2} + 1$

7. $-\dfrac{7}{18}$ **9.** $-\dfrac{120}{169}$ **11.** $\dfrac{2\sqrt{5}}{5}$ **13.** -2 **15.** $-\dfrac{1}{5}$

17. $-\dfrac{\sqrt{2 + \sqrt{2}}}{2}$ **19.** $\dfrac{3\sqrt{10}}{10}$ **21.** $\dfrac{5}{8}$ **23.** 1353

25. $2\sqrt{82}$ **27.** 3.9   **29.** yes   **31.** no   **33.** $\cos 2\beta = \cos^2 \beta - \sin^2 \beta = \cos^2 \beta - (1 - \cos^2 \beta) =$

$2 \cos^2 \beta - 1$ **35.** $\tan \dfrac{\alpha}{2} = \dfrac{\sin \dfrac{\alpha}{2}}{\cos \dfrac{\alpha}{2}} = \dfrac{\pm\sqrt{\dfrac{1 - \cos \alpha}{2}}}{\pm\sqrt{\dfrac{1 + \cos \alpha}{2}}} =$

$\pm\sqrt{\dfrac{1 - \cos \alpha}{1 + \cos \alpha}}$ **37.** $\tan \dfrac{\beta}{2} = \pm\sqrt{\dfrac{1 - \cos \beta}{1 + \cos \beta}} \cdot$

$\sqrt{\dfrac{1 - \cos \beta}{1 - \cos \beta}} = \pm\sqrt{\dfrac{(1 - \cos \beta)^2}{1 + \cos^2 \beta}} = \dfrac{1 - \cos \beta}{\pm\sqrt{\sin^2 \beta}} =$

$\dfrac{1 - \cos \beta}{\sin \beta}$ **41.** $\sin 4\alpha = \sin 2(2\alpha) =$

$2 \sin 2\alpha \cos 2\alpha$ **44.** complex   **45.** 38.7 ft

46. $\left(\dfrac{\cos \alpha + \cos \beta}{2}, \dfrac{\sin \alpha + \sin \beta}{2}\right)$ **47.** $3.1\ s$

49. $1.2\ s$ **55.** $\dfrac{\sqrt{10}}{10}$ **57.** $-\dfrac{\sqrt{3}}{3}$

Test Yourself, page 305

1. $2 + \sqrt{3}$ **3.** $-\dfrac{16}{65}$ **5.** yes   **7.** no   **9.** $-\dfrac{7}{25}$

11. $\dfrac{\cot \alpha - \tan \alpha}{\cot \alpha + \tan \alpha} = \dfrac{\dfrac{\cos \alpha}{\sin \alpha} - \dfrac{\sin \alpha}{\cos \alpha}}{\dfrac{\cos \alpha}{\sin \alpha} + \dfrac{\sin \alpha}{\cos \alpha}} \cdot \dfrac{\sin \alpha \cos \alpha}{\sin \alpha \cos \alpha} =$

$\dfrac{\cos^2 \alpha - \sin^2 \alpha}{\cos^2 \alpha + \sin^2 \alpha} = \cos 2\alpha$

Practice Exercises, pages 309–310

1. $\cos \dfrac{2\pi}{7} + \cos \dfrac{4\pi}{7}$ **3.** $\cos \dfrac{\pi}{6} - \cos \pi$

5. $\sin 118° + \sin 56°$ **7.** $\sin 170° - \sin 52°$

9. $ab^5 \sqrt[6]{32}$ **11.** $2 \cos \dfrac{4\pi}{11} \cos \dfrac{\pi}{11}$ **13.** $2 \sin 8.5$

$\cos 4.5$ **15.** $-2 \sin 49.5° \sin 24.5°$ **17.** $2 \cos$
$2.45 \sin 0.75$ **19.** 109   **21.** 37.4°   **23.** $0.04 \sin$
$990\pi x \cos 330\pi x$ **25.** 504 rpm   **34.** yes
35. yes   **36.** yes   **37.** yes

39. $\dfrac{2}{h} \sin \left(\dfrac{2x + h}{2}\right) \cos \dfrac{h}{2}$

41. $\dfrac{2}{h} \cos \left(\dfrac{2x + h}{2}\right) \cos \dfrac{h}{2}$ **43.** $\dfrac{\sin (2x + h)}{h \cos (x + h) \cos x}$

Practice Exercises, pages 314–316

1. $\dfrac{\pi}{3}, \dfrac{5\pi}{3}$ **3.** $\dfrac{\pi}{6}, \dfrac{5\pi}{6}$ **5.** $\dfrac{\pi}{4}, \dfrac{7\pi}{4}$ **7.** $\dfrac{5\pi}{6}, \dfrac{11\pi}{6}$ **9.** 0

11. 0.38, 2.76   **13.** 0, 2.82, π, 5.96   **15.** $\dfrac{\pi}{6}, \dfrac{\pi}{2}$,

$\dfrac{5\pi}{6}, \dfrac{3\pi}{2}$ **17.** $\angle A = 58°; b = 14.8; c = 27.1$

19. 3; π; π left; 1 down   **21.** $\dfrac{\pi}{2} < x < \dfrac{3\pi}{2}$

23. $\dfrac{\pi}{3} < x < \dfrac{2\pi}{3}$ **25.** neither; $f(-x) \neq f(x); f(-x) \neq$

$-f(x)$ **27.** $0, \dfrac{2\pi}{3}, \dfrac{4\pi}{3}$ **29.** $\dfrac{\pi}{12}, \dfrac{5\pi}{12}, \dfrac{13\pi}{12}, \dfrac{17\pi}{12}$

31. 0.12, 1.69, 3.26, 4.83   **33.** 9.05°   **35.** $2n\pi$,

$n \in Z$ **37.** $n\pi, \dfrac{\pi}{3} + 2n\pi, \dfrac{5\pi}{3} + 2n\pi, n \in Z$

39. $\left(\dfrac{2n - 1}{4}\right)\pi, n \in Z$ **41.** $\dfrac{\pi}{6} + n\pi, \dfrac{\pi}{2} + n\pi$,

$\dfrac{5\pi}{6} + n\pi, n \in Z$ **43.** $\dfrac{\pi}{9} + \dfrac{2n\pi}{3}, \dfrac{5\pi}{9} + \dfrac{2n\pi}{3}$,

$n \in Z$ **45.** $4x + 3y = 25$

Practice Exercises, pages 321–323

1. $\dfrac{3\pi}{2}$ **3.** $\dfrac{\pi}{3}, \dfrac{2\pi}{3}, \dfrac{4\pi}{3}, \dfrac{5\pi}{3}$ **5.** $\dfrac{7\pi}{6}, \dfrac{11\pi}{6}$ **7.** $\dfrac{\pi}{3}, \dfrac{5\pi}{3}$

9. $\dfrac{\pi}{6}, \dfrac{5\pi}{6}, \pi$ **11.** 1.23, 5.05   **13.** $\dfrac{\pi}{6}, \dfrac{\pi}{2}, \dfrac{5\pi}{6}, \dfrac{7\pi}{6}, \dfrac{3\pi}{2}$,

$\dfrac{11\pi}{6}$ **15.** 112π in./s   **17.** all real x **19.** $0 \leq x \leq$

0.64   **21.** 20 ml   **23.** $\dfrac{\pi}{6} + n\pi, \dfrac{5\pi}{6} + n\pi, n \in Z$

25. $\frac{\pi}{2} + n\pi$, $n \in Z$ **27.** no solution **29.** 1.83 + $n\pi$, $n \in Z$ **31.** 1.70 + $2n\pi$, 4.59 + $2n\pi$, $\frac{2\pi}{3}$ + $2n\pi$, $\frac{4\pi}{3}$ + $2n\pi$, $n \in Z$ **33.** The domains of both sine and cosine are all real numbers. The domains of tangent and secant do not include odd multiples of $\frac{\pi}{2}$, and the domains of cotangent and cosecant do not include multiples of π. **35.** 980.3451 cm/s² **38.** $\pm\frac{2\sqrt{5}}{5}$ **39.** $\frac{\pi}{6} \le x \le \frac{5\pi}{6}$ **41.** all real x **43.** $0 \le x \le \pi$ **45.** 0.06, 0.36, 1.11, 1.41, 2.16, 2.46, 3.21, 3.51, 4.25, 4.55, 5.30, 5.60 **47.** 1.17, 2.98, 4.31, 6.12

Test Yourself, page 323
1. $\cos\frac{\pi}{12} + \cos\frac{11\pi}{12}$ **3.** 2 cos 5.35 sin 1.85
5. 0.67, 5.61 **7.** 0.72, 5.56 **9.** $\frac{7\pi}{6}, \frac{11\pi}{6}$
11. $0 \le x \le 3.62$

Summary and Review, pages 324–325
1. $\frac{-\sqrt{6}-\sqrt{2}}{4}$ **3.** $-\frac{117}{125}$ **5.** $\sin\left(\frac{3\pi}{2}+\alpha\right) =$
$\sin\frac{3\pi}{2}\cos\alpha + \cos\frac{3\pi}{2}\sin\alpha = -1 \cdot \cos\alpha + 0 \cdot$
$\sin\alpha = -\cos\alpha$ **7.** no **9.** -2 **11.** $\cos\frac{\pi}{12} -$
$\cos\frac{7\pi}{12}$ **13.** 2 sin 2π cos $\frac{5\pi}{6}$ **15.** $\frac{\sin 2\alpha + \sin 6\alpha}{\sin 10\alpha - \sin 2\alpha} =$
$\frac{2\sin 4\alpha\cos(-2\alpha)}{2\cos 6\alpha\sin 4\alpha} = \frac{\cos(-2\alpha)}{\cos 6\alpha} = \frac{\cos 2\alpha}{\cos 6\alpha}$ **17.** $\frac{\pi}{3} <$
$x < \frac{5\pi}{3}$ **19.** $0 \le x < 1.16$

Chapter 7 Polynomial Functions

Practice Exercises, pages 334–336
1. $(3x - 4)x^2 + 7$ **3.** $((((2x + 3)x - 11)x - 15)x + 2)x + 6$ **5.** 120 ft² **7.** yes **9.** no
11. no **13.** -36 **15.** -6.684 **17.** $\frac{x^2}{2} +$
$\frac{9}{4}x + \frac{7}{8}$, $R = \frac{53}{8}$ **19.** $x(x + 3)(x + 2)$
21.

23. $(x - 2) \cdot (x^2 - 2x + 3)$, $R = 5$
25. $(x + 3) \cdot (x^3 - 5x + 15)$, $R = -36$

27. $(x - 1)(x^3 - x^2 - x)$, $R = -8$ **29.** $2x^3 + x^2 - \frac{1}{2}x - \frac{1}{4}$, $R = -\frac{5}{4}$ **31.** $3x^2 - \frac{13}{3}x + \frac{44}{9}$, $R = -\frac{70}{9}$ **33.** $x^2 - \frac{2}{3}x - \frac{1}{12}$, $R = \frac{1}{24}$
35. -2 **37.** 2 **39.** $f(n)$; $g(n)$ **41.** 3 h 50 min
45. 3 **47.** $-\frac{46}{7}$ **51.** $(x + 1)(x - 1)(x - 3)$
53. $2x^2 + 9$ **55.** -2 **57.** 0 **59.** -20

Practice Exercises, pages 340–342
1. 3 **3.** 4 **5.** 4 **7.** 4 (mult. 2) **9.** 0, 2, -1
11. 1 (mult. 3); -4 (mult. 2); 2 **13.** all real x, $x \ne 0$ **15.** even **17.** even **19.** neither
21. 1.11; 4.24 **23.** Let x represent the number of pens sold. $f(x) = 1500 + 0.35x$; $g(x) = 0.65x$
25. $f(x) = (x - 8)^2(x + 3)^3$ **31.** 0.8231; -0.8231 **33.** zeros: -3 (mult. 2), 0 (mult. 2); 3 relative extrema; $x^4 + 6x^3 + x^2 = x^2(x - 3)^2$
35. zeros: -2, 0, 1 (mult. 2); 3 relative extrema; $x^4 - 3x^2 + 2x = x(x + 2)(x - 1)^2$
37. zeros: -5, -2, -1, 1, 2; 4 relative extrema; $x^5 + 5x^4 - 5x^3 - 25x^2 + 4x + 20 = (x + 5)(x + 2)(x + 1)(x - 1)(x - 2)$ **39.** 7.3
45. $P(x) = 2(x + 2)(x - 1)(x - 3)$ **47.** $\frac{4\pi}{3}$
49. even **51.** even

Practice Exercises, pages 347–348
1. ± 1; ± 2; ± 3; ± 6 **3.** ± 1; ± 2; ± 5; ± 10
5. $-\frac{7\pi}{4}$ **7.** ± 1, ± 5, ± 25, $\pm\frac{1}{7}$, $\pm\frac{5}{7}$, $\pm\frac{25}{7}$
9. ± 1, ± 2, ± 4, ± 5, ± 10, ± 20, $\pm\frac{1}{3}$, $\pm\frac{2}{3}$, $\pm\frac{4}{3}$,
$\pm\frac{5}{3}$, $\pm\frac{10}{3}$, $\pm\frac{20}{3}$ **11.** $\frac{2\pi}{3} = 120°$; 2 **13.** 1; 2; 3
15. 1; ± 2.24 **17.** 2; -2 (mult. 2); 3 **19.** 1 + $\tan^2(-60°) = \sec^2(-60°)$, $1 + (-\sqrt{3})^2 = 2^2$, $4 = 4$ **21.** $-\frac{4}{5}$, 1; $\frac{3}{2}$ **23.** $-\frac{1}{2}$, $-\frac{1}{3}$, $\frac{2}{3}$
25. -3; -2; $\frac{1}{2}$, 2 **27.** 1-in. or 2-in. squares; $1 \times 8 \times 6$ in., $2 \times 6 \times 4$ in.
29.

$\overline{AB}$ and $\overline{BC}$ are perpendicular. $AB = 8$; $BC = 7$; $AC = \sqrt{113}$ $AB^2 + BC^2 = AC^2$

31. 0.62; 2.53; 3.76; 5.67 **33.** $11 \times 12 \times 13$ cm **35.** $\frac{1}{3}$ **37.** $\frac{3}{2}$, $\frac{7 \pm \sqrt{69}}{2}$ **39.** -1, 1, $\pm 2i$

Practice Exercises, pages 353–355

1. $(x - 4)(x - 2)(x + 3)$ 3. $(x - 3)^2(x - 1) \cdot (x + 4)$ 5. $(x - 2)^3(2x - 3)$ 7. $-2; 1 \pm \sqrt{5}$
9. $-2; 1; \pm i$ 11. $3; -3 \pm 2i$
13. $-\dfrac{15\sqrt{33}}{343} = -0.2512$ 15. $3 - 2i$ 19. 4 ft
21. $f(x) = x^2 - 2x - 4$ 23. $3 - 2i$;
$-\dfrac{1 \pm \sqrt{10}}{3}$ 25. $-2 - \sqrt{5}; \pm i$ 27. i;
$-i$ (mult. 2); $\dfrac{1 \pm \sqrt{33}}{4}$ 29. $f(x) = x^3 - 2x^2 - 4x$ 31. 3.0 m 33. $\sin y + \cos y \tan y = \sin y + \cos y \dfrac{\sin y}{\cos y} = \sin y + \sin y = 2 \sin y$
35. $x^2 - 8x + 25$ 37. $x^3 - 5x^2 - 23x + 135$
39. $x^8 - 28x^7 + 294x^6 - 1232x^5 - 99x^4 + 14,420x^3 - 21,560x^2 - 37,800x + 72,900$
40. $(-1, -1), (3, 27), (-2, -8)$ 41. $p(x) = x^3 - 4x^2 + x + 6$ 43. $p(x) = 2(x - \sqrt{2})^{12}$
47. $0.55, -0.40 \pm 0.22i$

Test Yourself, page 355
1. -291 3. not a factor
5.

7. $-5, 0, 1; 2$
9. $-7, -1, 1$
11. $(x + 3)(x - 2) \cdot (x - 4)$
13. $-2, 4, 2i, -2i$

Practice Exercises, pages 361–363
1. 2 or no pos., 2 or no neg. 3. 2 or no pos., 2 or no neg. 5. 2 and 3 7. -3 and $-2, 2$ and 3 9. 17,781 ft^2 11. $2; -3$ 13. $1; -2$
15. $3; -1$ 17. $30°, 90°, 150°$ 19. $\dfrac{4}{3}, -5$

25. 11.0 m/s 27. $-2.2; -1.5; 0.2$ 29. $-0.4; 0.8; 1.4$ 31. $0; -3; 4.4; 1.6$ 33. $-0.5; 0.7; -1.1; 1.3$ 35. $-\dfrac{16}{65}$ 37. $P(x)$ will take on every value between $P(3)$ and $P(4)$ in the interval [3.4]. 39. \$14 41. 1.5 43. -1.4

Practice Exercises, pages 368–370
1. 9 3. -2 5. 4 7. all integers 9. 1
11.

13.

15. $\dfrac{\pi}{6}$ 21. 45° or $\dfrac{\pi}{4}$ 23. 14 25. 35 m^2
27.

no intercepts; asymptotes: $x = 0$, $y = 0$

29.
intercept: $\left(0, \dfrac{1}{4}\right)$;
asymptotes: $x = 2$, $y = 0$

31.
intercepts: $\left(-\dfrac{5}{6}, 0\right)$, $\left(0, \dfrac{5}{3}\right)$;
asymptotes: $x = -3$; $y = 6$

33.
intercepts: $\left(\dfrac{3}{4}, 0\right)$, $\left(0, -\dfrac{3}{5}\right)$;
asymptotes: $x = 5$, $y = -4$

43. $\dfrac{\cot x \cot y - 1}{\cot x + \cot y}$ 53. 45°, 315° $\left(\dfrac{\pi}{4}, \dfrac{7\pi}{4}\right)$

Practice Exercises, pages 374–375
1.

3. 23.1
5. 2
7. 1.26
9. $\dfrac{3}{4}; -\dfrac{13}{4}$

11. 11 13. 16 15. 4 17. $x \neq k\left(\dfrac{\pi}{2}\right), k \in Z$
19. $f(V) = \sqrt{\dfrac{3V}{5\pi}}$; 1.5 in. 21. $V = \dfrac{\pi d^3}{6}$
23. 10 25. $2\pi; 1.4; 5.5; 2.4$
27. 1.9 29. 1.4 31. 2.15 33. $-0.78, 1.3$
34.

35. 81
37. $e - d$

Practice Exercises, pages 378–379

1. $\dfrac{3}{x} + \dfrac{2}{x-1}$ **3.** $\dfrac{2}{x-5} + \dfrac{1}{x+1}$ **5.** $\dfrac{3}{x} +$

$\dfrac{1}{(x+1)^2} + \dfrac{2}{x+1}$ **7.** $\dfrac{1}{x-1} - \dfrac{3}{x+1} + \dfrac{2}{x+2}$

9. $\dfrac{5}{x+1} - \dfrac{2}{x-2} + \dfrac{1}{(x-2)^2}$ **11.** odd

13. $0, \pi$ **15.** $\dfrac{34}{x+1} - \dfrac{31}{x+2} - \dfrac{58}{(x+2)^2}$

17. $\dfrac{2}{x} - \dfrac{1}{x+3} - \dfrac{20}{(x+3)^2}$ **19.** $-\dfrac{2}{x-1} +$

$\dfrac{2}{3x-1} + \dfrac{1}{2x+3}$ **21.** $-\dfrac{4}{x} + \dfrac{1}{x-1} + \dfrac{2}{(x-1)^2} +$

$\dfrac{3}{(x-1)^3}$ **23.** $\dfrac{2}{x} - \dfrac{1}{x-1} + \dfrac{2}{(x-1)^2} + \dfrac{1}{(x-1)^3}$

25. $\dfrac{5x^2 + 8x - 19}{x^3 + x^2 - 8x - 12}$ **27.** $\dfrac{1}{x^2+1} + \dfrac{2}{x-1}$

29. $\dfrac{x+3}{x^2+2} - \dfrac{2}{x-1} + \dfrac{1}{x+1}$

Test Yourself, page 379

1. 0 or 2 pos., 0 or 2 neg. **3.** $-0.41, 2.41$

5.   **7.** 2

9. $\dfrac{1}{x} - \dfrac{3}{x+1} + \dfrac{2}{(x+1)^2}$

Summary and Review, pages 380–381

1. 83 **3.** 421 **5.** -14

7.   **9.** $2; 1.5, -2.5$

11. $-1; 5; \pm 3i$

13. $1; \pm\sqrt{2}; \pm i$

15. 1 pos.; 1 neg. **17.** $-0.3; -3.7$

19. -12 **21.** 6 **23.** $\dfrac{3}{x+4} - \dfrac{2}{x-3}$

Chapter 8   Inequalities and Linear Programming

Practice Exercises, pages 390–392

1. $(-5, 4)$ **3.** $\left(\dfrac{13}{10}, \dfrac{33}{25}\right)$ **5.** $\left(\dfrac{10}{3}, \dfrac{5}{3}\right)$

7. $(0.62, 5.62), (-1.62, 3.38)$ **9.** $(-2, 3)$

11. no solution **13.** closure, assoc., comm., mult. ident., inv.

15. 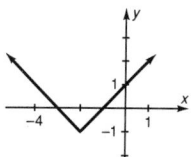 **17.** $0, \pi, 2\pi$

21. $\left(\dfrac{65}{11}, \dfrac{145}{11}\right)$

23. $(12, 0)$

24. maximum: $(3, 0)$

25. $c = 4.7$ ft; $\angle A = 33°$; $\angle B = 107°$

27. $(0, 3)$ **29.** no solution **31.** $(1.24, 0.65)$

35. 21,277.30 in.^{3} **36.** $3x + 2y = 0$ **37.** $y = \frac{1}{3}x + \frac{4}{3}$ **39.** $\left(\dfrac{q \pm \sqrt{q^2 - 4p}}{2}, \dfrac{q \mp \sqrt{q^2 - 4p}}{2}\right)$

41. $(0.79\pi, -0.78), (0.21\pi, 0.78)$ **43.** $a = d - 50; b = d + 20; c = d - 40$ **45.** $(-4, 4, -8)$

Practice Exercises, pages 398–400

1. $[1, 4]$ **3.** $(-6, 4)$ **5.** $(-\infty, 1] \cup [5, \infty)$

7.   **9.**

15. $x = \frac{1}{3}; \left(\frac{1}{3}, -\frac{20}{3}\right)$; no x-int.; y-int. $= (0, -7)$

17. $T \in [74, 75]$ **21.** $(-13, 15)$ **23.** $\left(-\infty, \dfrac{5}{3}\right) \cup$

$\left(\dfrac{5}{3}, \infty\right)$ **27.** $x \le \frac{1}{2}; \left(-\infty, \frac{1}{2}\right]$ **31.** $PR = QR = 2\sqrt{10}; PQ = 4\sqrt{5}$ **37.** $x > 3; (3, \infty)$

45. less than 29 lb/in.^{2} **47.** at least 3 hits

Practice Exercises, pages 404–405

1. $x \le 1$ or $x \ge 3$ **3.** $-2 < x < 0$ **5.** $1.5 < x < 8$ **7.** $x \le -2.92$ or $x \ge 3.42$

9. 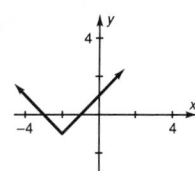 **11.** $\sin \dfrac{5\pi}{18} - \sin \dfrac{\pi}{18}$

13. $-8 < x < 1$

15. $-5 \le x \le 5$

17. $x \le \dfrac{-1 - \sqrt{11}}{2}$ or $x \ge \dfrac{-1 + \sqrt{11}}{2}$

23. $\angle B = 19°; \angle C = 21°; c = 2.23$

25. $-1.5 < x < -0.5$ **27.** $x < -3.5$ or $x > -2$ **28.** $1, -3, 4$ **29.** $\dfrac{3}{4} \le x \le 1$

 31. $\dfrac{1 - 2\sqrt{2}}{2} \le t \le \dfrac{1 + 2\sqrt{2}}{2}$ **37.** $0 < x < 2.35$

39. $-1.79 \le x \le -0.62$ or $1.62 \le x \le 2.79$

41. $-7.53 < x < -7$ or $0 < x < 0.53$

43. ex: $-4x^2 + 20x - 9 < 0$ **45.** ex: $-2x^2 < 0, -3x^2 < 0$ **47.** $x \le -1$ or $x \ge 1$

Practice Exercises, pages 409–411

1. $(-\infty, 0)$ **3.** $(-\infty, 0) \cup (0, 3)$ **5.** $(-\infty, -5.3] \cup [3, 5.3]$ **7.** $(-\infty, -3) \cup (-1.3, 1)$
9. $-3 \cup [6, \infty)$ **11.** $(-\infty, 2] \cup [8, \infty)$
15.

17.

21. $(-\infty, 1.26] \cup [1.91, \infty)$ **23.** $(-\infty, -2] \cup [-1, 2]$ **25.** $[-1.7, 0.1]$ or $[1.8, \infty)$
27. $(-\infty, -3]$ or $[-1.7, 1.7]$
31.

33.

35. $(-\infty, \infty)$ **37.** $[-1.7, 3]$ **39.** $[-2\pi, -1.8\pi] \cup \left[-\dfrac{\pi}{2}, 0.2\pi\right] \cup \left[\dfrac{3\pi}{2}, 2\pi\right]$ **43.** $7.04 \text{ ft} < r < 11 \text{ ft}$

Test Yourself, page 411

1. $\left(1, -\dfrac{2}{3}\right)$ **3.** $(2, -2), (3, -1)$ **5.** $(8, 25)$
7. $(-1.3, 1.4)$
9.

11.

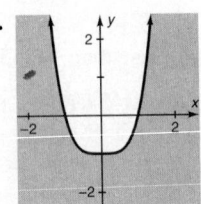

Practice Exercises, pages 415–417

1.

3.

11. $(-1, 7)$ **16.** $x = \pm 3; x = \pm i\sqrt{6}$ **17.** 1.7
19. The number of apples (x-coordinate) and the number of pears (y-coordinate) which can be eaten can be expressed as: (3, 0), (4, 0), (5, 0), (3, 1), (2, 1), (2, 2), (1, 2), (1, 3), (0, 3), (0, 4).

21.

23.

29. ex: $x + y \le 5$, $3x + 2y \le 12$ **33.** $55°, 235°$

Practice Exercises, pages 422–424

1. (2, 8) **3.** (6, 0) **5.** (4, 0) **7.** (18, 12)
9. $2\cos 44° \cos 34°$ **11.** \$176 **13.** 1.7, 4.58
15. (0, 4); 0.4 **17.** (10, 2); 1040 **19.** $x = \pm 0.71i, \pm 1.22$ **21.** 14π **23.** $2; \dfrac{\pi}{2}$

25. Ex: $C = 9y - 2x$ **27.** $b > 0$ and $a < \dfrac{b}{3}$
29. $a > 0$ and $a > 2b$

Practice Exercises, pages 428–431

1. 2 of each **3.** 10 regular, 0 deluxe **5.** 35 televisions; 75 refrigerators **7.** maximum at (1, 1) **9.** $f^{-1}(x) = \sqrt[3]{x + 3}$ **11.** $\angle C = 110.9°$; $\angle B = 41.1°$; $c = 69.6$ or $\angle C = 13.1°$; $\angle B = 138.9°$; $c = 16.9$ **15.** 377 in./s **19.** 10
21. 6 bags Growsome; 3 bags Growalot.

23. $C = ax + by$, where $0 < a < \dfrac{b}{2}$ **26.** $\dfrac{225}{4}$

27. 1600 yd of A; 0 yd of B **29.** 5 oz product I; 1 oz product II **33.** 10 reserved; 120 open

Test Yourself, page 431

1.

3. 15 bushels of peppers; 0 bushels of onions

Summary and Review, pages 432–433

1. $(-2, 3)$ **3.** $(-2, -1)$ **5.** $\left(\dfrac{4}{3}, 2\right]$ **9.** $\left(-\dfrac{7}{2}, 1\right)$
11. $\left(-\infty, -\dfrac{2}{3}\right) \cup (1, \infty)$ **15.** $(-\infty, -2.2) \cup (-1, 0.7)$
17. $\left[-\dfrac{1}{3}, 0\right) \cup (0, 8)$ **19.**

25. $3.5x + 4.5y \le 24$, $x \ge 0, y \ge 0$
27. 24 equine figures; 0 human figures

Chapter 9 Exponential and Logarithmic Functions

Practice Exercises, pages 443–445

1. 13 **3.** $\frac{1}{6}$ **5.** -36 **7.** $\frac{1}{100,000}$ **9.** $6xy$

11. $\frac{2xz}{y^2}$ **13.** $\frac{x^2}{y}$ **15.** $y^{\frac{2}{3}}$ **17.** $h+5$ **21.** 70.09

23. -2.94 **25.** $\frac{y^{\frac{3}{8}}z^{\frac{1}{4}}}{x}$ **27.** $\frac{y^4}{x^2z^{\frac{2}{5}}}$ **29.** $\frac{z^{\frac{1}{2}}}{x^{\frac{3}{2}}y^{\frac{1}{4}}}$

33. $0, \pm\sqrt{3}$ **35.** $(-\infty, -4] \cup \left[\frac{28}{5}, \infty\right)$ **37.** 0.10

39. 0.03 **41.** -0.69 **43.** \$2618.23 **45.** $\frac{1}{x^{\frac{1}{2}}y^{\frac{3}{4}}}$

47. y **49.** x^2 **51.** 139.3 ft/s **53.** 161,300 mi/s

Practice Exercises, pages 450–452

1. $D = \{x: x \in \mathscr{R}\}$; $R = \{y: y > 0\}$; x-int: none; y-int: (0, 1); increasing; one-to-one
3. $D = \{x: x \in \mathscr{R}\}$; $R = \{y: y > 0\}$; x-int: none; y-int: (0, 1); decreasing; one-to-one
5. $D = \{x: x \in \mathscr{R}\}$; $R = \{y: y > 1\}$; x-int: none; y-int: (0, 2); increasing; one-to-one
7. $D = \{x: x \in \mathscr{R}\}$; $R = \{y: y > 0\}$; x-int: none; y-int: $(0, e^{-3})$; increas-ing; one-to-one

9. $\frac{9}{5}$ **11.** $\frac{1}{e^{\frac{5}{6}}}$ **13.** 1.2 **15.** $\frac{3}{2}$ **17.** $\frac{1}{9}$

19. \$3145.73 **21.** 0.63 g/cm^2 **23.** $y = 3$
25. $y = 2$ **27.** $y = -2$ **31.** $\frac{1}{2}, -\frac{2}{3}$ **33.** -6
35. 2 **37.** $f^{-1}(x) = \sqrt[3]{x-1}$ **39.** 24

Practice Exercises, pges 458–460
1. 2.2304 **3.** 2.7726 **5.** $5^y = 625$; $y = 4$
7. $b^{\frac{1}{2}} = \frac{1}{4}$; $b = \frac{1}{16}$ **11.** $y = \frac{\sqrt{x}}{2}$; $D = \{x: x \geq 0\}$
13. $D = \left\{x: x > -\frac{9}{2}\right\}$; $R = \{y: y \in \mathscr{R}\}$; x-int: $(-4, 0)$; y-int: (0, 0.9542); asymptote: $x = -\frac{9}{2}$; increasing **15.** 16 **19.** $2x - 3$ **21.** 2.3 s

23. **25.**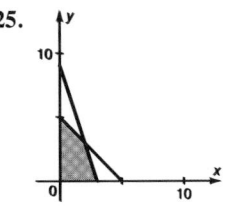

27. $D = \{x: x > -e^2\}$; $R = \{y: y \in \mathscr{R}\}$; x-int: $(-6.389, 0)$; y-int: $(0, -4)$; asymptote: $x = -e^2$; decreasing **33.** no; 7 is not in the domain of g.
35. $\pm 2.2, \pm 1.2i$ **39.** 3 **41.** $f(x) = \log_2(x+3)$
43. $f(x) = \log x - 5$ **45.** approx. 5411 years
47. The greater earthquake has 6.3 times the magnitude of the lesser quake.

Test Yourself, page 460

1. -49 **3.** $\frac{2y}{3x}$ **5.** $\frac{1}{4}$

7. 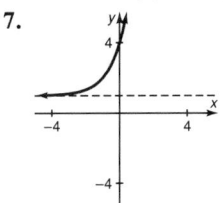 **9.** 8,285,213

Practice Exercises, pages 464–466
1. Let $\log_b M = u$. So $b^u = M$, $(b^u)^r = M^r$, $\log_b b^{ur} = \log_b M^r$, $ur = \log_b M^r$, $r \log_b M = \log_b M^r$. **3.** $\log_b x + 2 \log_b y - \log_b z$
5. $\frac{1}{5}[2 \log_b x + \log_b y]$ **7.** $\log \frac{3x^3}{y^3}$
9. $\ln 81 x^{\frac{7}{2}}y^4$ **15.** $[-1.5, 4]$ **17.** $\{x: x > -1\}$; $-\frac{5}{7}$
19. $2x^3 - 2$ **21.** $\log g + \log m + \log M - 2 \log d$ **23.** $\log_b \sqrt[4]{\frac{x}{y}}$ **25.** 9 **27.** $43°$
29. $D = \{x: x > -1\}$; $R = \{y: y \in \mathscr{R}\}$; x-int: 0; y-int: 0; asymptote: $x = -1$; increasing
31. $\{x: x > 1\}$; 2 **33.** $\{x: x > 0\}$; 0.59
35. 252 days **37.** $\{x: x > 2\}$; $\frac{20}{9}$
39. $\{x: x > 5\}$; 5.25 **41.** 1.3; 3.3 **43.** $\frac{10^{-14}}{[OH^-]}$
45. $g(x)$: $a = -2$, $h = 0$, $k = 2$ $h(x)$: $a = 1$, $h = -\frac{10}{3}$, $k = \log 3$

Practice Exercises, pages 472–474
1. 703.10 **3.** 2.72 **5.** 1.24 **7.** -0.02
9. 0.63 **11.** $x \geq 1.61$ **13.** 0.44 **15.** $5f(x)$
17. yes **19.** period: π; amplitude: 3; phase shift: $\frac{\pi}{2}$ to the left **21.** 17 years **23.** 0.86
25. -7.27 **27.** -1.10

29. 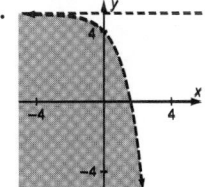 **31.**

33. 2 **35.** $-5 \le x \le 1$ or $3 \le x \le 9$ **37.** -1, $3 \pm 2i$ **39.** 1.95 **41.** (0.01, 2.95); $(2n\pi, \pi + 2n\pi)$ where $n \in Z$, $n \le 0$ **43.** $\dfrac{\ln 5a}{a}$ or $\dfrac{\ln 3a}{a}$

Practice Exercises, pages 478–481
1. growth **3.** growth **5.** 12 min **7.** 2.0
9. 6516 years **11.** no
13.

15. 4.2%
17.

19. $2; \dfrac{1}{2}$ **21.** $xy = k$ **23.** $r = -2.1\%$; 13 years
25. 2 h; 5.76 h **27.** 12 years **29.** $T_f = 82 + 98e^{-0.037t}$ **33.** $A = A_0 e^{-\frac{0.693t}{5570}}$

Test Yourself, page 481
1. $5 \log x + 2 \log y - \dfrac{1}{2} \log z$ **3.** $\{x: x > 0\}$; 16
5. 0.93 **7.** 5 years

Summary and Review, pages 482–483
1. $\dfrac{y^{16}}{x^{14}z^3}$ **5.** 1.83 **7.** $D = \{x: x > -3\}$;
$R = \{y: y \in \mathfrak{R}\}$; x-int: $(-2, 0)$; y-int: $(0, -1.1)$;
9. -0.4437 **11.** $6 \ln x + \dfrac{1}{2} \ln y - \ln 2 - 2 \ln z$
13. 8 **15.** 0.118 **17.** 0 or 3.347 **19.** 5000 years

Chapter 10 Polar Coordinates and Complex Numbers

Practice Exercises, pages 492–493
1.

3.

15. 6.16
17.

19.

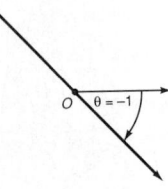

23. $\left(\dfrac{9\sqrt{3}}{2}, -\dfrac{9}{2}\right)$ **25.** (0.54, 0.84) **27.** $\left(9, \dfrac{\pi}{2}\right)$
29. $\left(1, \dfrac{2\pi}{3}\right)$ **31.** $c = 500 + 250d$; \$2750
33. 1500 years **35.** $x^2 + y^2 = 5$ **37.** $x = -1$
39. 20 ml **41.** $r^2 \cos^2 \theta = 12$ **43.** $3r \cos \theta - 2r \sin \theta = 1$ **45.** $2r^2 + 5r \cos \theta = 0$ **47.** $r^2 - 4r \sin \theta = 0$ **49.** $x^2 = 7y$ **51.** $3\sqrt{x^2 + y^2} + y = 1$

Practice Exercises, pages 501–502
1. pole, polar axis, $\theta = \dfrac{\pi}{2}$ **3.** $\theta = \dfrac{\pi}{2}$
5. $\theta = \dfrac{\pi}{2}$ **7.** pole **9.** pole
11.

13.

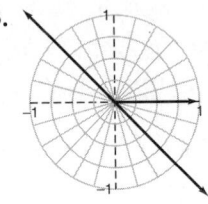

21. $y = -2$ **23.** $x = 2\sqrt{7}$
25. $x^2 + \left(y - \dfrac{11}{2}\right)^2 = \dfrac{11}{4}$
33. $\sin(\pi - \theta) = \sin[\pi + (-\theta)] = \sin \pi \cos(-\theta) + \cos \pi \sin(-\theta) = (0)[\cos(-\theta)] + (-1)(-\sin \theta) = \sin \theta$ **35.** 2 in. **39.** 7.2 L
41. $r^2 = \cos 2\theta$ **45.** $r = 1 + \cos \theta$

Practice Exercises, pages 506–508
1.

3.

7. $0 + 0i$ **9.** 3 **11.** $1 + 0i$ **13.** $\dfrac{\sqrt{3}}{2} - \dfrac{1}{2}i$
15. $-\dfrac{\sqrt{2}}{2} - \dfrac{\sqrt{2}}{2}i$ **17.** $0.4348 + 1.1184i$
19. 5 cis 0.93 **21.** 8 cis $\dfrac{3\pi}{2}$ **23.** 5.39 cis (-0.42) **25.** 6.71 cis (-0.46) **27.** 2 cis $\left(-\dfrac{\pi}{4}\right)$
29. a, b, c, and d real; $(a + bi) + (c + di) = (a + c) + (b + d)i$; $(a + bi)(c + di) = (ac - bd) + (ad + bc)i$ **31.** 3.739 years **33.** $a + bi \cdot \dfrac{a - bi}{a^2 + b^2} = \dfrac{a^2 + abi - abi - b^2i^2}{a^2 + b^2} = \dfrac{a^2 - b^2(-1)}{a^2 + b^2} = \dfrac{a^2 + b^2}{a^2 + b^2} = 1$ **35.** parabola **37.** 17.1 h

Test Yourself, page 508

1. $\left(-\dfrac{\sqrt{6}}{2}, \dfrac{\sqrt{2}}{2}\right)$ 3. $(\sqrt{41},\ 5.61)$ 5. $y = 8$

7. $r \cos \theta = -\sqrt{5}$ 9. pole   11. polar axis

13.

15. $-\sqrt{3} - i$

17. $8\sqrt{2}\left(\cos\dfrac{3\pi}{4} + i \sin\dfrac{3\pi}{4}\right)$

Practice Exercises, pages 513–515

1. $9 + 20i$ 3. $77.782 - 77.782i$

5.
```
          ↑ imaginary
(1.7 cis 29°)(3 cis 65°)
            •
              • 3 cis 65°
            • 1.7 cis 29°
                        real
  —6  +  + + + + + → 6
            • 
          —6 +
```

7. $x^2 - 10.5x + 13.5 = 0$

9. $-\dfrac{5}{17} + \dfrac{65}{17}i$

11. $x^2 - 2x + 50 = 0$

13. $\dfrac{\sqrt{2}}{4} - \dfrac{\sqrt{2}}{4}i$

15. $\dfrac{3}{9 + \pi^2} - \dfrac{\pi}{9 + \pi^2}i$ 17. $1.8\left(\cos\dfrac{5\pi}{8} + i \sin\dfrac{5\pi}{8}\right)$; $-0.69 + 1.66i$ 19. 6 cis 45°; $4.24 + 4.24i$

21. $39 - 18i$ 23. 39 V   25. rotation $\dfrac{3\pi}{2}$ counterclockwise   27. rotation $\dfrac{3\pi}{2}$ counter-

clockwise   29. $-4 + 2\sqrt{2}$ 31. 14 cis $\dfrac{3\pi}{2}$;

$0 - 14i$ 33. 9391   35. 3.33 cis (1.0278)

39. 4 cis $(0.75\pi) = -2\sqrt{2} + 2\sqrt{2}i$

43. $\dfrac{3\sqrt{15}}{2}[\cos (2.5261) + i \sin (2.5261)]$

45. $0.6019[\cos (67.935°) + i \sin (67.935°)]$

Practice Exercises, pages 520–521

1. $-625 + 0i$ 3. $9.24 \times 10^{-4} + (3.83 \times 10^{-4})i$

5. $1 + 0i$ 7. 190 ft²   9. $-128 - 128i$

11. $\dfrac{1}{24} - \dfrac{\sqrt{3}}{24}i$ 13. $1.204 \times 10^{-4} - 1.795 \times$

$10^{-4}i$ 15. $\{x: 0 < x < 2 \text{ or } x > 4\}$ 17. $1 + \sqrt{2}i,\ 1 - \sqrt{2}i$ 19. 66.99   21. 0.525 cis 3π

23. 1000 cis $\dfrac{\pi}{6}$ 25. $2.7557[\cos (4.7766) + i \sin$

$(4.7766)]$ 27. -27 29. $\dfrac{1}{8} - \dfrac{\sqrt{3}}{8}i$ 31. $-\dfrac{2}{25}$

35. 6.64 years; 6.33 years   37. Successive powers of z approach 0.   39. Successive powers of z remain on the unit circle.

41. $2 \cos \theta \sin \theta$ 43. $3 \sin \theta - 4 \sin^3 \theta$

45. $\sqrt{3} + i,\ -\sqrt{3} + i,\ -2i$

Practice Exercises, pages 526–527

1. 5 cis $\dfrac{\pi}{3}$, -5, 5 cis $\dfrac{5\pi}{3}$ 3. cis $\dfrac{\pi}{16}$,

cis $\dfrac{9\pi}{16}$, cis $\dfrac{17\pi}{16}$, cis $\dfrac{25\pi}{16}$ 5. 6 cis $\dfrac{\pi}{16}$, 6 cis $\dfrac{17\pi}{16}$

7. $\sqrt[6]{50}$ cis $\dfrac{\pi}{12}$, $\sqrt[6]{50}$ cis $\dfrac{9\pi}{12}$, $\sqrt[6]{50}$ cis $\dfrac{17\pi}{12}$

9. $\sqrt[6]{2}$ cis $\dfrac{7\pi}{12}$, $\sqrt[6]{2}$ cis $\dfrac{15\pi}{12}$, $\sqrt[6]{2}$ cis $\dfrac{23\pi}{12}$ 11. 12

13. $3, -3, 3i, -3i$ 15. $3^4 = 81$; $(-3)^4 = 81$; $(3i)^4 = 81$; $(-3i)^4 = 81$

21. $x^6 - 1 = (x^3 - 1)(x^3 + 1) = (x - 1)(x^2 + x + 1)(x + 1)(x^2 - x + 1)$; the roots are $1, -1$,

$-\dfrac{1}{2} + \dfrac{\sqrt{3}}{2}i$, $-\dfrac{1}{2} - \dfrac{\sqrt{3}}{2}i$, $\dfrac{1}{2} + \dfrac{\sqrt{3}}{2}i$, and $\dfrac{1}{2} - \dfrac{\sqrt{3}}{2}i$,

which agree with the results of Exercise 16.

23. $\sqrt[3]{52}$, $\sqrt[3]{52}$ cis $\dfrac{2\pi}{3}$, $\sqrt[3]{52}$ cis $\dfrac{4\pi}{3}$ 25. $\sqrt{6}$,

$-\sqrt{6}$, $\sqrt{7}$, $-\sqrt{7}$ 27. $\sqrt[5]{2}$ cis $\dfrac{\pi}{15}$, $\sqrt[5]{2}$ cis $\dfrac{7\pi}{15}$,

$\sqrt[5]{2}$ cis $\dfrac{13\pi}{15}$, $\sqrt[5]{2}$ cis $\dfrac{19\pi}{15}$, $\sqrt[5]{2}$ cis $\dfrac{25\pi}{15}$ 29. $\dfrac{1}{4}$ cis

$\dfrac{3\pi}{8}$, $\dfrac{1}{4}$ cis $\dfrac{7\pi}{8}$, $\dfrac{1}{4}$ cis $\dfrac{11\pi}{8}$, $\dfrac{1}{4}$ cis $\dfrac{15\pi}{8}$ 31. $x^3 - i =$

$(x + i)\left[x - \left(\dfrac{\sqrt{3}}{2} + \dfrac{1}{2}i\right)\right]\left[x - \left(-\dfrac{\sqrt{3}}{2} + \dfrac{1}{2}i\right)\right]$

33. $6x^2 - 11x + 10 = 6\left(x - \dfrac{11 + i\sqrt{119}}{12}\right)$

$\left(x - \dfrac{11 - i\sqrt{119}}{12}\right)$

Test Yourself, page 527

1. $24\left(\cos\dfrac{7\pi}{12} + i \sin\dfrac{7\pi}{12}\right)$; $-6.21 + 23.18i$

3. $\dfrac{1}{9}$ cis $\dfrac{\pi}{8}$; $0.10 + 0.04i$ 5. $24.49 + 59.13i$

7. 1   9. $-\dfrac{1}{9}$ 11. 7 cis $\left(-\dfrac{\pi}{9}\right)$, 7 cis $\dfrac{5\pi}{9}$, 7 cis $\dfrac{11\pi}{9}$

13. $\left(x - 4 \text{ cis } \dfrac{\pi}{8}\right)\left(x - 4 \text{ cis } \dfrac{5\pi}{8}\right)\left(x - 4 \text{ cis } \dfrac{9\pi}{8}\right)$

$\left(x - 4 \text{ cis } \dfrac{13\pi}{8}\right)$

Summary and Review, pages 528–529

3. $(5,\ 4.0689)$ 5. $\theta = \dfrac{\pi}{2}$ 11. $\dfrac{\sqrt{2}}{2} - \dfrac{\sqrt{2}}{2}i$

13. $2\sqrt{10}$ cis 0.32175   15. $\sqrt{5}$ cis 0

17. 3 cis $\dfrac{7\pi}{16}$; $0.5853 + 2.9424i$ 19. $-567 +$

$1944i$ 21. 5 cis $\dfrac{\pi}{2}$, 5 cis $\dfrac{7\pi}{6}$, 5 cis $\dfrac{11\pi}{6}$

23. $(x - 2\sqrt[3]{2})\left(x - 2\sqrt[3]{2} \text{ cis } \dfrac{2\pi}{3}\right)\left(x - 2\sqrt[3]{2} \text{ cis } \dfrac{4\pi}{3}\right)$

Chapter 11   Conic Sections

1. (0,0); 9   **3.** (0,1); 4   **5.** (7,−2); 5
7. (−4,6); 7   **9.** $25\sqrt{6}$ cm^2 **13.** $x^2 + y^2 = 25$
15. $(x + 2)^2 + (y − 4)^2 = 16$ **17.** $(x − 2)^2 +$
$(y − 6)^2 = 45$ **19.** $(x + 2)^2 + y^2 = 49$
21. $(x + 3)^2 + (y + 5)^2 = 36$ **23.** $(9 + 6\sqrt{3})$ in.
25. $(x − 3)^2 + (y − 1)^2 = 9$ **27.** $\left(x − \frac{3}{4}\right)^2 +$
$\left(y − \frac{7}{4}\right)^2 = \frac{170}{16}$ **29.** 45°   **31.** $\frac{18}{5}$ **33.** circle
35. circle   **37.** empty set   **39.** circle   **41.** (3,4); 1
43. (−7,1); 12   **47.** $(x − 5)^2 + (y − 1)^2 = \frac{400}{53}$
49. $\left(x + \frac{11}{2}\right)^2 + \left(y − \frac{5}{2}\right)^2 = \frac{125}{2}$
53. $168x^2 − 1690x + 168y^2 − 4056y + 28{,}561 = 0$

1. major axis: (0,6), (0,−6); minor axis: (5,0),
(−5,0); foci: $(0,\sqrt{11})$, $(0,−\sqrt{11})$; $e = \frac{\sqrt{11}}{6}$
3. major axis: (8,0), (−8,0); minor axis: (0,4),
(0,−4); foci: $(4\sqrt{3},0)$, $(−4\sqrt{3},0)$; $e = \frac{\sqrt{3}}{2}$
5. major axis: $(\sqrt{6},0)$, $(−\sqrt{6},0)$; minor axis:
$(0,\sqrt{2})$, $(0,−\sqrt{2})$; foci: (2,0), (−2,0); $e = \frac{\sqrt{6}}{3}$
7. major axis: (0,5), (0,−5); minor axis: (2,0),
(−2,0); foci: $(0,\sqrt{21})$, $(0,−\sqrt{21})$; $e = \frac{\sqrt{21}}{5}$
9. major axis: (5,0), (−5,0); minor axis: (0,3),
(0,−3); foci: (4,0), (−4,0); $e = \frac{4}{5}$ **11.** major
axis: $\left(0,\frac{\sqrt{15}}{3}\right)$, $\left(0,−\frac{\sqrt{15}}{3}\right)$; minor axis: $\left(\frac{\sqrt{3}}{3},0\right)$,
$\left(−\frac{\sqrt{3}}{3},0\right)$; foci: $\left(0,\frac{2\sqrt{3}}{3}\right)$, $\left(0,−\frac{2\sqrt{3}}{3}\right)$; $e = \frac{2\sqrt{5}}{5}$
13. $\left\{x: x \le −8 \text{ or } x \ge \frac{14}{3}\right\}$ **15.** $f^{-1}(x) = \sqrt[3]{x − 7}$
17. −0.9183   **19.** $\frac{(x − 1)^2}{11} + \frac{(y − 2)^2}{36} = 1$
23. center: (2,0); major axis: (2,4), (2,−4);
minor axis: (0,0), (4,0); foci: $(2,2\sqrt{3})$, $(2,−2\sqrt{3})$;
$e = \frac{\sqrt{3}}{2}$ **25.** center: (6,−4); major axis:
(0,−4), (12,−4); minor axis: (6,0), (6,−8); foci:
$(6 + 2\sqrt{5},−4)$, $(6 − 2\sqrt{5},−4)$; $e = \frac{\sqrt{5}}{3}$
27. center: (0,0); major axis: $(0,\sqrt{7})$, $(0,−\sqrt{7})$;
minor axis: (1,0), (−1,0); foci: $(0,\sqrt{6})$, $(0,−\sqrt{6})$;
$e = \frac{\sqrt{42}}{7}$ **29.** center: (5,1); major axis: (9,1),

(1,1); minor axis: (5,−1), (5,3); foci: $(5 + 2\sqrt{3},1)$, $(5 − 2\sqrt{3},1)$; $e = \frac{\sqrt{3}}{2}$ **31.** −32
33. major axis: $\left(\frac{5}{6},\frac{5}{2} + \sqrt{\frac{22}{3}}\right)$, $\left(\frac{5}{6},\frac{5}{2} − \sqrt{\frac{22}{3}}\right)$;
minor axis: $\left(\frac{5}{6} + \frac{\sqrt{22}}{3},\frac{5}{2}\right)$, $\left(\frac{5}{6} − \frac{\sqrt{22}}{3},\frac{5}{2}\right)$
35. major axis: $\left(\frac{3}{2} + \frac{\sqrt{21}}{6},−\frac{1}{3}\right)$, $\left(\frac{3}{2} − \frac{\sqrt{21}}{6},−\frac{1}{3}\right)$;
minor axis: $\left(\frac{3}{2},−\frac{1}{3} + \frac{\sqrt{7}}{6}\right)$, $\left(\frac{3}{2},−\frac{1}{3} − \frac{\sqrt{7}}{6}\right)$

1. vertices: (0,6), (0,−6); conjugate axis: (2,0),
(−2,0); foci: $(0,2\sqrt{10})$, $(0,−2\sqrt{10})$; asymptotes:
$y = \pm 3x$; $e = \frac{\sqrt{10}}{3}$ **3.** vertices: (9,0), (−9,0);
conjugate axis: (0,1), (0,−1); foci: $(\sqrt{82},0)$,
$(−\sqrt{82},0)$; asymptotes: $y = \pm\frac{1}{9}x$; $e = \frac{\sqrt{82}}{9}$
5. vertices: (11,0), (−11,0); conjugate axis:
(0,7), (0,−7); foci: $(\sqrt{170},0)$, $(−\sqrt{170},0)$;
asymptotes: $y = \pm\frac{7}{11}x$; $e = \frac{\sqrt{170}}{11}$ **7.** vertices:
(2,0), (−2,0); conjugate axis: (0,5), (0,−5);
foci: $(\sqrt{29},0)$, $(−\sqrt{29},0)$; asymptotes: $y = \pm\frac{5}{2}x$;
$e = \frac{\sqrt{29}}{2}$ **9.** vertices: (0,5), (0,−5); conjugate
axis: (3,0), (−3,0); foci: $(0,\sqrt{34})$, $(0,−\sqrt{34})$;
asymptotes: $y = \pm\frac{5}{3}x$; $e = \frac{\sqrt{34}}{5}$ **11.** vertices:
$\left(\frac{1}{3},0\right)$, $\left(−\frac{1}{3},0\right)$; conjugate axis: $\left(0,\frac{\sqrt{2}}{3}\right)$,
$\left(0,−\frac{\sqrt{2}}{3}\right)$; foci: $\left(\frac{\sqrt{3}}{3},0\right)$, $\left(−\frac{\sqrt{3}}{3},0\right)$; asymptotes:
$y = \pm\sqrt{2}x$; $e = \sqrt{3}$ **13.** 64   **15.** 10.42
17.
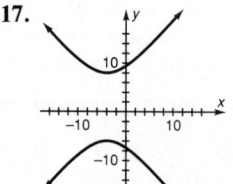
19. 219
21. $\frac{(y + 2)^2}{4} − \frac{(x + 1)^2}{9} = 1$;
center: (−1,−2);
vertices: (−1,0),
(−1,−4); foci:
$(−1,−2 + \sqrt{13})$,
$(−1,−2 − \sqrt{13})$;
asymptotes: $y + 2 = \pm\frac{2}{3}(x + 1)$
23. $\frac{(y − 4)^2}{28} − \frac{(x + 1)^2}{21} = 1$; center: (−1,4);
vertices: $(−1,4 + 2\sqrt{7})$, $(−1,4 − 2\sqrt{7})$; foci:
(−1,11), (−1,−3); asymptotes: $y − 4 = \pm\frac{4}{3}(x + 1)$

25. $y^2 - \frac{x^2}{7} = 1$; center: (0,0); vertices: (0,1), (0,−1); foci: (0,2√2), (0,−2√2); asymptotes: $y = \pm\frac{\sqrt{7}}{7}x$ **27.** 1358 rad/min   **29.** (−1,1), (−5,1)   **31.** (5,−5), (−5,5)   **33.** $\frac{(x-5)^2}{16} - \frac{(y-2)^2}{9} = 1$ **35.** $\frac{(x+3)^2}{100} - \frac{(y+4)^2}{44} = 1$ **37.** $3x^2 - y^2 - 12 = 0$ **41.** −2.87

Practice Exercises, pages 561–563

1. vertex: (0,−5); axis: $x = 0$; focus: $\left(0, -\frac{19}{4}\right)$; directrix: $y = -\frac{21}{4}$; opens up   **3.** vertex: (0,−3); axis: $x = 0$; focus: $\left(0, -\frac{25}{8}\right)$; directrix: $y = -\frac{23}{8}$; opens down   **5.** vertex: (4,0); axis: $y = 0$; focus: $\left(\frac{15}{4}, 0\right)$; directrix: $x = \frac{17}{4}$; opens left   **7.** vertex: (0,−2); axis: $x = 0$; focus: $\left(0, -\frac{25}{12}\right)$; directrix: $y = -\frac{23}{12}$; opens down   **9.** vertex: (3,−2); axis: $y = -2$; focus: (2,−2); directrix: $x = 4$; opens left   **11.** vertex: (4,1); axis: $x = 4$; focus: $\left(4, \frac{3}{2}\right)$; directrix: $y = \frac{1}{2}$; opens up   **13.** vertex: $\left(-\frac{25}{8}, 2\right)$; axis: $x = 2$; focus: $\left(-\frac{41}{8}, 2\right)$; directrix: $x = -\frac{9}{8}$; opens left   **15.** vertex: (−2,−1); axis: $x = -2$; focus: $\left(-2, -\frac{7}{12}\right)$; directrix: $y = -\frac{17}{12}$; opens up   **17.** vertex: (3,−4); axis: $x = 3$; focus: $\left(3, -\frac{15}{4}\right)$; directrix: $y = -\frac{17}{4}$; opens up   **19.** vertex: $\left(\frac{5}{4}, \frac{1}{8}\right)$; axis: $x = \frac{5}{4}$; focus: $\left(\frac{5}{4}, 0\right)$; directrix: $y = \frac{1}{4}$; opens down   **21.** $\cos\alpha = \frac{\sqrt{11}}{6}$; $\tan\alpha = -\frac{5\sqrt{11}}{11}$; $\csc\alpha = -\frac{6}{5}$; $\sec\alpha = \frac{6\sqrt{11}}{11}$; $\cot\alpha = -\frac{\sqrt{11}}{5}$ **23.** 305.6 cm²   **24.** 2π

27.

29. 101.5°, 258.4°, 120°, 240°   **31.** $(y+2)^2 = 24(x-2)$ **33.** $(x+8)^2 = -12(y-5)$ **35.** $(x+5)^2 = 8(y+3)$

37. $(y+2)^2 = -24(x+7)$ **39.** $(x+5)^2 = -24(y+1)$ **41.** $(x-8)^2 = \frac{9}{2}\left(y+\frac{7}{8}\right)$ **42.** $\frac{-5 \pm i\sqrt{47}}{4}$ **43.** $a = 2$, $b = -2$, $c = 1$ **47.** 55.4 ft   **48.** 0.345 s and 0.905 s   **49.** 42 ft

Test Yourself, page 563

1. (5,−6); 11   **3.** $(x-6)^2 + (y-1)^2 = 25$ **5.** point circle (7,−2)   **7.** major axis: (7,0), (−7,0); minor axis: (0,5), (0,−5); foci: (2√6,0), (−2√6,0); $e = \frac{2\sqrt{6}}{7}$ **9.** $\frac{(x-1)^2}{4} + \frac{(y+6)^2}{100} = 1$ **11.** conjugate axis: (9,0), (−9,0); vertices: (0,3), (0,−3); foci: (0,3√10), (0,−3√10); asymptotes: $y = \pm\frac{1}{3}x$; $e = \sqrt{10}$ **13.** $\frac{(y-3)^2}{16} - \frac{(x+2)^2}{4} = 1$ **15.** vertex: (0,−5); axis: $x = 0$; focus: $\left(0, -\frac{19}{4}\right)$; directrix: $y = -\frac{21}{4}$; opens up   **17.** $(x-2)^2 = 12(y-2)$

Practice Exercises, pages 568–569

1. $(x')^2 + (y')^2 + 10x' - 10y' + 34 = 0$ **3.** $2(x')^2 - 3(y')^2 - 12x' - 30y' - 32 = 0$ **5.** $y = 7x + 1$ **7.** hyperbola   **9.** parabola   **11.** hyperbola   **13.** $4(x')^2 - 3(y')^2 = 0$; (1,2)   **15.** $\frac{(x')^2}{1} + \frac{(y')^2}{4} = 1$; (3,−2)   **17.** $(y')^2 = 8x'$; (2,4)   **19.** $(x')^2 + (y')^2 = \frac{11}{2}$; (1,2)   **21.** $f'(t) = -16(t')^2$; (0,96)   **23.** $(x')^2 + (y')^2 = 25$; (1,2)   **25.** $\frac{(x')^2}{4} - (y')^2 = 1$; (1,−2)   **27.** $\frac{(x')^2}{\frac{8}{3}} + \frac{(y')^2}{2} = 1$; (−2,−1)   **29.** $x' = \frac{(y')^2}{8}$; (2,2)   **31.** $\frac{(x')^2}{16} + \frac{(y')^2}{9} = 1$; (−3,1)   **33.** $D = \{x: x \in \mathcal{R}\}$; $R = \{y: y \geq 0\}$ **35.** $x = \sqrt{3}$, $x = -\sqrt{3}$, $y = 1$ **39.** $\sqrt[3]{2}\left(\frac{\sqrt{3}}{2} - \frac{1}{2}i\right)$ **41.** $x^2 = -8(y-2)$ **43.** parabola

Practice Exercises, pages 574–575

1. circle, line; (3,4), (4,3)   **3.** line, parabola; $(1 + \sqrt{2}, \sqrt{2})$, $(1 - \sqrt{2}, -\sqrt{2})$ **5.** hyperbola, line: $\left(\frac{17}{5}, \frac{8}{5}\right)$ **7.** circle, parabola: (2√2,0), (−2√2,0)   **9.** circle, hyperbola; (3,1), (3,−1), (−3,1), (−3,−1)   **11.** circle, circle, no solution   **13.** parabola, parabola; (0,3), (3,0)   **15.** 5, 13

17. $\dfrac{37\pi}{18}, \dfrac{41\pi}{18}, \dfrac{49\pi}{18}, \dfrac{53\pi}{18}, \dfrac{61\pi}{18}, \dfrac{65\pi}{18}$ **19.** $-\dfrac{\pi}{9}$,

$-\dfrac{5\pi}{9}, -\dfrac{11\pi}{9}, -\dfrac{17\pi}{9}, -\dfrac{7\pi}{9}, -\dfrac{13\pi}{9}$ **21.** 7.5 ft,

18 ft **23.** -7 **27.** -2 **29.** 36 ft × 18 ft
31. $c = -11$; $d = -3$ **33.** hyperbola,
2 intersecting lines; (3,2), (2,1), $(-2,-1)$,
$(-3,-2)$ **35.** hyperbola, hyperbola; (3,1),
$(-3,-1)$, (1,3), $(-1,-3)$ **43.** 12 ft × 5 ft
45. 26 ft

Practice Exercises, pages 580–582
1. circle; $m_{\tan} = 1$; $m_{\text{normal}} = -1$ **3.** parabola;

$m_{\tan} = 1$; $m_{\text{normal}} = -1$ **5.** ellipse; $m_{\tan} = -\dfrac{\sqrt{5}}{10}$;

$m_{\text{normal}} = 2\sqrt{5}$ **7.** circle; tangent: $3x + \sqrt{7}\,y = 16$; normal: $\sqrt{7}\,x - 3y = 0$ **9.** hyperbola;
tangent: $x = 5$; normal: $y = 0$ **11.** hyperbola;
tangent: $y = -7$; normal: $x = 0$ **13.** parabola;
tangent: $y = -x - 3$; normal: $y = x - 9$
15. ellipse; tangent: $y = -3$; normal: $x = 0$
17. ellipse; tangent: $5x - \sqrt{15}\,y = 40$; normal:
$\sqrt{15}\,x + 5y = -8\sqrt{15}$ **19.** hyperbola; tangent:
$3x - \sqrt{30}\,y = 33$; normal: $\sqrt{30}\,x + 3y = -2\sqrt{30}$ **21.** $x^3 - 7x^2 + 11x + 3 = 0$ **23.** $y =$

$-\dfrac{a^2 x_0}{b^2 y_0}x + \left(y_0 + \dfrac{a^2 x_0^2}{b^2 y_0}\right)$ **25.** $y = \dfrac{2c}{y_0}x +$

$\left(y_0 - \dfrac{2cx_0}{y_0}\right)$ **27.** $y = -\dfrac{a^2 y_0}{b^2 x_0}x + y_0\left(1 - \dfrac{a^2}{b^2}\right)$

29. 2.12 **33.** $\dfrac{5}{16}$ **35.** 11.7 ft **37.** 16

Practice Exercises, pages 587–589
1. ellipse **3.** ellipse **5.** hyperbola **7.** circle
9. parabola **11.** ellipse **13.** parabola; $(3,\pi)$

15. ellipse; $\left(\dfrac{4}{3},\dfrac{\pi}{2}\right)$, $\left(4,\dfrac{3\pi}{2}\right)$ **17.** hyperbola;

$\left(\dfrac{1}{2},0\right)$, $(-1,\pi)$ **21.** yes **23.** $r = \dfrac{8}{3 + 2\sin\theta}$

25. $r = \dfrac{3}{1 - \cos\theta}$ **27.** $r = \dfrac{16}{1 + 2\cos\theta}$ **29.** $r =$

$\dfrac{16}{5 + 3\sin\theta}$ **31.** $1, -2, 3$ **33.** 1.5 h/rev
35. 10, 22

Test Yourself, page 589
1. $(x')^2 + (y')^2 = 36$; $(-3,5)$ **3.** $y' = 2(x')^2$;
$(-10,1)$ **5.** hyperbola, line; (1,5), $\left(-\dfrac{23}{15},-\dfrac{77}{15}\right)$

7. hyperbola, ellipse; (9,0), $(-9,0)$ **9.** hyperbola; $13x - 12y = 25$; $12x + 13y = 312$

11. ellipse; (0,1), $(0,-3)$ **13.** $r = \dfrac{4}{1 - \cos\theta}$

Summary and Review, pages 590–591
1. $(6,-1)$; 7 **3.** major axis: $(\pm 3,0)$; minor

axis: $(0,\pm\sqrt{5})$; foci: $(\pm 2,0)$; $e = \dfrac{2}{3}$

5. endpoints: $(\pm 8,0)$; vertices: $(0,\pm 2)$; foci:

$(0,\pm 2\sqrt{17})$; asymptotes: $y = \pm\dfrac{1}{4}x$; $e = \sqrt{17}$

7. vertex: $(-5,2)$; focus: $\left(-5,\dfrac{5}{2}\right)$; axis: $x = -5$;

directrix: $y = \dfrac{3}{2}$ **9.** $(x')^2 + (y')^2 = \dfrac{9}{4}$; origin at

$\left(\dfrac{1}{2},-\dfrac{7}{2}\right)$; circle **11.** hyperbola **13.** circles;

$(-5,0)$, (3,4) **15.** parabola; $\left(\dfrac{1}{6},\dfrac{3\pi}{2}\right)$

Chapter 12 Matrices and Vectors

Practice Exercises, pages 600–602

1. 1×5; row **3.** 2×3 **5.** 3×4 **7.** $\dfrac{8}{9}$

9. $\begin{bmatrix} 7 & 10 \\ 13 & 14 \\ 21 & 8 \end{bmatrix}$ **11.** $\begin{bmatrix} -5 & -4 \\ -9 & -6 \\ -9 & 6 \end{bmatrix}$ **13.** $\begin{bmatrix} 7 & 2 \\ 1 & 4 \end{bmatrix}$

15. $\begin{bmatrix} -21 & -6 \\ -3 & -12 \end{bmatrix}$ **17.** $[-2\sqrt{2} \quad -\sqrt{2} \quad -4\sqrt{2}]$

19. $\begin{bmatrix} \frac{1}{2} & \frac{3}{2} \\ 1 & 2 \\ 3 & \frac{7}{2} \end{bmatrix}$ **21.** (6,5,2) **23.** $\begin{bmatrix} 4 & -8 \\ -1 & -1 \\ 11 & 1 \end{bmatrix}$

25. $\begin{bmatrix} -47 & -27 \\ -100 & -80 \end{bmatrix}$ **27.** $\left[-\dfrac{1}{4} \quad -\dfrac{3}{4} \quad -\dfrac{1}{4} \quad -\dfrac{11}{4}\right]$

29. $\begin{bmatrix} 1 & 0 & -2 \\ 3 & -3 & 1 \end{bmatrix}$ **30.** $\left(-\dfrac{6}{17},\dfrac{9}{17}\right)$ **31.** 8; worst

33. 1000 **35.** $x = 2$; $y = -\dfrac{4}{5}$ **37.** $x = -3$;

$y = -5$ **39.** Portland; 6; Chicago; The new
matrix would give the increase in off-road miles,
auto restricted zones, and number of parks in
each city. **41.** ellipse **43.** $(-3,7,2)$

Practice Exercises, pages 608–610

1. [17] **3.** $\begin{bmatrix} 36 & -2 \\ 33 & -84 \end{bmatrix}$ **5.** undefined

7. $\begin{bmatrix} -25 \\ 18 \\ 10 \end{bmatrix}$ **9.** $\begin{bmatrix} 1 & 0 \\ 0 & 1 \end{bmatrix}$ **11.** $x = 4$; $y = -2$

13. $\pm\dfrac{\sqrt{3}}{3}, \pm\dfrac{\sqrt{2}}{2}i$ **15.** [$540 $663 $735]

17. $1938 **19.** $\begin{bmatrix} \$2.80 \\ \$4.00 \end{bmatrix}$ **21.** yes **23.** yes

25. yes **27.** 24 **29.** $(-2,3)$ **31.** $(-3,0)$
35. $\angle B = 38°$; $\angle C = 47°$; $a = 84$
43. $283,800

Practice Exercises, pages 616–618

1. Q **3.** R **5.**

$$
\begin{array}{c}
 & \begin{matrix} n_1 & n_2 & n_3 & n_4 & n_5 \end{matrix} \\
\begin{matrix} n_1 \\ n_2 \\ n_3 \\ n_4 \\ n_5 \end{matrix} &
\begin{bmatrix} 0 & 1 & 0 & 0 & 0 \\ 1 & 0 & 1 & 0 & 0 \\ 0 & 1 & 0 & 1 & 1 \\ 0 & 0 & 1 & 0 & 1 \\ 0 & 0 & 1 & 1 & 0 \end{bmatrix}
\end{array}
$$

7.

$$
\begin{array}{c}
 & \begin{matrix} n_1 & n_2 & n_3 & n_4 \end{matrix} \\
\begin{matrix} n_1 \\ n_2 \\ n_3 \\ n_4 \end{matrix} &
\begin{bmatrix} 0 & 1 & 1 & 1 \\ 1 & 0 & 1 & 1 \\ 1 & 1 & 0 & 1 \\ 1 & 1 & 1 & 0 \end{bmatrix}
\end{array}
$$

9.

$$
\begin{array}{c}
 & \begin{matrix} n_1 & n_2 & n_3 & n_4 & n_5 & n_6 \end{matrix} \\
\begin{matrix} n_1 \\ n_2 \\ n_3 \\ n_4 \\ n_5 \\ n_6 \end{matrix} &
\begin{bmatrix} 0 & 1 & 0 & 0 & 0 & 0 \\ 0 & 0 & 1 & 0 & 0 & 0 \\ 0 & 0 & 0 & 0 & 0 & 1 \\ 1 & 1 & 0 & 0 & 0 & 0 \\ 0 & 0 & 1 & 0 & 0 & 0 \\ 0 & 0 & 1 & 0 & 1 & 0 \end{bmatrix}
\end{array}
$$

21. 2

25. 15 **29.** 2 **31.** 13; 2 **33.** -14
37. $2x^3 - 6x^2 + 6x - 2$ **43.** 1.5

Practice Exercises, pages 624–625

1. $\begin{bmatrix} 7 & 3 \\ 5 & 2 \end{bmatrix}\begin{bmatrix} -2 & 3 \\ 5 & -7 \end{bmatrix} = \begin{bmatrix} -14 + 15 & 21 - 21 \\ -10 + 10 & 15 - 14 \end{bmatrix} = \begin{bmatrix} 1 & 0 \\ 0 & 1 \end{bmatrix}$ **3.** $\begin{bmatrix} 1 & -2 \\ -5 & 11 \end{bmatrix}$ **5.** no inverse

7. no inverse **9.** $\begin{bmatrix} -\frac{5}{6} & \frac{7}{6} & \frac{1}{2} \\ \frac{3}{2} & -\frac{3}{2} & -\frac{1}{2} \\ -\frac{7}{6} & \frac{5}{6} & \frac{1}{2} \end{bmatrix}$

11. $\begin{bmatrix} \frac{7}{48} & \frac{11}{96} & \frac{1}{96} \\ -\frac{11}{48} & \frac{17}{96} & \frac{19}{96} \\ -\frac{5}{24} & -\frac{1}{48} & \frac{13}{48} \end{bmatrix}$ **13.** no inverse **15.** $x > 4$

17. $x < 3$ **19.** $1 \le x \le 7$ **21.** type A: \$100;
type B: \$120 **23.** $\begin{bmatrix} -\frac{19}{2} \\ -\frac{13}{2} \end{bmatrix}$ **25.** no solution;

inverse does not exist **27.** $\begin{bmatrix} 6 \\ -2 \\ 3 \end{bmatrix}$ **29.** $\begin{bmatrix} \frac{80}{9} \\ \frac{43}{9} \end{bmatrix}$

31. $\begin{bmatrix} 3 \\ -2 \\ 2 \end{bmatrix}$ **33.** $\begin{bmatrix} 5 \\ 8 \\ 2 \end{bmatrix}$ **35.** $h^2 + 2xh - 5h$

37. $r = 10 \cos\theta$ **39.** $\begin{bmatrix} -3 \\ -9 \end{bmatrix}$ **41.** $\begin{bmatrix} -1 \\ 3 \\ -2 \end{bmatrix}$

Practice Exercises, pages 630–632

1. $(3, -5, 8)$ **3.** $(0, 2, -3)$ **5.** $(-2, 3, 1)$ **7.** no
solution **9.** $(-35, 30, -25)$ **11.** $(10, 8, -3)$
13. does not exist **15.** $x^2 + y^2 - 2x - 12y + 12 = 0$ **17.** $y = x^2 - 4x - 5$ **19.** $x^2 + y^2 - 5x - y - 6 = 0$ **21.** 0.4823 **23.** component I:
620 lb; component II: 1820 lb; component III:
2760 lb **25.** 1.3652 **27.** size I: 4 packages;
size II: 5 packages; size III: 6 packages
29. $10\sqrt{2}$ **31.** 360 **33.** mutual funds: \$1200;
government funds: \$3600; savings: \$200
35. $A = 3; B = -1; C = 2$ **37.** $(2, 4, 8)$
39. $(3, 4, 6)$ **41.** $x = 3a - b - 4c; y = -a + 2c; z = -2a + b + 3c$ **43.** $x = 3a; y = -a;$
$z = 2a$ **45.** X: 1600 gal/h; Y: 1400 gal/h;
Z: 1200 gal/h

Test Yourself, page 633

1. $\begin{bmatrix} -1 & -13 \\ -4 & 4 \\ 9 & 5 \end{bmatrix}$ **3.** $\begin{bmatrix} -6 & -6 \\ -5 & \frac{1}{2} \end{bmatrix}$ **5.** $\begin{bmatrix} -4 & -13 \\ -3 & -1 \\ 7 & 0 \end{bmatrix}$

7. $\begin{bmatrix} 26 & 44 \\ -27 & -45 \end{bmatrix}$ **11.** $\begin{bmatrix} 0 \\ -\frac{1}{2} \end{bmatrix}$ **13.** $(-1, 1, 2)$

Practice Exercises, pages 637–638

17. neither **19.** $\begin{bmatrix} 0 & 1 \\ 1 & 0 \end{bmatrix}\begin{bmatrix} a \\ b \end{bmatrix} = \begin{bmatrix} 0 \cdot a + 1 \cdot b \\ 1 \cdot a + 0 \cdot b \end{bmatrix} = \begin{bmatrix} b \\ a \end{bmatrix}$ **21.** $\begin{bmatrix} 7 & 1 \\ -2 & -1 \end{bmatrix}; \begin{bmatrix} 3 & 7 \\ 2 & 3 \end{bmatrix}$ **23.** $\begin{bmatrix} 0 & -1 \\ 1 & 0 \end{bmatrix}$

25. $\begin{bmatrix} -\frac{1}{2} & -\frac{\sqrt{3}}{2} \\ \frac{\sqrt{3}}{2} & -\frac{1}{2} \end{bmatrix}$ **27.** $\begin{bmatrix} -\frac{\sqrt{3}}{2} & \frac{1}{2} \\ -\frac{1}{2} & -\frac{\sqrt{3}}{2} \end{bmatrix}$ **31.** $R_{180°}$

33. $R_{270°}$ **35.** $-1, -2, \frac{3}{2}, 4$

39. 2 units left and 4 units down **41.** $\begin{bmatrix} x \\ y \end{bmatrix} + \begin{bmatrix} 5 \\ 2 \end{bmatrix} = \begin{bmatrix} x' \\ y' \end{bmatrix}$ **43.** $\begin{bmatrix} x \\ y \end{bmatrix} + \begin{bmatrix} -1 \\ 8 \end{bmatrix} = \begin{bmatrix} x' \\ y' \end{bmatrix}$

Practice Exercises, pages 643–644
9. neither **11.** all real numbers
13. $2\sqrt{5}$ **15.** $\frac{1}{2}$ **17.** $\sqrt{13}$ **19.** $2\sqrt{17}$ **21.** 5
23. $\sqrt{2}$ **25.** $\left(-\frac{7}{10}, -\frac{109}{20}\right)$ **27.** 139.76; 105.32
29. 1.49; 53.40 **31.** 21° **33.** $y = x - 1,$
$y = -x - 5$ **35.** 8.718; 277° **37.** $\mathbf{u} - \mathbf{v}$
39. $\frac{1}{2}(\mathbf{v} + \mathbf{u})$

Practice Exercises, pages 651–653

1. $8\mathbf{i} + 15\mathbf{j}$; $17\cos 61.9°\mathbf{i} + 17\sin 61.9°\mathbf{j}$; $\left(\frac{8}{17},\frac{12}{17}\right)$ **3.** $\sqrt{3}\mathbf{i} + \sqrt{5}\mathbf{j}$; $2\sqrt{2}\cos 52.2°\mathbf{i} + 2\sqrt{2}\sin 52.2°\mathbf{j}$; $\left(\frac{\sqrt{6}}{4},\frac{\sqrt{10}}{4}\right)$ **5.** $3x - 4y = -11$

7. $2x^2 + 15x - 8 = 0$ **9.** $5\mathbf{i} + 6\mathbf{j}$; $\sqrt{61}\cos 50.2°\mathbf{i} + \sqrt{61}\sin 50.2°\mathbf{j}$ **11.** $(\sqrt{13} - \sqrt{11})\mathbf{i} + (\sqrt{3} + \sqrt{2})\mathbf{j}$; $3.16\cos 84.8°\mathbf{i} + 3.16\sin 84.8°\mathbf{j}$

13. $-6 \le x \le 9$ **15.** $y = 3 - x$ **17.** $y = \pm\sqrt{x^2 + 1}$ **21.** $(-12,-5)$; $(x,y) = (31,13) + t(-12,-5)$; $x = 31 - 12t$, $y = 13 - 5t$ **25.** $x = \pm1$; $y = -1$ **29.** $(5,-18)$

31. $(-22,5)$ **33.** $(10,-89)$ **35.** no **37.** no

39. $y^2 = 4x^2(1 - x^2)$ **43.** $\dfrac{AC}{AM - CN}$

Practice Exercises, pages 657–658

1. 23 **3.** -3 **5.** $\frac{3}{4}$ **7.** $2 - \sqrt{15}$ **9.** yes

11. $180°$ **13.** $52.1°$ **15.** $119.9°$

23. perpendicular **25.** parallel **27.** neither

29. $\frac{50}{3}$; $-\frac{3}{2}$ **31.** $-\frac{5\sqrt{3}}{3}$; $-5\sqrt{3}$ **33.** $K = 0$;

$K = \pm2$ **35.** $\frac{\sqrt{10}}{3}$; $-\frac{3\sqrt{10}}{5}$ **37.** $4x + 3y = 1$

47. neither

Practice Exercises, pages 664–665

1. $(10,3,1)$ **3.** $(-19,2,-6)$ **5.** -90

7. $(40,-15,5)$ **9.** $(28,13,-5)$ **11.** $(-14,39,23)$

13. $(16,29,-41)$ **15.** $(48,87,-123)$ **17.** 5^{3m-n}

19. $99.9°$ **21.** 8^{a+3b} **23.** 1 **25.** $(x,y,z) = (-7,-3,2) + t(7,8,-8)$ **27.** $x = 7 - 2t$, $y = 1 + 3t$, $z = -3 + 4t$ **29.** -512

31. $-12x + 7y + 4z = -92$ **33.** 20

35. $4x - 30y + 42z = -100$ **37.** $4x - 3y - 3z + 10 = 0$

Test Yourself, page 665

5. $(5,14)$ **7.** $4\mathbf{i} + 7\mathbf{j}$; $\sqrt{65}\cos 60.3°\mathbf{i} + \sqrt{65}\sin 60.3°\mathbf{j}$ **9.** 38 **11.** parallel

13. perpendicular **15.** -50

Summary and Review, pages 666–667

1. $\begin{bmatrix} 1 & -\frac{11}{2} & 8 \\ 5 & -2 & 8 \\ -1 & 2 & 3 \end{bmatrix}$ **3.** $\begin{bmatrix} 2\sqrt{2} & -5\sqrt{2} & 8\sqrt{2} \\ 6\sqrt{2} & -2\sqrt{2} & -4\sqrt{2} \\ -4\sqrt{2} & 4\sqrt{2} & 2\sqrt{2} \end{bmatrix}$

5. $\begin{bmatrix} -8 & -2 & -5 \\ -7 & 1 & -11 \\ -10 & -13 & 19 \end{bmatrix}$ **7.** $\begin{bmatrix} -6 & 9 & -29 \\ 5 & 25 & -54 \\ -42 & -53 & 76 \end{bmatrix}$

9. $\begin{bmatrix} -\frac{1}{3} & -\frac{2}{3} \\ \frac{5}{3} & \frac{7}{3} \end{bmatrix}$ **11.** $\begin{bmatrix} 3 \\ -1 \\ -2 \end{bmatrix}$ **15.** $(6,11)$

17. $6\mathbf{i} + 8\mathbf{j}$; $10\cos 53.1°\mathbf{i} + 10\sin 53.1°\mathbf{j}$
19. $48°$ **21.** $(x,y,z) = (3,4,7) + (-4,-6,-12)t$; $x = 3 - 4t$, $y = 4 - 6t$, $z = 7 - 12t$

Chapter 13 Sequences and Series

Practice Exercises, pages 677–680

1. $-2, 1, 6, 13, 22$ **3.** $\frac{1}{2},\frac{1}{5},\frac{1}{10},\frac{1}{17},\frac{1}{26}$ **5.** 16

7. $a_n = 10(n - 1) + 1$ **9.** $a_n = \frac{1}{3^n}$ **11.** $12, 6, 3, \frac{3}{2}$ **13.** $a_1 = -12$ and $a_n = a_{n-1} + 5$

15. $a_1 = 10$ and $a_n = a_{n-1} + (n - 1)$ **17.** $y = \frac{1}{12}(x - 2)^2 + 1$ **19.** $\frac{x^2}{48} + \frac{y^2}{64} = 1$

21. $(x - 4)^2 + (y + 5)^2 = 265$ **23.** $a_n = 8n - 7$ **25.** $a_n = 1$ **27.** $1.1, 1.21, 1.4641, 2.1436, 4.5950$ **29.** $2.7183, 7.3891, 20.0855, 54.5982, 148.4132$ **45.** $1 + i, 2i, -4, 16, 256$

Practice Exercises, pages 687–689

1. arithmetic; 2 **3.** arithmetic; -6

5. geometric; $-\frac{1}{2}$ **7.** arithmetic; 0.02

11. $a_n = 21 - 6n$; -75 **13.** $a_n = (0.1)^{n-1}$; 1×10^{-15} **15.** $a_n = 5n - 1$ **17.** $-3\sqrt{33}$

23. $18, 54, 162$ or $-18, 54, -162$ **25.** none

27. $\begin{bmatrix} 7 & 6 & -3 \\ 2 & 2 & -1 \\ -6 & -5 & 3 \end{bmatrix}$ **29.** 50 **31.** restaurant A

33. After 5 years the second offer would be better for the job candidate, but after 10 years the original offer would be better for the job candidate. **35.** $b_n = 300(2^{n-1})$; 9600 **37.** 16 ft

Practice Exercises, pages 695–697

1. $\sum_{k=1}^{\infty} 4k$ **3.** $\sum_{k=1}^{\infty} 4^{k-1}$ **5.** $\sum_{k=1}^{\infty} k^3$ **7.** 147

9. 441 **11.** -874 **13.** 732 **15.** 9842 **17.** 207 **19.** 86.8 **21.** $-2.9\overline{3}, 8.9\overline{3}$

25. 2035.6 **27.** 168 **29.** 1475 **31.** $\sum_{k=1}^{n} \log(a_k)$

33. $\pm\sqrt[6]{2}$, $\sqrt[6]{2}\left(\pm\frac{1}{2} \pm \frac{\sqrt{3}}{2}i\right)$ **35.** $-\frac{1}{2}$

37. 79.57 cm **43.** Na **45.** 16

47. 15,690,529,510 **49.** $1275\pi + \dfrac{a(1 - a^{50})}{1 - a}$

51. 6570 **53.** $t_n = \sum_{k=1}^{n} k$; $S_n = \sum_{k=1}^{n} 2k - 1$

Practice Exercises, pages 702–705

1. 8   **3.** $n = 3$ **5.** P_{k+1}: $(ab)^{k+1} = a^{k+1}b^{k+1}$

7. P_{k+1}: $1^4 + 2^4 + 3^4 + \cdots + k^4 +$

$(k + 1)^4 = \dfrac{(k + 1)(k + 2)(2k + 3)(3k^2 + 9k + 5)}{30}$

9. $n! > n^2$ for $n > 3$ **11.** $x^2 - 4x + 5 = 0$

13. Since $3 = 1(1 + 2)$, P_1 is true. Assume P_k: $3 + 5 + 7 + \cdots + (2k + 1) = k(k + 2)$.
Then $3 + 5 + 7 + \cdots + (2k + 1) + (2k + 3) = k(k + 2) + (2k + 3) = k^2 + 2k + 2k + 3 = k^2 + 4k + 3 = (k + 1)(k + 3) = P_{k+1}$.

15. Since $1 = \frac{1}{2}(1)(3 \cdot 1 - 1)$, P_1 is true.

Assume P_k: $1 + 4 + 7 + \cdots + (3k - 2) = \frac{1}{2}k(3k - 1)$. Then $1 + 4 + 7 + \cdots + (3k - 2) +$

$(3k + 1) = \frac{1}{2}k(3k - 1) + (3k + 1) = \frac{1}{2}(3k^2 - k +$

$6k + 2) = \frac{1}{2}(3k^2 + 5k + 2) = \frac{1}{2}(k + 1)(3k + 2) =$

P_{k+1}.   **17.** $4096 \operatorname{cis} \dfrac{3\pi}{2} = -4096i$

31. $\sqrt[6]{2} \operatorname{cis} \dfrac{5\pi}{36}$, $\sqrt[6]{2} \operatorname{cis} \dfrac{17\pi}{36}$, $\sqrt[6]{2} \operatorname{cis} \dfrac{29\pi}{36}$, $\sqrt[6]{2} \operatorname{cis}$

$\dfrac{41\pi}{36}$, $\sqrt[6]{2} \operatorname{cis} \dfrac{53\pi}{36}$, $\sqrt[6]{2} \operatorname{cis} \dfrac{65\pi}{36}$

Test Yourself, page 705

1. $-3, 0, 5, 12, 21$ **3.** $a_n = \dfrac{1}{n + 1}$ **5.** $\dfrac{5}{4}, \dfrac{5}{16},$

$\dfrac{5}{64}, \dfrac{5}{256}$ **7.** $a_1 = -13$ and $a_{n+1} = a_n + 7$

9. A; -7 **11.** G; $\dfrac{1}{3}$ **13.** $a_n = 27\left(\dfrac{1}{3}\right)^{n-1}$;

5.645×10^{-6} **15.** 16, 32   **17.** $\displaystyle\sum_{k=1}^{\infty} 2(-0.3)^{k-1}$

Practice Exercises, pages 712–713

1. 720   **3.** 23,751   **5.** 11,440   **7.** $x^8 + 8x^7y + 28x^6y^2 + 56x^5y^3 + 70x^4y^4 + 56x^3y^5 + 28x^2y^6 + 8xy^7 + y^8$ **9.** $1 - 10x^3 + 40x^6 - 80x^9 + 80x^{12} - 32x^{15}$ **11.** 3; 16, 166   **13.** $n = 2$; $(2^2)! = 24$; $(2!)^2 = 4$ **15.** 91   **17.** 126; 9   **19.** $210a^6b^4$ **21.** $3003a^8b^6$ **23.** $4032m^5k^4$ **25.** $-48, 384x^3y^5$

27. $-960\sqrt{2}k^3$ **29.** $4^{\frac{1}{3}}$ **31.** 10.70326

33. 1.08243216   **35.** $3070.50   **39.** 2734.375

Practice Exercises, pages 718–719

1. $3, \frac{3}{8}, \frac{1}{9}, \frac{3}{64}, \frac{3}{125}, \frac{1}{72}$; convergent   **3.** $-1, -1,$
$-1, -1, -1, -1$; convergent   **5.** converges; 1
7. diverges   **9.** converges; 2   **11.** diverges

13. converges; $\frac{3}{4}$ **15.** diverges   **19.** 390

21. 189   **23.** converges; 0   **25.** diverges
27. converges; 0

29. $a = 10.4$; $\angle A = 85.6°$; $\angle B = 59.4°$ or $a = 4.3$; $\angle A = 24.4°$; $\angle B = 120.6°$ **31.** diverges
33. The side parallel to the building would be 90 ft and the other two sides would be 45 ft.
35. $e, e^2, e^3, e^4, e^5, e^6$; no; The terms in the sequence increase without bound.
43. The sequence will converge to 0 if $k < t$. It will converge to $\dfrac{c_k}{b_t}$ if $k = t$, and it will diverge if $k > t$.   **45.** $N > 20,000$

Practice Exercises, pages 725–727

1. 3, 9, 18, 30, 45   **3.** 1, 1.25, 1.3611, 1.423611, 1.4636111   **5.** The series in Exercise 1 diverges because the partial sums increase without bound. The series in Exercise 2 converges and the sum is 1.5.

7. $\dfrac{110}{99}$ **9.** $-\dfrac{3}{14}$ **11.** diverges   **13.** diverges

15. inconsistent system; no solutions   **17.** $\dfrac{117}{9}$

19. $-\dfrac{89,312,424}{10,000,000}$ **21.** As $n \to \infty$, $\frac{1}{2}n(n + 1)$
increases without bound. Since $1 + 2 + 3 +$

$\cdots + k = \frac{1}{2}k(k + 1)$, $\displaystyle\sum_{k=1}^{\infty} k$ is divergent.

23. $\dfrac{(n + 1)^2 - 1}{(n + 1)^2}$ **29.** 163.66 m   **31.** $90 billion

35. $\displaystyle\sum_{k=0}^{\infty} 2\left(\dfrac{1}{4}\right)^k$ **37.** No. The perimeter of the nth

figure is $S_n = \left(\dfrac{4}{3}\right)^{n-1}(3a)$. The limit of S_n is not

finite.   **39.** $\dfrac{e^2}{e - 1}$ **41.** 1   **43.** $8 + 4\sqrt{2}$

Practice Exercises, pages 733–735

1. $-\dfrac{5}{4} < x < \dfrac{3}{4}$ **3.** $-1 < x < 1$ **5.** $-5 <$

$x < 5$ **7.** $\displaystyle\sum_{k=0}^{\infty} \sqrt{11}x^k$ **9.** $\displaystyle\sum_{k=0}^{\infty} \dfrac{2\pi}{3}(2x)^k$ **11.** $\displaystyle\sum_{k=0}^{\infty} \left(\dfrac{5}{3}x\right)^k$

13. 0.745   **15.** 0.109778   **17.** 0.921061
19. $5(\cos 126.8699° + i \sin 126.8699°)$
21. $1408.1573 + 5162.0000\,i$ **23.** If $|x| \leq 1$,
then using three terms of the expansion gives a

good approximation.   **25.** $4e^{\frac{i\pi}{2}}$ **27.** $2e^{\frac{i\pi}{3}}$

29. $0.5211i$ **31.** $2 + 2i$ **33.** $2^{\frac{1}{4}}, 2^{\frac{1}{4}}i,$

$-2^{\frac{1}{4}}, -2^{\frac{1}{4}}i$ **35.** $\dfrac{5\sqrt{3}}{2} + \dfrac{5}{2}i, -\dfrac{5\sqrt{3}}{2} + \dfrac{5}{2}i, -5i$

37. $\sqrt[10]{2} \operatorname{cis} 9°$, $\sqrt[10]{2} \operatorname{cis} 81°$, $\sqrt[10]{2} \operatorname{cis} 153°$, $\sqrt[10]{2} \operatorname{cis} 225°$, $\sqrt[10]{2} \operatorname{cis} 297°$.   **39.** Using four terms: 0.5235258553; using calculator: 0.5235987756; using more terms would increase accuracy. **41.** If $|x| \le 1$, then using five terms of the expansion gives a good approximation. **45.** $\cos \pi = -1$ **47.** 1.25 mi

Test Yourself, page 735
1. $x^5 - 15x^4y + 90x^3y^2 - 270x^2y^3 + 405xy^4 - 243y^5$ **3.** $48,384x^5y^3$ **5.** diverges
7. converges; 0 **9.** $\frac{20}{9}$ **11.** diverges

13. $\frac{857}{2475}$ **15.** $-\frac{3}{2} < x < \frac{1}{2}$ **17.** $\sum_{k=0}^{\infty} 3(2x)^k$

Summary and Review, pages 736–737
1. $3, 1\frac{1}{4}, 1\frac{2}{27}, 1\frac{1}{32}, 1\frac{2}{125}$ **3.** 175 bacteria

5. geometric; $-\frac{1}{4}$ **7.** 31, 35, 39, 43 **9.** $-6\sqrt{3}$

11. -7 **15.** $-1,732,104x^5$ **17.** converges: $\frac{3}{2}$

19. converges, $\frac{10}{3}$ **21.** diverges **23.** $\sum_{k=0}^{\infty} 3.4(8x)^k$

Chapter 14 Probability

Practice Exercises, pages 745–747
5. 108 **7.** $(x - 17)^2 + (y - 9)^2 = 289$
11. 6 **13.** 3 **15.** 504 **17.** 1,213,056
19. 25,230 **21.** 32 **23.** 32 **25.** 48 **27.** 240
30. 120 **31.** 5040 **32.** 42 **33.** 495
34. $32x^5 - 80x^7 + 80x^9 - 40x^{11} + 10x^{13} - x^{15}$
35. 3584 **37.** 1584 **39.** 10 **41.** 6

Practice Exercises, pages 752–754
1. 3,628,800 **3.** *wxy, wyz, wxz, xyz* **5.** 012, 013, 023, 123, 120, 130, 230, 201, 213, 021, 031, 032, 132, 102, 103, 203, 210, 231, 301, 302, 312, 310, 320, 321 **7.** 100 **9.** 6,375,600 **11.** 21
13. 277,200 **15.** 330 **17.** 1,413,720

19. $\left\{x: x > \frac{4}{3}\right\}$ **21.** 2,193,360 **23.** 79

25. 45 **27.** 377,348,994 **29.** 136,138,860
31. 3 **32.** $\pm 10^{10}$ **33.** 5.1805 **37.** 2,704,156
41. 5040 **43.** 696,729,600 **45.** 4,989,600

Practice Exercises, pages 758–760
1. {HHHH, HHHT, HHTH, HHTT, HTHH, HTHT, HTTH, HTTT, THHH, THHT, THTH, THTT, TTHH, TTHT, TTTH, TTTT}
3. {HHTT, HTHT, HTTH, THHT, THTH, TTHH}; $P = \frac{3}{8}$ **5.** {HHTT, HTHT, HTTH, HTTT, THHT, THTH, THTT, TTHH, TTHT, TTTH, TTTT}; $P = \frac{11}{16}$ **7.** { }; $P = 0$ **9.** $\frac{1}{13}$

11. $\frac{1}{52}$ **13.** $\frac{3}{13}$ **15.** 1 to 3 **17.** 364 **19.** $\frac{56}{364}$

21. 1225 **23.** $\frac{13}{49}$ **24.** 7140 **25.** $\frac{1}{7140}$

27. $\frac{1}{7140}$ **29.** 7139 to 1 **30.** 20,901,888,000

31. $\frac{23}{1026}$ **33.** $\frac{11}{134}$ **37.** 2 to 7 **39.** 4.617 ×

10^{-6} **41.** $\frac{33}{100}; \frac{3}{50}$ **43.** $\frac{2}{5}$

Practice Exercises, pages 766–769
1. yes **3.** yes **5.** $\frac{7}{15}; \frac{1}{15}; \frac{8}{15}$ **7.** 0.30 **9.** 0.30

11. 0.90 **15.** dependent; General intelligence may be reflected in each grade. **17.** 0.144
18. 40,320 **19.** 594,048 **23.** $\frac{1}{4}$ **25.** $\frac{1}{36}$

27. $\frac{1}{17}$ **29.** $\frac{25}{102}$ **31.** $\frac{1}{5}$ **33.** $\frac{3}{14}$ **34.** $\frac{12}{35}$

35. 10.4% **36.** 64 **37.** 0.028 **39.** 0.0043
41. 0.0192 **43.** 0.0192; 0.0385

Test Yourself, page 769
1. 17,576,000 **3.** 742,560 **5.** 5040
7. {HHH, HHT, HTH, HTT, THH, THT, TTH, TTT} **9.** {TTT, TTH, THT, HTT}; $\frac{1}{2}$

11. independent; $\frac{5}{36}$

Practice Exercises, pages 773–776
1. yes; whether or not a patient experiences weight gain; $p = 0.05$; $n = 50$; $r = 4$ **3.** yes; getting a "heads" on a toss; $p = 0.65$; $n = 24$; $r = 12$ **5.** yes; whether or not the student answers correctly; $p = 0.5$; $n = 20$; $r = 14$
7. $P(0) = \frac{1}{8}$; $P(1) = \frac{3}{8}$; $P(2) = \frac{3}{8}$; $P(3) = \frac{1}{8}$;
9. 0.48 **11.** $P(0) = 0.16$; $P(1) = 0.48$;
$P(2) = 0.36$ **13.** $\frac{9}{16}$ **15.** $P(0) = \frac{9}{16}$;

$P(1) = \frac{3}{8}$; $P(2) = \frac{1}{16}$ **16.** 65,536 **17.** $\frac{1}{10}$

21. $P(2) = \frac{1}{36}$; $P(3) = \frac{2}{36}$; $P(4) = \frac{3}{36}$; $P(5) = \frac{4}{36}$; $P(6) = \frac{5}{36}$; $P(7) = \frac{6}{36}$; $P(8) = \frac{5}{36}$; $P(9) = \frac{4}{36}$; $P(10) = \frac{3}{36}$; $P(11) = \frac{2}{36}$; $P(12) = \frac{1}{36}$ **22.** $\frac{5}{18}$

23. $\frac{13}{18}$ **25.** 0.0018 **27.** 0.4437 **29.** 0.2206
31. 0.4925 **33.** 0.171 **34.** 0.132 **35.** 0.099
37. 0.0976 **39.** 0.0390 **41.** 29 **43.** 0.706
45. 706 to 294

Practice Exercises, pages 780–783

1. $2.50 **3.** $1.79 **5.** $P(0) = \frac{1}{12}$; $P(1) = \frac{1}{12}$;

$P(2) = \frac{2}{12}$; $P(3) = \frac{2}{12}$; $P(4) = \frac{2}{12}$; $P(5) = \frac{2}{12}$;

$P(6) = \frac{1}{12}$; $P(7) = \frac{1}{12}$ **7.** 0, 1, 2, 3, 4, 5, 6, 7, 8

9. 1 to 5 **11.** $2 **13.** $27.55 **14.** 0.0053

15. 0.8387 **17.** 2.3 **19.** $P(10) = \frac{5}{42}$, $P(11) =$

$\frac{7}{42}$, $P(12) = \frac{10}{42}$, $P(13) = \frac{9}{42}$, $P(14) = \frac{6}{42}$, $P(15) =$

$\frac{3}{42}$, $P(16) = \frac{2}{42}$ **21.** 40 to 2 **22.** $P(0) = \frac{1}{32}$,

$P(1) = \frac{5}{32}$, $P(2) = \frac{10}{32}$, $P(3) = \frac{10}{32}$, $P(4) = \frac{5}{32}$,

$P(5) = \frac{1}{32}$ **23.** 2.5 **25.** $8800 **27.** 6.68

29. 0.68 **35.** $f(k) = \dfrac{2400 - 2k}{k}$ **37.** $63.38

39. 4.5

Practice Exercises, pages 788–791

1. $P(V|A)$ **3.** $P(V|B)$ **5.** $P(M|C)$

7. $P(P \cap C)$ **9.** 0.7549 **11.** 0.93 **13.** $\frac{1}{221}$

16. $\frac{1}{3}$ **17.** 0.3029 **19.** 0.52 **21.** 0.4330

22. 0.1575 **23.** 0.1925 **25.** 0.4128 **27.** 0.4325

29. 0.3468 **31.** $\frac{1}{6}$ **33.** 0.1066 **37.** 5 to 3

Test Yourself, page 791

1. $P(0) = 0.015625$; $P(1) = 0.09375$; $P(2) =$
0.234375; $P(3) = 0.3125$; $P(4) = 0.234375$;
$P(5) = 0.09375$; $P(6) = 0.015625$ **3.** 0.0123
5. 3.35 **7.** 0.7226

Summary and Review, pages 792–793

1. 30 **3.** 591,600,030 **5.** {AA, AE, AI, AO,
AU, EA, EE, EI, EO, EU, IA, IE, II, IO, IU,
OA, OE, OI, OO, OU, UA, UE, UI, UO, UU}

7. {AA, AE, AI, EA, EE, EI, IA, IE, II}; $\frac{9}{25}$

9. independent; 0.0723 **11.** $P(3) = 0.4$;
$P(4) = 0.3$; $P(5) = 0.3$ **13.** 0.8788

Chapter 15   Statistics
and Data Analysis

Practice Exercises, pages 802–804

1. 5 **3.** 33 **5.** cannot tell **6.** $\frac{21}{40}$ **13.** 2.5

15. 41 **17.** cannot tell **25.** 64 **27.** 62.5%
29. 10,000 **33.** cannot tell **38.** If r is the
common ratio, $|r| > 1$. **39.** 1365; 32,760

Practice Exercises, pages 808–810

1. 73%; 27% **5.** Example: weight **7.** 90
9. 20 **11.** 55 **13.** 86; 12 **15.** 61 **17.** 1820

18. $\frac{1}{1820}$ **19.** $\frac{13}{1820}$ **21.** $m = 25,000$; lower

hinge $= 22,500$; upper hinge $= 30,000$; lower
extreme $= 17,500$; upper extreme $= 35,000$
23. 9 **29.** 11 **31.** 2 **37.** 2 **39.** 4
41. $Q_1 = 24$; $Q_3 = 28$; $IQR = 4$; potential
outlier; 36, 40; no serious outliers **43.** 20
and 32

Practice Exercises, pages 814–816

1. 495.6 **3.** 325,000 **5.** no mode **7.** 5.15

9. 5 **10.** $\frac{7}{20}$ **11.** 6.2 **13.** mode; The data is

not quantitative. **15.** mode; The manufacturer
needs to know how many shoes to make in each
size. **17.** mean **19.** Answers may vary.
Example: {Blue, Green, Blue, Brown, Hazel,
Brown} **21.** $1.09 **27.** 56 **29.** 84.8 **33.** 1.7

35. 2 **37.** $\frac{2261}{333}$ **38.** $243x^5 - 405x^4y^2 +$

$270x^3y^4 - 90x^2y^6 + 15xy^8 - y^{10}$ **45.** 7.23

Practice Exercises, pages 820–823

1. Answers may vary. **3.** 4.2 lb **5.** grams
7. grams **10.** $89.30 **11.** $30 **13.** 308.14
15. 452.78 **17.** $(x + 1)^2 = -8(y - 2)$

19. $\dfrac{x^2}{48} + \dfrac{(y - 4)^2}{64} = 1$ **21.** $(x - 8)^2 +$

$(y + 2)^2 = 325$ **27.** 6073 m **31.** 37.9 years
35. 1.8469×10^{-5} **36.** 2,324,784 **37.** 2.87
39. $26,100; $2200 **41.** 315.52 **43.** 2.47;
1.31 **45.** 11.7 and 30.9

Test Yourself, page 823
3. 405 **7.** 535 **9.** 308.59

Practice Exercises, pages 829–831

1. 68 **3.** $97\frac{1}{2}$ **5.** 0.815 **7.** b, d **9.** 400

11. 2.67; A score of 140 is 2.67 standard
deviations above the mean. **13.** $P(5) = 0.1000$;
$P(6) = 0.1000$; $P(7) = 0.1143$; $P(8) = 0.1429$;
$P(9) = 0.1571$; $P(10) = 0.1286$; $P(11) = 0.1143$;
$P(12) = 0.0857$; $P(13) = 0.0429$; $P(14) = 0.0143$
14. 8.79 **15.** 0.3857 **16.** 27 to 43 **17.** oral;
$z_{written} = 1.1667$; $z_{oral} = 1.2222$ **19.** 0.9015
21. 0.9057 **23.** 0.0897 **25.** 0.9525 **27.** 0.3446
29. 0.2709 **31.** 2.05 **35.** 93.8 min **37.** 3
years 3 months **38.** 124.75 **39.** 5.0825

7. The sample is random because each student is equally likely to be chosen. **9.** Examples: people unable to leave their houses, people whose demeanor discourages people from approaching them, people who do not talk to strangers, foreigners **11.** H_1: $\mu > 89$ **13.** H_1: $\mu \neq 2$ **14.** $\angle D = 27.04°$; $\angle E = 109.96°$; $e = 33.08$ **15.** $\angle R = 43.90°$; $\angle T = 82.10°$; $s = 16.34$ **17.** The means are normally distributed with $\mu_{\bar{x}} = 2.4$ cm and $\sigma_{\bar{x}} = 0.008$ cm. **19.** H_0: $\mu = 0.25$ lb; H_1: $\mu \neq 0.25$ lb **21.** H_0: $\mu = 115$; H_1: $\mu \neq 115$ **23.** yes; 15.24 is not in the interval 15.89 to 16.11. **24.** 520 **25.** 0.0735 **27.** yes; 1.92 is not in the interval 1.885 to 1.915. **31.** 49 **33.** $\bar{x} < 15.89$ **35.** $\bar{x} > 9.3379$

37. $\sigma_{\bar{x}} = \dfrac{\sigma}{\sqrt{n}}$, so the larger the sample size n, the smaller the standard error. A small $\sigma_{\bar{x}}$ suggests that the sample means are close to the population mean.

Practice exercises, pages 842–845

3. No, scatter plot does not approximate a line. **5.** Lines should be close to the line $y = 27.44 + 1.67x$. **7.** 161.04 **8.** 1.67; 27.44 **11.** 69.76 **13.** $y = 0.96x + 4.74$ **19.** negative **21.** positive **25.** $r = 0.998$; strong **27.** $\bar{x} = 74.6364$ **28.** 78.5 **29.** 365 mg **33.** no; The correlation coefficient should be closer to 0 than to 1 or -1. **35.** $r = 0.5285$; $y = 35.02 + 0.22x$

Test Yourself, page 845

1. $2\frac{1}{2}\%$ **3.** 0.0375 **5.** 0.175 **9.** $r = 0.998$; strong

Summary and Review, pages 846–847

3. P_{35} **7.** 251.85 **9.** -1.14 **11.** H_0: $\mu > 28.2$; H_1: $\mu \leq 28.2$; 0.56 **15.** -0.7315

Chapter 16 Limits and an Introduction to Calculus

Practice Exercises, pages 857–858

1. 2; 2; yes; $f(4) = 2$; equal **3.** -1; 2; no **5.** 2; 2; yes; $f(3) = 4$; not equal **7.** 3 **9.** 2 **11.** ∞ **13.** ∞ **15.** 41 **17.** 3 **19.** 3 **21.** -1 **23.** -4 **25.** 3 **27.** 0 **29.** -7 **31.** $\frac{4}{5}$ **33.** 0 **35.** does not exist **37.** $(-1,4)$, $(2,7)$ **39.** $(\pm\sqrt{10},0)$ **41.** ∞ **43.** 0

Practice Exercises, pages 863–864

1. 2 **3.** 19 **5.** 1 **7.** $-\frac{1}{2}$ **9.** $\frac{33}{7}$ **11.** -18 **13.** 2 **15.** $\frac{4}{9}$ **21.** 20 **23.** -1 **25.** 12 **27.** -10 **29.** ∞ **31.** $p(x) = (5x - 2)(4x + 3)(x - 3)$

Practice Exercises, pages 869–870

1. 0 **3.** 8 **5.** -2 **7.** 6 **9.** 5 **11.** $\{x: x \geq 4$ or $x \leq -4\}$ **13.** 4 **15.** $4c - 7$ **17.** -3 **19.** $\{x: -5 \leq x \leq 5\}$ **21.** $y = 4x + 4$ **23.** $6y = x + 15$ **25.** $6y = -x + 11$ **27.** $4c + 3$ **29.** $3c^2 + 5$ **31.** $-\dfrac{1}{2\sqrt{5 - c}}$ **33.** $\{x: x > -3\}$ **35.** 4.03 g/h; 4 g/h **37.** $y = -8x + 40$ **39.** $m_{f(x)} = \pm 2$ and $m_{g(x)} = \mp 2$ at $(\pm 1, 2)$ **41.** $2ad + b$

Practice Exercises, pages 874–875

1. $2x$; 2 **3.** $2x - 6$; 2 **5.** $2x + 15$; 2 **7.** $6x + 4$; 6 **9.** $6x + 8$; 6 **11.** $-12x - 12$; -12 **13.** $-\dfrac{4}{x^2}$ **15.** $\dfrac{3}{x^2}$ **17.** $-\dfrac{11}{(x + 3)^2}$ **19.** $\dfrac{1}{2\sqrt{x + 9}}$ **21.** $3x^2 + 9$ **23.** $15x^2 - 4x$ **25.** $\dfrac{5\sqrt{2}}{2} + \dfrac{\sqrt{2}}{2}i$, $-\dfrac{5\sqrt{2}}{2} - \dfrac{\sqrt{2}}{2}i$ **27.** $4 - 3i$, $-4 + 3i$ **29.** 24 **31.** none **33.** 4 **35.** $(8,8)$, $(4,-8)$ **37.** -5, $-\frac{2}{3}$, $\frac{1}{5}$ **39.** -1, $-\sqrt{2}$, $\sqrt{2}$, 6 **41.** $12x + 3$ **43.** $-\dfrac{b}{2a}$ **45.** $A\left(-\frac{2}{5},0\right)$; $B(0,4)$; $AB = \frac{2}{5}\sqrt{101}$

Test Yourself, page 875

1. 2 **3.** 8 **5.** $\frac{14}{9}$ **7.** no; Condition III is not satisfied. **9.** $3x^2 - 10x$; $6x - 10$ **11.** $\left(\frac{1}{2}, -\frac{3}{4}\right)$

Practice Exercises, pages 880–881

1. $2x$; 2 **3.** $2x + 8$; 2 **5.** $3x^2 + 10x$; $6x + 10$ **7.** $5x^4 + 21x^2 - 6$; $20x^3 + 42x$ **9.** $15x^2 - 12x$; $30x - 12$ **11.** $-\dfrac{13}{x^2}$ **13.** $-\dfrac{45\sqrt{x}}{2}$ **15.** $2x^3 + \dfrac{1}{x^4}$ **17.** 27 **19.** critical numbers: $x = 8$; increasing: $x > 8$; decreasing: $x < 8$; rel. min.: $(8,-61)$ **21.** critical numbers: $x = 0$; increasing everywhere; no rel. max. or rel. min. **23.** ∞ **25.** \$77.50 **27.** max: $(2,4)$; min: $(0,0)$ **29.** max: $(1,9)$; min: $(3,5)$ **38.** $y = 9x + 26$, $y = 9x - 6$

Practice Exercises, pages 884–886

1. 17 m/s; 2 m/s² **3.** -7 m/s; -2 m/s²

5. 42 m/s; -14 m/s² **7.** 18.05 m/s; 144.75 m/s²

9. 20, -20 **11.** $\frac{49\pi}{4}$ cm² **13.** 4.43 ft $\times$

2.43 ft $\times$ 0.79 ft **15.** 1222 cm² **17.** $96\sqrt{3}$ in.²

19. 68 **23.** $\begin{bmatrix} 78 \\ 80 \end{bmatrix}$ **25.** 144 ft **27.** 375,000 ft²

29. 15 **31.** none **33.** $a = 6$; $b = -36$

35. 12 mi apart at 2:48 p.m. **37.** 670 g

Practice Exercises, pages 892–893

1. $\frac{5n-1}{2}$ **3.** $\frac{50-3n-2n^2}{3}$ **7.** 78.75 units²

9. 31.5 units² **11.** 9.66 units² **15.** 22 ft

19. $\frac{74}{3}$ units² **21.** $\frac{26}{3}$ units² **23.** $\frac{7}{2}$ units²

27. 3.4 cal/cm² **29.** 95 animals/y

Test Yourself, page 893

1. $6x + 5$; 6 **5.** 1800 magazines; 200 magazines/y

Summary and Review, pages 894–895

1. does not exist **3.** yes; not equal **5.** 6

7. -4 **9.** $y = 2x - 5$ **11.** $4c - 1$

13. $-\frac{2}{x^2}$; $\frac{4}{x^3}$ **15.** (1,0) **17.** $4x^3 - 15x^2 + 16x$;

$12x^2 - 30x + 16$ **21.** $\frac{5}{3}$ ft $\times$ $\frac{5}{3}$ ft

23. $\frac{505}{6}$ units²

Additional Answers

Chapter 1 Functions
Practice Exercises, pages 15–17

28. add. inv.: $\frac{1}{2} + a = a + \frac{1}{2} = 0, a \notin \left\{0, \frac{1}{2}, \frac{1}{4}\right\}$; clos. add.: $\frac{1}{2} + \frac{1}{4} = \frac{3}{4}, \frac{3}{4} \notin \left\{0, \frac{1}{2}, \frac{1}{4}, \ldots\right\}$ mult.

ident.: $1 \notin \left\{0, \frac{1}{2}, \frac{1}{4}, \ldots\right\}$; mult. inv.: $\frac{1}{2} \cdot a = a \cdot \frac{1}{2} = 1, a \notin \left\{0, \frac{1}{2}, \frac{1}{4}, \ldots\right\}$

35. On a number line, mark off adjacent segments of lengths 2 and 4. At their common endpoint, construct a perpendicular. Then, bisect the segment of length 6 and use it to construct a circle. The far endpoints of the adjacent segments will be points on the circle, and the point of bisection will be the center. The vertex of the right angle will be at the point where the circle and the perpendicular intersect. The length of the altitude will be $\sqrt{8}$.

Practice Exercises, pages 21–23

1. **2.** **3.** **4.** **5.**

8. **9.** **10.** **11.** **12.**

    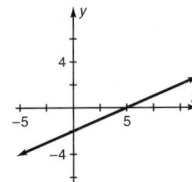

13. **14.** **15.** **21.** **22.**

    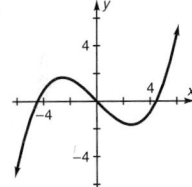

23. **24.** **27.** **28.** **29.**

30. **31.** **32.** **34.**

   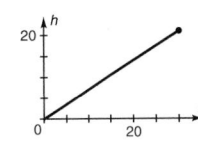

35. The graph is not a picture of the path of the object. It is a picture of the relationship between the height of the object and time. Thus, as time passes, the object rises, reaches a peak, and then falls as the graph indicates.

36.

38.

39.

43.

45.

Test Yourself, page 23

6. mult. ident.: 1 $\notin$ integers divisible by 4;
mult. inv.: $4 \cdot a = a \cdot 4 = 1$, $a \notin$ integers divisible by 4

7. closure, mult.: $\frac{1}{3} \cdot \frac{2}{3} = \frac{2}{9} \notin \left\{ \ldots, -\frac{1}{3}, 0, \frac{1}{3}, \frac{2}{3}, \ldots \right\}$;

mult. inv.: $\frac{2}{3} \cdot a = a \cdot \frac{2}{3} = 1$, $a \notin \left\{ \ldots, -\frac{1}{3}, 0, \frac{1}{3}, \frac{2}{3}, \ldots \right\}$

8.

9.

10.

11.

Class Exercises, pages 28–29

14.

$R = \{y : y > 0\}$

Practice Exercises, pages 29–31

44. Answers may vary. The statement is false. For example, $f(x) = \dfrac{x^2 - 10x + 25}{x - 5}$ and

$g(x) = x - 5$ can be written in the same form, $x - 5$, but are not equal since their domains are not the same.

Class Exercises, pages 35–36

1. $3x^2 + 2x + 6$, $D_{f+g} = \{x : x \in \mathcal{R}\}$; $3x^2 - 2x - 2$, $D_{f-g} = \{x : x \in \mathcal{R}\}$; $6x^3 + 12x^2 + 4x + 8$, $D_{f \cdot g} = \{x : x \in \mathcal{R}\}$;

$\dfrac{3x^2 + 2}{2x + 4}$, $D_{f/g} = \{x : x \neq -2\}$

2. $3x^3 + 1$, $D_{f+g} = \{x : x \in \mathcal{R}\}$; $-x^3 - 7$, $D_{f-g} = \{x : x \in \mathcal{R}\}$; $2x^6 - 2x^3 - 12$, $D_{f \cdot g} = \{x : x \in \mathcal{R}\}$; $\dfrac{x^3 - 3}{2x^3 + 4}$,

$D_{f/g} = \{x : x \neq \sqrt[3]{-2}\}$

3. $\sqrt{x - 1} + 3x$, $D_{f+g} = \{x : x \geq 1\}$; $\sqrt{x - 1} - 3x$, $D_{f-g} = \{x : x \geq 1\}$; $3x\sqrt{x - 1}$, $D_{f \cdot g} = \{x : x \geq 1\}$; $\dfrac{\sqrt{x - 1}}{3x}$,

$D_{f/g} = \{x : x \geq 1\}$

4. $\dfrac{2x - 2}{x^2 - 2x}$, $D_{f+g} = \{x : x \neq 0, x \neq 2\}$; $\dfrac{2}{x^2 - 2x}$, $D_{f-g} = \{x : x \neq 0, x \neq 2\}$; $\dfrac{1}{x^2 - 2x}$, $D_{f \cdot g} = \{x : x \neq 0, x \neq 2\}$; $\dfrac{x}{x - 2}$,

$D_{f/g} = \{x : x \neq 2\}$

Practice Exercises, pages 36–37

1. $7x$; $D_{f+g} = \{x: x \in \mathcal{R}\}$; $-x$; $D_{f-g} = \{x: x \in \mathcal{R}\}$; $12x^2$; $D_{f \cdot g} = \{x: x \in \mathcal{R}\}$; $\frac{3}{4}$; $D_{f/g} = \{x: x \neq 0\}$

2. $-x$; $D_{f+g} = \{x: x \in \mathcal{R}\}$; $5x$; $D_{f-g} = \{x: x \in \mathcal{R}\}$; $-6x^2$; $D_{f \cdot g} = \{x: x \in \mathcal{R}\}$; $-\frac{2}{3}$; $D_{f/g} = \{x: x \neq 0\}$

3. $\frac{2x^2 - x}{x - 2}$, $D_{f+g} = \{x: x \neq 2\}$; $\frac{-2x^2 + 7x}{x - 2}$, $D_{f-g} = \{x: x \neq 2\}$; $\frac{6x^2}{x - 2}$, $D_{f \cdot g} = \{x: x \neq 2\}$; $\frac{3}{2x - 4}$, $D_{f/g} = \{x: x \neq 0, x \neq 2\}$

4. $\frac{3x + 12}{x + 3}$, $D_{f+g} = \{x: x \neq -3\}$; $\frac{-5x - 12}{x + 3}$, $D_{f-g} = \{x: x \neq -3\}$; $\frac{-4x}{x + 3}$, $D_{f \cdot g} = \{x: x \neq -3\}$; $\frac{-x}{4x + 12}$, $D_{f/g} = \{x: x \neq -3\}$

5. $\sqrt{x} + 4x^2$, $D_{f+g} = \{x: x \geq 0\}$; $\sqrt{x} - 4x^2$, $D_{f-g} = \{x: x \geq 0\}$; $2x^{\frac{5}{2}}$, $D_{f \cdot g} = \{x: x \geq 0\}$; $\frac{1}{4x^{\frac{5}{2}}}$, $D_{f/g} = \{x: x > 0\}$

6. $\sqrt{2x} - x$, $D_{f+g} = \{x: x \geq 0\}$; $\sqrt{2x} + x$, $D_{f-g} = \{x: x \geq 0\}$; $\sqrt{2} x^{\frac{3}{2}}$, $D_{f \cdot g} = \{x: x \geq 0\}$; $\frac{\sqrt{2x}}{x}$, $D_{f/g} = \{x: x > 0\}$

36. $(f + g)(x)$ does not have to be one-to-one. For example, if $f(x) = x$, and $g(x) = -x$, then $(f + g)(x) = 0$, which is not one-to-one.

47.

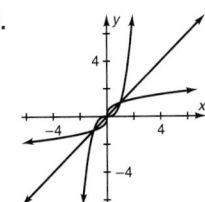

$f \circ g$ gives the line of reflection, $y = x$.

48. $R(x) = 40x - x^2$; $C(x) = 400 - 10x$; $P(x) = -x^2 + 50x - 400$

Class Exercises, page 41

1. $\{(-5, 1), (-3, 3), (-2, 4)\}$; function

2. $\{(c, a), (d, a), (e, b), (g, b)\}$; function

14.

 no

15.

 no

16.

 yes

17.

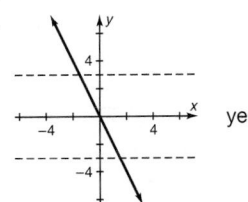 yes

18. Answers may vary. Students should conclude that plotting a limited number of points, such as only points where $x > 0$, may not give sufficient information for determining whether a function has an inverse.

Practice Exercises, pages 41–43

10.

11.

12.

13.

14.

15.

22.

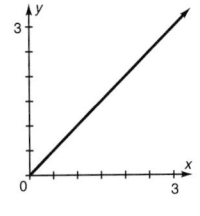

$D_f = \{x: x \geq 0\}$

23.

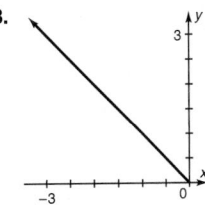

$D_f = \{x: x \geq 0\}$

24.

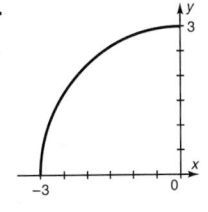

$D_f = \{x: 0 \leq x \leq 3\}$

25.

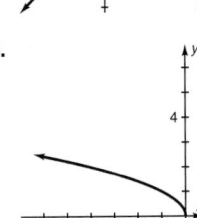

$D_f = \{x: x \geq 0\}$

29. Inverse functions;
$D_f = \{x: x \geq -2\}$; $R_f = \{y: y \geq 0\}$;
$D_g = \{x: x \geq 0\}$; $R_g = \{y: y \geq -2\}$

30. Inverse functions;
$D_f = \{x: x \in \mathcal{R}\}$; $R_f = \{y: y \in \mathcal{R}\}$
$D_g = \{x: x \in \mathcal{R}\}$; $R_g = \{y: y \in \mathcal{R}\}$

31. Not inverse functions;
$D_f = \{x: x \in \mathcal{R}\}$; $R_f = \{y: y \in \mathcal{R}\}$
$D_g = \{x: x \in \mathcal{R}\}$; $R_g = \{y: y \in \mathcal{R}\}$

32. Not inverse functions;
$D_f = \{x: x \in \mathcal{R}\}$; $R_f = \{y: y \in \mathcal{R}\}$
$D_g = \{x: x \in \mathcal{R}\}$; $R_g = \{y: y \in \mathcal{R}\}$

33. Inverse functions;
$D_f = \{x: x \neq 0\}$; $R_f = \{y: y \neq 1\}$
$D_g = \{x: x \neq 1\}$; $R_g = \{y: y \neq 0\}$

34. Not inverse functions;
$D_f = \{x: x \neq 0\}$; $R_f = \{y: y \neq 1\}$
$D_g = \{x: x \neq -1\}$; $R_g = \{y: y \neq 0\}$

35. Answers may vary. Refer students to Class Exercise 10 or Practice Exercise 7.

39. $f^{-1}(x) = \sqrt{x + 5} + 3$; $D_f = \{x: x \geq 3\}$

40. $f^{-1}(x) = x^2 + 2x + 1$; $D_f = \{x: x \geq 0\}$

42. $f^{-1}(x) = \dfrac{3 + \sqrt{4x - 7}}{2}$; $D_f = \left\{x: x \geq \dfrac{3}{2}\right\}$

43. Given function f, its inverse function is denoted f^{-1}. Given function f^{-1}, its inverse function is denoted $(f^{-1})^{-1}$. By definition of inverse functions, $f^{-1} \circ f = x$ and $f^{-1} \circ (f^{-1})^{-1} = x$, $f^{-1} \circ f = x = f^{-1} \circ (f^{-1})^{-1}$, hence $f = (f^{-1})^{-1}$.

44. If $a \neq 0$, the graph of $f(x) = ax + b$ is a non-horizontal line which would pass the horizontal line test and be a one-to-one function. If $a = 0$, the graph $f(x) = b$ is a horizontal line which would not pass the horizontal line test and is therefore not a one-to-one function.

45. Suppose a one-to-one function $f(x)$ has more than one inverse function, $g(x)$ and $h(x)$. Then $f(g(x)) = x$ for all x in the domain of $g(x)$ and $f(h(x)) = x$ for all x in the domain of $h(x)$. Thus $f(g(x)) = f(h(x))$ and $g(x) = h(x)$.

Class Exercises, page 47

4.
$D_f = \{x: x \in \mathcal{R}\}$
$R_f = \{y: y \in \mathcal{R}\}$

5.
$D_n = \{x: x \in \mathcal{R}\}$
$R_n = \{y: y \geq 0\}$

6.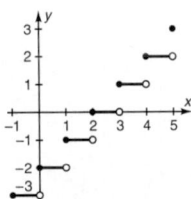
$D_t = \{x: x \in \mathcal{R}\}$
$R_t = \{y: y \in Z\}$

9.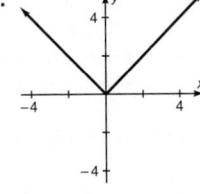

Practice Exercises, pages 47–49

1.
$D_f = \{x: x \in \mathcal{R}\}$
$R_f = \{y: y \geq 0\}$

2.
$D_g = \{x: x \in \mathcal{R}\}$
$R_g = \{y: y \geq 0\}$

3.
$D_f = \{x: x \in \mathcal{R}\}$
$R_f = \{y: y \in Z\}$

4.
$D_f = \{x: x \in \mathcal{R}\}$
$R_f = \{y: y \in Z\}$

5.
$D_f = \{x: x \in \mathcal{R}\}$
$R_f = \{y: y \geq 0\}$

6.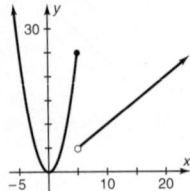
$D_g = \{x: x \in \mathcal{R}\}$
$R_g = \{y: y \geq 0\}$

7.
$D_n = \{x: x \in \mathcal{R}\}$
$R_n = \{y: y \in \mathcal{R}\}$

8.
$D_g = \{x: x \in \mathcal{R}\}$
$R_g = \{y: y \in \mathcal{R}\}$

9.
$D_m = \{x: x \in \mathcal{R}\}$
$R_m = \{y: y \leq 3\}$

10.
$D_t = \{x: x \in \mathcal{R}\}$
$R_t = \{y: y < 5, y = 6\}$

12. $f(x) = \begin{cases} x, x \ge 0 \\ -x, x < 0 \end{cases}$; This is the same as the definition in the lesson.

18.

20.

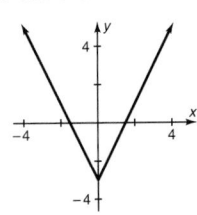

$D_f = \{x: x \in \mathcal{R}\}$
$R_f = \{y: y \ge -3\}$

21.

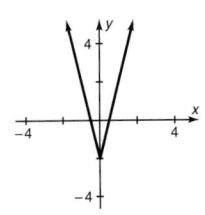

$D_g = \{x: x \in \mathcal{R}\}$
$R_g = \{y: y \ge -2\}$

22.

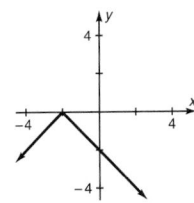

$D_h = \{x: x \in \mathcal{R}\}$
$R_h = \{y: y \le 0\}$

23.

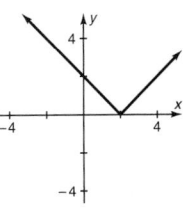

$D_g = \{x: x \in \mathcal{R}\}$
$R_g = \{y: y \ge 0\}$

24.

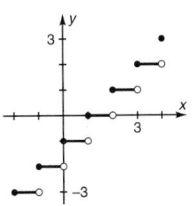

$D_f = \{x: x \in \mathcal{R}\}$
$R_f = \{y: y \in Z\}$

25.

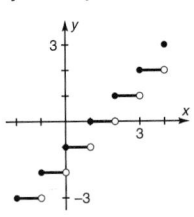

$D_g = \{x: x \in \mathcal{R}\}$
$R_g = \{y: y \in Z\}$

26.

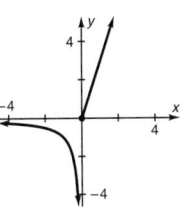

$D_f = \{x: x \in \mathcal{R}\}$
$R_f = \{y: y \in \mathcal{R}\}$

27.

$D_g = \{x: x \in \mathcal{R}\}$
$R_g = \{y: y < 0\}$

28.

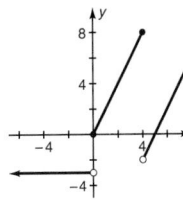

$D_h = \{x: x \in \mathcal{R}\}$
$R_h = \{y: y = -3, y > -2\}$

29.

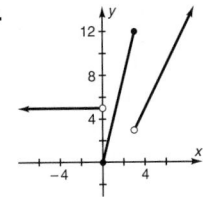

$D_g = \{x: x \in \mathcal{R}\}$
$R_g = \{y: y \ge 0\}$

31.

Increasing functions
are one-to-one functions.

32.

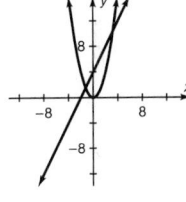

$(-1.2, 1.5), (3.2, 10.4)$

36.

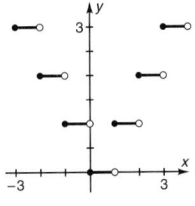

$D_f = \{x: x \in \mathcal{R}\}$
$R_f = \{y: y \in \text{nonnegative integers}\}$

37.

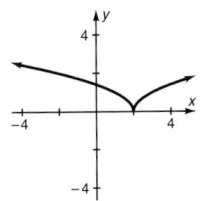

$D_g = \{x: x \in \mathcal{R}\}$
$R_g = \{y: y \ge 0\}$

38.

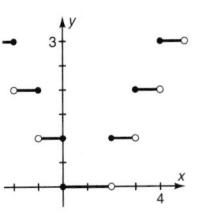

$D_h = \{x: x \in \mathcal{R}\}$
$R_h = \{y: y \in \text{nonnegative integers}\}$

39.

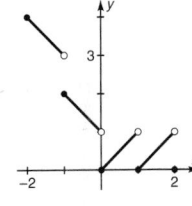

$D_f = \{x: x \in \mathcal{R}\}$
$R_f = \{y: 0 \le y \le 1,$
$2n - 1 < y \le 2n$ where
n is a positive integer$\}$

40. $f(x) = \begin{cases} -x^2, x \le 0 \\ x, x > 0 \end{cases}$

41. $f(x) = \begin{cases} -x^3, x \le 0 \\ -x, x > 0 \end{cases}$

42. $f(x) = \begin{cases} -x^2, x \le -1 \\ x, -1 < x \le 0, x > 1 \\ x^2, 0 < x < 1 \end{cases}$

43. $f(x) = \begin{cases} -x^3, x < -1, x > 1 \\ -x, -1 \le x \le 1 \end{cases}$

46. $f(x) = \begin{cases} 40, 0 < x \le 2 \\ 20 [\![-x]\!], 2 < x \le 8 \\ 160 + 30 [\![8 - x]\!], x > 8 \end{cases}$

44.

951

Test Yourself, page 49

5. $\dfrac{x^2 + 4x + 5}{x + 3}; D_{f+g} = \{x: x \neq -3\}$

6. $\dfrac{-x^2 - 4x - 1}{x + 3}; D_{f-g} = \{x: x \neq -3\}$

7. $\dfrac{2x + 2}{x + 3}; D_{f\cdot g} = \{x: x \neq -3\}$

8. $\dfrac{2}{x^2 + 4x + 3}; D_{f/g} = \{x: x \neq -1, -3\}$

15.

$D_f = \{x: x \in \mathcal{R}\}$
$R_f = \{y: y \in \mathcal{R}\}$

16.

$D_g = \{x: x \in \mathcal{R}\}$
$R_g = \{y: y = 0, y \text{ is an even integer}\}$

Chapter 2   Graphing Functions
Practice Exercises, pages 61–63

6.

7.

8.

9.

10.

11.

12.

13.

16.

17.

18.

19.

28.

29.

30.

31.

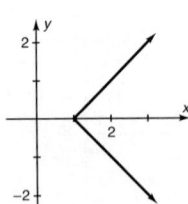

32. If f is symmetric to the y-axis and the origin, then $f(x) = f(-x)$, and $f(x) = -f(-x)$. This implies that $f(-x) = -f(-x)$, or that $f(x) = -f(x)$. Then f is symmetric to the x-axis and therefore cannot be a function.

36. The graph is symmetric to the line $x = 2$.

38.

39.

40.

Class Exercises, page 69

1.

2.

3.

4.

5.

6.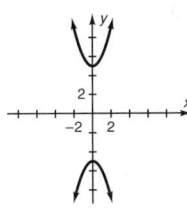

7. $y = \sqrt{x}$; shifted 3 units right

8. $y = x^2$; shifted 3 units left

9. $y = x^2$; shifted 2 units up

10. $y = [\![x]\!]$; reflected in x-axis, shifted 2 units left

11.

12.

13.

14.

15.

16.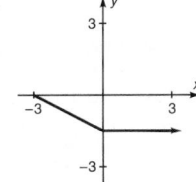

Practice Exercises, pages 69–72

18.

19.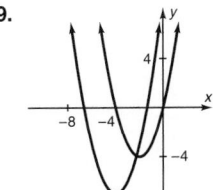

The graph of y_2 is the graph of y_1 with a 2 unit shift left and a 3 unit shift down.

20.

The graph of y_2 is the graph of y_1 with a 2 unit shift left.

21.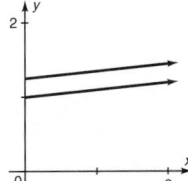

The graphs of the two equations are parallel.

22.

23.

24.

25.

26.

27.

28.

29.

31.

$y = x$

32.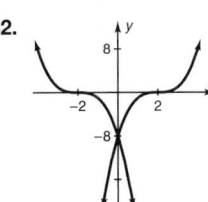

$x = 0$

35. closure, assoc., comm., add. ident.

36. Answers may vary. One example is $y = -x$, which is symmetric to the line $y = x$ and the origin.

45.
$y = -|x| - 1$

46.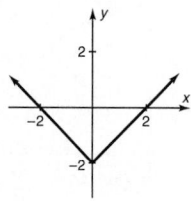
$y = |x| - 2$

47.
$y = [\![-x]\!] + 1$

48.
$y = [\![-x]\!] + 2$

50.

51.

52.

53.

Challenge, page 72

1. no; The volume of the cup is $\frac{40}{3}\pi$ cm³. Since the water level is one-half the height of the cup, the volume of the water is reduced by a factor of $\frac{1}{2} \cdot \left(\frac{1}{2}\right)^2$, so the water volume is $\frac{5}{3}\pi$ cm³.

Class Exercises, pages 76–77

6.

7.

Practice Exercises, pages 77–79

12.

21. closure, comm., assoc.

24. $\dfrac{x}{\frac{C}{A}} + \dfrac{y}{\frac{C}{B}} = 1$

33. A wall with no insulation has an R-factor of zero.

Practice Exercises, pages 84–86

9. $-0.4, 1.7$ **10.** $0.1 \pm 0.8i$ **11.** 1
12. $0, 0.7$ **13.** $-1.4, 1$ **14.** $-0.3 \pm 1.4i$

Test Yourself, page 86

11.

Class Exercises, page 91

11. Let x represent the number of 5 cent decreases. $R(x) = -50x^2 + 150x + 23{,}000$; A fare of \$1.07 will yield a maximum revenue.

Practice Exercises, pages 91–93

1.
x-int: $(\pm1,0)$; y-int: $(0,-4)$;
axis: $x = 0$; vertex: $(0,-4)$

2.
x-int: $(\pm1,0)$; y-int: $(0,3)$;
axis: $x = 0$; vertex: $(0,3)$

3.
x-int: $(-1,0)$, $(3,0)$; y-int: $(0,-3)$;
axis: $x = 1$; vertex: $(1,-4)$

Answers

4.

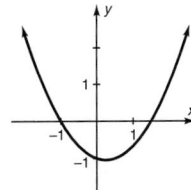

x-int: (−5,0), (1,0); y-int: (0,−5); axis: x = −2; vertex: (−2,−9)

5.

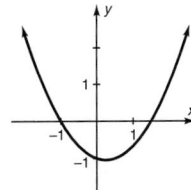

x-int: $\left(\frac{3}{2},0\right)$, (−1, 0); y-int: (0, −1); axis: $x = \frac{1}{4}$; vertex: $\left(\frac{1}{4}, -\frac{25}{24}\right)$

6.

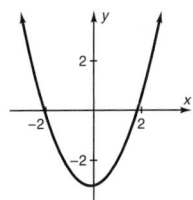

x-int: (1, 0), $\left(-\frac{5}{4}, 0\right)$; y-int: (0, −1); axis: $x = -\frac{1}{8}$; vertex: $\left(-\frac{1}{8}, -\frac{81}{80}\right)$

13.

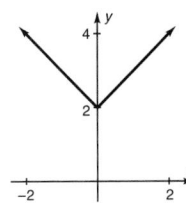

14. $f(x) = -(x - 2)^2 + 10$

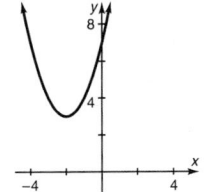

15. $f(x) = -2\left(x - \frac{1}{2}\right)^2 - \frac{1}{2}$

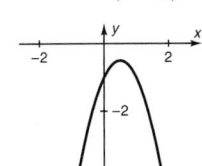

16. $f(x) = 3(x + 5)^2 - 79$

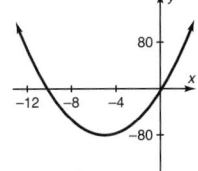

17. $f(x) = 6(x - 3)^2 - 47$

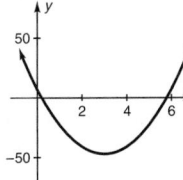

18. $f(x) = (x + 2)^2 + 3$

19. $f(x) = -2(x - 3)^2$

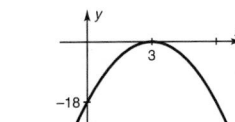

22. $R(x) = -0.40x^2 + 4.56x + 56.70$

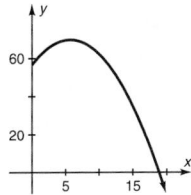

23. $f(x) = \frac{1}{2}(x - 1)^2 + \frac{3}{2}$

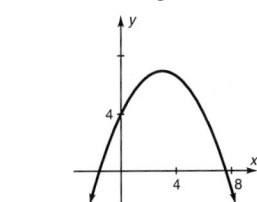

24. $f(x) = -\frac{1}{3}(x - 3)^2 + 7$

29.

36.

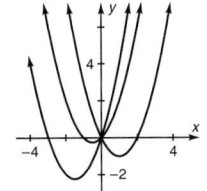

(±2.8, 0)

41. If −4ac = 0, there is one real zero.

If −4ac > 0, there are two real zeros.

If −4ac < 0, there is no real zero.

48. (−3.5, 0), (−1.5, 0), (0.5, 0), (2.5, 0), (4.5, 0)

47.

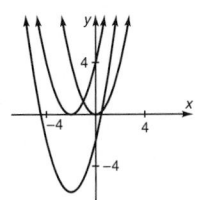

Practices Exercises, pages 97–99

11.

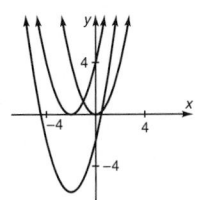

12. As a increases, the graph is compressed horizontally. As a decreases, the graph is stretched horizontally. Changes in b move the graph up or down.

14. There is always 1 real solution, since the function always crosses the x-axis exactly once.

955

Class Exercises, page 103

3. vertrex: $-\dfrac{b}{2a}$; $f(x_1) = 0$, $f(x_2) = 0$; $x_1 = \dfrac{-b + \sqrt{b^2 - 4ac}}{2a}$, $x_2 = \dfrac{-b - \sqrt{b^2 - 4ac}}{2a}$;

x-value of midpoint: $\dfrac{1}{2}\left(\dfrac{-b + \sqrt{b^2 - 4ac}}{2a} + \dfrac{-b - \sqrt{b^2 - 4ac}}{2a}\right) = \dfrac{1}{2}\left(\dfrac{-2b}{2a}\right) = -\dfrac{b}{2a}$

4. $PQ = QR = RS = PS = a$; $m_{\overline{PQ}} = m_{\overline{RS}} = 0$; $m_{\overline{PS}}$ and $m_{\overline{QR}}$ are undefined

5. $PQ = RS = a$; $PS = QR = \sqrt{b^2 + c^2}$; $m_{\overline{PQ}} = m_{\overline{RS}} = 0$; $m_{\overline{PS}} = m_{\overline{QR}} = \dfrac{c}{b}$

6. Let $A(0, 0)$, $B(a, 0)$, $C(a, a)$, and $D(0, a)$ represent the vertices of a square. Then $\overline{AC}$ and $\overline{BD}$ are the diagonals. So $m_{\overline{AC}} = 1$ and $m_{\overline{BD}} = -1$.

7. Let $A(2a, 0)$, $B(0, 2b)$, and $C(0, 0)$ represent the vertices of the right triangle. The midpoint of the hypotenuse is $M(a, b)$. $MA = MB$; $MC = \sqrt{(a - 0)^2 + (b - 0)^2} = \sqrt{a^2 + b^2}$; $MA = \sqrt{(a - 2a)^2 + (b - 2b)^2} = \sqrt{a^2 + b^2}$; Therefore, $MA = MB = MC$.

Practice Exercises, pages 104–106

8. Let $P(0, 2a)$, $Q(2b, 2a)$, $R(-2c, 0)$, and $S(2d, 0)$ represent the vertices of the trapezoid. Then $E(-c, a)$ and $F(b + d, a)$ are the midpoints of $\overline{PR}$ and $\overline{QS}$, respectively. $m_{\overline{PQ}} = \dfrac{2a - 2a}{2b - 0} = 0$; $m_{\overline{EF}} = \dfrac{a - a}{b + d + c} = 0$; $m_{\overline{RS}} = \dfrac{0 - 0}{2d + 2c} = 0$; Therefore, $\overline{EF}$ is parallel to $\overline{PQ}$ and $\overline{RS}$.

9. Add k to the x-coordinate and p to the y-coordinate.

10. Let $A(-a, 0)$, $B(a, 0)$, $C(b, c)$, and $D(-b, c)$ represent the vertices of the isosceles trapezoid. Then $\overline{AC}$ and $\overline{BD}$ are the diagonals.
$AC = \sqrt{(b + a)^2 + (c - 0)^2} = \sqrt{b^2 + 2ab + a^2 + c^2}$; $BD = \sqrt{(a + b)^2 + (0 - c)^2} = \sqrt{a^2 + 2ab + b^2 + c^2}$; Therefore, $AC = BD$.

11.

12. Let $P(2b, 2c)$, $Q(2d, 2c)$, $R(2a, 0)$, and $S(0, 0)$ represent the vertices of the trapezoid. Then $E(b, c)$ and $F(a + d, c)$ are the midpoints of $\overline{PS}$ and $\overline{QR}$, respectively. $RS = 2a$; $PQ = 2d - 2b$; $EF = a + d - b$; $\dfrac{1}{2}(RS + PQ) =$

$\dfrac{1}{2}(2a + 2d - 2b) = a + d - b = EF$

13. Let $A(0, 0)$, $B(a, 0)$, $C(a, b)$, and $D(0, b)$ be the vertices of a rectangle. Then $\overline{AC}$ and $\overline{BD}$ are the diagonals.
$AC = \sqrt{(b - 0)^2 + (a - 0)^2} = \sqrt{b^2 + a^2}$; $BD = \sqrt{(0 - b)^2 + (a - 0)^2} = \sqrt{b^2 + a^2}$

14.

midpoint of $\overline{LN}$: $(a + b, c)$;
midpoint of $\overline{MK}$: $(a + b, c)$; Since the segments have the same midpoint, they bisect each other.

22. Let $P(-2a, 0)$, $Q(0, 2b)$, and $R(2c, 0)$ represent the vertices of the triangle. Then $E(-a, b)$ and $F(c, b)$ are the midpoints of $\overline{PQ}$ and $\overline{QR}$, respectively. $ER = \sqrt{(2c + a)^2 + b^2}$; $PF = \sqrt{(c + 2a)^2 + b^2}$; Since the medians are equal, $ER = PF$. So $(2c + a)^2 + b^2 = (c + 2a)^2 + b^2$, $(2c + a)^2 = (c + 2a)^2$, $2c + a = c + 2a$ or $2c + a = -c - 2a$, $c = a$ or $c = -a$ (reject $c = -a$ because c and a would be the same point). Since $c = a$, $PQ = QR$ and the triangle is isosceles.

5

24.

$PN = \sqrt{a^2 + 2ab + b^2 + c^2}$; $LQ = \sqrt{b^2 - 4ab + 4a^2 + c^2}$;
$RM = \sqrt{4b^2 - 4ba + a^2 + 4c^2}$; $PR = \sqrt{4b^2 + 4c^2}$; $RQ = \sqrt{4b^2 - 8ba + 4a^2 + 4c^2}$;
$PQ = 2a$; $PN^2 + LQ^2 + RM^2 = 6a^2 - 6ab + 6b^2 + 6c^2$; $PR^2 + RQ^2 + PQ^2 = 8b^2 - 8ab + 8a^2 + 8c^2$;
$PN^2 + LQ^2 + RM^2 = \frac{3}{4}(PR^2 + RQ^2 + PQ^2)$

32. $m_{\overline{PM}} = \dfrac{\frac{y_1 + y_2}{2} - y_1}{\frac{x_1 + x_2}{2} - x_1} = \dfrac{y_1 + y_2 - 2y_1}{x_1 + x_2 - 2x_1} = \dfrac{y_2 - y_1}{x_2 - x_1}$; $m_{\overline{MQ}} = \dfrac{y_2 - \frac{y_1 + y_2}{2}}{x_2 - \frac{x_1 + x_2}{2}} = \dfrac{2y_2 - y_1 - y_2}{2x_2 - x_1 - x_2} = \dfrac{y_2 - y_1}{x_2 - x_1}$; $m_{\overline{PQ}} = \dfrac{y_2 - y_1}{x_2 - x_1}$; yes

Practice Exercises, pages 111–113

10. Since $x = h$ is a vertical line, the distance from $P(x_1, y_1)$ to $x = h$ is $|x_1 - h|$.

13.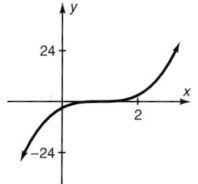

16. distance between two lines ≈ 3.29 in.; distance from buttonhole to one of the lines of stitching ≈ 1.65 in.

17. Each diagonal is the hypotenuse of an isosceles right triangle with legs of length a. Therefore, each hypotenuse has length $a\sqrt{2}$.

Chapter Test, page 116

11.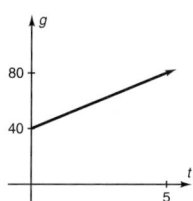

21. Let $P(0, 0)$, $Q(a, 0)$, $R(a + b, c)$, and $S(b, c)$ represent the vertices of the parallelogram. The midpoint of $\overline{PR} = \left(\frac{a + b + 0}{2}, \frac{c + 0}{2}\right) = \left(\frac{a + b}{2}, \frac{c}{2}\right)$, and the midpoint of $\overline{QS} = \left(\frac{a + b}{2}, \frac{0 + c}{2}\right) = \left(\frac{a + b}{2}, \frac{c}{2}\right)$. Since $\overline{PR}$ and $\overline{QS}$ have the same midpoint, they bisect each other.

Challenge

no; If $3 + i$ is a solution, then $3 - i$ must also be a solution. This would not be true if imaginary coefficients were allowed.

Chapter 3 Trigonometric Functions
Practice Exercises, pages 145–146

10.

11.

12.

13.

14.

15.

16.

17.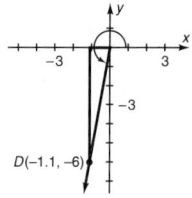

Class Exercises, page 149

For Exercises 1–4, see Solutions Manual for graphs.

1. $\sin\theta = \frac{3}{5}$; $\csc\theta = \frac{5}{3}$; $\cos\theta = \frac{4}{5}$; $\sec\theta = \frac{5}{4}$; $\tan\theta = \frac{3}{4}$; $\cot\theta = \frac{4}{3}$

957

2. $\sin \theta = \dfrac{\sqrt{5}}{5}$; $\csc \theta = \sqrt{5}$; $\cos \theta = -\dfrac{2\sqrt{5}}{5}$; $\sec \theta = -\dfrac{\sqrt{5}}{2}$; $\tan \theta = -\dfrac{1}{2}$; $\cot \theta = -2$

3. $\sin \theta = \dfrac{5}{13}$; $\csc \theta = \dfrac{13}{5}$; $\cos \theta = -\dfrac{12}{13}$; $\sec \theta = -\dfrac{13}{12}$; $\tan \theta = -\dfrac{5}{12}$; $\cot \theta = -\dfrac{12}{5}$

4. $\sin \theta = -\dfrac{4\sqrt{17}}{17}$; $\csc \theta = -\dfrac{\sqrt{17}}{4}$; $\cos \theta = -\dfrac{\sqrt{17}}{17}$; $\sec \theta = -\sqrt{17}$; $\tan \theta = 4$; $\cot \theta = \dfrac{1}{4}$

8. $\cos \theta = \dfrac{\sqrt{3}}{2}$; $\tan \theta = -\dfrac{\sqrt{3}}{3}$; $\csc \theta = -2$; $\sec \theta = \dfrac{2\sqrt{3}}{3}$; $\cot \theta = -\sqrt{3}$

9. $\tan \theta = \sqrt{3}$; $\csc \theta = \dfrac{2\sqrt{3}}{3}$; $\sec \theta = 2$; $\cot \theta = \dfrac{\sqrt{3}}{3}$

10. $\tan \theta = 0$; $\csc \theta$ is undefined; $\sec \theta = -1$; $\cot \theta$ is undefined

Practice Exercises, pages 150–151

For Exercises 1–6, see Solutions Manual for graphs.

1. $\sin \theta = -\dfrac{\sqrt{2}}{2}$; $\csc \theta = -\sqrt{2}$; $\cos \theta = \dfrac{\sqrt{2}}{2}$; $\sec \theta = \sqrt{2}$; $\tan \theta = -1$; $\cot \theta = -1$

2. $\sin \theta = \dfrac{\sqrt{21}}{7}$; $\csc \theta = \dfrac{\sqrt{21}}{3}$; $\cos \theta = \dfrac{2\sqrt{7}}{7}$; $\sec \theta = \dfrac{\sqrt{7}}{2}$; $\tan \theta = \dfrac{\sqrt{3}}{2}$; $\cot \theta = \dfrac{2\sqrt{3}}{3}$

3. $\sin \theta = \dfrac{5\sqrt{41}}{41}$; $\csc \theta = \dfrac{\sqrt{41}}{5}$; $\cos \theta = -\dfrac{4\sqrt{41}}{41}$; $\sec \theta = -\dfrac{\sqrt{41}}{4}$; $\tan \theta = -\dfrac{5}{4}$; $\cot \theta = -\dfrac{4}{5}$

4. $\sin \theta = -\dfrac{24}{25}$; $\csc \theta = -\dfrac{25}{24}$; $\cos \theta = -\dfrac{7}{25}$; $\sec \theta = -\dfrac{25}{7}$; $\tan \theta = \dfrac{24}{7}$; $\cot \theta = \dfrac{7}{24}$

5. $\sin \theta = -\dfrac{5\sqrt{29}}{29}$; $\csc \theta = -\dfrac{\sqrt{29}}{5}$; $\cos \theta = \dfrac{2\sqrt{29}}{29}$; $\sec \theta = \dfrac{\sqrt{29}}{2}$; $\tan \theta = -\dfrac{5}{2}$; $\cot \theta = -\dfrac{2}{5}$

6. $\sin \theta = \dfrac{\sqrt{2}}{2}$; $\csc \theta = \sqrt{2}$; $\cos \theta = \dfrac{\sqrt{2}}{2}$; $\sec \theta = \sqrt{2}$; $\tan \theta = 1$; $\cot \theta = 1$

18. $\sin \theta = -\dfrac{3\sqrt{13}}{13}$; $\tan \theta = \dfrac{3}{2}$; $\csc \theta = -\dfrac{\sqrt{13}}{3}$; $\sec \theta = -\dfrac{\sqrt{13}}{2}$; $\cot \theta = \dfrac{2}{3}$

19. $\cos \theta = \dfrac{3}{5}$; $\tan \theta = -\dfrac{4}{3}$; $\csc \theta = -\dfrac{5}{4}$; $\sec \theta = \dfrac{5}{3}$; $\cot \theta = -\dfrac{3}{4}$

20. $\sin \beta = \dfrac{2\sqrt{2}}{3}$; $\cos \beta = \dfrac{1}{3}$; $\tan \beta = 2\sqrt{2}$; $\csc \beta = \dfrac{3\sqrt{2}}{4}$; $\cot \beta = \dfrac{\sqrt{2}}{4}$

21. $\sin \phi = -\dfrac{5}{8}$; $\cos \phi = -\dfrac{\sqrt{39}}{8}$; $\tan \phi = \dfrac{5\sqrt{39}}{39}$; $\sec \phi = -\dfrac{8\sqrt{39}}{39}$; $\cot \phi = \dfrac{\sqrt{39}}{5}$

22. $\tan \theta = -\dfrac{2\sqrt{5}}{5}$; $\csc \theta = \dfrac{3}{2}$; $\sec \theta = -\dfrac{3\sqrt{5}}{5}$; $\cot \theta = -\dfrac{\sqrt{5}}{2}$

23. $\tan \theta = -\dfrac{3}{2}$; $\csc \theta = -\dfrac{\sqrt{13}}{3}$; $\sec \theta = \dfrac{\sqrt{13}}{2}$; $\cot \theta = -\dfrac{2}{3}$

24. $\tan \theta$ is undefined; $\csc \theta = 1$; $\sec \theta$ is undefined; $\cot \theta = 0$

25. $\tan \theta$ is undefined; $\csc \theta = -1$; $\sec \theta$ is undefined; $\cot \theta = 0$

26. $\sin \theta = \dfrac{2\sqrt{5}}{5}$; $\cos \theta = \dfrac{\sqrt{5}}{5}$; $\csc \theta = \dfrac{\sqrt{5}}{2}$; $\sec \theta = \sqrt{5}$; $\cot \theta = \dfrac{1}{2}$

27. $\sin \theta = -\dfrac{4\sqrt{17}}{17}$; $\cos \theta = -\dfrac{\sqrt{17}}{17}$; $\tan \theta = 4$; $\csc \theta = -\dfrac{\sqrt{17}}{4}$; $\sec \theta = -\sqrt{17}$

28. $\sin \theta = -\dfrac{2\sqrt{13}}{13}$; $\cos \theta = -\dfrac{3\sqrt{13}}{13}$; $\tan \theta = \dfrac{2}{3}$; $\csc \theta = -\dfrac{\sqrt{13}}{2}$; $\sec \theta = -\dfrac{\sqrt{13}}{3}$

29. $\sin \theta = \dfrac{8}{17}$; $\cos \theta = -\dfrac{15}{17}$; $\csc \theta = \dfrac{17}{8}$; $\sec \theta = -\dfrac{17}{15}$; $\cot \theta = -\dfrac{15}{8}$

35. $f(g(x)) = \dfrac{\sqrt{1 - x^2}}{|x|}$; $g(f(x)) = \dfrac{\sqrt{x^2 - 1}}{x^2 - 1}$

40. $\sin \dfrac{\pi}{4} = \dfrac{\sqrt{2}}{2}$; $\cos \theta = \dfrac{\sqrt{2}}{2}$; $\tan \theta = 1$; $\csc \theta = \sqrt{2}$; $\sec \theta = \sqrt{2}$; $\cot \theta = 1$

41.

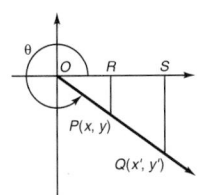

$\triangle POR \sim \triangle QOS$, and since corresponding sides are proportional, $\dfrac{OP}{OR} = \dfrac{OQ}{OS}$;

$\sec \theta = \dfrac{\sqrt{x^2 + y^2}}{x} = \dfrac{OP}{OR}$; $\sec \theta = \dfrac{\sqrt{(x')^2 + (y')^2}}{x'} = \dfrac{OQ}{OS}$

42. $m_l = \dfrac{y - 0}{x - 0} = \dfrac{y}{x}$; $\tan \theta = \dfrac{y}{x}$

Class Exercises, page 156

For Exercises 13–16, see Solutions Manual for graphs.

13. $\sin 150° = \dfrac{1}{2}$; $\csc 150° = 2$; $\cos 150° = -\dfrac{\sqrt{3}}{2}$; $\sec 150° = -\dfrac{2\sqrt{3}}{3}$; $\tan 150° = -\dfrac{\sqrt{3}}{3}$; $\cot 150° = -\sqrt{3}$

14. $\sin 315° = -\dfrac{\sqrt{2}}{2}$; $\csc 315° = -\sqrt{2}$; $\cos 315° = \dfrac{\sqrt{2}}{2}$; $\sec 315° = \sqrt{2}$; $\tan 315° = -1$; $\cot 315° = -1$

15. $\sin \dfrac{2\pi}{3} = \dfrac{\sqrt{3}}{2}$; $\csc \dfrac{2\pi}{3} = \dfrac{2\sqrt{3}}{3}$; $\cos \dfrac{2\pi}{3} = -\dfrac{1}{2}$; $\sec \dfrac{2\pi}{3} = -2$; $\tan \dfrac{2\pi}{3} = -\sqrt{3}$; $\cot \dfrac{2\pi}{3} = -\dfrac{\sqrt{3}}{3}$

16. $\sin \left(-\dfrac{2\pi}{3}\right) = -\dfrac{\sqrt{3}}{2}$; $\csc \left(-\dfrac{2\pi}{3}\right) = -\dfrac{2\sqrt{3}}{3}$; $\cos \left(-\dfrac{2\pi}{3}\right) = -\dfrac{1}{2}$; $\sec \left(-\dfrac{2\pi}{3}\right) = -2$; $\tan \left(-\dfrac{2\pi}{3}\right) = \sqrt{3}$; $\cot \left(-\dfrac{2\pi}{3}\right) = \dfrac{\sqrt{3}}{3}$

Practice Exercises, pages 157–158

2.

θ	$\sin \theta$	$\cos \theta$	$\tan \theta$	$\csc \theta$	$\sec \theta$	$\cot \theta$
0	0	1	0	undefined	1	undefined
$\dfrac{\pi}{2}$	1	0	undefined	1	undefined	0
π	0	-1	0	undefined	-1	undefined
$\dfrac{3\pi}{2}$	-1	0	undefined	-1	undefined	0

For Exercises 10–17, see Solutions Manual for graphs.

10. $\sin 120° = \dfrac{\sqrt{3}}{2}$; $\csc 120° = \dfrac{2\sqrt{3}}{3}$; $\cos 120° = -\dfrac{1}{2}$; $\sec 120° = -2$; $\tan 120° = -\sqrt{3}$; $\cot 120° = -\dfrac{\sqrt{3}}{3}$

11. $\sin 390° = \dfrac{1}{2}$; $\csc 390° = 2$; $\cos 390° = \dfrac{\sqrt{3}}{2}$; $\sec 390° = \dfrac{2\sqrt{3}}{3}$; $\tan 390° = \dfrac{\sqrt{3}}{3}$; $\cot 390° = \sqrt{3}$

12. $\sin (-60°) = -\dfrac{\sqrt{3}}{2}$; $\csc (-60°) = -\dfrac{2\sqrt{3}}{3}$; $\cos (-60°) = \dfrac{1}{2}$; $\sec (-60°) = 2$; $\tan (-60°) = -\sqrt{3}$; $\cot (-60°) = -\dfrac{\sqrt{3}}{3}$

13. $\sin (-135°) = -\dfrac{\sqrt{2}}{2}$; $\csc (-135°) = -\sqrt{2}$; $\cos (-135°) = -\dfrac{\sqrt{2}}{2}$; $\sec (-135°) = -\sqrt{2}$; $\tan (-135°) = 1$; $\cot (-135°) = 1$

14. $\sin \dfrac{10\pi}{3} = -\dfrac{\sqrt{3}}{2}$; $\csc \dfrac{10\pi}{3} = -\dfrac{2\sqrt{3}}{3}$; $\cos \dfrac{10\pi}{3} = -\dfrac{1}{2}$; $\sec \dfrac{10\pi}{3} = -2$; $\tan \dfrac{10\pi}{3} = \sqrt{3}$; $\cot \dfrac{10\pi}{3} = \dfrac{\sqrt{3}}{3}$

15. $\sin \left(-\dfrac{7\pi}{4}\right) = \dfrac{\sqrt{2}}{2}$; $\csc \left(-\dfrac{7\pi}{4}\right) = \sqrt{2}$; $\cos \left(-\dfrac{7\pi}{4}\right) = \dfrac{\sqrt{2}}{2}$; $\sec \left(-\dfrac{7\pi}{4}\right) = \sqrt{2}$; $\tan \left(-\dfrac{7\pi}{4}\right) = 1$; $\cot \left(-\dfrac{7\pi}{4}\right) = 1$

16. $\sin \left(-\dfrac{\pi}{3}\right) = -\dfrac{\sqrt{3}}{2}$; $\csc \left(-\dfrac{\pi}{3}\right) = -\dfrac{2\sqrt{3}}{3}$; $\cos \left(-\dfrac{\pi}{3}\right) = \dfrac{1}{2}$; $\sec \left(-\dfrac{\pi}{3}\right) = 2$; $\tan \left(-\dfrac{\pi}{3}\right) = -\sqrt{3}$; $\cot \left(-\dfrac{\pi}{3}\right) = -\dfrac{\sqrt{3}}{3}$

17. $\sin \dfrac{5\pi}{6} = \dfrac{1}{2}$; $\csc \dfrac{5\pi}{6} = 2$; $\cos \dfrac{5\pi}{6} = -\dfrac{\sqrt{3}}{2}$; $\sec \dfrac{5\pi}{6} = -\dfrac{2\sqrt{3}}{3}$; $\tan \dfrac{5\pi}{6} = -\dfrac{\sqrt{3}}{3}$; $\cot \dfrac{5\pi}{6} = -\sqrt{3}$

Class Exercises, pages 173–174

1. $\tan \phi \csc \phi \cos \phi = \dfrac{\sin \phi}{\cos \phi} \cdot \dfrac{1}{\sin \phi} \cdot \dfrac{\cos \phi}{1} = 1$

2. $(\sec \phi + 1)(\sec \phi - 1) = \sec^2 \phi - 1 = \tan^2 \phi$

3. $\cos \theta \csc \theta = \dfrac{\cos \theta}{1} \cdot \dfrac{1}{\sin \theta} = \cot \theta$

4. $(1 + \tan \beta)(1 - \cot \beta) = 1 - \cot \beta + \tan \beta - 1 = \tan \beta - \cot \beta$

5. $\dfrac{1 - \cos^2 y}{\sin y} = \dfrac{\sin^2 y}{\sin y} = \sin y$

6. $1 - \dfrac{1}{\sec^2 \theta} = 1 - \cos^2 \theta = \sin^2 \theta$

Practice Exercises, pages 174–175

3. $\dfrac{1}{1 - \sin \theta} + \dfrac{1}{1 + \sin \theta} = \dfrac{1 + \sin \theta + 1 - \sin \theta}{(1 - \sin \theta)(1 + \sin \theta)} = \dfrac{2}{1 - \sin^2 \theta} = \dfrac{2}{\cos^2 \theta} = 2 \sec^2 \theta$

4. $\dfrac{1 + \sin\theta}{\cos\theta} + \dfrac{\cos\theta}{1 + \sin\theta} = \dfrac{1 + \sin\theta}{\cos\theta} + \dfrac{\cos\theta\,(1 - \sin\theta)}{1 - \sin^2\theta} = \dfrac{1 + \sin\theta}{\cos\theta} + \dfrac{1 - \sin\theta}{\cos\theta} = \dfrac{2}{\cos\theta}$

5. $(\csc\theta + 1)(\csc\theta - 1) = \csc^2\theta - 1 = \cot^2\theta$

6. $\cos^4 x - \sin^4 x = (\cos^2 x + \sin^2 x)(\cos^2 x - \sin^2 x) = \cos^2 x - \sin^2 x$

7. $\cot^2\theta + \sec^2\theta - \tan^2\theta = \cot^2\theta + 1 = \csc^2\theta$

8. $\dfrac{1 + \tan^2 x}{\sec x} = \dfrac{\sec^2 x}{\sec x} = \sec x$

9. $\cos\phi\,(\sec\phi - \cos\phi) = \cos\phi\sec\phi - \cos^2\phi = 1 - \cos^2\phi = \sin^2\phi$

10. $\dfrac{\sec\theta - \csc\theta}{\csc\theta} = \dfrac{\sec\theta}{\csc\theta} - 1 = \dfrac{\frac{1}{\cos\theta}}{\frac{1}{\sin\theta}} - 1 = \dfrac{\sin\theta}{\cos\theta} - 1 = \tan\theta - 1$

For Exercises 24–29, answers may vary.

24. $\theta = \dfrac{\pi}{4}$ and $\phi = \dfrac{\pi}{4}$; $\tan\left(\dfrac{\pi}{4} + \dfrac{\pi}{4}\right)$ is undefined; $\tan\dfrac{\pi}{4} + \tan\dfrac{\pi}{4} = 2$

25. $\theta = \pi$ and $\beta = \dfrac{\pi}{6}$; $\cos\left(\pi - \dfrac{\pi}{6}\right) = -\dfrac{\sqrt{3}}{2}$; $\cos\pi - \cos\dfrac{\pi}{6} = -1 - \dfrac{\sqrt{3}}{2}$ **26.** $\theta = \dfrac{\pi}{3}$; $\sin\dfrac{2\pi}{3} = \dfrac{\sqrt{3}}{2}$; $2\sin\dfrac{\pi}{3} = \sqrt{3}$

27. $\phi = \dfrac{\pi}{3}$; $\dfrac{1}{2}\sec\dfrac{\pi}{3} = 1$; $\sec\dfrac{\pi}{6} = \dfrac{2\sqrt{3}}{3}$ **28.** $\theta = \dfrac{5\pi}{4}$; $\sqrt{\sin^2\dfrac{5\pi}{4}} = \dfrac{\sqrt{2}}{2}$; $\sin\dfrac{5\pi}{4} = -\dfrac{\sqrt{2}}{2}$ **29.** $\theta = \dfrac{\pi}{4}$; $\sqrt{1 - \sin^2\dfrac{\pi}{4}} = \dfrac{\sqrt{2}}{2}$; $-\cos\dfrac{\pi}{4} = -\dfrac{\sqrt{2}}{2}$

33. $\dfrac{1 - \cos\theta}{1 + \cos\theta} = \dfrac{(1 - \cos\theta)^2}{(1 + \cos\theta)(1 - \cos\theta)} = \dfrac{(1 - \cos\theta)^2}{1 - \cos^2\theta} = \dfrac{(1 - \cos\theta)^2}{\sin^2\theta} = \left(\dfrac{1 - \cos\theta}{\sin\theta}\right)^2 = (\csc\theta - \cot\theta)^2$

34. $\sec^2 x\csc^2 x = (\tan^2 x + 1)\csc^2 x = \dfrac{\sin^2 x}{\cos^2 x}\cdot\dfrac{1}{\sin^2 x} + \csc^2 x = \sec^2 x + \csc^2 x$

35. $\sin^4\alpha - \cos^4\alpha = (\sin^2\alpha + \cos^2\alpha)(\sin^2\alpha - \cos^2\alpha) = \sin^2\alpha - \cos^2\alpha = 1 - \cos^2\alpha - \cos^2\alpha = 1 - 2\cos^2\alpha$

36. $\dfrac{\cos\theta}{\csc\theta + 1} + \dfrac{\cos\theta}{\csc\theta - 1} = \dfrac{\cos\theta\csc\theta - \cos\theta + \cos\theta\csc\theta + \cos\theta}{\csc^2\theta - 1} = \dfrac{2\cos\theta\csc\theta}{\cot^2\theta} = \dfrac{2\cos\theta\cdot\frac{1}{\sin\theta}}{\frac{\cos^2\theta}{\sin^2\theta}} =$

$2\cos\theta\cdot\dfrac{1}{\sin\theta}\cdot\dfrac{\sin^2\theta}{\cos^2\theta} = 2\dfrac{\sin\theta}{\cos\theta} = 2\tan\theta$

37. $\sec^4\theta - 2\sec^2\theta\tan^2\theta + \tan^4\theta = (\sec^2\theta - \tan^2\theta)^2 = 1^2 = 1$

38. $\cot^2 x + \cos^2 x + \sin^2 x = \cot^2 x + 1 = \csc^2 x$

39. $\dfrac{\cos y}{1 + \sin y} + \dfrac{1 + \sin y}{\cos y} = \dfrac{\cos^2 y + (1 + \sin y)^2}{(1 + \sin y)\cos y} = \dfrac{\cos^2 y + 1 + 2\sin y + \sin^2 y}{(1 + \sin y)\cos y} = \dfrac{1 + 1 + 2\sin y}{(1 + \sin y)\cos y} =$

$\dfrac{2(1 + \sin y)}{(1 + \sin y)\cos y} = \dfrac{2}{\cos y} = 2\sec y$

40. $(\sin\beta + \cos\beta)^2\tan\beta = (\sin^2\beta + 2\sin\beta\cos\beta + \cos^2\beta)\tan\beta =$

$(1 + 2\sin\beta\cos\beta)\tan\beta = \tan\beta + 2\sin\beta\cos\beta\cdot\dfrac{\sin\beta}{\cos\beta} = \tan\beta + 2\sin^2\beta$

41. $\dfrac{\cos\theta}{1 + \sin\theta} = \dfrac{\cos\theta(1 - \sin\theta)}{1 - \sin^2\theta} = \dfrac{\cos\theta(1 - \sin\theta)}{\cos^2\theta} = \dfrac{1 - \sin\theta}{\cos\theta} = \sec\theta - \tan\theta$

42. $\dfrac{1}{\csc\theta + \cot\theta} = \dfrac{\csc\theta - \cot\theta}{(\csc\theta + \cot\theta)(\csc\theta - \cot\theta)} = \dfrac{\csc\theta - \cot\theta}{\csc^2\theta - \cot^2\theta} = \csc\theta - \cot\theta = \dfrac{1}{\sin\theta} - \dfrac{\cos\theta}{\sin\theta} = \dfrac{1 - \cos\theta}{\sin\theta}$

43. $\cos\theta = \sqrt{1 - \sin^2\theta}$; $\tan\theta = \dfrac{\sin\theta}{\sqrt{1 - \sin^2\theta}}$; $\csc\theta = \dfrac{1}{\sin\theta}$; $\sec\theta = \dfrac{1}{\sqrt{1 - \sin^2\theta}}$; $\cot\theta = \dfrac{\sqrt{1 - \sin^2\theta}}{\sin\theta}$

44. $\cos\theta = -\sqrt{1 - \sin^2\theta}$; $\tan\theta = -\dfrac{\sin\theta}{\sqrt{1 - \sin^2\theta}}$; $\csc\theta = \dfrac{1}{\sin\theta}$; $\sec\theta = -\dfrac{1}{\sqrt{1 - \sin^2\theta}}$; $\cot\theta = -\dfrac{\sqrt{1 - \sin^2\theta}}{\sin\theta}$

45. $(\sec\beta + \tan\beta)^3(\sec\beta - \tan\beta)^4 = [(\sec\beta + \tan\beta)(\sec\beta - \tan\beta)]^3(\sec\beta - \tan\beta) =$

$(\sec^2\beta - \tan^2\beta)^3(\sec\beta - \tan\beta) = \sec\beta - \tan\beta = \dfrac{1}{\cos\beta} - \dfrac{\sin\beta}{\cos\beta} = \dfrac{1 - \sin\beta}{\cos\beta}$

46. It is a contradiction because the range of sin θ is [−1, 1]. Other contradictions are $\sec \theta = \frac{1}{2}$, $\csc \theta = 0.5$, and $\cos \theta = 4$.

49. $\sqrt{(3\cos x + 4\sin x)^2 + (4\cos x - 3\sin x)^2} =$

$\sqrt{9\cos^2 x + 24\cos x \sin x + 16\sin^2 x + 16\cos^2 x - 24\cos x \sin x + 9\sin^2 x} =$

$\sqrt{25\cos^2 x + 25\sin^2 x} = \sqrt{25(\cos^2 x + \sin^2 x)} = \sqrt{25} = 5$

50.
$$\sqrt{\left(3\cos\frac{\pi}{8} + 4\sin\frac{\pi}{8}\right)^2 + \left(4\cos\frac{\pi}{8} - 3\sin\frac{\pi}{8}\right)^2} = 5$$

Test Yourself, page 175

13. $\sin^2\left(-\frac{\pi}{4}\right) + \cos^2\left(-\frac{\pi}{4}\right) = \left(-\frac{\sqrt{2}}{2}\right)^2 + \left(\frac{\sqrt{2}}{2}\right)^2 = \frac{1}{2} + \frac{1}{2} = 1$

14. $\dfrac{\cot 240° \tan 240°}{\sin 240°} = \dfrac{\frac{\sqrt{3}}{3}\cdot\sqrt{3}}{-\frac{\sqrt{3}}{2}} = \dfrac{1}{-\frac{\sqrt{3}}{2}} = -\dfrac{2\sqrt{3}}{3}$; $\csc 240° = \dfrac{1}{-\frac{\sqrt{3}}{2}} = -\dfrac{2\sqrt{3}}{3}$

15. $1 - \dfrac{1}{\csc^2 \phi} = 1 - \sin^2 \phi = \cos^2 \phi$

16. $1 + \dfrac{\sin^2 \theta}{\cos^2 \theta} = 1 + \tan^2 \theta = \sec^2 \theta = \sec \theta \cdot \dfrac{1}{\cos \theta} = \dfrac{\sec \theta}{\cos \theta}$

Chapter 4   Graphs and Inverses of Trigonometric Functions
Practice Exercises, pages 187–189

4.

5.

shifted 0.5 units down

6.
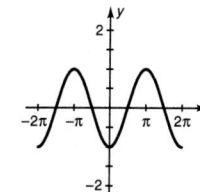
shifted π units right

7.

8.
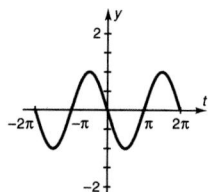
dilated $\frac{1}{2}$ unit vertically

9.
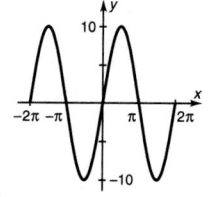
dilated 10 units vertically

10.
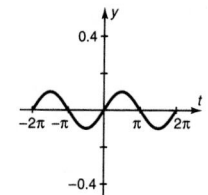
dilated 0.10 units vertically

11.

12.

shifted π units left

13.
reflected in x-axis;
dilated 4 units vertically

14.
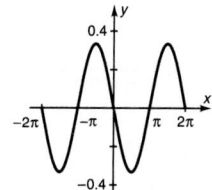
reflected in x-axis;
dilated $\frac{1}{3}$ units vertically

24. Since cos x is an even function, $\cos\left(\frac{\pi}{2} - x\right) = \cos\left(x - \frac{\pi}{2}\right)$. When graphed, this will give a cosine graph

shifted $\frac{\pi}{2}$ units right, which is the graph of sin x.

25. Since sin x is an odd function, $\sin\left(\frac{\pi}{2} - x\right) = -\sin\left(x - \frac{\pi}{2}\right)$. When graphed, this will give a reflection of the

sine graph shifted $\frac{\pi}{2}$ units right, which is the graph of cos x.

30.

shifted $\frac{\pi}{4}$ units right
and 2 units up

31.

reflected in x-axis;
shifted 3 units up

32.

reflected in x-axis;
shifted 3 units left

33.

34.

reflected in x-axis
where sin $x < 0$

35.

reflected in x-axis
where cos $x < 0$

36.

dilated 3 units vertically
and shifted 4 units up

37.

reflected in θ-axis; dilated
$\frac{1}{2}$ unit vertically; shifted 1

unit down

40.

42.

50.

51.

52.

53.

54.

Review, page 189

1. $\tan\theta \sec\theta = \dfrac{\sin\theta}{\cos\theta} \cdot \dfrac{1}{\cos\theta} = \dfrac{\sin\theta}{\cos^2\theta} = \dfrac{\sin\theta}{1 - \sin^2\theta}$

2. $\dfrac{\sec A}{\csc A} = \dfrac{\frac{1}{\cos A}}{\frac{1}{\sin A}} = \dfrac{\sin A}{\cos A} = \tan A$

16. $(1 - \cos x)^2 + (1 - \sin x)^2 = 1 - 2\cos x + \cos^2 x + 1 - 2\sin x + \sin^2 x = 3 - 2\cos x - 2\sin x$

17. $(\sec A + \cos A)^2 = \sec^2 A + 2\sec A \cos A + \cos^2 A = \dfrac{\cos^4 A + 2\cos^2 A + 1}{\cos^2 A}$

Class Exercises, page 196

9.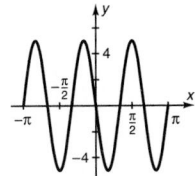

amp: 5; per: $\frac{2\pi}{3}$;

phase shift: $\frac{\pi}{3}$ right

vertical shift: none

10.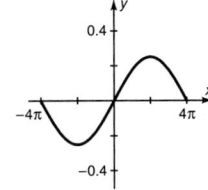

amp: $\frac{1}{4}$; per: 8π

phase shift: 2π right
vertical shift: none

11.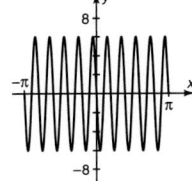

amp: 6; per: $\frac{\pi}{5}$;

phase shift: $\frac{\pi}{5}$ right

vertical shift: none

12.

amp: $\sqrt{2}$; per: $\frac{\pi}{2}$;

phase shift: $\frac{\pi}{12}$ right

vertical shift: none

14. maximum value: $|a|$; minimum value: $-|a|$; amplitude $= \frac{1}{2}\left[|a| - (-|a|)\right] = \frac{1}{2}(2|a|) = |a|$

Practice Exercises, pages 196–199

6.

7.

8.

9.

14.

16.

17.

For Exercises 26–31, see Solutions Manual for graphs.

26. amp: 2; per: π;

phase shift: $\frac{\pi}{4}$ right;

vertical shift: 1 down

27. amp: 4; per: π;
phase shift: π left;
vertical shift: 2 up

28. amp: 1; per: 8π;
phase shift: π right;
vertical shift: none

29. amp: 0.1; per: $\frac{2\pi}{3}$;

phase shift: $\frac{2\pi}{3}$ right;

vertical shift: none

30. amp: 3; per: 6π;

phase shift: $\frac{\pi}{2}$ right;

vertical shift: none

31. amp: $\sqrt{2}$; per: 10π;
phase shift: 1 right;
vertical shift: none

Practice Exercises, pages 205–207

10.

11.

12.

13.

14.

15.

28. increasing everywhere it is defined; never decreasing

29. increasing where defined on $(-2\pi, -\pi)$, $(0, \pi)$; decreasing where defined on $(-\pi, 0)$, $(\pi, 2\pi)$

30. never increasing; decreasing everywhere it is defined

31. $\left(-2\pi, -\frac{3\pi}{2}\right)$, $\left(-\frac{\pi}{2}, \frac{\pi}{2}\right)$; $\left(-\frac{3\pi}{2}, -\frac{\pi}{2}\right)$, $\left(\frac{\pi}{2}, \frac{3\pi}{2}\right)$

32. They agree at $x = 0$ and are continuous.

33. $D = \{x: x \geq 0\}$; $R = \{f(x): f(x) \geq -1\}$

34.

35.

36.

37.

38.

39.

46. 5; a horizontal translation which has the same period

47. 5; vertical translation which has the same period

48. 10; takes twice as long to complete a cycle

49. $\frac{5}{3}$; takes $\frac{1}{3}$ as long to complete a cycle

52.

53.

54.

55.

Class Exercises, page 211

3.

4.

9. The period of H is the least common multiple of the periods of $f(x)$ and $g(x)$.

10. no; The domain of $f + g$ is not defined at odd multiples of $\frac{\pi}{2}$, so the domain of f equals the domain of $f + g$. The domain of $f + g$ does not equal the domain of $\sin x$, since $\sin x$ is defined for all real x.

Practices Exercises, pages 211–213

1. $\left\{x: x \neq 0, x \neq \left(\frac{2k+1}{2}\right)\pi, k \in Z\right\}$

2. $\left\{\theta: \theta \neq \frac{k\pi}{2}, k \in Z\right\}$

4. $\left\{\phi: \phi \neq \frac{k\pi}{2}, k \in Z\right\}$

5.

6.

7.

8.

9.

10.

11.

12.

24.

25.

26.

27.

28.

29.

30.

31.

32.

34.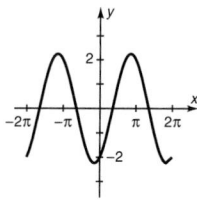

35. Let $P(x, y)$ be on the terminal side of angle t in standard position, and let $r = \sqrt{x^2 + y^2}$. Then $Q(-x, -y)$ is on the terminal side of $t - \pi$ and $\sin(t - \pi) = \dfrac{-y}{r} = -\sin t$.

38. The graph of $y = \cos t + \cos(t - \pi)$ is the graph of the line $y = 0$, which leads to the identity $\cos(t - \pi) = -\cos t$. Let $P(x, y)$ be on the terminal side of t in standard position, and let $r = \sqrt{x^2 + y^2}$. Then $Q(-x, -y)$ is on the terminal side of $t - \pi$, so $\cos(t - \pi) = \dfrac{-x}{r} = -\cos t$.

42.

43.

44.

45.

46.

47.

Test Yourself, page 213

1.

2.

3.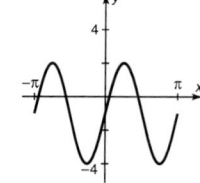

amp: 3; per: π;
phase shift: π right
vertical shift: 1 down

4.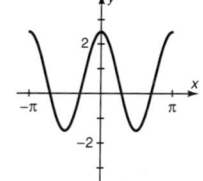

amp: 2; per: π;
phase shift: $\dfrac{\pi}{2}$ left
vertical shift: 0.5 up

965

5.

6.

7.

8.

9.

10.

Practice Exercises, pages 220–221

24. Answers may vary. Example: $\left[\frac{\pi}{2}, \frac{3\pi}{2}\right]$, $\left[\frac{3\pi}{2}, \frac{5\pi}{2}\right]$; These intervals will give all possible values of the sine once and only once.

Practice Exercises, pages 226–228

43.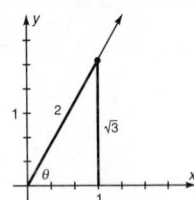

Let $\theta = \text{Sec}^{-1} 2$. Then $\sec \theta = 2$ and $\theta \in [0, \pi]$, so $\cos \theta = \frac{1}{2}$ and θ is in Quadrant I. Therefore, $\tan \theta = \sqrt{3}$ and $\theta \in \left(-\frac{\pi}{2}, \frac{\pi}{2}\right)$, so $\theta = \text{Tan}^{-1} \sqrt{3}$, and $\text{Sec}^{-1} 2 = \text{Tan}^{-1} \sqrt{3}$.

44. $\sin (\text{Arccsc } v) = \sin \left(\text{Arcsin } \frac{1}{v}\right) = \frac{1}{v}$ for all $v \in [-1, 1]$, $v \neq 0$

46. $Z = \begin{cases} \dfrac{5\sqrt{x^2 + 25}}{x^2 + 25}, & \text{if } x > 0 \\[2ex] -\dfrac{5\sqrt{x^2 + 25}}{x^2 + 25}, & \text{if } x < 0 \end{cases}$

47. $Z = \dfrac{7\sqrt{x^2 + 49}}{x^2 + 49}$

48. $f^{-1}(t) = \text{Tan}^{-1}(t + 1)$; $-\frac{\pi}{2} < f^{-1}(t) < \frac{\pi}{2}$; $t \in \mathcal{R}$; If $t = \frac{\pi}{4}$, then $f(t) = \tan \frac{\pi}{4} - 1 = 0$. If $f(t) = 0$, then $f^{-1}(t) = \text{Tan}^{-1}(0 + 1) = \frac{\pi}{4}$.

49. $g^{-1}(t) = \text{Cos}^{-1}(1 - t)$; $0 \le g^{-1}(t) \le \pi$; $0 \le t \le 2$; If $t = \frac{\pi}{3}$, then $g(t) = 1 - \cos \frac{\pi}{3} = 0.5$. If $g(t) = 0.5$, then $g^{-1}(t) = \text{Cos}^{-1}(1 - 0.5) = \frac{\pi}{3}$.

Practice Exercises, pages 233–236

15. $9x + 10y = 48$

18. $y = -110 \cos \frac{2\pi}{35}t + 114$

19. $y = 4 \cos \frac{\pi}{6}t$

24.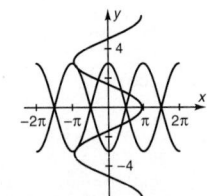

Summary and Review, pages 237–238

9.

10.

Chapter 6 Trigonometric Identities and Equations
Practice Exercises, pages 290–292

60. $\sin (\alpha + \beta) + \sin (\alpha - \beta) = \sin \alpha \cos \beta + \cos \alpha \sin \beta + \sin \alpha \cos \beta - \cos \alpha \sin \beta = 2 \sin \alpha \cos \beta$

64. $\cos (\alpha + \beta) \cos \beta + \sin (\alpha + \beta) \sin \beta = \cos [(\alpha + \beta) - \beta] = \cos \alpha$

65. $\sin (\alpha - \beta) \cos \beta + \cos (\alpha - \beta) \sin \beta = \sin [(\alpha - \beta) + \beta] = \sin \alpha$

66. $\cot(\alpha + \beta) = \dfrac{1}{\tan(\alpha + \beta)} = \dfrac{1}{\dfrac{\tan\alpha + \tan\beta}{1 - \tan\alpha\tan\beta}} = \dfrac{1 - \tan\alpha\tan\beta}{\tan\alpha + \tan\beta} \cdot \dfrac{\cot\alpha\cot\beta}{\cot\alpha\cot\beta} = \dfrac{\cot\alpha\cot\beta - 1}{\cot\beta + \cot\alpha} = \dfrac{\cot\alpha\cot\beta - 1}{\cot\alpha + \cot\beta}$

67. $\cot(\alpha - \beta) = \dfrac{1}{\tan(\alpha - \beta)} = \dfrac{1}{\dfrac{\tan\alpha - \tan\beta}{1 + \tan\alpha\tan\beta}} = \dfrac{1 + \tan\alpha\tan\beta}{\tan\alpha - \tan\beta} \cdot \dfrac{\cot\alpha\cot\beta}{\cot\alpha\cot\beta} = \dfrac{\cot\alpha\cot\beta + 1}{\cot\beta - \cot\alpha}$

Practice Exercises, pages 309–310

29. $2\cos\left(\dfrac{x+y}{2}\right)\sin\left(\dfrac{x-y}{2}\right) = 2\cos\left(\dfrac{x}{2} + \dfrac{y}{2}\right)\sin\left(\dfrac{x}{2} - \dfrac{y}{2}\right) = 2\left[\left(\cos\dfrac{x}{2}\cos\dfrac{y}{2} - \sin\dfrac{x}{2}\sin\dfrac{y}{2}\right)\left(\sin\dfrac{x}{2}\cos\dfrac{y}{2} - \cos\dfrac{x}{2}\sin\dfrac{y}{2}\right)\right] =$

$2\left(\cos\dfrac{x}{2}\sin\dfrac{x}{2}\cos^2\dfrac{y}{2} - \cos^2\dfrac{x}{2}\sin\dfrac{y}{2}\cos\dfrac{y}{2} - \sin^2\dfrac{x}{2}\sin\dfrac{y}{2}\cos\dfrac{y}{2} + \sin\dfrac{x}{2}\cos\dfrac{x}{2}\sin^2\dfrac{y}{2}\right) =$

$2\left[\sin\dfrac{x}{2}\cos\dfrac{x}{2}\left(\cos^2\dfrac{y}{2} + \sin^2\dfrac{y}{2}\right) - \sin\dfrac{y}{2}\cos\dfrac{y}{2}\left(\cos^2\dfrac{x}{2} + \sin^2\dfrac{x}{2}\right)\right] =$

$2\left(\sin\dfrac{x}{2}\cos\dfrac{x}{2} - \sin\dfrac{y}{2}\cos\dfrac{y}{2}\right) = 2\sin\dfrac{x}{2}\cos\dfrac{x}{2} - 2\sin\dfrac{y}{2}\cos\dfrac{y}{2} = \sin x - \sin y$

32. $\dfrac{\cos\beta - \cos 3\beta}{\sin 3\beta - \sin\beta} = \dfrac{-2\sin\left(\dfrac{\beta + 3\beta}{2}\right)\sin\left(\dfrac{\beta - 3\beta}{2}\right)}{2\cos\left(\dfrac{3\beta - \beta}{2}\right)\sin\left(\dfrac{3\beta - \beta}{2}\right)} = \dfrac{-2\sin 2\beta\sin(-\beta)}{2\cos 2\beta\sin\beta} = \dfrac{-(\sin 2\beta)(-\sin\beta)}{\cos 2\beta\sin\beta} = \dfrac{\sin 2\beta}{\cos 2\beta} = \tan 2\beta$

33. $\dfrac{\sin 2\beta - \sin 8\beta}{\cos 8\beta - \cos 2\beta} = \dfrac{2\cos\left(\dfrac{2\beta + 8\beta}{2}\right)\sin\left(\dfrac{2\beta - 8\beta}{2}\right)}{-2\sin\left(\dfrac{8\beta + 2\beta}{2}\right)\sin\left(\dfrac{8\beta - 2\beta}{2}\right)} = \dfrac{\cos 5\beta\sin(-3\beta)}{-(\sin 5\beta)(\sin 3\beta)} = \dfrac{-(\cos 5\beta)(\sin 3\beta)}{-(\sin 5\beta)(\sin 3\beta)} = \dfrac{\cos 5\beta}{\sin 5\beta}$

38. $\dfrac{2}{h}\cos\left(\dfrac{2x+h}{2}\right)\sin\dfrac{h}{2}$

39. $\dfrac{2}{h}\sin\left(\dfrac{2x+h}{2}\right)\cos\dfrac{h}{2}$

40. $-\dfrac{2}{h}\sin\left(\dfrac{2x+h}{2}\right)\sin\dfrac{h}{2}$

41. $\dfrac{2}{h}\cos\left(\dfrac{2x+h}{2}\right)\cos\dfrac{h}{2}$

42. $\dfrac{\sin h}{h\cos(x+h)\cos x}$

43. $\dfrac{\sin(2x+h)}{h\cos(x+h)\cos x}$

44. $\cos(x+y)\cos(x-y) = \dfrac{1}{2}\{\cos[(x+y)-(x-y)] + \cos[(x+y)+(x-y)]\} = \dfrac{1}{2}(\cos 2y + \cos 2x) =$

$\dfrac{1}{2}[(2\cos^2 y - 1) + (1 - 2\sin^2 x)] = \dfrac{1}{2}(2\cos^2 y - 2\sin^2 x) = \cos^2 y - \sin^2 x$

45. $\sin(x+y)\cos(x-y) = \dfrac{1}{2}\{\sin[(x+y)+(x-y)] + \sin[(x+y)-(x-y)]\} = \dfrac{1}{2}(\sin 2x + \sin 2y) =$

$\dfrac{1}{2}(2\sin x\cos x + 2\sin y\cos y) = \sin x\cos x + \sin y\cos y$

46. $\sin(x+y)\sin(x-y) = \dfrac{1}{2}\{\cos[(x+y)-(x-y)] - \cos[(x+y)+(x-y)]\} = \dfrac{1}{2}(\cos 2y - \cos 2x) =$

$\dfrac{1}{2}[(1 - 2\sin^2 y) - (1 - 2\sin^2 x)] = \dfrac{1}{2}(-2\sin^2 y + 2\sin^2 x) = \sin^2 x - \sin^2 y$

47. $-\sin(x+y)\sin(x-y) = -\dfrac{1}{2}\{[\cos(x+y) - (x-y)] - \cos[(x+y) + (x-y)]\} = -\dfrac{1}{2}(\cos 2y - \cos 2x) =$

$-\dfrac{1}{2}[(2\cos^2 y - 1) - (2\cos^2 x - 1)] = -\dfrac{1}{2}(2\cos^2 y - 2\cos^2 x) = \cos^2 x - \cos^2 y$

Practice Exercises, pages 314–316

34. $3\cos 2x = -7\sin x$ can be rewritten $6\sin^2 x - 7\sin x - 3 = 0$, which can be factored into $2\sin x - 3 = 0$, which has no solutions, and $3\sin x + 1 = 0$, which has two solutions; $3\cos 2x = -4\sin x + 1$ can be rewritten $6\sin^2 x - 4\sin x - 2 = 0$, which can be factored into $\sin x - 1 = 0$, which has 1 solution, and $3\sin x + 1 = 0$, which has two solutions.

Chapter 7   Polynomial Functions
Class Exercises, page 334

7. $2x^3 - 3x^2 + 2x - 4 = (x - 2)(2x^2 + x + 4) + 4$

8. $x^5 - 5x^2 = (x + 3)(x^4 - 3x^3 + 9x^2 - 32x + 96) - 288$

9. $4x^5 - 7x^3 + 9x^2 - 4x - 1 = (2x + 1)(2x^4 - x^3 - 3x^2 + 6x - 5) + 4$

Class Exercises, page 340

5.   **6.**   **7.**   **8.**

Practice Exercises, page 340-342

7.   **8.**   **9.**   **10.**   **11.**

12.   **14.**   **15.**   **16.**   **17.**

18.   **19.**

20. The minimum number of relative extrema a fourth degree polynomial can have is 1, since it must have either 1 or 3 relative extrema.

22.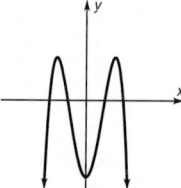

23. Let x represent the number of pens sold. $f(x) = 1500 + 0.35x$; $g(x) = 0.65x$

43.

32. zeros: $-2, 2, 3$; 2 relative extrema; $x^3 - 3x^2 - 4x + 12 = (x + 2)(x - 2)(x - 3)$

33. zeros: -3 (mult. 2), 0 (mult. 2); 3 relative extrema; $x^4 + 6x^3 + 9x^2 = x^2(x + 3)^2$

34. zeros: $-2, -1$ (mult. 3); 1 relative extrema; $x^4 + 5x^3 + 9x^2 + 7x + 2 = (x + 2)(x + 1)^3$

35. zeros: $-2, 0, 1$ (mult. 2); 3 relative extrema; $x^4 - 3x^2 + 2x = x(x + 2)(x - 1)^2$

36. zeros: $-3, 0$ (mult. 3), 4; 2 relative extrema; $x^5 - x^4 - 12x^3 = x^3(x + 3)(x - 4)$

37. zeros: $-5, -2, -1, 1, 2$; 4 relative extrema; $x^5 + 5x^4 - 5x^3 - 25x^2 + 4x + 20 = (x + 5)(x + 2)(x + 1)(x - 1)(x - 2)$

Practice Exercises, pages 347–348

20. Given the general cubic polynomial function $f(x) = px^3 + qx^2 + rx + e$ with a being a zero, then $pa^3 + qa^2 + ra + e = 0$, or $pa^3 + qa^2 + ra = -e$. So $a(pa^2 + qa + r) = -e$, and a divides into both the left and right side. If a divides into $-e$, it also divides into e, and is therefore a factor of e.

Practice Exercises, pages 361–363

49. Check students' programs. Make sure they solve for $p(a)$ and $p(b)$ to get y_1 and y_2, respectively, and then solve for the approximate zero at $x = x_1 - \dfrac{y_1}{y_2 - y_1}(x_2 - x_1)$.

Practice Exercises, pages 368–370

16. yes; $f(x)$ is the quotient of two polynomials and the denominator does not equal zero everywhere

17. yes; $f(x)$ is the quotient of two polynomials and the denominator never equals zero

19.

22.

26.
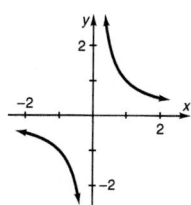

no intercepts;
asymptotes: $x = 0$, $y = 0$

27.
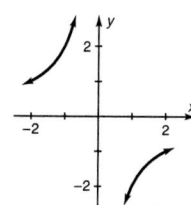

no intercepts;
asymptotes: $x = 0$, $y = 0$

28.
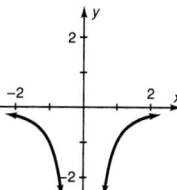

no intercepts;
asymptotes: $x = 0$, $y = 0$

29.
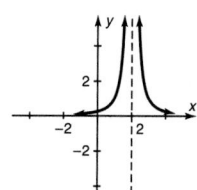

intercept: $\left(0, \frac{1}{4}\right)$;

asymptotes: $x = 2$, $y = 0$

30.
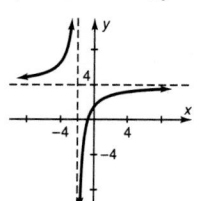

intercepts: $\left(-\frac{3}{4}, 0\right)$, $\left(0, \frac{3}{2}\right)$;

asymptotes: $x = -2$, $y = 4$

31.

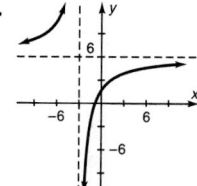

intercepts: $\left(-\frac{5}{6}, 0\right)$, $\left(0, \frac{5}{3}\right)$;

asymptotes: $x = -3$, $y = 6$

32.
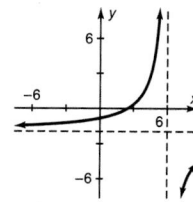

intercepts: $\left(\frac{5}{2}, 0\right)$, $\left(0, -\frac{5}{6}\right)$;

asymptotes: $x = 6$, $y = -2$

33.
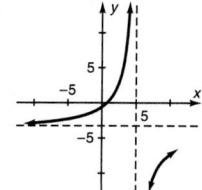

intercepts: $\left(\frac{3}{4}, 0\right)$, $\left(0, -\frac{3}{5}\right)$;

asymptotes: $x = 5$, $y = -4$

34.
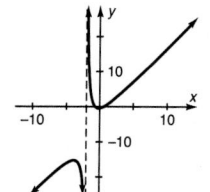

intercepts: $\left(\pm\frac{\sqrt{2}}{2}, 0\right)$, $\left(0, -\frac{1}{2}\right)$;

asymptotes: $x = -2$,
$\quad y = 2x - 2$

35.
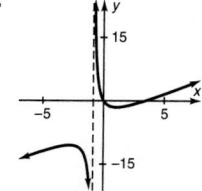

intercepts: $(0, 0)$, $(4, 0)$;
asymptotes: $x = -1$,
$\quad y = x - 5$

36.
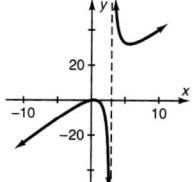

intercepts: $(0, 0)$, $\left(\frac{2}{3}, 0\right)$;

asymptotes: $x = 3$,
$\quad y = 3x + 7$

37.
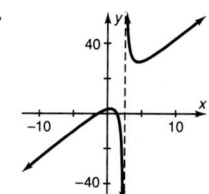

intercepts: $\left(\pm\frac{\sqrt{5}}{2}, 0\right)$; $\left(0, \frac{5}{2}\right)$;

asymptotes: $x = 2$,
$\quad y = 4x + 8$

38.

intercepts: $(-2, 0)$, $\left(0, -\frac{4}{3}\right)$;

asymptotes: $x = +1$,
$\quad x = -3$, $y = 1$

39.

intercepts: $(4, 0)$, $\left(0, -\frac{8}{3}\right)$;

asymptotes: $x = -1$,
$\quad x = 6$, $y = 1$

40.

intercepts: $(-2, 0)$, $(3, 0)$,

   $(0, 3)$;
asymptotes: $x = -1$, $x = 2$,
   $y = 1$

41.

intercepts: $(-1, 0)$, $(7, 0)$,

   $\left(0, \dfrac{7}{16}\right)$;

asymptotes: $x = 2$, $x = -8$,
   $y = 1$

42. asymptotes: $P = 0$, $I = 0$; If the current is increased by a factor of x, then the resistance is decreased by a factor of $\dfrac{1}{x^2}$.

44. The asymptotes are $x = -\dfrac{d}{c}$, $y = \dfrac{a}{c}$ if $a \neq 0$, and $y = 0$ if $a = 0$.

Practice Exercises, pages 378–379

10. Graph the original function and the function which represents the sum of the partial fractions. Their graphs should be identical.

Chapter 8   Inequalities and Linear Programming
Practice Exercises, pages 390–392

7.

8.

9.

10.

11.

29.

30.

31.

32.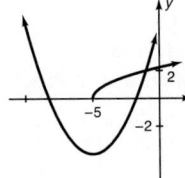

33. Answers may vary. If k is any integer, $x = k\pi + \dfrac{\pi}{4}$ and $y = (-1)^k \dfrac{\sqrt{2}}{2}$.

Class Exercises, page 398

5.

$\left(-\infty, \dfrac{1}{12}\right]$

6.

$\left(-\dfrac{9}{2}, 2\right]$

7.

$(-\infty, -3) \cup \left(\dfrac{13}{3}, \infty\right)$

8.

$\left(-\dfrac{1}{2}, \dfrac{1}{2}\right)$

9.

10.

11.

12.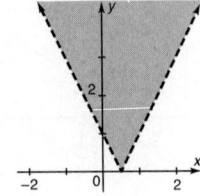

13. On the same set of axes, graph $F = \dfrac{9}{5}C + 32$ and $F = 68$. Determine by inspection the x-coordinates for which the line $F = \dfrac{9}{5}C + 32$ lies above the line $F = 68$.

Practice Exercises, pages 398–400

1. $[1, 4]$

2. $(2, 10]$

3. $(-6, 4)$

4. $(-\infty, 0] \cup [4, \infty)$

0   4

5. $(-\infty, 1] \cup [5, \infty)$

0 1   5

6. $(-\infty, 6) \cup (6, \infty)$

6

7.

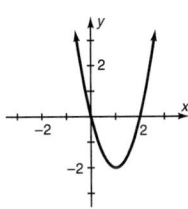

8. no; If $a < 0$ and $|a| > |b|$, then $a < b$, but $a^2 > b^2$.

15. axis: $x = \frac{1}{3}$; vertex: $\left(\frac{1}{3}, -\frac{20}{3}\right)$; no x-int; y-int: $(0, -7)$

17. between $74°$ and $75°$

21.

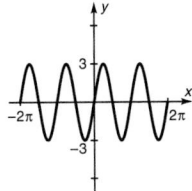

−13 0   15

$(-13, 15)$

22.

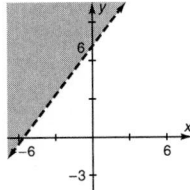

$-\frac{1}{2}$ 0 $\frac{3}{2}$

$\left(-\frac{1}{2}, \frac{3}{2}\right)$

23.

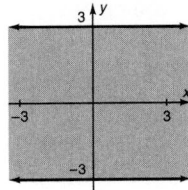

0 $\frac{5}{3}$

$\left(-\infty, \frac{5}{3}\right) \cup \left(\frac{5}{3}, \infty\right)$

24.

0

$\varnothing$

25.

28.

29.

33.

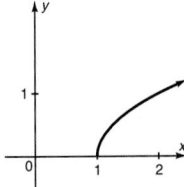

30. Quadrant I: $x > 0$; $y > 0$;   Quadrant II: $x < 0$; $y > 0$;   Quadrant III: $x < 0$; $y < 0$;   Quadrant IV: $x > 0$; $y < 0$

32. between 148 and 220 loaves

Practice Exercises, pages 404–405

10. The graph lies entirely above the x–axis and opens up. Thus, $a > 0$.

12. $x \le 2$ or $x \ge 4$

13. $-8 < x < 1$

14. $-3 < t < 3$

18.

19.

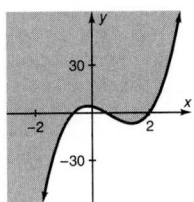

21. never true; Since $x^2 \ge 0$ for all real numbers, $x^2 + 9 \ge 9$.

36. If $a < 0$, then $x < z_1$ or $x > z_2$. If $a > 0$, then $z_1 < x < z_2$.

37. less than 2.35 in.

39. $-1.79 \le x \le -0.62$ or $1.62 \le x \le 2.79$

40. $-1 \le x \le 1.79$

41. $-7.53 < x < -7$ or $0 < x < 0.53$

Practice Exercises, pages 409–411

12.

13.

15.

17.

16. The inequality $x^3 + 8 \le 0$ is true for $x \le -2$.

19. See Solutions Manual for proof.

24. $(-\infty, 3.1)$

25. $[-1.7, 0.1]$ or $[1.8, \infty)$

26. $(-\infty, -0.8]$ or $[0.8, 2.8]$

27. $(-\infty, -3]$ or $[-1.7, 1.7]$

28.

29.

33.

34. $(-\infty, -4)$ or $(4, \infty)$

35. $(-\infty, \infty)$

36. $(-\infty, -1.2)$ or $(1.5, \infty)$

37. $[-1.7, 3]$

Test Yourself, page 411

3.

8.

9.

10.

11.

Class Exercises, page 415

9. number of roses = x-coordinate and number of day lilies = y-coordinate; (3, 17), (6, 16), (9, 15), (12, 14), (15, 13), (18, 12), (21, 11), (24, 10), (27, 9), (30, 8), (33, 7), (36, 6), (39, 5), (42, 4), (45, 3), (48, 2), (51, 1)

Practice Exercises, pages 415–417

For Exercises 1–9, 12–15, 21–28, and 36–41, see Solutions Manual for graphs.

18. number of electric clocks = x-coordinate and number of battery clocks = y-coordinate; (0, 0), (0, 1), (0, 2), (0, 3), (0, 4), (0, 5), (0, 6), (0, 7), (0, 8), (0, 9), (1, 0), (1, 1), (1, 2), (1, 3), (1, 4), (1, 5), (1, 6), (1, 7), (1, 8), (2, 0), (2, 1), (2, 2), (2, 3), (2, 4), (2, 5), (2, 6), (3, 0), (3, 1), (3, 2), (3, 3), (3, 4), (4, 0), (4, 1), (4, 2), (4, 3), (5, 0), (5, 1)

19. number of apples = x-coordinate and number of pears = y-coordinate; (3, 0), (4, 0), (5, 0), (3, 1), (2, 1), (2, 2), (1, 2), (1, 3), (0, 3), (0, 4)

32. Let x represent the number of red blocks and y the number of natural-colored blocks. $x > 0, y > 0, y < \frac{1}{3}x$, $1.7x + 1.5y \le 400$

42. As more and more time passes without a train, the probability that the next will be a southbound train approaches zero. The event and sample spaces both become smaller as time goes by, but the event space also occupies a progressively smaller percentage of the current sample.

43. Let S represent the number of hours the 60-w bulb is left on and H the number of hours the 100-w bulb is left on. $S \ge 0, H \ge 0, 1.3H + 0.8S < 800, S \le H - 50$

Class Exercises, pages 427–428

1. Let x represent the number of teak wastebaskets.
Let y represent the number of mahogony wastebaskets.
Maximize the objective function $P = 5x + 5y$
Constraints:
$\begin{cases} 2x + y \le 6 \\ x + 2y \le 6 \\ x \ge 0, y \ge 0 \end{cases}$

2. Let x represent the number of type A labelers.
Let y represent the number of type B labelers.
Maximize the objective function $P = 7x + 10y$
Constraints:
$\begin{cases} 5x + 6y \le 420 \\ x \le 60 \\ y \le 45 \\ x \ge 0, y \ge 0 \end{cases}$

3. Let x represent the number of bags of regular mix.
Let y represent the number of bags of deluxe mix.
Minimize the objective function $C = 2x + 7y$
Constraints:
$\begin{cases} 4x + 3y \ge 27 \\ x + y \ge 8 \\ 3x + 5y \ge 30 \\ x \ge 0, y \ge 0 \end{cases}$

4. Let x represent the number of packets of regular dressing.
Let y represent the number of packets of lite dressing.
Minimize the objective function $C = 0.03x + 0.02y$
$\begin{cases} 6x + 2y \ge 26 \\ 2x + 6y \ge 14 \\ x \ge 0, y \ge 0 \end{cases}$

Chapter 9 Exponential and Logarithmic Functions

Practice Exercises, pages 450–452

For Exercises 1–8, see Solutions Manual for graphs.

1. $D = \{x: x \in \mathcal{R}\}$; $R = \{y: y > 0\}$; x-int: none; y-int: (0, 1); increasing; one-to-one

2. $D = \{x: x \in \mathcal{R}\}$; $R = \{y: y > 0\}$; x-int: none; y-int: (0, 1); increasing; one-to-one

3. $D = \{x: x \in \mathcal{R}\}$; $R = \{y: y > 0\}$; x-int: none; y-int: (0, 1); decreasing; one-to-one

4. $D = \{x: x \in \mathcal{R}\}$; $R = \{y: y > 0\}$; x-int: none; y-int: (0, 1); decreasing; one-to-one

5. $D = \{x: x \in \mathcal{R}\}$; $R = \{y: y > 1\}$; x-int: none; y-int: (0, 2); increasing; one-to-one

6. $D = \{x: x \in \mathcal{R}\}$; $R = \{y: y > 0\}$; x-int: none; y-int: (0, 1); decreasing; one-to-one

7. $D = \{x: x \in \mathcal{R}\}$; $R = \{y: y > 0\}$; x-int: none; y-int: $(0, e^{-3})$; increasing; one-to-one

8. $D = \{x: x \in \mathcal{R}\}$; $R = \{y: y > -3\}$; x-int: $(-1.58, 0)$; y-int: $(0, -2)$; decreasing; one-to-one

10. If $b < 0$ and $x = \dfrac{1}{n}$, where n is an even integer, then b^x is not a real number.

23. $y = 3$

24. $y = 0$

25. $y = 2$

26. $y = 3$

27. $y = -2$

28. $y = 1$

29.

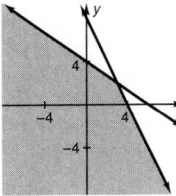

36. $P(x)$ can be used to approximate $f(x)$ for $x > -1.5$.

Practice Exercises, pages 458–460

For Exercises 13, 14, 26, and 27, see Solutions Manual for graphs.

13. $D = \left\{x: x > -4\frac{1}{2}\right\}$; $R = \{y: y \in \mathcal{R}\}$; x-int: $(-4, 0)$; y-int: (0, 0.95); asymptote: $x = -4\frac{1}{2}$; increasing

14. $D = \{x: x > -0.1\}$; $R = \{y: y \in \mathcal{R}\}$; x-int: (0.9, 0); y-int: (0, -1); asymptote: $x = -0.1$; increasing

23.

24.

25.

26.

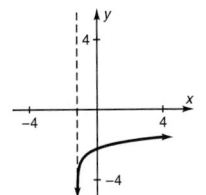

$D = \left\{x: x > -\frac{6}{5}\right\}$; $R = \{y: y \in \mathcal{R}\}$; x-int: (198.8, 0); y-int: (0, -2.2); asymptote: $x = -\frac{6}{5}$; increasing

27.

$D = \{x: x > -e^2\}$; $R = \{y: y \in \mathcal{R}\}$; x-int: $(-6.39, 0)$; y-int: $(0, -4)$; asymptote: $x = -e^2$; decreasing

28. Comparing the graphs results in the expression $-\log_b x = \log_{\frac{1}{b}} x$.

29.

30.

31.

Practice Exercises, pages 464–466

1. Let $\log_b M = u$. So $b^u = M$, $(b^u)^r = M^r$, $b^{ur} = M^r$, $\log_b b^{ur} = \log_b M^r$, $ur = \log_b M^r$, $r \log_b M = \log_b M^r$.

2. Let $\log_b M = x$ and $\log_b N = y$. So $b^x = M$ and $b^y = N$, $\dfrac{M}{N} = \dfrac{b^x}{b^y}$, $\dfrac{M}{N} = b^{x-y}$, $\log_b \dfrac{M}{N} = \log_b b^{x-y}$, $\log_b \dfrac{M}{N} = x - y = \log_b M - \log_b N$.

Practice Exercises, pages 478–481

6. 3.7%; $P = 389{,}910e^{0.037t}$; $P = 608{,}000$;

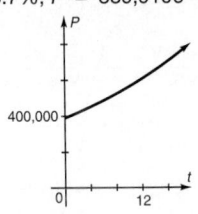

12. When $t = 0$, the population growth curve gives the present population.

13.

17.

Chapter 10   Polar Coordinates and Complex Numbers
Class Exercises, pages 491–492

1.

Examples: $(-1, 2\pi)$, $(1, 3\pi)$, $(-1, 0)$

2.

Examples: $\left(1.5, -\dfrac{\pi}{3}\right)$, $\left(1.5, \dfrac{5\pi}{3}\right)$, $\left(-1.5, -\dfrac{4\pi}{3}\right)$

3.

Examples: $\left(10, \dfrac{11\pi}{8}\right)$, $\left(-10, \dfrac{3\pi}{8}\right)$, $\left(-10, -\dfrac{13\pi}{8}\right)$

19. If $r < 0$, the point (r, θ) is $|r|$ units from the pole on the ray opposite the terminal side of the angle with measure θ. This point can be represented $[-r, (\theta + \pi)]$. Thus $x = -r \cos (\theta + \pi) = -r (-\cos \theta) = r \cos \theta$. Similarly, $y = -r \sin (\theta + \pi) = -r (-\sin \theta) = r \sin \theta$.

Practice Exercises, pages 492–493

For Exercises 8–14, see Solutions Manual for graphs.

1.

2.

3.

4.

5.
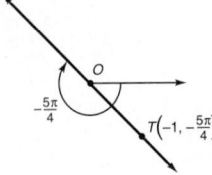

6. O
$W(0, 150°)$

7.

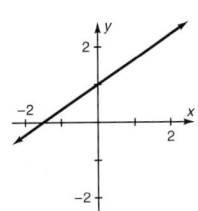

8. The coordinates of a point in the Cartesian system are interpreted differently than the coordinates of a point in the polar system.

9. Examples: $\left(-7, -\frac{11\pi}{6}\right)$, $\left(7, -\frac{5\pi}{6}\right)$, $\left(7, \frac{7\pi}{6}\right)$

10. Examples: $\left(2.8, \frac{\pi}{3}\right)$, $\left(2.8, -\frac{5\pi}{3}\right)$, $\left(-2.8, \frac{4\pi}{3}\right)$

11. Examples: $\left(29, -\frac{2\pi}{3}\right)$, $\left(29, \frac{4\pi}{3}\right)$, $\left(-29, \frac{\pi}{3}\right)$

12. Examples: $(11, -344°)$, $(-11, 196°)$, $(-11, -164°)$

13. Examples: $(6, 340°)$, $(6, -20°)$, $(-6, 160°)$

14. Examples: $\left(-5, \frac{5\pi}{4}\right)$, $\left(5, -\frac{7\pi}{4}\right)$, $\left(5, \frac{\pi}{4}\right)$

16.   **17.**   **18.**   **19.**

20.

21.

Class Exercises, pages 500–501

For Exercise 20, see Solutions Manual for graph.

1. $r = c$ is symmetric with respect to the pole, the polar axis, and the line $\theta = \frac{\pi}{2}$; $\theta = k$ is symmetric with respect to the pole

Practice Exercises, pages 501–502

For Exercise 54, see Solutions Manual for graph.

10.   **11.**   **12.**   **13.**   **14.**

15.   **16.**   **17.**   **18.**   **20.** $x = 9$

21. $y = -2$ **22.** $y = -3$ **23.** $x = 2\sqrt{7}$ 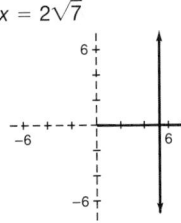 **24.** $(x - 1)^2 + y^2 = 1$ 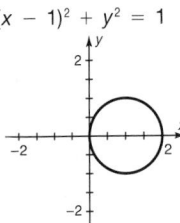 **25.** $x^2 + \left(y - \frac{\sqrt{11}}{2}\right)^2 = \frac{11}{4}$

26.   **27.**   **28.**   **29.**   **30.**

31.

32. $y = \frac{1}{2}x^2 - \frac{1}{2}$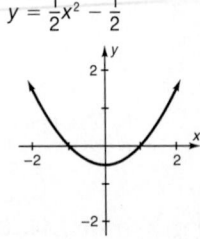

33. $\sin(\pi - \theta) = \sin[\pi + (-\theta)] =$
$\sin \pi \cos(-\theta) + \cos \pi \sin(-\theta) =$
$(0)[\cos(-\theta)] + (-1)(-\sin \theta) = \sin \theta$

34.

36. Since $f[\sin(\pi - \theta)]$ is equivalent to $f(\sin \theta)$, both graphs have symmetry with respect to the line $\theta = \frac{1}{2}\pi$.

37.

51. The graph of $r = f(\theta - \beta)$ is the graph of $r = f(\theta)$ rotated counterclockwise for $\beta > 0$ and clockwise for $\beta < 0$.

52. $r = a \cos \theta + b \sin \theta$, $r^2 = ar \cos \theta + br \sin \theta$, $x^2 + y^2 = ax + by$, $x^2 - ax + y^2 - by = 0$, $\left(x - \frac{a}{2}\right)^2 + \left(y - \frac{b}{2}\right)^2 = \frac{a^2 + b^2}{4}$; circle with center $\left(\frac{a}{2}, \frac{b}{2}\right)$ and radius $\frac{\sqrt{a^2 + b^2}}{2}$

54. $\left(\frac{5\sqrt{2}}{2}, \frac{\pi}{4}\right), \left(-\frac{5\sqrt{2}}{2}, \frac{5\pi}{4}\right)$ The pole is on both graphs but $0 = 5 \cos \frac{\pi}{2}$ for one and $0 = 5 \sin 0$ for the other.

Different coordinates for the same point in polar coordinates can prevent simultaneous solutions of equations from identifying all points of intersection.

Practice Exercises, pages 506–508

1.

2.

3.

4.

5.

6.

40.

41.

42.

43.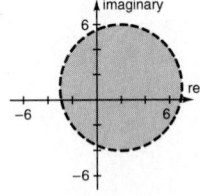

Test Yourself, page 508

44.

45.

12.

13.

14.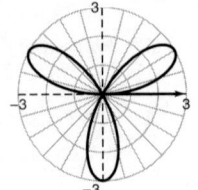

Practice Exercises, pages 513–515

37.

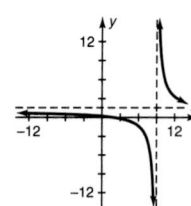

38. $\left[\frac{1}{2}\left(\sqrt{2} + \sqrt{2}\,i\right)\right]\left[\frac{1}{2}\left(\sqrt{2} + \sqrt{2}\,i\right)\right] = \frac{1}{2} + i + \frac{1}{2}i^2 = \frac{1}{2} + i - \frac{1}{2} = i$; The second root is

$-\frac{1}{2}\left(\sqrt{2} + \sqrt{2}\,i\right)$ because of the fact if $a^2 = b$, then $(-a)^2 = b$.

Practice Exercises, pages 526–527

For Exercises 1–10, 17–20, 42, 43, and 47, see Solutions Manual for graphs.

1. $5 \text{ cis } \frac{\pi}{3}, -5, 5 \text{ cis } \frac{5\pi}{3}$

2. $2 \text{ cis } \frac{\pi}{10}, 2i, 2 \text{ cis } \frac{9\pi}{10}, 2 \text{ cis } \frac{13\pi}{10}, 2 \text{ cis } \frac{17\pi}{10}$

3. $\text{cis } \frac{\pi}{16}, \text{cis } \frac{9\pi}{16}, \text{cis } \frac{17\pi}{16}, \text{cis } \frac{25\pi}{16}$

4. $9 \text{ cis } \frac{\pi}{15}, 9 \text{ cis } \frac{11\pi}{15}, 9 \text{ cis } \frac{21\pi}{15}$

5. $6 \text{ cis } \frac{\pi}{16}, 6 \text{ cis } \frac{17\pi}{16}$

6. $\sqrt[8]{10} \text{ cis } \frac{\pi}{24}, \sqrt[8]{10} \text{ cis } \frac{7\pi}{24},$
$\sqrt[8]{10} \text{ cis } \frac{13\pi}{24}, \sqrt[8]{10} \text{ cis } \frac{19\pi}{24},$
$\sqrt[8]{10} \text{ cis } \frac{25\pi}{24}, \sqrt[8]{10} \text{ cis } \frac{31\pi}{24},$
$\sqrt[8]{10} \text{ cis } \frac{37\pi}{24}, \sqrt[8]{10} \text{ cis } \frac{43\pi}{24}$

7. $\sqrt[6]{50} \text{ cis } \frac{\pi}{12}, \sqrt[6]{50} \text{ cis } \frac{3\pi}{4}, \sqrt[6]{50} \text{ cis } \frac{17\pi}{12}$

8. $\sqrt[6]{2} \text{ cis } \frac{11\pi}{36}, \sqrt[6]{2} \text{ cis } \frac{23\pi}{36}, \sqrt[6]{2} \text{ cis } \frac{35\pi}{36},$
$\sqrt[6]{2} \text{ cis } \frac{47\pi}{36}, \sqrt[6]{2} \text{ cis } \frac{59\pi}{36}, \sqrt[6]{2} \text{ cis } \frac{71\pi}{36}$

9. $\sqrt[6]{2} \text{ cis } \frac{7\pi}{12}, \sqrt[6]{2} \text{ cis } \frac{5\pi}{4}, \sqrt[6]{2} \text{ cis } \frac{23\pi}{12}$

10. $\sqrt[4]{2} \text{ cis } \frac{\pi}{3}, \sqrt[4]{2} \text{ cis } \frac{5\pi}{6}, \sqrt[4]{2} \text{ cis } \frac{4\pi}{3}, \sqrt[4]{2} \text{ cis } \frac{11\pi}{6}$

16. six sixth roots of unity: $1, \text{cis } \frac{\pi}{3}, \text{cis } \frac{2\pi}{3}, -1, \text{cis } \frac{4\pi}{3}, \text{cis } \frac{5\pi}{3}$ six sixth roots of 64: $2, 2 \text{ cis } \frac{\pi}{3}, 2 \text{ cis } \frac{2\pi}{3}, -2, 2 \text{ cis } \frac{4\pi}{3}, 2 \text{ cis } \frac{5\pi}{3}$

21. $x^6 - 1 = (x^3 - 1)(x^3 + 1) = (x - 1)(x^2 + x + 1)(x + 1)(x^2 - x + 1)$; The roots are $1, -\frac{1}{2} + \frac{\sqrt{3}}{2}i, -\frac{1}{2} - \frac{\sqrt{3}}{2}i,$
$-1, \frac{1}{2} + \frac{\sqrt{3}}{2}i,$ and $\frac{1}{2} - \frac{\sqrt{3}}{2}i,$ which agree with Exercise 16.

22. $5 \text{ cis } \frac{\pi}{4}, 5 \text{ cis } \frac{3\pi}{4}, 5 \text{ cis } \frac{5\pi}{4}, 5 \text{ cis } \frac{7\pi}{4}$ **23.** $\sqrt[3]{52}, \sqrt[3]{52} \text{ cis } \frac{2\pi}{3}, \sqrt[3]{52} \text{ cis } \frac{4\pi}{3}$ **24.** $0, \sqrt[5]{25}, \sqrt[5]{25} \text{ cis } \frac{2\pi}{5}, \sqrt[5]{25} \text{ cis } \frac{4\pi}{5}, \sqrt[5]{25} \text{ cis } \frac{6\pi}{5}, \sqrt[5]{25} \text{ cis } \frac{8\pi}{5}$

25. $\sqrt{6}, -\sqrt{6}, \sqrt{7}, -\sqrt{7}$ **26.** $\sqrt[6]{8} \text{ cis } \frac{\pi}{4}, \sqrt[6]{8} \text{ cis } \frac{11\pi}{12}, \sqrt[6]{8} \text{ cis } \frac{19\pi}{12}$ **27.** $\sqrt[5]{2} \text{ cis } \frac{\pi}{15}, \sqrt[5]{2} \text{ cis } \frac{7\pi}{15}, \sqrt[5]{2} \text{ cis } \frac{13\pi}{15}, \sqrt[5]{2} \text{ cis } \frac{19\pi}{15}, \sqrt[5]{2} \text{ cis } \frac{5\pi}{3}$

28. $\frac{1}{3} \text{ cis } \frac{\pi}{8}, \frac{1}{3} \text{ cis } \frac{5\pi}{8}, \frac{1}{3} \text{ cis } \frac{9\pi}{8}, \frac{1}{3} \text{ cis } \frac{13\pi}{8}$ **29.** $\frac{1}{4} \text{ cis } \frac{3\pi}{8}, \frac{1}{4} \text{ cis } \frac{7\pi}{8}, \frac{1}{4} \text{ cis } \frac{11\pi}{8}, \frac{1}{4} \text{ cis } \frac{15\pi}{8}$

30. $x^4 + 24 = \left(x - \sqrt[4]{24} \text{ cis } \frac{\pi}{4}\right)\left(x - \sqrt[4]{24} \text{ cis } \frac{3\pi}{4}\right)\left(x - \sqrt[4]{24} \text{ cis } \frac{5\pi}{4}\right)\left(x - \sqrt[4]{24} \text{ cis } \frac{7\pi}{4}\right)$

31. $x^3 - i = (x + i)\left(x - \text{cis } \frac{\pi}{6}\right)\left(x - \text{cis } \frac{5\pi}{6}\right)$ **32.** $x^3 - 27i = (x + 3i)\left(x - 3 \text{ cis } \frac{\pi}{6}\right)\left(x - 3 \text{ cis } \frac{5\pi}{6}\right)$

33. $6x^2 - 11x + 10 = 6\left(x - \frac{11 + i\sqrt{119}}{12}\right)\left(x - \frac{11 - i\sqrt{119}}{12}\right)$ **34.** $x^3 - 20 = (x - \sqrt[3]{20})\left(x - \sqrt[3]{20} \text{ cis } \frac{2\pi}{3}\right)\left(x - \sqrt[3]{20} \text{ cis } \frac{4\pi}{3}\right)$

35. $x^4 - 16i = [x - (1.8478 + 0.7654i)][x - (0.7654 + 1.8478i)][x - (-0.7654 + 1.8478i)][x - (-1.8478 + 0.7654i)]$

37. Answers may vary. Students' programs should determine the roots first in polar form, and then convert them to rectangular form.

42. $3, 3 \text{ cis } \frac{2\pi}{3}, 3 \text{ cis } \frac{4\pi}{3}$ Using the distance formula, it can be shown that the segments connecting the roots have equal length, and therefore the roots are vertices of an equilateral triangle.

43. $2 \text{ cis } \frac{\pi}{16}, 2 \text{ cis } \frac{9\pi}{16}, 2 \text{ cis } \frac{17\pi}{16}, 2 \text{ cis } \frac{25\pi}{16}$ Since the segments connecting the roots have equal length, and adjacent segments are perpendicular, the roots are vertices of a square.

47. The sum of the nth roots of unity for any n is zero.

Test Yourself, page 527

11. $7 \text{ cis } \left(-\frac{\pi}{9}\right), 7 \text{ cis } \frac{5\pi}{9}, 7 \text{ cis } \frac{11\pi}{9}$

12. $\frac{1}{2} \text{ cis } \frac{\pi}{8}, \frac{1}{2} \text{ cis } \frac{5\pi}{8}, \frac{1}{2} \text{ cis } \frac{9\pi}{8}, \frac{1}{2} \text{ cis } \frac{13\pi}{8}$

Chapter 11 Conic Sections
Practice Exercises, pages 538–540

For Exercises 32–39, see Solutions Manual for graphs.

32. circle **33.** circle **34.** circle **35.** circle **36.** point circle **37.** empty set **38.** point circle **39.** circle

50. By completing the square, $\left(x^2 + Dx + \frac{D^2}{4}\right) + \left(y^2 + Ey + \frac{E^2}{4}\right) = -F + \frac{D^2}{4} + \frac{E^2}{4}$, or $\left(x + \frac{D}{2}\right)^2 + \left(y + \frac{E}{2}\right)^2 =$

$\frac{D^2 + E^2 - 4F}{4}$. If this is a point circle, then $\frac{D^2 + E^2 - 4F}{4} = 0$, or $D^2 + E^2 - 4F = 0$.

51. Lines with slope of 3 tangent to the circle must be perpendicular to the radius, or perpendicular to line through

the origin with slope of $-\frac{1}{3}$, or $y = -\frac{1}{3}x$. Solve the equation $x^2 + \left(-\frac{1}{3}x\right)^2 = 40$ to get points of intersection,

which are $(6, -2)$ and $(-6, 2)$. Find the equation of the lines through the origin and each of these points to get
$3x - y - 20 = 0$ and $3x - y + 20 = 0$.

52. The midpoints are the locus of points which form a circle of radius a and center $\left(\frac{a}{2}, 0\right)$.

Class Exercises, page 546

1. major axis: $(0, 9)$, $(0, -9)$; minor axis: $(4, 0)$, $(-4, 0)$; foci: $(0, \sqrt{65})$,

$(0, -\sqrt{65})$; $e = \frac{\sqrt{65}}{9}$

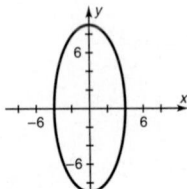

2. major axis: $(1, 6)$, $(1, -2)$; minor axis: $(-2, 2)$, $(4, 2)$; foci:

$(1, 2 + \sqrt{7})$, $(1, 2 - \sqrt{7})$; $e = \frac{\sqrt{7}}{4}$

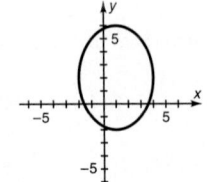

3. major axis: $(3, 0)$, $(-3, 0)$; minor axis: $(0, 2)$, $(0, -2)$; foci: $(\sqrt{5}, 0)$,

$(-\sqrt{5}, 0)$; $e = \frac{\sqrt{5}}{3}$

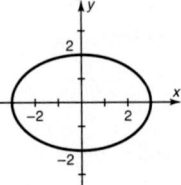

6. major axis: $\left(\frac{5}{6}, \frac{3}{2} + \frac{\sqrt{129}}{3}\right)$,

$\left(\frac{5}{6}, \frac{3}{2} - \frac{\sqrt{129}}{3}\right)$; minor axis:

$\left(\frac{5}{6} + \frac{\sqrt{43}}{3}, \frac{3}{2}\right)$, $\left(\frac{5}{6} - \frac{\sqrt{43}}{3}, \frac{3}{2}\right)$

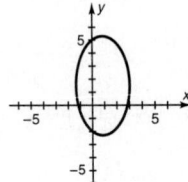

7. major axis: $\left(-1 + \frac{\sqrt{230}}{5}, \frac{1}{5}\right)$,

$\left(-1 - \frac{\sqrt{230}}{5}, \frac{1}{5}\right)$; minor axis:

$\left(-1, \frac{1}{5} + \frac{\sqrt{46}}{5}\right)$, $\left(-1, \frac{1}{5} - \frac{\sqrt{46}}{5}\right)$

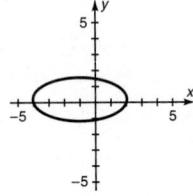

Practice Exercises, pages 546–548

For Exercises 1–12, 22–29, and 32–39, see Solutions Manual for graphs.

1. major axis: $(0, 6)$, $(0, -6)$; minor axis: $(5, 0)$, $(-5, 0)$; foci: $(0, \sqrt{11})$,

$(0, -\sqrt{11})$; $e = \frac{\sqrt{11}}{6}$

2. major axis: $(0, 8)$, $(0, -8)$; minor axis: $(7, 0)$, $(-7, 0)$; foci: $(0, \sqrt{15})$,

$(0, -\sqrt{15})$; $e = \frac{\sqrt{15}}{8}$

3. major axis: $(8, 0)$, $(-8, 0)$; minor axis: $(0, 4)$, $(0, -4)$; foci: $(4\sqrt{3}, 0)$,

$(-4\sqrt{3}, 0)$; $e = \frac{\sqrt{3}}{2}$

4. major axis: $(9, 0)$, $(-9, 0)$; minor axis: $(0, 7)$, $(0, -7)$; foci: $(4\sqrt{2}, 0)$,

$(-4\sqrt{2}, 0)$; $e = \frac{4\sqrt{2}}{9}$

5. major axis: $(\sqrt{6}, 0)$, $(-\sqrt{6}, 0)$; minor axis: $(0, \sqrt{2})$, $(0, -\sqrt{2})$;

foci: $(2, 0)$, $(-2, 0)$; $e = \frac{\sqrt{6}}{3}$

6. major axis: $(0, \sqrt{10})$, $(0, -\sqrt{10})$; minor axis: $(2\sqrt{2}, 0)$, $(-2\sqrt{2}, 0)$;

foci: $(0, \sqrt{2})$, $(0, -\sqrt{2})$; $e = \frac{\sqrt{5}}{5}$

7. major axis: $(0, 5)$, $(0, -5)$; minor axis: $(2, 0)$, $(-2, 0)$; foci: $(0, \sqrt{21})$,

$(0, -\sqrt{21})$; $e = \frac{\sqrt{21}}{5}$

8. major axis: $(\sqrt{2}, 0)$, $(-\sqrt{2}, 0)$; minor axis: $(0, 1)$, $(0, -1)$;

foci: $(1, 0)$, $(-1, 0)$; $e = \frac{\sqrt{2}}{2}$

9. major axis: $(5, 0)$, $(-5, 0)$; minor axis: $(0, 3)$, $(0, -3)$; foci: $(4, 0)$,

$(-4, 0)$; $e = \frac{4}{5}$

10. major axis: (4, 0), (−4, 0); minor axis: (0, 3), (0, −3); foci:

$(\sqrt{7}, 0), (-\sqrt{7}, 0); e = \dfrac{\sqrt{7}}{4}$

11. major axis: $\left(0, \dfrac{\sqrt{15}}{3}\right), \left(0, -\dfrac{\sqrt{15}}{3}\right)$;

minor axis: $\left(\dfrac{\sqrt{3}}{3}, 0\right), \left(-\dfrac{\sqrt{3}}{3}, 0\right)$;

foci: $\left(0, \dfrac{2\sqrt{3}}{3}\right), \left(0, -\dfrac{2\sqrt{3}}{3}\right); e = \dfrac{2\sqrt{5}}{5}$

12. major axis: $\left(0, \dfrac{\sqrt{14}}{2}\right), \left(0, -\dfrac{\sqrt{14}}{2}\right)$;

minor axis: $\left(\dfrac{\sqrt{2}}{2}, 0\right), \left(-\dfrac{\sqrt{2}}{2}, 0\right)$;

foci: $(0, \sqrt{3}), (0, -\sqrt{3}); e = \dfrac{\sqrt{42}}{7}$

22. center: (0, 4); major axis: (4, 4), (−4, 4); minor axis: (0, 2), (0, 6);

foci: $(2\sqrt{3}, 4), (-2\sqrt{3}, 4); e = \dfrac{\sqrt{3}}{2}$

23. center: (2, 0); major axis: (2, 4), (2, −4); minor axis: (0, 0), (4, 0);

foci: $(2, 2\sqrt{3}), (2, -2\sqrt{3}); e = \dfrac{\sqrt{3}}{2}$

24. center: (−2, 4); major axis: $(-2, 4 + 6\sqrt{2}), (-2, 4 - 6\sqrt{2})$; minor axis: (−8, 4), (4, 4); foci:

$(-2, 10), (-2, -2); e = \dfrac{\sqrt{2}}{2}$

25. center: (6, −4); major axis: (0, −4), (12, −4); minor axis: (6, 0), (6, −8); foci: $(6 + 2\sqrt{5}, -4)$,

$(6 - 2\sqrt{5}, -4); e = \dfrac{\sqrt{5}}{3}$

26. center: (0, 0); major axis: $(\sqrt{5}, 0)$, $(-\sqrt{5}, 0)$; minor axis: (0, 1), (0, −1);

foci: (2, 0), (−2, 0); $e = \dfrac{2\sqrt{5}}{5}$

27. center: (0, 0); major axis: $(0, \sqrt{7})$, $(0, -\sqrt{7})$; minor axis: (1, 0), (−1, 0); foci: $(0, \sqrt{6}), (0, -\sqrt{6})$;

$e = \dfrac{\sqrt{42}}{7}$

28. center: (−2, −1); major axis: $(-2 + \sqrt{3}, -1), (-2 - \sqrt{3}, -1)$; minor axis: (−2, 0), (−2, −2); foci: $(-2 + \sqrt{2}, -1), (-2 - \sqrt{2}, -1)$;

$e = \dfrac{\sqrt{6}}{3}$

29. center: (5, 1); major axis: (9, 1), (1, 1); minor axis: (5, −1), (5, 3); foci: $(5 + 2\sqrt{3}, 1), (5 - 2\sqrt{3}, 1)$;

$e = \dfrac{\sqrt{3}}{2}$

30. $\dfrac{x^2}{21,160,000} + \dfrac{y^2}{21,000,000} = 1$

32. major axis: (1, 1), (1, 3); minor

axis: $\left(\dfrac{1}{2}, 2\right), \left(\dfrac{3}{2}, 2\right)$

33. major axis: $\left(\dfrac{5}{6}, \dfrac{5}{2} + \dfrac{\sqrt{66}}{3}\right)$,

$\left(\dfrac{5}{6}, \dfrac{5}{2} - \dfrac{\sqrt{66}}{3}\right)$; minor axis:

$\left(\dfrac{5}{6} + \dfrac{\sqrt{22}}{3}, \dfrac{5}{2}\right), \left(\dfrac{5}{6} - \dfrac{\sqrt{22}}{3}, \dfrac{5}{2}\right)$

34. major axis: $\left(-1 + \dfrac{\sqrt{82}}{4}, \dfrac{3}{4}\right)$,

$\left(-1 - \dfrac{\sqrt{82}}{4}, \dfrac{3}{4}\right)$; minor axis:

$\left(-1, \dfrac{3}{4} + \dfrac{\sqrt{41}}{4}\right), \left(-1, \dfrac{3}{4} - \dfrac{\sqrt{41}}{4}\right)$

35. major axis: $\left(\dfrac{3}{2} + \dfrac{\sqrt{21}}{6}, -\dfrac{1}{3}\right)$,

$\left(\dfrac{3}{2} - \dfrac{\sqrt{21}}{6}, -\dfrac{1}{3}\right)$; minor axis:

$\left(\dfrac{3}{2}, -\dfrac{1}{3} + \dfrac{\sqrt{7}}{6}\right), \left(\dfrac{3}{2}, -\dfrac{1}{3} - \dfrac{\sqrt{7}}{6}\right)$

36. The graphs have the same intercepts, and the first graph is inscribed in the second.

37. The graphs have the same intercepts, and the first graph is inscribed in the second.

38. The graphs have the same endpoints, and the second graph is inscribed in the first.

39. The graphs have the same endpoints, and the second graph is inscribed in the first.

Class Exercises, pages 554–555

For Exercises 1–8, see Solutions Manual for graphs.

1. vertices: (7, 0), (−7, 0); conjugate axis: (0, 3), (0, −3); foci: $(\sqrt{58}, 0)$,

$(-\sqrt{58}, 0)$; asymptotes: $y = \pm\dfrac{3}{7}x$;

$e = \dfrac{\sqrt{58}}{7}$

2. vertices: (0, 8), (0, −8); conjugate axis: (5, 0), (−5, 0); foci: $(0, \sqrt{89})$,

$(0, -\sqrt{89})$; asymptotes: $y = \pm\dfrac{8}{5}x$;

$e = \dfrac{\sqrt{89}}{8}$

3. vertices: (3, 0), (−3, 0); conjugate axis: (0, 2), (0, −2); foci: $(\sqrt{13}, 0)$,

$(-\sqrt{13}, 0)$; asymptotes: $y = \pm\dfrac{2}{3}x$;

$e = \dfrac{\sqrt{13}}{3}$

4. vertices: (3, 0), (−3, 0); conjugate axis: (0, 4), (0, −4); foci: (5, 0),

(−5, 0); asymptotes: $y = \pm\dfrac{4}{3}x$;

$e = \dfrac{5}{3}$

5. vertices: (−2, 4), (8, 4); conjugate axis: (3, −2), (3, 10); foci: $(3 + \sqrt{61}, 4), (3 - \sqrt{61}, 4)$;

asymptotes: $y - 4 = \pm\dfrac{6}{5}(x - 3)$;

$e = \dfrac{\sqrt{61}}{5}$

6. vertices: (−1, 0), (−1, −4); conjugate axis: (−10, −2), (8, −2); foci: $(-1, -2 + \sqrt{85})$, $(-1, -2 - \sqrt{85})$; asymptotes:

$y + 2 = \pm\dfrac{2}{9}(x + 1); e = \dfrac{\sqrt{85}}{2}$

7. vertices: $(2 + 3\sqrt{3}, 3), (2 - 3\sqrt{3}, 3)$; conjugate axis: (2, 0), (2, 6); foci: (8, 3), (−4, 3); asymptotes: $y - 3 =$

$\pm\dfrac{\sqrt{3}}{3}(x - 2); e = \dfrac{2\sqrt{3}}{3}$

8. vertices: $(3, 2 + \sqrt{5}), (3, 2 - \sqrt{5})$; conjugate axis: (6, 2), (0, 2); foci: $(3, 2 + \sqrt{14}), (3, 2 - \sqrt{14})$; asymptotes: $y - 2 =$

$\pm\dfrac{\sqrt{5}}{3}(x - 3); e = \dfrac{\sqrt{70}}{5}$

Practice Exercises, pages 555–556

For Exercises 1–12 and 28–31, see Solutions Manual for graphs.

1. vertices: (0, 6), (0, −6); conjugate axis: (2, 0), (−2, 0); foci: (0, 2$\sqrt{10}$), (0, −2$\sqrt{10}$); asymptotes: $y = \pm 3x$; $e = \dfrac{\sqrt{10}}{3}$

2. vertices: (0, 8), (0, −8); conjugate axis: (3, 0), (−3, 0); foci: (0, $\sqrt{73}$), (0, −$\sqrt{73}$); asymptotes: $y = \pm\dfrac{8}{3}x$; $e = \dfrac{\sqrt{73}}{8}$

3. vertices: (9, 0), (−9, 0); conjugate axis: (0, 1), (0, −1); foci: ($\sqrt{82}$, 0), (−$\sqrt{82}$, 0); asymptotes: $y = \pm\dfrac{1}{9}x$; $e = \dfrac{\sqrt{82}}{9}$

4. vertices: (10, 0), (−10, 0); conjugate axis: (0, 4), (0, −4); foci: (2$\sqrt{29}$, 0), (−2$\sqrt{29}$, 0); asymptotes: $y = \pm\dfrac{2}{5}x$; $e = \dfrac{\sqrt{29}}{5}$

5. vertices: (11, 0), (−11, 0); conjugate axis: (0, 7), (0, −7); foci: ($\sqrt{170}$, 0), (−$\sqrt{170}$, 0); asymptotes: $y = \pm\dfrac{7}{11}x$; $e = \dfrac{\sqrt{170}}{11}$

6. vertices: (0, 13), (0, −13); conjugate axis: (12, 0), (−12, 0); foci: (0, $\sqrt{313}$), (0, −$\sqrt{313}$); asymptotes: $y = \pm\dfrac{13}{12}x$; $e = \dfrac{\sqrt{313}}{13}$

7. vertices: (2, 0), (−2, 0); conjugate axis: (0, 5), (0, −5); foci: ($\sqrt{29}$, 0), (−$\sqrt{29}$, 0); asymptotes: $y = \pm\dfrac{5}{2}x$; $e = \dfrac{\sqrt{29}}{2}$

8. vertices: (3, 0), (−3, 0); conjugate axis: (0, 2), (0, −2); foci: ($\sqrt{13}$, 0), (−$\sqrt{13}$, 0); asymptotes: $y = \pm\dfrac{2}{3}x$; $e = \dfrac{\sqrt{13}}{3}$

9. vertices: (0, 5), (0, −5); conjugate axis: (3, 0), (−3, 0); foci: (0, $\sqrt{34}$), (0, −$\sqrt{34}$); asymptotes: $y = \pm\dfrac{5}{3}x$; $e = \dfrac{\sqrt{34}}{5}$

10. vertices: (0, 1), (0, −1); conjugate axis: ($\sqrt{2}$, 0), (−$\sqrt{2}$, 0); foci: (0, $\sqrt{3}$), (0, −$\sqrt{3}$); asymptotes: $y = \pm\dfrac{\sqrt{2}}{2}x$; $e = \sqrt{3}$

11. vertices: $\left(\dfrac{1}{3}, 0\right)$, $\left(-\dfrac{1}{3}, 0\right)$; conjugate axis: $\left(0, \dfrac{\sqrt{2}}{3}\right)$, $\left(0, -\dfrac{\sqrt{2}}{3}\right)$; foci: $\left(\dfrac{\sqrt{3}}{3}, 0\right)$, $\left(-\dfrac{\sqrt{3}}{3}, 0\right)$; asymptotes: $y = \pm\sqrt{2}x$; $e = \sqrt{3}$

12. vertices: $\left(\dfrac{\sqrt{3}}{3}, 0\right)$, $\left(-\dfrac{\sqrt{3}}{3}, 0\right)$; conjugate axis: $\left(0, \dfrac{\sqrt{21}}{3}\right)$, $\left(0, -\dfrac{\sqrt{21}}{3}\right)$; foci: $\left(\dfrac{2\sqrt{6}}{3}, 0\right)$, $\left(-\dfrac{2\sqrt{6}}{3}, 0\right)$; asymptotes: $y = \pm\sqrt{7}x$; $e = 2\sqrt{2}$

16.

17.

18.

21. $\dfrac{(y + 2)^2}{4} - \dfrac{(x + 1)^2}{9} = 1$; center: (−1, −2); vertices: (−1, 0), (−1, −4); foci: (−1, −2 + $\sqrt{13}$), (−1, −2 − $\sqrt{13}$); asymptotes: $y + 2 = \pm\dfrac{2}{3}(x + 1)$

22. $\dfrac{(x - 1)^2}{\frac{4}{9}} - \dfrac{(y - 2)^2}{1} = 1$; center: (1, 2); vertices: $\left(\dfrac{5}{3}, 2\right)$, $\left(\dfrac{1}{3}, 2\right)$; foci: $\left(1 + \dfrac{\sqrt{13}}{3}, 2\right)$, $\left(1 - \dfrac{\sqrt{13}}{3}, 2\right)$; asymptotes: $y = \pm\dfrac{3}{2}(x - 1) + 2$

23. $\dfrac{(y - 4)^2}{28} - \dfrac{(x + 1)^2}{21} = 1$; center: (−1, 4); vertices: (−1, 4 + 2$\sqrt{7}$), (−1, 4 − 2$\sqrt{7}$); foci: (−1, 11), (−1, −3); asymptotes: $y - 4 = \pm\dfrac{2\sqrt{3}}{3}(x + 1)$

24. $\dfrac{(y + 2)^2}{9} - \dfrac{(x - 1)^2}{4} = 1$; center: (1, −2); vertices: (1, 1), (1, −5); foci: (1, −2 + $\sqrt{13}$), (1, −2 − $\sqrt{13}$); asymptotes: $y = \pm\dfrac{3}{2}(x - 1) - 2$

25. $\dfrac{y^2}{1} - \dfrac{x^2}{7} = 1$; center: (0, 0); vertices: (0, 1), (0, −1); foci: (0, 2$\sqrt{2}$), (0, −2$\sqrt{2}$); asymptotes: $y = \pm\dfrac{\sqrt{7}}{7}x$

26. $\dfrac{y^2}{11} - \dfrac{x^2}{1} = 1$; center: (0, 0); vertices: (0, $\sqrt{11}$), (0, −$\sqrt{11}$); foci: (0, 2$\sqrt{3}$), (0, −2$\sqrt{3}$); asymptotes: $y = \pm\sqrt{11}x$

28. (5, 2), (−3, 2)   29. (−1, 1), (−5, 1)   30. (4, 4), (−4, −4)   31. (5, −5), (−5, 5)

39. See Solutions Manual for proof.

42. Answers may vary. Students' programs should first convert the general equation to standard form, and then answer the remaining questions accordingly.

Class Exercises, page 561 See Solutions Manual for graphs.

1. vertex: (0, 3); axis: $x = 0$;

focus: $\left(0, \frac{13}{4}\right)$; directrix: $y = \frac{11}{4}$;

opens up

2. vertex: (0, −1); axis: $x = 0$;

focus: $\left(0, -\frac{5}{4}\right)$; directrix: $y = -\frac{3}{4}$.

opens down

3. vertex: (3, −2); axis: $y = -2$;
focus: (5, −2); directrix: $x = 1$;
opens right

4. vertex: (−5, 2); axis: $x = -5$;
focus: (−5, 1); directrix: $y = 3$;
opens down

5. vertex: (3, 1); axis: $y = 1$;
focus: (5, 1); directrix: $x = 1$;
opens right

6. vertex: $\left(\frac{5}{2}, \frac{5}{2}\right)$; axis: $x = \frac{5}{2}$;

focus: $\left(\frac{5}{2}, \frac{15}{8}\right)$; directrix: $y = \frac{25}{8}$;

opens down

Practice Exercises, pages 561–563 See Solutions Manual for graphs.

1. vertex: (0, −5); axis: $x = 0$; focus:

$\left(0, -\frac{19}{4}\right)$; directrix: $y = -\frac{21}{4}$;

opens up

2. vertex: (0, 2); axis: $x = 0$; focus:

$\left(0, \frac{9}{4}\right)$; directrix: $y = \frac{7}{4}$; opens up

3. vertex: (0, −3); axis: $x = 0$; focus:

$\left(0, -\frac{25}{8}\right)$; directrix: $y = -\frac{23}{8}$;

opens down

4. vertex: (−3, 0); axis: $y = 0$; focus:

$\left(-\frac{11}{4}, 0\right)$; directrix: $x = -\frac{13}{4}$;

opens right

5. vertex: (4, 0); axis: $y = 0$; focus:

$\left(\frac{15}{4}, 0\right)$; directrix: $x = \frac{17}{4}$; opens

left

6. vertex: (−1, 0); axis: $y = 0$; focus:

$\left(-\frac{5}{4}, 0\right)$; directrix: $x = -\frac{3}{4}$; opens

left

7. vertex: (0, −2); axis: $x = 0$; focus:

$\left(0, -\frac{25}{12}\right)$; directrix: $y = -\frac{23}{12}$;

opens down

8. vertex: (−5, −1); axis: $y = -1$;
focus: (−7, −1); directrix: $x = -3$; opens left

9. vertex: (3, −2); axis: $y = -2$;
focus: (2, −2); directrix: $x = 4$;
opens left

10. vertex: (7, −2); axis: $x = 7$;

focus: $\left(7, -\frac{1}{2}\right)$; directrix: $y = -\frac{7}{2}$;

opens up

11. vertex: (4, 1); axis: $x = 4$; focus:

$\left(4, \frac{3}{2}\right)$; directrix: $y = \frac{1}{2}$; opens up

12. vertex: (2, −1); axis: $x = 2$;

focus: $\left(2, -\frac{1}{4}\right)$; directrix: $y = -\frac{7}{4}$;

opens up

13. vertex: $\left(-\frac{25}{8}, 2\right)$; axis: $y = 2$;

focus: $\left(-\frac{41}{8}, 2\right)$; directrix: $x = -\frac{9}{8}$;

opens left

14. vertex: (−3, −3); axis: $y = -3$;

focus: $\left(-\frac{1}{2}, -3\right)$; directrix: $x =$

$-\frac{11}{2}$; opens right

15. vertex: (−2, −1); axis: $x = -2$;

focus: $\left(-2, -\frac{7}{12}\right)$; directrix: $y =$

$-\frac{17}{12}$; opens up

16. vertex: (−1, −1); axis: $y = -1$;

focus: $\left(-\frac{13}{20}, -1\right)$; directrix: $x =$

$-\frac{27}{20}$; opens right

17. vertex: (3, −4); axis: $x = 3$; focus:

$\left(3, -\frac{15}{4}\right)$; directrix: $y = -\frac{17}{4}$;

opens up

18. vertex: $\left(\frac{3}{2}, 0\right)$; axis: $x = \frac{3}{2}$; focus:

$\left(\frac{3}{2}, \frac{1}{16}\right)$; directrix: $y = -\frac{1}{16}$;

opens up

19. vertex: $\left(\frac{5}{4}, \frac{1}{8}\right)$; axis: $x = \frac{5}{4}$;

focus: $\left(\frac{5}{4}, 0\right)$; directrix: $y = \frac{1}{4}$;

opens down

20. vertex: $\left(\frac{7}{6}, -\frac{11}{12}\right)$; axis: $x = \frac{7}{6}$;

focus: $\left(\frac{7}{6}, -1\right)$; directrix: $y = -\frac{5}{6}$;

opens down

26.

27.

28.

51. Let $P(x, y)$ be a point on the parabola. Then $\sqrt{(x - c)^2 + y^2} = \sqrt{(x + c)^2}$, $(x - c)^2 + y^2 = (x + c)^2$, $x^2 - 2cx + c^2 + y^2 = x^2 + 2cx + c^2$, $y^2 = 4cx$, $x = \frac{1}{4c}y^2$.

Test Yourself, page 563

5. point circle (7, −2) **6.** circle (See Solutions Manual for graph.)

7.   **8.**   **9.**   **10.**   **11.**

12.   **13.**   **14.**   **15.**   **16.**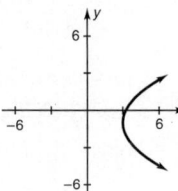

Practice Exercises, pages 568–569

6. ellipse **7.** hyperbola **8.** hyperbola **9.** parabola

10. parabola **11.** hyperbola **12.** ellipse **22.** Negative time corresponds to the time before the shell reaches its highest point.

For Exercises 23–32, see Solutions Manual for graphs.

23. $(x')^2 + (y')^2 = 25$, origin at (1, 2)

24. $(x')^2 + (y')^2 = 25$, origin at (2, 1)

25. $\dfrac{(x')^2}{4} - \dfrac{(y')^2}{1} = 1$, origin at (1, −2)

26. $\dfrac{(x')^2}{82} - \dfrac{(y')^2}{\frac{41}{2}} = 1$, origin at $\left(8, -\dfrac{1}{2}\right)$

27. $\dfrac{(x')^2}{\frac{8}{3}} + \dfrac{(y')^2}{2} = 1$, origin at (−2, −1)

28. $\dfrac{(x')^2}{1} + \dfrac{(y')^2}{9} = 1$, origin at (−2, 4)

29. $x' = \dfrac{1}{8}(y')^2$, origin at (2, 2)

30. $y' = -\dfrac{2}{5}(x')^2$, origin at $\left(\dfrac{3}{2}, \dfrac{7}{2}\right)$

31. $\dfrac{(x')^2}{16} + \dfrac{(y')^2}{9} = 1$, origin at (−3, 1)

32. $\dfrac{(y')^2}{9} - \dfrac{(x')^2}{25} = 1$, origin at (−3, 1)

33. $D = \{x : x \in \mathscr{R}\}; R = \{y : y \geq 0\}$

Class Exercises, pages 573–574

1.

2.

3.

4.

5.

6.

7.

8.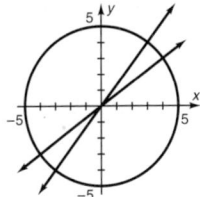

11. If the conics are a circle and a parabola or an ellipse and a parabola, the vertex is on the circle or ellipse. If they are a circle and a hyperbola or an ellipse and a hyperbola, the vertex of the hyperbola is tangent to the circle or ellipse. If they are a hyperbola and a parabola, the vertex of the parabola coincides with one vertex of the hyperbola. If they are a circle and an ellipse, the circle is tangent to a vertex of the ellipse.

Practice Exercises, pages 574–575   See Solutions Manual for graphs.

Practice Exercises, pages 580–582

1. circle; $m_{tan} = 1$; $m_{normal} = -1$

2. ellipse; $m_{tan} = -2$; $m_{normal} = \dfrac{1}{2}$

3. parabola; $m_{tan} = 1$; $m_{normal} = -1$

4. hyperbola; m_{tan} is undefined; $m_{normal} = 0$

5. ellipse; $m_{tan} = -\dfrac{\sqrt{5}}{10}$; $m_{normal} = 2\sqrt{5}$

6. parabola; $m_{tan} = 3$; $m_{normal} = -\dfrac{1}{3}$

7. circle; tangent: $3x + \sqrt{7}y = 16$; normal: $\sqrt{7}x - 3y = 0$

8. circle; tangent: $\sqrt{7}x - 3y = -16$; normal: $3x + \sqrt{7}y = 0$

9. hyperbola; tangent: $x = 5$; normal: $y = 0$

10. hyperbola; tangent: $x = -6$; normal: $y = 0$

11. hyperbola; tangent: $y = -7$; normal: $x = 0$

12. hyperbola; tangent: $y = 8$; normal: $x = 0$

13. parabola; tangent: $y = -x - 3$; normal: $y = x - 9$

14. parabola; tangent: $y = -x + 4$; normal: $y = x + 12$

15. ellipse; tangent: $y = -3$; normal: $x = 0$

16. ellipse; tangent: $y = 6$; normal: $x = 0$

17. ellipse; tangent: $5x - \sqrt{15}y = 40$; normal: $\sqrt{15}x + 5y = -8\sqrt{15}$

18. ellipse; tangent: $x - \sqrt{21}y = -25$; normal: $\sqrt{21}x + y = -3\sqrt{21}$

19. hyperbola; tangent: $3x - \sqrt{30}y = 33$; normal: $\sqrt{30}x + 3y = -2\sqrt{30}$

20. hyperbola; tangent: $x + 2\sqrt{10}y = -22$; normal: $2\sqrt{10}x - y = -3\sqrt{10}$

22. $y = -\dfrac{b^2 x_0}{a^2 y_0}x + \left(y_0 + \dfrac{b^2 x_0^2}{a^2 y_0}\right)$

23. $y = -\dfrac{a^2 x_0}{b^2 y_0}x + \left(y_0 + \dfrac{a^2 x_0^2}{b^2 y_0}\right)$

24. $y = \dfrac{b^2 x_0}{a^2 y_0}x + \left(y_0 - \dfrac{b^2 x_0^2}{a^2 y_0}\right)$

25. $y = \dfrac{2c}{y_0}x + \left(y_0 - \dfrac{2c x_0}{y_0}\right)$

26. $y = \dfrac{a^2 y_0}{b^2 x_0}x + y_0\left(1 - \dfrac{a^2}{b^2}\right)$

27. $y = -\dfrac{a^2 y_0}{b^2 x_0}x + y_0\left(1 + \dfrac{a^2}{b^2}\right)$

42. tangent line to ellipse at (x_0, y_0) is $y = -\dfrac{b^2 x_0}{a^2 y_0}x + \dfrac{b^2}{y_0}$, if $k = \pm\sqrt{a^2 m^2 + b^2}$ and $m = -\dfrac{b^2 x_0}{a^2 y_0}$, then $k =$

$\pm\sqrt{a^2\left(-\dfrac{b^2 x_0}{a^2 y_0}\right)^2 + b^2} = \pm\dfrac{ab}{a^2 |y_0|}\sqrt{b^2 x_0^2 + a^2 y_0^2} = \pm\dfrac{ab}{a^2 |y_0|}\sqrt{a^2 b^2} = \pm\dfrac{a^2 b^2}{a^2 |y_0|} = \pm\dfrac{b^2}{|y_0|}$ for $y_0 > 0$, $\dfrac{b^2}{y_0} > 0$,

for $y_0 < 0$, $\dfrac{b^2}{y_0} < 0$

43. tangent line to hyperbola at (x_0, y_0) is $y = \dfrac{b^2 x_0}{a^2 y_0}x - \dfrac{b^2}{y_0}$, if $k = \pm\sqrt{a^2 m^2 - b^2}$ and $m = \dfrac{b^2 x_0}{a^2 y_0}$, then

$k = \pm\dfrac{ab}{a^2|y_0|}\sqrt{b^2 x_0^2 - a^2 y_0^2} = \pm\dfrac{ab}{a^2|y_0|}\sqrt{a^2 b^2} = \pm\dfrac{b^2}{|y_0|}$ for $y_0 < 0$, $-\dfrac{b^2}{y_0}$ is positive, for $y_0 > 0$, $-\dfrac{b^2}{y_0}$ is negative

Practice Exercises, pages 587–589 See Solutions Manual for graphs.

Test Yourself, page 589

4.

5.

6.

7.

8. circle; tangent: $7x - y = 50$;
normal: $x + 7y = 0$

9. hyperbola; tangent: $13x - 12y = 25$;
normal: $12x + 13y = 312$

10. hyperbola; $\left(-\dfrac{8}{3}, 0\right), \left(\dfrac{8}{5}, \pi\right)$

11. ellipse; $\left(1, \dfrac{\pi}{2}\right), \left(3, \dfrac{3\pi}{2}\right)$

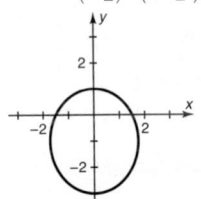

Chapter 12 Matrices and Vectors
Practice Exercises, pages 600–602

8. $\begin{bmatrix} 7 & 10 \\ 13 & 14 \\ 21 & 8 \end{bmatrix}$

9. $\begin{bmatrix} 7 & 10 \\ 13 & 14 \\ 21 & 8 \end{bmatrix}$

10. $\begin{bmatrix} 5 & 4 \\ 9 & 6 \\ 9 & -6 \end{bmatrix}$

11. $\begin{bmatrix} -5 & -4 \\ -9 & -6 \\ -9 & 6 \end{bmatrix}$

12. $\begin{bmatrix} -1 & 1 & -1 \end{bmatrix}$

13. $\begin{bmatrix} 7 & 2 \\ 1 & 4 \end{bmatrix}$

14. $\begin{bmatrix} 27 & 37 \\ 50 & 52 \\ 78 & 25 \end{bmatrix}$

15. $\begin{bmatrix} -21 & -6 \\ -3 & -12 \end{bmatrix}$

16. not possible; not conformable

17. $\begin{bmatrix} -2\sqrt{2} & -\sqrt{2} & -4\sqrt{2} \end{bmatrix}$

18. $\begin{bmatrix} 0 & 0 \\ 0 & 0 \end{bmatrix}$

19. $\begin{bmatrix} \dfrac{1}{2} & \dfrac{3}{2} \\ 1 & 2 \\ 3 & \dfrac{7}{2} \end{bmatrix}$

22. $\begin{bmatrix} 4 & -1 & 11 \\ -8 & -1 & 2 \end{bmatrix}$

23. $\begin{bmatrix} 4 & -8 \\ -1 & -1 \\ 11 & 1 \end{bmatrix}$

24. $\begin{bmatrix} -4 & -6 \\ -28 & -26 \end{bmatrix}$

25. $\begin{bmatrix} -47 & -27 \\ -100 & -80 \end{bmatrix}$

26. $\begin{bmatrix} 2 & 6 & \dfrac{16}{3} \end{bmatrix}$

27. $\begin{bmatrix} -\dfrac{1}{4} & -\dfrac{3}{4} & -\dfrac{1}{4} & -\dfrac{11}{4} \end{bmatrix}$

28. $\begin{bmatrix} 2 & 16 \\ 25 & -3 \end{bmatrix}$

29. $\begin{bmatrix} 1 & 0 & -2 \\ 3 & -3 & 1 \end{bmatrix}$

For Exercises 45–49, see Solutions Manual for proofs.

Class Exercises, page 615

3.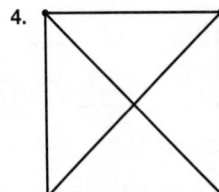

4.
$\begin{bmatrix} 0 & 1 & 1 & 1 \\ 1 & 0 & 1 & 1 \\ 1 & 1 & 0 & 1 \\ 1 & 1 & 1 & 0 \end{bmatrix}$
The adjacency matrix would have all 1's except for a diagonal of all 0's.

Practice Exercises, pages 616–618

9.

	n_1	n_2	n_3	n_4	n_5	n_6
n_1	0	1	0	0	0	0
n_2	0	0	1	0	0	0
n_3	0	0	0	0	0	1
n_4	1	1	0	0	0	0
n_5	0	0	1	0	0	0
n_6	0	0	1	0	1	0

10.

	n_1	n_2	n_3	n_4	n_5	n_6
n_1	0	1	0	0	1	0
n_2	1	0	0	0	0	0
n_3	0	0	0	1	0	1
n_4	1	0	1	0	0	0
n_5	0	0	0	0	0	0
n_6	0	0	0	0	0	0

17.

	A	B	C	D	E	F
A	0	0	1	0	0	0
B	0	0	0	1	0	0
C	0	0	0	0	1	0
D	0	0	0	0	0	1
E	1	0	0	0	0	0
F	0	1	0	0	0	0

no relation

18.

	A	B	C	D	E	F
A	0	0	0	1	0	0
B	0	0	0	0	1	0
C	0	0	0	0	0	1
D	1	0	0	0	0	0
E	0	1	0	0	0	0
F	0	0	1	0	0	0

no relation

19.

	A	B	C	D	E	F
A	0	0	0	0	1	0
B	0	0	0	0	0	1
C	1	0	0	0	0	0
D	0	1	0	0	0	0
E	0	0	1	0	0	0
F	0	0	0	1	0	0

	A	B	C	D	E	F
A	0	0	0	0	0	1
B	1	0	0	0	0	0
C	0	1	0	0	0	0
D	0	0	1	0	0	0
E	0	0	0	1	0	0
F	0	0	0	0	1	0

20. F; R^5 shows that the second person gives the first a message in 5 stages

22.

23.

28.
$$R = \begin{array}{c} A \\ B \end{array}\begin{array}{cc} A & B \\ \left[\begin{array}{cc} 0 & 1 \\ 1 & 1 \end{array}\right]\end{array}; \quad R^2 = \begin{array}{c} A \\ B \end{array}\begin{array}{cc} A & B \\ \left[\begin{array}{cc} 1 & 1 \\ 1 & 2 \end{array}\right]\end{array};$$

$$R^3 = \begin{array}{c} A \\ B \end{array}\begin{array}{cc} A & B \\ \left[\begin{array}{cc} 1 & 2 \\ 2 & 3 \end{array}\right]\end{array}; \quad R^4 = \begin{array}{c} A \\ B \end{array}\begin{array}{cc} A & B \\ \left[\begin{array}{cc} 2 & 3 \\ 3 & 5 \end{array}\right]\end{array}$$

38.

$$T = \begin{array}{c} A \\ B \\ C \\ D \end{array}\begin{array}{c}\begin{array}{cccc} A & B & C & D \end{array} \\ \left[\begin{array}{cccc} 0 & 0 & 1 & 0 \\ 1 & 0 & 0 & 1 \\ 0 & 1 & 0 & 0 \\ 1 & 0 & 1 & 0 \end{array}\right]\end{array}$$

39. $A = -1; B = 1; C = -1; D = 1;$ A winner is not determined because B and D are tied.

40.
$$T^2 = \begin{array}{c} A \\ B \\ C \\ D \end{array}\begin{array}{c}\begin{array}{cccc} A & B & C & D \end{array} \\ \left[\begin{array}{cccc} 0 & 1 & 0 & 0 \\ 1 & 0 & 2 & 0 \\ 1 & 0 & 0 & 1 \\ 0 & 1 & 1 & 0 \end{array}\right]\end{array}$$

41.
$$T + T^2 = \begin{array}{c} A \\ B \\ C \\ D \end{array}\begin{array}{c}\begin{array}{cccc} A & B & C & D \end{array} \\ \left[\begin{array}{cccc} 0 & 1 & 1 & 0 \\ 2 & 0 & 2 & 1 \\ 1 & 1 & 0 & 1 \\ 1 & 1 & 2 & 0 \end{array}\right]\end{array};$$

$A = -2; B = 2; C = -2; D = 2;$ A winner is not determined because B and D are tied.

42.
$$T^3 = \begin{array}{c} A \\ B \\ C \\ D \end{array}\begin{array}{c}\begin{array}{cccc} A & B & C & D \end{array} \\ \left[\begin{array}{cccc} 1 & 0 & 0 & 1 \\ 0 & 2 & 1 & 0 \\ 1 & 0 & 2 & 0 \\ 1 & 1 & 0 & 1 \end{array}\right]\end{array}; \quad T + T^2 + T^3 = \begin{array}{c} A \\ B \\ C \\ D \end{array}\begin{array}{c}\begin{array}{cccc} A & B & C & D \end{array} \\ \left[\begin{array}{cccc} 1 & 1 & 1 & 1 \\ 2 & 2 & 3 & 1 \\ 2 & 1 & 2 & 1 \\ 2 & 2 & 2 & 1 \end{array}\right]\end{array};$$

$A = -3; B = 2; C = -2; D = 3;$ D is the winner, B is in second place, C is in third place

Class Exercises, pages 623–624

9. $AB = \begin{bmatrix} 5 & 0 \\ 0 & 5 \end{bmatrix}$; $BA = \begin{bmatrix} 5 & 0 \\ 0 & 5 \end{bmatrix}$; since $AB = BA = 5\begin{bmatrix} 1 & 0 \\ 0 & 1 \end{bmatrix}$, $B^{-1} = \frac{1}{5}A$ and $A^{-1} = \frac{1}{5}B$

Practice Exercises, pages 624–625

1. $AB = \begin{bmatrix} -14 + 15 & 21 - 21 \\ -10 + 10 & 15 - 14 \end{bmatrix} = \begin{bmatrix} 1 & 0 \\ 0 & 1 \end{bmatrix}$

2. $AB = \begin{bmatrix} 16 - 15 & -24 + 24 \\ 10 - 10 & -15 + 16 \end{bmatrix} = \begin{bmatrix} 1 & 0 \\ 0 & 1 \end{bmatrix}$

18. The second row of PQ has only zeros as entries. If P has an inverse P^{-1}, the second row of PP^{-1} has a 1 in the second column (because it must be an identity matrix.) Since for *any* Q, PQ has all zeros in the second row, there exists no matrix P^{-1}.

22.
$$\begin{bmatrix} \frac{16}{10} - \frac{24}{40} & \frac{16}{5} - \frac{16}{5} \\ -\frac{3}{10} + \frac{12}{40} & -\frac{3}{5} + \frac{8}{5} \end{bmatrix} = \begin{bmatrix} 1 & 0 \\ 0 & 1 \end{bmatrix}; \quad \begin{bmatrix} \frac{16}{10} - \frac{3}{5} & -\frac{8}{10} + \frac{4}{5} \\ \frac{48}{40} - \frac{6}{5} & -\frac{24}{40} + \frac{8}{5} \end{bmatrix} = \begin{bmatrix} 1 & 0 \\ 0 & 1 \end{bmatrix}$$

Class Exercises, page 636

For Exercises 1–3 and 14–19, see Solutions Manual for graphs.

1. $\begin{bmatrix} 10 \\ 0 \end{bmatrix}$
2. $\begin{bmatrix} -32 \\ -13 \end{bmatrix}$
3. $\begin{bmatrix} \sqrt{2} \\ 2 \end{bmatrix}$
4. $\begin{bmatrix} 1 & 0 \\ 0 & 1 \end{bmatrix}$
5. $\begin{bmatrix} \dfrac{\sqrt{2}}{2} & -\dfrac{\sqrt{2}}{2} \\ \dfrac{\sqrt{2}}{2} & \dfrac{\sqrt{2}}{2} \end{bmatrix}$
6. $\begin{bmatrix} \dfrac{1}{2} & -\dfrac{\sqrt{3}}{2} \\ \dfrac{\sqrt{3}}{2} & \dfrac{1}{2} \end{bmatrix}$
7. $\begin{bmatrix} 0 & -1 \\ 1 & 0 \end{bmatrix}$

8. $\begin{bmatrix} -1 & 0 \\ 0 & -1 \end{bmatrix}$
9. $\begin{bmatrix} \dfrac{\sqrt{3}}{2} & -\dfrac{1}{2} \\ \dfrac{1}{2} & \dfrac{\sqrt{3}}{2} \end{bmatrix}$
10. $\begin{bmatrix} -\dfrac{1}{2} & -\dfrac{\sqrt{3}}{2} \\ \dfrac{\sqrt{3}}{2} & -\dfrac{1}{2} \end{bmatrix}$
11. $\begin{bmatrix} 0 & 1 \\ -1 & 0 \end{bmatrix}$
12. $\begin{bmatrix} \dfrac{1}{2} & \dfrac{\sqrt{3}}{2} \\ -\dfrac{\sqrt{3}}{2} & \dfrac{1}{2} \end{bmatrix}$
13. $\begin{bmatrix} 0.8290 & -0.5592 \\ 0.5592 & 0.8290 \end{bmatrix}$

14. $\begin{bmatrix} 3 \\ -4 \end{bmatrix}$
15. $\begin{bmatrix} 3 \\ -4 \end{bmatrix}$
16. $\begin{bmatrix} \dfrac{\sqrt{3}-1}{\sqrt{2}} \\ \dfrac{\sqrt{3}+1}{\sqrt{2}} \end{bmatrix}$
17. $\begin{bmatrix} 1 - \dfrac{\sqrt{3}}{2} \\ \sqrt{3} + \dfrac{1}{2} \end{bmatrix}$
18. $y = 2x + 1$
19. $y = 2x^2 - 4x + 3$

Practice Exercises, pages 637–638

For Exercises 1–12, see Solutions Manual for graphs.

1. $\begin{bmatrix} 2 \\ -4 \end{bmatrix}$
2. $\begin{bmatrix} 3 \\ 1 \end{bmatrix}$
3. $\begin{bmatrix} 0 \\ -3 \end{bmatrix}$
4. $\begin{bmatrix} 6 \\ 2 \end{bmatrix}$
5. $\begin{bmatrix} 2 \\ 0 \end{bmatrix}$
6. $\begin{bmatrix} \dfrac{\sqrt{2}}{2} \\ \dfrac{\sqrt{2}}{2} \end{bmatrix}$

7. $\begin{bmatrix} 0 \\ 2 \end{bmatrix}$
8. $\begin{bmatrix} 3 \\ 4 \end{bmatrix}$
9. $\begin{bmatrix} -5 \\ 12 \end{bmatrix}$
10. $\begin{bmatrix} 0 \\ -3 \end{bmatrix}$
11. $\begin{bmatrix} 2\sqrt{3} \\ -2 \end{bmatrix}$
12. $\begin{bmatrix} 0.2698 \\ 1.3882 \end{bmatrix}$

18. $\begin{bmatrix} 2 & 1 \\ -1 & -2 \end{bmatrix}\begin{bmatrix} x \\ y \end{bmatrix} = \begin{bmatrix} 2x + y \\ -x - 2y \end{bmatrix}$; The image of $A(3,1)$ is $A'(7,-5)$. The image of $B(-2,-3)$ is $B'(-7,8)$. The image of $C(4,-4)$ is $(4,4)$. Neither the size nor the shape of the figure is preserved under this transformation.

19. $\begin{bmatrix} 0 & 1 \\ 1 & 0 \end{bmatrix}\begin{bmatrix} a \\ b \end{bmatrix} = \begin{bmatrix} 0a + 1b \\ 1a + 0b \end{bmatrix} = \begin{bmatrix} b \\ a \end{bmatrix}$

20. $\begin{bmatrix} 0 & -1 \\ -1 & 0 \end{bmatrix}\begin{bmatrix} a \\ b \end{bmatrix} = \begin{bmatrix} 0a - 1b \\ -1a + 0b \end{bmatrix} = \begin{bmatrix} -b \\ -a \end{bmatrix}$

28. $\begin{bmatrix} -0.5592 & -0.8290 \\ 0.8290 & -0.5592 \end{bmatrix}$

37.

$\begin{bmatrix} \dfrac{\sqrt{2}}{2} & -\dfrac{\sqrt{2}}{2} \\ \dfrac{\sqrt{2}}{2} & \dfrac{\sqrt{2}}{2} \end{bmatrix}\begin{bmatrix} x \\ \dfrac{1}{x} \end{bmatrix} = \begin{bmatrix} \dfrac{x^2\sqrt{2} - \sqrt{2}}{2x} \\ \dfrac{x^2\sqrt{2} + \sqrt{2}}{2x} \end{bmatrix} = \begin{bmatrix} x' \\ y' \end{bmatrix}$;

$(y')^2 - (x')^2 = \dfrac{2x^4 + 4x^2 + 2}{4x^2} - \dfrac{2x^4 - 4x^2 + 2}{4x^2} = \dfrac{8x^2}{4x^2} = 2 = a^2$

44. When translating axes, the primed variables represent the same points as those in the original equation, except that they are viewed relative to a new set of axes. When translating a point, the primed variables represent coordinates of a different point in the same coordinate system.

Class Exercises, pages 642–643

1.
2.
3.
4.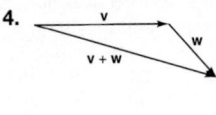

5. $\|4\mathbf{v}\| = 4\sqrt{13}$; $\|-2\mathbf{v}\| = 2\sqrt{13}$; $\|0.25\mathbf{v}\| = 0.25\sqrt{13} = 0.9014$

7.   **8.**

Practice Exercises, pages 643–644

For Exercises 1–23, see Solutions Manual for graphs.

24. For a vertical vector, the x-component is 0 and the absolute value of the y-component is equal to the norm of the vector.

Practice Exercises, pages 651–653

For Exercise 27, see Solutions Manual for graph.

14.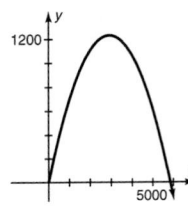

The vehicle reaches a maximum height of about 1200 miles.

19. no; The graph of $x = |t|$, $y = |t|$ is the same as that of $y = x$ only when $x \geq 0$ and $y \geq 0$.

20. $(-6, -4)$; $(x,y) = (23,7) + t(-6, -4)$; $x = 23 - 6t$, $y = 7 - 4t$

21. $(-12, -5)$; $(x,y) = (31,13) + t(-12, -5)$; $x = 31 - 12t$, $y = 13 - 5t$

22. Answers may vary. Example: $(2,4)$; $(x,y) = (6,2) + t(2,4)$; $x = 6 + 2t$, $y = 2 + 4t$

23. Answers may vary. Example: $(2,3)$; $(x,y) = (4,3) + t(2.3)$; $x = 4 + 2t$, $y = 3 + 3t$

24. horizontal force with magnitude 57.34 lb

26. Since $t = \frac{x - a}{c}$ and $t = \frac{y - b}{d}$, then $\frac{x - a}{c} = \frac{y - b}{d}$, or $xd - yc = ad - bc$, which is a linear function.

27. This skateboard ramp is much flatter.

41. Let t be the measure of the circle's rotation and let $P(x,y)$ begin at the origin. When $t = 0$, P is at the origin. When $t = \pi$, P is at the maximum point $(\pi a, 2a)$. When $t = 2\pi$, P is on the x-axis at $(2\pi a, 0)$. From the figure, $\angle PRQ = (180 - t)°$. So $\sin t = \sin (180 - t)° = \frac{PB}{a} = \frac{AQ}{a}$, and $\cos t = -\cos (180 - t)° = -\frac{BR}{a}$, which implies that $BR = -a \cos t$ and $AQ = a \sin t$. Since the circle rolls along the x-axis, $OQ = \overset{\frown}{PQ} = at$, and since $AP = BQ = a$, $x = OQ - AQ = at - \sin t$, and $y = BQ + BR = a - \sin t$, which represent the parametric equations.

Practice Exercises, pages 657–658

17.

19.

21.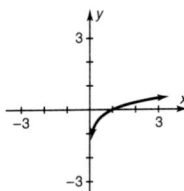

For Exercises 39–45, see Solutions Manual for proofs.

Practice Exercises, pages 664–665

22. divide each component by the norm of **v**, which is found using a similar method for the norm of a three-dimensional vector

24. $(x,y,z) = (5,4,1) + t(-5,1,-7)$

25. $(x,y,z) = (-7,-3,2) + t(7,8,-8)$

26. $(x,y,z) = (0,5,-6) + t(7,-4,3)$

27. $x = 7 - 2t$, $y = 1 + 3t$, $z = -3 + 4t$

28. $x = 5t$, $y = 5 - t$, $z = -6 + 7t$

30. $8x + 2y - 3z = 27$

31. $-12x + 7y + 4z = -92$

32. $6x - 6y - z = -92$

34. $20x + 30y + 30z = 220$

35. $4x - 30y + 42z = -100$

36. $56x + 30y - 42z = -140$

37. $40x - 30y - 30z = -100$

For Exercises 38–41 and 45–46, see Solutions Manual for proofs.

Test Yourself, page 665

For Exercises 1–3, see Solutions Manual for graphs.

1. $\begin{bmatrix} 1 \\ -5 \end{bmatrix}$

2. $\begin{bmatrix} -3 \\ -2 \end{bmatrix}$

3. $\begin{bmatrix} -\frac{\sqrt{2}}{2} \\ \frac{\sqrt{2}}{2} \end{bmatrix}$

Chapter 13   Sequences and Series

37. The user of the program will have to input the first two terms of the sequence, as well as the number of terms to be output. The third term will be the sum of the first two terms, and each subsequent term will be the sum of the previous two terms.

42. The choice of values for the first two terms of the Fibonacci sequence affects the values of all the terms.

44. The choice of values for the first two terms of the sequence affects the values of all of the terms.

Practice Exercises, pages 702–705

12. Since $1^2 = \frac{1(2)(3)}{6}$, P_1 is true. Assume P_k: $1^2 + 2^2 + \ldots + k^2 = \frac{k(k+1)(2k+1)}{6}$. Then $1^2 + 2^2 + \ldots + k^2 + (k+1)^2 =$

$\frac{k(k+1)(2k+1)}{6} + (k+1)^2 = \frac{2k^3 + 3k^2 + k}{6} + \frac{6k^2 + 12k + 6}{6} = \frac{2k^3 + 9k^2 + 13k + 6}{6} = \frac{(k+1)(k+2)(2k+3)}{6} = P_{k+1}$

13. Since $3 = 1(1+2)$, P_1 is true. Assume P_k: $3 + 5 + 7 + \ldots + (2k+1) = k(k+2)$. Then $3 + 5 + 7 +$
$\ldots + (2k+1) + (2k+3) = k(k+2) + (2k+3) = k^2 + 2k + 2k + 3 = k^2 + 4k + 3 =$
$(k+1)(k+3) = P_{k+1}$.

14. Since $2^2 = \frac{(2 \cdot 1)(1+1)(2+1)}{3}$, P_1 is true.   Assume P_k: $2^2 + 4^2 + \ldots + (2k)^2 = \frac{2k(k+1)(2k+1)}{3}$.

Then $2^2 + 4^2 + \ldots + (2k)^2 + [2(k+1)]^2 = \frac{2k(k+1)(2k+1)}{3} + [2(k+1)]^2 = \frac{4k^3 + 6k^2 + 2k}{3} + \frac{12k^2 + 24k + 12}{3}$

$= \frac{2(2k^3 + 9k^2 + 13k + 6)}{3} = \frac{2(k+1)(k+2)(2k+3)}{3} = P_{k+1}$

15. Since $1 = \frac{1}{2}(1)(3 \cdot 1 - 1)$, P_1 is true. Assume P_k: $1 + 4 + 7 + \ldots + (3k-2) = \frac{1}{2}k(3k-1)$.

Then $1 + 4 + 7 + \ldots + (3k-2) + (3k+1) = \frac{1}{2}k(3k-1) + (3k+1) = \frac{1}{2}(3k^2 - k + 6k + 2) =$

$\frac{1}{2}(3k^2 + 5k + 2) = \frac{1}{2}(k+1)(3k+2) = P_{k+1}$.

16. Since $5^1 = \frac{5^2 - 5}{4}$, P_1 is true.   Assume P_k: $5 + 5^2 + 5^3 + \ldots + 5^k = \frac{5^{k+1} - 5}{4}$.   Then $5 + 5^2 + 5^3 + \ldots + 5^k + 5^{k+1} =$

$\frac{5^{k+1} - 5}{4} + 5^{k+1} = \frac{5^{k+1} - 5}{4} + \frac{4 \cdot 5^{k+1}}{4} = \frac{5^{k+1} - 5 + 4 \cdot 5^{k+1}}{4} = \frac{5 \cdot 5^{k+1} - 5}{4} = \frac{5^{k+2} - 5}{4} = P_{k+1}$

18. Since $(ab)^1 = a^1 b^1$, P_1 is true.   Assume P_k: $(ab)^k = a^k b^k$.   Then $(ab)^{k+1} = (ab)^k(ab) = (a^k b^k)(ab) = (a^k a)(b^k b) = a^{k+1} b^{k+1} = P_{k+1}$

21. Since $1 \cdot 2 = \frac{1(1+1)(1+2)}{3}$, P_1 is true. Assume P_k: $1 \cdot 2 + 2 \cdot 3 + \ldots + k(k+1) = \frac{k(k+1)(k+2)}{3}$.

Then $1 \cdot 2 + 2 \cdot 3 + \ldots + k(k+1) + (k+1)(k+2) = \frac{k(k+1)(k+2)}{3} + (k+1)(k+2) =$

$\frac{k^3 + 3k^2 + 2k}{3} + \frac{3k^2 + 9k + 6}{3} = \frac{k^3 + 6k^2 + 11k + 6}{3} = \frac{(k+1)(k+2)(k+3)}{3} = P_{k+1}$.

22. Since $\frac{1}{1 \cdot 2} = \frac{1}{1+1}$, P_1 is true.   Assume P_k: $\frac{1}{1 \cdot 2} + \frac{1}{2 \cdot 3} + \ldots + \frac{1}{k(k+1)} = \frac{k}{k+1}$.   Then $\frac{1}{1 \cdot 2} + \frac{1}{2 \cdot 3} + \ldots + \frac{1}{k(k+1)} +$

$\frac{1}{(k+1)(k+2)} = \frac{k}{k+1} + \frac{1}{(k+1)(k+2)} = \frac{k(k+2)}{(k+1)(k+2)} + \frac{1}{(k+1)(k+2)} = \frac{k^2 + 2k + 1}{(k+1)(k+2)} = \frac{(k+1)(k+1)}{(k+1)(k+2)} = \frac{k+1}{k+2} = P_{k+1}$

23. Since $\frac{1}{2} = 1 - \frac{1}{2}$, P_1 is true.   Assume P_k: $\frac{1}{2} + \left(\frac{1}{2}\right)^2 + \ldots + \left(\frac{1}{2}\right)^k = 1 - \left(\frac{1}{2}\right)^k$.   Then $\frac{1}{2} + \left(\frac{1}{2}\right)^2 + \ldots + \left(\frac{1}{2}\right)^k + \left(\frac{1}{2}\right)^{k+1} =$

$1 - \left(\frac{1}{2}\right)^k + \left(\frac{1}{2}\right)^{k+1} = 1 - \left(\frac{1}{2^k} - \frac{1}{2^{k+1}}\right) = 1 - \left(\frac{2}{2^{k+1}} - \frac{1}{2^{k+1}}\right) = 1 - \frac{1}{2^{k+1}} = 1 - \left(\frac{1}{2}\right)^{k+1}$.

24. Since $a, > 1$, $a^2 > a^1$, so P_1 is true.   Assume P_k: $a^{k+1} > a^k$.   Then since $a > 1 > 0$, $(a^{k+1}) \cdot a > a^k \cdot a$ $a^{k+2} > a^{k+1} = P_{k+1}$

25. Since $2187 < 5040$, P_7 is true. Assume P_k: $3^k < k!$. Then $(3^k)(3) < (k!)(3)$ which is less than $(k!)(k + 1)$ since $k \geq 7$. So $3^k < (k + 1)! = P_{k+1}$.

26. Since $1 < 2^1$, P_1 is true. Assume P_k: $k < 2^k$. Then, $k + 1 < 2^k + 1 < 2^k + 2^k = 2 \cdot 2^k = 2^{k+1}$ $k + 1 < 2^{k+1} = P_{k+1}$

27. Since $4^1 - 1 = 3$ is a multiple of 3, P_1 is true. Assume P_k: $4^k - 1 = 3t$ for some integer t. Then $4^k = 3t + 1$, $(4^k)(4) = 4(3t + 1)$, $4^{k+1} = 12t + 4$, $4^{k+1} - 1 = 12t + 3 = 3(4t + 1)$ which is a multiple of 3, which is P_{k+1}.

28. Since $1^2 + 1 = 2$ is divisible by 2, P_1 is true. Assume P_k: $k^2 + k$ is divisible by 2, i.e. $k^2 + k = 2t$ for some $t \in \mathbb{Z}$. Then $(k + 1)^2 + (k + 1) = k^2 + 2k + 1 + k + 1 = k^2 + 3k + 2 = (2t)^2 + 3(2t) + 2 = 4t^2 + 6t + 2 = 2[2t^2 + 3t + 1] = P_{k+1}$, a multiple of 2

29. Since $a^1 < 1$ for all $0 < a < 1$, P_1 is true. Assume P_k: $a^k < 1$ for $0 < a < 1$. Then $a^k \cdot a < a$, $a^{k+1} < 1$ since $0 < a < 1$ which is P_{k+1}.

30. Since $e^1 > 2^1$, P_1 is true. Assume P_k: $e^k > 2^k$. Then $e^k \cdot e > 2^k \cdot 2$ or $e^{k+1} > 2^{k+1} = P_{k+1}$

31. $\sqrt[6]{2}\, \text{cis}\, \dfrac{5\pi}{36}$, $\sqrt[6]{2}\, \text{cis}\, \dfrac{17\pi}{36}$, $\sqrt[6]{2}\, \text{cis}\, \dfrac{29\pi}{36}$, $\sqrt[6]{2}\, \text{cis}\, \dfrac{41\pi}{36}$, $\sqrt[6]{2}\, \text{cis}\, \dfrac{53\pi}{36}$, $\sqrt[6]{2}\, \text{cis}\, \dfrac{65\pi}{36}$

For Exercises 41–43, see Solutions Manual for proofs.

Practice Exercises, pages 718–719

17.

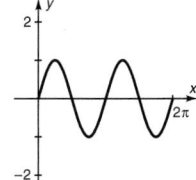

35. e, e^2, e^3, e^4, e^5, e^6; The sequence is not convergent because it increases without bound.

36. $\dfrac{1}{e}$, $\dfrac{1}{e^2}$, $\dfrac{1}{e^3}$, $\dfrac{1}{e^4}$, $\dfrac{1}{e^5}$, $\dfrac{1}{e^6}$; The sequence is convergent because the limit is 0.

39. $8 = 8$　　**40.** $15 = 15$　　**41.** $\dfrac{5}{3} = \dfrac{5}{3}$

Practice Exercises, pages 725–727

21. $S_k = 1 + 2 + 3 + \ldots + k = \dfrac{k(k + 1)}{2}$; $\lim\limits_{k \to \infty} S_k = \lim\limits_{k \to \infty} \dfrac{k(k + 1)}{2}$; As k increases without bound, $\dfrac{k(k + 1)}{2}$ increases without bound, so the series is divergent.

Practice Exercises, pages 733–735

34. The polynomial approximations are most accurate at x-values that are close to zero. To obtain more accurate approximations, you could use more terms of the series in the program.

38. See answer for Exercise 34, above.　　**41.** The series will give good approximations of $\ln(1 + x)$ for values of x between -1 and 1.

Chapter 14　Probability
Practice Exercises, pages 745–747　See Solutions Manual for diagrams.

Class Exercises, page 758

13. no; Probability is only a way of measuring uncertainty based on many trials. It is not an exact measure of predictability. In the long run, probabilities obtained using a frequency interpretation should be close to those obtained using the classical interpretation.

Practice Exercises, pages 788–791

14. If B_1, B_2, and B_3 are mutually exclusive events, one of which must occur,
$$P(B_1|A) = \dfrac{P(B_1) \cdot P(A|B_1)}{P(B_1) \cdot P(A|B_1) + P(B_2) \cdot P(A|B_2) + P(B_3) \cdot P(A|B_3)}$$

Chapter 15　Statistics and Data Analysis
See Solutions Manual for all histograms and tables.

Class Exercises, pages 801–802

7. 87, 90, 95, 98, 98, 99, 102, 102, 109, 109, 115, 120, 120, 122, 126, 130, 133, 134, 136, 136, 136, 139, 140, 140, 142, 142, 144, 148

Practice Exercises, pages 802–804

9. 2.0, 2.4, 2.5, 4.0, 4.8, 5.0, 5.5, 6.0, 6.0, 6.1, 7.1, 7.1, 8.0, 8.5, 12.0, 14.0, 26.7, 30.7, 31.2, 32.0

18. Since 44 saddles weigh less than 16 lb, and $44 > \frac{1}{2} \cdot 81$, then the statement is correct.

19. You do not know how many saddles in the 11–15 lb class weigh exactly 15 lb.

31. The rectangles for the rest of the data will be larger and therefore clearer.

Practice Exercises, pages 808–810

25.

0 2 4 6 8 10 12 14 16 18

32.

0 10 20 30 40

Practice Exercises, pages 814–816

24. no; The total weight of the crates is 5369 lb.

30, 31. Answers may vary.

Practice Exercises, pages 835–837

For Exercises 4–5 and 8–9, see Solutions Manual for examples.

Practice Exercises, pages 842–845

26. Answers may vary. One reason might be that female runners generally take shorter strides than male runners.

31. The more anxious the student is about math, the lower the student's scores will be.

32. very close to 1; Since the majority of people who graduate high school do so in 4 years, their high school graduation age is their eighth grade graduation age plus 4.

33. no; The correlation coefficient should be closer to 0 than to 1 or -1.

34. The scatter diagram should confirm your prediction in Exercise 33.

36. The model is based on known data and may change outside this range. This may result in large errors in prediction.

37. curvilinear; Growth is usually modeled using an exponential function which is curved.

40. Check students' programs. When testing their programs using the data in Example 1, the x-value will be the SAT score and the y-value will be the grade.

Chapter 16 Limits and an Introduction to Calculus See Solutions Manual for graphs.

Practice Exercises, pages 863–864

43. Since f is continuous at c, then $f(c)$ equals some real number n. Since g is continuous at c, $g(c)$ equals some real number m. $(f + g)(c) = f(c) + g(c) = m + n$, which is a real number by the closure property of addition. Therefore, $(f + g)(c)$ exists. Because they are continuous, $\lim_{x \to c} f(x)$ and $\lim_{x \to c} g(x)$ must also equal some real numbers, N and M respectively. $\lim_{x \to c} (f + g)(x) = \lim_{x \to c} f(x) + \lim_{x \to c} g(x) = N + M$, which is a real number. Therefore, $\lim_{x \to c} (f + g)(x)$ exists. Again, because f and g are continuous, $n = N$ and $m = M$. $\lim_{x \to c} (f + g)(x)$: $M + N$; $(f + g)(c) = n + m$; $M + N = m + n$; Therefore, $\lim_{x \to c} (f + g)(x) = (f + g)(c)$. Since all three conditions of continuity are satisfied, $f + g$ is continuous.

44. The continuity of a product of two continuous functions can be proven in a similar manner to the steps in Exercise 43. Substitute theorems regarding multiplication of functions for those regarding addition of functions.

Class Exercises, page 880

1. $14x$; 14

2. $-12x^3 + 10x$; $-36x^2 + 10$

3. $5x^4 + 6x + 4$; $20x^3 + 6$

4. $-18x^{-4} + 6x^2$; $72x^{-5} + 12x$

5. $\frac{1}{\sqrt{x}}$; $-\frac{1}{2x\sqrt{x}}$

6. $\frac{1}{3\sqrt[3]{x^2}}$; $-\frac{2}{9x\sqrt[3]{x^2}}$

7. critical number: $x = 2$; increasing: $x < 2$; decreasing: $x > 2$; relative max: $(2,4)$

8. critical number: $x = 0$; increasing: $x > 0$; decreasing: $x < 0$; relative min: $(0,0)$

9. critical numbers: $x = 0$, $x = \frac{3}{2}$; increasing: $x > \frac{3}{2}$; decreasing: $x < \frac{3}{2}$; relative min: $\left(\frac{3}{2}, \frac{85}{16}\right)$

Practice Exercises, pages 880–881

For Exercises 1–9, 19–22, and 31–37, see Solutions Manual.